MASERS

Selected Reprints with Editorial Comment

J. Weber
Professor of Physics
University of Maryland

GORDON AND BREACH Science Publishers
NEW YORK LONDON PARIS

Published 1967 by GORDON AND BREACH
Science Publishers, Inc.
150 Fifth Avenue, New York, N.Y. 10011

Editorial office for the United Kingdom:

Gordon and Breach, Science Publishers Ltd.
61 Carey Street, Chancery Lane
London W.C. 2, England

Editorial office for France:

Gordon and Breach
7-9 rue Emile Dubois
Paris 14

Library of Congress Catalog Card Number: 65-24874

Distributed in France by:

Dunod Editeur
92, rue Bonaparte
Paris 6, France

Distributed in Canada by:

The Ryerson Press
299 Queen Street West
Toronto 2B, Ontario

Printed in the United States of America
and Bound in Canada

MASERS

INTERNATIONAL SCIENCE REVIEW SERIES

Edited by Lewis Klein
Howard University, Washington, D. C.

VOLUME I

Lewis Klein, Dispersion Relations and the Abstract Approach to Field Theory

VOLUME II

Harry L. Morrison, The Quantum Theory of Many-Particle Systems

VOLUME III

D. McIntyre and F. Gornick, Light Scattering from Dilute Polymer Solutions

VOLUME IV

N. N. Bogoliubov, The Theory of Superconductivity

VOLUME V

P. K. Kabir, The Development of Weak Interaction Theory

VOLUME VI

M. E. Rose, Nuclear Orientation

VOLUME VII

P. H. Meijer, Group Theory and Solid State Physics (In Two Volumes)

VOLUME VIII

Part 1: C. Truesdell, The Mechanical Foundations of Elasticity and Fluid Dynamics

Part 2: C. Truesdell, The Rational Mechanics of Materials

Part 3: C. Truesdell, Foundations of Elasticity Theory

Part 4: C. Truesdell, Problems of Non-Linear Elasticity

VOLUME IX

J. Weber, Masers

VOLUME X

J. Weber, Lasers

Additional Volumes in Preparation

PREFACE

These volumes are an attempt to promote progress by assembling many of the original papers which contributed to the development and growth of this field. This work is dedicated to the many scientists and engineers whose papers appear here. The editor and publisher take pleasure in acknowledging the valuable assistance of these authors in making this publication possible.

CONTENTS

CONTENTS

Phonon Masers

CONTENTS

Techniques for Solid State Masers

Relaxation Phenomena

Materials, Preparation, Spectra

CONTENTS

Papers on Solid State Masers Not Listed Elsewhere

CONTENTS

INTRODUCTION AND EARLY HISTORY

Shortly after Roentgen discovered X-rays, physicians were employing this radiation for diagnostic purposes. Not all scientific discoveries are so quickly applied for the benefit of mankind. Several decades elapsed before useful engineering applications were found for the electron spin and for some other aspects of the quantum theory. There were several reasons for this. Thermionic electron emission dominated the first half century of modern communication engineering and electronics. The diode was a good rectifier. Triodes and multigrid electron tubes were soon amplifying signals from thermal fluctuation levels. When operated as oscillators they produced intense monochromatic sources with power outputs up to millions of watts, even for continuous operation.

Classical physics gave a good description of these devices. Engineers had little motivation to learn the principles of quantum theory, until 1948. At this time it was discovered that electrons and holes in semiconductors could perform, more conveniently, most of the functions of thermionic vacuum tubes.

By 1950 satisfactory solutions had been found for amplification, generation, and detection of electrical signals up to frequencies of several thousand megacycles. Techniques existing then did not seem capable of extension beyond another order of magnitude in frequency. This motivated a search for other methods.

The maser idea originated independently at the University of Maryland, Columbia University and the Lebedev Institute in Moscow.

It is interesting that effects due to having more particles in excited states had been discussed by W. E. Lamb[1] in 1950 and by Purcell and Pound[2] early in 1951. A study of these papers indicates that it was not appreciated that negative temperature systems in conjunction with a microwave cavity or waveguide could give coherent amplification through stimulated emission processes.

My work had its origins in a program of research in microwave spectroscopy. The mechanisms of absorption and emission taking place when a gas interacts with radiation had always seemed much more interesting than the structure of molecules. In the usual type of microwave spectroscope, microwaves from a source are incident on a detector. If a gas is subsequently introduced, an absorption of part of the incident radiation may be observed. What is the nature of this absorption? Suppose we have a pair of energy levels E_1 and E_2, with $E_2 > E_1$. If the radiation frequency ν is close to or equal to the value

$$\nu = \frac{E_2 - E_1}{h} ,$$

where h is Planck's constant, then absorption and emission processes may occur. The power absorbed is

$$P_{ABS} = W_{12} h\nu n_1 \qquad (1)$$

W_{12} is a transition probability and n_1 is the number of particles with energy E_1. Ordinarily there will be some excited particles present, say n_2 with energy E_2. The presence of resonance radiation acts as a kind of catalyst to stimulate the excited particles to emit radiation. The emitted power is

$$P_{EMITTED} = W_{21} h\nu n_2 \qquad (2)$$

It is known from quantum theory and the laws of radiation that $W_{12} = W_{21}$. The net power absorbed is

$$P_{NET} = W_{12} h\nu (n_1 - n_2) \qquad (3)$$

Power is always absorbed when radiation is sent through a substance in thermal equilibrium. This is a consequence of the fact that in thermal equilibrium n_1 exceeds n_2, with

$$n_2 = n_1 \; e^{-(E_2 - E_1)/kT} \qquad (4)$$

k is Boltzmann's constant and T is the absolute temperature. It is clear from expression (3) that amplification will result if $n_2 > n_1$, and this implies that the substance must not be in thermal equilibrium described by (4). We might wonder whether the emitted radiation would be coherent. I carried out detailed calculations in 1951 which indicated that for a substance coupled to the fields in a waveguide or resonant cavity the radiation would be coherent. It might be argued that inasmuch as the absorption is coherent, the emission should also be coherent.

If this is accepted there is the important problem of achieving $n_2 > n_1$. A pulsed symmetric top molecule amplifier was first considered, using polar molecules. Application of an electric field gives a Stark Effect linear in the applied field. If equilibrium is achieved and the electric field is suddenly reversed, one obtains $n_2 > n_1$ for a time corresponding to the thermal relaxation time. Calculations indicated that the intrinsic amplification using any gas at room temperature was insufficient for practical amplifiers to be constructed in this way. A pulsed oscillator was considered, but its power output would not have been large enough to be interesting. The use of a solid was suggested. An account of this work was submitted to the technical program committee of the Institute of Radio Engineers annual electron tube research conference early in 1952. The paper was accepted and presented to the 1952 conference at Ottawa. The summary was published[3] in 1953.

The idea of using a gas for a molecular amplifier had occurred also to C. H. Townes[4] and Basov and Prokhorov.[5] These physicists were able to achieve $n_2 > n_1$, by the simple expedient of selectively removing the ground state molecules from a molecular beam. The Columbia group was the first to develop a successful beam maser in 1954. While no practical amplifier was possible an escillator offered the possibility of a useful frequency standard. Other types of frequency standards had been developed which employed a microwave transition to control the frequency of a free electron type of oscillator by means of a feedback loop. The early gas beam type masers gave frequency stability comparable with but not as good as the cesium beam atomic clocks. At present it appears likely that the atomic hydrogen maser may give the best frequency stability.

In 1917 Einstein[6] had given a simple and clear discussion of radiation which included not only absorption and stimulated emission, but spontaneous emission as well. The latter effect is an emission by excited particles in the absence of resonance radiation. This is a small effect at microwave frequencies and increases as the cube of the frequency. Although it is small in the microwave region it is nonetheless a random process which determines the ultimate noise performance. The first beam type masers were not practical amplifiers. They did focus attention on the unsolved problems associated with use of the maser idea for useful amplifiers which would be superior in low noise performance to free electron devices. It required several important contributions to achieve these aims.

The three level method of achieving $n_2 > n_1$ was suggested by Basov and Prokhorov.[5] Again a very simple idea is involved. Suppose we have a three level system as shown in Fig. 3. In equilibrium $n_3 < n_2 < n_1$. Suppose we employ an intense source of radiation ν_{31} such that

$$\nu_{31} = \frac{E_3 - E_1}{h}$$

Initially particles leave E_1 at a more rapid rate than they leave E_3 because $n_1 > n_3$. Under saturation conditions this results in $n_1 \approx n_3$. The reduction of the population of E_1 and the enhancement of the population of E_3 may make either $n_3 > n_2$ or $n_2 > n_1$.

It was noted by Strandberg in 1955 that the use of low temperatures and paramagnetic ions would result in improved intrinsic amplification. How this comes about is discussed in the papers which follow. Bloembergen and Javan independently discovered the three level method. The synthesis of the three-level idea with the suggestions for the use of low temperatures and paramagnetic ions for a solid state maser was suggested by Bloembergen[7] in 1956. The first successful solid state maser action was achieved by Scovil, Feher and Seidel.[8]

The remaining problems involved search for the most appropriate solid. The use of chromium ions in ruby was suggested by C. Kikuchi.[9] Very successful ruby masers of the cavity type were readily developed. Further improvement in gain bandwidth product was accomplished by the development of travelling wave solid state masers.[10]

At low frequencies, in kilocycle regions where flicker noise is not dominant, the use of free electron vacuum tubes can result in amplifiers with internal noise temperatures well below one degree Kelvin. At twenty megacycles noise temperatures of approximately 20° Kelvin can be achieved. In the microwave region noise temperatures of several hundred degrees can be attained with travelling wave electron tubes. Solid state microwave maser systems give noise temperatures of a few degrees Kelvin and therefore represent a two order improvement in noise performance.

Research has continued on gas type masers for frequency standards. The atomic hydrogen type was suggested by N. F. Ramsey.[11] Separation of the ground state atoms is accomplished by a beam technique. However the excited atoms fill the entire microwave cavity. Special coatings are employed to prevent recombination and de excitation of the atoms by the walls. The lifetime of excited atoms under these conditions is several days. Frequency stability of the order of one part in 10^{15} was originally estimated. A part in 10^{12} or 10^{13} has been achieved up to the present time.

LASERS

We have already noted that the effect of spontaneous emission increases with the cube of the frequency. Actually the ultimate noise temperature[12] of any stimulated emission amplifier is given by

$$T = \frac{h\nu}{k \ln_e 2}$$

At optical frequencies this results in temperatures of the order of tens of thousands of degrees. A maser amplifier is therefore much less useful for detection than photo emission or photoconductive devices. However there was no reason why the maser principle could not be employed to give an optical source with unusual coherence properties.

It was noted by R. H. Dicke[13] that an assemblage of molecules could be placed in "superradiant" states where they would radiate coherently. In 1957 he discussed[14] the application of this to coherent optical radiation. His proposals involve coherence in spontaneous emission processes rather than the achievement of coherence due to stimulated emission.

To employ the maser principle in the optical region two problems had to be solved. One involved development of a relatively loss free cavity structure, the other required discovery of materials with suitable energy level schemes.

The use of a Fabry Perot interferometer was suggested by Dicke[15] and patented by him in 1958. The use of a Fabry Perot cavity and methods for achieving laser action were suggested independently by G. Gould in unpublished work of 1957 and 1958. Townes and Schawlow[16] suggested use of alkali atoms in the gas phase as the working substances. Later Schawlow[17] considered the use of ruby but expressed doubt that sufficient pumping power could be made available. Experiments employing the optically excited states of ruby[18,19] had been carried out by Wieder, Geschwind, Collins and Schawlow, and Maiman.[20]

The first laser was a solid state device, developed by T. H. Maiman.[21] It employed ruby. The energy level scheme (Fig. 4) illustrates the method of operation. Intense light from a pulsed flashlamp excites particles out of the ground state into the relatively broad band 3. Band 3 has the characteristic that fast radiationless transitions occur for particles in it, with most of these particles decaying to level 2, which is metastable. Fluorescence would ordinarily occur out of level 2. However the crystal has its ends polished to form a parallel plane Fabry Perot system. Thus we have a resonant cavity and more particles* in level 2 than in level 1. The device then fulfills the requirements for laser action and oscillates until the population of level 2 is depleted below the threshold condition. Figure 4 has been simplified in a number of respects. Thus level 2 consists of two levels with the relatively close spacing of 29 cm^{-1}. The fine structure of the state 1 has also been omitted. The early lasers had one end heavily silvered. The other end was lightly silvered to permit the emission of radiation.

Maiman's device employed pink ruby. Red ruby has a higher chromium concentration and a somewhat different energy level structure because of the chromium ion interactions. Laser action has been obtained employing both lines associated with the split level 2 (R_1 and R_2 lines) of pink ruby, and for the two lines (N_1 and N_2) of red ruby which involve transitions to terminal levels 100 cm^{-1} above the ground state.

As we remarked earlier the ruby laser in its original form was a pulsed optically pumped device. Javan[22] succeeded in developing a continuous source, using an electrical discharge in a mixture of gases. Optical pumping is more difficult to achieve in a gas because of the absence of a relatively broad band such as 3 (Fig. 4) into which ground state particles may be excited by a wide band source. Electron collisional excitation was suggested by Sanders[23] and Javan.[24] An electrical discharge in a gas has complex phenomena. Excitation and ionization by electron collision are taking place as well as stimulated emission, spontaneous emission, and imprisonment of resonance radiation. A thorough study of these processes is required in order to choose conditions which will lead to inverted populations. This can be achieved in a pure gas, but was originally achieved in a mixture of helium and neon. The method of more readily achieving greater population in the excited states may be understood from Fig. 5. The helium pressure was 1 mm Hg while the neon pressure was 0.1 mm Hg. The large ratio of helium to neon is desirable in the operation of the device. An electrical discharge excites both helium and neon atoms. Because the 2^3S level of He is nearly coincident with the 2s level of Ne, collisional transfer of excitation is relatively efficient. Because there are ten times as many helium atoms as neon, the discharge electrons can produce a relatively large ratio of helium to neon excited atoms. Atomic collisions then excite enough neon atoms so that there are more neon atoms in the 2s state of neon than in the 2p state. Maser action is then possible if a resonant structure is coupled to the gas.

Laser action using current carriers in gallium arsenide was achieved in 1962.[25,26,27,28] A forward biased gallium arsenide p-n junction is employed. Electron injection gives rise to more particles in excited states for allowed transitions between electron and hole states in or near the conduction and valence bands. Again a cavity resonator is obtained by polishing the front and back faces of the diode parallel to each other. This device represents a direct conversion of electrical energy to coherent radiation.

These developments have been accomplished by a search for new materials capable of maser action, by modified resonator structures, and by the achievement of continuous operation with several solid state materials.

RELATION OF MASERS TO FREE ELECTRON DEVICES

At first glance the masers appear to operate on a totally different principle from the free electron type of device. The difference is not so much in the mechanism of emission, but in the kind of quantum states employed. In this sense the name maser is somewhat unfortunate since it does imply that the earlier amplifiers did not make use of stimulated emission. A few remarks on the free electron devices and their connection with masers is therefore appropriate here.

Let us consider a vacuum tube oscillator, Fig. 6. This device converts the energy of a unidirectional voltage source into electromagnetic oscillations in the following way. First imagine the grid is negative, then a relatively few electrons enter the interaction region. Since both the radiofrequency and source voltage are positive these electrons will be acceler-

*Ordinarily we expect that flash pumping could produce at most equal populations of levels 1 and 3 (saturation). The presence of level 2 alters this by removing and storing particles which were excited to level 3. Thus we may, by pumping, achieve a higher population in level 2 than in the ground state.

Reprinted from REVIEWS OF MODERN PHYSICS, Vol. 31, No. 3, 681–710, July, 1959
Printed in U. S. A.

Masers *

J. WEBER

University of Maryland, College Park, Maryland

"It is strange that practical electronics remained untouched by these fundamental facts (electron spin) and could get along with the notion of the charged mass point or the minute charged sphere." [Arnold Sommerfeld, *Electrodynamics* (Academic Press, Inc., New York, 1948)].

I. INTRODUCTION

THE development of electronics during the first half of this century was based almost completely on the quantum states of translational energy of the free electron. Only recently did physicists recognize the fact that the spin states and the bound states of electrons in atoms and molecules could be employed for amplification. We give here an account of these technological advances together with a summary of the physics which made them possible.

The physical principles and experimental techniques required for development of paramagnetic amplifiers and molecular amplifiers were well established in the period 1945–1950. Such microwave amplifiers have much lower noise than those employing thermionic vacuum tubes. This low noise property has been the principal motivation for the large amount of work in this field.

The earliest work on molecular amplification started independently at three different laboratories.[1–3] It had a different motivation, namely, the hope that millimeter wave oscillators and amplifiers would result.

The word "maser" was coined by the Columbia group[2] as an acronym for "microwave amplification by the stimulated emission of radiation." This word appears in Webster's dictionary with the spellings "mazer" and "maser" and has the meaning "a large drinking cup, originally of a hard wood." The free electron vacuum tube amplifier may also be regarded as operating through the mechanism of the stimulated emission of radiation. In what follows, however, the word maser is taken to mean either a molecular amplifier or a paramagnetic solid state amplifier.

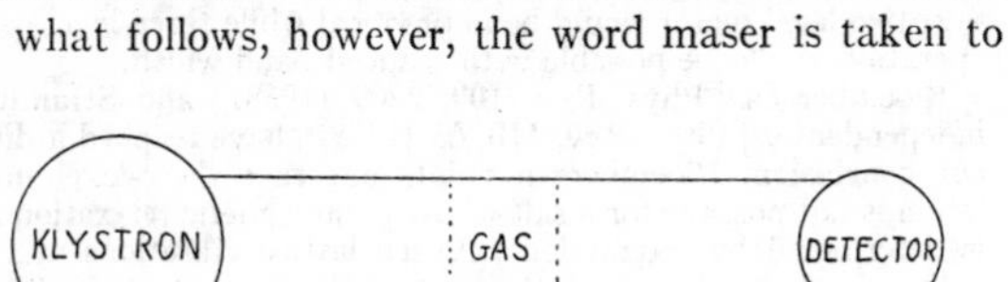

FIG. 1. Absorption of microwaves by a gas.

* This work was supported in part by the Office of Naval Research.

[1] J. Weber, Trans. Inst. Radio Engrs. Prof. Group on Electron Devices, PGED-3 (June, 1953).

[2] Gordon, Zeiger, and Townes, Phys. Rev. **95**, 282 (1954); Phys. Rev. **99**, 1264 (1955).

[3] N. G. Basov and A. M. Prokhorov, J. Exptl. Theoret. Phys. (U.S.S.R.) **27**, 431 (1954); Proc. Acad. Sci. (U.S.S.R.) **101**, 47 (1955); J. Exptl. Theoret. Phys. (U.S.S.R.) **28**, 249 (1955).

II. AMPLIFICATION BY SYSTEMS HAVING A HIGHER ENERGY STATE MORE DENSELY POPULATED THAN A LOWER STATE

A. General Principles

We follow the original[1] discussion of this principle of maser type amplification. In the experimental arrangement of Fig. 1, there is a microwave system which consists of a wave guide with gas inside, in thermal equilibrium. Such a gas may absorb microwaves, and this absorption can be described in the following terms.

Suppose the gas has a pair of energy levels (Fig. 2) with values E_1 and E_2, with $E_2 > E_1$. Let n_1 and n_2 be the numbers of particles with energies E_1 and E_2. Let the absolute temperature be denoted by T and Boltzmann's constant by k. Then we can write

$$n_2 = n_1 e^{-(E_2 - E_1)/kT}. \quad (1)$$

We suppose that electromagnetic radiation is present with frequency ν given by

$$\nu = (E_2 - E_1)/h. \quad (2)$$

The power absorbed by the gas can be written

$$P_A = W_{12} n_1 h\nu. \quad (3)$$

Here W_{12} is the transition probability for transitions from state 1 to 2 induced by radiation. Similarly the power emitted by the gas due to the stimulated emission of radiation is given by

$$P_E = W_{21} n_2 h\nu. \quad (4)$$

Neglecting spontaneous emission for the moment we can write $W_{21} = W_{12}$ and for the *net* power absorbed

$$P = W_{12}(n_1 - n_2) h\nu. \quad (5)$$

P will be positive and the gas will absorb power, if n_1 exceeds n_2. This will be the case in consequence of expression (1), if the gas is in thermal equilibrium. How-

FIG. 2.

ever, the net power absorbed can be made negative, and amplification will result, if $n_2 > n_1$. For the present we consider amplification by a one-quantum process, resulting from the nonequilibrium situation $n_2 > n_1$. The same considerations which lead to coherent absorption for $n_1 > n_2$ suggest that for[4] $n_2 > n_1$ the amplified signal will be coherent with the driving signal. The energy levels which are employed may be bound states of molecules, or spin states in a magnetic field. The low-temperature solid state masers use paramagnetic ions in an externally applied magnetic field.

B. Three-Level Method

Many methods have been proposed for obtaining a higher population density in an upper energy level than in a lower one. Most of these are not generally useful, but may nonetheless have special applications. A fairly complete survey is given in Sec. IV. First we present a summary of the three-level method, first proposed by Prokhorov,[3] and developed independently by Bloembergen,[5] and also by Javan; this appears to be by far the most generally useful one. We follow Bloembergen's treatment.

In a system with three energy levels, E_1, E_2, and E_3 (Fig. 3), let the selection rules be such that transitions are allowed between each level and either of the other two. In thermal equilibrium, the numbers of particles in the different states satisfy the relations,

$$n_1 > n_2 > n_3. \tag{6}$$

The frequencies ν_{32}, ν_{21}, ν_{31} are defined by the relations

$$\nu_{mn} = (E_m - E_n)/h. \tag{7}$$

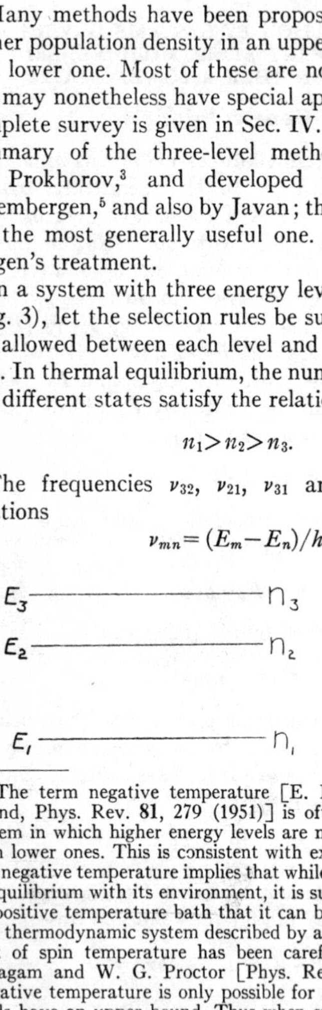

FIG. 3.

[4] The term negative temperature [E. M. Purcell and R. V. Pound, Phys. Rev. **81**, 279 (1951)] is often used to describe a system in which higher energy levels are more densely populated than lower ones. This is consistent with expression (1). The idea of a negative temperature implies that while part of a system is not in equilibrium with its environment, it is sufficiently isolated from its positive temperature bath that it can be considered as a separate thermodynamic system described by a temperature. The concept of spin temperature has been carefully considered by A. Abragam and W. G. Proctor [Phys. Rev. **109**, 1441 (1958)]. Negative temperature is only possible for a system whose energy levels have an upper bound. Thus when such a system is heated from 0°K to a temperature $+\infty$ the levels become equally populated. If it is heated further the temperature changes discontinuously to $-\infty$, and on further heating it eventually tends to minus 0°K at which point all particles are in the state of highest energy. As Bloembergen has remarked, negative temperature is hotter than hot. It has been suggested by Ramsey that the discontinuity at $+\infty$ could have been avoided if the reciprocal of temperature had been used. At negative temperatures resistances become negative and amplification is then possible.

[5] N. Bloembergen, Phys. Rev. **104**, 324 (1956).

An intense rf field of frequency ν_{31} will induce transitions between states 1 and 3. Since initially there are more particles in state 1, the particles will initially leave state 1 at a greater rate than return to it from state 3.

Saturation phenomena will result in which $n_3 \rightarrow n_1$. Under these nonequilibrium conditions we may expect either that $n_2 > n_1$ or $n_3 > n_2$. In the first case amplification is possible at frequency ν_{21} and in the second case at ν_{32}. In order to arrive at quantitative values relaxation[6]

[6] An important issue in the operation of a paramagnetic ion low-temperature maser is the mechanism of paramagnetic relaxation. We discuss briefly some pertinent aspects of this problem. It appears more complex than the corresponding nuclear magnetic resonance problem. One experimental fact is that it is possible to couple the saturation radiation to one set of spin levels and simultaneously saturate a second pair of levels at approximately the same spacing which is weakly coupled to the radiation field [Strandberg, Davis, Faughnan, Kyhl, and Wolga, Phys. Rev. **109**, 1988 (1958)]. Strandberg [Phys. Rev. **110**, 65 (1958)] has interpreted these results as evidence for the idea that there are anomalies in the phonon excitation, with the lattice modes with frequency near the spin resonance in equilibrium with the high-temperature saturated spin system. He considers this to be in part a consequence of the fact that the specific heat of the lattice vibrations at 4°K (calculated from say the Debye model) is several orders smaller than that of the paramagnetic spin system. Giordmaine, Alsop, Nash, and Townes [Phys. Rev. **109**, 302 (1958)] have described a series of experiments using paramagnetic resonance at 9000 Mc, at 1–4°K; $Gd_2Mg_3(NO_3)_{12}\cdot 24H_2O$), $K_3Cr(CN)_6$, and $Cu(NH_4)_2(SO_4)_2\cdot 6H_2O$) were used. They found that it was not possible to "burn a hole" in their resonances by saturation, indicating that their lines were homogeneously broadened. In the case of Cu, saturation of one line immediately saturated seven neighboring resonances. They were not able to observe the spin reversal by adiabatic rapid passage. No difference in absorption was noted in times as short as one msec after adiabatic rapid passage. They also observed that excitation due to a rapid sweep through a single resonance decayed very rapidly while that due to a slower sweep decayed at the normal rate, $T_1 \rightarrow 10$ sec. They interpreted these results as evidence for the idea that for some salts at low temperatures it is the lattice bath relaxation which limits the total relaxation rate. [Gorter, Van der Marel, and Bölger, Physica **21**, 103 (1955)]. They also remarked that for these salts the spin lattice relaxation time is several orders smaller than the observed values of T_1, and is of order 10^{-5} sec for Gd and 10^{-4} sec for Cu. In addition, they concluded that the breadth of the lattice modes is much larger than the width of the resonances in the diluted crystals (several hundred Mc for 1% paramagnetic concentration of the Cu salt), that the relaxation time T_1 is dependent on crystal size, and that the breadth of the lattice modes increases with increasing concentration of paramagnetic centers. They also suggested that for those salts described by the foregoing conditions, operation of an adiabatic rapid passage two-level maser would be impractical while three-level maser operation would be possible with reduced band width.

Bloembergen [Phys. Rev. **109**, 2209 (1958)] and Strandberg independently [Phys. Rev. **110**, 65 (1958)] have reached a different conclusion. Bloembergen points out that three-level maser iction is not possible for a salt whose paramagnetic relaxation rate is determined by interaction between lattice vibrations and the helium bath and for which the heat conduction between spin system and lattice is 1000 times better than between lattice and heat bath. Let ν_{31} be the saturation frequency and ν_{32} the amplification frequency and let these frequencies be widely spaced, with no overlapping of phonon bands. Then we have a negative spin temperature corresponding to levels 2 and 3. If the thermal contact with the phonons is very good then a band centered at frequency ν_{32} will start to gain energy, in order to attempt to reach equilibrium with the negative temperature spin system. Since the lattice vibration levels are those of harmonic oscillators, they have no upper bound. They cannot be saturated [R. Karplus and J. Schwinger Phys. Rev. **73**, 1020 (1948)] and the temperature associated with the ν_{32} band can never become negative. The steady state (nonequilibrium) situation would be one in which the spins of levels 2 and 3 are at a very high negative temperature and those effects must be included. Let w_{12} be the heat bath induced transition probability from state 1 to state 2, with corresponding meanings for w_{21}, w_{32}, w_{23}, w_{13}, and w_{31}. First suppose the system is in thermal equilibrium with no microwave fields applied. The number of particles leaving the state E_1 per sec must equal the number returning to it, so

$$n_1 w_{12} = n_2 w_{21}, \quad n_1 w_{13} = n_3 w_{31}. \tag{8}$$

Employing the Boltzmann factor enables us to write

$$w_{12}/w_{21} = n_2/n_1 = e^{-h\nu_{21}/kT}. \tag{9}$$

The w's are the reciprocals of the spin lattice relaxation times. Now suppose that a strong microwave field of frequency ν_{31}, and a weak microwave signal of frequency ν_{32} are present. Let W_{31} and W_{32} be the transition probabilities induced by these rf fields. The numbers of particles n_1, n_2, and n_3 occupying the three levels satisfy the relation,

$$n_1 + n_2 + n_3 = N. \tag{10}$$

For $(h\nu_{32})/(kT) \ll 1$, the populations satisfy the equations

$$\frac{dn_3}{dt} = w_{13}\left(n_1 - n_3 - \frac{Nh\nu_{31}}{3kT}\right) + w_{23}\left(n_2 - n_3 - \frac{Nh\nu_{32}}{3kT}\right) + W_{31}(n_1 - n_3) + W_{32}(n_2 - n_3),$$

$$\frac{dn_2}{dt} = w_{23}\left(n_3 - n_2 + \frac{Nh\nu_{32}}{3kT}\right) + w_{21}\left(n_1 - n_2 - \frac{Nh\nu_{21}}{3kT}\right) + W_{32}(n_3 - n_2), \tag{11}$$

$$\frac{dn_1}{dt} = w_{13}\left(n_3 - n_1 + \frac{Nh\nu_{31}}{3kT}\right) + w_{21}\left(n_2 - n_1 + \frac{Nh\nu_{21}}{3kT}\right) - W_{31}(n_1 - n_3).$$

These equations have the following approximate steady-state solution for the case in mind, $W_{31} \gg W_{32}$.

$$n_1 - n_2 = n_3 - n_2 = \frac{hN}{3kT}\left[\frac{-w_{23}\nu_{32} + w_{21}\nu_{21}}{w_{23} + w_{21} + W_{32}}\right]. \tag{12}$$

In case the numerator of (12) is positive, amplification is possible at frequency ν_{32}. In case it is negative, amplification is possible at the frequency ν_{21} and the W_{32} in the denominator of (12) must be replaced by W_{21}. The signal power emitted by the material is obtained by multiplying (12) by the signal induced transition probability W_{32} and the energy of one quantum.

$$P = \frac{Nh^2\nu_{32}(w_{21}\nu_{21} - w_{32}\nu_{32})W_{32}}{3kT(w_{23} + w_{21} + W_{32})}. \tag{13}$$

The situation described by (12) and (13) is qualitatively the same, but more complex, if $(h\nu/kT)$ is not small compared to 1. The procedures for calculating the transition probability W_{32} require a knowledge of the matrix elements of the interaction with the Maxwell field, and appropriate relaxation times. For the remainder of the section we consider a paramagnetic ion type of solid state amplifier. In this case the signal induced transition probability is given by

$$W_{32} = \left(\frac{2\pi}{h}\right)^2 |\langle 2|M_x|3\rangle|^2 \langle H_s^2(\nu_{32})\rangle_{\text{Av}} T_2. \tag{14}$$

Here M_x is the (x component) magnetic dipole operator, $\langle H_s^2(\nu_{32})\rangle_{\text{Av}}$ is the volume average squared magnetic field at the signal microwave frequency ν_{32}, and T_2 is the spin-spin relaxation time.

Expression (13) shows that the temperature T of the heat bath must be low. The three-level solid state masers which have so far been successfully operated have employed liquid helium cooling with temperatures in the range 1.25–4°K. In addition to increasing the amplification, the low temperatures partially improve the noise performance.

The power which is absorbed from the saturation†

---

lattice vibrations with which the spins are on "speaking terms" will be at a very high positive temperature. A high negative temperature means that the level populations associated with states 2 and 3 are almost equal, and therefore the maser would not operate in the observed manner. Bloembergen has solved the problem of three-level maser and phonon steady states in terms of the spin populations n_1, n_2, n_3 and the average lattice oscillator excitation quantum numbers in the three phonon bands, $n_{ph}(\nu_{32})$, $n_{ph}(\nu_{21})$, $n_{ph}(\nu_{31})$. His solution confirms that $n_3 - n_2$ is too small for maser operation if the contact between spins and phonons is better than between phonons and heat bath.

A possibility which has briefly been explored by the author is that the temperature associated with all three maser spin levels is positive, amplification occurring as a result of a two-quantum process involving absorption of a saturation frequency photon and emission of an amplification frequency photon. This is a kind of Raman process in which energy is conserved in both transitions. Direct calculation shows that this effect is too small, and that a low negative spin temperature needs to be assumed, in conjunction with single photon processes, in order to explain the operation of a maser.

It can be concluded that the paramagnetic relaxation mechanisms suggested by Giordmaine, Nash, and Townes do not apply to those salts which have been successfully used in a three-level maser.

Shapiro, Bloembergen, and Artman [Bull. Am. Phys. Soc. Ser. II, **3**, 317 (1958)] have reported additional indirect saturation experiments which they interpret as caused by higher order spin-spin interactions rather than by "hot phonons." This appears very reasonable because it is difficult to see how the lattice vibration modes could be tightly coupled to the saturated spin system without being similarly coupled to the negative temperature spin system. Further work by Bloembergen, Shapiro, Pershan, and Artman (Cruft Laboratory Technical Report No. 285, Harvard University, Cambridge, Massachusetts, October 15, 1958) has increased the evidence that the indirect saturation phenomena are indeed due to spin spin interactions. This follows the mechanism proposed by R. Kronig and C. J. Bouwkamp, Physica **5**, 521 (1938) and Physica **6**, 290 (1939).

† *Note added in proof.*—An interesting discussion of masers as heat engines has been given by H. E. D. Scovil and E. O. Schulz-

field of frequency ν_{31} is given by that needed to balance the tendency of collisions to restore equilibrium, and is

$$P_s=(h\nu_{31})^2 n_1/2T_1kT. \quad (15)$$

Here T_1 is the spin-lattice relaxation time.

Expressions (13), (14), and (15) lead to the following general criteria for selection of materials for a paramagnetic ion three-level maser. If the heat bath transition probabilities w_{21} and w_{23} are nearly equal, the frequencies ν_{21} and ν_{32} should be very unequal. However, if the frequencies ν_{21} and ν_{32} are approximately equal, then w_{21} and w_{23} should be very unequal. If ν_{21} is exactly equal to ν_{32} the device cannot operate since the same signal which induces transitions between states 2 and 1 will be effective in inducing transitions between 3 and 2. Amplification between one pair of states would be annulled by absorption associated with the other pair since (12) requires that $n_1-n_2\approx n_3-n_2$. In order to obtain large gain the temperature T has to be small. The spin should be at least 1, but preferably not more than $\frac{3}{2}$, otherwise the particles will be distributed among too many states. (Gd with a spin of $\frac{7}{2}$ is a notable exception.) It is also desirable that the nuclear spin be zero. Expression (15) requires that for small T, the spin-lattice relaxation time T_1 be as large as possible, otherwise excessive saturation power will be needed with consequent difficulty in maintaining low temperatures. Expressions (13) and (14) show that the product of total number of spins, N, and the spin-spin relaxation time T_2 should be as large as possible. Inasmuch as an increase in concentration of spins tends, in general, to decrease T_2 it is necessary to attain an optimum value of the product NT_2 by suitably diluting the paramagnetic ions. The zero field splitting ought to be of the same order of magnitude as the energy level difference associated with the signal frequency. This follows because mixing of the spin states is essential in order to have transitions allowed between all three levels. This is most favorable when the Zeeman and crystalline field terms are comparable.

It is possible, and in some cases desirable, to use a four-level system. A particularly elegant solution of the problem of four-level maser design employing ruby has been given by Kikuchi,[7] Makhov, Lambe, and Terhune with $E_4-E_2=E_3-E_1$. In the latter case a pumping frequency $\nu_{42}=\nu_{31}$ populates the third level and simultaneously depopulates the second level.

A generalization of (13), given by Kikuchi, is

$$P=\frac{Nh^2}{4kT}\left[\frac{w_{21}\nu_{21}-w_{32}\nu_{32}+w_{41}\nu_{41}+w_{43}\nu_{43}}{w_{21}+w_{23}+w_{14}+w_{34}+W_{32}}\right]W_{32}\nu_{32}. \quad (16)$$

The active material of a maser can be placed in a wave-guide transmission system or in a resonant cavity. In the former case we have a traveling wave amplifier with power output given by

$$P=P_oe^{\beta l}, \quad (17)$$

where l is the distance along the amplifier.

Differentiating this with respect to l leads to the gain coefficient β given by

$$\beta=dP/Pdl. \quad (18)$$

Here (dP/dl) is the power emitted per unit length and P is the power at the point where (dP/dl) is calculated, in accordance with expressions (13) or (16). Employing (14), this can be written

$$\beta=\frac{32\pi^3(n_3-n_2)|M_{32}|^2T_2\nu f}{hv_g}, \quad (19)$$

where f is a filling factor which may approach 1 and v_g is the group velocity.

Here the power P has been set equal to the energy density times the group velocity v_g. This equation shows that a slow wave structure (small group velocity) is a desirable method of obtaining a higher gain-band-width product. Slow wave structures proposed thus far are a ruby rod with a helix wrapped around it, considered by W. W. Anderson of Stanford University, and a rectangular wave guide with conducting fingers giving circular polarization, considered by DeGrasse, Schulz-DuBois,

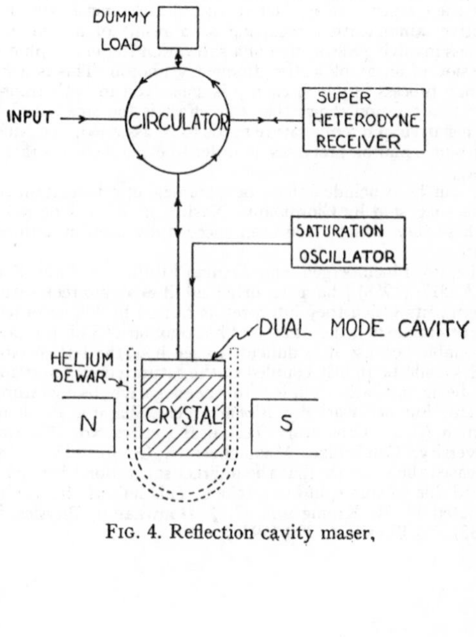

FIG. 4. Reflection cavity maser.

DuBois [Phys. Rev. Letters 2, 262 (1959)]. They consider a hot reservoir with temperature T_1 and filter allowing a band of frequencies in the vicinity of ν_{31} to pass, in thermal contact with a maser. Levels 2 and 3 are in thermal contact with a cold reservoir at temperature T_0, and coupled through a filter with pass band centered about ν_{32}. The signal frequency is ν_{21}. Ignoring relaxation processes within the maser, using the Boltzmann distribution law and requiring $n_2>n_1$ leads to the result that the maser efficiency ν_{21}/ν_{31} is that of the Carnot engine, $(T_1-T_0)/T_1$. They note the important result that instead of using a coherent microwave pump at ν_{31}, thermal excitation by two reservoirs as described above should make it possible to generate microwaves.

[7] Makhov, Kikuchi, Lambe, and Terhune, Phys. Rev. **109**, 1349 (L) (1958); also Kikuchi, Lambe, Makhov, and Terhune (to be published).

and Seidel of the Bell Telephone Laboratories. These structures could be employed either as transmission or reflection devices. Means must be provided to prevent output power from being fed back to the input, causing the amplifier to oscillate, and for preventing noise from the load from getting to the maser and being amplified. Transmission devices utilizing nonreciprocity would accomplish this.

The reflection cavity type of maser has undergone most development and appears capable of giving enough gain-band-width product for most purposes. A block diagram is sketched in Fig. 4. Here a nonreciprocal device, the microwave circulator,[8] prevents power from being fed back and causing oscillation, and keeps noise from the load out of the maser. Resonant cavity expressions for gain and noise performance are usually expressed in terms of the Q's (quality factors) of a cavity. The Q is defined by

$$Q=2\pi\nu E/P_a, \tag{20}$$

where E is the energy in the principal cavity mode and P_a is the rate of absorption of energy. The unloaded Q, usually denoted by Q_o, is defined by

$$Q_o=2\pi\nu E/P_{aw}, \tag{21}$$

where P_{aw} is the part of the absorbed power that is absorbed in the cavity walls. The magnetic Q, denoted by Q_m, is defined by

$$Q_m=-\frac{2\pi\nu E}{P_e}=\frac{-\nu\langle H^2(\nu)\rangle V_c}{4P_e}, \tag{22}$$

where P_e is the net power emitted by the active material.

Here V_c is the volume of the cavity and ν is the frequency being amplified. The denominator is given by expressions (13) or (16). The external Q, denoted by Q_e, is defined by

$$Q_e=2\pi\nu E/P_{en}, \tag{23}$$

where P_{en} is the net power output.

The cavity mode may be represented by the equivalent circuit in Fig. 5. G_m, G_o, and G_e are conductances associated with the spin system, the walls of the cavity, and the output load, respectively. From Fig. 5, a loaded Q may be defined as

$$Q_l^{-1}=Q_m^{-1}+Q_o^{-1}+Q_e^{-1}. \tag{24}$$

The voltage standing wave ratio in the transmission system which drives the cavity, B, is given in terms of the incident voltage V_i and the reflected voltage V_r, as

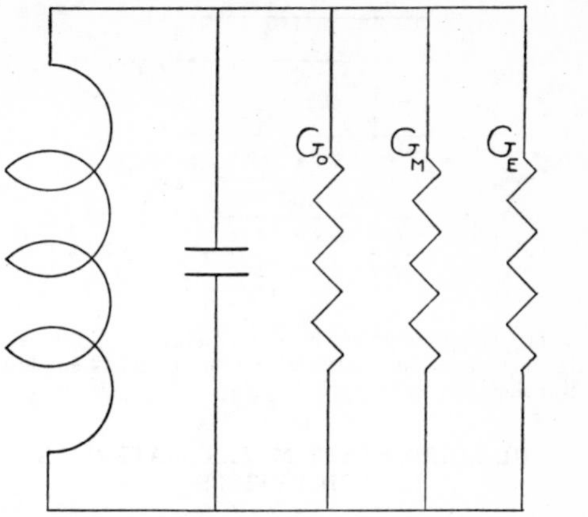

FIG. 5. Cavity equivalent circuit.

$$B=\frac{|V_i|+|V_r|}{|V_i|-|V_r|}=\frac{1+g}{1-g}. \tag{25}$$

Here g is the "voltage" gain defined by $g=|V_r/V_i|$. The power gain is g^2.

After solving (25) for g^2, we obtain

$$g^2=[(1-B)/(1+B)]^2. \tag{26}$$

The maser will oscillate if $-Q_m^{-1}>Q_o^{-1}+Q_e^{-1}$, and will amplify if $Q_o^{-1}+Q_e^{-1}>-Q_m^{-1}>Q_o^{-1}$. Let us consider some characteristics of an amplifier.

From transmission line theory, the voltage standing wave ratio B (at resonance), in terms of the conductances shown in Fig. 5, is

$$B=(G_m+G_o)/G_e=Q_e[Q_o^{-1}+Q_m^{-1}]. \tag{27}$$

This assumes that the input transmission line is matched to a conductance (G_m+G_o).

Use of (26) gives for the power gain,

$$g^2=\left[\frac{Q_e^{-1}-(Q_o^{-1}+Q_m^{-1})}{Q_e^{-1}+(Q_o^{-1}+Q_m^{-1})}\right]^2. \tag{28}$$

In terms of the loaded Q this takes the form

$$g^2=[2Q_lQ_e^{-1}-1]^2. \tag{29}$$

The band width is obtained by dividing the operating frequency by the loaded Q. For a low-temperature maser Q_o is so large that it may be neglected in (28). The product of the square root of power gain and band width is

$$g\Delta\nu=\frac{\nu[Q_e+|Q_m|]}{Q_e|Q_m|}. \tag{30}$$

For a high-gain device it is customary to adjust Q_e so that it equals the magnitude Q_m. Under these conditions (30) is approximately a constant, given by

$$g\Delta\nu\approx 2\nu/|Q_m|. \tag{31}$$

[8] Microwave circulators are not available below about 1400 mc/sec. Autler has proposed an ingenious arrangement [Lincoln Laboratory, MIT, Rept. M 37–27; Proc. Inst. Radio. Engrs. **46**, 1880 (1958)] using two masers in a "balanced" arrangement, which does not require use of a circulator. The two masers are at opposite ends of a coaxial or wave-guide "magic" tee. One of the maser arms is a quarter wavelength longer than the other. The antenna and receiver are connected to the other two arms. Thus the two maser outputs combine at the load. Noise from the load is amplified by the masers but is then radiated back out through the antenna.

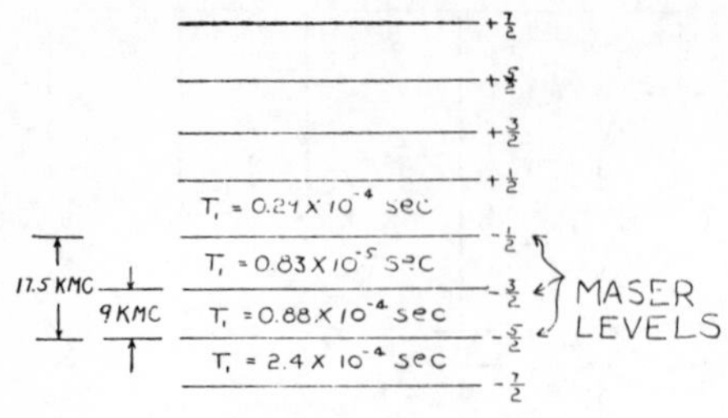

FIG. 6. Energy levels of the ground state of Gd^{+++} in ethyl sulfate, including spin-lattice relaxation times, as employed by Scovil, Feher, and Seidel.

III. SOLID STATE MASER MATERIALS AND DEVICES

The materials which have so far been successfully employed in three-level masers are[9,10] gadolinium ethyl sulfate, potassium chromicyanide,[11,12] and ruby.[7] We use the roman type g for the magnitude of the Zeeman tensor. This should not be confused with the italic g used for voltage gain.

Gadolinium ethyl sulfate was used in the first successful solid state maser.[10] The gadolinium ion is in an ^8S ground state having 7 electrons in a half-filled $4F$ shell. There is fine structure splitting into 7 lines with spacing which varies approximately as $3\cos^2\theta-1$, where θ is the angle between the constant magnetic field, H_o, and the crystalline field axis. If the steady magnetic field is normal to the crystalline symmetry axis, the spin Hamiltonian may be written[11] approximately as

$$\mathcal{H}=\mathrm{g}\beta_m H_o\cdot S_z-\tfrac{1}{2}D[S_z^2-\tfrac{1}{3}S(S+1)]+\tfrac{1}{2}D[S_x^2-S_y^2], \quad (32)$$

where β_m is the Bohr magneton, S is the spin operator, $\mathrm{g}=1.99$, $D=.02\ \mathrm{cm}^{-1}$, and the axis of quantization is parallel to that of the constant magnetic field, H_o. The first term of (32) represents the interaction with the field H_o which brings the transition to the required frequency. The second term makes the level spacings unequal, and the third term mixes the states, giving rise to transitions with $\Delta S_z=\pm 2$. The angle between H_o and the microwave magnetic field should be zero for the $\Delta S_z=\pm 2$ transitions and 90° for the $\Delta S_z=\pm 1$ transitions. Scovil, Feher, and Seidel used an angle of 45°. The energy levels and relaxation times of the ground state of Gd^{+++} in ethyl sulfate are shown in Fig. 6. Because the energy level separations are almost equal,

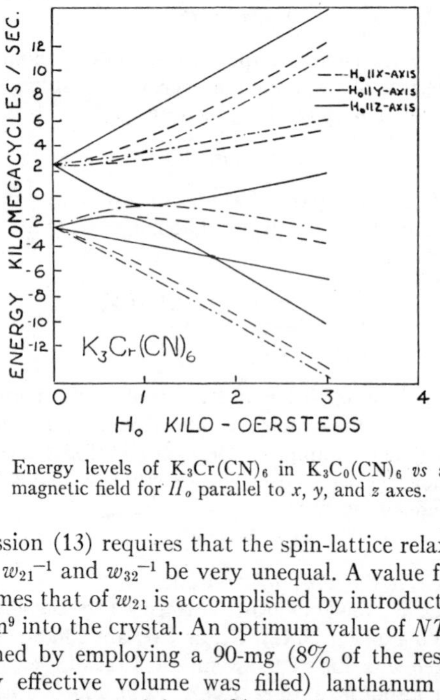

FIG. 8. Energy levels of $K_3Cr(CN)_6$ in $K_3Co(CN)_6$ *vs* applied magnetic field for H_o parallel to x, y, and z axes.

expression (13) requires that the spin-lattice relaxation times w_{21}^{-1} and w_{32}^{-1} be very unequal. A value for w_{32} ten times that of w_{21} is accomplished by introduction of cerium[9] into the crystal. An optimum value of NT_2 was obtained by employing a 90-mg (8% of the resonant cavity effective volume was filled) lanthanum ethyl sulfate crystal containing 0.5% Gd^{+++} and 0.2% Ce^{+++}. The device was operated at 1.2°K with a saturation frequency of 17.5 kmc/sec. Oscillations were obtained at 9 kmc/sec.

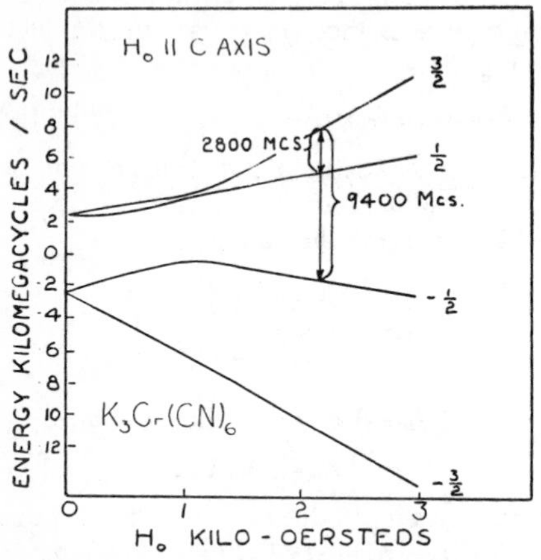

FIG. 7. Energy levels of $K_3Cr(CN)_6$ in $K_3Co(CN)_6$ *vs* applied magnetic field, for $H_o \|$ to the c axis.

The second material to be successfully used[12] in a solid state maser was potassium chromicyanide diluted in a cobalticyanide crystal [$K_3Co(CN)_6$]. In this case 0.5% Cr was used as the paramagnetic salt. This material appears to have the long spin-lattice relaxation time of 0.2 sec, at 1.25°K. The paramagnetic resonance spectrum of $K_3Cr(CN)_6$ arises from two differently oriented complexes per unit cell. The spin Hamiltonian is

$$\mathcal{H}=\beta_m\mathbf{H}\cdot\mathbf{g}\cdot\mathbf{S}+D[S_z^2-\tfrac{1}{3}S(S+1)]+E[S_x^2-S_y^2]. \quad (33)$$

[9] G. Feher and H. E. D. Scovil, Phys. Rev. **105**, 2, 760(L) (1957).

[10] Scovil, Feher, and Seidel, Phys. Rev. **105**, 2, 762(L) (1957); H. E. D. Scovil, Trans. Inst. Radio Engrs. Prof. Group on Microwave Theory and Techniques **6**, 29 (1958).

[11] B. Bleaney and K. W. H. Stevens, Repts. Progr. in Phys. **16**, 108 (1951).

[12] A. L. McWhorter and J. W. Meyer, Phys. Rev. **109**, 312 (1958); R. H. Kingston, Lincoln Laboratory, MIT, Rept. M 35–79; Artman, Bloembergen, and Shapiro, Phys. Rev. **169**, 1392 (1958); S. H. Autler and N. McAvoy, Phys. Rev. **110**, 280(L) (1958).

For cobalt as the diluent $D=0.083$ cm^{-1}, $E=0.011$ cm^{-1}, and the Zeeman tensor $\mathbf{g}$ is approximately isotropic and equal to 1.99. The direction cosines between the magnetic axes (x, y, and z) and the pseudo-orthorhombic crystalline axes (a, b, and c) are

	x	y	z
a	0.104	0	0.994
b	± 0.994	0	∓ 0.104
c	0	1	0

Energy level diagrams computed by McWhorter and Meyer are shown in Figs. 7 and 8. They used a dual mode coaxial cavity one half wavelength long at 2800 mc/sec operating in the *TEM* mode. For pumping, the cavity operated in the TE_{113} mode. The constant magnetic field H_o was applied, approximately parallel to the crystalline c axis, with operating conditions shown in Fig. 7. The upper two levels, labeled $+\frac{3}{2}$ and $+\frac{1}{2}$ were used for amplification and the second and fourth levels

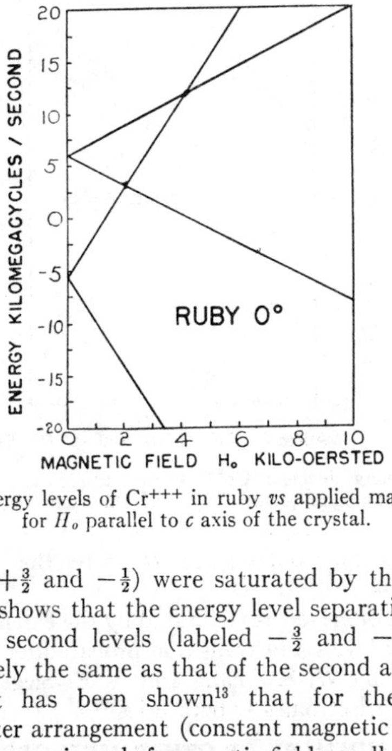

FIG. 9. Energy levels of Cr^{+++} in ruby *vs* applied magnetic field for H_o parallel to c axis of the crystal.

(labeled $+\frac{3}{2}$ and $-\frac{1}{2}$) were saturated by the rf field. Figure 7 shows that the energy level separation of the first and second levels (labeled $-\frac{3}{2}$ and $-\frac{1}{2}$) is approximately the same as that of the second and fourth levels. It has been shown[13] that for the Meyer-McWhorter arrangement (constant magnetic field parallel to the c axis and rf magnetic field parallel to the a axis) the transition probability for the first- to second-level transition is in fact 100 times greater than for the desired second and fourth levels. This is because the matrix elements are 4 times greater and the saturation radio-frequency magnetic field normal to the constant magnetic field favors the $\Delta m=1$ transitions. This implies that indirect saturation was accomplished by McWhorter and Meyer. They coupled strongly to levels 1 and 2 and succeeded in saturating levels 2 and 4 also.

This possibility of indirect saturation of one pair of levels by coupling to another pair which have the same energy separation is a useful aid in maser design. The total number of spins in the upper quartet of the chromium ion is approximately 10^{19}. A 10% filling factor was used. The calculated gain-band-width product $g\Delta\nu$, was 2.6×10^6 sec^{-1}. The measured value was 1.8×10^6 sec^{-1}. The small filling factor was chosen in order to be able to study the device without undue distortion of the cavity electromagnetic mode configurations. Practical amplifiers would therefore use a much larger filling factor, approaching unity. This gives a large increase in $g\Delta\nu$, of the order of 50. This is partly because there are more spins and partly because the increased dielectric constant enables a smaller cavity to be used.

The third material to be successfully used was ruby. Paramagnetic resonance in this material was investigated in the Soviet Union in 1955 and 1956,[14] and in the United States by Geusic.[15]

Again the Cr^{+++} ion is used, but the host crystal is Al_2O_3. The four nonequivalent sites are indistinguishable since the spin is less than two, and the crystal has trigonal symmetry. Maser action in ruby was first demonstrated by Makhov, Kikuchi, Lambe, and Terhune at the University of Michigan.[7] The spin Hamiltonian for Cr^{+++} in the Al_2O_3 lattice is given by

$$\mathcal{H}=\beta_m\mathbf{S}\cdot\mathbf{g}\cdot\mathbf{H}+D[S_z^2-\tfrac{1}{3}S(S+1)]. \qquad (34)$$

$\mathbf{g}$ is the Zeeman tensor with components $g_{zz}=g_{\parallel}$, $g_{xx}=g_{yy}=g_{\perp}$. This Hamiltonian leads to the eigenvalue equation[7]

$$(\epsilon^2-1)^2-\tfrac{5}{2}x^2\epsilon^2+\tfrac{9}{16}x^4-\frac{x^2(5g_{\parallel}^2\cos^2\theta-g_{\perp}^2\sin^2\theta)}{2g^2}+\frac{2\epsilon\lambda x^2(g_{\perp}^2\sin^2\theta-2g_{\parallel}^2\cos^2\theta)}{g^2}=0. \qquad (35)$$

Here

$$\epsilon=\frac{\text{Energy}}{|D|}, \quad x=g\frac{\beta_m H}{|D|},$$

$$D=-0.1913\ \text{cm}^{-1}=3.798\times10^{-17}\ \text{ergs},$$

$$\lambda=\frac{D}{|D|}, \quad g=1.986, \quad g^2=g_{\parallel}^2\cos^2\theta+g_{\perp}^2\sin^2\theta.$$

This equation is readily solved for the situations $\theta=0$, $\theta=\pi/2$, $g_{\perp}^2\sin^2\theta=2g_{\parallel}^2\cos^2\theta$. In the latter case, $\theta=\cos^{-1}(1/\sqrt{3})$ gives (assuming isotropic $\mathbf{g}$)

$$\epsilon(\pm\tfrac{3}{2})=\pm[1+(5/4)x^2+x(3+x^2)^{\frac{1}{2}}]^{\frac{1}{2}},$$

$$\epsilon(\pm\tfrac{1}{2})=\pm[1+(5/4)x^2-x(3+x^2)^{\frac{1}{2}}]^{\frac{1}{2}}.$$

[13] Standberg, Davis, Faughnan, Kyhl, and Wolga, Phys. Rev. **109**, 1988 (1958). See also Strandberg, Davis, and Kyhl, Fifth International Symposium on Low-Temperature Physics and Chemistry, Madison, Wisconsin (August 30, 1957).

[14] A. A. Manenkov and A. M. Prokhorov, Soviet Phys. JETP **1**, 611 (1955); M. M. Zaripov and Iv. Ia. Shamonin, Soviet Phys. JETP **3**, 171 (1956); J. E. Geusic, Phys. Rev. **102**, 1252 (1956).

[15] J. E. Geusic, Phys. Rev. **102**, 1252 (1956).

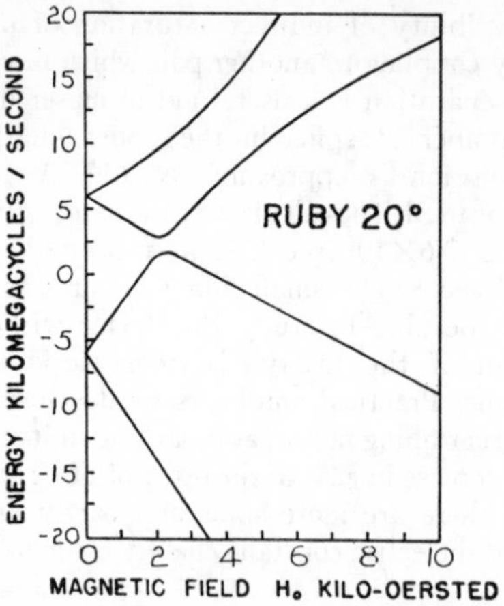

FIG. 10. Energy levels of Cr^{+++} in ruby *vs* applied magnetic field for H_o at 20° to *c* axis of the crystal.

Curves of energy levels as calculated with assistance of Dr. Schulz-DuBois are shown in Figs. 9–13. The four-level device using ruby has already been discussed. We are indebted to Professor Townes for the name "push-pull maser" for the four-level device of Makhov, Kikuchi, Lambe, and Terhune.‡

B. Characteristics of Some Ruby Masers

A ruby three-level maser has been developed by Alsop, Giordmaine, and Townes.[16] A large filling factor, approaching 0.9, is used. The "voltage gain" band-width product approaches 100 Mc, and the band width is approximately 5 Mc. The magnetic Q is about 400. The volume of the active material is about $\frac{1}{3}$ cm³. A rectangular cavity is used, operating in the TE_{011} mode

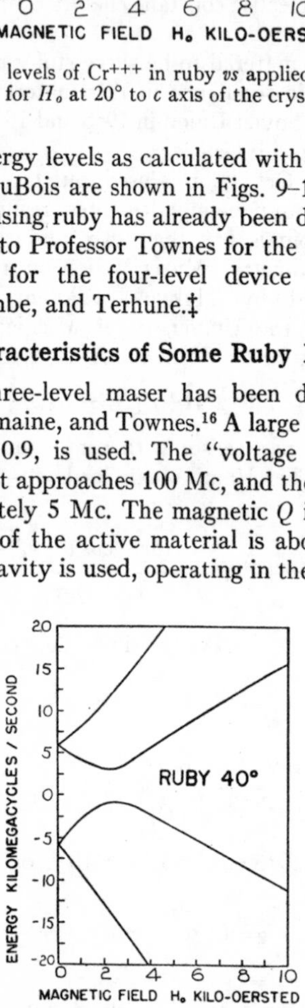

FIG. 11. Energy levels of Cr^{+++} in ruby *vs* applied magnetic field for H_o making an angle of 40° with the *c* axis of the crystal.

for the signal frequency and the TE_{012} mode for the saturation microwave field. The small cavity volume results from the high dielectric constant of ruby. About 30 mw of pumping power are required. The pump power is coupled to the wave guide by a remotely gear-controlled probe, and the signal power is coupled in by means of an iris. Liquid helium cooling with helium maintained at low pressure provided a bath temperature of 1.4°K.

Morris, Kyhl, and Strandberg[17] have described the ruby maser illustrated in Fig. 14. All four levels are employed. The chromium concentration is about 0.01%. Levels 1–3 and 2–4 are saturated at 23 kMc/sec. Levels 2–3 are employed for amplification. The device is tunable over the range 8400–9700 Mc/sec, and has the new feature that cavity resonance is not needed at the saturation frequency if a saturation power of 100 mw is employed. The fringing fields near the coupling hole

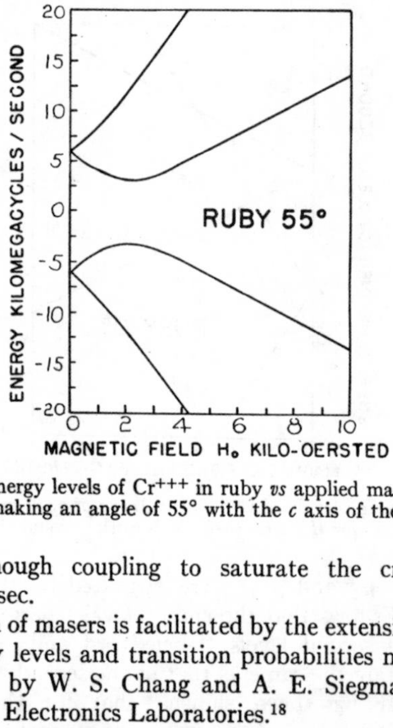

FIG. 12. Energy levels of Cr^{+++} in ruby *vs* applied magnetic field for H_o making an angle of 55° with the *c* axis of the crystal.

allow enough coupling to saturate the crystal at 23 kMc/sec.

Design of masers is facilitated by the extensive tables of energy levels and transition probabilities now being prepared by W. S. Chang and A. E. Siegman of the Stanford Electronics Laboratories.[18]

IV. SUMMARY OF OTHER METHODS FOR OBTAINING MASER ACTION

Bloch[19] showed, in 1946, that inversion of level populations can be obtained by "adiabatic rapid pas-

‡ *Note added in proof.*—The paramagnetic resonance absorption for Cr^{+++} ions in emerald has been reported by Geusic, Peter, and Schulz-DuBois [Bull. Am. Phys. Soc. Ser. II, 4, 21 (1959)]. The spin Hamiltonian is

$$\mathcal{H}=\beta_m[g_{\parallel}H_zS_z+g_{\perp}(H_xS_x+H_yS_y)]+D[S_z^2-\tfrac{1}{3}S(S+1)],$$
$$2D=-53.6\text{ kmc},\quad g_{\parallel}=1.973\pm0.002,\quad g_{\perp}=1.97\pm0.01.$$

[16] Alsop, Giordmaine, Mayer, and Townes, Astron. J. **63**, 301 (1958).

[17] Morris, Kyhl, and Strandberg, Proc. Inst. Radio Engrs. **47**, 80 (1959).

[18] W. S. Chang and A. E. Siegman, Stanford Electronics Lab. Tech. Rept. 156–1 (May 16, 1958). Their machine calculations are presented in the Appendix to this paper. Note carefully that their calculations were done using positive D. To use their curves and data for the correct negative sign of D, change the sign of their energies and regard their level labeled number four as having the lowest energy. Note their comments at the end of the Appendix.

[19] F. Bloch, Phys. Rev. **70**, 460 (1946). See also R. K. Wangsness and F. Bloch, Phys. Rev. **89**, 728 (1953).

sage" through resonance. We have again a system of spins in a "constant" magnetic field H_o. If a microwave magnetic field is applied at right angles to the "constant" magnetic field the spin system will precess about H_o. Suppose that H_o is smaller than the value required for resonance at the microwave angular frequency ω. If H_o is steady for a long time, and is then suddenly increased through resonance and beyond, the spin system is turned over. The magnetization vector will be antiparallel to H_o until equilibrium is restored by the spin-lattice relaxation mechanism. The passage through resonance must be adiabatic, but rapid enough so that the sweep occurs in a time short compared with the spin-lattice relaxation time. While the magnetization is antiparallel to the field there are more moments antiparallel than parallel. This means more particles in excited states than in the ground state. Such a system will therefore amplify.

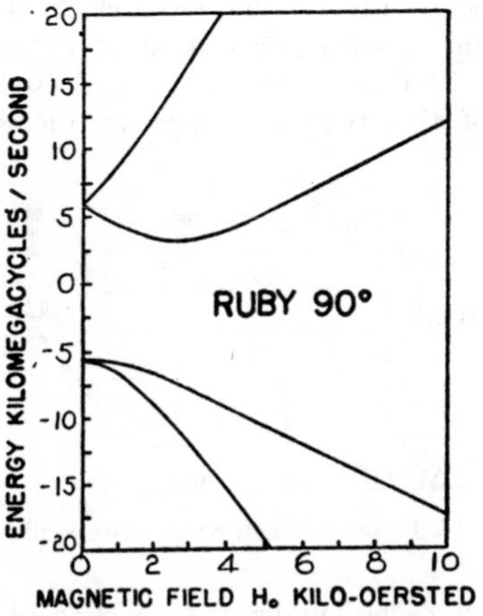

FIG. 13. Energy levels of Cr^{+++} in ruby *vs* applied magnetic field for H_o making an angle of 90° with the c axis of the crystal.

We assume the magnetic field H_o to be in the z direction. It is simpler to discuss the case where a circularly polarized rf field is applied, with its magnetic field in the x–y plane. The rf field is given by

$$H_x = H_1 \cos\omega t, \quad H_y = \mp H_1 \sin\omega t. \tag{36}$$

The $-$ sign refers to a positive gyromagnetic ratio and the $+$ sign to a negative one. The magnetization vector then satisfies the following equations.

$$\dot{M}_x - \gamma(M_y H_z - M_z H_y) + (M_x/T_2) = 0, \tag{37}$$

$$\dot{M}_y - \gamma(M_z H_x - M_x H_z) + (M_y/T_2) = 0, \tag{38}$$

$$\dot{M}_z - \gamma(M_x H_y - M_y H_x) + (M_z/T_1) = M_o/T_1. \tag{39}$$

γ is the gyromagnetic ratio, T_1 is the longitudinal (spin-lattice) relaxation time, T_2 is the transverse (spin-spin) relaxation time, and M_o is the value of the magnetization in the absence of a radio-frequency field.

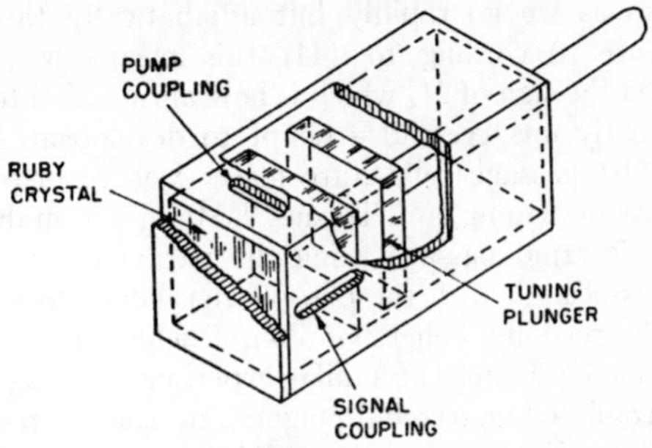

FIG. 14. Ruby maser of Morris, Kyhl, and Strandberg.

A quantity $\delta(t)$ is defined by the relation

$$\delta(t) = \frac{H_o(t) - (\omega/|\gamma|)}{H_1}. \tag{40}$$

$\delta(t)$ is zero at the resonant field $H_o = \omega/|\gamma|$. The magnetic field H_o is assumed to vary at a slow enough rate so that

$$|d\delta/dt| \ll |\gamma H_1|. \tag{41}$$

This is a statement of the adiabatic criterion. Subject to this condition Bloch gives the following solution of (37), (38), and (39):

$$M_x = \frac{M \cos\omega t}{(1+\delta^2)^{\frac{1}{2}}}, \tag{42}$$

$$M_y = \mp \frac{M \sin\omega t}{(1+\delta^2)^{\frac{1}{2}}}, \tag{43}$$

$$M_z = M\delta/(1+\delta^2)^{\frac{1}{2}}, \tag{44}$$

$$M(t) = \frac{1}{T_1} \int_{-\infty}^{t} \frac{\delta(t') e^{-[\theta(t)-\theta(t')]} M_o(t')}{[1+\delta^2(t')]^{\frac{1}{2}}} dt', \tag{45}$$

$$\theta(t) - \theta(t') = \frac{1}{T_1} \int_{t'}^{t} \left[\frac{\delta^2(t'') + (T_1/T_2)}{1+\delta^2(t'')} \right] dt''. \tag{46}$$

In order to discuss adiabatic rapid passage we assume that $\delta^2(t'')$ has been constant for a long time and then at time t_o is quickly increased through resonance, without violating (41). We have, for $\delta^2 \gg T_1/T_2$,

$$\theta(t) - \theta(t') = (t - t')/T_1. \tag{47}$$

The part of (45) resulting from the rapid change of δ is negligible. For the rest, since δ is large we have, from (45)

$$M(t) = \pm M(t_o). \tag{48}$$

Here the $+$ sign refers to the situation where δ was positive up to t_o (H_o larger than the resonant value, initially), and the $-$ sign refers to the situation where δ was negative up to t_o (H_o smaller than the resonant value, initially, then increased through resonance). Thus the sign of $M(t)$ does not change, but the sign of δ

changes as we go rapidly but adiabatically through resonance. According to (44) this means we have changed the sign of M_z which is now antiparallel to H_o.

An early unsuccessful attempt to develop an adiabatic fast passage solid-state maser was reported by Combrisson, Honig, and Townes.[20] Maser action due to adiabatic rapid passage using the paramagnetic electrons associated with the phosphorus donors in silicon was observed by Feher, Gordon, Buehler, Gere, and Thurmond.[21] Somewhat similar experiments using neutron irradiated quartz and magnesium oxide were done by Chester, Wagner, and Castle.[22] With a quartz sample containing $\sim 10^{18}$ spins the inverted state persisted for 2 msec at 4.2°K. A value of 5×10^6 sec^{-1} was obtained for the "voltage" gain-band-width product for gains between 8 and 21 db. This work was done at 9 kMc/sec with microwave powers for inversion of about 0.5 w, in 50–100 μsec pulses. A modulation structure of the pulsed power emitted from the cavity as the magnetic field is swept through resonance is observed. Senitzky[23] has suggested that this amplitude modulation of the power from the resonant cavity is due to the periodic transfer of energy between the cavity electromagnetic field and the spin system.

Purcell and Pound[24] were able to obtain inverted level populations in a magnetic resonance experiment using a single crystal of LiF which had a very long relaxation time. They removed their crystal from the strong field and inverted its spin system by means of other rapidly varying magnetic fields. When the crystal was reinserted in the strong field they were able to observe the return of the magnetization to its equilibrium value, from its "negative-temperature" state.

Weber studied the following method[1] in 1951. Consider a symmetric top molecule in an externally applied electrostatic field. The Stark effect has linear and quadratic terms. The linear effect is the dominant one if the field is not too strong. The energy levels are given by the formula

$$E_{JKM_j}{}^{(1)} = \frac{-\boldsymbol{\mu}\cdot\mathbf{E}KM_j}{J(J+1)}. \qquad (49)$$

$\boldsymbol{\mu}$ is the electric dipole moment, $\mathbf{E}$ is the Stark field, J, K, and M_j are the quantum numbers associated with the symmetrical top. If the electrostatic (Stark) field is applied normal to the microwave electric field the $\Delta M = \pm 1$ transition will be allowed, and the frequency for such a transition will be

$$\nu = \boldsymbol{\mu}\cdot\mathbf{E}K/J(J+1)h. \qquad (50)$$

If the gas is in equilibrium it will absorb microwaves at this frequency. There are more electric dipole moments parallel to the field than antiparallel to it. If the electrostatic field is suddenly reversed we have a negative temperature, and more dipole moments antiparallel than parallel to the field, and the device will amplify during roughly one relaxation time. A pulsed oscillator may be constructed as shown in Fig. 15. Here we have a resonant cavity with Stark electrode. If a square wave is applied there will be a microwave pulse emitted each time the field reverses and the TE_{10} mode (microwave electric field *parallel* to the Stark electrode) will be excited.

No experiments of this type were done because calculations showed that it would be difficult to achieve a useful gain-band width product in any gas-type maser amplifier, and the use of a solid was suggested.

A maser oscillator using a gas is, however, a very useful frequency standard, and compares favorably in many respects with a cesium beam clock. Work on an ammonia maser oscillator started at Columbia University in 1951 and the first maser oscillator and amplifier of this type was operated successfully by

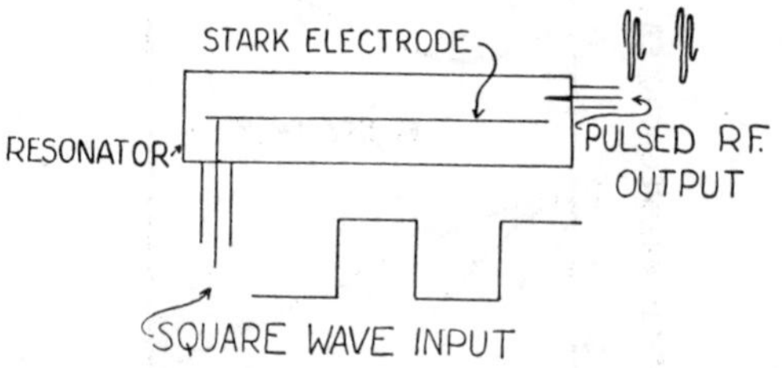

FIG. 15. Pulsed symmetric top maser oscillator.

Gordon and Zeiger[2] under the direction of Professor C. H. Townes in 1954. Similar work was done independently[3] by Basov and Prokhorov at the Lebedev Institute at about the same time. In addition to providing an exceptionally stable oscillator, the ammonia maser can also be employed as a very high resolution spectrometer. A sketch of the focuser and beam and cavity details is given in Fig. 16. The maser action is accomplished in the following way. The nitrogen atom in ammonia is in a potential which is symmetric on either side of the plane of the hydrogen atoms. In this kind of potential each harmonic oscillator level is split, and the ground state splitting provides microwave absorption lines of different frequencies for different rotational levels. In a Stark field the energy of the upper doublet level increases and that of the lower level decreases. The focuser of Fig. 16, provides an electric field with intensity approximately proportional to the displacement from the axis. If a molecular beam is now sent through the focuser the molecules in the lower doublet state drift outward to regions of lower energy and increasing field, and are removed. The center of the beam contains mostly higher energy particles. These

[20] Combrisson, Honig, and Townes, Compt. rend. **242**, 2451 (1956). Suggestions for a low-temperature adiabatic rapid passage maser were made independently by Strandberg in 1956.
[21] Feher, Gordon, Buehler, Gere, and Thurmond, Phys. Rev. **109**, 221 (1958).
[22] Chester, Wagner, and Castle, Phys. Rev. **110**, 281 (1958).
[23] I. R. Senitzky, Phys. Rev. Letters **1**, 167 (1958).
[24] E. M. Purcell and R. V. Pound, Phys. Rev. **81**, 279 (1951).

enter the resonant cavity and undergo stimulated emission. In this case, then, a higher population in excited states is achieved by the simple expedient of removing ground state particles from the beam.

The condition for sustained oscillation of a resonant cavity with volume V which contains n excited atoms or molecules may be obtained by setting the emitted power equal to the power lost in the cavity walls.

$$nW_{21}h\nu \geq P_w.$$

W_{21} is the transition probability. We write W_{21} in terms of the appropriate squared matrix elements $|\mu|^2$ and the line width $\Delta\nu$, and P_w in terms of the quality factor Q to obtain (Gordon, Zeiger, and Townes, see reference 2)

$$n \geq hV\Delta\nu / 4\pi|\mu|^2 Q.$$

The frequency range over which appreciable energy is distributed in a maser oscillator is given in terms of the

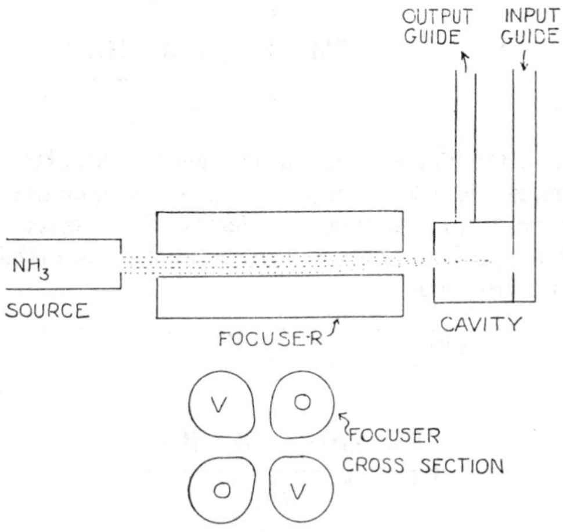

FIG. 16. Columbia ammonia maser.

total power output P, Boltzmann's constant, and the cavity wall temperature T as

$$\delta\nu = 4\pi kT(\Delta\nu)^2/P.$$

An upper state population ten times that of the lower state may be achieved in practice. The power output is approximately 10^{-9} w. An ammonia maser oscillator has been reported to have frequency stability over periods of one hour of the order of 1 part in 10^{10}. The stability is associated with the low noise property.

Another method of achieving inverted level populations in ammonia gas has been proposed by Dicke.[25] This uses a "hot grid" cell and again the quadratic Stark effect. A maser using this method of population inversion is being constructed by Dr. J. P. Wittke at RCA Laboratories.

Level population inversion can also be achieved by means of intense pulses of microwaves. For simplicity, consider, a two-level system with "permanent" electric dipole moment μ, driven at resonance[26] by a microwave field $E = E_o \sin(\omega t - \delta)$. The Hamiltonian is

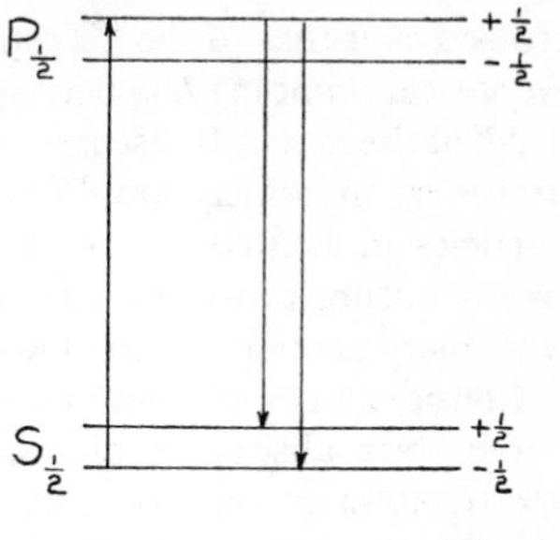

FIG. 17. Optical pumping.

$$\mathcal{H} = \mathcal{H}_o + \boldsymbol{\mu} \cdot \mathbf{E}_0 \sin(\omega t - \delta). \quad (51)$$

Let the wave functions with $E_o = 0$ be ψ_1 and ψ_2.

If we use this in the time-dependent Schroedinger equation and neglect sum frequency terms, an exact solution of the resulting equations gives for the wave function,

$$\Psi = \left[\cos\left(\frac{|\boldsymbol{\mu}_{12} \cdot \mathbf{E}_0| t}{2\hbar}\right)\right] \psi_1 e^{-i(E_1 t/\hbar)} + \left[\sin\left(\frac{|\boldsymbol{\mu}_{12} \cdot \mathbf{E}_0| t}{2\hbar}\right)\right] \psi_2 e^{-iE_2 t/\hbar}. \quad (52)$$

Here $\boldsymbol{\mu}_{12}$ is the dipole matrix element connecting the states 1 and 2. From this it follows that if the system is in the state ψ_1 at $t=0$, then at $t = (\pi\hbar)/(|\boldsymbol{\mu}_{12} \cdot \mathbf{E}_0|$, the microwave pulse has driven the system into state 2. This treatment is valid only for times short compared with the relaxation time since the effect of collisions is ignored.

Thus if we have thermal equilibrium at $t=0$ and apply a strong rf pulse of the correct length we can obtain inversion of level populations. This effect has been demonstrated by Dicke and Romer,[26] and by Kyhl, Standberg, Collins, and Park.[27]

The methods of optical pumping can also be employed[28] to achieve maser action. In Fig. 17 we have a system with a ${}^2S_{\frac{1}{2}}$ ground state and a ${}^2P_{\frac{1}{2}}$ excited state, in a magnetic field. In equilibrium almost all of the particles will be in the split S state. The $m = -\frac{1}{2}S$ state will have slightly more particles in it than the $m = +\frac{1}{2}$ state. Right circularly polarized optical resonance radiation will induce transitions with the selection rule $\Delta m = +1$. The excited particles can now spontaneously emit, either with $\Delta m = -1$, or 0. However this process only removes particles from the $m = -\frac{1}{2}S$ state and returns them to *both* the $m = -\frac{1}{2}$ and $m = +\frac{1}{2}$ states. Therefore the population of the ${}^2S_{+\frac{1}{2}}$ state will be in-

[25] J. P. Wittke, Proc. Inst. Radio Engrs. **45**, 291 (1957).

[26] R. H. Dicke and R. H. Romer, Rev. Sci. Instr. **26**, 915 (1955)

[27] Kyhl, Strandberg, Collins, and Park, Signal Corps Symposium on Solid State Masers, Fort Monmouth, New Jersey (June 12–13, 1958).

[28] W. H. Culver, Science **126** 810 (1957).

creased over that of the $^2S_{-\frac{1}{2}}$ state. A review of the work on optical pumping has been given by Kastler.[29]

All of the methods discussed so far use single quantum processes in which amplification results from more particles in excited states. A. Javan[30] has shown that two quantum processes can be used for amplification, with more particles in the lower state (Fig. 18).

Consider a two photon process in which a particle in a lower state absorbs a photon, then emits a photon, ending up in an excited state. Suppose the frequency of absorption corresponds to that of an intense (pump) oscillator and the emission is stimulated by a signal which it is desired to amplify. In this case we are obtaining emission in a particle transition from a state of lower energy to a state of higher energy. If all particles are in the ground state, amplification will result. Let the transition probability be W_{12} and let n_1 particles be in the ground state. The emitted power is $W_{12}n_1h\nu$. If the excited state has n_2 particles the reverse process may occur in which a photon of amplification frequency ν is absorbed and a pump frequency photon is emitted. The net power emitted will be $W_{12}h\nu(n_1-n_2)$, which is positive at positive temperatures.

For a *one* quantum process W_{12} may be written as

$$W_{12}=4\pi^2\tau|H_{12}'|^2/h^2. \qquad (53)$$

Here τ is the relaxation time and H' is the interaction matrix element. For a two quantum process H' is replaced by

$$\textstyle\sum_i H_{1i}'H_{i2}'/(E_1-E_i). \qquad (54)$$

The summation is over all intermediate states of the particle and the quantized electromagnetic field. In Raman spectroscopy the intermediate states are usually quantum states which are different from the initial and final states, because the diagonal interaction matrix elements ordinarily vanish. If the diagonal matrix elements do not vanish in either the initial or final state, no intermediate state is necessary. For example we may have a diagonal magnetic dipole matrix element in a product of the following type

$$\langle -\tfrac{1}{2}, N_1, N_2|H'|-\tfrac{1}{2}, N_1+1, N_2\rangle \times\langle -\tfrac{1}{2}, N_1+1, N_2|H'|N_2-1, N_1+1, +\tfrac{1}{2}\rangle. \qquad (55)$$

Here we use the nomenclature of quantum electrodynamics. The first bracket involves a matrix element between states in which the particle spin is $-\frac{1}{2}$, and the electromagnetic field oscillators of frequency ν_1 and ν_2 have N_1 and N_2 quanta, respectively, to a state with particle spin unchanged, N_1+1 quanta for the oscillator with frequency ν_1, and N_2 quanta for the oscillator with frequency ν_2. The second bracket then involves a final state in which the spin becomes $+\frac{1}{2}$ and the field oscillator of frequency ν_2 has lost a quantum. Three additional matrix elements, similar to (55) may be written. One of these corresponds to an intermediate state of the particle the same as the initial state but an absorption first of frequency ν_2 followed by emission of frequency ν_1. The other two matrix elements involve an intermediate state of the particle which is the same as the final state, with both possibilities for the order of absorption and emission. Some of these matrix elements may be small in comparison with the others, depending on circumstances of the experimental arrangement. The summation (54) may be written in terms of the (magnetic) dipole matrix elements M_{11} and M_{12} as

$$-\frac{[\mathbf{M}_{11}\cdot\mathbf{H}(\nu_1)][\mathbf{M}_{12}\cdot\mathbf{H}(\nu_2)]}{h\nu_1}+\frac{[\mathbf{M}_{12}\cdot\mathbf{H}(\nu_2)][\mathbf{M}_{22}\cdot\mathbf{H}(\nu_1)]}{h\nu_1}+\frac{[\mathbf{M}_{11}\cdot\mathbf{H}(\nu_2)][\mathbf{M}_{12}\cdot\mathbf{H}(\nu_1)]}{h\nu_2}-\frac{[\mathbf{M}_{12}\cdot\mathbf{H}(\nu_1)][\mathbf{M}_{22}\cdot\mathbf{H}(\nu_2)]}{h\nu_2}. \qquad (56)$$

$\mathbf{H}(\nu_1)$ is the magnetic field at frequency ν_1 and $\mathbf{H}(\nu_2)$ is the magnetic field at frequency ν_2. A corresponding expression would contain the electric field vectors for electric dipole transitions. The transition probability can be written as

$$W=\frac{4\pi^2\tau}{h^2}\left|-\frac{[\mathbf{M}_{11}\cdot\mathbf{H}(\nu_1)][\mathbf{M}_{12}\cdot\mathbf{H}(\nu_2)]}{h\nu_1}+\frac{[\mathbf{M}_{12}\cdot\mathbf{H}(\nu_2)][\mathbf{M}_{22}\cdot\mathbf{H}(\nu_1)]}{h\nu_1}+\frac{[\mathbf{M}_{11}\cdot\mathbf{H}(\nu_2)][\mathbf{M}_{12}\cdot\mathbf{H}(\nu_1)]}{h\nu_2}-\frac{[\mathbf{M}_{12}\cdot\mathbf{H}(\nu_1)][\mathbf{M}_{22}\cdot\mathbf{H}(\nu_2)]}{h\nu_2}\right|^2. \qquad (57)$$

The net power emitted by a two-level system which has n_1 particles in the lower state and n_2 particles in the upper state may then be written as

$$P=\frac{4\pi^2(n_1-n_2)\tau\nu_1}{h}\left|-\frac{[\mathbf{M}_{11}\cdot\mathbf{H}(\nu_1)][\mathbf{M}_{12}\cdot\mathbf{H}(\nu_2)]}{h\nu_1}+\frac{[\mathbf{M}_{12}\cdot\mathbf{H}(\nu_2)][\mathbf{M}_{22}\cdot\mathbf{H}(\nu_1)]}{h\nu_1}+\frac{[\mathbf{M}_{11}\cdot\mathbf{H}(\nu_2)][\mathbf{M}_{12}\cdot\mathbf{H}(\nu_1)]}{h\nu_2}-\frac{[\mathbf{M}_{12}\cdot\mathbf{H}(\nu_1)][\mathbf{M}_{22}\cdot\mathbf{H}(\nu_2)]}{h\nu_2}\right|^2. \qquad (58)$$

[29] A. Kastler, J. Opt. Soc. Am. 47, 460 (1957).
[30] A. Javan, Bull. Am. Phys. Soc. Ser. II, 3, 213 (1958).

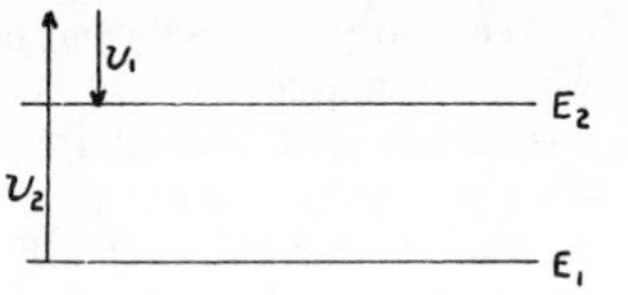

FIG. 18. Raman maser.

V. NOISE PERFORMANCE

Prior to 1950, methods had been developed for generation, amplification, and detection of signals in the electromagnetic spectrum from zero frequency to the mm wave-region. At frequencies below 10 mc/sec the noise performance is already better than is ordinarily required for communications in the presence of atmospheric and other external noise. Indeed, a well designed vacuum tube amplifier in the vicinity of 1 mc/sec is capable of noise performance corresponding to an internal temperature of about 25°K. Microwave amplifiers, on the other hand, did not have good low-noise performance, mainly because of electron stream fluctuations originating at a hot cathode. Inasmuch as this type of noise must be absent in a maser, it was suggested that molecular beam maser type amplifiers would have very little noise.[31] It was very gratifying that the important sources of low-temperature solid state maser noise which were understood in 1956, are sufficiently small to make possible sensitivities which may approach detection of single microwave photons.

We consider first the inherent spontaneous emission noise of a maser, disregarding circuit noise, at spin temperature approaching minus 0°K. The earlier discussion did not consider the effect of spontaneous emission. This is a purely random process[32] and therefore contributes noise. In an ensemble of charged particles, each having two energy levels, those which are in the upper state have a transition probability for transitions to the lower state of the form

$$W_{21}=f(\nu,\mu^2\cdots)[N+1], \tag{59}$$

in consequence of the interaction with the electromagnetic field.§

Here f is a function of frequency and squared matrix elements and N is the number of quanta per radiation oscillator. The one which adds to N gives the effect of spontaneous emission. Let us calculate an equivalent temperature for spontaneous emission. In thermal equilibrium at temperature T, according to the Bose-Einstein statistics, N would be

$$\frac{1}{e^{h\nu/kT}-1}. \tag{60}$$

The positive temperature which black surroundings would need, to emit input noise equivalent to the spontaneous emission, will be denoted by T_E. From (59) we see that this (equivalent) T_E corresponds to an equivalent $N=1$.

Expressions (60) and (59) allow us to write

$$1=e^{h\nu/kT_E}-1, \tag{61}$$

giving

$$T_E=h\nu/k\ \ln_e 2. \tag{62}$$

Suppose we ask the question: how many microwave photons will double the randomly fluctuating output of a maser whose spin temperature approaches -0°K. Let the averaging time of the receiver be τ and let the equivalent input noise energy during this interval be U_n. This is given by the product of the Nyquist formula noise power for T_E and the averaging time τ.

$$U_n=\left[\frac{h\nu}{e^{h\nu/kT_E}-1}\right]\Delta\nu\tau. \tag{63}$$

Here $\Delta\nu$ is the band width. $\Delta\nu\tau\approx 1$. Employing expression (61) gives

$$U_n=h\nu. \tag{64}$$

The equivalent input (noise) energy over the averaging time is that of one photon. If one microwave photon is incident during this interval it will double the average noise output and therefore we are justified in saying that a maser with no circuit noise and spin temperature approaching -0°K may detect single microwave photons, and a flux of $\Delta\nu$ photons per sec, with reasonably large probability.

The foregoing analysis gives exactly what would be predicted by the Nyquist formula for *any* resistance at a temperature -0°K. The Nyquist formula noise energy (delivered to a "matched" load) over the averaging time τ is given by

$$U_n=\frac{h\nu\Delta\nu\tau}{|e^{h\nu/kT}-1|}. \tag{63a}$$

In the limit as $T\to -0°$ (63a) becomes

$$U_n=h\nu\Delta\nu\tau\approx h\nu, \tag{64a}$$

in agreement with (64). This makes it clear that the residual noise in a low-temperature maser is of the same type as discussed by Johnson and Nyquist[33] long ago.

If the spin temperature is not close to minus 0°K (64a) becomes

$$U_n=\frac{h\nu\Delta\nu\tau}{|e^{h\nu/kT_{\text{spin}}}-1|}. \tag{64b}$$

[31] The Columbia work (Gordon, Zeiger, and Townes, reference 2) showed that good noise performance could be obtained with a molecular beam maser. Spontaneous emission from the molecules was not discussed. For a room temperature device this is small compared with input noise.

[32] It has been shown [J. Weber, Phys. Rev. **94**, 215 (1954)] that this type of noise is also present in conventional free electron amplifiers.

§ *Note added in proof.*—Expression (59) is given in Chapter V, *The Quantum Theory of Radiation*, by W. Heitler (Oxford University Press, London, 1954), third edition. It follows from the quantization of the Maxwell field. Each degree of freedom is like a harmonic oscillator and the $N+1$ arises from the squared harmonic oscillator matrix elements for downward transitions.

[33] J. B. Johnson, Phys. Rev. **32**, 47 (1928); H. Nyquist, Phys. Rev. **32**, 110 (1928).

For the case $(h\nu)/(kT)\ll 1$, the number of photons required to double the output is therefore

$$|kT_{\text{sp in}}/h\nu|. \tag{65}$$

Javan has remarked that the noise performance of a Raman type maser will be essentially the same as that of devices which employ greater populations of particles in excited states. This follows because the photon of frequency ν_1 (Fig. 18) can be spontaneously emitted in the absence of a signal, provided that intense "pump" radiation of frequency ν_2 is present.

A complete system will also have noise due to emission from circuit elements and the transmission system. A quantity which has been used to describe the performance of radio receivers is the noise figure, denoted by the symbol F. F is defined as the ratio of the total noise power output of the receiver to that part of the noise power output due to the source at the input of the receiver. An equivalent definition is that it is the quotient of the signal to noise power ratio at the input divided by the signal to noise power ratio at the output.

We now calculate the noise figure of a complete maser receiving system, considering first a traveling wave maser. Our approach is similar to that employed by Strandberg,[34] for two-level systems.[35] We consider three-level systems, taking effects of saturation[36] into account. Let $R_\nu d\nu$ be the number of modes per unit volume in a range $d\nu$ which can propagate, A be the cross-sectional area, and V_G the group velocity. The number of particles per unit volume in the states with energies E_1, E_2, and E_3 will be denoted by n_1, n_2, and n_3. Let β be the power gain per unit length. A quantity K is defined by the following relation

$$\beta = K(n_2 - n_1). \tag{66}$$

Let N be the average number of quanta per mode in the vicinity of the operating frequency ν_{21} and let p_ν be the energy per mode. The change in power as a consequence of energy exchanged in a differential length leads to

$$\begin{aligned} V_G A R_\nu d\nu (dp_\nu/dx) &= V_G A R_\nu d\nu [K n_2 h\nu (N+1) - K n_1 h\nu N - \alpha_c N h\nu \\ &\quad + \alpha_c p_\nu(T_c) - \alpha_{13} N h\nu + \alpha_{13} p_\nu(T_{13})]. \end{aligned} \tag{67}$$

In expression (67) $p_\nu(T_c)$ is the average energy per mode in equilibrium at the temperature of the waveguide walls T_c, and from statistical mechanics $p_\nu(T) = h\nu[e^{h\nu/kT}-1]^{-1}$, $p_\nu(T_{13})$ is the average energy per mode at the temperature T_{13} associated with particles in the energy levels with energies E_1 and E_3, α_c is the power absorption coefficient of the transmission system when the maser material is absent and $\alpha_{13}(\nu_{21})$ is the absorption coefficient at frequency ν_{21} associated with the particles in the energy levels E_1 and E_3. The first term on the right gives the effect of both stimulated and spontaneous emission in inducing transitions out of the state with energy E_2, the second term gives the absorption by particles in the ground state, the third term gives the effect of absorption by conducting walls or loss other than the active solid, the fourth term gives the emission from the walls, the fifth and sixth terms represent the effects of absorption and emission from particles undergoing transitions between the first and third states. We define the temperatures T_{12} and T_{13} by

$$n_1/n_2 = e^{h\nu_{21}/kT_{12}}, \quad n_1/n_3 = e^{h\nu_{31}/kT_{13}}. \tag{68}$$

Integrating expression (67) gives

$$(p_\nu)_{\text{out}} = (p_\nu)_{\text{in}} g^2 + \left[\frac{\beta p_\nu(T_{12}) - \alpha_c p_\nu(T_c) - \alpha_{13} p_\nu(T_{13})}{\beta - \alpha_c - \alpha_{13}}\right] \times (1-g^2). \tag{69}$$

Here g^2 is the power gain defined earlier. This tells us that the temperature of the environment of the maser enters in a subtle way, through the quantity $\alpha_c p_\nu(T_c)$. If the absorption coefficient of the environment, α_c, is small, then little noise is contributed even if T_c is not close to absolute zero. This is a consequence of Kirchhoff's law. Let the source temperature be T_s, the load temperature be T_L, and let the transmission line to the maser have a power loss factor t and a temperature T_t. Thermodynamic considerations enable us to express the output noise emission of the transmission line per cycle in terms of the input noise emission (per cycle) of the source, as

$$(p_\nu)_{\text{line}} = t p_\nu(T_s) + (1-t) p_\nu(T_t). \tag{70}$$

Expression (70) is $(p_\nu)_{\text{in}}$ for the maser.

We can now use (69), (70), and the previous definition of noise figure to write

$$\begin{aligned} F &= \frac{(p_\nu)_{\text{out}} + p_\nu(T_L)}{g^2 t p_\nu(T_s)} \\ &= 1 + \frac{1}{t p_\nu(T_s)} \Bigg\{ (1-t) p_\nu(T_t) + (1-g^{-2}) \\ &\quad \times \left[\frac{\alpha_c p_\nu(T_c) + \alpha_{13} p_\nu(T_{13}) - \beta p_\nu(T_{12})}{\beta - \alpha_c - \alpha_{13}}\right] + \frac{p_\nu(T_L)}{g^2} \Bigg\}. \end{aligned} \tag{71}$$

It was once thought that the saturation field would make a significant contribution to the noise because the temperature T_{13} associated with the (saturated) 1–3 system tends towards infinity. This is not the case; only a negligible contribution results, in the following way.[36]

[34] M. W. P. Strandberg, Phys. Rev. **106**, 617 (1957).

[35] Noise in maser type amplifiers has been discussed by Muller [Phys. Rev. **106**, 8 (1957)], Pound [Ann. Phys. **1**, 24 (1957)] and Shimoda, Takahasi, and Townes [J. Phys. Soc. Japan **12**, 686 (1957)]. The role of spontaneous emission was emphasized by R. H. Dicke at the Symposium on Amplification by Atomic and Molecular Resonance, Asbury Park, New Jersey (March 1, 1956).

[36] J. Weber, Phys. Rev. **108**, 537 (1957).

The quantity $\alpha_{13}(\nu_{21})$ may be written

$$\alpha_{13}(\nu_{21})=\frac{\chi n_1|\mu_{13}|^2}{kT_{13}}\left[\frac{\tau_{13}^{-1}}{4\pi^2(\nu_{21}-\nu_{31})^2+\tau_{13}^{-2}}\right], \quad (72)$$

where χ is a constant, and τ_{13} is the appropriate relaxation time.

β may be written in terms of χ and the 1–2 system relaxation time τ_{12}, as

$$\beta=\frac{\chi n_2|\mu_{12}|^2\tau_{12}}{|p_\nu(T_{12})|}. \quad (73)$$

The ratio of the terms involving α_{13} and β in the noise figure formula (71) is

$$\frac{\alpha_{13}p_\nu(T_{13})}{|\beta p_\nu(T_{12})|}=\frac{n_1|\mu_{13}|^2}{n_2|\mu_{12}|^2}\left[\frac{(\tau_{13}\tau_{12})^{-1}}{4\pi^2(\nu_{21}-\nu_{31})^2+\tau_{13}^{-2}}\right]. \quad (74)$$

For a typical amplifier in the microwave region, this gives a number of order 10^{-3}. Physically this is because a high-saturation temperature means a small absorption coefficient for the 1–3 system, consequently small noise emission.

In order to extend the previous results to a cavity type of maser we note that we have one mode with effective power width $(\pi/2)\Delta\nu$. $\Delta\nu$ is the band width over which the power exceeds one half of the maximum (exact resonance) power. The $\pi/2$ takes account of those parts of the response outside of the region where the power exceeds half the power at resonance. In order to calculate the noise we again employ detailed balancing on a power per cycle basis, making use of the definitions of the various Q's employed earlier. The noise power output per cycle is

$$P_{\text{noise}}=(g+1)^2\Bigg[tp_\nu(T_s)+(1-t)p_\nu(T_t)+\frac{Q_e}{Q_o}\left\{p_\nu(T_c)-\frac{1}{1+\gamma}(p_\nu(T_{12})+\gamma p_\nu(T_{13}))\right\}-\frac{g-1}{g+1}\left(\frac{p_\nu(T_{12})+\gamma p_\nu(T_{13})}{\gamma+1}\right)\Bigg]. \quad (75)$$

The noise figure is then given by

$$F=\frac{(g+1)^2}{g^2tp_\nu(T_s)}\Bigg[(1-t)p_\nu(T_t)+tp_\nu(T_s)+\frac{Q_e}{Q_o}\left\{p_\nu(T_c)-\frac{1}{1+\gamma}(p_\nu(T_{12})+\gamma p_\nu(T_{13}))\right\}-\frac{(g-1)}{(g+1)}\left(\frac{p_\nu(T_{12})+\gamma p_\nu(T_{13})}{1+\gamma}\right)\Bigg]+\frac{g^{-2}p_\nu(T_L)}{tp_\nu(T_s)}. \quad (76)$$

Here the quantity γ is defined by

$$\gamma=\frac{Q_m}{Q_{13}}=\frac{-\alpha_{13}(\nu_{21},T_{13})}{\beta}, \quad (77)$$

with Q_{13} the Q associated with energy absorption by the 1–3 system. The somewhat unusual appearance of (77) with the factor $(1+g)^2$ results from the fact that g^2 is the power gain at resonance. Different parts of the cavity response contribute noise, but with different effective gain.

The term noise temperature is often used, rather than noise figure. This may be defined in terms of the noise figure as

$$\left.\begin{array}{l}[e^{h\nu/kT_n}-1]^{-1}=(F-1)[e^{h\nu/kT_s}-1]^{-1}\\ T_n\approx(F-1)T_s, \quad \text{for } \dfrac{h\nu}{kT}\ll 1\end{array}\right\}. \quad (78)$$

Here T_n is the noise temperature, and T_s is the source temperature.

McWhorter and Arams[37] have measured the noise temperature of a complete solid state maser system and found it to be 20±5°K.

The use of the concept of noise figure or noise temperature was very meaningful for the older type of microwave amplifiers. We propose a method of describing the noise performance which seems better for very quiet amplifiers. The number of photons received over the receiver averaging time which will double the noise output can be employed as a "noise number" to specify the performance of a low noise receiver. We showed earlier that the minimum noise number of a maser is one. The connection between noise number N_n and noise temperature T_n is

$$N_n=[e^{h\nu/kT_n}-1]^{-1}+[e^{h\nu/kT_s}-1]^{-1}. \quad (79)$$

VI. MICROWAVE PHOTON COUNTERS

The maser makes use of stimulated emission. If *all* of the particles were in the upper state of a two-level maser, it could amplify without absorbing any of the incident photons. However, under these conditions the noise number is one, so that at least one incident photon is necessary in order that its randomly fluctuating output be doubled over the receiver averaging time. The incidence of one photon could be interpreted as a spontaneous fluctuation. In an earlier paper[36] we remarked that a maser is a voltage amplifier, not a power amplifier, and that all voltage amplifiers have spontaneous emission noise. Detectors such as nuclear counters must absorb energy in order to operate. However, unlike a maser, the internal fluctuations of a counter or power amplifier can be made arbitrarily

[37] McWhorter and Arams, Lincoln Laboratory, MIT, Rept. M 37–22. See also Alsop, Giordmaine, Townes, and Wang, Phys. Rev. **107**, 1450 (1957); J. C. Helmer, Phys. Rev. **107**, 902 (1957).

small. Such a device has essentially zero output until it detects a photon. It was proposed[36] that power amplifiers and detectors be developed which employ particles initially in their ground states. Methods for doing this are now being studied here. Consider a three-level system, in which the frequency ν_{21} (Fig. 19) for transitions from the first to the second state, is in the optical region. A lamp illuminates with intense light of frequency ν_{21} which can be linearly polarized. Then transitions from state 1 to state 2 are allowed, since $\Delta m=0$. Excited particles in state 2 can spontaneously emit only linearly polarized light. We employ a detector which counts circularly polarized optical frequency photons, which can be emitted only in certain directions. In order to detect microwave photons we arrange to have them circularly polarized. Then a microwave photon can be absorbed in a transition to state 3 or 4, since $\Delta m=1$. Excited particles in states 3 or 4 can now spontaneously emit circularly polarized photons which will be counted. Thus if no microwave photons are present we have particles in states 1 and 2 and only linearly polarized photons. The device has no output. As soon as a microwave (or infrared) photon is absorbed we have a particle in state 3 or 4, and when this particle emits, we have a circularly polarized photon, which is counted. This method is similar to that which has been employed in optical pumping experiments. The transition probability for this type of third-order process can be calculated in the following way. Let the wave function for atom and electromagnetic field be $\Phi(t)$.

$$\Phi(t)=\sum a_i(t)\Psi_i.$$

The Ψ_i are unperturbed wave functions of particle and electromagnetic field. Let the ground state be denoted by the subscript M. Let $a_M=1$ at $t=0$, and $a_j=0$ for $j\neq M$, at $t=0$. Let H' be the interaction part of the Hamiltonian. We quantize the electromagnetic field, H' is then not time dependent. Our process is one involving three photons. One is absorbed from the lamp, one is absorbed from the microwave field, and one is then spontaneously emitted. The third-order probability amplitude coefficient is given by

$$a_L^{(3)}=\frac{h^{-3}H_{LK}'H_{KN}'H_{NM}'}{\nu_{NM}}\times\left[\frac{1}{\nu_{KM}}\left\{\frac{e^{i2\pi\nu_{LM}t}-1}{i\nu_{LM}}-\frac{e^{i2\pi\nu_{LK}t}-1}{i\nu_{LK}}\right\}-\frac{1}{\nu_{KN}}\left\{\frac{e^{i2\pi\nu_{LN}t}-1}{i\nu_{LN}}-\frac{e^{i2\pi\nu_{LK}t}-1}{i\nu_{LK}}\right\}\right].$$

The intermediate states are denoted by the subscripts N and K. We are interested in three photon transitions of the type in which energy is conserved or nearly conserved in all three steps. The subscript N refers to the state in which a particular oscillator excited by the lamp has lost one photon. The subscript K refers to the state in which a particular microwave field oscillator has lost a photon. In order to calculate the probability that the particle has returned to the ground state with emission of a circularly polarized photon we must square the probability amplitude and integrate over all lamp photons, microwave photons, and emitted circularly polarized photons. We denote by $\rho(N)$, $\rho(K)$, and $\rho(L)$ the density of intermediate and final states. The transition probability is then

$$W=\frac{1}{h^6t}\int\left|\frac{H_{LK}'H_{KN}'H_{NM}'}{\nu_{NM}}\right|^2\times\left|\frac{1}{\nu_{KM}}\left\{\frac{e^{i2\pi\nu_{LM}t}-1}{\nu_{LM}}-\frac{e^{i2\pi\nu_{LK}t}-1}{\nu_{LK}}\right\}-\frac{1}{\nu_{KN}}\left\{\frac{e^{i2\pi\nu_{LN}t}-1}{\nu_{KN}}-\frac{e^{i2\pi\nu_{LK}t}-1}{\nu_{LK}}\right\}\right]^2\times\rho(E_L)\rho(E_K)\rho(E_N)dE_LdE_KdE_N.$$

We need to evaluate this expression, under conditions such that energy is conserved or nearly conserved in all steps. All denominators may vanish. An approximate solution can be obtained in the following way. When integrating over dE_N, we are integrating over all lamp photons which can be absorbed. Let the lamp have intensity which is zero except for a range $\Delta\nu_1$ on each side of that required for resonance. Let the lamp intensity be assumed constant over the range $2\Delta\nu_1$. A study of the integrand shows that it is not singular in the range where all denominators vanish. The integral over E_N is along the real frequency axis from $-\Delta\nu_1$ to $+\Delta\nu_1$. We can equally well integrate along a semicircle in the lower half complex frequency plane from $-\Delta\nu_1$ on the real axis to $+\Delta\nu_1$ on the real axis. The second pair of terms which have the factor $1/(\nu_{KN})$ may then be neglected in comparison with the pair of terms which have the factor $1/(\nu_{KM})$. This integration along the semicircle is now readily performed. The integration over E_K can be performed in the same way if the relaxation time for interaction with other particles is much smaller than the spontaneous emission lifetime. This leaves one integration which may then be handled in the same way as for one photon processes. The result

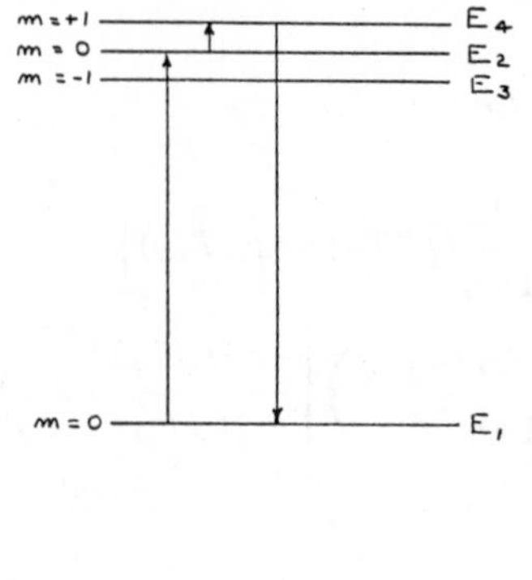

FIG. 19. Energy levels for quantum mechanical amplifier without spontaneous emission noise.

then gives the transition probability

$$W=\frac{16\pi^2\rho(E_N)\rho(E_K)\rho(E_L)\,|H_{LK}'H_{KN}'H_{NM}'|^2}{h^3\Delta\nu_{NM}\Delta\nu_{KM}}.$$

All quantities are evaluated at resonance. This predicts modified absorption (or emission) at one frequency due to intense radiation at a different frequency, for single particles. $\rho(N)$ is calculated from the average number of field oscillators excited by the lamp. It is reasonable to suppose that each lamp excited field oscillator is unlikely to have more than one photon. The remaining quantities require, for calculation, a detailed knowledge of the transitions and the experimental arrangements. The excited states of the rare earth salts may be suitable for such counters and are now being investigated by Mr. U. E. Hochuli.

At a meeting held at the National Academy of Sciences in April, 1958, Bloembergen independently proposed a microwave (or infrared) photon counter which operates on similar principles (Fig. 20).

Consider a solid with at least three low-lying levels and one or more optical levels. The solid, such as a salt of the rare earth elements, is cooled to such a low temperature that only the ground state is occupied. $kT\ll E_2-E_1$. Strong optical illumination takes place at the frequency $h^{-1}(E_4-E_2)$. This light is normally not absorbed because the level E_2 is empty, unless it is excited by an incident quantum E_2-E_1. Then the system gets raised to level E_4. The spontaneous emission from level E_4 to E_3 can be detected by a photomultiplier tube. Again, discrimination from the strong incident background can be made by directional, frequency, or polarization filters.

VII. MASERS AT LOW FREQUENCIES AND IN THE INFRARED

There has not been a great deal of motivation for development of masers at low frequencies. The theory previously given would appear to be applicable. Nuclear spin energy levels and the levels associated with nuclear quadrupole spectra are available in this part of the spectrum. The small nuclear moment gives a weaker interaction with radiation, but this tends to be compensated by longer transverse relaxation times. As noted by Braunstein[38] a nucleus of spin $I>2$ which possesses an electric quadrupole moment will yield at least three unequally spaced levels in a crystal of lower than cubic symmetry. If the crystalline field has large deviations from axial symmetry the $\Delta m=2$ transitions (necessary for saturation) begin to have significantly large transition probabilities.

Allais[39] obtained maser action in nuclear resonance experiments in the megacycle region. This followed the work of Abragam, Combrisson, and Solomon[39] in the kilocycle region.

In the infrared and optical parts of the spectrum the sensitivity of a maser will be expected to be less than that of photon counting devices. At 8000 A the spontaneous emission equivalent temperature is 18 000°K. Achievement of coherent amplification would be desirable. This is a useful concept only when large numbers of photons are involved so that the phase can be well defined.[40] The availability of highly monochromatic sources would extend the resolution of spectroscopy in these regions. One problem is to provide a device at infrared and optical frequencies which has the energy storage capacity ordinarily provided by an electromagnetic cavity resonator, with wide mode separations. Dicke has proposed[41] a number of arrangements which employ a standing wave system between parallel planes. Similar proposals have been made by Schawlow and Townes.[42] They suggest that a multimode cavity could be employed. Single modes might be selected by reducing the cavity to partially transparent end plates, with open sides. The great directivity associated with diffraction from sources which are many wavelengths on a side may make it possible to select particular modes and suppress unwanted ones. They carry out calculations for a system using potassium vapor.

VIII. PARAMETRIC AMPLIFIERS

During the past few years another type of microwave amplifier has been developed, which has promise of low noise performance approaching that of a maser. We describe it in classical terms because nothing seems to be gained by a quantum mechanical description. In Fig. 21 two oscillators are coupled by a time-dependent capacitor. Let the natural frequencies of the oscillators be ν_1 and ν_2, and let the capacity C_3 have the time dependence

$$C_3=C_o+C_t\sin[2\pi(\nu_1+\nu_2)t].$$

It has been known since at least the time of Lord Rayleigh that two harmonic oscillators with natural frequencies ν_1 and ν_2, with this kind of time-dependent coupling may be unstable.

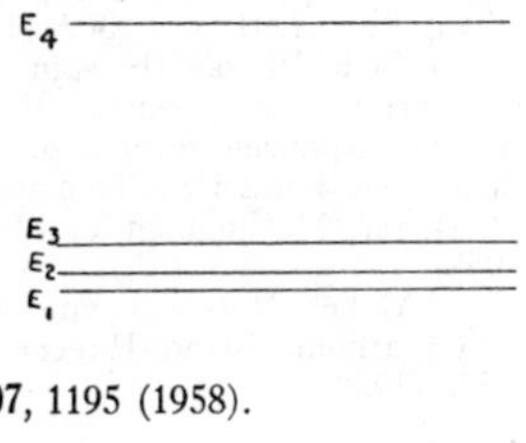

FIG. 20. Energy levels for quantum mechanical amplifier without spontaneous emission noise.

38 R. Braunstein, Phys. Rev. **107**, 1195 (1958).

39 Abragam, Combrisson, and Solomon, Compt. rend. **245**, 157 (1957); E. Allais, *ibid.* **246**, 2123 (1958).

40 W. Heitler, *The Quantum Theory of Radiation* (Oxford University Press, London), third edition, p. 65.

41 R. H. Dicke, U. S. Patent 2,851,652, issued September 9, 1958.

42 A. L. Schawlow and C. H. Townes, Phys. Rev. **112**, 1940 (1958); see also A. M. Prokhorov, J. Exptl. Theoret. Phys. **34**, 1658 (1958). Research activity is increasing along this line. Since low noise is not essential we suggest review of older methods in conjunction with parallel planes.

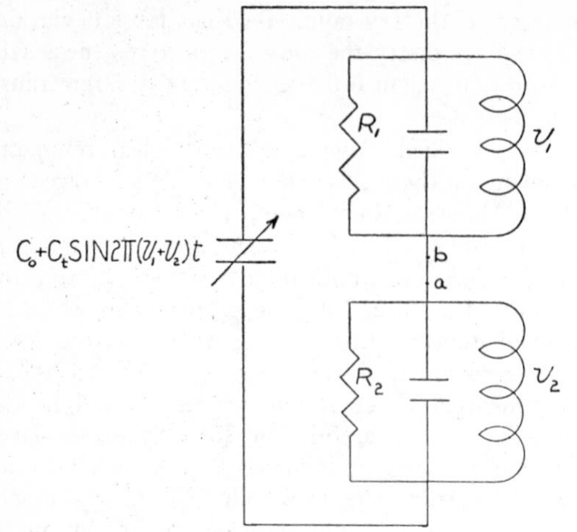

FIG. 21. Parametric amplifier.

Consider first a capacity alone with

$$C=C_t\sin[2\pi(\nu_1+\nu_2)t]$$

driven by a voltage $V=V_1\sin(2\pi\nu_1 t)+V_2\sin(2\pi\nu_2 t)$. The principal part[43] of the current is

$$i=-\pi\nu_1 C_t V_2\sin(2\pi\nu_1 t)-\pi\nu_2 C_t V_1\sin(2\pi\nu_2 t).$$

If, in the circuit of Fig. 21, a voltage $V_G\sin 2\pi\nu_1 t$ is applied between terminals *a* and *b*, the output voltage of frequency ν_1 can be shown to have increased amplitude

$$V_1=V_G\left[1-i2\pi C_o R_1\nu_1-\frac{\pi^2\nu_1\nu_2 C_t^2 R_1 R_2}{1-i2\pi\nu_2 C_o R_2}\right]^{-1}.$$

In deducing this we assume that the oscillator of frequency ν_1 has impedance R_1 at ν_1 and zero impedance at all other frequencies. A corresponding assumption is made concerning the oscillator of frequency ν_2. The time-dependent capacitor or inductance need have very little random fluctuations. The low noise properties of this type of amplifier were pointed out unequivocally by van der Ziel[44] in 1948. This pioneering theoretical work appears to represent the earliest solution to the problem of low noise microwave amplification. Experimental verification of the low noise properties was accomplished by Salzberg and Sard.[45] The noise figure of a parametric amplifier has been given as[43]

$$F=1+\frac{G_1}{G_g}+\frac{\nu_1}{\nu_2}\frac{G_{T1}}{G_g}+F_S+F_G,$$

where G_1 = effective conductance of unloaded amplifying resonant circuit, G_g = effective conductance coupled into the amplifying resonant circuit by the generator, G_{T1} = effective conductance of the loaded amplifying resonant circuit, ν_1 = amplifying frequency, ν_2 = idling frequency, F_S = shot noise, and F_G = gain fluctuation noise.

[43] We are following the treatment of H. Heffner and G. Wade, Meeting of Institute of Radio Engineers Professional Group on Electron Devices, Washington, D. C. (October, 1957).

[44] A. van der Ziel, J. Appl. Phys. **19**, 999 (1948).

[45] B. Salzberg and E. W. Sard, Proc. Inst. Radio Engrs. **46**, 1303 (1958).

The revival of interest in this type of amplifier appears to have started with the work of Suhl[46] and Weiss[47] on the ferromagnetic amplifier. Low noise "up frequency conversion" is also possible with parametric devices.[48] Room temperature operation is possible, with moderately good noise performance.

IX. APPLICATIONS OF MASERS TO EXPERIMENTAL PHYSICS AND RADIO ASTRONOMY

The very low noise, coupled with adequate gain-bandwith product, make the low-temperature solid state maser an obvious tool for radio astronomy and radar.‖ A modified Dicke-type radiometer in which a maser is used for pre-amplification has been described.[49] The ruby maser of Alsop, Giordmaine, and Townes, which was described earlier, was mounted near the focus of the Naval Research Laboratory 50-ft reflector in order to minimize transmission line losses. Liquid helium cooling was provided by a stainless steel Dewar with 3 l capacity which was maintained under partial vacuum. This allowed about 15 hr of observation before recharging was needed. The complete radiometer installation made it possible to observe with an rms output fluctuation of 0.03°K for an output time constant of 5 sec. The intermediate frequency amplifiers had a band width of 5 Mc.

The great stability of oscillators such as the cesium beam clock and the molecular beam masers make possible certain experimental tests of both special and general relativity. These possibilities have been discussed by Moller.[50] A molecular beam maser has been employed to repeat the Michelson-Morley experiment.[51] If there is a fixed ether a difference in frequency would

[46] H. Suhl Phys. Rev. **106**, 384 (1957); J. Appl. Phys. **28**, 1225 (1957).

[47] M. T. Weiss, Phys. Rev. **107**, 317 (1957).

[48] Herrmann, Uenohara, and Uhlir, Proc. Inst. Radio Engrs. **46**, 1301(L) (1958).

‖ *Note added in proof.*—Operation of a ruby maser at 60°K was reported by C. R. Ditchfield and P. A. Forrester [Phys. Rev. Letters **1**, 448 (1958)], and independently by T. H. Maiman (Hughes Aircraft Company Report). A maser employing a slow wave structure with band width of 67 mc per sec and gain of 13 decibels was described by R. W. DeGrasse (Bell Telephone Laboratories Report entitled "Slow Wave Structures for Unilateral Solid State Maser Amplifiers"). Amplifiers employing ruby which have wide tunability were reported by G. K. Wessel [380–450 mc, Proc. Inst. Radio Engrs. **47**, 590 (1959)], and by F. R. Arams and S. Okwit [850–2000 mc, Proc. Inst. Radio Engrs. **47**, 992 (1959)]. A proposal for generating higher frequencies than the pump frequency was made by A. E. Siegman and R. J. Morris [Phys. Rev. Letters **2**, 302 (1959)]. They suggest a staircase scheme in which say the spin populations of the lowest pair of states are reversed by adiabatic rapid passage, followed by adiabatic rapid passage reversal of the populations of levels 2 and 3. Then levels 3 and 1 can be employed for power generation.

[49] Mayer, McCullough, and Sloanmaker, Astrophys. J. **127**, 1 (1958).

[50] C. Moller, Nuovo cimento **6**, Suppl., 381 (1957).

[51] Cedarholm, Bland, Havens, and Townes, Phys. Rev. Letters **1**, 342 (1958).

be expected between two molecular beam type masers with beam velocities parallel and antiparallel to the earth's orbital motion. Let u be the velocity of the molecules relative to the cavity which is assumed to be moving with velocity v with respect to the fixed ether (u is parallel to v). It is assumed that the photons radiated by the molecules move with a velocity **c** relative to the fixed ether. The photon velocity relative to the cavity must be normal to u. This requires that **c** be tilted forward of the normal to u by an angle $\phi \approx (v/c)$. The expected doppler shift would be $\nu u\phi/c = uv\nu/c^2$. For a thermal velocity of 0.6 kMs/sec and for the earth's orbital velocity the difference in frequency between two *oppositely* directed beams is $2uv\nu/c^2$, which is $\sim$10 cps if $\nu = 23\,870$ Mc/sec. The experiment was done by mounting two maser oscillators on a rack which could be rotated about a vertical axis. The oscillators were adjusted so that their frequencies differed by a small amount. This difference was recorded and the apparatus was then rotated through 180°. A slight change of about 1/50 cps was observed under the best conditions of operation. This is smaller by a factor of 1000 than what would be expected on the basis of a fixed ether. Inasmuch as the special theory of relativity is one of the most securely established of all physical theories, such experiments may be regarded as a search for other effects such as perhaps an anisotropy of space in this part of our galaxy. The use of stable oscillators to test the gravitational red shift has also been considered.[50,52] This is perhaps more a test of whether or not these devices are natural clocks (whose intervals are invariants) than a test of the fundamental postulates of the general theory of relativity.

A series of experiments is being planned by the author to search for gravitational radiation. The theory of an antenna for such radiation has been discussed.[53] Two masses which are separated will have forces exerted upon them by a gravitational wave. The phase difference at the two masses results in one being driven relative to the other. Also strains can be set up in a material by a gravitational wave. Under some conditions it is desirable to make use of acoustical resonance, under other conditions where acoustic phase reversal is troublesome, it is better not to employ acoustical resonance. The gravitational wave interacts both with the mass of the piezoelectric crystal and the conducting masses shown. Very low-frequency search is planned. The output voltages are amplified as shown in Fig. 22. Liquid helium temperatures and low noise receivers may make it possible to observe correlation in the outputs, in the presence of electrical noise.

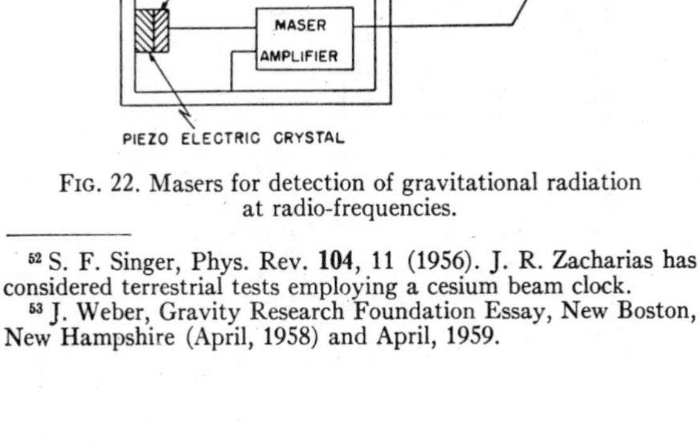

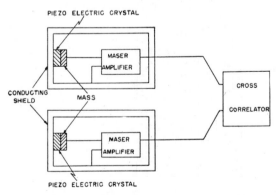

FIG. 22. Masers for detection of gravitational radiation at radio-frequencies.

[52] S. F. Singer, Phys. Rev. **104**, 11 (1956). J. R. Zacharias has considered terrestrial tests employing a cesium beam clock.

[53] J. Weber, Gravity Research Foundation Essay, New Boston, New Hampshire (April, 1958) and April, 1959.

X. CONCLUSION

The new microwave amplifiers are the result of electronics research to develop millimeter wave techniques, magnetic resonance research, and research in microwave spectroscopy. Maser amplifiers bring to the microwave region a detection sensitivity of the order of a few microwave photons. Most of these amplifiers employ the magnetic moment of the electron, and therefore fill in the gap in modern electronics pointed out by Sommerfeld. We may look forward to important advances in radio astronomy, spectroscopy and solid state physics, in consequence of improved ability to distinguish weak signals.

ACKNOWLEDGMENTS

We thank Professor Bloembergen, Professor Strandberg, and Professor Townes for helpful criticism and a profitable correspondence. Suggestions for improving the manuscript were also made by Dr. L. S. Nergaard and Dr. E. O. Schulz-DuBois. We acknowledge stimulating discussions with Dr. R. K. Wangsness and Professor R. A. Ferrell.

APPENDIX. MACHINE CALCULATIONS OF MATRIX ELEMENTS AND ENERGY LEVELS FOR RUBY¶

The following data are entirely the work of W. S. Chang and A. E. Siegman of the Stanford University Electronics Laboratories. We thank them for their kindness and cooperation in allowing this work to be published here.

The spin Hamiltonian used was

$$\mathcal{H} = g\beta_M \mathbf{H}_{dc}\cdot\mathbf{S} + D(S_z^2 - 5/4),$$

with $g=1.99$ and $2D=+11.46$ kmc/s. The small anisotropy in the g tensor was ignored.

¶ This material originally appeared as Tech. Rept. No. 156–2 under Air Force Contract AF33(600)-27784 of the Stanford Electronics Laboratories, Stanford University, California. A similar set of calculations have also been performed for the material potassium chromicyanide, $K_3Cr(CN)_6$, and reported earlier in Tech. Rept. No. 156–1 under the same contract. Because of the lower symmetry of the chromicyanide, the results are too lengthy to present here. Copies of the report can be obtained directly from the Stanford Electronics Laboratories. The support of this work by the Wright Air Development Center is gratefully acknowledged.

TABLE I(a). Ruby $\theta=10°$.

17453 49			50000 49	
64626 50N	50051 50N	36736 50	77941 50	
24804 47N	16853 49	98548 49 •	20405 48	for E_1
16158 48	98556 49N	16850 49 •	40671 47	for E_2
29417 45N	57731 46	20799 48	99978 49	for E_3
99986 49N	16344 48N	25300 46 •	17341 47	for E_4
18817 50	20007 50N	33252 49 •	1-2	
33277 49N	33277 49N	92644 47 •	2-3	
20548 47N	21808 47	51172 47 •	3-4	
16999 50N	16991 50N	40608 48 •	1-3	
17118 50	17127 50N	32422 48 •	2-4	
26263 49N	25668 49	43304 47	1-4	

17453 49			10000 50	
72064 50N	42862 50N	16288 50	98638 50	
41318 47N	16798 49	98466 49 •	46866 48	for E_1
89242 48	98534 49N	16764 49 •	11935 48	for E_2
19840 46N	38882 47	48205 48	99882 49	for E_3
99956 49N	29520 48N	82463 46 •	73835 46	for E_4
18657 50	20049 50N	33263 49 •	1-2	
38480 49N	38487 49N	31531 48 •	2-3	
10939 48N	11069 48	16925 47 •	3-4	
16911 50N	16835 50N	92312 48 •	1-3	
17157 50	17158 50N	58765 48 •	2-4	
23407 49N	23142 49	65152 47	1-4	

17453 49			15000 50	
79668 50N	35733 50N	39737 49 •	11937 51	
52844 47N	16691 49	98251 49 •	82286 48	for E_1
40030 48	98496 49N	16476 49 •	33220 48	for E_2
97454 46N	19060 48	86662 48	99605 49	for E_3
99918 49	40362 48	14941 47	23014 46	for E_4
18210 50	20260 50N	33512 49 •	1-2	
45328 49N	45401 49N	10387 49 •	2-3	
42584 48	42537 48N	29690 47 •	3-4	
16916 50N	16409 50N	15754 49 •	1-3	
17180 50N	17176 50	80461 48	2-4	
20950 49	21003 49N	76920 47 •	1-4	

17453 49			20000 50	
87539 50N	28974 50N	23629 50 •	14014 51	
60918 47N	16498 49	97748 49 •	13142 49	for E_1
47405 48	95305 49N	12460 49 •	27186 49	for E_2
12793 48N	24904 49	17029 49	95331 49	for E_3
99877 49	49432 48	21514 47	58699 46	for E_4
13570 50	23397 50N	38710 49 •	1-2	
47065 49N	54913 49N	99548 49 •	2-3	
45137 49	45107 49N	28066 48 •	3-4	
20122 50N	11086 50N	16809 49 •	1-3	
16601 50N	16598 50	94719 48	2-4	
18846 49	19007 49N	82257 47 •	1-4	

17453 49			25000 50	
95864 50N	43740 50N	21331 50 •	16093 51	
66087 47N	16141 49	96594 49 •	20212 49	for E_1
57094 47	11108 49N	18568 49	97629 49	for E_2
56523 48N	97894 49	18018 49	77442 48	for E_3
99836 49	57128 48	27512 47	28468 46	for E_4
12909 50N	18533 50N	43067 49 •	1-2	
67367 49	68455 49N	36998 49 •	2-3	
17136 50	17138 50N	11392 49 •	3-4	
19265 50N	17613 50	28622 49	1-3	
16617 49N	16626 49	94096 47	2-4	
16947 49	16996 49N	80871 47 •	1-4	

17453 49			30000 50	
10500 51N	62448 50N	14294 50 •	18174 51	
68019 47N	15452 49	93942 49 •	30586 49	for E_1
48383 47	93557 48N	29424 49	95112 49	for E_2
63276 48N	98148 49	17573 49	42498 48	for E_3
99796 49	63739 48	33155 47	22405 46	for E_4
11226 50N	17885 50N	61087 49 •	1-2	
87435 49	88034 49N	26571 49 •	2-3	
17187 50	17195 50N	12749 49 •	3-4	
17943 50N	17414 50	27904 49	1-3	
11871 49N	11877 49	69073 47	2-4	
14900 49	14918 49N	76059 47 •	1-4	

17453 49			35000 50	
11562 51N	79711 50N	72369 49 •	20257 51	
65428 47N	14131 49	88111 49 •	45125 49	for E_1
55808 47	10689 49N	43954 49	89181 49	for E_2
69049 48N	98172 49	17441 49	32132 48	for E_3
99757 49	69477 48	38421 47	34837 46	for E_4
70231 49N	17688 50N	83522 49 •	1-2	
11419 50	11485 50N	26872 49 •	2-3	
17200 50	17213 50N	13914 49 •	3-4	
16214 50N	15997 50	25027 49	1-3	
11756 49N	11779 49	66547 47	2-4	
12450 49	12497 49N	68489 47 •	1-4	

17453 49			40000 50	
12861 51N	94608 50N	18315 48 •	22341 51	
57376 47N	11992 49	77641 49 •	61867 49	for E_1
68069 47	12847 49N	60576 49	78517 49	for E_2
74094 48N	98161 49	17381 49	27167 48	for E_3
99721 49	74502 48	43117 47	20662 46	for E_4
59294 48N	17593 50N	10025 50 •	1-2	
14375 50	14466 50N	29690 49 •	2-3	
17205 50	17225 50N	14929 49 •	3-4	
13580 50N	13488 50	20351 49	1-3	
12579 49N	12576 49	76933 47	2-4	
96076 48	96045 48N	52662 47 •	1-4	

17453 49			45000 50	
14435 51N	10676 51N	68636 49	24485 51	
46566 47N	95477 48	64794 49 •	75566 49	for E_1
79205 47	14663 49N	74165 49	65451 49	for E_2
78548 48N	98140 49	17346 49	24255 48	for E_3
99686 49	78940 48	47503 47	27320 46	for E_4
57030 49	17537 50N	10173 50 •	1-?	
16660 50	16785 50N	32204 49 •	2-3	
17207 50	17234 50N	15827 49 •	3-4	
10597 50N	10557 50	15220 49	1-3	
13065 49N	13073 49	80524 47	2-4	
68736 48	68808 48N	39305 47 •	1-4	

17453 49			50000 50	
16218 51N	11683 51N	13903 50	26511 51	
37184 47N	75430 48	53728 49 •	84000 49	for E_1
86825 47	15735 49N	82539 49	54211 49	for E_2
82509 48N	98116 49	17324 49	22341 48	for E_3
99654 49	82887 48	51465 47	23836 46	for E_4
99216 49	17500 50N	93462 49 •	1-2	
17970 50	18126 50N	33587 49 •	2-3	
17207 50	17241 50N	16625 49 •	3-4	
81402 49N	81207 49	11171 49	1-3	
12997 49N	12991 49	82791 47	2-4	
48638 48	48596 48N	27000 47 •	1-4	

17453 49			55000 50	
18125 51N	12565 51N	20937 50	28597 51	
30440 47N	61370 48	45688 49 •	88739 49	for E_1
91833 47	16301 49N	87250 49	46052 49	for E_2
86054 48N	98091 49	17309 49	20989 48	for E_3
99624 49	86420 48	55099 47	21835 46	for E_4
12345 50	17474 50N	83745 49 •	1-2	
18649 50	18831 50N	34230 49 •	2-3	
17207 50	17247 50N	17339 49 •	3-4	
63995 49N	63888 49	84195 48	1-3	
12618 49N	12600 49	82495 47	2-4	
35445 48	35350 48N	18580 47 •	1-4	

17453 49			60000 50	
20100 51N	13381 51N	27965 50	30685 51	
25772 47N	51759 48	40041 49 •	91486 49	for E_1
95370 47	16608 49N	89983 49	40326 49	for E_2
89247 48N	98066 49	17299 49	19981 48	for E_3
99596 49	89601 48	58497 47	30984 46	for E_4
13739 50	17455 50N	75515 49 •	1-2	
19012 50	19215 50N	34526 49 •	2-3	
17206 50	17251 50N	17982 49 •	3-4	
51955 49N	51890 49	65877 48	1-3	
12114 49N	12118 49	79763 47	2-4	
26793 48	26810 48N	15690 47 •	1-4	

17453 49			65000 50	
22112 51N	14158 51N	34988 50	32772 51	
22478 47N	45030 48	36000 49 •	93185 49	for E_1
98073 47	16785 49N	91676 49	36231 49	for E_2
92136 48N	98043 49	17291 49	19201 48	for E_3
99569 49	92479 48	61619 47	38302 46	for E_4
14586 50	17440 50N	69045 49 •	1-2	
19220 50	19438 50N	34667 49 •	2-3	
17204 50	17255 50N	18563 49 •	3-4	
43424 49N	43380 49	53340 48	1-3	
11594 49N	11616 49	77066 47	2-4	
20974 48	21061 48N	14027 47 •	1-4	

17453 49			70000 50	
24148 51N	14913 51N	42007 50	34860 51	
20079 47N	40150 48	33016 49 •	94306 49	for E_1
10026 48	16896 49N	92794 49	33208 49	for E_2
94763 48N	98020 49	17285 49	18582 48	for E_3
99544 49	95095 48	64457 47	38247 46	for E_4
15131 50	17428 50N	63999 49 •	1-2	
19347 50	19578 50N	34737 49 •	2-3	
17202 50	17259 50N	19091 49 •	3-4	
37165 49N	37134 49	44421 48	1-3	
11103 49N	11121 49	75124 47	2-4	
16927 48	16991 48N	11321 47 •	1-4	

17453 49			75000 50	
26198 51N	15653 51N	49028 50	36948 51	
18272 47N	36487 48	30748 49 •	95087 49	for E_1
10210 48	16968 49N	93572 49	30905 49	for E_2
97163 48N	97998 49	17280 49	18075 48	for E_3
99521 49	97484 48	67097 47	40659 46	for E_4
15503 50	17418 50N	60020 49 •	1-2	
32419 49N	32596 49	37851 48	2-3	
13974 48	14044 48N	99553 46 •	3-4	
19430 50	19670 50N	34772 49 •	1-3	
10636 49N	10657 49	72886 47	2-4	
17200 50	17262 50N	19574 49 •	1-4	

Table I(b). Ruby $\theta=20°$.

34906 49			50000 49	
65368 50N	49333 50N	37805 50	77096 50	
89413 47N	30842 49	95044 49 •	38052 48	for E_1
31103 48	95069 49N	30821 49 •	14643 48	for E_2
23034 46N	21829 47	40713 48	99916 49	for E_3
99947 49	32345 48	11070 47	41471 46	for E_4
16039 50	20029 50N	58867 49 •	1-2	
61063 49N	61076 49N	33442 48 •	2-3	
83498 47	83075 47N	19082 47 •	3-4	
16213 50N	16181 50N	74688 48 •	1-3	
16662 50N	16651 50	62833 48	2-4	
47202 49	47302 49N	15828 48 •	1-4	

34906 49			10000 50	
74222 50N	41641 50N	18752 50	97111 50	
14771 48N	30538 49	94831 49 •	85000 48	for E_1
56798 48	95031 49N	30315 49 •	42024 48	for E_2
14878 47N	14020 48	93768 48	99549 49	for E_3
99827 49	58609 48	33527 47	28799 46	for E_4
15579 50	20176 50N	59093 49 •	1-2	
69877 49N	70032 49N	11065 49 •	2-3	
41003 48	41024 48N	48084 47 •	3-4	
15917 50N	15646 50N	16058 49 •	1-3	
16792 50N	16776 50	11538 49	2-4	
41744 49	41729 49N	23233 48 •	1-4	

34906 49			15000 50	
83397 50N	34329 50N	43895 48	11728 51	
18622 48N	29999 49	94296 49 •	14305 49	for E_1
78067 48	94857 49N	28679 49 •	10891 49	for E_2
65644 47N	61350 48	16888 49	98370 49	for E_3
99675 49	80302 48	59583 47	64534 46	for E_4
14390 50	20778 50N	60611 49 •	1-2	
79330 49N	80821 49N	33272 49 •	2-3	
14319 49	14318 49N	17613 48 •	3-4	
15845 50N	14300 50N	24415 49 •	1-3	
16833 50N	16818 50	15876 49	2-4	
36788 49	36802 49N	26254 48 •	1-4	

34906 49			20000 50	
93284 50N	28764 50N	15538 50 •	13758 51	
21020 48N	29155 49	93203 49 •	21415 49	for E_1
89064 48	89761 49N	18492 49 •	41232 49	for E_2
37388 48N	34269 49	31150 49	88550 49	for E_3
99510 49	98478 48	85679 47	90722 46	for E_4
88982 49	23721 50N	70165 49 •	1-2	
63055 49N	93695 49N	13519 50 •	2-3	
66513 49	66516 49N	82947 48 •	3-4	
18024 50N	71820 49N	17630 49 •	1-3	
15604 50N	15598 50	17893 49	2-4	
32205 49	32216 49N	26638 48 •	1-4	

34906 49			25000 50	
10413 51N	37067 50N	16782 50 •	15798 51	
22204 48N	27917 49	91235 49 •	29863 49	for E_1
42619 48	39749 49N	17202 49	90032 49	for E_2
10385 49N	86665 49	37134 49	31658 49	for E_3
99343 49	11389 49	11052 48	11805 47	for E_4
47650 49N	21462 50N	76345 49 •	1-2	
81185 49	10856 50N	12767 50 •	2-3	
15813 50	15824 50N	21604 49 •	3-4	
17658 50N	11132 50	30403 49	1-3	
62755 49N	62750 49	76655 48	2-4	
27817 49	27832 49N	25353 48 •	1-4	

34906 49			30000 50	
11621 51N	51996 50N	10241 50 •	17845 51	
22310 48N	26232 49	88093 49 •	39323 49	for E_1
31530 48	28905 49N	31622 49	90302 49	for E_2
12185 49N	91185 49	35181 49	17293 49	for E_3
99179 49	12712 49	13352 48	13702 47	for E_4
46180 49N	19397 50N	86467 49 •	1-2	
11291 50	12460 50N	85483 49 •	2-3	
16582 50	16615 50N	25205 49 •	3-4	
15368 50N	13077 50	35327 49	1-3	
39528 49N	39523 49	49135 48	2-4	
23575 49	23575 49N	22889 48 •	1-4	

34906 49			35000 50	
12974 51N	66101 50N	31387 49 •	19898 51	
21519 48N	24156 49	83723 49 •	49012 49	for E_1
30510 48	27536 49N	42441 49	86204 49	for E_2
13435 49N	92011 49	34448 49	12906 49	for E_3
99022 49	13857 49	15470 48	16114 47	for E_4
20062 49N	18689 50N	98067 49 •	1-2	
13132 50	14056 50N	74563 49 •	2-3	
16742 50	16798 50N	27757 49 •	3-4	
13594 50N	12494 50	32959 49	1-3	
33156 49N	33153 49	41743 48	2-4	
19538 49	19543 49N	19867 48 •	1-4	

34906 49			40000 50	
14478 51N	78841 50N	40509 49	21957 51	
20130 48N	21886 49	78484 49 •	57939 49	for E_1
31652 48	28099 49N	51718 49	80781 49	for E_2
14483 49N	92253 49	34092 49	10830 49	for E_3
98874 49	14858 49	17406 48	18325 47	for E_4
11013 49	18340 50N	10616 50 •	1-2	
14577 50	15457 50N	71176 49 •	2-3	
16803 50	16885 50N	29906 49 •	3-4	
11910 50N	11307 50	28997 49	1-3	
30316 49N	30317 49	38695 48	2-4	
15899 49	15910 49N	16716 48 •	1-4	

34906 49			45000 50	
16117 51N	90270 50N	11251 50	24019 51	
18500 48N	19672 49	73012 49 •	65412 49	for E_1
33273 48	29038 49N	59305 49	75023 49	for E_2
15393 49N	92314 49	33887 49	96257 48	for E_3
98734 49	15739 49	19165 48	19750 47	for E_4
40117 49	18133 50N	10982 50 •	1-2	
15680 50	16574 50N	70105 49 •	2-3	
16831 50	16940 50N	31772 49 •	3-4	
10345 50N	99856 49	24867 49	1-3	
28502 49N	28496 49	37041 48	2-4	
12830 49	12830 49N	13717 48 •	1-4	

34906 49			50000 50	
17867 51N	10061 51N	18442 50	26085 51	
16901 48N	17695 49	67861 49 •	71265 49	for E_1
34843 48	29897 49N	65199 49	69591 49	for E_2
16195 49N	92304 49	33756 49	88405 48	for E_3
98603 49	16521 49	20773 48	21343 47	for E_4
64277 49	17997 50N	11000 50 •	1-2	
16480 50	17406 50N	69755 49 •	2-3	
16844 50	16978 50N	33417 49 •	3-4	
89721 49N	87428 49	21161 49	1-3	
27018 49N	27010 49	35675 48	2-4	
10363 49	10362 49N	11227 48 •	1-4	

34906 49			55000 50	
19701 51N	11014 51N	25618 50	28154 51	
15474 48N	16022 49	63324 49 •	75702 49	for E_1
36215 48	30575 49N	69653 49	64810 49	for E_2
16910 49N	92260 49	33666 49	82886 48	for E_3
98481 49	17218 49	22245 48	23033 47	for E_4
83115 49	17900 50N	10814 50 •	1-2	
17047 50	18007 50N	69611 49 •	2-3	
16848 50	17008 50N	34881 49 •	3-4	
78171 49N	76620 49	18062 49	1-3	
25673 49N	25668 49	34375 48	2-4	
84392 48	84418 48N	92751 47 •	1-4	

34906 49			60000 50	
21595 51N	11907 51N	32779 50	30225 51	
14259 48N	14644 49	59464 49 •	79041 49	for E_1
37380 48	31084 49N	73002 49	60748 49	for E_2
17550 49N	92200 49	33600 49	78797 48	for E_3
98366 49	17844 49	23591 48	24486 47	for E_4
97441 49	17827 50N	10534 50 •	1-2	
17446 50	18437 50N	69518 49 •	2-3	
16846 50	17033 50N	36190 49 •	3-4	
68654 49N	67551 49	15548 49	1-3	
24427 49N	24423 49	33155 48	2-4	
69563 48	69602 48N	77257 47 •	1-4	

34906 49			65000 50	
23534 51N	12756 51N	39925 50	32298 51	
13244 48N	13518 49	56227 49 •	81571 49	for E_1
38368 48	31463 49N	75541 49	57347 49	for E_2
18128 49N	92132 49	33551 49	75647 48	for E_3
98259 49	18408 49	24825 48	25673 47	for E_4
10830 50	17771 50N	10226 50 •	1-2	
17731 50	18749 50N	69435 49 •	2-3	
16842 50	17053 50N	37369 49 •	3-4	
60857 49N	60038 49	13528 49	1-3	
23272 49N	23266 49	32011 48	2-4	
58111 48	58134 48N	64793 47 •	1-4	

34906 49			70000 50	
25505 51N	13573 51N	47056 50	34373 51	
12399 48N	12595 49	53520 49 •	83518 49	for E_1
39214 48	31747 49N	77496 49	54507 49	for E_2
18651 49N	92062 49	33513 49	73145 48	for E_3
98159 49	18920 49	25960 48	26774 47	for E_4
11661 50	17726 50N	99239 49 •	1-2	
17937 50	18979 50N	69354 49 •	2-3	
16835 50	17070 50N	38435 49 •	3-4	
54448 49N	53818 49	11899 49	1-3	
22202 49N	22194 49	30912 48	2-4	
49172 48	49183 48N	54957 47 •	1-4	

34906 49			75000 50	
27499 51N	14367 51N	54176 50	36449 51	
11695 48N	11835 49	51247 49 •	85042 49	for E_1
39946 48	31962 49N	79027 49	52125 49	for E_2
19128 49N	91991 49	33482 49	71113 48	for E_3
98065 49	19386 49	27006 48	27751 47	for E_4
12307 50	17689 50N	96411 49 •	1-2	
18091 50	19152 50N	69276 49 •	2-3	
16827 50	17085 50N	39404 49 •	3-4	
49138 49N	48638 49	10574 49	1-3	
21215 49N	21204 49	29872 48	2-4	
42109 48	42104 48N	47006 47 •	1-4	

TABLE I(c). Ruby $\theta=30°$.

52359 49			50000 49	
66856 50N	48388 50N	39534 50	75709 50	
17546 48N	41329 49	90895 49 •	61782 48	for E_1
44365 48	90933 49N	41270 49 •	28467 48	for E_2
75341 46N	44760 47	58917 48	99826 49	for E_3
99886 49	47653 48	24248 47	79319 46	for E_4
12895 50	20061 50N	75770 49 •	1-2	
81998 49N	82077 49N	65108 48 •	2-3	
17592 48	17511 48N	45626 47 •	3-4	
15264 50N	15196 50N	99631 48 •	1-3	
16137 50N	16111 50	90544 48	2-4	
62792 49	62930 49N	30804 48 •	1-4	

52359 49			10000 50	
77133 50N	40154 50N	22691 50	94596 50	
88808 48N	40699 49	90614 49 •	11148 49	for E_1
82139 48	90890 49N	40110 49 •	79164 48	for E_2
45562 47N	26721 48	13402 49	99060 49	for E_3
99619 49	86824 48	74774 47	12364 47	for E_4
12888 50	20330 50N	76694 49 •	1-2	
92392 49N	93215 49N	20691 49 •	2-3	
82211 48	82208 48N	15973 48 •	3-4	
14787 50N	14212 50N	19860 49 •	1-3	
16390 50N	16348 50	16924 49	2-4	
54615 49	54652 49N	44396 48 •	1-4	

52359 49			15000 50	
88253 50N	32964 50N	73738 49	11384 51	
35972 48N	39685 49	89958 49 •	17877 49	for E_1
11334 49	90461 49N	36680 49 •	18516 49	for E_2
17314 48N	99647 48	23668 49	96630 49	for E_3
99275 49	11940 49	13415 48	22440 47	for E_4
10686 50	21151 50N	80050 49 •	1-2	
99263 49N	10525 50N	54597 49 •	2-3	
25032 49	25030 49N	49350 48 •	3-4	
14418 50N	12060 50N	26391 49 •	1-3	
16410 50N	16365 50	23323 49	2-4	
47143 49	47200 49N	48886 48 •	1-4	

52359 49			20000 50	
10035 51N	28707 50N	43124 49 •	13337 51	
40209 48N	38298 49	88783 49 •	25188 49	for E_1
12987 49	85189 49N	24775 49 •	44274 49	for E_2
58677 48N	32565 49	38727 49	86053 49	for E_3
98897 49	14676 49	19414 48	31536 47	for E_4
67946 49	23020 50N	89646 49 •	1-2	
73366 49N	11780 50N	13473 50 •	2-3	
70029 49	70060 49N	14195 49 •	3-4	
14975 50N	60112 49N	17463 49 •	1-3	
15185 50N	15156 50	26091 49	2-4	
40370 49	40410 49N	48236 48 •	1-4	

52359 49			25000 50	
11353 51N	32817 50N	67653 49 •	15311 51	
42261 48N	36582 49	87010 49 •	32756 49	for E_1
10690 49	63971 49N	12347 48	76103 49	for E_2
12775 49N	65425 49	49206 49	55991 49	for E_3
98512 49	16996 49	25146 48	40838 47	for E_4
96914 48	22790 50N	98469 49 •	1-2	
30988 49	13027 50N	17439 50 •	2-3	
13067 50	13092 50N	28559 49 •	3-4	
14720 50N	40860 49	13346 49	1-3	
10648 50N	10535 50	19759 49	2-4	
34249 49	34289 49N	44852 48 •	1-4	

52359 49			30000 50	
12784 51N	43240 50N	19503 49 •	17303 51	
42710 48N	34631 49	84674 49 •	40158 49	for E_1
86546 48	49972 49N	18994 49	84065 49	for E_2
16633 49N	77091 49	49600 49	36332 49	for E_3
98133 49	18981 49	30467 48	49224 47	for E_4
34071 48N	20946 50N	10361 50 •	1-2	
89839 49	14196 50N	14389 50 •	2-3	
15143 50	15212 50N	36383 49 •	3-4	
13066 50N	81397 49	27057 49	1-3	
73330 49N	73255 49	14173 49	2-4	
28823 49	28855 49N	40137 48 •	1-4	

52359 49			35000 50	
14325 51N	54571 50N	47278 49	19310 51	
42074 48N	32579 49	81926 49 •	46999 49	for E_1
80022 48	45178 49N	29670 49	83752 49	for E_2
18954 49N	80431 49	48941 49	27859 49	for E_3
97769 49.	20693 49	35343 48	57004 47	for E_4
64746 48	19891 50N	10951 50 •	1-2	
11480 50	15231 50N	12540 50 •	2-3	
15754 50	15879 50N	41158 49 •	3-4	
11615 50N	89139 49	29409 49	1-3	
59131 49N	59066 49	11641 49	2-4	
24126 49	24154 49N	35074 48 •	1-4	

52359 49			40000 50	
15965 51N	65491 50N	11870 50	21327 51	
40799 48N	30557 49	78981 49 •	53023 49	for E_1
78777 48	43650 49N	37388 49	81453 49	for E_2
20726 49N	81662 49	48458 49	23524 49	for E_3
97425 49	22182 49	39782 48	63919 47	for E_4
21963 49	19295 50N	11434 50 •	1-2	
12917 50	16102 50N	11614 50 •	2-3	
15999 50	16185 50N	44841 49 •	3-4	
10380 50N	87126 49	28343 49	1-3	
51491 49N	51426 49	10292 49	2-4	
20167 49	20188 49N	30212 48 •	1-4	

52359 49			45000 50	
17689 51N	75798 50N	19151 50	23354 51	
39226 48N	28666 49	76042 49 •	58141 49	for E_1
79475 48	43300 49N	43376 49	78615 49	for E_2
22197 49N	82168 49	48134 49	20943 49	for E_3
97101 49	23486 49	43814 48	70251 47	for E_4
37747 49	18921 50N	11748 50 •	1-2	
13883 50	16811 50N	11114 50 •	2-3	
16115 50	16363 50N	47914 49 •	3-4	
93084 49N	81943 49	26238 49	1-3	
46517 49N	46450 49	94247 48	2-4	
16896 49	16914 49N	25878 48 •	1-4	

52359 49			50000 50	
19483 51N	85529 50N	26469 50	25388 51	
37579 48N	26959 49	73251 49 •	62396 49	for E_1
80876 48	43386 49N	48128 49	75735 49	for E_2
23462 49N	82364 49	47909 49	19243 49	for E_3
96798 49	24635 49	47476 48	75870 47	for E_4
52038 49	18666 50N	11912 50 •	1-2	
14576 50	17375 50N	10820 50 •	2-3	
16171 50	16484 50N	50556 49 •	3-4	
83789 49N	75900 49	23922 49	1-3	
42836 49N	42763 49	87888 48	2-4	
14233 49	14245 49N	22137 48 •	1-4	

52359 49			55000 50	
21331 51N	94772 50N	33787 50	27430 51	
35989 48N	25454 49	70688 49 •	65895 49	for E_1
82480 48	43621 49N	51938 49	73017 49	for E_2
24570 49N	82407 49	47746 49	18043 49	for E_3
96515 49	25656 49	50807 48	81083 47	for E_4
64349 49	18482 50N	11962 50 •	1-2	
15090 50	17820 50N	10635 50 •	2-3	
16197 50	16572 50N	52866 49 •	3-4	
75764 49N	69921 49	21710 49	1-3	
39882 49N	39807 49	82754 48	2-4	
12074 49	12085 49N	19015 48 •	1-4	

52359 49			60000 50	
23223 51N	10362 51N	41091 50	29476 51	
34518 48N	24143 49	68381 49 •	68769 49	for E_1
84080 48	43890 49N	55018 49	70539 49	for E_2
25552 49N	82370 49	47623 49	17152 49	for E_3
96252 49	26567 49	53841 48	85800 47	for E_4
74719 49	18343 50N	11937 50 •	1-2	
15478 50	18171 50N	10509 50 •	2-3	
16204 50	16640 50N	54906 49 •	3-4	
68857 49N	64368 49	19711 49	1-3	
37398 49N	37319 49	78404 48	2-4	
10325 49	10335 49N	16416 48 •	1-4	

52359 49			65000 50	
25149 51N	11215 51N	48376 50	31527 51	
33188 48N	23007 49	66327 49 •	71135 49	for E_1
85594 48	44149 49N	57530 49	68321 49	for E_2
26428 49N	82289 49	47526 49	16466 49	for E_3
96006 49	27384 49	56612 48	90092 47	for E_4
83383 49	18233 50N	11865 50 •	1-2	
15777 50	18449 50N	10420 50 •	2-3	
16200 50	16695 50N	56721 49 •	3-4	
62912 49N	59358 49	17948 49	1-3	
35248 49N	35165 49	74594 48	2-4	
89038 48	89121 48N	4261 48 •	1-4	

52359 49			70000 50	
27103 51N	12043 51N	55640 50	33583 51	
32000 48N	22024 49	64509 49 •	73097 49	for E_1
86994 48	44382 49N	59599 49	66350 49	for E_2
27216 49N	82184 49	47449 49	15920 49	for E_3
95777 49	28121 49	59148 48	93993 47	for E_4
90616 49	18146 50N	11766 50 •	1-2	
16011 50	18671 50N	10354 50 •	2-3	
16189 50	16741 50N	58346 49 •	3-4	
57782 49N	54897 49	16409 49	1-3	
33351 49N	33266 49	71193 48	2-4	
77405 48	77474 48N	12468 48 •	1-4	

52359 49			75000 50	
29078 51N	12852 51N	62883 50	35641 51	
30944 48N	21171 49	62900 49 •	74737 49	for E_1
88277 48	44587 49N	61320 49	64604 49	for E_2
27929 49N	82066 49	47386 49	15477 49	for E_3
95563 49	28788 49	61476 48	97559 47	for E_4
96677 49	18073 50N	11654 50 •	1-2	
16197 50	18851 50N	10304 50 •	2-3	
16173 50	16780 50N	59810 49 •	3-4	
53338 49N	50945 49	15071 49	1-3	
31659 49N	31571 49	68114 48	2-4	
67813 48	67870 48N	10971 48 •	1-4	

TABLE I(d). Ruby $\theta = 40°$

69813 49			50000 49	
68258 50N	47405 50N	41852 50	73811 50	
26912 48N	49068 49	86874 49 •	61592 48	for E_1
55900 48	86910 49N	48958 49 •	42875 48	for E_2
17264 47N	69979 47	74705 48	99717 49	for E_3
99807 49	61920 48	41262 47	10057 47	for E_4
10008 50	20098 50N	86421 49 •	1-2	
97346 49N	97605 49N	98061 48 •	2-3	
28478 48	28472 48N	80529 47 •	3-4	
14331 50N	14218 50N	11578 49 •	1-3	
15647 50N	15607 50	11545 49	2-4	
74075 49	74145 49N	46798 48 •	1-4	

69813 49			10000 50	
80255 50N	38751 50N	27869 50	91136 50	
44126 48N	48190 49	86577 49 •	12745 49	for E_1
10522 49	86797 49N	47164 49 •	11446 49	for E_2
96345 47N	38143 48	16676 49	98521 49	for E_3
99342 49	11371 49	13116 48	30786 47	for E_4
92676 49	20465 50N	88431 49 •	1-2	
10758 50N	10989 50N	29582 49 •	2-3	
12593 49	12594 49N	35662 48 •	3-4	
13568 50N	12823 50N	21268 49 •	1-3	
16027 50N	15935 50	22003 49	2-4	
63452 49	63585 49N	66531 48 •	1-4	

69813 49			15000 50	
93302 50N	31957 50N	16161 50	10909 51	
54992 48N	46901 49	85955 49 •	19533 49	for E_1
14599 49	86073 49N	42442 49 •	24017 49	for E_2
31366 48N	12013 49	28364 49	95085 49	for E_3
98725 49	15723 49	23895 48	55651 47	for E_4
78100 49	21284 50N	93334 49 •	1-2	
10941 50N	12196 50N	68186 49 •	2-3	
33391 49	33404 49N	96663 48 •	3-4	
12970 50N	10249 50N	25188 49 •	1-3	
16008 50N	15898 50	30321 49	2-4	
53895 49	54064 49N	71854 48 •	1-4	

69813 49			20000 50	
10739 51N	28685 50N	85182 49	12756 51	
61520 48N	45317 49	84969 49 •	26241 49	for E_1
17003 49	82167 49N	31315 49 •	44483 49	for E_2
78727 48N	28614 49	42276 49	85626 49	for E_3
98035 49	19392 49	34944 48	80800 47	for E_4
53652 49	22384 50N	10200 50 •	1-2	
81636 49N	13334 50N	12855 50 •	2-3	
70115 49	70221 49N	21158 49 •	3-4	
12634 50N	55159 49N	17068 49 •	1-3	
14944 50N	14850 50	34090 49	2-4	
45494 49	45671 49N	69720 48 •	1-4	

69813 49			25000 50	
12249 51N	31045 50N	71112 49	14642 51	
65062 48N	43557 49	83653 49 •	32597 49	for E_1
16750 49	72689 49N	13758 49 •	65164 49	for E_2
14326 49N	48090 49	52840 49	68483 49	for E_3
97323 49	22501 49	45540 48	10449 48	for E_4
28271 49	22469 50N	11016 50 •	1-2	
14742 49N	14362 50N	16876 50 •	2-3	
11000 50	11049 50N	35560 49 •	3-4	
12004 50N	28188 48	97516 47	1-3	
12392 50N	12324 50	31134 49	2-4	
38265 49	38430 49N	64075 48 •	1-4	

69813 49			30000 50	
13850 51N	37907 50N	10804 50	16560 51	
66602 48N	41736 49	82094 49 •	38394 49	for E_1
15532 49	63801 49N	15689 48	75403 49	for E_2
19471 49N	59623 49	56809 49	53278 49	for E_3
96619 49	25149 49	55375 48	12619 48	for E_4
18477 49	21557 50N	11529 50 •	1-2	
42581 49	15258 50N	16852 50 •	2-3	
13282 50	13410 50N	46607 49 •	3-4	
10940 50N	38977 49	14045 49	1-3	
99014 49N	98483 49	26035 49	2-4	
32161 49	32308 49N	57159 48 •	1-4	

69813 49			35000 50	
15531 51N	46523 50N	16800 50	18504 51	
66897 48N	39950 49	80402 49 •	43526 49	for E_1
14789 49	58774 49N	12123 49	78612 49	for E_2
23063 49N	64789 49	57853 49	43856 49	for E_3
95940 49	27418 49	64354 48	14578 48	for E_4
20902 49	20687 50N	11935 50 •	1-2	
75760 49	16016 50N	15875 50 •	2-3	
14312 50	14543 50N	54257 49 •	3-4	
98881 49N	54175 49	19756 49	1-3	
82492 49N	82022 49	22233 49	2-4	
27085 49	27212 49N	50183 48 •	1-4	

69813 49			40000 50	
17281 51N	55534 50N	23665 50	20468 51	
66338 48N	38265 49	78677 49 •	47975 49	for E_1
14499 49	56262 49N	19584 49	78998 49	for E_2
25766 49N	67136 49	58084 49	38143 49	for E_3
95298 49	29375 49	72482 48	16336 48	for E_4
28215 49	20061 50N	12270 50 •	1-2	
95321 49	16644 50N	15075 50 •	2-3	
14799 50	15146 50N	60022 49 •	3-4	
89694 49N	59213 49	21618 49	1-3	
71669 49N	71219 49	19633 49	2-4	
22907 49	23015 49N	43734 48 •	1-4	

69813 49			45000 50	
19088 51N	64488 50N	30869 50	22449 51	
65388 48N	36717 49	76991 49 •	51781 49	for E_1
14457 49	55035 49N	25176 49	78282 49	for E_2
27942 49N	68244 49	58092 49	34455 49	for E_3
94696 49	31074 49	79812 48	17906 48	for E_4
36848 49	19619 50N	12526 50 •	1-2	
10793 50	17159 50N	14522 50 •	2-3	
15045 50	15514 50N	64661 49 •	3-4	
81769 49N	59735 49	21739 49	1-3	
64023 49N	63577 49	17755 49	2-4	
19485 49	19578 49N	38035 48 •	1-4	

69813 49			50000 50	
20940 51N	73252 50N	38205 50	24445 51	
64230 48N	35318 49	75393 49 •	55019 49	for E_1
14539 49	54455 49N	29544 49	77138 49	for E_2
29763 49N	68754 49	58036 49	31918 49	for E_3
94135 49	32558 49	86420 48	19317 48	for E_4
45355 49	19296 50N	12708 50 •	1-2	
11668 50	17579 50N	14143 50 •	2-3	
15171 50	15763 50N	68532 49 •	3-4	
74908 49N	58239 49	21090 49	1-3	
58226 49N	57778 49	16306 49	2-4	
16686 49	16766 49N	33128 48 •	1-4	

69813 49			55000 50	
22830 51N	81802 50N	45586 50	26452 51	
62997 48N	34067 49	73908 49 •	57769 49	for E_1
14679 49	54206 49N	33052 49	75853 49	for E_2
31323 49N	68951 49	57963 49	30078 49	for E_3
93614 49	33863 49	92378 48	20574 48	for E_4
53193 49	19052 50N	12827 50 •	1-2	
12305 50	17923 50N	13877 50 •	2-3	
15230 50	15943 50N	71830 49 •	3-4	
68941 49N	55871 49	20120 49	1-3	
53596 49N	53143 49	15135 49	2-4	
14391 49	14460 49N	28942 48 •	1-4	

69813 49			60000 50	
24751 51N	90151 50N	52974 50	28469 51	
61768 48N	32954 49	72543 49 •	60110 49	for E_1
14844 49	54130 49N	35925 49	74558 49	for E_2
32680 49N	68975 49	57889 49	28690 49	for E_3
93131 49	35017 49	97763 48	21704 48	for E_4
60201 49	18862 50N	12897 50 •	1-2	
12787 50	18204 50N	13685 50 •	2-3	
15250 50	16082 50N	74681 49 •	3-4	
63730 49N	53183 49	19044 49	1-3	
49760 49N	49301 49	14152 49	2-4	
12500 49	12561 49N	25396 48 •	1-4	

69813 49			65000 50	
26696 51N	98324 50N	60350 50	30494 51	
60586 48N	31967 49	71299 49 •	62111 49	for E_1
15016 49	54144 49N	38314 49	73313 49	for E_2
33874 49N	68900 49	57819 49	27606 49	for E_3
92683 49	36044 49	10264 49	22722 48	for E_4
66382 49	18710 50N	12932 50 •	1-2	
13161 50	18435 50N	13543 50 •	2-3	
15246 50	16192 50N	77171 49 •	3-4	
59161 49N	50447 49	17966 49	1-3	
46498 49N	46033 49	13306 49	2-4	
10934 49	10987 49N	22396 48 •	1-4	

69813 49			70000 50	
28662 51N	10634 51N	67705 50	32526 51	
59471 48N	31089 49	70168 49 •	63831 49	for E_1
15186 49	54205 49N	40325 49	72145 49	for E_2
34934 49N	68767 49	57754 49	26739 49	for E_3
92269 49	36962 49	10707 49	23644 48	for E_4
71806 49	18585 50N	12942 50 •	1-2	
13458 50	18627 50N	13435 50 •	2-3	
15228 50	16282 50N	79364 49 •	3-4	
55136 49N	47795 49	16933 49	1-3	
43672 49N	43204 49	12565 49	2-4	
96288 48	96755 48N	19854 48 •	1-4	

69813 49			75000 50	
30644 51N	11423 51N	75038 50	34564 51	
58433 48N	30309 49	69143 49 •	65318 49	for E_1
15349 49	54288 49N	42037 49	71063 49	for E_2
35881 49N	68602 49	57694 49	26029 49	for E_3
91884 49	37786 49	11110 49	24476 48	for E_4
76561 49	18481 50N	12933 50 •	1-2	
13697 50	18788 50N	13351 50 •	2-3	
15199 50	16358 50N	81308 49 •	3-4	
51575 49N	45289 49	15967 49	1-3	
41190 49N	40719 49	11909 49	2-4	
85324 48	85734 48N	17685 48 •	1-4	

TABLE I(e). Ruby $\theta = 50°$.

87266 49			50000 49	
69599 50N	46507 50N	44662 50	71444 50	
36243 48N	64965 49	83184 49 •	67857 48	for E_1
65664 48	83198 49N	84802 49 •	56130 48	for E_2
32933 47N	92835 47	87535 48	99611 49	for E_3
99717 49	74794 48	61314 47	19011 47	for E_4
75117 49	20133 50N	93174 49 •	1-2	
10870 50N	10932 50N	12813 49 •	2-3	
39682 48	39731 48N	15375 48 •	3-4	
13478 50N	13312 50N	12450 49 •	1-3	
15218 50N	15148 50	13725 49	2-4	
82493 49	82631 49N	62600 48 •	1-4	

87266 49			10000 50	
83200 50N	37595 50N	34000 50	86795 50	
59674 48N	53971 49	82880 49 •	13503 49	for E_1
12599 49	82906 49N	52564 49 •	14308 49	for E_2
16858 48N	45722 48	19073 49	98043 49	for E_3
99009 49	13880 49	20181 48	66049 47	for E_4
68199 49	20562 50N	96363 49 •	1-2	
11754 50N	12223 50N	36488 49 •	2-3	
16560 49	16565 49N	67002 48 •	3-4	
12532 50N	11593 50N	21141 49 •	1-3	
15718 50N	15535 50	26692 49	2-4	
69812 49	70221 49N	88283 48 •	1-4	

87266 49			15000 50	
97949 50N	31289 50N	26111 50	10312 51	
74695 48N	52624 49	82335 49 •	19895 49	for E_1
17630 49	81881 49N	47348 49 •	27251 49	for E_2
47869 48N	12334 49	31062 49	94127 49	for E_3
98032 49	19338 49	37587 48	12101 48	for E_4
56484 49	21269 50N	10229 50 •	1-2	
11452 50N	13406 50N	74878 49 •	2-3	
39060 49	39110 49N	16277 49 •	3-4	
11710 50N	89166 49N	23041 49 •	1-3	
15681 50N	15432 50	36808 49	2-4	
58534 49	59077 49N	94188 48 •	1-4	

87266 49			20000 50	
11370 51N	28675 50N	22120 50	12025 51	
84143 48N	51097 49	81574 49 •	25765 49	for E_1
20908 49	78949 49N	37853 49 •	43553 49	for E_2
10032 49N	24116 49	43378 49	86232 49	for E_3
96909 49	23967 49	55753 48	17675 48	for E_4
41700 49	21913 50N	11016 50 •	1-2	
88112 49N	14448 50N	12158 50 •	2-3	
69451 49	69747 49N	30379 49 •	3-4	
10988 50N	52156 49N	16414 49 •	1-3	
14773 50N	14517 50	41666 49	2-4	
48861 49	49446 49N	90341 48 •	1-4	

87266 49			25000 50	
13031 51N	30272 50N	22554 50	13808 51	
89908 48N	49519 49	80656 49 •	31008 49	for E_1
22117 49	74000 49N	25539 49 •	58158 49	for E_2
16321 49N	35975 49	52807 49	75171 49	for E_3
95726 49	27882 49	73288 48	22915 48	for E_4
29607 49	21964 50N	11731 50 •	1-2	
41889 49N	15336 50N	15512 50 •	2-3	
98125 49	99151 49N	45878 49 •	3-4	
10198 50N	14648 49N	51200 48 •	1-3	
13073 50N	12837 50	40756 49	2-4	
40779 49	41349 49N	82332 48 •	1-4	

87266 49			30000 50	
14764 51N	35082 50N	26401 50	15632 51	
93264 48N	47976 49	79649 49 •	35598 49	for E_1
22176 49	69127 49N	14156 49 •	67298 49	for E_2
21953 49N	44121 49	58098 49	64775 49	for E_3
94547 49	31191 49	89536 48	27661 48	for E_4
24558 49	21507 50N	12251 50 •	1-2	
22558 48	16077 50N	16766 50 •	2-3	
11736 50	11971 50N	59083 49 •	3-4	
93446 49N	11962 49	44069 48	1-3	
11267 50N	11052 50	37024 49	2-4	
34136 49	34663 49N	73119 48 •	1-4	

87266 49			35000 50	
16555 51N	41619 50N	32149 50	17502 51	
95067 48N	46521 49	78611 49 •	39567 49	for E_1
22026 49	65645 49N	52947 48 •	71954 49	for E_2
26439 49N	48690 49	60691 49	56980 49	for E_3
93410 49	33995 49	10426 49	31876 48	for E_4
25240 49	20941 50N	12639 50 •	1-2	
34212 49	16687 50N	16922 50 •	2-3	
12826 50	13239 50N	69314 49 •	3-4	
85395 49N	27129 49	10264 49	1-3	
97826 49N	95803 49	33079 49	2-4	
28726 49	29200 49N	64132 48 •	1-4	

87266 49			40000 50	
18396 51N	48924 50N	38811 50	19407 51	
95880 48N	45179 49	77587 49 •	42978 49	for E_1
21969 49	63450 49N	13786 48	74090 49	for E_2
29993 49N	51080 49	61970 49	51485 49	for E_3
92335 49	36380 49	11745 49	35583 48	for E_4
28894 49	20446 50N	12944 50 •	1-2	
55922 49	17187 50N	16747 50 •	2-3	
13417 50	14033 50N	77273 49 •	3-4	
78281 49N	34926 49	13403 49	1-3	
86377 49N	84425 49	29702 49	2-4	
24332 49	24754 49N	55981 48 •	1-4	

87266 49			45000 50	
20275 51N	56536 50N	45897 50	21339 51	
96074 48N	43959 49	76604 49 •	45903 49	for E_1
22026 49	62115 49N	64921 48	74929 49	for E_2
32874 49N	52279 49	62631 49	47575 49	for E_3
91333 49	38421 49	12919 49	38828 48	for E_4
33724 49	20047 50N	13186 50 •	1-2	
70927 49	17595 50N	16520 50 •	2-3	
13732 50	14563 50N	83623 49 •	3-4	
72089 49N	38570 49	14919 49	1-3	
77462 49N	75550 49	26919 49	2-4	
20762 49	21135 49N	48846 48 •	1-4	

87266 49			50000 50	
22186 51N	64244 50N	53176 50	23293 51	
95885 48N	42859 49	75677 49 •	48415 49	for E_1
22159 49	61308 49N	10515 49	75097 49	for E_2
35264 49N	52822 49	62986 49	44709 49	for E_3
90407 49	40176 49	13964 49	41671 48	for E_4
38820 49	19730 50N	13376 50 •	1-2	
81669 49	17929 50N	16317 50 •	2-3	
13890 50	14938 50N	88806 49 •	3-4	
66694 49N	39923 49	15511 49	1-3	
70332 49N	68445 49	24612 49	2-4	
17849 49	18178 49N	42714 48 •	1-4	

87266 49			55000 50	
24123 51N	71957 50N	60535 50	25265 51	
95468 48N	41871 49	74815 49 •	50580 49	for E_1
22335 49	60822 49N	13758 49	74916 49	for E_2
37281 49N	52998 49	63178 49	42540 49	for E_3
89554 49	41696 49	14894 49	44167 48	for E_4
43761 49	19476 50N	13524 50 •	1-2	
89626 49	18205 50N	16151 50 •	2-3	
13956 50	15217 50N	93110 49 •	3-4	
61971 49N	40008 49	15584 49	1-3	
64477 49N	62609 49	22672 49	2-4	
15460 49	15750 49N	37489 48 •	1-4	

87266 49			60000 50	
26081 51N	79635 50N	67921 50	27252 51	
94920 48N	40984 49	74017 49 •	52455 49	for E_1
22533 49	60533 49N	16425 49	74552 49	for E_2
39008 49N	52962 49	63280 49	40852 49	for E_3
88771 49	43021 49	15722 49	46361 48	for E_4
48369 49	19269 50N	13638 50 •	1-2	
95693 49	18432 50N	16019 50 •	2-3	
13967 50	15433 50N	96732 49 •	3-4	
57812 49N	39391 49	15366 49	1-3	
59564 49N	57713 49	21015 49	2-4	
13486 49	13744 49N	33046 48 •	1-4	

87266 49			65000 50	
28056 51N	87263 50N	75306 50	29252 51	
94304 48N	40189 49	73283 49 •	54086 49	for E_1
22737 49	60368 49N	18656 49	74098 49	for E_2
40504 49N	52805 49	63327 49	39504 49	for E_3
88053 49	44182 49	16464 49	48303 48	for E_4
52586 49	19098 50N	13725 50 •	1-2	
10043 50	18622 50N	15913 50 •	2-3	
13945 50	15607 50N	99816 49 •	3-4	
54131 49N	38396 49	14988 49	1-3	
55369 49N	53536 49	19583 49	2-4	
11845 49	12074 49N	29270 48 •	1-4	

87266 49			70000 50	
30046 51N	94836 50N	82675 50	31262 51	
93659 48N	39474 49	72609 49 •	55515 49	for E_1
22941 49	60279 49N	20546 49	73606 49	for E_2
41810 49N	52577 49	63342 49	38407 49	for E_3
87394 49	45207 49	17129 49	50026 48	for E_4
56410 49	18954 50N	13790 50 •	1-2	
10421 50	18782 50N	15829 50 •	2-3	
13901 50	15749 50N	10246 50 •	3-4	
50856 49N	37207 49	14528 49	1-3	
51738 49N	49924 49	18330 49	2-4	
10471 49	10675 49N	26050 48 •	1-4	

87266 49			75000 50	
32048 51N	10235 51N	90024 50	33281 51	
93010 48N	38829 49	71990 49 •	56772 49	for E_1
23138 49	60240 49N	22168 49	73104 49	for E_2
42961 49N	52311 49	63337 49	37497 49	for E_3
86789 49	46116 49	17727 49	51563 48	for E_4
59862 49	18832 50N	13839 50 •	1-2	
10727 50	18916 50N	15761 50 •	2-3	
13845 50	15868 50N	10476 50 •	3-4	
47927 49N	35935 49	14032 49	1-3	
48558 49N	46765 49	17225 49	2-4	
93113 48	94945 48N	23297 48 •	1-4	

TABLE I(f). Ruby $\theta=60°$.

10471 50			50000 49	
70754 50N	45768 50N	47857 50	68664 50	
45080 48N	59683 49	79794 49 •	70995 48	for E_1
73510 48	79767 49N	59480 49 •	67200 48	for E_2
57507 47N	10940 48	97054 48	99520 49	for E_3
99625 49	85927 48	83456 47	40402 47	for E_4
53524 49	20164 50N	97495 49 •	1-2	
11725 50N	11849 50N	15290 49 •	2-3	
49949 48	49938 48N	29120 48 •	3-4	
12719 50N	12489 50N	12721 49 •	1-3	
14842 50N	14711 50	15531 49	2-4	
89144 49	89610 49N	77651 48 •	1-4	

10471 50			10000 50	
85708 50N	36726 50N	40781 50	81653 50	
74914 48N	58690 49	79459 49 •	13619 49	for E_1
14414 49	79188 49N	57050 49 •	16330 49	for E_2
27022 48N	48354 48	20572 49	97704 49	for E_3
98634 49	16163 49	28660 48	13241 48	for E_4
47874 49	20620 50N	10171 50 •	1-2	
12391 50N	13192 50N	41127 49 •	2-3	
19753 49	19768 49N	11685 49 •	3-4	
11652 50N	10536 50N	20127 49 •	1-3	
15472 50N	15110 50	30841 49	2-4	
74701 49	75812 49N	10945 49 •	1-4	

10471 50			15000 50	
10183 51N	30864 50N	36666 50	96034 50	
94620 48N	57435 49	78963 49 •	19401 49	for E_1
20428 49	77810 49N	51983 49 •	28737 49	for E_2
68578 48N	11366 49	32126 49	93763 49	for E_3
97191 49	22748 49	55058 48	24644 48	for E_4
39471 49	21200 50N	10826 50 •	1-2	
11698 50N	14381 50N	77183 49 •	2-3	
42612 49	42771 49N	26111 49 •	3-4	
10717 50N	7 221 49N	20730 49 •	1-3	
15463 50N	14915 50	42600 49	2-4	
61 36 49	63384 49N	11609 45 •	1-4	

10471 50			20000 50	
11888 51N	28669 50N	35960 50	11159 51	
10768 49N	56100 49	78363 49 •	24413 49	for E_1
24661 49	75323 49N	44240 49 •	41964 49	for E_2
12801 49N	19328 49	42809 49	87349 49	for E_3
95456 49	28381 49	83310 48	36265 48	for E_4
30761 49	21585 50N	11562 50 •	1-2	
92452 49N	15388 50N	11505 50 •	2-3	
68478 49	69244 49N	44243 49 •	3-4	
98761 49N	49499 49N	15447 49 •	1-3	
14679 50N	14038 50	48366 49	2-4	
50928 49	52664 49N	11042 49 •	1-4	

10471 50			25000 50	
13664 51N	29889 50N	38408 50	12812 51	
11638 49N	54790 49	77709 49 •	28701 49	for E_1
27059 49	72160 49N	35348 49 •	53019 49	for E_2
19348 49N	26336 49	50882 49	79642 49	for E_3
93583 49	33124 49	11076 49	47058 48	for E_4
24708 49	21580 50N	12210 50 •	1-2	
57561 49N	16214 50N	14340 50 •	2-3	
90558 49	92797 49N	62478 49 •	3-4	
90747 49N	22750 49N	78502 48 •	1-3	
13355 50N	12687 50	48498 49	2-4	
41960 49	43708 49N	99715 48 •	1-4	

10471 50			30000 50	
15497 51N	33588 50N	43103 50	14545 51	
12223 49N	53557 49	77042 49 •	32350 49	for E_1
28273 49	69208 49N	27145 49 •	60613 49	for E_2
25360 49N	31095 49	56057 49	72439 49	for E_3
91695 49	37079 49	13603 49	56576 48	for E_4
22349 49	21296 50N	12717 50 •	1-2	
24054 49N	16879 50N	15953 50 •	2-3	
10569 50	11035 50N	78153 49 •	3-4	
83230 49N	31739 48N	11614 48 •	1-3	
11909 50N	11243 50	45518 49	2-4	
34721 49	36378 49N	87769 48 •	1-4	

10471 50			35000 50	
17374 51N	38796 50N	49110 50	16342 51	
12618 49N	52425 49	76389 49 •	35453 49	for E_1
28944 49	66923 49N	20390 49 •	65327 49	for E_2
30419 49N	33821 49	59138 49	66583 49	for E_3
89875 49	40360 49	15857 49	64749 48	for E_4
22817 49	20919 50N	13110 50 •	1-2	
26698 48	17409 50N	16748 50 •	2-3	
11476 50	12258 50N	90681 49 •	3-4	
76462 49N	94968 48	36039 48	1-3	
10597 50N	99416 49	41575 49	2-4	
28924 49	30446 49N	76363 48 •	1-4	

10471 50			40000 50	
19285 51N	44853 50N	55806 50	18189 51	
12886 49N	51398 49	75766 49 •	38098 49	for E_1
29407 49	65299 49N	15026 49 •	68157 49	for E_2
34567 49N	35183 49	60954 49	62062 49	for E_3
88171 49	43084 49	17835 49	71668 48	for E_4
24897 49	20553 50N	13421 50 •	1-2	
22642 49	17831 50N	17121 50 •	2-3	
11975 50	13110 50N	10049 50 •	3-4	
70502 49N	17227 49	66960 48	1-3	
94829 49N	88403 49	37679 49	2-4	
24290 49	25664 49N	66187 48 •	1-4	

10471 50			45000 50	
21224 51N	51380 50N	62847 50	20077 51	
13067 49N	50474 49	75181 49 •	40365 49	for E_1
29792 49	64178 49N	10768 49 •	69840 49	for E_2
37963 49N	35727 49	62043 49	58591 49	for E_3
86604 49	45354 49	19557 49	77495 48	for E_4
27728 49	20230 50N	13674 50 •	1-2	
37429 49	18168 50N	17293 50 •	2-3	
12219 50	13723 50N	10818 50 •	3-4	
65283 49N	21782 49	86093 48	1-3	
85524 49N	79234 49	34165 49	2-4	
20576 49	21804 49N	57402 48 •	1-4	

10471 50			50000 50	
23185 51N	58170 50N	70051 50	21997 51	
13190 49N	49644 49	74636 49 •	42318 49	for E_1
30141 49	63407 49N	73423 48 •	70830 49	for E_2
40766 49N	35798 49	62707 49	55895 49	for E_3
85179 49	47258 49	21052 49	82403 48	for E_4
30817 49	19955 50N	13880 50 •	1-2	
48504 49	18438 50N	17373 50 •	2-3	
12311 50	14181 50N	11427 50 •	3-4	
60703 49N	24353 49	97453 48	1-3	
77734 49N	[illegible]1587 49	31093 49	2-4	
17583 49	18676 49N	49938 48 •	1-4	

10471 50			55000 50	
25164 51N	65108 50N	77326 50	23942 51	
13271 49N	48899 49	74133 49 •	44011 49	for E_1
30469 49	62876 49N	45416 48 •	71397 49	for E_2
43103 49N	35603 49	63118 49	53763 49	for E_3
83890 49	48865 49	22352 49	86553 48	for E_4
33904 49	19723 50N	14051 50 •	1-2	
56949 49	18657 50N	17407 50 •	2-3	
12313 50	14533 50N	11914 50 •	3-4	
56668 49N	25690 49	10377 49	1-3	
71158 49N	65156 49	28432 49	2-4	
15152 49	16125 49N	43637 48 •	1-4	

10471 50			60000 50	
27158 51N	72130 50N	84624 50	25908 51	
13324 49N	48229 49	73669 49 •	45488 49	for E_1
30777 49	62506 49N	22159 48 •	71699 49	for E_2
45071 49N	35262 49	63374 49	52046 49	for E_3
82727 49	50234 49	23485 49	90080 48	for E_4
36861 49	19526 50N	14192 50 •	1-2	
63509 49	18836 50N	17420 50 •	2-3	
12260 50	14813 50N	12309 50 •	3-4	
53094 49N	26253 49	10685 49	1-3	
65550 49N	59696 49	26128 49	2-4	
13161 49	14029 49N	38326 48 •	1-4	

10471 50			65000 50	
29164 51N	79199 50N	91920 50	27891 51	
13357 49N	47625 49	73242 49 •	46785 49	for E_1
31068 49	62247 49N	25694 47 •	71832 49	for E_2
46744 49N	34846 49	63531 49	50640 49	for E_3
81677 49	51408 49	24478 49	93097 48	for E_4
39632 49	19357 50N	14310 50 •	1-2	
68696 49	18983 50N	17422 50 •	2-3	
12177 50	15040 50N	12632 50 •	3-4	
49912 49N	26330 49	10781 49	1-3	
60722 49N	55016 49	24127 49	2-4	
11519 49	12294 49N	33840 48 •	1-4	

10471 50			70000 50	
31180 51N	86293 50N	99204 50	29888 51	
13375 49N	47080 49	72850 49 •	47931 49	for E_1
31341 49	62065 49N	14138 48	71858 49	for E_2
48180 49N	34396 49	63624 49	49471 49	for E_3
80730 49	52423 49	25352 49	95694 48	for E_4
42199 49	19212 50N	14409 50 •	1-2	
72861 49	19104 50N	17419 50 •	2-3	
12076 50	15229 50N	12899 50 •	3-4	
47067 49N	26102 49	10741 49	1-3	
56527 49N	50970 49	22381 49	2-4	
10151 49	10846 49N	30038 48 •	1-4	

10471 50			75000 50	
33204 51N	93399 50N	10647 51	31897 51	
13383 49N	46586 49	72488 49 •	48948 49	for E_1
31596 49	61937 49N	28545 48	71814 49	for E_2
49423 49N	33938 49	63676 49	48485 49	for E_3
79873 49	53307 49	26125 49	97944 48	for E_4
44562 49	19085 50N	14492 50 •	1-2	
76254 49	19207 50N	17414 50 •	2-3	
11968 50	15387 50N	13122 50 •	3-4	
44510 49N	25683 49	10613 49	1-3	
52853 49N	47442 49	20848 49	2-4	
90039 48	96286 48N	26801 48 •	1-4	

TABLE I(g). Ruby $\theta=70°$.

12217 50			50000 49	
71636 50N	45223 50N	51319 50	65539 50	
53100 48N	63657 49	76606 49 •	71413 48	for E_1
79208 48	76525 49N	63435 49 •	75513 48	for E_2
10063 48N	11645 48	10308 49	99455 49	for E_3
99539 49	94972 48	10656 48	78833 47	for E_4
34391 49	20187 50N	10018 50 •	1-2	
12368 50N	12609 50N	17121 49 •	2-3	
58015 48	58014 48N	53564 48 •	3-4	
12056 50N	11732 50N	12508 49 •	1-3	
14503 50N	14265 50	16882 49	2-4	
94767 49	95892 49N	91636 48 •	1-4	

12217 50			10000 50	
87606 50N	36133 50N	47925 50	75814 50	
89479 48N	62747 49	76204 49 •	13248 49	for E_1
15925 49	75576 49N	61054 49 •	17520 49	for E_2
43619 48N	45507 48	21214 49	97520 49	for E_3
98220 49	18172 49	38993 48	26968 48	for E_4
30449 49	20651 50N	10518 50 •	1-2	
12734 50N	14052 50N	43829 49 •	2-3	
22011 49	22065 49N	20743 49 •	3-4	
10960 50N	95991 49N	18568 49 •	1-3	
15331 50N	14584 50	34156 49	2-4	
78464 49	81429 49N	13063 49 •	1-4	

12217 50			15000 50	
10474 51N	30606 50N	47388 50	87959 50	
11443 49N	61662 49	75699 49 •	18340 49	for E_1
22962 49	73745 49N	56522 49 •	28975 49	for E_2
10102 49N	93084 48	31834 49	93796 49	for E_3
96123 49	25936 49	78359 48	51193 48	for E_4
25139 49	21129 50N	11208 50 •	1-2	
11671 50N	15343 50N	77363 49 •	2-3	
44484 49	44998 49N	43617 49 •	3-4	
10033 50N	70797 49N	18301 49 •	1-3	
15441 50N	14191 50	47069 49	2-4	
63694 49	68073 49N	13892 49 •	1-4	

12217 50			20000 50	
12271 51N	28666 50N	49588 50	10179 51	
13181 49N	60565 49	75164 49 •	22546 49	for E_1
28225 49	71229 49N	50377 49 •	39896 49	for E_2
17345 49N	13880 49	40790 49	88558 49	for E_3
93427 49	32641 49	12187 49	75691 48	for E_4
20313 49	21371 50N	11915 50 •	1-2	
92995 49N	16419 50N	11002 50 •	2-3	
66709 49	68860 49N	69165 49 •	3-4	
92184 49N	45919 49N	13974 49 •	1-3	
14773 50N	13172 50	52942 49	2-4	
51154 49	56241 49N	13135 49 •	1-4	

12217 50			25000 50	
14129 51N	29688 50N	53907 50	11707 51	
14417 49N	59531 49	74638 49 •	26022 49	for E_1
31710 49	68586 49N	43873 49 •	48635 49	for E_2
24731 49N	17068 49	47272 49	82839 49	for E_3
90415 49	38216 49	16415 49	97509 48	for E_4
17321 49	21329 50N	12526 50 •	1-2	
64196 49N	17264 50N	13536 50 •	2-3	
83633 49	89198 49N	92552 49 •	3-4	
84745 49N	25396 49N	85275 48 •	1-3	
13605 50N	11817 50	52776 49	2-4	
40975 49	46183 49N	11715 49 •	1-4	

12217 50			30000 50	
16032 51N	32786 50N	59568 50	13354 51	
15315 49N	58588 49	74142 49 •	28910 49	for E_1
33938 49	66281 49N	37986 49 •	54881 49	for E_2
31309 49N	18695 49	51491 49	77580 49	for E_3
87368 49	42716 49	20211 49	11551 49	for E_4
16296 49	21110 50N	13018 50 •	1-2	
37625 49N	17900 50N	15244 50 •	2-3	
94135 49	10474 50N	11137 50 •	3-4	
77961 49N	10540 49N	37699 48 •	1-3	
12282 50N	10425 50	49300 49	2-4	
32956 49	37920 49N	10149 49 •	1-4	

12217 50			35000 50	
17969 51N	37216 50N	65969 50	15094 51	
15982 49N	57739 49	73682 49 •	31329 49	for E_1
35423 49	64463 49N	33054 49 •	59135 49	for E_2
36769 49N	19168 49	54106 49	73164 49	for E_3
84485 49	46294 49	23468 49	12974 49	for E_4
16688 49	20828 50N	13414 50 •	1-2	
16083 49N	18368 50N	16334 50 •	2-3	
99560 49	11621 50N	12549 50 •	3-4	
71860 49N	53806 47N	20101 47 •	1-3	
11017 50N	91615 49	44678 49	2-4	
26733 49	31278 49N	86806 48 •	1-4	

12217 50			40000 50	
19932 51N	42478 50N	72746 50	16905 51	
16487 49N	56982 49	73262 49 •	33373 49	for E_1
36488 49	63089 49N	29034 49 •	62010 49	for E_2
41169 49N	18951 49	55706 49	69589 49	for E_3
81864 49	49127 49	26200 49	14079 49	for E_4
17911 49	20543 50N	13735 50 •	1-2	
50454 47	18712 50N	17030 50 •	2-3	
10167 50	12470 50N	13578 50 •	3-4	
66431 49N	59698 48	23010 48	1-3	
98937 49N	80753 49	40034 49	2-4	
21924 49	25996 49N	74005 48 •	1-4	

12217 50			45000 50	
21915 51N	48264 50N	79705 50	18771 51	
16877 49N	56307 49	72879 49 •	35116 49	for E_1
37306 49	62063 49N	25766 49 •	63971 49	for E_2
44687 49N	18371 49	56692 49	66719 49	for E_3
79538 49	51380 49	28472 49	14931 49	for E_4
19549 49	20280 50N	14000 50 •	1-2	
13110 49	18966 50N	17485 50 •	2-3	
10182 50	13111 50N	14322 50 •	3-4	
61625 49N	10132 49	40000 48	1-3	
69237 49N	71626 49	35810 49	2-4	
18194 49	21803 49N	63222 48 •	1-4	

12217 50			50000 50	
23914 51N	54389 50N	86748 50	20678 51	
17184 49N	55705 49	72531 49 •	38616 49	for E_1
37970 49	61293 49N	23089 49 •	65331 49	for E_2
47510 49N	17627 49	57307 49	64404 49	for E_3
77496 49	53190 49	30363 49	15593 49	for E_4
21350 49	20046 50N	14223 50 •	1-2	
22731 49	19156 50N	17792 50 •	2-3	
10090 50	13608 50N	14860 50 •	3-4	
57375 49N	12757 49	51316 48	1-3	
80953 49N	64001 49	32123 49	2-4	
15276 49	18462 49N	54274 48 •	1-4	

12217 50			55000 50	
25926 51N	60740 50N	93823 50	22618 51	
17428 49N	55167 49	72215 49 •	37916 49	for E_1
38529 49	60708 49N	20870 49 •	66289 49	for E_2
49794 49N	16827 49	57696 49	62517 49	for E_3
75711 49	54660 49	31943 49	16110 49	for E_4
23174 49	19840 50N	14411 50 •	1-2	
30157 49	19300 50N	18005 50 •	2-3	
99438 49	14002 50N	15254 50 •	3-4	
53609 49N	14375 49	58709 48	1-3	
73882 49N	57618 49	28957 49	2-4	
12970 49	15783 49N	46881 48 •	1-4	

12217 50			60000 50	
27948 51N	67245 50N	10090 51	24582 51	
17625 49N	54685 49	71928 49 •	39053 49	for E_1
39011 49	60259 49N	19008 49 •	66974 49	for E_2
51661 49N	16030 49	57946 49	60961 49	for E_3
74151 49	55869 49	33274 49	16519 49	for E_4
24946 49	19661 50N	14572 50 •	1-2	
35970 49	19412 50N	18159 50 •	2-3	
97727 49	14321 50N	15546 50 •	3-4	
50263 49N	15331 49	63398 48	1-3	
67823 49N	52243 49	26250 49	2-4	
11126 49	13614 49N	40767 48 •	1-4	

12217 50			65000 50	
29979 51N	73860 50N	10799 51	26566 51	
17786 49N	54250 49	71666 49 •	40054 49	for E_1
39435 49	59908 49N	17428 49 •	67469 49	for E_2
53205 49N	15265 49	58106 49	59663 49	for E_3
72784 49	56875 49	34405 49	16846 49	for E_4
26629 49	19503 50N	14710 50 •	1-2	
40586 49	19499 50N	18272 50 •	2-3	
95942 49	14585 50N	15764 50 •	3-4	
47280 49N	15846 49	66220 48	1-3	
62602 49N	47682 49	23932 49	2-4	
96352 48	11642 49N	35690 48 •	1-4	

12217 50			70000 50	
32017 51N	80553 50N	11507 51	28565 51	
17920 49N	53857 49	71428 49 •	40941 49	for E_1
39812 49	59630 49N	16071 49 •	67829 49	for E_2
54496 49N	14546 49	58210 49	58567 49	for E_3
71581 49	57722 49	35373 49	17111 49	for E_4
28208 49	19364 50N	14831 50 •	1-2	
44302 49	19569 50N	18358 50 •	2-3	
94178 49	14806 50N	15928 50 •	3-4	
44608 49N	16067 49	67747 48	1-3	
58073 49N	43781 49	21940 49	2-4	
84153 48	10382 49N	31450 48 •	1-4	

12217 50			75000 50	
34061 51N	87303 50N	12214 51	30577 51	
18031 49N	53501 49	71209 49 •	41732 49	for E_1
40151 49	59408 49N	14896 49 •	68092 49	for E_2
55585 49N	13876 49	58276 49	57632 49	for E_3
70519 49	58443 49	36209 49	17328 49	for E_4
29678 49	19241 50N	14936 50 •	1-2	
47333 49	19625 50N	18424 50 •	2-3	
92484 49	14994 50N	16054 50 •	3-4	
42206 49N	16090 49	68372 48	1-3	
54117 49N	40419 49	20218 49	2-4	
74072 48	91669 48N	27885 48 •	1-4	

Table I(h). Ruby $\theta=80°$.

13962 50			50000 49	
72188 50N	44891 50N	54929 50	62149 50	
60029 48N	67167 49	73513 49 •	69495 48	for E_1
82494 48	73376 49N	66951 49 •	80821 48	for E_2
21352 48N	10775 48	10556 49	99412 49	for E_3
99455 49	10163 49	13428 48	18832 48	for E_4
16819 49	20202 50N	10167 50 •	1-2	
12787 50N	13336 50N	18355 49 •	2-3	
63116 48	63168 48N	12019 49 •	3-4	
11530 50N	10971 50N	11857 49 •	1-3	
14252 50N	13711 50	17598 49	2-4	
99271 49	10257 50N	10489 49 •	1-4	

13962 50			10000 50	
88785 50N	35790 50N	55159 50	69417 50	
10300 49N	56387 49	73007 49 •	12514 49	for E_1
17073 49	72009 49N	64809 49 •	17968 49	for E_2
85619 48N	33851 48	20971 49	97341 49	for E_3
97616 49	19897 49	54707 48	67156 48	for E_4
14805 49	20665 50N	10714 50 •	1-2	
12565 50N	15128 50N	45704 49 •	2-3	
23151 49	23433 49N	45158 49 •	3-4	
10609 50N	85607 49N	16340 49 •	1-3	
15537 50N	13630 50	35597 49	2-4	
79600 49	89157 49N	15484 49 •	1-4	

13962 50			15000 50	
10653 51N	30467 50N	57824 50	79176 50	
13378 49N	65495 49	72426 49 •	16903 49	for E_1
25179 49	69605 49N	60985 49 •	28318 49	for E_2
18117 49N	52670 48	29938 49	93529 49	for E_3
94121 49	28944 49	11782 49	12830 49	for E_4
12254 49	21081 50N	11422 50 •	1-2	
10807 50N	16827 50N	78550 49 •	2-3	
43816 49	46192 49N	89160 49 •	3-4	
98751 49N	59917 49N	15025 49 •	1-3	
16032 50N	12566 50	47235 49	2-4	
60926 49	75663 49N	16791 49 •	1-4	

13962 50			20000 50	
12506 51N	28665 50N	62308 50	91417 50	
15520 49N	64627 49	71861 49 •	20377 49	for E_1
31566 49	66661 49N	56196 49 •	37440 49	for E_2
28323 49N	56691 48	36368 49	88560 49	for E_3
89204 49	36706 49	18849 49	18438 49	for E_4
10106 49	21250 50N	12114 50 •	1-2	
81673 49N	18150 50N	10963 50 •	2-3	
60116 49	68627 49N	12955 50 •	3-4	
91771 49N	37738 49N	11068 49 •	1-3	
15503 50N	10901 50	49889 49	2-4	
45234 49	62267 49N	15806 49 •	1-4	

13962 50			25000 50	
14412 51N	29588 50N	67866 50	10584 51	
17292 49N	63834 49	71342 49 •	23158 49	for E_1
36131 49	63809 49N	51407 49 •	44499 49	for E_2
37091 49N	47393 48	40340 49	83513 49	for E_3
83783 49	42790 49	25302 49	22560 49	for E_4
88671 48	21188 50N	12706 50 •	1-2	
55661 49N	19008 50N	13398 50 •	2-3	
68673 49	87330 49N	15793 50 •	3-4	
84705 49N	21522 49N	69736 48 •	1-3	
14269 50N	91490 49	46401 49	2-4	
33338 49	50119 49N	13772 49 •	1-4	

13962 50			30000 50	
16357 51N	32386 50N	73970 50	12199 51	
18569 49N	63129 49	70879 49 •	25415 49	for E_1
39303 49	61384 49N	47179 49 •	49611 49	for E_2
43762 49N	31456 48	42631 49	79103 49	for E_3
78709 49	47295 49	30540 49	25204 49	for E_4
84931 48	20995 50N	13191 50 •	1-2	
34643 49N	19503 50N	15115 50 •	2-3	
71141 49	10177 50N	17468 50 •	3-4	
77842 49N	10755 49N	37321 48 •	1-3	
12796 50N	76174 49	40671 49	2-4	
24867 49	40057 49N	11562 49 •	1-4	

13962 50			35000 50	
18331 51N	36412 50N	80344 50	13937 51	
19566 49N	62506 49	70470 49 •	27275 49	for E_1
41548 49	59441 49N	43651 49 •	53244 49	for E_2
48598 49N	13951 48	43961 49	75521 49	for E_3
74357 49	50574 49	34579 49	26786 49	for E_4
87215 48	20755 50N	13587 50 •	1-2	
18998 49N	19771 50N	16284 50 •	2-3	
70286 49	11270 50N	18359 50 •	3-4	
71509 49N	38821 48N	14159 48 •	1-3	
11378 50N	63850 49	34929 49	2-4	
18954 49	32164 49N	95855 48 •	1-4	

13962 50			40000 50	
20325 51N	41243 50N	86861 50	15763 51	
20362 49N	61959 49	70110 49 •	28827 49	for E_1
43194 49	57912 49N	40762 49 •	55845 49	for E_2
52080 49N	26987 47N	44772 49	72683 49	for E_3
70761 49	52981 49	37661 49	27701 49	for E_4
93038 48	20511 50N	13914 50 •	1-2	
76090 48N	19914 50N	17085 50 •	2-3	
68010 49	12103 50N	18796 50 •	3-4	
65843 49N	47170 47	17871 47	1-3	
10128 50N	54204 49	29954 49	2-4	
14796 49	26107 49N	79507 48 •	1-4	

13962 50			45000 50	
22335 51N	46609 50N	93465 50	17649 51	
21007 49N	61476 49	69791 49 •	30139 49	for E_1
44449 49	56709 49N	38397 49 •	57740 49	for E_2
54618 49N	17664 48N	45302 49	70437 49	for E_3
67821 49	54785 49	40030 49	28218 49	for E_4
10067 49	20281 50N	14188 50 •	1-2	
72370 47	19989 50N	17644 50 •	2-3	
65300 49	12750 50N	18985 50 •	3-4	
60346 49N	32399 48	12643 48	1-3	
90646 49N	46666 49	25861 49	2-4	
11816 49	21468 49N	66386 48 •	1-4	

13962 50			50000 50	
24358 51N	52345 50N	10012 51	19579 51	
21539 49N	61050 49	69509 49 •	31261 49	for E_1
45438 49	55752 49N	36446 49 •	59149 49	for E_2
56503 49N	30825 48N	45672 49	68642 49	for E_3
65412 49	56169 49	41881 49	28500 49	for E_4
10906 49	20073 50N	14420 50 •	1-2	
69162 48	20028 50N	18046 50 •	2-3	
62602 49	13261 50N	19042 50 •	3-4	
56458 49N	50078 48	20016 48	1-3	
81686 49N	40717 49	22542 49	2-4	
96284 48	17889 49N	55935 48 •	1-4	

13962 50			55000 50	
26390 51N	58341 50N	10682 51	21541 51	
21984 49N	60671 49	69259 49 •	32229 49	for E_1
46240 49	54981 49N	34819 49 •	60219 49	for E_2
57933 49N	42321 48N	45945 49	67189 49	for E_3
63420 49	57254 49	43352 49	28642 49	for E_4
11760 49	19887 50N	14619 50 •	1-2	
11606 49	20048 50N	18342 50 •	2-3	
60093 49	13674 50N	19030 50 •	3-4	
52602 49N	61348 48	25006 48	1-3	
74138 49N	35958 49	19849 49	2-4	
79848 48	15094 49N	47590 48 •	1-4	

13962 50			60000 50	
28431 51N	64526 50N	11356 51	23527 51	
22361 49N	60334 49	69035 49 •	33073 49	for E_1
46906 49	54351 49N	33448 49 •	61047 49	for E_2
59040 49N	52366 48N	46165 49	65996 49	for E_3
61756 49	58122 49	44543 49	28701 49	for E_4
12594 49	19720 50N	14792 50 •	1-2	
15226 49	20057 50N	18566 50 •	2-3	
57827 49	14013 50N	18981 50 •	3-4	
49201 49N	68442 48	28358 48	1-3	
67746 49N	32093 49	17648 49	2-4	
67229 48	12883 49N	40877 48 •	1-4	

13962 50			65000 50	
30478 51N	70853 50N	12032 51	25530 51	
22683 49N	60031 49	68834 49 •	33814 49	for E_1
47470 49	53830 49N	32279 49 •	61700 49	for E_2
59913 49N	61174 48N	46341 49	65002 49	for E_3
60352 49	58830 49	45522 49	28709 49	for E_4
13392 49	19572 50N	14943 50 •	1-2	
18070 49	20059 50N	18739 50 •	2-3	
55808 49	14296 50N	18915 50 •	3-4	
46189 49N	72765 48	30569 48	1-3	
62291 49N	28912 49	15831 49	2-4	
57350 48	11110 49N	35429 48 •	1-4	

13962 50			70000 50	
32530 51N	77287 50N	12711 51	27547 51	
22962 49N	59759 49	68653 49 •	34471 49	for E_1
47953 49	53393 49N	31273 49 •	62222 49	for E_2
60613 49N	68935 48N	46490 49	64165 49	for E_3
59153 49	59417 49	46339 49	28687 49	for E_4
14145 49	19440 50N	15075 50 •	1-2	
20342 49	20059 50N	18875 50 •	2-3	
54016 49	14535 50N	18842 50 •	3-4	
43508 49N	75223 48	31979 48	1-3	
57600 49N	26257 49	14315 49	2-4	
49484 48	96715 48N	30961 48 •	1-4	

13962 50			75000 50	
34587 51N	83805 50N	13391 51	29576 51	
23205 49N	59512 49	68489 49 •	35055 49	for E_1
48374 49	53022 49N	30399 49 •	62645 49	for E_2
61181 49N	75811 48N	46618 49	63450 49	for E_3
58121 49	59911 49	47029 49	28648 49	for E_4
14850 49	19322 50N	15193 50 •	1-2	
22183 49	20057 50N	18984 50 •	2-3	
52426 49	14739 50N	18767 50 •	3-4	
41109 49N	76411 48	32819 48	1-3	
53532 49N	24015 49	13038 49	2-4	
43122 48	84891 48N	27263 48 •	1-4	

TABLE I(i). Ruby $\theta = 90°$.

15707 50			50000 49	
72375 50N	44779 50N	58425 50	58729 50	
65592 48N	70405 49	70405 49 •	65592 48	for E_1
83105 48	70220 49N	70220 49 •	83105 48	for E_2
70412 49N	65600 48N	65584 48	70398 49	for E_3
70228 49	83112 48	83098 48	70212 49	for E_4
20000 42N	20207 50N	10214 50 •	1-2	
18873 46	19157 50N	25894 49 •	2-3	
75774 45N	64937 48N	29772 50 •	3-4	
15175 50N	14703 46	14979 45	1-3	
19176 50N	21057 46	28597 45	2-4	
16656 46	14974 50N	15933 49 •	1-4	

15707 50			10000 50	
89185 50N	35678 50N	61285 50	63578 50	
11507 49N	69767 49	69767 49 •	11507 49	for E_1
17784 49	68437 49N	68437 49 •	17784 49	for E_2
69768 49N	11508 49N	11507 49	69767 49	for E_3
68438 49	17784 49	17784 49	68436 49	for E_4
43000 43	20669 50N	10777 50 •	1-2	
17040 45	20399 50N	58696 49 •	2-3	
15520 45N	23886 49N	29057 50 •	3-4	
13191 50N	10520 45	29580 44	1-3	
19997 50N	29810 45	79800 44	2-4	
19460 45	12286 50N	22438 49 •	1-4	

15707 50			15000 50	
10713 51N	30423 50N	65288 50	72273 50	
15219 49N	69053 49	69053 49 •	15219 49	for E_1
27000 49	65352 49N	65352 49 •	27000 49	for E_2
69053 49N	15219 49N	15219 49	69053 49	for E_3
65352 49	27000 49	27008 49	65352 49	for E_4
90000 42	21064 50N	11491 50 •	1-2	
56000 44N	21035 50N	91975 49 •	2-3	
53800 44	46569 49N	27898 50 •	3-4	
11511 50N	26500 44N	60000 43 •	1-3	
19327 50N	27200 44N	12500 44 •	2-4	
17200 44N	95985 49N	22389 49 •	1-4	

15707 50			20000 50	
12585 51N	28664 50N	70050 50	84464 50	
18039 49N	68370 49	68370 49 •	18039 49	for E_1
34649 49	61639 49N	61639 49 •	34649 49	for E_2
68370 49N	18039 49N	18039 49	68370 49	for E_3
61639 49	34649 49	34649 49	61639 49	for E_4
23000 43	21211 50N	12179 50 •	1-2	
33000 43N	21211 50N	11990 50 •	2-3	
43000 43N	68549 49N	26536 50 •	3-4	
10132 50N	40000 42N	30000 43	1-3	
17545 50N	27600 44	16100 44	2-4	
14700 44	72880 49N	19336 49 •	1-4	

15707 50			25000 50	
14507 51N	29558 50N	75329 50	99308 50	
20223 49N	67756 49	67756 49 •	20223 49	for E_1
40372 49	58052 49N	58052 49 •	40372 49	for E_2
67756 49N	20223 49N	20223 49	67756 49	for E_3
58052 49	40372 49	40372 49	58052 49	for E_4
31000 43N	21142 50N	12765 50 •	1-2	
84000 43N	21150 50N	14064 50 •	2-3	
16900 44	86749 49N	25233 50 •	3-4	
90056 49N	49000 43N	82000 43 •	1-3	
15402 50N	38000 43N	42000 43 •	2-4	
22000 43N	55122 49N	15732 49 •	1-4	

15707 50			30000 50	
16467 51N	32264 50N	80970 50	11596 51	
21950 49N	67217 49	67217 49 •	21950 49	for E_1
44484 49	54965 49N	54965 49 •	44484 49	for E_2
67217 49N	21950 49N	21950 49	67217 49	for E_3
54965 49	44484 49	44484 49	54964 49	for E_4
22000 43N	20957 50N	13247 50 •	1-2	
26000 43N	21007 50N	15527 50 •	2-3	
58000 43	10084 50N	24120 50 •	3-4	
80805 49N	62000 43N	82000 43 •	1-3	
13390 50N	73000 43	35000 43	2-4	
22000 43	42205 49N	12587 49 •	1-4	

15707 50			35000 50	
18452 51N	36165 50N	86873 50	13381 51	
23341 49N	66746 49	66746 49 •	23341 49	for E_1
47441 49	52433 49N	52433 49 •	47441 49	for E_2
66746 49N	23341 49N	23341 49	66746 49	for E_3
52433 49	47441 49	47441 49	52433 49	for E_4
25000 43N	20728 50N	13643 50 •	1-2	
24000 43N	20855 50N	16551 50 •	2-3	
10700 44	11159 50N	23213 50 •	3-4	
73137 49N	44000 43N	65000 43 •	1-3	
11677 50N	16000 43N	35000 43 •	2-4	
28000 43N	32933 49N	10102 49 •	1-4	

15707 50			40000 50	
20457 51N	40860 50N	92970 50	15246 51	
24482 49N	66336 49	66336 49 •	24482 49	for E_1
49610 49	50386 49N	50386 49 •	49610 49	for E_2
66336 49N	24482 49N	24482 49	66336 49	for E_3
50386 49	49610 49	49610 49	50386 49	for E_4
25000 43	20496 50N	13972 50 •	1-2	
80000 42N	20720 50N	17278 50 •	2-3	
73000 43	11985 50N	22484 50 •	3-4	
66711 49N	70000 42	42000 43	1-3	
10267 50N	14000 43	20000 42 •	2-4	
12000 43N	26222 49N	81964 48 •	1-4	

15707 50			45000 50	
22476 51N	46092 50N	99212 50	17164 51	
25433 49N	65978 49	65978 49 •	25433 49	for E_1
51241 49	48726 49N	48726 49 •	51241 49	for E_2
65978 49N	25433 49N	25433 49	65978 49	for E_3
48726 49	51241 49	51241 49	48726 49	for E_4
34000 43	20278 50N	14249 50 •	1-2	
10000 42	20608 50N	17806 50 •	2-3	
38000 43	12631 50N	21895 50 •	3-4	
61267 49N	26000 43	56000 43	1-3	
91162 49N	58000 43	29800 43	2-4	
50000 42	21279 49N	67394 48 •	1-4	

15707 50			50000 50	
24506 51N	51700 50N	10556 51	19120 51	
26235 49N	65663 49	65663 49 •	26235 49	for E_1
52500 49	47367 49N	47367 49 •	52500 49	for E_2
65663 49N	26235 49N	26235 49	65663 49	for E_3
47367 49	52500 49	52500 49	47367 49	for E_4
20000 42	20078 50N	14484 50 •	1-2	
60000 42	20516 50N	18198 50 •	2-3	
	13146 50N	21416 50 •	3-4	
56608 49N	80000 42	60000 42 •	1-3	
81717 49N	11300 44	88000 43	2-4	
35000 43	17565 49N	56165 48 •	1-4	

15707 50			55000 50	
26546 51N	57578 50N	11201 51	21102 51	
26921 49N	65385 49	65385 49 •	26921 49	for E_1
53493 49	46242 49N	46242 49 •	53493 49	for E_2
65385 49N	26921 49N	26921 49	65385 49	for E_3
46242 49	53493 49	53493 49	46242 49	for E_4
21000 43	19898 50N	14687 50 •	1-2	
60000 42	20442 50N	18496 50 •	2-3	
55000 43	13564 50N	21021 50 •	3-4	
52583 49N	20000 42	11000 43	1-3	
73897 49N	21000 43	40000 42	2-4	
50000 42N	14719 49N	47402 48 •	1-4	

15707 50			60000 50	
28593 51N	63656 50N	11853 51	23105 51	
27512 49N	65138 49	65138 49 •	27512 49	for E_1
54294 49	45300 49N	45300 49 •	54294 49	for E_2
65138 49N	27512 49N	27512 49	65138 49	for E_3
45300 49	54294 49	54294 49	45300 49	for E_4
40000 42N	19737 50N	14864 50 •	1-2	
90000 42	20381 50N	18727 50 •	2-3	
25000 43	13909 50N	20692 50 •	3-4	
49075 49N	19000 43N	24000 43 •	1-3	
67351 49N	38000 43	27000 43	2-4	
12000 43	12498 49N	40469 48 •	1-4	

15707 50			65000 50	
30645 51N	69885 50N	12510 51	25123 51	
28028 49N	64918 49	64918 49 •	28028 49	for E_1
54951 49	44500 49N	44500 49 •	54951 49	for E_2
64918 49N	28028 49N	28028 49	64918 49	for E_3
44500 49	54951 49	54951 49	44500 49	for E_4
18000 43N	19592 50N	15019 50 •	1-2	
13000 43	20332 50N	18909 50 •	2-3	
62000 43	14197 50N	20414 50 •	3-4	
45993 49N	17000 43N	41000 43 •	1-3	
61812 49N	11000 43N	10000 43 •	2-4	
11000 43	10735 49N	34910 48 •	1-4	

15707 50			70000 50	
32703 51N	76231 50N	13173 51	27153 51	
28481 49N	64720 49	64720 49 •	28481 49	for E_1
55498 49	43816 49N	43816 49 •	55498 49	for E_2
64720 49N	28481 49N	28481 49	64720 49	for E_3
43816 49	55498 49	55498 49	43816 49	for E_4
15000 43N	19463 50N	15155 50 •	1-2	
12000 43	20291 50N	19055 50 •	2-3	
24000 43	14442 50N	20176 50 •	3-4	
43266 49N	26000 43N	44000 43 •	1-3	
57077 49N	20000 43	15000 43	2-4	
10000 43	93160 48N	30396 48 •	1-4	

15707 50			75000 50	
34764 51N	82668 50N	13839 51	29191 51	
28883 49N	64542 49	64542 49 •	28883 49	for E_1
55961 49	43223 49N	43223 49 •	55961 49	for E_2
64542 49N	28883 49N	28883 49	64542 49	for E_3
43223 49	55961 49	55961 49	43223 49	for E_4
32000 43	19346 50N	15277 50 •	1-2	
14000 43	20257 50N	19174 50 •	2-3	
12000 43	14652 50N	19971 50 •	3-4	
40838 49N	18000 43	29000 43	1-3	
52989 49N	56000 43	57000 43	2-4	
80000 42	81567 48N	26686 48 •	1-4	

θ in radians			H_{dc} in kilogauss	
E_1	E_2	E_3	E_4	E_j in Kmc/s
a_1	b_1	c_1	d_1	for E_1
a_2	b_2	c_2	d_2	for E_2
a_3	b_3	c_3	d_3	for E_3
a_4	b_4	c_4	d_4	for E_4
α	β	γ	1-2 transition	
α	β	γ	2-3 transition	
α	β	γ	3-4 transition	
α	β	γ	1-3 transition	
α	β	γ	2-4 transition	
α	β	γ	1-4 transition	

FIG. 23. Format of each sub-block in tables for ruby.

The energy eigenvectors $|j\rangle$ and the energy eigenvalues E_j are defined by the equations

$$\mathcal{H}|j\rangle = E_j|j\rangle$$

and

$$|j\rangle = a_j|\tfrac{3}{2}\rangle + b_j|\tfrac{1}{2}\rangle + c_j|-\tfrac{1}{2}\rangle + d_j|-\tfrac{3}{2}\rangle,$$

where $j=1$ through 4 denotes the four energy levels.

The axes were chosen so that the c axis of the ruby crystal is the z axis, the dc magnetic field H_{dc} lies in the x–z plane at an angle θ from the z axis, and the y axis is perpendicular to the plane containing H_{dc} and the c axis.

The transition probability matrix elements between levels k and l are given by

$$\frac{(\bar{H}')_{kl}}{\beta_M H_{rf}} = \frac{1}{\beta_M H_{rf}}\langle k|2\beta_M \mathbf{H}_{rf}\cdot\mathbf{S}|l\rangle = (\alpha\phi_1 + \gamma\phi_3) + j\beta\phi_2,$$

where H_{rf} is the peak amplitude of the linearly-polarized rf magnetic field, and ϕ_1, ϕ_2, ϕ_3 are the direction cosines of $\mathbf{H}_{rf}$ with respect to the x, y, z axes.

For each operating point, characterized by H_{dc} and θ, the four energy eigenvalues E_j in units of kmc/s, the eigenvector expansion coefficients $a_j\cdots d_j$ for each level j, and the values of α, β, γ for each possible transition are presented in tabular form in Tables I(a) through I(i). The tables cover $\theta=10°$ to $\theta=90°$ in 10° increments, with H_{dc} increasing from 500 gauss to 7500 gauss by 500 gauss increments in each table.

The format of each subblock in the tables is shown in Fig. 23. The numbers in the blocks are expressed in

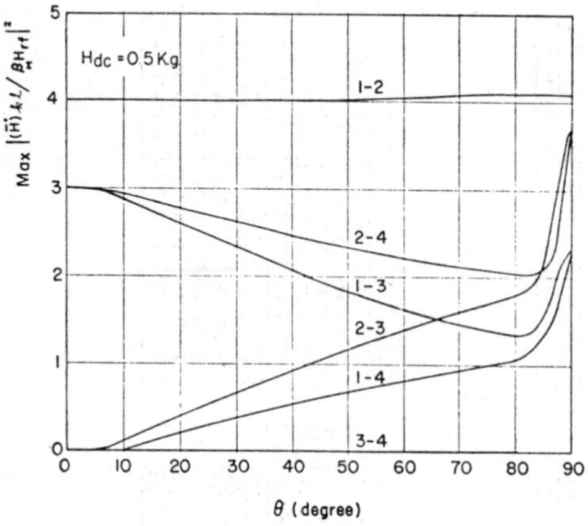

FIG. 24.

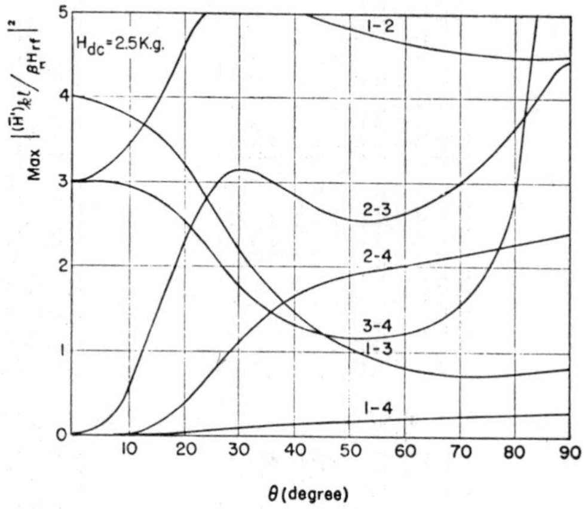

FIG. 26.

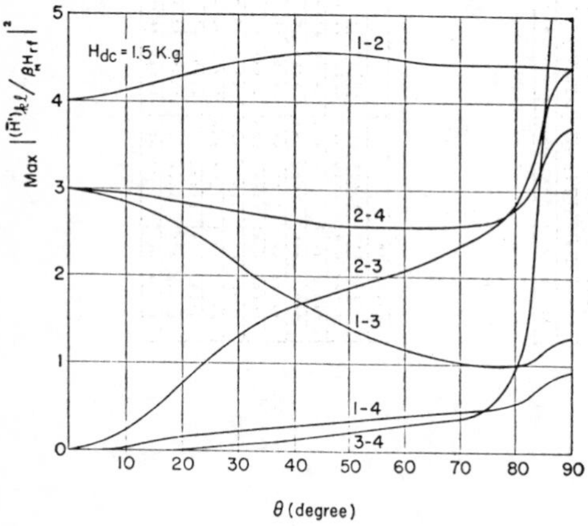

FIG. 25.

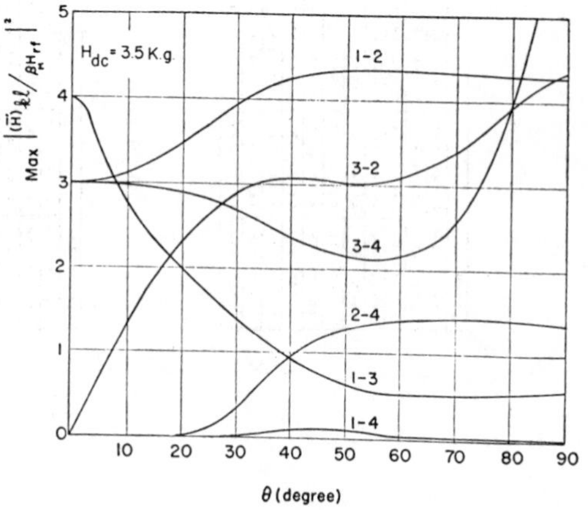

FIG. 27.

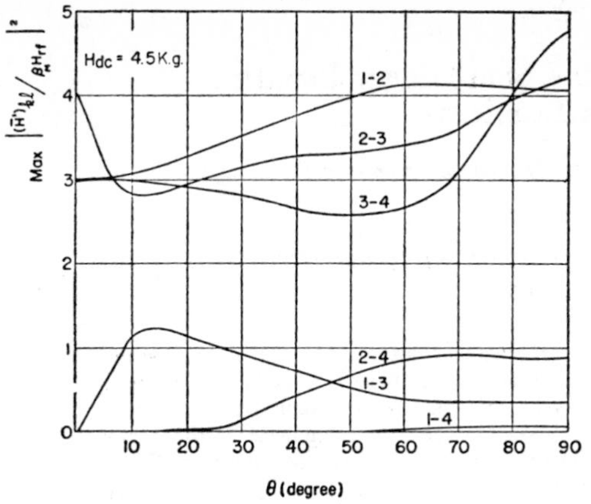

FIG. 28.

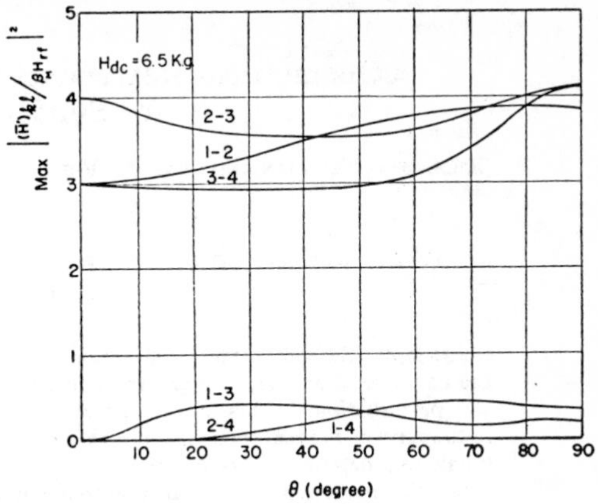

FIG. 30.

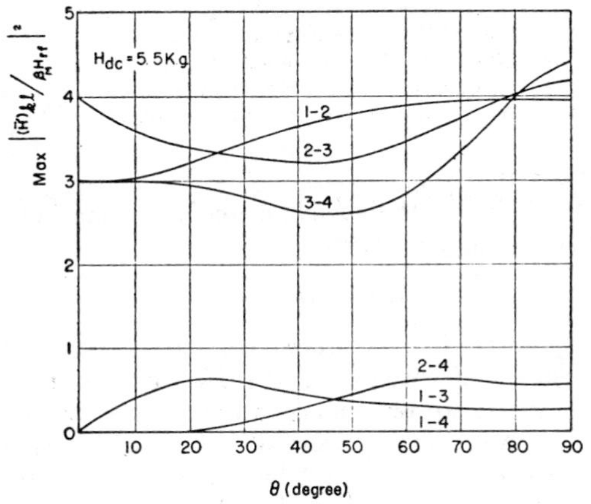

FIG. 29.

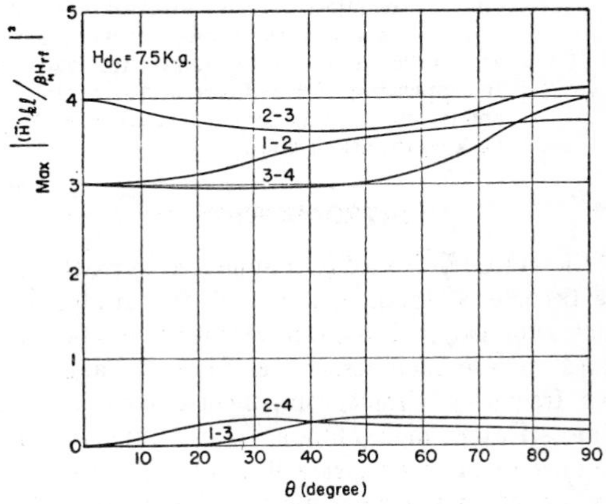

FIG. 31.

floating-point decimal form, since the blocks were prepared directly from the printed output of the computer to avoid transcription errors. The numbers can be converted to ordinary form by following the rule

$$abcde\ gh \equiv a \cdot bcde \times 10^{(gh\ 50)}.$$

The symbols *, N, or CR following a number indicate that the number is negative. For example, 56 423 51CR in the tables equals -56.423 in ordinary decimal form.

The maximum possible transition probability matrix element for optimum orientation of $\mathbf{H}_{rf}$ is either $\beta_M{}^2$ or $(\alpha^2+\gamma^2)$, whichever is larger. The maximum values for all the transitions have been plotted *vs* θ for several different values of H_{dc} in Figs. 24–31. The operation of the selection rules and the rapid variations in regions where levels curve strongly are very evident.

Since the calculations were performed, it has been found that D is negative, not positive as used in these calculations. This does not invalidate the calculations, but does require some simple modifications. To obtain correct answers for negative D, the signs of the E_j's should be reversed, and the signs of α and γ should be reversed. This of course does not change the squares of the matrix elements. When these corrections are made, the subscript J equals one in the tables and curves of this Appendix refers to the highest energy level, while J equals four refers to the lowest energy level. For example the subscript one dash two in the figures or tables refers to transitions between the two top-most levels of the ruby energy level spectrum.

Reprinted from JOURNAL OF APPLIED PHYSICS, Vol. 28, No. 1, 49–52, January, 1957

Geometrical Representation of the Schrödinger Equation for Solving Maser Problems

RICHARD P. FEYNMAN AND FRANK L. VERNON, JR., *California Institute of Technology, Pasadena, California*

AND

ROBERT W. HELLWARTH, *Microwave Laboratory, Hughes Aircraft Company, Culver City, California*
(Received September 18, 1956)

A simple, rigorous geometrical representation for the Schrödinger equation is developed to describe the behavior of an ensemble of two quantum-level, noninteracting systems which are under the influence of a perturbation. In this case the Schrödinger equation may be written, after a suitable transformation, in the form of the real three-dimensional vector equation $d\mathbf{r}/dt=\boldsymbol{\omega}\times\mathbf{r}$, where the components of the vector $\mathbf{r}$ uniquely determine ψ of a given system and the components of $\boldsymbol{\omega}$ represent the perturbation. When magnetic interaction with a spin $\frac{1}{2}$ system is under consideration, "r" space reduces to physical space. By analogy the techniques developed for analyzing the magnetic resonance precession model can be adapted for use in any two-level problems. The quantum-mechanical behavior of the state of a system under various different conditions is easily visualized by simply observing how $\mathbf{r}$ varies under the action of different types of $\boldsymbol{\omega}$. Such a picture can be used to advantage in analyzing various MASER-type devices such as amplifiers and oscillators. In the two illustrative examples given (the beam-type MASER and radiation damping) the application of the picture in determining the effect of the perturbing field on the molecules is shown and its interpretation for use in the complex Maxwell's equations to determine the reaction of the molecules back on the field is given.

INTRODUCTION

ELECTROMAGNETIC resonances in matter have become a fundamental tool for studying the structure of matter. Moreover, recently it has become of interest to use such resonances for radio and microwave frequency circuit components, such as highly stable oscillators, high Q filters, isolators, and amplifiers. The purpose of this paper will be to aid in the understanding of simple resonances and especially in the conception and design of microwave "atomic" devices (now commonly called MASER-type devices) which involve these simple resonances. In this paper we propose to do the following things: (a) To develop a simple but rigorous and complete geometrical picture of the Schrödinger equation describing the resonance behavior of a quantum system when only a pair of energy levels is involved (the resulting picture has the same form as the well-known three-dimensional classical precession of a gyromagnet in a magnetic field); (b) To note further properties of the model which permit its direct interpretation in terms of the physical properties which couple the quantum systems to the electromagnetic fields, and to state these explicitly for dipole transitions; (c) To illustrate the use of the picture by solving the particular cases of the beam MASER oscillator characteristics and "radiation damping."

Although the approach does not obtain results inaccessible to straight-forward calculation, the simplicity of the pictorial representation enables one to gain physical insight and to obtain results quickly which display the main features of interest.

FORMULATION

We will be concerned with an ensemble of spacially non-overlapping systems, e.g., molecules in a molecular beam, such that the wave function for any one individual system may be written

$$\psi(t)=a(t)\psi_a+b(t)\psi_b \tag{1}$$

during some time of interest. ψ_a and ψ_b are the two eigenstates of interest of the Hamiltonian for the single system corresponding to the energies $W+\hbar\omega_0/2$ and $W-\hbar\omega_0/2$ respectively. W is the mean energy of the two levels determined by velocities and internal interactions which remain unchanged. W will be taken as the zero of energy for each system. ω_0 is the resonant angular frequency associated with a transition between the two levels and is always taken positive.

It is usual to solve Schrödinger's equation with some perturbation V for the complex coefficients $a(t)$ and $b(t)$, and from them calculate the physical properties of the system. However, the mathematics is not always transparent and the complex coefficients do not give directly the values of real physical observables. Neither is it sufficient to know only the real magnitudes of a and b, i.e., the level populations and transition probabilities, when coherent processes are involved. We propose instead to take advantage of the fact that the phase of $\psi(t)$ has no influence so that only three real numbers are needed to completely specify $\psi(t)$. We construct three real functions (r_1,r_2,r_3) of a and b which have direct physical meaning and which define a 3-vector $\mathbf{r}$ whose time dependance is easily pictured:

$$\begin{aligned} r_1&\equiv ab^*+ba^*\\ r_2&\equiv i(ab^*-ba^*)\\ r_3&\equiv aa^*-bb^*. \end{aligned} \tag{2}$$

(*) always indicates complex conjugate. The time dependence of $\mathbf{r}$ can be obtained from Schrödinger's equation which gives

$$i\hbar da/dt = a[(\hbar\omega_0/2) + V_{aa}] + bV_{ab} \quad (3)$$

and similar equations for db/dt, da^*/dt, db^*/dt. The subscripts on V indicate the usual matrix elements. $V_{aa} = V_{bb} = 0$ for most all cases of interest, and whenever these can be neglected compared to $\hbar\omega_0/2$, V need be neither small nor of short duration for the results to be exact. Using Eqs. (3) to find the differential equation for $\mathbf{r}$ gives

$$d\mathbf{r}/dt = \boldsymbol{\omega}\times\mathbf{r} \quad (4)$$

where $\boldsymbol{\omega}$ is also a three vector in "$\mathbf{r}$" space defined by the three real components:

$$\begin{aligned}\omega_1 &\equiv (V_{ab}+V_{ba})/\hbar\\ \omega_2 &\equiv i(V_{ab}-V_{ba})/\hbar \quad (5)\\ \omega_3 &\equiv \omega_0.\end{aligned}$$

The $\times$ symbol has the usual vector product meaning. It is easily shown that the remaining real combination aa^*+bb^* is just equal to the length of the $\mathbf{r}$ vector, $(r_1^2+r_2^2+r_3^2)^{\frac{1}{2}}$, and is constant in time. It equals one when ψ is normalized to unity. The motion described by Eq. (4) is of the form for the precession of a classical gyromagnet in a magnetic field. Therefore, it is not surprising that in the case of transitions between the two magnetic levels of a spin $\frac{1}{2}$ particle, this mathematical $\mathbf{r}$ space will be equivalent to physical space with r_1, r_2, r_3 proportional to the expectation values of μ_x, μ_y, μ_z, and ω_1, ω_2, ω_3 proportional to the components of the magnetic field H_x, H_y, H_z respectively. Although in general the formalism does not represent physical space, by analogy any transitions under the stated conditions may be thought of rigorously in terms of the well-known classical vector model for spin precession. The extensive and explicit use of rotating coordinate procedures, as was introduced by Bloch, Ramsey, Rabi, and Schwinger[1,2] for special kinds of magnetic transitions, is generally applicable in dealing with the r space.

INTERPRETATION

The effect of the presence of the quantum systems on the surrounding electromagnetic field is observed in many resonance experiments or devices, so it is of interest to deduce such quantities as the energy given up by the systems and effective polarization densities which, in general, are not linear in the impressed fields. The internal energy, or expectation value of the unperturbed Hamiltonian H at any time t is

$$\langle H\rangle = \int \psi^* H\psi d(\text{Vol}) = (aa^*-bb^*)\hbar\omega_0/2 = r_3\hbar\omega_0/2 \quad (6)$$

or just r_3 in units of $\hbar\omega_0/2$. The total internal energy in any ensemble of these systems is of course the sum of the r_3 values (in units of $\hbar\omega_0/2$) in the region, or the projection on the 3 axis of the vector sum $\mathbf{R}=\sum_i \mathbf{r}^i$ over the region. In fact, any operator x such as the dipole moment operator, which is separable in the systems, has an expectation value of the form

$$x_{ab}\sum_i (a^i)^* b^i + x_{ba}\sum_i (b^i)^* a^i + x_{aa}\sum_i (a^i)^* a^i + x_{bb}\sum_i (b^i)^* b^i$$

and is therefore a linear combination of the r_1's, r_2's, and r_3's, or R_1, R_2, and R_3; it is proportional to a projection of $\mathbf{R}$ on some axis, plus perhaps a constant.

It remains to determine the proper projections for particular cases and also state explicitly the values of $\boldsymbol{\omega}$. Since all common microwave transitions such as hyperfine structure, spin flip, molecular rotational and inversion transitions are dipole transitions, we will examine only these cases.

For electric dipole $\Delta m=0$ transitions,

$$V_{ab} = -\mu_{ab}E \quad (7)$$

where μ_{ab} is the matrix element between the two states for the component of the dipole moment along the electric field E. If μ_{ab} is made real by proper choice of the phases of ψ_a and ψ_b, then

$$\begin{aligned}\omega_1 &= (V_{ab}+V_{ba})/\hbar = -(2\mu_{ab}/\hbar)E\\ \omega_2 &= i(V_{ab}-V_{ba})/\hbar = 0 \quad (8)\\ \omega_3 &= \omega_0\end{aligned}$$

ω_1 is the electric field strength in units of $-2\mu_{ab}/\hbar$. In this case

$$\langle\mu\rangle = a^*b\mu_{ab} + b^*a\mu_{ba} = r_1\mu_{ab}. \quad (9)$$

This means that the component of the polarization density P along the electric field will equal the average projection of $\mathbf{r}$ on the 1 axis in some small region of space and given in units of $\rho\mu_{ab}$ where ρ is the particle density.

In the case of magnetic dipole $\Delta m=0$ transitions, the same formulas apply substituting H for E and the appropriate magnetic dipole for μ.

In the case of electric or magnetic $\Delta m=\pm 1$ dipole transitions, considering E_x and E_y to be the relevant spacial components of either the electric or magnetic fields,

$$V = (-1/2)(\mu^+E^- + \mu^-E^+) \quad (10)$$

where $E^\pm \equiv E_x \pm iE_y$ and $\mu^\pm \equiv \mu_x \pm i\mu_y$. By the well-known properties of the $\mu^\pm$ operators:

$$\begin{aligned}V_{ab} &= -(1/2)\mu_{ab}^+(E_x - iE_y)\\ V_{ba} &= -(1/2)\mu_{ba}^-(E_x + iE_y). \quad (11)\end{aligned}$$

Choosing the phases of ψ_a and ψ_b such that μ_{ab}^+ is a real number γ, then $\mu_{ab}^+ = \mu_{ba}^-$ by their definitions, and:

$$\begin{aligned}\omega_1 &= -(\gamma/\hbar)E_x\\ \omega_2 &= -(\gamma/\hbar)E_y;\end{aligned} \quad (12)$$

thus $\boldsymbol{\omega}$ behaves in the 1–2 plane exactly as does E in

[1] Rabi, Ramsey, and Schwinger, Revs. Modern Phys. 26, 167 (1954).

[2] R. K. Wangsness, Am. J. Phys. 24, 60 (1956).

the $x-y$ plane of space. By noting that $\langle\mu^+\rangle=\gamma a^*b$ and $\langle\mu^-\rangle=\gamma b^*a$, we find:

$$\begin{aligned}\langle\mu_x\rangle&=(\gamma/2)r_1\\ \langle\mu_y\rangle&=(\gamma/2)r_2.\end{aligned}\tag{13}$$

If there exists a component μ_z such that $-\mu_z E_z=H$, then it can be seen that the mathematical "**r**" space reduces to physical space, as in the case of free spin $\frac{1}{2}$ Zeeman transitions. By similar procedures any kind of perturbation affecting only two levels can be thought of in terms of the familiar behavior of vectors rotating in space, according to $d\mathbf{r}/dt=\boldsymbol{\omega}\times\mathbf{r}$.

SAMPLE APPLICATIONS

Beam Type Maser Oscillator[3]

To examine how this viewpoint leads to the solution of a particular problem, we first solve the effect of a given field on the particles involved; secondly, we formulate the classical field equations in a way suitable to the experimental situation, and using the proper projections of the **r** vector we find the conditions which satisfy both Schrödinger's and Maxwell's equations simultaneously. Consider a beam of molecules which enters a microwave cavity which is near resonance with a $\Delta m=0$ transition of the molecule. The molecules have been prepared so that only those in the higher energy state enter the cavity. Assume for simplicity that the cavity mode shape is such that the molecules see an oscillatory field of constant amplitude and phase as they pass through the cavity. The oscillating ω_1 can be separated into two counter-rotating components in the 1–2 plane. For coherent perturbations such as this it is convenient to transform to a coordinate frame in which the appropriate component of ω_1 appears stationary, and neglect the other counter-rotating component. The rotating axes will be designated the *I*, *II*, and *III* axes. We take the *I* axis in the plane of the stationary driving torque which now has the following constant components (see Fig. 1):

$$\omega_I=1/2|\omega_1|$$
$$\omega_{II}=0$$
$$\omega_{III}=\omega_0-\omega.$$

ω is the frequency of the perturbation. The molecules enter the cavity with $\mathbf{r}=\mathbf{III}$ and at a time t later the components r_I and r_{II} can be seen by inspection of Fig. 1 to be

$$\begin{aligned}r_I&=\frac{\omega_I(\omega_0-\omega)}{\Omega^2}[1-\cos(\Omega t)]\\ r_{II}&=\frac{\omega_I}{\Omega}\sin(\Omega t).\end{aligned}\tag{14}$$

Ω is the magnitude $[\omega_I^2+(\omega_0-\omega)^2]^{\frac{1}{2}}$ of the driving torque as seen in the rotating frame.

[3] Gordon, Zeiger, and Townes, Phys. Rev. 95, 282 (1954).

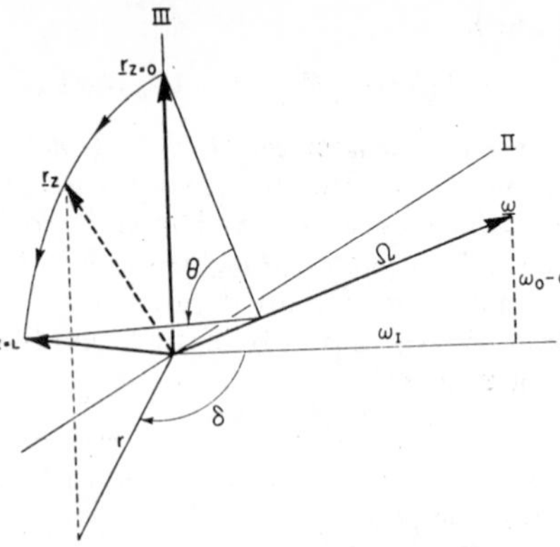

FIG. 1. MASER oscillator diagram in rotating coordinates.

To reduce these results to the stationary frame we choose the time reference such that $\omega_1=2\omega_I\cos(\omega t)$. Then $r_1=r(t)\cos[\omega t+\delta(t)]$ where $r(t)$ is the magnitude of the projection of **r** on the $1-2$ plane and $\delta(t)=\tan^{-1}r_{II}/r_I$. If we use complex quantities to represent time dependence at frequency ω, it is evident if ω_1 is represented by ω_I then r_1 is represented by (r_I+ir_{II}). Assuming all the molecules to have a velocity v then the complex polarization density P at a distance z along the cavity is the simple expression $\rho\mu_{ab}(r_I+ir_{II})$ with $t=z/v$.[4] In a thin beam, P_z, the polarization per unit length of beam is $(n/v)\mu_{ab}\times(r_I+ir_{II})$. n is number per second entering the cavity. Thus in practice one obtains the quantities of interest directly from the rotating frame.

The electric field configuration in the cavity has been assumed to be the normal configuration $\mathbf{E}_c(x,y,z)$ of the nondegenerate mode employed, where the normalization is taken such that $\int|\mathbf{E}_c|^2d\mathcal{V}=1$. $|\mathbf{E}_c|$ at the beam is taken to be the constant $f\mathcal{V}^{-\frac{1}{2}}$. $\mathcal{V}$ is the volume of the cavity. f is a form factor which would be unity were the field uniform throughout. The electric field may be written $\mathbf{E}=\mathbf{E}_c(x,y,z)\mathcal{E}(t)e^{i\omega t}$ where $\mathcal{E}$ is a real amplitude, constant in the steady state of oscillation. Then Maxwell's equations in complex form give

$$-\omega^2[\mathcal{E}\mathbf{E}_c+(4\pi\mathbf{E}_c/|\mathbf{E}_c|)P]+i(\omega\omega_c/Q)\mathbf{E}_c\mathcal{E}+\omega_c^2\mathbf{E}_c\mathcal{E}=0.\tag{15}$$

ω_c is the resonant frequency of the cavity and Q is quality factor of the cavity. Integrating Eq. (15) by $\cdot\mathbf{E}_c$ over the cavity volume gives in the case of a very thin beam

$$-\omega^2\left[\mathcal{E}+(4\pi n/v)\mu_{ab}\int_0^L f\mathcal{V}^{-\frac{1}{2}}(r_I+ir_{II})dz\right]+i(\omega\omega_c/Q)\mathcal{E}+\omega_c^2\mathcal{E}=0.\tag{16}$$

Performing the indicated integration, the imaginary

[4] J. Helmer, M. L. Report No. 311, Signal Corps Contract DA 36-039 SC-71178, Stanford University.

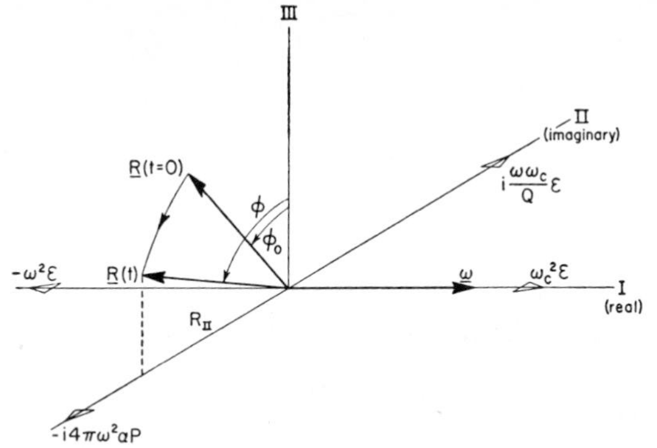

FIG. 2. Representation of "radiation damping" with the complex Maxwell's equations represented on the $I-II$ plane by the hollow arrows. $\mathbf{R}=\sum i\mathbf{r}^i$, $\alpha=fV^{-\frac{1}{2}}\mu_{ab}$, P=total polarization (or magnetization).

part of Eq. (16) gives

$$\frac{n}{n_{th}}=\frac{\theta^2}{2(1-\cos\theta)}. \tag{17}$$

$n_{th}\equiv\hbar\mathcal{V}v^2/2\pi f^2\mu_{ab}{}^2L^2Q$ and is the threshold number per second required to sustain oscillation. θ is the total angle $\Omega L/v$ through which each r precesses about the effective $\boldsymbol{\omega}$.

Equation (17) gives θ if n is known and thus the spread of frequencies at which oscillation is possible. To determine the magnitude of the electric field and the frequency of oscillation for a particular ω_c and cavity Q consider the real part of Eq. (16).

This may be written as

$$\frac{\omega_0-\omega}{\omega-\omega_c}=\frac{Q}{\pi Q_B}\frac{1-\cos\theta}{1-(\sin\theta)/\theta}\approx\frac{\omega_0-\omega}{\omega_0-\omega_c} \tag{18}$$

where $Q_B\equiv 2\pi\omega_0 L/v\approx\omega_0/\Delta\omega$ is a parameter describing the natural molecular resonance line width $\Delta\omega$. Given the amount of cavity detuning $\omega_0-\omega_c$ and θ from Eq. (17), Eq. (18) enables one to determine the frequency of oscillation ω and then $\mathcal{E}\sim\omega_I$ by using the definition of θ. These are essentially the results of Shimoda, Wang, and Townes,[5] though it appears here that no restrictions need be placed on ω to obtain them. Since the parameters θ, $\omega-\omega_0$, $\omega_I\sim\mathcal{E}$, the internal energy, and the dipole moment all appear as geometrical quantities in Fig. 1, it is easy to visualize the effects of changing any of them. Also, it is often easy to visualize, if not to solve, more complicated situations such as those which involve cavities with nonuniform modes, multiple cavities, or externally-driven cavities.

To picture the coupling of the molecules, governed by the Schrödinger equation, with the field, governed by Maxwell's equation, it is useful to think of the $I-II$ plane in the rotating frame as a complex plane representing relative time phase, with the II axis as the imaginary axis. Then the complex Maxwell's equation (16) can be drawn on the $I-II$ plane and the way in which the various quantities must vary to balance the equation to zero (or to some other driving force, if present) can be visualized. Imagining the $I-II$ plane as complex is especially useful when the $\mathbf{r}$ vectors throughout the cavity have all seen the same perturbation for the same length of time, in which case the integrals are just proportional at any time to the resultant $\mathbf{R}=\sum_i\mathbf{r}^i$ which behaves in the same manner as the individual $\mathbf{r}$'s, i.e., $d\mathbf{R}/dt=\boldsymbol{\omega}\times\mathbf{R}$. This picture is easily applied to the phenomenon of "radiation damping."[6,7]

Radiation Damping

To examine the spontaneous behavior of an ensemble of dipoles in an arbitrary state (represented by an $\mathbf{R}$) and enclosed in some small portion of a microwave cavity, we may write Maxwell's equations for the cavity as before. When the ensemble is in thermal equilibrium $\mathbf{R}$ is $-\mathbf{III}R_0$ where R_0 is given by the number present and Boltzmann statistics. Assume some other $\mathbf{R}$ state is obtained (this can be done by applying a short intense rf pulse at ω_0) and $\mathbf{R}$ is left tipped at an angle ϕ_0 to the III axis in the II, III plane ($R_I=0$). Further, we assume that the cavity is tuned to the molecular resonant frequency so that in this case $\omega=\omega_0=\omega_c$. Figure 2 is drawn for this case. $R_{II}=R_0\sin\phi$ is proportional to $\mathcal{E}$ from balancing imaginary parts of the diagram. We must now assume that $d\mathcal{E}/dt\ll(\omega_0/Q)\mathcal{E}$ and $(\omega_I/\omega_0)^2\ll 1$ as we have replaced time derivatives by $i\omega$ only. Now $d\mathbf{R}/dt=\boldsymbol{\omega}\times\mathbf{R}$ means that $d\phi/dt\sim\sin\phi$. So the radiation damping obeys $d\phi/dt\sim\sin\phi$ at resonance. The solution with constants evaluated is

$$\tan(\phi/2)=\tan(\phi_0/2)e^{t/\tau}. \tag{19}$$

$\tau=\mathcal{V}\hbar/4\pi f^2\mu_{ab}{}^2QR_0$ for $\Delta m=0$ transitions, and $\tau=\mathcal{V}\hbar/\pi f^2\gamma^2R_0Q$ for the case of $\Delta m\pm1$ transitions in a linearly polarized field (that is, a nondegenerate cavity mode). The case of a circularly polarized field involving two cavity modes and $\Delta m=\pm1$ transitions is more complicated and involves both $\langle\mu_x\rangle$ and $\langle\mu_y\rangle$ each coupling to a separate mode.

In conclusion, we wish to emphasize the usefulness of the geometrical model in visualizing and solving problems involving transitions between two levels. However, the way in which this model would be interpreted and used in a given situation depends upon the particular problem as is indicated by the two examples given. This technique of using the geometrical model does not make solutions of problems possible which were not solvable previously. However, even in many of these insoluble cases one can gain considerable insight into the behavior of the processes being investigated by observing how the parameters in the model vary.

[5] Shimoda, Wang, and Townes, Phys. Rev. **102**, 1308 (1956).

[6] N. Bloembergen and R. V. Pound, Phys. Rev. **95**, 8 (1954).

[7] R. H. Dicke, Phys. Rev. **93**, 99 (1954).

Reprinted from THE PHYSICAL REVIEW, Vol. 81, No. 2, 279–280, January 15, 1951
Printed in U. S. A.

A Nuclear Spin System at Negative Temperature

E. M. PURCELL AND R. V. POUND
Department of Physics, Harvard University, Cambridge, Massachusetts
November 1, 1950

A NUMBER of special experiments have been performed with a crystal of LiF which, as reported previously,[1] had long relaxation times both in a strong field and in the earth's field. These experiments were designed to discover the conditions determining the sense of remagnetization by a strong field when the initially magnetized crystal was put for a brief interval in the earth's field.

At field strengths allowing the system to be described by its net magnetic moment and angular momentum, a sufficiently rapid reversal of the direction of the magnetic field should result in a magnetization opposed to the new sense of the field. The reversal must occur in such a way that the time spent below a minimum effective field is so small compared to the period of the Larmor precession that the system cannot follow the change adiabatically. The experiments in zero field reported above[2] showed a zero field resonance at about 50 kc and therefore the following experiment was tried.

The crystal, initially at equilibrium magnetization in the strong (6376 gauss) field, was quickly removed, through the earth's field, and placed inside a small solenoid, the axis of which was parallel to a field of about 100 gauss, provided by a small permanent magnet. A 2 μfd condenser, initially charged to 8 kv, was discharged through the coil, with 500 ohms in series, in such a sense that the field in the coil reversed to about -100 gauss, with a time constant of about 0.2 μsec and decayed back to the original field with a time constant of 1 msec. The crystal was quickly returned, through the earth's field, to the strong magnet and the Li^7 resonance sampled. The operation could be done in 2 to 3 sec. A reversed deflection was found and it decayed, through zero, to the equilibrium state with the characteristic 5-min time constant. A typical record is shown in Fig. 1.

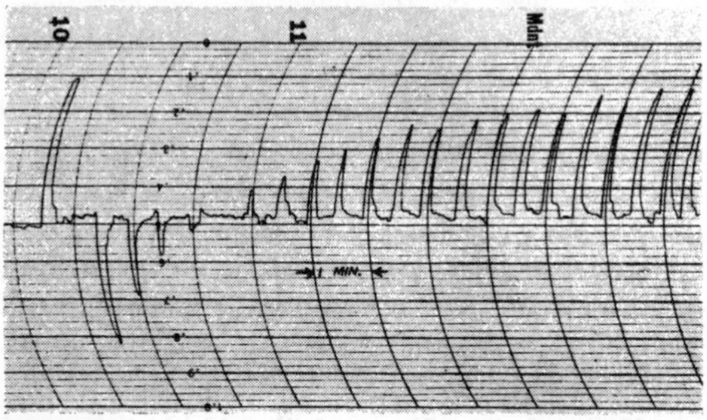

FIG. 1. A typical record of the reversed nuclear magnetization. On the left is a deflection characteristic of the normal state at equilibrium magnetization ($T \approx 300$°K), followed by the reversed deflection ($T \approx -350$°K), decaying ($T \rightarrow -\infty$) through zero deflection ($T = \infty$) to the initial equilibrium state.

The state of spin system just after this treatment is thought to be properly described by a negative spin temperature. The system loses internal energy as it gains entropy, and the reversed deflection corresponds to induced radiation. Statistically, the most probable distribution of systems over a *finite* number of equally spaced energy levels, holding the total energy constant, is the Boltzmann distribution with either positive or negative temperature determined by whether the average energy per system is smaller or larger, respectively, than the mid-energy of the available levels. The sudden reversal of the magnetic field produces the latter situation.

One needs yet to be convinced that a single temperature adequately describes the nuclear spin state. Bearing on this is the fact that the crystal passes through the earth's field after the inverted population is produced, on its way back to the main magnet. The retention of the reversed magnetization requires that the spin-only-state, in the earth's field, have an inverted population and be described by a suitably small (~ -1°K) negative temperature. Thus a very short time is required for the attainment of thermal equilibrium within the spin system itself (not the ordinary T_2, however).

A system in a negative temperature state is not cold, but very hot, giving up energy to any system at positive temperature put into contact with it. It decays to a normal state through infinite temperature.

This and related experiments indicate that the spin system is able to follow changes in even a small field adiabatically unless they occur in a time presumed to be less than about 20 μsec.

[1] R. V. Pound, Phys. Rev. 81, 156 (1951).
[2] N. F. Ramsey and R. V. Pound, Phys. Rev. 81, 278 (1951).

The maser principle is a statement of the fact that coherent amplification through the stimulated emission of radiation may occur for a system coupled to a waveguide or resonator if there are more particles in the upper of a pair of quantum states*. As noted earlier I had presented a discussion of this principle at the 1952 Ottawa electron tube research conference. It had been my intention to publish these results in a widely read journal. Early in 1953 Professor H.J. Reich of Yale University wrote to say that he had been chairman of the 1952 electron tube conference program committee, and was also editor of a (not so widely read) journal. As a result the conference summary report was published in the June 1953 Transactions of the Institute of Radio Engineers Professional Group on Electron Devices.

*Javan has noted (Bull. Am. Phys. Soc. Series II 3, 213, (1958)) that Raman processes could lead to amplification in systems in which the ground state is more heavily populated. This is discussed in the Reviews of Modern Physics paper which appears in the first part of this reprint volume.

AMPLIFICATION OF MICROWAVE RADIATION BY SUBSTANCES NOT IN THERMAL EQUILIBRIUM

by
J. Weber

Glenn L. Martin College of Engineering and Aeronautical Sciences
University of Maryland, College Park, Maryland

Introduction

This paper briefly discusses the possibility of obtaining coherent microwave radiation from crystals and gases. It will be shown that it is possible to obtain coherent microwave radiation by such methods, provided that a certain non equilibrium energy distribution is first produced. Methods are discussed for producing such a distribution. The amount of amplification which can be produced by such methods is very small under ordinary circumstances and does not appear to be able to compete with other methods. The method may have certain special applications.

Many substances show a strong selective absorption of radiation at certain frequencies in the microwave region. This absorption comes about in the following way. Let us consider that there are two energy levels E_1 and E_2 where $E_1 < E_2$.
Let N_1 be the number of oscillators in the state with energy E_1
Let N_2 be the number of oscillators in the state with energy E_2.
If we have equilibrium

$$N_2 = N_1 e^{-\left(\frac{E_2 - E_1}{kT}\right)}$$

where k is Boltzmann's constant
and T is the absolute temperature

Thus there will be, in equilibrium, always more oscillators in the lower energy state. Suppose we now apply radiation of frequency ν to the system where

$$\nu = \frac{E_2 - E_1}{h}$$

and h is Planck's constant. If the transition is allowed by the selection rules, the radiation will induce transitions for the oscillators with energy E_1 to the state with energy E_2. Also, the radiation will induce transitions downward (forced emission) of oscillators in the state E_2. It is well known from quantum theory that the transition probability up from E_1 to E_2 is the same as the transition probability down from E_2 to E_1; if we denote the transition probability from 1 to 2 as P_{12} and the transition probability from 2 to 1 as P_{21} then $P_{12} = P_{21}$. The rate of absorption of energy by oscillators in the lower state is $\text{Power}_{(\text{absorbed})} = P_{12}N_1(E_2-E_1) = P_{12}N_1 h\nu$. The rate of emission by oscillators in the upper state is

$$\text{Power}_{(\text{emitted})} = P_{21}N_2(E_2-E_1) = P_{12}N_2h\nu$$

If we have equilibrium, then from the Maxwell-Boltzmann distribution law,

$$N_2 = N_1 e^{-\frac{h\nu}{kT}} \approx N_1\left(1-\frac{h\nu}{kT}\right)$$

Therefore we obtain $P_{absorbed} - P_{emitted} = \frac{P_{12}(h\nu)^2N_1}{kT}$, and this is a positive quantity. Thus under ordinary circumstances we get absorption of radiation (ordinary microwave spectroscopy) because the transition probability up is the same as the transition probability down, but since there are more oscillators in the lower states, we get a net absorption.

A Method of Obtaining Amplification

We could get amplification if somehow the number of oscillators in the upper states could be made greater than the number in the lower states. A method of doing this is suggested by Purcell's[1] negative temperature experiment.

Suppose we apply a magnetic field to an ensemble of molecules of a gas, or nuclei of a crystal lattice. If the particles have a magnetic dipole moment this will give a resultant polarization. The distribution in angle of the various moments at equilibrium is given by

$$e^{\frac{\mu H\cos\theta}{kT}}$$

where:

- μ is the dipole moment
- H is the magnetic field
- θ is the angle between the dipole moment and the field.

It is known from the quantum theory that there is space quantization, only certain values of θ are allowed. Some of these are parallel to the field and some are anti-parallel. Suppose we have two states with values θ_1 and θ_2, then if we apply a radio-frequency field in the proper direction of frequency ν such that

$$h\nu = \mu H\left[\cos\theta_1 - \cos\theta_2\right],$$

and if the transition is allowed by the selection rules, we will get transitions from state one to state two. However the higher energy states are less heavily populated, and the substance will absorb radiation. If now we suddenly reverse the magnetic field then it will take time to restore equilibrium (relaxation time). During this brief time, because the field has been reversed, we will have more oscillators in the upper state than in the lower state. We have an "upside down" Boltzmann distribution and during this time an incident electromagnetic wave will be amplified, and the resultant pulse of radiation will be coherent.

Symmetric Top Molecules in Electric Fields

The same thing can be done (much more easily) with polar symmetric top molecules in an electric field which is reversed. We then obtain coherent pulses of the amplified driving signal. We can also imagine a gas flowing continuously through a region in which an electric field reversal takes place. In the region of field reversal we would get amplification so that continuous rather than pulsed radiation would be emitted. It is essential that the Stark effect be linear in the applied field, not quadratic, otherwise field reversal will not yield the desired energy distribution.

For the linear Stark effect in symmetric top molecules the frequency which could be amplified is given approximately by

$$\nu = \frac{\mu E K}{J(J+1)h}$$

where ν is the frequency
μ is the permanent dipole moment
E is the electric field (Stark field)
h is Planck's constant
J, and K are rotational quantum numbers associated with the symmetrical top. The Stark field has to be perpendicular to the microwave electric field.

An electromagnetic wave will grow if propagated in a gas with a "negative temperature" energy distribution. The real part of the propagation constant would be roughly given by

$$\alpha = -\frac{8\pi^3 \nu^2 N_1 |\mu_1|^2 \tau}{3ckT}$$

where ν is the frequency
N_1 is the number of molecules per unit volume in the originally lower state
$|\mu_1|^2$ is the squared matrix element corresponding to the dipole moment of the transition
τ is the pulse duration
c is the velocity of light
k is Boltzmann's constant
T is the absolute temperature.

It should be emphasized that we will get gain only during a very short period before the molecular energy distribution begins to approach the equilibrium value.

Collisions tend to restore equilibrium. The applied microwave field tends to equalize the population of the two levels because transitions out of a state are proportional to the population of that state. Thus if one state is more heavily populated than another, transitions from that state occur faster and this tends to equalize the level population. This effect of the microwave field on level population is called saturation.[2]

Rough calculations have been made of the gain and maximum power to be expected in the simple case of a gas at low pressure. The Stark effect in the ammonia rotation spectrum (not inversion spectrum) was considered. It was found that for a pressure of 10^{-2} mms of Hg. at ν = 30000 MCS., gains of the order of .02 decibels per meter could be obtained and the saturation power was of the order of 2 milliwatts per 100 cc's of gas. These figures could be enormously increased if a suitable transition (and relaxation time) could be found in either a solid or liquid.

1. E. M. Purcell and R. V. Pound, Phys. Rev. 81, 279, 1951.
2. R. Karplus and J. Schwinger, Phys. Rev. 73, 1020, 1948.

MASERS EMPLOYING GASES

The early gas beam masers did not have enough gain bandwidth product to be useful amplifiers, and their use as spectrometers was necessarily limited to molecules suitable for a given kind of excited state selector. The gas type maser has proved to be a very useful frequency standard.

The idea of employing an atomic or molecular transition as a standard was developed by Michelson in his determination of the standard meter in units of the red cadmium wavelength. In 1947, following suggestions of R. V. Pound, stabilization of a free electron oscillator by a spectral line was accomplished by Smith, Garcia de Quevedo, Carter, and Bennett.[1] In 1949 H. Lyons[2] and his associates constructed an ammonia clock at the U. S. National Bureau of Standards.

Substantial improvement in stability was achieved by use of a cesium beam[3,4] to control a crystal (vacuum tube) oscillator. The maser controls its own radiation and is a self contained source. Discussion of the relative merits of a cesium beam or thallium beam clock and a maser as frequency standards is given in a portion of Dr. Mockler's letter which is included here.

The following remarks are taken from a letter which Dr. Mockler sent me on February 6, 1963.

"Here at NBS we are in the process of critically comparing three devices that have the most obvious promise as primary frequency standards. These are the cesium beam, the thallium beam, and the hydrogen maser.

Cesium has the initial advantage because it has enjoyed the greater amount of developmental research. Our best stability (over a period of two weeks) for cesium is 2×10^{-13} and the accuracy is a little better than 1×10^{-11}. By accuracy, we mean just how closely we believe our experimental numbers approach the zero field hyperfine structure separation for the free atom as determined by various supplementary experiments including comparison with another independent Cs beam apparatus of somewhat different construction. We expect that we could obtain a precision of 2×10^{-13} any time that we run the machines for periods of about 12 hours which we do not ordinarily do. The difference frequency between our 2 existing cesium beams (designed NBS I and NBS II) has not changed more than 2×10^{-12} over the last 4 years even though the machines have been partially disassembled and moved from one laboratory to another and have had new deflecting magnets, C fields, C field shields, and frequency multiplier chains installed. These results have been most gratifying to us although requiring an enormous amount of rather tedious test procedures. We have observed our first beam in our new 3 meter (between oscillating fields) machine. It is behaving quite satisfactorily so far.

We now have a thallium beam operating—made from the older of our two cesium beam machines. We have chosen thallium—first suggested by Kusch—because it is much less sensitive to magnetic fields and the uncertainty in the C field is one of the important limitations on our accuracy for cesium. Our thallium beam has about the same stability as cesium so far. The best value is about 5×10^{-13}. Resettability is about 4×10^{-12}. We expect that this can be improved by improving the rigidity of our rf structure which is rather flimsy because of the smaller waveguide. Rotating the present cavity exciter for the purpose of measuring the phase difference between the two oscillating fields does not now give us the nice reproducibility that we get for cesium. (This is taken into account in the 4×10^{-12} figure.) This seems to be due to the fact that a change in stress on the structure shifts the phase. We are now in the process of improving this rf structure and we expect that we should be able to get an accuracy of 1×10^{-12} with this machine even though the machine has only a 55 cm separation between the oscillating fields. We are quite optimistic about thallium* although it has the disadvantage that the detector filament must be continuously oxidized and this now reduces its lifetime to about 1 month. There is some possibility of using a much hotter platinum detector wire where no oxidation is required but a substantially better vacuum is needed for it.

We are in the process of constructing a hydrogen maser. When finished—about July—we should be in a good position to make critical comparison of these three devices.

Although hydrogen is about 2000 times more sensitive to a magnetic field than is thallium, the line is only about 1 cps in breadth—much narrower than any line that can be obtained with an ordinary beam machine of sensible size. We expect then, for the hydrogen maser, that the uniform magnetic field within which the transitions occur can be reduced substantially less than they can be reduced in the corresponding atomic beam machine. If it could be reduced to say, 1 millioersted, then the sensitivity to the magnetic field is of no consequence since

$$\frac{\Delta\nu_H}{\nu_0} = 3.87 \times 10^{-6} \; H_0 \Delta H_0 \quad ,$$

where $\Delta\nu_H$ is the uncertainty in the maser frequency due to an uncertainty in the uniform field ΔH_0. H_0 is the magnitude of the uniform field and ν_0 = 1420 Mc is the hfs separation. However, one expects that the intensity of the maser signal will be reduced as H is decreased because of Majorana flop resulting from the inherent non-uniformity of the field. Whether one can reduce H_0 to the desired levels and still have sufficient signal has not yet been determined so far as I know. The hydrogen maser has an inherent frequency shift due to wall collisions and last summer this shift was 1×10^{-11}. If this can't be improved then the accuracy will be about 1×10^{-11}. Each bulb would probably have a slightly different shift and there would also likely be an "aging" effect as the surface conditions changed with time. It's hard for me to believe that someone could develop a sufficiently sophisticated theory for this shift to make a calculable correction. Even at worst, the hydrogen maser would be useful as a highly stable signal source over periods sufficient for many experiments even though it may not be useful as a primary standard.

To spare you some arithmetic I include below the relationships that compare the relative stabilities of Cs, Tl, and H with respect to a magnetic field.

$$\nu(Cs) = 9.193 \times 10^9 + 427 \overline{H_0^2}$$

$$\nu(Tl) = 2.131 \times 10^{10} + 20.4 \overline{H_0^2}$$

$$\nu(H) = 1.420 \times 10^9 + 2750 \overline{H_0^2}$$

$$\frac{\Delta\nu(Cs)}{\nu_0(Cs)} \cong 1 \times 10^{-7} \; H_0 \Delta H_0$$

$$\frac{\Delta\nu(Tl)}{\nu_0(Tl)} \cong 2 \times 10^{-9} \; H_0 \Delta H_0$$

$$\frac{\Delta\nu(H)}{\nu_0(H)} \cong 4 \times 10^{-6} \; H_0 \Delta H_0$$

$$\frac{\Delta\nu(Tl)}{\nu_0(Tl)} \approx \frac{1}{50} \; \frac{\Delta\nu(Cs)}{\nu_0(Cs)}$$

*R.E. Beehler and D.J. Glaze, "Experimental Evaluation of a Thallium Beam Frequency Standard". 17th Annual Frequency Control Symposium, Atlantic City, N.J., May 1963).

$$\frac{\Delta\nu(\mathrm{Tl})}{\nu_0(\mathrm{Tl})} \approx \frac{1}{2000} \frac{\Delta\nu(\mathrm{H})}{\nu_0(\mathrm{H})}$$

$$\frac{\Delta\nu(\mathrm{Cs})}{\nu_0(\mathrm{Cs})} \approx \frac{1}{40} \frac{\Delta\nu(\mathrm{H})}{\nu_0(\mathrm{H})}$$

Hans Dehmelt has suggested the ground state hfs transition (4 1 kMc) in the ion Hg^{199+} as a frequency standard. At extremely low pressures and using the techniques that Dehmelt has developed in ion spectroscopy one can make glowing estimates of accuracy and precision ($\sim 10^{-14}$).

It would certainly be interesting and of significant scientific value, I would suppose, to have a suitable gravitational clock in the form of a satellite to compare with atomic clocks. Position data could likely be improved with the kind of light sources now available."

REFERENCES

1. Smith, Garcia de Quevedo, Carter, and Bennett, J. A. P., **18**, 1112 (1947).
2. H. Lyons; Ann. N. Y. Acad. Sci., **55**, 831 (1952).
3. H. Lyons; Scientific American, p. 71, February 1957.
4. King, J. G., and Zacharias, J. R., Advances in Electronics and Electron Physics, **8**, 1-88 (1956).

The Maser—New Type of Microwave Amplifier, Frequency Standard, and Spectrometer*†

J. P. GORDON,‡ H. J. ZEIGER,§ AND C. H. TOWNES
Columbia University, New York, New York
(Received May 4, 1955)

A type of device is described which can be used as a microwave amplifier, spectrometer, or oscillator. Experimental results are given. When operated as a spectrometer, the device has good sensitivity, and, by eliminating the usual Doppler broadening, a resolution of 7 kc/sec has been achieved. Operated as an oscillator, the device produced a frequency stable to at least 4 parts in 10^{12} in times of the order of a second, and stable over periods of an hour or more to at least a part in 10^{10}. The device is examined theoretically, and results are given for the expected sensitivity of the spectrometer, the stability and purity of the oscillation, and the noise figure of the amplifier. Under certain conditions a noise figure approaching the theoretical limit of unity, along with reasonably high gain, should be attainable.

INTRODUCTION

A TYPE of device is described below can be used as a microwave spectrometer, a microwave amplifier, or as an oscillator. As a spectrometer, it has good sensitivity and very high resolution since it can virtually eliminate the Doppler effect. As an amplifier of microwaves, it should have a narrow band width, a very low noise figure and the general properties of a feedback amplifier which can produce sustained oscillations. Power output of the amplifier or oscillator is small, but sufficiently large for many purposes.

The device utilizes a molecular beam in which molecules in the excited state of a microwave transition are selected. Interaction between these excited molecules and a microwave field produces additional radiation and hence amplification by stimulated emission. We call an apparatus utilizing this technique a "maser," which is an acronym for "microwave amplification by stimulated emission of radiation."

Some results obtained with this device have already been briefly reported.[1] An independent proposal for a system of this general type has also been published.[2] We shall here examine in some detail the general behavior and characteristics of the maser and compare experimental results with theoretical expectations. Particular attention is given to its operation with ammonia molecules. The preceding paper,[3] which will hereafter be referred to as (I), discusses an investigation of the hyperfine structure of the microwave spectrum of $N^{14}H_3$ with this apparatus. Certain of its properties which are necessary for an understanding of the relative intensities of the hyperfine structure components are also discussed there.

BRIEF DESCRIPTION OF OPERATION

A molecular beam of ammonia is produced by allowing ammonia molecules to diffuse out a directional source consisting of many fine tubes. The beam then transverses a region in which a highly nonuniform electrostatic field forms a selective lens, focusing those molecules which are in upper inversion states while defocusing those in lower inversion states. The upper inversion state molecules emerge from the focusing field and enter a resonant cavity in which downward transitions to the lower inversion states are induced. A simplified block diagram of this apparatus is given in Fig. 1. The source, focuser, and resonant cavity are all enclosed in a vacuum chamber.

For operation of the maser as a spectrometer, power of varying frequency is introduced into the cavity from an external source. The molecular resonances are then observed as sharp increases in the power level in the cavity when the external oscillator frequency passes the molecular resonance frequencies.

At the frequencies of the molecular transitions, the beam amplifies the power input to the cavity. Thus the maser may be used as a narrow-band amplifier. Since the molecules are uncharged, the usual shot noise existing in an electronic amplifier is missing, and essentially no noise in addition to fundamental thermal noise is present in the amplifier.

If the number of molecules in the beam is increased beyond a certain critical value the maser oscillates. At the critical beam strength a high microwave energy density can be maintained in the cavity by the beam alone since the power emitted from the beam compensates for the power lost to the cavity walls and coupled wave guides. This oscillation is shown both experimentally and theoretically to be extremely monochromatic.

* Work supported jointly by the Signal Corps, the Office of Naval Research, and the Air Research and Development Command.
† Submitted by J. P. Gordon in partial fulfillment of the requirements of the degree of Doctor of Philosophy at Columbia University.
‡ Now at the Bell Telephone Laboratories, Inc., Murray Hill, New Jersey.
§ Carbide and Carbon Postdoctoral Fellow in Physics, now at Project Lincoln, Massachusetts Institute of Technology, Cambridge, Massachusetts.
[1] Gordon, Zeiger, and Townes, Phys. Rev. **95**, 282 (1954).
[2] N. G. Bassov and A. M. Prokhorov, J. Exptl. Theoret. Phys. (U.S.S.R.) **27**, 431 (1954). Also N. G. Bassov and A. M. Prokhorov, Proc. Acad. of Sciences (U.S.S.R.) **101**, 47 (1945).
[3] J. P. Gordon, preceding paper [Phys. Rev. **99**, 1253 (1955)].

APPARATUS

The geometrical details of the apparatus are not at all critical, and so only a brief description of them will be made. Two ammonia masers have been constructed with somewhat different focusers. Both have operated satisfactorily.

A source designed to create a directional beam of the ammonia molecules was used. An array of fine tubes is produced in accordance with a technique described by Zacharias,[4] which is as follows. A $\frac{1}{4}$ in. wide strip of 0.001-in. metal foil (stainless steel or nickel, for example) is corregated by rolling it between two fine-toothed gears. This strip is laid beside a similar uncorregated strip. The corregations then form channels leading from one edge of the pair of strips to the other. Many such pairs can then be stacked together to create a two-dimensional array of channels, or, as was done in this work, one pair of strips can be rolled up on a thin spindle. The channels so produced were about 0.002 in. by 0.006 in. in cross section. The area covered by the array of channels was a circle of radius about 0.2 in., which was about equal to the opening into the focuser. Gas from a tank of anhydrous ammonia was maintained behind this source at a pressure of a few millimeters of mercury.

This type of source should produce a strong but directed beam of molecules flowing in the direction of the channels. It proved experimentally to be several times more effective than a source consisting of one annular ring a few mils wide at a radius of 0.12 in., which was also tried.

The electrodes of the focuser were arranged as shown in Fig. 1. High voltage is applied to the two electrodes marked V, while the other two are kept at ground. Paul *et al.*[5,6] have used similar magnetic pole arrangements for the focusing of atomic beams.

In the first maser which was constructed the inner faces of the electrodes were shaped to form hyperbolas with 0.4-in. separating opposing electrodes. The distance of closest approach between adjacent electrodes was 0.08 in., and the focuser was about 22 in. long. Voltages up to 15 kv could be applied to these electrodes before sparking occurred. In the second maser the electrodes were shaped in the same way, but were separated from each other by 0.16 in. This allowed voltages up to almost 30 kv to be applied, and somewhat more satisfactory operation was obtained since higher field gradients could be achieved in the region between the electrodes. This second focuser was only 8 in. long. Teflon spacers were used to keep the electrodes in place. To provide more adequate pumping of the large amount of ammonia released into the vacuum system from the source the focuser electrodes were hollow and were filled with liquid nitrogen.

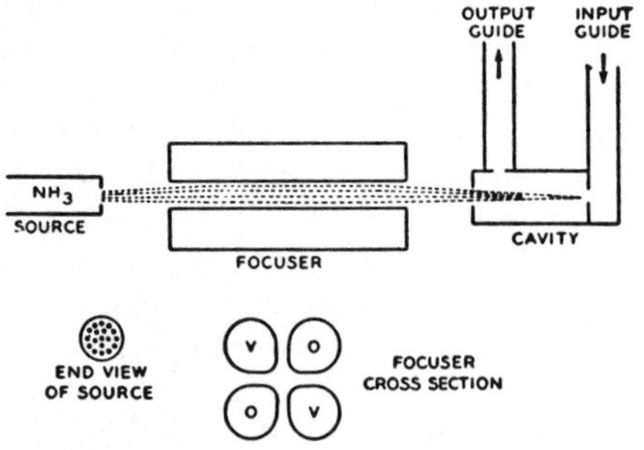

FIG. 1. Simplified diagram of the essential parts of the maser.

The resonant cavities used in most of this work were circular in cross section, about 0.6 in. in diameter by 4.5 in. long, and were resonant in the TE_{011} mode at the frequency of interest (about 24 kMc/sec). Each cavity could be turned over a range of about 50 Mc/sec by means of a short section of enlarged diameter and variable length at one end. A hole 0.4 in. in diameter in the other end allowed the beam to enter. The beam traversed the length of the cavity. The cavities were made long to provide a considerable time for the molecules to interact with the microwave field. Only one-half wavelength of the microwave field in the cavity in the axial direction was allowed for reasons which will appear later in the paper. Since the free space wavelength of 24-kMc/sec microwaves is only about 0.5 in., and an axial wavelength of about 9 in. was required in the cavity, the diameter of the cavity had to be very close to the cut-off diameter for the TE_{01} mode in circular wave guide. The diameter of the beam entrance hole was well beyond cutoff for this mode and so very little loss of microwave power from it was encountered. The cavities were machined and mechanically polished. They were made of copper or silver-plated Invar, and had values of Q near 12 000. Some work was also done with cavities in the TM_{01} mode which has some advantages over the TE_{01} mode. However, the measurements described here all apply to the TE_{011} cavities.

Microwave power was coupled into and out from the cavities in several ways. Some cavities had separate input and output wave guides, power being coupled into the cavity through a two-hole input in the end of the cavity furthest from the source and coupled out through a hole in the sidewall of the cavity. In other cavities the sidewall hole served as both input and output, and the end-wall coupling was eliminated. About the same spectroscopic sensitivity was obtained with both types of cavities.

Three MCF 300 diffusion pumps (Consolidated Vacuum Company, Inc.) were used to maintain the necessary vacuum of less than 10^{-5} mm Hg. Nevertheless, due to the large volume of gas released into the system through the source, satisfactory operation has

[4] J. R. Zacharias and R. D. Haun Jr., Quarterly Progress Report, Massachusetts Institute of Technology Research Laboratory of Electronics, 34, October, 1954 (unpublished).
[5] H. Friedberg and W. Paul, Naturwiss. 38, 159 (1951).
[6] H. G. Bennewitz and W. Paul, Z. Physik 139, 489 (1954).

not yet been attained without cooling the focuser electrodes with liquid nitrogen. At 78°K the vapor pressure of ammonia is considerably less than 10^{-6} mm Hg and so the cold electrode surfaces provide a large trapping area which helps maintain a sufficiently low pressure in the vacuum chamber. The pumping could undoubtedly be accomplished by liquid air traps alone; however the diffusion pumps alone have so far proven insufficient. The solidified ammonia which builds up on the focuser electrodes is somewhat of a nuisance as electrostatic charges which distort the focusing field tend to build up on it, and crystals form which can eventually impede the flow of gas. For the relatively short runs, however, which are required for spectroscopic work, this arrangement has been fairly satisfactory.

EXPERIMENTAL RESULTS

Experimental results have been obtained with the maser as a spectrometer and as an oscillator. Although it has been operated as an amplifier, there has as yet been no measurement of its characteristics in this role. Its properties as an amplifier are examined theoretically below.

The reader is referred to (I) for the results obtained from an examination of the hyperfine structure of the $N^{14}H_3$ inversion spectrum with the maser. Resolution of about seven kc/sec was obtained, which is a considerable improvement over the limit of about[7] 65 kc/sec imposed by Doppler broadening in the usual absorption-cell type of microwave spectrometer. This resolution can be improved still further by appropriate cavity design. The sensitivity of the maser was considerably better than that of other spectrometers which have had comparably high resolution.[8–10]

The factors which determine the sensitivity and resolution of the maser spectrometer are discussed in detail below, but we may make a general comment here. The sensitivity of the maser depends in part on the physical separation of quantum states by the focuser and thus on the forces exerted by the focuser on molecules in the various quantum states. For this reason its sensitivity is not simply related to the gas absorption coefficient for a given molecular transition. Each individual case must be examined in detail. Due to the focuser, for example, the sensitivity of the maser varies more rapidly with the dipole moment of the molecule to be studied than does that of the ordinary absorption spectrometer.

The experimental results obtained with the maser in its role as an oscillator agree with the theory given below and show that its oscillation is indeed extremely monochromatic, in fact more monochromatic than any other known source of waves. Oscillations have been produced at the frequencies of the 3–3 and 2–2 inversion lines of the ammonia spectrum, those for the 3–3 line being the stronger. Tests of the oscillator stability were made using the 3–3 line, so we shall limit the discussion to oscillation at this frequency. Other ammonia transitions, or transitions of other molecules could, of course, be used to operate a maser oscillator.

The frequency of the $N^{14}H_3$ 3–3 inversion transition is 23 870 mc/sec. The maser oscillation at this frequency was sufficiently stable in an experimental test so that a clean audio-frequency beat note between the two masers could be obtained. This beat note, which was typically at about 30 cycles per second, appeared on an oscilloscope as a perfect sine wave, with no random phase variations observable above the noise in the detecting system. The power emitted from the beams during this test was not measured directly, but is estimated to be about 5×10^{-10} watt.

The test of the oscillators was made by combining signals from the two maser oscillators together in a 1N26 crystal detector. A heterodyne detection scheme was used, with a 2K50 klystron as a local oscillator and a 30-Mc/sec intermediate-frequency (IF) amplifier. The amplified intermediate frequency signals from the two maser oscillators were then beat together in a diode detector, and their difference, which was then a direct beat between the two maser oscillator frequencies, displayed on an oscilloscope. The over-all band width of this detecting system was about 2×10^4 cps, and the beat note appeared on the oscilloscope with a signal to noise ratio of about 20 to 1.

It was found that the frequency of oscillation of each maser could be varied one or two kc/sec on either side of the molecular transition frequency by varying the cavity resonance frequency about the transition frequency. If the cavity was detuned too far, the oscillation ceased. The ratio of the frequency shift of the oscillation to the frequency shift of the cavity was almost exactly equal to the ratio of the frequency width of the molecular response (that is, the line width of the molecular transition as seen by the maser spectrometer) to the frequency width of the cavity mode. This behavior is to be expected theoretically as will be shown below. The two maser oscillators were well enough isolated from one another so that the beat note could be lowered to about 20 cps before they began to lock together. The appearance of this beat note has been noted above. As perhaps $\frac{1}{10}$-cycle phase variation could have been easily detected in a time of a second (which is about the time the eye normally averages what it observes), the appearance of the beat indicates a spectral purity of each oscillator of at least 0.1 part in 2.4×10^{10}, or 4 parts in 10^{12} in a time of the order of a second.

By using Invar cavities maintained in contact with ice water to control thermal shifts in their resonant frequencies, the oscillators were kept in operation for

[7] Gunther-Mohr, White, Schawlow, Good, and Coles, Phys. Rev. **94**, 1184 (1954).
[8] G. Newell and R. H. Dicke, Phys. Rev. **83**, 1064 (1951).
[9] R. H. Romer and R. H. Dicke, Phys. Rev. **98**, 1160(A) (1955).
[10] M. W. P. Strandberg and H. Dreicer, Phys. Rev. **94**, 1393 (1954).

periods of an hour or so with maximum variations in the beat frequency of about 5 cps or 2 parts in 10^{10} and an average variation of about one part in 10^{10}. Even these small variations seemed to be connected with temperature changes such as those associated with replenishing the liquid nitrogen supply in the focusers. Theory indicates that variations of about 0.1°C in temperature, which was about the accuracy of the temperature control, would cause frequency deviations of just this amount.

It was found that the oscillation frequency was slightly dependent on the source pressure and the focuser voltage, both of which affect the strength of the beam. These often produced frequency changes of the order of 20 cycles per second when either voltage or pressure was changed by about 25%. As the cavity was tuned, however, both these effects changed direction, and the null points for the two masers coincide to within about 30 cps. The frequency at which these effects disappear is probably very near the center frequency of the molecular response, so this may provide a very convenient way of resetting the frequency of a maser oscillator without reference to any other external standard of frequency.

THE FOCUSER

In (I) it was shown that forces are exerted by the nonuniform electric field of the focuser on the ammonia molecules, the force being radially inward toward the focuser axis for molecules in upper inversion states and radially outward for molecules in lower inversion states. Molecules in upper inversion states are therefore focused by the field, and only these molecules reach the cavity. Moreover, the quadrupole hyperfine splitting of the upper inversion state was shown to affect the focusing since the flight of the molecules through the focuser is adiabatic with respect to transitions between the different quadrupole levels. As a result the higher energy quadrupole levels are focused considerably more strongly than the lower energy ones. The further slight splitting of the various quadrupole states by the magnetic hyperfine interactions of the hydrogen nuclei has little effect since the molecules make many transitions between these closely spaced levels as they enter and leave the focuser. In regions of high field strength where hyperfine effects are unimportant and can be neglected the energy of the molecules in an electric field may be written as

$$W = W_{\text{rotation}}(J,K) \pm \left\{ \left(\frac{h\nu_0}{2}\right)^2 + \left(\frac{M_J K}{J(J+1)}\mu\mathcal{E}\right)^2 \right\}^{\frac{1}{2}}, \quad (1)$$

where ν_0 is the zero-field inversion frequency, J, K, and M_J specify the rotational state of the molecule relative to the direction of the field, μ is the molecular dipole moment, and $\mathcal{E}$ is the magnitude of the electric field.

With these considerations in mind, an approximate calculation of the total number of molecules in the upper inversion state which are trapped by the potential well of the focuser and delivered to the cavity is fairly straightforward. It involves some computation, since the line used for the oscillation (the main line of the $J=K=3$ inversion transition) is composed of three different but unresolved component transitions between quadrupole sublevels of the inversion states, and therefore the number of molecules trapped by the focuser must be calculated for each of these three sublevels and the results added. This calculation is outlined below. We shall consider in detail the properties of the first maser oscillator, with which the work reported in (I) was done.

The focuser electrodes form approximate equipotentials of the potential $V = V_0 r^2 \cos 2\theta$, where r and θ are cylindrical coordinates of a system whose z axis coincides with the axis of the focuser. 15 kv applied to the high-voltage focuser electrodes establishes an electric field whose magnitude is given by

$$\mathcal{E} = 200r, \quad (2)$$

where $\mathcal{E}$ is measured in esu and r is in cm. For simplicity we shall assume that the source is small in area and is located on the axis of the focuser. We shall also assume that all molecules which can travel farther than 0.5 cm from the focuser axis collide with the focuser electrodes and are removed from the beam. From (1) and (2) it is seen that the force ($\mathbf{f} = -\text{grad}W$) on the molecules is radial, and for small field strength is proportional to r. Furthermore it can be seen from energy considerations that all molecules which emerge from the source with radial velocity v_r less than v_{max}, where $\frac{1}{2}mv_{\text{max}}^2 = W(r=0.5\text{ cm}) - W(r=0)$ are held within the focuser by the electric field, while all molecules whose radial velocity is greater than v_{max} collide with the electrodes. Since v_{max} is a function of M_J (M_J is the projection of $\mathbf{J}$ on the direction of the electric field of the focuser) the number of molecules focused from a given zero-field quadrupole level depends on the high field distribution of these molecules among the various possible M states.

From kinetic theory, the number of molecules per second emerging from a thin-walled source of area S with radial velocity less than v_{max} is given by

$$N = PSv_0\Omega/(2\pi)^{\frac{1}{2}}kT, \quad (3)$$

where P is the source pressure, $v_0 = (kT/m)^{\frac{1}{2}}$ is the most probable velocity of molecules in the beam, T is the absolute temperature, and Ω is a solid angle defined by $\Omega = \pi(v_{\text{max}}/v_0)^2$. The number of molecules per second in a given quadrupole level which are focused is therefore

$$N(F_1) = \frac{PSv_0}{(2\pi)^{\frac{1}{2}}kT} f(JKF_1) \sum_{M_J} \varphi(F_1 M_J)\Omega(M_J), \quad (4)$$

where $f(JKF_1)$ is the fraction of molecules emerging from the source in the quadrupole state characterized by J, K, and F_1 ($\mathbf{F}_1=\mathbf{J}+\mathbf{I}_N$, where I_N is the spin of the nitrogen nucleus), and $\varphi(F_1, M_J)$ is that fraction of these molecules which, according to the discussion in (I), go adiabatically into the state characterized by the quantum number M_J as they enter the high electric field of the focuser. The total number of molecules per second in the upper inversion state which are delivered to the cavity by the focuser is then just the sum of the $N(F_1)$ for the three quadrupole levels, and so is

$$N(J,K)=\frac{PSv_0}{(2\pi)^{\frac{1}{2}}kT}f(JK)\Omega(JK), \quad (5)$$

where

$$\Omega(JK)=\sum_{F_1}\frac{f(JKF_1)}{f(JK)}\sum_{M_J}\varphi(F_1M_J)\Omega(M_J)$$

is an average solid angle for the upper inversion state, and $f(JK)$ is the fraction of molecules emerging from the source in the upper inversion state of the JK rotational level.

If each of these N molecules could be induced to make a transition to the lower inversion state while in the resonant cavity the total power delivered by the beam would be just $N(JK)h\nu_0$. Actually only about 50 to 75% average transition probability for the molecules in the beam can be obtained due to the variation of their velocities and spatial orientations. Assuming 50% transition probability, a source temperature of 300°K, and the geometry and voltage of the focuser given above, a calculation of the solid angle for the 3–3 line gives $\Omega(3\text{–}3)=4\times10^{-3}$ steradian, and available power of 1.5×10^{-9} watt per square millimeter of source area at 1 mm Hg source pressure.

It is estimated that the total number of molecules emerging from the source in the solid angle from which the upper inversion state molecules are selected is about 10^{15} per second. This estimate comes from knowledge of the number of molecules necessary to induce oscillation. This indicates that the present source is operating fairly inefficiently.

RESONANT CAVITY AND LINE WIDTH

The beam of molecules which enters the resonant cavity is almost completely composed of molecules in the upper inversion state. During their flight through the cavity the molecules are induced to make downward transitions by the rf electric field existing in the cavity. The transition probability for any particular molecule at low field strengths is given from first-order perturbation theory by

$$P_{ab}=\hbar^{-2}|\mu_{ab}|^2\left|\int_0^{L/v}\mathcal{E}(t)e^{-i2\pi\nu_0 t}dt\right|^2, \quad (6)$$

where μ_{ab} is the dipole matrix element for the transition, L is the length of the cavity, v is the velocity of the molecule, and $\mathcal{E}(t)$ is the rf electric field at the position of the molecule.

An average transition probability $\bar{P}_{ab}$ can be obtained for all molecules in the beam by averaging over the various velocities, trajectories, and values of $|\mu_{ab}|$ for the molecules in the several states which contribute to each spectral line. The power emitted from the beam is then just

$$P=Nh\nu\bar{P}_{ab}, \quad (7)$$

so $\bar{P}_{ab}$ as a function of the frequency of the applied field determines the line width of the molecular response.

Under the simplifying assumptions that the molecules all travel axially down the length of the cavity, that their velocity is uniform and equal to v_0, and that the cavity is a perfect cylinder with only one-half wavelength of rf field in the axial direction, we find that the emitted power has a maximum at the natural transition frequency ν_B, and a total width at half-maximum of $1.2v_0/L$. If the field is assumed to be uniform along the axis rather than one-half of a sine wave, the corresponding total width at half-maximum is $0.9v_0/L$. This line width of about v_0/L can alternatively be obtained from the uncertainty principle and the finite time of interaction of the molecules with the rf field. Thus $\Delta\nu\approx1/\Delta t$, where Δt is the time of flight of the molecule in the cavity, or L/v_0. The identity of the "Doppler broadening" of the spectral line has essentially disappeared. The sharpness of the molecular response as opposed to that obtained in the usual spectrometer may alternatively be attributed to the long wavelength of the rf field in the cavity in the direction of travel of the beam. If the cavity is excited in a mode in which there is more than one-half wavelength in the direction of travel of the beam, then the molecular emission line, as given by Eq. (6), has two peaks symmetrically spaced about the transition frequency. The frequency separation of these peaks can be associated with the Doppler shift.

Equations (6) and (7) show that for small rf field strengths the emitted power P is proportional to $\mathcal{E}_{\max}^2$ and thus to the energy stored in the cavity. For larger field strengths, of course, the molecular transitions begin to saturate and Eq. (6) is no longer sufficient for the calculation of P_{ab}. The effects of this saturation will be considered in detail in a later paper; however, we can say that P_{ab} must certainly be less than 1, and that if a high field strength is maintained in the cavity then the average transition probability $\bar{P}_{ab}(\nu_B)$ will be about 0.5. The total power available from the beam is therefore about $Nh\nu_B/2$. Power saturation in this case is rather similar to that in the usual molecular beam experiment, for which it has been considered by Torrey.[11]

Associated with the power emitted from the beam is an anomalous dispersion, that is, a sharp variation

[11] H. C. Torrey, Phys. Rev. **59**, 293 (1941).

in the dielectric constant of the cavity medium due to the beam. These two effects can be considered at the same time by thinking of the beam as a polarizable medium introduced into the cavity, whose average electric susceptibility is given by $\chi=\chi'+i\chi''$. The power emitted from the beam can then be shown directly from Maxwell's equations to be[12]

$$P=8\pi^2\nu_B W\chi'', \tag{8}$$

where W is the energy stored in the cavity. Thus, from Eqs. (7) and (8), χ'' is related to $\bar{P}_{ab}$ by

$$\chi''=Nh\bar{P}_{ab}/8\pi^2W. \tag{9}$$

The value of χ' is given from χ'' by Kramer's relation,[13] which for a sharp resonance line can be approximated by[14]

$$\chi'(\nu)=\frac{1}{\pi}\int_0^\infty \frac{\chi''(\nu')d\nu'}{\nu'-\nu}. \tag{10}$$

Figure 2 shows the form of χ' and χ'', calculated with the assumptions that all molecules are traveling parallel to the axis of the cavity with uniform velocity, that the cavity is excited in the TE_{011} mode, and that there is a small field strength in the cavity so that $P_{ab}\ll 1$ and Eq. (6) is valid. χ' and χ'' can also be found directly by calculation of the induced dipole moments of the molecules as they traverse the cavity.

If the Q of the cavity is defined in terms of net power loss (i.e., $dW/dt=-2\pi\nu W/Q_C$) then the presence of the

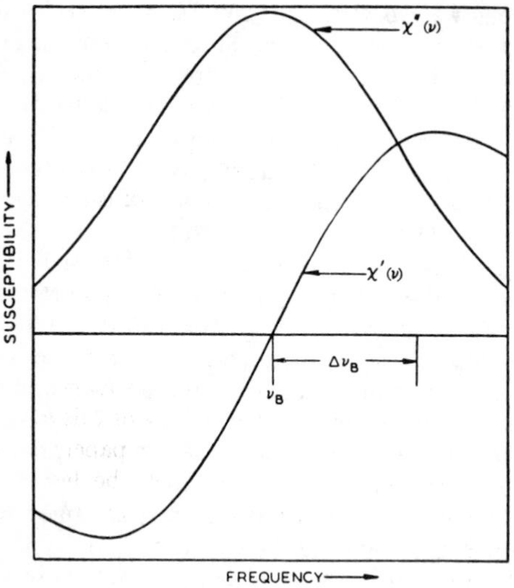

FIG. 2. Real and imaginary parts of the electric susceptibility χ of the molecular beam in the cavity. $\chi=\chi'+i\chi''$.

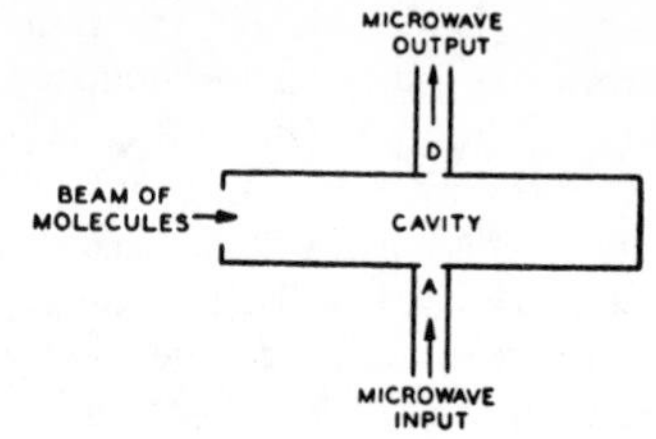

FIG. 3. Schematic diagram of the resonant cavity and molecular beam.

beam can be considered as causing a change in the effective Q_C given by $1/Q_{CB}=1/Q_C-4\pi\chi''$, where Q_{CB} and Q_C are respectively the cavity Q's with and without the beam, along with a shift in the resonant frequency of the cavity given by $\nu_{CB}=\nu_C(1-2\pi\chi')$ if $\chi'\ll 1$. These relations can also be easily derived directly from Maxwell's equations, and they will prove important in determining the properties of the maser.

THE MASER SPECTROMETER

Observed Line Shape as a Function of the Cavity Resonant Frequency

Consider the situation shown in Fig. 3. Power P_0 is incident on the cavity from wave guide A, and the power transmitted on out through wave guide D is detected as a function of the frequency of the input power. The power transmitted through the cavity in the absence of the beam is given by[12]

$$P_D(\nu)=\frac{P_0}{Q_AQ_D}\bigg/\left[\left(\frac{1}{2Q_L}\right)^2+\left(\frac{\nu-\nu_C}{\nu_C}\right)^2\right], \tag{11}$$

where Q_A and Q_D are defined in terms of the power losses from the cavity to wave guides A and D respectively, and Q_L is the loaded Q of the cavity, given by $1/Q_L=1/Q_C+1/Q_A+1/Q_D$. As was shown in the last section, the change in $P_D(\nu)$ caused by the presence of the beam can be described through variations in Q_C and ν_C near the transition frequency ν_B. Thus in the presence of the beam we find P_D modified to

$$P_{DB}(\nu)=\frac{P_0}{Q_AQ_D}\bigg/\left[\left(\frac{1}{2Q_L}-2\pi\chi''(\nu)\right)^2+\left(\frac{\nu-\nu_C+2\pi\nu_C\chi'(\nu)}{\nu_C}\right)^2\right]. \tag{12}$$

As long as the power output P_{DB} is not so high that nonlinearities in the molecular response are important, (12) gives the output power as a function of frequency in the presence of the beam and represents the spectrum which may be observed. For most spectroscopic applications we are interested in the case for which $\chi''(\nu)\ll 1/4\pi Q_L$ for all ν. For this case, an appropriate expansion of Eq. (12) shows that if $\nu_C=\nu_B$, where ν_B is the center frequency of the molecular response, then the presence of the beam shows up as a pip of the shape

[12] J. C. Slater, *Microwave Electronics* (D. Van Nostrand Company, Inc., New York, 1950).
[13] J. H. Van Vleck, *Massachusetts Institute of Technology Radiation Laboratory Report*, 735, see also *Radiation Laboratory Series* (McGraw-Hill Book Company, Inc., New York, 1948), Vol. 13, Chap. 8.
[14] G. E. Pake and E. M. Purcell, Phys. Rev. **74**, 1184 (1948).

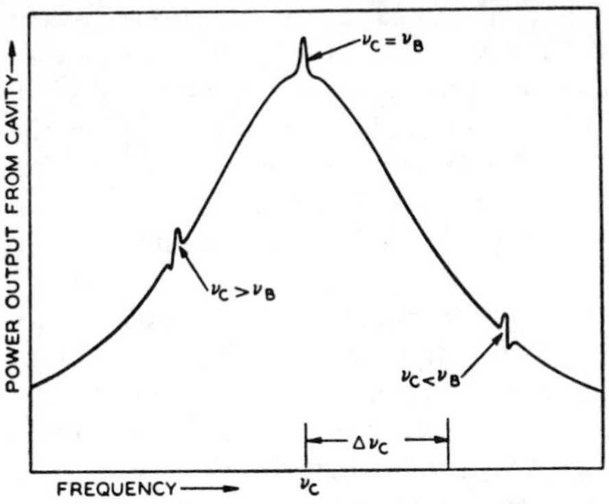

FIG. 4. Spectral line shapes as observed in the maser.

of χ'' superimposed on the cavity mode. The half-width $\Delta\nu_B$ of the molecular response is therefore defined as half the frequency separation of the half-maximum points of $\chi''(\nu)$. If the cavity frequency is altered so that the molecular line appears on the wings of the cavity mode, then the pip due to the beam assumes the shape of $\pm\chi'(\nu)$, the + or − sign depending on whether the line appears on the low or high frequency side of the cavity mode. These three situations are illustrated in Fig. 4.

Sensitivity of the Maser Spectrometer

We have here the usual problem occurring in microwave spectroscopy of detecting a small change in output power P_0 caused by the presence of the molecules. Assume that $\nu_C=\nu_B=\nu$ in Eq. (12). Then

$$P_{DB}=\frac{P_0}{Q_AQ_D}\bigg/\left(\frac{1}{2Q_L}-2\pi\chi''(\nu_B)\right)^2. \quad (13)$$

The change in output power which must be detected is then

$$\delta P_D=P_{DB}-P_D\cong P_0(4Q_L^2/Q_AQ_D)\times[8\pi Q_L\chi''(\nu_B)]. \quad (14)$$

Consider now the change in output voltage δV_D, which is proportional to $(P_D+\delta P_D)^{\frac{1}{2}}-P_D^{\frac{1}{2}}$ or to $\delta P_D/2P_D^{\frac{1}{2}}$ when $\delta P_D\ll P_D$. The noise voltage at the output of a linear detector is just $(FkT\Delta\nu)^{\frac{1}{2}}$, where $\Delta\nu$ is the band width of the detector and F is its over-all noise figure. Thus the voltage signal-to-noise ratio is given by

$$\delta V_D/V_N=[(\delta P_D)^2/4FkTP_D\Delta\nu]^{\frac{1}{2}}. \quad (15)$$

As long as the change in power δP_D due to the beam increases linearly with the power level P_D, the signal to noise ratio from (15) continues to increase. Hence the power input to the cavity should be increased until the transition begins to saturate. For saturation and a given Q_C, it can be shown that maximum sensitivity is achieved by using a small input coupling ($Q_A\gg Q_C$) and a matched output coupling ($Q_D=Q_C$). If we approximate the saturation condition by setting W equal to the level at which the power emitted by the beam is just $\frac{1}{2}Nh\nu_B$, then with a little algebra we find, from Eqs. (8), (14), and the known relationship of W to P_0,[12] that the change in output power δP_D is just $\frac{1}{2}Nh\nu_B$ (the beam emits $\frac{1}{2}Nh\nu_B$ of power, and due to the change in the input match caused by the beam, $\frac{1}{2}Nh\nu_B$ more power enters the cavity through the input coupling hole A. Thus the increase in power input to the cavity is twice the power emitted from the beam. Half of this increase emerges into wave guide D since it was assumed to be matched to the cavity. The power level P_D is now determined by the required energy W from the relation

$$P_D=2\pi\nu_BW/Q_C. \quad (16)$$

This, with (8), gives

$$P_D=P/4\pi\chi''(\nu_B)Q_C=Nh\nu_B/8\pi\chi''(\nu_B)Q_C. \quad (17)$$

Inserting these values for P_D and δP_D in (15) yields

$$\delta V_D/V_N=[\pi Q_CNh\nu_B\chi''(\nu_B)/2FkT\Delta\nu]^{\frac{1}{2}}. \quad (18)$$

This relation gives the sensitivity of the maser, once the value of $\chi''(\nu_B)$ for a given molecule is calculated. χ'' is, of course, related to the average transition probability $\bar{P}_{ab}$ by Eq. (9), so that Eq. (18) can easily be rewritten in terms of the transition probability.

For the ammonia 3–3 line, a calculation of the number of molecules in the 3–3 state necessary to make $\delta V_D/V_N=1$ was done, assuming $F=100$, $\Delta\nu=1$ cps, $Q_C=12\,000$, $T=300°$ and using an approximate calculation of $\chi''(\nu_B)$ based on the considerations of the previous section. The result was 10^9 molecules per second. It is estimated from the value of $\chi''(\nu_B)$ which is necessary to cause oscillation (see next section) that the number of upper inversion state molecules in the 3–3 rotational state in the beam when oscillations occur is at least 10^{13} molecules per second, and experimentally a number about four times this great was achieved. Thus, for ammonia, the maser should have good sensitivity, and the results described in paper (I) show that this is indeed the case.

In the case of the ammonia inversion spectrum, the focuser can effect an almost complete separation of the upper states from the lower states of the transitions. For some other transitions, this ideal state of affairs may not be attainable, but yet the focuser may preferentially focus one of the two states of the transition. In such a case all of the above considerations apply so long as one uses for N just the excess number of molecules in one of the two states. It is, of course, unimportant for spectroscopic purposes whether the more highly focused state is the upper or lower state of the transition. The high sensitivity attained in the observation of the ammonia spectrum with the maser gives promise that it may be generally useful as a microwave spectrometer of very high resolution.

THE MASER OSCILLATOR AND AMPLIFIER

By extending the considerations of the previous section to include amplification of the thermal noise which exists in the cavity, we can discuss the properties of the maser as an oscillator or amplifier. The results of this analysis, which is made below, are as follows:

(1) The center frequency ν_0 of the oscillation is given to a good approximation by the equation

$$\nu_0 = \nu_B + \frac{\Delta\nu_B}{\Delta\nu_C}(\nu_C - \nu_B), \tag{19}$$

where $\Delta\nu_C$ and $\Delta\nu_B$ are respectively the half-widths of the cavity mode and of the molecular emission line; and $\nu_C - \nu_B$ is the difference between the cavity resonant frequency ν_C and the line frequency ν_B.

(2) The total width at half-power of the spectral distribution of the oscillation is approximately

$$2\delta\nu = 8\pi kT(\Delta\nu_B)^2/P_B \tag{20}$$

where T is the temperature and P_B is the power emitted from the beam. Inserting in (20) values which approximate the experimental conditions, $T=300°\text{K}$, $\Delta\nu_B = 3\times10^3$ cps, $P_B = 10^{-10}$ watt, we find $2\delta\nu \approx 10^{-2}$ cps, or $\nu_B/\delta\nu = 5\times10^{12}$.

(3) If the beam is sufficiently strong, the maser may be used as an amplifier with a gain greater than unity and a noise figure very close to unity.

The argument goes along the following lines. Consider the situation of Fig. 3, the cavity with two wave guides. The whole system will be assumed to be in thermal equilibrium in the absence of the beam. Noise power of amount kT per unit band width is incident on the cavity from each wave guide, and the cavity walls emit noise power within the cavity. Of the noise power incident on the cavity from wave guide A, a certain amount within the frequency range of the cavity mode enters the cavity; part of this power is then absorbed by the cavity walls and part is transmitted on out through wave guide D. A similar situation holds for noise power incident on the cavity from wave guide D; some is absorbed in the cavity and some is transmitted through to wave guide A. The cavity walls emit noise power in the region of the cavity mode and some of this power goes out through each wave guide. When the beam is not present we have assumed the system to be in thermal equilibrium, so there must be kT per unit band width of noise power flowing away from the cavity down each wave guide and there must be kT of noise energy in the cavity mode, as required by the equipartition theorem.

In the presence of the beam thermal equilibrium is upset. The beam, since it is composed solely of upper inversion state molecules, and since the probability for spontaneous decay of these molecules to the lower states is negligible during the time they take to traverse the cavity, contributes no random noise of its own to the rf field of the cavity. What it does is merely to amplify, in a way described by its effect on the loaded Q and resonant frequency of the cavity, all of the noise signals which exist in the cavity. Thus to the noise sources in the wave guides the intrinsic Q of the cavity seems to have been altered; whereas to the noise source within the cavity, the loading on the cavity seems to have changed. In fact, the presence of the beam can be duplicated in the imagination by attaching to the cavity a third wave guide, with a negative Q equal to $\frac{1}{4}\pi\chi''(\nu)$ describing its coupling to the cavity, and by simultaneously shifting the resonant frequency of the cavity by an amount $-2\pi\nu_C\chi'(\nu)$.

From these considerations we will show that in the presence of the beam more than kT of power per unit bandwidth travels down each wave guide away from the cavity. The extra power, of course, comes from the beam. At a certain critical beam intensity this power suddenly becomes large, corresponding to sustained oscillations.

Let $\Delta\nu$ be some arbitrarily small element of the frequency spectrum at frequency ν. Within this range noise power of magnitude $kT\Delta\nu$ is incident on the cavity from each wave guide, independent of ν. Let $P_A\Delta\nu$ be the amount of noise power which enters the cavity from the incident power in wave guide A, and let $P_A'\Delta\nu$ be the total noise power re-emitted into wave guide A from inside the cavity. The presence of the beam will be indicated by an added subscript; i.e., P_{AB} will represent the value of P_A when the beam is present, etc. Similar definitions apply to the output guide D. Since the noise powers generated in the wave guides and in the cavity are completely incoherent with one another, we can simply add power coming from various sources to obtain the total power in any element of the system. Thus the total energy $W\Delta\nu$ stored in the cavity is merely the sum $\sum_i W_i\Delta\nu$ of all the energies due to power coming from the various different power sources. (W is energy per unit band width.)

Consider now the flow of power when no beam is present. The noise power entering the cavity from wave guide A is given by[12]

$$P_A = \frac{kT}{Q_AQ_L{}^A}\Big/\left[\left(\frac{1}{2Q_L}\right)^2 + \left(\frac{\nu-\nu_C}{\nu_C}\right)^2\right], \tag{21}$$

where $1/Q_L{}^x = \sum_{m\neq x} 1/Q_m$ is just proportional to all the losses from the cavity except that due to Q_x. Of this power P_A, some is absorbed in the cavity walls, and the rest is transmitted on out through wave guide D. The energy per unit band width stored in the cavity due to this power input is

$$W_A = P_AQ_L{}^A/2\pi\nu$$

$$= \frac{kT}{2\pi\nu Q_A}\Big/\left[\left(\frac{1}{2Q_L}\right)^2 + \left(\frac{\nu-\nu_C}{\nu_C}\right)^2\right]. \tag{22}$$

and the power transmitted on to the output wave guide D is $2\pi\nu W_A/Q_D$, or $P_A Q_L{}^A/Q_D$. Similar expressions hold for the noise power incident on the cavity from wave guide D. Furthermore, the cavity loss associated with Q_C may be assumed to be due to a third wave guide with coupling characterized by Q_C to a perfectly conducting cavity, so that the energy W_C emitted into the actual cavity from its wall has the same form as (22). The total energy stored in the cavity per unit frequency interval is hence

$$W=W_A+W_D+W_C$$

$$=\frac{kT}{2\pi\nu Q_L}\Big/\left[\left(\frac{1}{2Q_L}\right)^2+\left(\frac{\nu-\nu_C}{\nu_C}\right)^2\right], \quad (23)$$

where

$$1/Q_L=1/Q_A+1/Q_D+1/Q_C.$$

The total energy stored in the cavity, given by $\int_0^\infty W d\nu$, is easily shown to be equal to kT (we make the assumption that $Q_L \gg 1$, so that in the integration the approximation $\nu \approx \nu_C$ may be made) as required by the equipartition theorem. The net noise power flowing in the wave guides A or D is also easily shown to be zero, so that the system is indeed seen to be in thermal equilibrium.

Consider now the case when the beam is present. The noise power incident from each wave guide sees a cavity whose rates of internal loss has been reduced by an amount $4\pi\chi''(\nu)$ by the energy emitted from the beam and whose resonant frequency has been shifted by an amount $-2\pi\nu_C\chi'(\nu)$. Corresponding to Eq. (21), the power entering the cavity from wave guide A in the presence of the beam is

$$P_{AB}=\frac{kT}{Q_{LB}{}^A Q_A}\Big/\left[\left(\frac{1}{2Q_{LB}}\right)^2+\left(\frac{\nu-\nu_{CB}}{\nu_{CB}}\right)^2\right], \quad (24)$$

where $1/Q_{xB}=1/Q_x-4\pi\chi''(\nu)$ for any x and $\nu_{CB}=\nu_C[1-2\pi\chi'(\nu)]$, while that entering from wave guide D is similarly

$$P_{DB}=\frac{kT}{Q_{LB}{}^D Q_D}\Big/\left[\left(\frac{1}{2Q_{LB}}\right)^2+\left(\frac{\nu-\nu_{CB}}{\nu_{CB}}\right)^2\right]. \quad (25)$$

The noise energy stored in the cavity due to these two sources is

$$W_{AB}=\frac{P_{AB}Q_{LB}{}^A}{2\pi\nu}, \quad \text{and} \quad W_{DB}=P_{DB}Q_{LB}{}^D/2\pi\nu. \quad (26)$$

At the same time, the energy stored in the cavity due to its own internal noise source is changed as though the loading on the cavity has been altered while its internal loss was unaffected. This energy is therefore given by

$$W_{CB}=\frac{kT}{2\pi\nu Q_C}\Big/\left[\left(\frac{1}{2Q_{LB}}\right)^2+\left(\frac{\nu-\nu_{CB}}{\nu_{CB}}\right)^2\right]. \quad (27)$$

Due to the presence of the beam the net noise power emitted from the cavity into the output wave guide D is now no longer zero. The power emerging from the cavity is now

$$P_{DB}'=\frac{2\pi\nu}{Q_D}[W_{CB}+W_{AB}]$$

$$=\frac{kT}{Q_D Q_L{}^D}\Big/\left[\left(\frac{1}{2Q_{LB}}\right)^2+\left(\frac{\nu-\nu_{CB}}{\nu_{CB}}\right)^2\right]. \quad (28)$$

Thus the additional noise output in wave guide D due to the beam is, from (25) and (28),

$$P_{DN}\equiv P_{DB}'-P_{DB}$$

$$=\frac{kT}{Q_D}4\pi\chi''(\nu)\Big/\left[\left(\frac{1}{2Q_{LB}}\right)^2+\left(\frac{\nu-\nu_{CB}}{\nu_{CB}}\right)^2\right]. \quad (29)$$

The power which must be emitted from the beam to give this amount of power in wave guide D is just

$$P_N\equiv P_{DN}Q_D/Q_L=\frac{kT}{Q_L}4\pi\chi''(\nu)\Big/$$

$$\left[\left(\frac{1}{2Q_L}-2\pi\chi''(\nu)\right)^2+\left(\frac{\nu-\nu_C+2\pi\nu_C\chi'(\nu)}{\nu_C}\right)^2\right], \quad (30)$$

where ν_C has replaced ν_{CB} in the denominator of the last term in the denominator of this expression since $\nu_{CB}\approx\nu_C$. Note that (30) is just equivalent to (24) if the beam is thought of as a wave guide coupled to the cavity with a Q of $-1/4\pi\chi''$.

Expression (30) gives the complete spectrum of the power emitted from the beam due to amplification of the noise signals which are always present in the cavity. The necessary condition for the existence of oscillations as some cavity frequency is evidently that $\chi''(\nu_B)\approx\frac{1}{4}\pi Q_L$.

Assume that the cavity is tuned so that $|\nu_C-\nu_B| \ll \Delta\nu_C$, and then let the beam strength slowly increase so that χ'' increases. Then at the critical beam strength where $\chi''(\nu_B)\rightarrow 1/4\pi Q_L$, the total power $\int P_N d\nu$ emitted from the beam approaches infinity accordingly to (30). Obviously, the total power emitted from the beam cannot go to infinity, but is limited to about $\frac{1}{2}Nh\nu_B$. When the power level in the cavity reaches the point at which the molecular transition begins to saturate, χ'' and χ' become functions of the power level, and, of course, vary in such a way that $\int P_N d\nu$ is always less than $\frac{1}{2}Nh\nu_B$. We can, for simplicity, avoid the problem of dealing with this saturation merely by increasing χ'' until $\int P_N d\nu=\frac{1}{2}Nh\nu_B$ and examining the frequency spectrum of the power emitted from the beam at this level of output. Although χ'' is not independent of the electric field strength when saturation occurs, it varies much more slowly with time than does the oscillation, so that it may be considered constant in treating the short-term behavior of the microwave field.

As the critical number of molecules is reached, P_N becomes very large at frequencies very close to ν_B. Hence it is appropriate to expand χ' and χ'' about the center frequency ν_B. This gives approximately

$$\chi'=\chi_0\left(\frac{\nu-\nu_B}{\Delta\nu_B}\right)+\cdots,$$
$$\chi''=\chi_0\left[1-\frac{1}{2}\left(\frac{\nu-\nu_B}{\Delta\nu_B}\right)^2+\cdots\right]. \tag{31}$$

Writing Eq. (30) in terms of (31), and setting $\int P_N d\nu$ equal to P_B, where $P_B=\frac{1}{2}Nh\nu_B$, one obtains

$$P_N\approx 4kT(\Delta\nu_B)^2\bigg/\left[(\nu-\nu_0)^2+\left(\frac{4\pi kT}{P_B}(\Delta\nu_B)^2\right)^2\right], \tag{32}$$

where ν_0, the oscillation frequency, is given by the equation

$$\frac{\nu_0-\nu_B}{\nu_0-\nu_C}=-\frac{\Delta\nu_B}{\Delta\nu_C}, \tag{33}$$

or, as in (19),

$$\nu_0=\nu_B+(\nu_B-\nu_C)\Delta\nu_B/\Delta\nu_C \quad \text{if} \quad \Delta\nu_B/\Delta\nu_C\ll 1.$$

The total width $2\delta\nu$ at half-maximum power of this "noise" output is, from (32),

$$2\delta\nu=(8\pi kT/P_B)(\Delta\nu_B)^2 \tag{34}$$

as already stated in (20).

It should be remembered that (32) involves the assumption that the maser is a linear noise amplifier of very high gain. Actually, the noise properties of an oscillator depend to a considerable extent on the nonlinearities in its response, or the overload, and (32) does not accurately represent the precise noise spectrum of the maser as an oscillator. However, the approximate width of its noise spectrum is properly given by (34). As in the more usual types of oscillators, this oscillator actually maintains a nearly fixed amplitude of oscillation, but its phase slowly varies with time in a random way, corresponding to a noise spectrum of a width given approximately by (34). A more detailed discussion of noise will be given in a later publication.

The half-width of this oscillation signal is not to be confused with the half-width of the molecular response $\Delta\nu_B$. The latter represents the band width of the maser amplifier at low gain, whereas the former gives the band width of the oscillation signal. The oscillation frequency ν_0 can be varied throughout the range over which the molecules will amplify in accordance with (33) or (19). Hence care must be taken to keep the cavity frequency ν_C constant if it is desired to keep the oscillation frequency constant for any extended period of time.

Noise Figure and Band Width of the Amplifier

The noise figure of the maser amplifier may be easily found from the results of the foregoing sections. Assume that $\nu_C=\nu_B=\nu$, where ν is the frequency of the signal to be amplified. Also assume that the detector has a band width $\Delta\nu_{det}$ such that $\Delta\nu_{det}\ll\Delta\nu_B$. Equation (13) gives the signal power at the cavity output, while Eq. (29) gives the noise at the output in excess of kT. Thus we see that the signal-to-noise ratio at the output is just

$$\frac{P_0\bigg/\left[Q_AQ_D\left(\frac{1}{2Q_L}-2\pi\chi_0\right)^2\right]}{kT\Delta\nu_{det}\left[1+\frac{4\pi\chi_0}{Q_D}\bigg/\left(\frac{1}{2Q_L}-2\pi\chi_0\right)^2\right]}, \tag{35}$$

where $\chi''(\nu_B)=\chi_0$. At the input to the cavity, the signal to noise ratio is $P_0/kT\Delta\nu_{det}$. Therefore the noise figure F, which is just the ratio of these two quantities, is

$$F=Q_AQ_D\left[\frac{4\pi\chi_0}{Q_D}+\left(\frac{1}{2Q_L}-2\pi\chi_0\right)^2\right]. \tag{36}$$

At the same time, the power amplification available is, from (13), given simply by

$$\mu=P_{DB}/P_0=\left[Q_AQ_D\left(\frac{1}{2Q_L}-2\pi\chi_0\right)^2\right]^{-1}. \tag{37}$$

It can be shown from (37) that $\mu<1$ if $4\pi\chi_0<1/Q_C$, i.e., if there is a net loss of power within the cavity itself. Thus unless it is possible to produce oscillation by putting lossless reflections in all the wave guides so that $Q_L\rightarrow Q_C$, it is also impossible to create an amplifier with a gain greater than unity. In order to obtain a large gain μ, one must have $1/Q_L\approx 4\pi\chi_0$. If the gain is large, then a noise figure approaching unity is attainable by making $1/Q_A\approx +4\pi\chi_0\approx 1/Q_L$. This shows that for high amplification and at the same time a low noise figure, a fairly large input coupling to the cavity and a small output coupling is needed. Furthermore a sufficiently strong beam is required so that the maser is not too far from oscillation.

The maser acts as a regenerative amplifier, as can be seen from (12). Thus under conditions such that $4\pi\chi_0\approx 1/Q_L$ so that the midband gain is high, the band width becomes substantially smaller than $2\Delta\nu_B$.

It might also be noted that a certain amount of modulation of the amplified output is to be expected due to random variations of the number of molecules in the cavity at any time. These effects, however, are proportional to the input signal strength, and so are quite different from thermal noise signals which have no dependence on input power. Furthermore, they represent a modulation of only about one part in 10^6 since there are 10^{12} or more molecules in the cavity at any time. This type of modulation can be neglected when small input signals are considered and is not important under most circumstances. This shot effect and also the effect of power flow through the cavity on the frequency dependence of the amplification will be discussed in more detail in a subsequent paper.

Amplification may also be accomplished using one wave guide as both input and output, and the noise figure of such an amplifier can also approach unity. The amplified output signal might be coupled out and detected through a directional coupler, which would have to have a fairly small coupling so that little of the input power was lost to it. Then so long as the amplified input noise appearing at the detector was large compared to kT, the noise figure of this amplifier would be small.

The maser amplifier may be useful in a restricted range of applications in spite of its narrow band width because of its potentially low noise figure. For example, suppose that the signal to be amplified came from outer space, where the temperature is only a few degrees absolute. Then by making the coupling through the cavity fairly large so that little noise is contributed by the cavity itself, amplification should be attainable while keeping the noise figure, *based on the temperature of the signal source*, fairly low. This might prove to have a considerable advantage over electronic amplifiers. It might also be possible to tune the frequency of a maser amplifier through the use of the Stark or Zeeman effects on the molecular transition frequencies.

ACKNOWLEDGMENTS

The authors would like to express their gratitude to the personnel of the Columbia Radiation Laboratory who assisted in the construction of the experimental apparatus. They would also like to thank Dr. T. C. Wang and Dr. Koichi Shimoda for their assistance and suggestions during the later stages of this work.

Reprinted from THE PHYSICAL REVIEW, Vol. 126, No. 2, 603-615, April 15, 1962
Printed in U. S. A.

Theory of the Hydrogen Maser*

DANIEL KLEPPNER, H. MARK GOLDENBERG, AND NORMAN F. RAMSEY
Harvard University, Cambridge, Massachusetts
(Received December 15, 1961)

The behavior of the atomic hydrogen maser is analyzed for both stationary and transient operation. An expression for noise in the signal from the maser oscillator is derived by applying the previously developed theory of Shimoda, Wang, and Townes. A variety of relaxation phenomena are analyzed, including effects of chemical reaction with the surface and magnetic field inhomogeneities. Several mechanisms leading to frequency shifts in the maser are also analyzed, including cavity pulling and the Doppler effect.

I. INTRODUCTION

MOST attempts to observe radiofrequency or microwave spectral lines with high precision incorporate one or more of the following features: (a) observation of the resonance over a relatively long period of time in order to obtain a narrow resonance line; (b) observation of a spectral line which is as pure as possible so that there is no broadening due to different components of the line or to the environment of the atom or molecule concerned; (c) a technique for eliminating, or at least greatly reducing, the first-order Doppler shift; and (d) a means for obtaining a favorable signal-to-noise ratio such as is provided in the low-noise amplification which characterizes a maser oscillator.

Although most high-precision radiofrequency and microwave experiments depend upon one or more of the above characteristics, none of them in the past has attained high quality in all of these features in a single method. Atomic beam hyperfine structure resonance experiments are excellent with regard to purity of the spectral line, but the atoms have only moderately long lifetimes. The original ammonia maser was excellent with regard to signal-to-noise ratio but had only a short lifetime and used a complicated spectral line. Solid state masers are good with respect to all the criteria except for broadening of the lines by the influence of neighboring atoms in the material. Optical pumping experiments with buffer gases are excellent in every point except for the effects of perturbations due to the frequent collisions of the radiating atoms with the atoms of the buffer gas.

The hydrogen maser experiments described in the present paper originated in an effort to obtain a single device which was highly favorable in all of these features. Historically, the experiments were an outgrowth of the previously described successive oscillatory field technique[1] and of the atomic beam experiments with stored atoms.[2-4] The hydrogen maser also incorporates many of the features of beam maser developed by Townes and his associates.[5,6] The experiments are also related to the buffer gas experiments of Dicke[7,8] and others although no buffer gas is used in the hydrogen maser. A preliminary report on the hydrogen maser has been published[4] but no detailed analysis of its characteristics has been published previously.

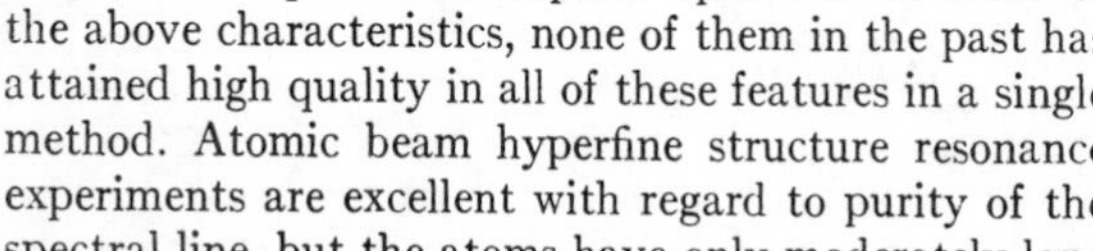

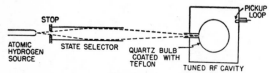

FIG. 1. Schematic diagram of the hydrogen maser.

The hydrogen maser consists of the apparatus shown schematically in Fig. 1. Atomic hydrogen from a radiofrequency discharge in the source passes through the inhomogeneous state-selecting magnetic field from a 6-pole permanent magnet. This field focuses atoms in the $[F=1, m=0]$ and $[F=1, m=1]$ states onto an aperture in a Teflon coated quartz bulb. The bulb is located in the center of a cylindrical radiofrequency cavity, operating in the TE_{011} mode, which is tuned to the $[F=1, m=0]\rightarrow[F=0, m=0]$ hyperfine transition frequency at approximately 1420.405 Mc/sec. The atoms make random collisions with the Teflon coated bulb wall and eventually leave the bulb through the entrance aperture. Due to their small interaction with the Teflon surface the atoms are not seriously perturbed even though they are retained in the bulb for more than a second and undergo up to 10^5 collisions with the wall during the storage time. Under these conditions the resonance line is so sharp that self-excited maser oscillations at the hyperfine frequency can take place.

The hydrogen maser has advantages in all of the desirable features listed above: (a) since the transition time is longer than one second the resonance line is narrow; (b) the hydrogen atom spends most of its time

* Work supported by the National Science Foundation and the Joint Program of the Office of Naval Research and the Atomic Energy Commission.

[1] N. F. Ramsey, Rev. Sci. Instr. **28**, 57 (1957); N. F. Ramsey, *Molecular Beams* (Oxford University Press, New York, 1956), p. 124.
[2] D. Kleppner, N. F. Ramsey, and P. Fjelstad, Phys. Rev. Letters, **I**, 232 (1958).
[3] H. M. Goldenberg, D. Kleppner, and N. F. Ramsey, Phys. Rev. **123**, 530 (1961).
[4] H. M. Goldenberg, D. Kleppner, and N. F. Ramsey, Phys. Rev. Letters **5**, 361 (1960).
[5] J. P. Gordon, H. J. Zeiger, and C. H. Townes, Phys. Rev. **95**, 282 (1954); N. G. Basov and A. M. Prokhorov, J. Exptl. Theoret. Phys. (U.S.S.R.) **27**, 431 (1954).
[6] K. Shimoda, T. C. Wang, and C. H. Townes, Phys. Rev. **102**, 1308 (1956).
[7] R. H. Dicke, Phys. Rev. **89**, 472 (1953).
[8] J. P. Wittke and R. H. Dicke, Phys. Rev. **103**, 620 (1956).

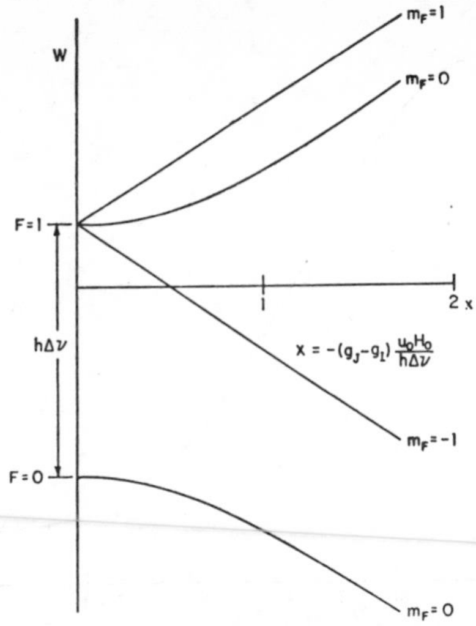

FIG. 2. Energy levels of the $^2S_{\frac{1}{2}}$ state of hydrogen.

in free space where it has a simple unperturbed hyperfine spectrum and the effects of wall collisions are small due to the low electric polarizability; (c) the effect of the first-order Doppler shift is greatly reduced by the fact that the velocity of the atom in the bulb, when suitably averaged, is close to zero; and (d) the ability of the device to operate as a self-excited maser oscillator provides the advantages of low noise amplification which characterize masers.

In the present paper the detailed theory and characteristics of the hydrogen maser are presented. Some preliminary experimental results have already been published[4] and details of the apparatus[9] and further results will be published subsequently.

II. STATIONARY OSCILLATION

Several authors have analyzed the behaviour of a two-level microwave beam maser.[6,10,11] The treatment of the ammonia maser by Shimoda, Wang, and Townes[6] (SWT) is the most comprehensive and the discussion of this section follows their analysis where possible. The chief differences are: (a) the transition of interest here is magnetic dipole, rather than electric dipole; (b) the lifetime of the atoms is described by an exponential distribution function instead of being constant; and (c) effects of confinement of the radiating atoms by the storage bulb must now be considered.

A. Preliminary Discussion

The ground state of hydrogen in a magnetic field $\mathbf{H}_0$ is described by the Hamiltonian

$$\mathcal{H}=ha\mathbf{I}\cdot\mathbf{J}-g_J\mu_0\mathbf{J}\cdot\mathbf{H}_0-g_I\mu_0\mathbf{I}\cdot\mathbf{H}_0. \quad (1)$$

The energy levels are illustrated in Fig. 2. In the presence of an oscillating magnetic field which lies in the direction of the static field so that $\mathbf{H}=(H_0+H_z\cos\omega t)\mathbf{k}$, the $(F=1, m_F=0)$ and $(F=0, m_F=0)$ states are connected by the following matrix element:

$$(0,0|\mathcal{H}|1,0)=(1,0|\mathcal{H}|0,0)=(g_J-g_I)\tfrac{1}{2}\mu_0H_z\cos\omega t \approx -\mu_0H_z\cos\omega t. \quad (2)$$

The wave function may be written

$$\psi=a_1\psi(0,0)+a_2\psi(1,0). \quad (3)$$

If at time $t=0$ the atom is in the $(F=1, m_F=0)$ state, then it can be shown[12] that at time t later

$$a_1(t)=-\exp\left[\frac{i}{2}(\omega-\omega_0)t\right]\frac{x}{[(\omega-\omega_0)^2+x^2]^{\frac{1}{2}}}\times\sin\{\tfrac{1}{2}[(\omega-\omega_0)^2+x^2]^{\frac{1}{2}}t\},$$
$$a_2(t)=\exp\left[\frac{-i}{2}(\omega-\omega_0)t\right]\left[\frac{-(\omega-\omega_0)}{[(\omega-\omega_0)^2+x^2]^{\frac{1}{2}}}\times\sin\{\tfrac{1}{2}[(\omega-\omega_0)^2+x^2]^{\frac{1}{2}}t\}+i\cos\{\tfrac{1}{2}[\omega-\omega_0)^2+x^2]^{\frac{1}{2}}t\}\right], \quad (4)$$

where $x=-\mu_0H_z/\hbar$, $\omega_0=[W(1,0)-W(0,0)]/\hbar$.

The average power radiated by a beam of I atoms per second initially in the (1,0) state is

$$\Delta P=Ih\nu\langle|a_1|^2\rangle_{\text{av}}, \quad (5)$$

(SWT use the symbol "n" instead of "I.") Here the average is over time spent in the cavity by the atoms. It will be shown below that the probability that an atom ceases to radiate by leaving the bulb or by having its radiation state relaxed is described by a simple exponential distribution function,

$$f(t)=\gamma\exp(-\gamma t), \quad (6)$$

in which case Eqs. (4) and (5) yield, after the indicated averaging,

$$\Delta P=\tfrac{1}{2}Ih\nu\frac{x^2}{\gamma^2+x^2+(\omega-\omega_0)^2}. \quad (7)$$

In the hydrogen maser the atoms, on the average, make many traversals of the storage bulb before leaving the cavity. As will be shown in Sec. IV-E, if H_z is not

---

[9] D. Kleppner, H. M. Goldenberg, and N. F. Ramsey, *Applied Optics* **1**, 55 (1962).

[10] H. M. Goldenberg, thesis, Harvard University, 1960 (unpublished).

[11] J. P. Gordon, H. J. Zeiger, and C. H. Townes, Phys. Rev. **99**, 1264 (1955); R. P. Feynman, F. L. Vernon, and R. W. Hellwarth, J. Appl. Phys. **28**, 49 (1957); W. E. Lamb and J. C. Helmer, Stanford University Microwave Laboratory Technical Report No. ML-311 (unpublished).

[12] N. F. Ramsey, *Molecular Beams* (Oxford University Press, New York, 1956), p. 119.

uniform throughout the storage bulb, we may replace x^2 by

$$\langle x\rangle^2=(\mu_0/\hbar)^2\langle H_z\rangle_b{}^2, \tag{8}$$

where $\langle H_z\rangle_b$ is averaged over the volume of the storage bulb. The energy stored in the resonant cavity is

$$W=\frac{1}{8\pi}\int_V H^2 dV. \tag{9}$$

(H is the peak value of the oscillating magnetic field and the average is over the volume of the resonant cavity.) $\langle H_z\rangle_b{}^2$ is related to the stored energy by $\langle H_z\rangle_b{}^2=(8\pi W/V)\eta$ where $\eta=\langle H_z\rangle_b{}^2/\langle H^2\rangle_V$. The value of η is plotted in Fig. 3, as a function of a/l, the ratio of storage bulb radius to cavity diameter, for a TE_{011} cavity with length and diameter equal. Combining the above expression with Eq. (7) yields

$$\Delta P=\tfrac{1}{2}Ih\nu\frac{\theta^2}{1+\theta^2+\delta^2}, \tag{10}$$

$$\theta^2=\langle x^2\rangle/\gamma^2=W/W_c,\quad W_c=(h/\mu_0)^2V\gamma^2/8\pi\eta,$$
$$\delta=(\omega-\omega_0)/\gamma. \tag{11}$$

The resonance curve is Lorentzian. The full resonance width at half-height, assuming $\theta^2\ll 1$, is

$$\Delta\omega_r=2\gamma. \tag{12}$$

B. Threshold Flux

For oscillation to occur, the power delivered to the cavity by the beam must equal the power dissipated in the cavity. The condition for this is

$$W=\frac{Q\Delta P}{\omega}=\frac{1}{2}\frac{Q}{\omega}Ih\nu\frac{\theta^2}{1+\theta^2}. \tag{13}$$

Near the threshold of oscillation $\theta\ll 1$, and from Eqs. (11) and (13), the minimum flux necessary for oscillation is

$$I_{\text{th}}=4\pi W_c/Qh=hV\gamma^2/8\pi^2\mu_0{}^2Q\eta. \tag{14}$$

As an example, if $V=10^4$ cm^3, $\gamma=3$ sec^{-1}, $Q=3\times10^4$, $\eta=3$, we have $I_{\text{th}}=10^{12}$ pps. With an incident beam $I>I_{\text{th}}$, the level of stored energy is given by

$$W/W_c=\theta^2=(I/I_{\text{th}})-1. \tag{15}$$

If the output coupling is represented by Q_1, then the output power is, using Eqs. (14) and (11),

$$P_0=\frac{\omega W_c}{Q_1}\left(\frac{I}{I_{\text{th}}}-1\right). \tag{16}$$

C. Effect of the Cavity Tuning on the Oscillator Frequency

In order to analyze the effect of cavity tuning and noise in the maser, the oscillating dipole moment due

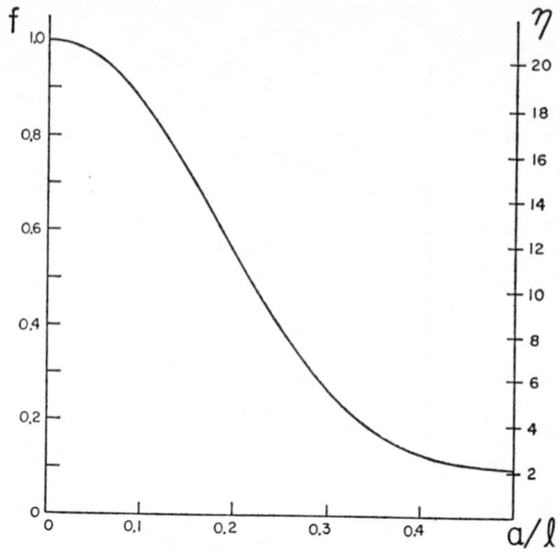

FIG. 3. The functions $\eta=\langle H_z\rangle^2/b\langle H^2\rangle_V$ and $f=\langle H_z\rangle_b{}^2/H_z{}^2(\max)$ $=0.047\eta$ for a storage bulb of radius a in a TE_{011} cavity with diameter and length equal to l.

to the stored atoms is calculated in the presence of an assumed oscillatory magnetic field. The electromagnetic field generated by the oscillating magnetization is then calculated, and the assumed field is made consistent with the field produced. The effects of thermal noise are ignored in this section but will be considered below.

The dipole moment operator is

$$\boldsymbol{\mu}(\text{op})=g_J\mu_0\mathbf{J}+g_I\mu_0\mathbf{I}. \tag{17}$$

The oscillating dipole moment of an atom in the cavity at any time is

$$\mu=\int\psi^*\boldsymbol{\mu}(\text{op})\psi d\tau=(a_2{}^*a_1+a_1{}^*a_2)\mu_0, \tag{18}$$

where g_J has been approximated by 2 and g_I by zero. (Vector notation has been omitted since the direction of the oscillating moment is parallel to the driving field, which is along the z axis.) When the perturbing field is $H_z\cos\omega t$, the dipole moment of an atom at time t which entered the field at time t_0 is, from Eqs. (4) and (18),

$$\mu(t-t_0)=\mu_0e^{i\omega t}\frac{x}{[(\omega-\omega_0)^2+x^2]^{\frac{1}{2}}}$$
$$\times\Bigg[\frac{i}{2}\sin\{[(\omega-\omega_0)^2+x^2]^{\frac{1}{2}}(t-t_0)\}$$
$$+\frac{(\omega-\omega_0)}{[(\omega-\omega_0)^2+x^2]^{\frac{1}{2}}}\sin^2\left\{[(\omega-\omega_0)^2+x^2]^{\frac{1}{2}}\frac{(t-t_0)}{2}\right\}\Bigg]$$
$$+\text{complex conj.}=\mu^\dagger e^{i\omega t}+\mu^{\dagger *}e^{-i\omega t}. \tag{19}$$

The oscillating magnetization $M(\mathbf{r})$, produced by the atoms in the cavity, is given by

$$M(\mathbf{r})=\frac{I}{\gamma V_b}\bar{\mu}(\mathbf{r})=\frac{I}{\gamma V_b}[\bar{\mu}^{\dagger}e^{i\omega t}+\bar{\mu}^{\dagger *}e^{-i\omega t}]. \quad (20)$$

The bar denotes an average over $(t-t_0)$, the time spent in the cavity. The probability that an atom has spent a time $(t-t_0)$ in the cavity is $\gamma\exp[-\gamma(t-t_0)]$. When the average is carried out, Eqs. (19) and (20) yield, assuming $\omega-\omega_0\ll x$.

$$M(\mathbf{r})=\frac{I\mu_0}{2\gamma V_b}\frac{x[\lambda+i\gamma]}{\gamma^2+x^2+(\omega-\omega_0)^2}e^{i\omega t}+\text{c.c.} \quad (21)$$

The magnetic field H generated by the oscillating magnetization can be calculated in the following fashion: It is assumed that the magnetization is so small that it does not seriously perturb the normal mode of the cavity, or the distribution of field in that mode $\mathbf{H}_n$. In this case the quality factor of the cavity containing the oscillating magnetization Q_m can be calculated from a result given by Slater[13] for a cavity containing a microwave current.

$$\frac{1}{Q_m}-2i\frac{\omega-\omega_c}{\omega_c}=\frac{1}{Q}+4\pi i\frac{\int\mathbf{M}^{\dagger}(\mathbf{r})\cdot\mathbf{H}_n^{\dagger *}(\mathbf{r})dV}{\int\mathbf{H}^{\dagger}(\mathbf{r})\cdot\mathbf{H}_n^{\dagger *}(\mathbf{r})dV}. \quad (22)$$

Here $\omega_c/2\pi$ is the resonant frequency and Q is the loaded quality factor of the cavity without stored atoms, while the frequency of oscillation is $\omega/2\pi$. Both the field and magnetization are expressed here in complex vector notation: $H\cos\omega t=\frac{1}{2}(\mathrm{H}e^{i\omega t}+\mathrm{H}e^{-i\omega t})=H^{\dagger}e^{i\omega t}+H^{\dagger *}e^{-i\omega t}$, and $\mathbf{M}=M^{\dagger}e^{i\omega t}+M^{\dagger *}e^{-i\omega t}$.

After some manipulation Eq. (22) can be rewritten, with the aid of Eq. (21),

$$\frac{1}{Q_m}-2i\frac{\omega-\omega_c}{\omega_c}=\frac{1}{Q}+i\frac{8\pi^2\mu_0^2I\eta}{h\gamma V}\left[\frac{\lambda+i\gamma}{\gamma^2+x^2+(\omega-\omega_c)^2}\right]. \quad (23)$$

For oscillation to occur $Q_m=\infty$, and Eq. (23) becomes, using Eq. (14),

$$1+2i\frac{(\omega-\omega_c)}{\omega_c}Q=\frac{I\gamma}{I_{\text{th}}}\left[\frac{\gamma-i(\omega-\omega_0)}{\gamma^2+x^2+(\omega-\omega_0)^2}\right]. \quad (24)$$

If $\omega\approx\omega_0$, and $\omega-\omega_0\ll x$, the real part of Eq. (24) gives Eq. (15), while the imaginary part can be written

$$\omega-\omega_0=2\left(\frac{\omega_c-\omega_0}{\omega_0}\right)Q\gamma. \quad (25)$$

If we define the quality factor of the resonance line by

$$Q_l=\omega_0/\Delta\omega_r=\omega_0/(2\gamma). \quad (26)$$

[13] J. C. Slater, Revs. Modern Phys. **18**, 441 (1946).

Equation (25) becomes

$$\frac{\omega-\omega_0}{\omega_0}=\frac{(\omega_c-\omega_0)}{\omega_0}\frac{Q}{Q_l}. \quad (27)$$

This is a familiar result. In the case of the conventional beam maser, the expression on the right is multiplied by a slowly varying function of the power radiated. When the lifetime of the atom is described by an exponential distribution function, however, cavity pulling is independent of the power level.

D. The Effect of Thermal Noise on the Oscillation

In order to calculate accurately the effect of thermal noise on the maser it is necessary to take into account the amplification of the noise by the maser itself. This is done by a perturbation method in which the thermal noise field in the cavity $H_n(t)$ is assumed to be small compared to the field H_0 produced by coherent radiation of the atoms. Details of this procedure are discussed in SWT, and only an outline of the calculation is given here.

The oscillating field in the cavity is assumed to be of the form

$$H_z=H_{z0}\cos\omega t+H_n(t). \quad (28)$$

Let

$$x=H_{z0}\mu_0/\hbar,\quad x_n(t)=2H_n(t)\mu_0/\hbar. \quad (29)$$

The quantity x_n may be written

$$x_n(t)=2x_n'\cos\omega t-2x_n''\sin\omega t, \quad (30)$$

where x_n' and x_n'' are functions of time defined by the equation. Equation (28) becomes, assuming x_n' and x_n'' are much less than x,

$$H_z=\hbar\mu_0^{-1}(x+x_n')\cos(\omega t+x_n''/x), \quad (31)$$

which shows that x_n' represents amplitude modulation and x_n'' represents phase modulation.

The effect of the noise is to induce a fluctuating oscillating dipole moment. The total oscillating moment can be written

$$\mu=\mu_s^{\dagger}e^{i\omega t}+\mu_n^{\dagger}(t)+\text{complex conjugate}. \quad (32)$$

The first term represents the contribution of the atoms with no noise present, and the second term represents the contribution due to the noise.

It is shown in SWT that

$$\mu_s^{\dagger}=\tfrac{1}{2}i\mu_0\sin xt, \quad (33)$$

$$\mu_n^{\dagger}(t)=-\tfrac{1}{2}\mu_0e^{i\omega t}\left[\int_{t_0}^{t}x_n''(t')\cos\{x(t'-t_0)\}dt' -i\cos\{x(t'-t_0)\}\int_{t_0}^{t}x_n'(t')dt'\right]. \quad (34)$$

The field which would be present in the cavity due to noise with no atoms present may be written

$$h_0(t)=h_n^{\dagger}e^{i\omega t}+h_n^{\dagger *}e^{-i\omega t}, \tag{35}$$

$$h_n^{\dagger}=2\hbar^{-1}(\xi_n'(t)+i\xi_n''(t))=2\hbar^{-1}\xi_n^{\dagger}(t). \tag{36}$$

$\xi_n'(t)$ and $\xi_n''(t)$ are derived from the spectral density in the cavity in the absence of the beam. In the following steps x_n' and x_n'' are found in terms of ξ_n' and ξ_n'', respectively, thereby giving the actual values for amplitude and frequency modulation in the oscillating maser.

For present purposes we need an equation similar to Eq. (24) but in which the dependence on the oscillating field is made explicit. This is obtained from Eq. (22) by using the value of $M(r)$ given by Eq. (20), assuming $Q_m=0$ and $Q(\omega-\omega_e)/\omega_c\ll 1$. If we solve the resultant equation for the field, we obtain

$$H_z^{\dagger}=-i\frac{4\pi Q\eta I}{V}\int_{-\infty}^{t}e^{-\gamma(t-t_0)}\mu^{\dagger}(t-t_0)dt_0+h_n^{\dagger}. \tag{37}$$

The first term on the right-hand side represents the field due to the oscillating magnetization, while the second term represents the thermal noise present with no magnetization. Using Eqs. (28), (33), (34), and (36), one obtains

$$\frac{x}{2}+\frac{x_n^{\dagger}}{2}-\frac{\xi_n^{\dagger}}{2}=\frac{4\pi^2 IQ\eta u_0^2}{Vh}\Bigg[\int_{-\infty}^{t}e^{-\gamma(t-t_0)}\sin(x(t-t_0))dt_0$$
$$+i\int_{-\infty}^{t}e^{-\gamma(t-t_0)}\bigg\{\int_{t_0}^{t}x_n''(t')\cos x(t'-t_0)dt'$$
$$-i\cos(x(t-t_0))\int_{t_0}^{t}x_n'dt'\bigg\}dt_0\Bigg]. \tag{38}$$

The first integral yields the same result as found in Sec. II-B. The other terms represent the effect of noise and can be written

$$\frac{x_n^{\dagger}}{2}-\frac{\zeta_n^{\dagger}}{2}=(1+\theta^2)\gamma^2\int_{-\infty}^{t}e^{-\gamma(t-t_0)}\bigg\{\cos(x(t-t_0))$$
$$\times\int_{t_0}^{t}x_n'(t')dt'+i\int_{t_0}^{t}\cos(x(t-t_0))x_n''(t')dt'\bigg\}dt_0, \tag{39}$$

where we have made use of the identity

$$8\pi^2 QI\eta u_0^2/Vh=I\gamma^2/I_{\text{th}}=(1+\theta^2)\gamma^2.$$

The real part of Eq. (39) can be solved for the case of noise components which lie within the resonance linewidth. With this restriction, $x_n'(t)$ may be considered constant, and the result is

$$2x_n'=\xi_n'(1+\theta^2)/\theta^2. \tag{40}$$

This result illustrates how the nonlinear properties of the maser oscillator tend to limit amplitude fluctuations, a familiar property of oscillators. As the oscillation level increases, the fractional amplitude fluctuation is suppressed. The fractional amplitude modulation, $x_n'/x=\xi_n'(1+\theta^2)/(2\gamma\theta^3)$, approaches zero with increasing radiated power.

In order to find the relation between x_n'' and ξ_n'' the time dependence of x_n'' must not be neglected. The reason for this that x_n'' represents a phase fluctuation which approaches infinity as time increases. The quantity of physical interest is the frequency fluctuation, and to determine this it is necessary to know how the phase x_n''/x increases in time. To do this we consider the spectral densities of ξ_n'' and x_n''. If df represents a frequency bandwidth differing from the oscillator frequency by f, we may write

$$\xi_n''(t)=\int_0^{\infty}\xi_n''(f)\cos(2\pi ft+\delta)df, \tag{41}$$

$$x_n''(t)=\int_0^{\infty}x_n''(f)\cos(2\pi ft+\delta')df, \tag{42}$$

where δ and δ' are phase angles, to be determined. With these substitutions, the imaginary part of Eq. (39) becomes

$$x_n''(f)\cos(2\pi ft+\delta')-\xi_n''(f)\cos(2\pi ft+\delta)$$
$$=(1+\theta^2)\gamma^2\int_{-\infty}^{t}e^{-\gamma(t-t_0)}\int_{t_0}^{t}x_n''(f)\cos(2\pi ft'+\delta)$$
$$\times\cos(x(t'-t_0))dt'dt_0. \tag{43}$$

The result of Eq. (43) is

$$\delta-\delta'=\pi/2 \tag{44}$$

and

$$x_n''(f)=\xi_n''(f)\frac{\gamma}{2\pi f}.$$

It is shown in SWT that

$$\frac{\langle\xi_n^2(f)\rangle_{\text{av}}}{x^2}=\frac{kTdf}{\omega_0 W/Q},$$

so that

$$\frac{x_n''^2}{x^2}=\frac{QkT}{\omega_0 W}\left(\frac{\gamma}{2\pi}\right)^2\int_{f_{\min}}^{f_{\max}}\frac{df}{f^2}, \tag{45}$$

($\langle\ \rangle$ here represents the time average.)

Both $f_{\max}$ and $f_{\min}$ must be less than the linewidth in order for the approximation in $\mu^{\dagger}(t)$ to be valid. The lower limit is determined by the observation time. If the phase is observed for time t, then the smallest frequency fluctuation observable is $f_{\min}\cong 1/(2t)$.

Assuming that $f_{\max}\gg f_{\min}$, i.e., that the observation time is large compared to $2/\Delta\omega_r$, Eq. (45) becomes

$$\langle x''^2\rangle/x^2=QkT\gamma^2 t/(2\pi^2\omega_0 W). \tag{46}$$

The fractional rms frequency fluctuation is therefore

$$\frac{\langle\Delta\omega^2\rangle^{\frac{1}{2}}}{\omega_0}=\frac{\langle x''^2\rangle^{\frac{1}{2}}}{xt\omega_0}=\frac{\Delta\omega_r}{2\sqrt{2}\pi\omega_0}\left(\frac{QkT}{\omega_0 Wt}\right)^{\frac{1}{2}}$$

$$=\frac{0.113}{Q_l}\left(\frac{QkT}{\omega_0 W_c t}\right)^{\frac{1}{2}}\frac{1}{\theta}=\frac{0.113}{Q_l}\left(\frac{kT}{Pt}\right)^{\frac{1}{2}}. \quad (47)$$

In the last expression, P represents the power delivered by the beam to the cavity. For example, if $Q_l=2\times10^9$, $P=4\times10^{-5}$ erg/sec, $t=1$ sec, $\langle\Delta\omega^2\rangle^{\frac{1}{2}}/\omega_0=1.5\times10^{-15}$.

III. TRANSIENT OPERATION

The radiation lifetime of atoms in the cavity γ^{-1} can be found in principle from the response of the maser to an applied signal when it is operated below oscillation threshold as a spectrometer. This method involves sweeping the frequency of a local signal generator across the resonance curve and detecting the power emitted by stimulated emission. In practice it presents several difficulties. The most serious of these is the necessity for controlling the power level of the signal generator in order to avoid power broadening of the resonance line. Spurious pickup in the detecting system can be a source of difficulty with the low power levels involved. Achieving the necessary frequency stability in the signal generator can be another serious source of difficulty. All of these problems are avoided by a transient technique which allows direct measurement of the radiation lifetime.

The atoms can be put in a radiative state by a short pulse of power at the resonance frequency applied to the cavity when the density of atoms is insufficient to cause oscillation. A signal at the resonance frequency is then generated in the cavity by the atoms and, as is shown below, if the system is sufficiently below the threshold of oscillation, the amplitude of the signal decreases with decay constant characterizing the lifetime. The effect is similar in principle to free precession in NMR. Since the transition of interest is a hyperfine transition, however, it is not correct to picture it in terms of a simple magnetic moment which undergoes a 90° pulse. Furthermore, since the radiation level is determined by stimulated emission, the term "free precession" is really a misnomer. For these reasons, the dynamical behavior of the system will be described in some detail.

It is assumed that the beam flux is well below the level necessary for oscillation. A pulse of rf is applied for a time $\tau\ll\gamma^{-1}$. The frequency ω_p is such that $|\omega_p-\omega_0|<x_1$, where the amplitude of the pulse H_p is related to x_1 by $x_1=\mu_0 H_p/\hbar$. At the end of the pulse the amplitude of the lower energy state is, from Eqs. (1) and (4),

$$a_1=\sin(\tfrac{1}{2}x_1\tau).$$

At a time t later,

$$a_1(t)=\sin[\tfrac{1}{2}(x_1\tau+xt)].$$

The rate at which an atom radiates energy is

$$\Delta P=h\nu\frac{d}{dt}(a_1(t)^2)=\tfrac{1}{2}h\nu x\sin(x_1\tau+xt). \quad (48)$$

(In this last step it must be remembered that if x is a slowly carrying function of time then xt is to be interpreted as $\int_0^t xdt$.) If the energy level in the cavity is so low that $xt\ll1$ for all time less than γ^{-1}, then the atom radiates at a maximum rate when $x_1\tau=\pi/2$. Since $\tau\ll\gamma^{-1}$, the total number of atoms initially in this state is approximately $I\gamma^{-1}$, and at time t the number of radiating atoms is $I\gamma^{-1}e^{-\gamma t}$. The power radiated at time t is, therefore,

$$\Delta P=\tfrac{1}{2}Ih\nu\gamma^{-1}xe^{-\gamma t}. \quad (49)$$

The energy in the cavity obeys the following equation

$$dW/dt=\Delta P-\omega W/Q. \quad (50)$$

Using Eq. (11), this leads to

$$\frac{d}{dt}\theta^2=\frac{Ih\nu\theta}{2W_c}e^{-\gamma t}-\frac{\omega\theta^2}{Q}. \quad (51)$$

The solution to this equation, assuming $\omega/Q\gg2\gamma$, is

$$\theta=\frac{\pi}{2\gamma\tau}e^{-\omega/(2Q)t}+\frac{IhQ}{4\pi W_c}e^{-\gamma t}. \quad (52)$$

The first term, which corresponds to decay of the stimulating pulse due to losses in the cavity, quickly becomes negligible compared to the second. After this time the field intensity decreases with the decay constant γ. The energy in the cavity decreases at twice this rate. If the maser is monitored with a linear detector, however, the observed signal is proportional to the field intensity, and therefore yields a direct measure of the lifetime of the atoms.

Near threshold, the above analysis does not hold due to the nonuniform fashion in which the atoms radiate when $xt\approx1$, and due to the necessity of taking into account the effect of atoms which enter the cavity after the pulse is over. The behavior of the system in this region has been analyzed,[10,14] but the results are not experimentally as useful due to the complexity of interpretation in the present case.

IV. RELAXATION PROCESSES

A variety of processes can limit the radiative lifetime of an atom in the storage bulb. Most of the processes are random and lead to time independent relaxation rates, so that the total relaxation rate is the sum of the rates for each process. Because of this it is possible to analyze the relaxation processes separately, with the

[14] R. H. Dicke, Phys. Rev. 93, 99 (1953); R. H. Dicke and R. H. Romer, Rev. Sci. Instr. 26, 915 (1955); S. Bloom, J. Appl. Phys. 27, 785 (1956).

understanding that the individual rates are to be added to obtain the total rate.

In the case of nuclear magnetic resonance, the dynamical equations of the magnetization are often described by the Bloch equations in terms of the relaxation times T_1 and T_2, the time constants which describe the return of magnetization in a given direction to its equilibrium value, and the decay of the oscillating dipole moment, respectively. These are not used in the present analysis because the Bloch equations do not apply due to the presence of hyperfine structure. It is important to remember, however, that a given perturbation frequently causes relaxation by both changing the magnetization along the axis of quantization and by causing loss of coherence between the oscillating moment and the rf field, and that these two rates may be considerably different. To emphasize this, the subscripts 1 and 2 will be used to identify decay rates due to each of these processes, respectively.

A. Escape from the Bulb

The escape rate of atoms from the bulb γ_0 is found by equating the incident beam flux I with the emergent flux, $N\bar{v}A_e/4K$, where N is the density, $\bar{v}$ is the mean velocity, A_e is the total escape area, and K is a numerical factor depending on the geometry of the first aperture. For a thin hole, $K=1$. If the volume of the storage bulb is V_b, then $N=I/(\gamma_0 V_b)$, and

$$\gamma_0=\bar{v}A_e/(4KV_b). \qquad (53)$$

As an example, for hydrogen at room temperature, $\bar{v}=3\times10^5$ cm/sec, and for a spherical bulb 16 cm in diameter with a thin exit aperture 2 mm in diameter, $\gamma_0=1\ \text{sec}^{-1}$.

B. Effect of Wall Collisions

Wall collisions fall conveniently into two categories: adiabatic and nonadiabatic. During an adiabatic collision no transitions of the atom between its states are induced but a small change in the spacing of the energy levels usually occurs. This eventually leads to a loss of coherence with the applied rf field due to randomness of the perturbations. In a nonadiabatic collision, the atom is effectively lost as far as further contributions to the radiation field are concerned due to a transition to some other state or to a chemical reaction with the surface. In this case, relaxation occurs during a single collision. The mean number of collisions an atom undergoes is then inversely proportional to the probability that a single collision is nonadiabatic.

1. Adiabatic Collisions

A convenient parameter in describing an adiabatic collision is the phase shift per collision

$$\varphi=\int\frac{\delta W(1,0)-\delta W(0,0)}{\hbar}dt. \qquad (54)$$

The integration is over the time of one collision, and δW is the difference in energy of a given state between the free space value and the value when surface forces are present. It is shown in reference 3 that the atom loses coherence after a number of collisions

$$n\approx 2/\varphi^2. \qquad (55)$$

This result was derived for a somewhat different situation from the present. In particular, it was assumed that there is no rf field present and that the adsorbtion energy is large compared with kT, so that the adsorbtion time is described by an exponential distribution function. Nevertheless, since the result is fundamentally due to the random nature of the perturbation, it is quite general and can be applied to the present case. (For example, it can be shown that the dispersion in φ is changed only slightly when the adsorbtion energy becomes less than kT, due to the relatively high dispersion in velocity and direction of the colliding atom.) If the collision rate is $\bar{v}/l$ then from Eq. (55) it follows that the relaxation rate is given by

$$\gamma_s=\tfrac{1}{2}(\bar{v}/l)\varphi^2. \qquad (56)$$

This type of relaxation process does not strictly lead to a Lorentzian resonance line. However, in the case where this is not the dominating process the line is approximately Lorentzian and the decay rate is still a useful parameter for describing the linewidth. An example of a case where this leads to a non-Lorentzian line is given in reference 3.

The phase shift φ is related to the frequency shift, as discussed below. For the case of hydrocarbon-like surfaces an upper limit to φ is[10] $\varphi<10^{-4}$ rad/col, leading to a value of $\gamma_s<10^{-4}\ \text{sec}^{-1}$.

2. Nonadiabatic Collisions: Chemical Reaction with the Surface

If there are no strong adsorbtion forces present, then physical adsorbtion does not by itself limit the radiative lifetime. Chemical reaction between the atom and the surface can occur, however, and this leads to a decay rate γ_s which is the probability per unit time that an atom undergoes such a reaction. This is found in the following manner: In order for a reaction to take place the incident atom must possess kinetic energy equal to E_a, the activation energy for that reaction. Departures of the atom from thermal equilibrium are usually negligible, so that the energy distribution may be found from a Maxwell-Boltzmann velocity distribution characterized by the temperature of the storage bulb. The probability that a particular collision leads to chemical reaction is obtained by finding the probability that the energy available for the reaction exceeds E_a. With the neglect of the difference between collisions of hydrogen with the same molecule when it is in the gas phase or on the surface, the following result for the rate r with which the atoms hit the surface with an energy greater than E_a may be derived by well-known procedure[15]

$$r=(2\bar{v}/\pi^{\frac{1}{2}}l)\exp(-E_a/kT), \tag{57}$$

$\bar{v}$ is the rms velocity $(3kT/m)^{\frac{1}{2}}$, and l is the mean distance between collisions. For a sphere, l is two-thirds the diameter. The temperature T is that of the storage bulb. The reaction rate differs from r by the steric factor[16] P which is introduced because not every collision satisfying the energy requirement leads to a reaction. The relaxation rate is therefore

$$\gamma_r=(2\bar{v}P/\pi^{\frac{1}{2}}l)\exp(-E_a/kT). \tag{58}$$

Both E_a and P are difficult to estimate accurately for a surface collision. For reactions in the gas phase, P is usually taken to be 0.1, although it can be much smaller. Since a surface collision may involve interaction with several of the surface molecules, P is probably larger than for a similar collision in the gas phase. A particular example of a possible surface reaction is the case of surface combination which occurs when atomic hydrogen reacts with a methyl group which is part of a hydrocarbon surface. An example of this is $H+CH_3\rightarrow H_2+CH_2$ where it is understood that the methyl group is bonded to a larger molecule. To estimate the activation energy for this reaction, one may consider a similar reaction which has been observed in the gas phase, $H+C_2H_6\rightarrow H_2+C_2H_5$. The activation energy for this is 6.4 kcal/mole (0.27 ev),[17] with a steric factor of about 5×10^{-3}. The activation energy for reactions involving hydrogen recombining with other paraffin hydrocarbons does not vary markedly from this value with the size of the molecule, so that it is a reasonable value to use for the present case. When it is substituted into Eq. (58), and assuming $P=1$, the result for a 16-cm-diam bulb at room temperature is $\gamma=0.7$ sec^{-1}. This is in approximate agreement with experimental observations which will be described in a later paper. The activation energy for corresponding reactions with flurocarbon is considerably higher than for the hydrocarbons, and the decay rate with a Teflon surface has been found to be considerably smaller than possible with a hydrocarbon surface.

C. Effect of Magnetic Field Inhomogeneities

A nonuniform static magnetic field in the storage bulb can cause relaxation in two ways. The atoms experience a time-varying field by virtue of their motion through the bulb, and this can induce Zeeman transitions analogous to the Majorana transitions of atomic beams. In addition, since the resonance frequency is slightly field dependent, and because different atoms have different histories in the bulb, due to the random nature of their paths, there is eventually a loss of coherence of the oscillating moment. The relaxation rates due to these processes will be designated γ_{H1} and γ_{H2}, respectively.

1. Relaxation Rate γ_{H1}

The effect of the inhomogeneities on the Zeeman states ($F=1$, $m_F=1, 0, -1$) is most easily analyzed by neglecting the ($F=0$) state, and considering a spin 1 system in the presence of a random perturbation. Transitions are induced among the states at a rate W, and the decay rate for an atom from the state of interest, ($F=1$, $m=0$), is $\gamma_{H1}=W_{1,0}+W_{-1,0}$. The subscripts denote m_F. It should be noted that γ_{H1} does not correspond to T_1^{-1}, since the quantity of interest is the rate of decay of an atom from a given state, not the rate of decay of magnetization. In the latter case, for a spin $\frac{1}{2}$ particle, the rate is twice as great.

The transition rate between two states, α and β, due to a random perturbation $\mathcal{H}_1(t)=AF(t)$, where A is one operator and $F(t)$ is a random function, is[18]

$$W_{\alpha\beta}=\hbar^{-2}|(\alpha|A|\beta)|^2J(\omega_{\alpha\beta}), \tag{59}$$

$J(\omega_{\alpha\beta})$ is the spectral density of $\langle[F(t)]^2\rangle_{\text{av}}$ and is given by the Fourier transform of the autocorrelation function of $F(t)$. The interaction Hamiltonian is

$$\mathcal{H}=-\gamma_F\hbar\mathbf{F}\cdot\mathbf{H}(t). \tag{60}$$

To a good approximation the components of the inhomogeneous magnetic field vary independently, so that $H(\mathbf{t})=H_x(t), H_y(t), H_z(t)$. When this is substituted in Eqs. (60) and (59) we have

$$W_{1,0}=W_{-1,0}=\tfrac{1}{2}\gamma_F^2J(\omega), \tag{61}$$

$$J(\omega)=\int_{-\infty}^{+\infty}[(H_x(t)+H_y(t)]\times[H_x(t+\tau)+H_y(t+\tau)]e^{-i\omega\tau}d\tau. \tag{62}$$

The cross products in the above equation vanish because $H_x(t)$ and $H_y(t)$ are independent and have zero average, so that $\langle H_x^2\rangle_{\text{av}}=\langle H_y^2\rangle_{\text{av}}=\frac{1}{2}\langle H_t^2\rangle_{\text{av}}$. The autocorrelation function of H_t, the transverse field, is $g(\tau)=\langle H_t(\tau)H_t(t+\tau)\rangle$, and the result is

$$\gamma_{H1}=W_{1,0}+W_{-1,0}=\gamma_F^2\int_{-\infty}^{+\infty}g(\tau)e^{-i\omega\tau}d\tau. \tag{63}$$

The integral in this equation, the spectral density of $\langle H_t^2\rangle_{\text{av}}$ at the transition frequency, is a complicated function of the storage bulb geometry, velocity distribution, and magnetic field. The mean time between collisions t_0 naturally presents itself as a sort of correlation time, since the motion of the atom is altered

[15] R. Fowler and E. A. Guggenheim, *Statistical Thermodynamics* (Cambridge University Press, London, 1956), Chap. XII.

[16] E. W. R. Steacie, *Atomic and Free Radical Reactions* (Reinhold Publishing Corporation, New York, 1954), p. 490.

[17] M. R. Berlie and D. J. LeRoy, Discussions Faraday Soc. 14, 50 (1953).

[18] A. Abragam, *The Principles of Nuclear Magnetism* (Oxford University Press, London, 1961), p. 270.

violently and nearly randomly on each wall collision, and in spite of the complexity of $g(\tau)$ it is possible to obtain approximate expression for the spectral density in the cases when ω is either much less or much greater than t_0^{-1}.

In the limit of low magnetic fields $\omega=\gamma_F H_0 \ll t_0^{-1}$ and the wall collision occurs rapidly with respect to ω^{-1}. In this case the atoms experience a field which assumes a new value after every collision, and if the wall collisions occur perfectly randomly in time, then[19]

$$g(\tau)=\langle H_t^2\rangle_{av}e^{-|\tau|/t_0}, \tag{64}$$

where the average of $\langle H_t^2\rangle_{av}$ is over either time or space. In this limit, we find

$$\gamma_{H1}(\omega\ll t_0^{-1})=2\gamma_F^2\langle H_t^2\rangle_{av}t_0. \tag{65}$$

This expression is not valid when $\omega \gtrsim t_0^{-1}$ for the following reason[20]: the assumption that the field changes discontinuously is not valid even in the low field case, although it introduces no appreciable error there since the relatively large intensity high-frequency components led to by this model have no effect when the resonance is at a low frequency. In the present case, however, the transitions are sensitive to the high-frequency components. Actually, the field is not discontinuous in time, since the atom does not alter position instantaneously, but its time derivative is discontinuous as long as the wall collision takes place in a time small compared to ω^{-1}. It can be shown that this causes the spectral density to fall off as ω^{-4}. Since the discontinuities in dH/dt occur at a surface collision, the spectral density is now sensitive only to the average field inhomogeneity at the surface, rather than the average throughout the bulb. Because of this it is necessary to assume a certain field configuration in order to estimate $J(\omega)$. The relaxation rate has been derived by Purcell[20] for the simplest type of symmetrical field inhomogeneity, where the inhomogeneous field is given in cylindrical coordinates by $H_\rho=2h\rho z/d^2 \cdot H_z=(h/a^2)(\rho^2-2z^2)$. The result is

$$\gamma_{H1}=\tfrac{1}{2}\gamma_F^2h^2\frac{t_0}{1+(\omega t_0/2)^4}. \tag{66}$$

As an example, in the low field region where $\omega t_0 \ll 1$, then the factor $(\omega t_0/2)^4$ may be neglected and using $\gamma_F=1.4\times10^6$ cps/oe, $t_0=3\times10^{-5}$ sec, the result is $\gamma_{H1}=3\times10^7 H_t^2$, so that for $H_t=10^{-4}$ oe, $\gamma_{H1}=0.3$ sec^{-1}.

This process leads to a non-Lorentzian line shape since it affects only the upper of the two resonance states. In the case where it is the dominating mechanism, the line shape does become Lorentzian, much as an ideal optical transition has a Lorentzian line shape even though the upper state has a very large decay rate and the lower state has a decay rate of zero. If there are several competing processes the situation is quite complicated, although it can be solved if the total decay rate for each of the states is known.[21]

2. *Relaxation Rate γ_{H2}*

The same comments regarding the line shape that were made in Sec. IV B(1) apply to phase decorrelation due to random motion through an inhomogeneous field. A simple method with which to obtain an estimate of γ_{H2} is to assume that the field has a separate value on either half of the storage bulb, $H_0\pm\Delta H/2$. Since field dependence of $(F=1, m_F=0)\rightarrow(F=0, m_F=0)$ is given by $\nu=\nu_0+\alpha H^2$, where $\alpha=2750$ cps/oe^2, the resonance frequencies on either side of the bulb then differ by $2\alpha H_0\Delta H$, assuming $\Delta H\ll H_0$. If the mean number of collisions an atom makes before leaving is n, then the mean time an atom spends in one half of the bulb, in excess of the other half, is $2n^{\frac{1}{2}}t_0$, and for coherence it is necessary to have $2n^{\frac{1}{2}}t_0(2\alpha H_0\Delta H)<1$. Therefore,

$$\gamma_{H2}=1/nt_0=t_0(16\alpha^2H_0^2\Delta H^2). \tag{67}$$

If, for example, $H_0=10^{-2}$ oe, $\Delta H=10^{-3}$ oe parallel to H_0, then with $t_0=3\times10^{-5}$ sec, we have $\gamma_{H2}\cong10^{-6}$ sec^{-1}.

If the transitions of interest are $(F=1, m_F=\pm1)\rightarrow(F=0, m_F=0)$, the π transitions, then there is a first-order field dependence, $\nu=\nu_0\pm\beta H$, where $\beta=1.4\times10^6$ cps/oe, and it follows that

$$\gamma_{H1}(\pi)=4\beta^2\Delta H^2t_0. \tag{68}$$

With the same field as above, $\gamma_{H1}(\pi)=240$ sec^{-1}. On the other hand, if the field varies due to inhomogeneities which are only perpendicular to the axis, then an inhomogeneity of 10^{-3} oe in the same field as above yields $\gamma_{H1}(\pi)=0.6$ sec^{-1}.

D. Spin Exchange Relaxation

At sufficiently high density of atomic hydrogen the dominating relaxation process is due to hydrogen-hydrogen collisions. The mechanism which leads to relaxation is chiefly spin exchange in which the electron spins of the colliding atoms exchange, leaving the atoms in hyperfine states different from the initial states. Wittke and Dicke[8] have analyzed this process, and their results have recently been confirmed by a detailed analysis of Mazo.[22] Measurements of the spin exchange cross section have been made in an EPR experiment by Hildebrandt, Booth, and Barth[23] and there is generally good agreement between theoretical and experimental results. The decay rate for spin exchange collisions γ_{se} is related to the number of hydrogen atoms per cm^3, N, by

$$\gamma_{se}\cong5\times10^{-10}N \text{ sec}^{-1}. \tag{69}$$

[19] W. B. Davenport and W. L. Root, *An Introduction to the Theory of Random Signals and Noise* (McGraw-Hill Book Company, Inc., New York, 1958), p. 103.

[20] E. M. Purcell (private communication).

[21] P. Kusch and V. W. Hughes, *Handbuch der Physik*, XXXVII/1 (Springer-Verlag, Berlin, Germany, 1959), p. 7.

[22] R. M. Mazo, J. Chem. Phys. **34**, 169 (1961).

[23] A. F. Hildebrandt, F. B. Booth, and C. H. Barth, Jr., J. Chem. Phys. **31**, 273 (1959).

This expression, which is valid for EPR, should be slightly modified for the hydrogen maser since in the latter there is initially a nonequilibrium distribution of states. On the other hand, this introduces only a minor change in γ_{se}, and Eq. 69 is still correct for an approximate estimate.

E. First-Order Doppler Broadening

So far the effect of the Doppler shift on the shape of the resonance has been neglected. This might seem to be a poor approximation since the normal Doppler broadening of the hyperfine line for a free hydrogen atom moving with thermal velocities is over 10 kc/sec, more than 10^4 times the resonance width of interest in the hydrogen maser. Doppler broadening does not, in fact, contribute appreciably to the linewidth due to the confinement of the radiating atoms to a region of constant phase and only slightly varying field amplitude. The possibility of inhibiting Doppler broadening in paramagnetic resonance experiments by limiting the motion of radiating atoms was first pointed out by Dicke who has analyzed the case of a radiating atom moving diffusively through a region of varying phase.[7,8] The present situation differs in that the atoms are confined to a region of almost constant phase and varying field amplitude, and their motion is random within a confined volume, rather than diffusive. For these reasons, a brief analysis of the effect of the atoms' motion is given.

The situation can be visualized classically. The resonance curve for the system when the atoms are assumed to be at rest, Eq. (7), corresponds to the spectrum of an ensemble of damped harmonic oscillators. If the resonance is not appreciably saturated, i.e., if $x \ll \gamma$, then the transition probability, i.e., the intensity of the resonance, is proportional to the driving oscillating magnetic field intensity x^2, so that the field radiated by each member of the fictitious ensemble is proportional to the local driving field. In the most general case the amplitude and phase of the local driving field vary with position in space. This causes the atoms to experience random amplitude and phase fluctuations due to their random motion. In the present case the atoms are confined in a resonant cavity in a region of almost constant phase where the amplitude varies according to the field distribution of the mode. The quantity of interest is the spectral density of the radiated power $P(\omega)$. $P(\omega)$ is the Fourier transform of the autocorrelation function of $x(t)$, $G(\tau) = \langle x(t)x(t+\tau)\rangle$. If the oscillators were randomly distributed throughout the bulb, but were at rest, then $x(t+\tau) = x(t)\exp(-\gamma|\tau|)$. (The exponential term expresses the fact that we are dealing with damped oscillation.) In this case

$$G(\tau) = \langle x^2\rangle_b \exp(-\gamma|\tau|). \tag{70}$$

The average is over the volume of the storage bulb.

The atoms actually move rapidly, making on the average more than 10^4 collisions before leaving the bulb. All correlation between positions at successive times is lost after a few wall collisions, and for τ greater than the time for a few collisions $x(t+\tau)$ is independent of t, except for the damping factor. In this case, we have approximately

$$G(\tau) = \langle x\rangle_b^2 \exp(-\gamma|\tau|). \tag{71}$$

The effect of motion is to reduce the power radiated at the center of the resonance line. This may be seen by evaluating the ratio of the spectral density at the center of the resonance curve for the two cases

$$\frac{P(0)\text{ moving}}{P(0)\text{ rest}} = \frac{\langle x\rangle_b^2}{\langle x^2\rangle_b} = \frac{\langle H_z\rangle_b^2}{\langle H_z^2\rangle_b}. \tag{72}$$

The area lost from the center of the spectrum appears in a broad pedestal having the full Doppler width, $\Delta = \bar{v}/\lambda$. The spectrum is approximately

$$P(\omega) = \langle x\rangle^2 \frac{1}{\gamma^2+\omega^2} + \frac{\Delta}{\gamma}(\langle x^2\rangle - \langle x\rangle^2)\frac{1}{\Delta^2+\omega^2}. \tag{73}$$

For a bulb located at a field maximum, $(\langle x^2\rangle - \langle x\rangle^2)/\langle x\rangle^2$ is typically $\frac{1}{10}(a/\lambdabar)^2$, where it is assumed that the radius of the bulb, a, is small compared to $\lambdabar$, the cavity wavelength $\times(2\pi)^{-1}$. Since $\gamma \approx \bar{v}/na$, where n is the mean number of collisions, the ratio of the second to first terms of Eq. (73) for $\omega = 0$ is approximately $a/(10n\lambdabar)$. Consequently the contribution of the broadened term is negligible to the spectrum at resonance, and it has negligible effect on the half-width of the spectrum. On the other hand, the motion of the atoms does have a significant effect on the intensity of the resonance. The loss of intensity at $\omega = 0$ is zero when the atoms are confined to a small volume at the region of maximum field, where $\langle x\rangle^2 = \langle x^2\rangle = x_{max}^2$. For larger regions, the intensity is reduced by the factor $f = \langle x\rangle^2/x^2(\max)$. This is related to the function η defined earlier by

$$f = \langle H^2\rangle_V \eta / H_z^2(\max). \tag{74}$$

In the case of a cylindrical cavity operating in the TE_{011} mode, $f = 0.0474\eta$. Both f and η are plotted in Fig. 3 for a spherical bulb of radius a in such a cavity, with length l.

F. Second-Order Doppler Broadening

Although broadening of the resonance by the first-order Doppler shift has been shown to be negligible, the second-order Doppler shift must also be considered. It is shown in Sec. VI-C that the total fractional shift of frequency due to the second-order Doppler effect at room temperature is approximately 10^{-10}. The velocities of the atoms are described by a Maxwellian distribution, and if there were no thermalization with the walls the resonance curve would be fractionally broadened by approximately the same amount as it is shifted. Thermalization does occur, however, and this reduces the effect. If the accommodation coefficient is p, and if the atoms make on the average n wall collisions, then the broadening effect is reduced by a factor approximately $(pn)^{\frac{1}{2}}$. Assuming $p=0.3$, $n=3\times10^4$, corresponding to a storage time of 1 sec, the broadening of the resonance line due to second-order Doppler shift is only about 1% of the resonance width, and therefore can be neglected.

G. Pressure Broadening

At easily obtainable pressures, collisions with inert atoms or molecules have negligible effect on the linewidth. Relaxation due to the presence of an impurity gas at elevated pressure has been observed. For instance, the relaxation rate due to O_2 has been found to be approximately

$$\gamma=2\times10^7 \text{ sec}^{-1}/\text{mm Hg}.$$

This effect is larger than can be accounted for by magnetic interaction and has not been fully interpreted as yet. It may be due to the formation of a short-lived excited molecule.

V. FREQUENCY SHIFTS IN THE MASER

Ideally the oscillation frequency of the maser is identical with the transition frequency between the levels of the atomic system as measured with atoms at rest in free space. The atoms are not free, though, since they interact with the surrounding electromagnetic system and, in the case of the present maser, with the walls of the storage bulb. In the following paragraphs some of the more important of the effects leading to a shift in frequency are discussed.

A. Wall Shift

The phase shift introduced in the wave function of an atom during a wall collision φ, defined in Eq. (54), causes a shift $\delta\omega$ in the resonance frequency given by

$$\delta\omega/\omega=\varphi/(\omega t_0), \tag{75}$$

where t_0 is the mean time between collisions. It is a difficult task to predict φ theoretically because of the uncertainty of the exact interaction potential and lack of knowledge of the microscopic wall structure. The experimental upper limit for φ for a surface treated with dimethyldichlorosilane is[10] $\varphi<10^{-4}$ rad, or, for a 16-cm-diam bulb, $\delta\omega/\omega<10^{-9}$. A lower limit to the expected shift with such a surface can be obtained from the following argument: The treated surface has very low adsorptive properties largely because it simulates a saturated hydrocarbon. The adsorption energy of atomic hydrogen on such surfaces is smaller than kT, and as a result the sticking time on the surface is comparable to the simple collision time with a free molecule. In a surface collision the impinging hydrogen atoms encounter methyl groups which are tightly bound to silicon atoms composing the underlying silica matrix. Such a collision should be similar but somewhat more severe than that with a single hydrogen molecule. The phase shift for the latter collision can be obtained from the measured value of the shift in the hyperfine frequency of hydrogen due to collisions with molecular hydrogen gas. This has been determined by Pipkin and his co-workers[24] and is -0.24 cps (mm Hg)$^{-1}$. Assuming an effective $H-H_2$ collision diameter of[25] 2.9×10^{-8} cm, the phase shift per collision is -3.9×10^{-3} rad/collision. This leads to a fractional shift in the frequency of the maser of $\delta\omega/\omega_0=-1.3\times10^{-13}$. The actual frequency shift with a saturated hydrocarbon surface should be higher than this value not only because the wall collision involves more than one perturbing molecule but because the small frequency shift in the molecular hydrogen buffer gas may be due to a partial cancellation of the dispersive attractive force effects by the effect of the exchange forces. The shift with a saturated flurocarbon surface, such as Teflon, may be smaller than the above value due to its relatively tight binding and small polarizability.

Since the wall shift is proportional to the collision rate, it can be determined by measuring the frequency of the maser as a function of the bulb size. This probably cannot be done with an accuracy of greater than 1% and the wall shift may therefore be the limiting factor in the absolute precision of the maser. Slow changes in the wall shift due to aging or contamination could cause long term fluctuations in the frequency. The answer to these problems can only be determined reliably by experiment.

B. First-Order Doppler Shift

The presence of running waves in the rf cavity can cause a shift in the resonance frequency due to the motion of the atoms. This occurs only if the atoms have a net effective translational velocity, as, for instance, if they enter one side of the bulb and relax before leaving through the entrance aperture. The situation is most easily described in terms of a running wave such as caused by the presence of a coupling loop placed asymmetrically in the cavity. (Effects of about the same size occur even if power is dissipated uniformly throughout the cavity walls due to generation of rf power within the storage bulb.) For the present, effects of saturation are neglected and an expression of the spectrum the atom experiences is derived by the same type of argument used in IV-E, to analyze the effect of Doppler broadening.

[24] L. W. Anderson, F. M. Pipkin, and J. C. Baird, Phys. Rev. Letters 4, 69 (1960).

[25] J. O. Hirschfelder, C. F. Curtiss, and R. B. Bird, *Molecular Theory of Gases and Liquids* (John Wiley & Sons, Inc., New York, 1954), p. 1082.

The rf field consists of a standing wave and a running wave and may be written

$$H(t)=\tfrac{1}{2}H_0e^{i(\omega_0t-kz)}+(\tfrac{1}{2}H_0+H_1)e^{i(\omega_0t+kz)}. \quad (76)$$

H_0 is the amplitude of the standing wave and H_1 is that of the running wave. The spectral density $J(\omega)$ is the Fourier transform of the autocorrelation function $G(\tau)$, which is

$$\begin{aligned}G(\tau)&=\langle H(t)H^*(t+\tau)\rangle_{\text{av}}\\&=\{(\tfrac{1}{2}H_0)^2\langle\exp[ik(z-z')]\rangle_{\text{av}}\\&\quad+(\tfrac{1}{2}H_0+H_1)^2\langle\exp[ik(z-z')]\rangle_{\text{av}}\\&\quad+(\tfrac{1}{2}H_0+H_1)\tfrac{1}{2}H_0\langle\exp[ik(z+z')]\rangle_{\text{av}}\\&\quad+(\tfrac{1}{2}H_0+H_1)\tfrac{1}{2}H_0\\&\quad\times\langle\exp[-ik(z+z')]\rangle_{\text{av}}\}\exp[-\gamma|\tau|]. \quad (77)\end{aligned}$$

If τ is large compared with t_0, the mean collision time, z and z', the position of the atom at time t and $(t+\tau)$, respectively, are independent. Since $J(\omega)$ is only of interest near the center of the spectrum, i.e., $\omega-\omega_0\ll t_0^{-1}$, the short time correlations can be neglected so that z and z' can be considered independent.

To simplify the calculation, the variation of field transverse to the axis of the cavity is neglected, and the bulb, which has a radius a, is treated as if it were one dimensional. If the center of the bulb is located at the center of the rf cavity, $z=0$, then a uniform density of the atom in the bulb is described by the distribution function $P(z)=1/2a$. If the atoms enter the bulb at one end and are relaxed uniformly throughout the bulb, the distribution is no longer uniform. In this case the distribution is approximately

$$P(z)=(1/2a)(1+z/na). \quad (78)$$

Here n is the mean number of collisions the atoms make before relaxing. If Eq. (78) is substituted in Eq. (77), the following result is obtained after some manipulation

$$G(\tau)=\left[H_0^2\frac{\sin^2(ak)}{(ak)^2}+2H_0H_1\left\{\frac{\sin^2 ak}{(ak)^2}+i\frac{\sin(ak)}{(ak)}\right.\right.$$
$$\left.\left.\times\frac{1}{n}\left(\frac{\cos(ka)}{(ka)}+\frac{\sin(ka)}{(ka)^2}\right)\right\}\right]\exp[-i\omega_0\tau-\gamma|\tau|]. \quad (79)$$

The imaginary part of $G(\tau)$ represents a frequency shift. This shift is obtained by evaluating $J(\omega)$, the Fourier transform of Eq. (79), and finding the position of the maximum of $J(\omega)$. Assuming $ak<1$, and using the relation $H_0/H_1=2Q_T/T_1$, where Q_T is the coupling Q, one obtains

$$\frac{\omega-\omega_0}{\omega_0}=\frac{2a}{3ln}\frac{1}{Q_TQ_l}. \quad (80)$$

The length of the resonant cavity is l.

As a numerical example, if $n=10^4$, $a/l=0.3$, $Q_T=10^4$, $Q_l=10^9$, the result is $(\omega-\omega_0)/\omega_0=2\times10^{-18}$. This is clearly a negligible effect.

A quantum mechanical treatment of this problem indicates that saturation does not appreciably affect this result, so that the first-order Doppler shift can be completely neglected as a source of frequency shift.

C. Second-Order Doppler Effect

The second-order Doppler effect does not average in the same manner as the first-order effect because of its dependence on the square of its velocity. The fractional shift introduced by this effect is

$$\frac{\omega-\omega_0}{\omega_0}=-\frac{1}{2}\frac{v^2}{c^2}=-\frac{3}{2}\frac{kT}{mc^2}, \quad (81)$$

where m is the mass of the atom, k is Boltzmann's constant, and T is the temperature. The fractional shift is seen to be the ratio of the thermal energy to the rest energy of the atom. For hydrogen its magnitude is $(\omega-\omega_0)/\omega_0=-3\times10^{-13}/°\text{K}$. The shift is three times smaller for tritium.

D. Cavity Pulling

The influence of the cavity tuning on the resonance has been discussed in Sec. II-C. It was shown there that a mistuning of the cavity by an amount $\omega_c-\omega_0$ shifts the frequency by an amount

$$\frac{\omega-\omega_0}{\omega_0}=\frac{\omega_c-\omega_0}{\omega_0}\frac{Q_c}{Q_l}, \quad (27)$$

where Q_c is the quality factor of the cavity. For a ratio Q_c/Q_l of 10^{-6}, and for a fractional shift no larger than 10^{-13}, the cavity must be tuned to approximately 100 cps. For this reason the cavity must be accurately tuned, and either temperature controlled or thermally compensated to a high degree.

E. Zeeman Effect

The second-order magnetic field dependence of the $(F=1, m=0)\rightarrow(F=0, m=0)$ transition is given by

$$\nu=\nu_0+2750H^2\text{ cps}, \quad (82)$$

where H is in oersted. The fractional shift in frequency due to ΔH, a small change in the field, is

$$(\nu-\nu_0)/\nu_0=3.9\times10^{-6}H\Delta H. \quad (83)$$

A fractional shift of 10^{-13} requires $H\Delta H\cong3\times10^{-8}$ or, for example, a field of 1 moe held constant to 3%. Although this represents a high degree of field stability, the use of the field dependent transitions in the maser to stabilize the magnetic field greatly simplifies the problem.

F. Effect of Neighboring States

The presence of atoms in other than $(F=1, m=0)$ can cause a change in the permeability of the cavity and thereby shift the resonance. The only states which make appreciable contributions to this are ($F=1$, $m=1$) and ($F=1, m=1$). The pulling effect of these states is very small, however, for the following reasons: Normally these states do not couple to the resonant mode because the static magnetic field is parallel, rather than perpendicular, to the oscillating field. In addition, the two states have effects of opposite sign, so that if care is taken to populate them equally they will have a negligible net effect even if the static magnetic field is not precisely parallel to the oscillating field.

ACKNOWLEDGMENTS

The authors wish to express appreciation to E. M. Purcell for his helpful comments on the analysis and interpretation of random relaxation mechanisms and to G. B. Kistiakowsky for an informative conversation on the role of surface reactions. In addition, they wish to thank H. Berg for many useful comments on the paper, and N. Fortson and E. Recknagel for helpful conversations. Numerical calculations were carried out by B. S. Mathur. One of the authors (H.M.G.) wishes to thank the National Science Foundation for a Predoctoral Fellowship during the course of this work.

After Eq. 66 replace paragraph with the following:

"As an example, in the low field region where $\omega t_o \ll 1$, then the factor $(\omega t_o/2)^4$ may be neglected and using $\gamma_F = 8.8 \times 10^6$/sec oe, $t_o = 3 \times 10^{-5}$ sec, the result is $\gamma_{H1} = 10^9 H_t^2$, so that for $H_t = 10^{-5}$ oe, $\gamma_{H1} = 0.1$ sec^{-1}."

Reprinted from THE PHYSICAL REVIEW, Vol. 138, No. 4A, A972–A983, 17 May 1965
Printed in U. S. A.

Hydrogen-Maser Principles and Techniques*

D. KLEPPNER,† H. C. BERG,‡ S. B. CRAMPTON,§ AND N. F. RAMSEY
Harvard University, Cambridge, Massachusetts

AND

R. F. C. VESSOT, H. E. PETERS, AND J. VANIER
Varian Associates, Beverly, Massachusetts

(Received 17 Decmeber 1964)

Techniques and design principles relevant to the construction and operation of a hydrogen maser are presented in detail. These include methods for the generation of atomic hydrogen, state selection, design of the microwave cavity, production of very low magnetic fields, coating the hydrogen storage bulb, and tuning the maser. A figure of merit is introduced which indicates the optimum choice of parameters.

I. INTRODUCTION

ALTHOUGH the hydrogen maser has proved useful both as a spectroscopic tool and as a frequency standard, only a portion of its theory has so far been described.[1] Most of the description of experiments with the maser have given the results but have omitted technical details.[2–8] In the present paper, the interrelation of the various physical effects governing the maser's behavior will be discussed along with relevant operational and technical considerations.

The hydrogen maser operates between the ground-state hyperfine levels of atomic hydrogen. For use as a frequency standard, the maser oscillates on the transition $(F=1, m_F=0) \rightarrow (F=0, m_F=0)$ at a frequency of approximately 1420 Mc/sec. Figure 1 is a schematic diagram. Molecular hydrogen is dissociated in the source and is formed into an atomic beam which passes through a state-selecting magnet. The emergent beam contains only atoms in the states $(F=1, m=1)$ and $(F=1, m=0)$. The beam passes into a storage bulb which has a specially prepared surface and in which the atoms remain for approximately 0.3 sec before escaping. The bulb is located in a cavity tuned to the hyperfine transition frequency. Stimulated emission occurs if the beam flux is sufficiently high and a signal is produced in the cavity. This signal is detected by means of a small coupling loop. The cavity is surrounded by magnetic shields to reduce the ambient field and a small uniform field is produced at the storage bulb by a solenoid.

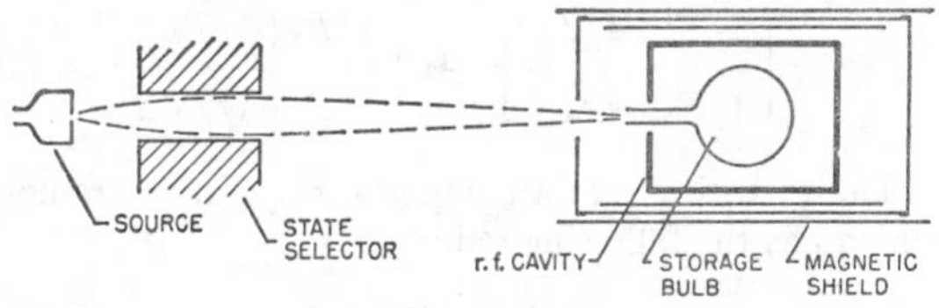

FIG. 1. Schematic diagram of the hydrogen maser.

In Sec. II, some formulas are presented which govern the choice of design parameters. Subsequent sections are: III. Source, IV. State Selector, V. Vacuum System, VI. Cavity, VII. Magnetic Shields, VIII. Storage Bulb, IX. Electronics, and X. Tuning Methods.

II. OPERATING CONDITIONS

Basic formulas governing the operation of the hydrogen maser have been published by Kleppner, Goldbenberg, and Ramsey[1] hereafter referred to as (KGR). Their results will be extended here in order to illustrate more clearly the interdependence of the design parameters. In particular, by including the effect of spin-exchange relaxation in the governing equations, it will be shown that for oscillation to occur on the transition $(F=1, m=0) \rightarrow (F=0, m=0)$ there is not only a minimum beam flux but also a *maximum* permissible flux. The analysis leads to a constraint condition governing the cavity geometry, storage-bulb size, and various relaxation times. Unless the constraint is satisfied, the maser will not oscillate, and the constraint equation leads to a useful figure of merit which predicts how suitable a given configuration will be.

Our starting point is KGR Eq. (7),

$$P=\tfrac{1}{2}I\hbar\omega\frac{x^2}{(1/T_b)^2+x^2+(\omega-\omega_0)^2}, \qquad (1)$$

where P is the power radiated by the atoms, I is the

* Work supported by the National Science Foundation and the Office of Naval Research (Harvard) and by the National Aeronautics and Space Administration and the Office of Naval Research (Varian).
† Alfred P. Sloan Foundation Fellow.
‡ Junior Fellow, Society of Fellows, Harvard University.
§ National Science Foundation Postdoctoral Fellow.
[1] D. Kleppner, H. M. Goldenberg, and N. F. Ramsey, Phys. Rev. 126, 603 (1962).
[2] H. M. Goldenberg, D. Kleppner, and N. F. Ramsey, Phys. Rev. Letters 5, 361 (1960); Appl. Opt. 1, 55 (1962).
[3] S. B. Crampton, D. Kleppner, and N. F. Ramsey, Phys. Rev. Letters 11, 338 (1963).
[4] H. C. Berg, D. Kleppner, and N. F. Ramsey, Bull. Am. Phys. Soc. 8, 379 (1963).
[5] S. B. Crampton, D. Kleppner, and H. G. Robinson, Bull. Am. Phys. Soc. 8, 351 (1963).
[6] S. B. Crampton and D. Kleppner, Bull. Am. Phys. Soc. 9, 451 (1964).
[7] H. G. Robinson, H. C. Berg, and S. B. Crampton, Bull. Am. Phys. Soc. 9, 564 (1964).
[8] E. N. Fortson, D. Kleppner, and N. F. Ramsey, Phys. Rev. Letters 13, 22 (1964).

net input flux, i.e., the difference in the flux of atoms entering in the state ($F=1$, $m=0$) and the state ($F=0$, $m=0$), ω_0 is the resonance frequency, and $x=\mu_0 H_z/\hbar$, where H_z is the oscillating field amplitude. T_b is the mean storage time of the bulb (denoted by γ^{-1} in KGR). Under the assumptions discussed below, this equation can be generalized to the case in which other relaxation processes occur. In particular, we shall distinguish between processes which relax the population difference between the two states of interest and those which relax the oscillating moment. In analogy with nmr terminology, we designate the decay times for the processes by T_1 and T_2, respectively. Then it can be shown that Eq. (1) becomes[9,10]

$$P=\tfrac{1}{2}I\hbar\omega\frac{x^2}{1/(T_1T_2)+x^2+(T_2/T_1)(\omega-\omega_0)^2}. \quad (2)$$

If the only relaxation mechanism is escape of atoms from the storage bulb, then $T_1=T_2=T_b$. However, we must also allow for hydrogen-hydrogen spin exchange (s.e.). For this process, $T_2=2T_1$,[11,12] where

$$(1/T_1)_{\text{s.e.}}=n\sigma\bar{v}_r. \quad (3)$$

Here σ is the hydrogen "spin-flip" cross section,[13] estimated by Mazo[14] to be 2.85×10^{-15} cm^2, $\bar{v}_r$ is the average relative hydrogen velocity $[\bar{v}_r=4(kT/\pi m)^{1/2}=3.58\times10^5$ cm/sec at $T=308°$K$]$, and n is the hydrogen density given by

$$n=I_{\text{tot}}T_b/V_b, \quad (4)$$

where I_{tot} is the total flux of atoms entering the storage bulb, and V_b is the storage-bulb volume. Normally, the states ($F=1$, $m=0$) and ($F=1$, $m=1$) are focused, so that $I_{\text{tot}}=2I$. If the state selection is imperfect, other states may be present so that I_{tot}/I can have a large value.

There are a variety of other possible relaxation processes,[11] some of which are discussed in KGR. For these, T_1 and T_2 are not in general the same. We shall allow for them by letting T_1' and T_2' stand for the total relaxation times due to all processes other than escape from the bulb and hydrogen spin exchange. Then

$$1/T_1=1/T_1'+(1/T_1)_{\text{s.e.}}+1/T_b,$$
$$1/T_2=1/T_2'+(1/T_2)_{\text{s.e.}}+1/T_b. \quad (5)$$

Here the subscript s.e. indicates that the relaxation mechanism is spin exchange.

We assume, for the present, that T_1' and T_2' are constants, insofar as they do not depend on the hydrogen atom flux or on the oscillation level of the maser. This is not necessarily true, since the structure of the storage-bulb wall may depend on the hydrogen density and the state populations, as will be discussed below.

To analyze the conditions for stationary oscillation of the maser, we proceed as in KGR by equating the radiated power to the dissipated power $\omega W/Q$ where W is the stored energy in the cavity. By substituting Eqs. (3), (4), and (5) in Eq. (2) with $\omega=\omega_0$ and rearranging, using $x^2=(\mu_0/\hbar)^2(8\pi W/V_c)\eta$, we arrive eventually at the following relation between the power radiated and the beam flux:

$$P/P_c=-2q^2(I/I_{\text{th}})^2+(1-cq)I/I_{\text{th}}-1. \quad (6)$$

P_c is defined by the following:

$$P_c=\omega\hbar^2V_c/8\pi\mu_0^2QnT_t^2, \quad (7)$$

where

$$1/T_t^2=(1/T_1'+1/T_b)(1/T_2'+1/T_b),$$
$$\eta=\langle H_z\rangle_{\text{bulb}}^2/\langle H^2\rangle_{\text{cavity}}, \quad (8)$$

and

$$V_c=\text{cavity volume.}$$

I_{th} is defined by

$$I_{\text{th}}=2P_c/\hbar\omega. \quad (9)$$

[Physically, I_{th} is the net threshold flux for oscillation to occur providing spin exchange can be neglected. In the presence of spin exchange, the net flux for oscillation is somewhat larger, and is given by I_{min}, as shown in Eq. (13) below.]

Also,

$$c=\left[\frac{1/T_b+1/T_1'}{1/T_b+1/T_2'}\right]^{1/2}+2\left[\frac{1/T_b+1/T_2'}{1/T_b+1/T_1'}\right]^{1/2}. \quad (10)$$

The quantity q is an important quality parameter which has the following value:

$$q=\frac{\sigma\bar{v}_r\hbar}{8\pi\mu_0^2}\frac{T_b}{T_t}\frac{V_c}{\eta V_b}\frac{1}{Q}\frac{I_{\text{tot}}}{I}. \quad (11)$$

From Eq. (6) it is apparent that the power radiated by the maser oscillator is a quadratic function of the beam flux. If we require that both the flux and the power be positive quantities, we obtain the following condition:

$$q<(c-2\sqrt{2})/(c^2-8). \quad (12)$$

It also follows that the maximum and minimum net beam fluxes for oscillation are given by

$$I_{\substack{\max\\ \min}}/I_{\text{th}}=\frac{1-cq\pm[1-2cq+(c^2-8)q^2]^{1/2}}{4q^2}. \quad (13)$$

Because of spin exchange, the resonance linewidth $\Delta\nu$ depends on the flux. It is given by the following

[9] S. B. Crampton, Ph.D. thesis, Harvard, 1964 (unpublished).
[10] P. L. Bender, Phys. Rev. **132**, 2154 (1963).
[11] H. C. Berg, Ph.D. thesis, Harvard, 1964 (unpublished). Also H. C. Berg, Phys. Rev. **137**, A1621, (1965).
[12] J. P. Wittke and R. H. Dicke, Phys. Rev. **103**, 620 (1956).
[13] L. C. Balling, R. J. Hanson, and F. M. Pipkin, Phys. Rev. **132**, 2154 (1964).
[14] R. M. Mazo, J. Chem. Phys. **34**, 169 (1961).

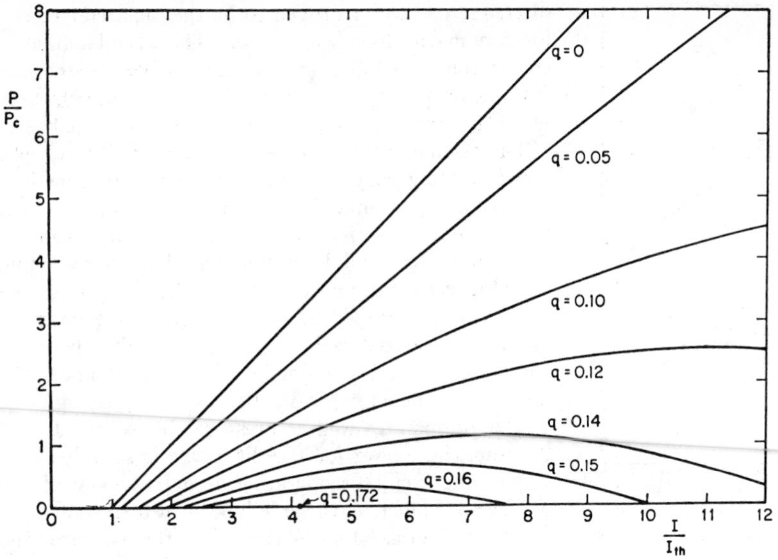

FIG. 2. P/P_c versus I/I_{th} for different values of the parameter q. This family of curves shows the strong influence of q on the operating conditions. If spin exchange is neglected, $q=0$ and radiated power increases monatonically with beam flux. For $q>0$, there is an upper limit to the flux for oscillation to occur and above a certain value ($q=0.172$) the maser cannot radiate at any beam flux. q is defined by Eq. (11).

expression:

$$\Delta\nu = 1/\pi T_2 = (1/\pi)[(1/T_2'+1/T_b)+(I/I_{th})q/T_t]. \quad (14)$$

To proceed further, we must choose a particular ratio for T_1' and T_2'. In the event that $T_1'=T_2'$, $c=3$, and we have

$$P/P_c = -2q^2(I/I_{th})^2+(1-3q)I/I_{th}-1, \quad (15)$$

$$q<3-2\sqrt{2}=0.172, \quad (16)$$

$$I_{\substack{\max\\ \min}}/I_{th} = \frac{1-3q\pm(1-6q+q^2)^{1/2}}{4q^2}, \quad (17)$$

$$\Delta\nu = (1/\pi T_t)(1+qI/I_{th}). \quad (18)$$

For purposes of tuning, to be discussed in Sec. X, it is essential that the ratio of the resonance widths at the extremes of permissible flux be large. This ratio is

$$r = \frac{\Delta\nu \max}{\Delta\nu \min} = \frac{1+q+(1-6q+q^2)^{1/2}}{1+q-(1-6q+q^2)^{1/2}}. \quad (19)$$

To illustrate the behavior of the maser as the factor q varies, Eq. (15) is plotted in Fig. 2 for a few values of q. Equations (17) and (19) are plotted in Fig. 3, which shows both r and the permissible extremes of flux as a function of q. It is evident from the figures that a relatively small decrease in q can take the maser from a state of critical dependence on flux, or even no oscillation at all, to a favorable region of oscillation.

In order for the maser to operate as an oscillator, it is essential that the inequality in (16) be satisfied. If we substitute Eq. (11) in Eq. (16), we obtain

$$T_b/T_t \times V_c/(\eta V_b)\times 1/Q\times I_{tot}/I < 3.47\times 10^{-4}. \quad (20)$$

As an example, let us insert the following typical values:

$$V_c/V_b=6.7,\ \eta=3,\ I_{tot}/I=2,\ Q=3\times 10^4.$$

Then, for oscillation,

$$T_b/T_t = 1+T_b/T_1 < 2.32. \quad (21)$$

If unwanted relaxation mechanisms are present, the bulb storage time must be decreased so that this inequality holds. Conversely, if a given bulb geometry and storage time are required, Eq. (21) can be used to set an upper limit on permissible relaxation.

If we assume $V_c=1.3\times 10^4$ cm^3, $T_b/T_t=1.3$, and $T_b=0.3$ sec, reasonable values in practice, then we have further

$$P_c=5.9\times 10^{-13}\ \text{W},$$
$$I_{th}=1.3\times 10^{12}\ \text{particles/sec},$$
$$q=0.097,$$
$$I_{\min}=1.9\times 10^{12}\ \text{particles/sec},$$

and

$$r=4.$$

The time T_2 can be measured by observing the decay of radiation when the maser is pulsed while operating below oscillation threshold.[11] In this condition, spin-exchange is usually negligible, so that if the relation between T_1' and T_2' is known, T_t can be determined from Eq. (8). The other quantities involved in q can be calculated in principle, though the quantity η is difficult to compute precisely, except for the case of simple geometry, such as a cylindrical bulb in a cylindrical cavity, which will be discussed in Sec. VIII. Alternatively, the cavity Q can be decreased by increasing the coupling until the maser ceases to operate at any flux. At this point, the inequality (12) becomes an equality. By measuring Q at this cutoff condition and

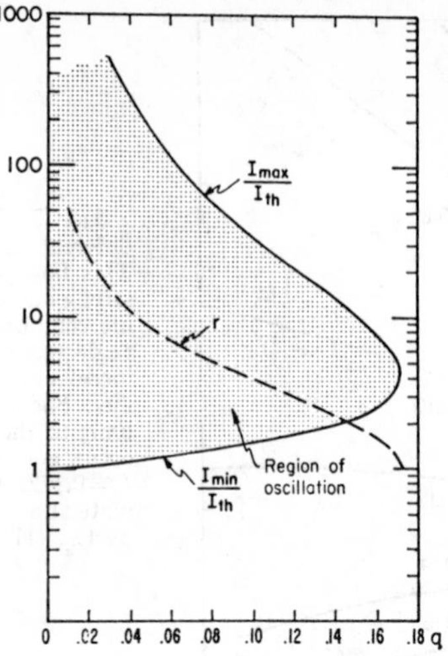

FIG. 3. I_{max}/I_{th} and I_{min}/I_{th} versus q. The maser can oscillate if the flux obeys $I_{min} \leqslant I \leqslant I_{max}$, indicated by the shaded region. The curve r gives the ratio I_{max}/I_{min} and is a useful measure of the amount by which the resonance line can be broadened by spin exchange.

at the normal operating condition, q can be determined for the latter case.

It should be pointed out that care must be used in applying this analysis. In some cases, T_1 is known once T_2 has been measured. For instance, in the case of spin-exchange collisions between hydrogen and a spin-$\frac{1}{2}$ or spin-1 background gas, $T_2 = \frac{4}{3}T_1$.[11] However, unless the relaxation mechanisms are understood, the ratio of T_1 to T_2 must be separately measured. Any mechanism which converts atoms to molecular form in effect behaves like a hole through the wall and decreases the storage time of the bulb T_b. In addition, two assumptions have been made which do not necessarily always hold. In the first place, the maser has been treated as a simple two-level system. This is not necessarily true if there is coupling with the remaining two hyperfine levels. As an example, relaxation due to motion of the atoms through an inhomogeneous magnetic field couples the three upper hyperfine states. The effect of this is, on the one hand, to relax the oscillating moment, and on the other hand, to feed atoms from the (1,1) and (1, −1) states into the (1,0) state as this is depleted by radiation to the ground state. A full analysis of this can be carried out using the density matrix formalism,[9] but for many purposes the process can be neglected by ensuring that magnetic relaxation is not large.

The second assumption is that the remaining relaxation processes are simply characterized by constant rates. In fact, there is evidence to indicate that part of the relaxation at the storage-bulb surface can occur at a rate proportional to the hydrogen density.[11] One effect of such a process is the enhancement of the value of σ entering Eq. (1), and this must be taken into account.

III. SOURCE

Of the three time-honored devices for dissociating molecular hydrogen—Wood's discharge, rf (or microwave) discharge, and thermal dissociator—the rf discharge has so far proven to be the most convenient for use in the hydrogen maser. The Wood's tube is cumbersome to build and operate, and the thermal dissociator produces a relatively hot beam which is difficult to focus. A simple rf discharge is described here.

The discharge takes place in a spherical Pyrex bulb, approximately $2\frac{1}{2}$ cm diam. The source aperture is a hole typically $\frac{1}{2}$ mm diam, though holes up to 1 mm diam function satisfactorily. The aperture can be connected to the bulb by a short length of Pyrex tubing or led directly through the wall of the bulb, as shown in Fig. 4. If desired, the flux to the source chamber pump can be reduced by using a multitube glass collimator instead of a simple hole.[15–17] Pressure in the discharge tube is typically 0.3 mm Hg, though the discharge operates well at pressures between 0.05 and 0.8 mm Hg. Power for the discharge is supplied by a single-tube oscillator operating at a frequency of 200 Mc/sec or higher. A variable link is used to couple the power to the discharge. A circuit for the oscillator and details of the coupling link are shown in Fig. 5. Tuning is facilitated by using a directional power meter in the transmission line. Matching must be done with the tube lit. Under typical conditions the oscillator tube will draw 150 mA at 400 V, and the input power to the discharge tube is 10 W. At higher power levels, the discharge tube should be cooled with forced air.

It is possible to treat the discharge tube walls to reduce recombination using phosphoric acid or Dri Film[18] (but not Teflon, which is decomposed by the discharge). The most satisfactory operation has been

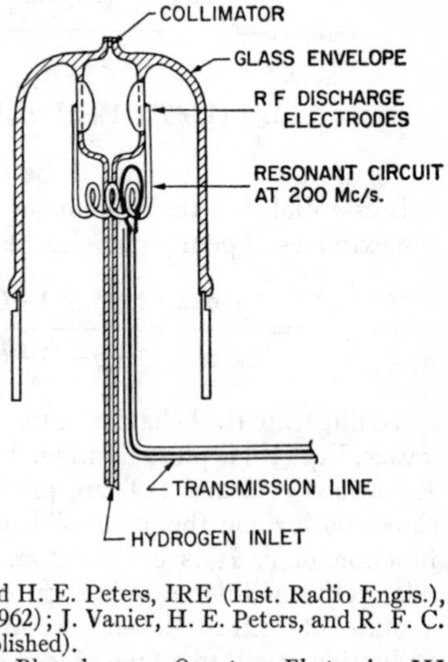

FIG. 4. Atomic hydrogen source.

[15] R. F. C. Vessot and H. E. Peters, IRE (Inst. Radio Engrs.), Trans. Instr. **11**, 183 (1962); J. Vanier, H. E. Peters, and R. F. C. Vessot, *ibid.* (to be published).

[16] P. Grivet and N. Bloembergen, *Quantum Electronics III* (Columbia University Press, New York, 1964), pp. 333–347; also pp. 409–417.

[17] The collimators described in Refs. 16 and 17 are effective at low source pressures but are not useful if high flux is desired. Finer collimators which are useful over a wider pressure range can be supplied by Permeonics, Inc., Southbridge, Massachusetts.

[18] Type SC-02 (dimethyldichlorosilane) General Electric Company, Silicone Products Department, Waterford, New York.

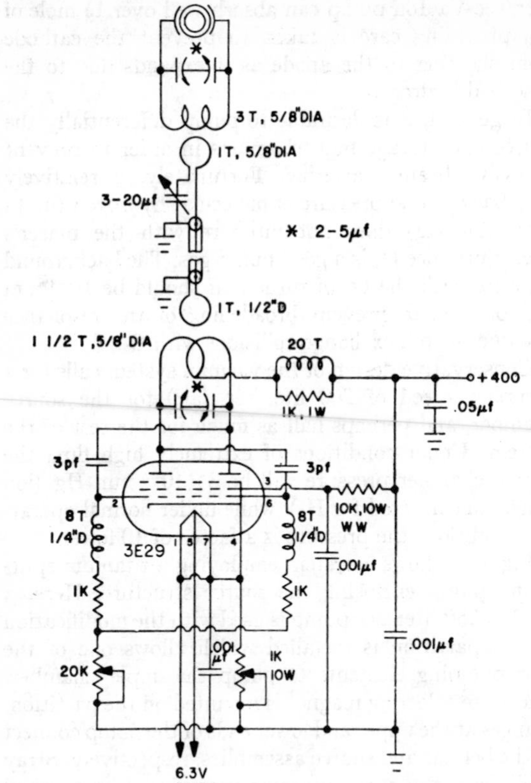

FIG. 5. Hydrogen discharge power oscillator.

obtained with untreated Pyrex. Normally, the tube must age for a few hours before the discharge acquires its characteristic red color. After long operation, the discharge tube becomes discolored by the decomposition of the glass; black borosilicate products appear on the inside surface of the tube. This does not appear to have a serious effect on the operation of the discharge.

Hydrogen may be introduced to the discharge by means of a conventional gas-handling system or through a combination purifier, pressure reducer, and flow controller consisting of a simple palladium leak. (Conventional regulators with variable leaks are difficult to reset and usually will not regulate pressure to better than 10%.) Both the leak and a servo system for controlling the source pressure are shown in Fig. 6. The source pressure is monitored by a Pirani gauge consisting of a thermistor bead suspended in the hydrogen inlet line. The gauge is housed in a thermally controlled box which also houses the resistance bridge and servo preamplifier. Flux through the palladium leak is controlled by varying its temperature with a heating coil.

IV. STATE SELECTOR

The hexapolar field proposed by Friedburg and Paul[19] is ideally suited to the hydrogen maser. This type of state selector has a large acceptance angle, but in general yields an atomic beam of relatively large area. Fortunately, the entrance to the storage bulb can be made large enough to accept a substantial part of the beam.

The design of a simple permanent six-pole magnet has been given by Christensen and Hamilton.[20] A magnet similar to their design has been constructed and has the following properties: gap diameter, $\frac{1}{8}$ in.; length, 3 in.; maximum field at pole tip (as measured by a rotating coil magnetometer), 9900 Oe. The magnet can be bolted or glued together with epoxy and is magnetized by passing approximately 500 A through 33 turns of wire wound on the poles or by using a pulsed magnetizer.[21]

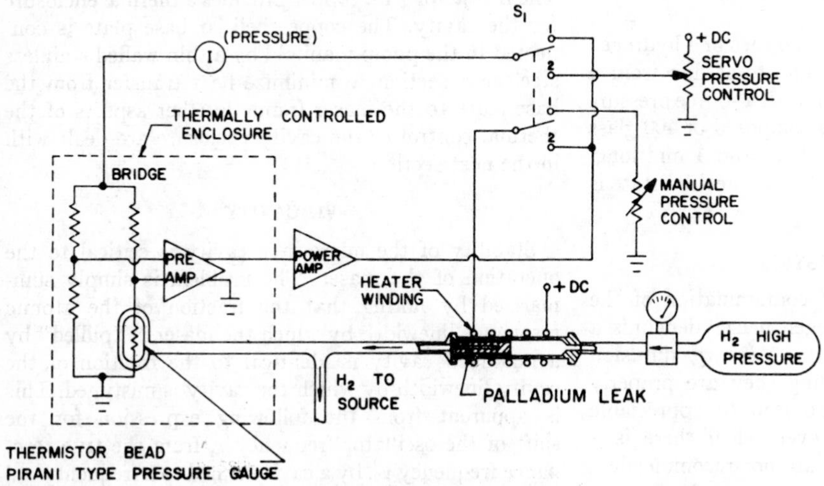

FIG. 6. Hydrogen gas-handling system and flow regulator. The palladium leak is made from an alloy pellet 70% palladium, 30% silver, approximately $\frac{1}{2}$-in. long, $\frac{3}{16}$-in. o.d., $\frac{1}{16}$-in. i.d. The Pirani-gauge preamplifier and bridge are similar to those in Fig. 8.

[19] H. Friedburg and W. Paul, Naturwiss. 38, 159 (1951).
[20] R. L. Christensen and D. R. Hamilton, Rev. Sci. Instr. **30**, 356 (1959).
[21] These magnets can be obtained commercially from Varian Company, Bomac Division, Beverly, Massachusetts.

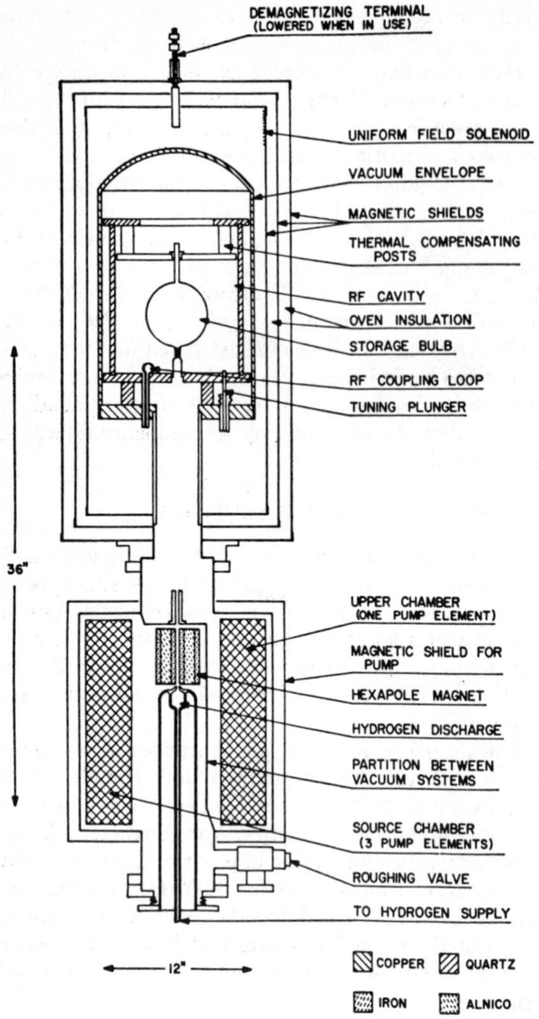

FIG. 7. Details of hydrogen maser.

Typical dimensions for the beam optics of a hydrogen maser are indicated in Fig. 7. The total flux from a collimated source is 10^{16} atom/sec with a source pressure of 0.1 mm Hg. The collimater is composed of 400 glass tubes forming a cylinder 1 mm diam and 1 mm long. The net flux of atoms to the bulb in the desired state is approximately 2×10^{12} atoms/sec.

V. VACUUM SYSTEM

Because of the possibility of contamination of the storage bulb surface, the hydrogen maser demands a relatively clean vacuum system. Mercury diffusion pumps are satisfactory, providing they are properly baffled. Oil diffusion pumps can lead to appreciable contamination of the surface, even when there is a very low residual pressure, and are not recommended. The most satisfactory pump appears to be an ion sputtering pump. These pumps have both high speed and high capacity for hydrogen. For example, a 75 liter/sec VacIon pump can absorb well over $1\frac{1}{2}$ mole of H_2, providing care is taken to prevent the cathode from shorting to the anode as it expands due to the absorbed hydrogen.

In general, it is desirable to pump differentially the source and storage bulb chambers in order to prevent excessive beam scattering. Fortunately, a relatively high background pressure of molecular hydrogen (up to 10^{-5} mm Hg) does not interfere with the maser's operation since H_2 is a good buffer gas. The background pressure with the beam turned off should be 10^{-8} mm Hg, or less, to prevent broadening of the resonance line due to spin exchange collisions with O_2.

Conservative design of the vacuum system calls for a pumping speed of 200 liter/sec (air) for the source chamber, and perhaps half as much for the rest of the system. Under conditions of extremely high flux, the source chamber pressure will be 3×10^{-5} mm Hg (ion gauge, uncorrected for H_2), while under normal operating conditions the pressure is a factor of 10 lower.

Figure 7 shows a system employing a titanium sputtering pump enclosing the source structure. Here, a VacIon 250-liter/sec pump is used with the modification that a partition is installed which allows one of the four pumping elements to pump the upper chamber. The state-selecting magnet is mounted on the partition. Flanges at the upper and lower ends of the pump connect to the bell jar and source assemblies, respectively. Stray fields from the pump magnets are reduced by a shield of $\frac{1}{16}$-in. Armco iron surrounded by a second shield of $\frac{1}{16}$-in. Mu Metal.

The microwave cavity must be evacuated to prevent atmospheric disturbance of the tuning.[15,16] This may be done by a separate roughing system, or, as shown in Fig. 7, by connecting it directly to the high-vacuum system. To afford thermal isolation from the bell jar, the cavity supports are three thin-walled quartz tubes. The bell jar of $\frac{1}{4}$-in. copper provides a thermal enclosure for the cavity. The copper bell-jar base plate is connected to the pump manifold by a thin-walled stainless steel neck section to minimize heat transfer from the base plate to the maser frame. Further aspects of the thermal control of the cavity enclosure are dealt with in the next section.

VI. CAVITY

Stability of the microwave cavity is critical to the operation of the maser. The problem is simply summarized by noting that the fraction of the atomic resonance linewidth by which the maser is "pulled" by a mistuned cavity is identical to the fraction of the cavity linewidth by which the cavity is mistuned. This is apparent from the following expression for the shift of the oscillator frequency ν, from the true resonance frequency ν_0, by a cavity tuned to a frequency ν_c.[1]

$$\frac{\nu-\nu_0}{\nu_0}=\frac{\nu_c-\nu_0}{\nu_0}\frac{\Delta\nu_r}{\Delta\nu_c}, \tag{22}$$

where $\Delta\nu_r$ and $\Delta\nu_c$ are the resonance and cavity linewidths, respectively.

In practice, the major source of drift of the maser is frequency pulling due to cavity drift. Although a particular cavity design is described here, it should be emphasized that other approaches are possible. In particular, it should be possible to stabilize the cavity frequency with a servo system. However, at the time of writing, such a system has not been put into operation.

The most convenient cavity mode is the cylindrical TE_{011} mode, since this has only azimuthal wall currents so that good contact between the cylinder and end plates is not required. The corresponding spherical mode should also be favorable, though it is difficult to construct.

The electrical properties of the TE_{011} mode are well described in the literature,[22] and only a few points will be summarized here. The unloaded cavity resonates with length and diameter both equal to 27.6 cm. The theoretical Q is 87 000 for silver-plated walls. In practice, $Q=60\,000$ is obtainable. The quartz storage bulb does not appreciably affect Q, but a bulb 15 cm in diameter with walls 1 mm thick will decrease the resonant length by about 5 cm.

Power is coupled from the cavity by a loop mounted in an end plate near the position of maximum magnetic field. A loop area $\approx 1\ \text{cm}^2$ will couple the cavity critically to a 50-Ω line.

Since thermal and mechanical stability are of great importance, it is desirable to make the cavity tube out of quartz. This is done commercially by grinding quartz pipe to the correct i.d. and then fusing a silver film to the inner surface.[23] A wall thickness of $\frac{5}{16}$ in. gives adequate mechanical strength, while the silver coating should be at least 0.001 in. to ensure minimum wall loss.

Because loading by the storage bulb changes the cavity length appreciably, the position of one end plate must be adjustable. For maximum stability the end plate should be mounted rigidly on spacers which are cut to bring the cavity within the range of a fine tuning control. For short term experiments involving frequent storage bulb changes, it is convenient to mount the end plate on a threaded drum with at least a 6-in. diam and a micrometer thread. After adjustment the end plate must be clamped in position.

Fine tuning can be accomplished by a tuning plunger or by coupling reactance to the cavity. A $\frac{1}{4}$-in.-diam plunger protruding through the end plate near the electric field maximum has a tuning sensitivity of approximately 7 kc/sec/in. The tuning range of the plunger is limited to about 70 kc/sec by the fact that it eventually couples in the TM_{111} mode. Other plungers have a tuning coefficient roughly proportional to their cross-sectional areas.

Reactance tuning is a very convenient fine-tuning method, since it is accomplished without mechanical adjustment. If the load coupled to the cavity by a line of impedance Z_0 is varied from Z_0 (i.e., a matched load) to $Z_0(1+jX)$, where $X\ll 1$, then the cavity will be detuned by an amount $\delta\nu_c$ given by[24]

$$\delta\nu_c = (-\beta/2Q)X. \tag{23}$$

β is the coupling coefficient.[25] A simple method for introducing the reactance is by coupling a fraction of the power from the cavity line with a directional coupler whose output is terminated by a crystal diode or a varactor. The reactance of the diode is adjusted by a biasing current. Although this presents a resistive as well as a reactive mismatch to the line, the coupling is sufficiently small so that the resultant power loss is negligible.

Preliminary tuning of the cavity to an accuracy of about 500 cps can be accomplished by conventional reflection techniques, providing care is taken not to vary the load reactance coupled to the cavity during the process. Final tuning is done with the maser itself, as described in Sec. X.

In general, it is necessary to regulate thermally the cavity to limit drift. Thermal sensitivity of the cavity can be reduced by mounting an end plate on metal spacers with a length chosen to shorten the cavity the necessary amount to compensate for the effect of expansion of the cylinder. A typical thermal coefficient for a partially compensated cavity is 1 kc/sec °C.

The system in Fig. 7 uses a cavity designed to provide as much thermal contact as possible among its components in order to reduce the effect of thermal gradients. Insofar as possible, the cavity is thermally isolated from the base structure. The base structure and bell jar assembly form an isothermal enclosure which is mounted so as to provide as little heat conduction as possible to the lower manifold. The bell jar is enclosed in an oven by a thermally insulated aluminum cylinder nesting outside the inner magnetic shield. A second similar oven encloses the first. Thermal control of the two ovens and the neck temperature results in the control of the bell jar temperature to about 0.01°C. Sensing and temperature correction are provided by the circuit shown in Fig. 8.

A word of caution about materials. Due to the requirements for very low magnetic fields, discussed in the next section, great care must be taken to avoid any ferromagnetic materials in the cavity. Stainless steels should not be used since at machined edges magnetically hard spots develop which cannot be removed by annealing. Even nickel plating over a nonmagnetic base material can cause difficulty. All cavity parts should be checked for magnetism during assembly.

[22] C. G. Montgomery, *Techniques of Microwave Measurement* (McGraw-Hill Book Company, Inc., New York, 1947), p. 297.
[23] Syncor Products Company, Malden, Massachusetts.

[24] Reference 22, p. 291.
[25] E. L. Ginzton, *Microwave Measurements* (McGraw-Hill Book Company, Inc., New York, 1957), p. 290.

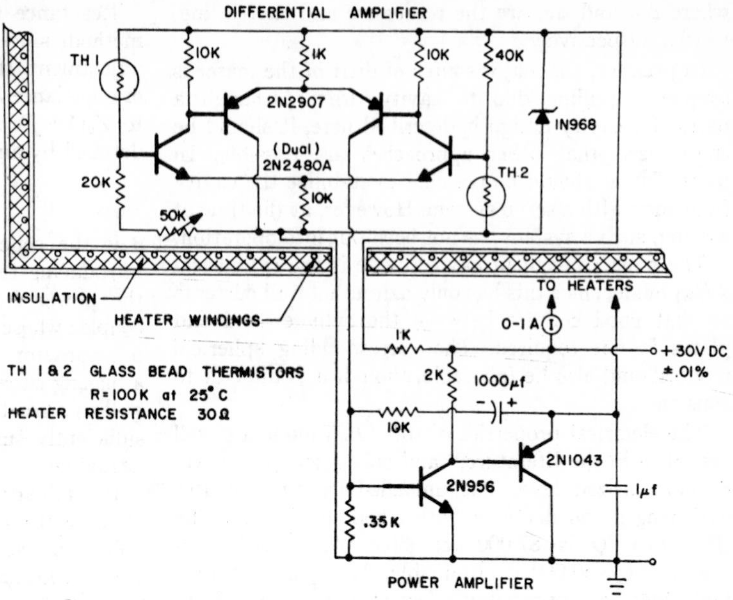

FIG. 8. Temperature sensing and servo systems.

VII. MAGNETIC SHIELDS

As a result of the quadratic field dependence of the transition $(F=1, m=0)\rightarrow(F=0, M=0)$, it is desirable to reduce the ambient field at the storage bulb to a very low value, preferably 1 mOe or less. The most satisfactory way to accomplish this is through the use of magnetic shields. Ideally, the shields completely eliminate the magnetic field, and then a small uniform field is applied with a solenoid.

In practice, the low-field limit at which the maser operates is determined by either (a) the magnitude of the residual field which may lie in an undesirable direction, or (b) the gradients in the residual field which can cause prohibitive relaxation as the Zeeman frequency is reduced. In the first case, the applied field must be large enough so that the oscillating moment is substantially parallel to the oscillating field. However, even then, owing to (b), gradients of the residual transverse field can cause relaxation owing to the random motion of the atoms. As discussed in KGR, this relaxation rate is uniform at low fields and drops rapidly when the Zeeman frequency exceeds the mean "rattle frequency" of the atoms in the bulb. Consequently, large gradients necessitate a relatively large uniform field. In poorly demagnetized shields, this means a field of 5 mOe or more.

The magnetic field dependence of the transition of interest is

$$\nu=\nu_0+2750\,H^2 \text{ cps}, \tag{24}$$

where H is the applied field in oersted.

The fractional shift of the frequency due to a small change in field is

$$\delta\nu/\nu=3.9\times10^{-6}\,H^2\,(\Delta H/H). \tag{25}$$

The maser has been operated at fields as low as 6×10^{-5} Oe, where field stability is no longer a significant problem.

In principle, it is possible to shield external fields to a high degree by the use of successive concentric shields. For the case of a uniform field at right angles to a series of three infinitely thin concentric cylinders, the shielding factor, i.e., the ratio of the applied external field H_0 to the net internal field H_i, is given[25a] by

$$\frac{H_0}{H_i}=\frac{1}{2}\frac{\mu_1 t_1}{r_1}\frac{\mu_2 t_2(s_{12}-s_{12}^2/2r_2)}{r_2^2}\frac{\mu_3 t_3(s_{23}-s_{23}^2/2r_3)}{r_3^2}, \tag{26}$$

where μ is the permeability of the shields, and the dimensions are as shown in Fig. 9. It is apparent from this that with moderately high permeability, very high shielding factors are obtainable.

A shield configuration which has proven successful in use consists of the following: The shields are composed of three coaxial cylinders fabricated from 0.025-in. Moly Permalloy. The innermost is 14 in. in diameter and 30 in. long; the middle shield is 16 in. in diameter and 32 in. long; and the outer shield is 18 in. in diameter and 36 in. long. The seams are spot-welded over $1\frac{1}{2}$-in. laps. (Mu Metal has also been used but is not as satisfactory as Moly Permalloy.) The inner two shields have end caps spun from Moly Permalloy. The shields were annealed by the manufacturer.[26] A 4-in.-diam hole through the end caps at one end does not appreciably deteriorate their performance. The static field is applied by means of a solenoid on an aluminum form just inside the inner shield. It is useful to have taps on the solenoid,

[25a] H. P. Wills, Phys. Rev. 9, 208 (1899).

[26] Allegheny Ludlum Steel Corporation, Brackenridge, Pennsylvania.

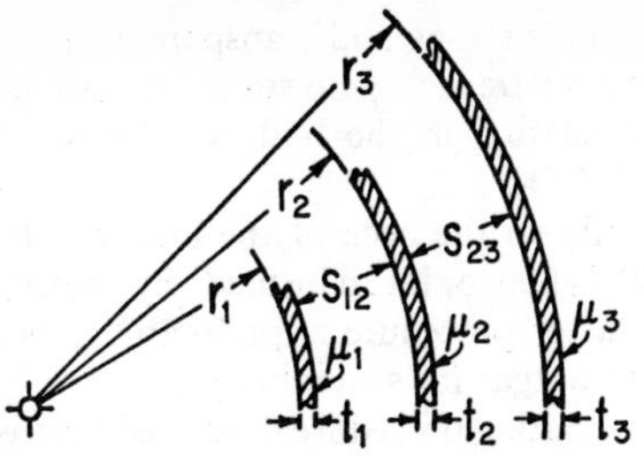

FIG. 9. Geometry of concentric cylindrical magnetic shields.

so that a few turns at each end can be energized separately. These coils can be used to reduce end effects. They are also useful for providing a small gradient for the magnetic-quenching tuning technique which will be described in Sec. X.

Proper demagnetization is critical to the shield's performance. A 60-cps demagnetizing current is passed through the center of the shields, using the vacuum can as a conductor. The resulting field is azimuthal, so that the demagnetizing flux lies completely in the shields. Current is obtained from a transformer made by winding seven turns of No. 4 copper cable around the toroidal core of a 20-A autotransformer. For fine current control, two Variacs in series are used to drive the transformer. Best results are obtained by slowly raising the current to its maximum value and then decreasing it to zero, taking about 1 min altogether.

Current up to 10^3 A is required to saturate the shields, but such strong demagnetizing current is seldom necessary. The best results are obtained by demagnetizing with maximum current of about 150 A. The residual fields appear to be caused primarily by spots of remnant magnetization in the shields. These spots vary in position and intensity from one demagnetization to another but are most commonly found along the seam of the innermost shield. The residual transverse field is generally quite nonuniform. Its maximum value is typically 10^{-5} to 10^{-4} Oe, based on measurements of the low-field radiation lifetime. Lower values are obtained from time to time.

By the demagnetization procedure described, very large external fields can be shielded. For instance, a powerful horseshoe magnet placed directly on the shields will cause a serious disturbance, but the disturbance is almost completely eliminated by demagnetization. Likewise, fields due to nearby large magnets on VacIon pumps can be shielded without undue difficulty. Apparently, the chief function of demagnetization is to raise the flux level to a point where the shield magnetization can favorably reorient itself.

Although large permanent fields are effectively reduced by the shields, they are much less effective at reducing small variations in the field, since the incremental permeability drops off rapidly at low fields. Addition of merely another shield does not help matters, since its shielding contribution is counterbalanced by the decrease in permeability of the inner shields which now operate at a lower field. Measurements made with a magnetometer indicate a shielding factor for small changes in the ambient field of about 600. (With the innermost shield made of Mu Metal, this figure is about 100.) During operation at favorable times, the field fluctuations at the storage bulb are about 10^{-7} Oe, as measured with the maser when it is operating on the field-dependent transition with a 10-sec sampling time. The rms fluctuations are almost 10 times smaller.

VIII. STORAGE BULB

A. Bulb Design

A number of considerations are involved in designing the storage bulb. The dimensions must be chosen so that the restriction on q given by Eq. (12) is satisfied, and preferably so that q is as small as possible. For this reason, it is desirable to maximize the filling factor[27] η' given by

$$\eta' = \frac{\langle H_z \rangle_{\text{bulb}}^2}{\langle H^2 \rangle_{\text{cavity}}} \frac{V_b}{V_c}. \tag{27}$$

A spherical bulb is the easiest to construct, and η' for that case may be determined using the plot of η in KGR (note the correction in footnote 27). For a cylindrical bulb of radius r and length l in a cylindrical cavity of radius R and length L, the following expression can be derived:

$$\eta' = \frac{32}{\pi^2} \frac{J_1^2(kr)}{J_0^2(kR)} \frac{\sin^2(\pi/2)(l/L)}{[1+(\pi/kL)^2]} \frac{L}{lk^2R^2}. \tag{28}$$

$J_n(x)$ is the nth-order Bessel function, $J_1(kR)=0$. From this it follows that η' is maximized by the choice $r=0.52R$, $l=0.74L$. Although the above formula neglects distortion of the fields in the cavity by the storage bulb, more detailed calculations show that η' is not significantly altered, providing the dimensions inserted in (28) refer to the actual dimensions of the cavity when it is loaded by the storage bulb. Two other considerations which enter the bulb design are the desired storage time and the collision rate. In order to avoid increasing q, the storage time must not be made long compared to the radiation lifetime. Because the wall shift is proportional to the collision rate, it is desirable to keep the bulb dimensions as large as possible. For this reason, a bulb somewhat larger than needed to maximize Eq. (7) may be desirable. The storage time T_b and mean distance between wall collisions λ are given by

$$T_b = 4V_b/\bar{v}A_a, \tag{29}$$

$$\lambda = 4V_b/A_b. \tag{30}$$

Here V_b=storage bulb volume, A_b=surface area of

[27] The symbol η' is chosen since η is the conventional nmr symbol for the filling factor. Unfortunately, η was used in KGR for the ratio of the field averages. The vertical scale of the plot of η in KGR has an error and should be divided by two.

bulb, A_a = area of the exit aperture, $\bar{v}$ = average velocity $= (8kT/\pi m)^{1/2}$. These formulas are derived in Appendix A. If a collimating tube is used instead of a simple aperture, then flow is reduced by a factor K, so that

$$T_b = (1/K)(4V_b/\bar{v}A_a). \qquad (31)$$

A table of values of K for tubes of various sizes is given by Dushman.[28] A collimating tube will also slightly alter λ, and a correction for this is presented in Appendix A.

The storage bulb is generally made of fused quartz with a diameter between $3\frac{1}{2}$ and $6\frac{1}{2}$ in. and a wall thickness of about 0.040 in. Atoms enter the bulb through a tube whose diameter and length are chosen for the desired lifetime. If it is important to make efficient use of the beam flux, the entrance aperture can be enlarged and several thin-walled tubes introduced to make a simple collimator.

B. Wall Coating

A number of materials have been used successfully for coating the storage bulb wall. At room temperature, both long-chain paraffin[2] and Dri-Film[15] surfaces have been used and yield times T_2' of about 0.3 sec in a 16-cm-diam bulb. The limit appears to be set by the chemical reaction of hydrogen with the wall. This problem is diminished by the use of Teflon, a fluorocarbon which also has the advantage of an appreciably smaller wall shift than paraffin or Dri-Film. At 35°C, a 16-cm-diam Teflon-coated storage bulb has a time T_2' of abut 3 sec and a fractional wall shift[3] of -2.1×10^{-11}. At higher temperatures, there is a decrease both in the wall shift and in the lifetime. At 100°C, T_2' is reduced by a factor of approximately 2, and the fractional wall shift is reduced by a factor of 3. The nature of the wall relaxation is discussed in Ref. 11.

The method for applying a Teflon film has been previously reported.[29] However, new techniques have been developed since then which simplify the procedure. The coating technique described in Ref. 29 is for TFE Teflon (du Pont TFE clear finish 852-201). The procedure described is improved by the use of hot white fuming nitric acid as the cleaning agent, rather than glass-cleaning solution. However, the entire coating process is simplified by the use of FEP Teflon (du Pont FEP Teflon product Code 120), since this forms a more uniform coat and several coats can be applied successively.[11] The FEP suspension is applied as described in Ref. 29. However, during the fusing process clean air is circulated through the bulb. Decomposition and waste products are thereby oxidized and removed as gases. The fusing oven temperature is brought up to 360°C during the course of an hour, held at that temperature for about 20 min, and then cooled, during the course of another hour. The film is strong and transparent and is inert to hot fuming nitric acid; however, it can be removed bodily by heating in the bulb a solution of 20% HF and 20% HNO_3.

The collimating tube in the neck of the bulb can be machined from solid Teflon, or it can be made by coating a pyrex plug. The latter procedure is preferable, since solid Teflon tends to outgas for several days.

Although the wall-coating procedure described here is quite reliable, the surfaces are not entirely inert, and it is possible that this is due to a contaminant in the Teflon. New surfaces are currently being investigated.

IX. ELECTRONICS

Systems for processing the maser signal will not be described in detail, since the procedure depends on the type of measurement to be made, and often to a large extent on the available equipment. However, there are a few points of general interest.

It is important to keep the maser operating into a constant load since reactance changes will cause frequency pulling, as discussed in Sec. VI. An isolator is invaluable for this purpose. The isolator is also helpful in decoupling two masers which are operating into converters powered by a common local oscillator. Isolation requirements are stringent, if frequency locking of the masers is to be avoided. This can be seen by the following argument: The initial phase of a maser is random, since the maser originally turns on due to noise signals. The phase of the maser is constantly perturbed by thermal noise power lying within the resonance bandwidth $kT\Delta\nu_r$. A coherent signal of less power cannot lock the maser, since random fluctuations due to noise are sufficient to randomize the maser phase with respect to the incident signal. Therefore, isolation sufficient to reduce the unwanted signal to less than $kT\Delta\nu_r$ will completely prevent locking. This required 80 to 90 dB of isolation. Fortunately, isolators with less than 1 dB of insertion loss and up to 60 dB of isolation are available.[30] It is usually possible to obtain the remaining 30 dB of isolation through the use of balanced mixers and balanced power dividers. If the maser frequencies are offset, the isolation requirements are considerably decreased. A number of systems for processing the maser signals are described in Refs. 15, 16, 31, and 32.

X. TUNING METHODS

Tuning the maser involves setting the magnetic field to a given value, and tuning the cavity. The magnetic field is easily measured by applying a small audio signal to the bulb by a single turn of wire placed

[28] S. Dushman, *Scientific Foundations of Vacuum Technique* (John Wiley & Sons, Inc., New York, 1962), p. 93.

[29] H. C. Berg and D. Kleppner, Rev. Sci. Instr. **33**, 248 (1962).

[30] Ferrotec, Inc., Newton, Massachusetts; also Mel. Labs., Palo Alto, California.

[31] Frequency **1**, 28 (1963).

[32] R. F. C. Vessot, H. Peters, and J. Vanier, Frequency **2**, 33 (1964).

around the cavity for that purpose. When the signal is at the Zeeman frequency, the oscillation level is markedly changed; usually the power is decreased. Alternatively, resonance of the Zeeman signal may be detected by using the fact that the hyperfine frequency is "pulled" when the Zeeman signal is close to resonance. The pulling is zero at resonance. Because the Zeeman line is as narrow as 1 cps under favorable conditions, it is convenient to apply a standard Zeeman frequency and then trim the magnetic field to resonance.

Cavity tuning is a more involved procedure. Normally, it is done using two masers, one acting as a frequency reference while the other is tuned. The most accurate tuning methods make use of the frequency pulling effect described in Eq. (21). The resonance width is varied by a method described below, and the cavity is tuned until the maser frequency is unperturbed by variations in the linewidth.

The following two-part method has proven useful:

(1) The resonance *width* is altered by operating the maser under two separate conditions (which we will denote by A and B), and the ratio $R=\Delta\nu_A/\Delta\nu_B$ is determined.

(2) The difference in pulling of the maser *frequency* under conditions A and B is measured. Knowledge of this figure, along with R, is sufficient to set the cavity to the correct frequency.

Here are details of the method:

(1) Determination of R. This is accomplished by offsetting the cavity frequency by some amount, typically 1 kc/sec. (The actual value of the offset need not be determined.) One simple way of accomplishing this is by switching an extra current through the diode of the reactance tuner described in Sec. VI. The amount by which the frequency of the maser changes as the cavity frequency is offset is measured. We denote this quantity by δ. δ is measured for each of the two operating conditions, A and B. From Eq. (22), it is easy to show that

$$R=\delta_A/\delta_B. \qquad (32)$$

(2) Setting the cavity. The cavity tuning is now left undisturbed, and the amount by which the frequency is shifted when the maser's condition is changed from A to B is measured. We denote this quantity by Δ.

Next, the maser is returned to condition A, and the frequency of the cavity is trimmed so that the maser frequency is increased by an amount

$$\delta_{\text{trim}}=\Delta/(R-1). \qquad (33)$$

At this point, the cavity is tuned. This can be checked by confirming that there is no frequency shift in going from A to B.

Any method for varying the resonance linewidth without shifting the resonance frequency can be used for the above procedure. However, for good sensitivity, the linewidth must be changed appreciably; R (or $1/R$) must be large compared to 1.

One method for varying the linewidth is to use spin exchange broadening. States A and B correspond to the maser operating near maximum and minimum flux, respectively. In this case, R is close to the quantity r introduced in Sec. II. [Since R is known from the result of Eq. (32), this method also allows us to find the quantity parameter q.] Another method for broadening the line is to apply an inhomogeneous magnetic field, providing care is taken not to shift the average field appreciably. The latter method has the advantage of convenience, but does not afford as much sensitivity as the former method.

A third method for cavity tuning is to plot ν versus ν_c for different values of $\Delta\nu_r$, as given in Eq. (21). The result is a family of straight lines intersecting at the point $\nu_c=\nu_0$.[31,33]

An important feature of all the above methods for cavity tuning is that the effect of a spin exchange frequency shift is eliminated; the cavity will be mistuned by just the right amount to cause the maser to oscillate on the true hyperfine frequency, regardless of flux.[3,9,32]

How well the maser can be tuned by these or other methods depends on how far q is below the critical value. Unless q is substantially below the maximum permissible value, the operating range is small, and the results will not be satisfactory.

ACKNOWLEDGMENTS

The authors wish to thank the following for their contributions to the work described in this paper: A. O. McCoubrey, H. G. Robinson, E. Recknagel, E. N. Fortson, B. S. Mathur, and L. Mueller.

APPENDIX: LIFETIME AND MEAN COLLISION DISTANCE OF ATOMS IN A STORAGE BULB

We assume that we have an enclosed region of space (i.e., a storage bulb) in which atoms are introduced and from which they effuse through a small aperture. It is assumed for the present that the mean free path is sufficiently long and the aperture is sufficiently small so that the density of atoms throughout the bulb is constant. Let V_b=volume of the bulb, A_b=total area of the enclosed surface, A_a=area of aperture, $\bar{v}$=mean velocity of atoms, N=total number of atoms in the bulb. Then the rate of loss of atoms from the bulb is $\frac{1}{4}(N/V_b)\bar{v}A_a$, and this can be shown to be equal to N/T, where T is the mean lifetime of atoms in the bulb. Hence

$$T=4V_b/\bar{v}A_a. \qquad (29)$$

It follows that the mean distance traveled by an atom before escape is $L=T/\bar{v}=4V_b/A_a$. However, we also

[33] J. Vanier and R. F. C. Vessot, Appl. Phys. Letters 4, 122 (1964).

have $L=n\lambda$, where n is the mean number of collisions an atom makes before escape, and λ is the mean distance between collisions. It can be shown that $n=(A_b+A_a)/A_a \simeq A_b/A_a$. Equating these two expressions for L then yields

$$\lambda=4V_b/A_b. \tag{30}$$

Application of this formula to a few simple geometries gives:

Sphere of radius R: $\lambda=4R/3$.

Cylinder of radius R and length L: $\lambda=2R/(1+R/2L)$.

Cube of side L: $\lambda=2L/3$.

The use of a collimating tube at the bulb entrance will increase the lifetime as described by Eq. (31) in the text. It also modifies λ, since the derivation above assumes a constant density throughout the bulb. In the neck, the density falls uniformly from the equilibrium density to 0, so that the average density is one-half that in the bulb. Since the rate of wall collision is proportional to the density, the mean wall collision rate is increased by a factor $1+\frac{1}{2}(V_t/V_b)$, where V_t is equal to the volume of the collimating tube and we have assumed $V_t \ll V_b$. The distance between collisions is then given by

$$\lambda=\frac{4V_b}{A_b}\frac{1}{1+\frac{1}{2}(V_t/V_b)}.$$

Maser Oscillation Observed from HCN Maser at 88.6 kMc*

In a previous publication,[1] the author reported observed stimulated emission from an HCN maser. At that time, no maser oscillation had been obtained.

Since the time of these earlier experiments, our HCN maser has been rebuilt. In its present form, the maser consists of a Fabry-Perot-type cavity with a plane and a spherically curved reflector ($Q=30,000$). The spacing between the two reflectors is arranged so that it results in a half confocal cavity.[2] This cavity is surrounded by two circular gas sources that shoot beams radially from many points of the periphery into the center of the circle, at which point the cavity is located. Each of these two planar beams passes through a state selector, which consists of two planes which are closely spaced and allow the gas beam to pass between them. Each plane is made of radially arranged rods which are charged alternatingly to positive and negative potentials of ±10,000 volts. The whole maser structure is contained in a copper cylinder which can be cooled by liquid nitrogen. Fastened on to this cylinder are copper fins that extend between the state selectors and freeze out that part of the gas beam that is rejected by them. The whole apparatus described above is mounted in a vacuum system.

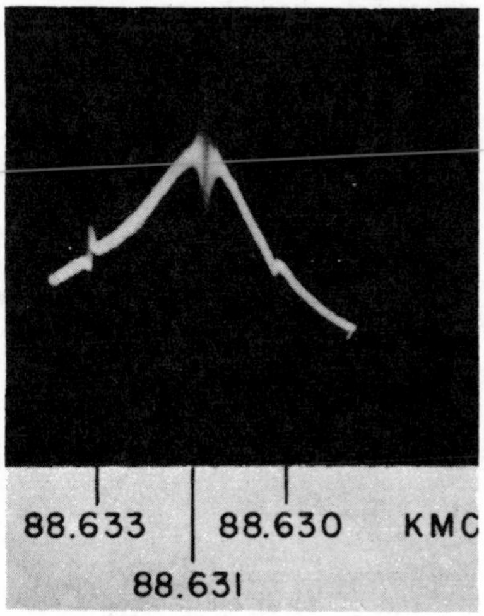

Fig. 1—The line on top of the cavity response curve sustains oscillation as indicated by the beat phenomenon between maser and probing signal.

Fig. 2—The upper trace indicates the rectified component of the maser signal at the output of the 70-Mc amplifier. The lower trace is the reference level with the maser turned off. The difference between these two levels is 16 db.

As in the previous maser,[1] a probing signal can be sent through the transmission-type cavity. Two waveguides are coupled to the cavity by small holes in the flat reflector plate.

Fig. 1 shows the emission spectrum with the strongest line at 88.631 kMc tuned to the peak of the cavity response curve. This line actually sustains oscillation. The picture shows the beat note of the maser oscillation with the probing signal superimposed on the picture of the emission line. This phenomenon needs some further explanation. The cavity allows several different modes to be resonant simultaneously. The maser apparently does not oscillate in the mode that is excited by the probing signal. This explains why the maser breaks into oscillation before any appreciable gain can be observed. The electronic gain reaches only about 5 db at the point where the maser breaks into oscillation, while the insertion loss of the empty cavity is about 10 db.

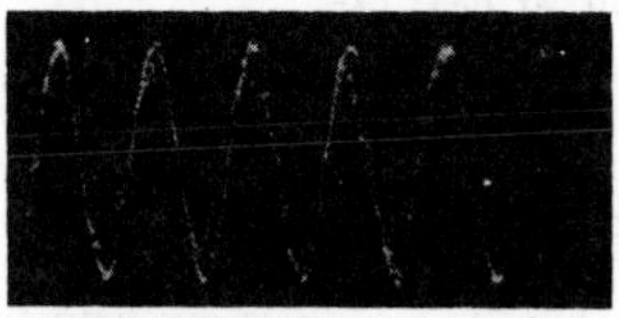

Fig. 3—Display of the 70-Mc signal resulting from heterodyning the maser output with a klystron.

The result of the maser output being heterodyned with a klystron is shown in Fig. 2. The resulting 70-Mc signal is amplified, rectified and displayed on the scope. No probing signal was passed through the cavity. The lower trace was obtained with the gas beam turned off and represents the rectified noise level. The upper trace shows the increase in level as a result of the maser output. The difference between the two levels is 16 db. The IF amplifier has a width of 20 Mc between 3-db points.

Fig. 3 shows a stroboscopic oscilloscope picture of the 70-Mc signal that is obtained by mixing the maser output with the signal from the klystron. Due to phase instability of the klystron, the scope did not achieve perfect synchronization, which explains the double trace.

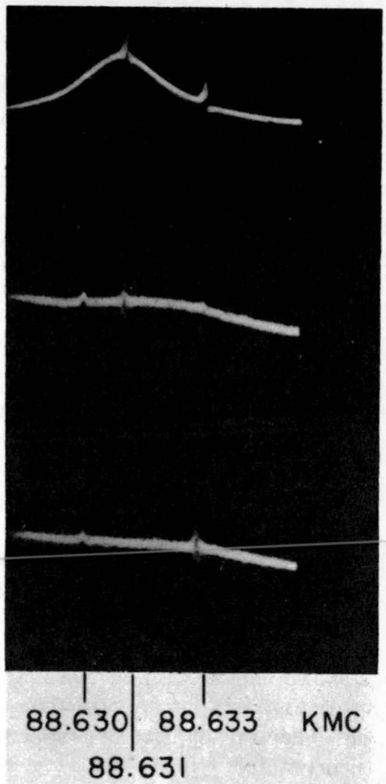

Fig. 4—Upper trace shows relative position of the two major emission lines. The two lower traces show the beat phenomenon between the maser output and the probing signal as one or the other line oscillates.

Fig. 4, finally, demonstrates that both of the stronger emission lines at 88.631 kMc and 88.633 kMc sustain maser oscillation. The upper trace shows both lines in their relative position on the cavity response curve. Subsequently, the cavity was tuned to each of the two lines in turn, and the beat note of the maser output with the probing signal (the latter at a much reduced level) is displayed in the two lower traces. As can be seen, both lines give rise to oscillation. The different traces in this picture were obtained by shifting the camera contrary to Fig. 2, where the camera stayed fixed.

DIETRICH MARCUSE
Bell Telephone Laboratories, Inc.
Holmdel, N. J.

* Received by the IRE, September 19, 1961.

[1] D. Marcuse, "Stimulated emission from HCN gas maser observed at 88.6 kmc," *J. Appl. Phys.*, vol. 32, p. 743; April, 1961.

[2] G. D. Boyd and J. P. Gordon, "Confocal multimode resonator for millimeter through optical wavelength masers," *Bell Sys. Tech. J.*, vol. 40, pp. 489–508; March, 1961.

Further Aspects of the Theory of the Maser*

K. SHIMODA,† T. C. WANG, AND C. H. TOWNES
Physics Department, Columbia University, New York, New York

(Received November 28, 1955)

The theory of the molecular transitions which are induced by the microwave field in a maser and the effects of various design parameters are examined in detail. It is shown that the theoretical minimum detectable beam intensity when the maser is used as a spectrometer for the 3–3 line of ammonia is about 10^9 molecules/sec under typical experimental conditions. Various systematic frequency shifts and random frequency fluctuations of the maser oscillator are discussed and evaluated. The most prominent of the former are the "frequency-pulling" effect, which arises from detuning of the cavity, and the Doppler shift due to the asymmetrical coupling of the beam with the two traveling wave components of the standing waves which are set up in the cavity. These two effects may produce fractional shifts as large as one part in 10^9. If adequate precautions are taken, however, they can be reduced to one part in 10^{10} or possibly less. The random fluctuations are shown to be of the order of one part in 10^{13} under typical operating conditions. For molecular beams in which the electric-dipole transition is used, the TM_{010} mode is usually the most suitable for the maser; while in atomic beams in which magnetic transitions are utilized, the TE_{011} mode is to be preferred.

I. INTRODUCTION

A DEVICE, which has been called a maser, involving a beam of molecules which give "Microwave Amplification by Stimulated Emission of Radiation," has already been described and much of the basic theory stated.[1,2] In the following discussion, we have examined in more detail certain aspects of the theory involved and explored some effects or conditions which were previously ignored or mentioned only briefly. In particular, the effects of saturation and of resonant cavity design are considered, and various types of noise and frequency shifts of the oscillator are treated.

II. ANALYSES OF THE MASER SPECTROMETER

A. Induced Emission and Saturation Effect

A beam of molecules (or atoms) in a certain quantum state passes through a resonant cavity tuned approximately to the frequency of transition of the molecules. The cavity is excited by a microwave generator through a coupled wave guide, which stimulates the transition of molecules and results in emission or absorption of microwaves. Assuming a low density of molecules in the beam, any direct interaction between the molecules, such as collision, can be neglected. The velocity of the molecules is not uniform, but all the molecules may be considered to be in the common microwave field and the emission or absorption waves from each molecule are superposed to produce the total emission or absorption.

Consider a molecule which is initially in state ψ_2 with energy W_2, and which is stimulated by a perturbation to emit or absorb microwave energy by transition to state ψ_1 with energy W_1. The wave function can at any time be expressed by

$$\psi = a_1\psi_1 + a_2\psi_2. \qquad (1)$$

As an initial condition at $t=t_0$, $|a_2|=1$ and $a_1=0$. The resonant frequency of the molecule is

$$\omega_0 = (W_2 - W_1)/\hbar. \qquad (2)$$

For simplicity of calculation, let us assume that the periodic perturbation

$$H' = -\mathbf{E}\cdot\boldsymbol{\mu}\cos\omega t \qquad (3)$$

is given to the molecule from $t=t_0$ to t. Here $\mathbf{E}$ is the electric field strength and $\boldsymbol{\mu}$ the dipole moment. The effect of field inhomogeneity in the cavity and of the thermal noise field will be discussed later.

The coefficients a_1 and a_2 as functions of t, ω, and E can then be obtained by perturbation theory as

$$a_1(t) = -e^{\frac{1}{2}i(\omega-\omega_0)t}\frac{x}{[(\omega-\omega_0)^2+x^2]^{\frac{1}{2}}} \times \sin\left\{[(\omega-\omega_0)^2+x^2]^{\frac{1}{2}}\left(\frac{t-t_0}{2}\right)\right\} \qquad (4)$$

and

$$a_2(t) = e^{-\frac{1}{2}i(\omega-\omega_0)t}\left\{-\frac{\omega-\omega_0}{[(\omega-\omega_0)^2+x^2]^{\frac{1}{2}}} \times \sin\left[[(\omega-\omega_0)^2+x^2]^{\frac{1}{2}}\left(\frac{t-t_0}{2}\right)\right] + i\cos\left[[(\omega-\omega_0)^2+x^2]^{\frac{1}{2}}\left(\frac{t-t_0}{2}\right)\right]\right\}, \qquad (5)$$

where

$$x = E\bar{\mu}/\hbar$$

and $\bar{\mu}$ is the matrix element between the two states for the component of the dipole moment along the direction of E.

The microwave power emitted from the beam of n

* Work supported jointly by the Signal Corps, the Office of Naval Research, and the Air Research and Development Command.
† Carbide and Carbon Postdoctoral Fellow, 1954–1955; now at Department of Physics, University of Tokyo, Tokyo, Japan.
[1] J. P. Gordon, Phys. Rev. **99**, 1253 (1955).
[2] Gordon, Zeiger, and Townes, Phys. Rev. **99**, 1264 (1955).

(See ERRATA p. 109)

molecules per second is given by

$$\Delta P = nh\nu_0 |a_1(L/v)|^2, \tag{6}$$

where L/v is the transit time of molecules with velocity v through the cavity of length L. If the nonuniform velocity distribution is taken into consideration, Eq. (6) should be replaced by

$$\Delta P = h\nu_0 \int_0^\infty n(v) \left| a_1\left(\frac{L}{v}\right)\right|^2 dv. \tag{7}$$

ΔP depends on E^2, the square of the electric field.

Assuming a uniform field distribution within the cross section of the cavity resonator, one obtains

$$E^2 = 8\pi W/AL, \tag{8}$$

where A is the area of the cross section, and W the stored microwave energy. To allow for the nonuniformity of the field distribution, this formula can be corrected to the form

$$E_e^2 = 8\pi W/A_e L,$$

where

$$A_e = \frac{\iint rn(r)d\theta dr \iint r|E(r,\theta)|^2 d\theta dr}{\iint r|E(r,\theta)|^2 n(r) d\theta dr},$$

$$E_e^2 = \frac{\iint r|E(r,\theta)|^2 n(r) d\theta dr}{\iint rn(r) d\theta dr}, \tag{9}$$

and $n(r)$ represents the density of the molecular beam. This assumes cylindrical symmetry, and also assumes that each molecule travels parallel to the axis so that it remains in a constant field.

Assuming a uniform molecular velocity as in (6), the emitted power may be written

$$\Delta P = nh\nu_0 \left(\frac{\theta^2}{\delta^2+\theta^2}\right) \sin^2(\delta^2+\theta^2)^{\frac{1}{2}}, \tag{10}$$

where

$$\theta^2 = W/W_c, \quad W_c = h^2 A v^2 / 8\pi^3 \bar{\mu}^2 L, \tag{11}$$

and

$$\delta = (\omega-\omega_0)(L/2v) = \pi(\nu-\nu_0)L/v. \tag{12}$$

Equation (10) shows that saturation of the spectral line becomes appreciable when

$$\theta \geqq 1, \quad \text{or} \quad W \geq W_c.$$

When the input power to the cavity is so small that there is no appreciable saturation, the emitted power is, from (10),

$$\Delta P = nh\nu_0 \theta^2 (\sin^2\delta/\delta^2). \tag{13}$$

This expression applies accurately only when $\delta \gg \theta \ll 1$ and for a uniform field distribution along the axis of the cavity. It gives a width to the line (frequency difference between half power points) of $2\Delta\nu = 0.89v/L$. If the field varies along the axis as $\sin(\pi z/2L)$, with z extending from 0 to L, as in the case of a TE mode, the line shape is given by

$$\Delta P \propto \left[\frac{\cos\delta}{1-(2\delta/\pi)^2}\right]^2, \tag{14}$$

which gives the line width $2\Delta\nu = 1.19v/L$. Equation (10) is not exact in this case, but it holds to a fairly good approximation if one takes, instead of (11),

$$W_c = h^2 A v^2 / 64\pi \bar{\mu}^2 L. \tag{15}$$

B. Detection of the Emitted Power

Consider a high-Q cavity resonator which has an output waveguide with coupling represented by Q_1, and an input waveguide of coupling Q_2. The beam of molecules is admitted into the cavity through another hole parallel to the axis of the cylinder. With the available power, P_a, in the input wave guide, the stored energy at the resonant frequency in the cavity is

$$W = (2/\pi\nu)(Q^2/Q_2)P_a, \tag{16}$$

where Q is the loaded Q of the cavity. The output power in the absence of the molecular beam is given by

$$P_0 = (2\pi\nu W/Q_1) = (4Q^2/Q_1Q_2)P_a. \tag{17}$$

In the presence of the beam, the increase of power in the output wave guide due to induced emission can be calculated as

$$\Delta P_0 = (2Q/Q_1)\Delta P, \tag{18}$$

assuming that the emitted power is small compared to the loss in the cavity.

Since the signal power to be compared to the noise power is[3]

$$\Delta P_s = (\Delta P_0)^2/4P_0,$$

the minimum detectable number of molecules per unit time, $n_{\min}$, can be calculated from the following condition:

$$\frac{Q^2}{Q_1^2}\left(\frac{(\Delta P_{\min})^2}{P_0}\right) = FkT\Delta f. \tag{19}$$

Here F is the over-all noise figure of the detector and amplifier, and Δf their effective band width. From Eqs. (10) and (19) with $\omega = \omega_0$, one obtains

$$n_{\min} = \frac{Q_1(P_0 FkT\Delta f)^{\frac{1}{2}}}{Qh\nu \sin^2\theta} = \frac{\theta}{\sin^2\theta}\,\frac{(Q_1)^{\frac{1}{2}}}{Q}\,\frac{(2\pi\nu W_c \cdot FkT\Delta f)^{\frac{1}{2}}}{h\nu}. \tag{20}$$

[3] C. H. Townes and S. Geschwind, J. Appl. Phys. 19, 795 (1948).

The optimum condition of the operating power level and couplings of wave guides can be evaluated by differentiating Eq. (20). This gives

$$\tan\theta = 2\theta,$$

which shows that for optimum sensitivity

$$\theta = 1.16, \quad W = 1.35W_c, \tag{21}$$

and

$$\theta/\sin^2\theta = 1.38. \tag{22}$$

The highest sensitivity can be obtained when the cavity is designed for minimum value of Q_1/Q^2. Assuming Q_0, the unloaded quality factor of the cavity, to be constant, the minimum value of Q_1/Q^2 is

$$\frac{Q_1}{Q^2} = \frac{2}{Q} = 4\left(\frac{1}{Q_0} + \frac{1}{Q_2}\right). \tag{23}$$

As will be shown later, the available input power of the order of milliwatt is much larger than the power in the cavity in most cases, so that $Q_2 \gg Q_0$. Hence

$$Q_1/Q^2 \simeq 4/Q_0, \quad Q_1 \simeq Q_0 \simeq 2Q, \tag{24}$$

for the optimum coupling. Then the minimum flow of molecules per unit time which can be detected is given by

$$n_{\text{min}} = \frac{6.92}{h}\left(\frac{W_c F k T \Delta f}{Q_0 \nu}\right)^{\frac{1}{2}}$$

$$= 0.44\frac{v}{\bar{\mu}}\left(\frac{A}{Q_0 L \nu}\right)^{\frac{1}{2}} (FkT\Delta f)^{\frac{1}{2}}, \tag{25}$$

using Eqs. (11), (20), (22), and (24).

If a cavity resonator is coupled by only one wave guide and one observes the change of power reflected from the cavity, the condition for the optimum coupling should have the same form as Eq. (24), resulting in the same equation for the optimum sensitivity.

As a specific example, consider a spectrometer for ammonia. The average velocity of molecules at a temperature T is given by kinetic theory as

$$v = (2/\pi^{\frac{1}{2}})(2RT/M)^{\frac{1}{2}} = 14\,551(T/M)^{\frac{1}{2}} \text{ cm/sec},$$

where M is the molecular weight, and R the gas constant. Letting $M=17$ and $T=290°$K, this expression gives $v=6.0\times10^4$ cm/sec. For the 3–3 line of NH_3, $\nu=2.4\times10^{10}$ cps and $\bar{\mu}=1\times10^{-18}$ cgs unit. The design of the cavity will be discussed in the following section, but the followlng values are taken as typical. Putting $A=1$ cm^2, $L=10$, one obtains for the 3–3 line of ammonia

$$W_c = 6.4\times10^{-11} \text{ erg}.$$

The optimum energy in the cavity is then found from Eq. (21). Using values $Q_1=Q_0=10^4$, and $Q=5\times10^3$, the net power flow from the cavity is

$$P_0 = 2\pi\nu W/Q_1 = 0.97\times10^{-10} \text{ watt}.$$

Thus, optimum sensitivity is reached with a very small flow of power.

To evaluate the spectrometer sensitivity, let us take, as an example, $F=100$, $\Delta f=10$ cps and $kT=4\times10^{-14}$ erg. Then Eq. (25) gives

$$n_{\text{min}} = 3.4\times10^9 \text{ sec}^{-1}.$$

Since the number of molecules focused into the cavity may be as great as 10^{13} to 10^{14} sec^{-1}, a signal-to-noise ratio of 10^4 to 10^5 can be expected for the 3–3 line of ammonia. This theoretically expected sensitivity of the maser spectrometer has been demonstrated experimentally by observation of the magnetic hyperfine components of the quadrupole satellites with a signal-to-noise ratio of 10 to 100, using an amplifier band width of 40 cps.[4] A further estimate of the practical limit of sensitivity will be given below, after a discussion of cavity design.

C. Figure of Merit for Cavity Resonators

Consider now the effect of cavity design on the strength of coupling between molecules and the electromagnetic field, and hence on the spectrometer sensitivity. Equation (25) shows that it is not simply Q_0 which determines the sensitivity, but the quantity Q_0L/A. The threshold condition for an oscillation to occur is also determined by the same factors. Furthermore, if the mode number n along the axis is not zero, but unity, the resonance line is broader by a factor $\pi^2/8$, and the coupling between molecules and electromagnetic field is correspondingly decreased. Hence a figure of merit M of the cavity resonator for producing induced transitions may be defined as

$$M = (LQ_0/A)(8/\pi^2)^n, \tag{26}$$

for $n=0$ or 1.

Because Q_0 is roughly proportional to the radius, a, of the cylindrical cavity resonator near cutoff, while A is roughly proportional to a^2, the largest values of M are expected in the lower modes of resonance. Therefore, values of M are computed and compared for some of the lower modes. The results for a cylindrical cavity with $L=12$ cm and a wavelength of 1.25 cm are shown in Table I. In this table ϵ is the skin depth multiplied by the specific permeability μ' of the wall material,

$$\epsilon = (c/2\pi)(\mu'\tau/\nu)^{\frac{1}{2}}. \tag{27}$$

TABLE I. Calculated values of parameters for cylindrical cavity resonator. $L=12$ cm, $\lambda=1.25$ cm.

Mode	Radius, a in cm	Narrow beam $A_e/\pi a^2$	Narrow beam $M\epsilon$	Broad beam $A_e/\pi a^2$	Broad beam $M\epsilon$	Q_0
TE_{111}	0.37	0.48	12.2	1.00	5.9	6100
TM_{010}	0.48	0.27	28.4	1.00	7.7	10 800
TM_{011}	0.48	0.27	22.2	1.00	6.0	10 400
TE_{211}	0.61	∞	0	1.00	2.9	8100
TE_{011}	0.76	∞	0	1.00	4.1	17 800

[4] K. Shimoda and T. C. Wang, Rev. Sci. Instr. **26**, 1148 (1955).

Here τ is the electric resistivity. For copper at a frequency of 2.4×10^{10},

$$\epsilon=4.27\times10^{-5}\text{ cm.} \tag{28}$$

The third and fourth columns in Table I assume a sharp narrow beam entering the cavity along its axis. The fifth and sixth columns are for a uniform intensity of beam throughout the cross section of the cavity. The actual values lie somewhere between these two extreme cases. The table indicates that the TM_{010} mode of the cylindrical cavity is the best with a figure of merit about three times that for the TE_{011} mode, which was used in most of the experiments reported earlier.[1,2]

Similar results for rectangular cavities with cross section $a\times b$ are shown in Table II. Although the TE_{011} mode in the rectangular cavity has a fairly large value of M, it should be noted that it is obtained with a small cross section. When the focused beam of molecules is not rather sharp, the value of M is counterbalanced by the loss of the beam. For a uniform beam of very large cross section, M times the cross-sectional area of the cavity is, in fact, a more appropriate figure of merit than M itself. Hence for a rectangular guide, the TM_{110} mode is probably preferable in most cases. This cavity is also convenient since the resonant frequency may be tuned by changing the width, a or b.

A cylindrical TM_{010} cavity for the 3–3 line of ammonia and a tunable TM_{110} mode rectangular cavity were constructed and tested. The holes to admit the beam of molecules were about 8 mm in diameter in both cavities, but the leakage of microwave energy from them was practically negligible compared with the losses through the wave guide and in the cavity walls. The cylindrical TM cavity was constructed for a maser oscillator and found, as may be expected from Table I, to produce oscillations with a flow of molecules about three times smaller than the minimum required for a TE_{011} mode with the same Q. The rectangular TM cavity was constructed to be tunable in the range from 22 500 Mc/sec to 26 400 Mc/sec. It had one wave guide with nearly optimum coupling, and the loaded Q was measured to be near 4000. This value is only a little lower than the expected value of loaded Q ($\frac{1}{2}Q_0$). It was found that a rather precise parallelism of walls is required for a large value of Q.

Increasing the length of the cavity will decrease the line width and increase M and sensitivity. However, the longer the cavity, the closer the resonant frequencies of the different axial modes and the more parallel stream of molecules is necessary. By the proper choice of coupling or by other devices, some modes can of course be suppressed.

Table II. Calculated values of parameters for rectangular cavity resonators. $L=12$ cm, $=1.25$ cm.

Mode	Dimensions a (cm)	b (cm)	Narrow beam A_e/ab	M_ϵ	Broad beam M_ϵ	Q_0
TE_{011}	0.63	$\ll$0.63	0.50	15.4	7.7	$\ll$5000
TE_{011}	0.63	0.31	0.50	15.5	7.8	3700
TE_{011}	0.63	0.63	0.50	10.3	5.2	4900
TM_{110}	0.89	0.89	0.25	26.0	6.5	10 100

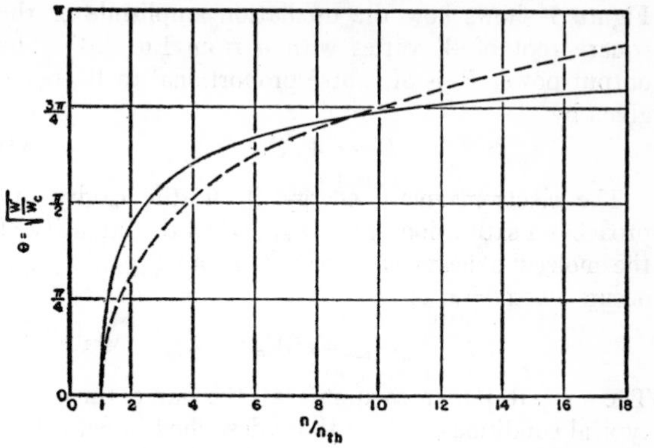

Fig. 1. The amplitude of oscillation, $\theta=(W/W_c)^{\frac{1}{2}}$ *versus* n/n_{th} as given by Eq. (31). The dashed line shows a crude estimate for nonuniform velocities.

An estimate of the practical limit of sensitivity of a maser spectrometer can be made with the following conditions. Using the TM_{010} mode of a cylindrical cavity resonator made of copper, one obtains $A=0.5$ cm^2 and $Q_0=10^4$ with $L=20$ cm and $\nu=2.4\times10^{10}$ cps. Equation (25) then gives

$$n_{\min}=5.4\times10^7\text{ sec}^{-1}$$

for the 3–3 line of ammonia, if an amplifier with $F=10$ and $\Delta f=0.1$ cps is used. Decreasing the velocity of molecules by reducing the temperature T_s of the source can increase the sensitivity slightly since, from (25), $n_{\min}$ is proportional to v and therefore to $T_s^{\frac{1}{2}}$. Also, cooling the cavity will increase the sensitivity by increasing Q_0.

III. THEORY OF THE MOLECULAR OSCILLATOR

A. Simple Theory of the Maser Oscillator

If a large number of molecules in the upper energy level is focused into the cavity resonator, a self-sustained oscillation can be obtained. The power loss from the microwave oscillation in the cavity is compensated by the emitted power from the molecular beam. This condition is given by the following formula, using Eq. (10) at $\omega=\omega_0$:

$$\frac{1}{Q}=\frac{\Delta P}{\omega W}=\frac{nh}{2\pi W_c}\frac{\sin^2\theta}{\theta^2}. \tag{29}$$

Because $\sin^2\theta/\theta^2\simeq1$ for small values of θ, the threshold rate of flow of molecules, n_{th}, required to build up oscillation in the cavity is

$$n_{\text{th}}=2\pi W_c/Qh=h v^2 A/4\pi^2\bar{\mu}^2 LQ. \tag{30}$$

If n molecules enter the cavity per unit time, Eq. (29) may be written

$$n/n_{\text{th}}=\theta^2/\sin^2\theta. \tag{31}$$

Figure 1 shows how the oscillation amplitude or the square root of W varies with n from Eq. (31). The output power P_0 is of course proportional to W, being given by

$$P_0=\omega W/Q_1. \quad (32)$$

The electromagnetic energy W in the cavity approaches a saturation value W_{sat}, when the intensity of the molecular beam is increased. From Eq. (31), this occurs when $\theta=\pi$, or

$$W_{sat}=\pi^2 W_c. \quad (33)$$

The output power saturates at the same time. For typical conditions such as those described in Sec. II.C, the output power at saturation is about 10^{-9} watt. However, more power can be obtained, even if such saturation occurs, by increasing the output coupling (decreasing Q_1).

For a certain intensity of the molecular beam, the output coupling to get maximum output of molecular oscillation may be calculated by eliminating θ in the following two equations:

$$\tan\theta/\theta=1+(Q_0/Q_1),$$
$$\sin 2\theta/2\theta=(2\pi W_c/nQ_0 h). \quad (34)$$

These expressions come from using Eqs. (29) and (32) and optimizing P_0 with respect to Q_1. Using optimum coupling given by Eq. (34), the maximum output power can be calculated as

$$P_{0,\max}=\omega W_c/Q_1. \quad (35)$$

Although expressions (34) and (35) apply accurately only for the case of uniform velocity, they can serve as qualitative guides for the case of a distribution of molecular velocities.

If the velocity distribution is taken into account, the stored energy W and the output power would continue to increase with increasing the intensity of the molecular beam instead of reaching a saturation value. When molecules with different velocities are put in a common electric field, the induced emission from all molecules is superimposed. An estimated curve for the beam of molecules with nonuniform velocities is shown by the dashed curve in Fig. 1.

Experimental tests of a maser oscillator were made using ammonia molecules in the 3-3 state and a cavity of $Q=12\,000$ operating in the TE_{011} mode. The minimum focuser voltage required to start oscillation with a source pressure of 6 mm Hg was found to be 11 kv. For a TM_{010} mode cavity with $Q=10\,000$, the minimum focuser voltage for oscillation was 6.9 kv at the same source pressure. At a source pressure of 1.2 mm Hg, the critical focuser voltage was 15 kv for the same TM_{010} cavity. Since for a fixed source pressure, the number of molecules entering the cavity is roughly proportional to the square of the focuser voltage,[1,2] the above results show clearly that for the TM_{010} cavity, the threshold number of molecules, n_{th}, was about three times smaller than that for the TE_{011} cavity.

The threshold intensities of the molecular beam calculated from Eq. (30) are $n_{th}=4\times10^{13}$ sec^{-1} and 1×10^{13} sec^{-1} for the TE_{011} and TM_{010} cavities, respectively. The ratio of these two numbers agrees reasonably well with the above results. The actual number of effective molecules per unit time in the experimental apparatus at a source pressure of 6 mm Hg and focuser voltage of 15 kv is hence probably close to

$$n=5\times10^{13}\ \text{sec}^{-1}.$$

This number is also consistent with estimates from the amount of total flow and directivity of the beam from the source.

B. Frequency Deviation of the Molecular Oscillator

Frequency shifts and noise in the molecular oscillation can be analyzed in detail by the method shown below. First the oscillating induced dipole moment of the molecular beam is calculated, assuming the electromagnetic field in the cavity. Secondly the electromagnetic field generated by the oscillating polarization of molecules is calculated and finally the assumed field and that generated by the molecules are made consistent, or equated in case there is no noise. In this section the noiseless case is treated.

The dipole moment of a molecule in the beam at anytime is

$$p=\int\psi^*\mathbf{u}\psi d\tau=a_2^*a_1\mathbf{u}_{21}e^{i\omega_0 t}+a_1^*a_2\mathbf{u}_{12}e^{-i\omega_0 t}, \quad (36)$$

where it has been assumed that ψ has the form (1). With the perturbing field given by (3), the dipole moment of a molecule at $z=v(t-t_0)$ is, when one uses (4) and (5),

$$p(t)=\bar{\mu}e^{i\omega t}\frac{x}{[(\omega-\omega_0)^2+x^2]^{\frac{1}{2}}}\times\left(\frac{i}{2}\sin\{[(\omega-\omega_0)^2+x^2]^{\frac{1}{2}}(t-t_0)\}+\frac{\omega-\omega_0}{[(\omega-\omega_0)^2+x^2]^{\frac{1}{2}}}\sin^2\{[(\omega-\omega_0)^2+x^2]^{\frac{1}{2}}\times(t-t_0)/2\}\right)+\text{complex conj.}$$
$$=p^\dagger e^{i\omega t}+p^{\dagger *}e^{-i\omega t}. \quad (37)$$

The oscillating polarization density, $P(z)$, produced by molecules in the beam is given by

$$P(z)=(n/vA)p(z). \quad (38)$$

The electric field E generated by the oscillating polarization may now be calculated. The polarization is small enough that it may be considered as a small perturbation of the normal mode of oscillation of the cavity, or of the distribution of electric field, $\mathbf{E}_n$. In this case, the frequency and the quality factor Q_m for the cavity with the molecular beam can be calculated from a result given by Slater[5] for a cavity containing a microwave current:

$$\frac{1}{Q_m}-2i\frac{\omega-\omega_c}{\omega_c}=\frac{1}{Q}+4\pi i\frac{\int \mathbf{P}^\dagger\cdot\mathbf{E}_n{}^{\dagger *}dV}{\int \mathbf{E}^\dagger\cdot\mathbf{E}_n{}^{\dagger *}dV}. \quad (39)$$

Here $\omega_c/2\pi$ is the resonant frequency and Q the loaded quality factor of the cavity without the beam. The electric field and polarization are expressed by the complex vector quantities: $\mathbf{E}\cos\omega t=\frac{1}{2}\mathbf{E}e^{i\omega t}+\frac{1}{2}\mathbf{E}e^{-i\omega t}=\mathbf{E}^\dagger e^{i\omega t}+\mathbf{E}^{\dagger *}e^{-i\omega t}$ and $\mathbf{P}=\mathbf{P}^\dagger e^{i\omega t}+\mathbf{P}^{\dagger *}e^{-i\omega t}$. Actually, $\mathbf{E}$ and $\mathbf{P}$ are parallel in the case considered, so that vector rotation is not important.

For a stationary state of oscillation, the damping should be zero and Q_m should be infinity, so that (39) becomes

$$\frac{1}{Q}+2i\frac{\omega-\omega_c}{\omega_c}=-4\pi i\int \mathbf{P}^\dagger\cdot\mathbf{E}_n{}^{\dagger *}dV\Big/\int \mathbf{E}^\dagger\cdot\mathbf{E}_n{}^{\dagger *}dV. \quad (40)$$

If the distribution of the polarization in the cross section of the cavity is proportional to the field distribution of the resonant mode, the following equation is obtained from the TM_{mn0} mode:

$$\int \mathbf{P}^\dagger\cdot\mathbf{E}_n{}^{\dagger *}dV\Big/\int \mathbf{E}^\dagger\cdot\mathbf{E}_n{}^{\dagger *}dV=\frac{2}{L}\int_0^L P^\dagger(z)\frac{dz}{E}. \quad (41)$$

If the distributions of $\mathbf{P}$ and $\mathbf{E}$ in the cross section are different, the above equation does not hold exactly, but the discrepancy of the distributions usually causes only a slight deviation from Eq. (41). Therefore the following result is obtained, assuming $Q[(\omega-\omega_c)/\omega_c]\ll 1$:

$$\tfrac{1}{2}E=-i\frac{4\pi Q}{L}\left(1-2iQ\frac{\omega-\omega_c}{\omega_c}\right)\int_0^L P^\dagger(z)dz. \quad (42)$$

By using Eq. (38), Eq. (42) may be written

$$\tfrac{1}{2}E=-i\frac{4\pi nQ}{vAL}\left(1-2iQ\frac{\omega-\omega_c}{\omega_c}\right)\int_0^L p^\dagger(z)dz. \quad (43)$$

Since $p(z)$ has been given as a function of $x=E\bar{\mu}/\hbar$, the condition of stationary oscillation is obtained from Eqs. (43) and (37) as

$$\frac{x}{2}=\frac{4\pi^2Qn\bar{\mu}^2}{vhAL}\left(1-2iQ\frac{\omega-\omega_c}{\omega_c}\right)\times\int_0^L\left\{\sin[(\omega-\omega_0)^2+x^2]^{\frac{1}{2}}\frac{z}{v}-i\frac{\omega-\omega_0}{[(\omega-\omega_0)^2+x^2]^{\frac{1}{2}}}\times\left[1-\cos[(\omega-\omega_0)^2+x^2]^{\frac{1}{2}}\frac{z}{v}\right]\right\}dz,\quad \text{for } \omega-\omega_0\ll x. \quad (44)$$

From the real part of Eq. (44), the amplitude of oscillation $E=x\hbar/\bar{\mu}$ can be obtained. Remembering that $\theta^2=W/W_c$, or $\theta=Lx/2v$ from Eqs. (8) and (11), one can thus obtain Eq. (31) when $\omega=\omega_0$.

If $\omega-\omega_0$ is considerably smaller than the line width ($\omega-\omega_0\ll v/L$, or $\omega-\omega_0\ll x$, since x is comparable with v/L), then $[(\omega-\omega_0)^2+x^2]^{\frac{1}{2}}$ can be approximated as x and the imaginary part of Eq. (44) gives

$$2Q\frac{\omega-\omega_c}{\omega_c}\int_0^L \sin\frac{x}{v}z\,dz+\frac{\omega-\omega_0}{x}\int_0^L\left(1-\cos\frac{x}{v}z\right)dz=0. \quad (45)$$

Integration of Eq. (45) gives

$$\frac{\omega-\omega_0}{\omega_0}=2Q\frac{(v/L)}{\omega_0}\,\frac{1-\cos 2\theta}{1-\sin 2\theta/2\theta}\,\frac{\omega_c-\omega}{\omega_c}. \quad (46)$$

If the Q of the line is defined by

$$Q_l=\frac{\nu_0}{2\Delta\nu}=\frac{\nu_0}{(0.89v/L)}, \quad (47)$$

then Eq. (46) shows that the fractional deviation of the frequency of the molecular oscillation is

$$\frac{\omega-\omega_0}{\omega_0}=\frac{Q}{Q_l}\,\frac{1}{2.8}\,\frac{1-\cos 2\theta}{(1-\sin 2\theta/2\theta)}\,\frac{\omega_c-\omega_0}{\omega_0}. \quad (48)$$

This is similar to the expression previously given for "pulling" of the oscillation by the cavity.[2] However, it is more complete in allowing for saturation of the molecular response. If the oscillation is weak so that saturation does not occur, $\theta\ll 1$ and Eq. (48) reduces to

$$\frac{\omega-\omega_0}{\omega_0}=1.07\frac{Q}{Q_l}\,\frac{\omega_c-\omega_0}{\omega_0}. \quad (49a)$$

Or, under more normal conditions when $\theta\simeq\frac{1}{2}\pi$, Eq. (48) is

$$\frac{\omega-\omega_0}{\omega_0}=0.72\frac{Q}{Q_l}\,\frac{\omega_c-\omega_0}{\omega_0}. \quad (49b)$$

The effect of saturation on frequency deviations of the above type is shown in Fig. 2. Since the factor

[5] J. C. Slater, Revs. Modern Phys. 18, 441 (1946).

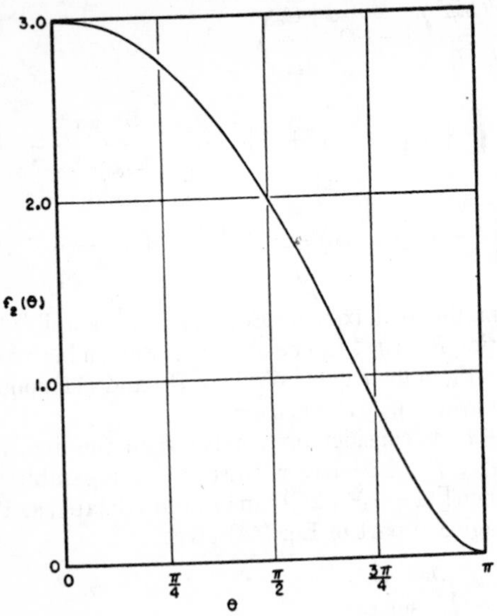

FIG. 2. A curve for $f_2=(1-\cos2\theta)/(1-\sin2\theta/2\theta)$, giving the dependence of frequency pulling by cavity tuning on the amplitude of oscillation θ. See Eq. (48).

$(1-\cos2\theta)(1-\sin2\theta/2\theta)^{-1}$ decreases with increasing θ, the frequency deviation will decrease with increasing beam intensity. This may well be the origin of frequency variations with source pressure and with focusing field which have been observed. Both of these vary the number of molecules entering the cavity, and hence vary θ. Qualitative features of the observed variations agree with what may be expected from Eq. (48). However, it must be remembered that in deriving the precise form of Eq. (48), it was assumed that molecules of uniform velocity flow through the cavity and that the saturation does not depend on the distance of the molecules from the axis. Neither of these assumptions is strictly correct.

Bassov and Prokhorov have indicated[6] that if the "natural frequency" of the resonator is tuned to the center frequency of the spectral line, the frequency of molecular oscillation will be shifted by

$$(\omega-\omega_0)/\omega_0\simeq-1/(2QQ_l).$$

It may be worthwhile to note that this type of frequency shift is, however, just due to the change of resonant frequency of the cavity by damping, since

$$\omega_c=\omega_{\mathrm{nat}}(1-1/2Q^2),$$

where ω_{nat} is the "natural frequency" used by Bassov and Prokhorov, and ω_c is the actual resonant frequency as ordinarily measured. A frequency shift of $\omega/2Q^2$ in the cavity pulls the frequency by the amount $\omega/2QQ_l$. Hence if the actual resonant frequency is tuned to the frequency of the spectral line, there is no shift of the frequency of oscillation as indicated by expression (48).

[6] N. G. Bassov and A. M. Prokhorov, Discussions Faraday Soc. **19**, 96 (1955).

There are several other types of systematic shifts in the frequency of oscillation. They include shifts due to unbalanced traveling waves in the cavity, changes in the resonant frequency of the cavity due to the polarization or dielectric constant of molecules in states other than those of interest, the effect of molecular collisions within the cavity, and also shifts due to Stark and Zeeman effects. Some of these will not be examined in much detail, since they are usually considerably less important than the "pulling" due to the cavity which was discussed above.

The frequency shift caused by the presence of traveling waves in the cavity which produce a net flow of power in one direction may be regarded as a type of Doppler shift. Thus if there is net power flow along the length of the cavity in the direction of the molecular velocity, the oscillation frequency may be expected to increase, since the frequency experienced by the moving molecules tends to correspond to the fixed molecular resonance frequency. Conversely, if there is a net flow of power in a direction opposite that of the molecular motion, the oscillation frequency should be somewhat decreased. The amount of frequency change due to traveling waves can in fact be approximately calculated by making a Fourier analysis of the apparent frequencies seen by the moving molecules. However, in order to be consistent with the formulation developed here and to show roughly the effect of saturation, this frequency shift is calculated in another, perhaps less transparent, manner.

When a small fraction of unbalanced traveling waves are present in a TM_{010} cavity, the electric field may be written

$$E=E_0\cos\omega t+E_1\cos(\omega t-\beta z)\simeq(E_0+E_1)\cos\omega t+E_1\beta z\sin\omega t, \quad (50)$$

where $E_1\ll E_0$, $\beta L\ll1$, and $E_1\cos(\omega t-\beta z)$ represents a flow of microwave power along the cavity in the direction of the molecular velocity, i.e. the positive z direction if $E_1\beta$ and E_0 have the same sign. The oscillating dipole moment of the molecules in the cavity due to the stimulating field given by (50) may be expressed as

$$p_0{}^\dagger e^{i\omega t}+p_1{}^\dagger e^{i\omega t}+\text{complex conj.}$$

Here p_0 is the dipole moment produced by the field E_0 and p_1 the small change in dipole moment due to E_1. Allowing the electric field produced by the polarization of molecules in the cavity to equal the presupposed field (50), one obtains in analogy with Eq. (43)

$$\tfrac{1}{2}\left[x+x_1-\frac{ix_1\beta}{L}\int_0^L zdz\right]=\frac{-2inv}{\bar{\mu}n_{\mathrm{th}}L^2}\left[1-2iQ\frac{\omega-\omega_c}{\omega_c}\right]\int_0^L(p_0{}^\dagger+p_1{}^\dagger)dz, \quad (51)$$

where $x=E_0\bar{\mu}/\hbar$ and $x_1=E_1\bar{\mu}/\hbar$.

The frequency of oscillation may be obtained from the imaginary part of Eq. (51). If the cavity frequency ω_c is tuned very close to the oscillating frequency ω, the terms in $\omega-\omega_c$ may be neglected and the imaginary part of (51) is, to a good approximation,

$$-\frac{x_1\beta}{2}\int_0^L zdz=-\frac{2n}{\bar{\mu}n_{\text{th}}}\frac{v}{L}\int_0^L \text{Re}(p_0{}^\dagger+p_1{}^\dagger)dz. \quad (52)$$

Now p_0 is obtained from (37) as

$$\text{Re}(p_0)=\bar{\mu}\frac{\omega-\omega_0}{x}\sin^2\left[\frac{x}{2}(t-t_0)\right], \quad (53)$$

and p_1 can be calculated by a perturbation calculation similar to that given in Sec. III.C. For this purpose, Eq. (67) has to be replaced by (50); then p_1 can be obtained from (78) by substituting x_1 and $-x_1\beta vt$ for x_n' and x_n'', respectively, in that equation. One obtains,

$$\text{Re}(p_1)=-\frac{\bar{\mu}}{2}\frac{x_1}{x}\beta v\left\{(t-t_0)\sin[x(t-t_0)]-\frac{2}{x}\sin^2\left[\frac{x}{2}(t-t_0)\right]\right\}. \quad (54)$$

Using (53) and (54), Eq. (52) can be written as

$$\frac{x_1\beta L}{4}=\frac{n}{n_{\text{th}}}\frac{v^2}{L^2}\int_{t-L/v}^{t}\left\{\frac{2}{x}\left(\omega-\omega_0-\frac{x_1}{x}\beta v\right)\sin^2\left(\frac{x}{2}(t-t_0)\right)+\frac{x_1}{x}\beta v(t-t_0)\sin[x(t-t_0)]\right\}dt_0.$$

After integration the following equation is obtained, using $\theta=Lx/2v$:

$$\frac{x_1}{x}\beta v\theta^2=\frac{n}{n_{\text{th}}}\left[(\omega-\omega_0)\left(1-\frac{\sin 2\theta}{2\theta}\right)-\frac{x_1}{x}\beta v\left(\cos 2\theta+1-\frac{\sin 2\theta}{\theta}\right)\right].$$

Using n/n_{th} as given by Eq. (31), the fractional deviation of the frequency of oscillation is

$$\frac{\omega-\omega_0}{\omega_0}=\frac{x_1}{x}\frac{2\beta v}{\omega_0}\left[1-\frac{\theta\sin^2\theta}{2\theta-\sin 2\theta}\right]. \quad (55)$$

The traveling waves in the cavity may be considered to be due to the loss through an output coupling hole at one end of the cavity with a value of Q_t, which can be shown to be

$$Q_t=\frac{\omega_0 W}{S}=\frac{2\pi^2 L}{\lambda^2\beta}\frac{x}{x_1},$$

because the stored energy is $W=KLx^2$, and the power flow S is given by $S=2K(\beta c^2/\omega_0)xx_1$. When one uses this Q_t and the Q_l given in (47), Eq. (55) becomes

$$\frac{\omega-\omega_0}{\omega_0}=\frac{2\pi}{0.89}\frac{1}{Q_tQ_l}\frac{L^2}{\lambda^2}\left[1-\frac{\theta\sin^2\theta}{2\theta-\sin 2\theta}\right]. \quad (56)$$

It should be noted from Eq. (55) that the sign of the shift reverses, if the velocity v of the beam changes sign, or hence if the direction of power flow due to the traveling waves reverses with respect to the molecular velocity. For small saturations, $\theta\ll 1$ and the bracketed factor in (55) or (56) is 0.25. For $\theta=\frac{1}{2}\pi$ it is 0.5. In a real oscillator, there is of course a distribution of molecular velocities and of effective values of θ. However, as an approximation, the bracketed factor may be assumed to equal 0.5, and this assumption gives

$$\frac{\omega-\omega_0}{\omega_0}\simeq\frac{3.5}{Q_tQ_l}\frac{L^2}{\lambda^2}. \quad (57)$$

This equation shows that, the closer the output coupling, the larger will be the frequency shift. The shift given by (57) may be seen to have roughly the same form as the shift mentioned by Bassov and Prokhorov[6] and discussed above. However, it has a quite different origin.

Assuming the values, $L=10$ cm, $\lambda=1.25$ cm, and $Q_l=4\times10^6$, the fractional frequency shift produced by the traveling waves is about 2×10^{-9} for $Q_t=3\times10^4$. If the load impedance changes by 10 percent, a change in frequency of about two parts in 10^{10} will be produced. The frequency shift caused by the output coupling can be very much reduced by placing the coupling hole just halfway between the two ends of the cavity, so that traveling waves progress from both ends of the cavity symmetrically.

In addition to the effect of the asymmetrical location of the output coupling holes described above, the variation of the molecular emission along the length of the beam in the cavity will give rise to corresponding unbalanced traveling waves and, therefore, a corresponding frequency shift. A shift of this kind will be of the same order of magnitude as that due to the asymmetrical coupling of the output hole, since the power emitted from the molecules is of the same order of magnitude as the output power. The molecular transition probability is connected with p_0 and p_1 in Eqs. (53) and (54) which vary along the length of the cavity. However, in obtaining the result given in Eq. (56), the molecular emission is effectively averaged over the molecular path in the cavity. A detailed analysis of the frequency shift due to the variation in beam emission has not been made. However, it should be noted that when little saturation occurs, the molecules deliver most of their energy toward the end of their path in the cavity, whereas for the highly saturated case, most of the energy is delivered near their entrance into the cavity. Thus the power delivered by the molecules flows in one direction for the case of little saturation, and in the reverse direction for high saturation. In some intermediate condition, the frequency shift due to variation in molecular emission should become zero. A frequency shift due to this type of traveling waves could be reduced considerably by sending two similar molecular beams into opposite ends of the cavity. This method, with the output coupling at the middle of the cavity, would probably reduce frequency shifts due to traveling waves to considerably less than one part in 10^{10}, depending on the accuracy of the symmetry.

Consider now the change in resonant frequency of the cavity due to the presence of ammonia molecules in states other than those between which the desired transition takes place. The change in dielectric constant at frequency ν, due to the presence of other rotational state, is given by

$$\Delta\epsilon=\sum_i \frac{2\pi N_i}{3h}\frac{|\mu_i|^2}{\nu-\nu_i}, \qquad (58)$$

where N_i is the density of the molecules in the ith rotational state in the cavity, μ_i the matrix element of the molecular dipole moment, and ν_i the inversion frequency of the ith rotational state. Since the only molecules which are focused are those in the upper inversion state, the contribution of molecules in the lower inversion states is neglected in the above expression. The effect of the (2,2) line on the frequency of the (3,3) line is considered as typical, since it is the nearest strong line. For an intensity of the molecular beam which is about ten times the threshold value for molecular oscillation at the (3,3) line, the change of dielectric constant due to the (2,2) line is estimated as $\Delta\epsilon(2,2)=8\times10^{-9}$. In this estimate, $\mu_i=1$ debye, $\nu-\nu_i=1.5\times10^8$ cps and $N_i=n_i/vA=4\times10^9$ cm^{-3} are used. Then the resonant frequency of the cavity is shifted by $-\frac{1}{2}\Delta\epsilon$, and the frequency of oscillation will be effected by about one part in 10^{11}. A precise calculation of this frequency shift of course requires a summation over all rotational states. However, its approximate magnitude is indicated by considering only the (2,2) state, which produces the largest shift.

It is difficult to isolate the aforementioned frequency shift experimentally, since the simultaneous existence of various states in the cavity cannot be prevented. However, if the relative populations of these states are changed, a small frequency shift might be expected. Since the focusing efficiency is a function of the rotational state as well as the focusing field, fluctuations in focuser voltage of ten percent may give rise to frequency shifts of about one part in 10^{12} due to changes in dielectric constant of gases in the cavity.

When ammonia molecules interact with each other the inversion spectrum is modified, and this effect produces the usual pressure broadening. In addition to a broadening of the inversion transition, there may be a frequency shift of the center of the line, which is proportional to the pressure broadening. Such a shift has not been observed for any microwave line, and for the inversion spectrum of NH_3 it has been shown to be less than a few percent of the line width.[7] However, in principle, some shift of this type must occur. An upper limit for the resulting effect on the frequency of a maser oscillator can be obtained by assuming that the resonance width of molecules in the cavity is broadened by about ten percent due to collisions with other molecules in the cavity. The pressure broadening is probably less than this in most cases, and the maser would not oscillate very well if it were much larger. Assuming a resonance width $Q_l\simeq5\times10^6$, the upper limit for the fractional shift is then a few thousandths of $1/(5\times10^6)$, or a few parts in 10^{10}. An additional type of frequency shift by molecular interaction which is proportional to the square of the pressure[8] has been observed, but this is quite negligible for the pressures used in the maser.

Every spectroscopic frequency is affected to some extent by electric or magnetic fields; these effects are referred to as Stark or Zeeman effects, respectively. Stark effects in the inversion spectrum of NH_3 have been discussed in a number of places.[9] They shift the inversion spectrum and disturb the coupling of the various nuclear spins to the molecular rotational motion. The uncoupling of nuclear spins is to a good approximation identical in the upper and lower inversion states, so that it does not shift the frequency of transitions which involve no change in the hyperfine states, and on which the oscillation frequency depends. The fractional change in frequency is hence approximately $(E\bar{\mu}/h\nu_0)^2$, where E is the field strength in esu, $\bar{\mu}$ the dipole matrix element, ν_0 the inversion frequency, and h is Planck's constant. Specifically, the fractional frequency shift for the most sensitive component ($M_J=3$) of the NH_3 (3,3) line is very close to $10^{-9}E_v^2$, where E_v is in volts/cm. Thus if surface charges or varying contact potentials within the cavity produce field strengths as large as 1/30 volt/cm, the resulting fractional change in frequency is about 10^{-12}.

"First-order" Zeeman effects split each hyperfine component of the inversion spectrum of NH_3 by approximately $g_J\mu_nH$, where g_J is the molecular g-factor, μ_n the nuclear magneton, and H the magnetic field in oersteds. In terms of frequency, this is about 1 kc/sec per oersted. The splitting is symmetric about the undisplaced transition, and hence for small H it corresponds only to some broadening of the line without a shift of its center.

"Second-order" Zeeman effects do shift the line center by a fractional amount which is roughly $(g_J\mu_nH/h\nu_0)^2$, or $2\times10^{-15}H^2$, where H is again in oersteds. Such a shift is usually negligible. It is about 10^6 times smaller than similar effects in atoms such as Cs, since the molecular magnetic moment is of the order of a nuclear magneton

[7] R. R. Howard and W. V. Smith, Phys. Rev. **79**, 128 (1950).
[8] H. Margenau, Phys. Rev. **76**, 1423 (1949).
[9] J. M. Jauch, Phys. Rev. **72**, 715 (1947); Coles, Good, Bragg, and Sharbaugh, Phys. Rev. **82**, 877 (1951).

rather than a Bohr magneton. Partial uncoupling of the nuclear spins from the molecular rotation occurs in molecules subjected to a magnetic field, but as in the case of Stark effect this does not change the frequency of oscillation because the transitions of interest involve no change in hyperfine energy.

First-order Zeeman effects can shift the frequency of oscillation if the oscillation does not occur very near the resonance frequency. For, if the cavity is tuned off resonance to a frequency ν_c, the oscillation frequency is "pulled" by approximately

$$\Delta\nu = (Q/Q_l)(\nu_c - \nu_0)$$

from expression (49). If the magnetic field H changes by a small amount, there is an incipient splitting which changes the line width slightly, and hence changes Q_l and $\Delta\nu$. This effect can be minimized by tuning so that $\nu_c = \nu_0$, and can in fact be useful as a test for the condition $\nu_c = \nu_0$, when oscillation should occur very near resonance.

C. Random Noise in the Maser Oscillator

Two kinds of effects give random fluctuations in the output of a maser oscillator: one comes from fluctuations in the number of molecules in the beam, which may be called "shot" noise, and the other from random fluctuations of the fields inside the cavity due to thermal noise and to "zero-point" fluctuations. We shall consider first the shot noise.

Let the number of molecules which may radiate and which enter the cavity in a time interval t be

$$N = nt.$$

The fluctuation in this number is then $\sqrt{N} = \sqrt{(nt)}$. The output of the maser oscillator is

$$P_0 = Knh\nu, \tag{59}$$

where K depends on θ and Q_1/Q, but is normally of the order of unity. The shot effect may hence be expected to produce an average fluctuation in power during a time t of approximately

$$(\langle \Delta P_0^2 \rangle_{\text{Av}})^{\frac{1}{2}} = KN^{\frac{1}{2}}h\nu/t = Kh\nu(n/t)^{\frac{1}{2}}.$$

The fractional fluctuation of amplitude of the electric field E is, from (59) and the above equation

$$\frac{(\langle \Delta E^2 \rangle_{\text{Av}})^{\frac{1}{2}}}{E} = \frac{1}{2(nt)^{\frac{1}{2}}}. \tag{60}$$

It must be remembered, however, that the field strength cannot change much more rapidly than the time required for a molecular transition to occur, or than the inverse of the frequency width of the molecular response. This time is approximately

$$\tau = 2Q_l/\omega. \tag{61}$$

In a typical case, it has a value $\tau = 10^{-4}$ sec and $n = 10^{14}$ sec^{-1}, so that the fractional fluctuation is at most $(\langle \Delta E^2 \rangle_{\text{Av}})^{\frac{1}{2}}/E \simeq 5\times 10^{-6}$ which is small enough usually to be negligible. The smallness of this fluctuation results from the large number, i.e., $n\tau = 10^{10}$, of molecules in the cavity at all times.

In addition to an amplitude fluctuation, there is a phase fluctuation during the correlation time τ of the oscillation which is approximately equal to the fractional change in amplitude, or

$$(\langle \Delta\phi^2 \rangle_{\text{Av}})^{\frac{1}{2}} = \frac{1}{2(n\tau)^{\frac{1}{2}}}. \tag{62}$$

Such phase fluctuations which occur during each correlation time add together in a random way to produce a root-mean-square phase change of

$$t(\langle \Delta\omega^2 \rangle_{\text{Av}})^{\frac{1}{2}} = \left(\frac{t}{\tau}\langle \Delta\phi^2 \rangle_{\text{Av}}\right)^{\frac{1}{2}} = \frac{1}{2\tau}\left(\frac{t}{n}\right)^{\frac{1}{2}},$$

after a time interval t. Hence the fluctuation of frequency is obtained by using (59) and (61) as

$$\frac{(\langle \Delta\omega^2 \rangle_{\text{Av}})^{\frac{1}{2}}}{\omega_0} = \frac{1}{4Q_l}\left(\frac{Kh\nu}{P_0 t}\right)^{\frac{1}{2}} \simeq \frac{1}{Q_l}\left(\frac{h\nu}{P_0 t}\right)^{\frac{1}{2}}. \tag{63}$$

The magnitude of frequency fluctuations due to this effect will be shown below to be considerably smaller than that due to thermal noise at normal temperatures.

The molecular oscillator builds up initially from the thermal noise fields present in the cavity. During the stationary state of oscillation, thermal noise in the cavity shifts the frequency and amplitude of oscillation in a random manner. Although the precise behavior of thermal fluctuations in the cavity depends on the presence of molecular beam amplification, a rough estimate which ignores the effect of the saturation of the beam will first be described.

Assuming that the noise power, $kT\Delta f$, is independent of the oscillation in the cavity, the average fractional fluctuation of amplitude and phase of the molecular oscillation is approximately

$$(\langle \Delta E^2 \rangle_{\text{Av}})^{\frac{1}{2}}/E \simeq (\langle \Delta\phi^2 \rangle_{\text{Av}})^{\frac{1}{2}} \simeq (kT\Delta f/P_0)^{\frac{1}{2}}, \tag{64}$$

where Δf is determined by the length of the time t used for measuring the frequency of the oscillator. When the frequency is observed during a time interval t, the transfer function, that is the frequency characteristics for the frequency modulation noise fluctuating at a frequency f, is proportional to

$$(1/f)\sin(\pi f t).$$

This transfer function gives the effective band width of

$$\Delta f \simeq 1/t. \tag{65}$$

From (64), (65), and (61) the fractional fluctuation of

the frequency of oscillation due to thermal noise is

$$\frac{(\langle\Delta\omega^2\rangle_{\text{Av}})^{\frac{1}{2}}}{\omega_0} \simeq \frac{1}{2Q_l}\left(\frac{kT}{P_0 t}\right)^{\frac{1}{2}}. \tag{66}$$

The maximum frequency fluctuation which can occur is found by setting t equal to the minimum response time τ in (66), which gives

$$\frac{(\langle\Delta\omega^2\rangle_{\text{Av}})^{\frac{1}{2}}}{\omega_0} \simeq \frac{1}{2Q_l}\left(\frac{kT}{P_0 \tau}\right)^{\frac{1}{2}}.$$

For typical conditions this quantity is approximately 10^{-10}, which is the fractional frequency change occurring in the time $\tau \simeq 10^{-4}$ sec. For $t=1$ sec, this is reduced to 10^{-12}.

Comparison of Eqs. (63) and (66) shows that

$$\frac{\langle\Delta\omega^2\rangle_{\text{Av (shot noise)}}}{\langle\Delta\omega^2\rangle_{\text{Av (thermal noise)}}} \simeq \frac{h\nu}{kT}.$$

At room temperature and microwave frequencies this ratio is about 3×10^{-3}; hence shot noise can be neglected compared to thermal noise.

It should be noted that spontaneous emission of radiation by the molecules also produces random fluctuations. Their nature is, however, precisely the same as that of fluctuations due to thermal radiation and considerably smaller. For our purposes, spontaneous emission may be considered as an added thermal fluctuation corresponding to a temperature of $h\nu/k$, which for microwave frequencies is only one or two degrees absolute.

The theory of fluctuations of the oscillator, as simplified above, might lead one to suppose that successive changes in both phase and amplitude add in a random manner, so that the amplitude of the oscillating electric field would at times go through zero. This does not actually occur for the same reason that it does not occur in most other oscillators: the nonlinearities in the oscillator's response ensure that the amplitude stays within certain narrow limits rather than increasing or decreasing in a random way. However, as in most other oscillators, the phase variation is quite random and may increase indefinitely as indicated by the above discussion in a way which is proportional to $\sqrt{t}$.

To allow for the effect of molecular amplification and nonlinearities on the thermal noise, a more complete theory is described. In the following discussion the noise field, $E_n(t)$, due to thermal noise is calculated by a perturbation technique, assuming that $E_n(t)$ is small compared to the field E_0 produced by emission of radiation from the molecules.

The electric field in the cavity resonator may be written

$$E = E_0 \cos\omega t + E_n(t), \tag{67}$$

where ω is the frequency of oscillation, E_0 is assumed to be constant, and $E_n(t)$ is a small field associated with thermal noise. If one uses

$$x = E_0\bar{\mu}/\hbar, \quad x_n(t) = 2E_n(t)\bar{\mu}/\hbar, \tag{68}$$

the Schrödinger equation for the wave function $\psi = a_1\psi_1 + a_2\psi_2$ requires

$$\dot{a}_1 = \tfrac{1}{2}i\{x[e^{i(\omega-\omega_0)t} + e^{i(\omega+\omega_0)t}] + x_n e^{-i\omega_0 t}\}a_2,$$
$$\dot{a}_2 = \tfrac{1}{2}i\{x[e^{-i(\omega-\omega_0)t} + e^{-i(\omega+\omega_0)t}] + x_n e^{+i\omega_0 t}\}a_1. \tag{69}$$

If the oscillation occurs near the molecular resonance, then $(\omega-\omega_0)^2 \ll x^2$, and $(\omega-\omega_0)t \simeq 0$ for the time of passage of the molecules through the cavity. Furthermore $e^{i(\omega+\omega_0)t}$ fluctuates very rapidly during the time of transition when a_1 and a_2 are changing more slowly, so that the terms in (69) including this exponential average to zero and may be neglected to a good approximation. Terms such as $x_n e^{-i\omega_0 t}$ cannot similarly be omitted because x_n varies rapidly with time in such a way that the product $x_n e^{-i\omega_0 t}$ does not necessarily average to zero during the transition.

Let the solution of (69) for $x_n=0$ be $a_1^{(0)}$ and $a_2^{(0)}$, which are given in expressions (4) and (5) as

$$a_1^{(0)} = -\sin[\tfrac{1}{2}x(t-t_0)],$$
$$a_2^{(0)} = i\cos[\tfrac{1}{2}x(t-t_0)], \tag{70}$$

when $(\omega-\omega_0)^2 \ll x^2$ as assumed above. Here t_0 is the time at which a molecule enters the cavity. The solution when $x_n \neq 0$ may be written

$$a_1 = a_1^{(0)} + a_1^{(1)},$$
$$a_2 = a_2^{(0)} + a_2^{(1)}, \tag{71}$$

and then (69) becomes

$$\dot{a}_1^{(1)} = \tfrac{1}{2}i(xa_2^{(1)} + x_n e^{-i\omega_0 t}a_2^{(0)}),$$
$$\dot{a}_2^{(1)} = \tfrac{1}{2}i(xa_1^{(1)} + x_n e^{i\omega_0 t}a_1^{(0)}), \tag{72}$$

if terms in the product of the two small quantities $a_1^{(1)}$ and x_n or $a_2^{(1)}$ and x_n are neglected.

The quantity x_n in (69) or (72) due to noise may be written

$$x_n = 2x_n' \cos\omega t - 2x_n'' \sin\omega t, \tag{73}$$

in which case expression (67) for the field becomes

$$E = \frac{\hbar}{\bar{\mu}}(x + x_n')\cos\left(\omega t + \frac{x_n''}{x}\right), \tag{74}$$

which makes it evident that x_n' gives the amount of amplitude modulation and x_n''/x the phase modulation. Making the substitutions (73) and

$$a_1^{(1)} = Ae^{\frac{1}{2}ix(t-t_0)} - Be^{-\frac{1}{2}ix(t-t_0)},$$
$$a_2^{(1)} = Ae^{\frac{1}{2}ix(t-t_0)} + Be^{-\frac{1}{2}ix(t-t_0)}, \tag{75}$$

into Eq. (72), one finds

$$A=-\tfrac{1}{4}[x_n'+ix_n''e^{-ix(t-t_0)}],$$
$$\dot{B}=+\tfrac{1}{4}[x_n'+ix_n''e^{+ix(t-t_0)}]. \qquad (76)$$

Again in obtaining expression (76) it must be remembered that very rapidly varying terms such as $e^{i(\omega+\omega_0)t}$ average to zero and may be omitted to a good approximation.

Now the oscillating dipole moment of the molecule is given by

$$p=\bar{\mu}e^{i\omega_0 t}(a_1^{(0)}a_2^{(0)*}+a_1^{(1)}a_2^{(0)*}+a_1^{(0)}a_2^{(1)*}) + \text{complex conj.}$$
$$=p_0^\dagger e^{i\omega t}+p_n^\dagger(t)+\text{complex conj.} \qquad (77)$$

Using Eqs. (70) and (75) together with (76), one obtains

$$p_0^\dagger=\tfrac{1}{2}i\bar{\mu}\sin(xt),$$

$$p_n^\dagger(t)=-\tfrac{1}{2}\bar{\mu}e^{i\omega_0 t}\left[\int x_n''\cos\{x(t-t_0)\}dt - i\cos\{x(t-t_0)\}\int x_n'dt\right]. \qquad (78)$$

The electric field produced by the polarization of molecules can be calculated in the same way as described in the former section, using (39), (41), and (43). The total field is the sum of fields produced by molecules in the beam and those generated by thermal agitation in the wall of the cavity. It may be written, as $Q[(\omega-\omega_c)/\omega_c]\ll 1$,

$$E^\dagger=-i\frac{4\pi Qn}{vAL}\int_0^L p^\dagger(z)dz+e_n^\dagger, \qquad (79)$$

where $E^\dagger$ is defined as in Eqs. (39) and (67), and $e_n^\dagger e^{i\omega_0 t}+e_n^{\dagger *}e^{-i\omega_0 t}$ is the primary thermal noise which would occur without the presence of the molecular beam. After some manipulation, Eq. (79) can be rewritten as

$$\frac{x}{2}+\frac{x_n^\dagger}{2}-\frac{\xi_n^\dagger}{2}=\frac{4\pi^2 Q_n\bar{\mu}^2}{hAL}\Bigg[\int_{t-L/v}^{t}\sin(x(t-t_0))dt_0 + i\int_{t-L/v}^{t}\left\{\int_{t_0}^{t}x''\cos(x(t-t_0))dt - i\cos(x(t-t_0))\int_{t_0}^{t}x_n'dt\right\}dt_0\Bigg], \qquad (80)$$

where $x_n^\dagger$ is defined by $x_n^\dagger e^{i\omega t}+x_n^{\dagger *}e^{-i\omega t}$, that is, $x_n^\dagger=x_n'+ix_n''$ from (73). In addition,

$$\xi_n^\dagger(t)=2\frac{e_n^\dagger\bar{\mu}}{\hbar}=\xi_n'(t)+i\xi_n''(t). \qquad (81)$$

The first integral in (80), which gives the field strength of precisely the frequency $\omega_0/2\pi$ and which is independent of the noise, yields the same results as were found above in Sec. III.B. The remaining terms represent the noise fluctuations and can be written as

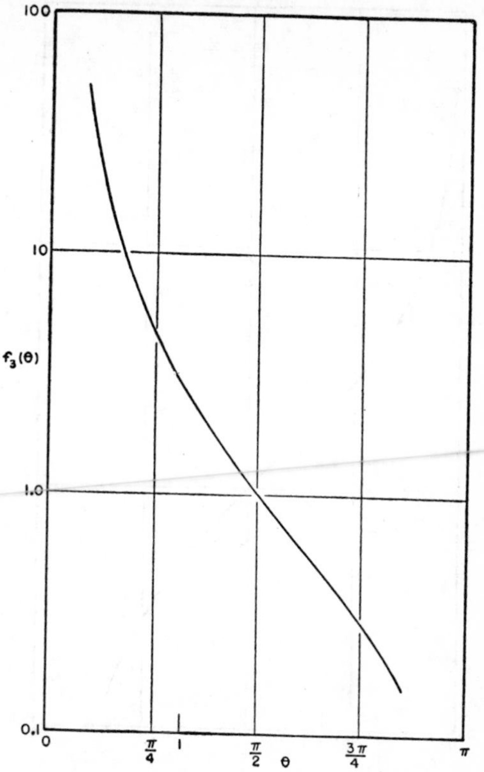

FIG. 3. A curve for $f_3=1/(1-\theta\cot\theta)$, giving the dependence of amplitude fluctuations due to thermal noise on the amplitude of oscillation θ. See Eq. (84).

$$x_n'=\left[2\frac{n}{n_{\text{th}}}\frac{v^2}{L^2}\int_{t-L/v}^{t}\cos\{x(t-t_0)\}\int x_n'dtdt_0\right]+\xi_n', \qquad (82)$$

$$x_n''=\left[2\frac{n}{n_{\text{th}}}\frac{v^2}{L^2}\times\int_{t-L/v}^{t}\int_{t_0}^{t}x_n''\cos\{x(t-t_0)\}dtdt_0\right]+\xi_n''. \qquad (83)$$

From these equations, amplitude noise x_n' and phase noise x_n''/x can be computed.

Equation (82) may be simply solved for the important case of noise components which differ from the frequency of oscillation by an amount smaller than the line width. For these components, x_n' varies much more slowly than does $\cos(xt)$, so that as a first approximation (82) can be integrated by assuming x_n' to be constant. Using expression (31) for n/n_{th} and $\theta=xL/2v$, one obtains the following from this integration:

$$2x_n'=\frac{\xi_n'}{1-\theta\cot\theta} \qquad (84)$$

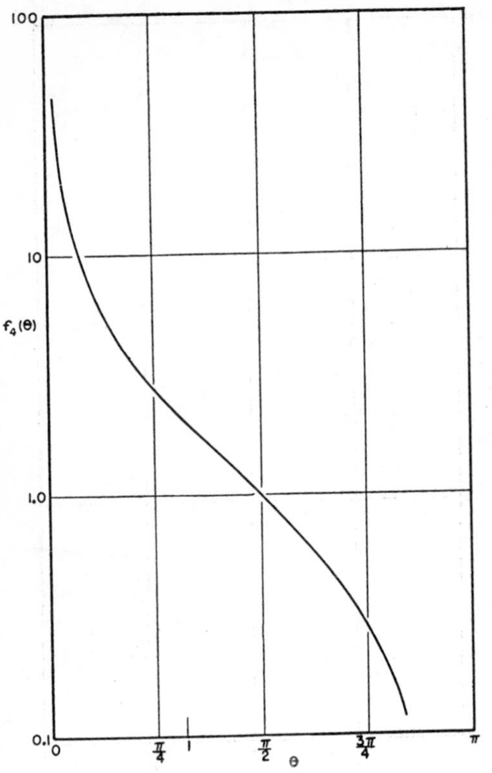

FIG. 4. A curve for $f_4=\pi\sin^2\theta/(2\theta-\sin 2\theta)$, giving the dependence of frequency fluctuations due to thermal noise on the amplitude of oscillation θ. See Eqs. (92).

This expression shows that the magnitude of AM noise depends strongly on the amplitude of oscillation, as can be seen from Fig. 3. Since the primary noise, ξ_n', is independent of frequency, x_n' is also independent of frequency near the center of the molecular transition frequency where the approximations involved in obtaining (84) are valid. The frequency distribution of noise outside this range can also be estimated in a similar way by using $a_1^{(0)}$ and $a_2^{(0)}$ as given by Eqs. (4) and (5) so long as $\omega-\omega_0\ll\omega_0$, but such a calculation would be very tedious. Presumably the spectrum of amplitude noise is not far different from the line shape.

Evaluation of the fluctuation of phase from Eq. (83) is somewhat more difficult. If the phase fluctuation is computed from (83) by assuming that x_n'' in the integrand is constant, then (83) becomes, after integration, $x_n''=x_n''+\xi_n''$. This indicates that x_n'' must approach infinity, corresponding to the indefinite increase in the phase error with increasing time as was found in the simpler discussion above. In order to obtain a finite result for x_n'' and to examine the way in which it approaches large values with increasing time, it is necessary to allow variation of x_n'' in the integrand.

Consider the thermal noise $\xi_n''(t)$ in a small band width df about a frequency which differs from the oscillator frequency by f. Then ξ_n'' which is a function of time can be written in the form

$$\xi_n''=\int_0^\infty \xi_n''(f)\cos(2\pi ft+\delta)df, \qquad (85)$$

where δ is a phase angle. x_n'' must have the similar form,

$$x_n''=\int_0^\infty x_n''(f)\cos(2\pi ft+\delta')df,$$

where $x_n''(f)$ and δ' may be assumed to be constants with respect to time.

Substitution of these expressions into Eq. (83) gives, with the assumption $f\ll v/\pi L$,

$$x_n''(f)=\xi_n''(f)\frac{v}{\pi fL}\frac{\sin^2\theta}{(1-\sin 2\theta/2\theta)}, \qquad (86)$$

and $\delta-\delta'=\frac{1}{2}\pi$.

Because ξ_n'' represents a component in the primary thermal noise given by (79) and (81), $\langle[\xi_n''(f)]^2\rangle_{\text{Av}}$ is actually independent of frequency f. From (85), (81), (68), and (64), one has

$$\frac{\langle[\xi_n''(f)]^2\rangle_{\text{Av}}}{x^2}=\frac{\frac{1}{2}\langle\xi_n^2(f)\rangle_{\text{Av}}}{x^2}=\frac{2\langle e_n^2(f)\rangle_{\text{Av}}}{E_0^2}=\frac{kTdf}{\omega_0 W/Q}, \qquad (87)$$

where $\xi_n(f)$ and $e_n(f)$ represents the amplitude of Fourier components at the frequencies $(\omega_0/2\pi)\pm f$. Thus the mean square of x_n'' is obtained as

$$\frac{\langle x_n''^2\rangle_{\text{Av}}}{x^2}=\frac{QkT}{\omega_0 W}\left\{\frac{v}{\pi L}\frac{\sin^2\theta}{[1-(\sin 2\theta/2\theta)]}\right\}^2\int_{f_{\min}}^{f_{\max}}\frac{df}{f^2}, \qquad (88)$$

where $f_{\min}$ and $f_{\max}$ are the minimum and maximum frequencies respectively for the range of values of f which are considered. Both $f_{\max}$ and $f_{\min}$ must be much less than the line width in order that Eq. (86) be approximately correct. Assuming $f_{\max}\gg f_{\min}$, expression (88) is

$$\frac{\langle x''^2\rangle_{\text{Av}}}{x^2}=\frac{QkT}{\omega_0 W f_{\min}}\left[\frac{v}{\pi L}\frac{2\theta\sin^2\theta}{2\theta-\sin 2\theta}\right]^2. \qquad (89)$$

If fluctuations are observed during a time interval t, the minimum frequency of fluctuation which can be observed is approximately

$$f_{\min}\simeq 1/2t. \qquad (90)$$

From (74), the root mean square of the fractional fluctuation of frequency is

$$\frac{(\langle\Delta\omega^2\rangle_{\text{Av}})^{\frac{1}{2}}}{\omega_0}=\frac{(\langle x''^2\rangle_{\text{Av}})^{\frac{1}{2}}/x}{\omega_0 t}. \qquad (91)$$

Thus one obtains from (89), (90), and (91)

$$\frac{(\langle\Delta\omega^2\rangle_{\text{Av}})^{\frac{1}{2}}}{\omega_0}=\frac{v}{\pi\omega_0 L}\left(\frac{2QkT}{\omega_0 Wt}\right)^{\frac{1}{2}}\frac{2\theta\sin^2\theta}{2\theta-\sin 2\theta}.$$

Using $\theta^2 = W/W_c$, and $Q_l = \omega_0 L/(0.89\times 2\pi v)$, the frequency fluctuations can be written

$$\frac{(\langle\Delta\omega^2\rangle_{Av})^{\frac{1}{2}}}{\omega_0} = \frac{0.16}{Q_l}\left(\frac{QkT}{\omega_0 W_c t}\right)^{\frac{1}{2}} \frac{\sin^2\theta}{2\theta - \sin 2\theta}. \quad (92)$$

This is very similar to the approximate expression (66) obtained earlier, since $\omega_0 W/Q$ is a typical value of emitted power from the molecular beam for $\theta = 1$. Dependence of the frequency fluctuation on power is given by the last factor in (92), which is plotted in Fig. 4. This figure shows that the amount of FM noise increases by a large factor when the oscillation is weak. It must be remembered that Eq. (92) is not exact because of the approximation used in its derivation. In addition, the distribution of molecular velocities and matrix elements over molecules in the beam tends to make expression (92) even less accurate. However, it probably represents the major features of noise fluctuations reasonably well.

As a typical example, let $\theta = \frac{1}{2}\pi$, $W_c = 2\times 10^{-11}$ erg, $Q = 5000$, and $Q_l = 5\times 10^6$, then

$$\frac{(\langle\Delta\omega^2\rangle_{Av})^{\frac{1}{2}}}{\omega_0} \simeq 10^{-13} t^{-\frac{1}{2}}.$$

This calculated fluctuation is somewhat smaller than the upper limit set by experimental observations.[2]

ACKNOWLEDGMENTS

The authors are grateful for discussions with Professor W. E. Lamb, Jr., Dr. J. P. Gordon, and Dr. Ali Javan which have influenced and improved the above work.

Errata: Further Aspects of the Theory of the Maser

K. Shimoda, T.C. Wang, and C.H. Townes

Equation (35) should read:

$$P_{0,max} = \omega\,\theta^2 W_c / Q_1$$

Page 1313: Lower left part of page after the words is obtained, delete

assuming $Q[(\omega - \omega_c)/\omega_c] \ll 1$

Correct equations (42), (43), and (44) to read:

$$\tfrac{1}{2}E = \frac{-i4\pi Q}{L}\left(1 + (2iQ)\left(\frac{\omega - \omega_c}{\omega_c}\right)\right)^{-1} \int_0^L P\dagger(z)\,dz \quad (42)$$

$$\tfrac{1}{2}E = \frac{-i4\pi nQ}{vAL}\left(1 + (2iQ)\left(\frac{\omega - \omega_c}{\omega_c}\right)\right)^{-1} \int_0^L p^{\dagger}(z)\,dz \quad (43)$$

$$\frac{x}{2} = \frac{4\pi^2 Qn\mu^{-2}}{vhAL} \left(1 + (2iQ)\left(\frac{\omega - \omega_c}{\omega_c}\right)\right)^{-1} \frac{x}{[(\omega - \omega_o)^2 + x^2]^{\frac{1}{2}}}$$

$$X \int_o^L \{\sin[(\omega - \omega_o)^2 + x^2]^{\frac{1}{2}} \frac{z}{v} - \frac{i(\omega - \omega_o)}{[(\omega - \omega_o)^2 + x^2]^{\frac{1}{2}}} \qquad (44)$$

$$X [1 - \cos [(\omega - \omega_o)^2 + x^2]^{\frac{1}{2}} \frac{z}{v}]\} dz$$

Delete the words: for $\omega - \omega_o \ll x$

Delete the entire paragraph starting with:

If $\omega - \omega_o$ is considerably smaller .... and delete equation 45.

Above equation (46) delete the words: Integration of Eq. (45) and substitute the words: Imaginary part of Eq. (44)

Page 1314, correct equation (51) to read:

$$\tfrac{1}{2}[x + x_1 - \frac{ix_1\beta}{L} \int_o^L zdz]$$

$$= \frac{-2inv}{\bar{\mu} n_{th} L^2} \left[1 + 2iQ\left(\frac{\omega - \omega_c}{\omega_c}\right)\right]^{-1} \int_o^L (p_o^\dagger + p_1^\dagger) dz \qquad (51)$$

Page 1318 equations (69) should read

$$\dot{a}_1 = \tfrac{1}{2}i\ \{x[e^{i(\omega-\omega_o)t} + e^{-i(\omega+\omega_o)t}] + x_n e^{-i\omega_o t}\}\ a_2$$

$$\dot{a}_2 = \tfrac{1}{2}i\ \{x[e^{-i(\omega-\omega_o)t} + e^{+i(\omega+\omega_o)t}] + x_n e^{+i\omega_o t}\}\ a_1$$

Page 1319 equation (76) change A to $\dot{A}$.

Equation 82 should read:

$$x_n{}' = [\frac{2nv^2}{n_{th}L^2}\int_{t-L/_v}^{t} \cos\ \{x(t-t_o)\} \int_{t_o}^{t} x'_n\, dt dt_o] + \xi_n{}'$$

NONLINEAR EFFECTS OF THE INTERACTION OF RESONANCE FIELDS IN THE MOLECULAR GENERATOR AND AMPLIFIER

V. M. KONTOROVICH and A. M. PROKHOROV

Institute for Radiophysics and Electronics, Academy of Sciences, Ukrainian S.S.R. and
P. N. Lebedev Physics Institute, Academy of Sciences, U.S.S.R.

Submitted to JETP editor June 7, 1957

J. Exptl. Theoret. Phys. (U.S.S.R.) 33, 1428-1430 (December, 1957)

The position of the possible frequencies of generation and amplification, with saturation by an auxiliary field taken into account, is investigated on the basis of an analysis of the polarizability of a quantum system situated in two resonance fields. It is shown that an amplifier or a generator can operate at two frequencies which depend on the amplitude as well as on the frequency of the auxiliary field.

BASOV and Prokhorov[1] have considered a molecular generator and amplifier that does not utilize a molecular beam. In this case an auxiliary field of higher frequency is required for obtaining active molecules.

In contrast to the generator with a beam, where, with any kind of excitation (state selection), only the number of active molecules obtained plays a role, in generators and amplifiers with an auxiliary field the molecules must be situated simultaneously in two resonance fields with a common resonance level. In this case the auxiliary field will affect the shapes of the lines and the positions of the resonant frequencies of the transition used. Similar effects were observed by Burgess and Norberg[2] in the hyperfine spectrum of the $(SO_3)_2NO^{--}$ radical and are easily explained on the basis of the quantum theory of dispersion.

Let two resonance fields with frequencies ω_1 and ω_2 act simultaneously on a quantum system with a nonequidistant discrete spectrum; let these frequencies be close to the transition frequencies ω_{mn} and ω_{mq} between any levels of the system (these levels will be called resonance levels), under the condition that one of the resonance levels be common to both fields.

We shall give an expression for the Fourier component of the average dipole moment of a gas, in which τ is the average time between collisions of a molecule, obtained under the usual assumptions,[3] but in the presence of two fields with frequencies

$$|\omega_1 - \omega_{mn}| \lesssim 1/\tau, \quad |\omega_2 - \omega_{mq}| \lesssim 1/\tau$$

and a common resonance level m. The perturbed Hamiltonian is $\hat{H}(t) = \hat{H}_0 + \hbar\hat{V}(t)$, where the perturbation has the form

$$\hat{V}(t) = \hat{\Phi}^{\pm} e^{\mp i\omega_1 t} + \hat{\Psi}^{\pm} e^{\mp i\omega_2 t}$$

(summation over ±). The resonance part of the density matrix $\hat{D}$ is determined from the equation

$$\left(\frac{\partial}{\partial t} + i\omega_{ab} + \frac{1}{\tau}\right) D_{ab} + i\sum_k (V_{ak}(t) D_{kb} - D_{ak} V_{kb}(t)) = \frac{\rho_a^0 - \rho_b^0}{\omega_{ab}} \left(\frac{\partial \hat{V}}{\partial t}\right)_{ab}, \tag{1}$$

where

$$\hat{\rho}^0 = \exp(-\hat{H}_0/kT)/\mathrm{Sp}\exp(-\hat{H}_0/kT)$$

is the equilibrium distribution function in the absence of a field. Near resonance with $|V| \gtrsim 1/\tau$ (strong field) it is necessary to take into account the second term in (1), because of which the equation for $\hat{D}$ becomes linear with variable coefficients, which leads to "nonlinear" effects. For definiteness let [illegible], We seek a solution of the form

$$\hat{D} = \hat{R} + \hat{Q}^{\pm} e^{\mp i\omega_1 t} + \hat{S}^{\pm} e^{\mp i\omega_2 t} + \hat{T}^{\pm} e^{\mp i(\omega_2 - \omega_1)t}.$$

in which we retain only the resonance matrix elements

$$R_{mm},\ R_{nn},\ R_{qq},\ Q^{+}_{mn},\ Q^{-}_{nm},\ S^{+}_{mq},\ S^{-}_{qm},\ T^{+}_{nq},\ T^{-}_{qn}.$$

The resonance part of the average dipole moment of the system is (omitting the indices of degeneracy)

$$\mathbf{d}(t) = 2\,\mathrm{Re}\,\{\mathbf{d}_{nm}Q^{+}_{mn}e^{-i\omega_1 t} + \mathbf{d}_{qm}S^{+}_{mq}e^{-i\omega_2 t} + \mathbf{d}_{qn}T^{+}_{nq}e^{-i(\omega_2-\omega_1)t}\}. \tag{2}$$

In the limiting case of a strong field Ψ and of a weak Φ

$$Q^{+}_{mn} = \Phi^{+}_{mn}\left\{\frac{A+Bi}{\Delta\omega_1 - \Delta\Omega_1 - i/\tau} + \frac{C+Di}{\Delta\omega_1 - \Delta\Omega_2 - i/\tau}\right\}, \tag{3}$$

where

$$\Delta\omega_1 = \omega_{mn} - \omega_1,\quad \Delta\omega_2 = \omega_{mq} - \omega_2,\quad \Delta\Omega_{1,2} = \Delta\omega_2/2 \mp \sqrt{(\Delta\omega_2/2)^2 + |\Psi|^2},$$

$$A = (\gamma_1\Delta\omega_2 - \gamma_2\Delta\Omega_1)/(\Delta\Omega_2 - \Delta\Omega_1),\quad A + C = \gamma_2,\quad B = (\gamma_3 - \gamma_2)/\tau\,(\Delta\Omega_2 - \Delta\Omega_1),\quad B + D = 0.$$

$$\gamma_k = \gamma_{mn} - k\gamma_{mq}\frac{|\Psi|^2}{\Delta\omega_2^2 + \tau^{-2} + 4|\Psi|^2},$$

and where k = 1, 2, 3; $|\Psi|^2 \equiv |\Psi_{mq}|^2$, and

$$\gamma_{mn} = (\omega_1/\omega_{mn})\,(\rho^0_m - \rho^0_n),\quad \gamma_{mq} = (\omega_2/\omega_{mq})\,(\rho^0_m - \rho^0_q).$$

From formula (3) it is evident that in general the absorption curve has two maxima.

Let $|\Psi|^2 \gg \Delta\omega_2^2,\ \tau^{-2}$. Then the positions of the two absorption maxima are given by the relations

$$(\Delta\omega_1)_1 = -|\Psi| + \Delta\omega_2/2 - \gamma_{mq}/8\gamma_2\tau^2|\Psi|,\quad (\Delta\omega_1)_2 = |\Psi| + \Delta\omega_2/2 + \gamma_{mq}/8\gamma_2\tau^2|\Psi|, \tag{4}$$

and the values of $I = Q^{+}_{mn}/\Phi^{+}_{mn}$ at these points are given by

$$I_1 = \tau\left\{\frac{\gamma_2}{2} + \frac{\Delta\omega_2}{4|\Psi|}\gamma_{mn}\right\},\quad I_2 = \tau\left\{\frac{\gamma_2}{2} - \frac{\Delta\omega_2}{4|\Psi|}\gamma_{mn}\right\}. \tag{5}$$

As is evident from (5), in this case the absorption curve has two approximately equal maxima, almost symmetrical relative to $\Delta\omega_1 = 0$.

If $|\Psi|^2,\ \tau^{-2} \ll \Delta\omega_2^2$, the positions of the maxima are

$$(\Delta\omega_1)_1 = -|\Psi|^2/\Delta\omega_2,\quad (\Delta\omega_1)_2 = \Delta\omega_2,$$

and their magnitude is given by

$$I_1 = \tau\left\{\gamma_{mn} - \frac{|\Psi|^2}{\Delta\omega_2^2}(\gamma_{mn} + \gamma_{mq})\right\},\quad I_2 = \tau\frac{|\Psi|^2}{\Delta\omega_2^2}(\gamma_{mn} - \gamma_{mq}).$$

In general the real part of the polarizability vanishes at three points. For $|\Psi|^2 \gg \Delta\omega_2^2,\ \tau^{-2}$, the positions of these points are

$$\Delta\omega_1 = \begin{cases} -|\Psi| + {}^1\!/_2\Delta\omega_2 + (2\gamma_3 - \gamma_2)/2\gamma_2\tau^2|\Psi| \\ \Delta\omega_2\,(\gamma_1/\gamma_2) \\ |\Psi| + {}^1\!/_2\Delta\omega_2 - (2\gamma_3 - \gamma_2)/2\gamma_2\tau^2|\Psi|. \end{cases}$$

The formulas obtained allow us to draw the following conclusions about the molecular generator and amplifier with auxiliary radiation:

1. If the auxiliary radiation is large, then the amplifier can operate at two frequencies.
2. The molecular generator is excited at those frequencies for which the real part of the polarizability is equal or close to zero. Therefore, for the type of generator considered, oscillations can arise at three frequencies, the oscillations being unstable for the central frequency.
3. The frequency of the oscillations of the generator will depend on both the frequency and amplitude of the auxiliary field.

Note added in proof (November 16, 1957). We note that the solution of (1) for both fields of arbitrary intensity is very cumbersome, but does not lead to results new in principle. Because of the transitions through the common level, which is an intermediate one, the absorption maximum is split for the frequency ω_1 as well as for ω_2.

[1] N. G. Basov and A. M. Prokhorov, J. Exptl. Theoret. Phys. (U.S.S.R.) 28, 249 (1955), Soviet Phys. JETP 1, 184 (1955); Usp. Fiz. Nauk 57, 485 (1955).
[2] J. H. Burgess and R. E. Norberg, Phys. Rev. 100, 752 (1955).
[3] R. Karplus and J. Schwinger, Phys. Rev. 73, 1020 (1948).

Translated by J. Heberle

Reprinted from JOURNAL OF APPLIED PHYSICS, Vol. 31, No. 2, 396–399, February, 1960

Operating Characteristics of a Molecular-Beam Maser*†

H. G. VENKATES‡ AND M. W. P. STRANDBERG
Department of Physics and Research Laboratory of Electronics, Massachusetts Institute of Technology, Cambridge, Massachusetts
(Received April 27, 1959)

General expressions for the emitted power and the frequency pulling in an ammonia maser have been deduced. The operating characteristics of the maser have been deduced by introducing a mean-square time of flight of molecules in the cavity.

I. INTRODUCTION

WE are concerned here with a two-level maser[1,2] in which a molecular beam of ammonia, effusing from narrow channels, passes through an inhomogeneous electric field. We shall assume that the field possesses a cylindrical symmetry about the z axis with its gradient in the radial direction. The two levels in question are those that give rise to the 3-3 inversion line of ammonia. When it emerges from the field (focuser) the beam is state-selected; the molecules transmitted by the focuser are mostly in the inversion state of higher energy. The state-selected beam then enters a tuned microwave cavity in which it emits power by decay into the inversion state of lower energy.

K. Shimoda[3] makes a realistic approach to the theory of the two-level maser by taking into consideration the Maxwell law for the distribution of velocities in the beam. His method consists essentially of treating the focuser as serving a twofold purpose: (a) ideal state selection, and (b) velocity selection of the active molecules by restricting the range of the radial and the axial components of the velocity. This range is determined by the maximum value of the electrostatic field of the focuser, and the dimensions of the focuser and of the cavity. The theory has the merit of simplicity in so far as it avoids the detailed computation of molecular trajectories, and considers only the approximate limiting trajectories of the molecules in the focuser and cavity in order to get reasonably correct relationships among the parameters. In this connection, two classes of molecules are considered—those which pass freely through the cavity, and those which collide with its walls and are reflected away. In order to deal with large power output from the beam, Shimoda has indicated an approximation procedure in which he introduces a certain average velocity of molecules computed from their density in the cavity.

It is shown in the present paper that a closer approximation to the correct theory requires the introduction of a mean-square time of flight in the cavity computed from the flux of molecules in the cavity rather than from the density.

II. GENERAL EXPRESSIONS FOR EMITTED POWER AND FREQUENCY PULLING

An outline of the theory is indicated in Appendix I. We have the following limits for the velocity components for molecules passing freely through the cavity:

$$v_r=0 \text{ to } v_c$$
$$v_z=(L/R)v_r \text{ to } (l/2R)v_r; \qquad (1)$$

for molecules colliding with the walls of the cavity

$$v_r=0 \text{ to } v_c$$
$$v_z=0 \text{ to } (L/R)v_r. \qquad (2)$$

The approximate limiting trajectories are shown in Figs. 1 and 2.

In expressions (1) and (2) L is the length of the cavity; l, the length of the focuser; R, the cross-section radius of the cavity and the focuser; v_c, the critical velocity in the radial direction determined from the condition $W_c=\frac{1}{2}mv_c^2$, where W_c is the Stark energy corresponding to the maximum value of the field which occurs at the surface of the focuser. With these limits the emitted power is given by

$$P_B=G^2(N\hbar\omega_1)\frac{4\alpha}{\sqrt{\pi}}\frac{AR^2}{L^2}\frac{1}{\Delta^2}\left[\int_{x=0}^{a}\int_{y=y}^{b}\sin^2\left(\frac{\Delta L}{2\alpha}\frac{1}{x}\right)\times\exp(-x^2)xydxdy+\int_{x=0}^{a}\int_{y=0}^{y}\sin^2\left(\frac{\Delta L}{2\alpha}\frac{1}{y}\right)\times\exp(-x^2)xydxdy\right], \qquad (3)$$

where N is the density of molecules in the beam in the higher-energy inversion state; α is the most probable velocity in the beam source; $G=(E\bar{\mu}/\hbar)$, with E the rf field amplitude in the cavity, and $\bar{\mu}$ the electric dipole moment of the molecule; A is the cross-section area of the cavity; ω_0 is the resonant frequency of the molecule;

* This work was supported in part by the U. S. Army (Signal Corps), the U. S. Air Force (Office of Scientific Research, Air Research and Development Command), and the U. S. Navy (Office of Naval Research): and in part by the Ministry of Education, Government of India, and the Indian Institute of Technology, Kharagpur, India.

† This paper is based on a thesis submitted to the Department of Physics, Massachusetts Institute of Technology in partial fulfillment of the requirements for the degree of Doctor of Science, August, 1958.

‡ Present address: Department of Physics, Indian Institute of Technology, Kharagpur, India.

[1] Gordon, Zeiger, and Townes, Phys. Rev. **99**, 1264 (1955).
[2] Shimoda, Wang, and Townes, Phys. Rev. **102**, 1308 (1956).
[3] K. Shimoda, J. Phys. Soc. Japan **12**, 1006 (1957).

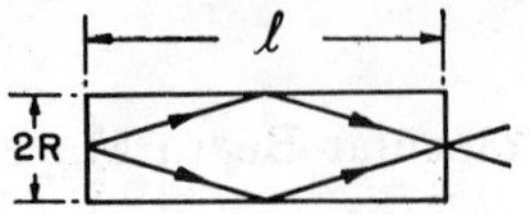

FIG. 1. Focuser.

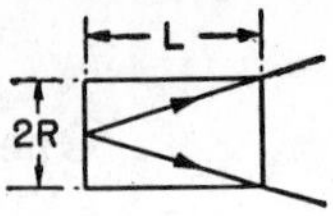

FIG. 2. Cavity.

ω_1 is the oscillation frequency; and $\Delta=(\delta^2+G^2)^{\frac{1}{2}}$, with $\delta=\omega_1-\omega_0$.

The variables and limits are defined by

$$x=\frac{v_z}{\alpha};\quad y=\frac{L}{R}\frac{v_r}{\alpha}$$

$$a=\frac{L}{R}\frac{v_c}{\alpha};\quad b=\frac{1}{2}\frac{l}{R}\frac{v_c}{\alpha}$$

and for the frequency pulling we have

$$\frac{\omega_1-\omega_c}{\omega_c}=-8\sqrt{\pi}N\frac{\mu^2\delta}{\hbar\Delta^2}\frac{R^2}{L^2}\times\left\{\int_{y=0}^{a}\int_{x=y}^{b}\left[1-\frac{\sin(\Delta L/\alpha x)}{\Delta L/\alpha x}\right]\times\exp(-x^2)ydydx+\int_{y=0}^{a}\int_{x=0}^{y}\left(1-\frac{\sin(\Delta L/\alpha y)}{\Delta L/\alpha y}\right)\times\exp(-x^2)xdxdy\right\}. \quad (4)$$

III. APPROXIMATION METHODS

The integrals in (3) and (4) are hard to evaluate. Hence it is desirable to consider limiting cases and approximation procedures. If, now, we restrict ourselves to small signals when $\Delta L/\alpha x$ and $\Delta L/\alpha y$ are to be considered small, we obtain for the frequency pulling

$$\frac{\omega_1-\omega_0}{\omega_0}=\frac{\omega_c-\omega_1}{\omega_c}\frac{3}{\langle\tau_0{}^2\rangle/\langle\tau\rangle}\frac{2Q}{\omega_0}. \quad (5)$$

We also get Shimoda's expression for the emitted power at the resonant frequency:

$$P_B=(G^2/4)(N'\hbar\omega_1)\langle\tau^2\rangle. \quad (6)$$

The quantities $\langle\tau_0\rangle$ and $\langle\tau^2\rangle$ that have the dimension of $(\text{time})^2$, and $\langle\tau\rangle$ that has the dimension of time, have been defined and evaluated in Appendix II. The flux of molecules and the density of molecules in the cavity are given by

$$N'=\frac{4N\alpha}{\sqrt{\pi}}A\frac{R^2}{L^2}\left[\int_{y=0}^{a}\int_{x=y}^{b}\exp(-x^2)yxdxdy+\int_{y=0}^{a}\int_{x=y}^{b}\exp(-x^2)yxdxdy\right] \quad (7a)$$

and

$$n=\frac{4N}{\sqrt{\pi}}\frac{R^2}{L^2}\left[\int_{y=0}^{a}\int_{x=y}^{b}y\exp(-x^2)dxdy+\int_{y=0}^{a}\int_{x=0}^{y}\frac{x^2}{y}\exp(-x^2)dxdy\right]. \quad (7b)$$

The evaluation of the integrals involved in the mean times leads to the following expression for P_B in the small-signal case:

$$P_B=\frac{1}{2}G^2\frac{1}{\sqrt{\pi}\alpha^3}(N\hbar\omega_1)AL^2\left(1+\log\frac{l}{2L}\right)v_c{}^2. \quad (8)$$

In order to put the theory in reasonably explicit form for large signals, we proceed along Shimoda's lines, and consider, first, the case of a beam of uniform velocity v_0 traversing the cavity parallel to its axis. The power emitted is given by

$$P_B=\frac{G^2}{4}(N'\hbar\omega_1)\frac{4}{\Delta^2}\sin^2\left(\frac{\Delta\tau_0}{2}\right), \quad (9)$$

where $\tau_0=(L/v_0)$.

For small signals this formula approximates to

$$P_B=(G^2/4)(N'\hbar\omega_1)\tau_0{}^2. \quad (10)$$

Upon comparing (10) and (6) we obtain the correspondence

$$\tau_0\rightarrow\langle\tau^2\rangle^{\frac{1}{2}}. \quad (11)$$

In generalizing the theory to large signals in the case involving velocity distribution we can make use of this correspondence. The final result is

$$P_B=\frac{G^2}{4}(N'\hbar\omega_1)\frac{4}{\Delta^2}\sin^2(\tfrac{1}{2}\Delta\langle\tau^2\rangle^{\frac{1}{2}}). \quad (12)$$

This formula replaces, for practical purposes, the complicated general formula (3). Setting $\theta=\frac{1}{2}\Delta\langle\tau^2\rangle^{\frac{1}{2}}$, we obtain

$$\frac{N'}{N_0'}=\frac{\theta^2}{\sin^2\theta} \quad (13)$$

and

$$\frac{v_c}{v_{c0}}=\frac{\theta}{\sin\theta}. \quad (14)$$

In (14) v_{c0} is determined by the potentials on the focuser rods that are required to start the oscillation, and v_c is determined by the higher potentials applied to the rods. The saturation condition, $\theta=\pi$, as given by

(13) and (14) enables plotting of the field amplitude in the cavity agsainst applied potential on which v_c depends. N_0' is the flux corresponding to the minimum oscillation condition. The saturation energy density is given by

$$W_{\text{sat}}^{(\theta)}=\frac{\pi^2}{4}\frac{\hbar^2}{\bar{\mu}^2}\frac{l^2}{L}\frac{1}{1+\log(l/2L)}v_c^2. \quad (15)$$

The oscillation condition is given by

$$\frac{1}{Q}\leqslant\frac{4\sqrt{\pi}}{\hbar}\frac{N\langle\mu^2\rangle}{\alpha^3}v_c^2L\left(1+\log\frac{l}{2L}\right)\frac{\sin^2\theta}{\theta^2}. \quad (16)$$

A similar set of formulas has been given by Shimoda[3] with $\beta=\frac{1}{2}\Delta\langle\tau\rangle$ replacing θ in (13) and (14). Thus

$$\frac{N'}{N_0'}=\frac{\beta^2}{\sin^2\beta} \quad (17)$$

and

$$\frac{v_c}{v_{c0}}=\frac{\beta}{\sin\beta}. \quad (18)$$

The saturation energy stored in the cavity is, then,

$$W_{\text{sat}}^{(\beta)}=\frac{\pi^2}{32}\frac{\hbar^2}{\bar{\mu}^2}L\left(1+\frac{l}{2L}\right)v_c^2. \quad (19)$$

It may be noted that Shimoda's formulas will follow if we assume the approximate relationship

$$N'=n\Delta L\frac{\langle\tau\rangle}{\langle\tau^2\rangle} \quad (20)$$

between the flux and the density that have been expressed by (7a) and (7b), and then make τ_0 correspond to $\langle\tau\rangle$ by comparing the two formulas for the emitted power, both of which involve the density, one relating to a beam with a velocity distribution, and the other to a beam with uniform velocity.

The two sets of formulas (13), (14), (15) and (17), (18), (19) are different as long as the correspondences $\tau_0\rightarrow\langle\tau\rangle$ and $\tau_0\rightarrow\langle\tau^2\rangle^{\frac{1}{2}}$ are not identical. For a typical case of $l=2L$, $\langle\tau^2\rangle^{\frac{1}{2}}$ is nearly three times as great as $\langle\tau\rangle$. A difference arises, therefore, between the two sets of formulas in regard to the determination of the field amplitude as a function of applied potential, and of the saturation characteristics. In fact, for the typical case we have

$$W_{\text{sat}}^{(\theta)}=16W_{\text{sat}}^{(\beta)}.$$

Since the density is not so accurately determinable, we may bypass the approximate relationship (20), and hence the density from (7b). We thereby obtain the more accurate relationships (13), (14), and (15) and a closer approximation to the order of magnitude of the output power and saturation characteristics.

APPENDIX I

The emitted power and the frequency pulling are given by

$$P_B=4\pi\omega_1Wx''$$

$$\frac{\omega_1-\omega_c}{\omega_c}=-2\pi x'$$

where ω_c is the resonant frequency of the cavity, W is the energy stored in the cavity, and x' and x'' are the real and imaginary parts of the susceptibility defined by

$$\frac{\int P\dagger\cdot E_a\dagger^*dv}{\int E\dagger\cdot E\dagger^*dv}=x'+jx''.$$

The polarization is given by

$$P=P\dagger e^{j\omega t}+P\dagger^*e^{-j\omega t}=\int p\delta n,$$

where δn is given by Maxwell's law of velocity distribution,

$$\delta n=\frac{AN}{\alpha^3\sqrt{\pi}}\exp(-v^2/\alpha^2)v_rdv_rdv_z,$$

and p is given by

$$p=\int\mu\psi\psi^*dv.$$

The wave functions are those given by Shimoda, Wang, and Townes.[2] The real and imaginary parts of the susceptibility are, then,

$$x'=\frac{4N}{\sqrt{\pi}}\frac{\bar{\mu}^2\delta}{\hbar\Delta^2}\frac{R^2}{L^2}\left\{\int_{y=0}^{a}\int_{x=y}^{b}\left[1-\frac{\sin(\Delta L/\alpha x)}{\Delta L/\alpha x}\right]\right.$$
$$\times\exp(-x^2)ydydx$$
$$\left.+\int_{y=0}^{a}\int_{x=0}^{b}\left[1-\frac{\sin(\Delta L/\alpha y)}{\Delta L/\alpha y}\right]\exp(-x^2)xdxdy\right\}$$

and

$$x''=\frac{2}{L}\frac{4N}{\sqrt{\pi}}\frac{\bar{\mu}^2\alpha}{\hbar\Delta^2}\frac{R^2}{L^2}\left\{\int_{y=0}^{a}\int_{x=y}^{b}\sin^2[(\Delta L/2\alpha)(1/x)]\right.$$
$$\times\exp(-x^2)xydxdy$$
$$\left.+\int_{y=0}^{a}\int_{x=0}^{b}\sin^2[(\Delta L/2\alpha)(1/y)]\exp(-x^2)xydxdy\right\}.$$

APPENDIX II

The mean times introduced in the main discussion are defined by

$$\langle\tau^2\rangle=\frac{L^2}{\alpha^2}\frac{\int_{y=0}^{a}\int_{x=y}^{b}\frac{y}{x}\exp(-x^2)dxdy+\int_{y=0}^{a}\int_{x=0}^{y}\frac{x}{y}\exp(-x^2)dxdy}{\int_{y=0}^{a}\int_{x=y}^{b}xy\exp(-x^2)dxdy+\int_{y=0}^{a}\int_{x=y}^{y}xy\exp(-x^2)dxdy},$$

$$\langle\tau\rangle=\frac{L}{\alpha}\frac{\int_{y=0}^{a}\int_{x=y}^{b}\frac{y}{x}\exp(-x^2)dxdy+\int_{y=0}^{a}\int_{x=y}^{b}\frac{x}{y}\exp(-x^2)dxdy}{\int_{y=0}^{a}\int_{x=y}^{b}y\exp(-x^2)dxdy+\int_{y=0}^{a}\int_{x=0}^{y}\frac{x^2}{y}\exp(-x^2)dxdy},$$

$$\langle\tau_0\rangle=\frac{4}{\alpha\sqrt{\pi}}\frac{R^2}{L}\left[\int_{y=0}^{a}\int_{x=y}^{b}\frac{y}{x}\exp(-x^2)dxdy+\int_{y=0}^{a}\int_{x=0}^{y}\frac{x}{y}\exp(-x^2)dxdy\right].$$

Explicit expressions for these quantities are

$$\langle\tau^2\rangle=2\left(\frac{L}{l}\right)^2\left(1+\log\frac{l}{2L}\right)\left(\frac{R}{v_c}\right)^2,$$

$$\langle\tau\rangle=4\left(\frac{R}{v_c}\right)\frac{1}{1+(l/2L)},$$

and

$$\langle\tau_0\rangle=\frac{2}{\alpha^3\sqrt{\pi}}Lv_c^2\left(1+\log\frac{l}{2L}\right).$$

In all of this the approximation is made that $a \ll 1$ and $b \ll 1$.

Reprinted from THE PHYSICAL REVIEW, Vol. 107, No. 6, 1728–1729, September 15, 1957

Experimental Determination of the Noise Figure of an Ammonia Maser

J. P. GORDON AND L. D. WHITE
Bell Telephone Laboratories, Murray Hill, New Jersey

(Received July 22, 1957)

THE recent theoretical work[1–3] on the noise produced by the active media of masers can be combined with previous microwave circuit theory[4] to yield a prediction for the noise figure of an ammonia maser.[5] We have measured the noise figure of an ammonia maser and compared the result with the predicted value.

A block diagram of the apparatus is shown in Fig. 1. Each maser was of the reflection type, i.e., there was only one microwave port in the maser cavity. The maser's output was separated from its input by a circulator.[6,7] The first maser was modulated on and off at 35 cps by applying a square-wave voltage between the two halves of the cavity.

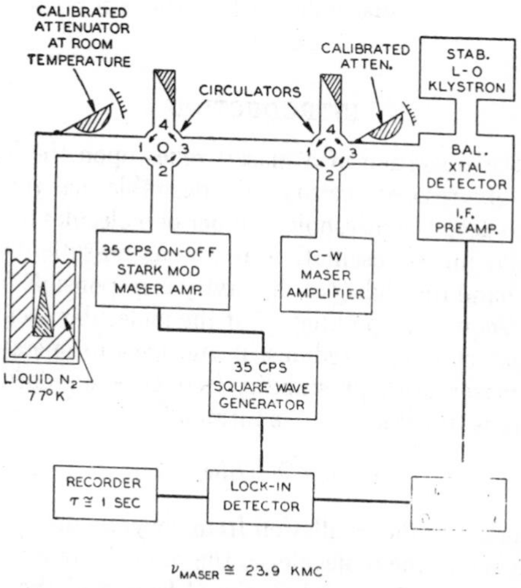

FIG. 1. Block diagram of apparatus.

The noise measurement consisted of changing the temperature of the input load by a known amount by changing the attenuation of the calibrated input attenuator and then varying the calibrated attenuator following the second maser in such an amount as to keep the dc recorder signal constant.

With the variable input attenuator at zero the loss between the liquid nitrogen cooled (77°) attenuator and the maser cavity was 0.69±0.10 db. These losses were at room temperature, 300°K. As a result, the thermal noise at the input to the maser cavity corresponded to a temperature of $77\times0.853+300\times0.147=110$°K. With the variable-input attenuator set at 20 db, the noise at the input to the maser cavity corresponded to a temperature of 298°K. When the effective input temperature of the maser was thus increased from 110°K to 298°K, the microwave power increase was measured to be 3.0±0.1 db. Thus the noise originating in the maser was equivalent to that which would result if the maser were noiseless but had, at its input, thermal radiation from a load at 78±20°K. In terms of noise figure,[8] F, this effective noise temperature is equivalent to $F=1+78/300=1.26$ or 1.0 db.[9]

The theoretical prediction of the effective noise temperature may be obtained by considering the maser as a lossless cavity with three suitably terminated ports. The cavity losses are represented by a port connected to a matched load at the cavity temperature, T_c. The actual microwave port is represented by a second port connected to the microwave line. The beam is represented by the third port terminated at an appropriate position by a susceptance $g(\nu)+jb(\nu)$ at the "effective beam temperature," T_B (negative for a maser). The frequency dependence of the susceptance characterizes the beam resonance. The size of each port is characterized by a Q which is the ratio of the energy stored in the cavity to the energy per radian dissipated (or generated, in the case of the beam) via the mechanism being represented. For high gain the effective noise temperature, T_N, is given approximately by $T_N \cong (T_c/Q_0+|T_B|/Q_B)(1/Q_B-1/Q_0)^{-1}$. The value of T_B obtained from calculations involving the focuser voltages, geometry, and solid angles is $-\frac{1}{4}$°K. The measured value of Q_0/Q_B is of the order of $5\frac{1}{2}$. Thus $|T_B|Q_0/(T_cQ_B)\ll1$ and $T_N\cong T_c/[(Q_0/Q_B)-1]$. In this case $T_c=300$°K, $Q_0/Q_B=5.44$, and the predicted effective-noise temperature was 68±4°K, where the uncertainty results from the errors in the measurements leading to the value for Q_0/Q_B.

A second measurement yielded 72±15°K for the effective noise temperature. The predicted value was 64±5°K.

The agreements between the experimental and theoretical values are good. The contribution to the noise from the beam was too small to be measured, but from these results an upper limit of about 20°K can be placed on the absolute value of the effective beam temperature.

We should like to acknowledge many helpful discussions with Professor C. H. Townes.

[1] Shimode, Takahasi, and Townes, J. Phys. Soc. Japan **12**, 686 (1957).
[2] R. V. Pound, Ann. Phys. **1**, 24 (1957).
[3] M. W. P. Strandberg, Phys. Rev. **106**, 617 (1957).
[4] John C. Slater, *Microwave Electronics* (D. Van Nostrand Company, Inc., Princeton, 1950), Chap. 4.
[5] Gordon, Zeiger, and Townes, Phys. Rev. **99**, 1264 (1955).
[6] C. L. Hogan, Bell System Tech. J. **31**, 1 (1952), see p. 25.
[7] E. A. Ohm, Trans. Inst. Radio Engrs. Microwave Theory and Techniques **MTT-4**, 210 (1956).
[8] H. T. Friis, Proc. Inst. Radio Engrs. **32**, 419 (1944).
[9] The reference temperature is here taken to be the actual room temperature, 300°K.

Twin Cavity for NH_3 Masers

J. BONANOMI, J. HERRMANN, J. DE PRINS, AND P. KARTASCHOFF
Laboratoire Suisse de Recherches Horlogères and Institut de Physique de l'Université, Neuchâtel, Switzerland

(Received July 25, 1957)

A system of two coupled cavities is described replacing the single cavity of an NH_3 maser. Using this system the curve of the oscillation frequency against cavity temperature presents a plateau, thus reducing considerably the "pulling" effects of the cavity.

INTRODUCTION

THE operation of a maser[1] relies upon the high Q of a resonant cavity. It is desirable that this Q be high to keep the threshold number of molecules required to build up the oscillation as low as possible. On the other hand the high Q of the cavity is responsible for the large frequency "pulling"[1,2] of the molecular oscillator. This effect is very tedious, if one tries to operate the NH_3 maser as a high-stability frequency standard. The pulling is described by the formula[1]

$$\omega-\omega_0=Q_c/Q_l(\omega_c-\omega_0), \tag{1}$$

in which ω is the oscillation frequency, ω_0 the resonant frequency of the molecule, ω_c the resonant frequency of the cavity, and Q_c and Q_l the Q factors of the cavity and the spectral line, respectively. This formula is very well satisfied experimentally. In a typical case of a TE_{011} cavity, 20 cm long, ω varies very linearly with temperature; the temperature coefficient being about 4×10^{-8}/°C for brass, and 2×10^{-9}/°C for Invar. An Invar cavity does not seem to be a sufficient remedy, because in addition to the dependence on temperature, the oscillation frequency depends on other uncontrollable factors (e.g., corrosion), affecting the dimensions of the cavity.

In a first attempt[3] to eliminate the effects of pulling, we used several criteria to obtain a frequency which was independent of the cavity dimensions. Though these criteria proved very reliable, the actual measurements were rather tiresome. This paper describes a high Q twin cavity, which eliminates most of the drawbacks of the high Q single cavities. The twin cavity consists of two identical cavities, soldered together and coupled through a hole in the common wall. The molecular beam crosses only one of the cavities.

THEORY

We have to describe the behavior of two coupled cavities, in one or which there exists a polarization $\boldsymbol{P}$. From Maxwell's equations, eliminating $\boldsymbol{H}$, we get for $\boldsymbol{E}$, assumed proportional to $e^{i\omega t}=e^{ikct}$,

$$k^2\boldsymbol{E}-\text{curl curl}\boldsymbol{E}=-4\pi k^2\boldsymbol{P}. \tag{2}$$

The two cavities are denoted C_1 and C_2. In both of them the series of normal modes $\boldsymbol{E}_a$ is known.[4] These normal modes are the solutions of the following equation

$$\text{curl curl}\boldsymbol{E}_a=k_a^2\boldsymbol{E}_a \quad (ck_a=\omega_a).$$

It is sufficient to consider only one mode for each cavity. $\boldsymbol{E}_1$ will be nonvanishing in C_1, $\boldsymbol{E}_2$ in C_2.

Using a perturbation method given by Casimir,[5] we put for the electric field

$$\boldsymbol{E}=\sum_{a=1}^{2} e_a(\boldsymbol{E}_a+\boldsymbol{E}_a')e^{i\omega t}, \tag{3}$$

where $\boldsymbol{E}_a$, the functions defined above, are real and $\boldsymbol{E}_a'$ are supposed small but in general complex. By analogy a similar equation holds for $\boldsymbol{H}$.

The polarization $\boldsymbol{P}$ exists only in C_1 and may be written[2]

$$\boldsymbol{P}=p_1\boldsymbol{E}_1e^{i\omega t}.$$

If we multiply (2) by $\boldsymbol{E}_1$ and by $\boldsymbol{E}_2$, respectively, and integrate over the entire volume, we get the two coupled equations,

$$\left(\frac{\omega}{\omega_1}-\frac{\omega_1}{\omega}-\frac{i}{Q_1}\right)e_1=K_1e_2-4\pi p_1,$$
$$\left(\frac{\omega}{\omega_2}-\frac{\omega_2}{\omega}-\frac{i}{Q_2}\right)e_2=K_2e_1, \tag{4}$$

where

$$\frac{1}{Q_a}=\frac{c}{\omega_a}\int \boldsymbol{H}_a(n\times\boldsymbol{E}_a')dS \quad (a=1, 2),$$

$$K_1=\frac{c}{\omega_1}\int \boldsymbol{H}_1(n\times\boldsymbol{E}_2')dS,$$

$$K_2=\frac{c}{\omega_2}\int \boldsymbol{H}_2(n\times\boldsymbol{E}_1')dS.$$

The value of p_1 may be taken from reference 2, so that

$$-4\pi iQ_1\frac{p_1}{e_1}=\frac{n}{n_{th}}\left(1+i\frac{\omega-\omega_0}{\omega_0}\frac{2\pi}{3}Q_l\right),$$

[1] Gordon, Zeiger, and Townes, Phys. Rev. 99, 1264 (1955).
[2] Shimoda, Wang, and Townes, Phys. Rev. 102, 1308 (1956).
[3] Bonanomi, De Prins, Herrmann, and Kartaschoff, Helv. Phys. Acta 30, 288 (1957),
[4] J. C. Slater, *Microwave Electronics* (D. Van Nostrand Company, Inc., New York, 1950).
[5] H. B. G. Casimir, Philips Research Repts. 6, 162 (1951).

with the same notation, but neglecting saturation. Finally we arrive at the equation, describing the properties of the twin-cavity maser,

$$1+\frac{\kappa^2}{1+\alpha_2^2}+i\left(\alpha_1-\frac{\alpha_2\kappa^2}{1+\alpha_2^2}\right)=\frac{n}{n_{th}}\left(1+i\frac{\omega-\omega_0}{\omega_0}\frac{2\pi}{3}Q_l\right), \quad (5)$$

where

$$\alpha_a=Q_a\left(\frac{\omega}{\omega_a}-\frac{\omega_a}{\omega}\right) \quad \text{and} \quad \kappa^2=K_1K_2Q_1Q_2.$$

This equation reduces for $\kappa=0$ (vanishing coupling) to the single-cavity case treated by Shimoda *et al.*[2] In the actual experiment the cavities were identical, which means $\alpha_1=\alpha_2=\alpha$, or $\omega_1=\omega_2=\omega_c$ and $Q_1=Q_2=Q_c$. The cavity frequency is varied by sweeping the temperature. This mode of operation guarantees that the condition $\omega_1=\omega_2$ remains satisfied.

Equating the phases of both sides of (5), we obtain the frequency of oscillation as a function of the frequency of the cavity

$$\frac{\omega-\omega_0}{\omega_0}=\frac{3}{2\pi}\frac{1}{Q_l}\frac{\alpha(1+\alpha^2-\kappa^2)}{1+\alpha^2+\kappa^2}. \quad (6)$$

One sees immediately that for $\kappa^2=1$ (critical coupling) the curve of Eq. (6) has a point of inflection with a horizontal tangent at the point $\alpha=0$.

Equating the absolute values of both sides of (5) gives the amplitude condition of oscillation. At the point $\omega_c=\omega_0$ and for $\kappa^2=1$ this condition gives for the

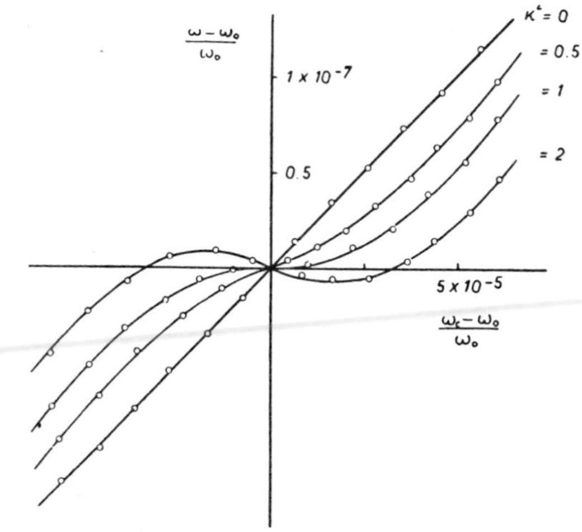

FIG. 1. Maser frequency as a function of twin cavity frequency for different values of the coupling parameter κ. The points are experimental, the curves being calculated from Eq. 6. The constants in this Eq. are in good agreement with the values computed from the experimental conditions (copper plated brass cavities, molecular line width of 3 kc/s).

number of molecules necessary to sustain oscillation

$$n=2n_{th}, \quad (7)$$

where n_{th} is the threshold number for a single cavity.

EXPERIMENT

The measurements are in complete agreement with the above derived Eqs. In Fig. 1 we have plotted the measured points together with curves computed from Eq. (6). The agreement between the theoretical and measured parameters of the curves is as good as could be expected. The plateau of the experimental curve, where the relative frequency variations remain within $\pm2\times10^{-10}$, is 0.5°C wide for a brass cavity; this temperature interval corresponds to a detuning of 1×10^{-5} or 0.25 Mc/sec. On the other hand Eq. (7) is also satisfied within experimental error.

Instead of coupling together two modes of two separated cavities, we also tried to use two modes within the same cavity. The experiment was performed with the modes TE_{011} coupled to the two degenerate modes TM_{111}, and the amount of coupling was variable. The result was that oscillations built up simultaneously at two and even three frequencies, one for each mode.

CONCLUSIONS

The following is a list of several advantages offered by twin cavities as compared to single cavities:

(1) The measurements are made with a stable and not with a swept frequency as described in reference 3.

(2) Corrosion and other effects affecting the cavity dimensions detune both cavities by the same amount. Such a parallel detuning of both cavities does not alter the oscillation frequency at the plateau, but only the temperature at which the plateau occurs. Merely the difference in detuning between the two cavities and not the detuning itself is active in "pulling" the oscillator frequency.

(3) The temperature coefficient at the plateau is much lower for a twin cavity made of brass than for a single cavity made of Invar. Temperature control needs to be only very rough, and bad thermal insulation from the wave guide and the supports is not harmful.

(4) Since the twin cavity can be operated at a reasonably high amplitude, it needs to be coupled only very loosely to the detecting system. This prevents possible "pulling" effects from the outside.

(5) Though one would expect the effects of state selector voltage and beam intensity to remain unchanged with respect to a single cavity, the observed effects are actually three times smaller in the twin cavity case (for the 3,3 line). These effects are sensitive to the geometrical configuration.

A disadvantage, presumably not of practical importance, of the twin cavity is that the frequency at the plateau differs from the molecular frequency ω_0 by an amount depending on how exactly the condition $\omega_1=\omega_2$

is approximated by the initial adjustment of the cavities.

A twin cavity has been in use for a few weeks as a frequency standard and has proved very well suited for this purpose.

ACKNOWLEDGMENTS

We want to thank Professor H. Mugeli and Professor J. Rossel for their interest and encouragement in this work, and Dr. W. Seeds for reading and correcting the manuscript.

Reprinted from JOURNAL OF APPLIED PHYSICS, Vol. 29, No. 4, 714–717, April, 1958

Maser Oscillator with One Beam through Two Cavities*

WILLARD H. WELLS
Jet Propulsion Laboratory, California Institute of Technology, Pasadena, California
(Received November 11, 1957)

A two-cavity beam type of maser is studied by a geometrical representation of the Schrödinger equation developed by Feynman, Vernon, and Hellwarth. By this method complicated effects may be readily visualized. As an example, the qualitative explanation will be developed for the experimental observation that a cavity in a maser will oscillate simultaneously at two frequencies (differing by 1000–5000 cps) under certain conditions when the beam is first passed through another cavity. A possible amplifier application is noted.

INTRODUCTION

THE maser consisting of two cavities with a single molecular beam passing through both is a device of considerable interest as a spectrometer[1] and as an oscillator. For example, it is superior to the ordinary maser as a frequency standard because the distance between cavities adds to the effective time of interaction between the molecules and the electric field.[2] The two-cavity maser will be studied by a method which is especially useful in finding the approximate behavior of a complicated maser system.

As an example, we develop the theory of a recent experimental observation by Higa.[3] In his experiment the two cavities were first tuned to the molecular frequency under conditions such that each maintained oscillations without the other. The first cavity through which the beam passed, hereafter called A, was then detuned. Oscillations in the second cavity, B, were observed to follow the frequency of A up to a critical point a few kilocycles from the molecular frequency. With further detuning of A, cavity B began to oscillate simultaneously at the molecular frequency to which it was tuned and the frequency of A.

This behavior can be understood in a crude manner as a combination of two effects. First, the molecules entering cavity B are still ringing with the polarization they received in A. Second, when cavity A is detuned the molecules enter B with considerably more than $(1/2)^{\frac{1}{2}}$ amplitude in the excited state. Thus B is capable of oscillations as though A had been omitted.

We proceed to examine in more detail the theory of these effects using a geometric representation of the Schrödinger equation developed by Feynman, Vernon, and Hellwarth[4] in a paper hereafter referred to as C. We shall adhere to their notation throughout with a few additions such as subscripts A and B for the two cavities. It will be necessary to refer to C in reading this paper. The geometry will not only yield quantitative results, but it also enables us to visualize the behavior qualitatively with much less effort. We treat the subject in two parts: first, cavity B oscillating at the frequency $\omega_A/2\pi$ of A; second, cavity B oscillating at $\omega_B/2\pi$, the frequency to which it is tuned, but modulated at $|\omega_A-\omega_B|/2\pi$ owing to the ringing of the beam at $\omega_A/2\pi$. In the first part we study the behavior qualitatively, then develop the quantitative results corresponding to Eqs. (17) and (18) of C. In the second part we study the behavior qualitatively only, then examine the transition to this type of oscillation from that of the first part. Throughout we shall approximate the distribution of molecular velocities by a single average value.

CAVITY B AT FREQUENCY OF A

Since we shall be discussing the perturbation of a single molecule as it passes through two cavities, it seems advisable to first note an essential fact which is missing in this restricted point of view, namely, that a molecule entering cavity B has no memory of the frequency $\omega_A/2\pi$ at which it was perturbed in A, but that the beam as a whole does remember. The single molecule entering is in some state given by

$$\psi(t)=a(t)\varphi_a e^{-iE_a t/\hbar}+b(t)\varphi_b e^{-iE_b t/\hbar}. \tag{1}$$

If $\mu(t)$ is its oscillating dipole moment and μ_{ab} the corresponding matrix element, and if phases are such that a and b are real we have

$$\mu(t)=\langle\psi^*(t)|\mu|\psi(t)\rangle=2ab\mu_{ab}\cos\left(\frac{E_a-E_b}{\hbar}t\right) \tag{2}$$

$$=\text{const.}\times\cos(\omega_0 t).$$

In Eq. (2) we have ω_0 but no trace of ω_A. However, each molecule lasts in cavity B only about 1/5000 second, and out of this 5-kilocycle line width the molecules are coherent only at ω_A. This is illustrated in Fig. 1.

To apply the method of C we shall trace the orbits or $\mathbf{r}$ vectors on the surface of a sphere which they intersect. Figure 2 shows the diagram in the rotating coordinate system. The driving torque in A is labeled Ω_A. The orbit in cavity A is labeled $\mathbf{r}_A$ at the end of which an energy E_A has been delivered to the electromagnetic field. As was pointed out in C the projection of $\mathbf{r}$ on the I, II plane is the polarization phasor. That component along

* This paper presents one phase of research carried out at the Jet Propulsion Laboratory, California Institute of Technology, under Contract No. DA-04-495-Ord 18, sponsored by the Department of the Army, Ordnance Corps.
[1] A. Javan and T. C. Wang, Bull. Am. Phy. Soc. 2, 209 (1957).
[2] N. F. Ramsey, Phys. Rev. 78, 695 (1950).
[3] W. H. Higa, Rev. Sci. Instr. 28, 726 (1957).
[4] Feynman, Vernon, and Hellwarth, J. Appl. Phys. 28, 49 (1957).

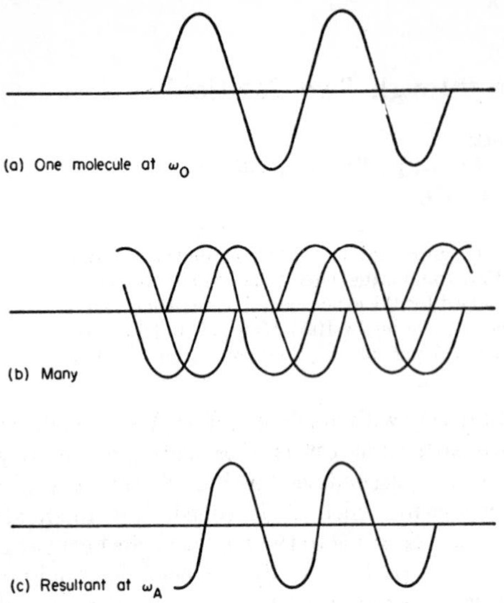

FIG. 1. Frequency memory.

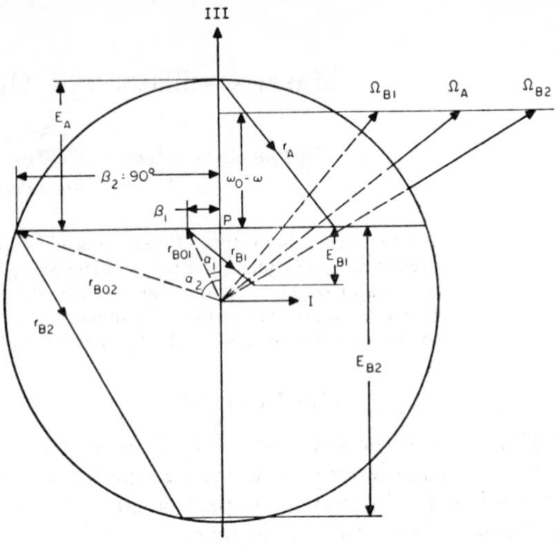

FIG. 2. Cavity B at frequency of A.

the II axis has the proper phase to drive the field. The phase of the field is indicated by the projection of Ω_A on the I, II plane which we take to be the I axis as in C.

Since the $\mathbf{r}$ vector merely precesses about the 3 (or III) axis between cavities and since the phases of the electric field in A and B are in general different, we are free to reorient phasors in B. Therefore, we shall slice the sphere at the latitude of the $\mathbf{r}$ vector when the molecule emerges from A and reorient vectors as desired to visualize the perturbation in B. The phase of the field in B will have some relation to the phase of the oscillating dipole moment of the incoming molecule. As we shall see, this phase relation depends on the amplitude of oscillation in B and other factors. For convenience in the diagram we reorient the molecular phase to obtain this dependence instead of Ω_A so that the I axis is always to the right.

To visualize the orbit in B which satisfies Maxwell's equations some trial and error will be necessary. We write Eq. (16) of C in the form,

$$\mathcal{E}=\frac{K\int_0^{L/v}\dot{r}dt}{(\omega_{CB}{}^2-\omega^2)-(i\omega\omega_{CB}/Q)}, \tag{3}$$

where $\mathbf{r}=r_1+ir_2$ and $K=4\pi n\omega^2\mu_{ab}f\mathcal{V}^{-\frac{1}{2}}$. $\mathcal{E}$ must be real since the phase has been defined by choosing the projection of Ω on the I, II plane to be the I direction. For orbits such as $\mathbf{r}_{B1}$ and $\mathbf{r}_{B2}$ in Fig. 2 the phase of the integral in Eq. (3) can be quickly estimated and compared with the denominator. Clearly the integral over $\mathbf{r}_{B1}$ is nearly pure negative imaginary, and the integral over $\mathbf{r}_{B2}$ has a negative real and negative imaginary part. Having found an orbit with the proper phase, the magnitude of $\mathcal{E}$ from Eq. (3) can be compared to the value of ω_I which was used to generate the orbit, remembering that $\omega_I=\mu_{ab}E/\hbar$. This is the consistency check of the first trial. New orbits giving integrals of the same phase are tried until $\mathcal{E}$ comes out consistent with ω_I.

We take note of a few facts that aid in using the diagram efficiently. The point P indicates the azimuth of the $\mathbf{r}$ vector at which the molecules have the proper phase to drive the field. Consider a cavity with small Q, small oscillations, and $\omega\approx\omega_{CB}$. Its orbit, like $\mathbf{r}_{B1}$, will remain near P, since the numerator of Eq. (3) must be nearly pure negative imaginary, and $\theta=\Omega L/v$ is small. A quite different case is one in which the cavity has the orbit $\mathbf{r}_{B2}$. This orbit delivers the energy E_{B2} to the field, almost the maximum energy available. Here $\theta=180°$ (large Ω or L/v), and the molecule enters and leaves in quadrature. To obtain $\mathbf{r}_{B2}$ we must have $\omega>\omega_{CB}$ as seen from the phase of Eq. (3). The behavior is asymmetric for $\omega>\omega_{CB}$ compared to $\omega<\omega_{CB}$, since we have taken $\omega_0>\omega$.

The large size of $\mathbf{r}_{B1II}$, the driving component of $\mathbf{r}_{B1}$, suggests that it is a good orbit for an amplifier with a very weak input introduced into cavity B. However, the phase relation between the incoming signal and the oscillations in A must be considered in such an application.

We shall carry out the solution corresponding to Eqs. (17) and (18) of C, but unwieldy equations will result. We define α and β as the colatitude and azimuth, respectively, of $\mathbf{r}_{B0}$, the initial $\mathbf{r}_B$ vector. We measure β from P to the left in Fig. 2. Using the notation of C[5]

[5] In C the 2π is misplaced in the definition of Q_B. It should read $Q_B=\omega_0 L/2\pi v$.

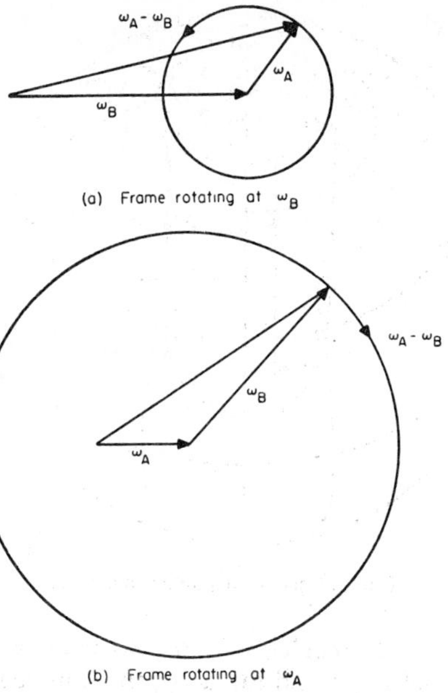

FIG. 3. Two frequencies $\Omega_{I,II}$ when $\omega_B > \omega_A$.

the equations corresponding to Eq. (14) of C are

$$r_{IB} = \frac{\omega_I(\omega_0-\omega)}{\Omega^2}[1-\cos(\Omega t)]\cos\alpha - \left[\frac{\omega_I^2}{\Omega^2}+\frac{(\omega_0-\omega)^2}{\Omega^2}\cos(\Omega t)\right]\sin\alpha\sin\beta + \frac{(\omega_0-\omega)}{\Omega}\sin(\Omega t)\sin\alpha\cos\beta,$$

$$r_{IIB} = -\frac{\omega_I}{\Omega}\sin(\Omega t)\cos\alpha - \frac{(\omega_0-\omega)}{\Omega}\sin(\Omega t)\sin\alpha\sin\beta - \cos(\Omega t)\sin\alpha\cos\beta. \tag{4}$$

Defining γ to be the angle between I and Ω, i.e.,

$$\tan\gamma = \frac{\omega_0-\omega}{\omega_I} = \frac{\hbar(\omega_0-\omega)\mathcal{V}_B^{\frac{1}{2}}}{\mu_{ab} f_{BB}},$$

we have corresponding to Eqs. (17) and (18) of C;

$$\frac{n}{n_{thB}} = \left|\frac{\theta_B^2}{2\cos\alpha(1-\cos\theta_B)+\tan\gamma\sin\alpha\sin\beta(1-\cos\theta_B)+\sin\alpha\cos\beta\sin\theta_B\sec\gamma}\right|, \tag{5}$$

$$\frac{\omega_0-\omega}{\omega-\omega_{CB}} = \frac{Qn_{thB}}{2\pi Q_B n} \frac{\theta^2}{\cos\alpha\left(1-\dfrac{\sin\theta_B}{\theta_B}\right) - \sin\alpha\sin\beta\left(\cot\gamma+\tan\gamma\dfrac{\sin\theta_B}{\theta_B}\right) + \dfrac{\sin\alpha\cos\beta}{\cos\gamma}\dfrac{1-\cos\theta_B}{\theta_B}}. \tag{6}$$

Equations (5) and (6) relate θ and β when γ, α, n, n_{th}, Q, Q_B, ω_0, ω_{CB}, and ω are known, thus implicitly solving the problem. Although they could have been obtained without diagrams, their complexity demonstrates the usefulness of diagrams in estimating the behavior of a two-cavity maser.

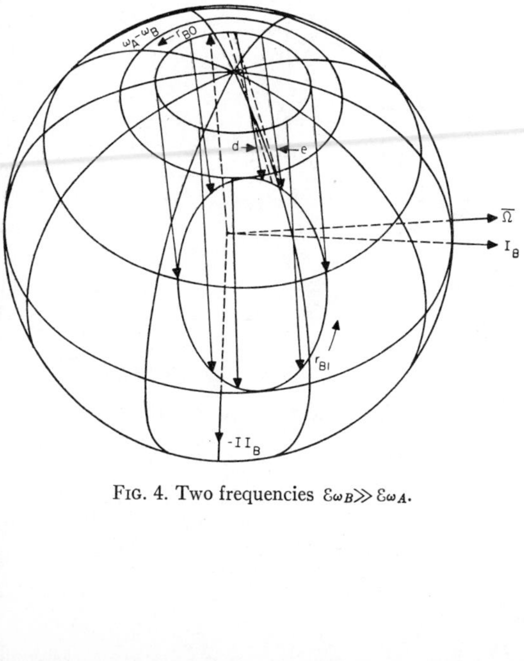

FIG. 4. Two frequencies $\mathcal{E}\omega_B \gg \mathcal{E}\omega_A$.

Limiting cases of Eqs. (5) and (6) are interesting. For example, when A is oscillating exactly at ω_0 but not saturating, and B has small oscillations, we have $\gamma=0$, $\alpha>0$, θ_B small. Then Eq. (5) becomes

$$\frac{n}{n_{thB}} \approx \frac{\theta_B}{\theta_B\cos\alpha+\sin\alpha\cos\beta}, \tag{7}$$

which shows that as long as A is oscillating making $\alpha>0$ we have oscillations in B for $n<n_{thB}$.[1] This is just molecular ringing. However, when $\alpha=0$ we must have $n>n_{th}$ for oscillations, just the single cavity case.

CAVITY B OSCILLATING AT TWO FREQUENCIES

When a cavity oscillates at two frequencies we can look at the rotating coordinate system of either frequency, say $\omega_B/2\pi$. Then $\omega_{III}=\omega_0-\omega_B$ and $\omega_{I,II}$ is the sum of two vectors, $1/2|\omega_{1B}|$ in the I direction and $1/2|\omega_{1A}|$ precessing at a frequency of $(\omega_A-\omega_B)/2\pi$. This is illustrated in Fig. 3(a).

Figure 4 shows the two-frequency diagram for cavity B in which the amplitude of ω_B is much greater than ω_A. The coordinate system is rotating at ω_B. Ω wobbles owing to ω_A. The average position $\bar{\Omega}$ is shown. Since the beam is ringing at ω_A when it enters B, the starting point, r_{B0}, of the B orbit in this frame precesses with the difference frequency $(\omega_A-\omega_B)/2\pi$. This precession is the circle around the top pole, the area of which we shall call the polar cap. At first we suppose that Ω is constant. Then the orbits r_B, which appear as straight lines in Fig. 4, would all be parallel arcs subtending equal angles $(\Omega L/v)$. The locus of their end points r_{B1} would be a circle. However, the response time of the amplitude of the field is very short compared to the period, $2\pi/|\omega_A-\omega_B|$, of r_{B0}. Therefore, the strength of oscillations varies with the frequency $|\omega_A-\omega_B|/2\pi$ following the variation in the latitude of r_{B1}. Since ω_1 is proportional to E, Ω is longer and more nearly parallel to I when the oscillations are strong. This distorts the orbits and locus of r_{B1} into the shape shown in Fig. 4.

This completes the qualitative discussion of modulated oscillations at $\omega_B/2\pi$ which are approximately equivalent to simultaneous oscillations at frequencies $\omega_A/2\pi$ and $\omega_B/2\pi$. We shall not attempt quantitative results, but conclude by examining the critical conditions for oscillations at ω_B.

In order for the oscillations at ω_B to be coherent for the period $2\pi/|\omega_A-\omega_B|$, the orbits which start in the $+II$ hemisphere must reach over the polar cap so that the final latitude is lower than the initial. Otherwise these molecules absorb power from the field. To state the critical condition more precisely we represent an increment of time, Δt, by those orbits or parts of orbits which describe the states of the molecules present in B during Δt. Such an increment is indicated by dotted lines in Fig. 4. At the beginning of Δt molecule d is just entering and e is leaving B. At the end d has traveled half the length. We define $\theta_c(t)$ to be the arc across the polar cap along the average orbit during t to $t+\Delta t$. Then $\Omega_c(t)\equiv\theta_c(t)v/L$ is that value of Ω which will drive the orbit across the cap. The critical condition may now be stated as the requirement that during each Δt_i the beam must provide just sufficient energy to maintain oscillations during the next Δt_{i+1} such that $\Omega(t_{i+1})>\Omega_c(t_{i+1})$.

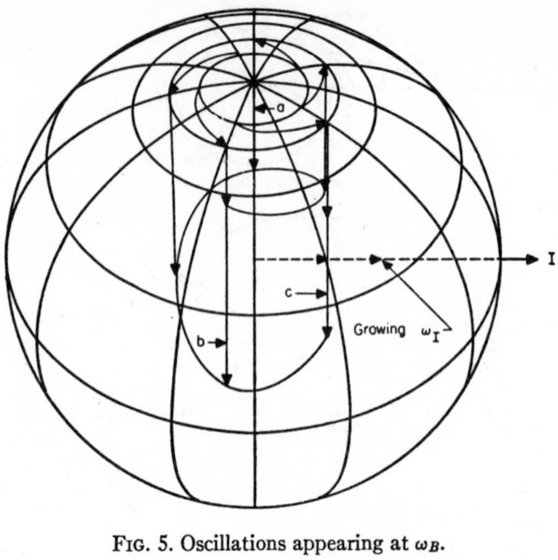

FIG. 5. Oscillations appearing at ω_B.

One can make a rough check on this condition using the geometry of Fig. 4 and $\Delta t=\omega_c/Q$, the time constant for decay of oscillations in an empty cavity. The required energy then is just the energy in the cavity mode at the amplitude $\mathcal{E}_c\approx\hbar\Omega_c/\mu_{ab}$.

In Fig. 5 we show pictorially the idea of how cavity B changes from oscillations at ω_A to modulated oscillations at ω_B. We suppose that the cap has just been shrunk, for example by detuning cavity A. The arrows spiraling outward depict an orbit such as r_{B1} of Fig. 2 as seen in the frame rotating at ω_B instead of ω_A. The growing ω_I barely succeeds in maintaining coherent oscillations by bringing orbit a over the polar cap. Orbits b and c begin to resemble Fig. 4.

ACKNOWLEDGMENT

The author is grateful to Dr. W. H. Higa for suggesting this paper and for helpful discussions of his experiments.

Reprinted from THE REVIEW OF SCIENTIFIC INSTRUMENTS, Vol. 31, No. 10, 1164–1165, October, 1960

Advantage of a Cascaded-Cavity NH_3 Maser over the Single Cavity Maser

FRIEDRICH H. REDER AND CHARLES J. BICKART
U. S. Army Signal Research and Development Laboratory, Fort Monmouth, New Jersey

(Received June 15, 1960; and in final form, August 8, 1960)

IN the conventional maser, the NH_3 beam, emerging from the separator, enters a single microwave cavity which is tuned to the transition frequency of the molecules. The excited molecules radiate coherently in the cavity through the mechanism of induced emission. Part of the radiated power is absorbed in the cavity walls, another part is extracted from the cavity through a waveguide coupled to the cavity and may be used for driving a frequency translating device. Another, usually negligible, fraction might be lost by radiation through the beam entrance and exit holes. It was shown elsewhere[1] that such a simple maser frequency standard is quite susceptible to many disturbing influences, the most troublesome being the cavity pulling effect. For the reduction of this cavity frequency-pulling effect, Bonanomi[2] has introduced the use of a twin-cavity system (two critically coupled cavities side by side, with the beam passing only through one cavity). Such a cavity arrangement utilizes the flat phase curve characteristic at resonance for reducing the cavity pulling effect. It still leaves us, however, with the problem of perturbing influences from varying impedances reflected back into the cavity through the waveguide coupling hole. This effect is particularly disturbing in a practical maser frequency standard in which the maser drives an electronic frequency translator. In order to keep the system in lock under even moderate environmental conditions of shock and vibration, the cavity coupling has to be considerably larger (between 3 db undercoupled and matched) than one could tolerate under laboratory conditions. Ferrite isolators are helpful to some extent but do not provide a completely satisfying solution. The need for an output waveguide presents in addition some problems for temperature control of the frequency determining cavity. It would, therefore, be desirable to devise a maser in which the frequency controlling cavity has no output waveguide and can, therefore, be isolated to a maximum extent.

This can be accomplished by putting the beam emerging from the cavity through a second cavity mounted directly behind. Some theoretical and experimental aspects of such a cascaded-cavity system were investigated by Javan[3] and Wells[4] and some experiments were conducted by Higa.[5] It is not known, however, whether any of these investigators drew the practical conclusions discussed here.

During early fall of 1959 we experimented with a maser frequency standard having a cascaded-cavity system. The cavities were similar to each other and about 4 cm long. Their distance was 2 cm. Each cavity was first connected with its own frequency translator. Both translators gave output signals at 325^+ Mc and the frequencies were measured with a precision of three parts in 10^{10} in terms of an atomic Cs beam frequency standard. The following results were found: (1) With roughly the same coupling coefficient (3 db undercoupled), the output power from the second cavity was only about 6 db less than that from the first one. The output frequencies of the two cavities were identical. (2) Mechanical tuning of the second cavity changed only its output power level but had no detectable influence on its frequency. (3) Mechanical tuning of the first cavity changed the output frequencies of both cavities in the same way.

This last result made us first suspect that the second cavity was just picking up power leaking through the beam coupling holes of the first cavity. We could easily show, however, that this was not the case by inserting a dielectric beam flag between the two cavities which killed the output from the second cavity without disturbing the performance of the first cavity. A further proof followed: Holding a strong bar magnet first to the middle of each Invar cavity gave no measureable effect, and then, holding it to the space between the two cavities did not influence the frequency of the signal from the first cavity but had a large frequency changing influence on the signal from the second cavity.

The conclusion was that only the first cavity was oscillating in the usual manner explained by the maser theory.

The beam emerging from this cavity was, however, still so strongly polarized[6] that there was no need for the second cavity to stimulate emission and to fulfill the usual feedback loop requirement. The beam radiated by itself and the second cavity served only as a convenient pickup antenna for the molecular ringing without having a distinct influence on the output frequency.

This makes it possible to build a maser frequency standard with two cascaded cavities. The first and only frequency determining cavity has to have no microwave output-power coupling hole, should have a relatively low Q to prevent saturation (which reduces at the same time frequency pulling), and can be isolated thermally, electrically, and mechanically to the largest possible extent from the rest of the system. The second cavity has no pronounced influence on the frequency, can therefore be matched to the output waveguide, and does not have to be temperature controlled. Varying load impedances (e.g., that of a mixer) cannot influence the output frequency anymore. However, the space between the two cavities has to be shielded electrically and magnetically by putting, e.g., an Invar sleeve over it which can be mounted on the second cavity and should enclose part of the first cavity without touching it (1 mm distance). It is furthermore believed that the second cavity can be made so short that this method will also reduce the Doppler effect[1] observed in masers of common design.

[1] K. Shimoda, T. C. Wang, and C. H. Townes, Phys. Rev. **102**, 1308 (1956).
[2] J. Bonanomi, J. Herrmann, J. DePrins, and P. Kartaschoff, Rev. Sci. Instr. **28**, 879 (1957).
[3] A. Javan and T. C. Wang, Bull. Am. Phys. Soc. Ser. II **2**, 209 (1957).
[4] W. H. Wells, J. Appl. Phys. **29**, 714 (1958).
[5] W. H. Higa, Jet Propulsion Laboratory, External Rept. No. 381 (1957), and 477 (1958).
[6] S. Bloom, J. Appl. Phys. **27**, 785 (1956).

$N^{15}H_3$ Double-Beam Maser as a Primary Frequency Standard*

JEAN DE PRINS†

Summary—**Ammonia masers are studied concerning their use as frequency standards. They oscillate on the $J=K=3$ inversion line of $N^{15}H_3$. Single beam masers allow the realization of a frequency standard with a stability of 2–3.10^{-11}, and an accuracy of about 10^{-9}. Experiments on double beam masers suggest that their use makes it possible to obtain a stability of the order of 10^{-12} and an accuracy better than 10^{-10}.**

THE INVENTORS of the ammonia maser have from the very first recognized its possibilities as a frequency standard [1].

The frequency of a maser ν_M is in a good approximation related to the natural frequency ν_0 of the transition used, and to the frequency ν_c of the cavity by the relation [2]

$$\frac{\nu_M - \nu_0}{\nu_0} = Q_c \frac{\Delta_l}{\nu_0} f(\theta) \left(\frac{\nu_c - \nu_0}{\nu_0}\right) \tag{1}$$

where Q_c is the quality factor of the cavity, $\Delta\nu_l$ is the line width, $f(\theta)$ is a saturation factor. In principle, it is thus possible to tune the frequency of the maser oscillator through the use of the Zeeman effect. If a magnetic field is modifying $\Delta\nu_l$, the cavity will be tuned ($\nu_c = \nu_0$) when the frequency ν_M of the maser is independent of the magnetic field applied to the cavity. The corresponding maser frequency is defined as being the "characteristic frequency" which differs from the natural frequency ν_0 due to secondary effects. The use of the maser as a primary frequency standard requires that these two frequencies be brought into coincidence. It is desirable that this characteristic frequency be equal to the natural frequency ν_0 of the transition used.

Since the oscillation conditions are relatively critical, it is desirable that the maser oscillate on the most intensive of the lines of the inversion spectrum of natural ammonia $N^{14}H_3$, characterized by the quantum number $J=K=3$. Previous studies have shown that in this case the characteristic frequencies of the masers strongly depend on the experimental conditions [3]–[8]. This is due to the multiplicity of the line resulting from the quadrupole interaction of the N^{14} nucleus of nuclear spin one. The quadrupole coupling constant is greater by about 3 kHz for the lower inversion state than for the higher state [9].

The result of this is that the line 3-3 of $N^{14}H_3$ is formed by three components of different intensities and separated in frequencies by 1.7 kHz and 0.6 kHz. The intensity of these different components depends on the experimental conditions, and mainly on the state selector characteristics. The maser frequency oscillations, being an average of the frequencies of these components, will vary with the variations of their respective intensities and consequently with the experimental conditions. It is thus essential for the use of the maser as a frequency standard to utilize a single line.

One solution is to use the 3-2 line of $N^{14}H_3$. For this line the quadrupole interaction factor of the nitrogen nucleus proportional to

$$\left(1 - \frac{3K^2}{J(J+1)}\right)$$

* Received August 17, 1962. Presented at the 1962 International Conference on Precision Electromagnetic Measurements as Paper No. 7.2.

† University of Brussels, Brussels, Belgium.

is zero. The total number of molecules required to build up an oscillation is unfortunately higher than for beam 3-3 and this leads to serious inconveniences, as we shall see later. In particular, our experiments show that the line width $\Delta\nu_l$ increases linearly with the number of molecules used.

A second solution which is preferable is to use the line 3-3 of the isotopic ammonia $N^{15}H_3$. The basic equation (1) is valid only if the molecule undergoes an induced transition in a high-frequency field that is stationary. In practice this condition is not realized because the energy emitted by the molecule is not uniformly distributed along the cavity [2]. The dissymetry results from the divergence of the beam and from the fact that the transition probability depends on the interaction time of the molecule with the high-frequency field. This gives rise to a progressive wave component which tends to equalize the energy distribution in the cavity. The frequency emitted by the molecules in the presence of this progressive wave will be displaced by the Doppler effect.

As suggested by Shimoda, Wang, and Townes [2] the progressive wave appearing in the cavity can be greatly reduced by symmetrizing the phenomena with the aid of a second beam of opposite direction. It is to verify this hypothesis and to make the maser a primary frequency standard that we have constructed in the "Laboratoire Suisse de Recherches Horlogères" two experimental prototypes of a double beam maser.

Description of the Apparatus

Apparatus No. 1

Ammonia enriched to 95 per cent of $N^{15}H_3$ can be commercially obtained. Since this product is expensive the maser has been built with the intent of recovering the ammonia used during the measurements.

Apparatus No. 1 permits the independent adjustment of the two beams entering the cavity. Each beam is formed by a nozzle, fed from a stainless steel reservoir, and produces a beam of ammonia molecules which, passing through a state selector, is enriched in molecules in the higher inversion state by the action of an inhomogeneous electrostatic field.

A "needle valve" regulates the debit of the $N^{15}H_3$ beam. The beam intensity of 10^{16} to 10^{18} molecules/sec is measured by the pressure before the nozzle. The nozzle (diameter 3.5 mm) is formed by an array of fine parallel channels (0.1 mm diameter, 5 mm long). The state selector uses a quadrupolar electric field and consists of four cones of stainless steel, the axes of which converge toward the nozzle. A voltage up to 20 kv is applied between neighboring cones.

The cavity of a maser must have a high quality factor and a good frequency stability. For this reason, we chose a copper-plated brass cylindrical cavity, 17-cm long, of mode TM_{010} without movable parts.

A frequency adjustment is affected by varying the temperature of the whole cavity. The choice of the mode is conditioned by the method of measurements. We need a mode with $n=0$ or 1, and one which is not degenerated with another mode (*e.g.*, TE_{011} and TM_{111}).

For the tuning of the cavity, the magnetic field must be orientated in the direction corresponding to the σ components of the Zeeman effects. In our case two rectangular coils produce a magnetic field, the intensity of which is limited to one-oersted.

The focusing voltage and the number of molecules in the two beams can be independently adjusted in Apparatus No. 1, but the alignment of the cavity with the nozzles and the state selection is only roughly possible.

Apparatus No. 2

This apparatus was specially designed so that an alignment of the components within 0.1 mm is possible. Furthermore the construction ensures that the characteristics of the two beams are identical. Indeed, the high voltage generator is the same for both state selectors, and the symmetrical construction of the ammonia distribution system provides, on the two nozzles, an identical number of molecules.

The components are identical to those used in Apparatus No. 1 with the exception of the nozzles, which here have a diameter of 5 mm and are formed by channels of 0.3 mm diameter and 5 mm long. The nozzle directivity in Apparatus No. 2 is therefore about three times smaller than in No. 1.

Method for the Measurement of the Characteristic Frequency

The frequency of a quartz clock 1 MHz determined by a Cesium standard is compared to the maser frequency. The measurement is made in two stages.

1) The frequency of the maser is compared to that of an adjustable auxiliary 8.5 MHz quartz oscillator. This latter frequency is multiplied by 2681 so that a microwave reference signal is obtained of a frequency nearly equal to that of the maser. After superheterodyne detection and amplification, the beat frequency between these two signals is measured by a frequency meter and is graphically recorded.

To determine the characteristic frequency, the temperature of the cavity is slightly changed so that the frequency of the cavity is slowly displaced through the natural frequency ν_0. At the same time, a sawtooth generator establishes in the cavity a magnetic field which varies linearly from 0 to 1 oersted at a repetition rate of 1 cps. The recording of the beat frequency immediately shows the passage through zero of the frequency modulation produced by the magnetic field, and thus easily permits the determination of the characteristic frequency. The frequency of the auxiliary oscillator is thus known in comparison with that of the maser.

2) During the measurements described above, the frequency of the quartz oscillator 1 MHz is compared to the frequency of the auxiliary oscillator by classical methods using electronic counters.

The measurement of the characteristic frequency is made with a precision of 2.10^{-11}.

Experimental Results

Effect of the Progressive Wave in the Cavity

The experiments made with Apparatus No. 1 bring out the effect of the progressive wave component in the cavity. We have measured the frequency of the maser as a function of the number of molecules in one beam. The voltages of the two state selectors and the number of molecules in the other beam are kept constant. We observed the frequency variation of the maser predicted by the progressive wave theory [2]. The frequency goes through an extremum when the two beams are identical (Fig. 1).

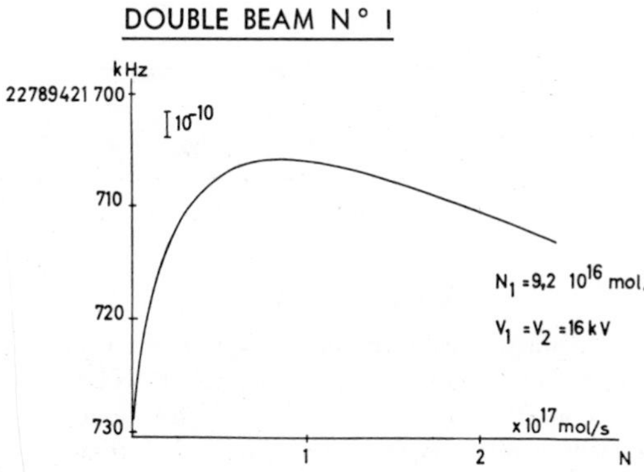

Fig. 1—Influence of traveling wave on maser frequency.

Influence of the Experimental Parameters on the Characteristic Frequency

The frequency of the double beam maser is within the experimental errors independent of the voltage applied on the state selector (Fig. 2). On the other hand the frequency varies in function of the number of molecules N in the beam, but not with the oscillation amplitude. Indeed this latter varies strongly with the voltage applied to the state selectors and the experiment shows that in this case the frequency does not vary.

The following results suggest a linear relation between the frequency and the number of molecules in the cavity, this number being proportional to $N^{2/3}$: 1) A plot of frequency vs $N^{2/3}$ gives a straight line within experimental error (Figs. 3, 4). 2) The difference in nozzle directivities produces different numbers of molecules in the cavity and thus different slopes, the ratio of which corresponds approximately to the ratio of nozzle directivities. 3) For maser oscillation on the 3-2 $N^{14}H_3$ line, the influence of the number of molecules should be 12 times larger due to the larger threshold number of molecules required for oscillation. The experiment effectively gives this order of magnitude. 4) The number of molecules in the cavity varies only by 2 per cent when the voltage applied to the state selector passes from 0 to 20 kv [3]. If we admit a frequency variation proportional to the number of molecules in the cavity, the effect of the high voltage variations in Apparatus No. 1 for a number of molecules lower than 3.10^{17} mol s^{-1} is less than 10^{-11} and thus not measurable.

The complete theoretical justification of this frequency variation is more difficult. In fact the measurements of line width show a broadening proportional to the number of molecules, thus indicating that there are interactions between the molecules in the cavity. We would attribute to these interactions the frequency variations as a function of number of molecules.

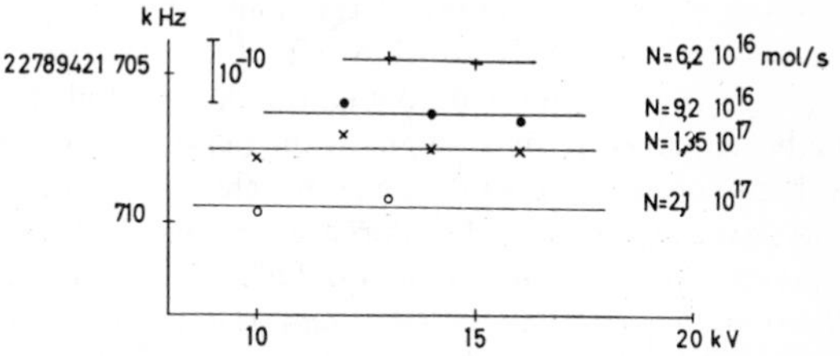

Fig. 2—Frequency variations of double-beam maser with experimental conditions.

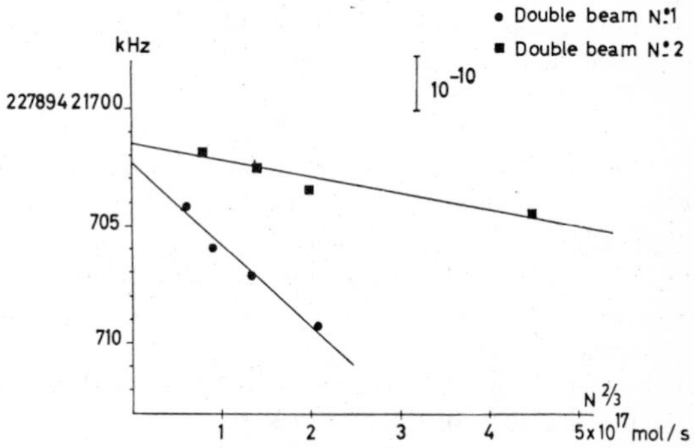

Fig. 3—Frequency of the double-beam masers vs number of molecules in the beam.

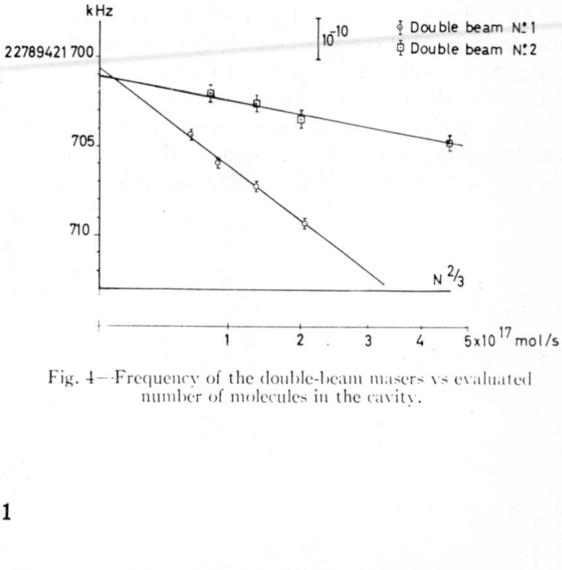

Fig. 4—Frequency of the double-beam masers vs evaluated number of molecules in the cavity.

Stability and Accuracy of the Double-Beam Maser

1) *Stability:* The number of molecules in the beam is easily measurable and reproducible within a few per cent. This reproducibility ensures the reproducibility of the frequency to within a few units in 10^{12}. One can thus be certain that for a given apparatus the long-term stability is also of a few 10^{-12}.

2) *Accuracy:* If we accept the hypothesis of a linear frequency variation as a function of the number of molecules, we can extrapolate the frequency to zero number of molecules in the cavity. The extrapolated value is identical for the two double-beam masers. The frequency is 22,789,421,701 ± 1 Hz in the A-1 scale (Cs 9,192,631,770 Hz).

To evaluate the accuracy of the double-beam maser, it is necessary to know to what extent the progressive wave has been eliminated. We can make the following rough evaluations: In a single-beam maser, increasing the high voltage applied to the state selector from 10 to 20 kv gives an increase of the progressive wave effect by about 40 per cent [3]. In the double-beam maser, the corresponding increase is less than the measurement error of 2.10^{-11} and we may estimate that the total maximum progressive wave effect is lower than 10^{-10}.

In spite of the uncertainty subsisting as to the true cause of the frequency variation in terms of the number of molecules, our results clearly establish that the accuracy of the double-beam maser exceeds 10^{-10}.

Conclusion

The essential qualities of an atomic frequency standard are high signal-to-noise ratio, high operating frequency within the region where frequency multiplication is possible, and relative insensitivity to external parameters. All these qualities are fulfilled by the double-beam $N^{15}H_3$ maser.

The maser signal-to-noise ratio is high, and thus the frequency stability of the signal is excellent. The short time stability of one maser was found to be 2.10^{-12} for a measuring time of 0.2 sec. Another advantage of the ammonia maser is its great insensitivity to the magnetic field. There only appears a second-order Zeeman effect which induces a fractional shift of the line center of roughly 2.10^{-15} H^2 hertz where H is in oersteds. This is about 10^6 times less than the effect for atoms such as Cs, and about 10^{10} times smaller than for hydrogen.

Our experiments show the interest of more precise measurement techniques. Actually, the precision is limited by the fluctuation of the comparison quartz oscillator, which amounts to 2.10^{-11} for 0.2 sec measuring time. Such fluctuations should be eliminated if the auxiliary quartz oscillator is replaced by a maser. Preliminary experiments have indicated a measurement precision of 4.10^{-12} (Fig. 5). A system using this technique is under construction at the University of Brussels.

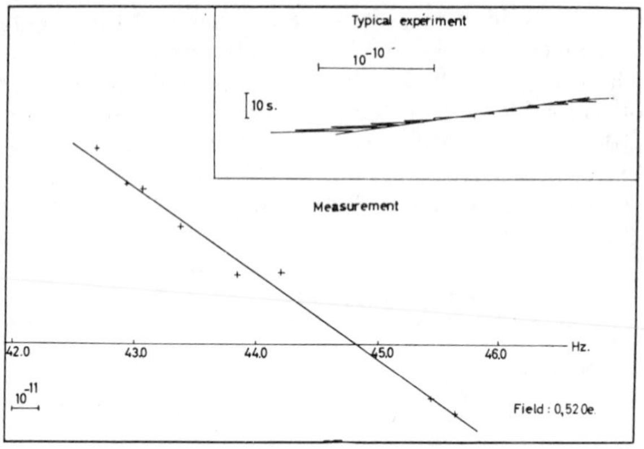

Fig. 5—Frequency measurement with two masers

Acknowledgment

The author wishes to thank C. Menoud for his collaboration in the final experimentation, and P. Kartaschoff for the construction of certain electronic devices. Dr. G. Severne has kindly corrected the English text.

References

[1] J. P. Gordon, H. J. Zeiger, and C. H. Townes, "The maser new type of microwave amplifier, frequency standard and spectrometer," *Phys. Rev.*, vol. 99, pp. 1264–1274; August, 1955.

[2] K. Shimoda, P. C. Wang, and C. H. Townes, "Further aspect of the theory of the maser," *Phys. Rev.*, vol. 102, pp. 1308–1321; June, 1956.

[3] F. S. Barnes, "Operating Characteristics of an Ammonia Beam Maser," Proc. IRE, vol. 47, pp. 2085–2098; December, 1959.

[4] J. C. Helmer, "Small signal analysis of molecular beam," *J. Appl. Phys.*, vol. 30, pp. 118–120; January, 1959.

[5] A. M. Mitchell and E. Sandback, "Measurements of the frequency of an ammonia maser in England and Australia," *Nature*, vol. 185, pp. 834–835; March, 1960.

[6] R. C. Mockler, J. Barnes, R. Beehler, H. Salazar, and L. Fey, "The ammonia maser as an atomic frequency and time standard," IRE Trans. on Instrumentation, vol. I-7, pp. 201–202; December, 1958.

[7] K. Shimoda, "Characteristics of the beam type maser," Part I: *J. Phys. Soc. Japan*, vol. 12, pp. 1006–1016; 1957; Part II: *J. Phys. Soc. Japan*, vol. 13, pp. 939–947; 1958.

[8] J. Bonanomi, J. De Prins, J. Hermann, and P. Kartaschoff, "Stabilité d'étalons de fréquence à NH^3," *Helv. Phys. Acta*, vol. 30, pp. 288–290; 1955.

[9] J. P. Gordon, "Hyperfine structure in the inversion spectrum of NH_3," *Phys. Rev.*, vol. 99, pp. 1253–1263; August, 1955.

Reprinted from IRE TRANSACTIONS
ON *INSTRUMENTATION*
Volume I-11, Numbers 3 and 4, December, 1962

The Ammonia Beam Maser as a Standard of Frequency*

J. A. BARNES†, D. W. ALLAN†, AND A. E. WAINWRIGHT†

INTRODUCTION

The ammonia beam maser has presented certain problems when considered as a primary standard of frequency. These problems come about because the maser's frequency of oscillation is quite dependent upon a variety of parameters. Also, with several of these parameters there is no unambiguous way of selecting a particular value for the parameter. In the past these parameters have been difficult to control and caused undesirable drift rates.

Recently a servomechanism has been installed which has eliminated cavity-tuning effects;[1] *i.e.*, the cavity is continuously tuned to be at the resonant frequency of the molecule. The method will be shown later. The elimination of this parameter has also reduced the effects of the other parameters.

In the case of ammonia beam pressure and focusing voltage, there is no clear-cut way of selecting values in order to get the maser to oscillate at the "proper Bohr frequency."

In part, some of the trouble arises from the fact that the quadrupole moment of N^{14} in ordinary ammonia causes an asymmetric splitting of the $J=3$, $K=3$ inversion line. This trouble can be avoided by using $N^{15}H_3$ instead of the ordinary ammonia. The present experimental work has been confined to $N^{14}H_3$; however, as soon as a system capable of recirculating the ammonia is completed, data will be taken on $N^{15}H_3$. A considerable improvement in reproducibility when using $N^{15}H_3$ has been reported by others.[2]

With all of its problems, the ammonia beam maser using $N^{14}H_3$ has demonstrated a resettable frequency of better than $\pm 3\times 10^{-11}$.

ZEEMAN MODULATION

It has been shown[3] that the cavity-pulling of the maser frequency is given approximately by

$$\nu_0 - \nu = \frac{\Delta\nu_l}{\Delta\nu_c}(\nu_0 - \nu_c) \tag{1}$$

where ν_0 is the natural resonance frequency of the ammonia molecule; ν is the frequency of oscillation of the maser; ν_c is the resonant frequency of the cavity; $\Delta\nu_l$ is the natural line width of the ammonia transition in the maser; and $\Delta\nu_c$ is the cavity bandwidth. It has been suggested by Shimoda, *et al.*[1,4] that a small magnetic field will cause a Zeeman splitting of the ammonia line and thus cause an effective broadening of the ammonia line width. If the cavity is tuned to a frequency other than ν_0, a frequency shift of the maser is observed with the application of the magnetic field.

Under the influence of a magnetic field, the line width is given approximately by (see Appendix)

$$\Delta\nu_l = \sqrt{(\Delta\nu_0)^2 + (\Delta\nu_H)^2} \tag{2}$$

where $\Delta\nu_0$ is the unperturbed line width for the ammonia transition and $\Delta\nu_H$ is the amount the lines are split by the magnetic field. (See Fig. 1.) It has been found[5] that $\Delta\nu_H$ is given by

$$\Delta\nu_H = \alpha H$$

where the constant α is approximately 718 cps/oersted.

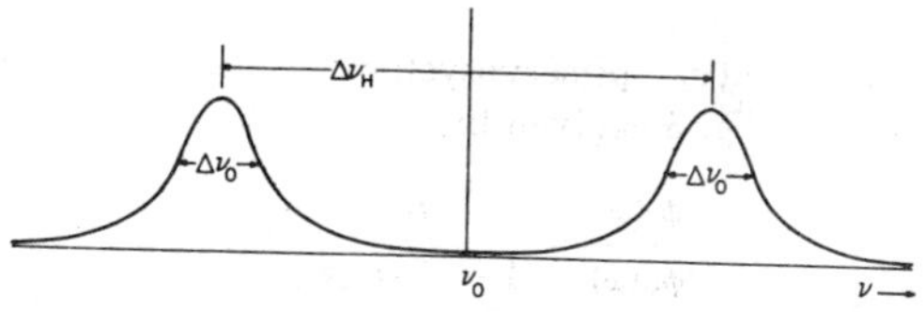

Fig. 1—Zeeman splitting of $J=3$, $K=3$ line of $N^{14}H_3$.

In order to obtain a continuous correction to the cavity tuning, the authors have found it desirable to apply a sinusoidally varying magnetic field to the maser; *i.e.*,

$$H = H_0 \sin \omega_m t.$$

Thus the line width will be given by

$$\Delta\nu_l = \sqrt{(\Delta\nu_0)^2 + (\alpha H_0)^2 \sin^2 \omega_m t}$$
$$= \sqrt{(\Delta\nu_0)^2 + \tfrac{1}{2}(\alpha H_0)^2 - \tfrac{1}{2}(\alpha H_0{}^2)\cos 2\omega_m t}.$$

* Received August 28, 1961. Presented at the WESCON Conf., San Francisco, Calif.; August 22–25, 1961.

† National Bureau of Standards, Boulder, Colo.

[1] J. C. Helmer, "Maser oscillators," *J. Appl. Phys.*, vol. 28, pp. 212–215; February, 1957.

[2] J. De Prins and P. Kartashoff, "Applications of Hertzian Spectroscopy to the Measurement of Frequency and Time," publication of Laboratoire suisse de recherches horlogeres, Neuchatel, Switzerland. (Topics on Radiofrequency Spectroscopy, August 1–17, 1960, International School of Physics, "Enrico Fermi," Varenna—Villa Monastero.)

[3] The reader is referred to J. P. Gordon, H. J. Zeiger, and C. H. Townes, "The maser," *Phys. Rev.*, vol. 99, pp. 1264–1274; August, 1955. While this is an approximate formula, it is sufficient to indicate the functional dependence of the maser frequency. Also a more elaborate theory[1] still suggests that $\partial\nu/\partial H=0$ determines the natural resonant frequency which, incidentally, differs from other possible means of obtaining this frequency.

[4] K. Shimoda, T. C. Wang, and C. H. Townes, "Further aspects of the maser theory," *Phys. Rev.*, vol. 102, pp. 1308–1321; June, 1956.

[5] C. K. Jen, "Zeeman effect in microwave spectra," *Phys. Rev.*, vol. 74, pp. 1396–1406; November, 1948.

Applying the binomial theorem one obtains

$$\Delta\nu_l \approx \Delta\nu_0 \sqrt{1 + \frac{x^2}{2}}$$

$$- \tfrac{1}{2}\Delta\nu_0 \sqrt{1 + \frac{x^2}{2}}\left(\frac{x^2}{2 + x^2}\right) \cos 2\omega_m t + \cdots \quad (3)$$

where $x \equiv \alpha H_0/\Delta\nu_0$ and the approximation is valid to the degree that

$$\frac{x^2}{2 + x^2} \ll 1.$$

Substitution of (3) into (1) gives

$$\nu = \nu_0 - \frac{\Delta\nu_0}{\Delta\nu_c}\sqrt{1 + \frac{x^2}{2}}\,(\nu_0 - \nu_c)$$

$$+ \frac{\Delta\nu_0}{\Delta\nu_c}\,\frac{1}{2\sqrt{2}}\,\frac{x^2}{\sqrt{2 + x^2}}\,(\nu_0 - \nu_c) \cos 2\omega_m t. \quad (4)$$

There are two things of interest in (4); first, the frequency of the modulation term is twice the frequency of the Zeeman field, as one would expect and, second, this modulation term is proportional to $\nu_0 - \nu_c$. It is this latter property which enables one to simply construct a servosystem that will continually control the cavity tuning.

The authors have found that the most convenient and most noise-free method of demodulation is that of phase demodulation. The block diagram of the system used is shown in Fig. 2 and the equivalent servodiagram of the maser-crystal-oscillator phase-lock system is shown in Fig. 3. In Fig. 3 the transfer functions of the various components are indicated below the components.

From the theory of servosystems, the total transfer function for Fig. 3 is given by

$$\frac{\phi_0(\omega)}{\phi_m(\omega)} = \frac{K_1K_2K_3}{1 + K_1K_2K_3}\,. \quad (5)$$

From this it follows that

$$\alpha(\phi_m(\omega) - \phi_0(\omega)) = V_1 = \alpha\phi_m(\omega)\left(1 - \frac{K_1K_2K_3}{1 + K_1K_2K_3}\right)$$

$$= \alpha\phi_m(\omega)\left(\frac{1}{1 + K_1K_2K_3}\right). \quad (6)$$

Substitution of the transfer functions into (6) yields

$$V_1(\omega) = \alpha\phi_m(\omega)\left[\frac{\omega^2\tau - j\omega}{\omega^2\tau + \alpha\beta - j\omega}\right]. \quad (7)$$

It is apparent that the bracketed expression in (7) has its maximum value when $\omega^2\tau \gg \alpha\beta$ which makes (7) have the value

$$V_1(\omega) \approx \alpha\phi_m(\omega). \quad (8)$$

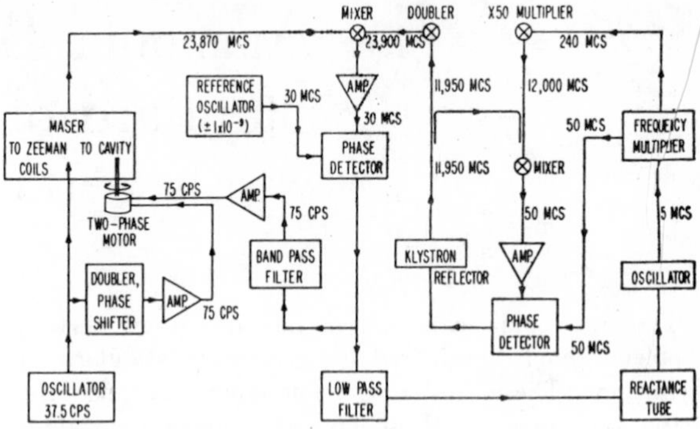

Fig. 2—Block diagram of complete system.

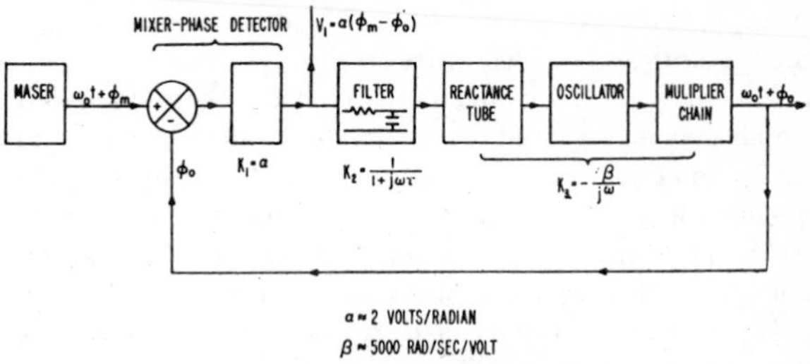

Fig. 3—Equivalent servodiagram for oscillator-maser phase-lock system.

As is customary in dealing with transfer functions, the quantities $\phi_m(\omega)$, $\phi_0(\omega)$ and $V_1(\omega)$ are the Fourier transforms of the time-dependent functions. Thus the voltage $V_1(t)$ can be obtained by taking the inverse Fourier transform of (8)

$$V_1(t) = \alpha\phi_m(t), \quad (9)$$

since α is a constant, and provided all important frequency components satisfy the relation $\omega^2\tau \gg \alpha\beta$.

Returning to (4), which can be written in terms of the total phase $\Phi(t)$,

$$\Phi(t) = \omega t + \phi_m(t) = 2\pi\left[\nu_0 - \frac{\Delta\nu_0}{\Delta\nu_c}\sqrt{1 + \frac{x^2}{2}}\,(\nu_0 - \nu_c)\right]t$$

$$+ \frac{\Delta\nu_0}{\Delta\nu_c}\,\frac{1}{2\sqrt{2}}\,\frac{x^2}{\sqrt{2 + x^2}}\left(\frac{\nu_0 - \nu_c}{2\nu_m}\right) \sin 2\omega_m t. \quad (10)$$

Comparison of (9) and (10) gives

$$V_1(t) = \gamma(\nu_0 - \nu_c) \sin 2\omega_m t \quad (11)$$

where γ is the constant

$$\gamma = \left(\frac{\alpha}{4\sqrt{2}\nu_m}\right)\left(\frac{\Delta\nu_0}{\Delta\nu_c}\right)\left(\frac{x^2}{\sqrt{x^2 + 2}}\right) \quad (12)$$

and $(2\omega_m)^2\tau \gg \alpha\beta$.

Eq. (11), then, represents the demodulated signal from the maser. It should be noted here that the phase-locked crystal oscillator's frequency is determined by the maser frequency and thus this servosystem serves a double purpose: 1) as a low-noise phase demodulator, and 2) as a precise frequency divider to facilitate comparison with other systems, *e.g.*, the cesium beam.

For the NBS maser system, γ has the value of approximately 3.5 mv per part in 10^{10} of $N^{14}H_3$ maser frequency. While this seems like a sufficiently sensitive detection system, it must be remarked that there still exist significant noise sources which will tend to limit the precision of balance. The most important of these sources is the crystal oscillator used in the maser phase-lock system. Any phase jitter of this oscillator signal after multiplication to K band will be detected as noise in the phase demodulator. It is interesting to note that if the maser is detuned one part in 10^{10}, the peak phase modulation on the maser is only about 0.14° at K band!

The oscillator which is used in the NBS maser system has demonstrated the most nearly pure spectrum of any oscillator analyzed to date.[6] In fact, except for a very small white-noise pedestal, it is difficult to be sure whether the maser or this oscillator has the more nearly monochromatic signal. Although some noise may be eliminated by narrow banding the demodulator, this process cannot be carried too far or the Nyquist conditions for stability of the servosystem will be violated.

The serveloop for the cavity tuning is completed by applying the amplified signal from the phase demodulator to one phase of a two-phase motor which in turn controls the depth of a small plunger in the maser's resonant cavity. The reference for the other phase of the motor is obtained by doubling the frequency of part of the signal from the Zeeman modulating field supply.

Due to inherent noise in the system, it has been found that a better time-averaged frequency is obtained from the maser if the gain is advanced to the point where small oscillations about the null modulation point just begin. Under these conditions, the servomotor is oscillating back and forth at a rate of about 2 cps, and at an amplitude of about ± 5 parts in 10^{10} in terms of maser frequency. An 8-sec average of oscillator frequency shows a standard deviation of about 3 parts in 10^{11}.

Returning to the condition on (11) that

$$(2\omega_m)^2\tau \gg \alpha\beta,$$

it is possible to determine the minimum time constant of the phase-lock filter. For the NBS system, the product $(\alpha\beta)$ is about 10^4 sec^{-1} and thus $\tau \gg 0.05$ sec. Typically, τ is chosen to be about 0.5 sec to 1.0 sec. Since this time constant must be taken this long, again the stability of the crystal oscillator must be very good or deterioration of the maser stability will result.

[6] J. A. Barnes and L. E. Heim, "A high-resolution ammonia-maser-spectrum analyzer," IRE TRANS. ON INSTRUMENTATION, vol. I-10, pp. 4–8; June, 1961.

BASIC MEASURING SCHEME

Quite an elaborate system is involved in detecting and dividing down the maser frequency. It is the purpose of this section to outline this system. See Fig. 2.

A 5-Mc crystal oscillator drives a multiplier chain. From this chain, 240 Mc is fed into a crystal multiplier; the 50th harmonic (12,000 Mc) of this and an 11,950-Mc signal from a klystron are fed into a crystal mixer. The 50-Mc beat note resulting is sent through an IF amplifier and then phase compared with 50 Mc from the multiplier chain. The phase difference is used as an error voltage to correct the klystron's frequency; hence, the klystron is phase locked to the 5-Mc crystal oscillator.

The klystron signal is sent to a crystal doubler giving 23,900 Mc. This signal goes in one side of a balanced crystal mixer. The maser's signal at approximately 23,870 Mc provides the reference into the other side of the above mixer. The 30-Mc beat note resulting goes to an IF amplifier and then to a phase detector. A frequency synthesizer, stable to better than a part in 10^8, is used as the reference into the other side of the phase detector. (One part in 10^8 at this reference gives a stability of about 1 part in 10^{11} at maser frequency.) The phase error resulting is then sent to a reactance tube which in turn corrects the frequency of the above-mentioned 5-Mc crystal oscillator. Therefore, the 5-Mc signal is phase locked to the maser's frequency, and hence the maser's stability can be analyzed by looking at the 5-Mc crystal oscillator or any multiple of it as derived from the multiplier chain.

EXPERIMENTAL RESULTS

Maser Frequency Dependence on Operating Conditions

It has been the intent of the authors to find most, if not all, parameters that give instability and that cause frequency shifts; also, the control of critical parameters has been of concern. Some of the frequency-dependent parameters are beam pressure, electrode focusing voltage, Zeeman modulation voltage, fluctuations in the magnetic field of the earth, background pressure in the maser's vacuum system, alignment of beam nozzles and electrodes with respect to the resonant cavity, temperature effects, and a few other influences, most of which are quite minor.

In connection with the beam pressure a variety of nozzles have been tried including klystron grid material, crimped foil, and special drilled single-hole nozzles. Most of the data have been taken with 0.02-inch single-hole nozzles; this is by no means the optimal nozzle to use, and this nozzle is used mainly for symmetry reasons in the NBS double-beam maser. Beam pressures typically used are in the vicinity of 6 mm of mercury; such a pressure gives a molecular mean free path (λ) of 8×10^{-4} cm. Since λ is smaller than the nozzle hole diameter, this disallows a Maxwellian velocity distribution, but rather gives cloud diffusion which has a radial molecular intensity distribution. This system gives very uniform flow as can be illustrated from the frequency-time statistics, but quite a large consumption of ammonia (about 1 gr/hr).

Data were taken to determine the optimal beam pressure to use for frequency stability, and a typical family of curves is shown in Fig. 4. In another experiment the beam pressure was run up to about 14 mm of mercury to observe the continuation of the curves shown. It was found that the curves continued to approach each other and the second derivative became negative. This change in slope is attributed to a significant increase in the background pressure caused by the high flux of molecules.

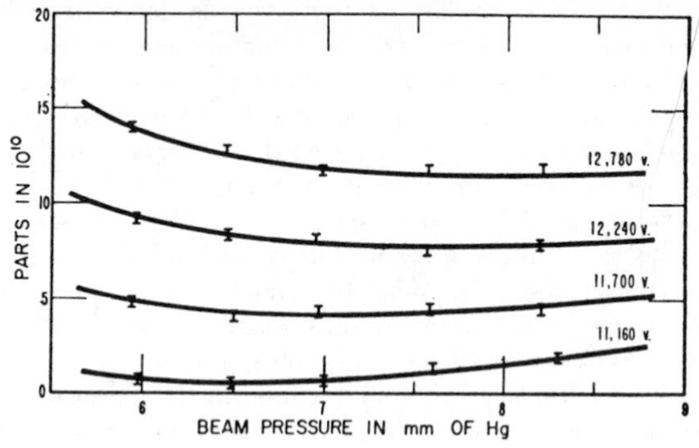

Fig. 4—Relative shift in maser frequency vs beam pressure.

By analyzing Fig. 4 one can quite easily observe the behavior of the focusing voltage V_F vs maser frequency since there is a 540-v difference between each of the curves in the family of curves plotted. The slope of maser frequency as a function of focusing voltage is positive with a positive second derivative also; the magnitude of the slope is in the vicinity of 1 part in 10^{10} of maser frequency per 200 v. This is rather severe for frequency stability, and the voltage has to be read to about 0.2 per cent in order to get resettability to 1 part in 10^{11}. This, of course, puts stringent requirements on the high-voltage power supply. One can further observe by analyzing Fig. 4 that the slope of frequency vs focusing voltage decreases for increasing beam pressures.

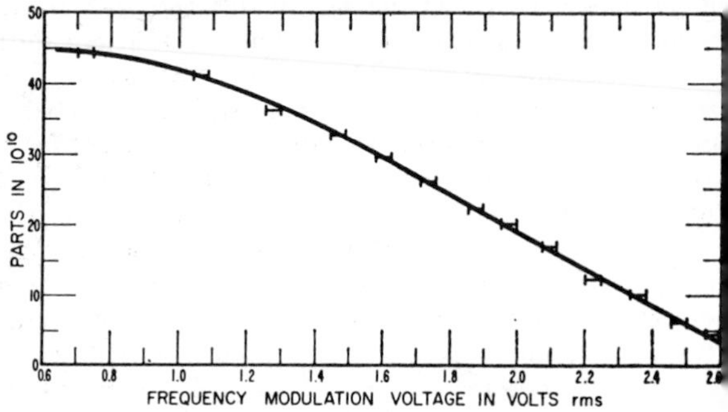

Fig. 5—Relative maser frequency vs modulation voltage applied to magnetic field coils.

Another curve of interest is maser frequency vs the Zeeman frequency modulation voltage (see Fig. 5). If the Zeeman splitting coefficients are linear (the theory states they are to a first approximation—second-order effects are of the order[4] of 2×10^{-15} H^2—for all molecular frequency components within the range of the resonant cavity) then the slope of frequency vs modulation voltage should be zero. But the contrary result is that the curve has a negative slope of about 5 parts in 10^9 at maser frequency per oersted (rms); 2 volts rms applied to the magnetic-field coils of the NBS maser corresponds very closely to 1 oersted (rms) in the cavity. A similar effect has been observed on $N^{15}H_3$.[2]

With a slope as previously stated for maser frequency vs Zeeman modulation voltage, one might wonder if fluctuations in the earth's magnetic field would cause frequency shifts. From experiments performed it was found that the slope of this curve is essentially the same as for an ac field. Since the earth's magnetic field is about 0.56 oersted, a net shift of the maser's frequency of about 3 parts in 10^9 would be expected. Also, it was predicted that during fairly severe magnetic storms a frequency shift in the vicinity of 1 part in 10^{11} could be observed; an experiment was performed and an actual correlation was shown to exist. Since the shift due to magnetic storms is so small, it could be easily eliminated with a μ-metal shield around the maser's resonant cavity.

Prior to the installation of the cavity-tuning servo-loop, background pressure changes caused sizeable frequency shifts; for example, when the liquid-nitrogen cold traps on the maser's vacuum system were filled, of course the background pressure would change, and frequency shifts as high as 1 part in 10^9 were observed. Since the installation of the above-mentioned servo-loop, cold trap filling and fairly large changes in the background pressure cause no measurable frequency shifts. Pressures typically used in the maser's vacuum system are 2×10^{-6} mm of mercury; no frequency shift has been observed up to pressures of 6×10^{-6} mm. Higher frequency shifts than this have been indicated though very marginal up to 1×10^{-5} mm.

The NBS maser has been taken apart and reassembled several times; each time a frequency shift has occurred along with changes in the parametric curves of Figs. 4 and 5, although the basic character of the curves has not changed. If pains are taken to duplicate alignment and configuration of nozzles, focusers, and cavity, the shift can be kept within 3 parts in 10^{10}—showing the critical nature alignment plays in the maser as a frequency standard. However, for any one alignment and configuration the stability for short term and long term is shown in Figs. 6 and 7. Such stability brings the maser to the status of a very good secondary standard.

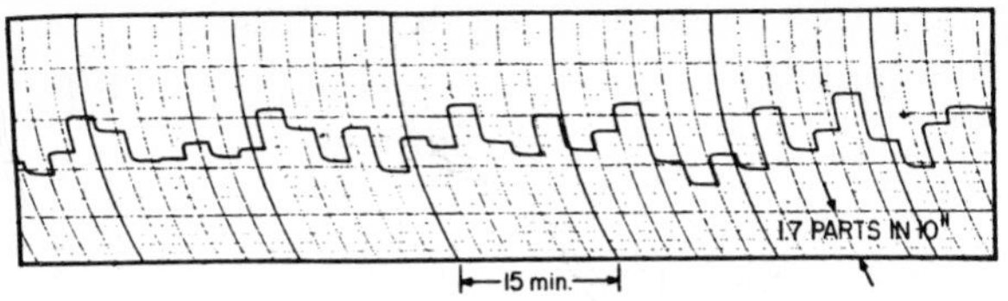

Fig. 6—Frequency of maser as a function of time. Each step represents an average frequency over an interval of approximately 78 sec. The record is 1½ hr long.

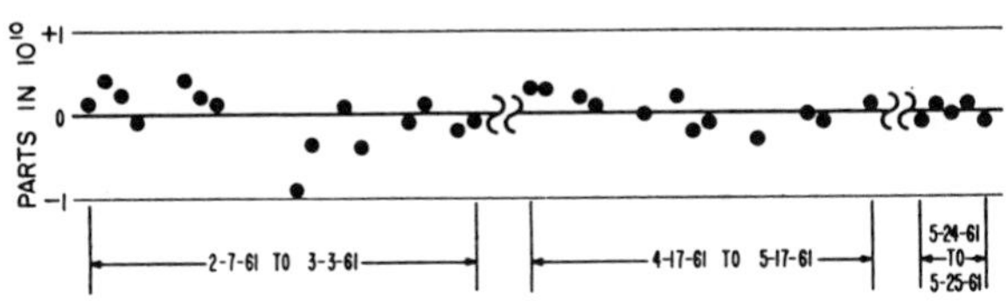

Fig. 7—NBS double-beam ammonia maser vs cesium beam (National Frequency Standard).

Maser Stability

In order to test the long- and short-term stability of the maser, comparisons have been made with a very stable (drift rate of about 6×10^{-12}/hr) quartz crystal oscillator and with the National Frequency Standard, cesium beam.

For short-term comparisons the oscillator that is phase locked to the maser is mixed with the oscillator mentioned above, and the period of the beat note is measured. Eight-second averages gave a standard deviation of 3 parts in 10^{11}; a large part of this is due to the oscillating cavity-tuning servoloop because the short-term stability of the free-running maser is only a few parts in 10^{12}.

The reader will remember that the period of oscillation of the cavity-tuning servoloop is about ½ sec; so if the time of averaging is long compared with the period of oscillation, the statistics should average out this oscillatory characteristic. Therefore, 78-sec period averages were taken, and a typical trace of the relative frequency fluctuations is shown in Fig. 6. This trace is 96 min long and gives a standard deviation of the mean of 1.3 parts in 10^{12}.

The long-term stability of the maser has been obtained by direct comparisons with the cesium beam. A plot of the day-by-day comparisons is shown in Fig. 7. Note that there are three sections; each one represents a new alignment and hence a different frequency (not indicated); the mean of each set is plotted on the same axis. Since the cesium beam usually has a standard deviation of the mean of less than 1 part in 10^{11} for any one measurement and the standard deviation for the plot in Fig. 7 is 3 parts in 10^{11}, one concludes that there is an unknown parameter in the maser system which is not in statistical control. It is felt at present that this is probably temperature-dependent elements in the maser system.

Conclusion

The experimental results show that an ammonia beam maser using the $J=3$, $K=3$ transition in ordinary $N^{14}H_3$ can be a very reliable secondary standard of frequency. As long as the alignment of the maser is not disturbed, its frequency is resettable to a precision which makes it quite competitive with the cesium beam and gas cell. The authors see no reason why such a maser system could not be run for years without deterioration of its resettability. With an improved servosystem, the short-term stability could probably approach that of the free-running maser itself and thus have this advantage over either the cesium beam or gas cell which depends on a quartz crystal oscillator for their short-term stability.

Perhaps one of the most encouraging aspects of the system is that everyone who has used $N^{15}H_3$ has reported a marked improvement over $N^{14}H_3$ in all operating parameters as theory predicts. It is hoped that the change to $N^{15}H_3$ may relegate this maser servosystem to a competitive primary standard of frequency.

Appendix

When a magnetic field is applied to the ammonia molecule, the spectral line for $J=3$, $K=3$ is split as shown in Fig. 1. Such a splitting, of course, changes the effective line width $\Delta\nu_l$ of the transition. Since this effective line width must be a function of the magnitude of the splitting only, it is reasonable, at least as far as functional dependence is concerned, to assume that the effective line width is related to the second moment of the perturbed line by the relation

$$\left(\frac{\Delta\nu_l}{2}\right)^2 = \frac{\int P(\nu)(\nu-\nu_0)^2 d\nu}{\int P(\nu) d\nu} \tag{13}$$

where $P(\nu)$ is the probability of transition for the frequency ν, and ν_0 is the center of gravity of the line.

By a simple application of the parallel axis theorem one obtains

$$\left(\frac{\Delta\nu_l}{2}\right)^2 = \left(\frac{\Delta\nu_0}{2}\right)^2 + \left(\frac{\Delta\nu_H}{2}\right)^2 \tag{14}$$

or equivalently

$$\Delta\nu_l = \sqrt{(\Delta\nu_0)^2 + (\Delta\nu_H)^2}. \tag{15}$$

Acknowledgment

The authors wish to acknowledge the great amount of assistance given by R. E. Beehler and C. S. Snider in the comparisons with the cesium beam, and Dr. R. C. Mockler for some enlightening discussions and comments.

Reprinted from JOURNAL OF APPLIED PHYSICS, Vol. 31, No. 3, 458–463, March, 1960

Focusing Molecular Beams of NH_3*

J. C. HELMER AND F. B. JACOBUS, *Varian Associates, Palo Alto, California*

AND

P. A. STURROCK, *W. W. Hansen Laboratories of Physics, Stanford, California*
(Received August 28, 1959;

The problem of forming molecular beams for use in ammonia masers is examined. It is shown theoretically and experimentally that through the use of a new type of parabolic focuser with a "point source" effuser, the molecular flow may either be reduced by a factor of 8, for the same power output, or the power output may be increased by a factor of 2 for the same molecular flow. A theory of beam formation in a multitube effuser is described. This shows that the most intense molecular beam is formed by an effuser of small overall diameter. Design considerations are discussed for parabolic, upper-state focusers, and for coaxial, lower-state focusers. The operation of a system is described, using a lower-state focuser and an ionization detector, in which lower-state molecules produced by maser oscillation may be detected.

I. INTRODUCTION

AN investigation of the properties of the ammonia beam maser[1] leads directly to a study of the formation and focusing of the molecular beam. In addition, it is desirable to know how to obtain the most intense molecular beam, and how to make the most efficient use of the molecules leaving the effuser. The following discussion summarizes some of the results of a three year study of NH_3 beams as used in the ammonia maser.

II. NONUNIFORM FOCUSERS

Focusers used in the past have been uniform in cross section from effuser to cavity. These produce beams of uniform cross section. Consider now a beam whose cross-sectional area varies in a more or less arbitrary way from the molecular source to the cavity, as shown in Fig. 1. The number of molecules N leaving the source and entering the cavity is given by

$$N=I_1A_1\Omega_1=I_2A_2\Omega_2,$$

where A_1, A_2 are the areas of the source and cavity apertures; Ω_1, Ω_2 are the solid capture angles occupied by the molecular trajectories, averaged over A_1 and A_2; and I_1, I_2 are the beam intensities at the source and the cavity apertures. Since the volume of phase space occupied by the beam is constant, we have

$$A_1\Omega_1=A_2\Omega_2, \tag{1}$$

and hence

$$I_2=I_1.$$

In maser application the minimum molecular bandwidth, $\Delta f_{\min}$, is determined by Ω_2, so that

$$\Delta f_{\min}\simeq 2v/\lambda(\Omega_2/\pi)^{\frac{1}{2}}, \tag{2}$$

* Supported by the U. S. Army Signal Corps under Contract No. DA-36-039 sc-73266.

[1] Gordon, Zeiger, and Townes, Phys. Rev. 99, 1264 (1955).

where v is the axial molecular velocity and λ is the wavelength of the molecular line. If Δf_{min} and therefore Ω_2 are to be held constant, the only way that the molecular flux may be increased is to increase I_1, the source intensity. We will consider this problem in Sec. III. The value of Ω_2 is determined by the strength of the focusing fields. Increasing the strength of the focusing fields increases the molecular flux and the minimum molecular bandwidth at the same time. For sufficiently short cavities, the change in Δf_{min} may be ignored, but in long cavities where Δf_{min} is greater than the "transit time" bandwidth, the change in Δf_{min} is an important, complicating factor.[2]

In practice, the capture solid angle at source, Ω_1, is much smaller than the solid angle, Ω_e, occupied by the molecules leaving the effuser. The total gas input to the device is therefore $I_1A_1\Omega_e$, independent of Ω_1. It follows that if a focuser can be designed such that A_1 is reduced while maintaining the same value of Ω_2, a substantial reduction in the gas input may be achieved. This problem has been solved by P. A. Sturrock.[3] A solution exists for the molecular trajectories in a harmonic potential well, such that the envelope of the beam defines a paraboloid of revolution. Sturrock shows that the focusing fields which form this beam are provided by quadrupole electrodes which lie on the surface of the paraboloid. The paraboloid may be cut at any two planes, normal to the axis, and these define the entrance and exit apertures. It is assumed that the area of the molecular source is equal to the area A_1 of the entrance aperture. The design of such a focuser is particularly simple, since the entrance and exit apertures uniquely define the parabola. If R_1 is the radius of the input aperture and R_2 the radius of the output aperture, then the beam radius R is given by

$$R=\left(\frac{Z}{L}(R_2^2-R_1^2)+R_1^2\right)^{\frac{1}{2}}, \quad (3)$$

where L is the length of the focuser and Z is the distance along the beam axis. In practice, the focusing electrodes have circular cross sections which match the radius of curvature of the theoretical hyperbolic equipotentials, at the closest approach to the beam axis. This condition is obtained when the diameter of the focusing electrode is equal to the beam diameter, where the beam diameter is defined by the inscribed circle which grazes the electrodes.

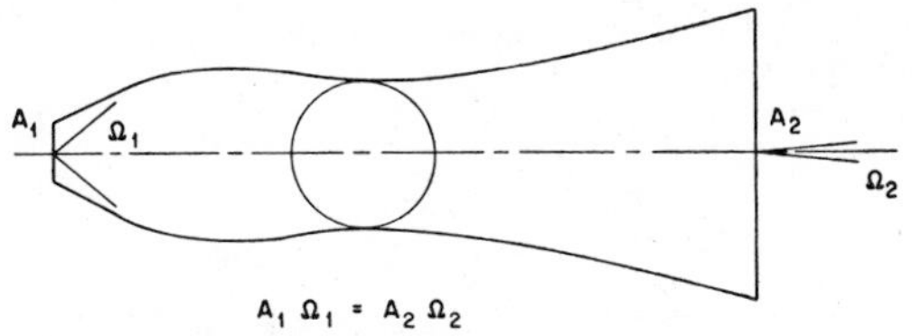

FIG. 1. Arbitrary beam envelope.

To obtain the maximum beam transmission, the period in space of the molecular trajectories must change sufficiently slowly along the length of the beam. In a given focuser this condition can be obtained by applying a sufficiently high potential. This condition will hold if the applied potential is of a value such that a uniform focuser of length L and radius R_2 is one-quarter of a focusing period long or more. Therefore, the length of the parabolic, quadrupole focuser will be the same as the length of a uniform quadrupole focuser with the same applied potential and exit aperture R_2. If the molecular sources have the same intensities I_1, then the beams emerging from the two focusers will be identical. But, under the condition $\Omega_e \gg \Omega_1$, which is true in practice, the total gas input is reduced, using the parabolic focuser, by the factor A_1/A_2. The limit to which this situation may be carried is reached when R_1 becomes so small that breakdown occurs due to the applied potential. However, this type of focuser is favored by the experience that breakdown usually occurs across insulators, and if not, then it is always possible to obtain higher electric fields, before breakdown, with conductors of small diameter than with conductors of large diameter. Secondly, this geometry favors the production of molecular beams of greater intensity than has been obtained in uniform focusers. This is discussed in Sec. III.

The parabolic shape is not the only possible shape for a nonuniform focuser. The shape is primarily determined by an upper limit on the allowed rate of variation. This upper limit is given by a solution of the harmonic oscillator equation with time varying force constant,

$$(d^2r/dt^2)+\omega^2(t)r=0. \quad (4)$$

Subject to the condition that

$$d\omega/\omega^2dt \ll 1, \quad (5)$$

a solution of (4) is[4]

$$r=A\left(\frac{\omega(0)}{\omega(t)}\right)^{\frac{1}{2}} \exp \pm j\int_0^t \omega dt, \quad (6)$$

where A is a constant. A feature of Eq. (6) is that

$$|dr/dt|_{max}\times|r|_{max}=\text{const.} \quad (7)$$

This is a specific example of the law expressed in Eq. (1). For maximum beam transmission, the condition (5) is a little too strong and it is sufficient that

$$d\omega/\omega^2dt \leq 1 \quad (8)$$

or, if $T=2\pi/\omega$ is the period of oscillation, then

$$dT/2\pi dt \leq 1. \quad (9)$$

[2] J. C. Helmer, J. Appl. Phys. 30, 118 (1959).
[3] P. A. Sturrock, "Research on atomic and molecular resonance devices," Varian Associates Engineering Report No. 218-3Q, January, 1958 (to be published).

[4] For example, see the WKB approximation.

In a quadrupole focuser, the Stark energy is

$$W=C|E|^2, \quad |E|=V_0r/R^2, \tag{10}$$

where C is a molecular constant, E is the electric field strength, R is the inscribed radius of the focuser, and V_0 is the applied voltage. It follows that

$$T=\frac{2\pi}{\omega}=2\pi\left(\frac{mr}{dW/dr}\right)^{\frac{1}{2}}=\frac{2\pi R^2}{V_0(2C/m)^{\frac{1}{2}}}, \tag{11}$$

where m is the molecular mass. For a nonuniform focuser, we therefore require that

$$\frac{1}{2\pi}\frac{dT}{dt}=\frac{d}{dt}\left(\frac{R^2}{V_0(2C/m)^{\frac{1}{2}}}\right)\leq 1. \tag{12}$$

If V_0 and C are constant with length $z(z=vt$, where v is the axial velocity), then the shape of a focuser in which $dT/dt=$const is given by

$$R^2=At+B. \tag{13}$$

This is the equation of the parabolic focuser. The parabolic focuser is the shortest nonuniform focuser, however, it is only necessary in general to satisfy Eq. (9). This relation may be satisfied by a *linear* taper in which at $R=R_2$, $dT/2\pi dt=1$. Then it follows that, for $R<R_2$, $dT/2\pi dt<1$.

In NH_3 and in other molecules as well, a complicating effect is the change in molecular constants at high field strength. In ammonia, the Stark energy undergoes a transition from second order to first order for field strengths above 30 000 v/cm. At the small end of a nonuniform focuser, field strengths in excess of 200 000 v/cm are easily obtained. In this region, $W\sim|E|$ and a linear taper is more nearly the optimum electrode shape. These remarks also hold for the focusing of linear molecules which have rotational constants above 30 kmc. Molecules with small rotational constants will not focus properly in high fields due to a sign reversal in the slope of the Stark energy.

III. MOLECULAR EFFUSERS

The limiting intensity I of a molecular effuser is determined by mean-free-path considerations in much the same way that molecular flow is limited in a thin hole. Due to the frequent crossings of the molecular paths on the exit side of a thin hole, the molecular density remains roughly constant for a distance along the axis about equal to the diameter of the hole. If a molecule can get through this region, it enters the inverse-square-law region of molecular density where the collision probability rapidly vanishes. Thus, the maximum intensity of molecular effusion is reached when the pressure at the entrance side of the hole is such that the molecular mean-free-path is equal to the diameter of the hole.

For long single tubes, we have instead the requirement that the mean-free-path be greater than the length of the tube. Effusers for intense molecular beams usually consist of bundles of such tubes. In addition, the effuser is operated at a sufficiently high entrance pressure so that the gas enters a tube in viscous flow. We may imagine a condition such that as we travel along the tube the pressure drops until the mean-free-path is equal to the remaining tube length. From this transition region the gas streams out in molecular flow. If this picture is correct then the angle between half intensity points in the molecular beam thus formed is given by

$$\theta=2d/(\lambda), \tag{14}$$

where d is the tube diameter and λ is the mean-free-path at the transition region. Since λ is inversely proportional to the pressure at the transition region, it follows that the central beam intensity will be proportional to the angular beam width.

If the effuser consists of a bundle of diameter D of such tubes then, as we have described for the case of a thin hole, a region of constant beam density will exist in front of the effuser, and the length ℓ of this region along the axis will be

$$\ell\simeq D/\theta \tag{15}$$

The maximum beam intensity is determined by the condition that a molecule be able to pass through this region of constant density without collision. Our calculations suggest that

$$I_{\max}\sim(t/Dd)^{\frac{1}{2}}, \tag{16}$$

where t is the transparency of the effuser. Thus, greater intensity is obtainable from effusers of high transparency t and small diameter D. In our opinion, it is this relation which explains the confusing results obtained by various workers in the field in comparing large, multi-tube effusers, with smaller ones.

According to the above remarks, it is a fortunate circumstance that the parabolic focuser uses a small diameter source, for with this combination we have the choice of either reducing the total gas flow for the same beam intensity, or achieving a higher beam intensity with the same gas flow.

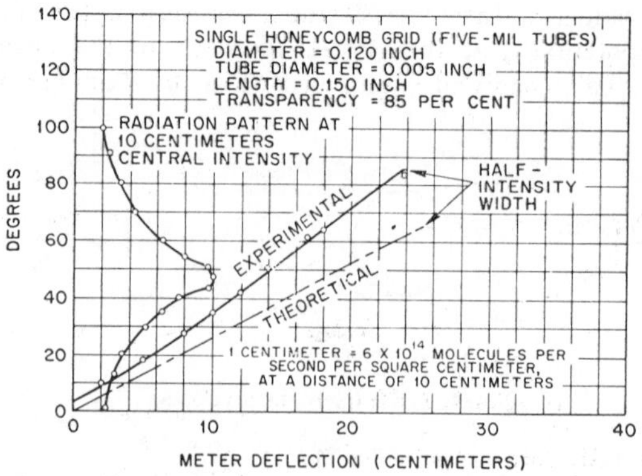

FIG. 2. Beam pattern and beam width (single honeycomb grid, five-mil tubes).

IV. LOWER-STATE FOCUSING

It will be described in Sec. V how interesting experiments can be carried out with lower-state focusers.[5] A lower-state focuser must have strong electric fields along the axis, and the obvious configuration which achieves this is a coaxial line with voltage applied between the center conductor and the outside conductor. The catastrophic increase in field strength as the center conductor is approached prevents this focuser from being a true focuser in the sense of imparting periodic motion to the lower-state molecules. Molecules which enter this focuser must ultimately strike either the inner or the outer conductor if the focuser is infinitely long. However, molecules of certain classes are strongly deflected and their radial velocities are reversed. These consist of molecules with large angular momentum and inward directed radial velocities, and molecules of small angular momentum with outward directed radial velocities. The latter class could have periodic motion if the center conductor were cut away at intervals. Calculations show that the beam transmission is optimized when the diameter ratio between the outer and inner conductor is between 3 and 4. In addition, at the operating potential the coaxial focuser should have about the same length as a quadrupole focuser of the same diameter (inscribed circle diameter) and potential.

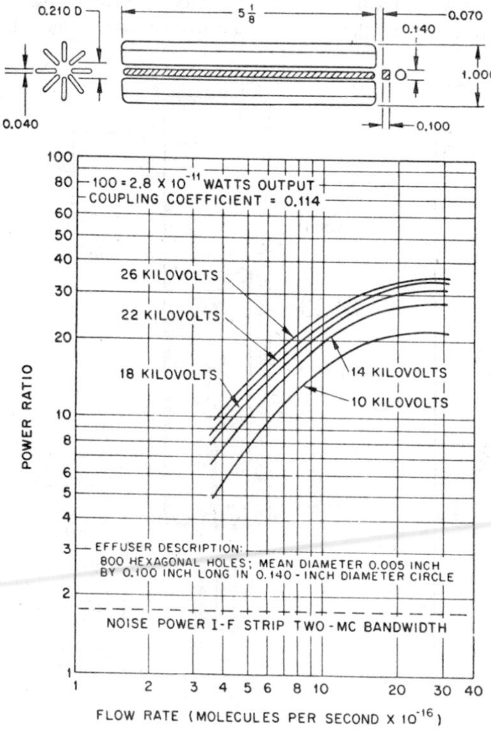

FIG. 3. Power ratio *vs* flow rate for eight-pole focuser (all dimensions in inches).

[5] See also W. H. Higa, Proceedings of the 11th Annual Symposium on Frequency Control (May, 1957), p. 352.

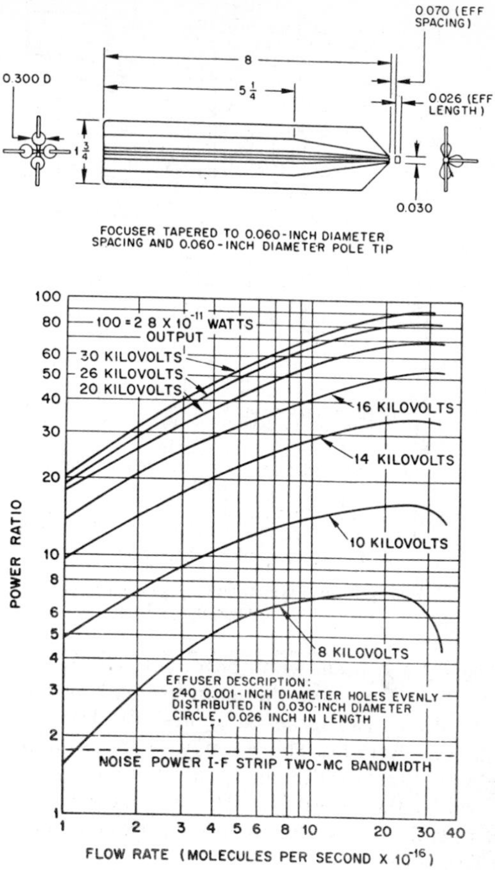

FIG. 4. Power ratio *vs* flow rate for parabolic focuser with 240-hole effuser (all dimensions in inches).

V. EXPERIMENTAL RESULTS

A. Effusers

It was suggested by Jepsen[6] that short lengths of klystron grid stock could be promising as molecular effusers. These grids are made by plating fine aluminum wire, of diameter equal to the tube diameter in the effuser, with a thin layer of copper. The plated wire is cut in six inch lengths and stacked in a copper pipe until the pipe is full. The pipe is then swaged so that the wire cross sections deform and fill the empty spaces. A molecular effuser is made by cutting off a desired length and etching out the aluminum, leaving a thin wall, copper honeycomb structure. The technique may be used with wire diam of 0.001 in. and above. A transparency of 85% is obtained with 0.005-in. wire.

The beam pattern for a 0.140-in. diam grid with 0.005-in. diam tubes was measured with a Pirani gauge and a rotating grid mount. The Pirani gauge was calibrated by the beam formed by a small, thin hole, with a known pressure behind it. The results are shown in Fig. 2. The nearly linear relation between central

[6] R. L. Jepsen (private communication).

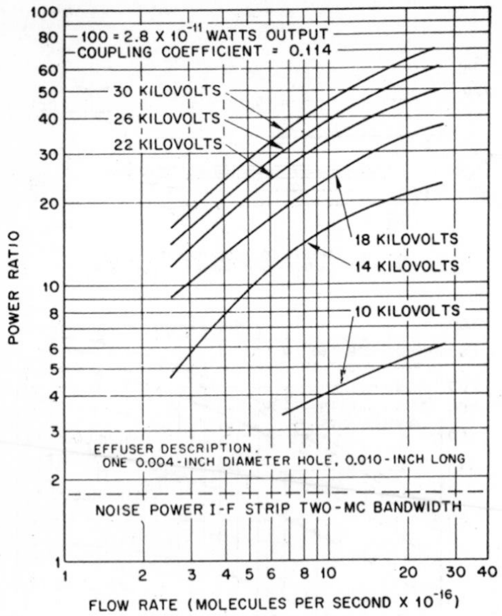

FIG. 5. Power ratio *vs* flow rate for parabolic focuser with single-hole effuser.

intensity and beam width bears out the prediction of Eq. (14). If we take the mean-free-path of ammonia molecules as two inches at a pressure of 10^{-3} mm of Hg, then, from Eq. (14) we may compute the relation between beam width and central intensity. This is shown by the dashed line. The agreement here is very good, and it lends support to the arguments presented in Sec. III.

Grids of the type described above have been used extensively in this laboratory for molecular effusers with uniform focusers, in which the beam diameter is about 0.375 in. The rather small diameter of the effuser has not been a disadvantage as at first we thought it might be. In fact, the performance of larger diameter effusers, made up from 3 or 7 of these grids mounted in parallel, as measured by the microwave power output of the maser, has been noticeably poorer. And the 7 grid effuser produced much less power output than the 3 grid effuser. These results support the general idea that the most intense molecular beams are produced by effusers of small diameter and high transparency.

B. Parabolic Focusers

For reference, Fig. 3 shows the maser power output when the beam is formed by an eight-pole focuser using the klystron grid effuser described in part A. In Fig. 4 is shown the same measurement for a parabolic quadrupole focuser, using a 0.030-in. diam effuser containing 240, 0.001-in. diam tubes. In comparison with Fig. 3, we see that at a relative power of 20 the parabolic focuser uses a factor of 8 less gas flow, while the maximum output, at constant flow rate, is greater by a factor of 2. This again agrees qualitatively with the predicted results. The amount of gas saved should be given by the area ratio of the exit and entrance apertures, about 25. At least part of the reason that only a factor of 8 is obtained is that at the very high fields produced in the entrance aperture, about 200 kv per centimeter, the Stark effect is well into the linear region. The design of the focuser is based on the second order Stark effect which, if it were to hold at the input aperture, would produce considerably higher deflections than are actually obtained.

Of additional interest is the performance of the parabolic focuser with a single 0.004-in. diam tube for the effuser; shown in Fig. 5. It does not perform quite as well as the multitube effuser with the parabolic focuser, but it is quite superior to the uniform, eight-pole focuser with the klystron grid effuser.

All of these measurements were made with a six-inch long cavity. We suggest that the quadrupole, parabolic focuser performs best with such a long cavity. This is due to the better defocusing of lower-state molecules which travel close to the beam axis. In the case of uniform focusers which have more than four poles, there is a definite tendency for the production of beams which, within a small axially directed solid angle, are deficient in upper state population excess.[7] However, it is just these molecules which are put to the best use in very long cavities.

It is found that the easiest way of measuring total gas flow is to allow the maser to exhaust a glass bulb

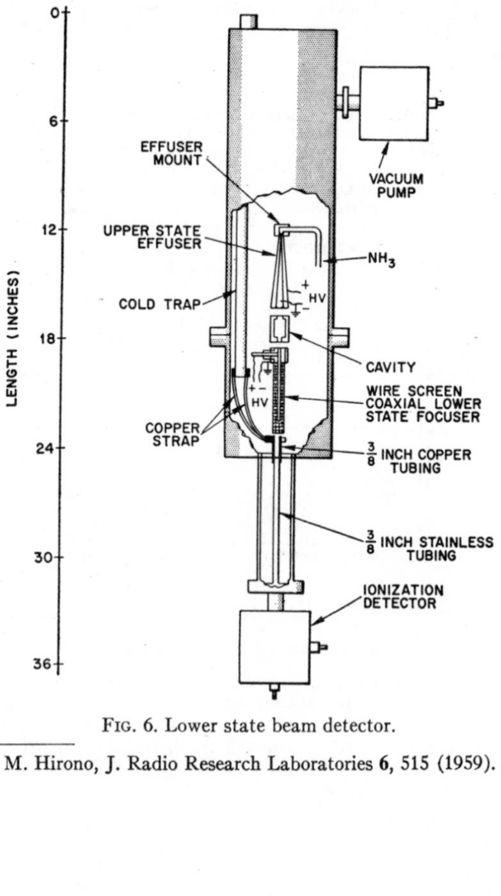

FIG. 6. Lower state beam detector.

[7] M. Hirono, J. Radio Research Laboratories **6**, 515 (1959).

of known volume, containing NH_3. The pressure in the bulb is monitored by an oil monometer whose reference end is connected to vacuum. If the flow conditions in the effuser are molecular, then the pressure in the bulb is a simple exponential function of time, from which the initial flow rate is easily deduced. There is no reason to suppose that the flow conditions are molecular, however, in all cases, a perfect exponential decay of pressure with time is observed.

C. Lower State Focusing

Through the use of a lower-state focuser it is possible to detect oscillation in the cavity by detecting the lower state molecules which are produced by the oscillation. The experimental setup for such a system is shown in Fig. 6. If there is no oscillation, upper state molecules passing into the lower state focuser are defocused and do not reach the ionization detector. Oscillation produces lower state molecules which are focused by the lower state focuser into the ionization detector, resulting in an increase in detector current. By using an all metal vacuum system, pumped by a small VacIon† high vacuum pump and a liquid nitrogen cold trap, we obtain an increase in detector current of five per cent due to oscillation, with a voltage signal to noise ratio of 15. The ionization gauge, a modified VacIon high vacuum pump, has a time constant of three minutes due to adsorption and desorption of molecules on the surfaces of the entrance tube and chamber. The principle of operation of this gauge, with its long entrance tube, is the same as the more conventionally used Pirani gauge.[8] In addition, it may be shown that the gauge sensitivity is independent of the pumping speed of the gauge. In this application, the main advantage of a VacIon pump is its high current sensitivity, 800 times greater than the filament type ion gauge, and the very important fact that it keeps itself clean.

The lower state beam detector has two potential uses. Due to the fact that it counts only those molecules which pass through the cavity without hitting the walls, it may be used as a spectrometer of very high resolution. In addition, it may be used as a detector of infrared oscillation in the ammonia beam.

† Registered U. S. Patent Office.

VI. ACKNOWLEDGMENT

This work has benefited considerably from the contributions, advice, and encouragement of R. L. Jepsen, M. W. Muller, and W. L. Beaver. Many of the experiments would have been impossible without the expert technical assistance of E. B. Hodges, R. E. Uhlenberg, and W. W. Wood.

[8] N. F. Ramsey, *Molecular Beams* (Clarendon Press, Oxford England, 1956).

Reprinted from JOURNAL OF APPLIED PHYSICS, Vol. 31, No. 3, 463–471, March, 1960

Molecular Beam Formation by Long Parallel Tubes*

J. A. GIORDMAINE AND T. C. WANG†
Columbia University, New York, New York
(Received August 13, 1959)

The characteristics of molecular beams formed by sources consisting of long tube arrays are measured for several sources. The peak beam intensity and the beam width are calculated when collisions in the source are taken into account under the assumption that a limited region of Knudsen type flow occurs near the low-pressure end of the source. The peak beam intensity and the beam width are calculated to vary as the square root of the total flow rate for source pressures giving useful directivity, in good agreement with the observations. Considerations in the design of sources are discussed.

I. INTRODUCTION

IN recent years, several types of molecular beam devices have been constructed in which beams of high intensity are required from sources having an area of the order of 1 cm^2. An example of such a system is the ammonia maser,[1] in which the necessary peak beam intensity is approximately 10^{19} molecules per second per steradian. In order to reduce pumping requirements in such systems, arrays of long parallel tubes[2] have been used as beam sources. In this way the peak intensity has been increased in some systems by a factor of about 20 compared to a cosine law source for the same total flow. In this paper we discuss the properties of molecular flow in such sources and report on the characteristics of several different types of sources.

* Work supported jointly by the U. S. Army Signal Corps, the Office of Naval Research, and the Air Force Office of Scientific Research.

† Present address: Arthur D. Little, Inc., Cambridge, Massachusetts.

[1] Gordon, Zeiger, and Townes, Phys. Rev. 99, 1264 (1955).

[2] This technique was first used by J. R. Zacharias; see N. F. Ramsey, *Molecular Beams* (Clarendon Press, Oxford, 1956), p. 363.

We shall make use of the following symbols:

- a tube radius, cm
- L tube length, cm
- n molecular density, molecules cm^{-3}
- n_0 density at the high-pressure end of the tube
- A cross-sectional area of tube, cm^2
- $d\omega$ element of solid angle, steradians
- θ angle between a given direction and the tube axis
- $\bar{c}$ average molecular velocity, cm sec^{-1}
- λ mean free path, cm
- σ molecular diameter, cm
- $I(\theta)$ beam intensity in the direction θ, molecules $(steradian)^{-1}$ sec^{-1}
- z distance into tube, measured from low-pressure end, cm
- N rate of flow through the tube, molecules sec^{-1}
- $\bar{\lambda}$ average mean free path over the length of the tube, where

$$\bar{\lambda} \equiv L\left(\int_0^L dz/\lambda(z)\right)^{-1}. \qquad (1)$$

Depending on the ratio of the molecular mean free path to the radius and length of the tube, several modes of molecular flow can be defined for the purposes of the present work. It will be assumed through that $L \gg a$.

Mode I. $\bar{\lambda} \gg L$. In this mode of flow the tube is "transparent," i.e., a molecule at the high pressure end of the tube traveling in the direction of the tube axis passes through the tube without a collision. The peak intensity and the flow rate are proportional to the pressure behind the source.

The peak intensity is

$$I(0)d\omega = \frac{n_0 \bar{c} a^2}{4} d\omega \qquad (2)$$

and the flow rate is given[3] by

$$N = \frac{2\pi}{3} \frac{n_0 \bar{c} a^3}{L}. \qquad (3)$$

The beam shape, that is, $I(\theta)/I(0)$ is determined almost completely by the tube geometry and is independent of n_0 and N. The beam shape under these conditions is calculated below on the basis of certain reasonable assumptions.

Mode II. $\bar{\lambda} \gtrsim L$; $\lambda \gg a$ throughout the tube. In this mode the tube is no longer transparent, and the peak intensity no longer proportional to the pressure behind the source. Equation (3) remains valid for the flow rate. The beam shape for Mode II is a function of flow rate as well as the tube geometry. If $\bar{\lambda} \gg L$ the beam shape is determined almost completely by a and N, with no direct dependence on L. Under this condition the tube is referred to as "opaque."

[3] L. B. Loeb, *The Kinetic Theory of Gases* (McGraw-Hill Book Company, Inc., New York, 1934), 2nd edition, p. 294.

Mode III. $\bar{\lambda} \ll L$; $\lambda \gg a$ for $z < L_0$; $\lambda \lesssim a$ for $L > z > L_0$, where $L_0 \gg a$. In this mode, Knudsen type flow ($\lambda \gg a$) is a valid approximation only over a limited region L_0 near the discharge end of the tube. Neither peak intensity nor flow rate is any longer proportional to the pressure behind the source.

As the pressure behind the source is further increased, the molecular beam becomes less well defined. It will become clear that useful collimation is usually provided only for flow described by one of these three modes.

Clearly the optimum collimation for a given tube is obtained in collision-free flow (Mode I). However, to obtain peak intensities of the order of $I(0) = 10^{19}$ sec^{-1} cm^{-2} $sterad^{-1}$ according to Eq. (2), source pressures of the order of several tenths of mm are indicated. At such pressures the mean free path is of the order of 10^{-2} cm, so that long-tube collision-free flow could occur only in tubes of radius considerably less than 10^{-3} cm. At present, densely packed arrays of such narrow bore tubes are not available. For this reason, sources giving high beam intensities are operated under Mode II or III conditions, in which the peak intensities and collimation are essentially determined by intermolecular collisions in the tubes.

All of the experimental work reported below was carried out under Mode II and III conditions.

II. EXPERIMENTAL TECHNIQUE

The angular distribution of intensity from the tube arrays was studied by use of the apparatus shown in Fig. 1. The sources were mounted so as to allow rotation about an axis through the center of the source face and perpendicular to the tube axes.

The detector was a Pirani gauge in which the chambers and slits were milled in a pair of lapped stainless steel blocks.[4] The four platinum ribbon elements were soldered to springs which kept the ribbons taut in the channels. The characteristics of the gauge are shown in Table I. The gauge was used in a conventional

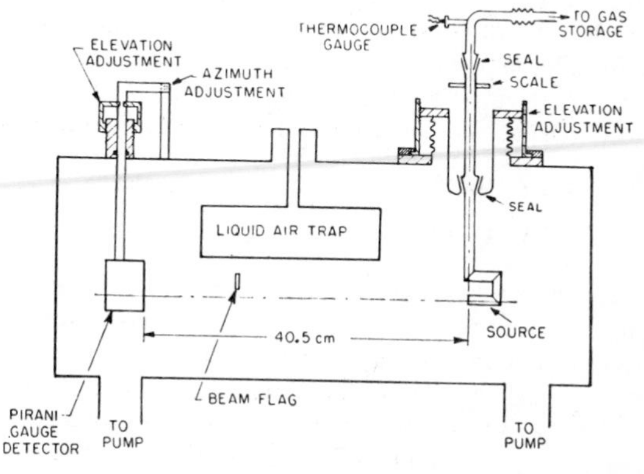

FIG. 1. Experimental apparatus, showing the mounting and relative positions of the source and detector.

[4] R. S. Julian, Ph.D. Thesis, Massachusetts Institute of Technology, Cambridge, Massachusetts (1947). This gauge is described by N. F. Ramsey, reference 2, p. 392.

Wheatstone bridge circuit with a mirror galvanometer. The gauge mounting allowed for adjustment of height and azimuth, and the final alignment of the gauge was carried out by adjustment of the gauge for maximum response with the beam from the source being studied.

The sources and detectors were mounted in a molecular beam can which was already available.[5] Two MCF 300 pumps and one MCF 700 pump were used, as well as a liquid nitrogen trap. Nevertheless, can pressures with the sources operating were in the range 1 to 6×10^{-5} mm.

The source-detector spacing was 40.5 cm. As a result of the high can pressure, the measured beam intensities had to be corrected for attenuations of between 10% and 55% between the source and the detector.

Flow rates through the sources could be measured by observing the rate of change of pressure in a bulb of approximately 5 liter volume connected to the source. The bulb pressures were measured by a thermocouple gauge (Hastings Model AP-1) mounted at the neck of the bulb. Pressures at the source were measured by a second thermocouple gauge mounted near the source. The thermocouple gauges were calibrated for CO_2 at

TABLE I. Design of Pirani gauge.

Chamber dimension:	$0.100\times0.020\times1.75$ in.
Slit cross section:	0.006×0.188 in.
Slit length:	0.247 in.
Ribbon dimensions:	$0.00005\times0.015\times1.59$ in.
Gauge sensitivity (CO_2):	1 cm deflection $\sim1.6\times10^{13}$ molecules cm^{-2} sec^{-1}

pressures of a few tenths of a mm and higher against a mechanical pressure gauge (Wallace-Tiernan FA-160).

The Pirani gauge was calibrated by observing the flow rate through one of the sources (A) and the integrated beam intensity as indicated by the gauge, taking into account the beam attenuation in the can. The flow rates quoted below were obtained from the integrated angular distribution patterns and the Pirani gauge calibration factor.

Beam attenuation in the can was calculated using a mean free path derived from the quoted[6] values for CO_2.

$$\lambda=2.95\times10^{-3}\text{ cm}\quad 0°\text{C, 1 mm pressure}$$

$$\lambda=3.34\times10^{-3}\text{ cm}\quad 26°\text{C, 1 mm pressure.}$$

Because of the small angular aperture of the Pirani gauge, it was necessary to apply a correction for decreased effective detection sensitivity with sources B and C, which had larger diameters than source A. The sensitivity was calculated to be less than that with source A by 19% and 15%, respectively.

All of the results quoted are for CO_2. Attempts were made to observe source behavior using NH_3. However,

TABLE II. Characteristics of long tube sources.

Source	Tube length cm	Effective radius of single tube cm	No. of tubes	Over-all source diameter cm	Approximate shape of tube cross section
A	0.66	1.65×10^{-2}	224	0.51	Hexagonal
B	0.31	2.35×10^{-3}	1.28×10^{4}	1.3	Circular
C	0.95	2.69×10^{-3}	1.80×10^{4}	1.1	Triangular

the Pirani gauge detected NH_3 very sluggishly, with low sensitivity and little reproducibility. This behavior may have been caused by adsorption of the gas in the detector.

The over-all accuracy of the flow rate measurements is estimated as about ±20%. The peak intensities are known to the same absolute accuracy. Ratios of peak intensity to flow rate are known to about ±5%.

The three sources studied in this investigation are described in Table II.

Source A, an extended klystron grid structure, had a honeycomb cross section, with the individual tubes separated by walls of approximately 0.001-in. thickness. Source B consisted of an aligned stack of photographically etched metal foils,[7] with the holes of circular cross-section arranged in hexagonal format. The alignment accuracy was such that the optical transparency of the stack was about 85% that of a single foil. Source C was prepared by rolling together two strips of nickel foil, one finely corrugated, the other flat, onto a thin spindle.[8] Source A was surrounded by a sleeve whose front edge was flush with the front of the source. The sleeves for sources B and C protruded about 3 and 2 mm respectively in front of the source face.

The effective radius quoted in Table II is defined as the perimeter of the tube cross section divided by 2π. The effective radius is equal to the actual radius for source B. The tube radii were measured with a magnifying optical projector and are minimum radii for the entire tube length. As a result of nonuniformity in the source construction, they may be up to 10% smaller than the average cross section for source B and 20% for C.

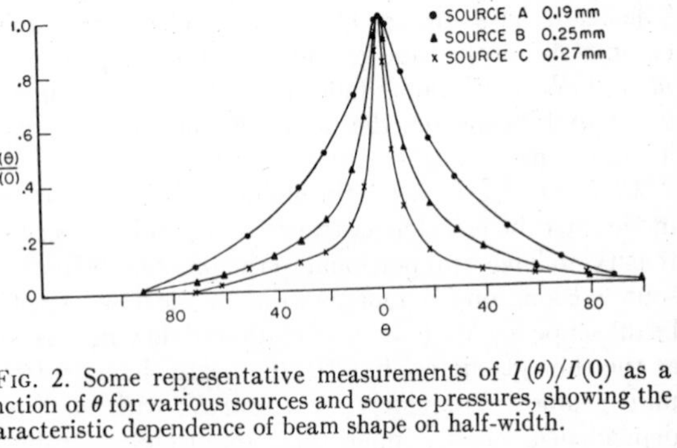

FIG. 2. Some representative measurements of $I(\theta)/I(0)$ as a function of θ for various sources and source pressures, showing the characteristic dependence of beam shape on half-width.

[5] Heberle, Reich, and Kusch, Phys. Rev. **101**, 612 (1956).
[6] *Smithsonian Physical Tables* (1954), ninth edition.

[7] This source was kindly loaned by Mr. J. P. Cedarholm.
[8] J. R. Zacharias and R. D. Haun, Jr., Quarterly Progress Report, M.I.T. Research Laboratory of Electronics, 34, October, 1954 (unpublished).

TABLE III. Beam formation by long tube sources.

Source	Pressure behind source mm	Peak intensity molecules sec^{-1} sterad^{-1}	Total flow molecules sec^{-1}	Half-width of beam at half-intensity degrees
A	0.024	1.42×10^{17}	8.91×10^{16}	5.0
	0.060	3.19	1.87×10^{17}	8.3
	0.110	5.70	5.26	15.0
	0.190	9.66	1.21×10^{18}	21.1
B	0.03	9.16×10^{17}	2.69×10^{17}	3.5
	0.075	1.49×10^{18}	4.56	4.3
	0.15	2.80	1.25×10^{18}	6.0
	0.25	3.73	2.28	9.1
	0.44	5.01	4.61	15.7
C	0.035	3.05×10^{17}	5.42×10^{16}	2.5
	0.13	7.87	1.81×10^{17}	3.3
	0.265	1.30×10^{18}	3.88	4.5
	0.61	2.29	1.03×10^{18}	5.7
	1.28	3.74	2.18	7.8
	1.90	4.79	3.58	11.3

III. EXPERIMENTAL RESULTS

Typical beam shapes produced by the sources are shown in Fig. 2. The beam shapes are shown normalized to the same peak intensity. These illustrations are reproduced to indicate the changing character of the beam shape with source pressure that was observed for all three sources, rather than to compare the effectiveness of the various sources. For a given beam width of half-intensity, the beam shapes were approximately the same for each source.

The experimental data are collected in Table III. The values quoted are corrected for beam attenuation in the can and for the limited angular aperture of the detector.

The source pressures shown in Table III are accurate to about ±0.03 mm. As a result of this low relative accuracy, the flow rates at the lowest pressures, where Knudsen flow would be expected throughout the tube, could not be compared quantitatively with the prediction of Eq. (2). In what follows, we shall be concerned with the flow rates themselves as the variable, irrespective of whether Knudsen flow is a valid approximation throughout the tube.

The peak intensity and the beam width varied approximately as the square root of the total flow rate for all the observations. The dependence on N is shown in Figs. 3 and 4. The intensities and flow rates plotted are those per single tube, i.e., the observed quantities divided by the number of tubes.

In the theoretical section we derive an approximate theory predicting this behavior quantitatively over the range of flow rates observed.

IV. THEORY

A. Peak Intensity

In this section the peak intensity is calculated as a function of the flow rate for a single tube of circular cross section. The approximate generalization to tubes of arbitrary cross section is discussed briefly at the end of this section.

We assume that, at least near the low-pressure end of the tube, the mean free path λ is much larger than the tube radius a, and that this condition obtains for a distance L_0 into the tube, where $L_0 \gg a$. This assumption of Knudsen type flow over at least a limited region will be seen to be valid for cases in which a beam of useful directivity is formed. We are thus considering flow in Modes I, II, and III.

The second assumption is that in the limited region of Knudsen flow the density of molecules in the tube n is related to the distance into the tube z by the relation:

$$n = rz \tag{4}$$

where r is a constant determined by the flow rate, the mean molecular velocity $\bar{c}$, and the tube radius. This assumption is strictly valid for $z \gg a$ only, since end corrections for $z \lesssim a$ are neglected. However, it will be

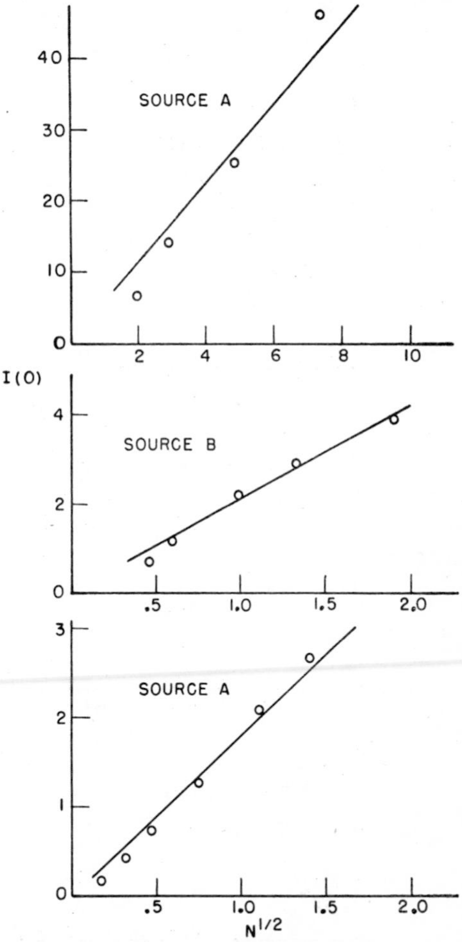

FIG. 3. Peak intensity per tube as a function of the square root of the total flow rate per tube. The units of $N^{\frac{1}{2}}$ are (molecules per second)$^{\frac{1}{2}}\times10^7$, and of $I(0)$ (molecules per steradian per second)$\times10^{14}$. *Note added in proof.* The bottom graph, incorrectly labeled Source *A*, refers to Source *C*.

seen that the peak intensity in cases of high collimation is determined mainly by the behavior of n for $z \gg a$, where this assumption is valid.

Consider an element of tube volume $\pi a^2 dz$ at a distance z from the low-pressure end of the source. The number of collisions per second in this volume element is $(\pi a^2 dz n\bar{c})/2\lambda$.

Let σ be the equivalent molecular diameter for collisions, as defined by

$$\lambda = 1/(\sqrt{2}\pi\sigma^2 n). \tag{5}$$

The number of collisions in $\pi a^2 dz$ is $(\pi^2 n^2 \sigma^2 \bar{c} a^2 dz)/\sqrt{2}$ from which arise $(\pi n^2 \sigma^2 \bar{c} a^2 dz d\omega)/2\sqrt{2}$ molecules traveling within the solid angle $d\omega$ in the direction of the tube axis toward the detector.

The fraction of these molecules undergoing collision in the distance dz' is dz'/λ or $\sqrt{2}\pi\sigma^2 n dz'$. The fraction of molecules leaving the element $\pi a^2 dz$ in the direction $d\omega$ which leave the source without a further collision is $\exp[-\pi\sigma^2 r z^2/\sqrt{2}]$.

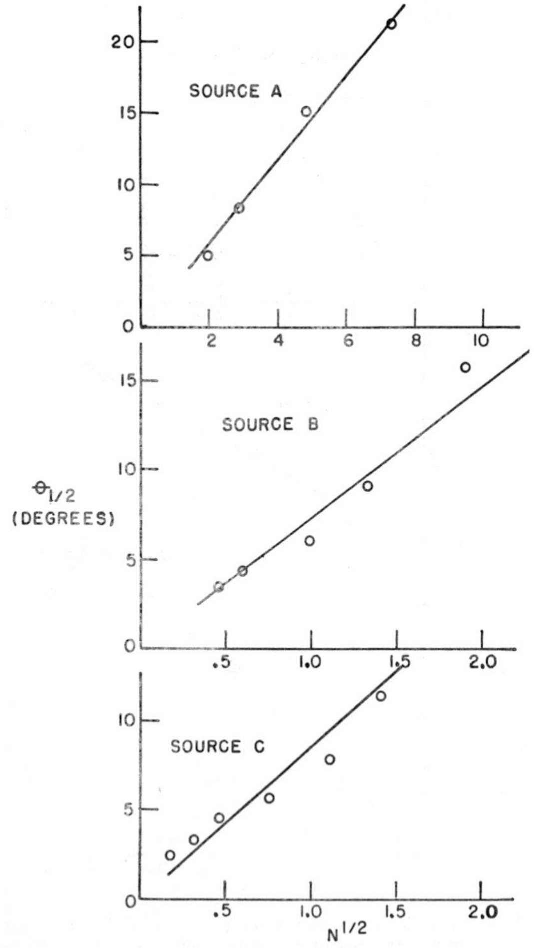

FIG. 4. Half-width of beam at half-intensity as a function of the square root of the total flow rate per tube. The units of $\theta_{\frac{1}{2}}$ are degrees, and of $N^{\frac{1}{2}}$ (molecules per second)$^{\frac{1}{2}}\times 10^7$.

Thus the total contribution to the peak intensity $I(0)d\omega$ from the collisions in the volume element $\pi a^2 dz$ is

$$I(0,z)d\omega dz = \frac{\pi\sigma^2 \bar{c} a^2 n^2}{2\sqrt{2}} \exp\left(\frac{-\pi\sigma^2 r z^2}{\sqrt{2}}\right) d\omega dz$$
$$= \frac{\pi\sigma^2 \bar{c} a^2 r^2 z^2}{2\sqrt{2}} \exp\left(\frac{-\pi\sigma^2 r z^2}{\sqrt{2}}\right) d\omega dz. \tag{6}$$

The total contribution to $I(0)$ from collisions throughout the tube is

$$I_t(0)d\omega$$
$$= \int_0^L I(0,z)d\omega dz = \frac{\pi\sigma^2 \bar{c} a^2 r^2 d\omega}{2\sqrt{2}} \int_0^L \exp\left(\frac{-\pi\sigma^2 r z^2}{\sqrt{2}}\right) z^2 dz$$
$$= \frac{a^2 r^{\frac{1}{2}} \bar{c} d\omega}{2^{7/4}\pi^{\frac{1}{2}}\sigma}\left[\int_0^{L'} \exp(-y^2)dy - L' \exp(-L'^2)\right]$$
$$= \frac{a^2 r^{\frac{1}{2}} \bar{c} d\omega}{2^{7/4}\pi^{\frac{1}{2}}\sigma} \int_0^{L'} \exp(-y^2)dy - \frac{a^2 r \bar{c} L d\omega}{4} \exp(-L'^2), \tag{7}$$

where L is the tube length and

$$L' = \frac{\pi^{\frac{1}{2}}\sigma r^{\frac{1}{2}} L}{2^{\frac{1}{4}}}.$$

An additional contribution to $I(0)$ arises from molecules which pass through the entire tube length without a collision. It can be shown by a development similar to that of Eq. (7) that this contribution is

$$I_s(0)d\omega = \frac{a^2 r \bar{c} L d\omega}{4} \exp(-L'^2). \tag{8}$$

The total intensity in the peak direction is

$$I(0)d\omega = I_t(0)d\omega + I_s(0)d\omega$$
$$= \frac{a^2 r^{\frac{1}{2}} \bar{c} d\omega}{2^{7/4}\pi^{\frac{1}{2}}\sigma} \int_0^{L'} \exp(-y^2)dy. \tag{9}$$

The peak intensity is given explicitly in terms of the total flow rate by using Eq. (3) for Knudsen flow, or

$$r = \frac{3N}{2\pi \bar{c} a^3}. \tag{9a}$$

Substituting Eq. (9a) into Eq. (9), we obtain

$$I(0) = \frac{3^{\frac{1}{2}} \bar{c}^{\frac{1}{2}} a^{\frac{1}{2}} (N)^{\frac{1}{2}}}{4\ 2^{\frac{1}{4}} \pi\sigma} \int_0^{L'} \exp(-y^2)dy, \tag{10}$$

where

$$L' = \frac{3^{\frac{1}{2}}\sigma L (N)^{\frac{1}{2}}}{2^{\frac{3}{4}} \bar{c}^{\frac{1}{2}} a^{\frac{3}{2}}}.$$

Formula (10) gives the peak intensity as a function of flow rate at all flow rates at which the source has appreciable directivity.

Simplified forms of Eq. (10) are useful in special limiting cases.

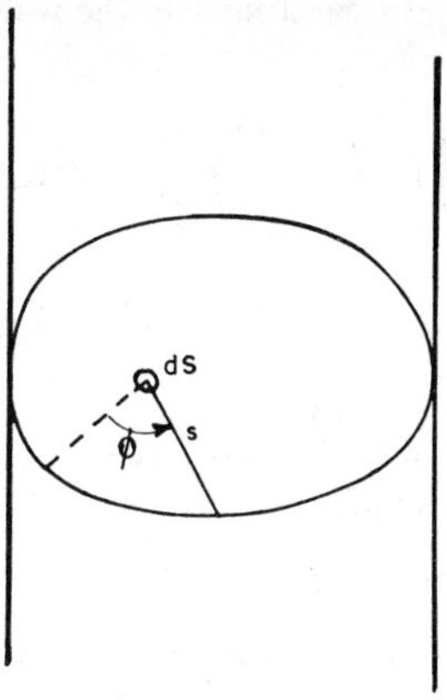

FIG. 5. Element of tube cross section, illustrating Eq. (13).

Case 1: Source Transparent: $L' \ll 1$

In this limit, the collisions in the source play a completely negligible role. In the limit of very low pressures and flow rates,

$$I(0) = \frac{(\pi a^2) n_0 \bar{c}}{4\pi} \tag{11}$$

where n_0 is the molecular density at the high pressure end of the source. Equation (11) is just the expression for the peak intensity of molecules effusing from a hole of area πa^2 in a container of molecules of density n_0, where $\lambda \gg a$.

Case 2: Source Opaque: $L' \gg 1$

In this limit, the density in the source is so large that the probability of a molecule passing through the source without a collision is negligible. In the limit of L' large compared to unity,

$$I(0) = \frac{3^{\frac{1}{2}} \bar{c}^{\frac{1}{2}} a^{\frac{1}{2}}}{8\, 2^{\frac{1}{4}} \pi^{\frac{1}{2}} \sigma} (N)^{\frac{1}{2}}. \tag{12}$$

The criterion for the validity of Eq. (12) to an accuracy of 1% is

$$L' \geqslant 2.5$$

or

$$L \geqslant \frac{2.5\, 2^{\frac{3}{4}} \bar{c}^{\frac{1}{2}} a^{\frac{3}{2}}}{3^{\frac{1}{2}} \sigma (N)^{\frac{1}{2}}} = \Lambda. \tag{12a}$$

This criterion is satisfied for all the measurements reported above and will generally be satisfied in application of long tube sources to molecular beam devices. From Eq. (12a) it follows that for a source tube of radius a carrying N molecules per second, increasing the length of the tube beyond Λ has a negligible effect on the source characteristics.

A special case of Eq. (12) arises when $\lambda \gg a$ throughout the tube. From Eqs. (3) and (12)

$$I(0) = \frac{2^{\frac{1}{4}} (\pi a^2) \bar{c} n_0^{\frac{1}{2}}}{8\pi\sigma L^{\frac{1}{2}}}. \tag{12b}$$

Equation (12b) expresses the peak intensity explicitly in terms of the pressure behind the source.

For tubes of uniform but noncircular cross section, Eq. (3) becomes[9]

$$N = \frac{1}{8} \bar{c} \frac{n_0}{L} \int dS \int_0^{2\pi} s\, d\phi, \tag{13}$$

where dS is an element of cross-sectional area and s is the distance measured at an angle ϕ with a fixed direction in the plane of the cross section, from the element dS to the boundary. The cross section is shown in Fig. 5.

An approximate expression for N for tubes of uniform and almost circular cross section is[10]

$$N = \frac{4}{3} \bar{c} \frac{n_0}{L} \frac{A^2}{P}, \tag{14}$$

where A is the cross-sectional area of the tube and P is the perimeter. From the derivation of Eq. (10) and from Eq. (14), it follows that for tubes of noncircular cross section the effective radius a_{eff} to be used in Eq. (10) and (12) is

$$a_{eff} = \frac{P}{2\pi}. \tag{15}$$

In Table IV values of $I(0)/(N)^{\frac{1}{2}}$ predicted by Eq. (12) are compared with the observed values derived from the best straight lines drawn through the origin and the experimental points in Figs. 3 and 4.

The constants used in Eq. (12) are the following, interpolated for $T = 20°C$ from observed values[6] for CO_2.

$\bar{c} = 3.74 \times 10^4$ cm sec^{-1}

$\lambda = 3.2 \times 10^{-3}$ cm at 1 mm pressure

$\sigma = 4.6 \times 10^{-8}$ cm [calculated from Eq. (5)].

For sources A and B the agreement between the theoretical and the experimental values is within the estimated experimental error. The agreement for C is less satisfactory; the discrepancy may be due in part to the use of the approximations Eq. (14) and Eq. (15) for the effective radius where the cross section is far from circular, and to the uncertainties in the average cross section for this source.

TABLE IV. Comparison of predicted and observed peak intensities.

	$\frac{I(0)}{(N)^{\frac{1}{2}}}$ molecules per steradian per second (molecules per sec)$^{-\frac{1}{2}}$	
Source	Observed	Calculated from Eq. (12)
A	5.6×10^7	5.5×10^7
B	2.1×10^7	2.1×10^7
C	1.8×10^7	2.2×10^7

[9] E. H. Kennard, *Kinetic Theory of Gases* (McGraw-Hill Book Company, Inc., New York, 1938), p. 304.
[10] L. B. Loeb, reference 3, p. 292.

The agreement observed indicates that Eq. (12) is a useful approximation in predicting peak intensity in terms of the flow rate and the constants of the tube and gas. The peak intensity appears to be determined essentially by the density gradient r and to be insensitive to end effects.

B. Beam Width

In this section the beam width is calculated for tubes of circular cross section for two of the limiting cases described in Part A, (a) "transparent source," (b) "opaque source." In both cases we make the assumption of uniform pressure gradient, in (a) over the entire tube, and in (b) over a limited region near the end of the tube. In applying Eq. (4) we again make the assumption of zero pressure at the end of the tube. It would be expected that the beam shape would be considerably more sensitive to the neglect of end corrections than the peak intensity. However in cases of high collimation, the beam intensity for angles up to the angle of half-maximum intensity is still determined largely by the pressures at points distant from the end of the tube. For this reason it seems useful to present the theory in this approximation.

(a) Transparent Source

In this limit the effect of collisions is neglected. Consider the contribution of the molecules leaving the exposed portion of the surface strip dz to the intensity in the direction θ measured from the tube axis (Fig. 6). If it is assumed that the molecules leave each surface element with an angular distribution proportional to the cosine of the angle with the normal to the surface, it is easily seen that the strip of width dz makes a contribution

$$I(\theta,z)dzd\omega=\frac{a\bar{c}}{2\pi}n(z)\sin\theta\left[1-\left(\frac{z\tan\theta}{2a}\right)^2\right]^{\frac{1}{2}}dzd\omega$$

$$=\frac{a\bar{c}r}{2\pi}\sin\theta z\left[1-\left(\frac{z\tan\theta}{2a}\right)^2\right]^{\frac{1}{2}}dzd\omega. \quad (16)$$

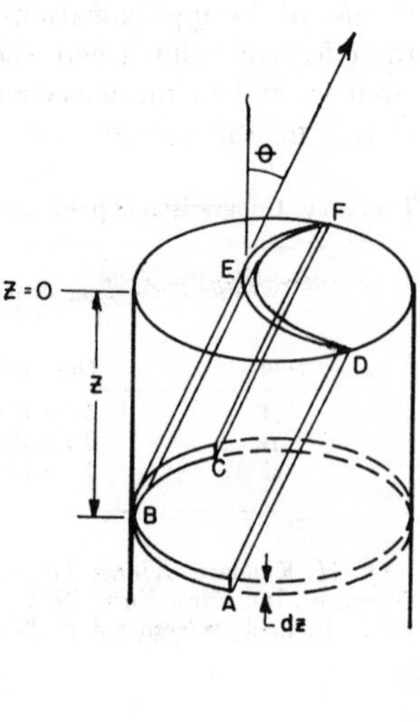

FIG. 6. Tube geometry, showing division of the exposed tube surface into strips ABC of width dz.

(*i*) $\pi/2>\theta\geqslant \tan^{-1}(2a/L)$.—Integrating over the wall area contributing to $I(\theta)d\omega$,

$$I(\theta)d\omega=\frac{a\bar{c}r\sin\theta d\omega}{2\pi}\int_0^{2a/\tan\theta}z\left[1-\left(\frac{z\tan\theta}{2a}\right)^2\right]^{\frac{1}{2}}dz \quad (16a)$$

$$=\frac{2a^3\bar{c}r}{3\pi}\frac{\cos^2\theta}{\sin\theta}d\omega. \quad (17)$$

(*ii*) $\tan^{-1}(2a/L)>\theta\geqslant 0$.—For θ in this range, the exposed area of the cross section at $z=L$ is

$$A=2a^2[\cos^{-1}y-y(1-y^2)^{\frac{1}{2}}].$$

where $y=(L\tan\theta/2a)$. The contribution from molecules passing through the source without colliding with the walls is then

$$I_1(\theta)d\omega=A\cos\theta\frac{n_0\bar{c}}{4\pi}d\omega.$$

The contribution from the walls, by analogy with Eq. (16a) is

$$I_2(\theta)d\omega=\frac{a\bar{c}r\sin\theta d\omega}{2\pi}\int_0^L z\left[1-\left(\frac{z\tan\theta}{2a}\right)^2\right]^{\frac{1}{2}}dz.$$

The total intensity is then

$$I(\theta)d\omega=\frac{a^2n_0\bar{c}\cos\theta d\omega}{2\pi}$$

$$\times\{\cos^{-1}y-y(1-y^2)^{\frac{1}{2}}+\tfrac{2}{3}y[1-(1-y^2)^{\frac{3}{2}}]\}. \quad (18)$$

Formulas (17) and (18) give the intensity distribution for all θ. From Eq. (17) and (18) the value of at which $I(\theta)=[I(0)/2]$ is

$$\theta_{\frac{1}{2}}=\frac{1.68a}{L} \quad (19)$$

for $a\ll L$. As expected the half-width at half-intensity in this limit is of the order of a/L. Since this mode of source operation is not of great use we do not discuss it further.

(b) Opaque Source

We again make the assumption of a cosine distribution for molecules, leaving the walls of the source. We shall be concerned only with tubes which are opaque according to the criterion of Eq. (12a).

The contribution to $I(\theta)d\omega$ of molecules leaving the wall element dz and undergoing no further collisions will be given by Eq. (16) modified by a suitable attenuation factor. Molecules in this category travel a distance $z/\cos\theta$ within the tube and suffer an attenuation

$$\exp\left(\frac{-\pi\sigma^2rz^2}{\sqrt{2}\cos\theta}\right).$$

The contribution to $I(\theta)d\omega$ from dz is then

$$I_1(\theta,z)dzd\omega=\frac{a\bar{c}r\sin\theta}{2\pi}z\left[1-\left(\frac{z\tan\theta}{2a}\right)^2\right]^{\frac{1}{2}}\times\exp\left(\frac{-\pi\sigma^2rz^2}{\sqrt{2}\cos\theta}\right)dzd\omega$$

or (20)

$$I_1(\theta,z')dz'd\omega=\frac{2^{\frac{1}{4}}a^2\cos^{\frac{3}{2}}\theta r^{\frac{1}{2}}\bar{c}}{\pi^{\frac{3}{2}}\sigma}kz'(1-z'^2)^{\frac{1}{2}}\times\exp(-k^2z'^2)d\omega dz',$$

where the substitutions of Eq. (21) have been made.

$$z'=\frac{z\tan\theta}{2a}$$
$$k=\frac{2a}{\tan\theta}\left(\frac{\pi\sigma^2r}{\sqrt{2}\cos\theta}\right)^{\frac{1}{2}} \qquad (21)$$

In addition to the molecules whose final collision before leaving the source is made with the tube wall, we must consider those diverted into $d\omega$ by collisions with other molecules. We divide the tube volume contributing to the intensity in the direction of $d\omega$ into elementary volumes as follows (Fig. 6). The volume element dV associated with dz is defined as that bounded by the exposed portion ABC of the curved strip dz, by the envelope of lines in the direction of θ passing through the boundary of the strip dz, and by the projection DEF in the direction of θ of the strip dz onto the tube cross section at $z=0$. The length of this element is $z/\cos\theta$ and the cross sectional area is

$$2a\sin\theta\left[1-\left(\frac{z\tan\theta}{2a}\right)^2\right]^{\frac{1}{2}}dz.$$

Using reasoning analogous to that used in deriving Eq. (7), the contribution to $I(\theta)d\omega$ from collisions in an elementary volume element is

$$I_2(\theta,z')dz'd\omega=\frac{2^{5/4}a^2r^{\frac{1}{2}}\bar{c}\cos^{\frac{3}{2}}\theta(1-z'^2)^{\frac{1}{2}}dz'}{\sigma\pi^{\frac{3}{2}}}\times\int_0^{kz'}y^2\exp(-y^2)dy. \qquad (22)$$

Combining Eqs. (20) and (22), the total contribution of the wall element dz' and the associated volume element is

$$I(\theta,z')dz'd\omega=\frac{2^{\frac{1}{4}}a^2r^{\frac{1}{2}}\bar{c}\cos^{\frac{3}{2}}\theta d\omega dz'}{\sigma\pi^{\frac{3}{2}}}(1-z'^2)^{\frac{1}{2}}\times\int_0^{kz'}\exp(-y^2)dy.$$

The integrated intensity arising from all the contributing elements is

$$I(\theta)d\omega=\frac{2^{\frac{1}{4}}a^2r^{\frac{1}{2}}\bar{c}\cos^{\frac{3}{2}}\theta d\omega}{\sigma\pi^{\frac{3}{2}}}\times\int_0^1(1-z'^2)^{\frac{1}{2}}\int_0^{kz'}\exp(-y^2)dydz'. \qquad (23)$$

Substituting for r from Eq. (9a), Eq. (23) becomes

$$I(\theta)d\omega=\frac{3^{\frac{1}{2}}a^{\frac{1}{2}}\bar{c}^{\frac{1}{2}}\cos^{\frac{3}{2}}\theta(N)^{\frac{1}{2}}d\omega}{2^{\frac{1}{4}}\pi^2\sigma}\times\int_0^1(1-z'^2)^{\frac{1}{2}}\int_0^{kz'}\exp(-y^2)dydz'. \qquad (23a)$$

Typical beam shapes calculated from Eq. (23a) are shown in Fig. 7. It is noted that these curves are qualitatively similar in shape to those observed (Fig. 2). In cases of high collimation, the angle $\theta_{\frac{1}{2}}$ at which $I(\theta)=[I(0)/2]$ is given approximately by

$$\theta_{\frac{1}{2}}\approx\frac{2^{\frac{3}{4}}3^{\frac{1}{2}}\sigma}{1.78a^{\frac{1}{2}}\bar{c}^{\frac{1}{2}}}(N)^{\frac{1}{2}}. \qquad (24)$$

Expression (24) follows from Eq. (23a) in the approximation $\cos\theta\sim 1$.

The predictions of Eq. (24) are compared with the measured half-widths (Fig. 4) in Table V. $\theta_{\frac{1}{2}}$ is the half-width of the beam at half-maximum intensity. Although the theory is relevant only for sources of circular cross section, the predictions for all the sources are included in Table V, by making use of the effective radius Eq. (15). The observed half-widths are larger than the theoretical values by about 60% in the case of A and B which have cross sections close to circular. The deviation is about 100% in the case of C.

A major source of the discrepancy in Table V is the inadequacy of the relation $n=rz$ near $z=0$. Since $n\neq 0$ at the end of the tube, it would be expected that the observed intensity would be less than the intensity predicted by Eq. (23a) for angles away from the peak. It is noted that Eq. (23a) reduces to Eq. (12) at $\theta=0$.

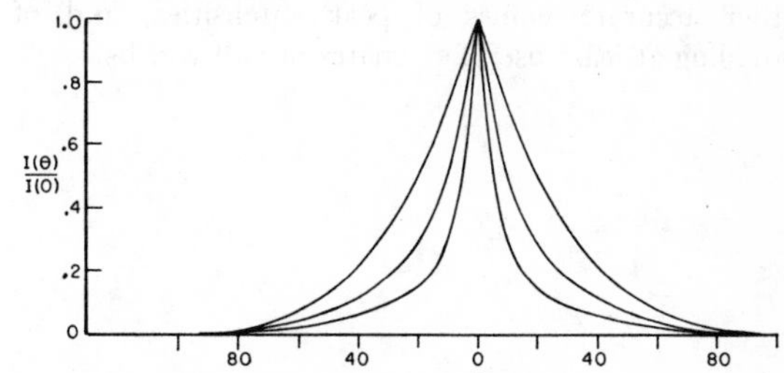

FIG. 7. $I(\theta)/I(0)$ as a function of θ, calculated from Eq. (23a) or (26), showing the beam shapes corresponding to half-widths at half-intensity of 5°, 10°, and 20°.

TABLE V. Comparison of predicted and observed beam widths.

Source	$\theta_{\frac{1}{2}}/(N)^{\frac{1}{2}}$ degrees (molecules $sec^{-1})^{-\frac{1}{2}}$ Observed	Calculated from Eq. (24)
A	2.9×10^{-7}	1.8×10^{-7}
B	7.3×10^{-7}	4.6×10^{-7}
C	8.4×10^{-7}	4.3×10^{-7}

In the limit of $N/a\rightarrow 0$ it can be shown that

$$\int_0^{\pi/2} I(\theta)2\pi\sin\theta d\theta\rightarrow N/2 \qquad (25)$$

where $I(\theta)$ is given by Eq. (23). At values of N/a reported on in the present work, the integral in Eq. (25) is somewhat less than $N/2$. It would be expected from Eq. (25) that the half-widths predicted by Eq. (24) would be small by a factor of the order of 2.

A formula predicting the proper peak intensity, and with integrated intensity normalized to N rather than $N/2$, can be obtained by substituting $2k$ for k in the integration limit in Eq. (23a). This somewhat *ad hoc* procedure leads to Eq. (26)

$$I'(\theta)d\omega=\frac{3^{\frac{1}{2}}a^{\frac{1}{2}}\bar{c}^{\frac{1}{2}}\cos^{\frac{3}{2}}\theta(N)^{\frac{1}{2}}d\omega}{2^{\frac{1}{4}}\pi^2\sigma}\times\int_0^1(1-z'^2)^{\frac{1}{2}}\int_0^{2kz'}\exp(-y^2)dydz'. \qquad (26)$$

The half-width predicted by Eq. (26) is

$$\theta_{\frac{1}{2}}'\approx\frac{2^{7/4}3^{\frac{1}{2}}\sigma(N)^{\frac{1}{2}}}{1.78a^{\frac{1}{2}}\bar{c}^{\frac{1}{2}}} \qquad (27)$$

which is twice the value of Eq. (24) and in better accord with the observations. The beam shape $I'(\theta)/I(0)$ predicted by Eq. (26) for a given half-width at half-intensity is identical with that of Eq. (23a), illustrated in Fig. 7.

Further sources of the discrepancy are the protruding sleeves discussed earlier, and molecular collisions outside the source. Thus it appears that the theory in its present state of refinement is capable of predicting rather accurate values of peak intensities, and of providing at least useful estimates of half-widths.

V. SOURCE DESIGN CONSIDERATIONS

Under the assumptions and restrictions described in Sec. IV, the peak intensity and half-width of the beam are given approximately by

$$I(0)=\frac{3^{\frac{1}{2}}\bar{c}^{\frac{1}{2}}a^{\frac{1}{2}}(N)^{\frac{1}{2}}}{8\,2^{\frac{1}{4}}\pi^{\frac{1}{2}}\sigma} \qquad (12)$$

$$\theta_{\frac{1}{2}}=\frac{2^{7/4}3^{\frac{1}{2}}\sigma(N)^{\frac{1}{2}}}{1.78a^{\frac{1}{2}}\bar{c}^{\frac{1}{2}}}. \qquad (27)$$

Expressions (12) and (27) refer to flow per single tube.

For an array of tubes in a fixed total area, it follows from (12) that the available peak intensity for a fixed total flow rate varies as $a^{-\frac{1}{2}}$, while the half-width varies as $a^{+\frac{1}{2}}$, as long as the tube walls do not occupy an appreciable fraction of the available total area. As sources are made with increasingly fine tubes, the fractional area of the source taken up by the tube walls necessarily becomes greater, and tube alignment usually becomes increasingly difficult. As a result an optimum tube radius exists which depends on the details of the source construction, but which is probably of the order of 1 to 2×10^{-3} in.

The critical source length is that length at which the source becomes opaque. Increasing the source length beyond this point does not change the available collimation of the source. For a given peak intensity the critical source length Λ can be obtained from the opacity criterion Eq. (12a) and from Eq. (12).

$$\Lambda\approx\frac{2.5\,2^{\frac{1}{4}}\bar{c}a^2}{8\pi^{\frac{1}{2}}\sigma^2I(0)} \qquad (25)$$

where $I(0)$ refers to the peak intensity per single tube.

VI. CONCLUSION

The characteristics of long tube sources can be predicted theoretically to a useful approximation on the basis of a simplified model of the pressure distribution in the source.

ACKNOWLEDGMENTS

This work was proposed by Professor P. Kusch. The authors wish to thank him and Professor C. H. Townes for valuable discussions and advice.

SENSITIVITY OF MICROWAVE SPECTROMETERS USING MASER TECHNIQUES

C. H. Townes*
Institute for Defense Analyses, Washington, D. C.
(Received October 10, 1960)

The minimum detectable absorption coefficient for an absorbing medium in a microwave waveguide has been written[1]

$$\alpha_{\min} = 2e\alpha_0(2k_eT_e\Delta\nu/P_0)^{1/2}, \tag{1}$$

where α_0 is the absorption coefficient per unit length of the waveguide, e the Napierian base, k Boltzmann's constant, P_0 the microwave power used, T_e the effective noise temperature of the amplifying system, and $\Delta\nu$ its bandwidth. Most microwave spectrometers have involved noise temperatures T_e of 10 000°K or greater. It is obvious that use of maser amplifiers can very much decrease T_e in expression (1) and thus improve spectrometer sensitivity. It will be shown here that additional large gains even beyond the reduction of T_e in expression (1) can be obtained by suitable use of maser-like techniques, assuming that sensitivity is limited only by random noise.

If the microwave power is sent into a perfect maser amplifier following partial absorption in a waveguide, one might expect that the noise temperature T_e would be as low as $h\nu/k$.[2] But this is not true, since the waveguide is normally at a temperature above $h\nu/k$ and radiates noise into the amplifier, making T_e comparable with the waveguide temperature T_g. Consider now the addition along the length of the waveguide of molecules in an excited state, which can undergo stimulated emission to a lower state. The noise radiated by the waveguide, including the excited molecules, is characterized by the temperature[2]

$$T_g' = \frac{h\nu}{k}\,\frac{a}{b-a}, \tag{2}$$

where a is the total probability of stimulated emission per unit time per photon and b is the total probability of absorption per unit time per photon. b includes all losses in the waveguide. As excited molecules are added, a approaches b and T_g becomes very large. However, the net absorption in the waveguide decreases since $\alpha_0 = (b-a)/C$, where C is the velocity of light, and hence $\alpha_{\min}$ appears to decrease without limit even with $\Delta\nu$ and P_0 fixed. A more complete analysis can be easily obtained with the help of expressions (14) and (15) of reference 2 for the waveguide case or of expressions (58) for the resonant cavity spectrometer.

If n_0 photons are introduced into a waveguide, the noise fluctuation when $b > a$ is

$$\Delta n = \left[n_0\left(\frac{a+b}{b-a}\right)\right]^{1/2} e^{(a-b)t/2}. \tag{3}$$

The signal due to a small change ϵ in $(b-a)$ associated with gas absorption is

$$S = n_0\, e^{(a-b)t}\epsilon t. \tag{4}$$

If this is regarded as a peak signal, and the rms signal is equated to Δn, then $\Delta n = S/\sqrt{2}$. After optimization with respect to the time t, one has from (3) and (4)

$$\epsilon = e[2(b-a)(b+a)/n_0]^{1/2}. \tag{5}$$

A similar expression is obtained when $a > b$, except that $(b-a)$ becomes $(a-b)$. If b is due to normal absorption, then

$$b = \alpha_0(CkT_g/h\nu), \tag{6}$$

where T_g is the temperature of the waveguide walls. Furthermore $a \approx b$ so that (5) gives for the minimum detectable absorption coefficient

$$\alpha_{\min} = 2e(\alpha_0\alpha_0')^{1/2}(2kT_g\Delta\nu/P_0)^{1/2} \tag{7}$$

Here $\alpha_0' = (b-a)/C$ can in principle be made as small as desired by adding excited molecules to increase a. The power level introduced into the waveguide is $P_0 = n_0h\nu\Delta\nu$. Expression (7) should be compared with (1). When $T_e = T_g$, (1) gives approximately the best sensitivity obtainable by a perfect amplifier following the waveguide. (7) gives further increased sensitivity when excited atoms are added within the absorption cell. (7) also assumes that the following amplifier used is sufficiently good so that its effective noise temperature is much less than T_g', which is not impractical to achieve.

Consider now a cavity spectrometer, for which the minimum detectable absorption coefficient is normally given by[3]

$$\alpha_{\min} \approx \frac{2\pi}{Q_c\lambda}\left(\frac{4kT_e\Delta\nu}{P_0}\right)^{1/2}$$

$$\approx \frac{2}{\lambda}\left(\frac{2\pi kT_e\Delta\nu}{WQ_c\nu}\right)^{1/2}, \qquad (8)$$

where Q_c is the cavity quality factor, λ the wavelength, and W the microwave energy stored in the cavity. Following Shimoda, Takahasi, and Townes,[2] the average number of photons in a cavity when $b > a$ is

$$\bar{n} = c/(b-a), \qquad (9)$$

and the noise fluctuation is

$$\Delta n = (bc)^{1/2}/(b-a). \qquad (10)$$

Here c is the probability per unit time of introduction of a photon by any process (including spontaneous emission) other than stimulated emission. The signal due to a small change ϵ in $b-a$ is from (9)

$$S = c\epsilon/(b-a)^2. \qquad (11)$$

For signal equal to noise, from (10) and (11),

$$\epsilon_{\min} = (b/c)^{1/2}(b-a) = (bc)^{1/2}/\bar{n} = [(b-a)b/\bar{n}]^{1/2}. \qquad (12)$$

The last form of (12) shows the similarity with expression (5) for the waveguide. Sensitivity is best when c is as small as possible, i.e., when $c = a$. Since also $a \approx b$, and $\bar{n} = W/h\nu$,

$$\epsilon_{\min} = b(n\Delta\nu/W)^{1/2}, \qquad (13)$$

or

$$\alpha_{\min} = \frac{4\pi}{\lambda Q_c}\frac{kT_c}{h\nu}\left(\frac{h\Delta\nu}{W}\right)^{1/2}, \qquad (14)$$

where T_c is the wall temperature of the cavity, and $b = 2kT_c/h\nu$.

Expression (14) is to be compared with (8). If a perfect amplifier is used outside the cavity, $T_e \approx T_c$ and (8) gives

$$\alpha_{\min} = \frac{2}{\lambda}\left(\frac{2\pi kT_c}{WQ_c}\frac{\Delta\nu}{\nu}\right)^{1/2}. \qquad (15)$$

If the cavity is cooled so that $kT_c < h\nu$, then (8) may be written

$$\alpha_{\min} \approx \frac{2}{\lambda}\left(\frac{2\pi h\Delta\nu}{WQ}\right)^{1/2}. \qquad (16)$$

The minimum detectable absorption coefficient given by (14), which applies when excited molecules are appropriately introduced directly into the cavity where absorption is to be detected, can hence be markedly less than the best achievable with external amplification alone, as given by either (15) or (16). It is interesting to express (14) in terms of the minimum detectable number of absorbing atoms or molecules. If a approaches b, spontaneous emission is amplified more and more and the bandwidth $\Delta\nu$ to which the cavity system will respond becomes smaller, since $\Delta\nu = \nu(b-a)/a$.[2] Let a approach b until W builds up to the point of saturation of the molecules to be detected. Then if α is expressed in terms of the total number of molecules N (in upper and lower states) producing the absorption, one can show that (14) gives for the minimum number N which can be detected in a time $1/\Delta\nu$

$$N_{\min} \approx \frac{16Q_L}{Q_c}\frac{kT_c}{h\nu}\frac{kT_N}{h\nu}, \qquad (17)$$

where Q_c is the quality factor for the cavity before insertion of molecules in the excited state, and Q_L is $\nu/\delta\nu$ for the absorption line. Here the linewidth $\delta\nu$ is assumed due to relaxation processes alone; otherwise expression (17) is somewhat modified. T_N is the temperature of the absorbing material, which would usually be the same as T_c for the cavity walls, and we assume $kT_N \gg h\nu$. It is evident that some conditions allow detection of only a few molecules, if limitations are due to random noise only. Note also that (17) is independent of the matrix element for the absorption. The time required for detection of the number of atoms given by (17) is

$$t = 1/\Delta\nu = 3hV/(8\pi\mu^2 Q_L^{\,2}), \qquad (18)$$

where μ^2 is the square of the matrix element for the transition being detected, and V the cavity volume. Thus the matrix element does affect the time required for such measurement. For $|\mu| = 10^{-18}$ esu, $V = 1\ \text{cm}^3$, and $Q_L = 10^6$, (18) gives $t \approx 10^{-3}$ sec. Hence the time required for sensitivities indicated by (17) is not excessively long.

A spectrometer involving some of the above principles, utilizing excited molecules directly in the cavity and a change in $b-a$, has actually already been demonstrated without perhaps its potentiality and general applicability being fully realized. This was the experiment of Shimoda and Wang[4] on an oscillating beam-type maser. There the sensitivity was found to be much greater than that for an ordinary cavity-type spectrometer; the factor of improvement obtained in practice was not precisely measured but was of the order of 50.

Various alternative situations can be worked out theoretically, and a number of types of arrangements to take advantage of the possibilities indicated above for increasing sensitivity can be rather easily seen. One such would be to insert paramagnetic material, for which a resonance is to be detected, into a microwave cavity at very low temperature and also containing ruby. The ruby would be "pumped" so that for it $a > b$, and for the entire cavity a approaches b until the system is approximately at the point of oscillation and the noise output is greater than that produced by any following amplifier. The desired resonance should be then detectable by sweeping it through the center of response of the cavity and excited ruby.

---

*On leave from Columbia University, New York, New York.

[1]C. H. Townes and A. L. Schawlow, Microwave Spectroscopy (McGraw-Hill Book Company, New York, 1955), p. 414.

[2]K. Shimoda, H. Takahasi, and C. H. Townes, J. Phys. Soc. Japan 12, 686 (1957).

[3]See reference 1, p. 437.

[4]K. Shimoda and T. C. Wang, Rev. Sci. Instr. 26, 1148 (1955).

Reprinted from THE REVIEW OF SCIENTIFIC INSTRUMENTS, Vol. 30, No. 1, 9–16, January, 1959
Printed in U. S. A.

Theory of the Cavity Microwave Spectrometer and Molecular Frequency Standard*

YARDLEY BEERS
Physics Department, New York University, University Heights, New York 53, New York
(Received September 15, 1958; and in final form, November 10, 1958)

A short section of a wave guide is considered as a nonresonant absorption cell and then as a resonant cavity. It is shown that the latter gives a better signal-to-noise ratio by a factor which depends upon the relative intensity of the various noise sources but which increases with the Q. It is shown that the voltage signal-to-noise ratio is proportional to the square root of the product of the volume and the Q and otherwise is independent of the shape. This result leads to the conclusion that it is possible in theory to build microwave spectrometers having signal-to-noise ratios some 50 db larger or capable of detecting absorption coefficients some 300 times smaller than spectrometers which are now widely used. However, practical considerations probably would prevent this advantage from being realized completely. These results are applied to a frequency standard using an absorption line. It is shown that it is possible to build a standard using the 3,3 line of NH_3 with a fractional stability of about 4×10^{-12} over an extended interval of time. Some discussion of spectrometers with long nonresonant cells is also included.

THE cavity microwave gas spectrometer has some theoretical advantages in regard to sensitivity over the wave guide which seem to have been overlooked in the decade in which the microwave spectroscopy of gases has been an established field of science. The wave-guide spectrometer has been accepted as the standard instrument for this research because of its simplicity and the ability to operate over a wide-frequency range. The use of the conventional cavity spectrometer has been restricted to special purposes, not requiring a wide band width, because it can be tuned over a wide range only with difficulty, and also because likelihood of saturation generally requires a more complicated circuit, which further reduces the flexibility. However, it will be seen that the properties which lead to the flexibility of the wave-guide spectrometer are the ones which cause a loss of sensitivity.

* Supported by the Electronics Branch of the U. S. Office of Naval Research and the Air Force Office of Scientific Research.

The author reached these conclusions while planning a high-resolution experiment leading to the development of a molecular frequency standard. The popular trend in the development of such devices is to employ one or another of the various ingenious schemes,[1–4] which have been devised for producing line widths smaller than the Doppler width or else atomic beam magnetic resonance techniques. However, as is well known and as will be discussed further, the stability of a standard depends not only upon the line width but also upon the signal-to-noise ratio. Therefore, a standard based upon a simple cavity absorption cell under some conditions may have a superior stability because of its high sensitivity even though the line width is not the minimum obtainable. Another advantage is that such a

[1] G. Newell, Jr., and R. H. Dicke, Phys. Rev. **83**, 1064L (1951); **87**, 297(A) (1951).
[2] Gordon, Zeiger, and Townes, Phys. Rev. **99**, 1264 (1955).
[3] R. H. Romer and R. H. Dicke, Phys. Rev. **99**, 532 (1955).
[4] J. P. Wittke and R. H. Dicke, Phys. Rev. **103**, 620 (1956).

cell may be permanently sealed off from a vacuum system and may be operated without associated heat sources or refrigerants.

A preliminary report of part of this work has been published previously.[5]

THE WAVE-GUIDE SPECTROMETER

For the sake of clarity, let us first review the wave-guide spectrometer, which will be represented in terms of its well-established transmission line analog. Consider a section having a length l and a voltage absorption coefficient α caused by losses in the conductors and insulation. Let V_0 be the voltage supplied to the detector in the absence of a sample. The sample has a power absorption coefficient γ, or a voltage absorption coefficient of $\gamma/2$. Let the noise in the system be represented by an instantaneous voltage $\dot{V}_n$ at the input of the detector. Then the instantaneous output current (which is proportional to the output voltage) may be written as

$$i = g(V_0 e^{-\gamma l/2} + V_n)^2, \qquad (1)$$

where g is a constant. Equation (1) assumes that the output current is proportional to the square of the input voltage.

In practice γ is small compared to unity, and V_n is small compared to V_0. Therefore we may employ a power series expansion and retain only the leading terms,

$$i = gV_0{}^2 - gV_0{}^2\gamma l + 2gV_0 V_n. \qquad (2)$$

The first term is a constant for all practical purposes and is of no interest. The second term represents the contributions to the output current due to signal and the third term the contributions to the output due to noise.

Equation (2), even within the approximations we have made, is not quite correct, as the signal term includes only the effect of the sample through absorption. There is another effect. If the input impedance of the detector is equal to the characteristic impedance of the transmission line without the sample present, the introduction of the sample changes the characteristic impedance, and the presence of the resulting reflected wave causes a further change in the detector input voltage, this change being 90° out of phase with that due to the absorption. It can be shown by use of transmission line theory[6] that the effects of reflection and absorption may both be included by replacing the physical length l by an equivalent

$$l' = \left(l^2 + \frac{\lambda^2}{16\pi^2}\right)^{\frac{1}{2}}, \qquad (3)$$

assuming that reflections at the sending end are negligible. λ is the wavelength in free space.

Then the output current signal-to-noise ratio may be seen, with reference to Eqs. (2) and (3), to be in magnitude

$$S_0 = \frac{V_0 \gamma l'}{2V_n} \qquad (4)$$

$$= \frac{V_0 \gamma l'}{2(2F_0 kTZ_0 B)^{\frac{1}{2}}} = \frac{\gamma l' P_0{}^{1/2}}{2(2F_0 kTB)} \qquad (5)$$

where $k =$ Boltzmann's constant, $T =$ absolute temperature, $Z_0 =$ characteristic impedance, $B =$ noise band width of detector, and $F_0 =$ noise figure.

S_0, as given by Eq. (4), gives the ratio of instantaneous values, and we note that it is proportional to γ and inversely proportional to V_n. We may infer, then, that the rms signal-to-noise ratio is the same.

This calculation, of course, is based upon a discontinuous or "step function" introduction of the sample. Most practical spectrometers employ a modulation method, which is the equivalent of periodically introducing and removing the sample. Because of the small shot effect, the noise figure F_0 decreases with an increase in the modulation frequency. The practical upper limit of the frequency is reached when the modulation frequency approaches the line width, when the line shape is distorted. Ordinarily we can assume from experience that, with optimum adjustment, small shot effects are negligible and that the signal-to-noise ratio with a modulation system differs from that given by Eq. (4) or (5) by a factor of the order of unity, which we shall neglect. With high-resolution experiments, however, the sensitivity may be poorer than that calculated because the narrow line width does not permit the adequate reduction of small shot noise, but this loss of sensitivity is not characteristic of any one type of spectrometer.

The length appears explicitly in the numerator in Eqs. (4) and (5) and is involved implicitly in V_0 and F_0. It should be recalled that V_0 is the voltage at the detector input. With a fixed signal source, it decreases exponentially, and this effect is in opposition to the explicit factor in the numerator. Also F_0 is a function of V_0. Arbitrarily large values of V_0 cannot be used because of either saturation of the sample, or a deterioration of the noise figure, or both. Several authors[7–10] have made assumptions concerning how F_0 varies with V_0 and have shown that there exists an optimum length of the order of $1/\alpha$, if oscillator noise is neglected or somewhat larger than $1/\alpha$ if it is not

[5] Y. Beers, Bull. Am. Phys. Soc. Ser. II, **3**, 213 (1958).
[6] See, for example, A. B. Bronwell and R. E. Beam, *Theory and Application of Microwaves* (McGraw-Hill Book Company, Inc., New York, 1947).

[7] W. Gordy, Revs. Modern Phys. **20**, 668 (1948).
[8] Gordy, Smith, and Trambarulo, *Microwave Spectroscopy* (John Wiley and Sons, Inc., New York, 1953).
[9] S. Geschwind, Ann. N. Y. Acad. Sci. **55**, 751 (1952).
[10] C. H. Townes and A. L. Schawlow, *Microwave Spectroscopy* (McGraw-Hill Book Company, Inc., New York, 1955).

neglected.[11] Only in the K band and in the millimeter wave regions, it is practical in the laboratory to achieve lengths comparable to the optimum because of space or economic restrictions. However, in the present paper we shall be thinking in terms of much shorter lengths, and for most purposes we shall consider the voltage throughout the length of a line terminated by its characteristic impedance as constant.

THE CAVITY SPECTROMETER

Now that we have considered a section of transmission line short compared to $1/\alpha$ as a nonresonant absorption cell, let us consider using it as a resonant cavity. One method whereby this may be accomplished is shown in Fig. 1. This line is shown at the extreme right. For the sake of definiteness, it is assumed to be an odd number of quarter-wavelengths long and to be terminated by a short-circuit at the right end, but this assumption is not a basic restriction as it can be seen by modifications of the arguments to be presented that they can be made to apply to any arbitrary length. The input impedance of this section at the left end is known from transmission line theory[6] to be a pure resistance

$$Z = Z_0/(\alpha l), \tag{6}$$

which, with a short length and with small losses, is large compared to Z_0. This input is matched through a step-up transformer of turns ratio n (or equivalent) to another transmission line of characteristic impedance Z_{01}. (In practice it is most unlikely that Z_{01} and Z_0 would differ by more than a factor of 2 or 3, and for most of our calculations we may place $Z_{01} \doteqdot Z_0$, even though the lines may not be identical.) Then

$$n^2 Z_{01} = Z_0/(\alpha l), \tag{7}$$

or

$$n^2 \doteqdot 1/(\alpha l),$$

Standard transmission line theory[6] gives

$$Q = \pi/(\alpha\lambda). \tag{8}$$

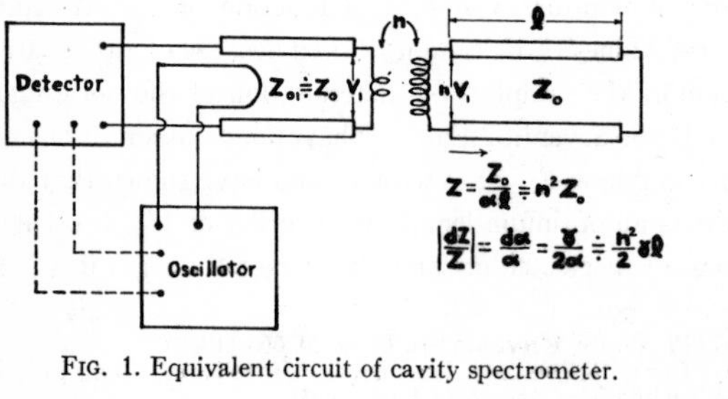

FIG. 1. Equivalent circuit of cavity spectrometer.

[11] W. M. P. Strandberg *Microwave Spectroscopy* (John Wiley and Sons Inc., New York, 1954).

Then

$$n^2 \doteqdot \frac{Q\lambda}{\pi l}. \tag{9}$$

The left end is connected to the input of a detector whose input impedance is matched to Z_{01}. (Feher[12] showed that an accurate impedance match is undesirable because the sample causes a discontinuous change in the standing wave ratio. However, this point is academic, at least for gas spectrometers, because the absorption is so small and because it is rarely possible to make the standing wave ratio less than 1.1.) An oscillator is coupled to the line on the left, but we shall assume that the coupling is so weak that the impedance relations which we have postulated are not appreciably affected, and therefore no important part of the reflected wave caused by the introduction of the sample is absorbed by the oscillator. This oscillator produces a voltage V_1 at the detector and also at the input of the step-up transformer.

The imminence of saturation of the sample depends upon the average voltage in the absorption cell. Therefore, to avoid saturation effects the detector voltage V_1 often must be considerably lower, probably by the ratio n, than the voltage V_0 employed with the nonresonant cell. This lower voltage is likely to be below that required for optimum noise figure. To obtain the optimum noise figure, therefore, it may be necessary to supply additional power to the detector by an alternate route which circumvents the sample. This supplementary feed may be derived from the same oscillator through a directional coupler or a bridge network as suggested by the dotted lines in Fig. 1. Or it may be derived from a separate oscillator, which usually is tuned to another frequency, and then the detector feeds an IF amplifier tuned to their difference in frequencies, and the detecting system becomes a superheterodyne.

Theoretically, neglecting small shot noise, the single oscillator scheme is capable of giving nearly the same signal-to-noise ratio as the superheterodyne system. Contrary to the theory, Feher[12] found that the optimum performance of the single oscillator system was 10 db poorer, but, as he was concerned with magnetic resonance, his modulation frequency was lower than used with gas spectroscopy, and his apparatus would be more vulnerable to small shot noise in his oscillator. In the superhetrodyne scheme the effects of small shot noise would have been reduced. On the other hand, the single oscillator scheme avoids the problem of local oscillator tracking. However, the adjustment of the phase and amplitude of the supplementary feed in the single oscillator system is very critical. Therefore, it is questionable which system is the less inconvenient when a large variation in signal frequency is desired. In addition there is the problem of retuning the

[12] G. Feher, Bell System Tech. J. **36**, 449 (1957).

resonator frequency to that of the oscillator. For these reasons the cavity spectrograph has been used mainly in applications where the frequency has not been required to change, especially in work with paramagnetic gases with which it has been possible to search for unknown resonances by sweeping the magnetic field.

The circuit shown in Fig. 1, of course, is not unique. However, other circuits which might be reasonably considered, such as one where the oscillator is connected to one end and the detector to the other, would not have signal-to-noise ratios differing by more than 3 db or so, if at all. As we are not interested in such small differences, we shall consider the present circuit as representative.

The presence of the sample causes the input impedance of the cell as given by Eq. (6) to change by the fractional amount

$$\frac{dZ}{Z} = -\frac{Z_0}{Z\alpha^2 l}d\alpha$$

$$= -\frac{\gamma}{2\alpha}, \qquad (10)$$

which is transmitted without change to the input of the transformer causing the generation of a reflected wave in the left-hand line. The voltage associated with this reflected wave appears at the detector input with a magnitude

$$v_1 = \frac{V_1\gamma}{4\alpha}. \qquad (11)$$

Then the voltage signal-to-noise ratio

$$S_1 = \frac{V_1\gamma}{4\alpha(2F_1kTZ_{01}B)^{1/2}} \qquad (12)$$

$$= \frac{V_1 Q\gamma\lambda}{4\pi(2F_1kTZ_{01}B)^{1/2}} = \frac{Q\gamma\lambda P_1^{1/2}}{4\pi(2F_1kTZ_{01}B)^{1/2}} \qquad (13)$$

In general, the noise figure F_1 in the resonant method is not equal to F_0 because of the difference in voltage applied to the detector.

COMPARISON OF NONRESONANT AND RESONANT METHODS

The voltage signal-to-noise ratio of the resonant spectrometer relative to that of the nonresonant one is given from Eqs. (5), (7), (8), and (12) as

$$\frac{S_1}{S_0} = \frac{V_1}{2\alpha l' V_0}\left(\frac{F_0}{F_1}\right)^{1/2} \qquad (14)$$

$$= \frac{n^2 l V_1}{2l' V_0}\left(\frac{F_0}{F_1}\right)^{1/2} \qquad (15)$$

$$= \frac{Q\lambda V_1}{2\pi\alpha l' V_0}\left(\frac{F_0}{F_1}\right). \qquad (16)$$

In these equations several quantities have canceled out. The characteristic impedances were canceled by the approximation $Z_0 \doteq Z_{01}$.

Case I. $V_1 = V_0$

Then $F_0 = F_1$, and,

$$\frac{S_1}{S_0} = \frac{1}{2\alpha l'} \qquad (17)$$

$$= \frac{Q\lambda}{2\pi l'}. \qquad (18)$$

With short lengths of line $\alpha l' \ll 1$, and Eq. (17) shows that a definite advantage is obtained by using resonant operation. Since Eq. (3) shows that l' cannot decrease below $\lambda/(4\pi)$, this advantage remains finite. Equation (18) is essentially the same result as that obtained by Townes and Schawlow.[10] This equation has the simple interpretation that in resonant operation the cell can be considered as a wave guide of length $Q\lambda/(2\pi)$. Unfortunately, it appears that many workers have been content to accept this statement as the final word concerning the comparison of the two modes of operation, and, recognizing the greater vulnerability of the resonant cell to saturation, have dismissed resonant operation as being either impractical or, at least, undesirable. However, this reasoning has overlooked several important points. To be sure, we must consider saturation, and therefore we must make the realistic assumption that the rms field as averaged over the volume of the cell is just equal to that used in nonresonant operation. This assumption is made in the following case.

Case II. $nV_1 = \sqrt{2}V_0$

The relative signal-to-noise ratio can then be found from Eqs. (14), (15), and (16). However, in general the noise figure will vary with power level and the behavior depends upon how the noise is distributed between the oscillator and the detector. We consider two limiting situations.

(a) Detector Noise Predominates

Then by use of supplementary feed of the detector we can always make F_1 equal to F_0 (or perhaps even smaller). Placing $F_1 = F_0$ we obtain

$$\frac{S_1}{S_0} = \frac{1}{l'}\left(\frac{l}{2\alpha}\right)^{1/2} \qquad (19)$$

$$= \frac{ln}{l'\sqrt{2}} \qquad (20)$$

$$= \frac{1}{l'}\left(\frac{Q\lambda l}{2\pi}\right)^{1/2}. \qquad (21)$$

(b) Oscillator Noise Predominates

We can assume that the noise voltage is proportional to V_1 and therefore approximately F_1 is equal to F_0/n^2. Then

$$\frac{S_1}{S_0}=\frac{1}{\alpha l'\sqrt{2}} \tag{22}$$

$$=\frac{n^2 l}{l'\sqrt{2}} \tag{23}$$

$$=\frac{Q\lambda}{\pi l'\sqrt{2}}. \tag{24}$$

We note that in both (a) and (b) we obtain superior performance with the resonator for short lengths of transmission line since then $Q\lambda \gg l$, and $n \gg 1$, and, other things being constant, there is always an advantage in raising the Q, although quantitatively the advantage depends upon just how the noise is distributed. In practice the noise is likely to be intermediate between (a) and (b).

Case III. Variable Q, Constant Volume of Sample, and Constant V_1

The variation of Q merely results in a variation in the degree of saturation. Feher[12] has shown in this case that the signal is independent of the Q. An application of the methods used here confirms his result, but the details will not be given for the sake of brevity. This case seems to be merely of academic importance because it is unrealistic to assume an arbitrary constant value of V_1 since a variation of V_1 is a readily available method of optimizing the sensitivity.

RELATION OF SENSITIVITY TO VOLUME

Equation (12) indicates that, for maximum sensitivity, the voltage absorption coefficient of the transmission line, α, should be made as small as possible. A reduction in α requires expansion of the transverse dimensions. Such a process obviously implies that the volume is the limiting economic factor either because of the cost of the cavity itself, or, in the case of rare gases, because of the cost of the sample. Therefore the most significant calculation of the sensitivity relates it explicitly to the volume. Optimum sensitivity requires that the sample operate on the verge of saturation. With this assumption we shall show that the sensitivity is proportional to the square root of the product of the volume and the Q and that it is independent of the shape except for the implicit dependence of the Q upon the shape.

From the definition of Q we may write

$$Q=\frac{\langle E^2\rangle_{\text{Av}} V\nu}{4P}, \tag{25}$$

where

$\langle E^2\rangle_{\text{Av}}$ = square of peak value of electric intensity in esu averaged over the volume of the cavity,
V = volume in cm^3,
ν = resonant frequency of line and of cavity, and
P = power dissipated within cavity in ergs/sec.

Strandberg[11] has given a condition for the onset of saturation, when the saturation effect causes the line widths to increase by $\sqrt{2}$ as follows

$$E=\frac{h\Delta\nu}{|\mu|}, \tag{26}$$

where $|\mu|$ is the dipole matrix element pertaining to the transition, where the relaxation time has been expressed as $1/(2\pi\Delta\nu)$, where $\Delta\nu$ is the half-width at half-power of the line at small values of E, and where h = Planck's constant.

We place E^2 in Eq. (25) equal to the square of the value given by Eq. (26) and solve for

$$P=\frac{h^2\Delta\nu^2 V\nu}{4Q|\mu|^2}. \tag{27}$$

With reference to Fig. 1 we see that $P=V_1^2/Z_{01}$. If we solve for V_1 and substitute into Eq. (13), the resulting voltage signal-to-noise ratio is

$$S_1=\frac{hc\gamma}{8\pi|\mu|}\left(\frac{\Delta\nu}{\nu}\right)\left(\frac{QV\nu}{2F_1kTB}\right)^{\frac{1}{2}}, \tag{28}$$

where c = velocity of light.

The minimum detectable absorption coefficient $\gamma_{\min}$ is found by placing $S_1=1$ in Eq. (28) and solving for $\gamma=\gamma_{\min}$. If all of the constants are evaluated ($T=300°$K), the result is

$$\gamma_{\min}=3.64\times10^{-11}|\mu|\left(\frac{\nu}{\Delta\nu}\right)\left(\frac{F_1B}{QV\nu}\right)^{\frac{1}{2}}, \tag{29}$$

where now $\Delta\nu$ and ν are given in Mc, $|\mu|$ in debyes (10^{-18} esu), V in cm^3, B in cps, and $\gamma_{\min}$ in cm^{-1}.

To see the significance of these calculations, let us consider a spectrometer employing a 10-foot cell made of standard K-band wave guide without Stark modulation. For such a cell $\alpha l'$ is approximately 0.16. Equations (19) and (22) indicate that about 10-db improvement could be obtained by changing from nonresonant to resonant operation. Such a cell has a volume of about 8 cubic inches. If the original cell were replaced by a cube of the same volume, the Q would increase by a factor of about 17 because the Q is proportional to the ratio of volume to surface area. According to Eq. (28) the sensitivity would improve by about 12 db or a total of about 22 db relative to the nonresonant cell. However, except with very rare gases, it would be economically feasible to employ a much larger volume, perhaps one cubic foot. Such a volume would give a further improvement of 31 db, partly because of the explicit effect of the volume and partly because of the increase in Q. Thus it is theoretically possible to obtain an improvement of some 50 db over a 10-foot K-band nonresonant cell, which is typical of what is being used in many laboratories. With reference to the derivation of Eq. (29) it can be seen that a signal-to-noise ratio of 50 db is equivalent to an improvement in the minimum detectable signal of about 300.

However, there are obstacles to hinder or prevent the obtainment of this theoretical improvement. For one thing, we have passed over the question of modulation. The effectiveness of Stark modulation, which can be easily incorporated in the wave-guide absorption cell, has been well demonstrated. It is doubtful that a uniform strong Stark field can be introduced into a large cavity of approximately cubical shape without spoiling the microwave characteristics. Therefore some less effective method must be used. One possibility is source modulation. Another possibility is Zeeman modulation. With Zeeman modulation the cavity has some advantage over the wave guide because the volume is more centralized, and therefore the magnetic field can be produced more conveniently. Also, because of the less frequent collisions with the walls, smaller line widths can be obtained, and Zeeman modulation can be carried out with smaller fields. (With free radicals, the cavity has a distinct advantage as the lifetime is greater because of less frequent wall collisions. These, being paramagnetic, can be modulated easily by the Zeeman effect.) A second general difficulty with cavities is vulnerability to microphonics, which cannot be predicted. A third difficulty is that it is generally impossible to sweep over a large frequency range. The problem of frequency coverage with a large cavity is complicated by the interaction of various resonant modes. A high Q cavity, furthermore, is likely to drift out of tune due to temperature changes. In spite of these difficulties, the cavity spectrograph in practice should yield some of the advantage predicted, and it should be particularly useful for looking for hyperfine splittings in previously discovered lines, where it is not required to cover a wide range.

The remarks made in the last paragraph pertain to cavity spectrographs of conventional design. A multimode cavity employing a rotating metal vane to mix modes and capable of being swept over a wide range has been known for some time.[13] Also Verdier[14] has recently reported an apparatus using a parallel plate cavity for use with Stark modulation, but apparently this does not have a high Q and appears to have a sensitivity comparable to that obtainable with a conventional wave-guide system. Collier[15] has described a coaxial cavity system for Stark modulation having high sensitivity but incapable of giving a uniform Stark field.

[13] G. E. Becker and S. H. Autler, Phys. Rev. **70**, 300 (1946); W. E. Lamb, Jr., Phys. Rev. **70**, 308 (1946).

[14] P. H. Verdier, Rev. Sci. Instr. **29**, 646 (1958).

LONG NONRESONANT CELLS

Let us digress to consider the design of a broad-band spectroscope for search work. For this work, the nonresonant cell, especially if equipped with Stark modulation, holds definite advantages even though the sensitivity may be inferior theoretically. The example of the 10-foot K-band cell which has been cited, while typical, does not represent quite the practical limit of such a device. Lengths of the order of 40 feet could be used and probably have been used. Such lengths are close to optimum or may even exceed it. With them $\alpha l' \geqslant 1$ because of the additional loss due to the Stark electrode. The earlier discussion has shown that the resonant operation of such a cell would be disadvantageous, or at best, would provide no advantage.

However, if a nonresonant cell with Stark modulation is desired for search work at K band, a section of K-band wave guide of optimum length is not necessarily the best choice. Other choices are provided by the use of wave guides of various larger cross sections, such as S- and X-band wave guides. The best choice depends upon several different factors. To illustrate the various questions which arise, let us consider replacing a section of K-band wave guide of approximately "optimum" length l_1 and area of cross section A_1 by a section of wave guide of larger area A_2 and length l_2. (For simplicity the distinction between l and l' will be neglected here.) With the K-band wave guide the average "voltage" is D_1 times the output voltage V_0. Let the ratio of the analogous ratio in the larger wave guide be D_2. Let us suppose that in both cases the average "voltage" is adjusted for the same degree of saturation, a condition which prevails when the average power per unit area of cross section is the same.

Two special cases come to mind. First suppose that the economic limitation is one of constant volume. Then, excluding the variation in the noise figure F_0, Eq. (2) shows that the sensitivity with the larger wave guide would be $[D_1(A_1)^{\frac{1}{2}}]/[D_2(A_2)^{\frac{1}{2}}]$ times that obtained with the K-band wave guide. D_1 is somewhat larger than unity, while D_2 is unlikely to be much larger than unity as the larger wave guide would have a smaller α. Therefore for small changes (such as from K-band to X-band wave guide) this combination of factors is approximately unity, while, for larger changes, it would become smaller than unity. In addition, the sensitivity depends upon the noise figure F_0 which in turn depends upon the detector voltage. In the usual case where saturation is reached at a lower voltage level than minimum noise figure, considerations of noise

[15] R. J. Collier, Rev. Sci. Instr. **25**, 1205 (1954).

figure suggest a slight advantage in favor of the larger wave guide. Thus, under conditions of nonresonant operation at constant volume, there is little advantage one way or the other in replacing the K-band wave guide with larger wave guide. However, with the larger wave guide, once lines have been discovered by the nonresonant method, additional sensitivity in principle could be obtained by switching over to resonant operation for investigation of hyperfine splittings.

The other case which is of interest is when the economic limitation is one of constant length. In this case the relative sensitivity, excluding noise figure, of the larger wave guide is $[D_1(A_2)^{\frac{1}{2}}]/[D_2(A_1)^{\frac{1}{2}}]$, and clearly under almost all conditions a large increase in the area would be desirable. One practical limitation on the area results from the fact that ultimately the noise figure increases with detector voltage. Another limitation results from the difficulty of insuring the excitation of only the desired mode, and the criticalness of adjustments of impedance match may impede search work.

There are several factors in addition to sensitivity which can influence the choice of wave-guide size. With strong lines with which the line width is limited by collisions with the walls, greater resolution can be obtained with the larger wave guide. Greater pumping speeds are possible with the larger wave guide, especially at constant volume, and there is less difficulty with wall contamination. Also unstable molecules have longer lifetimes. On the other hand, greater Stark splittings can be obtained at the same voltage with the smaller wave guide.

USE OF CAVITY SPECTROMETER AS A FREQUENCY STANDARD

In this treatment the only type of frequency standard that we shall consider is one employing an absorption spectral line.

It is well known[10,16] that the optimum way of comparing the frequency of an external source with that of a line is not to attempt to set upon the peak of the line but to make observations at two frequencies, one higher and one lower than the center of the line, and, when the two signals are equal, the average of the frequencies corresponds to the line center. This comparison can be made manually or automatically by an electronic circuit. Neglecting the "pulling" effect to be discussed in the following, the precision of the comparison process is limited by noise. An evaluation of the precision can be made by calculating the rms fluctuation in frequency corresponding to the minimum detectable change in absorption coefficient.

It may be shown by differentiation of the expression for the shape of a Lorentzian line that the rms standard deviation of the frequency ϵ has a minimum with respect to variation of the operating frequency ν' given by

$$\frac{\epsilon}{\nu}=1.54\left(\frac{\Delta\nu}{\nu}\right)\left(\frac{\Delta\gamma}{\gamma_m}\right), \tag{30}$$

when

$$\nu'=\nu\pm\frac{\Delta\nu}{\sqrt{3}}. \tag{31}$$

Here ν is the center frequency of the line, $\Delta\gamma$ is the minimum detectable change in absorption coefficient, and γ_m is the absorption coefficient at the center of the line.

Equations (30) and (31) are independent of the type of instrument except that it is assumed that the deflection of the output indicator is linear with γ. If the deflection obeys a different relationship or if a different line shape is assumed, the only effect on Eq. (30) is to change the constant. Then, of course, Eq. (31) no longer holds. The last factor on the right-hand side of Eq. (30) can be recognized being essentially the reciprocal of the sensitivity when expressed in appropriate fashion. In most instruments, a change in the parameters to cause an increase in one of the factors on the right, causes the other to decrease. Therefore the optimum design of the instrument involves finding the optimum compromise between these factors.

Since the instruments we are considering here are ones for which the voltage is proportional to γ, the last factor on the right is to be equated to $1/S_1$. (In anticipation of this step, we have expressed signal-to-noise ratios in voltage rather than in power.) If S_1 is given by Eq. (29),

$$\frac{\epsilon}{\nu}=5.6\times10^{-11}\frac{|\mu|}{\gamma_m}\left(\frac{F_1B}{QV\nu}\right)^{\frac{1}{2}}. \tag{32}$$

The quantity on the left denotes the rms fractional fluctuation in frequency for an interval of time $1/B$. It is to be noted that the line-width parameter has canceled out, and therefore there is no explicit advantage in using a molecule with a narrow line width as far as present considerations are concerned. A similar result was obtained previously by Townes and Schawlow[10] for the special case of the nonresonant wave-guide spectrometer. If there are several molecules having lines near the desired frequency ν, the selection of one for optimum performance should be made mainly on the basis of the largest γ_m, since the practical range of variation of $|\mu|$ is not large. The molecules with the largest γ_m are generally light ones, which have large line widths.

Equation (32) is based upon the assumption that the resonant frequency of the cavity is precisely synchronized to the center of the line. In practice, the synchronization cannot be perfect, especially when drifts of the cavity due to thermal expansion are considered. Gordon, Zeigler, and Townes[2] have shown that there results, because of the detuning of the cavity, a fractional error in the measured

[16] H. Lyons, Ann. N. Y. Acad. Sci. **55**, 831 (1952).

value of the frequency in the amount of

$$\frac{\delta\nu}{\nu}=2Q\left(\frac{\Delta\nu}{\nu}\right)\left(\frac{D}{\nu}\right), \tag{33}$$

where D is the difference between the cavity and line frequencies. Thus this "pulling" effect is more serious with high Q cavities than with low Q ones, and with broad lines than with sharp ones. Fluctuations in measured frequency due to thermal drift may be considerably larger than those due to noise as given by Eq. (32). If long-term stability is of prime importance, it may be necessary to limit the Q at the sacrifice of sensitivity. For this reason and also to simplify the design of the servomechanism used to stabilize the frequency of the oscillator to that of the spectral line, it would be desirable to include some special technique for narrowing the line.

The only known line narrowing scheme which could be used with a cavity absorption cell of conventional design is the use of a buffer gas devised by Wittke and Dicke.[4] The use of this technique is limited, however, to work with magnetic resonance in monatomic gases. In this method the major component of the gas occupying the cavity is an inactive nonpolar buffer gas while the active component has a very small partial pressure. The line width is determined by collisions between the active atoms and is proportional to their partial pressure. However, a study of the equation on page 624 of Wittke and Dicke's paper[4] suggests that the voltage signal-to-noise ratio at the verge of saturation is proportional to the partial pressure. (In this paper, this equation is said to give the power absorbed per atom but an unpublished project report of the same authors, which gives the derivation of this equation, and their reference 14 indicate that this is the power absorbed per N atoms; i.e., it is the total power absorbed.) Therefore with reference to Eq. (30) we see that (ϵ/ν) is independent of the pressure. Hence, if it is desired to aid the design of the servomechanism by narrowing the line width, the use of a low partial pressure is desirable, as there would be no deterioration in the short period stability.

On the other hand, if the principal objective is to reduce pulling effects, lowering the Q of the cavity appears to be a more favorable method than the use of a buffer gas since Eq. (33) shows that the pulling effect is reduced in proportion to the Q, while Eq. (32) shows that the short term stability deteriorates only in proportion with the square root of the Q.

The ideas of this section should be clarified by a numerical example. Suppose a cubic copper-plated Invar cavity of 1 cu ft is used with the 3,3 line of NH_3. The following values apply: $|\mu|=1.1$ debye, $\nu=23\,870$ Mc, and $\gamma_m=7.9\times10^{-4}$ cm^{-1}. The loaded Q is estimated to be 7×10^4. Assume $F_1=100$ (20 db), $B=1$ cps, and that $(\Delta\nu/\nu)=2.0\times10^{-6}$ (approximately $\sqrt{2}\times$Doppler width). Then $(\epsilon/\nu)=1.1\times10^{-13}$.

If we assume the frequency temperature coefficient of the cavity is 10^{-6}/C° (approximately equal to the coefficient of linear expansion of Invar) and that the temperature fluctuates by an amount of 0.1 C° between retunings of the cavity, $(D/\nu)=10^{-7}$. Then $(\delta\nu/\nu)=2.8\times10^{-9}$. These errors can be equalized by lowering the Q to 92, when both are equal to 3.7×10^{-12}. This is a precision comparable to what can be obtained by other methods.

Reprinted from THE REVIEW OF SCIENTIFIC INSTRUMENTS, Vol. 32, No. 1, 23–27, January, 1961
Printed in U. S. A.

Comparison of the Sensitivities of the Beam Maser and Cavity Absorption Spectrometers*

YARDLEY BEERS
Department of Physics, New York University, University Heights, New York 53, New York

(Received August 26, 1960)

A formula for the signal-to-noise ratio of a maser spectrometer is derived by considering it as a special case of a cavity spectrometer. This formula is consistent with evaluations made by previous authors but is more convenient for comparison with an absorption cavity spectrometer. In applications where high resolution is not a requirement, the pressure and power level in an absorption spectrometer may be made very large so that its sensitivity can be superior to that of the maser. However, if it is operated to obtain the highest possible resolution, its sensitivity may or may not be superior to that of the maser, depending upon the frequency and upon other conditions. In the situation of greatest interest, in which the linear dimensions of the cavity are scaled in proportion to the wavelength and in which it is sufficiently large to make the effect of collisions between the molecules and the walls negligible, it is shown that the sensitivity of the maser relative to the absorption spectrometer varies inversely with the frequency. The theory is illustrated by calculations pertaining to spectrometers designed for the ND_3 inversion spectrum at 1500 Mc. From these calculations it can be inferred that, with the best available techniques, the two instruments would have about equal sensitivity in the region of 1500 to 2000 Mc, while at lower frequencies the maser would have higher sensitivity and the absorption spectrometer would have higher sensitivity at higher frequencies.

EVER since the invention of the beam maser, its sensitivity frequently has been compared to that of an absorption spectrometer, but, because molecular parameters were present or because the postulated type of absorption spectrometer was not optimum, the significance of such comparisons has not been entirely clear. In particular, it has been difficult to see how the relative sensitivity varies with frequency. In the present formulation, essentially no molecular parameters appear in the expression for the relative sensitivity, and the relative advantages of the two instruments can be seen more clearly.

In one of the first beam maser papers, Gordon, Zeiger, and Townes[1] have given a formula for voltage signal-to-noise ratio of a beam maser. For coherence of presentation, another approach will be followed here. It can be shown that the results of the present treatment are consistent with their formula.

The beam maser can be considered as a special case of a cavity spectrometer. The present author has derived[2] the following formula for the voltage signal-to-noise ratio of such a device

$$S=\frac{hc\gamma}{8\pi\bar{\mu}}\left(\frac{\Delta\nu}{\nu}\right)\left(\frac{QV\nu}{2FkT'B}\right)^{\frac{1}{2}}, \quad (1)$$

where γ is the power absorption coefficient of the gas, ν is the resonant frequency, both of the line and of the cavity, $\Delta\nu$ is the half-width at half-power of the line, $\bar{\mu}$ is the dipole matrix element pertaining to the transition, Q is the unloaded quality factor of the cavity, V is its volume, F is the noise figure of the detector, B is its noise bandwidth, T' is a reference temperature, and h, c, and k have their usual meanings.

Equation (1) has been derived upon the assumption of a reaction type resonator whose impedance is matched to the impedance of the detector and which is highly mismatched to the generator. However, it can be expected that, under conditions of optimum adjustment, this formula can be expected to apply to a transmission type resonator to a very good approximation. This formula has also been based upon the assumption that the power level has been adjusted to be on the verge of saturation: that is, to cause the linewidth to be approximately the square root of two times its value at vanishingly small power levels.

Before adapting this formula to beam masers, this author should insert some remarks upon the significance of the quantity S which he should have included in his previous paper.[2] This quantity is a convenient figure of merit for a spectrometer. It may or, more likely, may not equal the effective signal-to-noise ratio at the output of the detector or receiver. Even with detectors or receivers which are linear in the sense of precisely reproducing the true line shape or the modulation of the input signal, there may be a variety of nonlinear effects of other types which can cause the output to differ from the quantity S. In addition, subjective effects may produce a similar result. For one thing, the output due to signal alone is never observed, but the effective signal output is the difference in output due to signal plus noise and the output due to noise alone. It may be shown[3] that the ratio of the effective output signal-to-noise ratio is then appreciably less than S when S is of the order of unity or smaller: In other words, under these conditions, noise may be said to suppress the signal. On the other hand, it is well known that certain types of detectors, such as wide band frequency-modulated receivers and some superregenerative receivers,

* Supported by the Electronics Branch of the U. S. Office of Naval Research and by the Air Force Office of Scientific Research.

[1] J. P. Gordon, H. J. Zeiger, and C. H. Townes, Phys. Rev. **99**, 1265 (1955).

[2] Y. Beers, Rev. Sci. Instr. **30**, 9 (1959).

[3] W. H. Jordan in *Microwave Receivers*, edited by S. N. Van Voorhis, MIT Radiation Lab. Series (McGraw-Hill Book Company, Inc., New York, 1948), Vol. 23, Sec. 7. 9.

tend to suppress noise or to exaggerate signal once S is appreciably larger than unity. Finally, with a maser, positive feedback may cause the signal to become exaggerated with respect to noise. In fact, it is possible that the maser may go into oscillation. Nevertheless, even in the case of oscillation, the quantity S has some significance since it gives some indication of the purity of the signal.

In adapting Eq. (1) to the beam maser, it is convenient to introduce the basic formula for the absorption coefficient,[4]

$$\gamma=\frac{8\pi^2\nu^2 N f\bar{\mu}^2}{3ckT\Delta\nu}, \tag{2}$$

where N is the total number of molecules per unit volume, f is the fraction of these which are in the state from which the transition originates, and T is the temperature of the gas. When Eqs. (1) and (2) are combined,

$$S=\frac{\pi N f h\nu\bar{\mu}}{3kT}\left(\frac{QV\nu}{2FkT'B}\right)^{\frac{1}{2}}. \tag{3}$$

It is to be noted that the only factors in Eq. (3) which depend upon geometry when this formula is applied to an absorption spectrometer are Q and V. Since the Q is approximately proportional to the ratio of volume to surface area, it is obvious that for a given volume, maximum sensitivity is obtained with the minimum surface area: that is, with the linear dimensions approximately equal. It will be shown that optimum performance of a beam maser requires a different relation between the dimensions.

To adapt Eq. (3) to the beam maser two modifications are needed. The first is to undo an assumption which has been incorporated in the derivation of Eq. (2) and therefore is implicit in Eq. (3). It has been assumed in Eq. (2) that $h\nu$ is small compared to kT and, therefore, that there are nearly as many downward transitions per unit time due to stimulated emission as there are upward transitions due to absorption. γ and S are proportional to the net number of upward transitions. The focuser of the maser, however, ideally eliminates all the molecules of one of these states, and the net number of transitions is equal to the actual number leaving that state. With the maser, usually the upper state is retained yielding an emission signal, but since only the magnitude is of interest, this fact can be overlooked. The effect of the focuser can be included by multiplying Eqs. (2) and (3) by the factor $KT/(h\nu)$.

Secondly, it is necessary to evaluate Nf, the number of molecules per unit volume in the state from which the transition originates, in terms of quantities which are of direct interest with the maser. If N_m molecules are emitted per unit time by the effuser, $N_m f$ per unit time are in the state from which the transition originates and, with $h\nu$ small compared to kT, the number per unit time in the state on which the transition terminates is nearly the same. Because of the action of the focuser, the net excess of the number in the state of origin over the number in the state of termination actually entering the cavity per unit time is $N_m f\Omega$, where Ω can be considered the efficiency of the focuser. Previous authors have defined Ω geometrically as the solid angle which the emergent beam subtends at the effuser, and this definition provides a means of obtaining a numerical estimate of it.[1] The pressure in the cavity is assumed to be so low that effectively no collisions between molecules take place. Under these conditions the presence of molecules in still other states has no effect. Then the effective number of molecules in the cavity is $N_m F\Omega$ multiplied by the time each remains in the cavity, which is $L/\bar{v}$, where L is the length of the cavity and $\bar{v}$ is the average speed. The number per unit volume is this quantity divided by the volume V. With a properly designed cavity $L/\bar{v}$ is approximately $1/(\Delta\nu)_m$, the half-width at half-power of the line which is observed in the maser at low power levels. After these substitutions are made, the resulting sensitivity of the maser is

$$S_m=\frac{\pi N_m f\Omega\bar{\mu}}{3(\Delta\nu)_m}\left(\frac{Q_m\nu}{2FkT'BV_m}\right)^{\frac{1}{2}}. \tag{4}$$

In Eq. (4) the subscript "m" has been added to several symbols to facilitate comparison with the absorption spectrometer, whose symbols will be denoted by the subscript "a."

$(\Delta\nu)_m$ is inversely proportional to the length. Q_m is approximately proportional to the volume V divided by the surface area. Then for a cavity whose length is considerably greater than the radius r, S_m is approximately proportional to $(L/r)^{\frac{1}{2}}$. This condition is very different than that with an absorption spectrometer.

By expressing the imaginary part of the susceptibility in terms of the absorption coefficient in the original formula of Gordon, Zeiger, and Townes,[1] and by making other substitutions which have been used here, it is possible to derive a formula which is identical with Eq. (4) except that the numerical factor $\pi/[3(2)^{\frac{1}{2}}]$ is replaced by $(\pi/3)^{\frac{1}{2}}$. In view of the assumptions which have been made concerning the optimum power level in the two derivations, and in view of the accuracy which is required in a practical calculation, the agreement between the two formulas can be considered good.

$N_m f\Omega$ represents the net number of particles of the state from which the transition originates entering the resonator per second. The minimum number required for detection may be found by placing $S_m=1$ and solving. The result which is obtained is identical with one obtained previously

[4] See, for example, C. H. Townes and A. L. Schawlow, *Microwave Spectroscopy* (McGraw-Hill Book Company, Inc., New York, 1955), Sec. 13–3.

by Shimoda, Wang, and Townes[5] except for a numerical coefficient, their coefficient being smaller by a factor of about 3. However, they made a third assumption regarding the optimum power level and assumed a transmission cavity matched to the load. Therefore, the agreement can be considered fairly good. In the numerical example which follows, the coefficients from the present theory will be used for the sake of consistency.

The relative sensitivity of the two instruments may be found by dividing Eq. (3) by Eq. (5) with the subscript "a" inserted where appropriate.

$$\frac{S_m}{S_a}=\frac{N_m\Omega}{N_a(\Delta\nu)_m}\left(\frac{kT}{h\nu}\right)\left(\frac{Q_m}{Q_aV_aV_m}\right)^{\frac{1}{2}}. \tag{6}$$

In the derivation of Eq. (6) the factors f and $FkT'B$ have canceled out. It has been assumed that the same detection system has been used with both instruments. The maser, as is well known, is capable of yielding nearly a perfect noise figure. However, its power output is so low that, if the benefit of its low noise figure is to be realized, it must be followed by another low noise device such as a solid-state maser or a parametric amplifier. On the other hand, these may also be used with the absorption spectrometer. Therefore, no serious error is made by assuming the noise figures equal.

The significance of Eq. (6) may be illustrated first by considering its frequency dependence under several sets of assumptions. For simplicity, it will be assumed that the same cavity is used in both applications: That is, $Q_a=Q_m$ and $V_a=V_m=V$, although this condition cannot yield optimum performance of both instruments. The situation which is of greatest interest is when the cavity is large enough not to limit resolution by wall collisions and when the dimensions are scaled in proportion to the wavelength. N_m depends only upon the properties of the beam source and is independent of the frequency. On the other hand, if the contribution to the linewidth due to collisions is to be held to some constant fraction of the Doppler width, N_a must be made proportional to the frequency since the Doppler width is proportional to the frequency. Gordon, Zeiger, and Townes[1] have shown that Ω is inversely proportional to the Stark energy. In the usual case of a molecule having a quadratic Stark effect and having a transition between two isolated levels, this in turn is approximately inversely proportional to the frequency. $(\Delta\nu)_m$ is inversely proportional to the length of the cavity, and, therefore, in view of the hypothesis of scaling the cavity dimensions, it is proportional to the frequency. V is, of course, inversely proportional to the cube of the frequency. Then, including the explicit inverse first power dependence, it can be seen that the over-all effect is to make the ratio S_m/S_a inversely proportional to the frequency. Then it is of interest to determine the frequency at which this ratio becomes unity. The numerical examples concerning the detection of the (3,3) line of ND_3 which will be given somewhat later suggest that with present techniques this frequency is in the neighborhood of from 1500 to 2000 Mc. It should be noted, however, that with relaxation of the requirement that the pressure in the absorption cell be held low enough to cause the resolution to be limited by Doppler effect, N_a may be made arbitrarily large, and then S_a may be made large compared to S_m at all frequencies.

It is also of some interest to consider situations in which the volume can be considered approximately constant. The constraints upon the dimensions required for resonance will be neglected. One possibility is that the dimensions are so large that within the range of frequency being considered the resolution of the absorption spectrometer is limited by Doppler effect. In such a case, $(\Delta\nu)_m$ is constant, and the only quantities to vary implicitly with the frequency are N_a and Ω. Then the ratio of S_m to S_a varies inversely with the cube of the frequency. On the other hand, if the cavity is sufficiently small that the resolution in the absorption spectrometer is limited by collisions with the walls, N_a is constant, and the ratio of S_m to S_a varies inversely with the square of the frequency.

To illustrate these formulas further, consider the numerical example of a maser designed for the (3,3) inversion transition of ND_3, the instrument being a scaled-up version of the type of instrument which has been built in many laboratories for the observation of the (3,3) line of NH_3. Shimoda, Wang, and Townes[5] in 1956 reported values of $N_mf\Omega$ up to 10^{14}/sec for NH_3. With ND_3, f is about 2×10^{-2} at room temperature and is about one-half that for NH_3. On the other hand, the frequency is lower by a factor of 14, and Ω can be expected to be proportionately larger. Also, no doubt, the technology of effusers has improved since 1956. Therefore it seems reasonable to expect that 10^{15}/sec with ND_3 can be obtained. Conditions for resonance make it impractical to use a cavity radius smaller than about 0.4 wavelength, while the danger of collisions of the molecules with the side walls usually makes it impractical to use a cavity length greater than 5 free space wavelengths (although in some cases considerably longer cavities have been used). With these assumptions, along with a wavelength of approximately 20 cm, the volume is 2.10×10^4 cm^3.

With this length, $(\Delta\nu)_m$ can be assumed to be 3.2×10^2 cps, slightly more than one-tenth of the Doppler width. A nominal value for Q of 1×10^4 is assumed, although at this frequency probably higher values can be obtained. FB is assumed to be 10/sec and T' is assumed to be 290°K, $\bar{\mu}=1.3\times10^{-18}$ esu cm. The computed value of S_m from Eq. (4) is 1.3×10^5.

[5] K. Shimoda, T. C. Wang, and C. H. Townes, Phys. Rev. **102**, 1308 (1956).

With the contribution to the linewidth due to wall collisions in an absorption spectrometer approximately equal to the contribution from the Doppler effect, $N_a = 4.2\times10^{12}/\text{cm}^3$. Then if the same resonator is used as an absorption spectrometer, Eq. (3) yields a value of $S_a = 1.9\times10^4$. However, this cavity is not of optimum design for use as an absorption spectrometer. A larger volume could be used. (A resonator having six times this volume is being placed into operation in the writer's Laboratory as this paper is being written.) Furthermore, the shape which has been described is not optimum because, if the dimensions are made more equal, a higher Q can be obtained for any given volume. Therefore, it can be surmised that with a suitably designed cavity, an absorption spectrometer of nearly equal sensitivity could be made for use with the ND_3 transitions. From these calculations it can be concluded that between 1500 and 2000 Mc the two devices can be made to have about equal sensitivity. At lower frequencies, the maser potentially has greater sensitivity than an absorption spectrometer operated under conditions of maximum resolution, while above this region the reverse is true.

As stated previously, this calculation has neglected feedback: that is, the tendency for the maser to oscillate. Shimoda, Wang, and Townes[5] have derived the following formula for the minimum number of molecules per second required for oscillation:

$$(N_m f\Omega)_{\text{osc}} = \frac{hV_m(\Delta\nu)_m{}^2}{2\pi^2\bar{\mu}^2 Q_m}. \quad (7)$$

It is possible to choose numerical values such that, when the quantity calculated from Eq. (7) is substituted into Eq. (6), a value of S_m less than unity is obtained, even though a very low value of F is assumed. The fallacy in such a calculation is that Eq. (7) has been based upon the assumption that the field inside the cavity is essentially coherent: That is, that the contributions of noise to the field are negligible. Thus such a value of S_m less than unity generally indicates that Eq. (7) is being used under conditions for which it is not valid. Under other conditions, where the maser can reasonably be expected to oscillate, the largeness of S_m gives a qualitative indication of the purity of the emitted frequency. With the numerical values which have been assumed for the ND_3 maser, Eq. (7) yields a value of 4.2×10^{13}/sec, while earlier it was said that 10^{15}/sec should be expected. Thus this maser should oscillate and should give a reasonably monochromatic signal.

The advantage of oscillation is an aid to spectroscopic investigations as well as in applications as a frequency standard. However, this advantage is obtainable at a price. Cavities of the type described for maser operation operate in modes such that the resonant frequency depends critically upon the diameter, and therefore it is not practical to build them with tuning ranges of more than 1%, and often it is necessary to build a new resonator for almost every spectral line. Even with the ND_3 spectrum,[6–8] where a large number of lines occur in a small region, three or four of these resonators are required for a comprehensive investigation. In view of the fact that each would be of the order of 1 m in length, the cost would be considerable, not counting the more elaborate pumping system and focus voltage supply required for the maser. On the other hand, an absorption spectrometer can employ a cavity operating in other modes which can be tuned over a wide range, and a single resonator can cover more than the entire significant portion of the ND_3 spectrum. At the same time, the expected line width of about 3 kc should be small enough to resolve most of the expected hyperfine splittings.

As the frequency is decreased below 1500 Mc, the maser should become superior in sensitivity in accordance with the discussion which has been presented. However, the frequency would have to be considerably lower before this advantage would become important, and at such a long wavelength it would probably not be economically practical to use cavities 5 free space wavelengths long to narrow the line width. However, the Doppler width, which is proportional to the frequency, would be so small compared to most hyperfine splittings that such a line narrowing feature would not be required. As is well known, ammonia has an unusually high value of f and a very favorable value of $\bar{\mu}$. There appears to be no molecule with the same relative advantages for transitions at lower frequencies, and therefore there are few, if any, transitions which are capable of providing an oscillating beam maser below 1500 Mc.

The discussion in this paper has been based upon maser techniques which have been used for some time. At high frequencies the Fabry-Perot type of cavity[9,10] is capable of giving higher Q and longer path lengths than the conventional cavities upon which the present discussion has been based. The limitations of size undoubtedly make them impractical at frequencies as low as 1500 Mc. Furthermore, with present techniques, coupling losses are large, and the effective noise figures would be inferior, but this difficulty probably will be reduced by further development. Ramsey[11] has described a maser in construc-

[6] H. Lyons, L. J. Rueger, R. G. Nuckolls, and M. Kessler, Phys. Rev. **81**, 630 (1951).

[7] R. G. Nuckolls, L. J. Rueger, and H. Lyons, Phys. Rev. **89**, 1101 (1953).

[8] G. Herrmann, J. Chem. Phys. **29**, 875 (1958).

[9] A. L. Schawlow and C. H. Townes, Phys. Rev. **112**, 1940 (1958).

[10] W. Culshaw, IRE Trans. on Microwave Theory Tech., **MTT-8**, 182 (1960).

[11] N. F. Ramsey, Proceedings of the 14th Annual Symposium on Frequency Control, U. S. Army Signal Research and Development Laboratory, Fort Monmouth, New Jersey (unpublished, 1960).

tion in his Laboratory employing atomic hydrogen and collisions with specially treated walls to increase the effective length to one many times greater than can be obtained with conventional techniques, but this method appears to be very restricted in its application to spectroscopy.

ACKNOWLEDGMENT

During the later stages of the preparation of this manuscript, the author held a summer position with the National Bureau of Standards at Boulder, Colorado. During this period he received great help through discussions with Dr. R. C. Mockler.

Reprinted from THE JOURNAL OF CHEMICAL PHYSICS, Vol. 40, No. 2, 257–273, 15 January 1964
Printed in U. S. A.

Hyperfine Structure in the Microwave Spectrum of HDO, HDS, CH_2O, and CHDO: Beam-Maser Spectroscopy on Asymmetric-Top Molecules*

P. THADDEUS
Columbia Radiation Laboratory, Columbia University, New York, New York, 10027 and Goddard Institute for Space Studies, NASA, New York, New York 10027

L. C. KRISHER
Columbia Radiation Laboratory and Department of Chemistry, Columbia University, New York, New York 10027

AND

J. H. N. LOUBSER†
Columbia Radiation Laboratory, Columbia University, New York, New York 10027

(Received 15 August 1963)

Hyperfine structure in the $2_{20}\rightarrow 2_{21}$ rotational transition of HDO at 10 278.2 Mc/sec and HDS at 11 283.8 Mc/sec, and in the $2_{11}\rightarrow 2_{12}$ rotational transition of CH_2O at 14 488.6 Mc/sec and CHDO at 16 038.1 Mc/sec, has been investigated with a high-resolution beam maser microwave spectrometer. Linewidths of 5 kc/sec have been obtained. The hyperfine Hamiltonian for an arbitrary number of nuclei with quadrupole, spin–rotation, and spin–spin interactions is discussed, and the matrix elements of the Hamiltonian and the intensities of hyperfine transitions calculated in terms of the tabulated $6j$ coefficients. Quadrupole and spin–rotation constants and bond lengths which have been determined are, for the 2_{20} state of HDO: $(eq_JQ)_D=79.3\pm0.3$ kc/sec, $C_H=-43.47\pm0.11$ kc/sec, $C_D=-2.33\pm0.02$ kc/sec; for the 2_{21} state of HDO: $(eq_JQ)_D=79.6\pm0.3$ kc/sec, $C_H=-43.63\pm0.13$ kc/sec, $C_D=-2.20\pm0.02$ kc/sec; for the 2_{20} state of HDS: $(eq_JQ)_D=42.9\pm0.4$ kc/sec, $C_H=-25.03\pm0.13$ kc/sec, $C_D=-0.47\pm0.02$ kc/sec; for the 2_{21} state of HDS: $(eq_JQ)_D=43.3\pm0.4$ kc/sec, $C_H=-25.45\pm0.13$ kc/sec, $C_D=-0.22\pm0.02$ kc/sec; for CH_2O: $C_H(2_{11})-C_H(2_{12})=2.26\pm0.13$ kc/sec, $C_H(2_{11})=0.65\pm0.50$ kc/sec, $\langle 1/r_{HH}^3\rangle^{-\frac{1}{3}}=1.898\pm0.017$ Å; for CHDO: $(eV_{\xi\xi}Q)_D=170.0\pm2.0$ kc/sec (where $V_{\xi\xi}$ is the second derivative of the electrostatic potential along the CD bond), $C_H(2_{11})-C_H(2_{12})=2.42\pm0.50$ kc/sec, $C_D(2_{11})-C_D(2_{12})=0.25\pm0.10$ kc/sec, $C_H(2_{11})=0.2\pm1.0$ kc/sec, $C_D(2_{11})=0.13\pm0.20$ kc/sec, and $\langle 1/r_{HD}^3\rangle^{-\frac{1}{3}}=1.88\pm0.10$ Å. The $V_{\xi\xi}$ calculated from the deuteron quadrupole coupling constants are, for HDO: 1.56×10^{15} statvolt/cm²; for HDS: 0.76×10^{15} statvolt/cm²; and for CHDO: 0.83×10^{15} statvolt/cm².

I. INTRODUCTION

THE great majority of stable molecules have $^1\Sigma$ electronic ground states for which the total magnetic field produced by the electrons is small, and the effect of nuclear electric quadrupole moments rather than magnetic dipole moments is predominant in the hyperfine structure (hfs) of the rotation (or inversion) spectrum. In microwave spectroscopy, quadrupole hfs is usually well resolved, and has been extensively studied.

The quadrupole moment of the deuteron is several orders of magnitude smaller than that characteristic of most nuclei, however, and produces hfs which is near the limit of resolution of most microwave spectrometers. Deuteron quadrupole hfs has been observed by microwave spectroscopy for only a few molecules, and the coupling constant has been measured for only several cases to an accuracy of better than 10%.[1] At the same time, because of the precision to which the electronic wavefunction for molecular hydrogen can be calculated, the deuteron quadrupole moment is known much more accurately than the quadrupole moments of other nuclei,[2] and a measurement of its coupling constant in other molecules therefore allows an accurate determination of the gradient of the molecular electric field.

There are also other interactions which lie near or beyond the limit of resolution imposed by Doppler broadening, which gives at room temperature for light molecules a linewidth of about 50 kc/sec in the centimeter region. A $^1\Sigma$ ground state has zero electronic angular momentum only in the idealized case that the nuclear frame is fixed in space, or "clamped." Under rotation, higher electronic states with nonzero angular momentum are slightly excited, producing a small molecular magnetic field and a magnetic hyperfine interaction proportional to **I·J**. These "spin–rotation" interactions were first observed in molecular hydrogen, and subsequently many alkali halides, with molecular beam magnetic resonance techniques.[3] A number have also been observed by high-resolution microwave absorption spectroscopy.[4,5] The energies of the **I·J** interactions

* Work supported in part by the Joint Services (the U.S. Army, the Office of Naval Research, and the Air Force Office of Scientific Research) and in part by the National Science Foundation.

† Present address: Physics Department, University of the Orange Free State, Bloemfontein, South Africa.

[1] R. Bersohn, J. Chem. Phys. **32**, 85 (1960).

[2] J. P. Auffray, Phys. Rev. Letters **6**, 120 (1961).

[3] N. F. Ramsey, *Molecular Beams* (Oxford University Press, Oxford, England, 1956), Chap. 8.

[4] R. L. White, Rev. Mod. Phys. **27**, 276 (1955).

[5] C. H. Townes and A. L. Schawlow, *Microwave Spectroscopy* (McGraw-Hill Book Company, Inc., New York, 1955), Chap. 8.

are typically of the order of a few tens of kilocycles per second, but may be as large as 100 kc/sec or greater for molecules with large rotational constants.

The direct magnetic dipole–dipole, or "spin–spin," interactions between nuclei are still smaller, with typical energies of a few kilocycles per second. This interaction depends only on the dipole moments and masses of the nuclei and the geometry of the nuclear frame of the molecule. These are usually more accurately found by other methods, and this interaction is not as interesting, therefore, from the point of view of molecular structure as the hyperfine terms previously discussed. In certain rare cases, however, such as CH_2O studied here, a very precise measurement of a spin–spin interaction may allow calculation of an internuclear distance to an accuracy as great as or exceeding that already known.

Two general methods have been used to investigate these various interactions in $^1\Sigma$ molecules. Since Doppler broadening decreases in direct proportion to the frequency of a transition, while there is no systematic decrease of the hyperfine interactions, absorption spectroscopy at low microwave and radio frequencies offers the possibility of observing hfs that cannot be resolved in the centimeter region. There is a systematic decrease of the intensity of absorption lines, however, that is roughly proportional to the cube of the frequency for rotational transitions, which severely limits the applicability of this method. Treacy and Beers[6] have used this approach to observe two rotational transitions in HDO which lie as low as 825 and 487 Mc/sec.

The second approach consists in selectively observing a limited class of molecules whose velocity spread along the direction of signal propagation is a small fraction of the average thermal velocity. This is most commonly done with a molecular beam, which, if well collimated, permits in practice a reduction in Doppler broadening by a factor of 10 to 100. This technique has, of course, been employed for some time in high-resolution optical spectroscopy. With a microwave spectrometer operating on this principle, Strandberg and Dreicer[7] have observed a linewidth of only 12 kc/sec for the ammonia 3, 3 inversion line. Using the same transition, Newell and Dicke[8] have devised an ingenious method, employing spatial as well as temporal Stark modulation, for observing only those molecules moving at a given velocity with respect to the wavefronts of the microwaves. A linewidth of about 10 kc/sec was observed.

In practice, both of these schemes suffer from low sensitivity. In the centimeter region they have only been applied to the intense ammonia inversion spectrum, and even in this case the sensitivity was not high enough to allow investigation of hfs.[9]

The first spectrometer of comparable resolution to overcome this limitation on sensitivity was the ammonia beam maser of Gordon, Zeiger, and Townes,[10] which also used a molecular beam to reduce Doppler broadening. In addition, however, an electrostatic state selector was employed to increase the population difference between the states of the transition. It was the unique feature of the maser that instead of increasing the population of the lower state of the transition with respect to the upper state, it was found possible to remove effectively the lower-state molecules from the beam. The hfs of the transition was therefore observed in emission instead of absorption. A linewidth of 7 kc/sec and a signal-to-noise ratio of about 1000 with superheterodyne detection and oscilloscope display were obtained for the ammonia 3, 3 line. This sensitivity allowed new features of the inversion spectrum (due mainly to magnetic interactions of the protons) to be investigated.[11]

In this paper we report the results obtained from a beam-maser study of the light asymmetric-top molecules HDO, HDS, CH_2O, and CHDO. These molecules are nearly symmetric tops, and their rotational spectrum possesses closely spaced pairs of levels due to the lifting of the $\pm K$ symmetric-top degeneracy (Fig. 1). These K-type doublets resemble in some respects the inversion doublets of ammonia. In particular, if transitions between the two components of a doublet are allowed, the two states will repel each other under the Stark effect to typically very high fields, due to the isolation of the doublets from other rotational states. Electrostatic state selection is therefore feasible. Moreover, as in the case of ammonia, the great majority of rotational intervals for these molecules lie in the millimeter or submillimeter region, and the lower rotational states are well populated.

The spectrometer used in this investigation and the techniques of frequency measurement have been described elsewhere.[12] Therefore, only those experimental considerations which are peculiar to a given molecule, such as the preparation of the sample, are discussed in detail.

II. THEORY OF HFS

In this section we summarize the theory of hfs for $^1\Sigma$ molecules, in particular for asymmetric rotors. The

[6] E. B. Treacy and Y. Beers, J. Chem. Phys. **36**, 1473 (1962).

[7] M. W. P. Strandberg and H. Dreicer, Phys. Rev. **94**, 1393 (1954).

[8] G. Newell and R. H. Dicke, Phys. Rev. **83**, 1064 (1951).

[9] Recently in the millimeter region a molecular beam spectrometer has been used in studies of the rotational spectrum of the alkali halides with good signal strength and linewidths of about 100 kc/sec. See J. R. Rusk and W. Gordy, Phys. Rev. **127**, 817 (1962).

[10] J. P. Gordon, H. J. Zeiger, and C. H. Townes, Phys. Rev. **99**, 1264 (1955).

[11] J. P. Gordon, Phys. Rev. **99**, 1253 (1955).

[12] P. Thaddeus and L. C. Krisher, Rev. Sci. Instr. **32**, 1083 (1961).

interaction terms diagonal in the rotational states and the relation between the hyperfine coupling constants and the more basic nuclear and molecular properties are brought together and presented under a systematic notation. Finally, the problem of writing down the matrix elements for an arbitrary number of nuclei in a given representation in terms of the tabulated $6j$ coefficients is considered, and the calculation of intensities is briefly discussed.

Foley[13] originally considered the coupling of two similar nuclei with electric quadrupole moments in a diatomic molecule. His work was extended to dissimilar nuclei and to symmetric- and asymmetric-top molecules by Bardeen and Townes,[14] Myers and Gwinn,[15] and Robinson and Cornwell.[16] The case of three nuclei with quadrupole moments has been treated by Bersohn,[17] who indicated how his results could be generalized to an arbitrary number of nuclei.

In an attempt to understand certain previously unresolved features of the ammonia inversion spectrum, Gunther-Mohr, Townes, and Van Vleck[18] undertook a systematic investigation of all hyperfine effects which could be observed under the highest microwave resolution then available. Their treatment was comprehensive enough to explain the results which Gordon[11] soon afterward obtained with the first beam maser. These new features were magnetic in origin, due either to the direct dipole–dipole interactions between various nuclei, or to the $\mathbf{I}\cdot\mathbf{J}$ interactions between the nuclei and the molecular magnetic field. A review of the theory of the $\mathbf{I}\cdot\mathbf{J}$ interactions and of the microwave work up to 1955 is given by White[4] and in the monograph by Townes and Schawlow.[5] Ramsey[3] also gives an extensive discussion of these interactions, with particular attention to linear and diatomic molecules.

The work of Gunther-Mohr, Townes, and Van Vleck on NH_3 has been extended to the deuterated ammonias by Hadley,[19] while hfs in planar molecules with two off-axis spins and one axial quadrupolar nucleus has been treated by Okaya.[20] The problem of the coupling of an arbitrary number of nuclei having, in general, both a magnetic dipole and an electric quadrupole moment has been considered in some detail by Posener.[21]

a. Hamiltonian

The hfs of the molecules studied in this work is interpreted on the basis of the Hamiltonian given by

[13] H. M. Foley, Phys. Rev. **71**, 747 (1947).
[14] J. Bardeen and C. H. Townes, Phys. Rev. **73**, 627 (1948).
[15] R. J. Myers and W. D. Gwinn, J. Chem. Phys. **20**, 1420 (1952).
[16] G. W. Robinson and C. D. Cornwell, J. Chem. Phys. **21**, 1436 (1953).
[17] R. Bersohn, J. Chem. Phys. **18**, 1124 (1950).
[18] G. R. Gunther-Mohr, C. H. Townes, and J. H. Van Vleck, Phys. Rev. **94**, 1191 (1954).
[19] G. F. Hadley, J. Chem. Phys. **26**, 1482 (1957).
[20] A. Okaya, J. Phys. Soc. (Japan) **11**, 249 (1956).
[21] D. W. Posener, Australian J. Phys. **11**, 1 (1958).

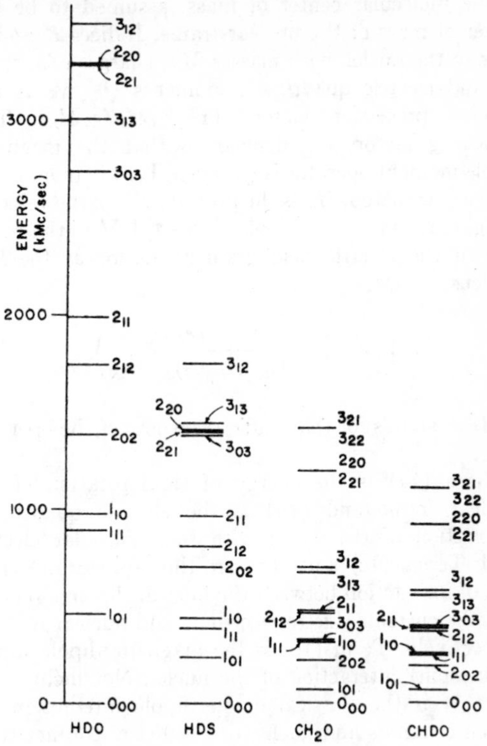

FIG. 1. The lower rotational levels of HDO, HDS, CH_2O, and CHDO, calculated in the rigid rotor approximation.

Gunther-Mohr, Townes, and Van Vleck[18]:

$$\mathcal{H}=\sum_g A_g(J_g-L_g)^2 \tag{1a}$$

$$+\tfrac{1}{6}\sum_K \frac{eQ_K}{I_K(2I_K-1)}\mathbf{V}:\times\{\tfrac{3}{2}[\mathbf{I}_K\mathbf{I}_K+(\mathbf{I}_K\mathbf{I}_K)^{\mathrm{tr}}]-I_K(I_K+1)\mathbf{1}\} \tag{1b}$$

$$+\frac{e\mu_N}{c}\sum_{i,K} g_K r_{iK}^{-3}[\mathbf{r}_{iK}\times(\mathbf{v}_i-\gamma_K\mathbf{v}_K)]\cdot\mathbf{I}_K \tag{1c}$$

$$-\frac{e\mu_N}{c}\sum_{K,L\neq K} Z_L g_K r_{LK}^{-3}[\mathbf{r}_{LK}\times(\mathbf{v}_L-\gamma_K\mathbf{v}_K)]\cdot\mathbf{I}_K \tag{1d}$$

$$+\mu_N^2\sum_{K,L>K} g_K g_L r_{LK}^{-3}\times[(\mathbf{I}_L\cdot\mathbf{I}_K)-3r_{LK}^{-2}(\mathbf{I}_L\cdot\mathbf{r}_{LK})(\mathbf{I}_K\cdot\mathbf{r}_{LK})]. \tag{1e}$$

J_g and L_g are, respectively, in units of $\hbar$, the components of the total angular momentum excluding nuclear spins, and the electronic orbital angular momentum, along the principal axis of inertia of the molecule. The A_g are the rotational constants given, in terms of the principal moments of inertia, by $A_g=\hbar^2/2I_g$. The index i refers to the electrons, with charges $-e$ and positions and velocities $\mathbf{r}_i$ and $\mathbf{v}_i$ with respect to the molecular center of mass, assumed to be the center of mass of the nuclear frame. Indices K and L refer to the nuclei, with masses M_K, charges eZ_K, spins I_K, and electric quadrupole moments Q_K. γ_K is the Thomas precession factor[22] $(1-Z_KM_P/g_KM_K)$. The nuclear g factors are defined so that the magnetic dipole moment operator is $\boldsymbol{\mu}_K=g_K\mu_N\mathbf{I}_K$, where μ_N is the nuclear magneton. M_P is the proton mass, c the velocity of light, $\mathbf{r}_{ij}=\mathbf{r}_i-\mathbf{r}_j$, and $r_{ij}=|\mathbf{r}_i-\mathbf{r}_j|$. $\mathbf{V}$ is the negative of the electric field gradient tensor at the Kth nucleus:

$$V_{\alpha\beta}=\sum_{i,L\neq K}\frac{\partial^2}{\partial x_{K_\alpha}\partial x_{K_\beta}}\left(\frac{eZ_L}{r_{LK}}-\frac{e}{r_{iK}}\right).$$

$(\mathbf{I}_K\mathbf{I}_K)^{\text{tr}}$ stands for the dyadic transpose of the operator $\mathbf{I}_K\mathbf{I}_K$.

Term (1a) is the energy of rigid rotation of the nuclear frame and (1b) is the electric quadrupole interaction of the nuclei with the molecular electric field. Terms (1c) and (1d) are the (spin–orbit) energies of interaction between the nuclear dipole moments and the currents due to electronic and nuclear motion, respectively. Term (1e) is the magnetic dipole–dipole (spin–spin) interaction of the nuclei. Not included in Eq. (1) is the classical dipole–dipole interaction between electrons and nuclei, or the Fermi contact term proportional to $\mathbf{S}_i\cdot\mathbf{I}_K$. For $^1\Sigma$ molecules, rotation of the nuclear frame slightly excites higher electronic orbital states, but not higher spin states (to the same order in perturbation theory, in any case), and these terms do not therefore contribute to the hfs.[18]

The terms in the Hamiltonian of Eq. (1) are written in order of descending magnitude for most $^1\Sigma$ molecules. The first term, the energy of rotation of the nuclear frame, is of the order of 10^5 times the largest hyperfine term for all the molecules considered here. Terms off-diagonal in the rotational states are therefore neglected,[23] and the perturbation problem reduces to the averaging of the Hamiltonian over a given asymmetric rotor wavefunction. The result of this averaging, together with the diagonal terms of the $\mathbf{I}\cdot\mathbf{J}$ interaction considered below, we will call the hyperfine Hamiltonian. For a given rotational state this will be a function of $\mathbf{J}$, the various nuclear spins $\mathbf{I}_K$, and the hyperfine coupling constants.

The result of averaging the quadrupole term (1b) over an asymmetric rotor wavefunction was originally studied by Bragg,[24] and is reviewed by Townes and Schawlow[25] and Posener.[21] For the Kth nucleus

$$\mathcal{H}_{\text{quadrupole}}=\frac{(eq_JQ)_K}{2I_K(2I_K-1)J(2J-1)}\times[3(\mathbf{I}_K\cdot\mathbf{J})^2+\tfrac{3}{2}(\mathbf{I}_K\cdot\mathbf{J})-I_K(I_K+1)J(J+1)]. \quad (2)$$

The q_J, in general, vary from rotational state to state, and may be expressed in terms of the diagonal elements $V_{gg}=\partial^2V/\partial g^2$ of the electric field gradient tensor, when this tensor is written in the principal axis system of the molecule. For an asymmetric rotor[25,26]

$$q_J=2\sum_g\langle J_g^2\rangle V_{gg}/(J+1)(2J+3). \quad (3)$$

The $\langle J_g^2\rangle$ are the average values of the square of the components of J along the principal inertial axes of the molecule

$$\langle J_a^2\rangle=\tfrac{1}{2}[J(J+1)+E(\kappa)-(\kappa+1)\partial E(\kappa)/\partial\kappa], \quad (4a)$$

$$\langle J_b^2\rangle=\partial E(\kappa)/\partial\kappa, \quad (4b)$$

$$\langle J_c^2\rangle=\tfrac{1}{2}[J(J+1)-E(\kappa)+(\kappa-1)\partial E(\kappa)/\partial\kappa], \quad (4c)$$

where a, b, and c refer, respectively, to the least, intermediate, and greatest principal axes of inertia. $E(\kappa)$ is the energy parameter of an asymmetric rotor with asymmetry parameter $\kappa=(2B-A-C)/(A-C)$, and is tabulated by Townes and Schawlow.[27]

The three V_{gg} are not independent, but satisfy Laplace's equation: $\sum_gV_{gg}=0$. It is often a good approximation to assume that the field gradient tensor is cylindrically symmetric about a molecular bond, in which case the tensor is determined by the single derivative $V_{\xi\xi}$ along the bond direction ξ.

The result of averaging the spin–spin term (1e) over an asymmetric rotor wavefunction is given by Posener.[21] It is also presented by Ramsey[3] for diatomic molecules, and by Gunther-Mohr *et al.*[18] for ammonia.

This interaction may be put in a form in the molecule-fixed frame of reference which allows the well-known results given above for the quadrupole interaction to be applied, and at the same time suggests a consistent notation. If we define the two symmetric dyadics

$$\mathbf{S}=\tfrac{1}{2}(\boldsymbol{\mu}_K\boldsymbol{\mu}_L+\boldsymbol{\mu}_L\boldsymbol{\mu}_K), \quad (5)$$

$$\mathbf{R}=r_{KL}^{-5}(-3\mathbf{r}_{LK}\mathbf{r}_{LK}+r_{LK}^2\mathbf{1}), \quad (6)$$

then the spin–spin interaction for the two nuclei labeled K and L can be written as a contraction of these dyadics, in analogy to the quadrupole interaction

$$\mathcal{H}_{\text{spin-spin}}=\mathbf{S}:\mathbf{R}. \quad (7)$$

[22] N. F. Ramsey, Phys. Rev. **90**, 232 (1953). The sign for the term Z_KM_P/g_KM_K given in Refs. 18 and 21 is in error.

[23] Second-order hyperfine effects, produced by the hyperfine matrix elements connecting different rotational states, may be expected to modify the hyperfine levels by an energy of the order of the (hyperfine energy)^2/rotational energy, or of the order of 1 cps for the molecules considered here.

[24] J. K. Bragg, Phys. Rev. **74**, 533 (1948).

[25] See Ref. 5, Chap. 6.

[26] J. K. Bragg and S. Golden, Phys. Rev. **75**, 735 (1949).

[27] See Ref. 5, p. 527.

R, like **V**, may be averaged over an asymmetric rotor wavefunction to give

$$\langle \mathbf{R} \rangle = \frac{d_J}{J(2J-1)} \{\tfrac{3}{2}[\mathbf{JJ}+(\mathbf{JJ})^{\mathrm{tr}}] - J(J+1)\mathbf{1}\}. \quad (8)$$

d_J is calculated from the dyadic **R** when written in the principal axis frame, in the same way that q_J is calculated from **V**.

$$d_J = 2\sum_g \langle J_g^2 \rangle R_{gg}/(J+1)(2J+3). \quad (9)$$

If Eq. (8) is now substituted into Eq. (7), the tensor contraction can be written in terms of scalar-product operators, and the spin–spin interaction becomes

$$\mathcal{H}_{\text{spin-spin}} = [g_L g_K \mu_N^2 d_J / J(2J-1)] \times \{\tfrac{3}{2}[(\mathbf{I}_L\cdot\mathbf{J})(\mathbf{I}_K\cdot\mathbf{J}) + (\mathbf{I}_K\cdot\mathbf{J})(\mathbf{I}_L\cdot\mathbf{J})] - (\mathbf{I}_L\cdot\mathbf{I}_K)\mathbf{J}^2\}. \quad (10)$$

The rotation of the nuclear frame produces a small magnetic field which contributes to hfs in first order. If we make the substitution $\mathbf{v}_K = \boldsymbol{\omega}\times\mathbf{r}_K$, and $\omega_g = 2A_g J_g/\hbar$, then the term (1d) for the Kth nucleus can be written in the reference frame fixed in the molecule as

$$\mathcal{H}_{\text{nuclear } \mathbf{I}\cdot\mathbf{J}} = \mathbf{I}_K\cdot\mathbf{N}\cdot\mathbf{J}, \quad (11)$$

where **N** is a tensor whose components in the principal axis system of the molecule are

$$N_{g'g} = -(2eg_K\mu_N A_g/\hbar c)\sum_{L\neq K} Z_L r_{LK}^{-3} \times [\mathbf{r}_{LK}\cdot(\mathbf{r}_L - \gamma_K\mathbf{r}_K)\delta_{gg'} - (\mathbf{r}_{LK})_g(\mathbf{r}_L-\gamma_K\mathbf{r}_K)_{g'}]. \quad (12)$$

We may again use the results quoted for the quadrupole interaction to average **N** over an asymmetric rotor wavefunction. We find that

$$\langle \mathbf{N} \rangle = 2\sum_g \langle J_g^2\rangle N_{gg}/J(2J-1)(J+1)(2J+3) \times \{\tfrac{3}{2}[\mathbf{JJ}+(\mathbf{JJ})^{\mathrm{tr}}] - J(J+1)\mathbf{1}\}, \quad (13)$$

and Eq. (11) becomes, using the commutation rules for the components of angular momentum

$$\mathcal{H}_{\text{nuc. } \mathbf{I}\cdot\mathbf{J}} = [\sum_g \langle J_g^2\rangle N_{gg}/J(J+1)]\mathbf{I}_K\cdot\mathbf{J}. \quad (14)$$

From Eq. (12) it can be seen that the diagonal elements N_{gg}, and therefore the **I·J** constant due to nuclear rotation, are always negative.

For $^1\Sigma$ molecules, Term (1c) in the Hamiltonian, the interaction of the nuclei with the orbital motion of the electrons, makes no contribution to the hfs in first order. The cross terms in (1a), however, proportional to $J_g L_g$, connect excited electronic states to the $^1\Sigma$ ground state, and (1c) makes a second-order contribution to the hfs.[28]

The perturbation calculation is carried out in detail by White[4] and by Townes and Schawlow.[5] Written in the molecular frame, the interaction has the same form as Eq. (11). For the Kth nucleus

$$\mathcal{H}_{\text{electronic } \mathbf{I}\cdot\mathbf{J}} = \mathbf{I}_K\cdot\mathbf{E}\cdot\mathbf{J}. \quad (15)$$

E is a tensor fixed in the molecular frame with components

$$E_{g'g} = 2(e/c)g_K\mu_N A_g \times \sum_{i,n} \frac{\langle 0|L_g|n\rangle\langle n|\rho_{g'}|0\rangle + \langle 0|\rho_{g'}|n\rangle\langle n|L_g|0\rangle}{W_n - W_0}. \quad (16)$$

The summation over n is over all excited electronic states, and $\boldsymbol{\rho}$ stands for $r_{iK}^{-3}\mathbf{r}_{iK}\times(\mathbf{v}_i-\gamma_K\mathbf{v}_K)$.

The averaging proceeds as in the previous case. If we include the contribution due to rotation of the nuclear frame from Eq. (14), we find for the total **I·J** interaction for the Kth nucleus

$$\mathcal{H}_{\mathbf{I}\cdot\mathbf{J}} = [\sum_g \langle J_g^2\rangle (N_{gg}+E_{gg})/J(J+1)]\mathbf{I}_K\cdot\mathbf{J}. \quad (17)$$

Several points should be noted. While the components of **N** can be accurately calculated on the basis of Eq. (12) and the molecular geometry, the tensor **E** can only be roughly estimated due to our ignorance of excited state electronic wavefunctions. Electrons which are spherically symmetric about a given nucleus, however, do not contribute to the **I·J** constant for that nucleus, since for these electrons $\langle 0|L_g|n\rangle$ is zero. It can be shown also[5] that those electrons which are spherically distributed about other nuclei contribute in the same way as the nuclear charges, but with opposite sign, to **N**. For molecules with many-electron atoms, the observed **I·J** constant is therefore the difference between two larger numbers. To determine the sum of Eq. (16) *over the excited states of the valence electrons* from the experimental constants, the components of **N** should be calculated with an effective nuclear charge equal to Z minus the number of closed-shell electrons.

The second-order perturbation treatment[5] of (1c) reveals a second hyperfine term having the same dependence on **I** and **J** as the quadrupole interaction, and usually referred to as the pseudoquadrupole effect. This interaction is typically of the order of a few cycles per second and is not further considered here. Higher-order terms in the perturbation expansion producing a pseudomagnetic dipole interaction between nuclei and decoupling of the electronic spins were considered by

[28] This must not be confused with the "second-order" hyperfine interactions between different rotational states mentioned above. For the **I·J** interactions arising from the term (1c) in the Hamiltonian, such effects can appear only to third order in the perturbation expansion.

Gunther-Mohr *et al.*[18] for ammonia, and found to be equally small.

We are now in a position to write down the hyperfine Hamiltonian for all the molecules studied. Hfs for HDO, HDS, and CHDO is due to a proton and a deuteron, and therefore the Hamiltonian is

$$\mathcal{H}=\frac{(eq_JQ)_D}{2I_D(2I_D-1)J(2J-1)}\times[3(\mathbf{I}_D\cdot\mathbf{J})^2+\tfrac{3}{2}(\mathbf{I}_D\cdot\mathbf{J})-\mathbf{I}_D{}^2\mathbf{J}^2]+C_H(\mathbf{I}_H\cdot\mathbf{J})+\frac{g_Dg_H\mu_N{}^2d_J}{J(2J-1)}\{\tfrac{3}{2}[(\mathbf{I}_D\cdot\mathbf{J})(\mathbf{I}_H\cdot\mathbf{J})+(\mathbf{I}_H\cdot\mathbf{J})(\mathbf{I}_D\cdot\mathbf{J})]-(\mathbf{I}_H\cdot\mathbf{I}_D)\mathbf{J}^2\}+C_D(\mathbf{I}_D\cdot\mathbf{J}). \quad (18)$$

For CH_2O, hfs is due only to the two protons. In the coupling scheme

$$\mathbf{I}_1+\mathbf{I}_2=\mathbf{I},$$

$$\mathbf{I}+\mathbf{J}=\mathbf{F},$$ the Hamiltonian is:

$$\mathcal{H}=C_H\mathbf{I}\cdot\mathbf{J}+\frac{g_H{}^2\mu_N{}^2d_J}{J(2J-1)}\times\{\tfrac{3}{2}[(\mathbf{I}_1\cdot\mathbf{J})(\mathbf{I}_2\cdot\mathbf{J})+(\mathbf{I}_2\cdot\mathbf{J})(\mathbf{I}_1\cdot\mathbf{J})]-(\mathbf{I}_1\cdot\mathbf{I}_2)\mathbf{J}^2\}. \quad (19)$$

B. Matrix Elements

In Eqs. (2), (10), and (17) the hyperfine interactions are given as products of the diagonal operators $\mathbf{J}^2$ and $\mathbf{I}_K{}^2$, and the scalar products $\mathbf{I}_L\cdot\mathbf{J}$ and $\mathbf{I}_L\cdot\mathbf{I}_K$. To calculate the hfs due to an arbitrary number of nuclei, it is most convenient to select a representation in which off-diagonal matrix elements of the Hamiltonian are as small as possible. For N distinguishable nuclei, numbered in order of decreasing coupling to $\mathbf{J}$, the appropriate representation is

$$|I_1\cdots I_N, J, F_1\cdots F_{N-1}, F\rangle, \quad (20)$$

defined by the coupling scheme

$$\mathbf{J}+\mathbf{I}_1=\mathbf{F}_1,\quad \mathbf{F}_1+\mathbf{I}_2=\mathbf{F}_2,\quad \vdots \quad \mathbf{F}_{N-1}+\mathbf{I}_N=\mathbf{F}. \quad (21)$$

The matrix elements of $\mathbf{I}_L\cdot\mathbf{J}$ and $\mathbf{I}_L\cdot\mathbf{I}_K$ diagonal in the total angular momentum F, and all the intermediate angular momenta F_i, can be calculated from the vector model. The quickest and most elegant way of calculating the off-diagonal elements is to use the Wigner $6j$ coefficients[29,30] which are now tabulated[31] for all integral and half-integral values of the coupling spins up to 8. In the above representation we find that

$$\langle F_1'\cdots F_{L-1}'|\mathbf{I}_L\cdot\mathbf{J}|F_1\cdots F_{L-1}\rangle =(-1)^r\{J(J+1)(2J+1)[(2F_1'+1)(2F_1+1)]\cdots[(2F_{L-1}'+1)(2F_{L-1}+1)]I_L(I_L+1)(2I_L+1)\}^{\frac{1}{2}}\times\begin{Bmatrix}F_0' & F_1' & I_1\\ F_1 & F_0 & 1\end{Bmatrix}\cdots\begin{Bmatrix}F_{L-2}' & F_{L-1}' & I_{L-1}\\ F_{L-1} & F_{L-2} & 1\end{Bmatrix}\begin{Bmatrix}F_L & I_L & F_{L-1}'\\ 1 & F_{L-1} & I_L\end{Bmatrix}, \quad (22)$$

where

$$r=(L-1)+\sum_{i=1}^{L-1}(F_{i-1}'+I_i+F_i)+(F_{L-1}+I_L+F_L),$$

and, for $K<L$,

$$\langle F_K'\cdots F_{L-1}'|\mathbf{I}_L\cdot\mathbf{I}_K|F_K\cdots F_{L-1}\rangle =(-1)^s\{I_K(I_K+1)(2I_K+1)[(2F'_K+1)(2F_K+1)]\cdots[(2F'_{L-1}+1)(2F_{L-1}+1)]I_L(I_L+1)(2I_L+1)\}^{\frac{1}{2}}\times\begin{Bmatrix}I_K & F_K' & F_{K-1}\\ F_K & I_K & 1\end{Bmatrix}\begin{Bmatrix}F_K' & F_{K+1}' & I_{K+1}\\ F_{K+1} & F_K & 1\end{Bmatrix}\cdots\begin{Bmatrix}F_{L-2}' & F_{L-1}' & I_{L-1}\\ F_{L-1} & F_{L-2} & 1\end{Bmatrix}\begin{Bmatrix}F_L & I_L & F_{L-1}'\\ 1 & F_{L-1} & I_L\end{Bmatrix}, \quad (23)$$

where

$$s=(L-K)+(F_{K-1}+I_K+F_K')+\sum_{i=K+1}^{L-1}(F_{i-1}'+I_i+F_i)+(F_{L-1}+I_L+F_L).$$

The { } are the $6j$ coefficients, tabulated in Ref. 31. Where it simplifies the notation we have let $J=F_0=F_0'$ and $F=F_N$. $\mathbf{I}_L\cdot\mathbf{J}$ and $\mathbf{I}_L\cdot\mathbf{I}_K$ are diagonal in the F_i not lying in the explicit ranges $F_1\cdots F_{L-1}$ and $F_K\cdots F_{L-1}$, respectively. The product of $6j$ symbols immediately on either side of the suspension points in Eq. (22)

[29] A. R. Edmonds, *Angular Momentum in Quantum Mechanics* (Princeton University Press, Princeton, New Jersey, 1960), 2nd ed.
[30] B. R. Judd, *Operator Techniques in Atomic Spectroscopy* (McGraw-Hill Book Company, Inc., New York, 1963).
[31] M. Rotenberg, R. Bivens, N. Metropolis, J. K. Wooten, *The 3j and 6j Symbols* (The Technology Press, Massachusetts Institute of Technology, Cambridge, Massachusetts, 1959).

reduces to one symbol when $L=2$, and vanishes when $L=1$, leaving for the entire chain only the symbol on the far right. Likewise in Eq. (23), when $L=K+1$ the intermediate product vanishes, leaving for the entire chain the product of the symbol on the far left and that on the far right.

For the case of the spin–spin interaction, which couples three spins, it is most convenient in practice first to calculate the scalar product operators and then perform the matrix products of Eq. (10). The quadrupole interaction couples only two spins, however, and while the matrix elements may be calculated in this way, using Eq. (2), it is even simplier to revert to the tensor form of the operator

$$\mathcal{H}_{\text{quadrupole}}=\tfrac{1}{6}\mathbf{V}:\mathbf{Q},$$

which can easily be shown to become for the Lth nucleus in the above representation[32]

$$\langle F_1'\cdots F_{L-1}'\,|\,\mathcal{H}_{\text{quadrupole}}\,|\,F_1\cdots F_{L-1}\rangle=(-1)^t\,(eq_JQ)_L$$
$$\times\left[\frac{(2J+1)(2J+2)(2J+3)}{8J(2J-1)}[(2F_1'+1)(2F_1+1)]\cdots[(2F_{L-1}'+1)(2F_{L-1}+1)]\frac{(2I_L+1)(2I_L+2)(2I_L+3)}{8I_L(2I_{L-1})}\right]^{\frac{1}{2}}$$
$$\times\begin{Bmatrix}F_0' & F_1' & I_1\\ F_1 & F_0 & 2\end{Bmatrix}\cdots\begin{Bmatrix}F_{L-2}' & F_{L-1}' & I_{L-1}\\ F_{L-1} & F_{L-2} & 2\end{Bmatrix}\begin{Bmatrix}F_L & I_L & F_{L-1}'\\ 2 & F_{L-1} & I_L\end{Bmatrix},\qquad(24)$$

where

$$t=\sum_{i=1}^{L-1}(F_{i-1}'+I_i+F_i)+(F_{L-1}+I_L+F_L).$$

In an asymmetric rotor there may exist one or more pairs of equivalent nuclei—identical isotopes with the same molecular environment and hyperfine coupling constants. The protons in H_2O, CH_2O, and NH_2D are an example of such a pair, which always defines a twofold axis of symmetry for the molecule. If there are more than two equivalent nuclei the molecule will have a higher-fold symmetry axis, and will be a symmetric or spherical rotor (for example, NH_3 or CH_4).

The Hamiltonian for equivalent nuclei is most conveniently written in a representation where the total angular momentum of the pair

$$\mathbf{I}_S^{(1)}+\mathbf{I}_S^{(2)}=\mathbf{I}_S\qquad(25)$$

is well defined. The various $\mathbf{I}_S$ for equivalent pairs may then be coupled together, and to the $\mathbf{I}_L$ of the other nuclei in the molecule, by the coupling scheme (21).

The requirement that the total wavefunction be either symmetric or antisymmetric on exchange of equivalent nuclei, however, restricts the values of I_S which can occur in a given rotational state. The symmetry of the rotational wavefunction $\psi_{JK_{-1},K}$ on exchange is a simple function of K_{-1} and K if inversion of the molecule is not considered.[33] For example, in the case of planar CH_2O where the symmetry axis is the least principal axis of inertia, the rotational state is symmetric under exchange of the protons when K_{-1} is even, and antisymmetric when K_{-1} is odd. The symmetry of the spin state depends only on whether I_S is odd or even. Since the state for which I_S has its greatest value, $2I_S^{(1)}$, is always symmetric, in the case of integral-spin nuclei even I_S states will be symmetric and odd I_S states antisymmetric. The converse will be true for half-integral-spin equivalent nuclei. In either case, only every other value of I_S is allowed.

It often happens that when a given hyperfine interaction is summed over an equivalent pair, terms off-diagonal in I_S vanish, and the result is formally equivalent to the coupling of the single angular momentum $\mathbf{I}_S$ to the rest of the molecule. In particular, it is clear that

$$\mathcal{H}_{\mathbf{I}\cdot\mathbf{J}}=C_S\mathbf{I}_S^{(1)}\cdot\mathbf{J}+C_S\mathbf{I}_S^{(2)}\cdot\mathbf{J}=C_S\mathbf{I}_S\cdot\mathbf{J},\qquad(26)$$

and it is also easily shown that the spin–spin interactions of $\mathbf{I}_S^{(1)}$ and $\mathbf{I}_S^{(2)}$ with the Lth nucleus sum to

$$\mathcal{H}_{ss}=\frac{g_Sg_L\mu_N^2(d_J)_{SL}}{J(2J-1)}\times\{\tfrac{3}{2}[(\mathbf{I}_S\cdot\mathbf{J})(\mathbf{I}_L\cdot\mathbf{J})+(\mathbf{I}_L\cdot\mathbf{J})(\mathbf{I}_S\cdot\mathbf{J})]-(\mathbf{I}_S\cdot\mathbf{I}_L)\mathbf{J}^2\}.\qquad(27)$$

The quadrupole interactions of an equivalent pair, and their mutual spin–spin interaction, however, connect states which differ in $\mathbf{I}_S$ by 2. In a representation where $\mathbf{I}_S$ is well defined, the elements off-diagonal in $\mathbf{I}_S$ cannot therefore be simply written down in terms of the matrix elements given above, although the correct expressions may be derived without difficulty as chains of $6j$ symbols in terms of the general matrix elements of tensor operators.[29] The elements diagonal in $\mathbf{I}_S$, however, may be written in terms of the above expressions.[34] Moreover, in the common case of two equivalent spin $\frac{1}{2}$ nuclei such as the protons in CH_2O or NH_2D, no terms off-diagonal in $\mathbf{I}_S$ can exist, and all hyperfine interactions vanish when $\mathbf{I}_S=0$. When $\mathbf{I}_S=1$ the mutual spin–spin interaction gives the quadrupole-

[32] See Ref. 29, pp. 111, 115.
[33] See Ref. 5, Chap. 4.
[34] See Ref. 3, Chap. 3.

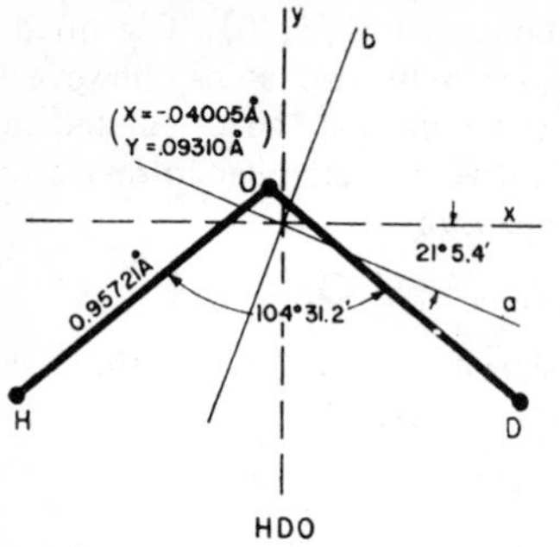

FIG. 2. Geometry of the HDO molecule.

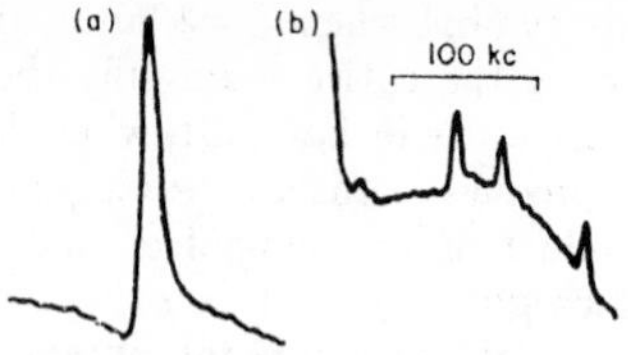

FIG. 3. Observed hfs of the $2_{20}\rightarrow 2_{21}$ transition of HDO. (a) is the strong central line, the sum of the six unresolved $\Delta F=\Delta F_1=0$ transitions; (b) shows the high-frequency hyperfine satellites seen against the background of the cavity response. The weak "forbidden" $3\frac{5}{2}\rightarrow 1\frac{3}{2}$ transition can be seen to the extreme left, at the foot of the central line. The low-frequency satellites were observed to be slightly weaker than the high-frequency ones (see text).

like term

$$\mathcal{H}_{\text{mutual }ss}=\frac{g_S{}^2\mu_N{}^2(d_J)_{SS}}{2I_S(2I_S-1)J(2J-1)}\times[3(\mathbf{I}_S\cdot\mathbf{J})^2+\tfrac{3}{2}(\mathbf{I}_S\cdot\mathbf{J})-\mathbf{I}_S{}^2\mathbf{J}^2], \quad (28)$$

We have obtained the important result that the hyperfine Hamiltonian, even when equivalent nuclei are present, can often be written in terms of simple products of the operators whose matrix elements are given explicitly by Eqs. (22) and (23).

c. Hyperfine Intensities

Due to the complicated dependence of the state selection process on both the parameters of the molecule and apparatus, there is no simple correspondence between the intensities of transitions observed in absorption and those observed in emission with a beam maser. Details of the calculation of absolute intensities are discussed in Ref. 12.

Although the state selection of various hyperfine levels is often quite preferential, it is found in practice that, for hfs of a few hundred kilocycles per second or less, the passage of a molecule out of the high electric field region of the state selector is highly nonadiabatic, and relative intensities of hyperfine transitions subsequently observed as the molecules pass through the resonant cavity of the maser may be calculated, as in absorption spectroscopy, on the assumption that all hyperfine states are essentially equally populated. HDO has the largest coupling constants of the molecules which we have studied, and the low-frequency hyperfine satellites are observed to be slightly weaker than the high-frequency ones, due to preferential state selection of the higher hyperfine levels of the 2_{20} state. A similar but more pronounced effect has been observed for the quadrupole satellites of the NH_3 inversion line.[11]

In fitting the theoretical to the observed spectrum we have therefore, as is usually done, taken the hyperfine intensities proportional to the square of the electric dipole moment matrix elements, summed over the degenerate magnetic states of the transition.[35] That is, in the representation (20),

$$S_{\alpha'F,\alpha'F}=\sum_{m_F',m_F}|\langle\alpha',F',m_F'|\mu_E|\alpha,F,m_F\rangle|^2, \quad (29)$$

where μ_E is the component of the dipole moment along the electric field, and α stands for all the intermediate F_i. It is one of the well-known results of atomic spectroscopy that the summation over m_F and m_F' gives[36]

$$S_{\alpha'F',\alpha F}=|C_{\alpha'F',\alpha F}|^2, \quad (30)$$

where, in arbitrary units,

$$C_{\alpha F,\alpha'F'}=(-1)^u\{[(2F_1'+1)(2F_1+1)]\cdots[(2F_N'+1)(2F_N+1)]\}^{\frac{1}{2}}\times\begin{Bmatrix}F_0' & F_1' & I_1\\ F_1 & F_0 & 1\end{Bmatrix}\cdots\begin{Bmatrix}F_{N-1}' & F_N' & I_N\\ F_N & F_{N-1} & 1\end{Bmatrix}, \quad (31)$$

$$u=\sum_{i=1}^{N}(I_i+F_{i-1}'+F_i)+N,$$

and, as before, we let $J=F_0=F_0'$ and $F=F_N$ for notational compactness.

In the event that various F_i are not good quantum numbers, we must transform C into the representation where the Hamiltonian is diagonal. In matrix notation

$$\mathsf{C}'=\mathsf{A}_i\mathsf{C}\mathsf{A}_f{}^{-1},$$

where A_i and A_f are the unitary matrices which diagonalize the hyperfine Hamiltonians of the initial and final rotational states, respectively, of the transition.

[35] E. U. Condon and G. H. Shortley, *The Theory of Atomic Spectra* (Cambridge University Press, Cambridge, England, 1959) p. 98.
[36] See Ref. 29, p. 76.

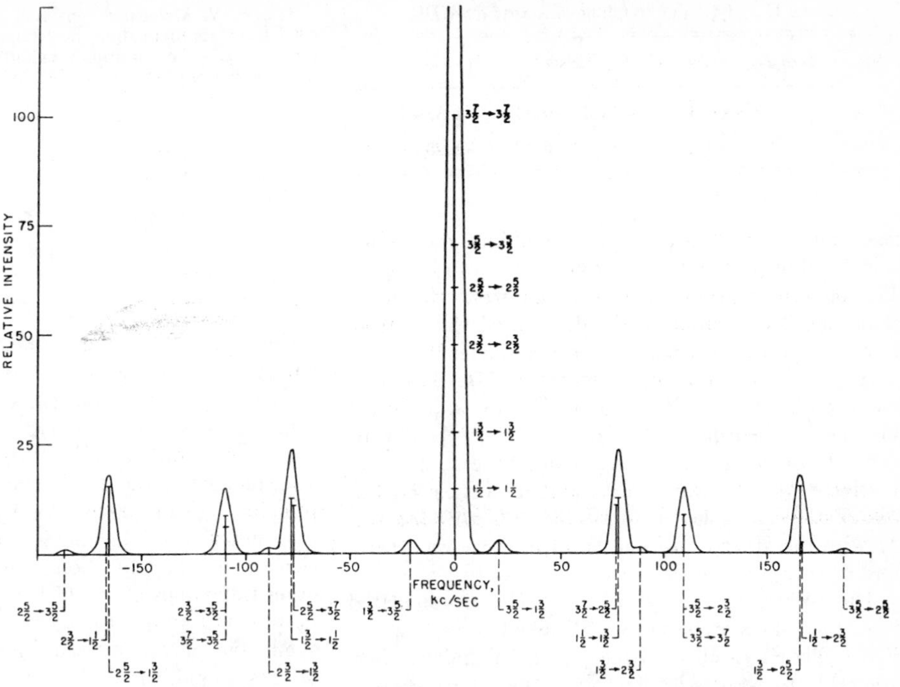

FIG. 4. Calculated hfs of the HDO $2_{20}\to2_{21}$ transition.

In theory the line shape of transitions observed with a beam maser is also a complicated function of the parameters of the apparatus, since it depends on the velocity distribution of the molecules emerging from the state selector, and may be modified by collision of the more divergent molecules with the cavity walls. In practice, however, we have found the true lineshape to be well approximated by a Gaussian, and we have used this lineshape, adjusting the full half-width of about 5 kc/sec slightly from molecule to molecule, to calculate the theoretical spectra presented in this work.

III. EXPERIMENTAL RESULTS

a. HDO[37]

The water molecule has been extensively studied in the infrared, and its geometry is well known. The

TABLE I. Molecular constants of HDO, calculated in the rigid rotor approximation, neglecting electrons, from the geometry of Fig. 2. The rotation constants and asymmetry parameter are: $A=694.45$ kMc/sec, $B=273.80$ kMc/sec, $C=196.37$ kMc/sec, and $\kappa=-0.6891$.

State	$\langle J_a^2\rangle$	$\langle J_b^2\rangle$	$\langle J_c^2\rangle$	$g_Hg_D\mu_N^2d_J$ (kc/sec)
2_{20}	3.9794	1.2607	0.7603	−2.470
2_{21}	4.0000	1.0000	1.0000	−2.446

[37] Preliminary results have appeared in Nuovo Cimento **13**, 1060 (1959).

TABLE II. Hyperfine intervals of the HDO $2_{20}\to2_{21}$ transition, measured relative to the strong central line which is the sum of the $\Delta F=\Delta F_1=0$ transitions. The uncertainties quoted are probable errors.

Transition $F_1F\to F_1'F'$	Frequency (kc/sec)
$1\frac{1}{2}\to2\frac{3}{2}$	
$+1\frac{3}{2}\to2\frac{5}{2}$	167.07±0.40
$3\frac{5}{2}\to2\frac{3}{2}$	
$+3\frac{5}{2}\to3\frac{7}{2}$	109.91±0.30
$3\frac{7}{2}\to2\frac{5}{2}$	
$+1\frac{1}{2}\to1\frac{3}{2}$	77.91±0.30
$3\frac{5}{2}\to1\frac{3}{2}$	18.80±0.30
$F_1F\to F_1F$	0.00±0.20
$1\frac{3}{2}\to3\frac{5}{2}$	−20.01±0.30
$2\frac{5}{2}\to3\frac{7}{2}$	
$+1\frac{3}{2}\to1\frac{1}{2}$	−77.41±0.30
$2\frac{3}{2}\to3\frac{5}{2}$	
$+3\frac{7}{2}\to3\frac{5}{2}$	−109.04±0.30
$2\frac{3}{2}\to1\frac{1}{2}$]	
$+2\frac{5}{2}\to1\frac{3}{2}$	−165.86±0.30

TABLE III. Hyperfine coupling constants for HDO.

State	$(eq_JQ)_D$(kc/sec)	C_H(kc/sec)	C_D(kc/sec)
2_{20}	79.3±0.3	−43.47±0.11	−2.33±0.02
2_{21}	79.6±0.3	−43.63±0.13	−2.20±0.02

least and intermediate principal axes of inertia of HDO, calculated neglecting the electrons, are shown in Fig. 2. The molecular geometry was taken from the high-resolution investigation of the deuterated waters from 1.25 to 4.1 μ by Benedict, Gailar, and Plyler.[38]

Hfs in the microwave spectrum of HDO has been observed by Posener,[39,40] and by Treacy and Beers.[6] Posener studied in particular the (2_{20}, 2_{21}) K-type doublet which we selected as being the easiest to investigate with a beam maser, and found the central line of the hfs to lie at 10 278.2455±0.0010 Mc/sec. As with the other transitions studied, there was therefore no search problem.

The rotational energy levels of HDO, calculated from the rotation constants of Table I, are shown in Fig. 1. The Stark effect of the (2_{20}, 2_{21}) doublet is very favorable to state selection, since the adjacent rotational states lie several hundred kilomegacycles away.

Other closely spaced pairs of levels exist in HDO, moreover, which are suitable for beam-maser study. The lowest lying K-type doublet (1_{10}, 1_{11}) is split by about 80 kMc, while the (3_{30}, 3_{31}) doublet studied by Treacy and Beers, which lies above the (2_{20}, 2_{21}) doublet and is not shown in Fig. 1, is split by 825 Mc/sec. If a TM_{010} cavity of the type used in the present experiments were used for the $3_{30}\rightarrow 3_{31}$ transition, it would be large (about 28 cm in diameter), but by that

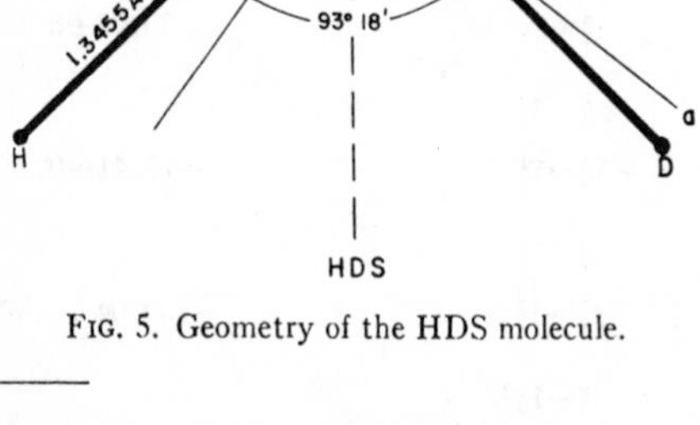

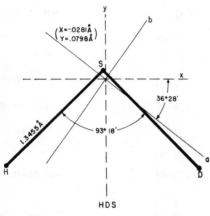

FIG. 5. Geometry of the HDS molecule.

[38] W. S. Benedict, N. Gailar, and E. K. Plyler, J. Chem. Phys. **24**, 1139 (1956).
[39] D. W. Posener, Australian J. Phys. **10**, 276 (1957).
[40] D. W. Posener, Australian J. Phys. **13**, 168 (1960).

TABLE IV. Molecular constants of HDS, calculated in the rigid rotor approximation, neglecting electrons, from the geometry of Fig. 5. The rotation constants and asymmetry parameter are: $A=290.24$ kMc/sec, $B=145.25$ kMc/sec, $C=96.81$ kMc/sec, and $\kappa=-0.4991$.

State	$\langle J_a^2\rangle$	$\langle J_b^2\rangle$	$\langle J_c^2\rangle$	$g_Hg_D\mu_N^2d_J$ (kc/sec)
2_{20}	3.941	1.446	0.613	−0.745
2_{21}	4.000	1.000	1.000	−0.661

token could be made long enough to allow exceptionally narrow lines 1 kc/sec or less in width.

The other water molecules H_2O and D_2O have a comparable series of K-type doublets. The doublet transitions, however, are of the ^aQ branch, and require a component of the dipole moment along the a (least) principal axis of inertia. For H_2O and D_2O this axis is perpendicular to the dipole moment, and the matrix element for the transition vanishes. Unfortunately, no other transitions exist which are nearly as favorable for beam-maser study. In the case of HDO, however, the symmetry of the molecule about the dipole axis is destroyed, and the a and b inertial axes are rotated by 21° (Fig. 2). In absorption spectroscopy, the $2_{20}\rightarrow 2_{21}$ transition is a rather strong microwave line with an absorption coefficient of 3×10^{-5} cm^{-1}.

The HDO sample was prepared by mixing equal parts of ordinary and heavy water, the exchange of hydrogen proceeding very rapidly to yield 50% HDO. Since only about 1 mm Hg of vapor pressure is needed behind the effuser, it is possible to cool the vapor in a salt–ice bath. In practice, however, this was found to give only a small improvement in intensity.

The observed hfs of the $2_{20}\rightarrow 2_{21}$ transition is shown in Fig. 3. The hyperfine intervals were measured as described in Ref. 12, and are listed in Table II.

Since the hfs is observed to be very symmetrical, and the most intense $\Delta F=\Delta F_1=0$ transitions overlap, it is evident that the hyperfine coupling constants are very nearly the same in the 2_{20} and the 2_{21} states. This equality of the coupling constants is expected when the K-type doublet is close to a symmetric-top level for which $K>1$.[18] On the assumption of the equality of the constants in the two rotational states, and with the

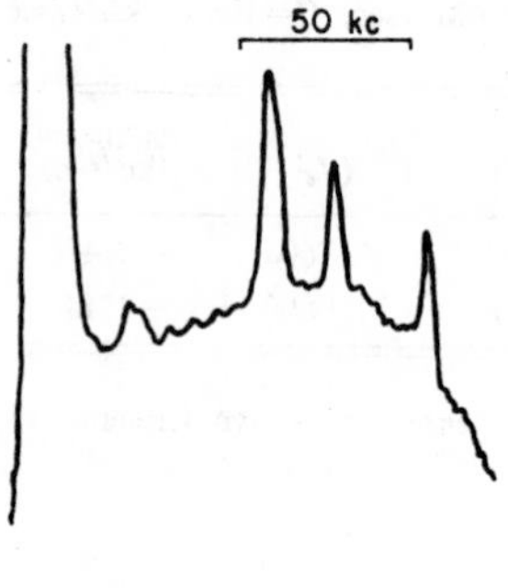

FIG. 6. The observed high-frequency hyperfine components and the central line of the $2_{20}\rightarrow 2_{21}$ transition of HDS.

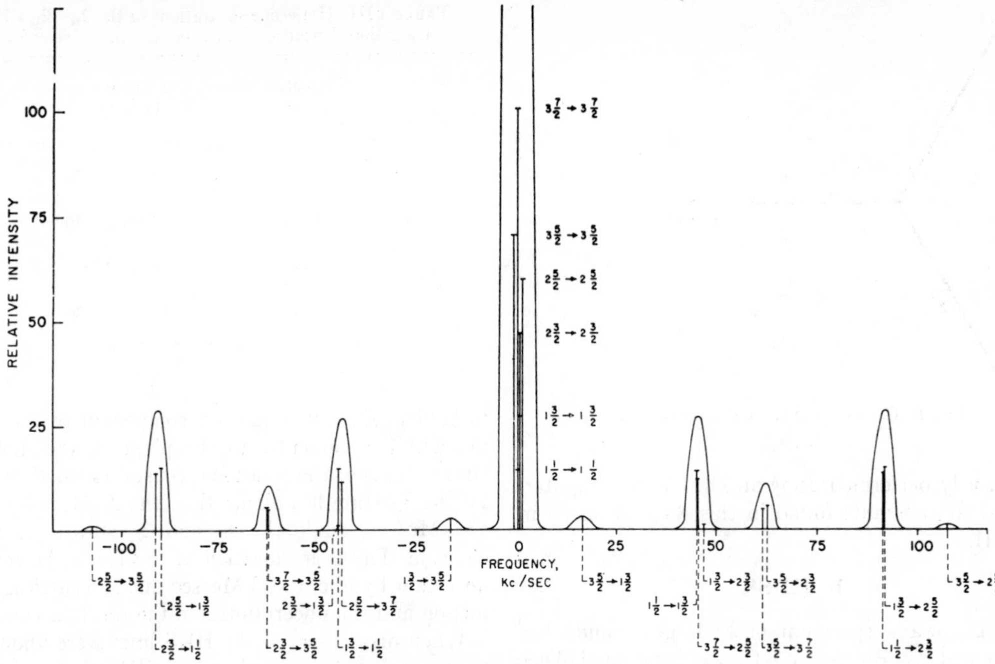

FIG. 7. Calculated hfs of the HDS $2_{20}\to2_{21}$ transition.

TABLE V. Hyperfine intervals of the HDS $2_{20}\to2_{21}$ transition, measured relative to the strong central line which is the sum of the $\Delta F=\Delta F_1=0$ transitions. The uncertainties quoted are probable errors.

Transition $F_1F\to F_1'F'$	Frequency (kc/sec)
$1\frac{1}{2}\to2\frac{3}{2}$ $+1\frac{3}{2}\to2\frac{5}{2}$	91.9 ± 0.4
$3\frac{5}{2}\to2\frac{3}{2}$ $+3\frac{5}{2}\to3\frac{7}{2}$	62.3 ± 0.4
$3\frac{7}{2}\to2\frac{5}{2}$ $+1\frac{1}{2}\to1\frac{3}{2}$	45.8 ± 0.4
$3\frac{5}{2}\to1\frac{3}{2}$	15.6 ± 0.4
$F_1F\to F_1F$	0.0 ± 0.4
$1\frac{3}{2}\to3\frac{5}{2}$	-17.4 ± 0.4
$2\frac{5}{2}\to3\frac{7}{2}$ $+1\frac{3}{2}\to1\frac{1}{2}$	-45.6 ± 0.5
$2\frac{3}{2}\to3\frac{5}{2}$ $+3\frac{7}{2}\to3\frac{5}{2}$	-62.4 ± 0.5
$2\frac{3}{2}\to1\frac{1}{2}$ $+2\frac{5}{2}\to1\frac{3}{2}$	-89.5 ± 0.5

spin–spin constant d_J of Eq. (9) calculated in advance from the known molecular geometry (Table I), a close fit of the calculated to observed spectrum was obtained on the basis of the Hamiltonian of Eq. (18). The theoretical spectrum, calculated using a Gaussian linewidth with full half-width of 5 kc/sec, is shown in Fig. 4.

In the $|F_1, F\rangle$ representation, the terms off-diagonal in F_1, due mainly to the $\mathbf{I}\cdot\mathbf{J}$ interaction of the proton, are appreciable with respect to the diagonal energies due to the deuteron quadrupole coupling. The magnetic interaction therefore plays an important role in even a qualitative understanding of the spectrum, and the intensities calculated in the $|F_1, F\rangle$ representation are only approximately correct. The transitions 1, $3/2\leftrightarrow$ 3, 5/2 in particular are forbidden in the $|F_1, F\rangle$ representation, but are reasonably strong for HDO. One may be seen quite clearly as a close satellite of the central line in Fig. 3.

As long as the constants to be varied, $(eq_JQ)_D$, C_H, and C_D were kept the same in either rotational state, it proved feasible to perform the fitting calculations on a desk calculator. A somewhat closer least-squares fitting, varying all six constants independently, was

TABLE VI. Hyperfine coupling constants for HDS.

State	$(eq_JQ)_D$(kc/sec)	C_H(kc/sec)	C_D(kc/sec)
2_{20}	42.9 ± 0.4	-25.03 ± 0.13	-0.47 ± 0.02
2_{21}	43.3 ± 0.4	-25.45 ± 0.13	-0.22 ± 0.02

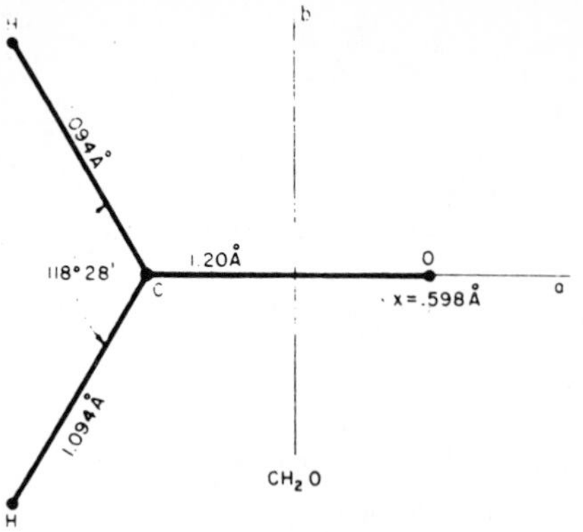

FIG. 8. Geometry of the CH_2O molecule.

subsequently performed using an IBM 7090 computer. The best fit constants found in this way are listed in Table III.

b. HDS[41]

The microwave spectrum of hydrogen sulfide has been studied by Burrus and Gordy[42] and by Hillger and Strandberg.[43] No hfs has been reported prior to the present work.

Dousmanis[44] has calculated the geometry of H_2S from the measured frequencies of Hillger and Strandberg; his results are shown in Fig. 5. The rotational levels of HDS are shown in Fig. 1. The $2_{20}\rightarrow 2_{21}$ transition lies at 11 283.83 Mc/sec, about 1000 Mc/sec higher in frequency than in HDO.

It is seen that the ($2_{20}\rightarrow 2_{21}$) doublet is surrounded by the (3_{13}, 3_{03}) oblate symmetric top K-type doublet. Such nearby states can sometimes sufficiently modify the Stark effect of a given level to destroy the possibility of state selection. In the present case, however, the dipole-moment matrix elements that connect the 2_{20} and 3_{13} states and the 2_{21} and 3_{03} states are very small, and the ${}^cQ$ branch $3_{13}\rightarrow 3_{03}$ transition is strictly forbidden, since it requires a component of the dipole moment perpendicular to the plane of the molecule. On the basis of the rotational constants listed in Table IV the 3_{13} state lies higher than the 2_{20} state by about 57 kMc/sec, while the 3_{03} and 2_{21} states practically coincide. The exact location of the levels, however, is uncertain by about 20 kMc/sec due to centrifugal distortion and the uncertainties in the rotation constants.

When first observed the HDS lines were about four times weaker, compared to the HDO lines, than expected, and we attributed this to inhibition of state selection. However, a carefully prepared sample, made by reacting deuterated sulfuric acid with iron sulfide, finally gave the strong signals shown in Fig. 6, and it appears that in fact the state-selection process is quite efficient.

Hydrogen sulfide has a vapor pressure of several hundred millimeters of Hg at dry-ice temperatures, and it was found that the source could be cooled with a dry-ice–acetone mixture to produce roughly an improvement of 2 in signal strength. As with HDO, the short hydrogen exchange time permits a sample containing at best only 50% HDS.

The measured hyperfine intervals are listed in Table V. The fitting of the calculated to the observed spectrum was done in the same way as for HDO: the spin–spin constants d_J were calculated in advance, and the three constants $(eq_JQ)_D$, C_H, and C_D, considered equal in the 2_{20} and 2_{21} states, were varied to give a best fit using the Hamiltonian of Eq. (18). Subsequently, these constants were varied independently in the two rotational states with an IBM 7090 computer to give a slightly better fit. The theoretical spectrum is shown in Fig. 7. The line envelope was calculated assuming a Gaussian line shape with full half-width of 4 kc/sec. The best-fit hyperfine constants are listed in Table VI.

TABLE VII. Rotation constants and asymmetry parameters for CH_2O and CHDO, calculated in the rigid rotor approximation, neglecting electrons, from the geometry of Fig. 8 and Fig. 11. The $\langle J_g\rangle$ for the rotational levels of interest are independent of κ. $\langle J_a^2\rangle$, $\langle J_b^2\rangle$, $\langle J_c^2\rangle$ are 1, 4, 1 and 1, 1, 4 for the 2_{11} and 2_{12} states, respectively.

	A (kMc/sec)	B (kMc/sec)	C (kMc/sec)	κ
CH_2O	283.75	39.52	34.69	−0.9612
CHDO	198.69	35.59	30.18	−0.9358

TABLE VIII. Hyperfine separations of the $2_{11}\rightarrow 2_{12}$ CH_2O transition. Uncertainties quoted are probable errors.

Transition $F\rightarrow F'$	Frequency (kc/sec)
$2\rightarrow 2$	10.12 ± 0.20
$3\rightarrow 3$	0.00 ± 0.30
$1\rightarrow 2$	-8.5 ± 1.0
$1\rightarrow 1$	-20.73 ± 0.30

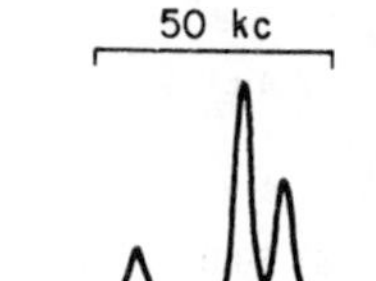

FIG. 9. Observed hfs of the $2_{11}\rightarrow 2_{12}$ transition of CH_2O. A single $\Delta F=1$ transition can be seen just to the left of the strongest line.

[41] Preliminary results have appeared in Bull. Am. Phys. Soc. **5**, 74 (1960).
[42] C. A. Burrus and W. Gordy, Phys. Rev. **92**, 274 (1953).
[43] R. E. Hillger and M. W. P. Strandberg, Phys. Rev. **83**, 575 (1951).
[44] See G. R. Bird and C. H. Townes, Phys. Rev. **94**, 1203 (1954).

TABLE IX. Hyperfine coupling constants for CH_2O and CHDO.

Molecule	$(eV_{\xi\xi}Q)_D$ (kc/sec)	$C_H(2_{11})-C_H(2_{12})$ (kc/sec)	$C_H(2_{11})$ (kc/sec)	$C_D(2_{11})-C_D(2_{12})$ (kc/sec)	$C_D(2_{11})$ (kc/sec)	$(1/r^3)^{-\frac{1}{3}}$ (Å)
CH_2O	···	2.26±0.13	0.65±0.50	···	···	1.898±0.017
CHDO	170.0±2.0	2.42±0.50	0.2±1.0	0.25±0.10	0.13±0.20	1.88±0.10

c. CH_2O[45]

Bragg and Sharbaugh,[46] Lawrance and Strandberg,[47] and Hirakawa, Miyahara, and Shimoda[48] have studied the microwave spectrum of the common species of formaldehyde. Magnetic hfs, the only kind occuring, was first observed by Okaya,[49] who resolved two of the three intense $\Delta F=0$ hyperfine components of the $4_{14}\rightarrow 4_{13}$ K-type doublet transition at 48 285 Mc/sec. More recently, Takuma, Shimizu, and Shimoda[50] have investigated the $3_{12}\rightarrow 3_{13}$ K-type doublet transition near 28 975 Mc/sec with a beam maser, and have resolved all three $\Delta F=0$ components. They were able to determine the difference $C_H(3_{12})-C_H(3_{13})$, and the proton–proton distance. They have also succeeded in using a beam maser at radio frequencies to observe rotational transitions and hfs at 4.57 and 18.275 Mc/sec.[51–53]

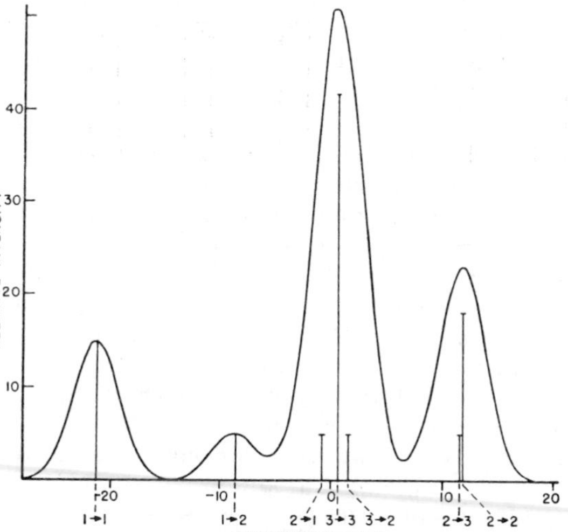

FIG. 10. Calculated hfs of the CH_2O $2_{11}\rightarrow 2_{12}$ transition.

We have studied the K-type doublet transition $2_{11}\rightarrow 2_{12}$ which lies at 14 488.65 Mc/sec. A linewidth of 5 kc/sec was obtained, and a sensitivity great enough to allow detection of one of the four possible $\Delta F=1$ transitions. This allowed a calculation of the $\mathbf{I}\cdot\mathbf{J}$ constant for either rotational state, and the proton–proton distance.

The molecular geometry is shown in Fig. 8, and the molecular constants are listed in Table VII. The bond lengths and the HCH angle were taken with slight modification from the paper of Lawrance and Strandberg.[47] CH_2O is a very nearly prolate symmetric top, with an asymmetry parameter $\kappa=-0.9612$, so that the prolate K-type doublets are in general split by a much smaller frequency than for HDO and HDS. The $(2_{11}, 2_{12})$ doublet, for example, in HDO is split by several hundred kilomegacycles.

From the rotational energy levels of CH_2O (Fig. 1), it can be seen that the $(2_{11}, 2_{12})$ doublet is well located from the point of view of state selection. Although the density of rotational states is greater than for HDO, with consequent smaller fractional population of a given state, the large component of the dipole moment along the a (least) principal axis of inertia makes formaldehyde very favorable for beam-maser study.

We first succeeded in observing the $2_{11}\rightarrow 2_{12}$ transition with a formaline solution as the source of vapor, the water which came off being removed with a dry-ice trap, since formaldehyde has a vapor pressure of more than 10 mm Hg at −80°C. It was subsequently found that heating the polymer *para*-formaldehyde to about 130°C gave a copious flow of the monomer and much

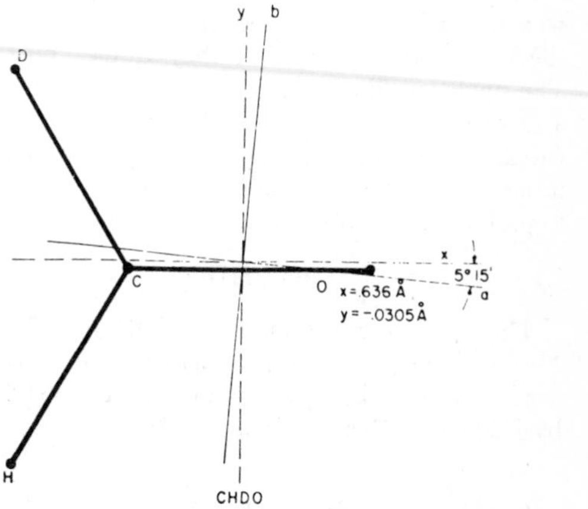

FIG. 11. Geometry of the CHDO molecule.

[45] Preliminary results have appeared in J. Chem. Phys. **31**, 1677 (1959).
[46] J. K. Bragg and A. H. Sharbaugh, Phys. Rev. **75**, 1774 (1949).
[47] R. B. Lawrance and M. W. P. Strandberg, Phys. Rev. **83**, 363 (1951).
[48] H. Hirakawa, A. Miyahara, and K. Shimoda, J. Phys. Soc. (Japan) **11**, 334 (1956).
[49] A. Okaya, J. Phys. Soc. (Japan) **11**, 258 (1956).
[50] H. Takuma, T. Shimizu, and K. Shimoda, J. Phys. Soc. (Japan) **14**, 1595 (1959).
[51] K. Shimoda, H. Takuma, and T. Shimizu, J. Phys. Soc. (Japan) **15**, 2036 (1960).
[52] See also the article by K. Shimoda in the *Proceedings of the International School of Physics "Enrico Fermi," Topics on Radiofrequency Spectroscopy* (Academic Press Inc., New York, 1962).
[53] H. Takuma, J. Phys. Soc. (Japan) **16**, 309 (1961).

TABLE X. Hyperfine separations of the $2_{11}\to2_{12}$ CHDO transition. Uncertainties quoted are probable errors.

Transition $F_1F\to F_1'F'$	Frequency (kc/sec)
$1\frac{3}{2}\to1\frac{3}{2}$	30.93 ± 0.30
$1\frac{1}{2}\to1\frac{1}{2}$	20.00 ± 0.30
$3\frac{7}{2}\to3\frac{7}{2}$ $+3\frac{5}{2}\to3\frac{5}{2}$	0.00 ± 0.30
$2\frac{5}{2}\to2\frac{5}{2}$	-49.03 ± 0.40
$2\frac{3}{2}\to2\frac{3}{2}$	-57.30 ± 0.40

stronger lines. Cooling of the effuser, as with HDS, was found to give some increase in signal intensity.

The observed hfs is shown in Fig. 9. Since $K_{-1}=1$ for the (2_{11}, 2_{12}) doublet, the hyperfine coupling constants vary greatly between the two rotational states,[18] and the $\Delta F=0$ transitions are well separated. The hfs, however, is due to magnetic interactions alone, and the entire structure is only some 35 kc/sec wide, or about half the Doppler width in conventional absorption spectroscopy. A single $\Delta F=1$ transition can be clearly made out next to the most intense central line.

Frequency intervals were measured to within 1 kc/sec using the Radiation Laboratory's frequency standard as described in Ref. 12; they are listed in Table VIII. A reasonably close fit to the observed spectrum was first obtained using the Hamiltonian of Eq. (19), with the spin–spin constant d_J for the 2_{11} and 2_{12} states being calculated from the molecular geometry of Fig. 8. A closer fit was then obtained by slightly varying the proton–proton distance. The best fit gave $\langle 1/r^3\rangle^{-1/3}=1.898\pm0.017$ Å. This contrasts with the value found by Shimoda *et al.*[50] of 1.82 ± 0.04 Å, but is in good agreement with the value of 1.92 Å obtained from the geometry of Fig. 8.

From the theoretical spectrum of Fig. 10 it can be seen that all but one of the $\Delta F=1$ lines lie so close to the $\Delta F=0$ transitions that they cannot be resolved. The single one discerned in Fig. 9, however, has allowed a determination of the absolute values of $C_H(2_{11})$ and $C_H(2_{12})$, only the difference being determined by the intervals between the main $\Delta F=0$ lines. The various hyperfine constants are listed in Table IX.

d. CHDO[45]

The $2_{11}\to2_{12}$ transition for CHDO lies about 1500 Mc/sec higher in frequency than that for CH_2O. The exact frequency has been found to be 16 038.08 Mc/sec by Hirakawa, Oka, and Shimoda.[54]

[54] H. Hirakawa, T. Oka, and K. Shimoda, J. Phys. Soc. (Japan) **11**, 1207 (1956).

The rotation of the inertial axes shown in Fig. 11 was calculated, neglecting the electrons, on the assumption that the bond lengths and the HCH angle are the same as those for CH_2O. The intensity of the $2_{11}\to2_{12}$ transition was as strong as expected, compared to the same transition in CH_2O, indicating that nearby levels did not hinder state selection. In particular, the 3_{03} level, shown in Fig. 1 immediately above the 2_{11} level, is not expected to give any difficulty, since the ${}^cR$ branch transition $2_{11}\to3_{03}$ is strictly forbidden.

As for CH_2O, the CHDO vapor was produced by heating the polymer paraformaldehyde. The sample, prepared by the Volk Company, was specified to be 90% CHDO, due to the stability of this molecule against H–D exchange. Dry-ice cooling of the vapor gave some increase in the signal strength.

The observed hfs is shown in the oscilloscope trace of Fig. 12. It may be qualitatively interpreted in the following way: the deuteron quadrupole interaction splits both the upper and lower rotational state into a triplet. The coupling constant $(eq_JQ)_D$ is quite different in either case since $K_{-1}=1$,[18] so that the three most intense $\Delta F_1=0$ transitions are widely spaced—they correspond in Figs. 12 and 13 to the central line, and the two strong doublets on either side. The doublet structure in turn is due to the magnetic coupling of the proton—the central transition is also split, but not sufficiently so to be resolved. The remaining structure is due to the hyperfine transitions for which ΔF or $\Delta F_1\neq0$.

The measured hyperfine intervals are given in Table X. Using the Hamiltonian of Eq. (18) there are seen to be in principle a total of eight hyperfine constants to be varied to fit the observed spectrum. Considerable simplicity resulted, however, in initially using the proton–proton distance calculated from CH_2O, and in calculating the $(eq_JQ)_D$ from the quadrupole coupling constant along the bond, assuming that the electric field was cylindrically symmetric about the C–D bond direction. The $\Delta F_1=\Delta F=0$ transitions were then fit to within 1 kc/sec in terms of only three constants: $(eV_{\xi\xi}Q)_D$, $C_H(2_{11})-C_H(2_{12})$, and $C_D(2_{11})-C_D(2_{12})$. $C_H(2_{11})$, $C_D(2_{11})$, and $\langle 1/r^3\rangle^{-1/3}$ were then varied to fit as well as possible the shape and frequency of the manifold of the other hyperfine components. All calculations were performed on a desk computer. The best-fit hyperfine constants are listed in Table IX. The theoretical spectrum of Fig. 13, calculated using a Gaussian line shape with full half-width of 5 kc/sec, reproduces all aspects of the observed hfs. Relative

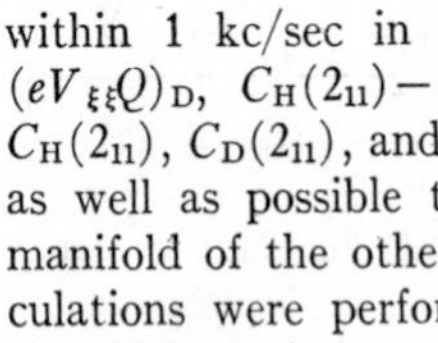

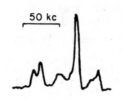

FIG. 12. Observed hfs of the $2_{11}\to2_{12}$ transition of CHDO.

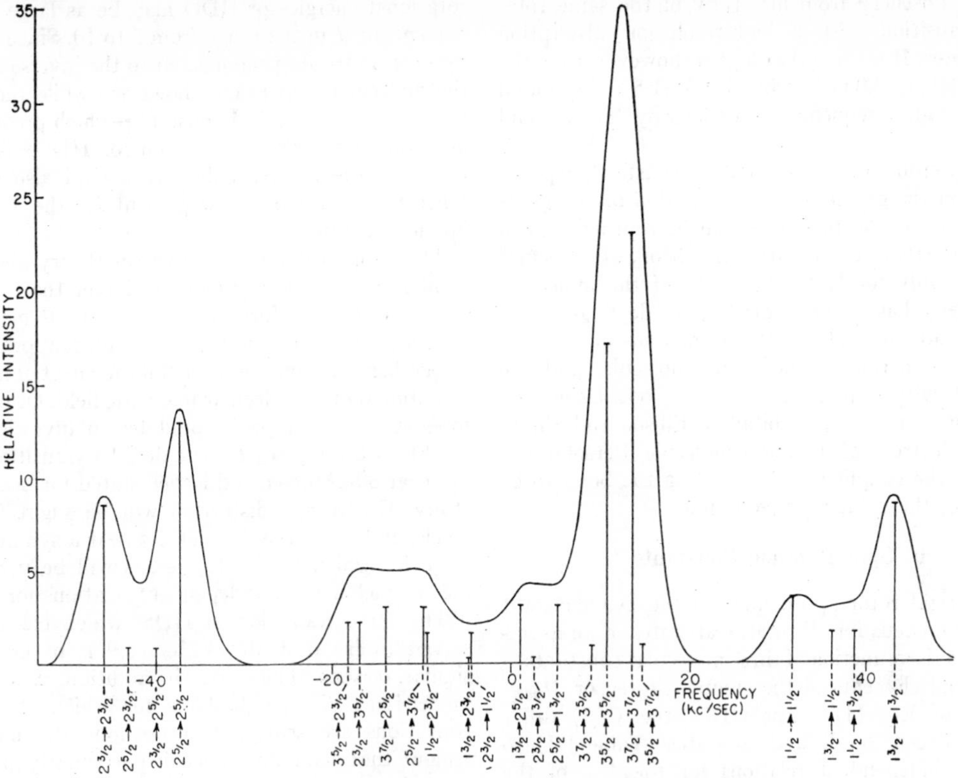

FIG. 13. Calculated hfs of the CHDO $2_{11}\rightarrow 2_{12}$ transition.

intensities were calculated in the $|F_1, F\rangle$ frame, since off-diagonal terms in the Hamiltonian are relatively small.

IV. MOLECULAR CONSTANTS

a. Electric Field Gradients

The hfs of HDO, HDS, and CHDO is well interpreted on the assumption that the electric field at the deuteron is nearly cylindrically symmetric about the bond. The coupling constants along the bond, $(eV_{\xi\xi}Q)_D$, derived from the $(eq_JQ)_D$ of Tables III, VI, and IX, are listed in Table XI. The $V_{\xi\xi}$ are calculated taking the deuteron quadrupole moment to be[2] $Q=2.82\times 10^{-27}$ cm^2.

Since $(eq_JQ)_D$ has been found for two rotational states in each molecule, we can also, in principle, calculate the asymmetry parameter for the field gradient tensor,

$$\eta=(V_{\zeta\zeta}-V_{\chi\chi})/V_{\xi\xi}, \tag{32}$$

where ζ and χ are directions perpendicular to the bond direction ξ, and perpendicular and parallel, respectively, to the plane of the molecule. The η found for HDO and HDS are also given in Table XI. For CHDO the complexity of the hfs has allowed only a rough upper limit to be set on the value of this parameter.

The quadrupole coupling constant along the bond of 318.6±2.4 kc/sec, which we have found for HDO, is in good agreement with the value of 315±7 kc/sec

TABLE XI. Quadrupole coupling constants along the OD, SD, and CD bonds.

Molecule	$(eV_{\xi\xi}Q)_D$ (kc/sec)	$V_{\xi\xi}$ (statvolt/cm²)	η
HDO	318.6±2.4	1.56×10^{15}	0.06±0.16
HDS	154.7±1.6	0.76×10^{15}	−0.12±0.13
CHDO	170.0±2.0	0.83×10^{15}	$\lvert\eta\rvert<0.15$

TABLE XII. Comparison of measured and calculated values of C_H for HDO.

State	C_H(calc.) − C_H(meas.) (kc/sec)
$5_{41}(5_3)$	0.84
$5_{42}(5_2)$	0.83
$3_{30}(3_3)$	1.36
$3_{31}(3_2)$	1.31
$2_{20}(2_2)$	−1.85
$2_{21}(2_1)$	−2.47

found by Posener[39] from his study of the same rotational transition with a high-resolution absorption spectrometer. It is somewhat higher, however, than the values of 310.3±3.0 kc/sec and 314.3±1.5 kc/sec found from the radio frequency transitions by Treacy and Beers.[6]

The deuteron quadrupole coupling constant, depending only on the ground-state distribution of charge, is one of the molecular properties which, in principle, can be most directly calculated from the theory of molecular structure. Only for HDO, however, of the molecules studied here, has an attempt been made to evaluate the field gradient at the deuteron in terms of the electronic wavefunction of the entire molecule, and the agreement with experiment is not good. Using the self-consistent molecular orbitals of Ellison and Shull[55] for all 10 electrons of the water molecule, Bersohn[1] has calculated the coupling constant along the bond to be about twice the value we have found.

b. Spin–Rotation Constants

In the rigid rotor approximation the **I·J** constant of a given nucleus for all rotational states of an asymmetric rotor is a function of three molecular constants—the diagonal elements of the symmetric tensor $M_{gg}=N_{gg}+E_{gg}$ of Eq. (17). For HDO, the $\langle J_g^2\rangle$ differ enough between the 2_{20} and 2_{21} states (Table III) to allow two independent relations for the M_{gg} of the proton to be established from the hfs. The work of Treacy and Beers[6] determines four further equations for the M_{gg}, only two of which are independent, however, since the $\langle J_g^2\rangle$ vary only slightly between the 3_{30} and 3_{31} states, or the 5_{42} and 5_{41} states.

Their least-squares fitting of the three M_{gg} to the experimental data has revealed a clear discrepancy between theory and experiment.[6] No substantial improvement results if the least-squares fitting is repeated with our more recent value of C_H for the 2_{20} and 2_{21} states (Table III), and with the more precise determination of the water geometry of Benedict, Gailar, and Plyler[37] used to calculate the $\langle J_g^2\rangle$. We find that $M_{aa}=-43.78$ kc/sec, $M_{bb}=-41.15$ kc/sec, and $M_{cc}=-60.30$ kc/sec. A revised version of Treacy and Beers' Table IV, calculated on the basis of these constants and the $\langle J_g^2\rangle$ of our Table I, is given in Table XII. By way of comparison, if the M_{gg} are calculated on the basis of the three independent equations furnished by the four lowest-lying rotational levels studied, the 2_{20}, 2_{21}, 3_{30}, and 3_{31} states, we find that $M_{aa}=-55.8$ kc/sec, $M_{bb}=-18.9$ kc/sec, and $M_{cc}=-19.8$ kc/sec.

Since all our calculations are based on the rigid rotor approximation, it is tempting to consider that centrifugal distortion, which is notoriously large for light asymmetric rotors, may be the cause of this discrepancy. The effect of centrifugal distortion on the rotational energies of HDO may be as large as a few percent for J in the range from 5 to 10. Since the rotation constants are proportional to the inverse square of the molecular dimensions, however, while the nuclear contribution to the **I·J** constant—which predominates over the electronic contribution for HDO—is proportional to the inverse cube, we should also expect a centrifugal effect of a few percent for the M_{gg} of the 5_{42} and 5_{41} states.

The actual discrepancy between theory and experiment is seen to be considerably larger than this; if it is confirmed by further experiment it may prove necessary to abandon the rigid rotor approximation altogether, and consider in detail the effect of molecular vibration on the molecular magnetic field. Of particular interest in this respect would be an investigation of the hfs of the $1_{10}\rightarrow 1_{11}$ K-type doublet transition, which lies near 80 kMc/sec and is well suited for beam-maser study. Centrifugal distortion will be slight for these levels, and, since the doublet lies near a symmetric-top state for which $|K|=1$, the hfs will be very asymmetric, yielding two independent relations for the M_{gg}.

The same transition in HDS, which has been observed to lie at 51.073 kMc/sec,[43] is of interest for similar reasons. There are, in addition, a number of higher-lying K-type doublets for which the doublet transitions are scattered throughout the microwave region[43] that make this molecule particularly interesting from the point of view of the **I·J** interactions.

Takuma[53] has evaluated the M_{gg} for CH_2O from the various observations of hfs,[45,50] which yielded five independent relations for the three constants. All of the experimental results were well interpreted on the basis of the rigid rotor approximation. He found that $M_{aa}=30.2\pm2.7$ kc/sec, $M_{bb}=-3.0\pm3.4$ kc/sec, and $M_{cc}=-13.2\pm3.4$ kc/sec.

V. CONCLUSIONS

The present work has shown the value of a molecular beam in increasing resolution, and state selection in increasing sensitivity, in the investigation of molecular hfs. The properties found from experiment—electric field gradients, and magnetic interaction constants—have not so far been calculated for many polyatomic molecules. These calculations, however, and particularly those of field gradients, are coming within reach of modern computing techniques and our knowledge of molecular structure.

It is important to emphasize that the present results were obtained without recourse to the most sensitive detection techniques now available. The use of stabilized microwave oscillators, and narrow-band phase-sensitive detection, should allow an improvement in sensitivity by a factor of from 10 to 100, and the study of similar hfs in many microwave transitions. The extension of the present techniques to the rotational and rotation-inversion transitions of other light asymmetric rotors, to the rotational transitions of linear

[55] F. O. Ellison and H. Shull, J. Chem. Phys. **23**, 2358 (1955).

and symmetric-top molecules, and, perhaps, to molecules with hindered rotation, can be expected.

ACKNOWLEDGMENTS

We should like to acknowledge the support of Professor C. H. Townes, who gave aid and guidance at all times. The staff of the Radiation Laboratory offered invaluable assistance during the course of this work; we would like to thank C. Dechert, T. Bracken, and I. Beller in particular. H. Lecar assisted in the taking of data, while several of the experimental techniques described were inspired by A. Javan. A correspondence with D. W. Posener concerning HDO was of great interest, as were a variety of conversations with A. Okaya, B. P. Dailey, R. Bersohn, and M. Karplus. Professor R. Jastrow kindly made available the computing facilities of the Institute for Space Studies, and Ohseun Koh and Daniel Fife contributed greatly by writing the machine program used in the final fitting of the HDO and HDS spectra. T. Psaropolos prepared many of the illustrations.

Hyperfine Structure in the Inversion Spectrum of $N^{14}H_3$ by a New High-Resolution Microwave Spectrometer*

J. P. GORDON†
Columbia University, New York, New York

(Received May 4, 1955)

The hyperfine structure of the inversion spectrum of $N^{14}H_3$ has been reexamined with an ultra-high resolution spectrometer. Lines whose total width at half-maximum is seven kc-sec have been obtained in this spectrometer. Such narrow lines allow resolution of magnetic hyperfine structure caused by reorientation of the spins of the hydrogen nuclei. The new structure has been satisfactorily explained to within the experimental error of about 1 kc/sec by considering the various interactions of the magnetic moments of the hydrogen nuclei with the molecular fields. The interaction energy of the nitrogen nucleus has been remeasured with higher resolution than was possible previously, and indications were found that $|eqQ|$ for the lower inversion state is larger by about 0.01% than that for the upper state. The sign of eqQ was directly determined to be negative. A theoretical treatment of the magnetic interactions has been made which is slightly different from that which has previously been used. The method allows some simplification of the form of the magnetic interactions.

INTRODUCTION

THE inversion spectrum of the symmetric top molecule $N^{14}H_3$ has been the subject of a great deal of study ever since it was first observed by Cleeton and Williams in 1934.[1,2] Hyperfine structure in this spectrum due to quadrupole interaction of the nitrogen nucleus was first noticed in 1946 by Good.[3] Quite recently, a thorough theoretical and experimental study of the hyperfine structure of this spectrum has been carried out by Gunther-Mohr *et al.*[4,5] which explained a doubling of the $K=1$ lines in terms of the magnetic interactions of the hydrogen nuclei with the molecular magnetic fields.

A significant increase in experimental resolution afforded by the molecular beam spectrometer described in this paper has made it desirable to remeasure once again in greater detail the hyperfine structure of this spectrum. Previously undetected structure caused by the reorientation of the spins of the hydrogen nuclei has been observed and theoretically explained to within experimental error. The theoretical analysis of Gunther-Mohr *et al.* has been extended to include evaluation of the mutual spin-spin interaction of the three hydrogen nuclei, and simplification of some of the terms of the Hamiltonian has been effected through the use of the symmetry properties of the molecule.

* Work supported jointly by the Signal Corps, the Office of Naval Research, and the Air Research and Development Command.

† Now at the Bell Telephone Laboratories, Inc., Murray Hill, New Jersey.

[1] C. E. Cleeton and N. H. Williams, Phys. Rev. **46**, 235 (1934).

[2] The reader is referred to C. H. Townes and P. Kisliuk, National Bureau of Standards Circular, 518, June 23, 1952 (unpublished), in which will be found a summary of the experimental and theoretical work on this molecule together with a survey of the literature and a tabulation of microwave transition frequencies.

[3] W. E. Good, Phys. Rev. **70**, 213 (1946).

[4] Gunther-Mohr, White, Schawlow, Good, and Coles, Phys. Rev. **94**, 1184 (1954).

[5] Gunther-Mohr, Townes, and Van Vleck, Phys. Rev. **94**, 1191 (1954).

THEORY

The experimental[4] and theoretical[5] papers by Gunther-Mohr *et al.* form the background for the following work. For convenience, they will be referred to as GM I and GM II respectively.

The rotational state of the molecule in zero field will be specified by the following quantum numbers:

- $\mathbf{J}$ total molecular angular momentum excluding nuclear spins.
- K projection of $\mathbf{J}$ on the molecular axis of symmetry.
- $\mathbf{I}_N$ spin of the nitrogen nucleus.
- $\mathbf{I}_i$ ($i=1, 2, 3$) spin of the ith hydrogen nucleus.
- $\mathbf{I}$ sum of the spins of the three hydrogen nuclei.
- $\mathbf{F}_1$ sum of $\mathbf{J}$ and $\mathbf{I}_N$ (this is a good quantum number because the quadrupole interaction energy of the nitrogen is considerably larger than the magnetic interaction energy of the hydrogens).
- $\mathbf{F}$ sum of F_1 and $\mathbf{I}$.
- M_F projection of F on some axis fixed in space.

The calculation of the various matrix elements will be made in the molecular frame coupling scheme, as described by Van Vleck[6] and GM II. The molecular frame scheme is based on the fact that if one refers all angular momenta to set of axes fixed in the molecule, then $\mathbf{F}$, $\mathbf{I}_N$, and $\mathbf{I}$ form a set of commuting angular momenta, just as in the laboratory frame, $\mathbf{J}$, $\mathbf{I}_N$, and $\mathbf{I}$ form a commuting set. In the molecular frame, however, the commutation relations of $\mathbf{F}$ and $\mathbf{F}_1$ change sign: i.e., $[F_x,F_y]=-iF_z$; where x, y, and z now refer to axes fixed in the molecule. The "internal" angular momenta $\mathbf{I}$ and $\mathbf{I}_N$, however, retain the old commutation relations. If one reverses the signs of these internal angular momenta, setting $\mathbf{I}_N'=-\mathbf{I}_N$, $\mathbf{I}'=-\mathbf{I}$, then all of the angular momenta commute with the anomalous sign, and one has the molecular frame coupling scheme

$$\mathbf{F}_1=\mathbf{F}+\mathbf{I}', \quad \mathbf{J}=\mathbf{F}_1+\mathbf{I}_N',$$

[6] J. H. Van Vleck, Revs. Modern Phys. **23**, 213 (1953).

to an understanding of the spectroscopic results. A more general and complete discussion, including the properties of the apparatus as a microwave amplifier and oscillator, is given in the following paper.

Most attempts by previous workers to utilize a molecular beam for microwave spectroscopy have failed to be very successful because of a lack of sensitivity. The electrostatic focuser used here, allows both a sizeable beam, and large signals from a given number of molecules in the beam. Consider first a gas in thermal equilibrium which is irradiated by microwaves at the frequency of one of the transitions of the gas molecules. An absorption of energy invariably takes place. There will be molecules in both the higher and lower energy states of the transition, and the microwaves will excite transitions both up and down with equal probability. The total rate of upward transitions will, however, be slightly larger than the rate of downward transitions, since the Boltzmann distribution gives the lower state a population larger than the upper by approximately $N(h\nu/kT)$, where N is the total number of molecules in the lower state. For $T=300°K$, $kT/10^6h$ equals 6.63 $\times 10^6$ Mc/sec, and so $h\nu/kT$ is approximately 1/250 at the frequency of 1.25-cm microwaves. At this frequency, then, the net effect is produced by only 1/250 of the molecules which are capable of absorbing energy. In the present apparatus, only molecules in upper inversion states reach the cavity. Since they can all contribute energy to the exciting microwave field, there results a substantial improvement in the sensitivity of the apparatus. The fact that the upper inversion states are focused means that the molecular response to the exciting radiation is an emission of energy, so that emission lines are observed rather than absorption lines.

Cylindrical cavities were used, which resonated in the TE_{011} mode at the frequency of interest. In order to provide a long interaction region and so to cut down the line width (this is discussed in detail in the following paper), the cavities were made approximately four inches in length. They were tuned by means of short sections of enlarged diameter and variable length at one end. The beam entered through a circular hole in the other end. In order to make cavities of this length for the TE_{011} mode, their diameters had to be very close to the cut-off values. This restricted the tuning range of each cavity to about 50 Mc/sec, and so a new cavity usually had to be constructed for each line which was examined. The cavities were made of copper and had values of Q near 12 000. Suprisingly little radiation from the beam entrance hole was encountered, even though the hole diameter was two thirds of the diameter of the cavity.

Emission lines whose total width at half-maximum is seven kc/sec have been obtained, and it is estimated that from two to four kc/sec of this width is due to spurious frequency modulation of the microwave signal from the 2K50 klystron which was used to induce the transitions, rather than to the actual width of the spectral lines.

The field of the focuser exerts forces on the molecules due to their induced dipole moments. In zero field the ammonia molecule has no average dipole moment because of the inversion, while with increasing field, the inversion is slowly quenched and an average dipole moment appears. If hyperfine effects are neglected the energies of the inversion states may be written for all field strengths as

$$W=W_0\pm\left[\left(\frac{h\nu_0}{2}\right)^2+\left(\mu\mathcal{E}\frac{MK}{J(J+1)}\right)^2\right]^{\frac{1}{2}}, \qquad (6)$$

where W_0 is the average energy of the upper and lower inversion levels, ν_0 is the inversion frequency in zero electric field, μ is the permanent dipole moment the molecule would have if the inversion did not occur, $\mathcal{E}$ is the magnitude of the electric field, and M is the projection of J on the direction of the field. Since the changes in magnitude and direction of the field the molecule sees as it travels through the focuser occur very slowly compared to the rate of precession of J around the field, J maintains its orientation with respect to the field direction during the whole flight of of the molecule. Therefore M is a constant of the motion.

The focuser, as shown in Fig. 2, is composed of four cylindrical electrodes whose inner faces are shaped to form hyperbolae. Two opposing electrodes are maintained at a high voltage V, while the other two are kept at ground. This arrangement produces an electric potential in the gap between the electrodes of the form $\varphi=\varphi_0 r^2\cos 2\theta$; where r and θ are cylindrical coordinates of a system whose axis is the axis of the focuser. The magnitude of the electric field produced by this potential is proportional to r. The force exerted on the molecules by this field is, from (6),

$$f_r=-\frac{\partial W}{\partial r}=\mp\frac{[\mu MK/J(J+1)]^2\mathcal{E}d\mathcal{E}/dr}{\{(h\nu_0/2)^2+[\mu\mathcal{E}MK/J(J+1)]^2\}^{\frac{1}{2}}}. \qquad (7)$$

It is radial and proportional to r for small field strengths. The force is directed inward for molecules in upper inversion states (negative sign) and outward for molecules in lower inversion states (positive sign).

Under the assumption of small electric fields, the number of molecules in the upper state and with a given value of M which are held in the focuser by the restoring force is approximately proportional to M^2. This can be seen as follows. Assume that the source consists of a small hole located on the axis of the focuser from which molecules effuse in all directions. Assume further that all molecules which can travel farther away from the axis of the focuser than a distance of r_0 collide with the focuser electrodes and are lost from the beam. It can easily be shown that all molecules whose initial velocity perpendicular to the axis of the focuser is less than a

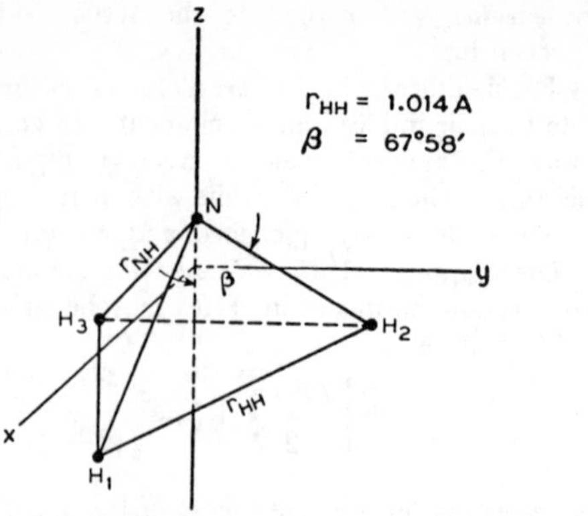

FIG. 1. Geometrical structure of the ammonia molecule.

and such relations as

$$\mathbf{I}'^2=\mathbf{I}^2=I(I+1),\quad \mathbf{F}\cdot\mathbf{I}'=-\mathbf{F}\cdot\mathbf{I}.$$

The matrix elements of Condon and Shortley[7] may be used for this coupling scheme, provided one reverses the signs of all the imaginary ones. The molecular frame has a distinct advantage, for calculations, in that the positions of the nuclei are fixed in the coordinate system (except for vibrations) and it becomes unnecessary to know the matrix elements of the direction cosines which determine the angular position of the molecule in space.

The interactions which are important in the hyperfine structure of the inversion spectrum of ammonia are listed in Table I.[8] They include the effects previously evaluated in GM II, with the addition of the mutual spin-spin interaction of the magnetic moments of the hydrogen nuclei. The reader is referred to GM I and GM II for the evaluation of any constants not explicitly defined here. The combined effect of these interactions satisfactorily fits almost all the experimental data to within the accuracy of measurement. The few apparent discrepancies which still remain will be discussed later.

We shall proceed to a calculation of the hydrogen spin-spin interaction. Reference should be made to Fig. 1 which shows the structure of the molecule and the positions of the nuclei with respect to the molecular axes. The z axis is the axis of symmetry of the molecule, the xz plane contains hydrogen No. 1, and the projection of the position of hydrogen No. 2 on the xy plane lies in its second quadrant. The origin of the coordinate system is taken at the center of gravity of the molecule. The x, y, and z axes form a right-handed set of coordinates.

[7] E. U. Condon and G. H. Shortley, *Theory of Atomic Spectra* (Cambridge University Press, London, 1951).

[8] Some errors noticed in GM I and GM II are corrected here and in Eq. (5). These errors include: (a) The function f of Eq. (5) is written incorrectly in GM II. (b) in GM I and II, the magnetic constants α and ρ should be replaced in all equations by $\alpha/2$ and $\rho/2$. These constants, of course, keep the same definitions as before. (c) in GM II, Appendix III, Eq. (A23), the proportionality constant $\Omega_1(J,I_N)/[J(J+1)]$ should be replaced by $\varphi(J,I_N')/[J(J+1)]$ where $\varphi(J,I_N')=2\Omega_2(J,I_N)-\mathbf{I}_N\cdot\mathbf{J}$.

The energy of the spin-spin interactions among t[he] three hydrogen nuclei is given by[9]

$$G_1^{HH}=(g_H\mu_0)^2 r_{HH}^{-3}\times\sum_{i<j}\left[\mathbf{I}_i\cdot\mathbf{I}_j-3r_{HH}^{-2}(\mathbf{I}_i\cdot\mathbf{r}_{ij})(\mathbf{I}_j\cdot\mathbf{r}_{ij})\right],\quad ($$

where r_{HH} is the distance between hydrogen nuclei, an[d] $\mathbf{r}_{ij}$ is the vector distance between hydrogen nuclei [i] and j. As shown in the Appendix, the only matr[ix] elements of this interaction which affect the spectru[m] in an observable way are those which are diagonal in [K] and if only these elements are considered, it is show[n] there that the interaction can be written in the equiva-lent form:

$$G_1^{HH}=-\tfrac{1}{4}(g_H\mu_0)^2 r_{HH}^{-3}(\mathbf{I}^2-3\mathbf{I}_z^2),\quad ($$

where I_z is the projection of I on the molecular sym[metry] axis. This term may then be evaluated in [a] similar way to that by which the term $(\mathbf{I}_{Nz}^2-\mathbf{I}_N^2/$ is evaluated in GM II, giving the result:

$$G_1^{HH}=-\tfrac{1}{4}(g_H\mu_0)^2\langle v|r_{HH}^{-3}|v\rangle\times\frac{\varphi(F_1,I')\varphi(J,F_1)}{F_1(F_1+1)}\left(1-\frac{3K^2}{J(J+1)}\right),\quad ($$

TABLE I. Interactions important in the hyperfine structure of t[he] inversion spectrum of $N^{14}H_3$.

Energy term	Physical interpretati[on]
$-eqQ\left(1-\frac{3K^2}{J(J-H)}\right)\Omega_1(J,I_N)$	Nitrogen quadrupole interaction
$\left[a+\frac{(b-a)K^2}{J(J+1)}\right](\mathbf{I}_N\cdot\mathbf{J})$	Nitrogen magneti[c] interaction with m[o]lecular rotation
$\left[A+\frac{cK^2}{J(J+1)}-\delta_{K1}(-1)^{J+v}B\right](\mathbf{I}\cdot\mathbf{J})$	Hydrogen magnet[ic] interaction with molecular rotatio[n]
$g_Hg_N\mu_0^2 r_{NH}^{-3}\sum_{i=1,2,3}[(\mathbf{I}_i\cdot\mathbf{I}_N)-3(\mathbf{I}_i\cdot\mathbf{r}_{iN})(\mathbf{I}_N\cdot\mathbf{r}_{iN})$ or $\mathfrak{D}_1(\mathbf{I}\cdot\mathbf{I}_N-3I_zI_{Nz})+3\mathfrak{D}_2(I_{1y}I_{Ny}-I_{1x}I_{Nx})$	Hydrogen-nitroge[n] spin-spin interaction
$(g_H\mu_0)^2 r_{HH}^{-3}\sum_{i<j}[\mathbf{I}_i\cdot\mathbf{I}_j-3(\mathbf{I}_i\cdot\mathbf{r}_{ij})(\mathbf{I}_j\cdot\mathbf{r}_{ij})]$ or $-\frac{1}{4}\mathfrak{D}_3(I^2-3I_z^2)$,	Hydrogen-hydroge[n] spin-spin interaction

where

$$\mathfrak{D}_1=g_Hg_N\mu_0^2\langle v|r_{NH}^{-3}(1-\tfrac{3}{2}\sin^2\beta)|v\rangle,$$
$$\mathfrak{D}_2=g_Hg_N\mu_0^2\langle v|r_{NH}^{-3}\tfrac{3}{2}\sin^2\beta|v\rangle,$$
$$\mathfrak{D}_3=(g_H\mu_0)^2\langle v|r_{HH}^{-3}|v\rangle,$$
$$A=\tfrac{1}{2}(\alpha+\rho),\quad B=\tfrac{1}{2}(\rho-\alpha),\quad C=\gamma-\tfrac{1}{2}(\alpha+\rho);$$

α, ρ, and γ are proportional to the magnetic fields at the positio[n] of hydrogen nucleus 1 (see Fig. 1) caused by rotations of th[e] molecule about the x, y, and z axes, respectively (see GM II).

[9] The notation here for the Hamiltonian is patterned aft[er] GM II.

where $\langle v|r_{HH}^{-3}|v\rangle$ indicates that r_{HH}^{-3} is to be averaged over the inversion, and

$$\varphi(A,B)=\frac{6(\mathbf{A}\cdot\mathbf{B})^2-3(\mathbf{A}\cdot\mathbf{B})-2A(A+1)B(B+1)}{(2A+3)(2A-1)}. \quad (4)$$

It can be shown from symmetry arguments that the total hydrogen spin depends on K, so that when K is a multiple of 3, I is $\frac{3}{2}$, while for all other values of K, $I=\frac{1}{2}$. Since states with $I=\frac{1}{2}$ must have $I_z^2=\frac{1}{4}$, it can be seen from Eq. (2) that G_1^{HH} is zero in this case. Thus this interaction does not affect the hyperfine structure of the energy levels unless K is a multiple of three. When K is a multiple of three, however, it forms an important component of the magnetic structure. In computing the magnitude of the coupling constant $(g_H\mu_0)^2\langle v|r_{HH}^{-3}|v\rangle$ we have used for $\langle v|r_{HH}^{-3}|v\rangle$ merely the inverse cube of the equilibrium value of r_{HH} which was obtained using the values given by Herzberg[10] for the hydrogen nitrogen distance r_{HH} and the apex angle β which are illustrated in Fig. 1. These values are $r_{HH}=1.014\times10^{-8}$ cm, $\beta=67°58'$. The coupling constant was thus calculated to be 27.7 kc/sec, and this value provides a good fit to the experimental spectrum.

Combining this result with those of GM II, we arrive at the final form of the complete hyperfine energy. This equation is valid, as explained below, so long as the quadrupole energy term is large compared to the magnetic terms.

$$\begin{aligned}W_{JJKF_1F}=&-\langle v|eQq|v\rangle\left(1-\frac{3K^2}{J(J+1)}\right)\Omega_1(J,I_N)\\&+\left[a+\frac{(b-a)K^2}{J(J+1)}\right](\mathbf{I}_N\cdot\mathbf{J})\\&+\left[A+\frac{CK^2}{J(J+1)}\right]\frac{(\mathbf{I}\cdot\mathbf{F}_1)(\mathbf{F}_1\cdot\mathbf{J})}{F_1(F_1+1)}\\&+2g_Hg_N\mu_0^2\langle v|r_{HH}^{-3}(1-\tfrac{3}{2}\sin^2\beta|v\rangle\\&\times\frac{(\mathbf{F}_1\cdot\mathbf{I})\Omega_2(J,I_N)}{F_1(F_1+1)}\left(1-\frac{3K^2}{J(J+1)}\right)\\&-\tfrac{1}{4}(g_H\mu_0)^2\langle v|r_{HH}^{-3}|v\rangle\frac{\varphi(F_1,I')\varphi(J,F_1)}{F_1(F_1+1)}\\&\times\left(1-\frac{3K^2}{J(J+1)}\right)-\delta_{K1}(-1)^{J+5}2\mathbf{F}, \quad (5)\end{aligned}$$

where

$$2f=\langle v|r_{HH}^{-3}\tfrac{3}{2}\sin^2\beta|v\rangle 2g_Hg_N\mu_0^2\times\frac{(\mathbf{F}_1\cdot\mathbf{I})\Omega_2(J,I_N)}{F_1(F_1+1)}+B\frac{(\mathbf{I}\cdot\mathbf{F}_1)(\mathbf{F}_1\cdot\mathbf{J})}{F_1(F_1+1)},$$

[10] G. Herzberg, *Infra-Red and Raman Spectra* (D. Van Nostrand and Company, Inc., New York, 1945).

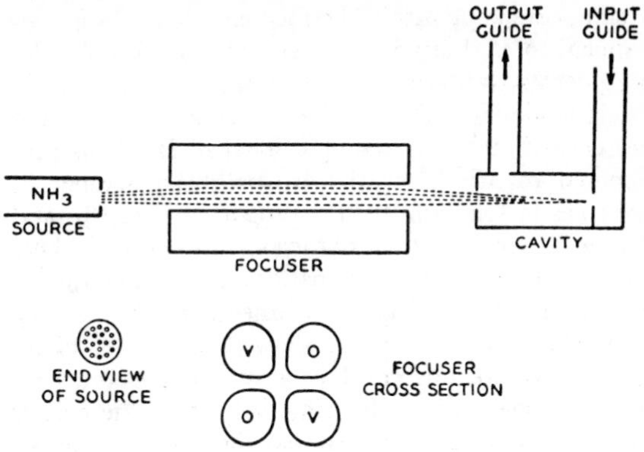

FIG. 2. Block diagram of the molecular beam oscillator.

$$\Omega_1(J,I_N)=\frac{3(\mathbf{I}_N\cdot\mathbf{J})^2+\frac{3}{2}(\mathbf{I}_N\cdot\mathbf{J})-I_N(I_N+1)J(J+1)}{(2J-1)(2J+3)2I_N(2I_N-1)},$$

$$\Omega_2(J,I_N)=\frac{3(\mathbf{I}_N\cdot\mathbf{J})^2+2J(J+1)(\mathbf{I}_N\cdot\mathbf{J})-I_N(I_N+1)J(J+1)}{(2J-1)(2J+3)}.$$

In addition to this expression, the magnetic terms of Table I have matrix elements off diagonal in F_1 which might be expected to contribute measurable shifts in some of the lines where the quadrupole splittings are small. For the 3–2 line, in particular, the factor $[1-3K^2/J(J+1)]$ is equal to zero, so that the quadrupole coupling energy disappears, F_1 is no longer a good quantum number, and expression 5 is no longer valid. Of the lines we measured, the largest effect of terms off-diagonal in F_1 appears in the 4–3 line, since for this line the quadrupole splittings were small and the magnetic energies large. In this case some of the individual hyperfine structure components are shifted by as much as two kc/sec, but this did not produce a detectable change in the envelope of all components of the lines.

EXPERIMENTAL CONSIDERATIONS

The experimental results were obtained by use of an ultra-high resolution spectrometer.[11] A block diagram of this spectrometer is shown in Fig. 2. Ammonia gas at room temperature is maintained in the source at 5 to 20 mm pressure. Molecules emerge from the source through a group of fine tubes and travel through an electrostatic focuser in which a highly nonlinear electric field focuses the molecules which are in upper inversion states. Molecules in lower inversion states are defocused and so removed from the beam. The beam then traverses a high-Q resonant cavity tuned to an inversion frequency, and there transitions are induced by microwave radiation from a 2K50 klystron. We shall discuss here only those properties of the apparatus which are necessary

[11] Gordon, Zeiger, and Townes, Phys. Rev. 95, 282 (1954).

given v_{m0} are kept within the focuser, where v_{m0} is proportional to M. For any axial velocity v_z, all molecules in a given M state which emerge from the source within a solid angle $\Omega_M=\pi(v_{m0}/v_z)^2$ are thus kept within the focuser, and since v_{m0} is proportional to M, Ω_M is proportional to M^2. Since Ω_M is small, the number of molecules in solid angle Ω_M is proportional to Ω_M, and thus to M^2. Actually none of the assumptions made here is exactly correct, the principal deviation being due to the decrease in polarizability of the molecule at strong fields. However, calculations show that the results are not changed by this effect in a very important way. Hence we shall assume for simplicity, that the field is relatively weak ($\mu\mathcal{E}\ll h\nu_0$), so that the number of upper state molecules trapped by the potential minimum of the focuser, and thus delivered to the cavity, is proportional to M^2.

We shall see that as the molecules enter, traverse, and leave the focuser, very few transitions are made between the various quadrupole levels of a given inversion state. This fact plus the dependence of the focusing strength on M will be shown to have the effect of substantially increasing the relative populations of the higher energy quadrupole levels inside the cavity. The quadrupole satellites on the high-frequency side of the main line are made relatively strong by this effect.

Neglecting for a moment the effects of the hydrogen spins, we see that in small electric fields, J and the nitrogen spin I_N are coupled together by the quadrupole interaction and the stationary states of the molecule may be represented by the quantum numbers J, I_N, F_1, and M_F, where $\mathbf{F}_1=\mathbf{J}+\mathbf{I}_N$ and M_F is the projection of $\mathbf{F}_1$ along the direction of the field. At high fields, $\mathbf{J}$ and $\mathbf{I}_N$ are decoupled and separately quantized along the field direction. At all intermediate fields, the stationary states have a one to one correspondence with the low- or high-field states. If a molecule exists at low field in a particular quantum state and then the field is increased infinitely slowly (adiabatic approximation) the state of the molecule will progress through the intermediate configurations and at high field will be found in a particular high-field state. If the field is turned on within a finite time, then transitions will be possible, and the molecule may then be found in any of several high-field states.

The criterion for whether such transitions will take place is discussed in most textbooks on quantum mechanics. Let $\hbar\omega_{km}$ be the energy difference between states k and m. Then if there is only a small fractional change in $\hbar\omega_{km}$ in a time given by $1/\omega_{km}$, few transitions between states k and m are to be expected. The most probable velocity of the ammonia molecules in the beam is about 4×10^4 cm/sec and the distance they travel in entering or leaving the focuser is about one centimeter, so that they take about 2.5×10^{-5} second to enter the field. The quadrupole level splittings are of the order of 1.5 Mc/sec, so that for transitions to occur between these levels, the energy differences between quadrupole states must undergo large fractional changes in times of the order of $[2\pi\times1.5\times10^6]^{-1}$ or about 10^{-7} sec. This time is short, however, compared to the time required for the molecule to enter or leave the fields, so that we should expect few transitions.

In addition, each of the quadrupole levels is further split in zero field by the magnetic interactions of the hydrogen spin, which are listed in Table I. These zero field magnetic hyperfine splittings are only of the order of 50 kc/sec, however, so that in the case of these energy splittings the time $1/\omega_{km}$ is of the same order as the time of entry of the molecules into the focuser. We should thus expect many transitions between these levels, and in our computing theoretical line shapes, we have assumed that in the cavity all the magnetic hyperfine sublevels of a given quadrupole level are equally populated.

As an example of the intensity shifts produced by adiabatic focusing we shall take the case of the 3–3 line, which is one of those experimentally measured. Since eqQ is negative, Eq. (5) shows that the $F_1=3$ state has the highest energy, followed by the $F_1=4$ and 2 states respectively. Of the seven low-field M_F states with $F_1=3$, four go at high fields to $|M|=3$ states, two to $|M|=2$, and one to $|M|=1$. The other low-field states are somewhat similarly distributed among the high-field states. However, there is a significant trend for low-energy low-field states to go predominantly into the low-energy high-field states. Following our assumption that the number of molecules in a given M state which reach the cavity is proportional to M^2, the population of each F_1 level in the cavity must be weighted according to the factor $(2F_1+1)^{-1}\sum_M N(M)M^2$, where $N(M)$ is the number of low-field states which go into the particular high-field state with quantum number M. For the 3–3 line, these weighting factors are 45/7, 37/9, and 2/5 respectively for the states $F_1=3$, 4, and 2. The high-energy quadrupole levels thus have substantially greater populations in the cavity. The relative intensities of the transitions originating from the various quadrupole levels must be weighted by these factors.

The effect of this varying of the weight-factor was experimentally observed as a variation in intensity of the transitions. Under conditions of thermal equilibrium, the hyperfine pattern of the 3–3 line should be almost exactly symmetrical intensitywise, and in particular the two transitions $F_1=3\rightarrow2$ and $F_1=2\rightarrow3$ equal in intensity. Actually, while the $F_1=3$ to 2 quadrupole satellite was quite strong (see Fig. 4), the $F_1=2$ to 3 quadrupole satellite on the low frequency side of the main line was just barely observable.

The relative intensities of the quadrupole satellites were used to provide a direct check on the sign of eqQ. Under the correct assignment of a negative eqQ, both quadrupole satellites on the high frequency side of the main line originate from the same quadrupole level and thus their relative intensities are unchanged by the

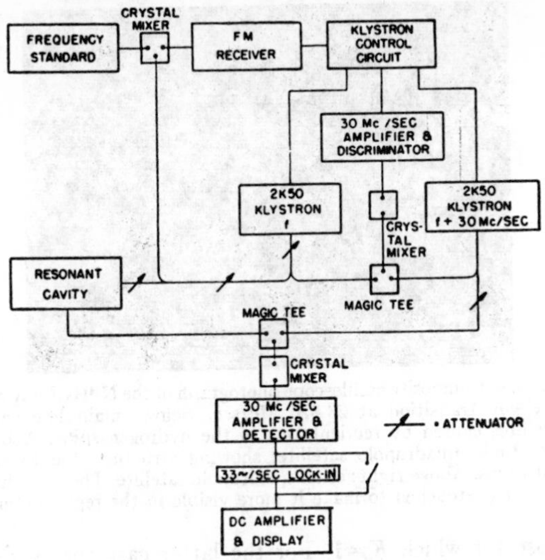

FIG. 3. Block diagram of the heterodyne detection system used in the experimental work.

adiabatic focusing, while the quadrupole satellites on the low frequency side originate from different quadrupole levels, and so have different intensities. The $K=1$ line also checked the sign of *eqQ*, since the details of its asymmetric hyperfine structure depend on the relative sign of *eqQ* and the nuclear spin-spin interaction. The sign of the latter interaction is of course known from the nuclear magnetic moments. This determination also shows that *eqQ* is negative.

The large changes in the relative populations of the quadrupole levels due to focusing also allow the possibility of producing direct quadrupole transitions in the beam in the region between the focuser and the cavity. The cavity would then be used as a detector, the quadrupole resonances being observed by the changes in intensity of the quadrupole satellites of the microwave transitions.

ELECTRONICS AND MEASUREMENT TECHNIQUE

A block diagram of the heterodyne detection system used in this work appears in Fig. 3. The carrier power from the signal klystron $K1$ plus power emitted from the beam is mixed in a 1N26 crystal with power from a second klystron $K2$ which is maintained by an automatic frequency control AFC circuit at a frequency 30 Mc/sec away from that of $K1$. A tuned intermediate-frequency (IF) amplifier with a band width of about 2.5 Mc/sec then amplifies the resulting 30-Mc/sec signal. The output of this amplifier is detected in a diode second detector, and then fed through a low-pass filter to an oscilloscope. Alternatively, the output from the second detector may be sent to a 33-cps lock-in detector which is synchronized with mechanical beam chopper inside the vacuum system.

Most of the measurements were taken without the lock-in circuit. Klystrons $K1$ and $K2$ were frequency-modulated by applying to their repellers a sawtooth sweep voltage at a rate of about 20 cps from an oscilloscope. The output of the diode second detector was then fed through a low pass filter with a bandpass of about 200 cps, and displayed on the scope. The emission lines appeared on the scope, as in Fig. 4 when the klystron $K1$ swept through the ammonia transition frequencies.

The line frequencies were measured in the usual way by means of standard frequency markers at 30-Mc/sec intervals generated by multiplication up from a 50-kc/sec quartz crystal oscillator whose frequency is monitored directly against radio station WWV.[12] An AM receiver tuned to the frequency difference between the ammonia line frequency and the nearest standard marker picks up the beat note between the signal klystron and the standard marker. As the klystron sweeps, a pip emerges from the receiver which is displayed on the oscilloscope along with the emission line pattern. Calibration of the receiver setting gives the line frequency when the pip is centered on the line.

The lock-in detector was also used during a few of the frequency measurements. In this case the difference between the signal klystron frequency and a nearby standard frequency was fed into an FM reciver, and the discriminator output of the receiver was used as an *AFC* to fix the frequency of the signal klystron at a point determined by the receiver tuning. Point by point measurements at intervals of a few kilocycles were then made in order to take advantage of the long time-constants (about $\frac{1}{3}$ sec) afforded by the lock-in circuit. The increase in sensitivity afforded by the reduced band width of the lock-in system was, however, offset by a decrease in resolution caused by the introduction of spurious frequency modulation into the klystron signal from noise in the frequency standard. In addition this method was considerably more cumbersome and time-consuming and hence was not used very much.

The equivalent band with for a detecting system of the type used has been discussed by Geschwind,[13] who showed that it is

$$\Delta\nu=[(\Delta\nu_1)(\Delta\nu_2)]^{\frac{1}{2}},$$

where $\Delta\nu_1=2.5\times10^6$ cps is the band width of the IF amplifier, and $\Delta\nu_2$ is the band width of the output circuit of the diode second detector. In the first and most frequently used measuring technique discussed above, $\Delta\nu_2$ was about 200 cps, so that

$$\Delta\nu=(2.5\times10^6\times2\times10^2)^{\frac{1}{2}}=2.2\times10^4 \text{ cps}.$$

An increased signal-to-noise ratio is therefore possible if the band width of the detecting system is reduced.

---

[12] Gordy, Smith, and Trambarulo, *Microwave Spectroscopy* (John Wiley and Sons, Inc., New York, 1953).

[13] S. Geschwind, thesis, Columbia University, 1951 (unpublished). See also Ann. N. Y. Acad. Sci. **55**, 751 (1952), Article 5.

The measurements were made difficult by the width of the frequency standard marker pips. This width is caused by spurious frequency modulation of the standard and klystron signals. At best, the marker pips could be narrowed to about 10 or 15 kc/sec, and the center of the pips could only be determined to about 1 kc/sec. The situation, plus the fact that drifts in the klystron control circuits made it difficult to keep the lines on the scope for very long, made the measurements accurate only to about one kilocycle, or about one seventh of the line width. In addition, most of the lines measured were unresolved structures whose shapes could not be accurately calculated because of the effects of the focuser on the populations of the various hyperfine levels. Thus, while measurements could be repeated to an accuracy of about 1 kc/sec, errors in the determinations of the positions of incompletely resolved lines were perhaps somewhat greater. The theoretical frequencies listed in Table II represent our best estimate of the frequencies determined from the theoretical patterns, which should correspond to the measured frequencies.

THE MEASUREMENTS

Measurements were taken on the hyperfine structure of the 1–1, 2–2, 3–3, and 4–3 lines of the NH_3 inversion spectrum. These measurements allowed accurate experimental values to be obtained for the constants A and C of the hydrogen magnetic interaction [see Eq. (5)]. They also provided accurate checks on the previously determined magnetic constants B, a, and b, and of the quadrupole coupling constant eqQ and its dependence on J and K. A slight asymmetry of the hyperfine structure of the 3–3 line was observed and explained by assuming that the magnitude of eqQ is 4 ± 1 kc/sec larger in the lower inversion state than in the upper; however, an apparent slight asymmetry in the structure of the 4–3 line is still unexplained.

Best values for the magnetic constants are, in kc/sec,

$$A=-17.3\pm0.5,\quad B=-14.1\pm0.3,\quad C=-2.0\pm1.0,$$
$$a=6.66\pm0.2,\quad b=6.66\pm0.2,$$

and the quadrupole coupling constant is given by

$$\langle eqQ\rangle_{\mathrm{Av}}=4089\{1+7.7\times10^{-5}[J(J+1)+K^2]\}\pm1.5\ \mathrm{kc/sec},$$

where $\langle eqQ\rangle_{\mathrm{Av}}$ is the average of the quadrupole coupling constants for the upper and lower inversion levels. This result was chosen to provide a best fit to both our data and those of GM I. Our own data on the relatively low J and K lines are somewhat better fitted by a formula

$$\langle eqQ\rangle_{\mathrm{Av}}=-4092.4[1+5\times10^{-5}J(J+1)]\pm1.5\ \mathrm{kc/sec},$$

which, however, does not agree well at high J and K with the results of GM I.

The magnetic structures of the inversion lines may be divided into two classes; those for which $K=1$, and those for which $K\neq1$. For the latter case the K degeneracy (this is discussed in some detail in GM II) is not lifted by the hyperfine interactions. Hence the hyperfine structure of the upper and lower inversion levels is almost identical, and so the hyperfine structure of lines with $K\neq1$ is almost symmetrical about the position of a line undisplaced by hyperfine structure. The only departure from symmetry for which we have allowed is the difference in the quadrupole coupling constants for the upper and lower inversion states.

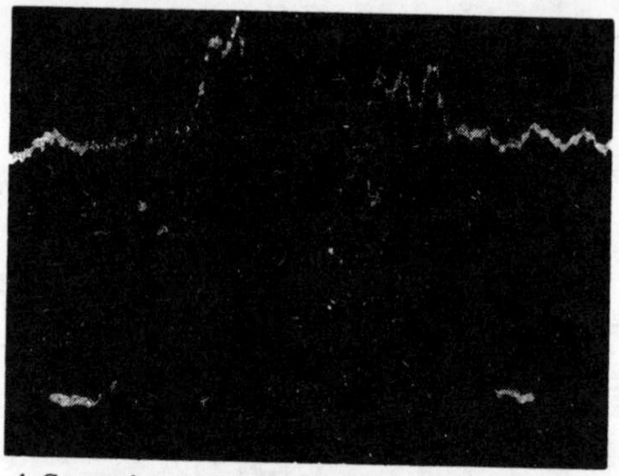

FIG. 4. Composite oscilloscope photograph of the $N^{14}H_3$ $J=K=3$ inversion transition at 23 870 Mc/sec. Below: main line with satellites caused by reorientation of the hydrogen spins. Above left: Inner quadrupole satellite, showing structure due to the hydrogens. Above right: outer quadrupole satellite. The main line has been retouched to make it more visible in the reproduction.

Figures 4 and 5 show the experimental and theoretical structures, respectively, of the 3–3 line. This is the most intense of the observed lines and is an example of the structure to be expected for the $K\neq1$ lines. The main line, composed of the twelve individual hyperfine transitions for which $\Delta F=\Delta F_1=0$, is closely flanked on either side by the magnetic satellites. The satellite on the high-frequency side of the main line is composed of the nine transitions for which $\Delta F=+1$, $\Delta F_1=0$, while the one on the low frequency side has $\Delta F=-1$, $\Delta F_1=0$. At frequency intervals of 1.7 and 2.3 Mc/sec on either side of the main line lie the quadrupole satellites, each of which as its own magnetic structure. This magnetic hyperfine structure of both the main line and the quadrupole satellites had not previously been observed due to lack of resolution or sensitivity. Because of the adiabatic focusing, the quadrupole satellites on the low-frequency side of the main line are considerably weaker than those on the high-frequency side, and only the upper two are shown in Fig. 4. It is to be noticed that the slight asymmetry of the magnetic satellites of the main line is well accounted for by the assumed variation of the quadrupole coupling constant.

Figure 6 shows the theoretical pattern for the 1–1 line. Because of the removal of the K degeneracy by the magnetic interactions in this case, the symmetry of the structure has disappeared. This line was weaker than any of the others, so somewhat larger experimental errors were incurred. It is the only one of the $K=1$ lines which was measured.

TABLE II. Hyperfine spectrum of NH_3. Frequencies are given in kc/sec relative to a theoretical line undisplaced by hyperfine structure. The theoretical frequencies listed are best estimates of the measured positions, after allowances for the observed line shapes and the width of the frequency standard pips.

Component	Transitions $F_1F-F_1'F'$	Experimental frequency	Theoretical frequency
$J=1$, $K=1$; $A+\frac{1}{2}C=-18.3\pm0.3$ kc/sec, $B=-14.1\pm0.3$ kc/sec			
Main line	$2, 5/2 \rightarrow 2, 5/2$		
	$1, \frac{3}{2} \rightarrow 1, \frac{3}{2}$	-15.6	-14.8
	$2, \frac{3}{2} \rightarrow 2, 5/2$		
	$1, \frac{1}{2} \rightarrow 1, \frac{3}{2}$		
	$2, \frac{3}{2} \rightarrow 2, \frac{3}{2}$		
	$2, 5/2 \rightarrow 2, \frac{3}{2}$	13.7	13.0
	$1, \frac{3}{2} \rightarrow 1, \frac{1}{2}$		
	$1, \frac{1}{2} \rightarrow 1, \frac{1}{2}$		
Inner quadrupole satellites	$2, \frac{3}{2} \rightarrow 2, \frac{1}{2}$	-624.2	-622.9
	$2, 5/2 \rightarrow 1, \frac{3}{2}$	-591.3	-590.6
	$2, \frac{3}{2} \rightarrow 1, \frac{3}{2}$		
	$1, \frac{1}{2} \rightarrow 2, \frac{3}{2}$	575.2	572.6
	$1, \frac{3}{2} \rightarrow 2, \frac{3}{2}$		
	$1, \frac{3}{2} \rightarrow 2, 5/2$	619.2	617.8
Outer quadrupole satellites	$0, \frac{1}{2} \rightarrow 1, \frac{1}{2}$		1569.0
	$0, \frac{1}{2} \rightarrow 1, \frac{3}{2}$		1526.9
	$1, \frac{1}{2} \rightarrow 0, \frac{1}{2}$	1540.3	1540.8
	$1, \frac{3}{2} \rightarrow 0, \frac{1}{2}$		

Component	Transitions	No. individual contributing lines	Experimented frequency	Theoretical frequency
$J=2$, $K=2$; $A+\frac{1}{3}C=-18.6\pm0.2$ kc/sec				
Main line	$\Delta F_1=\Delta F=0$	6	$+0.3$	-0.3
Magnetic satellites	$\Delta F_1=0$, $\Delta F=-1$	3	-42.2	-42.0
	$\Delta F_1=0$, $\Delta F=+1$	3	41.1	40.7
Inner quadrupole satellites	$F_1=3\rightarrow 2$, $\Delta F=-1$	2	-1297.3	-1297.3
	$F_1=3\rightarrow 2$, $\Delta F=0$	1		-1255
	$F_1=2\rightarrow 3$, $\Delta F=0$	1	1255.2	1256.0
	$F_1=2\rightarrow 3$, $\Delta F=+1$	2	1296.5	1296.6
Outer quadrupole satellites	$F_1=1\rightarrow 2$, $\Delta F=0$	1		-2099.8
	$F_1=1\rightarrow 2$, $\Delta F=+1$	2	-2056.4	-2057.5
	$F_1=2\rightarrow -1$, $\Delta F=-1$	2	2056.8	2057.5
	$F_1=2\rightarrow 1$, $\Delta F=0$	1	2100.6	2099.8

Component	Transitions	No. individual contributing lines	Experimented frequency	Theoretical frequency
$J=3$, $K=3$; $A=\frac{3}{4}C=-18.8\pm0.2$ kc/sec				
Main line	$\Delta F_1=\Delta F=0$	12		-0.5
Magnetic satellites	$\Delta F_1=0$, $\Delta F-1$	9	-71.0	-71.0
			-62.5	-62.5
	$\Delta F_1=0$, $\Delta F=+1$	9	60.9	61.0
			70.4	70.3
Inner quadrupole satellites	$F_1=4\rightarrow 3$, $\Delta F=0$	3		
	$F_1=4\rightarrow 3$, $\Delta F=-1$	4		-1689.4
				-1680.0
	$F_1=3\rightarrow 4$, $\Delta F=+1$	4	1680	1679.2
			1689.0	1688.6
	$F_1=3\rightarrow 4$, $\Delta F=0$	3		
Outer quadrupole satellites	$F_1=2\rightarrow 3$, $\Delta F=0$	3		-2365.3
				-2383.8
	$F_1=2\rightarrow 3$, $\Delta F=+1$	4		-2323.5
				-2311.2
				-2302.1
	$F_1=3\rightarrow 2$, $\Delta F=-1$	4	2303.0	2302.1
			2311.0	2311.2
			2323.0	2323.5
	$F_1=3\rightarrow 2$, $\Delta F=0$	3	2365.0	2364.8
			2383.5	2383.0
$J=4$, $K=3$; $A+0.45C=-18.2\pm0.2$ kc/sec				
Main line	$\Delta F=\Delta F_1=0$	12	-1.7	0
Magnetic satellites	$\Delta F_1=0$, $\Delta F=-1$	9	-82.0	-81.5
			-65.5	-65.5
	$\Delta F_1=0$, $\Delta F=+1$	9	64.8	65.5
			81.6	81.5
Inner quadrupole satellites	$F_1=5\rightarrow 4$, $\Delta F=-1$	3	-460.9	-462.4
	$F_1=4\rightarrow 5$, $\Delta F=+1$	3	-464.2	462.6
Outer quadrupole satellites	$F_1=3\rightarrow 4$, $\Delta F=+1$	3	-638.4	638.0
	$F_1=4\rightarrow 3$, $\Delta F=-1$	3	638.8	638.2

Table II is a list of all the experimentally measured frequencies, along with the corresponding frequencies determined from theoretical plots of the line structures. In most cases, the observed structures were the envelopes of groups of unresolved or partially resolved individual lines. If these structures had several resolved peaks, then wherever possible the positions of the various peaks were measured. In cases where the envelope was a weak unresolved asymmetric structure, the measurement usually corresponded more nearly to the midpoint between the two frequencies at which the emission was at half-maximum rather than to the point of maximum emission. This was so since the width of the frequency standard pip used for measuring was as broad or broader than the line structures involved, and such a piper could be much more easily centered between the steeply sloping sides of a peak than on its relatively indistinct maximum. In some cases errors greater than one kc/sec could be expected, since effects of the adiabatic focusing on the populations of the various hyperfine levels could not be exactly calculated, therefore the calculation of the line shapes for the unresolved structures was subject to some error.

From the spacings of the magnetic satellites of each of the three measured $K\neq 1$ lines, values of the quantity $\{A+CK^2/[J(J+1)]\}$ could be obtained to an accuracy of about 0.2 kc/sec. These values are shown in Table II. From them the values of A and C given above were calculated. A best fit was then found for the 1–1 line using these values of A and C and varying B. The value of B so obtained is also given above. Theoretically $\{A+CK^2/[J(J+1)]\}$ and B could both be obtained from the structure of this line, but since its intensity was small and the errors correspondingly large, it seemed better to determine A and C from the other lines.

Constants for the magnetic energy associated with orientation of the hydrogen nuclei were used to calculate the structures of the quadrupole satellites, and to obtain the positions of lines displaced only by the hyperfine interactions of the nitrogen nucleus. These displacements were then used to calculate values of $\langle eqQ\rangle_{\mathrm{Av}}$ and of $\{a+(b+a)K^2/[J(J+1)]\}$, the quadrupole and magnetic dipole coupling constants. The second expression given above for the value of $\langle eqQ\rangle_{\mathrm{Av}}$ as a function of J and K seemed to fit our data best, and it was used to calculate the theoretical line frequencies listed in Table II. The first expression for $\langle eqQ\rangle_{\mathrm{Av}}$ agrees better with the results of GM I at high values of J and K, but it increases some of the discrepancies between our own theoretical and experimental results for the case of the 1–1 line. It was, however, thought to be the best available compromise between the present work and that of GM I. The form of the dependence of $\langle eqQ\rangle_{\mathrm{Av}}$ on J and K given in GM I was used simply because this form could not be well determined from the few lines which were measured under high resolution.

These results give a considerable amount of information about the electric and magnetic fields existing within the molecule, which should be explainable in terms of a satisfactory molecular theory. All three components of the molecular magnetic field at the position of the hydrogen nuclei are now known to good accuracy, as well as the two different components of the magnetic field and the gradient of the electric field at the position of the nitrogen nucleus, (which had been previously determined with good accuracy). Some discussion of the interpretation of these constants has been made in GM I.

One expects small variations of eqQ with J and K on account of the centrifugal distortion of the molecule, which produces changes in the inversion wave function. Similarly, a slight change in eqQ from upper inversion level to lower inversion level can be expected. The change of 4 kc/sec which explained satisfactorily the asymmetry of the 3–3 line was also applied on calculating the hyperfine structures of the other lines, but produced no changes in the spectra which would be detectable with the present apparatus. A remaining discrepancy which has not yet been explained is the apparent displacement of the main line of the 4–3 transition. Table II shows that the main line appears to be displaced by about 3 kc/sec away from the average frequency of the two inner quadrupole satellites. Since these measurements were taken rather carefully, this shift appears to be outside of experimental error. In this line the quadrupole splittings are small, so that the asymmetry cannot be accounted for by the small change in quadrupole coupling constant.

The change in eqQ from the upper state to lower can be qualitatively discussed with a relatively crude model. In the lower inversion state, the inversion wave function is a symmetrical function of z, the coordinate which

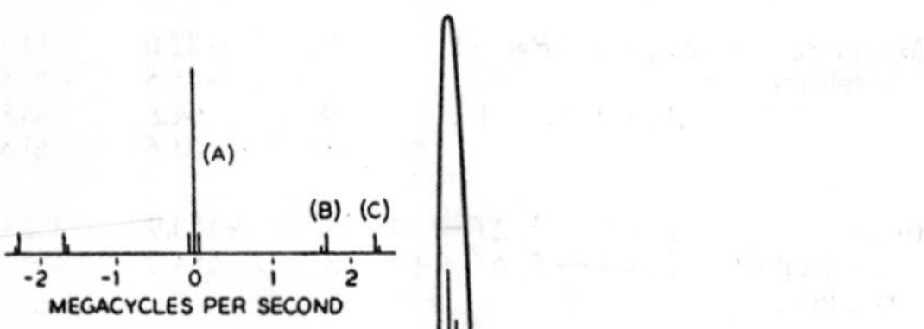

FIG. 5. Theoretical pattern of the hyperfine structure of the $J=K=3$ inversion transition. $\mathbf{F}_1=\mathbf{J}+\mathbf{I}_N$, where I_N is the spin of the nitrogen nucleus. The box at the upper left shows the complete spectrum. Below, the components (a), (b), and (c) of the complete spectrum are shown expanded. Frequency displacements from the position of a line undisplaced by hyperfine structure are shown on the figure. The positions and heights of the solid lines indicate the frequencies and intensities of the various hyperfine structure components of this transition. A total width at half-maximum of 7 kc/sec for each individual component was chosen to give a good fit to the observed spectrum. The intensity of the main line has been reduced by a factor of five.

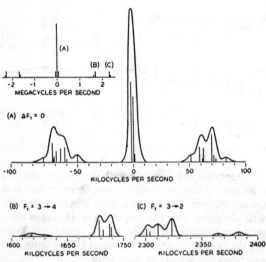

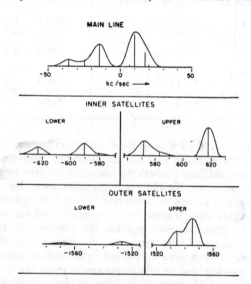

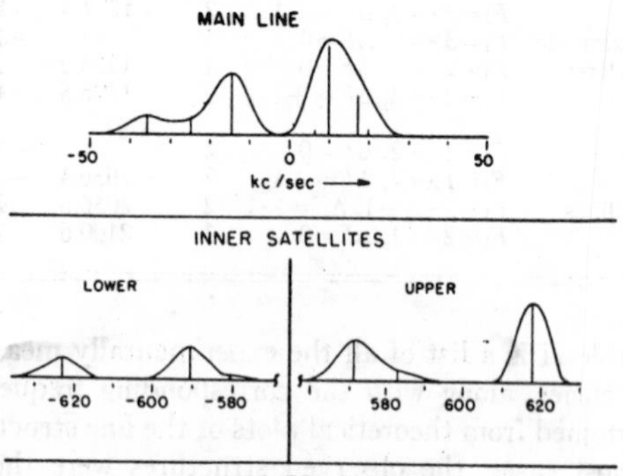

FIG. 6. Theoretical pattern of the $J=K=1$ inversion transition. Note that the symmetry of the hyperfine structure, which was evident in the 3,3 transition, is not present in this case. The total width at half-maximum of each hyperfine component of the transition is chosen as 10 kc/sec. Frequency displacements from the position of a line undisplaced by hyperfine structure are shown on the figure.

gives the position of the nitrogen nucleus on the symmetry axis of the molecule. In the upper state, the inversion wave function is an odd function of z. The nitrogen thus spends more of its time near the plane of the three hydrogens when the molecule is in the lower state. In its most probable configuration, the bond angles of the molecule are only slightly less than the tetrahedral angle. The quadrupole coupling constant is considerably smaller than would be expected if the five bonding electrons combined to form a completely covalent tetrahedral bond. This is due to the partially ionic character of the bond.[14] If, however, we neglect the ionic character and assume a completely covalent bond, we shall observe the proper trend in eqQ. For the tetrahedral bond, the two nonbonding electrons would be represented by $\frac{1}{2}s+\frac{1}{2}\sqrt{3}p_z$ hybrid orbitals, where z is the molecular axis. The value of $q_z=\partial^2V/\partial z^2$ at the position of the nitrogen may be considered as produced by only one of these nonbonding electrons, since the other plus the three bonding electrons form a symmetrical structure for which $q_z=0$. This results in a value $q_z=\frac{3}{4}q_p$, where q_p is the value of $\partial^2V/\partial z^2$ produced by a pure p_z orbital. For the planar configuration of the molecule, through which it must go while inverting, the three bonding electrons should be in sp^2 hybrid orbitals, while the two nonbonding electrons would both be in pure p_z orbitals. It can be shown that in this configuration $q_z=q_p$, which is larger in magnitude than that given by the tetrahedral structure. Thus one should expect the observed larger magnitude for quadrupole coupling in the symmetric lower inversion state, in which the nitrogen spends more time near the plane of the hydrogens.

APPENDIX. SIMPLIFICATION OF TERMS OF THE HAMILTONIAN INVOLVING THE OFF-AXIS NUCLEI

In the hyperfine structure problem in ammonia, one is frequently interested in matrix elements of the form

$$\langle\gamma JK|O|\gamma'J'K'\rangle, \tag{A1}$$

where O is a general operator which contains the spins of the hydrogen nuclei, and $J_z=K$. In other symmetric top molecules similar matrix elements will appear in which O contains the properties of the off axis nuclei. Some simplification of O may be effected by considering the symmetry properties of the molecule.

In the case of ammonia, the three hydrogen nuclei must obey Fermi-Dirac statistics, which means that any physically allowed state of the molecule must obey the equation

$$P_{ij}{}^{\sigma}P_{ij}{}^{x}|\psi\rangle=-|\psi\rangle \quad i\neq j, \tag{A2}$$

where $P_{ij}{}^{x}$ and $P_{ij}{}^{\sigma}$ represent exchange of space and spin coordinates, respectively, of hydrogen nuclei i and j. We shall find it to our advantage to confine our attention to those states of the molecule which satisfy the less restrictive equation

$$P_{ijk}{}^{\sigma}P_{ijk}{}^{x}|\psi\rangle=|\psi\rangle \quad i\neq j\neq k, \tag{A3}$$

where $P_{ijk}=P_{ij}P_{jk}$. States can be constructed satisfying Eq. (A3) which are separable into the product of a spin function and a space function and can be treated without difficulty.[15] The space functions are to be eigenfunctions of the angular momentum operator J_z, which commutes with both $P_{ijk}{}^{x}$ and $P_{ijk}{}^{\sigma}$. The final state function satisfying Eq. (A2) will of necessity be formed of linear combinations of functions satisfying Eq. (A3), so that no generality is lost in this procedure.

The operation $P_{123}{}^{x}$ is equivalent to a rotation of the molecule through an angle of $2\pi/3$ around its axis of symmetry, and thus can be written in the form $P_{123}{}^{x}=e^{\frac{2}{3}\pi iJ_z}$. Also $P_{123}{}^{\sigma}$ can be expressed in terms of the hydrogen spins I_i.[16] It has the effect of interchanging hydrogen spins; i.e., $(P_{123}{}^{\sigma})^{-1}\mathbf{I}_2P_{123}{}^{\sigma}=\mathbf{I}_1$, etc. In view of Eq. (A3) we may write

$$\begin{aligned}\langle\gamma JK|O|\gamma'J'K'\rangle\\ &=\langle\gamma JK|(P_{123}{}^{x})(P_{123}{}^{\sigma})^{-1}OP_{123}{}^{\sigma}P_{123}{}^{x}|\gamma'J'K'\rangle\\ &=\langle\gamma JK|(P_{132}{}^{x})^{-1}(P_{132}{}^{\sigma})^{-1}OP_{132}{}^{\sigma}P_{132}{}^{x}|\gamma'J'K'\rangle.\end{aligned} \tag{A4}$$

Allowing only the P^x operators to operate on the state functions, and averaging the three resulting expressions gives

$$\begin{aligned}\langle\gamma JK|O|\gamma'J'K'\rangle\\ &=\tfrac{1}{3}\langle\gamma JK|O+e^{\frac{2}{3}\pi i(K'-K)}P_{132}{}^{\sigma}OP_{123}{}^{\sigma}\\ &\quad+e^{-\frac{2}{3}\pi i(K'-K)}P_{123}{}^{\sigma}OP_{132}{}^{\sigma}|\gamma'J'K'\rangle.\end{aligned} \tag{A5}$$

In the particular case of ammonia we shall be interested in matrix elements diagonal in K and those joining the two degenerate states $+K$ and $-K$. Application of Eq. (A5) to the various interactions, particularly those diagonal in K, will reduce them to a simpler form.

We shall illustrate the method by applying it to the mutual spin-spin interaction of the hydrogens. This energy term [see Eq. (5)] transforms under rotations as a second degree spherical harmonic.[17] It can therefore have matrix elements joining state of $I=\frac{3}{2}$ to states of $I=\frac{3}{2}$ and $I=\frac{1}{2}$, but has no matrix elements joining two states of $I=\frac{1}{2}$. It will therefore contribute a term diagonal in K for the states with K a multiple of 3. All other nonzero matrix elements of this interaction (it can change J, K, F_1 by a maximum of two) are between states which are nondegenerate in the rotational energy, and so these matrix elements can be ignored. We are interested therefore only in matrix elements diagonal

[14] J. Bardeen and C. H. Townes, Phys. Rev. **73**, 97 (1948).

[15] For example, $P_{123}{}^{x}$ operating on the rotation vibration function $\psi_v{}^{JKM}$ multiplies it by $e^{i2\pi K/3}$. Thus we choose a spin function with the property that $P_{123}{}^{\sigma}$ operating on its multiplies it by $e^{-i2\pi K/3}$.

[16] P. A. M. Dirac, *The Principles of Quantum Mechanics* (Clarendon Press, Oxford, 1947), third edition, p. 222.

[17] J. H. Van Vleck, *Theory of Electric and Magnetic Susceptibilities* (Oxford University Press, London, 1932).

in K. Substituting $K'=K$ in Eq. (A5) gives

$$O \rightarrow \tfrac{1}{3}\{O+P_{132}{}^{\sigma}OP_{123}{}^{\sigma}+P_{123}{}^{\sigma}OP_{132}{}^{\sigma}\}. \quad \text{(A6)}$$

This operation immediately reduces (1) to (2) with only a small amount of algebra, after (1) is expanded in terms of the molecular axes.

To demonstrate the application of the method to interactions which have matrix elements of interest which are off-diagonal in K, we shall apply it to the hydrogen-nitrogen spin-spin interaction. This part of the Hamiltonian may be written

$$G^{\mathrm{HN}}=g_{\mathrm{H}}g_{\mathrm{N}}\mu_0{}^2r_{\mathrm{HH}}{}^{-3} \times\sum_i[\mathbf{I}_i\cdot\mathbf{I}_{\mathrm{N}}-3r_{\mathrm{HN}}{}^{-2}(\mathbf{I}_i\cdot\mathbf{r}_{i\mathrm{N}})(\mathbf{I}_{\mathrm{N}}\cdot\mathbf{r}_{i\mathrm{N}}), \quad \text{(A7)}$$

where r_{HN} is the hydrogen-nitrogen distance, and $\mathbf{r}_{i\mathrm{N}}$ is the vector distance between the ith hydrogen and the nitrogen. This interaction can lift the K degeneracy for $K=\pm1$, as shown in GM II, and so we shall be interested in the diagonal elements and those joining $K=\pm1$ to $K=\mp1$. Again, all other nonzero matrix elements are off-diagonal in the rotational energy. For the diagonal part we may make the substitution (A6), which here has the effect of replacing I_i by $I/3$, and so we obtain

$$\langle K|G_1{}^{\mathrm{HN}}|K\rangle=g_{\mathrm{H}}g_{\mathrm{N}}\mu_0{}^2\langle K|r_{\mathrm{HN}}{}^{-3}[\mathbf{I}\cdot\mathbf{I}_{\mathrm{N}} -\sum_i r_{\mathrm{HN}}{}^{-2}(\mathbf{I}\cdot\mathbf{r}_{i\mathrm{N}})(\mathbf{I}_{\mathrm{N}}\cdot\mathbf{r}_{i\mathrm{N}})]|K\rangle. \quad \text{(A8)}$$

Expanding this in terms of the molecular axes then results in

$$\langle K|G_1{}^{\mathrm{HN}}|K\rangle=2g_{\mathrm{H}}g_{\mathrm{N}}v_0{}^2\langle K|r_{\mathrm{HN}}{}^{-3}(1-\tfrac{3}{2}\sin^2\beta) \times(I\cdot I_{\mathrm{N}}-3I_zI_{\mathrm{N}z})|K\rangle. \quad \text{(A9)}$$

Now we are here interested also in those matrix elements which join the two degenerate states of $K=\pm1$, so we must evaluate $\langle K=\pm1|G_1{}^{\mathrm{HN}}|K'=\mp1\rangle$ Application of (7) reduces this matrix to the form

$$\langle K=\pm1|G_1{}^{\mathrm{HN}}|K'=\mp1\rangle =g_{\mathrm{H}}g_{\mathrm{N}}\mu_0{}^2\langle K=\pm1|r_{\mathrm{HN}}{}^{-3}[-(9/4)\sin^2\beta \times(I_{1x}{}'\mp iI_{1y}{}')(I_{\mathrm{N}x}{}'\mp iI_{\mathrm{N}y}{}')]|K'=\mp1\rangle, \quad \text{(A10)}$$

or

$$\langle K=\pm1|G_1{}^{\mathrm{HN}}|K'=\mp1\rangle =g_{\mathrm{H}}g_{\mathrm{N}}\mu_0{}^2\langle K=\pm1|r_{\mathrm{HN}}{}^{-3}(9/2)\sin^2\beta \times(I_{1y}I_{\mathrm{N}y}-I_{1x}I_{\mathrm{N}x})|K=\mp1\rangle. \quad \text{(A11)}$$

Since (A9) and (A11) give all the matrix elements of interest, we see that the complete interaction can be replaced by the somewhat simplified form:

$$G_1{}^{\mathrm{HN}}\rightarrow g_{\mathrm{H}}g_{\mathrm{N}}\mu_0{}^2r_{\mathrm{HN}}{}^{-3}[(1-\tfrac{3}{2}\sin^2\beta)(\mathbf{I}\cdot\mathbf{I}_{\mathrm{N}}-3I_zI_{\mathrm{N}z}) +(9/2)\sin^2\beta(I_{1y}I_{\mathrm{N}y}-I_{1x}I_{\mathrm{N}x})]. \quad \text{(A12)}$$

Evaluation of the off-diagonal matrix elements (A11) may be made according to the standard methods of Condon and Shortley, remembering our choice of spin functions, or the equivalent Hamiltonian (A12) may be treated by the methods of GM II.

The method may easily be extended to the treatment of the $I\cdot J$ interaction, and yields the same result as that obtained in GM II. (Note the correction to GM II given in reference 8.)

ACKNOWLEDGMENTS

The author would like to express his appreciation to the personnel of the Columbia Radiation Laboratory who assisted in the construction of the experimental apparatus. Dr. H. J. Zeiger and Dr. T. C. Wang contributed greatly to the experiment in various stages. In particular the author is indebted to Professor C. H. Townes for suggesting this research and for his continued advice and guidance.

A NEW EXPERIMENTAL TEST OF SPECIAL RELATIVITY

By J. P. CEDARHOLM
I.B.M. Watson Laboratory
AND
PROF. C. H. TOWNES
Columbia University, New York

EXPERIMENTS which have tested special relativity have usually been forced to rely on great delicacy and precision in order to detect or examine the small differences between predictions of special relativity and those of alternate theories. This is because these differences appear multiplied by a very small quantity $(v/c)^2$, where c is the velocity of light and v is some relative velocity which is generally much smaller than c. While giving a clear-cut support to special relativity over some other theories such as a simple ether, experiments have not generally measured the small terms in $(v/c)^2$ with impressive fractional accuracy. Michelson and Morley's first experiment[1], for example, was of remarkable precision. But it was searching for a change in light-path of only about one part in 10^8 due to the motion of the Earth about the Sun on the basis of the then current ether theory, and was able to set an upper limit no less than 1/40 of this, or an ether drift of about one-sixth the orbital velocity of the Earth. Subsequent very refined experiments[2] of a similar type succeeded, a half-century later, in setting an upper limit on any ether drift of 1/20 the velocity of the Earth around the Sun. Others[3] even suggested the existence of an ether drift as large as about one-fifth of the orbital velocity of the Earth. The advent of very high precision atomic clocks suggests that still more exacting experimental tests may now be made; one such, which is now more or less completed, is reported here.

The experiment compares the frequencies of two maser oscillators[4] with their beams of ammonia molecules pointed in opposite directions, but both parallel to a supposed direction of motion through the ether. If both masers are rotated 180°, and their frequencies again compared, a change in relative frequency should be found due to motion of the masers through the ether, assuming the molecular vibrations are unchanged by such motion. A precision of one part in 10^{12} has been achieved in this frequency comparison, and failure to find a frequency change of the predicted type allows setting the upper limit on an ether drift as low as 1/1,000 of the orbital velocity of the Earth. This precision also provides a test for some other effects which will be discussed below.

The effect on the frequency of a beam-type maser oscillator of motion through the ether was first worked out by Møller[5]. A brief, somewhat intuitive explanation of this shift follows. In this device, ammonia molecules in an excited state travel at thermal velocities along the axis of a circular cylindrical cavity, giving it energy. If the cavity is stationary in the ether, the standing waves may be considered to be made of travelling waves with wave-fronts nearly parallel to the axis. As the molecule moves along the axis, there is then no Doppler shift. If the apparatus is moving axially through the ether at velocity v, the wave-fronts must tilt at an angle $\alpha = v/c$ in order to follow this axial velocity. Hence, molecules travelling at velocity u through the cavity produce a frequency shifted by the Doppler effect of an amount $\nu u\alpha/c = \nu uv/c^2$. Here ν is the molecular frequency. Since $uv\nu/c^2$ depends on the relative direction of u and v, two masers with oppositely directed beams should have frequencies which differ by $2uv\nu/c^2$ due to this effect. If each is rotated 180°, the total change in their frequency difference is $4uv\nu/c^2$.

A more precise derivation of this effect is obtained from the fact that special relativity predicts the same result as does an ether theory, provided that the FitzGerald contraction $\sqrt{\left(1 - \frac{V^2}{c^2}\right)}$ is introduced for any length parallel to the motion v through the ether, and also that the proper time of any clock or oscillator is modified by the same factor $\sqrt{\left(1 - \frac{V^2}{c^2}\right)}$ due to this motion. In other words, any effect due to motion through a simple ether is just compensated by appropriate changes in scale for length and time which correspond to the Lorentz transformation. If, then, an ether theory is used without FitzGerald contraction and time dilation, the expected shift in frequency may be computed from an examination of the effects of these changes of scale for length and time.

Consider first the FitzGerald contraction. Its effect on the frequency of maser oscillation is very small and may be neglected because this frequency is rather insensitive to the dimensions and resonant frequency of the cavity[4].

The time dilation, however, produces the effect we seek. If the cavity moves through the ether at a velocity v and the molecule through the cavity at velocity u, then the molecular velocity through the ether is $V = u+v$, and the molecular time will be slow, for an observer in the framework of the ether, for the factor:

$$\sqrt{\left\{1 - \frac{(u+v)^2}{c^2}\right\}} \approx 1 - \frac{u^2}{2c^2} - \frac{uv}{c^2} - \frac{v^2}{c^2}$$

But time in the actual laboratory framework, which is fixed with respect to the cavity, is slow by the factor:

$$\sqrt{\left(1 - \frac{v^2}{c^2}\right)} \approx 1 - \frac{v^2}{2c^2}$$

Hence the molecule would appear slow to an observer in the laboratory by the difference between these two, or by the factor:

$$1 - \frac{u^2}{2c^2} - \frac{uv}{c^2}$$

The first small correction is the well-known transverse Doppler effect, and is independent of ether drift. The second small correction is the discrepancy uv/c^2 which would occur if we were to accept a simple ether and no time dilation in the proper oscillation of the molecule, as postulated in Møller's original discussion[5].

The above derivation makes it clear that failure to see any change in time equivalent to the small fractional amount uv/c^2 may be explained away by the assumption of a time dilation for those who wish to adhere to an ether with such peculiarities. Hence the experiment is more closely related to the Kennedy–Thorndike experiment[6] than to that of Michelson and Morley. A null result in the latter needs, of course, only a FitzGerald contraction for an explanation in terms of an ether theory.

For performance of the present experiment, two ammonia beam masers were mounted with oppositely directed beams on a rack which rotated about a vertical axis. The frequencies of these oscillators are near 23,870 Mc./s. The thermal velocity u = 0·6 km./s. for NH_3 at room temperature. If the orbital velocity of the Earth is assumed to be the rate of motion through the ether, then v = 30 km./s. and the frequency change $4uv\nu/c^2$ = 20 c./s. when the masers are rotated 180° from an initial east–west position at noon or midnight.

During a small fraction of a second the relative frequency of the two masers fluctuates randomly about $\frac{1}{10}$ c./s. Over somewhat longer periods, such as those required for measurement before and after rotation, the average frequency difference does not vary more than about $\frac{1}{50}$ c./s. or one part in 10^{12}. Hence the 20 c./s. variation expected on an ether theory would be very easily detected. Variation of about 1 c./s. on rotation of the two masers was in fact observed. However, this variation could be eliminated by magnetically shielding the masers, and without shielding it remained constant to within about $\frac{1}{50}$ c./s. as the Earth rotated throughout a 24-hr. run. This shows that no more than about $\frac{1}{50}$ c./s. shift could be attributed to an ether drift.

The experiment involving rotation of the two masers was carefully done for the first time on September 20, 1958[7]. No proper effect as large as $\frac{1}{50}$ c./s. was found. Hence, since the orbital velocity of the Earth of 30 km./s. would have given an effect of 20 c./s., the ether drift could not have been larger than 1/1,000 of this value, or 30 m./s. It is, of course, possible for the motion of the Earth to be just cancelled by the motion of the solar system through the ether at some particular time of the year. The experiment has now been repeated at the Watson Laboratory during 24-hr. runs at approximately three-month intervals throughout the year. In none of these runs was any effect as large as $\frac{1}{50}$ c./s. found.

The present experiment sets an upper limit on an ether-drift velocity about one-fiftieth that allowed by previous experiments. This is in part because the effect measured is linear in the ether drift velocity v. An experiment of the Michelson–Morley type is designed to detect a fractional change of the form $\frac{1}{2}v^2/c^2$, which is an order of magnitude larger than the term uv/c^2 discussed here. An upper limit of 1/400 of $\frac{1}{2}v^2c^2$ has been set by the very careful experiments of Joos[2] with a Michelson interferometer. However, since this term is second order in v, the upper limit given for the ether-drift velocity is one-twentieth of the orbital velocity of the Earth, or 1·5 km./s. The present experiments have the advantage that the expected effect is linear in v, and also that two clocks can now be compared with much greater precision than can two distances. This experiment, involving a comparison of two maser oscillators to an accuracy of one part in 10^{12}, may perhaps represent the most precise experiment so far reported.

For most physicists, a confirmation of the fundamental postulate of special relativity that no absolute motion can be detected comes as no surprise, and a more precise experimental test may not even seem important because this postulate is so intuitively satisfactory and firmly accepted. It should be noted, however, that the positive detection of an effect in the present experiment could give some new information without necessarily contradicting the general principles of relativity. The motion of the Earth involves velocity relative to other parts of the solar system, as well as to the fixed stars and external galaxies. Hence this relative motion might, in principle, produce some anisotropy in space and some shift in relative frequency of the two masers when they are rotated by 180°.

Dicke[8] has suggested that an effect due to motion with respect to fixed masses in the universe should be present which is of the order of the fine structure constant, α, times the effect due to ether drift. This would correspond to a frequency shift in the present experiment of the order of $\frac{1}{7}$ c./s. Reasons given by Dicke why such a shift might occur are speculative, but very interesting. The present results allow no shift larger than $\frac{1}{50}$ c./s., which gives some indication against a term of the order $4\alpha uv\nu/c^2$.

Optical maser oscillators[9] should also lend themselves to interesting experiments on relativity, since they will probably be capable of examining changes in length as small as one part in 10^{12}. An optical maser oscillator could be constructed with a resonance between two étalon plates which is narrower in frequency than the atomic resonance supplying energy. In this case the frequency would depend primarily on the spacing between the plates, rather than on the atomic frequency. It is estimated that the oscillation would be monochromatic to about one part in 10^{11}. This suggests an experiment in which the oscillations of two optical masers are beat together in a photocell. One of the masers may be rotated about a vertical axis. On the basis of an ether theory, the beat frequency should then vary by an amount $\pm\ v^2\nu/2c^2$, for the same reasons that the Michelson–Morley experiment was expected to show a variation of path length. The fraction v^2/c^2 is 10^{-8}, so that its presence could probably be tested with excellent precision.

1 Michelson, A. A., and Morley, E. W., *Amer. J. Sci.*, **34**, 333 (1887).
2 Joos, G., *Ann. Phys.*, **7**, 385 (1930).
3 Miller, D. C., *Revs. Mod. Phys.*, **5**, 203 (1933). See, however, Shankland, R. S., McCuskey, S. W., Leone, F. C., and Kuerti, G., *ibid.*, **27**, 167 (1955).
4 Gordon, J. P., Zeiger, H. J., and Townes, C. H., *Phys. Rev.*, **99**, 1264 (1955).
5 Møller, C., *Nuovo Cimento*, **6**, Supp., 381 (1957).
6 Kennedy, R. J., and Thorndike, E. M., *Phys. Rev.*, **42**, 400 (1932).
7 Cedarholm, J. P., Bland, G. F., Havens, B. L., and Townes, C. H., *Phys. Rev. Letters*, **1**, 342 (1958).
8 Dicke, R. H., Proc. Symp. Quantum Electronics, Columbia Univ. Press (to be published).
9 Schawlow, A. L., and Townes, C. H., *Phys. Rev.*, **112**, 1940 (1958).

Reprinted from JOURNAL OF APPLIED PHYSICS, Vol. 33, No. 7, 2370-2372, July, 1962

High Resolution Ammonia ($N^{14}H_3$) Maser

F. HOLUJ,* H. DAAMS, AND S. N. KALRA*
Division of Applied Physics, National Research Council, Ottawa, Canada
(Received January 12, 1962)

A $N^{14}H_3$ maser based on Ramsey's principle of separated oscillatory fields has been used to increase the resolution over a conventional maser. A single component of the 3.3 inversion line of $N^{14}H_3$ can be isolated. This type of maser overcomes the difficulties arising from the composite structure of the line.

THE resolution of a $N^{14}H_3$ maser has been considerably increased by using a three-cavity system satisfying the conditions of Ramsey's separated oscillatory fields technique.[1] A single cavity $N^{14}H_3$ maser oscillating at the main $J=K=3$ inversion line corresponding to transitions $\Delta F_1=0$ suffers from two main disadvantages both as a high resolution spectrometer and as a frequency standard.[2]

The cavity pulling. This pulling obeys approximately the relation[2-5]

$$\nu-\nu_0=(Q/Q_l)(\nu_c-\nu_0), \quad (1)$$

where Q=loaded cavity Q, Q_l=emission line Q, ν=maser frequency, ν_0=center of line frequency, and ν_c=cavity frequency. Detuning the cavity frequency ν_c by a few megacycles pulls the maser frequency from the natural line frequency by a few kilocycles.

The fine structure of the inversion 3.3 line. The main inversion line is a composite line. It consists of three components corresponding to $F_1=2$, 3, 4. In a maser the various components occur in ratio $F_1=3:4:2$ $=1:0.92:0.05$.[4] These figures demonstrate that only the two components $F_1=3$ and $F_1=4$ need be considered. The presence of two components has the effect of continuously varying the frequency of oscillations as a function of molecular beam flux in the cavity, which is dependent on the state selector voltage and the source pressure.

These disadvantages have been largely overcome in the present experiment using Ramsey's separated oscillatory fields.[1] Theory shows that in Ramsey's arrangement, cavity pulling of a maser frequency can be expressed, using notation of reference 3, as

$$\omega-\omega_0=\frac{2Q}{2\tau\omega_0}\left[(1-\cos 2\theta)\Big/\left(1-\frac{\sin 2\theta}{2\theta\tau}+\frac{T}{2\tau}\theta\sin\theta\right)\right](\omega_c-\omega_0), \quad (2)$$

where T is the molecular time of flight between the two oscillatory regions, and 2τ is the combined time of flight through the two oscillatory regions. Equation 2 is valid for $\theta\gg(\omega-\omega_0)\tau/2$ and $T(\omega-\omega_0)/2\rightarrow 0$. In the case when $\theta\rightarrow 0$, Eq. (2) reduces to Eq. (1). The cavity pulling is substantially reduced however, since the cavity Q is lowered and the Q_l increased. An expression for the linewidth can be derived from the probability amplitude.

$$|a_1(2\tau+T)|^2=\frac{4\mu^2E^2\sin^2[(\omega-\omega_0)\tau/2]}{\hbar^2\,[(\omega-\omega_0)\tau/2]^2}\times\cos^2\left[\frac{\omega-\omega_0}{2}(\tau+T)\right], \quad (3)$$

and is valid for $|\omega-\omega_0|\tau/2\gg\mu E\tau/\hbar$. The linewidth for a cavity system for which $T/\tau\approx 4$ is, therefore, $2\Delta\nu=0.15/\tau$. For comparison, in a single cavity maser, the linewidth is[2] $2\Delta\nu=0.89/\tau$. Ramsey's arrangement can, therefore, be expected to improve the performance of a molecular beam maser. Experimental results fully justify theoretical predictions.

Figure 1 shows a diagrammatic arrangement of the maser; a, b, and c form a cavity system; f_1, f_2 and S_1, S_2

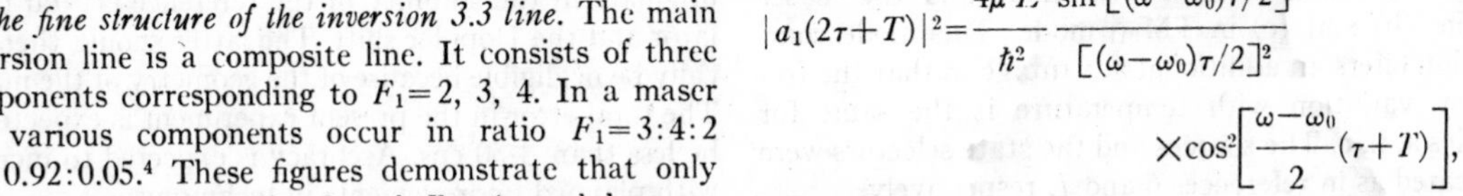

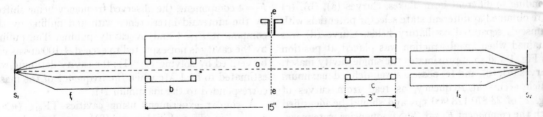

FIG. 1. Diagrammatic arrangement of the maser. a, b, and c form the cavity arrangement. f_1, f_2, and S_1, S_2 are identical state selectors and sources, respectively.

* Present address: Essex College, Assumption University, Windsor, Ontario, Canada.

[1] N. F. Ramsey, Phys. Rev. **78**, 695 (1950).
[2] J. Bonanomi, J. Hermann, J. de Prins, and P. Kartaschoff, Rev. Sci. Instr. **28**, 879 (1957).
[3] K. Shimoda, T. C. Wang, and C. H. Townes, Phys. Rev. **102**, 1308 (1956).
[4] K. Shimoda, J. Phys. Soc. Japan **12**, 1006 (1957).
[5] J. P. Gordon, H. J. Zeigler, and C. H. Townes, Phys. Rev. **99**, 1264 (1955).

NRC 6872

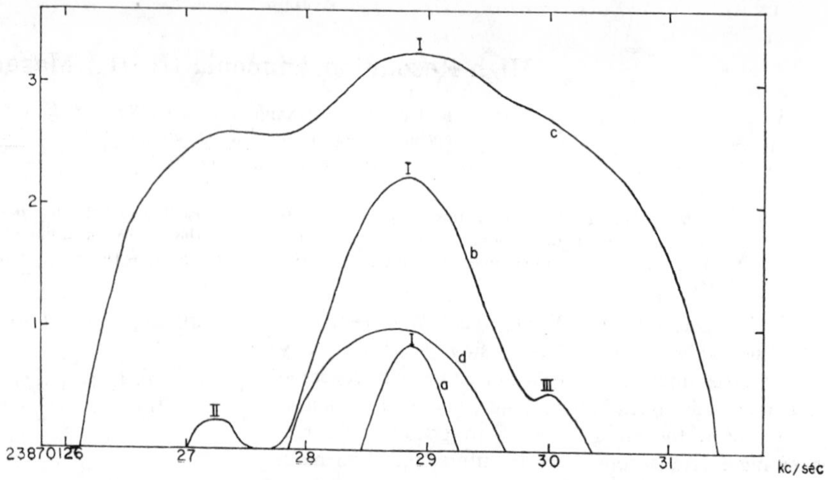

FIG. 2. Maser oscillation modes. Amplitude of oscillation in arbitrary units is plotted against frequency of oscillation. Curves (a), (b), and (c) were obtained at different state-selector potentials with Ramsey's separated oscillatory fields type of maser. Curve (d) was obtained with an obstruction in between the two maser cavities.

are identical state selectors and sources of $N^{14}H_3$ molecules, respectively. Care has been taken to ensure a geometrical symmetry of cavity system, state selectors and sources. Electrical symmetry of the cavity system is very important. Cavity (a) can be looked upon as a phase controller of the two maser cavities (b) and (c). Equality of phase in the two maser cavities can be assured by strongly overcoupling them to the phase controller. Strongest coupling was achieved when the cavity (a) oscillated in TM_{015} mode and the maser cavities (b) and (c) in TM_{011} mode. This mode combination offers an additional advantage in that the frequency variation with temperature is the same for cavities a, b, c. The sources and the state selectors were fabricated as in references 6 and 7, respectively.

Self-sustained oscillations occur at relatively high molecular beam fluxes. This is a consequence of high cavity losses (the cavity system Q is of the order of 2500), and of the fact that molecules with collimation 0.01 rad or better are the only ones that can pass through both cavities b, c. The amplitude and frequency of maser oscillation were measured at intervals of time as the cavity temperature was allowed to drift continuously.

Figure 2 shows the maser oscillation modes corresponding to different beam fluxes. Curves (a), (b), (c) were obtained at different state selector potentials with Ramsey's separated oscillatory fields. Curve (d) was obtained when an obstruction was placed at position *e-e* Fig. 1 and so approximates the single cavity maser. Curves (a), (b), and (c) possess a well-defined maximum which occurs at frequency, as read from curves of Fig. 2, of 23 870 128 900 cps and should be identified with the component $F_1=3$. The frequencies were measured in terms of a quartz crystal oscillator calibrated against a Cs^{133} atomic beam resonator of assumed frequency of 9 192 631 770 cps. The error of reading the graph is estimated at ± 10 cps and can presumably be reduced by applying an experimental technique developed originally by J. de Prins *et al.*,[8] which consists of Zeeman modulating the maser and determining the maser frequency at which the cavity pulling is zero. Possible sources of error arise from the experimental technique rather than from an inherent instability of the maser. Other errors of somewhat greater magnitude than the error of reading the graphs are expected to originate in the stability of the reference crystal oscillator and the Doppler shift. The latter should theoretically be negligible because of the geometry of the maser. The total error in the present experiment is expected to be less than ± 50 cps. Accuracy is expected to increase with planned improvements in technique.

Curve (b) displays additional two maxima II and III. II occurs at a frequency 1590 cps lower than peak I and should be identified with one of the outer maxima of the transition probability curve calculated for Ramsey's separated oscillatory fields. A corresponding maximum on the high-frequency side of the peak I is masked due to its interference with the component $F_1=4$, thus giving rise to maximum III, curve (b) of Fig. 2. This maximum, which occurs close to 1160 cps above peak I, does not, however, represent a natural frequency of the $F_1=4$ component, the observed frequency being shifted by the aforesaid interference with and pulling by the component $F_1=3$ and by cavity pulling. The pulling by the cavity is not expected to exceed $+100$ cps as can be verified by solving Eq. (1); the cavity detuning was estimated to be 1 Mc when the frequency of the maser corresponded to the maximum III.

A similar experiment using cavities TE_{01n} ($n>5$, 7, . . .) in place of TM_{015} and TM_{011} is planned. Such cavity combinations, because of their larger diameter,

[6] G. R. Hanes, J. Appl. Phys. 31, 2171 (1960).
[7] J. C. Helmer and F. B. Jacobus, J. Appl. Phys. 31, 458 (1960).
[8] J. de Prins and P. Kartaschoff, "Applications de la spectroscopie hertzienne à la mesure des fréquences et du temps," Topics on Radio Frequency Spectroscopy Conference, August 1–17, 1960.

would require less collimated molecular beams and thus lower molecular source pressures. This improvement is to some extent nullified by lower figure[3] of merit for TE cavities. Alternatively, they would permit a design of cavities with larger distances between the two oscillatory regions.

It has been shown that by using a cavity structure based on Ramsey's separated oscillatory technique the resolution of $N^{14}H_3$ maser spectrometer can be increased to the point where a single component of the central 3.3 line of $N^{14}H_3$ is resolved. This type of maser oscillator shows no dependence of frequency on beam flux within the accuracy of measurement of ± 10 cps. The cavity pulling effect is also greatly reduced.

Reprinted from JOURNAL OF APPLIED PHYSICS, Vol. 31, No. 5, 941–942, May, 1960

Proposed Molecular Amplifier and Coherent Generator for Millimeter and Submillimeter Waves*

WALTER GORDY AND MONROE COWAN†
Department of Physics, Duke University, Durham, North Carolina
(Received February 4, 1960)

In an attempt to construct a coherent quantum mechanical submillimeter wave generator or amplifier through stimulated emission of molecules in molecular beams, as in the ammonia maser,[1,2] practical difficulties arise in the design for an effective state selector for securing the needed excess population in the upper, emitting state. These difficulties result partly from the increasing number of sublevels (as J increases) but primarily from the decreasing sensitivity of molecules to field gradients with an increase in rotational frequency. Upon first thought it seems that one should be able to overcome the latter difficulty by using $K=0$, $M=0$ levels of symmetric-top molecules which have first-order Stark effects and are sensitive to deflection by inhomogeneous electric fields up to very high frequencies. For molecules without nuclear coupling, the first-order energy is

$$E_{JKM}=\frac{-\mu \mathcal{E} MK}{J(J+1)},$$

and in a field gradient $(\partial \mathcal{E}/\partial x)$ the molecules would experience a deflecting force

$$f_x=\frac{-E_{JKM}}{\partial x}=\frac{\mu KM}{J(J+1)}\left(\frac{\partial \mathcal{E}}{\partial x}\right).$$

By choosing molecules such as CH_3F or PH_3 which have rotational states of low J that give rise to submillimeter wave lines, one can keep the denominator of this expression relatively small and the deflecting force effective up to very high submillimeter wave frequencies, of the order of 3×10^{12} cps (wavelength 0.1 mm). However, one encounters the difficulty that the lower as well as the upper J levels are deflected in the same direction for the sublevels with the same sign of M. This not only decreases the angular separation achieved but also imposes the difficulty that one must focus into the emission cavity molecules which are deflected by the inhomogeneous field in the same direction as those rejected.

It has occurrred to us how one can avoid the above difficulties by employing as the stimulated emitters states of symmetric-top molecules with $M=0$ but $K\neq0$. The states have no first-order Stark effect and are, relative to the $M\neq0$, $K\neq0$ states, essentially insensitive to field gradients. Thus by passing a collimated beam of symmetric-top molecules through an electric field gradient one can scatter out of the beam the $M\neq0$ states while leaving the $M=0$ states relatively well focused into the cavity. The upper state, $J+1$, K, $M=0$, however, will not have greater population in the cavity than the lower state, J, K, $M=0$. Hence, one will not achieve maser action by this state selection alone. If, however, a homogeneous Stark or Zeeman field is applied on the molecules in the microwave emission cell so as to lift the M degeneracy with the direction of the field arranged relative to the mode lines (or the microwave radiation field) in such a way that the $\Delta M=\pm1$ transitions are stimulated, it is apparent that stimulated emission will occur between the upper $J+1$, K, $M=0$ to the lower, J, K, $M=\pm1$ levels (which by the preselection are depleted in population). The counter absorption, J, K, $M=0$ to $J+1$, K, $M=\pm1$ can also occur; but because of the marked difference in the splitting of the $M=\pm1$ levels for different J values for first-order, Stark, or Zeeman effect [in each case the splitting varies inversely as $J(J+1)$], the latter absorption will occur at a different frequency and will not cancel the emission. Also, the $\Delta M=0$ transitions will be separated in frequency from the desired emission lines.

Thus by a combination of an inhomogeneous field outside the radiation cell and an homogeneous (Stark or Zeeman) field inside the cell, amplification of submillimeter waves can be achieved through stimulated $J+1\rightarrow J$, $K\rightarrow K$, $M\rightarrow M\pm1$ transitions where $K\neq0$ and $M\neq0$. An energy level diagram indicating these transitions with a selected case is given in Fig. 1.

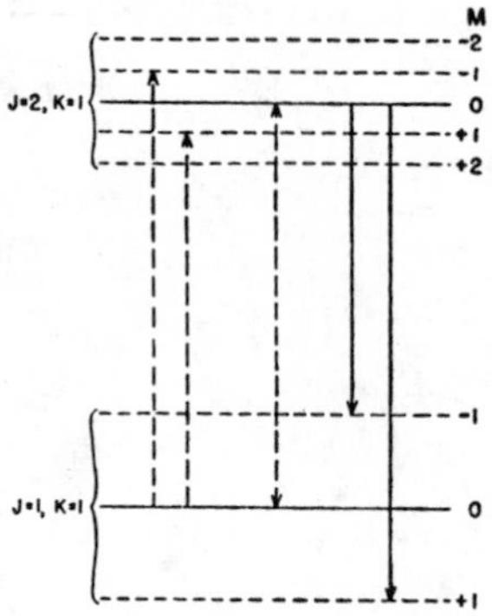

FIG. 1. Energy level diagram for $J=1$, $K=1$ and $J=2$, $K=1$ levels showing populated $M=0$ substates in solid lines and the depleted $M\neq0$ states in broken horizontal lines. The solid vertical lines pointing downward indicate the transitions employed for the maser action.

We are attempting to construct millimeter and submillimeter amplifiers and generators based upon the above principle, one type employing the Stark and the other the Zeeman splitting. In this laboratory, cells for observing $\Delta M=\pm1$ components of rotational transitions in absorption have already been designed and successfully applied for both Stark[3] and Zeeman[4] effects. We shall first employ a parallel plate cell for Stark effect and a cylindrical, high Q cavity for the Zeeman cell.

Although the quantum mechanical amplifier proposed here may perhaps be applied most simply with symmetric-top molecules, it is by no means limited to them. The principle of applying a homogeneous field in combination with an inhomogeneous one for state separation in masers is applicable to quantum mechanical systems of other types. Certain asymmetric-top molecules are also usable. Furthermore this amplifier is not limited to millimeter or submillimeter wavelengths but can be used for lower frequencies as well. Because the second-order effect is superimposed on the first-order effect, the spacing of the Stark sublevels for a given J and K are not exactly equal, and the transition $\Delta J=0$, $\Delta K=0$, $M=0\rightarrow+1$ can similarly be employed for low-frequency maser action after the $M\neq0$ states are removed. Unlike the zero-field maser, the one proposed here is tunable over a limited range, and yet with easily obtainable field homogeneities it can be made highly monochromatic.

An early maser proposed by Weber[5] employing stimulated emission between Stark levels of particular rotational states of symmetric-top molecules is entirely different from the one described here. Weber proposed a pulsed Stark field to obtain the excess population in upper states somewhat as Purcell and Pound achieved excess population of upper states in a nuclear resonance experiment to accomplish the first observation of stimulated emission.[6]

* This research was supported by the United States Air Force through the Air Force Office of Scientific Research of the Air Research and Development Command.
† National Science Foundation Postdoctoral Fellow.
[1] J. P. Gordon, H. J. Zeiger, and C. H. Townes, Phys. Rev. **95**, 282 (1954); **99**, 1264 (1955).
[2] N. G. Bassov and A. M. Prokhorov, J. Exptl. Theoret. Phys. **28**, 249 (1955).
[3] Bhattacharya, Gordy, and Fujii, Bull. Am. Phys. Soc. Ser. II, **2**, 213 (1957).
[4] J. T. Cox and W. Gordy, Ph[...] Rev. **101**, 1298 (1956).
[5] J. Weber, I.R.E. Trans. o[...] on Devices ED-3, 1 (1953).
[6] E. M. Purcell and R. V. [...] hys. Rev. **81**, 279 (1951).

SOLID STATE MASERS

General Principles and Development of Amplifiers

Adequate gain bandwidth product together with extremely low noise performance was achieved by use of paramagnetic ions in a host crystal at liquid helium temperatures.

The use of a concentrated magnetic material for a three or four level maser yields negative results. The spin spin relaxation effects are so great that the pump radiation heats up the entire spin system, to one temperature. For maser action the temperatures associated with certain pairs of energy levels must be negative while other pairs of levels should be at essentially infinite temperature. There is a critical value for the concentration of the paramagnetic ion, roughly one per cent, above which no maser action can usually be obtained at any temperature.

The first solid state masers employed a resonant cavity as described in the Reviews of Modern Physics Paper earlier in this volume. Further increase in gain bandwidth product was accomplished by the development of amplifiers of the travelling wave type.

The papers which follow will deal with the general principles, with the development of both cavity and travelling wave amplifiers, with the theoretical and experimental aspects of the spin lattice and spin spin interactions, and with materials and their spectra.

PHYSICAL REVIEW VOLUME 104, NUMBER 2 OCTOBER 15, 1956

Proposal for a New Type Solid State Maser*

N. BLOEMBERGEN
Cruft Laboratory, Harvard University, Cambridge, Massachusetts
(Received July 6, 1956)

The Overhauser effect may be used in the spin multiplet of certain paramagnetic ions to obtain a negative absorption or stimulated emission at microwave frequencies. The use of nickel fluosilicate or gadolinium ethyl sulfate at liquid helium temperature is suggested to obtain a low noise microwave amplifier or frequency converter. The operation of a solid state maser based on this principle is discussed.

TOWNES and co-workers[1,2] have shown that microwave amplification can be obtained by stimulated emission of radiation from systems in which a higher energy level is more densely populated than a lower one. In paramagnetic systems an inversion of the population of the spin levels may be obtained in a variety of ways. The "180° pulse" and the "adiabatic rapid passage" have been extensively applied in nuclear magnetic resonance. Combrisson and Honig[2] applied the fast passage technique to the two electron spin levels of a *P* donor in silicon, and obtained a noticeable power amplification.

Attention is called to the usefulness of power saturation of one transition in a multiple energy level system to obtain a change of sign of the population difference between another pair of levels. A variation in level populations obtained in this manner has been demonstrated by Pound.[3] Such effects have since acquired wide recognition through the work of Overhauser.[4]

Consider for example a system with three unequally spaced energy levels, $E_3>E_2>E_1$. Introduce the notation,

$$h\nu_{31}=E_3-E_1 \quad h\nu_{32}=E_3-E_2 \quad h\nu_{21}=E_2-E_1.$$

Denote the transition probabilities between these spin levels under the influence of the thermal motion of the heat reservoir (lattice) by

$$w_{12}=w_{21}\exp(-h\nu_{21}/kT),\quad w_{13}=w_{31}\exp(-h\nu_{31}/kT),$$
$$w_{23}=w_{32}\exp(-h\nu_{32}/kT).$$

The w's correspond to the inverse of spin lattice relaxation times. Denote the transition probability caused by a large saturating field $H(\nu_{31})$ of frequency

* Supported by the Joint Services.
[1] Gordon, Zeiger, and Townes, Phys. Rev. **99**, 1264 (1955).
[2] Combrisson, Honig, and Townes, Compt. rend. **242**, 2451 (1956).
[3] R. V. Pound, Phys. Rev. **79**, 685 (1950).
[4] A. W. Overhauser, Phys. Rev. **92**, 411 (1953).

ν_{31} by W_{13}. Let a relatively small signal of frequency ν_{32} cause transitions between levels two and three at a rate W_{32}. The numbers of spins occupying the three levels n_1, n_2, and n_3, satisfy the conservation law

$$n_1+n_2+n_3=N.$$

For $h\nu_{32}/kT \ll 1$ the populations obey the equations[5]:

$$\frac{dn_3}{dt}=w_{13}\left(n_1-n_3-\frac{N}{3}\frac{h\nu_{31}}{kT}\right)+w_{23}\left(n_2-n_3-\frac{N}{3}\frac{h\nu_{32}}{kT}\right)+W_{31}(n_1-n_3)+W_{32}(n_2-n_3),$$

$$\frac{dn_2}{dt}=w_{23}\left(n_3-n_2+\frac{N}{3}\frac{h\nu_{32}}{kT}\right)+w_{21}\left(n_1-n_2-\frac{N}{3}\frac{h\nu_{21}}{kT}\right)+W_{32}(n_3-n_2), \quad (1)$$

$$\frac{dn_1}{dt}=w_{13}\left(n_3-n_1+\frac{N}{3}\frac{h\nu_{31}}{kT}\right)+w_{21}\left(n_2-n_1+\frac{N}{3}\frac{h\nu_{21}}{kT}\right)-W_{31}(n_1-n_3).$$

In the steady state the left-hand sides are zero. If the saturating field at frequency ν_{31} is very large, $W_{31} \gg W_{32}$ and w's, the solution is obtained

$$n_1-n_2=n_3-n_2=\frac{1}{3}\frac{hN}{kT}\frac{-w_{23}\nu_{32}+w_{21}\nu_{21}}{w_{23}+w_{12}+W_{32}}. \quad (2)$$

This population difference will be positive, corresponding to negative absorption or stimulated emission at the frequency ν_{32}, if

$$w_{21}\nu_{21} > w_{32}\nu_{32}. \quad (3)$$

If the opposite is true, stimulated emission will occur at the frequency ν_{21}. The following discussion could easily be adapted to this situation. The power emitted by the magnetic specimen is

$$P_{\mathrm{magn}}=\frac{Nh^2\nu_{32}}{3kT}\frac{(w_{21}\nu_{21}-w_{32}\nu_{32})W_{32}}{w_{23}+w_{12}+W_{32}}. \quad (4)$$

For a magnetic resonance line with a normalized response curve $g(\nu)$ and $g(\nu_{\max})=T_2$, the transition probability at resonance is given by

$$W_{32}=\hbar^{-2}|(2|M_x|3)|^2H_x^2(\nu_{32})T_2. \quad (5)$$

For simplicity it has been assumed that the signal field $H(\nu_{32})$ is uniform in the x direction over the volume of the sample. A similar expression holds for W_{31}.

For the moment we shall restrict ourselves to the important case that the signal excitation at frequency ν_{32} is small, $W_{32} \ll w_{23}+w_{31}$. No saturation effects at this transition occur and a magnetic quality factor can be defined by

$$-1/Q_{\mathrm{magn}}=\frac{4P_{\mathrm{magn}}}{\nu_{23}\langle H^2(\nu_{32})\rangle_{\mathrm{Av}}V_c}. \quad (6)$$

Q_{magn} is negative for stimulated emission, $P_{\mathrm{magn}}>0$. V_c is the volume of the cavity, and $\langle H^2\rangle_{\mathrm{Av}}$ represents a volume average over the cavity. The losses in the cavity, exclusive of the magnetic losses or gains in the sample, are described by the unloaded quality factor Q_0. The external losses from the coupling to a wave guide or coaxial line are described by Q_e. Introduce the voltage standing wave ratio β for the cavity tuned to resonance,

$$\beta=(Q_e/Q_0)+(Q_e/Q_{\mathrm{magn}}).$$

The ratio of reflected to incident power is

$$\frac{P_r}{P_i}=\frac{(1-\beta)^2}{(1+\beta)^2}.$$

There is a power gain or amplification, when β is negative or, $-Q_{\mathrm{magn}}^{-1}>Q_0^{-1}$. Oscillation will occur when

$$-Q_{\mathrm{magn}}^{-1}>Q_0^{-1}+Q_e^{-1}=Q_L^{-1},$$

where Q_L is the "loaded Q." The amplitude of the oscillation will be limited by the saturation effect, embodied by the W_{32} in the denominator of Eq. (4). The absolute value of $1/Q_{\mathrm{magn}}$ decreases as the power level increases. In the oscillating region the device will act as a microwave frequency converter. Power input is at the frequency ν_{13}, a smaller power output at the frequency ν_{23}. The balance of power is dissipated in the form of heat through the spin-lattice relaxation and through conduction losses in the cavity walls. For $-Q_{\mathrm{magn}}=Q_L$, $\beta=-1$, and the amplification factor would be infinite. The device will act as a stable c.w. amplifier at frequency ν_{23}, if

$$Q_0^{-1}+Q_e^{-1}>-Q_{\mathrm{magn}}^{-1}>Q_0^{-1}. \quad (7)$$

The choice of paramagnetic substance is largely dependent on the existance of suitable energy levels and the existence of matrix elements of the magnet moment operator between the various spin levels. The absorption and stimulated emission process depend directly on this operator, but the relaxation terms (w) also depend on the spin angular momentum operator via spin-orbit coupling terms. It is essential that all off-diagonal elements between the three spin levels under consideration be nonvanishing. This can be achieved by putting a paramagnetic salt with a crystalline field splitting δ in a magnetic field, which makes an angle with the crystalline field axis. The magnitude of the field is such that the Zeeman energy is comparable to the crystalline field splitting. In this case the states with magnetic quantum numbers m_s are all scrambled. This situation is usually avoided to unravel paramagnetic resonance spectra, but occasionally "forbidden lines" have been observed, indicating mixing of the m_s states. For our

[5] In case $h\nu_{31}\sim kT$, the Boltzmann exponential factors cannot be approximated by the linear terms. The algebra becomes more involved without changing the character of the effect.

purposes the mixing up of the spin states by Zeeman and crystalline field interactions of comparable magnitude is essential. The energy levels and matrix elements of the spin angular momentum operator can be obtained by a numerical solution of the determinantal problem of the spin Hamiltonian.[6] The number of electron spin levels may be larger than three. One may choose the three levels between which the operation will take place. The analysis will be similar, but algebraically more complicated. One has a considerable amount of freedom by the choice of the external dc magnetic field, to adjust the frequencies ν_{23} and ν_{13} and to vary the values of the inverse relaxation times w. It is advisable—although perhaps not absolutely necessary—to operate at liquid helium temperature. This will give relatively long relaxation times (between 10^{-2} and 10^{-4} sec), and thus keep the power requirements for saturation down. The factor T in the denominator of Eq. (4) will also increase the emission at low temperature. Although the order of magnitude of the w's is known through the work of Leiden school,[7] there is only one instance where w's have been measured for some individual transitions.[8] Van Vleck's[9] theory of paramagnetic relaxation should be extended to the geometries envisioned in this paper. If a Debye spectrum of the lattice vibrations is assumed, the relaxation times will increase with decreasing frequency at liquid helium temperature, where Raman processes are negligible. This implies that the condition (3) should be easily realizable when $\nu_{32}<\nu_{21}$.

Important applications as a microwave amplifier could, e.g., be obtained for $\nu_{32}=1420$ Mc/sec, corresponding to the interstellar hydrogen line, or to another relatively low microwave frequency used in radar systems. The frequency ν_{31} could be chosen in the X band, $\nu_{31}=10^{10}$ cps. To obtain well scrambled states with these frequency splittings one should have crystalline field splittings between 0.03 cm^{-1} and 0.3 cm^{-1}. Paramagnetic crystals which are suggested by these considerations are nickel fluosilicate[10] and gadolinium ethyl sulfate.[11] These crystals have the additional advantage that all magnetic ions have the same crystalline field and nuclear hyperfine splitting is absent, thus keeping the total number of possible transitions down. The use of magnetically dilute salts is indicated to reduce the line width, increase the value of T_2 in Eq. (5) and to separate the individual resonance transitions.

A single crystal 5% Ni 95% Zn Si $F_6\cdot 6H_2O$ has a line width of 50 oersted ($T_2=1.2\times10^{-9}$ sec) and an average crystalline field splitting $\delta=0.12$ cm^{-1} for the Ni^{++} ions. With an effective spin value $S=1$ there are indeed three energy levels of importance. The spin lattice relaxation time is about 10^{-4} sec at 2°K as measured in a saturation experiment by Meyer.[12] Further dilution does not decrease the line width, as there is a distribution of crystalline fields in the diluted salt.

A single crystal of 1% Gd 99% La $(C_2H_5SO_4)_3\cdot 9H_2O$ has an effective spin $S=7/2$. In zero field there are four doublets separated respectively by $\delta=0.113$ cm^{-1}, 0.083 cm^{-1}, and 0.046 cm^{-1} as measured at 20°K. These splittings are practically independent of temperature. The line width is 7 oersteds due to the distribution of local fields arising from the proton magnetic moments. This width could be reduced by a factor three by using the deuterated salt. The relaxation time is not known, but should be about the same as in other Gd salts,[7] which give $T_1\sim10^{-2}$ sec at 2°K.

In the absence of detailed calculations for the relaxation mechanism, we shall take $w_{12}=w_{13}=w_{32}=10^4$ sec^{-1} for the nickel salt and equal to 10^2 sec^{-1} for the gadolinium salt. The matrix elements $(2|M_z|3)$, etc., can be calculated exactly by solving the spin determinant. For the purpose of judging the operation of the maser using these salts, we shall take the off-diagonal elements of magnetic moment operator simply equal to $g\beta_0$, where $g=2$ is the Landé spin factor and β_0 is the Bohr magneton. For the higher spin value of the Gd^{+++} some elements will be larger but this effect is offset by the distribution of the ions over eight rather than three spin levels. Take $T=2$°K and $Q_0=10^4$, which is readily obtained in a cavity of pure metal at this temperature. A coaxial cavity may be used which has a fundamental mode resonating at the frequency $\nu_{32}=1.42\times10^9$ cps and a higher mode resonating at $\nu_{31}\approx10^{10}$ cps. Take the volume of the cavity $V=60$ cm^3 and $H_s^2=6\langle H^2\rangle_{Av}$. If these values are substituted in Eqs. (4)–(6), the condition (7) for amplification is satisfied if $N>3\times10^{18}$ for nickel fluosilicate and $N>3\times10^{17}$ for gadolinium ethyl sulfate ($N>10^{17}$ for the deuterated salt). The minimum required number of Ni^{++} ions are contained in 0.02 cm^3 of the diluted nickel salt. The gadolinium salt, diluted to 1% Gd, contains the required number in about the same volume. The critical volume is only 0.006 cm^3 for the deuterated salt. Crystals of appreciably larger size can still be fitted conveniently in the cavity. A c.w. amplifier or frequency converter should therefore be realizable with these substances. A larger amount of power can be handled by these crystals than by the P impurities in silicon which have a very long relaxation time, and require an intermittant operation, and where it is harder to get the required number of spins in the cavity.

So far we have assumed that the width corresponds to the inverse of a true transverse relaxation time T_2.

[6] See, e.g., Bleaney and K. H. W. Stevens, Repts. Progr. in Phys. 16, 108 (1953).
[7] See, e.g., C. J. Gorter, *Paramagnetic Relaxation* (Elsevier Publishing Company, Amsterdam, 1948).
[8] A. H. Eschenfelder and R. T. Weidner 92, 869 (1953).
[9] J. H. Van Vleck, Phys. Rev. 57, 426 (1940).
[10] R. P. Penrose and K. H. W. Stevens, Proc. Phys. Soc. (London) A63, 29 (1949).
[11] Bleaney, Scovil, and Trenam, Proc. Roy. Soc. (London) A223, 15 (1954).
[12] J. W. Meyer, Lincoln Laboratory Report 1955 (unpublished).

Actually the width $1/T_2^*$ is due to an internal inhomogeneity broadening with normalized distribution $h(\nu)$ and $h(\nu_{max})\approx T_2^*$ in both cases. The response curve for a single magnetic ion is probably very narrow indeed, $g(\nu_{max})=T_2\approx T_1$, and $T_1=10^{-4}$ should be used in Eq. (5) rather than $T_2^*=1.2\times10^{-9}$ sec. The response to a weak threshold signal at ν_{32} now originates, however, from a small fraction of the magnetic ions. If $\gamma H(\nu_{32})<1/T_1\approx10^4$ cps, then only T_2^*/T_1 of the ions contribute to the stimulated emission and the net result is the same as calculated above. In most applications the incoming signal will be so weak that this situation will apply, even with a power amplification of 30 or 40 db.

For use as an oscillator or high level amplifier with a field $H(\nu_{32})$ in the cavity larger than $1/\gamma T_1$, one has essentially complete saturation ($W_{32}\gg w_{23}+w_{13}$) in Eq. (4) for those magnetic ions lying in a width $2\pi\Delta\nu=\gamma H(\nu_{32})$ in the distribution $h(\nu)$. One has then for the power emitted instead of Eqs. (4) and (5)

$$P_{magn}=\frac{h^2\nu_{32}}{3kT}N(-w_{32}\nu_{32}+w_{21}\nu_{21})\gamma H(\nu_{31})T_2^*. \quad (8)$$

The power is proportional to the amplitude of the radio frequency field rather than its square. This effect has been discussed in more detail by Portis.[13] It will limit the oscillation or amplification to an amplitude which can be calculated by using Eq. (8) in conjunction with Eqs. (6) and (7).

The driving field $H(\nu_{31})$ will necessarily have to satisfy the condition $\gamma H(\nu_{31})>w_{31}=T_1^{-1}$ to obtain saturation between levels 1 and 3. The power absorbed in the crystal will be proportional to the amplitude $H(\nu_{31})$, and is in order of magnitude given by

$$P_{abs}\sim N\frac{h^2\nu_{13}^2}{3kT}w_{13}\gamma H(\nu_{31})T_2^*. \quad (9)$$

This equation looses its validity if $\gamma H(\nu_{31})>T_2^{*-1}$. In this case the whole line would be saturated, but such excessive power levels will not be used. For $T_1^{-1}<\gamma H(\nu_{31})<T_2^{*-1}$, the effective band width of the amplifier is determined by $H(\nu_{31})$. It is about 0.5 Mc/sec for $H(\nu_{31})=0.2$ oersted. The power dissipated in a specimen of fluosilicate ten times the critical size is 0.5 milliwatt under these circumstances. For the gadolinium salt, also ten times the critical size, either deuterated or not, the dissipation is only 0.005 milliwatt. There should be no difficulty in carrying this amount out of the paramagnetic crystal without excessive heating. The power dissipation in the walls under these conditions will be 5 milliwatts. Liquid helium will boil off at the rate of only 0.01 cc/min due to heating in the cavity. Since helium is superfluid at 2°K, troublesome vapor bubbles in the cavity are eliminated.

The noise power generated in this type of amplifier should be very low. The cavity with the paramagnetic salt can be represented by two resonant coupled circuits as discussed by Bloembergen and Pound.[14] Noise generators are associated with the losses in the cavity walls, kept at 2°K, and with the paramagnetic spin abosrption which is described by an effective spin temperature, associated with the distribution of the spin population. The absolute value of this effective temperature also has the order of magnitude of 1°K. The input is from an antenna, which sees essentailly the radiation temperature of interstellar space. Reflected power is channeled by a circulating nonreciprocal element[15] into a heterodyne receiver, or, if necessary, into a second stage Maser cavity. The circulator makes the connection: antenna→maser cavity→heterodyne receiver→dummy load→antenna. If the antenna is not well matched, the dummy load may be a matched termination kept at liquid helium temperature to prevent extra power from entering the cavity. The input arm of the cavity at frequency ν_{31} will be beyond cutoff for the frequency ν_{32}. The coaxial line passing the signal at ν_{32} between cavity and circulator will contain a rejection filter at frequency ν_{31} to prevent overloading and noise mixing at the mixer crystal of the super heterodyne receiver.

It may be concluded that the realization of a low-noise c.w. microwave amplifier by saturation of a spin level system at a higher frequency seems promising. The device should be particularly suited for detection of weak signals at relatively long wavelength, e.g., the 21-cm interstellar hydrogen radiation. It may also be operated as a microwave frequency converter, capable of handling milliwatt power. More detailed calculations and design of the cavity are in progress.

[13] A. M. Portis, Phys. Rev. 91, 1071 (1953).

[14] N. Bloembergen and R. V. Pound, Phys. Rev. 95, 8 (1954).

[15] C. L. Hogan, Bell System Tech. J. 31, 1 (1952).

Reprinted from THE PHYSICAL REVIEW, Vol. 105, No. 2, 762–763, January 15, 1957
Printed in U. S. A.

Operation of a Solid State Maser

H. E. D. SCOVIL, G. FEHER, AND H. SEIDEL
Bell Telephone Laboratories, Murray Hill, New Jersey
(Received December 3, 1956)

A MASER of the same type as that proposed by Bloembergen[1] has been successfully operated at 9 kMc/sec. Since the basic theory has been covered in the reference, it will not be reviewed here.

We require a magnetically dilute paramagnetic salt having at least three energy levels whose transitions fall in the microwave range and which may be easily saturated. The ion $Gd^{+++}|4f^7, {}^8S\rangle$ seems a suitable choice since its eight energy levels give the choice of several modes of maser operation. Of the three salts of Gd^{+++} which have been investigated by paramagnetic resonance[2] the diluted ethyl sulfate appears very desirable. This salt has been investigated in detail by Bleaney *et al.*,[3] Buckmaster,[4] and Feher and Scovil.[5]

If an external magnetic field is applied perpendicular to the magnetic axis, the spin Hamiltonian may be written[3]

$$\mathcal{H}=g\beta H_0\cdot S_z-\tfrac{1}{2}B_2^0[S_z^2-\tfrac{1}{3}S(S+1)]+\tfrac{1}{4}B_2^0[S_+^2+S_-^2], \quad (1)$$

where some small terms have been neglected, $g=1.99$, $B_2^0\approx 0.02\ \mathrm{cm}^{-1}$, and the axis of quantization is parallel to H_0. The first term is the usual Zeeman energy and is varied to bring the transitions to the desired operating frequency. The second term disturbs the equality of the level spacings (essential for the device) as shown in Fig. 1. The third term admixes states, thereby permitting $\Delta S_z=\pm 2$ transitions which are also essential. The angle between the dc magnetic field and the microwave magnetic field should be zero for the $\Delta S_z=\pm 2$ transitions and 90° for the $\Delta S_z=\pm 1$ transitions. A convenient compromise of 45° between both microwave fields and H_0 was chosen for the structure employed.

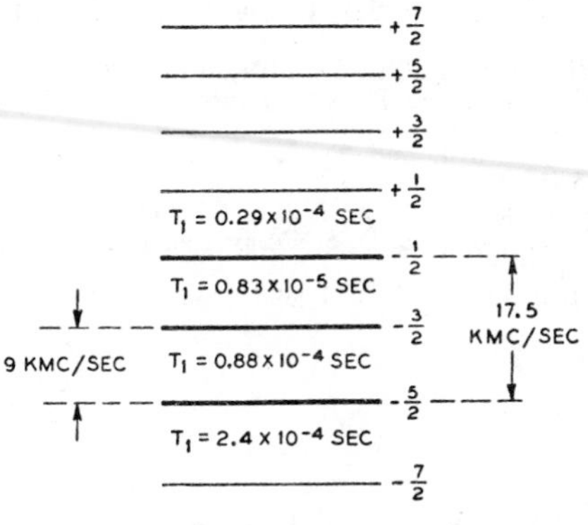

FIG. 1. The energy levels of the ground state of Gd^{+++} in the ethyl sulfate for a large applied magnetic field. The heavy lines identify the maser levels. Spin-lattice relaxation times between levels are shown.

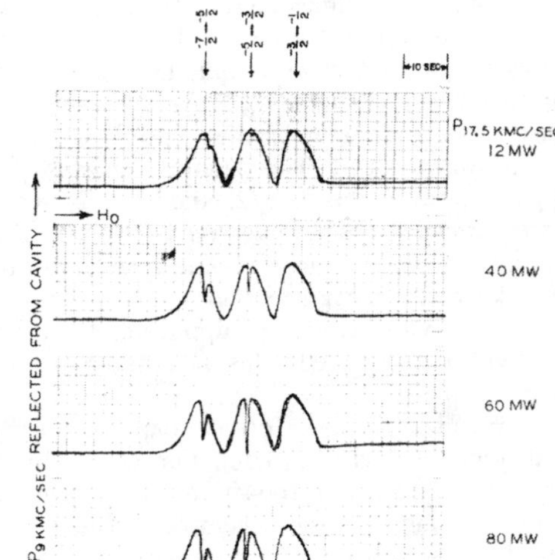

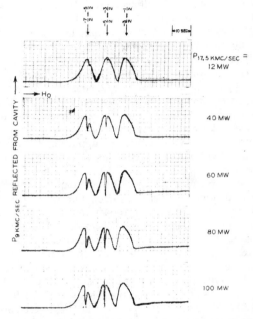

FIG. 2. The power reflected from the 9-kMc/sec cavity as the magnetic field was swept to cover three $\Delta S_z\pm 1$ transitions for different 17.5-kMc/sec power levels. The spacing between two lines is about 200 oersteds.

The negative temperature (a term introduced by Purcell and Pound[6] to designate the fact that a higher energy level is more densely populated than the lower one) at complete saturation of the $\Delta S_z=\pm 2$ transition will depend essentially upon two parameters: the separations of the energy levels and the ratio of the relaxation times. In a given material the first parameter is fixed. Our attempts were directed toward varying the second parameter in order to obtain lower negative temperatures. A relaxation time ratio of 1:10 between two neighboring transitions was obtained by introducing cerium into the crystal.[5] In order to obtain the full benefit of this large relaxation time ratio for a 9-kMc/sec maser, a dc magnetic field of 2850 oersteds was applied at an angle of 17° from the perpendicular direction of the crystal.[5] Although Eq. (1) refers to the perpendicular direction, the energy levels and transition probabilities are only slightly modified at this small angle. A 90-mg (8% filling factor) lanthanum ethyl sulfate crystal containing $\approx$0.5% Gd^{+++} and $\approx$0.2% Ce^{+++} was used in contact with liquid helium at 1.2°K. A saturating magnetic field at 17.52 kMc/sec was used to induce transitions between the $|-5/2\rangle$ and $|-\frac{1}{2}\rangle$ states as shown in Fig. 1. The signal at 9.06 kMc/sec was applied between the $|-5/2\rangle$ and $|-3/2\rangle$ states. The maser embodies a microwave cavity simultaneously resonant at these two frequencies. The almost critically coupled 9-kMc/sec cavity had a loaded $Q\approx 8000$. The 17.5-kMc/sec cavity perversely supporting a spurious mode provided a $Q\approx 1000$; this fortunately proved sufficient.

Figure 2 shows the 9-kMc/sec monitoring signal reflected from the cavity as a function of H_0. In the first trace three $\Gamma S_z=\pm 1$ transitions are shown, the peaks representing essentially complete reflection as a result of the high magnetic losses associated with the material. The observed resonance line appears broadened since the absorption is not a small perturbation on the cavity as resonance is approached. The succeeding traces show the reflections associated with the $|-5/2\rangle \rightarrow |-3/2\rangle$ transition as the 17.5-kMc/sec power is increased. In the third trace the salt is lossless, corresponding to an essentially infinite spin temperature.

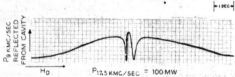

FIG. 3. The central line of the last trace of Fig. 2 is shown on an expanded time scale.

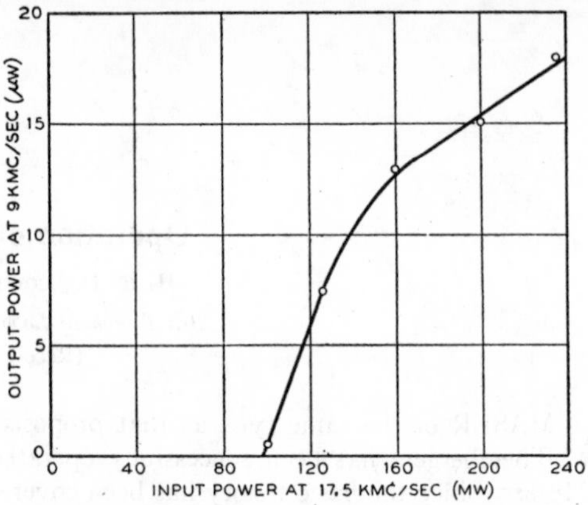

FIG. 4. The 9-kMc/sec output power of the oscillating maser as a function of the saturating power.

The fourth trace shows the onset of negative spin temperatures and the partial overcoming of the losses associated with the empty cavity. In the fifth trace the reflected power exceeds the incident power and oscillations have commenced. Before oscillations commence, a region of amplification must exist. Figure 3 shows the last trace on an expanded time scale.

At this stage, the 9-kMc/sec monitoring signal was turned off. The dc magnetic field was adjusted to a value resulting in maximum 9-kMc/sec output power from the oscillating maser. The power output was measured with a barretter as a function of the saturating 17.5-kMc/sec power. The results are shown in Fig. 4.

The required saturating power could be materially reduced by the use of a 17.5-kMc/sec cavity having a higher Q. The purpose of this work was merely to show the feasibility of this device.

We should like to acknowledge the generous cooperation of many members of the Bell Telephone Laboratories, and in particular, to thank Mr. M. G. Gussak.

[1] N. Bloembergen, Phys. Rev. **104**, 324 (1956).
[2] K. D. Bowers and J. Owen, Repts. Progr. in Phys. **18**, 304 (1955).
[3] Bleaney, Scovil, and Trenam, Proc. Roy. Soc. (London) **A223**, 15 (1954).
[4] H. A. Buckmaster, Can. J. Phys. **34**, 150 (1956).
[5] G. Feher and H. E. D. Scovil, preceding Letter [Phys. Rev. **105**, 760 (1957)].
[6] E. M. Purcell and R. V. Pound, Phys. Rev. **81**, 279 (1951).

Reprinted from THE PHYSICAL REVIEW, Vol. 109, No. 4, 1399–1400, February 15, 1958
Printed in U. S. A.

Maser Action in Ruby*

G. MAKHOV, C. KIKUCHI, J. LAMBE, AND R. W. TERHUNE
The University of Michigan Engineering Research Institute, Ann Arbor, Michigan

(Received January 2, 1958)

A THREE-LEVEL maser was proposed by Bloembergen,[1] and first operated by Scovil, Feher, and Seidel.[2] In our endeavor to find paramagnetic materials suitable for maser applications, we have investigated the electron-spin resonance properties of ruby (Al_2O_3:Cr). This note reports briefly the results of our studies.

According to several investigators[3-5] the zero-field splitting in ruby is 0.38 cm^{-1}. The ground state of the trivalent chromium ion, Cr^{+++}, which is responsible for the coloring of ruby, behaves as $S=\frac{3}{2}$. The dependence of the energy levels of ruby on the magnetic field was calculated for the polar angle 54° 44′.[6] Experiment has indicated that the "forbidden" transition $-\frac{3}{2}\rightarrow\frac{1}{2}$ is quite intense for this orientation. Calculations showed that for $H=4200$ gauss, the pumping frequency corresponding to this transition should be 24 kMc/sec, and the signal frequency corresponding to the $-\frac{1}{2}\leftrightarrow\frac{1}{2}$ transition should be approximately 9.3 kMc/sec.

A cylindrical cavity was designed and built so as to excite the TE_{114} and TE_{011} modes, respectively, at the above frequencies. A ruby crystal, with about 0.1% chromium concentration, was placed at the center of the cavity on the end of an axially located quartz rod. The crystal was mounted so as to make the c axis normal to the cavity axis. A selected Varian VA-96 klystron, rated at 120 mw, was used for pumping.

At room temperature, K- and X-band absorption lines characteristic to ruby were observed, and no interaction of any kind between the two bands was detected. The initial evidence of stimulated microwave emission in ruby was obtained at liquid helium temperature (4.2°K), with a sample of about three cubic millimeters in volume. Subsequently, the volume of the sample was increased to approximately two tenths of a cubic centimeter. Evidence of oscillations and amplification was obtained with the latter sample.

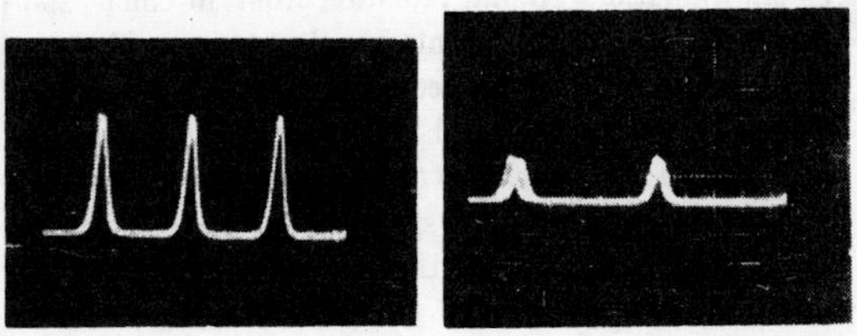

(a) (b)

FIG. 1. X-band (9.22 kMc/sec) pulses emitted by ruby under constant H, fixed pumping frequency, and no external X-band signal. Figure 1(a) shows that the pulse interval is about 0.3 msec corresponding to maximum power available. Figure 1(b) shows the effect of reduced pumping power.

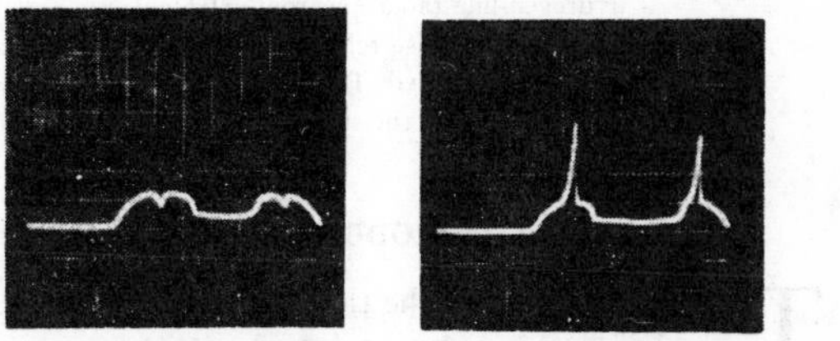

(a) (b)

FIG. 2. The traces (a) and (b) were obtained before and after application of pumping power, respectively, which was maintained below oscillation level. To observe amplification, a small frequency-modulated X-band signal was applied to the cavity.

Figures 1(a) and 1(b) demonstrate the dependence of emitted X-band power on pumping power in the absence of an external X-band signal. It is interesting to note that both the pulse-height and the repetition rate decrease with decreased pumping power. The pulse interval was found to be approximately 0.3 millisecond for maximum K-band power at our disposal. The radiated frequency was 9.22 kMc/sec for $H=4230$ gauss and pumping frequency of 24.2 kMc/sec.

Figures 2(a) and 2(b) show the effects of amplification. The traces were taken before and after application of K-band power, respectively. The small downward pips in Fig. 2(a) indicate the position of cavity resonance. Net gain up to 20 db has been observed. For this presentation, a small frequency-modulated X-band signal was applied to the cavity.

Details of this study will be published at a later date. In the meantime we should like to point out that ruby possesses a number of physical properties which contribute to its usefulness as a maser medium, such as very high chemical stability, good thermal conductivity, and low dielectric losses.

We wish to thank R. Ager and M. Bair for their capable technical assistance during the progress of this investigation.

* This research was supported by Project Michigan (administered by the U. S. Army Signal Corps) and the Air Force Office of Scientific Research.

[1] N. Bloembergen, Phys. Rev. **104**, 324 (1956).
[2] Scovil, Feher, and Seidel, Phys. Rev. **105**, 762 (1957).
[3] A. A. Manenkov and A. M. Prokhorov, J. Exptl. Theoret. Phys. S.S.S.R. **28**, 762 (1955) [translation: Soviet Physics JETP **1**, 611 (1955)].
[4] M. M. Zaripov and Iu. Ia. Shamonin, J. Exptl. Theoret. Phys. S.S.S.R. **30**, 291 (1956) [translation: Soviet Physics, JETP **3**, 171 (1956)].
[5] J. E. Geusic, Phys. Rev. **102**, 1252 (1956).
[6] $\theta=\cos^{-1}(1/\sqrt{3})$.

An Operational Ruby Maser for Observations at 21 Centimeters with a 60-Foot Radio Telescope

J. V. JELLEY* AND B. F. C. COOPER†
Harvard College Observatory, Cambridge 38, Massachusetts

(Received April 28, 1960; and in final form, September 20, 1960)

A maser preamplifier designed for radiometry at a wavelength of 21 cm is described. The maser is mounted at the focus of the 60-ft reflector of the Harvard College Observatory and is being used principally for observations of hydrogen-line radiation from extra-galactic nebulae. An automatic gain stabilization system for the maser using a modulated-noise reference signal is described and an example of an observation made with this stabilization scheme is included. The total input noise temperature of the radiometer is 85°K, without the gain stabilization, and 148°K with the stabilization.

I. INTRODUCTION

THE potentialities of the three-level solid-state maser amplifier as a sensitive low noise instrument for radio astronomy were pointed out by Bloembergen[1] in his original paper in which the device was first proposed. The first confirmation of the predicted low noise temperatures was made by McWhorter, Meyer, and Strum[2] following in the wake of the early experiments by Scovil, Feher, and Seidel,[3] McWhorter and Meyer,[4] and others. These early three-level masers, and the first maser to operate at 1420 Mc (the frequency of the interstellar hydrogen line), constructed by Artman, Bloembergen, and Shapiro,[5] were all laboratory instruments quite unsuited to operational use at the focus of a large radio telescope. The first application of a maser to radio astronomy was made by Giordmaine, Alsop, Mayer, and Townes[6] who developed an X-band instrument which was used at the focus of the 50-ft antenna at the Naval Research Laboratory in Washington for studies of thermal and other continuum radiations from point sources.

Observations in radio astronomy at the present time may be divided into two main groups, those concerned with emissions in the continuous spectrum and those centered around studies of galactic and extra-galactic hydrogen at frequencies close to 1420 Mc, the emission frequency for neutral atomic hydrogen. The design of a maser and its associated radiometer, for optimum performance, depends for a variety of reasons on the applications intended for the equipment. For a radiometer with an over-all input noise temperature T_N, a pre-detector bandwidth Δf, and a post-detector integration time τ, the minimum detectable signal is set by recorder fluctuations of equivalent rms value,

$$\langle \Delta T_N^2 \rangle^{\frac{1}{2}} = T_N / (\Delta f \tau)^{\frac{1}{2}}. \qquad (1)$$

Thus, for a given source and antenna, it is clear from Eq. (1) that for work in the continuum the system sensitivity increases with the bandwidth. For hydrogen-line observations, however, the optimum sensitivity occurs when Δf is matched to the line width for the hydrogen under investigation; the latter in turn will depend on the nature of the source. The observed bandwidths for hydrogen radiation may vary between say a few kilocycles for the narrow absorption lines caused by localized gas clouds between the earth and point sources having a continuous spectrum (e.g., the frequency profile for the source Cassiopeia A), to a few megacycles for the Doppler-broadened emission radiation from an edge-on spiral galaxy.

The maser radiometer described in this paper is constructed to operate at the focus of a large telescope and has been specifically designed for observations in the 21-cm band. At the present stage of development, the cavity maser proved to be the only feasible type to build at this comparatively low frequency; such a regenerative device has however a limited bandwidth of around 2 Mc. Although we have seen in the foregoing that for hydrogen work it is in principle only necessary to have a narrow bandwidth, there are reasons, nevertheless, why a wide-band amplifier would have advantages.

In general, an object emitting 21-cm line radiation will be seen against a continuum background because of galactic radiation, ground radiation from antenna "spill-over," and solar radiation entering the antenna side lobes.

There are a variety of receiving systems currently in use in radio astronomy, and it is important to appreciate their relative merits prior to designing a maser radiometer for the 21-cm field. Broadly speaking, the various types of radiometers may be grouped into five classes. In the first, I, the frequency comparison system, a continuous recording is made of the difference in signal power levels between two frequency channels in the receiver, one channel tuned

* On leave from the Atomic Energy Research Establishment, Harwell, England.
† On leave from the Commonwealth Scientific and Industrial Research Organization, Sydney, Australia.
[1] N. Bloembergen, Phys. Rev. **104**, 323 (1956).
[2] A. L. McWhorter, J. W. Meyer, and P. D. Strum, Phys. Rev. **108**, 1642 (1957).
[3] H. E. D. Scovil, G. Feher, and H. Seidel, Phys. Rev. **105**, 762 (1957).
[4] A. L. McWhorter and J. W. Meyer, Phys. Rev. **109**, 312 (1958).
[5] J. O. Artman, N. Bloembergen, and S. Shapiro, Phys. Rev. **109**, 1392 (1958).
[6] J. A. Giordmaine, L. E. Alsop, C. H. Mayer, and C. H. Townes, Proc. IRE **47**, 1062 (1959).

to the hydrogen frequency (suitably corrected for Doppler shifts) and the other to a neighboring band. In this way, it is possible to balance out the continuum background radiation. This system has proved to be very satisfactory but requires that all stages preceding the selective filters, which are usually in the IF stages, have a relatively broad band and a very stable frequency response. In the second group, II, in effect a variant of I, the frequency comparison is performed on a time-sharing basis, i.e., there is only a single channel but the response frequency of the radiometer is alternately switched between the line frequency and the comparison frequency. Both these systems compensate for gain variations, at least to first order.

In the next two systems, III and IV, the radiometer measures total antenna power, and the hydrogen-line component from a source is obtained by comparing runs with the equipment tuned first to the line frequency and then away from this frequency. In total-power radiometers, it is essential that gain variations be either very small and slow, or that some form of gain stabilization be used. The most common type of radiometer in this class, III, uses the well-known Dicke comparison system,[7] in which the input of the receiver is alternately switched between the antenna and a comparison load. In the variant of this system described by Drake and Ewen[8] in 1958, the comparison load is adjusted to have a temperature set close to that of the antenna temperature. Compensation for receiver gain variations is achieved in this system. In system IV, there is no comparison switching, and two courses are then open: either one builds a receiver with extreme care and attention to voltage and temperature control, so that the gain remains constant to the required accuracy (typically 1 part in 3×10^4 over several minutes), or one adopts some form of gain stabilization.

Finally, there is the phase-switching radiometer, system V, which is used with interferometers having two antennae, and in polarimeters. This system does not concern us here, but is included for completeness.

Since the specific problem is to design a radiometer for a single antenna, with a cavity maser, to be used primarily for hydrogen work, we conclude that each of the four types of radiometer just described presents difficulties. System I cannot be used with a cavity maser, because the bandwidth is inadequate. The frequency-switching system II could conceivably be adopted with a narrow-band cavity maser, but would require, to a high degree of precision, simultaneous variation of cavity tuning, magnetic field, and local oscillator. The technical problems associated with this mode of operation seemed insoluble within a reasonable period of time. The Dicke system III was favored, but at the time when this project was started (1958) no reliable broad-band low noise switch was commercially available. Later, in 1959, a switched circulator became available, and a Dicke system was developed which replaced the gain stabilization described here. This development is described by Cooper in an accompanying note in this issue.

It was decided, therefore, to resort to system IV, and to build a direct radiometer with automatic gain stabilization operating on the pump circuit in the maser. Laboratory tests had already shown that gain variations in the maser, caused by changes in liquid helium level and distortions that occurred when the instrument was tilted, etc. precluded use of the maser without a stabilization circuit.

One of the central problems in applying the Bloembergen maser to practical radio astronomy was the incorporation of suitable gain stabilization. The other problems, of a more technical nature, stemmed from operational requirements such as rigidity, compactness, weight, reliability, and serviceability. Most important of all, a complicated and sensitive laboratory instrument had to be simplified so that an observing team without special training in solid-state physics or microwave radio techniques could handle it easily.

II. MASER MATERIAL AND CAVITY

Because of its excellent thermal, mechanical, and dielectric properties, ruby was chosen for the active material of the maser; the crystal, which contained $\sim$0.05% of chromium, was cut from a boule supplied by the Linde Corporation. In order to minimize magnet weight it was originally hoped to operate the maser on a low field mode, with a field of $\sim$200 gauss. This plan, however, proved impractical owing to cross-relaxation effects in this mode, effects which others had found in developing L-band masers. The present maser operates at a field of 2000 gauss, an orientation of $\theta=90°$ between the field and the crystalline c axis, and requires a pump frequency of 11.27 kMc for a signal frequency of 1420 Mc. With this arrangement, and with the levels numbered in order of their energy, pumping occurs between levels 1 and 3, and signal amplification takes place between levels 2 and 1 after inversion of the population in these levels.

The essential features of the cavity are shown in Fig. 1. The X-band waveguide, which also forms the main structural component of the unit and carries the pump power, tapers down to the cavity which is made from a piece of K_u-band waveguide. The bottom of this guide is closed by a plug on which is mounted a TEM-strip resonator for the signal frequency. Two slabs of ruby almost entirely fill the resonator, one on each side of the tongue, to obtain the maximum filling factor. The length of the tongue required for resonance is very much less than $\lambda/4$ in free space, owing to the high dielectric constant for ruby, $\epsilon\sim10$. The tip of the tongue protrudes a little from the

[7] R. H. Dicke, Rev. Sci. Instr. **17**, 268 (1946).
[8] F. D. Drake and H. I. Ewen, Proc. IRE **46**, 53 (1958).

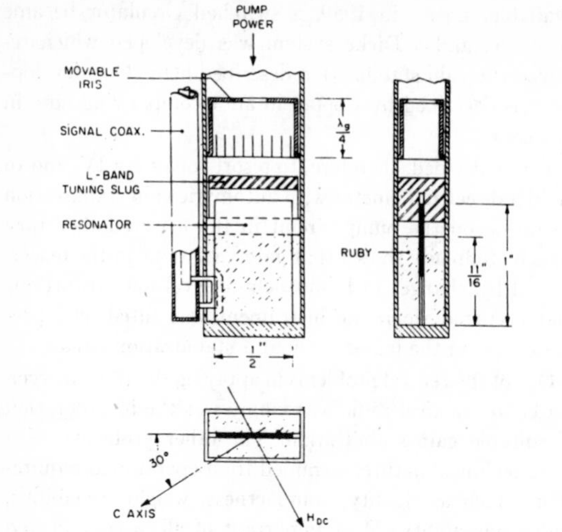

FIG. 1. Details of maser cavity.

ruby, and a Teflon slug slides over this to provide dielectric tuning over a range ~50 Mc. The resonator is made as wide as possible for maximum unloaded Q at 1420 Mc.

Coupling at the signal frequency is achieved by a flattened loop which protrudes into the cavity between the slabs of ruby and whose insertion may be varied. To achieve sufficient penetration of the loop, the resonant tongue is made like a sandwich of three metal strips with the center one cut away to form a slot. A strip of Mylar is folded into this slot to insulate the coupling loop. The loop is connected to a 50-ohm coaxial line which goes up through the helium and out of the maser. This line, which serves both for the input and output signals, is fitted with a hermetic seal near its lower end to prevent entry of liquid helium and consequent impedance variations due to the changing liquid level. However, the inner space is exposed to helium gas through small holes placed well above the liquid level. In this way the formation of solid air, CO_2, and ice is minimized.

Pump power is admitted to the cavity through a movable iris diaphragm held firmly in the guide with $(\lambda_g/4)$ spring fingers. The cavity, which resonates in a TE mode and is not seriously perturbed by the tongue resonator, is somewhat overcoupled at the pump frequency so that its tuning is not very critical.

The signal coupling and tuning controls, and the pump tuning, are all brought out on shafts through the maser head plate. The first two can be operated remotely, in the observatory, while the third is preset before a run.

Under saturation conditions for the pump levels, a negative magnetic Q of approximately 140 is readily obtained at a signal frequency of 1420 Mc in a bath temperature of 4.2°K, corresponding to a gain-bandwidth product of 20 Mc. The gain-bandwidth product could have been doubled by lowering the bath temperature to 1.5°K by pumping on the helium. The inconvenience of running a large pump and its long vacuum line mounted on the telescope did not seem to be justified by the prospect of an increase in bandwidth from 2 to 4 Mc. The maser is therefore normally run at a gain of 20 db and a bandwidth of 2 Mc.

III. MAGNET AND CRYOSTAT

The magnetic field, of the required strength and homogeneity, was obtained from a one-piece C-shaped permanent magnet to which soft-iron pole pieces and shims were added. The magnet, of Alnico V steel and weighing 44 lb was obtained from the Indiana Steel Products Company (type 36C280B) and was subsequently fitted with cylindrical pole pieces $3\frac{1}{2}$ in. in diameter, which gave an air gap of $2\frac{1}{8}$ in. between the flat faces. After magnetization to saturation, which was carried out at the Raytheon Manufacturing Company, the gap flux was 2200 gauss; this was subsequently reduced to 2010 gauss. The addition of trim-

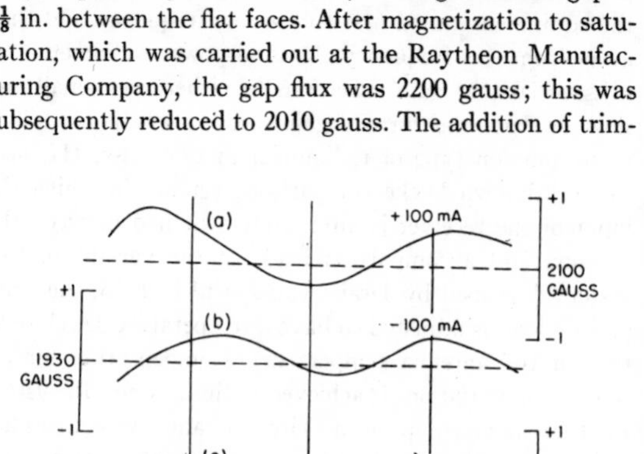

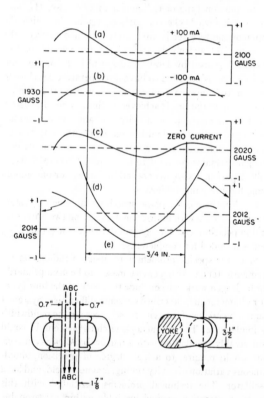

FIG. 2. Homogeneity curves for permanent magnet with 500-ohm trimming coils. (a) Field plot along the line BB with 100-ma current producing a field aiding the permanent field. (b) Field plot along the line BB with 100-ma current producing a field opposing the permanent field. (c) Field plot along the line BB with zero current in the trimming coils. (d) Field plot along the line AA adjacent to south pole with zero current in the trimming coils. (e) Field plot along the line CC adjacent to north pole with zero current in the trimming coils.

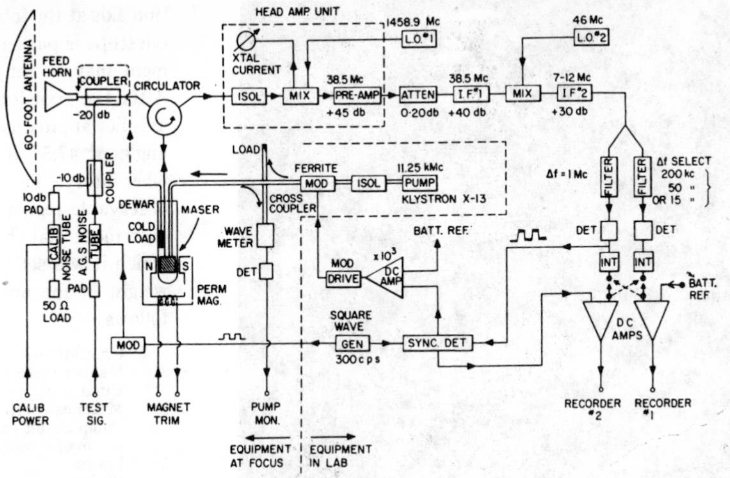

FIG. 3. Block diagram of complete radiometer.

ming coils mounted on the pole pieces enables the field to be varied over a range of ±100 gauss, for tuning purposes, with a current variation of ±100 ma. Over this range the flux in the air gap varies linearly with the current, and there is no depreciation of the flux at zero current after repeated cycling.

A homogeneity of better than ±5 parts in 10^4 was obtained over a spherical volume $\frac{3}{4}$ in. in diameter, at the center of the gap, by the use of single-step shims placed on the pole faces; the outside diameter of the shims was $3\frac{1}{2}$ in., the same as the pole diameter. The homogeneity curves shown in Fig. 2 were obtained with these shims, which were of width $\frac{9}{16}$ in. and depth 0.070 in. This degree of homogeneity was more than adequate for the bandwidth of the system, even if the crystal were oriented with the wide dimension lying along the axis of the field. In practice the orientation is such that this dimension lies at an angle of ~60° to the field axis.

Since Alnico V steel has a small temperature coefficient, the setting of the magnet current varies a little with ambient temperature for a given signal frequency. The over-all weight of the magnet, 60 lb with pole pieces and coils, might have been somewhat lower if an oriented ferrite ceramic magnet such as Indox V had been used. This material, however, has a much higher temperature coefficient than Alnico, and would have created problems in field stability.

The stainless steel helium cryostat, constructed by Hofman Laboratories, Inc., was designed with a narrow neck in the helium section, and with supports in the tail section. Thus the unit could be tilted over to angles of up to 50° from the vertical, without undue loss of helium or breakdown of the thermal insulation in the tail, even when fully charged with nitrogen and helium. All the vacuum surfaces are gold-plated to reduce heat loss from radiation, and provision is made for repumping the vacuum spaces from time to time. The double walls of the nitrogen and helium vessels are interconnected. The outside diameter of the tail of the Dewar is $1\frac{7}{8}$ in. and the inside diameter of the helium vessel is $1\frac{3}{8}$ in., because there is a radiation shield between these two surfaces.

The capacities of the nitrogen and helium vessels are 6.2 and 3.3 liters, respectively. With a full charge of both coolants, the maser in the Dewar, the pump power on, and the equipment mounted vertically, the nitrogen charge lasts 30 hr and the helium 16 hr.

IV. AUXILIARY EQUIPMENT AND PACKAGE ASSEMBLY

A block diagram of the maser, the associated equipment in the preamplifier (also mounted at the focus of the telescope), and the rest of the radiometer, are shown in Fig. 3, while Fig. 4 shows a photograph of the package mounted at the focus. In a maser of the reflection cavity type, an all-important component is a circulator which must have good isolation and, if it is not cooled, a low insertion loss. For this component, a Raytheon coaxial three-port unit, type CLL5, was used. This unit was adjusted for optimum performance at 1420 Mc; it has an insertion loss of 0.35 db and an isolation of >20 db, and is operated at ambient temperature.

As seen from Fig. 3, the input circuit also contains a 20-db directional coupler through which noise from a modulated noise tube may be injected into the circuit at the antenna input; this noise is used, as explained in Sec. V, as a reference signal in the automatic gain stabilizing system. A second noise tube serves to inject for calibration purposes a very small signal which enters through a second directional coupler in cascade with the first. The only other signal-frequency component is an L-band isolator mounted in the preamplifier unit to prevent local

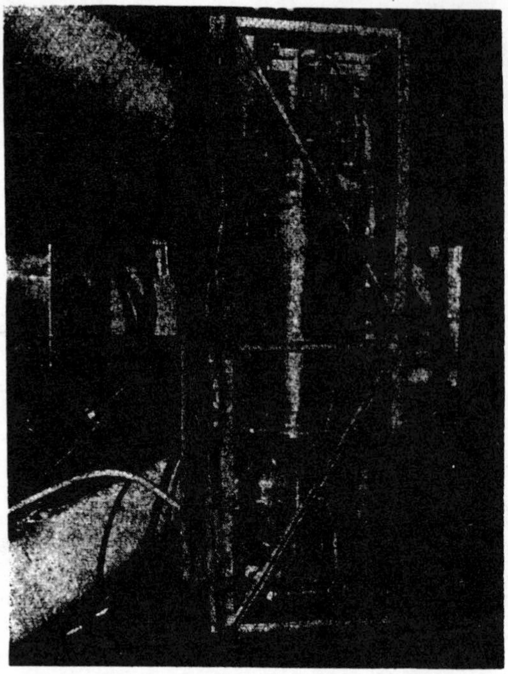

FIG. 4. Maser package mounted at focus of 60-ft reflector.

oscillator power from entering the maser via the circulator due to mismatches in the antenna horn.

The pump circuit is built up as follows: About 100 mw of pump power at 11.27 Mc, generated by a Varian Associates X-13 klystron, passes through an isolator (to reduce frequency pulling by the maser cavity), then through a "Gyraline" ferrite modulator, via a directional coupler to the waveguide feed in the maser. The ferrite modulator is used in the gain stabilization system (see Sec. V). The directional coupler passes a small signal to a wavemeter and a crystal detector, to tune up the pump circuit and monitor the pump power.

Other items installed in the maser package include a two-tube modulator circuit for driving the noise tube, electric motors for turning the maser controls, a facility for injecting a tuning signal into the maser (via the noise tube when this is switched off), filament transformers for the klystron and modulator, a thermistor temperature-sensing element, and an air blower to provide circulation.

The maser assembly is built into a braced aluminum framework of dimensions 48×15×15 in. which in turn is bolted to a rigid aluminum backplate with an internal honeycomb structure. The rigidity of the system is especially important for the $\theta=90°$ orientation in a ruby maser. With a constant magnetic field the maser gain drops by 3 db for a change of crystal orientation of $\pm 0.5°$.

The entire package is mounted on a subsidiary declination axis at the focus of the 60-ft reflector, so that when the telescope is parked in its normal stow position, the instrument may be set up vertically during a helium transfer. After the transfer, the package is tilted over so that its axis lies approximately parallel to the polar axis, i.e., at an angle of 47.5° from the zenith, at the latitude of the Obervatory. The telescope is then moved round to the observable region of the sky, which is limited by the requirement that the angle of tilt never exceeds the angle at which it was set immediately after the transfer. The total weight of the unit is approximately 200 lb, made up as follows:

Cryostat (with coolants)	35 lb
Magnet (with poles and coils)	60
Circulator	9
Maser assembly	2
Pump circuit components and waveguides	10
Motors for control of tuning and coupling	10
Frame	20
Backplate, cover, secondary declination axis, and mounting castings	50
Miscellaneous components	5
Total	200 lb

V. AUTOMATIC GAIN STABILIZATION AND RECORDING SYSTEM

For reasons discussed in the Introduction, the instrument has so far been used as a total-power radiometer. With the bandwidths and integration times used here, it is theoretically possible to detect signals of the order of 0.001 of the total input noise temperature. However, to realize this sensitivity, the gain must be held constant within comparable limits for the duration of an observation. The maser itself exhibits gain variations of about ± 0.1 db or $\pm 2.3\%$ over a half-hour period, and the reduction of these variations to a figure approaching $\pm 0.1\%$ is carried out in the following manner.

Artificial noise from a 10 100°K Bendix type TD 40 noise tube, in an A.I.L. type 70A mount, is coupled through a nominal 20-db coupler at the input of the maser. The noise tube is square wave modulated at a recurrence frequency of $\sim$300 cps. A standard noise step of equivalent temperature $\sim$100°K thus appears at the output of the radiometer. This noise step is picked out in a phase-sensitive detector and compared with a fixed reference voltage (see Fig. 3). The error signal from this comparison, after amplification, is applied to a ferrite modulator in the pump circuit where it controls the pump power and thereby the maser gain. A small range of gain control, amounting to about 2 db, is provided so that the maser is never far from saturation and very little bandwidth is sacrificed. This range is adequate to take care of gain drifts over a long period, and, when the operating point moves too close to the limits of the control range, the gain is reset manually to the middle of the range.

An A.G.S. loop gain of about 50 is provided so that the

residual gain variations are reduced to an acceptable figure, which in practice is limited by the stability of the noise lamp itself. This stability appears to be about one part in a thousand, provided the discharge current is regulated to at least 1 in 150 ma, the normal running value.

It is important to the success of this scheme that the gain of stages following the maser should remain very constant. If the gain of these stages should vary, while at the same time the over-all gain is held constant, the contribution of the second stage to the input noise temperature will change. Such a change would be equivalent to a spurious input signal. Fortunately, it is possible to maintain gain stability in the post-maser stages to better than one part in a thousand by careful regulation of supply voltages and ambient temperature.

Once the gain is stabilized within close limits it is possible to record the second detector output at high sensitivity in the usual way by balancing it against a stable dc reference voltage. This is done in the "Recorder No. 1" channel of Fig. 3. However there would appear to be some advantage in balancing the second detector output against the synchronous detector output, since both of these outputs are affected in the same ratio by the small gain fluctuations which are not removed by the A.G.S. action. Since two recorder channels were available, both schemes have been tried with the present maser. There is also the possibility of using a wide bandwidth for the A.G.S. channel when the signal channel bandwidth must be restricted for improved resolution of the hydrogen line. This reduces the fluctuation level in the A.G.S. channel and improves the signal-to-noise ratio in the narrow recording channel.

An analysis of the performance of the present modulated-noise comparison scheme relative to that of an ideal continuous dc comparison radiometer is presented in Appendix A. It is shown that a slight improvement in performance might result from the use of a 13-db input coupler in place of the present nominal 20-db coupler.

In Appendix B the dynamic performance of the A.G.S. system is analyzed and the effect of the feedback on the recorder fluctuations is discussed.

VI. NOISE TEMPERATURE MEASUREMENTS

With the antenna pointing to the zenith and away from the galactic plane, the total input noise temperature of the system was measured by injecting an accurately calibrated noise signal into the input coaxial cable and thus determing the resultant increase in noise power level with a precision IF attenuator. The over-all system temperature was measured to be (85±5)°K. This figure includes all contributions of noise, except those introduced by the gain-stabilization system, disconnected during the measurements.

An independent measurement of the antenna "spillover" was then made by connecting the input coaxial cable, first to a matched termination immersed in the helium bath and then to the antenna horn. This operation gave a figure of (20±5)°K, believed to be largely antenna "spillover," but which also included small contributions from genuine sky background at 21-cm wavelength, and possibly even smaller effects from atmospheric attenuation.

The antenna horn used in the present experiments produces (at the edge of the 60-ft reflector), a 20-db illumination taper that reduces spillover considerably more than does the conventional 10-db illumination taper. However, the reduced spillover is accompanied by a loss of some 10% in antenna gain.

The measured figure of (85±5)°K for the over-all temperature agrees closely with the figure calculated from the expected contributions from the various components of the system. These contributions are estimated to be made up as follows:

Antenna spillover (measured pointing to zenith, away from the galactic plane)	20°K
Input coaxial cable from antenna feed horn (0.2 db)	15
Input directional coupler (insertion loss)	5
Circulator (0.35 db)	25
Maser input coaxial cable (0.1 db)	7
Maser spontaneous emission (theoretical)	2
Second-stage contribution (1000°K with 20-db maser gain)	10
Total	84°K

The appreciable contribution, 15°K, from the input coaxial cable is caused by the use of 4.5 ft of RG-17/u cable which was later replaced by a coaxial line $1\frac{5}{8}$ in. in diameter having a loss of only 0.05 db and contributing <4°K.

When the gain stabilization is operating in normal use, the over-all input temperature of the system will be augmented, as explained in Appendix A. When the noise lamp runs at an equivalent temperature of 10 100°K half the time, terminated by a matched load at ambient temperature the remainder of the time, the additional noise introduced into the system via the input directional coupler (nominally 20 db, see Fig. 3), will be $(10\,100+300)/2\times 83=63$°K, where the factor 83 represents the measured coupling factor (19.3 db). Thus the total system temperature of the entire radiometer, with gain stabilization, is $85+63=148$°K.

Deductions for the over-all operational sensitivity follow. For example, in typical observations involving drift scans, a pre-detector bandwidth of 200 kc is used for the hydrogen-line filter in conjunction with a post-detector integration time constant of 50 sec. Insertion of these figures into Eq. (1) shows that under these conditions the rms fluctuations at the recorder correspond to ±0.05°K which agrees satisfactorily with observed fluctuations.

Finally, the noise temperature of the calibration signal, derived from the second noise tube, is determined from the

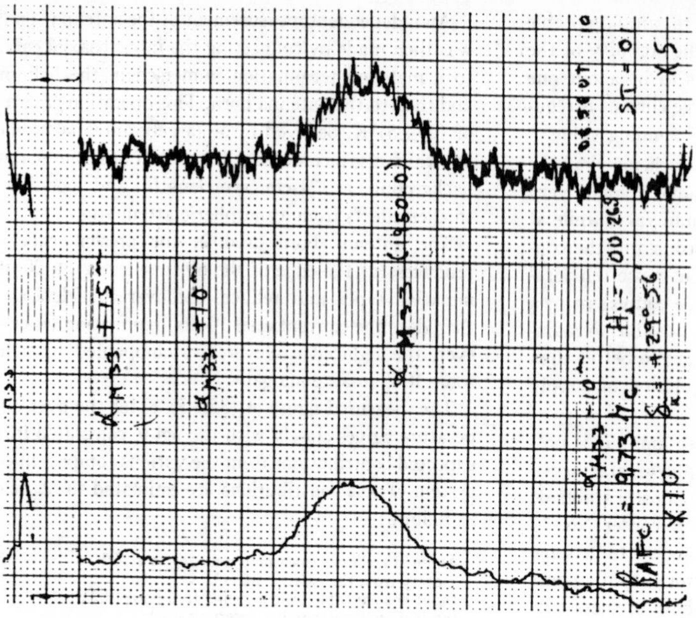

FIG. 5. Drift scan of the nebula M33 using a bandwidth of 200 kc. Lower tracing from Recorder No. 1 using a 50-sec integration time. Upper tracing from Recorder No. 2 using a 10-sec integration time.

attenuation of the pad and the two directional couplers in cascade (see Fig. 3). The magnitude of the calibration signal is therefore −39.3 db relative to 10 100°K, i.e., 1.2°K.

VII. PRELIMINARY OBSERVATIONS

Figure 5 shows drift curves taken on the spiral nebula M33 at a frequency of 1421.2 Mc with a bandwidth of 200 kc. This frequency allows for the Doppler shift caused by the approach velocity of the source. The lower tracing is on Recorder No. 1 with an integration time constant of 50 sec. The upper tracing is from Recorder No. 2 with an integration time constant of 10 sec. The measured peak antenna temperature is 1.6°K for an antenna beam width of 52′. The fluctuation level is approximately 0.1°K root mean square in the upper tracing, and approximately 0.05°K in the lower tracing. These fluctuation levels are in reasonable agreement with the values calculated according to the theory given in Appendix A.

The drift curve of Fig. 5 may be compared with that of Fig. 6 which was taken on the same nebula. Here the conventional radiometer was used without the maser preamplifier, but with the same bandwidth and a 10-sec integration time. In this instance, the deflection produced by M33 is just detectable, allowing for the fact that the time of transit is already known. The conventional receiver has a 900° noise temperature but has the advantage that the radiation in the signal channel is continuously compared with wide-band radiation in an adjacent comparison channel.

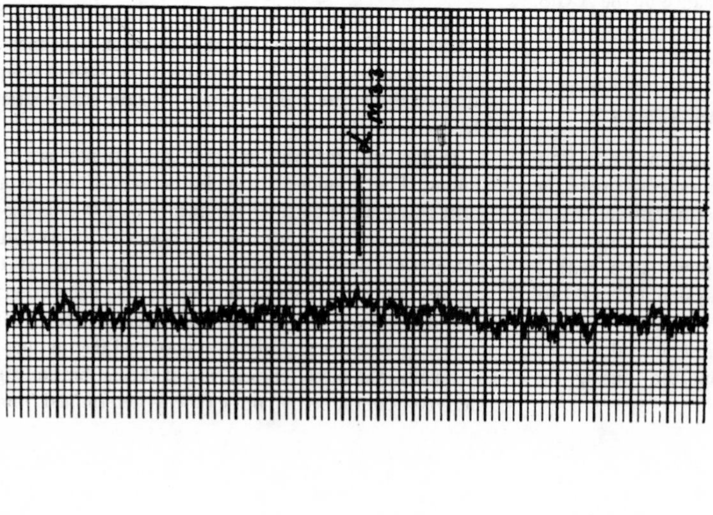

FIG. 6. Drift scan of M33 without maser preamplifier. Bandwidth 200 kc. Integration time 10 sec.

VIII. FUTURE DEVELOPMENTS

A Dicke comparison system is now being developed, which will use a switched circulator, with an electromagnet as the rf switch. This circulator will be situated in front of the existing circulator, so that the maser input will alternately "see" the antenna and a comparison noise source derived from a mixture of noise from room temperature and from a cold load in the helium bath. The existing A.G.S. system then may not be required and greater stability will probably be achieved.

The development of a traveling wave maser at 1420 Mc is the next and urgent step required. Although so far such a maser has not been built at this frequency, the results obtained by DeGrasse *et al.*[9] at 6000 Mc are sufficiently encouraging to make the effort well worth while. The main advantages to be gained from a TW maser used at L-band are the following: (i) An amplifying bandwidth of about one-third of the magnetic line width of the active material, which is 25 Mc for ruby. This might be even larger if stagger tuning were used, with an inhomogeneous magnetic field. (ii) Large, tunable bandwidth, determined by the properties of the slow-wave structure. (iii) Reduction of input losses, because of the elimination of the circulator.

A large bandwidth for hydrogen work would simplify the problems of frequency scanning and permit the use of a frequency comparison system. For work in the continuum, a large bandwidth would lead directly to an increase in the ultimate sensitivity of the equipment. The recent development by Autler[10] of a high flux solenoid using superconducting niobium, points to the hope of a great reduction in weight of a maser unit, and at the same time to a high degree of stability of the magnetic field.

Finally, if at 21 cm the maser survives the competition with parametric amplifiers, traveling wave beam tubes, and other devices, long periods of extended observation would justify the use of a compact helium liquifier with recycling of the helium. Operational considerations and expense together would warrant this development.

ACKNOWLEDGMENTS

The Harvard Observatory Maser Project was carried out as a joint project between the Harvard College Observatory and the Division of Engineering and Applied Physics. The work was initiated by Professor T. Gold, whose enthusiasm and foresight were the dominant factors in the progress attained with this 21-cm maser under operational conditions. We wish to express our appreciation to Professor Gold, and to Professor N. Bloembergen of the Gordon McKay Laboratory who assisted and advised us throughout the project and has shown constant interest and encouragement. We are also very grateful to Professor A. E. Lilley who succeeded Gold and assisted greatly in the task of establishing the astronomical research program for the staff and students at the Agassiz Station of the Harvard Observatory. During the last six months Dr. S. J. Goldstein has given freely of his time in integrating the maser into the radiometer, at considerable sacrifice to his own observing program. Valuable assistance in the installation and operation of the maser has also been given by W. Weiler.

In conclusion we express our gratitude to the National Science Foundation and the Office of Naval Research who generously provided the funds with which this work was carried out.

APPENDIX A

Figure of Merit of Modulated Noise Comparison System

The signal-to-noise ratio of the second recording channel of Fig. 3 will be first considered with the automatic gain stabilization inoperative. Let the total input noise temperature of the radiometer be T_1 and let the square-wave modulated noise of the equivalent noise temperature T_2 be injected into the input, so that the noise temperature follows the waveform of Fig. 7(a). Let the corresponding waveform at the second detector output be as shown in Fig. 7(b). For convenience in assessing the noise perform-

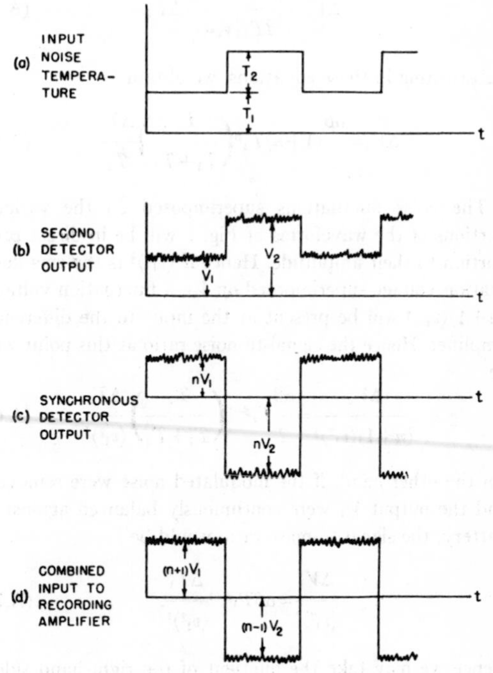

FIG. 7. Waveforms in A.G.S. system.

[9] R. W. DeGrasse, D. C. Hogg, E. A. Ohm, and H. E. D. Scovil J. Appl. Phys. **30**, 2013 (1959).
[10] S. H. Autler, Rev. Sci. Instr. **31**, 369 (1960).

ance of the system, the synchronous detector will be assumed to have no built-in filtering so that its switching action essentially generates the waveform of Fig. 7(c). For balance in the difference amplifier, waveform (c) must be multiplied by a suitable factor to make its dc level equal and opposite to the dc level of the second detector. The combined waveform of the two voltages applied to the difference amplifier is then that shown in Fig. 7(d), where the factor n is adjusted to make $(n+1)V_1 \approx (n-1)V_2$.

The net dc level at the input to the difference amplifier may then be written as

$$V_3 = \tfrac{1}{2}[(n+1)V_1 - (n-1)V_2]. \quad \text{(A.1)}$$

To assess the effect of a signal producing an increment of antenna temperature ΔT_1, we write

$$V_1 = \alpha T_1^{\beta} \quad \text{(A.2)}$$

and

$$V_2 = \alpha(T_1 + T_2)^{\beta}, \quad \text{(A.3)}$$

where α is a constant involving the power gain up to the detector, the bandwidth, and the detector efficiency, and β is an index describing the power law of the detector, i.e., $\beta = \frac{1}{2}$ for a linear detector and $\beta = 1$ for a square-law detector.

The unbalance produced at the input of the difference amplifier due to the signal ΔT_1 is then expressed by the equation

$$\Delta V_3 = \left|\frac{dV_3}{dT_1}\right|_{V_3=0} \cdot \Delta T_1. \quad \text{(A.4)}$$

Substituting in these equations, we obtain

$$\Delta V_3 = \frac{\alpha\beta}{2}(1+n)T_1^{\beta}\left(\frac{T_2}{T_1+T_2}\right)\frac{\Delta T_1}{T_1}. \quad \text{(A.5)}$$

The noise fluctuations superimposed on the various portions of the waveforms of Fig. 7 will be in direct proportion to their amplitude. Hence if $\langle v_1^2\rangle^{\frac{1}{2}}$ is the rms fluctuation voltage superimposed on V_1, a fluctuation voltage $(n+1)\langle v_1^2\rangle^{\frac{1}{2}}$ will be present at the input to the difference amplifier. Hence the signal-to-noise ratio at this point will be

$$\frac{\Delta V_3}{(n+1)\langle v_1^2\rangle^{\frac{1}{2}}} = \frac{\alpha\beta}{2}T_1^{\beta-1}\left(\frac{T_2}{T_1+T_2}\right)\frac{\Delta T_1}{\langle v_1^2\rangle^{\frac{1}{2}}}. \quad \text{(A.6)}$$

On the other hand, if the modulated noise were removed and the output V_1 were continuously balanced against a battery, the signal-to-noise ratio would be

$$\frac{\Delta V_1}{\langle v_1^2\rangle^{\frac{1}{2}}} = \alpha\beta T_1^{\beta-1}\frac{\Delta T_1}{\langle v_1^2\rangle^{\frac{1}{2}}}. \quad \text{(A.7)}$$

Hence we may take the quotient of the right-hand sides of Eqs. (A.6) and (A.7) as a figure of merit M of the modulated noise comparison system, as expressed in the equation,

$$M = \tfrac{1}{2}(1 + T_1/T_2)^{-1}. \quad \text{(A.8)}$$

According to this equation, the largest possible ratio (T_2/T_1) should be employed to minimize the recorder fluctuations, and when $T_2 \gg T_1$ the system is approximately equivalent to a Dicke radiometer in which the signal is effective for half of the time and the reference noise predominates for the other half.

In this analysis, we have assumed that during the half cycle when the noise tube is off it is contributing nothing to the input noise temperature T_1. However, on referring to Fig. 3, it is evident that when the noise tube is dead, the input to the circulator will still "see" a contribution from the termination at the far end of the tube, in addition to the input noise T_1. This noise component, which increases the effective value of T_1, depends on the physical temperature T_0 of the termination, and the coupling factor C of the input directional coupler, expressed as a power factor. It is thus no longer true that the optimum performance of the system will occur when $T_2 \gg T_1$, because a high value of T_2 implies a tight coupling factor and hence a large contribution to T_1.

To calculate the influence of this effect, let T_d denote the noise lamp temperature when fired, and let T_n be the radiometer noise temperature, excluding contributions entering via the input directional coupler. If we assume that when the noise tube is fired, the terminating pad at the far end is isolated from the circuit, the corrected values for T_1 and T_2 will be

$$T_1 = T_n + T_0/C \quad \text{(A.9)}$$

and

$$T_2 = (T_d - T_0)/C. \quad \text{(A.10)}$$

Revision of the earlier analysis shows that Eq. (A.8) should now be written in the form,

$$M = \frac{T_n}{2T_1(1+T_1/T_2)} \quad \text{(A.11)}$$

$$M = \frac{CT_n(T_d - T_0)}{2[C^2T_n^2 + CT_n(T_d+T_0) + T_dT_0]}. \quad \text{(A.12)}$$

With the assumption that $T_d \gg T_0$, it can be shown that there is an optimum coupling factor,

$$C_{\text{opt}} = (T_dT_0)^{\frac{1}{2}}/T_n, \quad \text{(A.13)}$$

which gives a maximum value to M, as expressed by the equation

$$M_{\max} = \frac{(T_d - T_0)}{2[T_d + T_0 + 2(T_dT_0)^{\frac{1}{2}}]} \quad \text{(A.14)}$$

$$\therefore M_{\max} \approx \{2[1 + 2(T_0/T_d)^{\frac{1}{2}}]\}^{-1} \quad \text{for} \quad T_d \gg T_0. \quad \text{(A.15)}$$

In the existing equipment in which $T_d = 10\,100°K$, $T_0 \sim 300°K$, $T_n \sim 80°K$, $C = 83(19.3\text{ db})$, we have $M = 0.28$.

The optimum coupling factor would be $C_{opt} = 20(13\text{ db})$ for which $M_{max} = 0.35$. Further improvement could be achieved by refrigerating the noise-lamp termination, thus lowering T_0.

APPENDIX B

Analysis of Automatic Gain Stabilization System

Figure 8 reproduces the portions of the radiometer, required for this analysis, in a simplified block schematic form.

The effectiveness of the A.G.S. circuit in controlling low frequency gain variations such as might be troublesome in the recording circuits will be considered. A single smoothing time constant RC will be assumed in the A.G.S. loop. This is essentially true of the present radiometer.

Let the maser gain be subject to a small low frequency perturbation which is the resultant of its inherent instability and the control signal fed back through the ferrite modulator. The instantaneous maser power gain may then be written in the form

$$G = G_0 + \bar{g}e^{j\omega t}, \tag{B.1}$$

where G_0 is the steady gain and $\bar{g}$ is a quantity describing the low frequency component in amplitude and phase. Let

$$\bar{g} = \bar{g}_1 + \bar{g}_2, \tag{B.2}$$

where $\bar{g}_1$ is the inherent gain variation and $\bar{g}_2$ is the component due to the control signal.

Similarly the output of the synchronous detector is written

$$V_d = V_{d0} + \bar{v}_d e^{j\omega t}, \tag{B.3}$$

where V_{d0} is the dc component and $\bar{v}_d$ is the ac component resulting from the maser gain variations. The very much higher frequency component due to the modulated noise control signal is ignored here.

For the linear detector used here we have

$$\frac{\bar{v}_d}{V_{d0}} = \frac{1}{2}\frac{\bar{g}}{G_0}. \tag{B.4}$$

After filtering, the ac component at the input to the comparison amplifier is

$$\bar{v}_d' = \bar{v}_d/(1+j\omega\tau), \tag{B.5}$$

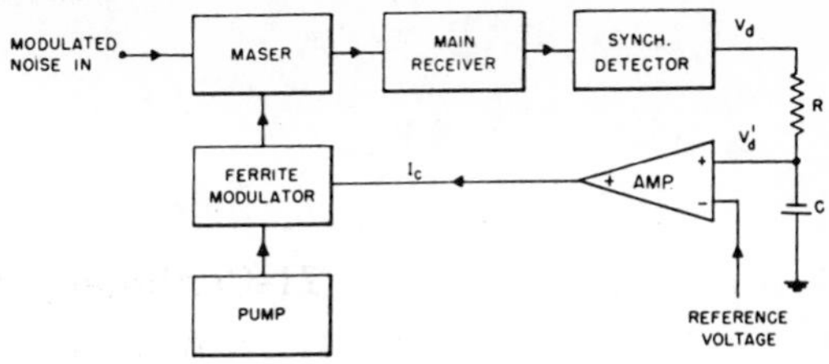

FIG. 8. Simplified schematic of A.G.S. loop.

where $\tau = RC$. This component gives rise to an alternating current component in the pump modulator, of the form,

$$\bar{\imath}_c = S\bar{v}_d', \tag{B.6}$$

where S is the transconductance of the control amplifier. For small variations it is sufficiently accurate to take the maser gain as varying linearly with modulator current, i.e.,

$$\bar{g}_2/G_0 = -\alpha\bar{\imath}_c, \tag{B.7}$$

where α is a constant. Here the minus sign has been introduced to obtain the correct phase relationship.

Manipulation of the foregoing equations leads to the result

$$\bar{g}/\bar{g}_1 = [1 + A(1+j\omega\tau)^{-1}]^{-1}, \tag{B.8}$$

where

$$A = \tfrac{1}{2}\alpha S V_{d0}. \tag{B.9}$$

The quantity $A(1+j\omega\tau)^{-1}$ will be recognized as the open-loop gain of the control system, which determines the amount by which the gain fluctuations are reduced.

With high open-loop gain, the difference voltage at the input to the control amplifier is reduced to a small value in the frequency range $0 < \omega < 1/RC$. Thus, in addition to suppressing gain drifts in the maser, the A.G.S. also removes low frequency noise fluctuations from the synchronous detector output. This takes place by feedback of out-of-phase gain-fluctuation "noise" around the A.G.S. loop. The smoothing of the synchronous detector output voltage is then accompanied by a compensating increase in the low frequency fluctuations of the second detector voltage, and the total noise input to the second recording channel is therefore the same whether or not A.G.S. is employed. Again, with A.G.S. in action, the second detector carries virtually all of the fluctuations which affect the recorders, and both recording channels should therefore be expected to show the same signal-to-noise ratio when used with the same predetector bandwidth. This has been observed in practice.

Reprinted from THE PHYSICAL REVIEW, Vol. 110, No. 1, 280–281, April 1, 1958
Printed in U. S. A.

21-Centimeter Solid-State Maser*

S. H. AUTLER† AND NELSON MCAVOY‡
Lincoln Laboratory, Massachusetts Institute of Technology, Lexington, Massachusetts
(Received February 3, 1958)

A 3-LEVEL solid-state maser[1] using $K_3Co(CN)_6$ doped[2] with $\frac{1}{2}$% $K_3Cr(CN)_6$ has been operated as an amplifier at 1382 Mc/sec. The design is somewhat different from a previously reported one which operates in the same frequency range.[3] Saturating power is supplied at 9070 Mc/sec through a wave guide while a coaxial line terminated in a probe serves as both input and output for the amplified power. The band width has been varied from about 1 Mc/sec to less than 50 kc/sec by changing the probe insertion and thus the external coupling. At an operating temperature of 1.25°K the product of voltage gain and band width is about 1.85×10^6 sec^{-1} over a considerable range.

A means of obtaining a reasonably large filling factor and still saturating all spins is to use a cavity with dimensions small compared to a wavelength at the signal frequency. With a coaxial cavity (Fig. 1) shortened by capacitative loading at one end, a filling factor of approximately 0.5 is obtained. Pumping is possible in several higher-order modes but best results were obtained for the 9070-Mc/sec mode.

The maser operates at a magnetic field of about 1200 gauss, making an angle of 18° with the *a* axis and 90° with the *b* axis of the crystal.[2] It can be seen from Fig. 2 of reference 2 that in this region emission can occur between levels 2 and 3 and saturation between 2 and 4, where the levels are designated in order of increasing energy.

It is of some interest that we were unable to make a maser amplifier work using the same cavity and a crystal containing 1% Cr. The reason for this is not yet understood, but a possible explanation is that the additional power required for saturation at the higher concentration raises the lattice temperature, reducing the spin-lattice relaxation time, which results in still greater power requirement for saturation, etc.

The measured gain band width product is less than one-fifth the theoretical value for $\Delta M=\pm1$ transition. Although a calculation of the wave functions in the operating region would be quite involved, it is likely that mixing of the states has greatly reduced the transition probability between levels 2 and 3. Relatively weak paramagnetic absorption observed in the absence of saturating power confirms this, and better maser performance should be obtainable by operating at lower magnetic fields (200–300 gauss) where stronger absorption is observed. This would require a somewhat lower pumping frequency than 9 kMc/sec.

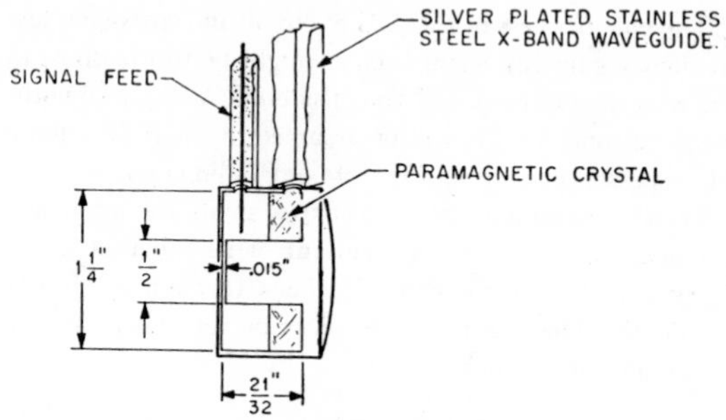

FIG. 1. Cross-sectional view of maser cavity.

About 28 milliwatts of saturating power is required, which is considerably greater than that reported by McWhorter and Meyer.[2] A reduction should be obtained by using a cavity mode at the saturating frequency which has no magnetic field nodes within the crystal.

A new design for a tunable maser which incorporates these improvements is being constructed and may be useful in radio astronomy for observing Doppler-shifted hydrogen radiation.

* The research reported in this document was supported jointly by the Army, Navy, and Air Force under contract with the Massachusetts Institute of Technology.
† Staff Member, Lincoln Laboratory, Massachusetts Institute of Technology, Lexington, Massachusetts.
‡ Visiting staff.
[1] N. Bloembergen, Phys. Rev. **104**, 324 (1956).
[2] A. L. McWhorter and J. W. Meyer, Phys. Rev. **109**, 312 (1958).
[3] Ortman, Bloembergen, and Shapiro, Phys. Rev. **109**, 1392 (1958).

A Tunable Maser Amplifier with Large Bandwidth*

This note describes a solid-state single-cavity X-band maser that has a 20-mc bandwidth at 10-db gain with a bath temperature of 4.2°K. Previous cavity masers[1] have been restricted to small bandwidths. The present system can be tuned from 8400 to 9700 mc. The performance of the maser is offered as further experimental support for the phonon saturation mechanism proposed previously.[2,3]

The maser crystal is ruby ($Al_2O_3 \cdot Cr_2O_3$), chromium being the paramagnetic ion. The chromium concentration is approximately 0.01 per cent. Maser action in ruby has been reported by Makhov and others.[4] The Cr^{+++} ion spin 3/2 system produces four energy levels in an applied magnetic field. For the 54°44′ polar orientation of the c axis, the 1–3 and 2–4 transition frequencies are degenerate for all fields. The maser is operated in this orientation at fields of approximately 4000 gauss. The 1–3 and 2–4 transitions are saturated by pumping power near 23 kmc; population inversion is achieved between levels 2 and 3 with subsequent amplification at approximately 9100 mc.

A large ruby crystal (1 cm×1 cm×½ cm) is placed in the short-circuited end of a 1-cm square waveguide. A moving plunger provides the other wall. Since the crystal dielectric constant is high,[5] at X-band the perturbed TE_{10} mode propagates in the crystal and is cut off in the rest of the waveguide. X-band fields are almost entirely confined to the crystal. Since the fields near the plunger are small, a Q_0 of 2000 is realized without plunger-wall contact. Coupling to the feeding K-band and X-band waveguides is furnished by the coupling slits shown in Fig. 1. To provide variable coupling and resulting gain and bandwidth control, the X-band waveguide is fitted with a sliding quarter-wavelength impedance transformer. A circulator is used in the signal circuit to give unidirectional gain and maximum gain-bandwidth. Plunger displacement tunes the TE_{10} resonance over a large frequency range. Maser operation is accomplished throughout this range by appropriately tuning the magnetic field and pumping frequencies as the cavity is being tuned.

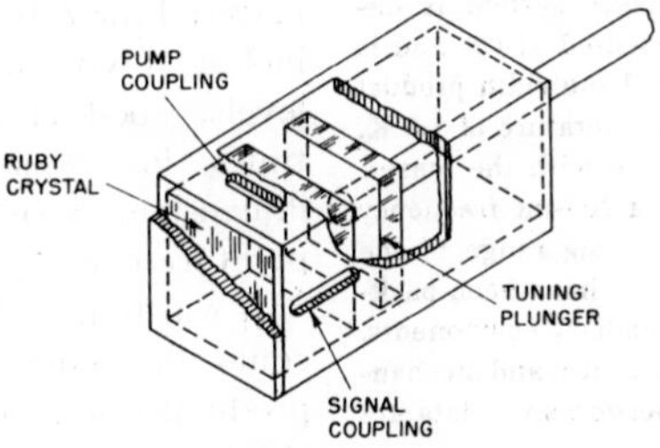

Fig. 1—Maser cavity.

This device has the unusual feature of complete maser action in the absence of cavity resonance at the pumping frequency. It is this characteristic that allows the amplifier to be operated at any frequency in the signal tuning range. If the maser is to be continuously tuned, operation cannot be restricted to those few frequencies at which the cavity is simultaneously resonant at the signal and pumping frequencies. We have observed that complete saturation can be achieved in the absence of a cavity resonance at the pumping frequency. Under these conditions, pumping power appears to be coupled to the crystal primarily by the fringing fields near the coupling hole.

The voltage gain-bandwidth product[6] was measured at representative frequencies in the tuning range, and is essentially constant at 43 mc with a bath temperature of 4.2°K. At 1.5°K, the product increases to approximately 65 mc. Magnetic absorption, observed in the absence of pumping power, yields a magnetic absorption Q of approximately 350. This value checks with expected absorption Q, as calculated from the known spin concentration. Furthermore, the absorption Q is essentially equal to the magnitude of the magnetic negative Q, as computed from the observed gain-bandwidth and cavity Q_0. At a small-signal gain of 11.5 db, the gain is constant for small-signal levels and is down by 3 db at 25 μw of input power. Since the negative and absorption magnetic Q's are approximately equal in magnitude, the effective input noise temperature of the crystal alone is approximately equal to the bath temperature, 4.2°K.[7] Furthermore, since the forward losses in the X-band circulator are 0.1 db, and the signal waveguide losses are small, the over-all effective input noise temperature is expected to be no higher than 20°K. This temperature and the saturating input signal power would give a dynamic range of 100 db, if a 6-mc bandwidth is assumed. The incident pumping power for saturation is approximately 15 mw when the cavity is nonresonant at the pump frequency and reduces to approximately 3 mw when the cavity is resonant. This reduction is the result of improved matching In each case the gain-bandwidth is approximately the same. There is reason to believe that the crystal may require as little as 30 μw saturating power.

One reason for the small gain-bandwidths of previous solid-state masers is that small filling factors were used. Accepted theory specifies that the crystal should not extend beyond regions of large pumping rf magnetic field. Spins in small or zero pumping fields are expected to be absorptive at the signal frequency. However, the performance of our maser indicates that the cavity negative resistance is essentially independent of pumping-field configuration, since the gain-bandwidth is the same in the resonant and nonresonant cases. This, as well as the near equality of magnetic absorption and negative Q's, indicates that pump transitions are uniformly saturated throughout the crystal with nonuniform saturating fields. A possible explanation is offered by the phonon saturation mechanism that has recently been proposed.[2,3]

R. J. Morris
R. L. Kyhl
M. W. P. Strandberg
Dept. Elect. Eng., Phys.,
and Res. Lab. Electronics,
Mass. Inst. Tech.
Cambridge 39, Mass.

* Received by the IRE, August 5, 1958. This work was supported in part by the U. S. Army (Signal Corps), the U. S. Air Force (Office of Sci. Res., Air Res. and Dev. Command), and the U. S. Navy (Office of Naval Res.).

1 A. L. McWhorter and J. W. Meyer, "Solid-state maser amplifier," *Phys. Rev.*, vol. 109, pp. 312–318; January 15, 1958.

2 M. W. P. Strandberg, C. F. Davis, Jr., B. W. Faughnan, R. L. Kyhl, and G. J. Wolga, "Operation of a solid-state quantum-mechanical amplifier," *Phys. Rev.*, vol. 109, pp. 1988–1989; March 15, 1958.

3 M. W. P. Strandberg, "Spin-lattice relaxation," *Phys. Rev.*, vol. 110, pp. 65–69; April 1, 1958.

4 G. Makhov, C. Kikuchi, J. Lambe, and R. W. Terhune, "Maser action in ruby," *Phys. Rev.*, vol. 109 pp. 1399–1400; February 15, 1958.

5 $\epsilon/\epsilon_0 = 11.53$, parallel to c axis, semi color and 9.53, perpendicular.

6 $(G^{1/2}-1)Bw = 2f_0/|Q_{neg}|$ = "voltage gain-bandwidth product" is nearly constant for high gains. Q_{neg} is the net negative cavity Q, including losses; f_0 is the operating frequency.

7 $T_{\text{amplifier}} \approx (|Q_{neg}|/Q_{abs})T_{\text{bath}}$.

Reprinted from the PROCEEDINGS OF THE IRE
VOL. 47, NO. 1, JANUARY, 1959

PRINTED IN THE U.S.A.

Packaged Tunable L-Band Maser System*

F. R. ARAMS†, SENIOR MEMBER, IRE, AND S. OKWIT†, ASSOCIATE MEMBER, IRE

***Summary*—A low-noise tunable *L*-band maser system is described. The maser uses a pink ruby crystal oriented at 90° and is tunable from 850 to 2000 mc. The voltage-gain bandwidth product is as high as 37.5 mc at a liquid helium bath temperature of 1.5°K. An *L*-band circulator has been developed for use with the maser. It has an insertion loss of 0.3 db, operates over a 200-mc frequency range at *L*-band, and determines the usable tuning range of the circulator-maser system. The maser and circulator have been packaged into an operational unit that includes all auxiliary components, and has a system noise factor of 0.5 db (35°K). Electrical and mechanical features of the system are described and performance data are given.**

I. Introduction

THE low-noise characteristic of the three-level solid-state maser amplifier has stimulated the interest of workers in a number of fields where the ultimate in receiver sensitivity is required. Radio astronomers, for example, are particularly interested in using a maser as a preamplifier for a 21-cm interstellar hydrogen-line receiver. Because of the Doppler shift in the frequency of the hydrogen line in receding galaxies, an *L*-band maser amplifier, which covers 1420 mc and tunes down in frequency, is of great practical interest. A packaged tunable maser system is described that tunes over a 200-mc frequency range at *L*-band.

Fixed-frequency *L*-band masers have been operated using chromium-doped potassium cobalticyanide.[1,2] Furthermore, gadolinium-doped hydrated lanthanum ethyl sulfate with cerium impurity[3] and chromium-doped aluminum oxide (ruby) had given satisfactory operation at higher microwave frequencies.[4–7] Ruby was chosen for our maser, because of its excellent physical, mechanical, and chemical characteristics, even though it had not previously to our knowledge been used as a material for *L*-band maser operation. Its characteristics include favorable "zero-field" splitting of the energy levels, good crystal line width, favorable relaxation times, low dielectric loss, machinability to accurate dimensions, resistance to cracking upon repeated temperature cycling, chemical inertness, and availability.

It was found[8] that *L*-band maser operation using ruby could be achieved, and satisfactory gain-bandwidth products obtained. In our design we placed emphasis on the feature of tunability. A tuning range from 850 to 2000 mc was obtained. Since a low-loss four-port *L*-band circulator was not available, such a unit, having a 200-mc frequency range for use with the maser, was developed.[9]

The maser and circulator were then packaged with the necessary auxiliary equipment to form a complete low-noise *L*-band preamplifier having a system noise factor of 0.5 db (35°K).

II. System Description

A schematic diagram of the maser system is shown in Fig. 1. The signal received by the antenna is directed by the four-port circulator into the single-port cavity maser; the amplified signal leaves the maser by the same

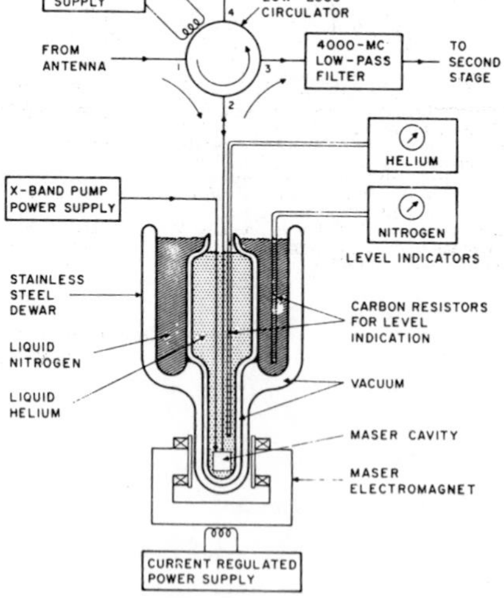

Fig. 1—Schematic diagram of maser system.

* Original manuscript received by the IRE, August 19, 1959; revised manuscript received, December 21, 1959. This work was supported by the U. S. Department of Defense, and was presented at the 1959 PGMTT Symposium, Harvard University, Cambridge, Mass.; June 2, 1959.

† Airborne Instruments Lab., Cutler-Hammer, Inc., Melville, L. I., N. Y.

[1] J. O. Artman, N. Bloembergen, and S. Shapiro, "Operation of a three-level solid-state maser at 21 cm," *Phys. Rev.*, vol. 109, pp. 1392–1393; February 15, 1958.

[2] S. Autler and N. McAvoy, "21-centimeter solid-state maser," *Phys. Rev.*, vol. 110, pp. 280–281; April, 1958.

[3] H. E. D. Scovil, G. Feher, and H. Seidel, "Operation of a solid-state maser," *Phys. Rev.*, vol. 105, pp. 762–763; January 1, 1957.

[4] G. Makhov, C. Kikuchi, J. Lambe, and R. W. Terhune, "Maser action in ruby," *Phys. Rev.*, vol. 109, pp. 1399–1400; February 15, 1958.

[5] R. W. DeGrasse, E. O. Schulz-DuBois, and H. E. D. Scovil, "Three-level solid-state traveling wave maser," *Bell Sys. Tech. J.*, vol. 38, pp. 305–334; March, 1959.

[6] T. H. Maiman, "Solid-state masers—design and performance," *Proc. NSIA-ARDC Conf. on Molecular Electronics*, Washington, D. C.; November 13, 1958.

[7] J. A. Giordmaine, L. E. Alsop, C. H. Mayer, and C. H. Townes, "A maser amplifier for radio astronomy at *X*-band," PROC IRE, vol. 47, pp. 1062–1069; June, 1959.

[8] F. R. Arams, S. Okwit, and A. Penzias, "Maser action in ruby at 21 cm," *Bull. Amer. Phys. Soc.*, ser. II, vol. 4, p. 21; January 28, 1959.

[9] F. R. Arams, G. Krayer, and S. Okwit, "Low-loss *S*- and *L*-band circulators," 1959 IRE NATIONAL CONVENTION RECORD, pt. 3, pp. 126–133.

port and is directed by the circulator to the second stage. A low-pass filter having a cutoff frequency of 4000 mc is placed at the output of the maser system to prevent feed-through of pump power into the receiver. At this location, the filter will not adversely affect system noise factor.

A matched load is connected to the fourth port of the circulator. This load can be refrigerated if it is necessary to reduce its noise contribution caused by antenna mismatch (which reflects load noise into the maser).

The maser cavity (which is described more fully in Section III) is located near the bottom of a 2-inch inner diameter stainless-steel double Dewar flask. The inner portion of the Dewar flask is filled with $2\frac{1}{4}$ liters of liquid helium, which is allowed to enter the maser cavity. One charge of liquid helium yields approximately 16 hours of operation. The outer jacket of the Dewar flask is filled with liquid nitrogen to reduce liquid helium evaporation. The Dewar flask is constricted at the bottom to a $2\frac{1}{4}$-inch outer diameter to keep the dimensions of the maser electromagnet to a minimum. The maser electromagnet employs a 5-inch diameter pole-face and provides a magnetic field that is homogeneous within ± 5 gauss out of 2000 gauss over the volume occupied by the ruby crystal.

Liquid level indicators are provided for the refrigerants. These use three carbon resistors connected in parallel and located at various heights in the Dewar flask. Liquid levels are displayed on two ammeters. A relay-actuated warning light indicates when a new charge of liquid helium is required.

The *X*-band pump power circuitry (shown in Fig. 2) consists of 1) a Varian X-13, 100-mw, klystron with a dial mounted on its tuning shaft that is directly calibrated in frequency, 2) an isolator that helps to stabilize the klystron by protecting it from load variations, 3) a variable attenuator that allows for pump power level adjustment, and 4) a 20-db bidirectional coupler to sample the pump output that is detected and displayed on a microammeter (this monitors the pump power level). The power reflected from the maser cavity is also sampled by the bidirectional coupler, detected, and fed to an oscilloscope to permit observation of the maser cavity resonance. For this purpose, the klystron is frequency-modulated using sawtooth modulation from the klystron power supply. A reaction frequency meter is included to permit accurate determination of pump frequency.

III. Tunable Maser Cavity Design

For maser operation, it is desirable that the cavity containing the paramagnetic material (ruby) be resonant at both the signal and pump frequencies. Furthermore, it is desirable that 1) these two cavity resonances be independently tunable, 2) the tuning be accomplished from the top of the Dewar flask while the cavity is in the liquid helium, and 3) the cavity coupling at the signal frequency be adjustable so that gain and bandwidth can be varied during operation.

The cavity design used, which meets all of these requirements, is shown in Fig. 3. This structure has the additional feature of simple mechanical design for making the required tuning and coupling adjustments.

The signal-frequency mode consists of a quarter-wavelength TEM-mode resonator.[1] This resonator is a thin-rod center conductor between parallel ground planes provided by the broad walls of a small *X*-band waveguide. This type of structure has the advantages that 1) resonant wavelength is proportional to rod length, 2) cavity coupling remains reasonably constant with frequency, and 3) the RF magnetic field distribution over the paramagnetic material remains essentially unchanged while the cavity is tuned. Because the TEM mode is dominant, the problem of spurious responses is minimized. A tuning range of more than one octave is obtained simply by varying the length of the center-conductor rod. The rod length is reduced by a factor of about three because of the high dielectric constant of the ruby. This is desirable at *L*-band to keep physical dimensions small. The unloaded Q of this structure is 550 at room temperature and increases to 1100 at 4.2°K.

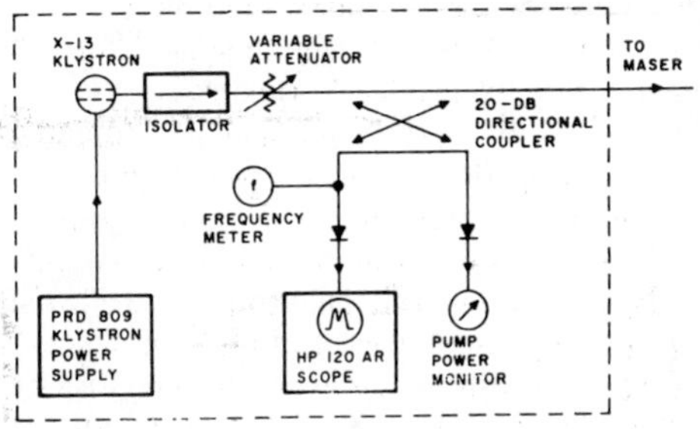

Fig. 2—Schematic diagram of *X*-band pump power supply.

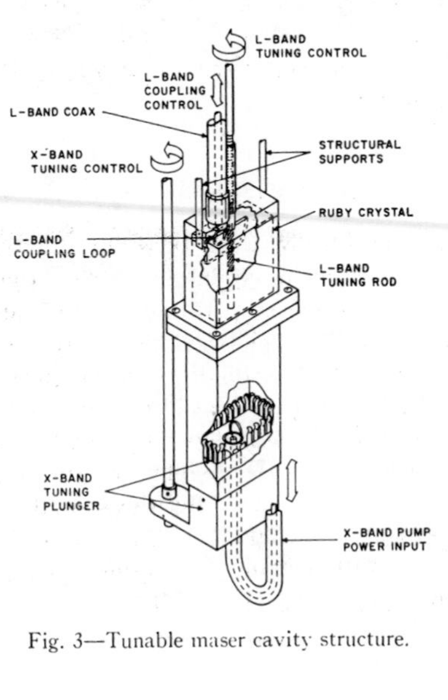

Fig. 3—Tunable maser cavity structure.

The waveguide region not occupied by the rod is beyond cutoff for the signal frequency. Therefore, a contacting plunger located in this region can serve as the tuning element for the X-band pump resonance (which operates in a TE_{107} mode) without affecting the L-band resonance (Fig. 3). The X-band pump power is loop-coupled into the cavity, through the backplate of the X-band tuning plunger, by means of a coaxial line having a bead-supported center conductor. Such a line has an X-band dissipative loss of only a few tenths of a db, has a much smaller cross section compared with waveguide, and the coupling remains reasonably constant over a broad tuning range. The X-band cavity is conveniently tuned from the top by a tuning rod directly connected to the tuning plunger. All low-temperature moving joints (except where electrical contact is required) consist of metal-to-teflon bushings.

Two factors were considered in choosing the 0.036-inch diameter of the L-band tuning rod: 1) the diameter should be as small as possible to minimize its effect on the X-band resonant frequency, and 2) the diameter dimension should yield a high unloaded Q at the L-band signal frequency. Measurements showed that the X-band resonance goes through a cyclical variation of only ± 3 mc when the L-band resonance is tuned. The X-band tuning plunger is, as previously stated, in a region beyond cutoff for the L-band mode. Thus, the two resonances are independently tunable.

The coupling to the L-band mode is accomplished by means of a loop that penetrates into a thin slot in the ruby. The loop is oriented in a plane parallel to the broad waveguide dimension to minimize coupling to the X-band pump resonance. The coupling is variable from the top of the Dewar flask by means of a micrometer head that moves the L-band coaxial line in the vertical direction. This varies the penetration of the coupling loop into the maser cavity. Two other micrometer heads located at the top of the Dewar flask are used to tune the L- and X-band cavity resonances. The cavity assembly and the superstructure are shown in Figs. 4 and 5, respectively.

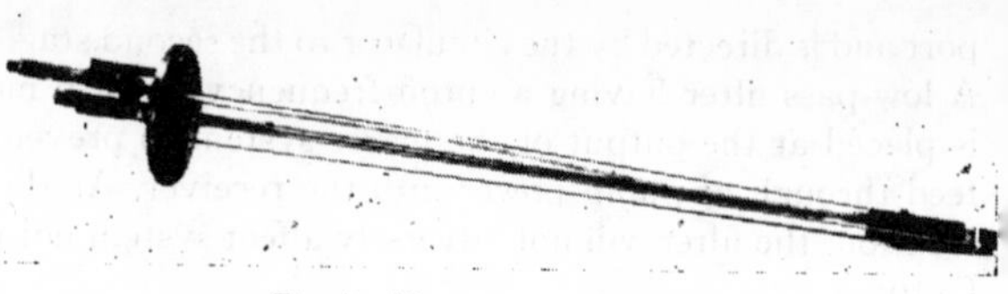

Fig. 4—Maser cavity assembly.

Fig. 5—Cavity superstructure.

IV. Maser Performance

The relationship between the pump and signal resonant frequencies of the cavity and the external magnetic field required for maser operation are determined by the inherent quantum-mechanical properties of the paramagnetic crystal. These quantum-mechanical properties (energy levels, RF transition probabilities, and relaxation times) are strongly dependent upon the external magnetic field H and the angular orientation θ between the external magnetic field and the crystal C-axis.

Best L-band maser performance was obtained for an angular orientation θ of 60° at high magnetic fields ($H \approx 2000$ gauss). The energy level diagram for ruby when θ is equal to 90° is shown in Fig. 6. It shows four (low-lying) energy levels, since Cr^{+++} in Al_2O_3 has a spin $S=3/2$. The L-band signal transition and X-band pump transition that were used are between levels 1 and 2, and levels 1 and 3, respectively. The high-field 90° operating point is attractive on theoretical grounds because the calculated signal and pump transition probabilities are high.[10,11] At this operating point, the signal transition probability is maximum when the microwave signal magnetic field is nearly perpendicular to the external magnetic field and parallel to the ruby C-axis. This condition is realized to a fair degree in our design, since the ruby crystal that we utilized had its C-axis oriented in a plane parallel to the broad face of the X-band waveguide, and at 60° to the L-band tuning rod (see Fig. 3), and the signal magnetic field is elliptically shaped for slabline TEM mode employed.

[10] W. S. Chang and A. E. Siegman, "Characteristics of Ruby for Maser Applications," Electron Devices Laboratory, Stanford University, Stanford, Calif., Tech. Rept. 156-2, Figs. 14 and 15; September 30, 1958. Also, J. Weber, "Masers," *Rev. Mod. Phys.*, vol. 31, pp. 681–710; July, 1959.

[11] E. O. Schulz-DuBois, H. E. D. Scovil, and R. W. DeGrasse, "Use of active material in three-level solid-state masers," *Bell Sys. Tech. J.*, vol. 38, pp. 335–352; March, 1959.

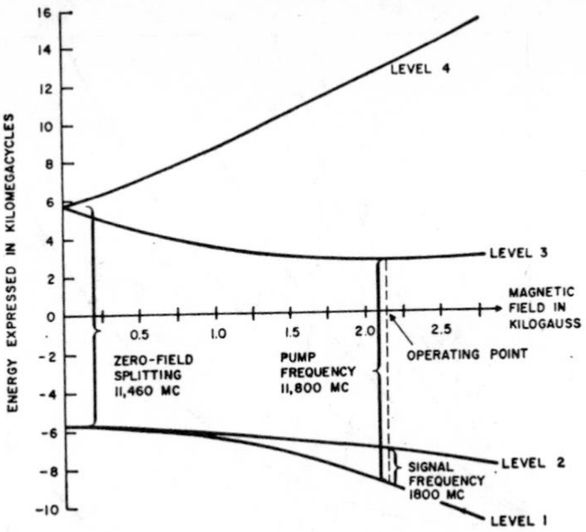

Fig. 6—Energy levels utilized for *L*-band maser.

Measurements of the voltage-gain bandwidth product at high magnetic fields were made at liquid helium bath temperatures of 4.2°K and 1.5°K. The results of these measurements are listed in Table I.

Table I shows that a voltage-gain bandwidth product of 37.5 mc was measured at 1750 mc for a temperature of 1.5°K. Thus, for a half-power bandwidth of 3.75 mc, a gain of 20 db will be obtained. Furthermore, operation was also obtained at an operating temperature of 4.2°K, where a voltage-gain bandwidth product as high as 20 mc was measured.

The gain-bandwidth products measured were used to calculate the effective magnetic Q. For such calculations, Fig. 7 and (3) (Appendix I) can be used, under the condition that the cavity unloaded Q is much greater than the external Q. The effective magnetic Q calculated at 1200 mc (Table I) is 140 and 210 for operation at 1.5°K and 4.2°K, respectively. The magnetic Q is approximately constant over the *L*-band region. There is a deterioration in magnetic Q at the low-frequency end that is probably due to cross-relaxation effects.[12] The pump power that was required varied between 5 and 150 mw for the various measurements.

A four-level experiment was also performed for θ equal to 90° at high magnetic fields. Here, pumping was done between levels 1 and 4, with the signal transition again between levels 1 and 2. Maser operation at a liquid helium bath temperature of 4.2° K was readily obtained at frequencies from 850 to 1750 mc (Table II). However, the measured voltage-gain bandwidth product did not show the expected improvement of greater than 100 per cent (assuming equal relaxation times between all levels) over the three-level arrangement. This may have been due in part to the limited pumping power available from the 20-kmc klystron that was used. Of the 50 mw available from a Raytheon QK306 klystron, only an estimated 10 mw reached the maser cavity. This power level was insufficient to saturate the 20-kmc pump transition, which has a low calculated transition probability.[10]

[12] N. Bloembergen, S. Shapiro, P. S. Pershan, and J. O. Artman, "Cross-relaxation in spin systems," *Phys. Rev.*, vol. 114, pp. 445–459; April 15, 1959.

TABLE I

SUMMARY OF *L*-BAND MASER PERFORMANCE (THREE-LEVEL OPERATION)

Liquid Helium Bath Temperature (°K)	Signal Frequency (mc)	Voltage-Gain Bandwidth Product Measured (mc)	Voltage-Gain Bandwidth Product Determined from External Q Measurement (mc)	Pump Frequency (mc)	Magnetic Field (gauss)
4.2	2000	*	*	12,150	2260
4.2	1815	20	22	11,860	2150
4.2	1200	11	13	10,950	1740
4.2	1010	9	12	10,700	1650
4.2	850	*	*	10,460	1510
1.5	1750	37.5	37.5	11,795	2100
1.5	1200	19	20	10,845	1740

* Not measured.

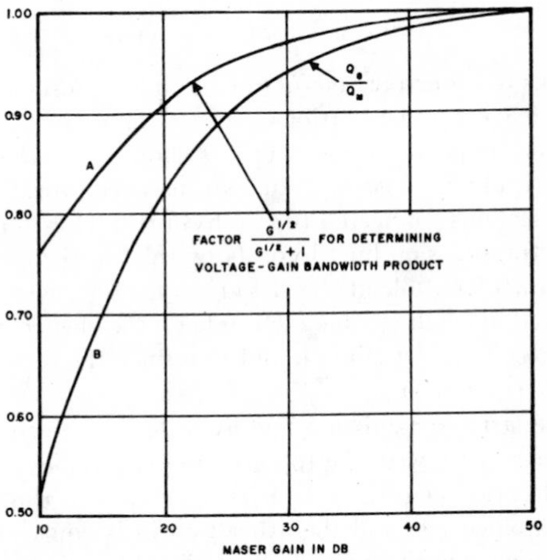

Fig. 7—Relationship of external Q to gain-bandwidth product and magnetic Q for cavity maser [when the cavity unloaded $Q(Q_u)$ is much greater that the external $Q(Q_e)$]. Curve A: Correction factor, due to finite gain, on gain-bandwidth product determined from external-Q measurement. Curve B: Relationship of external Q to magnetic Q as a function of gain.

TABLE II

SUMMARY OF *L*-BAND MASER PERFORMANCE (FOUR-LEVEL OPERATION)

Liquid Helium Bath Temperature (°K)	Signal Frequency (mc)	Voltage-Gain Bandwidth Product Measured (mc)	Pump Frequency (mc)
4.2	1750	13	21,750
4.2	1005	6	19,180
4.2	855	5	18,420

For convenient reference, we have plotted the energy levels in ruby in a manner that is particularly suitable for three-level tunable maser operation [Fig. 8(a) and 8(b)]. By plotting pump frequency as a function of magnetic field, with angular orientation θ and signal frequency as parameters, the variation in pump frequency and magnetic field for a given signal tuning range are readily determined. The region of operation used in our maser is indicated by a heavy line in Fig. 8(b).

This form of plotting the energy levels brings out an interesting and useful point, namely, that the ruby crystal can be readily oriented to 90° by varying the crystal orientation until the dc magnetic field required for resonance absorption is maximized. As Fig. 8(b) shows, this alignment technique can be applied to either the pump or signal transition.

V. Low-Loss Circulator

This is a four-port circulator having an insertion loss near 0.3 db and isolations greater than 23 db over a 200-mc frequency range.[9] Fig. 9 shows the circulator. Electrically, it consists of dual 90° non-reciprocal phase-shift sections connected to two hybrids.[13] Our unit used strip-transmission-line hybrids with transitions to a MgMnAl-ferrite-loaded *L*-band waveguide, which was reduced in height to one inch to keep the electromagnet dimensions at a minimum and to reduce the ferrite material requirements.

The strip-transmission-line hybrids are shown in detail in Fig. 10, with the top ground plane removed. The ring hybrid is equivalent in its operation to the waveguide folded tee, and the other hybrid is equivalent to the waveguide short-slot hybrid. The use of the strip-transmission-line hybrids results in reasonable physical size.

VI. Package Description and Performance

A. Description of Package

The over-all maser system is housed in two standard relay cabinets (Fig. 11). The smaller cabinet contains the maser cavity structure, stainless-steel Dewar flask, and maser magnet. The larger cabinet contains the associated auxiliary equipment, including (from top to bottom in Fig. 11):

1) oscilloscope to view either the pump or signal frequency cavity resonance and to observe and optimize maser action;
2) current-regulated power supplies to drive circulator and maser electromagnets;

[13] C. L. Hogan, "Elements of non-reciprocal microwave devices," Proc. IRE, vol. 44, pp. 1345–1368; October, 1956.

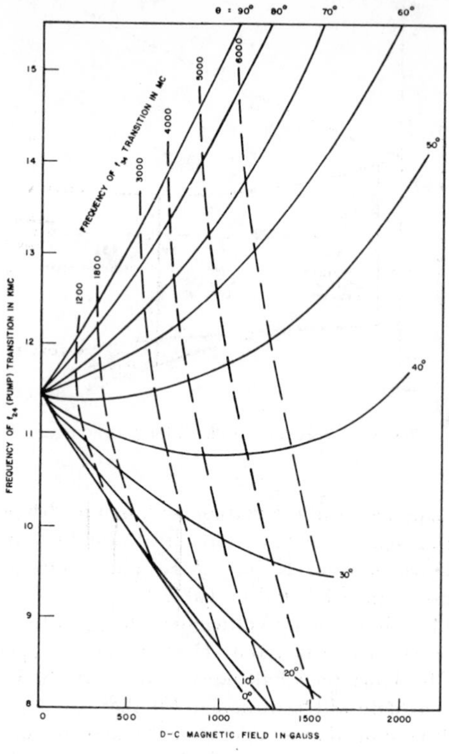

(a)

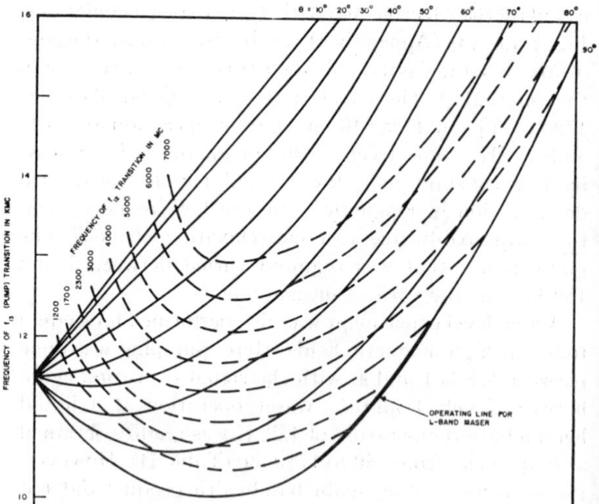

(b)

Fig. 8—Frequency relationships for three-level ruby maser as a function of magnetic field and angular orientation. (a) Upper three energy levels. (b) Lower three energy levels.

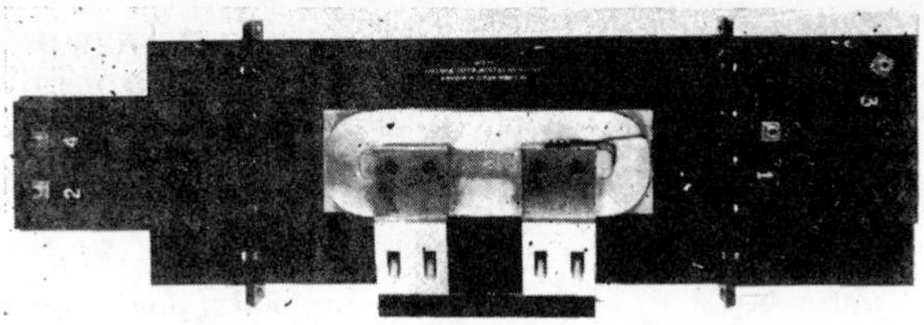

Fig. 9—Low-loss *L*-band circulator.

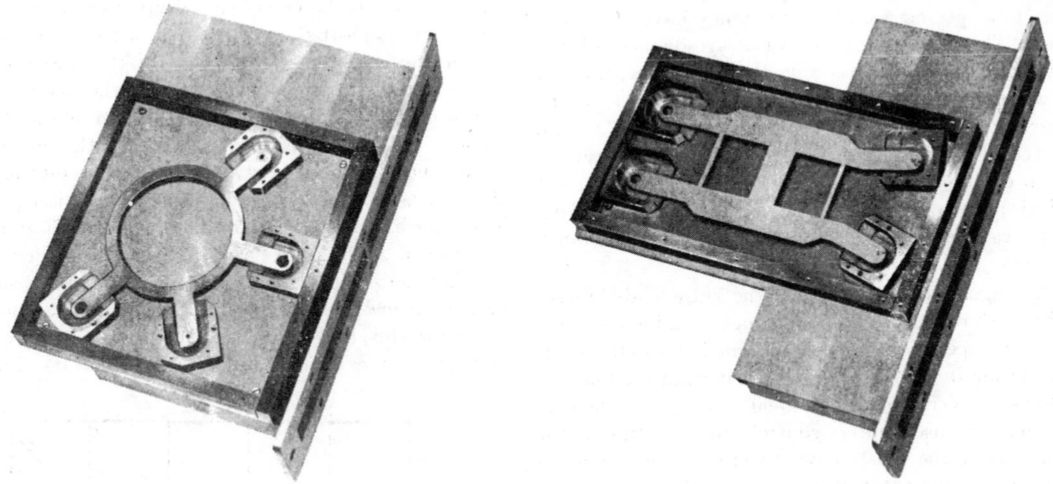

Fig. 10—Strip transmission line hybrids used n *L*-band circulator. (a) 180° 3-db hybrid. (b) 90° 3-db hybrid.

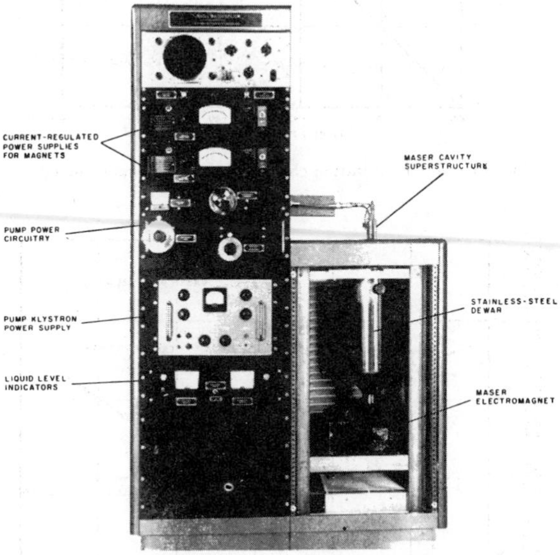

Fig. 11—Packaged maser system.

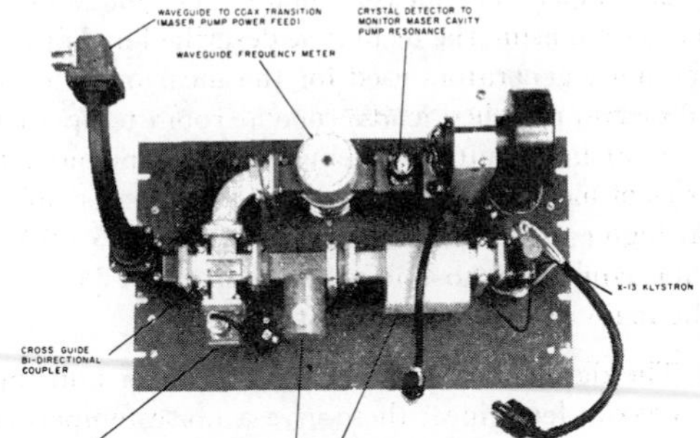

Fig. 12—Pump power circuitry.

3) pump power circuitry, including klystron, isolator, variable attenuator, frequency meter, bidirectional coupler, and detectors (shown in detail in Fig. 12);
4) klystron power supply; and
5) liquid level indicators for the refrigerants.

The circulator (which cannot be seen in Fig. 11) is located in the rear of the larger cabinet and is connected to the maser by a low-loss strip transmission line having $1\frac{1}{2}$-inch ground-plane spacing. The input to the maser system consists of $1\frac{5}{8}$-inch coaxial line.

B. General Performance

The maser is easily tuned to any operating frequency over the 200-mc range by adjusting the dc magnetic field, the pump frequency, and the two cavity resonances. All the adjustments necessary for tuning the maser to a specific operating frequency have been calibrated. The signal-frequency cavity-resonance adjustment can be set to any specified frequency within ± 2 mc with the calibrated micrometer head. One of the required adjustments, the dc magnetic field, is critical and requires fine tuning. The other two adjustments (pump cavity resonance and pump frequency) are not critical; maser operation can be obtained with the pump cavity resonance and pump frequency detuned as much as 75 mc.

The angular orientation θ of the ruby-loaded maser cavity with respect to the dc magnetic field is not critical. Maser operation has been obtained, without serious degradation in gain-bandwidth product, at angular deviations of several degrees from 90° throughout the tuning range. Consequently, controls for fine-tuning the alignment of the maser cavity were deemed unnecessary. A mechanical feature ensures that the maser cavity structure is correctly oriented when it is inserted into the system.

C. System Noise Temperature

Noise-temperature measurements were made on the maser system using the technique described in Appendix I. The noise generators used for the measurement consisted of two matched loads—one at room temperature and one at liquid nitrogen temperature (Appendix II). A series of measurements, made with the maser operating at high gains, yielded a noise factor of 0.5 ± 0.1 db, which is equivalent to a noise temperature of 35°K.

The main contributing noise sources are:

1) The dissipative losses of the circulator and input coaxial feed lines; these give a noise temperature of approximately 28°K (0.4 db).
2) The second-stage amplifier and other components at the output of the maser having an over-all noise factor of 7.2 db (1230°K). The amplifier consists of a balanced mixer utilizing 1N21EMR crystals and a 30-mc IF amplifier. Its measured noise factor was 6.6 db. With a net maser system gain of 23 db, this contribution is 6.15°K.
3) The maser signal frequency spin temperature, which is calculated to be 1.5°K, for a bath temperature of 4.2°K, assuming equal idler and signal spin-lattice relaxation times.

Thus, good correlation is obtained between the calculated and measured noise temperatures.

D. Maser Saturation Characteristics

A saturation curve that was measured on the maser system is shown in Fig. 13. As can be seen, the gain drops 3 db at a power output of -35 dbm. This yields a dynamic range of 68 db for a post-receiver bandwidth of 1 mc.

Susceptibility of the maser to nearby CW signals is shown in Fig. 14. The power level of the interfering signal, at which the maser gain drops 3 db at its center frequency, is plotted as a function of the frequency of the interfering signal. The shape of the measured response can be closely determined from the frequency response of the active maser cavity. The measurement was made with a three-cavity filter between the maser and the second-stage receiver to ensure that the interference effect measured was primarily due to the maser proper. The filter had a 3-db bandwidth of 15 mc and an insertion loss of 25 db at 15 mc from center frequency.

It is essential that the input level of interfering signals be kept below the microwatt range (Figs. 13 and 14). To insure this, it is desirable to use a preselector cavity and/or passive ferrite limiter that has its limiting

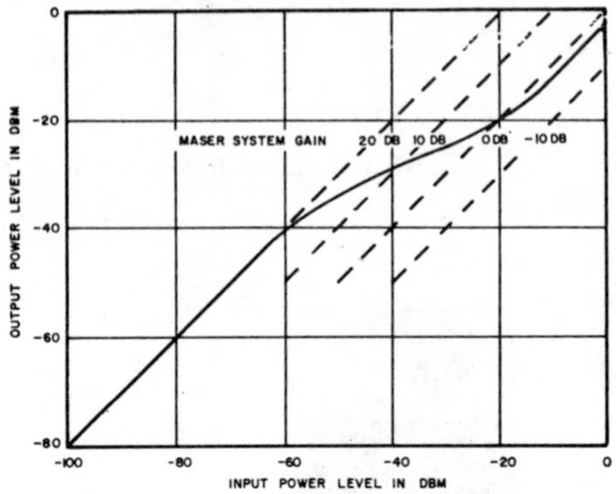

Fig. 13—Maser saturation characteristic due to main signal.

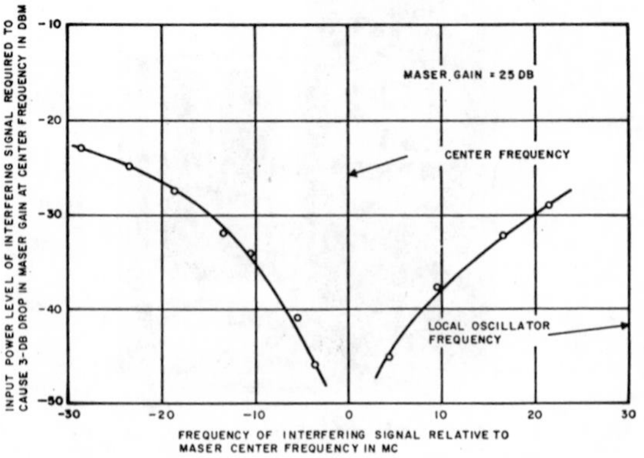

Fig. 14—Maser saturation characteristic due to nearby signals.

threshold at microwatt power levels.[14] These can be placed in the low temperature bath to minimize their noise contribution. The relatively low saturation power level (and relatively long recovery time) of the ruby maser is a result of the relatively long spin-lattice relaxation time of the idler transition, which (for θ equal to 90°) is in the tens of milliseconds at 4.2°K. Future masers will show marked improvements in saturation level and recovery time by using new materials or "impurity-doped" ruby to reduce the idler relaxation time.

To prevent maser saturation effects due to the local oscillator in the second-stage receiver, a balanced mixer should be used. A balanced mixer provides a local-oscillator isolation of 30 db, which, in combination with the circulator isolation and maser cavity selectivity, is more than sufficient to prevent maser saturation effects due to local-oscillator power leakage.

E. Gain Stability

The results of a number of stability measurements at a helium bath temperature of 4.2°K and a maser gain of 22 db yielded a long-term peak-to-peak drift of ±0.55 db, and a short-term peak-to-peak stability of ±0.1 to ±0.2 db over a period of several hours. These figures represent the fluctuations of a complete receiver with the maser front end fed by a standard signal generator. Hence, a portion of the output variation must be ascribed to parts of the measurement setup rather than the maser.

Turbulence in the liquid helium appears to be responsible for some of the short-term gain variations observed in the maser. This effect is reduced by the use of polyfoam loading of the microwave structure. The fluctuations are also significantly reduced by reducing the helium bath temperature below the λ-point (2.2°K), where the liquid helium becomes a superfluid.

The parameter having the greatest detrimental effect on long-term gain stability was found to be the maser magnetic field, which is controlled by a current-regulated power supply. This is evident when it is noted that the regulation must be substantially better than the magnetic line width of the ruby, which is about 1 per cent of the external magnetic field that was used. The electromagnet is designed to permit maser operation over the entire 850 to 2000 mc tuning range of the cavity. Improved stability can be obtained by using a permanent magnet employing an adjustable mechanical shunt or bucking coils for tuning, since a variation in magnetic field of about 6 per cent is needed to cover the 200 mc tuning range of the maser system.

VII. Conclusion

It can be concluded that a cavity maser can be satisfactorily operated over frequency bands greater than one octave. In packaging such a maser together with a circulator for field operational use, the usual 12-inch diameter laboratory magnet and other highly precise supplementary equipment have been eliminated without detrimental effect on gain-bandwidth product, noise figure, and other system parameters. The resulting equipment is reasonably compact and easily operated by semi-skilled personnel.

Appendix I

Techniques for Measuring Maser Gain-Bandwidth Product

The voltage-gain-bandwidth product was determined by two methods. In the first method, gain and half-power bandwidth were measured directly, using the setup shown in Fig. 15. Maser gain is measured by noting the increase in generator output required to maintain a constant output meter reading when the maser is disconnected from the circuit and replaced by a short-circuit at point A of Fig. 15.

In the second method, the external Q of the maser cavity was measured with the pump power and magnetic field turned off. The voltage-gain bandwidth product $G^{1/2}B$ can then be calculated since, for the condition of high gain ($G^{1/2} \gg 1$), it is approximately

$$G^{1/2}B \approx \frac{2f}{Q_e}. \quad (1)$$

where f is the signal frequency and Q_e is the external Q. The more exact expression[15] for $Q_u \gg Q_e$ is

$$G^{1/2}B = \frac{2f}{Q_e}\left[\frac{G^{1/2}}{G^{1/2}+1}\right]. \quad (2)$$

The bracketed term in (2) is the correction factor on the approximation. It is plotted in Fig. 7, and is seen to be less than 10 per cent for gains greater than 20 db.

For comparison with theoretical computations of maser performance, it is desirable to determine Q_m, the magnetic Q, which is a measure of the negative resistance introduced by the paramagnetic maser material.

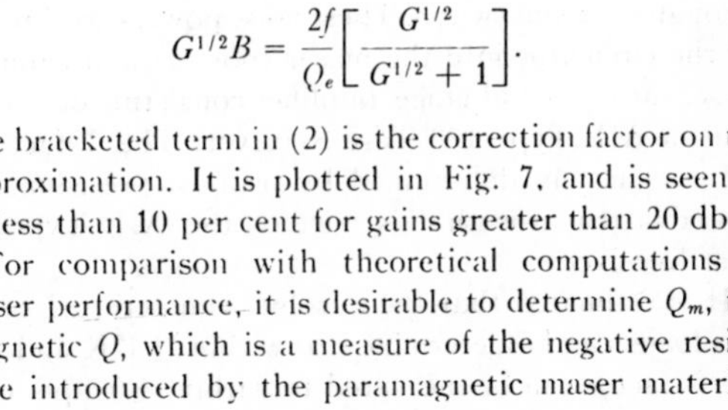

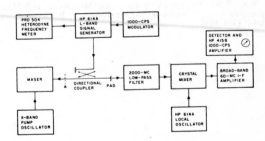

Fig. 15—Measurement setup for maser gain and bandwidth.

[14] R. W. DeGrasse, "Low-loss gyromagnetic coupling through single crystal garnets," *J. Appl. Phys.*, vol. 30, suppl. 4, pp. 155.S–156.S; April, 1959.

[15] J. O. Artman, "The Solid-State Maser," *Proc. Symp. on Role of Solid-State Phenomena in Electric Circuits*, Polytechnic Inst. of Brooklyn, Brooklyn, N. Y., sec. 3, p. 77; April, 1957.

The magnetic Q is related to Q_e by the expression

$$\frac{Q_e}{Q_m} = \frac{G^{1/2} - 1}{G^{1/2} + 1}, \tag{3}$$

and is plotted in Fig. 7. Obviously, $Q_e \approx Q_m$ for high gains. The correction factor is less than 20 per cent for gains greater than 20 db.

Appendix II

Measurement of System Noise Temperature

Of the several methods used for the measurement of noise temperature,[16] the Y-factor method appeared to be most satisfactory for low noise temperatures. In this method, the output noise power of the receiver, when the input source resistance is at a high temperature T_2, is compared with the output noise power of the receiver when the input source resistance is at a lower temperature T_1. The ratio of these two noise powers is called the Y-factor, which is related to the noise temperature, T_e, by the expression

$$T_e = \frac{T_2 - T_1}{Y - 1} - T_1. \tag{4}$$

The accuracy with which T_e can be determined depends upon how accurately T_1, T_2, and Y are known.

Fig. 16 shows the experimental arrangement used for the noise measurement. The available noise power from the two loads (one maintained at a liquid nitrogen temperature of 77.3°K, and the other at room temperature) is alternately coupled to port 1 of the circulator through a coaxial switch. These noise powers are directed by the circulator into the maser (port 2) and from the maser into a second-stage amplifier consisting of a mixer and an AIL Type 130 Test Receiver. The Y-factor is then accurately determined by using a precision calibrated attenuator that is part of the AIL Type 130 Test Receiver.

It is estimated that the absolute temperature of the two loads can be determined to within ±1°K and that the Y-factor can be measured to within ±0.5 per cent.

[16] M. Wind, "Handbook of Electronic Measurements," Microwave Res. Inst., Polytechnic Inst. of Brooklyn, Brooklyn, N. Y., ch. 13; 1954–1955.

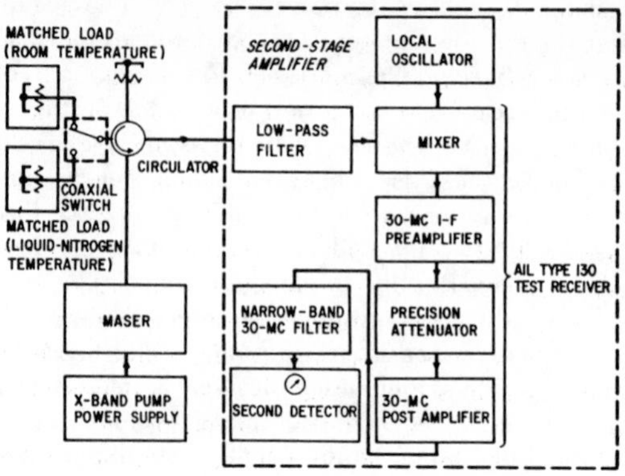

Fig. 16—Measurement setup for maser system noise temperature.

Application of these errors to a variational form of (4) yields a calculated over-all measurement accuracy of better than ±3°K.

In measuring low noise temperatures, the following precautions were taken.

1) The two noise generators (ambient temperature load and the liquid nitrogen load) were well matched.
2) Linearity measurements of the second-stage amplifier were made over a 40-db range. The linearity was found to be within ±0.05 db. In addition, the bandwidth of the second stage was made narrower than that of the first stage, to eliminate bandwidth corrections from the noise-factor measurement.
3) The over-all receiving system was tested for spurious responses. Since broad-band noise sources were used, all spurious responses must be known to reduce the measurement data accurately. All spurious responses were found to be negligible.

Acknowledgment

The advice and aid of C. H. Townes and A. Penzias of Columbia University during the early phases of the project are gratefully acknowledged. The authors also wish to express their gratitude to their co-workers, J. G. Smith and M. Grace, who helped with the packaging and with the measurements.

A UHF Ruby Maser*

A ruby maser has been operated at signal frequencies tunable over the range 380–450 mc. In the experimental arrangement, the magnetic levels $M=+\frac{1}{2}$ and $M=-\frac{1}{2}$ of paramagnetic pink ruby were used for the signal, and X-band pumping was carried out between levels $M=+\frac{3}{2}$ and $M=+\frac{1}{2}$. At the required low magnetic field strength of approximately 70 oe, maser operation was observed to be only slightly dependent on the angle between the dc magnetic field and the crystal axis; amplification and oscillation were obtained for any angle of orientation, with optimum performance at 90°. The observed slight dependence of the maser action on the angle of orientation at the low fields used here is expected on theoretical grounds.

In the mode of operation used, the X-band pumping frequency (approximately 11.8 kmc) is not a critical parameter so that tuning of the signal frequency over the range 380–450 mc required neither adjustment of the pump source nor variation of the magnetic field with regard to magnitude or direction. This feature makes the UHF ruby maser especially suitable for applications in which tuning is desired.

The ruby crystal (4 cm^3 in volume) was located at the center of a teflon loaded cavity which was excited in a TE_{011} pump mode. The construction and tuning of the signal frequency lumped circuit was carried out in a manner similar to that used by Kingston[1] in the design of a potassium-chromicyanide maser. The dc magnetic field was supplied by a small permanent magnet in which the field strength was adjusted by varying the gap between the pole faces.

As an amplifier, typical operational data included a gain of 15 db and a bandwidth of 100 kc with the maser at a temperature of 1.7°K. As an oscillator, the power output was less than 1 μw.

G. K. Wessel
Electronics Lab.
General Electric Co.
Syracuse, N. Y.

* Received by the IRE, December 15, 1958.

[1] R. H. Kingston, "A UHF solid-state maser," Proc. IRE, vol. 46, p. 916; May, 1958.

Reprinted from the PROCEEDINGS OF THE IRE
VOL. 47, NO. 4, APRIL, 1959

PRINTED IN THE U.S.A.

PROJECT ECHO

The Dual Channel 2390-mc Traveling-Wave Maser

By R. W. DE GRASSE, J. J. KOSTELNICK, and H. E. D. SCOVIL

(Manuscript received April 26, 1961)

Reflected 2390-mc signals from the Echo I satellite were received by a horn-reflector antenna and amplified by solid state traveling-wave masers. This paper describes the design of the dual channel maser amplifiers for this experiment. Each maser has sufficient gain (>33 db) to override the noise of the following stage. Unconditional stability is obtained by the use of distributed ferrimagnetic isolator elements. Their instantaneous bandwidth is 13 mc, centered at 2390 mc. The effective input noise temperature is 8°K.*

I. INTRODUCTION

This paper discusses the design of an S-band traveling-wave maser for the Project Echo satellite communication experiment.[1] The masers described here were used at Bell Telephone Laboratories, Holmdel, New Jersey, receiving terminal to amplify the 2390-mc signals reflected from the passive Echo I satellite and received by the 20-foot horn-reflector antenna.[2]

The 2390-mc signal was transmitted with circular polarization. Imperfections in the transmission path such as a not perfectly spherical satellite could lead to deviations from the originally circular polarization. Such effects would show up in terms of a signal having the opposite sense of circular polarization. A quarter-wave plate in the antenna feed converted both senses of circular into orthogonal senses of linear polarization, which were then fed separately to the inputs of two masers. Thus one maser received the polarization as transmitted and served as pre-

* Although this equipment was designed by the Bell System as part of its research and development program, it was operated in connection with Project Echo under Contract NASW-110 for the National Aeronautics and Space Administration.

amplifier for the signal channel. The other maser served as a preamplifier for a monitoring channel which received data on the imperfections of the transmission path.

The system used frequency modulation. It required a receiving bandwidth of approximately 1 mc centered at 2390 mc for the signal. A slightly wider bandwidth was required, however, since continuous sky-noise monitoring was desired at 2388 mc; this frequency was outside but close to the signal channel. Further receiving system details are given in the accompanying paper by Ohm.[3]

II. SIGNAL REQUIREMENTS

The system objective called for masers with the following requirements:

1. two identical amplifiers for duplex operation;
2. lowest possible noise temperature;
3. bandwidth greater than 3 mc;
4. long-term gain stability;
5. at least 33 db gain;
6. dynamic range greater than 60 db;
7. sufficient running time between helium transfers to permit operation for a full sequence of neighboring satellite passes;
8. center frequency 2390 mc.

Because of items 2, 4, and 6, it was decided that traveling-wave masers would be the most desirable. It was shown previously[4] that these general objectives could be met at 6 kmc. Apart from the frequency, the main differences were the requirement for a higher gain and no electronic tuning. This suggested the use of the 6-kmc traveling-wave maser as a basis for design, the main departure being a much narrower-bandwidth slow-wave structure with greater slowing.

Item 7 suggested a batch helium system using a stainless steel dewar with sufficient liquid storage capacity to give the required running time.

The two amplifiers were located in the same dewar and magnetic field, in order to obtain duplex operation.

III. THE ACTIVE MATERIAL (RUBY)

Chromium-doped aluminum oxide (ruby) was the one material which was proved to have the requisite properties. Fortunately, essentially complete information was available on the maser properties of this material at 2390 mc from the work of Geusic.[5] In particular it was known that 0.05 per cent chromium was optimum and that the $\theta = 90°$, high-field, single-pump operation was best.

The value of $\chi''_{\pm}$ for circular polarization is given by Equation (12) of Ref. 4. Geusic obtained the inverted state densities ($\bar{\rho}_n - \bar{\rho}_{n'}$) directly from a measurement of the inversion ratio, $\chi''_{\text{pump on}}/\chi''_{\text{pump off}}$. From the inversion ratio of 3.6 at 4.2°K he computed $-\chi_+''$ and $-\chi_-''$, the inverted susceptibilities, for the two senses of circular polarization defined with respect to the applied dc magnetic field. He gives $\chi_+'' = -0.018$ and $\chi_-'' = -0.0021$ when the material is pumped to saturation, the principal axis of the susceptibility tensor being along the C-axis of the crystal.

IV. THE INTERACTION BETWEEN THE ACTIVE MATERIAL AND THE SLOW-WAVE STRUCTURE

The gain in a length of structure, l, is given by Equation (5) of Ref. 4 as

$$G = e^{-\chi''_{\max} F(\omega v_g) l},$$

where $\chi''_{\max}$ is the magnitude of the diagonalized χ'' tensor, and the filling factor, F, is defined by

$$F = \frac{\int H \cdot \chi'' \cdot H^* \, ds}{\chi''_{\max} \int H^2 \, ds}$$

Since $\chi''_{\max}$ is a property of the material and may be computed from Geusic's values for $\chi''_{\pm}$, we find $\chi''_{\max} = 1.4 \, \chi''_+$. In order to obtain the largest gain, one should maximize F. This would occur if the structure were completely filled with ruby and if the RF fields everywhere had the correct ellipticity. In practice, however, this cannot be done. The comb structure cannot be conveniently filled with active material between the fingers, and some air dielectric has to be left near the tips in order to control the frequency and bandwidth. Further, the RF field configuration is controlled by the structure, and the ellipticity is different in different regions. In principle, the C-axis of the crystal can be oriented to give the best value for F. Unfortunately, at the time this device was built, large boules could not be obtained with the optimum orientation. It was necessary, therefore, to use the C-axis at 60° to the axis of the comb.

The 6-kmc maser was loaded with ruby on only one side, and the ratio of the db gains in the opposite directions of propagation was 3.5. A ratio of about 2 was expected at 2.4 kmc, because of the increased ellipticity of the susceptibility tensor. It was decided, therefore, that a design would be attempted in which both sides of the slow-wave structure would be loaded with ruby in order to obtain maximum gain. In obtaining this increase in gain, we paid the penalty of reciprocal electronic gain. This led to a rather difficult job for the isolator, since short-circuit stability required the isolator reverse loss to now exceed twice the ruby gain.

The RF magnetic field patterns of the comb are not known exactly; nevertheless it was possible to make a reasonable estimate of the product $\chi''_{max}F$, and hence obtain the magnetic Q_m at 4.2°K. This approximate computation gave

$$Q_m = \frac{1}{\chi''_{max}F} \approx 190.$$

The electronic gain may be rewritten [Equation (22) of Ref. 4] as

$$G = 27.3\left(\frac{SN}{Q_m}\right),$$

where S is the slowing factor and N the number of free space wavelengths in the length of the structure. Assuming an amplifier length of 5 inches and a $Q_m = 190$,

$$G \approx 1.4(10^{-1}S).$$

If the structure and isolator forward loss is assumed to be about 12 db, we see that a slowing factor of about 340 is required for operation at 4.2°K. As this was considered somewhat excessive, it was decided to operate at a pumped helium temperature of about 1.6°K. At this temperature cross-relaxation reduces the inversion ratio to about 2.5. Taking this into account, we obtain a required slowing of 190.

It is now possible to estimate the number of sections required in the slow-wave structure and the structure bandwidth from Equation (38) of Ref. 4,

$$SN = N_s \frac{f_0}{2\pi} \frac{d\varphi}{df},$$

where f_0 is the frequency at which the circuit fingers have an electrical length of one-quarter wavelength, N_s is the total number of sections in the structure, and $d\varphi/df$ is the rate of change of phase shift per section with frequency. Using an empirical relationship between structure bandwidth B_s and $d\varphi/df$, which is

$$\frac{d\varphi}{df} \approx \frac{k\pi}{B_s},$$

where $k \sim 0.6$, then

$$SN = 0.3N_s \frac{f_0}{B_s},$$

and putting in values we obtain

$$\frac{B_s}{N_s} \approx 3.8,$$

where B_s is in megacycles. In the final design, 25 sections were used, which indicates an approximate structure bandwidth of 95 mc, i.e., about 4 per cent. Previous experience showed that fabrication difficulties were often encountered with smaller percentage bandwidths.

V. THE SLOW-WAVE STRUCTURE

One difficulty with the use of the comb structure at low frequencies is the increase in size if the structure is simply scaled in dimensions. The nominal finger length is $\lambda/4$. This dimension is along the direction of the applied dc magnetic field; consequently, it will be a determining factor in the magnet gap size. The actual finger length required can be reduced by capacitive loading at the finger tips and by utilizing the dielectric constant of the ruby maser material.

The 6-kmc traveling-wave maser employed a finger length of 0.87 $\lambda/4$. In order to keep the magnet size down, the Echo maser was designed to use a length of 0.64 $\lambda/4$. The outer walls of the comb structure, which form the pump frequency waveguide, are 0.400 by 0.850 inches, which is close to X-band waveguide inside dimension. These dimensions give a 0.050-inch gap between the finger tips and the waveguide wall and increase the fringe capacity considerably. The final structure employed an array of 25 fingers having a diameter of 0.070 inch and a pitch of 0.214 inch. The unloaded phase shift per section, φ, versus frequency, f, curve for this structure is shown in Fig. 1 as curve A. The effects of dielectric loading are illustrated by curves B and C. The length of the loading along the fingers determines, to a good approximation, the upper cutoff frequency of the structure. The position of the lower cutoff frequency is then determined by the height of the loading perpendicular to the fingers. Full-height loading, without essentially changing the bandwidth, as in B, lowers the pass band.

In order to obtain maximum gain, full-height loading of the ruby is indicated near the base of the fingers where the RF magnetic fields are strongest. Consequently, the final amplifier design was based on the loading shown in Fig. 1. Under this condition the lower cutoff is deter-

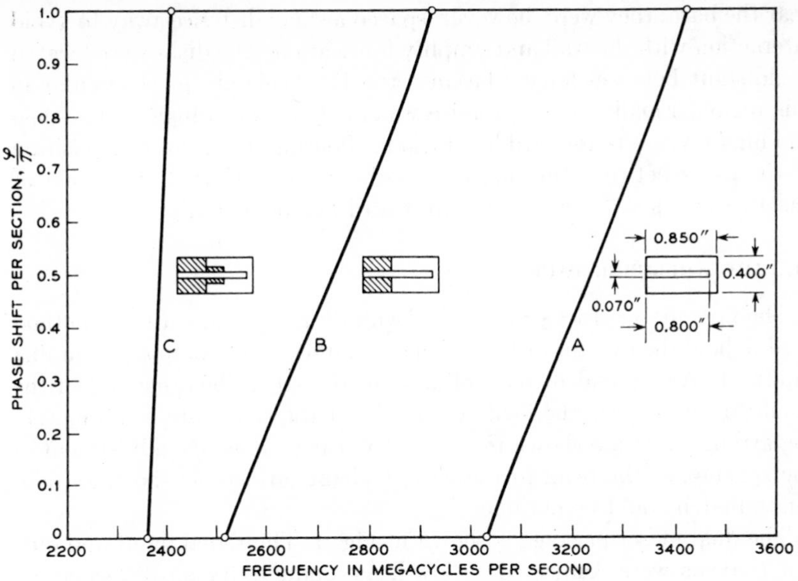

Fig. 1 — Unloaded phase shift per section vs. frequency.

mined primarily by the length of the full-height ruby loading, and is little effected by the partial-height loading. The high-frequency cutoff is determined primarily by the length of ruby directly in contact with the fingers.

VI. THE ISOLATOR

Development of a satisfactory isolator was essential to the design, since the ruby gain was reciprocal. An important aspect of the isolator design was the adjustment of geometry in order to obtain ferrimagnetic resonance at the ruby paramagnetic resonance field. A geometry approaching a thin disk was required, and polycrystalline iron garnet disks with an aspect ratio of 8:1 were used.

Isolator tests were carried out in a crossed-wire strip-line structure in order to determine the performance of the material. Ref. 6 shows typical curves.

The actual volume of yttrium iron garnet which could be used to obtain sufficient reverse loss was determined by the aspect ratio and the physical limitations imposed by the structure dimensions. The remaining parameter was the location of the disks in the signal RF magnetic field. The high field near the base called for placement of the disks in a plane near the base; they were, however, spaced a small distance away to avoid interaction with the wall and simplify fabrication. The disks were located equidistant between fingers because the RF fields are most circular in this region. Finally, a compromise was made between high reverse loss and high reverse-to-forward loss ratio in choosing the transverse position of the disks between the fingers and the waveguide wall. The isolator has a reverse loss >120 db and a forward loss of ~ 10 db.

VII. THE AMPLIFIER PACKAGE

The final maser cross section is shown in Fig. 2 along with the method used to hold the isolator disks, which are mounted in a composite alumina sandwich. An equivalent piece of alumina is used on the other side of the comb to symmetrize the loading. Details of the coaxial-to-comb matching arrangement are shown in Fig. 3. By using successive adjustment of the spacing, *d*, the bend in the wire, and the adjustable short, an adequate match could be obtained.

The dual maser package is shown in Fig. 4. The signal input and output coaxials were connected to low-heat-conductivity air-dielectric coaxial cables. The input cables have a diameter of 0.750 inch and an impedance of 70 ohms. Low electrical loss is important in these cables, since they have a higher noise contribution than any other single part of the amplifier. The output cables are 0.50 inch in diameter with a 50-ohm impedance. The pump frequency waveguide is Ku-band, and a 3-db top-wall short-slot coupler is provided to divide the incoming pump power equally for the two maser amplifiers.

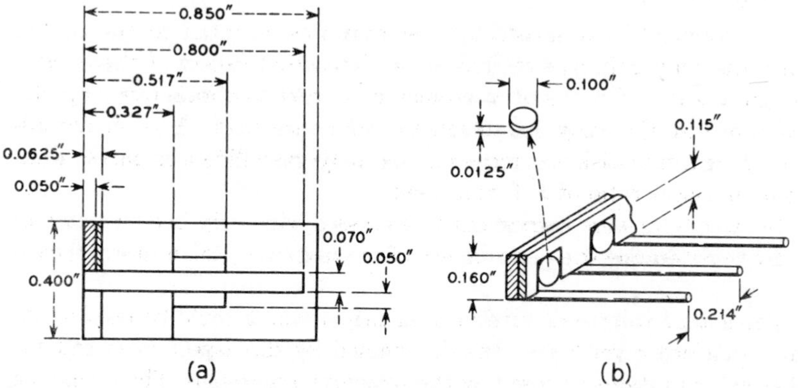

Fig. 2 — (a) Maser cross section including isolator; (b) placement of garnet disks relative to comb structure.

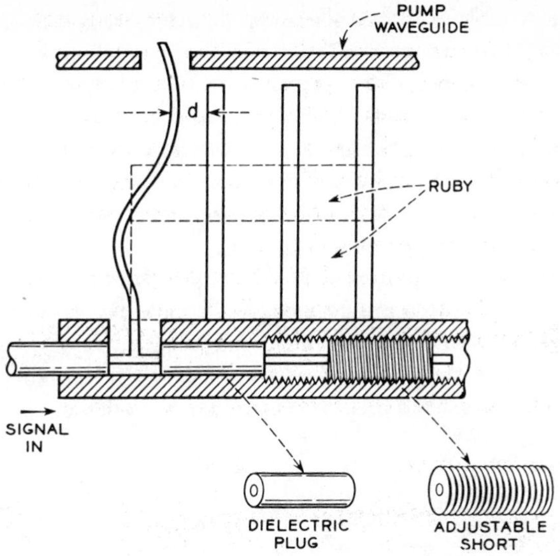

Fig. 3 — Coaxial-to-comb matching arrangement.

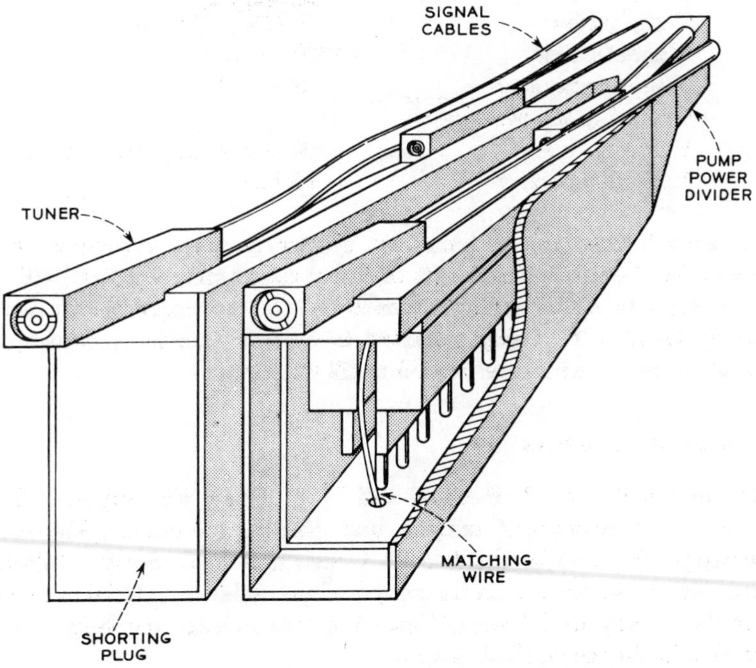

Fig. 4 — Two-maser package.

The cable assembly and traveling-wave maser structure are located in a stainless steel dewar with a 10-liter helium capacity. The tip of the dewar is between the poles of a permanent magnet whose field can be adjusted with movable shunts. The dewar and magnet are mounted in a frame which also contains the microwave pump klystron, the automatic frequency control discriminator and associated waveguide, the automatic nitrogen transfer controls, temperature and level monitoring meters, and the vacuum control valves and gauges.

The entire assembly is mounted just beneath the antenna feed in the cab at the back of the antenna, which also houses the remainder of the microwave receiver and the monitoring and calibration equipment. The vacuum pump is remotely located at the base of the antenna.

The dual maser amplifier characteristics are as follows:

Center frequency:	2390 mc
Instantaneous bandwidth:	13 mc
Tuning range:	±10 mc
Gain, channel I:	36 db
Gain, channel II:	33 db
Pump frequency:	13 kmc
Pump power:	70 mw per channel
Magnetic field:	2530 oersteds
Noise temperature:	8 ± 1°K
Operating temperature:	1.8°K
Running time:	20 hours (approximately)
Helium capacity:	10 liters

The noise temperature is somewhat greater than the expected 5°K. This is believed due to excess loss in the input cables and mismatch, which together seem to contribute approximately 7°K, the maser proper contributing about 1°K. Using standard laboratory transfer procedures, about 12 liters of helium are needed to fill the dewar.

VIII. ACKNOWLEDGMENTS

We are indebted to P. P. Cioffi and D. C. Hogg, who supplied the variable shunt permanent magnet and stabilized pumping klystron respectively. We wish to thank J. E. Geusic and E. O. Schulz-DuBois for making measurements on the ruby and the isolator material, as well as for their many useful suggestions. We acknowledge the help of D Halvorsen in the mechanical design.

The device was installed in the antenna in collaboration with E. A.

Ohm, who was responsible for the cryogenic transfer system used in the field.

The use of this device in Project Echo was in connection with National Aeronautics and Space Administration Contract NASW-110.

APPENDIX

Some Remarks on a Double-Valued ωβ Diagram

At one stage of the design considerable difficulty was experienced when the device persisted in being unstable. These oscillations were quite unexpected, since they occurred well within the passband of the amplifier and at a frequency where the isolator seemed to give excellent reverse loss. It had also been observed that the passband with the isolator magnetic field at resonance was much narrower than when it was off resonance, and that sometimes a minimum in transmission would appear in the passband. It is now believed that these effects can be explained by an anomolous mode of propagation.

As previously mentioned, the height of the loading primarily controls the lower cutoff, while the width primarily controls the upper cutoff. By the use of a small-height dielectric loading, the upper cutoff of the empty structure can be shifted below the lower cutoff. Under these conditions the structure is backward wave; i.e., the phase and group

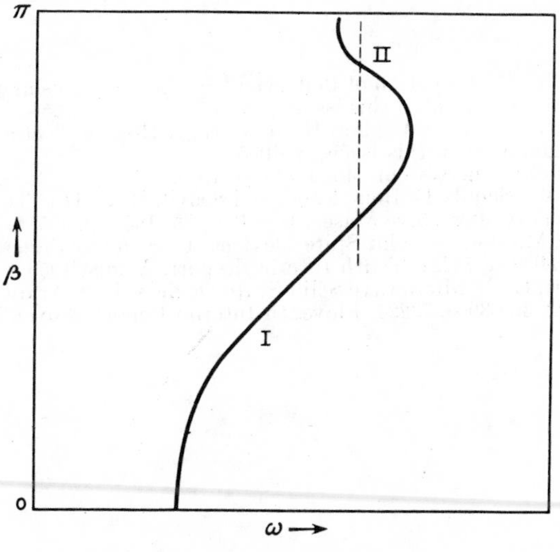

Fig. 5 — Double mode of propagation.

velocities have opposite directions. In our design we wished to use a narrow passband and consequently the loading was chosen such that small changes in the loading could shift the structure from forward to backward. Under these conditions curves such as shown in Fig. 5 can occur. Notice that the upper and lower cutoff frequencies are close together as indicated by the 0 and π phase-shift points. However, in the nominal passband of the structure the phase shift is double-valued.

This double mode has a particularly bad effect upon a traveling-wave maser. Consider operation at a frequency within the double mode region as indicated by the dotted line of Fig. 5. The mode labeled I has a forward phase velocity and a forward group velocity. With the correct direction of magnetic field and an isolator, we will obtain normal unilateral gain in the forward direction. However, under the same conditions, unilateral gain in mode II will be in the reverse direction because the group velocity is backward for the phase velocity which corresponds to low isolator loss. Oscillation can now occur—the wave travels forward in the structure on mode I, is reflected by any mismatch into mode II, and returns to the input of the amplifier on mode II. The result is a feedback path with potentially high gain.

These effects have since been encountered in masers at other frequencies when attempting to obtain very narrow bandwidths. Frequently a change of only a few mils in the dielectric loading is sufficient to cure the difficulty.

REFERENCES

1. Jakes, W. C., Jr., Participation of Bell Telephone Laboratories in Project Echo and Experimental Results, this issue, p. 975.
2. Crawford, A. B., Hogg, D. C., and Hunt, L. E., A Horn-Reflector Antenna for Space Communication, this issue, p. 1095.
3. Ohm, E. A., Receiving System, this issue, p. 1065.
4. DeGrasse, R. W., Schulz-DuBois, E. O., and Scovil, H. E. D., The Three-Level Solid State Traveling-Wave Maser, B.S.T.J., **38,** 1959, p. 305.
5. Geusic, J. E., Microwave Solid-State Devices, U. S. Army Signal Corps Contract DA-36-039 sc-73224, Tenth Interim Report, August 1959.
6. Schulz-DuBois, E. O., Microwave Solid-State Devices, U. S. Army Signal Corps Contract DA-36-039 sc-73224, Eleventh Interim Report, November 1959.

The Three-Level Solid State Traveling-Wave Maser*

By R. W. DeGRASSE, E. O. SCHULZ-DuBOIS, and H. E. D. SCOVIL

(Manuscript received December 18, 1958)

Broadband very-low-noise microwave amplification can be obtained from solid state maser action in a propagating microwave structure. Such a traveling-wave maser produces unilateral amplification with a high degree of gain stability. The theory of the traveling-wave maser is developed and used to compare the gain, bandwidth and gain stability of the traveling-wave maser with that of the cavity maser. The general requirements for traveling-wave maser slow-wave structures are discussed. Theoretical analysis and experimental results are presented for the comb-in-waveguide slow-wave structure.

A traveling-wave maser consisting of a ruby-loaded comb structure was tested. A gain of 23 db at 6 kmc with a bandwidth of 25 mc was obtained. Further performance characteristics of this amplifier and one using gadolinium ethyl sulfate are given. Experimental verification of the low noise temperature of solid state masers was obtained.

I. INTRODUCTION

The three-level solid state maser, as proposed by Bloembergen,[1] employs a microwave pump signal to alter the thermal equilibrium of a

* This work was supported in part by the U. S. Army Signal Corps under Contract DA-36-039 sc-73224.

paramagnetic salt in such a manner that an otherwise absorptive medium becomes emissive when stimulated by radiation at the signal frequency. Successful application of this principle to produce microwave amplification was reported by Scovil *et al.*,[2,3] who used microwave cavities to couple the microwave radiation to the paramagnetic salt. Several laboratories[4,5] have since operated such cavity-type masers.

Microwave amplification can also be obtained by stimulating radiation from active material in a propagating structure. Effective coupling of the microwave fields to the paramagnetic salt is obtained by slowing the velocity of propagation of the microwave energy through the structure. The active material produces an equivalent negative resistance in the slow-wave structure, and a propagating wave having an exponentially increasing amplitude is obtained.

However, if a slow-wave structure is simply filled with the active material, the device will be reciprocal and have gain in both directions. It would therefore require excellent input and output matches and presumably external isolation to obtain unilateral gain. Unidirectional traveling-wave amplification can be obtained in a slow-wave structure which has definite regions of circular polarization of the magnetic field if a maser material is employed which has circularly polarized signal-frequency transitions. The maser material is then loaded in the structure in such a manner that it is coupled to the structure only for one direction of wave propagation. Then, the maser will have high gain in one direction and little or no gain in the reverse direction.

Unidirectional gain alone is not enough to ensure freedom from regenerative instability. One might add reciprocal loss, as in the case of the traveling-wave tube. However, the traveling-wave tube has an electron beam to carry the microwave energy past the loss region, with very little forward attenuation; in the case of the traveling-wave maser, only the one propagation wave is present and the attenuation subtracts directly from the forward gain. Unidirectional loss may be obtained in the same manner as the unidirectional gain, that is, by excitation of a magnetic material through a circularly polarized magnetic field. For the magnetic material, one may use either an absorptive ferrimagnetic material or an absorptive paramagnetic material whose thermal equilibrium is not disturbed by the microwave pump power.

II. TRAVELING-WAVE MASER THEORY

The amplification in a traveling-wave maser is obtained from power transferred to the microwave circuit by coherent excitation of the paramagnetic spins due to the magnetic fields of the circuit. This effect can be represented classically in the constitutive equation of electromagnetic theory†

$$B = \mu_0(H + M_m), \tag{1}$$

where μ_0 is the permeability of free space and M_m is the magnetic moment per unit volume of maser material. The magnetic moment, M_m, is computed from the quantum mechanical treatment of the paramagnetic spin system. From this analysis may be obtained a complex permeability, given by

$$\chi' - j\chi'' = \frac{M_m}{H}. \tag{2}$$

The real part of the permeability, χ', will produce reactive effects in the microwave circuit, while the imaginary part can produce gain or loss. In most cases, the magnetic permeability depends upon the orientation of the magnetic field, H; thus, it is in general a tensor quantity.

If we have a microwave structure uniform in the z direction and partially filled with a maser material, the rate of change of power in the circuit with distance is given by

$$\frac{dP}{dz} = -\frac{1}{2}\omega\mu_0 \int_{A_m} H\cdot\chi''\cdot H^*\,dS, \tag{3}$$

where the integration is performed over the cross section of the maser material, A_m. The power in the waveguide is given by

$$P = \frac{1}{2} v_g\mu_0 \int_{A_s} H^2\,dS, \tag{4}$$

where v_g is the group velocity in the waveguide circuit, and the integration is performed over the entire waveguide cross section, A_s. The gain in a length of structure, l, is then given by

$$G = \frac{P(l)}{P(0)} = \exp\left[-\chi''_{\max}F(\omega/v_g)l\right], \tag{5}$$

where $\chi''_{\max}$ is the magnitude of the diagonalized χ'' tensor, and the filling factor, F, is defined by

$$F \equiv \frac{\int_{A_m} H\cdot\chi''\cdot H^*\,dS}{\chi''_{\max}\int_{A_s} H^2\,dS} \tag{6}$$

† All equations are given in MKS units.

Rather than use the exact tensor representation for χ'', it is convenient to obtain a value for χ'' which reflects the magnetic field orientation. In a cavity maser, χ'' would be defined for linear polarization. In a traveling-wave maser, however, it is desirable to obtain nonreciprocal effects by using circularly polarized magnetic fields to excite the signal transition in the maser material.

In a maser material with small zero field splitting, such as gadolinium ethyl sulfate, the signal transitions have nearly pure circular polarization. Thus, if the magnetic fields of the circuit are resolved into circular polarized components, H_+ and H_-, the filling factor and gain (in decibels) are given by

$$F_+ = \frac{\int_{A_m} H_+^2 \, dS}{\int_{A_s} (H_+^2 + H_-^2) \, dS}, \tag{7}$$

$$G_{db} = -27.3 \chi_+'' F_+ \frac{fl}{v_g}, \tag{8}$$

where f is the signal frequency.

The permeability for positive circular polarization, χ_+'', can be calculated using the notation of Schulz-DuBois.[6] He obtains for the rate of transition per ion from a state $\bar{n}$ to a state $\bar{n}'$,

$$w_{\bar{n}\to\bar{n}'}(S_+) = \frac{1}{2}\left(\frac{\pi g \beta}{h}\right)^2 g(f - f_0) \mid \langle \bar{n}' \mid S_+ \mid \bar{n} \rangle \mid^2 H_+^2, \tag{9}$$

where positive circular polarization is assumed as indicated by S_+. The power absorbed per unit volume of material is then

$$P = (\rho_{\bar{n}} - \rho_{\bar{n}'}) hf w_{\bar{n}\to\bar{n}'}(S_+), \tag{10}$$

where $\rho_{\bar{n}}$ is the density of ions in energy state $\bar{n}$ per unit volume.

The power absorbed per unit volume is given classically in terms of χ_+'' as

$$P = \tfrac{1}{2} \omega \mu_0 \chi_+'' H_+^2 . \tag{11}$$

Thus, χ_+'' is given by

$$\chi_+'' = \frac{\pi}{2\mu_0 h} (g\beta)^2 (\rho_{\bar{n}} - \rho_{\bar{n}'}) g(f - f_0) \mid \langle \bar{n}' \mid S_+ \mid \bar{n} \rangle \mid^2. \tag{12}$$

If the equilibrium spin populations are inverted by making $\rho_{\bar{n}'}$ greater than $\rho_{\bar{n}}$, χ_+'' will be negative and amplification is obtained. The various conditions for maser population inversion have been discussed by Scovil.[3] A companion paper in this issue[7] discusses this problem in more detail.

For the case of propagation of energy in the reverse direction through the amplifier, the magnetic field sense of polarization will reverse and the filling factor will become

$$F_- = \frac{\int_{A_m} H_-^2 \, dS}{\int_{A_s} (H_+^2 + H_-^2) \, dS}. \tag{13}$$

The degree of nonreciprocity of gain is then determined by the ratio, R_m, given by

$$R_m = \frac{\int_{A_m} H_+^2 \, dS}{\int_{A_m} H_-^2 \, dS}. \tag{14}$$

This ratio must be optimized in the selection of a suitable slow-wave structure for use in the amplifier.

As was mentioned before, nonreciprocity in gain is not enough to insure that the amplifier will not have regenerative effects due to mismatched input and output terminations. Thus, it is necessary to also include some nonreciprocal loss for isolation. Both ferrimagnetic and paramagnetic isolators have been used. By increasing the concentration of the active ion in the maser crystal, it is possible to prevent maser action. Such a high-concentration crystal will have energy levels which are identical to the maser material; thus, it will provide nonreciprocal loss at the desired magnetic field and orientation. Ferrimagnetic isolators can be designed to operate at the magnetic field required by the maser material by using shape anisotropy to change the frequency of ferrimagnetic resonance.

The isolator loss is determined by (5). If we retain the convention that H_+ produces excitation of magnetic spins for propagation in the direction of amplification, and H_- for the reverse direction, then the isolator loss in the reverse direction is given by

$$L = 27.3\chi''_{i+} F_{i-} \frac{fl}{v_g}, \tag{15}$$

where

$$F_{i-} = \frac{\int_{A_i} H_-^2 \, dS}{\int_{A_s} (H_-^2 + H_+^2) \, dS} \tag{16}$$

and χ''_{i+} is the lossy permeability of the isolator. The ratio of reverse loss to forward loss, R_i, then is the figure of merit of the isolator:

$$R_i = \frac{\int_{A_i} H_-^2 \, dS}{\int_{A_i} H_+^2 \, dS}. \tag{17}$$

In general, the figure of merit of a paramagnetic isolator will be about the same as that of the paramagnetic maser material. Since χ''_i is usually much greater for a ferrimagnetic than for a paramagnetic, it is possible to locate a ferrimagnetic isolator of small cross section in a region which will optimize R_i.

Some loss, L_0, will occur in the TWM structure due to the usual resistive losses in the conductors. This loss is reduced below the usual room temperature value by a factor of 2 to 4 by operation at liquid helium temperatures. In some cases this insertion loss can be quite high, and care must be exercised in the selection of a circuit. Uniform current distribution and the largest possible surface area in the circuit conductors are desirable.

In discussing TWM circuits, it is useful to rewrite the factor fl/v_g as the product of the slowing factor, S, and the number of free space wavelengths in the length of the structure, N, where

$$S = \frac{c}{v_g}, \quad N = \frac{l}{c/f}. \tag{18}$$

Then the over-all maser forward gain and reverse loss equations are

$$G = 27.3SN\left(-\chi''_+ F_+ - \chi''_{i+} \frac{F_{i-}}{R_i}\right) - L_0, \tag{19}$$

$$L = 27.3SN\left(\chi''_+ \frac{F_+}{R_m} + \chi''_{i+} F_{i-}\right) + L_0. \tag{20}$$

For short-circuit stability of the amplifier, L must exceed G. In some cases, it may even be desirable to have L as much as 20 db greater than G, in order to eliminate any regenerative gain effects due to load changes. It is often convenient to refer to the product $\chi''_+ F_+$ as the inverse of the magnetic Q of the maser material. The magnetic Q will be defined for amplification in the forward direction as a positive number,

$$Q_m = \frac{-1}{\chi''_+ F_+}. \tag{21}$$

Thus, the gain of the maser material only is simply

$$G = 27.3 \frac{SN}{Q_m}. \tag{22}$$

The frequency variation of the TWM gain is given primarily by the term $g(f - f_0)$ in (12). If a Lorentzian line shape is assumed for the maser material, then

$$g(f - f_0) = \frac{2}{\pi B_m} \frac{1}{1 + \left(2\frac{f - f_0}{B_m}\right)^2}, \tag{23}$$

where B_m is the bandwidth over which χ'' is greater than one half its peak value. If we assume that the permeability is an analytic function, then it follows that, for the Lorentzian line shape,

$$\chi_+' = -2\frac{f - f_0}{B_m} \chi_+''. \tag{24}$$

This rapid variation of χ_+' in the vicinity of the amplifying region will produce some perturbation in the phase velocity characteristics of the slow-wave structure. However, in a broadband maser slow-wave structure this effect will be negligible. Using the frequency variation of (23), we obtain for the 3-db bandwidth of a traveling-wave maser

$$B = B_m \sqrt{\frac{3}{G_{db} - 3}}. \tag{25}$$

This derivation of bandwidth assumes a Lorentzian line shape. The actual emission line shape of a maser material depends upon a number of factors, and, at the present state of the art, is best determined experimentally.

The bandwidth variation given by (25) is quite different from that predicted for the cavity maser and it is apparent that the gain-bandwidth product increases at high gain, rather than reaching a constant as in the case of the cavity maser (CM).

The bandwidth variation with gain has been plotted in Fig. 1 for a traveling-wave and a cavity maser. The cavity maser was assumed to have a magnetic Q equal to that of the TWM. For a typical case, we may take 0.05 per cent Cr^{+++} in Al_2O_3, for which B_m is 60 mc for operation at 6 kmc with the magnetic field at 90° to the crystal axis. In this operation, a magnetic Q of 150 is obtainable at 1.5°K. The gain of a cavity maser has been calculated, taking into account the effect of χ'

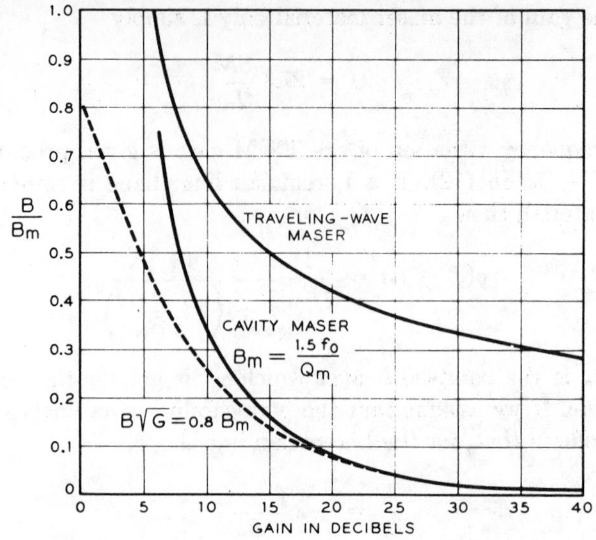

Fig. 1 — Normalized maser bandwidth, B/B_m, as a function of gain for the cavity maser and the traveling-wave maser.

from (24), as

$$G_{\text{CM}}^{1/2} = \frac{(1 - jb_0)(1 + jb_m) - R_0/R_m}{(1 + jb_0)(1 + jb_m) + R_0/R_m}, \tag{26}$$

where

$$b_0 = \left|\frac{R_0}{R_m}\right| \frac{2\Delta f}{f_0} Q_m, \tag{27}$$

$$b_m = 2\,\frac{\Delta f}{B_m}, \tag{28}$$

R_0 = the effective load impedance of the circulator,

R_m = the effective resistance of the maser material

and

Q_m = the magnetic Q of the maser material.

In the limit of large gain, the gain-bandwidth product approaches a constant given by (26) as

$$G_{\text{CM}}^{1/2} B = \frac{2}{\left(\dfrac{Q_m}{f_0} + \dfrac{1}{B_m}\right)}. \tag{29}$$

For the assumed maser operation in ruby,

$$G_{CM}^{1/2}B = 0.8\ B_m . \tag{30}$$

The gain-bandwidth curve from (30) is plotted as a dashed line in Fig. 1. It is interesting to note that, for relatively low gains in the cavity maser, the true bandwidth given by (26) is somewhat greater than is estimated from the limiting gain-bandwidth figure of merit.

The required amplifier slowing and length can be determined from (22). Taking the above example for ruby operation at 6 kmc with Q_m equal to 150 and a structure length of 2 wavelengths (10 cm), we find that a slowing of about 90 is required in the slow-wave structure in order to give a gain of 30 db. An amplifier designed without geometric or resonant slowing, but using the dielectric constant of ruby, would require a length of about 300 cm. The TWM bandwidth for the assumed Lorentzian line shape would be 20 mc. A cavity maser designed using the same material would have a bandwidth of about 1.5 mc. It should also be pointed out that, since a broadband structure is used in the TWM, stagger tuning of the maser material along the maser structure can lead to even greater bandwidths.

The TWM has another important advantage over the cavity maser in that the useful slow-wave structure bandwidth may be an order of magnitude, or more, greater than the maser material bandwidth. Therefore, the center frequency of the maser passband can be tuned electronically over a wide frequency range simply by changing the pump frequency and the dc magnetic field. Thus, a TWM with a 20-mc passband may be tuned over a 200- to 500-mc frequency range at 6 kmc.

An important consideration in maser amplifiers is the sensitivity of the gain to a slight change in the material inversion as measured by χ''. We may, therefore, define the ratio of percentage change in gain to the percentage change in χ'' as a measure of this gain sensitivity, s_g. The gain sensitivity factors for a cavity maser and a traveling-wave maser are respectively,

$$\text{CM}: s_g = \sqrt{G}, \tag{31}$$

$$\text{TWM}: s_g = \log_e G. \tag{32}$$

These two equations are plotted in Fig. 2. They show that, at a gain of 30 db, the stability of a TWM is better by a factor of 4.6 than that of the cavity maser. Ultimately, gain stability in a maser is obtained by stabilization of the material χ'' through temperature regulation and regulation of the pump power. It is also advantageous to use sufficient pump power to saturate the pump transition and, hence, make χ'' relatively insensitive to pump power. These techniques are applicable to both the cavity and the traveling-wave maser, but the stability factor, which is given by s_g , is always better in the TWM case. Gain stability may be an important factor in system applications as it has been in noise figure measurements, where the gain fluctuations are equivalent to actual system noise.

The gain stability to load changes of a TWM is also much better than that of a cavity maser. This problem is particularly bad in the case of the cavity maser, because of the dependence of the gain upon the iris coupling factor. This leads to gain changes due to thermal expansion and vibration effects.

The power output of a cavity maser, as well as that of a TWM, is limited by the total volume of active maser material present in the structure. In the case of the cavity maser, this volume is quite small, whereas a TWM uses a long interaction region and the volume of material is greater, often by an order of magnitude. As a result, in the case of the TWM a much wider dynamic range is to be expected, with output powers an order of magnitude greater. It is also possible to optimize output power by proper design of the slow-wave structure in order to increase active material volume.

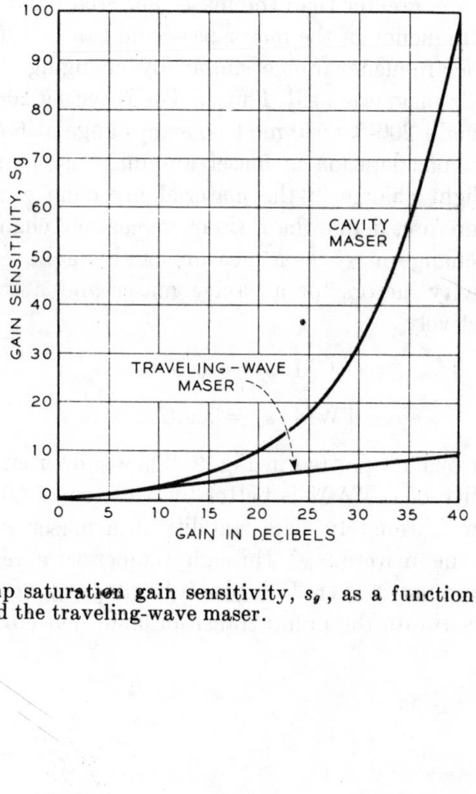

Fig. 2 — Pump saturation gain sensitivity, s_g , as a function of gain for the cavity maser and the traveling-wave maser.

Just as in the case of the cavity maser, some provision must be made in the propagating structure to allow either a propagating or cavity mode at the pump frequency in order to energize the emissive transition in the material. Finally, ease of fabrication and small size are necessary to the practical realization of the TWM.

III. SLOW-WAVE MASER STRUCTURES

There are three classes of structures suitable for slowing propagation for use with the TWM. The first class uses geometric slowing, such as one obtains in a helix where the energy is propagated on a long circuitous path. The second class uses resonant slowing, as is obtained in a periodic structure in which the energy is internally reflected in the various periods of the structure. The third class employs dielectric slowing and may be used in combination with either of the first two classes. The simple helix structure has an advantage in that it will produce high slowing over a very wide bandwidth of frequency, whereas periodic structures obtain slowing at the expense of tunable bandwidths. However, the circular polarization present on a helix structure has a plane which rotates around the axis of the helix. As a consequence, one requires a spiraling dc magnetic field in order to have the dc field perpendicular to the circularly polarized RF field.

The flattened helix structure of Fig. 3 is a possible broadband slow-wave structure which does have planar regions of circularly polarized magnetic field. The plane of circular polarization is perpendicular to the flat side of the helix and to the direction of propagation. Changes in the sense of polarization are indicated by the arrows.

The second class of slow-wave structures, the periodic type, has a definite passband with associated upper and lower cutoff frequencies.

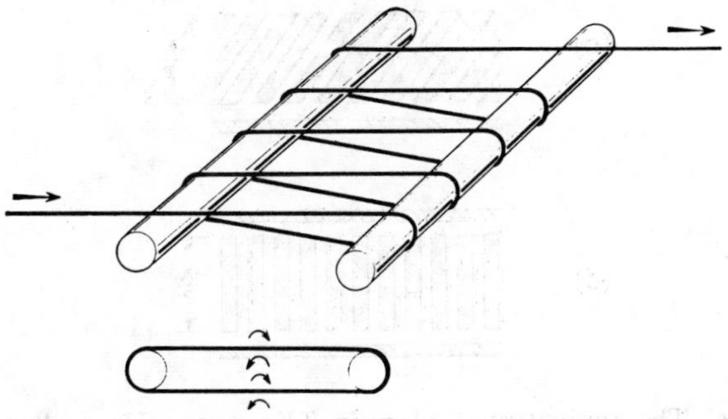

Fig. 3 — Flattened helix structure for broadband nonreciprocal gain.

In general, the narrower the structure passband, the higher is the slowing. It is quite possible to obtain slowing factors of 100 to 1000 in a periodic structure, while 10 to 100 is typical of a helix or other geometrically slowed structure.

It is interesting to note that, while many traveling-wave electron devices require constant phase velocity, the traveling-wave maser requires constant group velocity. As a result, various periodic structures which are very narrowband for tube applications, such as the comb structure, will have wide TWM bandwidths.

Also, it is essential to keep in mind that the structure must propagate at the desired pump frequency. This can be accomplished by propagating the pump power in a waveguide mode and locating the slow-wave structure in the waveguide in such a manner that the two structures are not coupled.

The TE_{10} mode in rectangular waveguide has an equipotential plane, as indicated by the cross section A-A in Fig. 4(a). Thus a planar arrangement of conductors in this cross section will have a minimum of coupling

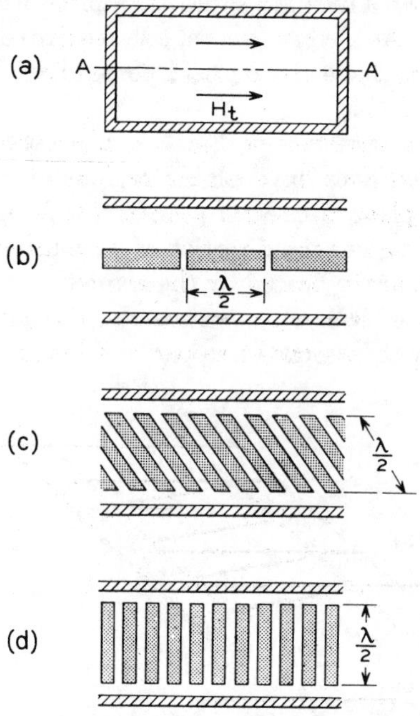

Fig. 4 — (a) The equipotential plane in TE_{10} waveguide and three parallel plane structures consisting of half-wave strip-line resonators: (b) end-coupled; (c) slant-coupled; (d) side-coupled.

to the waveguide mode. The flattened helix of Fig. 3 could be used in such a waveguide, although some coupling of the two modes would result. Three periodic-type structures consisting of coupled half-wave strip resonators are shown in Figs. 4(b), (c) and (d). The end-coupled arrangement of Fig. 4(b) is least desirable of these structures because the magnetic field is linearly polarized. The structure of Fig. 4(c), suggested by H. Seidel,[8] has mutual magnetic field coupling, which is variable by changing the slant angle. The structures of both Figs. 4(c) and 4(d) have regions of circular polarization of the magnetic field. The plane of circular polarization is perpendicular to the long dimension of the resonators of Fig. 4(d), and the sense of polarization is opposite above and below the plane of the strips.

Another set of slow-wave structures having planar conductors is shown in Fig. 5. Fig. 5(a) consists of an array of half-wave rods shorted to the side walls. Because of its symmetry, it can be shown that there is no component of Poynting's vector, $E \times H$, in the direction of the waveguide propagation. Consequently, it is a nonpropagating structure and has been suggested for use in the Easitron.[9] It is interesting because it points out the separate effects of electric and magnetic coupling between adjacent rods. A perturbation of the enclosing waveguide, such

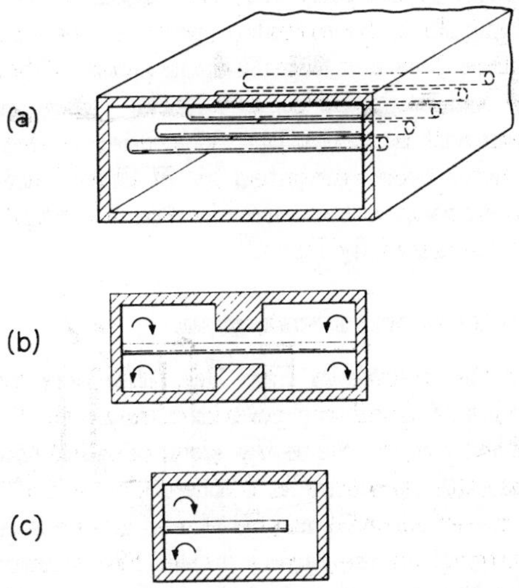

Fig. 5 — Structures consisting of planar arrays of conductors with electrical connection to the waveguide walls; the plane of circular polarization is perpendicular to the fingers and the arrows indicate changes in the sense of polarization: (a) Easitron zero passband structure; (b) Karp propagating structure; (c) comb propagating structure.

as that of the Karp[10] type of structure, in Fig. 5(b), produces a propagating passband in the structure. Thus, the Easitron structure may be called a zero passband structure in which the effect of electric and magnetic coupling between rods just cancels. The general properties of propagating parallel arrays has been discussed by Pierce.[11] Although the structure of Fig. 4(b) is similar to the Easitron, this structure will propagate, due to the fringe capacity at the ends of the resonators. The comb structure of Fig. 5(c) will have characteristics very similar to Fig. 4(d), since it is essentially Fig. 4(d) with a shorting plane along the center line, which is an equipotential plane for the slow-wave structure. A comb-type structure was used by Millman.[12] This structure had rather broad fingers, however, as required for effective electron beam interaction.

A rather extensive study of periodic slow-wave structures is given by Leblond and Mourier.[13, 14] A method for calculating the characteristics of such structures which takes into account coupling between nonadjacent wires was developed by Fletcher[15] and applied to the interdigital line. The interdigital line may be thought of as two comb structures attached to opposite walls of the waveguide with fingers interleaved. The interdigital line does not, in general, produce as much slowing as a comb structure, since, in its passband, the signal wave is propagated at the velocity of light along the circuitous path between adjacent fingers. Thus, the propagation does not depend upon a critical balance of finger to finger coupling and can take place without fringe capacity at the finger tips or a side-wall perturbation. A number of design curves for digital structures have been computed by Walling[16] using the theory of Fletcher. Nonreciprocal attenuation in the interdigital circuit has been analyzed and measured by Haas.[17]

IV. THE COMB-TYPE SLOW-WAVE STRUCTURE

As indicated by the arrows in Fig. 5(c), the comb-type slow-wave structure has regions of circularly polarized magnetic field above and below the plane of the fingers. Since the sense of polarization is reversed in the two regions, the structure is particularly suited to the TWM application.[18] The maser material can be placed on one side of the fingers and the isolator material on the opposite side. The magnetic field varies from a maximum at the shorted end of the rod to zero at the end. Since the electric field does just the opposite, it is possible to place a high dielectric material, such as ruby, in a region where effective magnetic interaction is obtained without incurring substantial dielectric loading, which might adversely effect the structure characteristics.

The microwave pump power is propagated through a waveguide enclosing the comb structure, such as in Fig. 6. The TE_{10} waveguide mode will produce strong longitudinal fields near the waveguide wall and transverse fields in the center of the guide. The dc magnetic field is applied in the direction of the fingers of the structure. Thus, for a maser crystal against the waveguide wall nearest the base of the fingers, $\Delta S = \pm 1$ pump transitions would be excited, while $\Delta S = 0$ pump transitions would be most strongly excited for a centrally located crystal. In our operation, both gadolinium ethyl sulfate and ruby maser materials have $\Delta S = 0$ pump transitions. Thus, it is necessary either to move the crystal away from the waveguide wall slightly, which reduces the gain, or to use a higher pump power, in order to invert the spin population throughout the crystal. The waveguide structure can, of course, be extended beyond the slow-wave structure. A waveguide short and coupling iris can then be used to obtain resonant enhancement of the pumping fields and, hence, better coupling to the pump transition in the crystal.

A perturbation measurement has been made, using a small sphere of ferrimagnetic material to measure the circularly polarized components of the magnetic field in such a comb structure. The absorption of the sphere at ferrimagnetic resonance is a measure of the circularly polarized filling factor per unit volume, which we will call F_+^*. The result of such a measurement is plotted in Fig. 7. The dashed line in Fig. 7(b), labeled F_-^*, is obtained either by reversing the direction of propagation through the structure or by reversing the dc magnetic field. The circularly polarized filling factor, F_+, and the figure of merit, R, can be obtained by integrating the appropriate curve over the cross section. This one

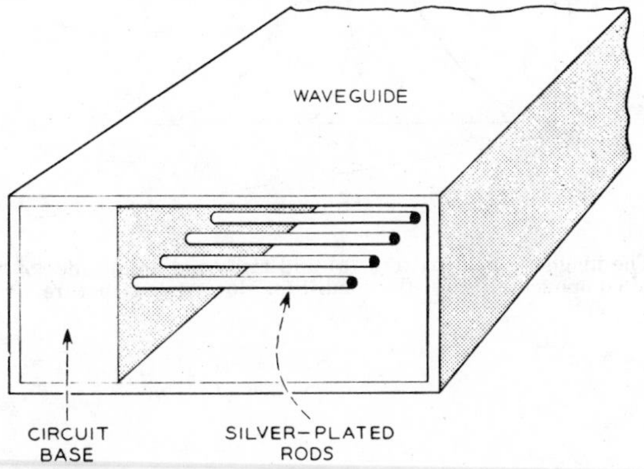

Fig. 6 — The comb-type slow-wave structure.

measurement is not sufficient to get the exact filling factor because the structure is not uniform. The filling factor should be calculated from measurements made over the volume of one period of the structure. The measurement of Fig. 7 predicts a forward-to-reverse gain ratio of about 15 for maser material between one side of the fingers and the wall. In actual tests on gadolinium ethyl sulfate, a value of R_m of 10 was obtained. Careful placement of ferrimagnetic sphere isolators in the same structure gave a value for R_i of 30.

The gain and tunable bandwidth of a maser using the comb structure can be computed from the phase-versus-frequency characteristics of the slow-wave structure. A useful equivalent circuit for this calculation is given in Fig. 8(a). The capacity, C_1, represents the fringe capacity at the ends of the fingers. The transmission line impedances, Z_{01} and Z_{02}, can be computed from the TEM characteristic impedance of the finger in waveguide transmission line at the upper and lower cutoff frequencies. When the phase shift between fingers is zero, the electric field pattern, Z_{++}, is that shown on the left in Fig. 8(b). The electric field pattern at

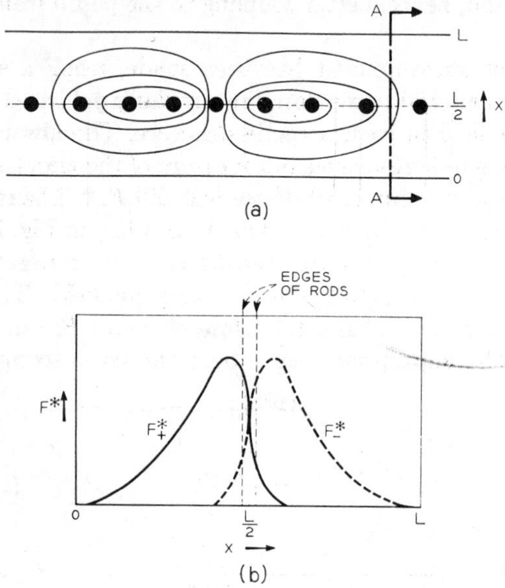

Fig. 7 — The magnetic field pattern (a) and measured amplitudes of circular polarized field components (b) for the comb-type slow-wave structure.

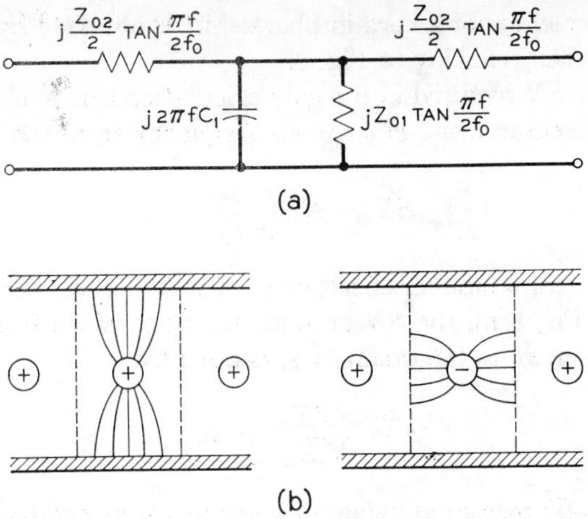

Fig. 8 — (a) Equivalent circuit for the comb structure and (b) the cutoff-frequency TEM mode electric field patterns.

the other cutoff frequency of the structure, Z_{+-}, is that corresponding to π phase shift, indicated on the right in Fig. 8(b). The impedances Z_{++} and Z_{+-} can be obtained analytically or by means of the usual electrolytic tank or resistance card analog computers. These cutoff impedances are related to those in the equivalent circuit by

$$Z_{01} = Z_{++}, \tag{33}$$

$$Z_{02} = \frac{4Z_{+-}}{1 - \dfrac{Z_{+-}}{Z_{++}}}. \tag{34}$$

The determinental equation for the circuit of Fig. 8(a) is

$$j2\pi f C_1 + \left(\frac{1}{Z_{01}} + \frac{2}{Z_{02}} \sin^2 \varphi/2\right) \tan \frac{\pi f}{2f_0} = 0, \tag{35}$$

where φ is the phase shift per section and f_0 is the frequency at which the circuit fingers have an electrical length of one-quarter wavelength. Solution of this transcendental equation is simplified by use of the curve in Fig. 9. The abscissa is the signal frequency normalized to f_0. The ordinate is $X_{co}Y(\varphi)$, which is given by

$$X_{co} = \frac{1}{2\pi f_0 C_1}, \tag{36}$$

$$Y(\varphi) = \frac{1}{Z_{01}} + \frac{4}{Z_{02}} \sin^2 \varphi/2. \tag{37}$$

The signal frequency for a certain phase shift is obtained by computing $X_{co}Y(\varphi)$, and then referring to Fig. 9.

The product SN required in the gain calculation can be obtained from experimental measurement of φ versus frequency from the equation

$$SN = N_s \frac{f_0}{2\pi} \frac{d\varphi}{df}, \tag{38}$$

where N_s is the total number of sections in the structure. For the equivalent circuit of Fig. 8(a), the SN product can be obtained from the curve of Fig. 10, which gives the quantity s, defined by

$$s \equiv \frac{SNX_{co}}{N_s Z_{02}} \sin \varphi. \tag{39}$$

Experimentally measured values of φ versus f were compared with the values calculated from the equivalent circuit, for a comb structure in which the end capacity, C_1, could be varied. The resulting calculations are shown in Fig. 11.

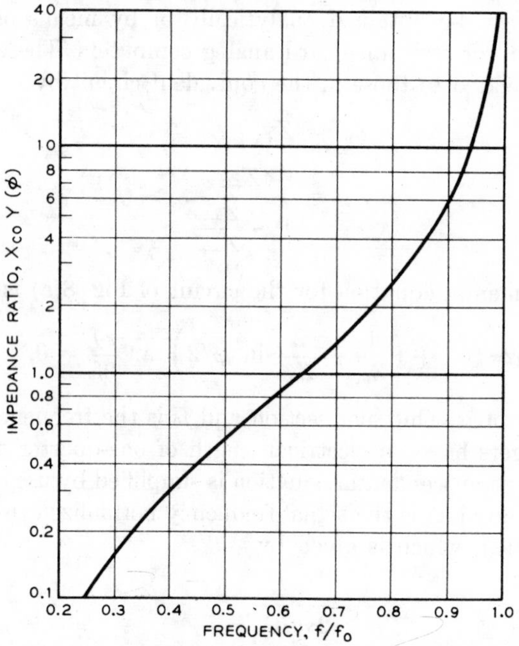

Fig. 9 — The curve, $X_{co}Y(\varphi)$ vs. f, used to solve equation (35).

The three curves were computed from the equivalent circuit analysis using the measured values of Z_{++} and Z_{+-}. The fringe capacity was determined by using the measured frequency for 0.2π phase shift. It should be mentioned that the equivalent circuit does not fully take into account the effect of coupling between nonadjacent fingers, an effect which may be important in this particular circuit.

A rather wide passband was obtained with the particular choice of parameters, even with rather large spacing between the finger ends and the opposite waveguide wall. Also, because of the wide bandwidth, the slowing varies over a wide range. The increase in slowing at the high-frequency end of the band is partially compensated for by the reduction

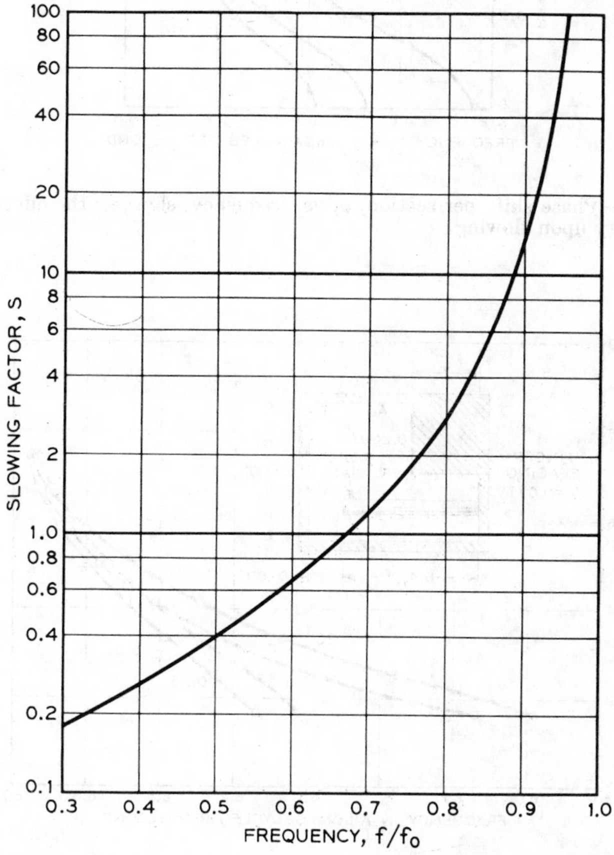

Fig. 10 — The slowing factor, s, as a function of frequency, used to determine SN from (39).

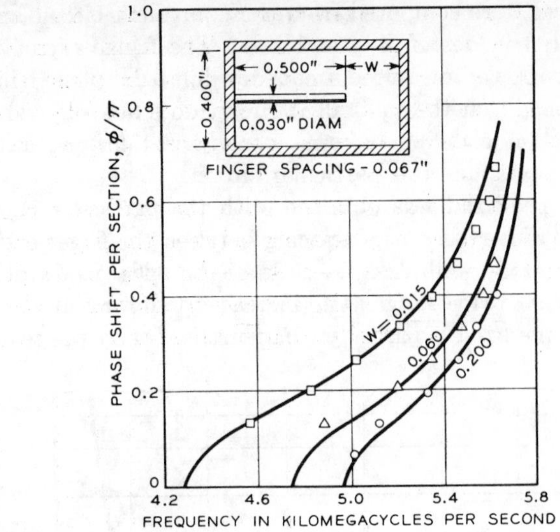

Fig. 11 — Phase shift per section, φ, vs. frequency, showing the effect of end wall capacity upon slowing.

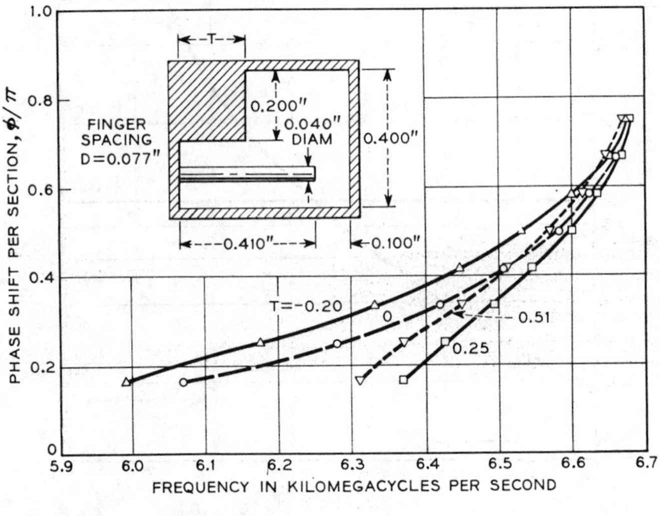

Fig. 12 — Phase shift per section, φ, vs. frequency showing the effect of a side wall perturbation upon slowing.

in the filling factor due to an increase in the stored energy between the fingers.

The structure passband can be decreased by reducing the waveguide height and increasing the distance between fingers. Too great a reduction in waveguide height will make the comb fingers a rather serious perturbation of the waveguide pump mode and will degrade the maser gain nonreciprocity factor, R_m. On the other hand, increasing the distance between fingers increases the over-all length of the amplifier.

Several methods for reducing the bandwidth of the comb structure have been tried. The first consisted of building a structure in which a wall perturbation could be moved across the width of the structure. The cross section of this test structure is shown in Fig. 12, along with the measured results obtained. The curve for $T = -0.2$ inch is for the case where the sliding side wall perturbation is pulled back from the base of the fingers. In this case, the bandwidth is increased. However, with $T = 0.25$ the bandwidth is reduced by a factor of 2 and relatively constant slowing is obtained over the band.

A second method for reducing the bandwidth is that shown in Fig. 13. The tips of the structure fingers are dielectrically loaded with a polystyrene strip having holes for the fingers. The dielectric increases the finger-to-finger capacity without greatly increasing the finger-to-wall capacity. Thus, this capacity would be in shunt with Z_{02} in the equivalent circuit of Fig. 8. It is apparent from the results in Fig. 13 that very narrow bandwidths can be obtained in this manner. However, the varia-

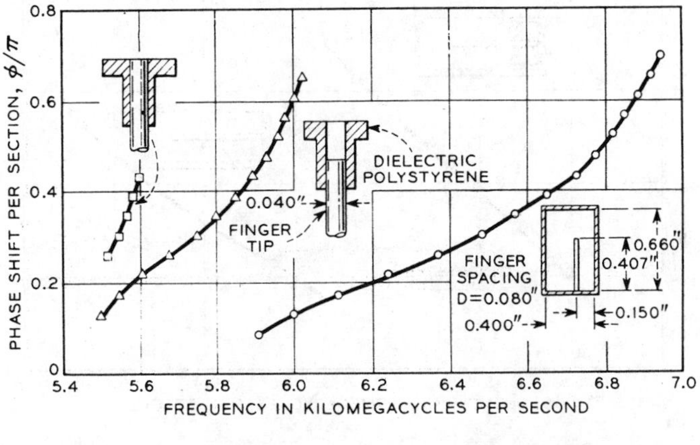

Fig. 13 — Phase shift per section, φ, vs. frequency, showing the effect of finger-to-finger capacity upon the slowing.

tions in structure dimensions become rather critical. Thus only a few points on the φ-f curve could be obtained using the structure resonance. This was also due in part to the high losses resulting from the high slowing.

The full-length ruby maser employed a slow-wave structure whose φ-f characteristics are shown in Fig. 14. Notice that the unloaded structure has a wider passband than the final amplifier with dielectric loading of the ruby on both sides of the structure. In this case, the slowing was improved by not loading the ruby to the full height of each side of the waveguide. Thus, in this case, bandwidth narrowing is obtained by selective location of the maser material itself.

A number of different coupling schemes have been employed to match a 50-ohm coaxial cable into the comb structure. The matching arrangement shown in Fig. 15 gives quite broadband results. It has been found that a good impedance match can be obtained only over that frequency range for which the slowing factor is relatively constant. A VSWR less than 1.5 is typical over the useful band of the structure. Rapid variation of measured VSWR is observed which can be attributed to periodic variations in the structure which result in internal resonances. In actual maser operation, these internal resonances should be suppressed by the nonreciprocity of the structure.

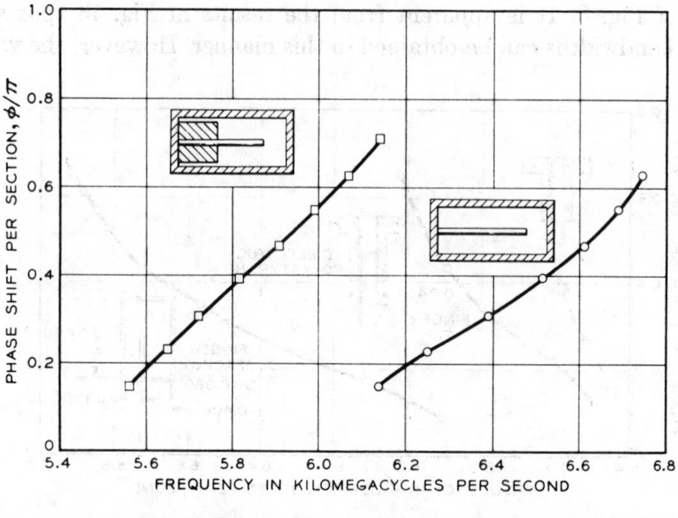

Fig. 14 — Phase shift per section, φ, vs. frequency for the comb structure used in the full-length ruby maser; the unloaded structure characteristic is compared with that of the ruby loaded structure.

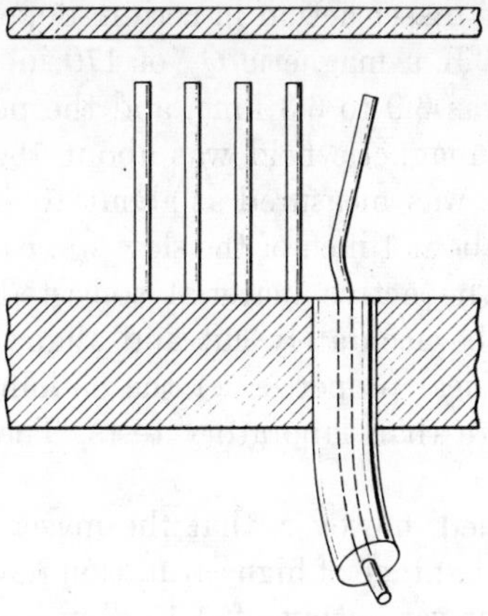

Fig. 15 — Detail of the coaxial-to-comb-structure impedance match.

V. GADOLINIUM MASER TEST SECTION RESULTS

The first TWM tests were performed using gadolinium ethyl sulfate as the active maser material and yttrium iron garnet as the isolator material. The cross section of this TWM is shown in Fig. 16. The slow-wave structure was similar to that of Fig. 12, since it employed a perturbation of the side wall to narrow the passband. Of course, the maser material dielectric constant also affected the structure characteristics and a certain optimum loading could be obtained.

Since the maser operation in gadolinium requires the pump magnetic field to be parallel to the applied magnetic field, a slab of dielectric was added against the waveguide wall to enhance the transverse RF waveguide magnetic field.

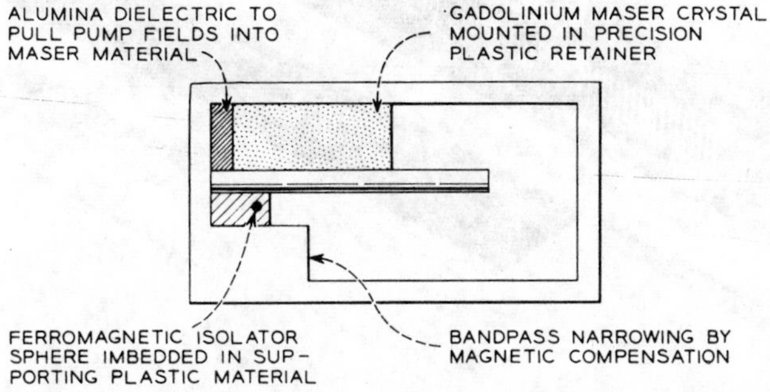

Fig. 16 — Cross section of gadolinium maser, showing location of active material and polycrystalline yttrium iron garnet isolators.

The "impurity dope" maser action in cerium-doped gadolinium ethyl sulfate produced at 1.6°K a magnetic Q_m of 170 in the structure used. The signal frequency was 6.0 to 6.3 kmc, and the pump frequency was 11.7 to 12.3 kmc. The magnetic field was about 1800 gauss. The nonreciprocity factor, R_m, was measured as about 10. The maser gain obtained was 12 db with about 1 inch of the slow-wave structure filled with the gadolinium salt. The active material consisted of three separate crystals which had to be accurately cut and aligned. Thus, it became apparent that the physical properties of the gadolinium salt were not too well suited for more than laboratory tests. The gadolinium bandwidth, B_m, was 30 mc.

It should be mentioned, however, that the maser operation in gadolinium does have the advantage of high saturation power and fast saturation recovery time. A power output of +15 dbm was obtained and the saturation recovery time was measured as about 20 microseconds.

The magnetic field required by the maser material is in the vicinity of that for ferrimagnetic resonance in a sphere. Hence, it was possible to use spheres of a gallium-substituted yttrium iron garnet, which was found to have a relatively high χ'' at liquid helium temperature. Spheres of yttrium iron garnet were located in the A-A cross section indicated in Fig. 7(a). By careful location of the spheres, approximately one per finger, an isolation ratio of 50 was obtained at room temperature. The isolation ratio at 1.5°K was 30.

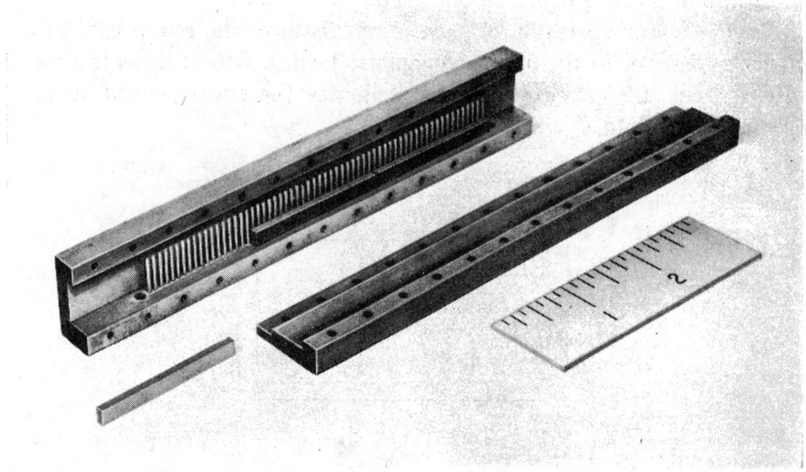

Fig. 17 — View of the disassembled comb structure for the ruby maser, with two pieces of ruby material shown in position.

The first high-gain full-length TWM was constructed using pink ruby which had approximately 0.05 per cent Cr^{+++} in the Al_2O_3 parent crystal. The slow-wave structure is shown in Fig. 17 with one side of the waveguide removed. Two pieces of ruby are shown in position, and a third is in the foreground. The comb structure has a length of 5 inches and consists of 62 brass rods approximately 0.4 inch long. The phase-shift characteristics of this structure were given in Fig. 14.

The holes for insertion of the coaxial input and output matches are visible at the ends of comb structure of Fig. 17. Fig. 18 is a cutaway drawing of the complete TWM assembly, showing the waveguide flanges which are added to the ends of the structure for attachment of a movable short and the pump waveguide coupling iris. This drawing also shows the location of the 0.05 per cent ruby amplifying material and the 1 per cent ruby isolator material. Notice that the 1 per cent ruby is spaced away from the circuit fingers by an alumina slab. This reduces the

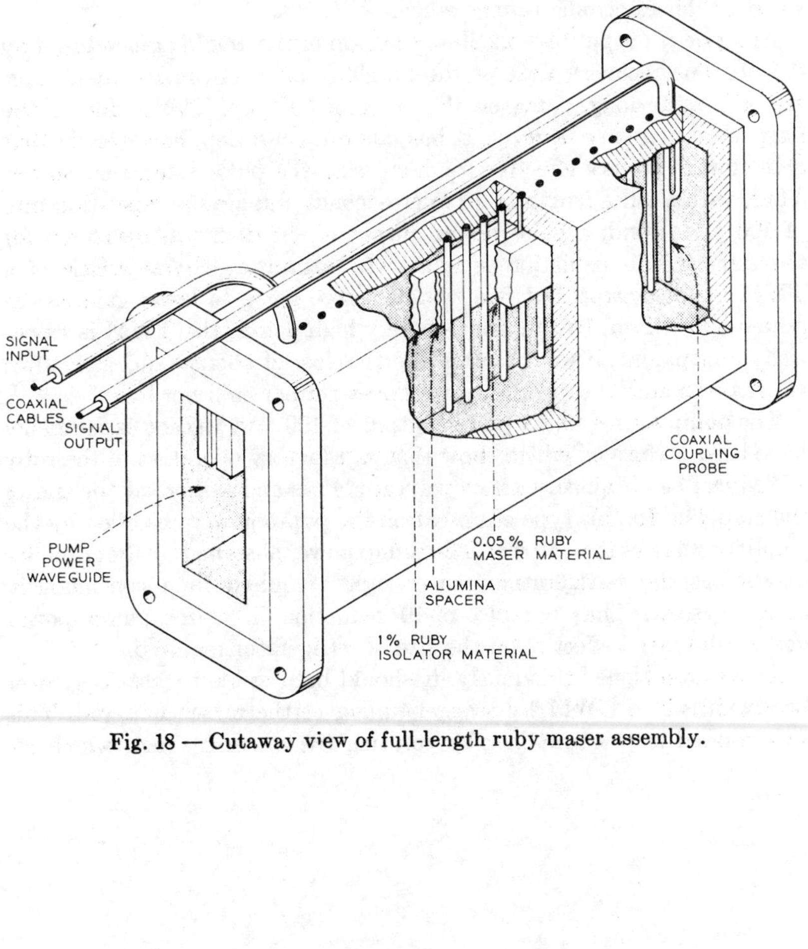

Fig. 18 — Cutaway view of full-length ruby maser assembly.

coupling of the isolator to the forward propagating circuit wave, thus improving the isolation ratio, R_i.

This TWM gives a net forward gain of 23 db and a net reverse loss of 29 db, including the input and output coaxial cables extending into the 1.5°K helium bath. With the dc magnetic field off, the structure gave a loss, L_0, of 3 db. The electronic gain of the maser material, the first term in (19), was 30 db, and the loss of the isolator was 35 db. Thus, the ratios R_m and R_i are about 3.5 and 8.5 respectively. The improved figure of merit for the isolator is due to the addition of the alumina slab. The high loss of the isolator, in spite of the spacer, is due to the increased Cr concentration.

The 3-db bandwidth of the TWM was measured as 25 mc at a center frequency of 5.8 kmc. This bandwidth is somewhat in excess of that predicted by an assumption of Lorentzian line shape as used in Fig. 1. The passband of the structure allows amplification over a frequency range of 5.75 to 6.1 kmc. The pump frequency must be tuned from 18.9 to 19.5 kmc and the dc magnetic field varied from 3.93 to 4.07 kilogauss to cover this electronic tuning range.

At a power output of -22 dbm, the gain of the amplifier is reduced by 0.5 db. The recovery time of the amplifier after saturation by a large signal is quite long, being on the order of 10^{-1} sec. This is due to the long relaxation time in ruby. It has one compensation, however, in that spin storage is very effective for increasing the pulse saturation power. Thus, with a pulse length of 10 microseconds and a pulse repetition rate of 100 per second, a pulse power output of $+8$ dbm was measured for the same 0.5-db reduction in gain. The saturation characteristic of a TWM is not abrupt, but is a smooth curve going to lower gain as the power is increased. In the limit of very high power, the TWM is essentially transparent. It will have an insertion loss of about 3 db, since after the maser material saturates, it produces neither gain nor loss.

The pump source had a power output of 100 mw. Recent experiments have been performed which show that satisfactory operation of the ruby TWM can be obtained with no waveguide iris and a short at the end of the amplifier. In this type of operation the pump power absorbed by the amplifier was less than 10 mw. The pump power absorbed by the amplifier determines the refrigeration power input required in a continuously cooled system. Thus a factor-of-10 reduction in maser pump power has a substantial effect upon the size of refrigerator required.

As was mentioned previously, it should be possible to obtain greater bandwidths in a TWM by stagger-tuning of the maser material. This was verified in this amplifier by rotating the maser magnet, which resulted in tuning of the three maser crystals to different frequencies. A bandwidth of 67 mc at a gain of 13 db was measured.

VII. TWM NOISE-TEMPERATURE MEASUREMENT

Because of the high gain stability inherent in the TWM it was possible to perform a quite accurate measurement of noise temperature. Also, since the TWM is a unilateral two-port amplifier by itself, no external isolators or circulators are required when it is used, for instance, as a radar preamplifier.

The experimental system for the noise-temperature measurement is shown in Fig. 19. Two noise sources, which are matched loads maintained at different temperatures, are connected alternatively to the TWM input with an electrically operated waveguide switch. Isolators were included at the input and output of the TWM. Although the TWM is short-circuit stable, small gain fluctuations can be produced by changes in the input VSWR. Since gain fluctuations on the order of 0.02 db are significant in this measurement, an input isolator was included to eliminate gain changes when the waveguide switch is operated. An isolator was included on the output of the TWM to insure that no excess noise from the traveling-wave tube (TWT) would be fed back into the TWM

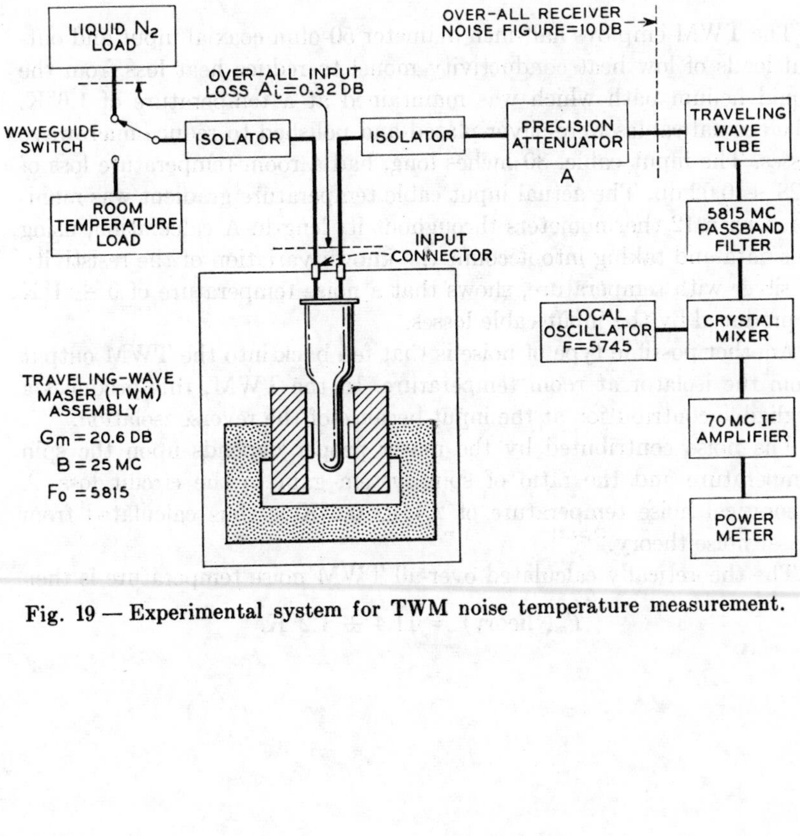

Fig. 19 — Experimental system for TWM noise temperature measurement.

and prevent maser gain changes because of the precision attenuator setting.

The microwave detecting system consisting of the TWT, filter, crystal mixer, etc., had an over-all noise figure of 10 db. The actual noise temperature measurement is made by switching the noise source and adjusting the precision attenuator to maintain constant output power at the power meter.

A total of 37 separate measurements were made over a period of about 30 minutes, and the resulting noise temperature was calculated to be

$$T_m = 10.7 \pm 2.3°K.$$

Approximately two-thirds of the estimated error was a statistical variation in the observed attenuator reading. About half of this attenuator reading variation can be attributed to gain fluctuations in the system of about ±0.03 db during any one measurement and the other half to observational error. The remaining error is principally due to an error of ±0.02 db in the determination of the input circuit loss, A_i.

Since the above-measured noise temperature is referred to an input connector at room temperature, it is a useful system temperature and the noise figure of the resulting preamplifier TWM is

$$F = 1.037 \pm 0.008 \; (0.16 \pm 0.03 \text{ db}).$$

The TWM employs half-inch diameter 50-ohm coaxial input and output leads of low heat conductivity monel to reduce heat loss from the liquid helium bath which was maintained at a temperature of 1.6°K. The coaxial cables were silver plated and polished to reduce microwave losses. The input cable, 30 inches long, had a room temperature loss of 0.28 ± 0.02 db. The actual input cable temperature gradient was monitored with 12 thermometers throughout its length. A calculation, using this data and taking into account the known variation of the resistivity of silver with temperature, shows that a noise temperature of 9 ± 1°K is produced by the input cable losses.

Another possible type of noise is that fed back into the TWM output from the isolator at room temperature. In the TWM, this produces a negligible contribution at the input because of the reverse isolation.

The noise contributed by the maser proper depends upon the spin temperature and the ratio of spin system gain to the circuit loss. A theoretical noise temperature of 2.4 ± 0.2°K is thus calculated from maser noise theory.[19,20,21]

The theoretically calculated over-all TWM noise temperature is then

$$T_m(\text{theory}) = 11.4 \pm 1.2°K.$$

Since it is apparent that most of the above noise is contributed by the input cable, a second experiment is planned which will exclude the input cable loss and allow a more direct measurement of the actual noise temperature of the maser amplifier proper.

VIII. FUTURE STUDIES

An extensive investigation of the ferrimagnetic properties of various ferrite and garnet materials at liquid helium temperatures is being carried out by F. W. Ostermayer of Bell Telephone Laboratories. A number of materials look promising for application as isolators in the ruby TWM. A ferrimagnetic isolator can be expected to have lower forward loss, higher reverse isolation, and low pump-power absorption.

Further reduction of the TWM tunable bandwidth will increase the gain. Thus it should be possible to obtain useful wideband gain at a somewhat higher bath temperature, such as 4.2°K.

It appears that, by using high pump-frequency-to-signal-frequency ratios, it will be possible to build low-frequency traveling-wave masers with about the same percentage tunable bandwidth as the present 6 kmc amplifier. Accordingly, a number of suitable circuits are being investigated.

IX. ACKNOWLEDGMENT

The initial slow-wave structure investigation for TWM application was begun by H. Seidel, whose assistance is gratefully acknowledged. We would also like to thank A. Pohly for technical assistance and G. Shimp for computation and plotting of curves.

REFERENCES

1. Bloembergen, N., Proposal for a New-Type Solid State Maser, Phys. Rev., **104,** October 1956, p. 324.
2. Scovil, H. E. D., Feher, G. and Seidel, H., Operation of a Solid State Maser, Phys. Rev., **105,** January 1957, p. 762.
3. Scovil, H. E. D., The Three-Level Solid State Maser, Trans. I.R.E., **MTT-6,** January 1958, p. 29.
4. McWhorter, A. L. and Meyer, J. W., Solid State Maser Amplifier, Phys. Rev., **109,** January 15, 1958, p. 312.
5. Makhov, G., Kikuchi, C., Lambe, J. and Terhune, R. W., Maser Action in Ruby, Phys. Rev., **109,** February 15, 1958, p. 1399.
6. Schulz-DuBois, E. O., Paramagnetic Spectra of Substituted Sapphires—Part I: Ruby, B.S.T.J., **38,** January 1959, p. 271.
7. Schulz-DuBois, E. O., Scovil, H. E. D. and DeGrasse, R. W., this issue, p. 31.
8. Seidel, H., private communication.
9. Walker, L. R., unpublished manuscript.

10. Karp, A., Traveling-Wave Tube Experiments at Millimeter Wavelengths with a New, Easily Built Space Harmonic Circuit, Proc. I.R.E., **43,** January 1955, p. 41.
11. Pierce, J. R., Propagation in Linear Arrays of Parallel Wires, Trans. I.R.E., **ED-2,** January 1955.
12. Millman, S., A Spatial Harmonic Amplifier for 6-mm Wavelength, Proc. I.R.E., **39,** September 1951, p. 1035.
13. Leblond and Mourier, Etude des Lignes a Barraux a Structure Périodique pour Tubes Electroniques U.H.F., Ann. de Radioélect. **9,** April 1954, p. 180.
14. Leblond and Mourier, Etude des Lignes a Barraux a Structure Périodique—Deuxieme Partie, Ann. de Radioélect., **9,** October 1954, p. 311.
15. Fletcher, R. C., A Broadband Interdigital Circuit for Use in Traveling-Wave-Type Amplifiers, Proc. I.R.E., **40,** August 1952, p. 951.
16. Walling, J. C., Interdigital and Other Slow-Wave Structures, J. Elect. and Cont., **3,** September 1957, p. 239.
17. Haas, L. K. S., Unilateral Attenuation in the Interdigital Circuit, WADC TR 57-239, Wright-Patterson Air Force Base, Ohio, May 1957.
18. DeGrasse, R. W., Slow-Wave Structures for Unilateral Solid State Maser Amplifiers, I.R.E., WESCON Conv. Record, August 1958.
19. Shimoda, K., Takahasi, H. and Townes, C. H., J. Phys. Soc. Japan, **12,** 1957, p. 686.
20. Pound, R. V., Ann. Phys., **1,** 1957, p. 24.
21. Strandberg, M. W. P., Inherent Noise of Quantum-Mechanical Amplifiers, Phys. Rev., **106,** May 15, 1957, p. 617.

The Coupled-Cavity Transmission Maser-Analysis

T. R. O'MEARA

***Summary*—This paper discusses an analysis of a maser amplifier structure (developed at Hughes Research Laboratories) consisting of a cascade of iris-coupled $\pi/2$ cavities intermixed with isolators. Starting from the basic media susceptibility, narrow-band equivalent networks and matrix representations are derived for maser and isolator cavities. A rational function approximation to the over-all gain function is thereby derived by matrix methods. From one viewpoint, the over-all amplifier may be regarded as a negative-resistance inverse-feedback amplifier. The key design parameter is shown to be the isolator round-trip attenuation. Excess isolation yields an overly rounded gain-frequency characteristic, while deficient isolation yields a characteristic with excess ripple or instability in the extreme cases. The feedback effects associated with intermediate "optimum" values of isolation reduce the effective gain per cavity below the normal gain of a single cavity, but in return one obtains a reduced gain sensitivity which may be reduced to a value comparable to or lower than that of the pure traveling-wave maser.**

I. Introduction

THE MASER amplifier structure to be discussed in this paper is illustrated in Fig. 1. Details of construction are discussed in a companion paper [1]. It is a slow-wave microwave structure containing an activated or pumped-maser material with interspersed isolators, commonly known as a traveling-wave maser. From one viewpoint, the "slowing" structure slows the excitation wave sufficiently to permit a larger interaction with the maser material [2], [3], [4]. A less documented viewpoint is to regard maser gain as the reverse of incidental dissipation; as is well known, the first order effect of dissipation (or reverse dissipation) on the loss (or gain) function is proportional to group delay [5], and inversely proportional to circuit Q.

There exist a number of weak points in the usual slow-wave approach. The slow-wave structure power gain has been generally computed from the group velocity or slowing factor which, in turn, is generally computed on the assumption that there exists an image parameter match. Since the basic structures are not image terminated in an operational amplifier, the true group velocity near the band-pass edges and consequently the gain are subject to considerable doubt in conventional theory. In traveling-wave masers, the fundamental limitation on bandwidth has usually been set by the paramagnetic resonance line width rather than by the structure pass band. However, since the tunable bandwidth of a tunable maser *is* related to the structure bandwidth, it is important that this be accurately known.

In contrast to the slow-wave approach, passive micro-

Manuscript received October 2, 1963; revised February 24, 1964.
The author is with the Hughes Research Laboratories, Malibu, Calif.

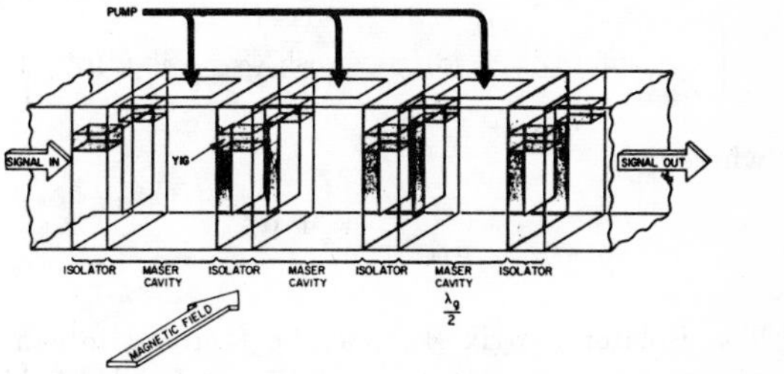

Fig. 1—The Hughes coupled-cavity maser amplifier structure.

wave filters constructed of M structures, large in wavelengths ($\lambda/4$ or $\lambda/2$ dimensions are common), have been approximated by lumped-parameter networks with considerable success [6]. These equivalent lumped-parameter networks are much easier to analyze or synthesize than their distributed parameter counterparts.

This same general approach is also applicable to active filters including maser amplifiers, although so far as is known, it has not been previously attempted in the literature. With a filter approach, we may gain an understanding of many of the effects observed in the laboratory which are probably inexplicable by the usual traveling-wave concepts. For example, one may show how the maser activity and isolators influence bandwidth and band shape.

First we will develop a chain-matrix description of the three basic components which comprise the structure as follows: 1) the isolator, 2) the resonant active cavity, and 3) the coupling irises. These will be combined to obtain a matrix description of the over-all amplifier and its gain. Such a description yields the gain as a rational function of a frequency displacement variable, permitting more detailed analysis as well as an examination of a number of design problems.

The present analysis is basically concerned with an iterative structure, since we feel that the practical advantages of such structures outweigh their limitations. Furthermore, the active iterative filter, with proper control of the intercavity isolation, yields a much more satisfactory gain characteristic than the corresponding passive filter. The cryogenics present difficulty in tuning adjustments on an operating amplifier, providing one potent argument for structural simplicity.

II. Matrix Description of the Isolator

The isolators will be modeled by nonreciprocal transmission lines assumed to have the same characteristic impedance for waves in either direction and the same phase constant β but differing attentuation constants

α_1 and α_2. The electrical length will be assumed to be frequency independent.[1] Thus the isolator will be described by a chain matrix A_{is} such that

$$A_{is} = e^{\alpha_1 l_{is}} e^{-\alpha_{(+)} l_{is}} \cdot \begin{bmatrix} \cosh(\alpha_{(+)} + j\beta) l_{is} & Z_{is} \sinh(\alpha_{(+)} + j\beta) l_{is} \\ \frac{1}{Z_{is}} \sinh(\alpha_{(+)} + j\beta) l_{is} & \cosh(\alpha_{(+)} + j\beta) l_{is} \end{bmatrix} \quad (1)$$

where

$$\alpha_{(+)} = \frac{\alpha_1 + \alpha_2}{2}. \quad (2)$$

The isolator matrix A_{is} may be factored into a non-phase-shifting (or resistive) portion and a phase-shifting (or line-like) portion as indicated in Fig. 2. Thus

$$A_{is} = [\bar{A}][\tilde{A}_{is}] \quad (3)$$

where

$$A_{is} = e^{\alpha_1 l_{is}} \begin{bmatrix} \cosh(\theta/2) & Z_{is} \sinh(\theta/2) \\ \frac{1}{Z_{is}} \sinh(\theta/2) & \cosh(\theta/2) \end{bmatrix} e^{-\theta/2} \quad (4a)$$

$$\tilde{A}_{is} = \begin{bmatrix} \cos(\beta l)_{is} & jZ_{is} \sin(\beta l)_{is} \\ \frac{j}{Z_{is}} \sin(\beta l)_{is} & \cos(\beta l)_{is} \end{bmatrix} \quad (4b)$$

and

$$\theta = (\alpha_1 + \alpha_2) l_{is}. \quad (5)$$

The $\bar{A}_{is}$ matrix may be represented by various equivalent networks which must include gyrators or equivalent nonreciprocal elements.

Note that the isolator transmission line (of characteristic impedance Z_{is}) may be shifted "across" the $\bar{A}_{is}$ portion of the isolator because their matrices are commutative.

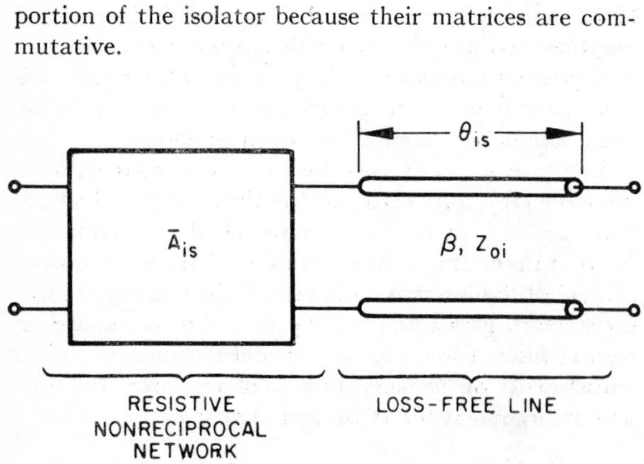

Fig. 2.

[1] The actual variation in electrical length with frequency introduces an additional bandwidth narrowing as in a passive filter [6] and may be included in much the same way, but only at the price of considerable complication in the analysis. This is because it becomes a selective element which, unlike the $\lambda_g/2$ cavity, is not activated.

III. A Network Description of the Maser Cavity Including the Coupling Irises

The passive isolator-deactivated structure strongly resembles the filters discussed by W. W. Mumford [6], although we consider iterative rather than maximally flat couplings. We would follow a modified Mumford analysis except for the following two reasons: 1) he derives an equivalent lumped-parameter resonator as a parallel tuned circuit rather than a series tuned circuit, and Kyhl [7], [8] has already illustrated a series type representation for a one-port $\lambda_g/2$ maser resonator which compares closely to our two-port circuit; and 2) we wish to make the transformer action of the irises explicit rather than implicit, as in Mumford's paper, because we feel this demonstrates more clearly their relation to the negative resistance gain.

A. The Maser Cavity

In the interest of brevity we will use a semiheuristic approach to the development of the narrow-band equivalent network for the masering cavity. A more rigorous (and lengthy) development based on transmission lines is presented O'Meara [1a]. First, note that masering action is usually a rather weak effect, the resulting imaginary component of the susceptibility being typically less than 1 per cent of the real part. Thus we look for an equivalent network based on a small perturbation of known equivalent network representations of passive $\lambda_g/2$ cavities. Such a cavity is conveniently represented in the low-pass case by a single series inductance plus an inverting transformer. This transformer, which plays no essential role in the operation of these amplifiers will be ignored in subsequent development. The impedance of the equivalent series element is [9], [10]

$$Z_c = s \frac{\pi K_g}{\omega_o Y_o} \quad (6)$$

where K_g is the guide wavelength factor

$$K_g = \left[1 - \frac{1}{\mu_r \epsilon_r} \left(\frac{\omega_c}{\omega_o}\right)^2\right]^{-1} \quad (7)$$

and Y_0 is the (passive) characteristic admittance of the guide. The frequency variable s represents the displacement from center frequency. Now, assuming that this equivalent inductance is the result of a magnetic energy storage throughout the masering volume, the active impedance should be directly proportional to the active permeability

$$\mu_r^* = \mu_r(1 + \chi) \quad (8)$$

where the susceptibility χ is assumed to be complex (as a result of masering action) and small (typically of the order of 10^{-2}). The susceptibility is assumed to be

$$\chi = \frac{j\chi_m''}{1 + j\tau\Delta\omega_m}, \quad (9)$$

where the parameter χ_m'' is the peak value of the absorptive-emissive component, τ is the reciprocal of the material half-line width, and

$$\Delta\omega_m = \omega - \omega_m \tag{10}$$

is the frequency departure from the material line resonance center frequency ω_m. Under these assumptions the masering impedance may be approximated as

$$Z_m \doteq \frac{\pi K_g}{\omega_o Y_o}\left[\frac{s^2 + s\left(s_{mo} + \frac{1}{\tau}\right) - \frac{\omega_o \chi_m''}{2\tau} + \frac{s_{mo}}{\tau}}{s + \frac{1}{\tau}}\right] \tag{11a}$$

where

$$s = j\Delta\omega_m = j(\omega - \omega_m) \tag{11b}$$

$$s_{mo} = j\omega_{mo} = j(\omega_m - \omega_o), \tag{11c}$$

and where ω_{mo} is the frequency displacement (if any) between the line resonance and the $\lambda_g/2$ resonant frequency, *i.e.*,

$$\omega_{mo} = \omega_m - \omega_o. \tag{11d}$$

If the cavity resonance frequency at ω_o and the line resonance at ω_m are synchronously tuned, the s_{mo} in (11a) vanishes, giving an effective series impedance

$$Z_m \doteq \frac{\pi K_g}{\omega_o Y_o}\left[s - \frac{\frac{\chi_m''\omega_o}{2\tau}}{s + \frac{1}{\tau}}\right]. \tag{12}$$

This impedance has one equivalent-network representation as illustrated in Fig. 3. When short circuited on one side, this network is a low-pass equivalent to the (one-port) Fig. 2 network of Kyhl [7], if Kyhl's series inductance is resonated.

On the other hand, if the maser line center frequency ω_m is tuned to the operating frequency ω as in a tunable maser[2] then s in (11a) vanishes giving

$$Z_m \doteq \frac{\pi K_g}{\omega_o Y_o}\left[s_{mo} - \frac{\chi_m''\omega_o}{2}\right]. \tag{13}$$

Now if we redefine s_{mo} in (13) as s, comparison to (12) demonstrates that we have in effect obtained infinite linewidth in our tunable maser. One may define an equivalent Q for this "tunable" maser by the definition

$$Q_{me} = \frac{\omega_o L_o}{2(R_m - R_o)} \doteq \frac{1}{\chi_m''}\left(1 - \frac{Q_o}{Q_m}\right)^{-1}. \tag{14}$$

The tunable situation, corresponding to (13), will be of dominant interest in this paper.

[2] This is most generally effected by changing the magnetic field.

B. The Coupling Irises

If the cavity were operated without coupling irises, the band-center frequency would be the $\lambda_g/2$ resonant frequency. However, the irises, which are needed to obtain reasonable gains, also introduce a detuning reactance X_{ir}, as may be seen from the equivalent transformer and transmission line representation[3] of Fig. 4. These iris reactances are easily eliminated by a frequency translation[4]

$$\bar{s} = s - j\frac{2X_{ir}}{L_o}, \tag{15a}$$

where for an equivalent iris line impedance of 1Ω

$$X_{ir} = \frac{b}{1 + b^2}. \tag{15b}$$

If δ_o is the percentage frequency shift associated with this translation, or in other terms the fractional separation between the $\lambda_g/2$ frequency and the operating frequency, then

$$\delta_o = \frac{-2X_{ir}}{\omega_o L_o} = \frac{-2b}{(1 + b^2)\pi K_g}. \tag{16}$$

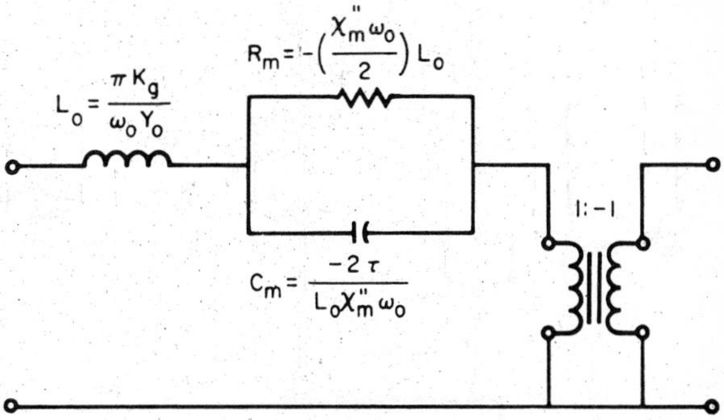

Fig. 3—An approximate lumped-parameter representation of a $\lambda_g/2$ maser cavity with the cavity synchronously tuned to the maser line.

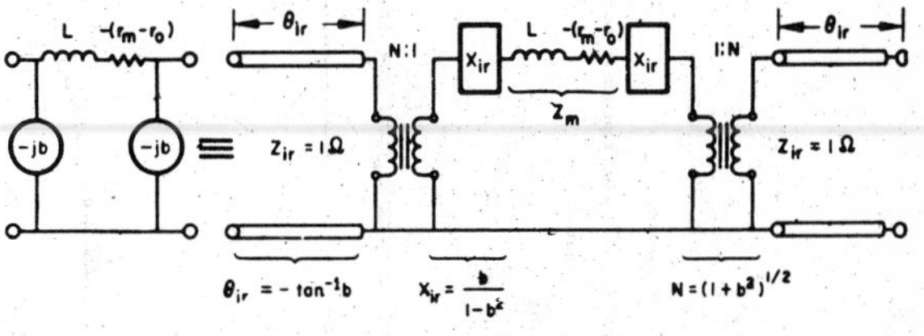

Fig. 4—Approximation equivalent network representation of the maser cavity and its coupling irises (with infinite linewidth).

[3] Note that all reactances and line lengths are assumed to be frequency independent in this representation. This network is a special case presented by G. G. Montegomery, *et al.*, Fig. (4.22a), p. 107, [9], with

$$Z_{11} = Z_{22} = Z_{12} = -jb^{-1}.$$

[4] This frequency translation is an expression of the iris detuning effect upon $\lambda_g/2$ cavity.

IV. The Effect of the Iris Transformers and the Effective Isolator Line Length

The ideal transformers of Fig. 4 may be removed by increasing all maser impedances by a factor of N, where

$$N^2 = 1 + b^2, \quad (17)$$

giving the equivalent network of Fig. 5 with an effective maser impedance, z_m, normalized to a one ohm cavity impedance, such that

$$z_m = N^2 Z_m = N^2(sL_o + R_o - R_m)Y_o. \quad (18)$$

The function of the iris-transformers can thus be regarded as that of increasing the effective negative resistance so that the effective power generated by the source current flowing through this negative resistance may be appreciable, compared with the source power. In this way, reasonable gains are obtained. In payment one accepts an enhanced inductance which reduces bandwidth. The maser-cavity-transformer portion of the microwave network may now be described by a transmission matrix

$$[A_m] = \begin{bmatrix} 1 & z_m \\ 0 & 1 \end{bmatrix}. \quad (19)$$

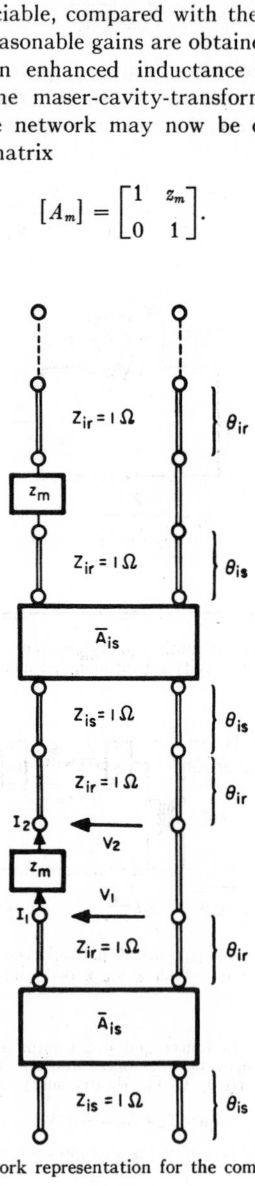

Fig. 5—A network representation for the combined amplifier.

The frequency independent lines at the beginning and the end of the amplifier of Fig. 5 introduce phase shifts only, but the internal lines are another matter. These lines may be shifted (as mentioned in section II) to either side of a reduced isolator and combined. Since we wish degenerative feedback at midband, the net phase shift in a signal passing round trip from one maser resistance through two irises and the isolator should be 180 degrees. In other terms, we require a total forward path (midband) phase shift of

$$\theta_{ie} = \theta_{is} + 2\theta_{ir} = \pm \pi/2 \text{ rad}. \quad (20)$$

Further, as will be shown, a frequency independent phase shift of $\pi/2$ is a sufficient condition for symmetry in the gain frequency function. From the equivalent network of Fig. 4, we see that the phase shift from two irises,

$$2\theta_{ir} = -2 \tan^{-1} b, \quad (21)$$

is a function of b and hence of the required transformation ratio N. Thus (21) specifies the required isolator line length under normal circumstances.

Henceforth, the iris and isolator phase-shifting lines will be combined and considered as a portion of the isolator. Note that the forward attenuation $e^{\alpha_1 l_{is}}$ introduces only a loss constant, in the over-all transmission matrix, and will be ignored in subsequent development. Under these assumptions and with the isolator characteristic impedance normalized to one ohm, (3) may be written as

$$[A_{is}] = je^{-\theta/2}[\overline{A}_{is}], \quad (22)$$

where

$$[\overline{A}_{is}] = \begin{bmatrix} \sinh \theta/2 & \cosh \theta/2 \\ \cosh \theta/2 & \sinh \theta/2 \end{bmatrix}. \quad (23)$$

The j multiplier may be shifted to the end of the network or its matrix representation, resulting in an additional amplifier phase shift which, however, does not otherwise affect the amplifier gain characteristic. The remaining isolator matrix (23) still contains the both isolation properties and the impedance inverting properties normally associated with $\lambda_g/4$ lines.

V. The Gain-Frequency Function of the Over-All Amplifier and Some Degenerate Cases

Consider the over-all amplifier consisting of M-identical maser and isolator cavities coupled with identical irises, such as just discussed. One may avoid tedious expansions by utilizing the results of the existing theory of iterated networks [11], [12]. The simplest method commences with a unitary matrix as the basic transmission block. Thus, using (22) the over-all transmission matrix for M cavities and M isolators[5] becomes

$$\begin{bmatrix} A_{11} & A_{12} \\ A_{21} & A_{22} \end{bmatrix}$$

$$= e^{-M\theta/2}\{j[\overline{A}_{is}][A_m]\}^M$$

$$= (j)^M e^{-M\theta/2}\begin{bmatrix} \sinh\theta/2 & (\cosh\theta/2 + z_m\sinh\theta/2) \\ \cosh\theta/2 & (\sinh\theta/2 + z_m\cosh\theta/2) \end{bmatrix}^M \quad (24a)$$

where

$$z_m = p - d = N^2(sL_o + R_o - R_m)Y_o. \quad (24b)$$

The matrix elements in the expansion of (24a) are not of dominant interest. Rather, one desires the insertion gain expression.

$$g = \frac{2}{A_{11} + A_{12} + A_{21} + A_{22}} = \frac{2}{O_M}. \quad (25)$$

As shown by Armstrong [11], the denominator characteristic polynomial P_M is expressible as a sum of Chebyshev polynomials. Thus for source and load normalized to one ohm,

$$(j)^{-M} H^{-M/2} O_M = 2T_M(x) + (a_{12} + a_{21})U_{M-1}(x)$$
$$= 2T_M(x)$$
$$+ \frac{2}{1+H}[j2H^{1/2} + x(1-H)]U_{M-1}(x), \quad (26a)$$

where a_{11}, a_{12}, a_{21} and a_{22} are the matrix elements of (24a),

$$H = e^{-\theta} \quad (26b)$$

and

$$x = \frac{1}{2}[a_{11} + a_{22}]$$
$$= j\frac{H^{-1/2}}{2}\left[1 - H + (1+H)\frac{z_m}{2}\right]. \quad (26c)$$

By letting $p = j\Omega$ and expressing d in terms of an equivalent single cavity gain g_{os} a more useful expression for x is obtained

$$x = \frac{-H^{-1/2}}{2}\left[\frac{(1+H)\Omega}{2} - j\left(\frac{1+H}{g_{os}} - 2H\right)\right]. \quad (27)$$

Note that T_M and U_{M-1} in (26a) and (26b) are Chebyshev polynomials of the first and second kinds [13].

$$T_M(x) = \cos(M\cos^{-1}x) \quad (28a)$$

$$U_{M-1}(x) = \frac{\sin(M\cos^{-1}x)}{\sqrt{1-x^2}}. \quad (28b)$$

The second definition differs somewhat from that used by Armstrong [11].

Some properties of (26) are worth noting. Because T_M is of degree M while U_{M-1} is of degree $M-1$, one polynomial is even while the other is odd, and consequently $T_M(x)$ and $jU_{M-1}(x)$ are either both real or both imaginary (for real p or s). Thus the gain is a function of a polynomial in p with real coefficients and consequently the magnitude of the gain function is symmetrical (about $p/j=0$), a consequence of our choice in effective isolator line length.

Several degenerate cases are of interest. If the isolators and the maser resistance are deactivated, then $H=1$, $g_{os}=1$ and (27) becomes

$$x = j\frac{z_m}{2} = j\frac{p}{2} = -\frac{\Omega}{2} \quad (29)$$

and the absolute value of the insertion gain reduces to

$$|g_o| = \left[1 + \left(\frac{\Omega}{2}\right)^2 U_{M-1}{}^2\left(\frac{\Omega}{2}\right)\right]^{-1/2}. \quad (30)$$

Allowing for the difference in notation in both frequency variable and the ordering of the Chebyshev polynomial (30) agrees with (186) of Lawson and Fano,[6] representing the λ/4-coupled cavity chain.

Let the isolation become very large, such that $H \to 0$. The gain function becomes

$$G = g^2 = \left(\frac{2}{p+2-d}\right)^{2M}. \quad (31)$$

Thus the over-all gain function becomes simply the product of the individual cavity gain functions.

Eq. (27) has been used to compute the characteristic polynomials, O_M,

$$O_M = \sum_{ko}^{M} K_k(z_m)^k \quad (32)$$

corresponding to the inverse gain function, for M values 1 through 4. The results (powers of j are deleted) are as listed in Table I. Of particular interest is the fact that the constant term is $K_0 = 2$ (33) while the leading term is

$$K_m = \left(\frac{1+H}{2}\right)^{M-1}. \quad (34)$$

For $H=1$ (no isolation) and $d=0$, the filter reduces to a passive reciprocal filter with characteristic polynomials as listed by O'Meara [1a], [15].

[5] It must be recognized that because of the extra isolator in the actual amplifier the forward gain or voltage transfer function will differ from that of (24a) by some phase shift factor. However, the magnitude of the forward gain function is not changed by these terminal isolators, except possibly for a small, constant reduction in gain resulting from forward isolator loss.

[6] See page 681 of Ref. 14.

TABLE I
CHARACTERISTIC POLYNOMIALS OF THE ACTIVE FILTER

M	O_M
1	$= \frac{1}{2}[z_m + 2]$
2	$= \frac{1}{2}[(1+H)z_m^2 + 4z_m + 4]$
3	$= \frac{1}{4}[(1-H)^2 z_m^3 + 2(1+H)(3-H)z_m^2 + 12z_m + 8]$
4	$= \frac{1}{8}\left\{(1+H)^3 z_m^4 + 2(1+H)^2(4-2H)z_m^3 + 4(1+H)(6-3H+H^2)z_m^2 + 32z_m + 16\right\}$
5	$= \frac{1}{16}\left\{(1+H)^4 z_m^5 + 2(1+H)^3(5-3H)z_m^4 + 4(1+H)^2(10-8H+3H^2)z_m^3 + 8(1+H)(10-6H+3H^2-H^3)z_m^2 + 80z_m + 32\right\}$

VI. THE "OPTIMUM" ISOLATION FUNCTION FOR THE GENERAL AMPLIFIER

With more than two maser cavities, sufficient freedom does not exist under the assumptions (identical isolators and identical irises) to achieve any desired gain function, *e.g.*, equal ripple gain with prescribed ripple. Thus other techniques must be found for choosing the isolator round-trip attenuation to produce a desirable gain-frequency function. This is a central problem of this paper.

It is known from (31) that excess isolation results in a gain-function pole distribution with the poles nearly coincident [16], producing an excessively rounded gain-frequency function, with an excessively shrunken bandwidth. On the other hand, an extreme deficit of isolation will lead to instability. However, under-isolation has a more immediate effect in producing both a large gain peak at the band edges, and excessive ripple elsewhere in the pass band. An "optimum" intermediate value of isolation exists which compromises between these two conditions.

One method of choosing the isolator round-trip attenuation would be to establish first order flatness in the gain frequency characteristic. This technique proved prohibitively laborious, both in deriving equations and in solving them for $M>4$. However, the $M=2$ results are illustrated in Fig. 6. The $M=2$, 3, and 4 cases are available to the interested reader in O'Meara's report [1a].

Some lower and upper bounds upon the isolation developed by O'Meara [1a] are illustrated in Fig. 6. Unfortunately, the limits are sufficiently widely spaced that the practical problem of finding an optimum H for a given g_{os} is not yet solved. However, it is possible to compute gain-frequency functions for specific cases and thereby estimate optimum isolation. As an example, consider the gain-frequency curves of a 10-cavity maser illustrated in Fig. 7. Observe that the optimum round-

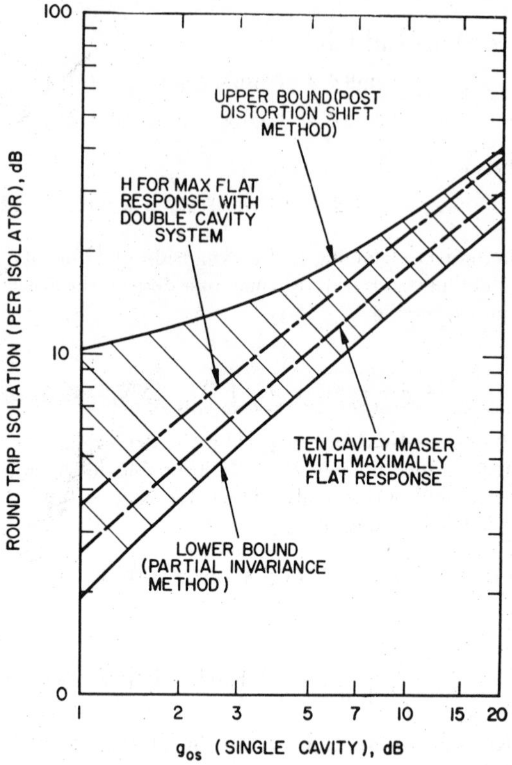

Fig. 6—Design ranges for optimum round-trip isolation.

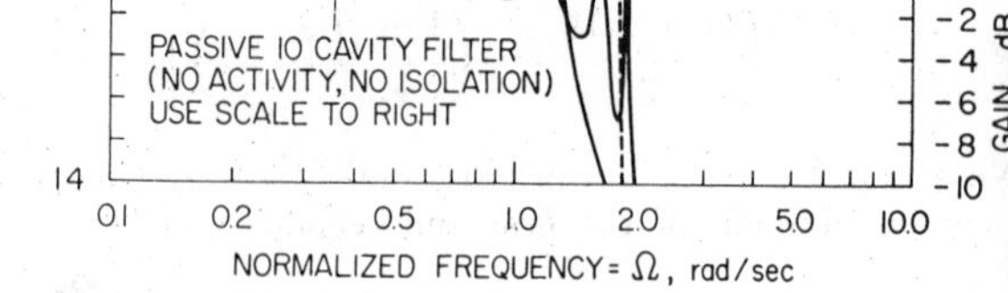

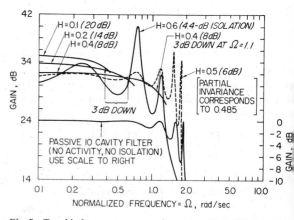

Fig. 7—Tunable-frequency-response for a ten cavity maser, $g_{os}=1.53$.

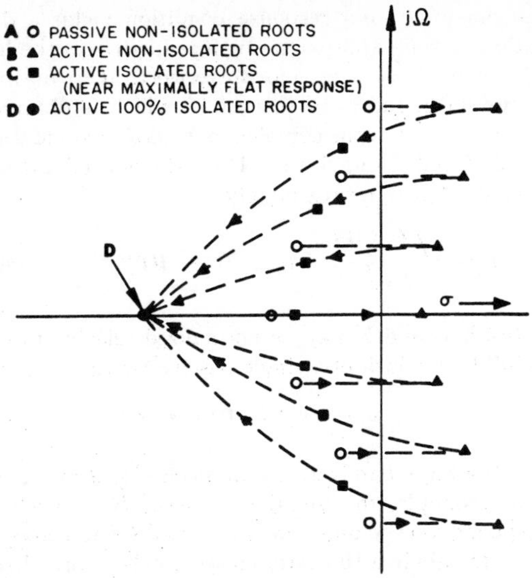

Fig. 8—A root-locus description of the isolater action (7-cavity amplifier).

trip isolation for this amplifier falls in the range[7]

$$0.4 < H < 0.43$$

and one pays a price in excess bandwidth shrinkage or excess gain ripple for H values which fall very far under or over these limits. From similar computations, it is estimated that near maximally flat isolation values fall on the design curves illustrated in Fig. 6.

Root locus concepts may serve to give a better understanding of the isolator function, as indicated in Fig. 8. The roots of $O_M(p)$, in the passive nonisolated case, will fall on a contour in the complex p-plane illustrated by position "A." If one first activates the amplifier, leaving the isolators inoperative, however, all roots are shifted equally[8] to the right in the p plane, with some or all of the roots shifting into the right half plane, as illustrated in the "B" position. Instability thereby results. The effect of large isolation is to make all the roots coalesce to a point "D" on the real or axis. Therefore, in the root locus migration, with increasing H, all roots must eventually cross back into the left half plane, restoring stability. The "optimum" H might thus yield the intermediate position illustrated as C of Fig. 8. This root-locus diagram also illustrates why the bandwidth of the final amplifier is less than that of the passive filter. The quantitative aspects of bandwidth shrinkage will be considered in a later section.

VII. Gain Loss

Unfortunately, the over-all effective band-center gain G_0 is only approximately given by the product of the individual cavity gains G_o'

$$G_o' = (g_{os})^{2M} = \left(\frac{2}{2-d}\right)^{2M} \qquad (35)$$

since the inverse feedback action associated with nonvanishing H values reduces the gain somewhat below this value. This is a price one pays for the considerable gain bandwidth improvement and the slight sensitivity improvement associated with a proper choice in isolation. The over-all loss[9] in gain G_L may be expressed as

$$G_L = 20\log_{10}\left[\frac{O_M\big|_{s=0}}{O_M\big|_{H=0}}\right] = 20\log_{10}\left[1-\left(\frac{g_{os}}{2}\right)^M F_M(H,d)\right] \qquad (36)$$

where $F_M(H, d)$ is the difference in the polynomials O_M,

$$F_M(H,d) = 2^{M-1}\left[O_M\Big|_{s=0} - O_M\Big|_{\substack{s=0\\H=0}}\right]. \qquad (37)$$

With normal designs, of moderate to large gain, the contributions of terms in (37) containing powers of H beyond the first are quite small and consequently a good approximation to (36) may be shown to be

$$G_L \doteq 20\log_{10}\left[1+(M-1)H(g_{os}-1)^2\right]dB. \qquad (38)$$

Table I compares some values of gain loss computed via (38) to the exact values. It is seen that (38) errs on the pessimistic side.

TABLE II
Some Computations of Gain Loss Resulting from Inverse Feedback

M	g_{os}	H	g_o^1(db)	g_o(db)	G_L(db) Exact	G_L(db) Via (38)
10	1.53	0.4	36.95	32.13	4.82	6.08
10	1.53	0.15	36.95	34.45	2.50	2.79
4	3.0	0.20	38.2	28.0	10.2	10.62
6	2.0	0.333	36.1	28.6	7.5	8.53

VIII. Tunable Bandwidth and Sensitivity

The basic reasons for using more than a single cavity in any negative resistance amplifier are twofold: 1) to improve gain bandwidth, and 2) to reduce the gain sensitivity to variations in activity (*e.g.*, pumping). Each of

[7] The value $H=0.43$ gives a single excess gain peak of approximately 0.12 db at $\Omega=0.190$, while $H=0.40$ is monotonic.

[8] Assuming all cavities are equally active. This is called a "predistortion" transformation in filter theory.

[9] This loss in gain is entirely from feedback action; the loss resulting from forward isolator attenuation must be computed and added separately.

these points will be discussed in more detail in the sections which follow.

A. Bandwidth Considerations

There are two aspects of tunable bandwidth to be discussed. The first involves the practical problem of finding the theoretical expected bandwidths of the activated, isolated amplifiers and of relating these bandwidths to other parameters, more easily measured, of the corresponding passive filter. The second aspect concerns the gain-bandwidths obtainable with this particular structure and compares these to some competitive amplifiers[10] and to theoretical limits.

Although most of the bandwidth measures given below will be given in terms of normalized bandwidth Ω_β, these are readily converted to true bandwidths via the equation

$$\overline{BW} = \frac{1}{4}\frac{\Omega_\beta \omega_o}{Q_{me}}\left(\frac{g_{os}}{g_{os}-1}\right) \quad (39)$$

where Q_{me} is the effective Q as already defined by (14).

It is convenient to have a means of finding the potential active bandwidth by passive (outside the dewar) measurements. The unloaded filter outer peaks shift but little with internal losses, providing a good measure of bandwidth. The outer peak is given by

$$\Omega_p = 2\cos\left(\frac{\pi}{M+1}\right). \quad (40)$$

In contrast, the outer peak of the loaded (passive lossfree) filter may be obtained from (30) as

$$\Omega_p' = 2\cos\left(\frac{\pi}{M}\right). \quad (41)$$

Although no general, exact formula for bandwidth has been found for the active-isolated amplifiers with intermediate values of isolation, there is a way of estimating bandwidth for responses which approach maximal flatness; that is, responses which are as flat as permitted by the constraints. Note from (26) that the gain is of the form

$$g = 2[K_M p^M + \cdots \overline{K}_o]^{-1} \quad (42)$$

where K_M is as given by (34) while $\overline{K}_o$ is the summation of K_o, as defined in (33), plus the contributions from d in the other terms of (32). Consequently, the midband gain is

$$g_o = 2(\overline{K}_o)^{-1}. \quad (43)$$

[10] It is the gain-tunable bandwidth of the maser which compares most nearly with the (instantaneous) gain-bandwidth of the tunnel diode and the parametric amplifier.

If the maximally-flat response condition yields a distribution of poles approximating a semicircle in the left hand p plane (*i.e.*, a pseudo-Butterworth distribution) then the mean radius of this circle, which is obtained from the product of the complex roots, is a good measure of the 3 db half bandwidth.[11] Thus, the normalized full "Ω" bandwidth is approximately

$$\Omega_\beta \doteq 2\left(\frac{\overline{K}_o}{K_M}\right)^{1/M} = 4 g_o^{-1/M}(1+H)^{(1-M)/H}. \quad (44)$$

This full bandwidth may be normalized relative to the 3 db full bandwidth of a single passive cavity, giving

$$\Omega_{\beta r} \doteq g_o^{-1/M}(1+H)^{(1-M)/M}. \quad (45)$$

For $M=2$ the bandwidth expression (45) is exact. As another example, the isolation value of $H=0.4$ which corresponds very closely to a maximally-flat response with 32 db gain in a 10-cavity maser, yields a normalized ($\Omega_{\beta r}$) bandwidth of 0.505 while (45) predicts a bandwidth of 0.502. By increasing H to 0.43 one may widen the relative bandwidth to approximately 0.615 at the price of a 0.12 db gain ripple over the bandwidth. Although the bandwidth shrinks less rapidly than with a 100 per cent isolated system, it still remains smaller than that of the passive filter.

Substituting (39) in (45) gives the (denormalized) relative bandwidth B_r as

$$B_r = \frac{1}{Q_{me}}\left(\frac{g_{os}}{g_{oe}}\right)\frac{(1+H)^{(1-M)/M}}{(g_{os}-1)}. \quad (46)$$

The resulting increase in B_r with increasing M is illustrated[12] in Fig. 9. The increase with M is very rapid at first, becoming nearly linear at higher values of M. The limiting behavior is explored in the Appendix. It is therein shown that for large M

$$(B_r Q_{me}) \approx \frac{M}{\ln G_o}. \quad (47)$$

This value is illustrated in Fig. 11 and therein compared to more exact curves based on specific computer results.

It is interesting to compare (47) with one kind of theoretical limit, which is structure independent. As mentioned in the introduction, maser negative resistance gain action may be regarded as a type of inverse incidental dissipation. It has been long known that small values of incidental dissipation (either positive or

[11] As the actual critical frequency distributions tend to be somewhat elliptical (which the major axis in the Ω direction) this assumption generally gives a pessimistic estimate of bandwidth for $M>10$. However, computer checks indicate that (44) is a good compromise for most design values.

[12] The curves are based on specific values of M, g_{os} and H associated with specific computer examples.

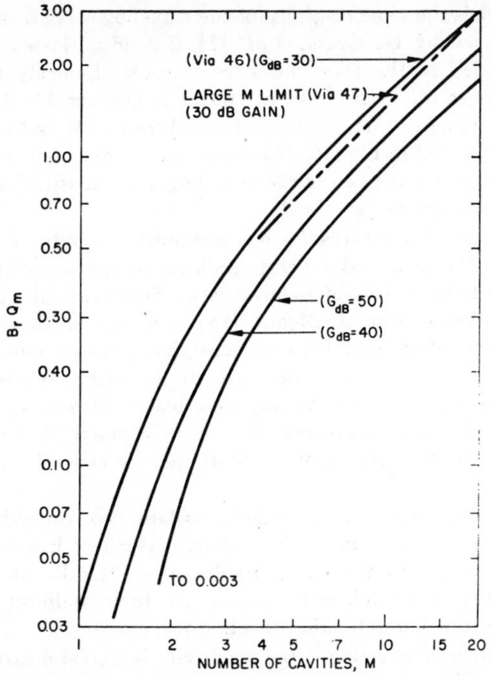

Fig. 9—Some approximations to tunable percentage bandwidth as a function of number of cavities (with constant over-all gain as a parameter).

negative) may be well approximated in terms of the group delay function T_g, and the cavity Q of a band-pass filter as [5], [19]

$$G_{dB} \doteq \frac{8.69\omega_o T_g(\omega_o)}{2Q}. \tag{48}$$

Now it is also known that the maximum uniform group delay which can be obtained from M resonators may be related to the bandwidth (in cycles) B_g, over which the delay is uniform, by the formula [20]

$$T_g B_g = \frac{\eta M}{2} < \frac{M}{2} \tag{49}$$

while η is a delay area efficiency. Combining (48) and (49) one may derive

$$B_r Q = \eta \frac{\pi}{2} \frac{M}{\ln G_o} \tag{50}$$

which compares closely to, but is somewhat larger than (47), for large η.

An equation may be derived for the direct-coupled Butterworth response maser [21] which, in the limit of large M and large $B_r Q_m$, reduces to the same form as (47). Thus, as shown by O'Meara [1a], one obtains

$$\lim_{M\to\infty} B_r Q_{me} = \frac{4}{\pi}\left(\frac{M}{\ln G_o}\right) \tag{51}$$

giving a gain-bandwidth factor 27 per cent greater than that of the isolator-coupled maser. Actually, for a typical design (an $M=10$ and $B_r Q=1.6$) (51) gives an optimistic result while (47) is pessimistic; the gains are nearly identical (33.2 db vs 32.13 db).

Gain-bandwidth may also be increased by compensation with passive network elements [22], [23] (*i.e.*, cavities). However, as one usually does not double the bandwidth (a 30 per cent increase is more typical) by doubling the total number of elements (one passive for each active element) and as it costs little more to insert an active as opposed to a passive cavity in a dewar, it appears that there is very little point to these compensation schemes with masers.[13]

B. Sensitivity

A fundamental problem with all negative-resistance amplifiers is that small changes in negative resistance or loading produce relatively large changes in gain. The maser amplifier provides no exception, although it is usual to operate in a saturated condition such that changes in pump power have relatively little influence on negative resistance [16].

While the computation of the exact gain sensitivity is, in general, tedious, some special cases are relatively simple. The easiest is for infinite ($H=0$) isolation. With infinite isolation, the over-all band-center gain G_o is given by (35). Thus the gain sensitivity $S_{r_m}^{G}$ at band benter with respect to changes in R_m (or x_m'') is [1a][14]

$$S_{r_m}^{G_o}(\Omega = 0) \frac{dG_o/G_o}{d(r_m)/r_m} = g_o M(d + R_o)$$

$$= 2M(G_o^{1/2M} - 1)\left(\frac{R_m}{R_m - R_o}\right). \tag{52}$$

This result agrees with Stitch's (20C) [18], with $M=1$, as it should. On the other hand, as M becomes large it is readily shown that

$$\lim_{M\to\infty} 2M(G_o^{1/2M} - 1) = \ln G_o \tag{53}$$

and, therefore

$$\lim_{M\to\infty} S_{r_m}^{G} = \left(\frac{r_m}{r_m - r_o}\right)\ln G_o \tag{54}$$

[13] It should be emphasized that we refer only to the problem of increasing tunable bandwidth. Compensating for instantaneous bandwidth is another matter.

[14] The corresponding sensitivity for a coupled series of reflection type cavities is given by Kyhl and Strandberg [17] (in the notation of this paper as $(dG_o/G_o)(dr_m/rm) = M(G^{1/2M} - G^{-1/2M})$. The M factor in Strandberg's (15) was omitted and he presumes $r_o = 0$. The reflection type cavity series has the advantage for low values of M, but this advantage rapidly vanishes as M becomes modestly large.

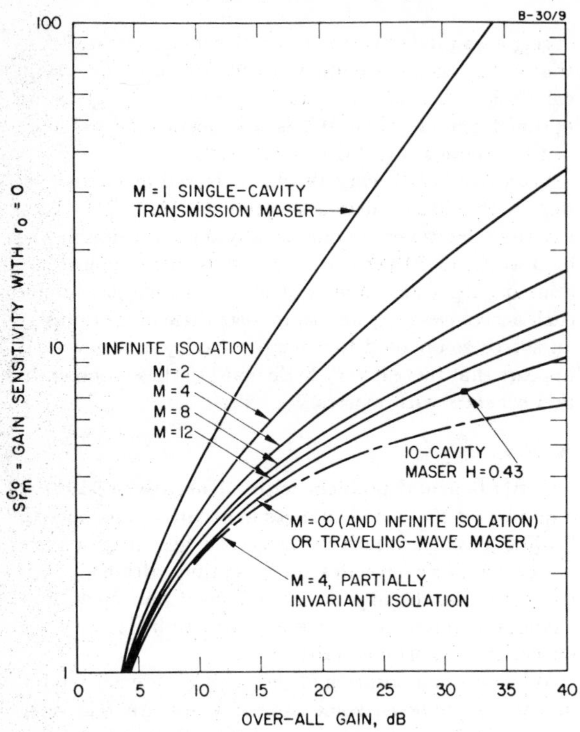

Fig. 10—Gain sensitivity of coupled cavity masers to variations in activity.

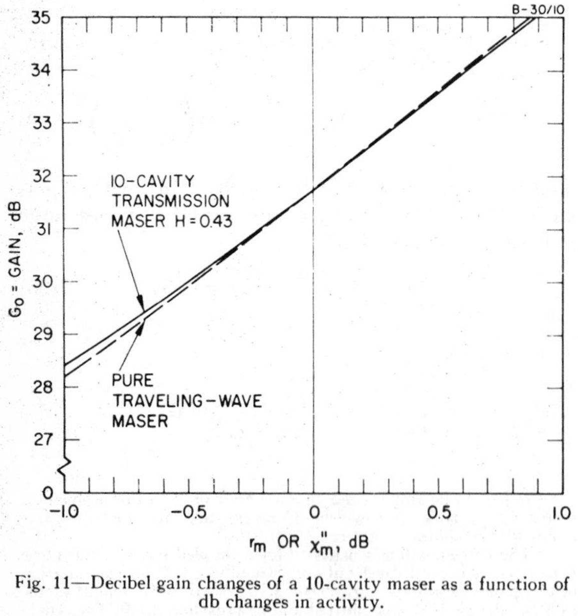

Fig. 11—Decibel gain changes of a 10-cavity maser as a function of db changes in activity.

which is the same result as for the traveling wave maser, as given by De Grass, *et al.* [2], if residual losses are included in the traveling-wave formula. Ignoring the factor $[R_m/R_m - R_o)]$, the $H=0$ sensitivities for $M=1, 2, 4, 8, 12$ and ∞ have been computed from (53) and (54) and plotted in Fig. 10. It is seen that M does not have to be very large before the traveling-wave sensitivity is approached rather closely.

None of these results has obtained any advantage from the potential inverse feedback action associated with finite values of isolator ratio. Some special cases are discussed by O'Meara [1a] and one of these is illustrated in Fig. 10. One sees that improvement is possible and one may decrease the sensitivity slightly below that of the traveling wave maser. However, the case illustrated corresponds to more feedback than one can afford to use from a gain-frequency control viewpoint.

The sensitivity with a value of isolation corresponding to a near optimum H in a 10-cavity maser has been computed for one particular gain value (31.7 db) and is plotted as a single point in Fig. 10. It falls almost on top of the curve for the traveling-wave maser.

One may question if the sensitivity is a good measure of the actual gain changes and if so over what ranges. Fig. 11 compares the actual gain changes occurring with a 10-cavity maser and a pure traveling-wave maser for variations in r_m measured in db. It is seen that the two curves are nearly identical with the 10-cavity maser having an almost insignificant advantage. As both curves are nearly linear over a range of ± 1 db variation in R_m (or χ_m''), the sensitivity is indeed a good measure. Similar computations near the band-edge frequencies of the 10-cavity maser yield lesser variation in gain.

IX. Conclusions

The maser amplifier which has been analyzed proves to be fairly complex in spite of numerous approximations and the fact that many degrees of freedom have been eliminated by the choice of an iterative structure. Consequently, exact theoretical formulae are not available for all parameters of interest. However, certain interim conclusions may be drawn. Probably the four most significant conclusions are the following:

1) Unlike the nonisolated iterative passive filter, the band-pass ripple may be held to quite low values by the proper choice in round-trip isolation.
2) The product of gain in db and relative bandwidth is linearly proportional to the number of cavities (in first order theory) if the number of cavities is reasonably large, given optimal isolation values.
3) The gain-tunable-bandwidth product obtainable with this structure is comparable to that obtained with competitive structures (using equally active cavities or reactive elements).

4) It may often be good practice to employ a larger number of cavities than dictated by gain-bandwidth requirements in order to improve stability, that is, to reduce the sensitivity to cavity loadings or activity (*e.g.*, pumping).

Although we have not succeeded in developing exact formal equations for either round-trip isolation or bandwidth, by combining computer results and various approximations we have been able to prepare design curves which should permit a choice in these parameters sufficient for normal engineering applications.

Appendix

Limiting Gain-Bandwidth as the Number of Resonators Becomes Large

From (46), it is noted that

$$B_r Q_{me} = \left(\frac{g_{os}}{g_{oe}}\right)\left(\frac{1+H}{g_{os}-1}\right)^{(1-M)/M} \tag{55}$$

Also note that the difference between g_{oe} and g_{os} is a second order effect in the parameter ($\ln G_o/2M$). Specifically, it is readily derived from (38) that

$$1 - \frac{g_{oe}}{g_{os}} \approx H\left(\frac{\ln G_o}{2M}\right)^2 \approx \left(\frac{\ln G_o}{2M}\right)^2. \tag{56}$$

Second, note from Fig. 6 that an optimum H is related to g_{os}, roughly as

$$\ln H \approx -K \ln g_{os} \tag{57}$$

where K is a constant whose exact value is uncertain, but lies roughly in the range

$$2 < K < 2.5. \tag{58}$$

Using a series expansion for H values near unity and ignoring the second order distinction between g_{oe} and g_{os} gives

$$1 + H \approx 2 - K \ln g_{oe} = 2\left(1 - \frac{K \ln G_o}{4M}\right). \tag{59}$$

Since the $g_{os}-1$ factor in (55) is small to begin with, second-order corrections of the form (56) become important. Thus

$$\frac{g_{os}}{g_{oe}}(g_{os}-1)^{-1} \approx \left[1 - \frac{g_{oe}}{g_{os}} + \frac{\ln G_o}{2M}\right]^{-1}$$
$$\approx \frac{2M}{\ln G_o}\left[1 + \frac{\ln G_o}{2M}\right]^{-1}. \tag{60}$$

Substituting (59) and (60) in (55) gives a large M approximation

$$B_r Q_{me} \approx \frac{M}{\ln G_o}\left[1 + \left(1 - \frac{K}{2}\right)\frac{\ln G_o}{2M}\right]^{-1}$$
$$\approx \frac{M}{\ln G_o}. \tag{61}$$

List of Symbols

$A_{11}, A_{12}, A_{21}, A_{22}$	Matrix element of the over-all amplifier matrix.
A_{is}	Transmission matrix description of an isolator.
$\overline{\overline{A}}_{is}$	A reduced isolator matrix which includes the inversion and isolation functions of an effective $\lambda/4$ isolator but excludes phase shift effects.
$\overline{A}_{is}$	The resistive part of an isolator matrix.
A_m	Transmission matrix describing a maser cavity.
$b = B/Z_o$	Normalized iris susceptance.
$B_r = \dfrac{\omega_{3db} - \omega_{db3}}{\omega_o(1+\delta)}$	Relative bandwidth of an M-cavity maser.
$d = N^2(r_m - r_o)Y_o$	A transformed effective maser cavity resistance; also a predistortion shift in the complex frequency plane (assuming a normalized cavity inductance of 1 Henry).
$g_o = \sqrt{G_o}$	Band-center transducer voltage gain of an M-cavity maser.
$g_{o\cdot}$	Band-center transducer voltage gain of a single-cavity maser.
G_L	Gain loss (in db) as a result of inverse feedback action.
$g_{oe} = (g_o)^{1/M}$	Band-center effective transducer voltage gain of a single-cavity in an M-cavity maser.
G_{db}	Over-all power gain in db.
$H = \exp(\alpha_1 + \alpha_2)l_{is}$	Round-trip attenuation of a single isolator as a voltage ratio.
$K_g = (\lambda_g/\lambda)^2 = \left[1 - \dfrac{1}{\mu_r\epsilon_r}\left(\dfrac{\omega_c}{\omega_o}\right)^2\right]^{-1}$	Guide wavelength factor.
$L_o = \dfrac{\pi K_g}{\omega_o Y_o}$	Equivalent low-pass inductance of a $\lambda/2$ cavity.

M	Number of maser cavities.
$N = 1 + b^2$	Turns ratio of the effective transformer in a transformer and line representation of an iris.
$O_M = \sum K_k(z_m)^k$	A polynomial in z_m, whose reciprocal gives the transducer gain.
$p = \sigma + j\Omega$	Normalized low-pass complex frequency variable.
$Q_m = \dfrac{1}{\chi_m''} = \dfrac{\omega_o L}{2R_m}$	Maser medium Q.
$Q_{me} = \dfrac{\omega_o L}{2(R_m - R_o)} = \left[\dfrac{1}{\chi_m''}\left(1 - \dfrac{R_o}{R_m}\right)\right]^{-1}$	Effective Q of a resonant network representing a waveguide filled with a medium having a susceptibility x_m.
R_o	A residual (passive) loss resistance in a $\lambda/2$ maser cavity resulting from wall or dielectric losses.
R_m	A resistance introduced by the maser action within a material filling a waveguide.
s	A low-pass or displacement complex frequency variable.
$s_{mo} = j(\omega_m - \omega_o)$	Frequency displacement between the line resonance center frequency and the (iris-short-circuit) cavity resonant frequency.
$S_l^k = \dfrac{d[\ln k]}{d[\ln l]}$	Sensitivity of k to the parameter l.
$T_M(x) = \cos(M \cos^{-1} x)$	Chebyshev polynomial of the first kind.
$U_{M-1}(x) = \dfrac{\sin(M \cos^{-1} x)}{\sqrt{1 - x^2}}$	Chebyshev polynomial of the second kind.
$x = j\dfrac{H^{-1}/2}{2}\left[1 - H \ (1 + H)\dfrac{z_m}{2}\right]$	Complex argument of a Chebyshev polynomial.
X_{ir}	Equivalent series reactance resulting from an iris susceptance.
$Y_o = (Z_o)^{-1}$	Characteristic admittance of a passive waveguide or line.
$Z_m = sL_o + R_o - R_m$	Effective series impedance representing a $\lambda/2$ maser cavity.
$z_m = N^2 Z_m Y_o = p - d$	Effective transformed low-pass impedance of a $\lambda/2$ maser cavity, normalized to the waveguide characteristic impedance of.
α_1	Forward path attenuation constant in an isolator-waveguide section.
α_2	Backward path attenuation constant in an isolator-waveguide section.
$\alpha_{(+)} = \dfrac{\alpha_1 + \alpha_2}{2}$	Average attenuation constant.
$\delta = \delta\omega/\omega_o$	Relative frequency shift resulting from iris detuning.
$\Delta\omega_o = \omega - \omega_o$	A frequency departure from the $\lambda/2$ resonant frequency.
$\Delta\omega_m = \omega - \omega_m$	A frequency departure from the material line center frequency.
$\omega_{mo} = \omega_m - \omega_o$	Frequency displacement between the line resonance and the $\lambda_g/2$ resonant frequency.
$\theta = \ln H = (\alpha_1 + \alpha_2) l_{is}$	Round-trip attenuation of a single isolator in nepers.
θ_{is}	Electrical length of the isolator, in radians.
θ_{ir}	Electrical length of the effective line in a transformer and line representation of a single iris.
λ_g	Guide wavelength.
μ_r	Relative permeability of a passive medium.
$\mu_r^* = \mu_r(1 + \chi)$	Complex permeability of an active maser medium.
τ	Maser material reciprocal half-line width.
χ	Complex susceptibility of a maser medium.
χ_m''	Peak value of imaginary part of χ.

ω	Band-pass frequency variable.
ω_c	Cutoff frequency in a waveguide.
ω_m	Maser medium line center frequency.
ω_0	Passive iris-short-circuit $\lambda/2$ resonance frequency of a line or cavity.
Ω	A normalized low-pass frequency variable.
Ω_p	Outer-peak (normalized) frequency of a loss-free unloaded passive filter.
Ω'_p	Outer-peak (normalized) frequency of a loss-free loaded passive filter.

ACKNOWLEDGMENT

The author wishes to thank K. Higa of the Hughes Computing Department, Malibu, Calif., for programming and running the computations leading to the preparation of Fig. 7.

REFERENCES

[1a] T. R. O'Meara, "An Analysis of the Isolator-Coupled-Cavity Transmission Maser, Parts I and II," Hughes Research Labs., Malibu, Calif., Research Rept. No. 259; April, 1963.
[1b] F. E. Goodwin, J. E. Kiefer and G. E. Moss, "The Coupled-Cavity Transmission Maser—Engineering Design," Hughes Research Labs., Maliblu, Calif., Research Rept. No. 252; August, 1962.
[2] R. W. DeGrasse, E. O. Schulz-DuBois, and H. E. O. Scovil, "The three-level solid state traveling-wave maser," *Bell Sys. Tech. J.*, vol. 39, pp. 1–47; March, 1959.
[3] "Solid-State Maser Research Report No. 2," Bell Telephone Labs. Contract No. DA-36-039 SC-85357, 2nd Quarterly Rept.; December 20, 1960.
[4] A. E. Siegman, "Microwave Solid State Masers," McGraw-Hill Book Co., Inc., New York, N. Y.; 1964.
[5] H. W. Bode, "Network Analysis and Feedback Amplifier Design," D. Van Nostrand Co., Inc., New York, N. Y., pp. 216–222; 1945.
[6] W. W. Mumford, "Maximally flat filters in waveguide," *Bell Sys. Tech. J.*, vol. 27, pp. 648–714; October, 1948.
[7] R. L. Kyhl, R. A. McFarlane, and M. W. D. Strandberg, "Negative *L* and *C* in solid-state masers, "Proc. IRE, vol. 50, pp. 1608–1623; July, 1962.
[8] R. L. Kyhl, "Negative *L* and *C* in solid-state masers," Proc. IRE, (*Correspondence*), vol. 48, p. 1157; June, 1960.
[9] C. G. Montgomery, R. H. Dicke and E. M. Purcell, "Principles of Microwave Cicruits," M.I.T. Rad. Lab. Ser., McGraw-Hill Book Co., Inc., New York, N. Y.; 1948.
[10] S. B. Cohn, "Direct-coupled resonator filters," Proc. IRE, vol. 45, pp. 187–196; February, 1957.
[11] H. L. Armstrong, "Note on the use of Tchebyscheff functions in dealing with iterated networks," IRE Trans. on Circuit Theory, vol. CT-2, pp. 169–170; June, 1955.
[12] L. Storch, "On the chain matrix of cascaded networks," IRE Trans. on Circuit Theory (*Correspondence*), vol. CT-3, pp. 297–298; December, 1956.
[13] "Tables of Chebyshev Polynomials $S_n(x)$ and $C_n(x)$", U. S. Dept. of Commerce, National Bureau of Standards, Applied Mathematics Series, U. S. Government Printing Office, Washington, D. C., 1952.
[14] G. L. Ragan, "Microwave Transmission Circuits," vol. 9, M.I.T. Rad. Lab. Ser., McGraw-Hill Book Co., Inc., New York, N. Y.; 1948.
[15] T. R. O'Meara, "Generating arrays for ladder network transfer functions," IEEE Trans. on Circuit Theory (*Correspondence*), vol. CT-10, p. 285; June, 1963.
[16] G. E. Valley and H. Wallman, "Vacuum Tube Amplifiers," vol. 18, M.I.T. Rad. Lab. Ser., McGraw-Hill Book Co., Inc., New York, N. Y.; 1948.
[17] M. W. P. Strandberg, "Unidirectional paramagnetic amplifier design," Proc. IRE, vol. 48, pp. 1307–1320; July, 1960.
[18] M. L. Stitch, "Maser amplifier characteristics for transmission and reflection cavities," *J. Appl. Phys.*, vol. 29, pp. 782–789; May, 1958.
[19] E. A. Guillemin, "Communication Networks," John Wiley and Sons, New York, N. Y. vol. II, pp. 445–448; July, 1947.
[20] E. S. Kuh, "Synthesis of lumped parameter precision delay lines," Proc. IRE Convention Record, vol. 45, pp. 160–174; December, 1957.
[21] L. Weinberg, "Synthesis using tunnel diodes and masers," IRE Trans. on Circuit Theory, vol. CT-8, pp. 66–75; March, 1961.
[22] H. J. Carlin, *et al.*, "Comments on design theory of optimum negative-resistance amplifiers," Proc. IRE, vol. 49, pp. 1687–1688; November, 1961.
[23] D. C. Youla and L. I. Smilen, "Optimum negative-resistance amplifiers," Proc. Symp. on Active Networks and Feedback Systems, Polytechnic Press, Polytechnic Inst. of Brooklyn, N. Y.; April 19–21, 1960.

The Coupled-Cavity Transmission Maser-Engineering Design

F. E. GOODWIN, MEMBER, IEEE, J. E. KIEFER, MEMBER, IEEE AND G. E. MOSS, MEMBER, IEEE

Summary—**The experimental design of an *X*-band microwave maser amplifier which uses a new type of slow-wave circuit is described. A detailed theoretical analysis of the circuit is presented in a companion paper [1]. The slow-wave circuit consists of a cascade of iris-coupled ruby resonators separated by garnet isolators. This unit provides significant reduction in size and weight over previously reported maser slow-wave circuits.**

The microwave properties of the solid ruby resonator are treated in detail, and the passive bandwidth of the single transmission cavity and its relation to the iris susceptance are shown. Experimental techniques involved in obtaining and measuring precise iris susceptance are presented. A step-by-step procedure for designing an amplifier having a given gain and tuning range is also presented.

Typical performance characteristics include a gain of 30 db, instantaneous bandwidth of 25 Mc, and a noise temperature of 15°K. An electronic tuning range of 200 Mc has been achieved in one configuration with a 20 db gain and a 25-Mc bandwidth. The weight of the maser-dewar unit, filled with 6 liters of helium for 24 hours of operation is less than 40 pounds. The design of the dewar enables the cryogenic system to work over a wide range of vertical angles, thus facilitating the use of the maser at the feed of a large steerable antenna.

I. Introduction

SOON after the first generation of solid-state maser amplifiers were developed, it became apparent that the instability associated with these reflection-type cavity devices would prevent their use for many applications. The benefits derived from the very low noise were reduced by the instability and complexity of the maser and the associated cryogenics. With the development of the traveling-wave maser, greater stability was achieved, and, in addition, great improvements in gain-bandwidth product were obtained. To date, operating traveling-wave masers which utilize slow-wave structures are of four types: the comb structure [2], the meander line [3], the Karp structure [4], and the coupled resonant cavity structure. One of these, the comb-structure maser amplifier, has been developed by several laboratories.

This paper reports on the coupled resonant cavity type maser developed at this laboratory. The primary advantage of this type of structure over the others is its inherent smaller size while it still yields comparable or improved performance characteristics. This reduction in size may be seen to be possible by considering the four basic structures shown in Fig. 1. Each of these structures must be oriented with the static magnetic field in a particular way. To permit unilateral absorption or isolation, the ferromagnetic element is placed in the region of a circularly polarized RF magnetic field, where the static magnetic field must then be perpendicular to the RF field. This requirement follows directly from [5], [6]

$$\frac{d\overline{M}}{dt} = \gamma(\overline{M} \times \overline{H})$$

where $\overline{M}$ is the magnetization, $\overline{H}$ is the magnetic field and γ is the gyromagnetic ratio. The comb structure, meander line and Karp structure are similar in that the plane of RF circular polarization is perpendicular to the plane of the structure. It is thus necessary to orient the static magnetic field parallel to the plane of these structures. However, the waveguide filter structure has the circular RF polarization in the plane of the waveguide and thereby permits the static magnetic field to be directed perpendicular to the plane of the structure. This is a very real advantage over the other types of structures in that the magnet gap length may be considerably reduced thus permitting a much smaller magnet to be used to furnish the necessary field. The static field for an *X*-band coupled-cavity type maser is provided by a small permanent magnet weighing 10 to

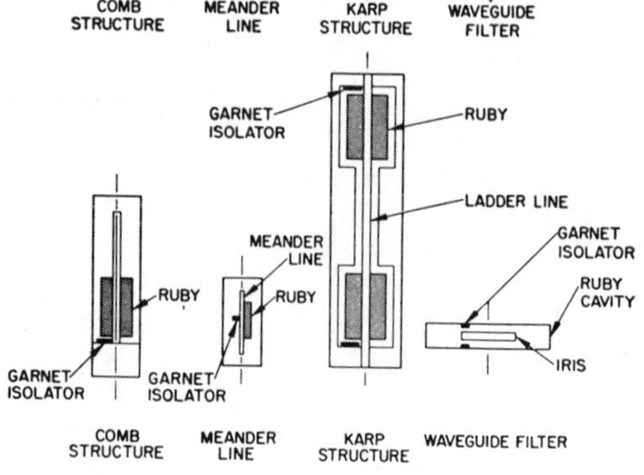

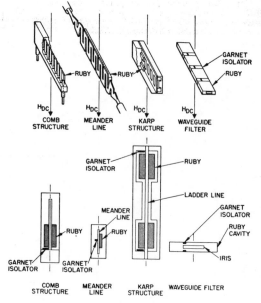

Fig. 1—Four basic traveling-wave maser structures.

Manuscript received October 15, 1963; revised received February 24, 1964.

The authors are with Hughes Research Laboratories, Malibu. Calif.

Fig. 2—Complete maser amplifier.

20 ounces which is fixed directly to the maser structure. The relative smallness of the magnet permits it to be cooled along with the maser without excessive expenditure of liquid helium. This type of structure can be readily adapted to use a superconducting magnet, but it has been found that the fields required for operation at X-band frequencies may be more easily provided by a permanent magnet.

The elimination of the large magnet facilitates the design of the maser-dewar unit to fulfill practical operating requirements for size, weight and variable angular orientation. In many systems these requirements are imposed by the necessity for locating the maser very close to the feed of a large steerable antenna. Design features of the liquid helium dewar allow operation at all elevation angles encountered while fixed to a steerable antenna. Fig. 2 illustrates the complete maser along with its associated control unit. The dewar, as shown in Fig. 2 (and in Fig. 15), is capable of maintaining the maser at the operating temperature of 4.2°K for over 24 hours with a 6-liter charge of liquid helium.

Closed cycle refrigerators capable of liquid helium temperatures are becoming less expensive and more reliable. These are finding ready application to maser systems where liquid helium availability and storage is a problem. The coupled-cavity maser discussed in this paper has been designed to be readily adaptable to a liquid helium refrigerator.

II. Maser RF Assembly

The maser RF assembly (illustrated in Fig. 3) includes an input-output and pump waveguide flange block, Fiberglas heat exchanger tube and maser unit. The configuration of the heat exchanger tube is such that the escaping helium vapor is forced to flow in contact with the neck tube of the dewar. The space between the waveguides and inside the Fiberglas tube is filled with foamed epoxy to prevent undesirable circulation of gas. The signal input and output waveguides are made of either stainless steel or metallized Fiberglas. At the bottom of the neck, where the waveguide joins the maser, the waveguide is transformed into a solid, alumina-filled waveguide by means of a matching transition. The design of the matching device is considered in Section IV and illustrated in Fig. 9. The dielectric-filled waveguide serves the following three purposes: 1) to keep liquid helium and frozen gases out of the waveguide in the bath, thereby preventing mismatches and instability, 2) to reduce the line impedance to that of the active coupled-cavity filter (the maser amplifying structure) and 3) to reduce the physical size.

The coupled-cavity structure consists of a number of transmission-type cavities which are in cascade and separated from each other by interstage garnet isolators. Pump power is brought into the cavities through a pump distribution waveguide circuit which lies adjacent to the coupled cavities. Each cavity has a pump slot in its side, and the cavities form a slot array for the pump power. Both resonant and nonresonant pump arrays have been used successfully. The arrangement of the structure is shown in disassembled form in Fig. 4.

The magnetic field for the maser is provided by a small Alnico V permanent magnet located within the dewar. Carefully shaped [7] Armco pole pieces assure the required high degree of homogeneity of field (see Fig. 5). A trimming coil mounted on the magnet allows small variations of the field magnitude necessary for initial adjustment and for fine frequency tuning of the maser. Two modes of control of the magnitude of the field are possible. By applying regulated direct current to the trimming coil, the field magnitude may be continuously varied. If long time operation at a given field is required, the field magnitude may be fixed by discharging a charged capacitor through the trimming coil. Varying the charging voltage varies the final field to which the magnet is charged, and when the desired field is established, the magnet control may be turned off. (This feature is desirable because it removes the dependence of the magnetic field stability, and thus the gain stability of the maser from the direct current supply.) Also, by eliminating the continuous current through the trimming coil, a significant heat load to the liquid helium bath is removed.

A superconducting lead shell surrounding the maser assembly provides the magnetic shielding found necessary to eliminate the gain fluctuations of the maser due to variations in external magnetic fields.

One electrical advantage of the waveguide filter, or coupled-cavity maser, is that the structure pass band may be reduced arbitrarily without changing the front-to-back ratio of the isolators. Since the isolators are not in a region of high RF field, the net forward loss remains small even when structure pass bands are reduced to 0.2 percent. The reduced pass band, however, increases

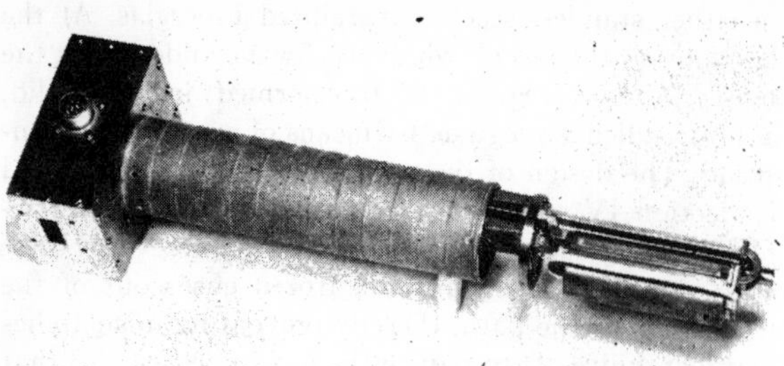

Fig. 3—Maser RF assembly.

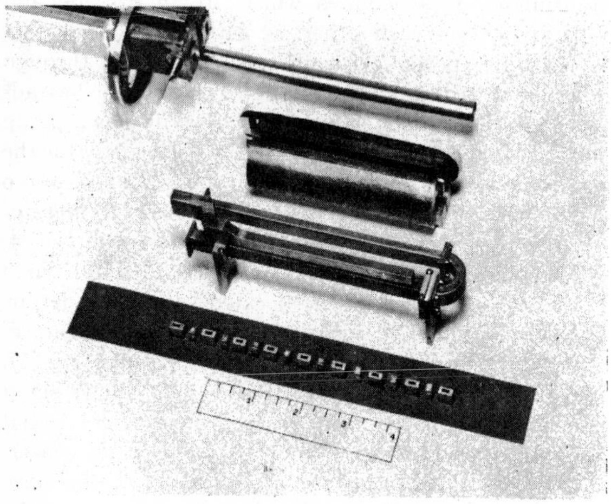

Fig. 4—Disassembled RF structure.

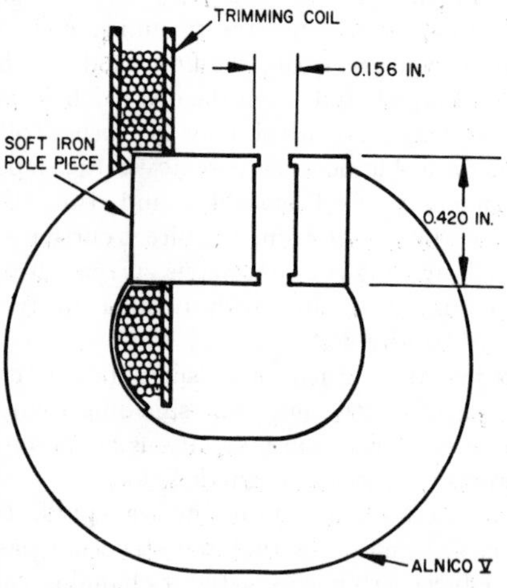

Fig. 5—Cross section of maser magnet.

the gain as shown by the approximate relationship [8]

$$G(dB) \simeq \frac{8.6M}{Q_m \overline{BW}},$$

where

$M \equiv$ number of resonators
$Q_m \equiv$ magnetic Q of material
$\overline{BW} \equiv$ structure pass band (fractional).

With an arbitrarily narrow pass band, high net gain may be achieved by using maser materials of relatively high magnetic Q, such as would be the case when operating a ruby maser at temperatures higher than that of liquid helium. It has been shown [9] that amplification can be achieved in a ruby reflection-type-cavity maser at temperatures as high as 77°K. Thus, it would be possible to extend the operation of the multiple-resonator transmission device to higher temperatures, although the required pump power may set the upper limit to practical operating temperature. For the purposes of this paper, however, we consider only operation at 4.2°K, the temperature of liquid helium at 1 atmosphere of pressure, where the over-all performance capabilities of the coupled-cavity transmission maser are the most practical.

III. Microwave Properties of the Solid Ruby Resonator

Resonator Frequency

The resonant cavities which form the slow-wave structure consist of rectangular papallelepipeds of ruby constructed to be resonant in the TE_{011} mode. Silver plating is used to form the conductive wall of the cavity. To form the coupling irises of the resonator this plating is removed from precisely determined areas. A filling factor of unity is assured with this type of construction as well as high stability of the cavity resonant frequency. Two dimensions of the resonator are fixed by the structure cross section, while the third (the dimension parallel to the direction of propagation through the structure) is used to fix the resonant frequency.

To determine the resonant frequency of the cavity, the effective dielectric permittivity of ruby for this configuration must be known. Ruby is an electrically anisotropic crystal and as such has a tensor dielectric permittivity. In addition, ruby is uniaxial, which means that the dielectric permittivities are such that $\epsilon_x = \epsilon_y \neq \epsilon_z$ where the z direction is parallel to the optical axis. ϵ_x, ϵ_y and ϵ_z are called the principal dielectric permittivities of the crystal. For clarity, let $\epsilon_z = \epsilon_\parallel$ and $\epsilon_x = \epsilon_y = \epsilon_\perp$. The principal dielectric permittivities for ruby have been measured at 9 kMc and are shown as a function of temperature in Fig. 6. The effective refractive index n of ruby may be determined by the ellipsoid of revolu-

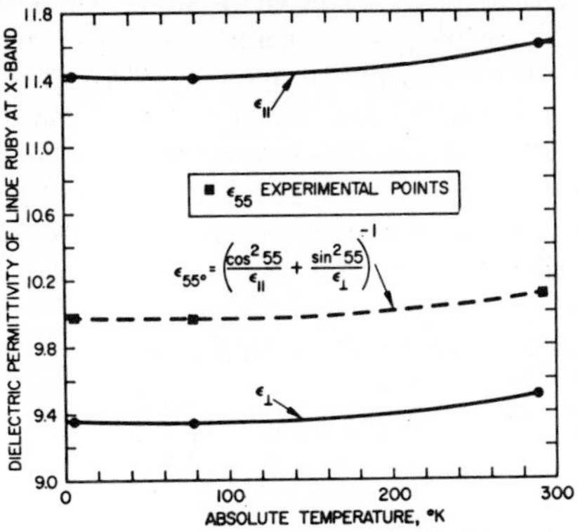

Fig. 6—Relative dielectric permittivity of Linde ruby as a function of temperature.

tion about the optical axis

$$\frac{1}{n^2} = \frac{\cos^2\theta}{n_\parallel^2} + \frac{\sin^2\theta}{n_\perp^2}$$

where θ is the angle between the electric vector and the optical axis. Therefore, the effective dielectric permittivity ϵ for ruby is given by

$$\frac{1}{\epsilon} = \frac{\cos^2\theta}{\epsilon_\parallel} + \frac{\sin^2\theta}{\epsilon_\perp}.$$

The resonators are normally constructed such that $\theta = 55°$; the effective dielectric permittivity for this configuration is also given by Fig. 6. The length of the ruby resonator can thus be found for a predetermined unloaded resonant frequency f_u and width a from the relation

$$\text{ruby length} = \frac{c/2f_u}{\sqrt{\epsilon - \left(\frac{c}{2f_u a}\right)^2}} \text{ cm} \tag{1}$$

where $c = 3 \times 10^{10}$ cm/sec.

The relative impedance of the coupling irises pulls the resonant frequency of the cavity to some loaded frequency f_0. The fractional deviation δ_f is given by [10]

$$\delta_f = \frac{f_0 - f_u}{f_u} \cong \left(\frac{b}{2Q_L}\right) \tag{2}$$

where Q_L is the loaded Q of the cavity and $b = B/Y_0$, the normalized susceptance of the coupling irises which are assumed to be identical.

B. Loaded Q

The loaded Q of the cavity has special significance since the power gain G of the maser depends upon the ratio of this quantity to the magnetic quality factor of the maser material Q_m [11]. For any given set of operating conditions, the magnetic Q is optimized and remains fixed. Thus the gain depends on the loaded Q, and therefore on iris susceptance. The conventional expression for the loaded Q of a waveguide resonator is given by [12]

$$(\overline{BW})^{-1} = Q_L = \frac{b^2 + 1}{4\left[1 - \left(\frac{f_c^2}{f_0}\right)\right]} \tan^{-1}\left(\frac{2b}{b^2 - 1}\right) \tag{3}$$

where f_0 is the cavity resonant frequency and f_c is the waveguide cut-off frequency.

Another expression for loaded Q, which is obtained from transmission line theory is

$$(\overline{BW})^{-1} = Q_L = \frac{\pi - 2\tan^{-1}\left(\frac{1}{b}\right)}{\left[1 - \left(\frac{f_c}{f_0}\right)^2\right] \ln\left[\left(\frac{2}{b}\right)^2 + 1\right]} \tag{4}$$

for $b > 2$.

For the middle of the waveguide band and large b, (3) and (4) reduce to $\pi b^2/2$. Eq. (4) and its reciprocal, fractional bandwidth $\overline{BW}$, are plotted in Fig. 7 for several values of (f_c/f_0). It can be seen that there is excellent correlation with experimental $\overline{BW}$ points.

C. Magnetic Q

The magnetic Q is defined as the reciprocal of the imaginary part of the paramagnetic susceptibility χ'' and is given by [9]

$$Q_m = \frac{1}{\chi''} = \frac{h\nu_s}{8\pi(n_2 - n_1)\langle\mu^2\rangle F}$$

where h is Planck's constant, ν_s is the signal frequency, n_1 and n_2 are the number of ions in spin states 1 and 2, $<\mu^2>$ is the average squared dipole moment of the maser transition and F is the cavity filling factor. For the particular case of the symmetric or four-level "push-pull" mode, Q_m reduces to

$$Q_m = \frac{kT\Delta\nu_m}{2\pi N_0\langle\mu^2\rangle(\nu_p - \nu_s)}, \tag{5}$$

where k is Boltzmann's constant, T is the absolute temperature, $\Delta\nu_m$ is the line width of the transition, N_0 is the number of maser ions per cm^3 and ν_p is the pump frequency which is fixed by ν_s.

Eq. (5) which is plotted in Fig. 8 represents the minimum or best possible value of Q_m. In practice, this value is never realized because it is degraded by several factors, such as broadening of the paramagnetic line width by inhomogeneous magnetic field or by crystal imperfections, incomplete saturation of pump transition (incomplete inversion), lower than unity filling factor, or local heating of the ruby by high pump power.

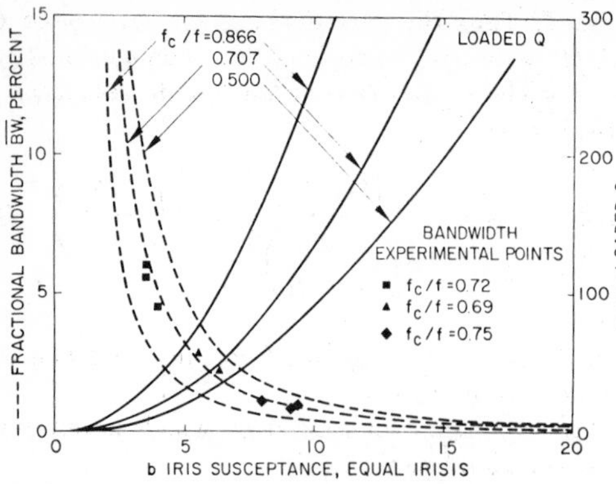

Fig. 7—Passive bandwidth of transmission cavity as a function of iris susceptance (equal irises).

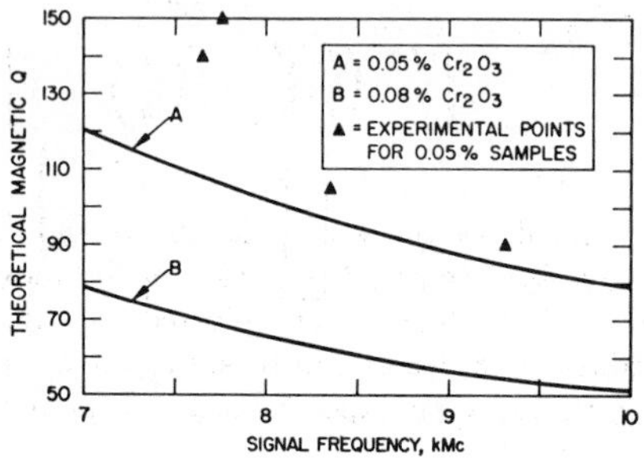

Fig. 8.—Magnetic Q as a function of frequency for ruby at $\theta = 54.7°$.

D. Iris Susceptance Measurements

We have seen that the gain of the maser and relative bandwidth of the ruby filter structure depend upon the iris susceptance. The key to this maser design, therefore, is the achievement of precise iris susceptances. A simple and accurate method for attaining precision irises is to remove the silver plating from the area of the coupling iris by fine sandblasting through a thin metal template of a predetermined size.

The shape of the iris is a critical factor in coupling between the rubies because a favorable field distribution in the isolator must be maintained. The optimum shape of the iris is rectangular with the E dimension (height of the iris) about half that of the ruby. The width of the iris then determines its susceptance. Two methods used for measuring the iris susceptance are the following:

1) *The Reflection Coefficient Method*—The standard method of measuring a susceptance is by measuring the reflected power from an iris. In this case, since dielectric filled waveguide is used, great care must be taken that the iris is backed up by a matched termination. The reflection coefficient ρ is related to the iris susceptance by

$$\rho = \left[\left(\frac{2}{b}\right)^2 + 1\right]^{-1/2} = \left(\frac{P_{\text{reflected}}}{P_{\text{incident}}}\right)^{1/2}.$$

This method is satisfactory for determining the susceptance of an iris on the thin metal template used as a pattern for cutting irises on the rubies.

2) *The Del Method*—After the iris has been cut on a ruby, it is possible to determine its susceptance by measuring the detuning or frequency pulling introduced by the reactive nature of the iris. The resonant frequency of the cavity with the iris shorted is compared with the resonant frequency with the iris open circuited. A quarter wavelength ruby shorted at the iris end provides the open circuit. The relation of the amount of frequency detuning δ_f to the iris susceptance of a conventional half-wave transmission line is given by

$$\delta_f = \frac{f_0 - f_u}{f_u} = \frac{1}{\pi} \tan^{-1}\left(\frac{1}{b}\right),$$

which for the case of waveguides becomes

$$\delta_f = \frac{f_0 - f_u}{f_u} = \frac{1}{\pi}\left[1 - \left(\frac{f_c}{f_0}\right)^2\right] \tan^{-1}\left(\frac{1}{b}\right).$$

IV. Broad-Band Impedance Match into a Dielectric Filled Waveguide

Relatively good broad band RF matches from a standard waveguide into a dielectric-filled waveguide can be obtained with the transition shown in Fig. 9 [13] on the next page. For frequency independent impedance match, the height of the two waveguides must be equal at the junction and their widths must be related by

$$\frac{a_1}{a_2} = \sqrt{\frac{\epsilon_2}{\epsilon_0}}$$

where $\epsilon_2/\epsilon_0 = 9.4$ for alumina. The optimum stub diameter is $0.8\ a_2$, and its optimum position is $a_2/2$ from the junction. The depth of the stub is adjusted for best match. A typical VSWR of 1.16 or less can be obtained over a 25 per cent band with the X-band device.

V. The Coupled-Cavity Filter Structure

O'Meara [1] has described the equivalent network of the ruby cavity and has analyzed the combined M-cavity amplifier network. His analysis yielded essential design relations and optimum values of parameters. In this and the sections that follow, repeated reference is made to his analysis of the isolator-iris effective line length, the optimum isolation for general M-cavity system and the gain-frequency functions. Computed data from this analysis of a 15-cavity maser amplifier are compared with experimental results.

A. Passive, Nonisolated Structure

The bandwidth $\overline{BW}$ of a single passive-transmission ruby cavity has been given as a function of iris susceptance [(4)] and plotted in Fig. 7. When the number of cavities M of the system is increased from 1, it can be shown that the structure bandwidth decreases to a minimum for $M = 2$, increases for $M > 2$, and approaches that of a single cavity again for larger M. Therefore,

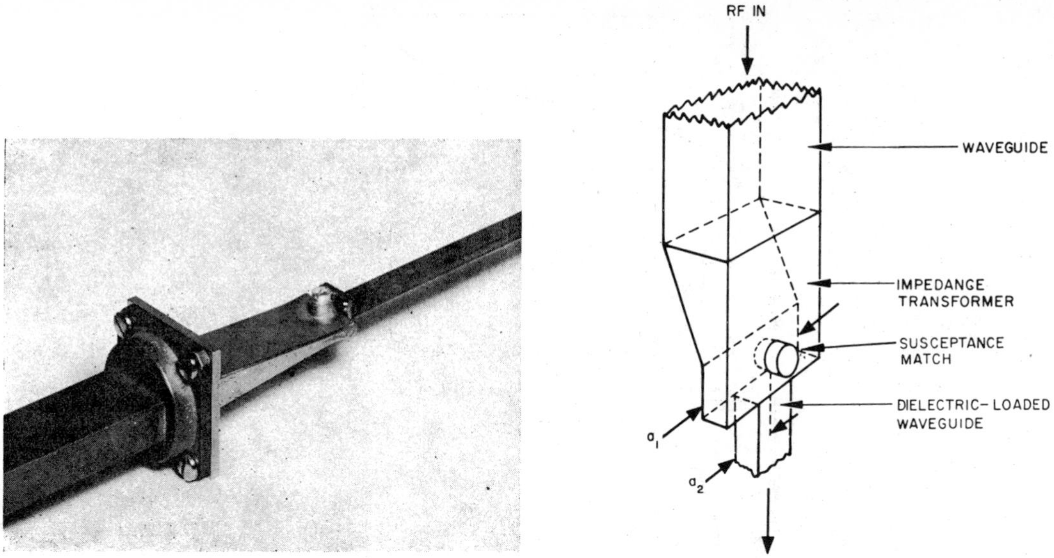

(a) (b)

Fig. 9—Broad-band impedance transition from standard to dielectric-filled waveguide.

(4) holds for large M and is nearly correct for $M=4$. Experimental results agree with this prediction to a high degree of accuracy for $M>4$.

The measured phase-frequency diagram for a passive 15-resonator structure is given in Fig. 10 (opposite) where $\beta l/\pi$ is the normalized phase shift per cavity. Fig. 10 also illustrates the calculated single cavity bandwidth $\overline{BW}$ compared with both the measured reflected and the transmitted power over the region of the pass band. It can be seen that the bandwidth of the 15-resonator filter is 425 Mc, or slightly less than the calculated $\overline{BW}=440$ Mc. A good passive filter characteristic is necessary for a good active maser amplifier. This of course requires precise control of the iris susceptance and ruby resonator center frequencies.

B. The Isolator

Three important functions of the isolators are directly related to their physical length. First, the isolator must be long enough to provide sufficient separation between cavities so that the mutual coupling between irises is small. For this case, the net susceptance of the coupling element is twice the susceptance of a single iris. This gives the desired filter characteristic for the maser structure.

The second function of the isolator length is related to the symmetry of the structure pass band. It can be shown [1] that a symmetric pass band may be obtained if quarter-wave coupling between elements is provided. The electrical length of each isolator βl must then satisfy the requirement

$$\beta l + 2 \tan^{-1} b = \pm \frac{\pi}{2}$$

where b is the iris susceptance.

The third function of the isolator electrical length is to provide isolation to the active maser amplifier. The optimum isolation, discussed below, is determined by the gain of the individual cavities, and since the isolation is nearly a linear function of length, the optimum length is established.

C. Active Isolated Structure

When the structure is cooled to liquid helium temperatures and pump power is provided to the rubies, the filter becomes active. In order for the filter to provide stable gain, isolation is required. The minimum interstage isolation necessary to prevent oscillation, which was determined by the partially invariant method [1], is approximately twice the single cavity gain. Because large ripple in the gain-frequency response is undesirable, an isolation of twice the single cavity gain is regarded as a lower bound. A maximally flat gain-frequency response is obtained with an interstage isolation of approximately three times the gain per stage. In practice, a value of two and one-half is adequate to produce smooth gain characteristics. The optimum value is not a linear function of the gain per stage, so the curves should be consulted for exact values (O'Meara [1], Fig. 6).

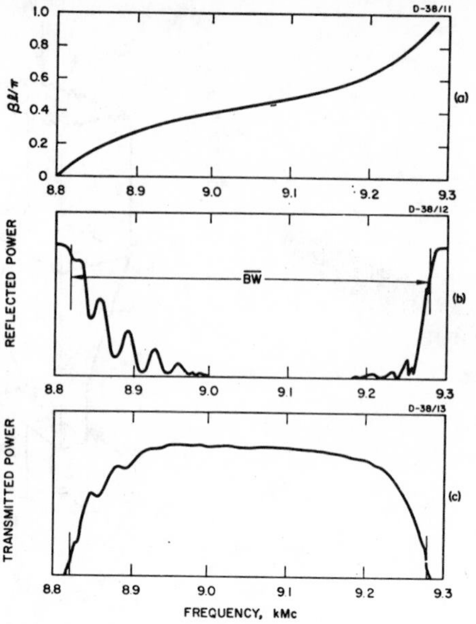

Fig. 10—Passive transmission and reflection characteristics of the 15-cavity maser.

D. Tunability and Gain Characteristic

The fractional active (tunable) bandwidth of an M-resonator maser amplifier is given to a good approximation by the relation [1]

$$B_r \doteq \frac{1}{Q_m}\left(\frac{g_{os}}{g_{oe}}\right)\frac{(1+H)^{(1-M)/M}}{(g_{os}-1)} \quad (6)$$

where g_{oe} is the effective single cavity voltage gain, g_{os} is the isolated single cavity voltage gain, and H is the round trip attenuation per isolator as a voltage ratio. The isolator attenuation is assumed to be that which yields a maximally flat structure response. The product B_rQ_m computed as a function of M for several values of total amplifier gain is given in Fig. 11. The passive structure bandwidth $\overline{BW}$ for large M may be determined from the single cavity gain by using the relationship [11].

$$g_{os} = \frac{\overline{BW}Q_m}{\overline{BW}Q_m - 1}\,. \quad (7)$$

In practice the gain per cavity is reduced by feedback through the noninfinite isolator. The theoretical gain loss per stage as a function of the isolated single cavity gain with the interstage isolation as the parameter is shown by the curves of Fig. 12. The effect of interstage isolation on the active bandwidth of the maser is illustrated by the curves of Fig. 13 which show the gain-frequency characteristics of a 15-resonator maser for a series of isolator attenuation values. It has also been found experimentally that the minimum isolation required for stable maser gain results in an active bandwidth which is reduced nearly 50 per cent from that of the passive structure.

The signal frequency of the maser amplifier, which is determined by the 2→3 transition of the ruby spin system, is a function of the magnetic field. It is plotted in Fig. 14 for the frequency interval from 7 to 10 Gc. The amplification band may be tuned either up or down in frequency by increasing or decreasing the magnetic field strength. The exact eigenvalues for either the signal or pump frequency can be obtained from the spin-Hamiltonian or from published tables [14].

E. Amplifier Bandwidth

The instantaneous amplifier (3 db) bandwidth is determined by the shape of the ruby line and is given by the expression for a conventional traveling-wave maser

$$\text{Amplifier bandwidth} \equiv \Delta\nu_m\sqrt{\frac{3}{G_{dB}-3}}\,.$$

F. Isolator Alignment and Tracking

The ferromagnetic resonant frequency of a ferrite depends upon the magnitude of the applied static magnetic field, the magnetic properties of the material and the size and shape of the specimen being considered. Kittel has shown [5] that the resonant frequency ω of a ferrite sample in the form of an ellipsoid with principal axes parallel to the x, y, z coordinate axes is given by

$$\omega = \gamma\{[H_z + (N_y - N_z)M_z][H_z + (N_x - N_z)M_z]\}^{1/2}$$

where N_x, N_y and N_z are the demagnetizing factors which are functions of this size and shape of the sample, M_z is the saturation magnetization of the material and

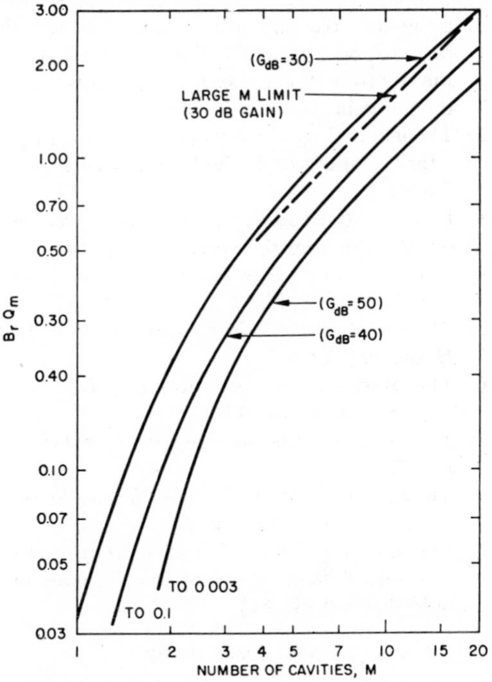

Fig. 11—Some approximations to tunable percentage bandwidth as a function of a number of cavities with over-all gain as the parameter.

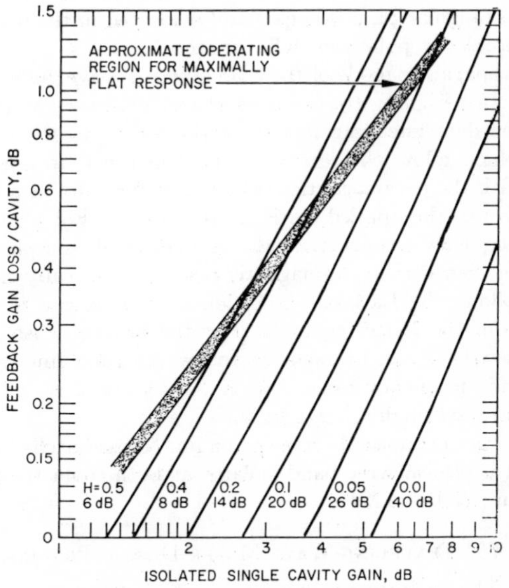

Fig. 12—Inverse feedback gain loss as a function of single cavity gain with M as a parameter.

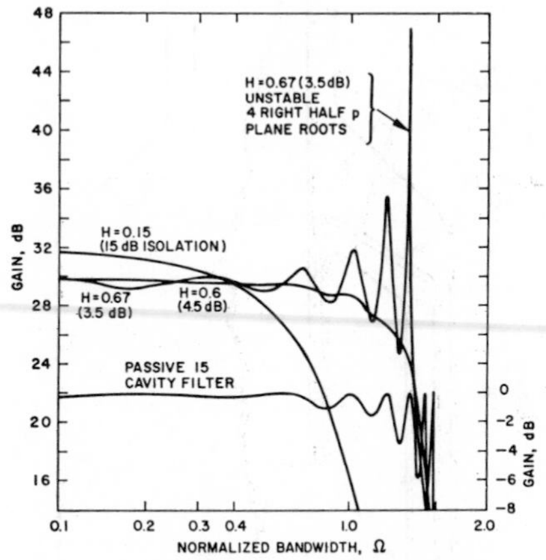

Fig. 13—Theoretical frequency response for a 15-cavity maser, $g_{os}=1.288$.

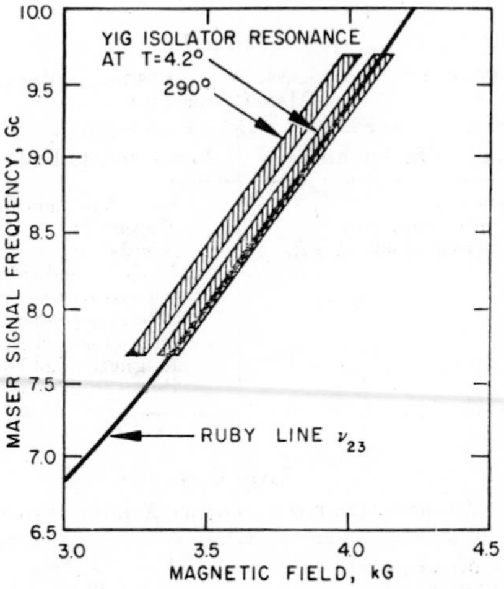

Fig. 14—Ruby γ_{23} signal transition and isolator tracking as a function of magnetic field ($\theta=54.7°$).

H_z is the static magnetic field. γ is the magneto-mechanical ratio which for electron spin is numerically 2.8 Mc/G.

The ferrite best suited for use as the maser isolator material was found to be polycrystalline yttrium-iron-garnet (YIG) which has a saturation magnetization of about 2200 G at 4.2°K. The ferrite is in the form of a rectangular parallelepiped and is located in the plane of circularly polarized RF magnetic field of the TE_{01} propagating mode of the solid alumina waveguide.

In designing the isolators, it was necessary to adjust the demagnetizing factors of the ferrite to the values which allow the ferromagnetic resonance to coincide with the paramagnetic resonance of the ruby as a function of the applied static magnetic field. For a narrow frequency of operation, this is a relatively simple matter. Since the paramagnetic resonance of ruby nearly follows the Larmour condition $\omega = \gamma H$, it can be seen from the Kittel equation that the isolator absorption frequency can be made to follow the ruby line over a wide frequency range only if $N_x = N_y$ or if N_x and N_y are very small relative to N_z.

Fig. 14 shows the absorption line (cross-hatched area) of a typical wide band isolator at both room temperature and at 4.2°K.

VI. Traveling-Wave Maser Design Procedure

The performance specifications of the maser amplifier determine its configuration. Specifications which are particularly relevant are listed in Table I, along with the parameters to be determined. The design data for a tunable X-band maser which is now operational is given in Table II.

TABLE I

Performance Specifications and Essential Parameters of Maser Amplifier

Amplifier Specifications	Parameters to Be Determined
Net gain	Electronic gain G_{db}
Center frequency	Magnetic Q
Tunable bandwidth B_r	Number of cavities M
	Passive bandwidth $\overline{BW}$
	Iris susceptance b
	Interstage isolation H
	Isolator length θ_{is}
	Magnetic field
	Pump frequency

TABLE II

Design Data for a Tunable X-Band Maser

Center frequency	9.3 Gc
Net gain	20 db min
Electronic gain	30 db
Magnetic Q	90
Number of cavities M	15
Interstage isolation H	0.53 (5.5 db)
Effective single cavity gain g_{oe}	1.26 (2.0 db)
Isolated single cavity gain g_{os}	1.3 (2.3 db)
Tunable bandwidth B_r	0.025 (230 Mc)
Structure bandwidth $\overline{BW}$	0.048 (440 Mc)
Coupling iris susceptance b	3.7
Optimum isolator length	1.04 rad

The general maser design parameters are determined as follows:

1) The electronic gain should be sufficient to overcome the structure loss. The gain-to-loss decibel ratio for operation at 4.2°K is about 6:1, making the electronic gain about 20 per cent higher than the net gain required (in decibels).
2) The magnetic Q of ruby can be obtained from Fig. 8 for the "push-pull" mode at any frequency from 7 to 10 Gc.
3) From B_r, Q_m, and G, the number of cavities M is established from the curves of Fig. 11.
4) Optimum interstage isolation H is determined from O'Meara's Fig. 6 [1].
5) The single cavity gain g_{os} may be found from g_{oe}, H and Fig. 12.
6) The passive structure bandwidth $\overline{BW}$ may then be determined from (7).
7) The coupling iris susceptance b is found from Fig. 7.
8) The optimum isolator length θ_{is} may be obtained from $\theta_{is} + 2 \tan^{-1} b = \pm \pi/2$.
9) The magnetic field and pump frequency can be determined from the spin-Hamiltonian or from published tables [14].

VII. Cryogenics

The liquid helium dewar (Fig. 15) designed for the coupled-cavity maser is a single fluid type with a fluid capacity of about 6 liters. Radiation protection for the

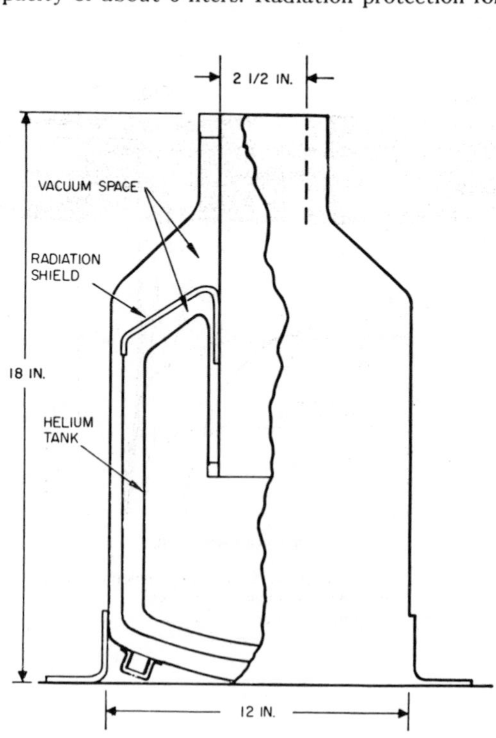

Fig. 15—Cross section of dewar.

liquid helium chamber is provided by a copper shield surrounding the chamber. The shield is connected to the neck of the dewar and during operation is maintained at about 80°K by the helium vapor passing through the neck. The helium chamber and the dewar neck form a re-entrant type structure in which the wall temperature is essentially constant throughout. As a result, the helium liquid does not contact "hot" areas within the dewar with subsequent boil-off, regardless of the position of the dewar. This feature, in addition to the single fluid type dewar permits the dewar to be operated in any angular position from vertical to horizontal.

VIII. Operational Maser Performance

To date, Hughes has developed several masers for systems application in the frequency range of 7600 to 9500 Mc. The operating characteristics of these masers were varied with the application from a net gain of 40 db tunable over 40 Mc/sec to a net gain of 20 db with 200 Mc/sec tunability. The instantaneous 3 db bandwidth ranged from 10 Mc/sec for the high gain masers to 30 Mc/sec for the masers with reduced gain. The noise temperature of the maser is less than 20°K with typical measured values of 12 to 13°K. Measurements of stability indicate a gain drift of less than ± 0.1 db for a period of more than 20 hours of continuous operation, and less than ± 0.2 db when the unit was continuously tilted ± 85 degrees from the vertical.

IX. Conclusions

The coupled resonant cavity type traveling-wave maser has been analyzed as an active microwave filter in this and a companion paper [1], and a design procedure has been established. The important design parameters have been shown which demonstrate the wide range of performance characteristics possible with this type of structure.

The more practical advantages of the coupled-cavity transmission maser over previously reported traveling-wave masers are its reduced size and competitive performance at 4.2°K. These advantages may be particularly important in cases where it is necessary to integrate the maser with mobile equipment or with a closed cycle refrigerator.

References

[1] T. R. O'Meara, "The coupled-cavity transmission maser analysis," IEEE Trans. on Microwave Theory and Technique, vol. MTT 12, pp. 336; January, 1964.

[2] R. W. DeGrasse, E. O. Schultz-DuBois and H. E. D. Scovil, "Three-level solid-state traveling-wave maser," *Bell System Tech. J.*, vol. 38, pp. 305–334; March, 1959.

[3] J. C. Cromack, "A Wide-Tuning Range S-Band Traveling-Wave Maser," Electron Devices Laboratory, Stanford Electronics Laboratory, Stanford, Calif. Tech. Rept., No. 155–5; April, 1963.

[4] G. I. Haddad and J. E. Rowe, "S-band ladder-line traveling-wave maser," IRE Trans. on Microwave Theory and Technique, vol. MTT-10, pp. 3–8; January, 1962.

[5] C. Kittel, "On the theory of ferromagnetic resonance absorption," *Phys. Rev.*, vol. 73, pp. 155–161; January, 1948.

[6] F. Block, "Nuclear induction," *Phys. Rev.*, vol. 70, pp. 460–474; October, 1946.

[7] M. E. Rose, "Magnetic field corrections in the cyclotron," *Phys. Rev.*, vol. 53, pp. 715–719; May, 1938.

[8] P. H. Vartanian, "Research and Development of a Solid State Paramagnetic Maser," Microwave Engineering Laboratories, Inc., AF Cambridge Res. Ctr., Bedford, Mass., Third Quarterly Progress Report on Contract No. AF 19(604)-4071; 10 December 1958 through March 1959.

[9] T. H. Maiman, "Temperature and concentration effects in a ruby maser," in "Quantum Electronics, A Symposium," Columbia University Press, New York, N. Y., pp. 324–327; 1960.

[10] R. Beringer, "Frequency pulling by reactive loads," in "Technique of Microwave Measurements," C. G. Montgomery, Ed., McGraw-Hill Book Co., New York, N. Y., MIT Rad. Lab. Ser., vol. 11, pp. 291–293. 1947,

[11] M. L. Stitch, "Maser amplifier characteristics for transmission and reflection cavities," *J. Appl. Phys.*, vol. 29, pp. 782–789; May, 1958.

[12] G. L. Ragan, "Microwave Transmission Circuits," MIT Rad. Lab. Ser., vol. 9, pp. 653–661; 1948.

[13] F. E. Goodwin and G. E. Moss, "Broadband impedance matching into dielectric filled waveguides," IEEE Trans., on Microwave Theory and Technique, vol. MTT-11, pp. 36–39; January, 1963.

[14] W. S. Chang and A. E. Siegman, "Characteristics of Ruby for Maser Applications," Electron Devices Laboratory, Stanford Electronics Laboratory, Stanford, Calif.; Tech. Rept. No. 156–2; September, 1958.

Reprinted from IEEE TRANSACTIONS
ON MICROWAVE THEORY AND TECHNIQUES
Volume MTT-12, Number 3, May, 1964

Traveling-Wave Maser with Instantaneous Bandwidths in Excess of 100 Mc*

An *S*-band traveling-wave maser has been operated with 3-db amplification bandwidths as great as 126 Mc centered at a frequency of 2280 Mc, with electronic gains greater than 16 db. The maser utilized a comb-type slow-wave structure loaded on both sides of the comb with $6\frac{1}{2}$ inches of X-ray oriented ruby of nominal 0.05 per cent chromium concentration. The external magnetic field was oriented at $\theta = 90°$ to the ruby *c* axis, and the helium bath temperature was 1.8°K.

These broad bandwidths, more than twice the nominal 60-Mc intrinsic linewidth of ruby,[1] were obtained by stagger-tuning the applied external magnetic field (H_{dc}). The staggered field causes the imaginary part of the magnetic susceptibility $\chi''(f)$, which is usually assumed to have a Lorentzian line shape, to broaden and take on a new effective shape dependent upon the distribution of the magnetic field. This results in a corresponding change in the maser gain vs frequency characteristic $G(f)$, since $G(f) = K\chi''(f)$, where $G(f)$ is the gain in db and K is a constant determined by the microwave propagating structure. An analysis of this technique has been independently presented by Ostermeyer.[2]

Photographs of oscilloscope displays of maser amplification bandwidth under increasing staggered-field conditions are shown in Fig. 1. The field staggering was accomplished by periodically shimming one of the pole pieces of an electromagnet with thin rectangular slabs of high-permeability material. The amplitude of the peak-to-peak field variations on the ruby were controlled by adjusting the proximity of the shimmed pole piece to the slow-wave structure. The average value of the external field for all the measurements was approximately 2.46 kilogauss, and the peak-to-peak variations were as high as 70 gauss. It should be pointed out that under homogeneous field conditions, the maser yielded net gains of 30 db (with a net reverse loss of 100 db), an instantaneous bandwidth of 21 Mc, and an electronic tuning range in excess of 240 Mc.[3]

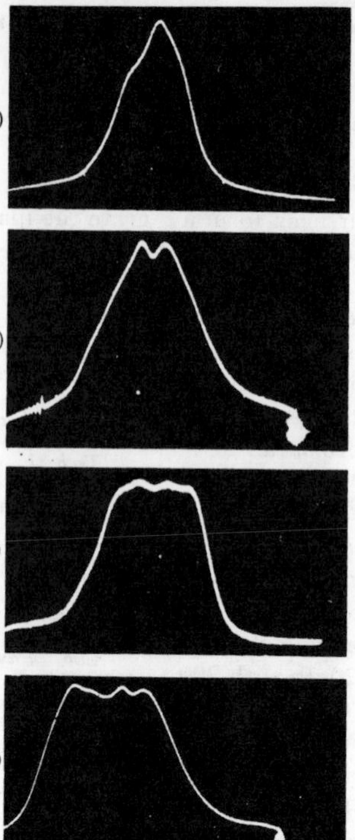

Fig. 1—Oscilloscope display of the maser amplification bandwidth under different field staggering conditions (center frequency≈2280 Mc). (a) 3-db bandwidth = 46 Mc; electronic gain = 25.5 db. (b) 3-db bandwidth = 58 Mc; electronic gain = 23.5 db. (c) 3-db bandwidth = 100 Mc; electronic gain = 18.5 db. (d) 3-db bandwidth = 126 Mc; electronic gain = 16.5 db.

A detailed bandwidth measurement of the trace shown in Fig. 1 (c) is plotted in terms of net gain in Fig. 2. It can be seen that a maximum net gain of 11 db is obtained with a 3-db bandwidth of 100 Mc. The structure loss was 7.5 db. This high structure loss was due, in part, to the magnetic broadening in some of the ferrite isolator disks produced by the inhomogeneous field. It is believed that with proper ferrite disk design, this loss can be reduced.

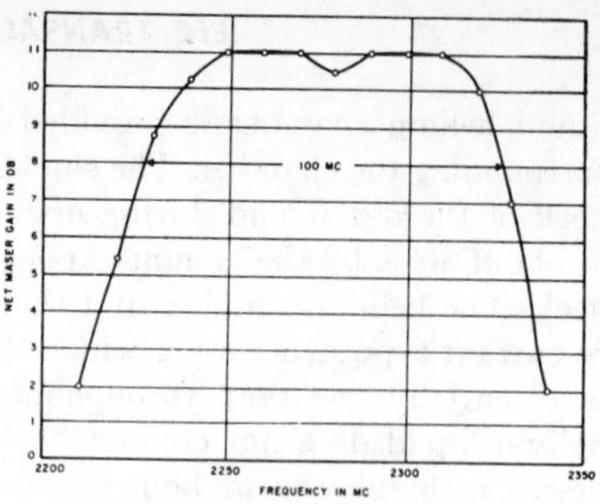

Fig. 2—Detailed amplification band of stagger-tuned TWM [see Fig. 1(c)].

All of the above broad bandwidth measurements were obtained with one CW pump source operating at a fixed frequency of 12.62 kMc. This single-frequency source of power sufficiently saturated the wings of the pump transition so that no serious bandwidth degradation effects occurred. A qualitative picture of the degree of wing saturation is shown in the plot of Fig. 3, where the relative gain of a similar maser (with a homogeneous field) is plotted as a function of signal frequency for a fixed CW pump frequency and optimized magnetic field.[4] From this curve, it can be seen that the signal can be tuned over a 120-Mc band before the gain decreases by 3 db. If maser bandwidths much greater than 120 Mc are desired with high gain-bandwidth efficiency, it might be necessary to employ two pump sources operating at different frequencies, or to use one pump source that is frequency modulated at a rate much greater than the pump-transition relaxation time.

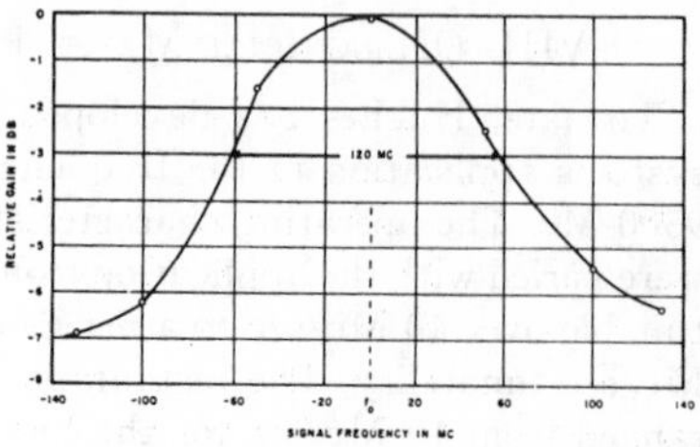

Fig. 3—Relative gain vs signal frequency for fixed pump frequency and optimized magnetic field. $f_0 = 2250$ Mc; $f_p = 12.65$ kMc; pump power = 200 mw; H_{dc} = optimized for maximum gain; $T_{bath} = 1.8°K$.

It is worthwhile mentioning that two different stagger-tuned field configurations were successfully used.

1) Periodic staggering along the direction of propagation.
2) A linear field variation perpendicular to the direction of propagation.

Either of the above configurations are desirable for low-noise considerations. (It would be undesirable to have a portion of the signal spectrum traveling through a significant length of slow-wave structure experiencing loss before being amplified.) In the first configuration, the periodic staggering effectively divides the structure into many sections, each of which yields gain to the entire signal spectrum. The second configuration has the effect of dividing the ruby into long parallel filaments, each filament yielding gain to a small portion of the frequency band over the entire length. It is believed that this latter technique is more effective in maintaining the maser low-noise properties.

It should also be pointed out that the conditions desired in the staggered field for broadbanding are a variation in the amplitude of the H_{dc} vector and an unperturbed angular orientation. When the angular orientation of the field varies, broadening is obtained but with the additional decrease in gain caused by the reduced transition probability. This is an expensive trade of gain for bandwidth. Unfortunately, in the experiments discussed in this note, a considerable amount of angular inhomogeneity was present. Further work is being done to correct this situation.

S. Okwit
J. G. Smith
Airborne Instruments Lab.
Melville, L. I., N. Y.

* Received by the IRE, April 24, 1961. This work was supported in part by the USAF Aeronautical Systems Div., under Contract AF33(600)-38862.

[1] J. E. Geusic, R. W. DeGrasse, E. O. Schulz-DuBois and H. E. D. Scovil, "The Three Level Solid State Maser," Bell Telephone Labs., Murray Hill, N. J., 9th Interim Rept. on Microwave Solid-State Devices, U. S. Army Signal Corp Contract DA-36-039-sc-73224, pp. 7–10; May, 1959.

[2] F. W. Ostermeyer, "Stagger Tuning of Traveling Wave Masers," Bell Telephone Labs., Murray Hill, N. J., Rept. No. 2, U. S. Army Signal Corps Contract DA-36-039-sc-85357, pp. 17–24; December, 1960.

[3] S. Okwit, J. G. Smith, and F. R. Arams, "Tunable *s*-band traveling-wave maser for telemetry systems," Proc. IRE (Correspondence), vol. 49, pp. 1078–1079; June, 1961.

[4] S. Okwit, F. R. Arams, and J. G. Smith, "Design of a Molecular Amplifier Group," Airborne Instruments Lab., Melville, L.I., N.Y., Rept. No. 5945-2; June, 1960.

Reprinted from the PROCEEDINGS OF THE IRE
VOL. 49, NO. 7, JULY, 1961

Packaged Electronically Tunable *S*-Band Traveling-Wave Maser System*

S. OKWIT†, SENIOR MEMBER, IRE AND J. G. SMITH†

Summary—An *S*-band traveling-wave maser that operates over an 11 per cent tuning range is tuned by a single "frequency-calibrated" dial from 2120 to 2380 Mc. The maser has a relatively constant gain of 30 db and an instantaneous bandwidth of 22 Mc. It uses a comb-type slow-wave structure loaded on both sides with a $6\frac{1}{2}$ in length of 0.065 per cent chromium-doped ruby. Ferrimagnetic disks of yttrium iron garnet are periodically distributed in the slow-wave structure and provide sufficient reverse loss for short-circuit stability (100 db).

A relatively high gain per unit length of active ruby was realized because of: 1) optimization of the *C* axis orientation with respect to the dc and RF magnetic fields, 2) utilization of a four spin flip cross-relaxation process and 3) loading both sides of the comb structure with active ruby.

The traveling-wave maser and all the necessary auxiliary components have been packaged into an operational unit. The noise temperature of the system is about 10°K, and the short-term and long-term stabilities are ±0.05 db and ±0.1 db, respectively. A series of detailed measurements on the important electrical characteristics are described, and the performance data is presented. The system has been designed and successfully tested to meet military field environmental specifications.

I. Introduction

THE THREE-LEVEL solid-state maser proposed by Bloembergen [1] has stimulated wide interest in many fields where the ultimate in microwave receiver sensitivity is desired. Such masers have found applications in radio astronomy [2]–[6], satellite and intercontinental communications such as Project ECHO [7], and radar [8].

In the early development of practical maser amplifiers, the emphasis was placed on cavity masers. However, cavity masers have many undesirable characteristics such as small voltage gain-bandwidth products, relatively poor stability, difficult procedures required for tuning, etc. More recently emphasis has been placed on the use of distributed structures that have nonreciprocal gain [9]–[12]. This technique has eliminated or minimized all of the disadvantages of the cavity maser, and thus contributes a significant advance to the state of the art.

This paper describes the design considerations, operating characteristics and system performance of a traveling-wave maser operating in the 2120- to 2380-Mc telemetry band which is capable of military field applications.

* Received November 13, 1961; revised manuscript received, February 8, 1962. The work was supported by the USAF, Aeronautical Systems Division under Contract AF33(600)–38862.

† Airborne Instruments Laboratory, A Division of Cutler-Hammer, Inc, Deer Park, N. Y.

II. Design Considerations

A. Paramagnetic Crystal

Three-level solid-state masers have been operated using five paramagnetic crystals: gadoliniun ethyl sulfate [13], potassium chromi-cyanide [14], ruby [15], rutile [16] and emerald [17]. Of these five materials, ruby is the most desirable for operation in the microwave frequency range (below *K* band) because of its excellent electrical, physical and chemical characteristics. Consequently, ruby was chosen and used in all of the experiments discussed in this paper.

B. Gain and Bandwidth Characteristics

Amplification is obtained in a traveling-wave maser (TWM) by stimulating emission from an active material within a propagating structure. The electronic gain (in decibels) of a TWM is given by [9].

$$G_{db} = 27.3\,\frac{SNF}{Q_m}, \tag{1}$$

where

S = Slowing factor = Velocity of light/group velocity,
N = Active length of TWM expressed in free-space wavelengths,
Q_m = Magnetic Q of the paramagnetic material,
F = Filling factor (a measure of the spatial interaction efficiency of the electro-magnetic wave and the paramagnetic spin system).

The 3-db bandwidth that results from operating the TWM at a given gain is [9]

$$B = B_m\left(\frac{3}{G_{db} - 3}\right)^{1/2}, \tag{2}$$

where B_m is the line width of the paramagnetic crystal (about 60 Mc for ruby). Eq. (2) shows that, for a gain of 30 db, the maser 3-db bandwidth would be about 20 Mc.

C. Slow-Wave Structure

To obtain appreciable gain in a TWM, it is necessary to strongly couple the microwave RF signal to the crystal. There are several techniques for doing this [18]; however, the most desirable technique is to use a resonant slow-wave circuit as the propagating structure. Several different types of resonant slow-wave structures were investigated and evaluated. The comb structure,

Fig. 1—Comb-type slow-wave structure.

which was first used in a TWM by DeGrasse, *et al.* [9], was determined to be the most suitable for our application.

A photograph of the structure that was evolved is shown in Fig. 1. Both sides of the comb structure were loaded with rectangular ruby slabs to increase the filling factor. (This is discussed further in Section IIIB.) Figs. 2 and 3 show the measured ω-β characteristics of the structure (measured at liquid-helium temperatures) and the slowing factors calculated from these characteristics. The slowing over the 2120- to 2380-Mc tuning range is relatively constant—that is, 72 at band center and increasing to about 83 at the band edges. The lower and upper cutoff frequencies are 2080 and 2480 Mc, respectively, which yield an overall bandwidth of 400 Mc. Only about 65 per cent of this over-all bandwidth was found to be useable because of matching considerations. The SWR over this 65 per cent band was measured to be less than 1.5 with an average insertion loss of about 4 db (see Fig. 4).

D. Isolator Methods

To achieve gain stability in the presence of generator and load variations, the maser must have unilateral forward gain and reverse loss. There are two practical solutions to this problem [18].

1) An inactive ruby crystal (heavily doped to prevent inversion of the signal transition) used as an isolator.
2) A ferrimagnetic material (such as polycrystalline YIG) used as an isolator.

Each of these solutions requires the use of a microwave structure with well-defined regions of circular or elliptical polarization.

In addition, the method of obtaining isolation should have the same static magnetic field requirements for isolator resonance as it does for maser action.

1) Inactive Ruby Crystal

The inactive ruby crystal method is ideal insofar as the coincident field requirement is concerned. However, for the frequencies of interest the amount of isolation that can be obtained for a circularly polarized field is

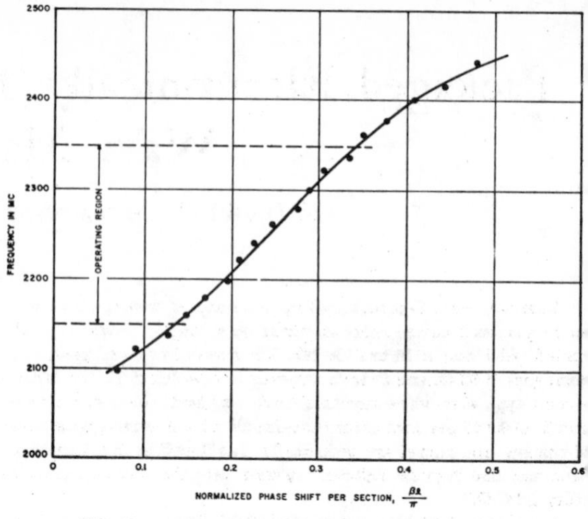

Fig. 2—ω-β characteristic of final comb structure.

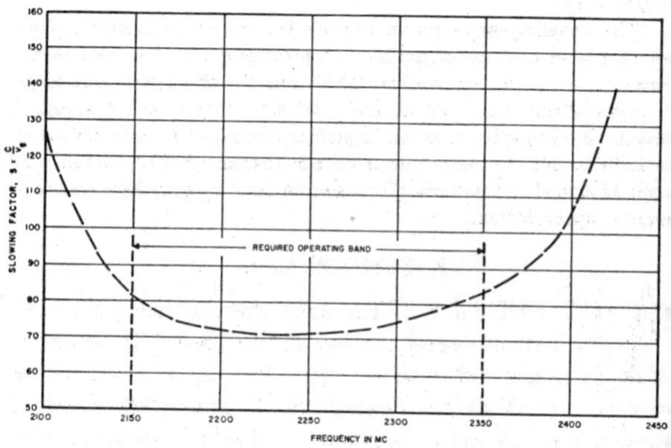

Fig. 3—Slowing factor of final comb structure.

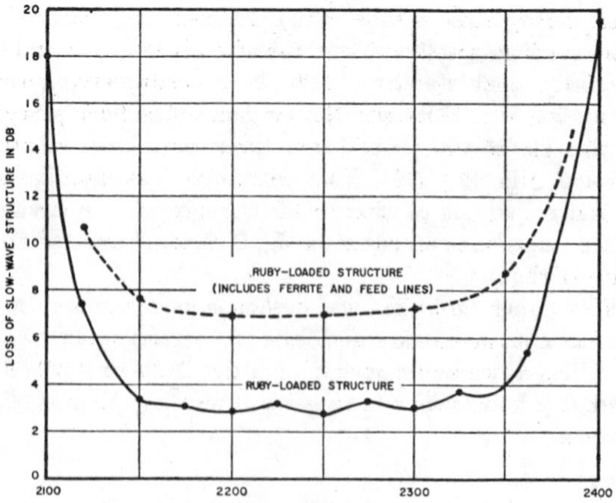

Fig. 4—Dissipative losses of TWM structure.

insufficient for the degree of stability desired. This can be seen from the following:

The loss of the inactive material in the forward direction can be expressed as

$$L_{db}^{+} = 27.3 \frac{SN}{Q_m^{+}} \tag{3}$$

and the loss in the reverse direction as

$$L_{db}^{-} = 27.3 \frac{SN}{Q_m^{-}} \tag{4}$$

where the entire ruby is assumed to be contained in the plane of circular polarization, and where Q_m^+ and Q_m^- are the ruby magnetic Q's associated with the forward and reverse directions, respectively. The figure of merit of the ruby isolator is thus

$$F = \frac{L_{db}^{-}}{L_{db}^{+}} = \frac{Q_m^{+}}{Q_m^{-}} \cdot \tag{5}$$

The Q_m is inversely proportional to the square of the signal transition matrix elements of the perturbation Hamiltonian. Hence, using the notations of [19] and [20] (corrected for negative D values), we obtain

$$F = \left[\frac{\langle E_1 | 2\beta H_{rf}^{+} \cdot S | E_2 \rangle}{\langle E_1 | 2\beta H_{rf}^{-} \cdot S | E_2 \rangle}\right]^2, \tag{6}$$

where H_{rf}^+ and H_{rf}^- are the right and left circularly polarized RF magnetic fields for the forward and reverse directions of propagation.

The circular polarization for the orientation used is defined in the Y-Z plane, where the X direction is parallel with the dc magnetic field (see the coordinate system of Fig. 5).

$$H_{rf}^{+} = iHy \cos \omega_s t - H_z \sin \omega_s t. \tag{7}$$

$$H_{rf}^{-} = iHv \cos \omega_s t + H_z \sin \omega_s t. \tag{8}$$

The perturbation Hamiltonian ($2\beta H_{rf} \cdot S$) then becomes

$$2\beta(iH_y S_y - H_z S_z) \quad \text{for } H_{rf}^{+}. \tag{9}$$

$$2\beta(iH_y S_y + H_z S_z) \quad \text{for } H_{rf}^{-}. \tag{10}$$

Substituting into (6) yields

$$\left[\frac{(\beta_i + \gamma_r)}{(\beta_i - \gamma_r)}\right]^2, \tag{11}$$

where β_i and γ_r are coefficients of the direction cosines of the y and z components of the magnetic moment. These coefficients have been tabulated and plotted as a function of magnitude and angular orientation of the dc magnetic field [19]. Using the tables in [19], (11) has been evaluated as a function of frequency for an H_{dc} angular orientation of 90° with respect to the C axis. Fig. 6 is a plot of the results obtained. The maximum figure of merit that can be obtained for a circularly polarized field in the 2120- to 2380-Mc range is about 4.[1] which is not efficient enough to obtain high reverse loss and good stability without seriously degrading the forward gain. In addition, this method has the disadvantage of absorbing pump power.

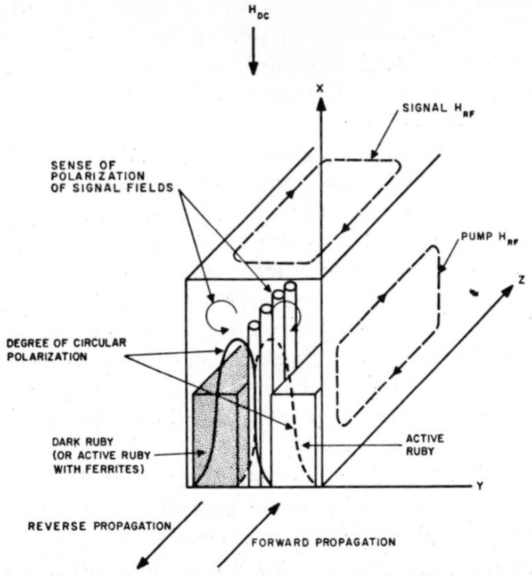

Fig. 5—Circular polarization in comb structure.

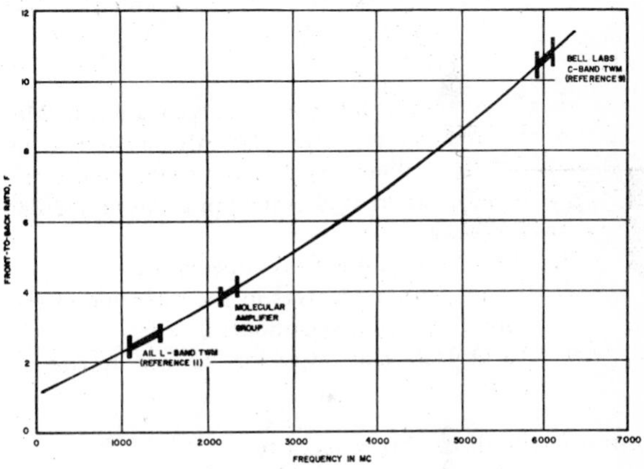

Fig. 6—Theoretica. front-to-back ratio of signal transition (1-2) of ruby crystal for circular polarization.

2) *Ferrimagnetic Material*

The ferrite-isolator method eliminates the disadvan-

[1] It is possible to obtain infinite figures of merit for specific combinations of 1) C axis orientation with respect to the RF magnetic fields, and 2) field ellipticity in the ruby crystal. However, even though the figure of merit can be infinite, the resulting matrix elements become small and this causes a decrease in field interaction and a subsequent low reverse loss-per-unit-length. This is discussed in more detail in Section IIIB.

It is more practical in this discussion to use circular polarization since we will also be dealing with ferrimagnetic resonance.

tages that occur in the inactive ruby crystal—that is, poor figure of merit, and pump power absorption. However, the problem of obtaining coincident dc magnetic fields for isolator resonance and TWM amplification must be solved.

Since the TWM operates at liquid-helium temperatures, a ferrite whose resonance line width does not broaden excessively at low temperatures must be used. A broadening in line width causes degradation in the figure of merit. The best ferrite now available for use at low temperatures (in the 2120- to 2380-Mc region) is polycrystalline YIG. This material has little line broadening when cooled to liquid-helium temperatures [21] and has a saturation magnetization of 1750 gauss at room temperature (changing to about 2480 gauss at 4.2°K).

The problem of coincident magnetic fields can be solved by choosing a ferrite geometry whose demagnetizing fields [22] cause coincidence. The ferrite resonance condition is given by the general Kittel equation [23]

$$\frac{f_r}{\gamma} = \{(H_z-(N_z-N_x)4\pi M_s][H_z-(N_z-N_y)4\pi M_s]\}^{1/2} \quad (12)$$

where

f_r = Frequency of ferrimagnetic resonance, in Mc.
γ = Gyromagnetic ratio = 2.8 Mc/oersted (this definition differs by 2π from that in most references, where it is defined in terms of angular frequency).
H_z = Applied magnetic field in oersteds.
N = Demagnetizing factors in the direction of the three Cartesian coordinates.
$4\pi M_s$ = Saturation magnetization of the ferrite in gauss.

For a ferrite disk, (12) reduces to

$$\frac{f_r}{\gamma} = H_z - (N_z - N_t)4\pi M_s, \quad (13)$$

where $N_x = N_y = N_t$.

Furthermore, for a ferrite sphere,

$$\frac{f_r}{\gamma} = H_z \quad (14)$$

since N_x and $N_y = N_z$.

Fig. 7 is a plot of resonant frequency vs applied magnetic field H_z for the following:

1) Ruby crystal with C axis at 90° with respect to H_z.
2) Ferrite sphere.
3) Computed values for YIG disks with various t/d ratios at room temperature ($4\pi M_s = 1750$ gauss).

Superimposed on Fig. 7 are measured values taken at room temperature of YIG disks with several t/d

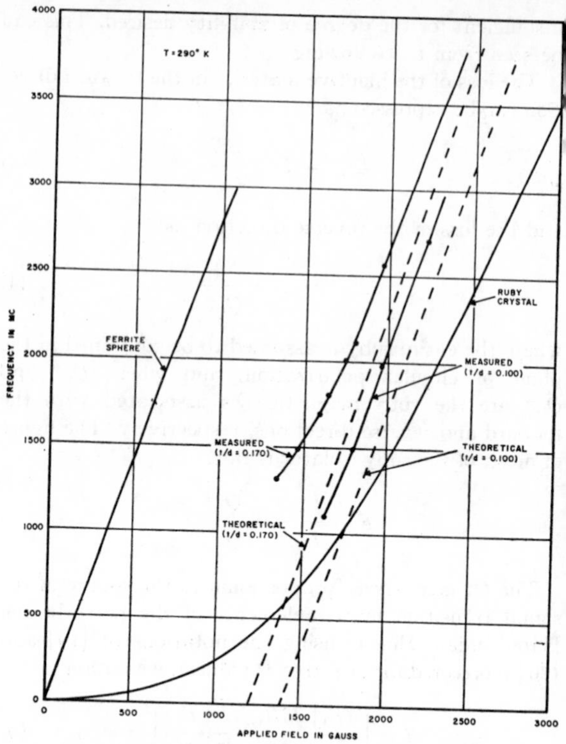

Fig. 7—Resonant frequency vs applied magnetic field for ruby crystal and YIG ferrite disks.

ratios. The measured magnetic field required for resonance is lower than that predicted theoretically. It was also observed that at low fields the slope of the measured data deviates considerably from the 2.8 Mc/oersted straight-line relationship. We believe this is due to the fact that the ferrite is not completely saturated.

Measurements of the polycrystalline YIG disks were made at 4.2°K and 77°K (Fig. 8). This figure shows that 1) the field requirements at 4.2°K and 77°K are almost identical (implying that the saturation magnetization does not change greatly from 77°K to 4.2°K), 2) the optimum t/d ratio for coincidence is about 0.105 and 3) the slope of the measured values deviates from the 2.8-Mc/oersted straight-line relationship by more than the room-temperature measurements (Fig. 7). This deviation is to be expected since the saturation magnetization has increased from 1750 gauss at room temperature to about 2480 gauss at low temperatures. Thus, the ferrite is further away from saturation at 4.2°K. Furthermore, the 1-db bandwidth of the ferrite resonance is about 150 gauss, which is caused in part by low-temperature broadening as well as by the slight differences in the effective t/d ratios of the disks that result from 1) the dimensional tolerances, and 2) the tilting caused by mounting variations. (A slight amount of broadening is a desirable effect for tuning considerations.)

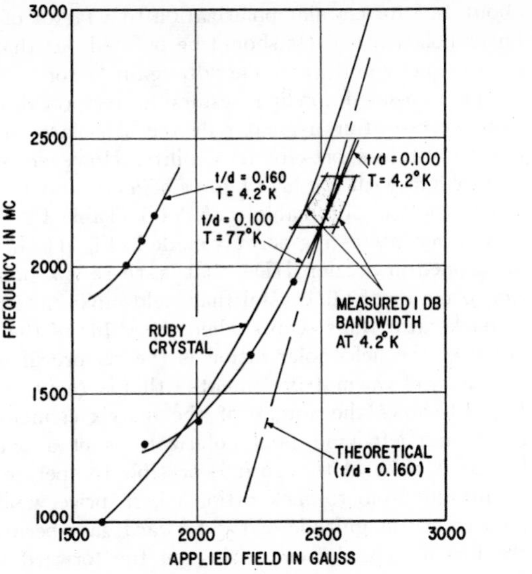

Fig. 8—Resonant frequency vs applied magnetic field for YIG ferrite disks at 77° K and 4.2° K.

TABLE I

YIG Isolator Characteristics at 4.2°K

Frequency (Mc)	Forward Loss (db)	Reverse Loss (db)	Figure of Merit
2100	3.3	90	27.3
2150	3.5	102	29.1
2200	3.4	106	31.2
2250	3.6	106	29.5
2300	3.4	103	30.3
2350	3.7	117	31.6

A set of experiments determined the magnitudes of the forward and reverse magnetic loss at 4.2°K. The resulting data are given in Table I, and indicate clearly that the reverse loss across the 2120- to 2380-Mc operating band is greater than 100 db (which is sufficient to operate a 50-db gain maser with short-circuit stability). The figure of merit of the isolator disks is about 30. (This is about half of the measured figure of merit at room temperature.)

III. Maser Operation

A. General Description

The optimum operating parameters of a maser, such as the relationship of the signal frequency, the pump frequency and the external magnetic field required to obtain maser operation, depend upon the quantum mechanical properties (energy levels, RF transition probability and relaxation times) of the paramagnetic crystal. These quantum mechanical properties are strongly dependent upon the magnitude of the external magnetic field and its angular orientation θ, with respect to the crystal C axis. All of the experiments performed used ruby (Cr^{+++} in Al_2O_3), with the C axis oriented at 90° with respect to the external magnetic field. Fig. 9 is the energy level diagram for a 90° oriented ruby, and shows four low-lying energy levels since ruby has a spin of $S=3/2$. The signal and pump transitions used are between energy levels (1-2) and (1-3), respectively. The 90° orientation was used because it yields the lowest magnetic Q, and hence the greatest maser gain per unit length. This low magnetic Q is obtained because of the unique combination of high RF signal transition probability and high inversion ratio.

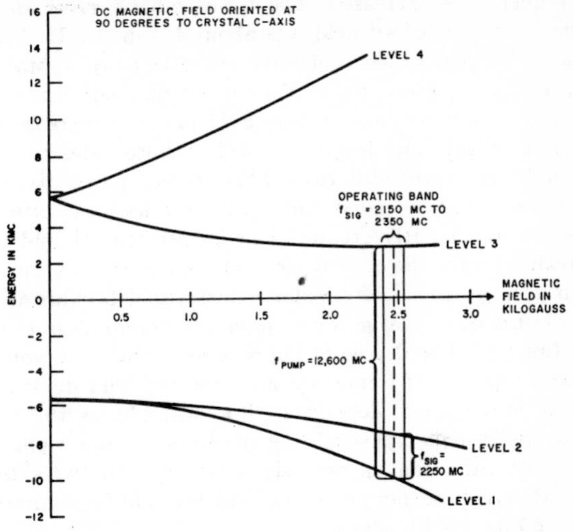

Fig. 9—Energy level diagram of 90° oriented ruby maser.

A discussion of the methods used to realize the low available magnetic Q and other factors that maximize the maser gain per unit length follows.

B. Maser Gain per Unit Length

Once the slowing factor S of the slow-wave structure has been adjusted to a maximum (upper limit set by bandwidth considerations), the maser gain can be increased in two ways:

1) Maximizing the ratio of the filling factor to the magnetic Q,
2) Increasing the structure length.

The simplest technique is to increase the structure length. However, this is not very desirable since the longer the structure the larger and heavier the electromagnet that supplies the external magnetic field must be. The more advantageous technique is to first maximize the gain per unit length and then adjust the overall length to obtain the proper gain.

1) *Optimum Ruby Loading of Comb Structure, and C Axis Orientation with Respect to RF Fields*

In Section IID, it was pointed out that the matrix elements of the RF signal transition are elliptically polarized, and become increasingly linearly polarized as the frequency is decreased. The front-to-back ratio for a circularly polarized field was about 4:1 in the 2120- to 2380-Mc region. Consequently, if active ruby crystal is placed completely in the plane of circular polarization, one can achieve theoretically a 25 per cent increase in the gain per unit length by loading both sides of the comb structure with ruby [24], as compared to the conventional one-sided loading. In practice an improvement significantly greater than 25 per cent should be realized since the crystals are not completely contained in a single plane of circular polarization, but are distributed over a large region having different degrees of ellipticity. The degree of improvement obtained would be a function of frequency since the RF field distribution is frequency dependent. For example, as the RF magnetic fields approach the condition of linear polarization,[2] the gain in decibels obtained with two-sided loading approaches twice that which would be obtained with one-sided loading.

Since the square of the matrix element parallel to the *C* axis is about four times that of the perpendicular component, a considerable improvement should be obtained by aligning the *C* axis relative to the RF magnetic fields in a manner that maximizes the interaction—$(S \cdot H_{rf})^2_{max}$. Since the region of the ω-β diagram used for maser operation in our structure is near the lower β end (Fig. 2), the best crystal alignment is one in which the *C* axis is almost parallel to the direction of propagation [24]. (A crystal conforming to this alignment is here defined as a 0° crystal.) Use of a standard crystal would result in a *C* axis alignment of about 60° in relation to the direction of propagation. This is a result of the ruby crystal growth pattern. Fig. 10 shows the two crystal configurations, with their relative orientations with respect to the microwave structure geometry and magnetic fields.

The actual improvement that can be obtained by two-sided loading compared with one-sided loading, and 0° *C* axis orientation compared with 60° *C* axis orientation, is a function of the polarization seen by the ruby weighted by the square of the matrix elements, and the RF energy distribution across the crystal. A qualitative measure of the improvement that is expected has been obtained for the frequency range in the region of 2500 gauss by calculating $(S \cdot H_{rf})^2$ as a function of the average field ellipticity in the structure. (This calculation assumes that the α-direction cosine coefficient [19] is zero.) Fig. 11 is a plot of this calculation and shows that the 0° ruby is vastly superior to the 60° ruby for elliptical polarizations, where the major axis lies in the direction of propagation. The maximum improvement is obtained for a linearly polarized field, h_z, and decreases as circular polarization is approached. In addition, 0° two-sided loading yields improvements from a factor of about 1.25 for circular polarization to a factor of 2 for linear polarization. (It should be pointed out that this improvement multiplies the "db" gain factor.)

The two-sided loading results in reciprocal maser gain, necessitating a greater degree of isolator reverse loss to obtain short-circuit stability. However, this is no problem with the high figures of merit and the high susceptibilities obtainable with YIG (Table I).

Another interesting point is made in Fig. 11, and was mentioned in Section IID—that is, there is a polarization plane for the 0° crystal that yields an infinite front-to-back ratio. This occurs when the value of the ellipticity of the field polarization is the reciprocal of the ellipticity of the matrix elements—that is, $\langle h_z/h_y \rangle \approx 0.35$. Fig. 12 shows the square of the matrix elements for right- and left-hand field polarizations of a one-side loaded 0° ruby. Although it is possible to operate with an infinite front-to-back ratio, a high price would be paid in the magnitude of the forward gain because of the low matrix element acting on the forward wave. In addition, the magnitude of the reverse loss caused by a dark ruby would also be small because of poor interaction.

A series of experiments were performed to determine the difference in electronic gain that is obtained with a 0° and a 60° crystal *C* axis orientation (Table II). In the measurements, a slow-wave structure $1\frac{7}{8}$ in in length, operating in the 1800- to 2000-Mc region, was loaded on both sides, first with a set of 0° crystals and then with a set of 60° crystals; both crystals being of the same chromium concentration. The structure slowing factors measured for the 0° ruby loading was found to be 39 per cent greater than the 60° crystal. This was expected because of the nonisotropic dielectric constant of ruby, which varies from 9.5 to 12 depending upon the *C* axis orientation.

Table II shows that the 0° ruby does yield a considerable degree of improvement over the 60° ruby (from 45 to 67 per cent greater db of gain), because of its higher matrix element. In addition, the gain of the 0° ruby slightly decreases with increasing frequency, though the gain of the 60° ruby increases directly with frequency. This results in a decreasing gain improvement with increasing frequency as was expected (Fig. 11). The region of the ω-β diagram that was used in this structure was almost identical to the region used in the 2120- to 2380-Mc structure. Thus, the results apply qualitatively to the higher frequency.

This investigation resulted in the use of 0° ruby crystals in a two-sided loading configuration for the final slow-wave structure.

2) *Chromium Concentration of Ruby*

Several maser experiments were conducted using ruby with chromium concentrations of 0.065 and 0.125 per cent. These concentrations are considerably higher than the nominal 0.05 per cent used in most masers, and were expected to increase the relative signal absorp-

[2] For a forward wave comb structure, linear polarization is approached as the operating frequency approaches the lower cutoff frequency.

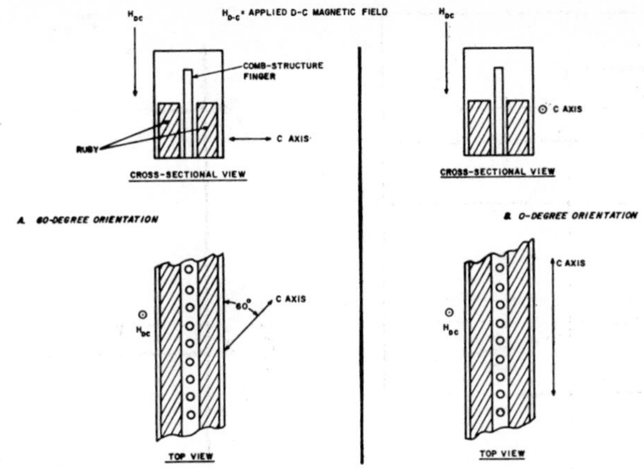

Fig. 10—*C*-axis orientations of ruby crystal with respect to comb structure.

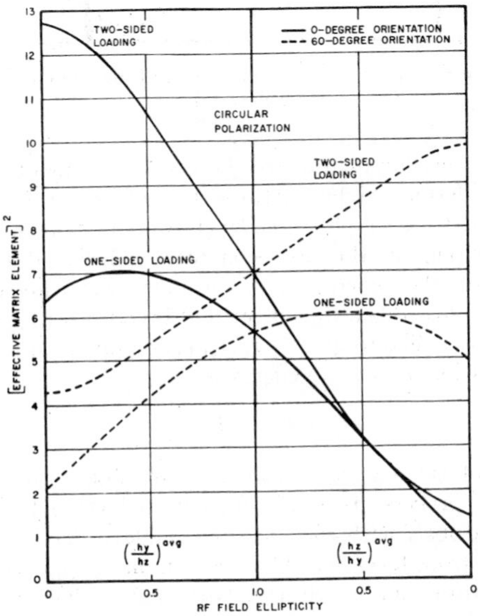

Fig. 11—Square of effective matrix elements as a function of magnetic field ellipticity and loading.

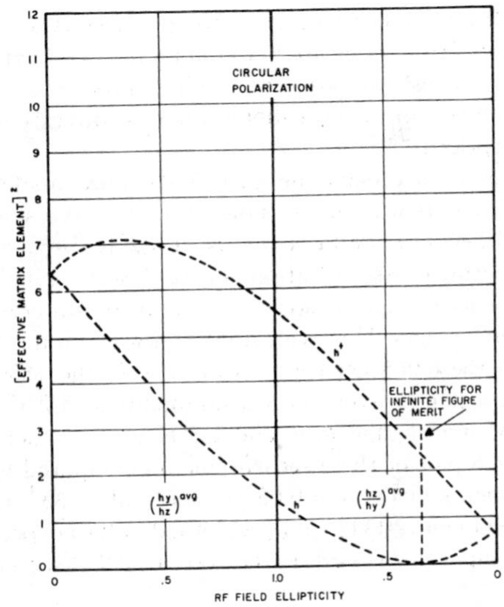

Fig. 12—Square of effective matrix elements of right- and left-hand elliptical polarizations for singly loaded 0° ruby crystal.

TABLE II

Maser Gain Characteristics for 0° and 60° Ruby Crystals

Frequency (Mc)	Bath Temperature (°K)	Electronic Gain of 60° Crystal (db)	Electronic Gain of 0° Crystal (db)	Adjusted* Gain of 0° Crysta (db)	Gain Ratio Improvement (0° Adjusted / 60°)
1800	1.8	4.25	9.8	7.1	1.67
1850	1.8	4.25	9.7	7.0	1.65
1900	1.8	4.50	9.3	6.7	1.49
1950	1.8	4.60	9.1	6.6	1.45

* The gain adjustment is made because of the greater structure slowing (39 per cent) of the 0° ruby. The ratio of the slowing factors was nearly constant across the 1800 to 2000 Mc region.

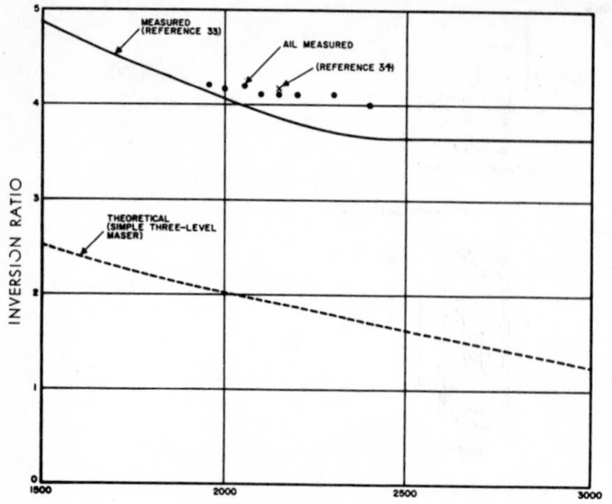

Fig. 13—Inversion ratio of ruby crystal as a function of frequency (for $\theta = 90°$).

tion by 25 and 70 per cent, respectively [25]. Assuming that the concentrations are low enough not to affect the inversion ratios[3] by cross-relaxation processes,[4] the maser gain per unit length should increase directly with the absorptions.

A series of inversion measurements were made on both crystals. It was not possible to obtain inversion in the 0.125 per cent crystal at 1.8°K or 4.2°K, because of the competing cross-relaxation effects as well as higher-order processes that destroy temperature differences in the spin system. However, inversion was obtained at 1.8°K on the 0.065 per cent crystal across the 1850 to 2350 Mc region. (Inversion measurements at 4.2°K did not show any change from the 1.8°K measurements.) Fig. 13 is a plot of these measurements compared with measurements made on a 0.05 per cent ruby [33], on a 0.06 per cent ruby [34], and theoretical values expected from a simple three-level maser system. All three independent measurements are in good agreement, but are considerably higher (greater than a factor of 2) than predicted by a simple three-level system. This anomalous behavior of the inversion ratio is believed to be caused by the shortening of the idler relaxation time due to a cross-relaxation effect that involves a four-spin flip process. The frequency relationship involved in the conservation of Zeeman energy is

$$f_p + f_{idl} = 2f_{3-4}. \tag{15}$$

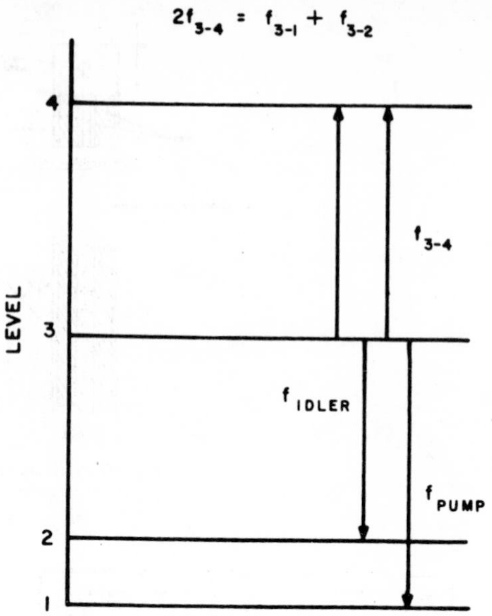

Fig. 14—Energy level diagram of four-level spin flip process in ruby crystal.

Fig. 14 is an energy level diagram illustrating the spin flip process; two spin flips from level 3-4 occur simultaneously with one spin flip from level 3-2 and one spin flip from level 3-1. The Zeeman energy gained by the 3-4 transition nearly equals the energy lost by the 3-1 and 3-2 transitions, thus nearly conserving the Zeeman energy. Roberts and Tenney [35] have obtained a solution to the rate equations for this mode of operation, and have given the following expression for the inversion ratio

$$R = \left(\frac{f_p}{f_s}\right)\left\{\frac{22 - \dfrac{50}{4P - 3}}{19 - \dfrac{25}{4P - 3}}\right\} - 1 \tag{16}$$

where

f_p = Pump frequency,
f_s = Signal frequency,
$P = W_c/w$ = Ratio of cross-relaxation transition probability (W_c) to thermal relaxation probability (w).

[3] The inversion ratio R is defined as [26]

$$R = \frac{T_b}{T_s} = \frac{1 - \left(\dfrac{\tau_s}{\tau_{idl}}\right)\left(\dfrac{f_{idl}}{f_s}\right)}{1 + \left(\dfrac{\tau_s}{\tau_{idl}}\right)}$$

where

T_s = Signal-frequency spin temperature,
T_b = Maser bath temperature,
τ_s = Spin-lattice relaxation time of signal transition
τ_{idl} = Spin-lattice relaxation time of idler transition,
f_{idl} = Idler frequency,
f_s = Signa' frequency.

[4] The cross-relaxation process [27]–[32] involves the direct exchange of energy between neighboring paramagnetic ions; the spin-lattice relaxation involves an energy exchange between the paramagnetic ions and the lattice vibrations. Bloembergen [27] has shown that the probability of a cross-relaxation process occurring is high if the conservation of Zeeman energy in the spin system is satisfied to within a few line widths. Consequently, since the probability is proportional to the proximity of the spins, it would be expected to be dependent upon concentration.

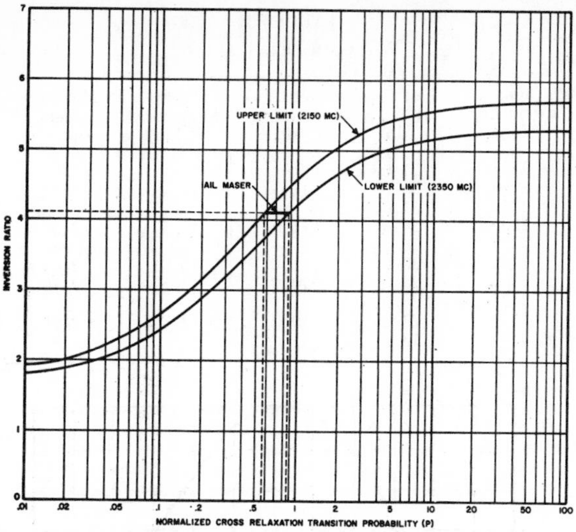

Fig. 15—Calculated inversion ratios of four-level spin flip process.

This equation has been plotted in Fig. 15 for signal frequencies of 2120 and 2380 Mc, as a function of W_c/w. This curve shows that

1) As $W_c \rightarrow 0$, $R \rightarrow$ the values predicted by the simple three-level system (Fig. 13),
2) As $W_c \rightarrow \infty$, $R \rightarrow$ a value greater than 5.7.

To obtain the magnitude of inversion ratios measured, W_c/w must be about 0.55 and 0.85 for the 2120 and 2380 Mc signal frequencies. It is believed that these values are reasonable because the Zeeman energy in the spin system is conserved to within about 4 line widths at 2380 Mc and about 6 line widths at 2120 Mc.

To further investigate the cross-relaxation effect, a series of maser gain recovery measurements were made on a full-length maser structure having about 30 db of gain. It has been shown [30] that a transition involved in a cross-relaxation process will have a recovery characteristic, after being saturated by a high-level pulse, that is represented by two or more relaxation times. If the saturating pulse is short compared to the cross-relaxation time, these multiple time constants can be observed. Fig. 16 is a typical photograph of the recovery time of the maser, operating at a bath temperature of 1.8°K, after being saturated by a 3-msec high-power pulse. The actual recovery times are obtained by plotting the data on semi-log paper and determining the slopes (Fig. 17). It appears that the recovery process is described by three relaxation times, two of which are easily determined to be about 90 msec and 270 msec. The third relaxation time is estimated to be about 5 msec.

C. Maser Gain and Instantaneous Bandwidth

Following the evaluation of maser operation as a function of C axis orientation, loading, and chromium

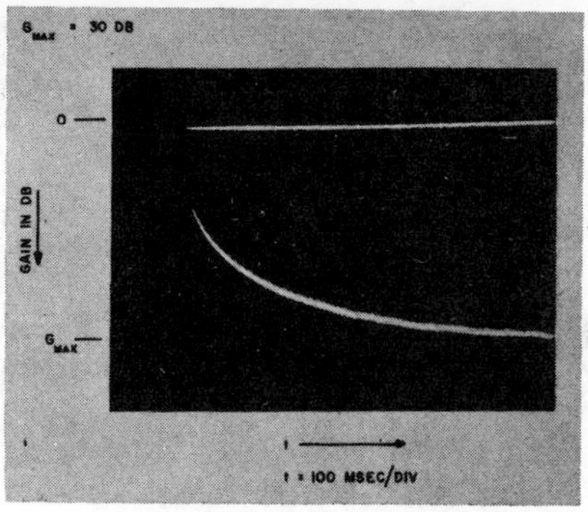

Fig. 16—Recovery time of TWM.

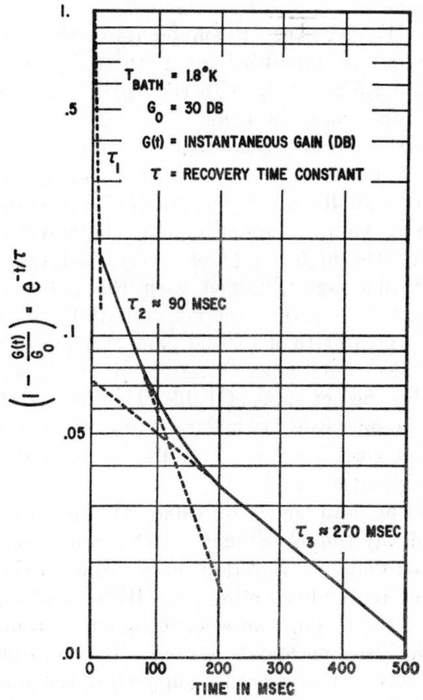

Fig. 17—Recovery time of TWM showing multiple relaxation times.

concentration, a series of gain and bandwidth measurements were made across the 2120 to 2380 Mc frequency band. The final slow-wave structure configuration used in these measurements consisted of a comb that was loaded on both sides with 0° X-ray oriented ruby (C axis oriented in a plane parallel to the direction of propagation), and on one side with polycrystalline YIG isolator disks. The active length of the ruby was $6\frac{1}{2}$ in, having a chromium concentration of 0.065 per cent. Fig. 18 is a photograph of the slow-wave structure assembly. The comb is folded in half; the two sections lie side by side having a common wall and are connected in series by means of a small section of coaxial cable. This was done to minimize the size and weight of the magnet needed

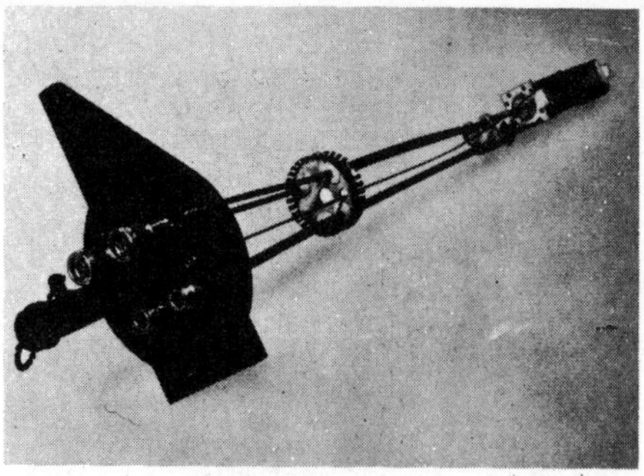

Fig. 18—TWM structure.

TABLE III
TWM Gain Performance

Signal Frequency (Mc)	Net Gain at 1.8°K (db)	Net Gain at 4.2°K (db)	Pump Frequency (kMc)	Magnetic Field (gauss)
2125	21.0	—	—	—
2150	30.0	11.1	12.48	2395
2175	31.0	—	—	—
2200	29.5	11.0	12.53	2420
2225	28.5	—	—	—
2250	30.0	11.4	12.61	2445
2300	28.0	10.4	12.70	2470
2325	28.0	—	—	—
2350	27.0	10.0	12.79	2495
2375	13.0	—	—	—

to give the high degree of field homogeneity necessary for high gain.

Table III gives the measurements of the net maser gain made at liquid-helium bath temperatures of 4.2°K and 1.8°K, along with the associated pump frequencies and magnetic fields.

Table III makes it clear that the gain data taken at 1.8°K is 1) nearly constant across the tuning range, being close to 30 db, and 2) has no regenerative effects in the tuning band. These desirable characteristics are caused by the high degree of reverse isolation (about 100 db) that was obtained with the polycrystalline YIG disks. In addition, the net gain at 1.8°K is about 2.8 times greater than the net gain at 4.2°K. Comparing the electronic gains (total circuit losses shown in Fig. 4 plus the net gains of Table III) that are obtained at the two operating bath temperatures, it can be seen that they correlate well with that predicted by the bath temperature ratio.

All of the data shown in Table III was obtained by electronically tuning the maser with a single frequency-calibrated dial that simultaneously adjusted the pump frequency (delay-line voltage of a BWO) and magnetic field (current through an electromagnet). No mechanical tuning was necessary because of a multiple resonance effect in the structure supporting the pump frequency. The amount of pump power required for saturation was about 100 mw.

It was found that the maser gain was not a critical function of the pump frequency. Furthermore, the signal frequency, when being pumped with a fixed CW frequency, could be tuned about 120 Mc before a 3-db gain degradation was observed (Fig. 19). This wing saturation effect is desirable because it eases tracking of the pump frequency and magnetic field when tuning the maser.

Fig. 20 is a plot of a typical instantaneous bandwidth curve measured at 2189 Mc. There is a slight hump on the high-frequency side of the amplification band. Furthermore, the measured bandwidth is slightly greater than predicted by the nominal 20-oersted ruby line width, operating at 30-db gain. These are the results of a slight stagger-tuning effect caused by slight

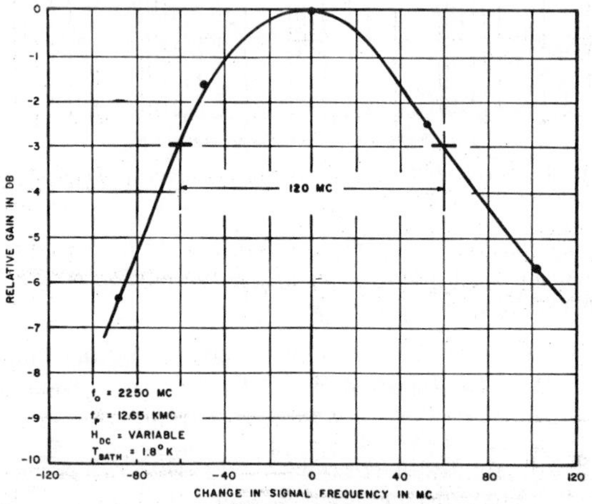

Fig. 19—Gain vs change in signal frequency for fixed pump frequency and optimized magnetic field.

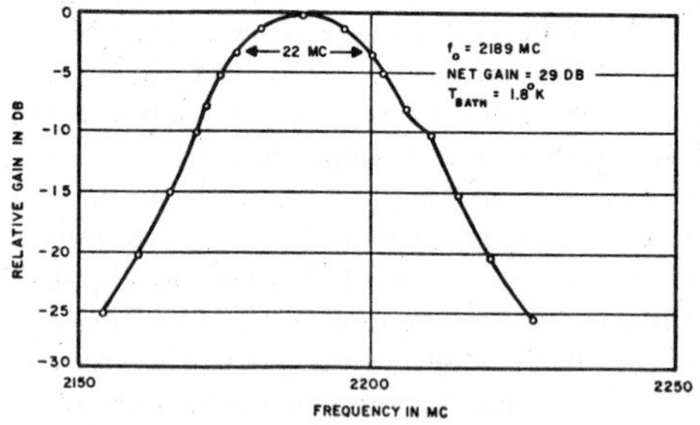

Fig. 20—Instantaneous bandwidth of TWM.

variations in the relative C axis orientations of the four ruby slabs that were used.

Several experiments were performed in which an attempt was made to produce amplification bandwidths in excess of the line width of the material. Bandwidths in excess of 125 Mc were obtained with electronic gains of 16.5 db by stagger-tuning the applied magnetic field [36].

Fig. 21 shows photographs of oscilloscope displays of the maser bandwidth under increasing staggered field conditions. The field staggering was accomplished by

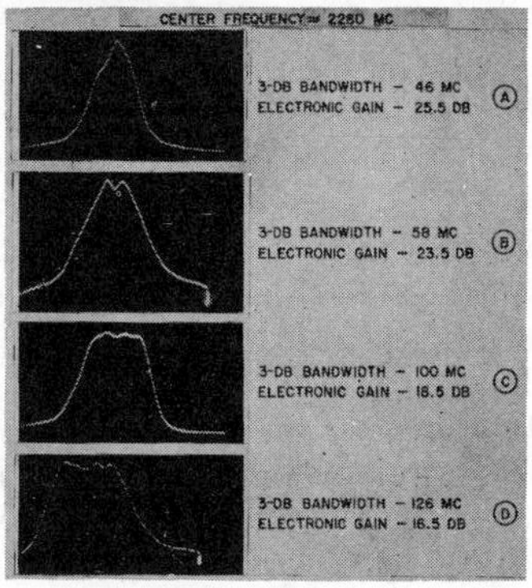

Fig. 21—Oscilloscope display of maser amplification bandwidth under different field-staggering conditions.

periodically shimming one of the pole pieces of an electromagnet with thin rectangular slabs of high-permeability material.

IV. System Performance

A. General Description

The maser amplifier can easily be tuned to any operating frequency in the 2120- to 2380-Mc band by simply adjusting a single frequency-calibrated dial. This dial simultaneously sets the external magnetic field (current through an electromagnet) and pump frequency (delay line voltage of a BWO) to the proper value. By using the calibrated dial, the amplification frequency can easily be set to within ±3 Mc of the desired signal. This is sufficiently accurate for most applications since the maser instantaneous bandwidth is about 22 Mc.

If a more accurate frequency setting is required, a mirrored scale ammeter, located on the front panel of the power supply, can be used to tune the maser to within ±0.5 Mc of the desired frequency. The ammeter reads the current through the electromagnet thus setting the magnitude of the external magnetic field to the proper value. The magnetic field is the only critical adjustment since the pump frequency may deviate considerably from the required values (Fig. 19).

B. Important Characteristics

1) Receiver Noise Temperature

Measurements of the over-all maser receiver input noise temperature T_e were made using an AIL Type 70 Hot-Cold Body Standard Noise Generator in a *Y*-factor measurement. The hot and cold loads of the noise generator were at boiling-water and liquid-nitrogen temperatures, respectively.

A series of 10 separate measurements was made at each of 10 different frequencies across the amplifier tuning band; the results of these measurements are shown in Table IV.

TABLE IV

Results of Receiver Noise Temperature Measurements*

Signal (Mc)	Net Maser Gain (db)	T_e(°K)	T_2(°K)	T_m(°K)
2170	31	12.4	2420	10.5
2200	29.5	13.5	2345	10.9
2220	28	15.8	2290	12.2
2230	29	15.1	2420	12.0
2250	30	15.5	2050	13.4
2270	28	15.4	2345	11.7
2280	28	12.8	2295	9.2
2300	28	13.6	2350	9.9
2330	27.5	14.3	2350	10.1
2350	27	15.1	2520	10.1

* All of the noise temperatures tabulated are average values.
T_e = Over-all receiver noise temperature including second-stage noise contributions (measured data). We were able to measure T_e to within ±2°K because of the high degree of stability of the maser.
T_2 = Second-stage noise temperature (measured data).
T_m = Maser noise temperature including feed-line losses (calculated from T_e and T_2).

Table IV shows that T_m varies ±2.1°K across the band, being as low as 9.2°K at 2280 Mc. This minimum is considerably greater than the maser spin temperature, which is less than 1°K (determined from inversion measurements). There are two main contributing noise sources responsible for the temperature degradation.

1) The dissipative losses of the coaxial input feed line, which is located in the helium bath, and which was designed to be as short as possible with as large a diameter as possible, consistent with keeping the cryogenic heat conduction losses low. The dissipative loss of the feed line measured at 290°K was about 0.2 db. The actual noise contribution caused by this loss was not accurately known because of the temperature gradient on the feed line.
2) The noise contributed by the dissipative losses of the slow-wave structure. The magnitude of this contribution depends upon the ratio of the gain-per-unit length to the loss-per-unit length of the structure, and the temperature of these losses. The contribution caused by this mechanism is small compared to feed-line losses.

It is believed that these losses can be further decreased, thus yielding maser system noise temperatures closer to the spin temperature.

2) Maser Gain Saturaiion and Dynamic Range

A series of gain saturation measurements was made on the maser under three different input signal conditions.

1) Continuous wave,
2) Pulsed (duty cycle = 0.1, pulse width = 100 μsec),
3) Pulsed (duty cycle = 0.01, pulse width = 100 μsec).

Fig. 22 plots the results of these measurements, and shows that the maser input power saturation level (defined as the power required to decrease the gain by 3 db) increases with decreasing duty cycle—that is, −54 dbm, −44 dbm and −34 dbm for the signals 1), 2) and 3) above. The resulting dynamic ranges (for a 1-Mc post-receiver

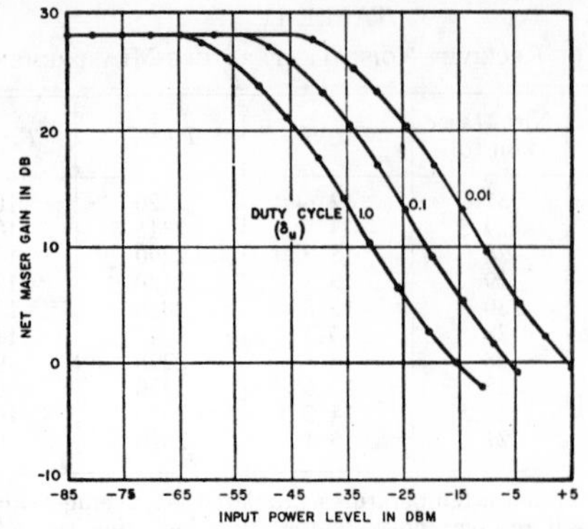

Fig. 22—TWM gain saturation vs input signal power as a function of duty cycle.

bandwidth) are 75 db, 85 db and 95 db. The increase in pulse saturation power is caused by the long spin storage time of the ruby, and is effective for pulse signals that are short with respect to it. The spin-lattice relaxation time T_1 of ruby is in the hundreds of milliseconds, which is quite long compared to the pulse width generally used in high-resolution systems.

The saturation output power of the maser is a constant. Thus, if the system saturation measurements were made with lower maser gains, the level of input power causing saturation would increase, resulting in greater dynamic ranges.

3) Recovery Time

Fig. 16 is a photograph of the recovery time of the maser, after being saturated with a 3-msec high power pulse. The actual recovery times were determined by the plot shown in Fig. 17. The recovery process is described by several relaxation times, caused by a four-level spin-flip cross-relaxation mechanism. The time required for the maser to recover to within 3 db of its presaturated gain is about 50 msec. Hence, one can see the added advantage of a relatively fast recovery time in addition to the greater inversion ratios that can be obtained with the cross-relaxation mechanism.

Furthermore, marked improvements in recovery time might be obtained in future masers by impurity-doping of the idler transition of the ruby to reduce the idler relaxation time. (This was done in the cerium-doped gadolinium ethyl sulfate maser [13].) In addition, the proper use of low power level ferrimagnetic limiters, with the masers should yield rapid recovery times.

4) Gain Stability

Several gain stability measurements at a helium bath temperature of 1.8°K, and a maser gain of 30 db, yielded a long-term peak-to-peak drift of ±0.1 db and a short-term peak-to-peak stability of better than ±0.05 db over a period of several hours. Fig. 23 is a photograph of the output of a recorder from a typical stability run of one hour. The fluctuations represent the instabilities of a complete maser IF receiver, fed by a standard signal generator. Thus, a significant portion of the variation must be ascribed to the measurement technique rather than the maser.

The parameter that was considered to have the greatest effect on the maser long-term stability was the magnet, since the field stability must be considerably better than the magnetic line width of the ruby (which is less than 1 per cent of the external magnetic field). To minimize this problem, the magnet design consisted of a permanent magnet with a pair of "tickler" coils to give the necessary field variation required for tuning. This technique made it possible to use a relatively small current regulated power supply, and minimized coil-heating problems.

5) Signal Desensitization

Fig. 24 shows the gain saturation effect (desensitization) of nearby interfering signals. The power level of the interfering signal required to decrease the maser gain by 3 db at its center frequency is plotted as a function of the interfering signal. The shape of the measured response closely follows the maser amplification characteristic. Fig. 25 is a block diagram of the test setup used for the measurements. The filter, which is located between the maser and the second-stage amplifier, insured that the interference effect measured was caused by the maser and not the second stage. In addition, to give added isolation, the interference signal was CW, while the probing signal was square-wave modulated, detected, and amplified at 1000 cps.

6) Environmental Tests

The maser amplifier was subjected to an environmental testing program in accordance with MIL-E-4158. The tests included in this program were as follows:

1) High-altitude storage (40,000 ft),
2) High-altitude operating (10,000 ft),
3) Low-temperature storage (−80°F),
4) Low-temperature operating (−20°F),
5) High-temperature storage and operating (160°F),
6) Humidity (seven cycles),
7) Rain,
8) Salt spray,
9) Sand and dust,
10) Radio interference,
11) Shock,
12) Vibration.

The units successfully passed all tests. However, the resonance phase of the vibration tests on the vacuum pump and power supply had to be modified for the vertical plane. The low-frequency amplitude to which these two units were subjected had to be decreased to about one-half the specified value because of bottoming of the shock mounts.

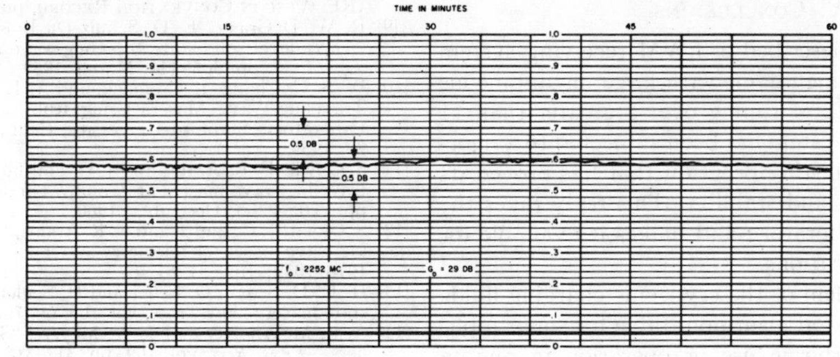

Fig. 23—Recorder display of gain stability for TWM.

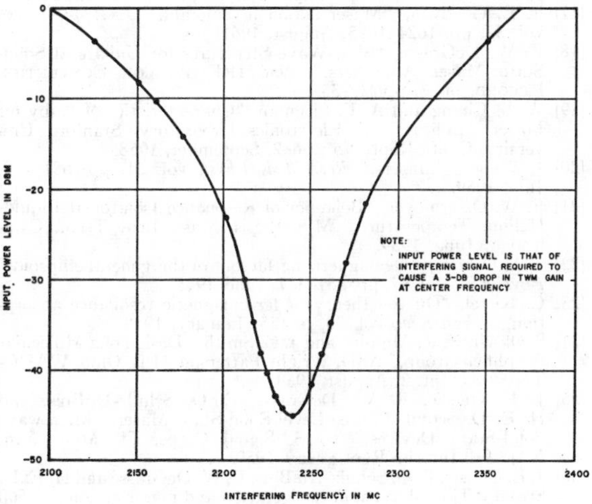

Fig. 24—TWM gain desensitization as a function of nearby interference signal.

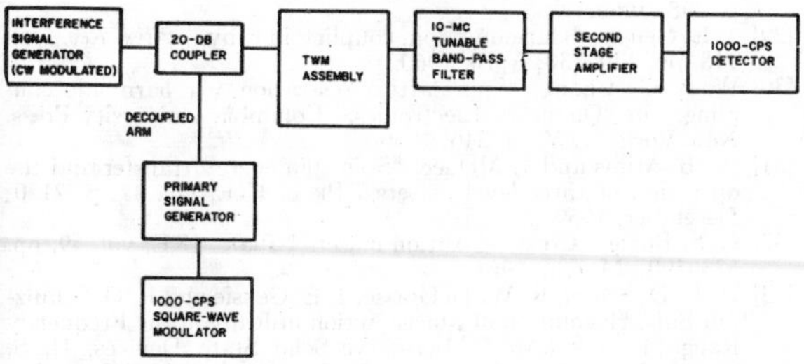

Fig. 25—Test setup used to measure maser gain desensitization.

(a)

(b)

Fig. 26—Packaged units of TWM system. (a) TWM assembly. (b) Remote-control power supply.

7) *Package Description*

The over-all system consists of three units—1) the TWM assembly, 2) the remote-control power supply and 3) the vacuum pump. These units can be separated by as much as 100 feet to permit the TWM assembly to be mounted as close to the antenna feed as practicable. A photograph of the packaged TWM assembly and the remote control power supply is shown in Figs. 26(a) and (b), respectively.

V. Conclusions

This report has described a TWM receiving system that has low noise, high gains with large instantaneous bandwidths and ease of tuning over a greater than 11 per cent band. The system has been subjected to a rigorous environmental testing program that has proved its inherent ruggedness and stability. This truly takes the maser out of the laboratory and makes it available for military field applications.

The logistic problem of the cryogenic charging fluids must still be considered insurmountable for some applications, such as airborne use or operation in remote geographical areas where the refrigerants are not readily available. However, a considerable effort is being placed on miniaturized, reliable closed-cycle refrigerating systems within the cryogenics field. Furthermore, it is believed that such closed systems, having a high degree of reliability and long-time trouble free operation, will be available in the near future.

In future systems, a weight reduction in the assembly containing the TWM structure is desirable to facilitate mounting problems, and make possible airborne application. The magnet is the major portion of the weight of this assembly (110 pounds), and work now in progress on the feasibility of replacing the heavy magnet assembly with a 3-pound superconducting magnet is proving successful. This work will be reported at a later date. In maser applications where the magnetic field is not too high, niobium wire can successfully be used [37]. At the higher frequencies, where the magnitude of the magnetic fields required increases, the newly discovered high-field high-current-density super-conducting materials such as Nb_3Sn [38] and NbZr [39] can be used.

With the successful application of closed cryogenic systems and superconducting magnets, the maser will unquestionably be a practical lightweight low-noise amplifier for all types of applications including airborne.

Acknowledgment

The authors gratefully acknowledge the stimulating discussions of Dr. F. R. Arams and his assistance in determining the optimum crystal orientation. In addition, the authors express their gratitude to J. Wolczok and J. Baris for help with the measurements and packaging.

References

[1] N. Bloembergen, "Proposal for a new type solid-state maser," *Phy . Rev.*, vol. 109, pp. 324–327; October 15, 1956.
[2] J. O. Artman, *et al.*, "Operation of a three-level solid-state maser at 21 cm," *Phys. Rev.*, vol. 109, pp. 1392–1393; February, 1958.
[3] F. R. Arams, S. Okwit and A. Penzias, "Maser action in ruby at 21 cm," *Bull. Amer. Phys. Soc.*, vol. 4, p. 21; January, 1959.
[4] B. F. C. Cooper and J. V. Jelley, "Maser for Radio Astronomy Observations at 21 cm," presented at meeting of Northeast Electronics Res. and Engrg., Boston, Mass.; November, 1959.
[5] J. A. Giordmaine, L. E. Alsop, C. H. Mayer and C. H. Townes, "A maser amplifier for radio astronomy at *X*-band," Proc. IRE, vol. 47, pp. 1062–1069; June, 1959.
[6] W. W. Higa, "A Maser System for Radio Astronomy," Jet Propulsion Laboratory, Rept. No. 32–103; June 15, 1961.
[7] J. R. Pierce, "Exotic radio communications," *Bell Labs. Rec.*, vol. 37, p. 323; September, 1959.
[8] R. L. Forward, F. E. Goodwin and J. E. Kiefer, "Application of a Solid-State Ruby Maser to an *X*-Band Radar System," 1959 IRE Wescon Convention Record, pt. 1, pp. 119–125.
[9] R. W. DeGrasse, E. O. Schulz-Du Bois, and H. E. D. Scovil, "Three-level solid-state traveling-wave maser," *Bell Sys. Tech. J.*, vol. 38, pp. 305–334; March, 1959.
[10] W. S. C. Chang, J. Cromack, and A. E. Siegman, "Cavity and Traveling-Wave Masers Using Ruby at *S*-Band," Electronics Laboratory, Stanford University, Calif., Rept. No. 155-2; July 28, 1959.
[11] S. Okwit, F. R. Arams and J. G. Smith, "Electronically tunable traveling-wave masers at *L* and *S* bands," Proc. IRE, vol. 48, pp. 2205–2206; December, 1960.
[12] S. Okwit, J. G. Smith and F. R. Arams, "Tunable *S*-band traveling-wave maser for telemetry systems," Proc. IRE, vol. 49, pp. 1078–1079; June, 1961.
[13] H. E. D. Scovil, G. Feher and H. Seidel, "Operation of a solid-state maser," *Phys. Rev.*, vol. 105, pp. 762–763; January, 1957.
[14] A. L. McWhorter and J. W. Meyers, "Solid-state maser amplifiers," *Phys. Rev.*, vol. 109, pp. 312–318; January, 1958.
[15] G. Makhov, C. Kikuchi, J. Lambe and R. W. Terhune, "Maser action in ruby," *Phys. Rev.*, vol. 109, pp. 1399–1400; February, 1958.
[16] H. Gerritsen and H. Lewis, "Operation of a chromium-doped titania maser," *J. Appl. Phys.*, vol. 31, p. 608; March, 1960.
[17] F. E. Goodwin, "Maser action in emerald," *J. Appl. Phys.*, vol. 32, pp. 1624–1625; August, 1961.
[18] R. W. DeGrasse, "Slow-Wave Structures for Unilateral Solid-State Maser Amplifiers," 1958 IRE Wescon Convention Record, pt. 3, pp. 29–35.
[19] W. S. Chang and A. E. Siegman, "Characteristics of Ruby for Maser Applications," Electronics Laboratory, Stanford University, Calif., Rept. No. 156–2; September, 1958.
[20] J. Weber, "Masers," *Rev. Mod. Phys.*, vol. 31, pp. 681–710; July, 1959.
[21] F. W. Ostermeyer, "Behavior of Resonance Isolator at Liquid-Helium Temperature," M.S. thesis, Mass. Inst. Tech., Cambridge; June, 1959.
[22] J. A. Osborn, "Demagnetizing factors of the general ellipsoid," *Phys. Rev.*, vol. 67, pp. 351–357; June, 1945.
[23] C. Kittel, "On the theory of ferromagnetic resonance absorption," *Phys. Rev.*, vol. 73, p. 155; January, 1948.
[24] S. Okwit, F. R. Abrams, and J. G. Smith, "Design of a Molecular Amplifier Group," ASD, Wright-Patterson AFB, Ohio, WADC-TN-59-392, pt. 2; August, 1959.
[25] J. E. Geusic, R. W. DeGrasse, E. O. Schulz-DuBois, and H. E. D. Scovil, "Three-Level Solid-State Maser," Microwave Solid-State Devices," U. S. Signal Corps, Ft. Monmouth, N. J., 9th Interim Rept.; May, 1959.
[26] J. E. Geusic, E. O. Schulz-Du Bois, R. W. DeGrasse and H. E. D. Scovil, "Three-level spin refrigeration and maser action at 1500 Mc," *J. Appl. Phys.*, vol. 30, pp. 113–114; July, 1959.
[27] N. Bloembergen, S. Shapiro, P. S. Pershan, and J. O. Artman, "Cross-relaxation in spin systems," *Phys. Rev.*, vol. 144, pp. 445–459; April, 1959.
[28] W. H. Higa, "Excitation of an *L*-band ruby maser," in "Quantum Electronics," Columbia University Press, New York, N. Y., p. 298; 1960.
[29] J. E. Geusic, "Harmonic spin coupling in ruby," *Phys. Rev.*, vol. 118, pp. 129–130; April, 1960.
[30] W. S. C. Chang, "Spin lattice relaxation via harmonic coupling," in "Quantum Electronics," Columbia University Press, New York, N. Y., p. 346; 1960.
[31] W. B. Mims and J. McGee, "Spin-spin energy transfer and the operation of three-level masers," Proc. IRE, vol. 47, p. 2120; December, 1959.
[32] G. S. Bogle, "Cross-relaxation masers," Proc. IRE, vol. 49, pp. 573–590; March, 1961.
[33] H. E. D. Scovil, R. W. DeGrasse, J. E. Geusic and E. O. Schulz-Du Bois, "Evolution of Maser Action in Ruby in the Frequency Range 1 to 9 kMc," Microwave Solid State Devices, U. S. Signal Corps., Ft. Monmouth, N. J., 10th Interim Rept.; August, 1959.
[34] F. R. Arams, "Microwave Cross-Relaxation Masers," Doctoral dissertation, Polytechnic Inst. of Brooklyn, N. Y.; June, 1961.
[35] R. W. Roberts and H. D. Tenney, "Research and Development of a Solid-State Paramagnetic Maser," USAF, Cambridge, Mass., AFCRC-TN-60-552, No. 7; April, 1960.
[36] S. Okwit and J. G. Smith, "Traveling-wave masers with instantaneous bandwidths in excess of 100 Mc," Proc. IRE, vol. 49, p. 1210; July, 1961. ×
[37] S. Autler, "Superconducting electromagnets." *Rev. Sci. Instr.*, vol. 31, p. 369; April, 1960.
[38] J. E. Kunzler, E. Buehler, F. S. L. Hsu and J. H. Wernick, "Superconductivity in Nb_3Sn at high current density in a magnetic field of 88 Kgauss," *Phys. Rev. Lett.*, vol. 6, p. 89; February, 1961.
[39] T. G. Berlincourt, R. R. Harke and D. H. Leslie, "Superconductivity of high magnetic fields and current densities in some NbZr alloys," *Phys. Rev.*, vol. 6, pp. 671–674; June, 1961.

A C-BAND MASER DICKE-RADIOMETER SYSTEM[†]

By

J. A. DeGruyl*, H. Hvatum**, S. Okwit*, and J. G. Smith*

A C-Band Maser Dicke-Radiometer System that uses a low-noise traveling-wave maser (TWM) as the RF amplifier and a helium-cooled Y-junction circulator as the RF switch was designed, developed, and installed on the 85-foot parabolic antenna at the National Radio Astronomy Observatory (NRAO). Figure 1 is a photograph of the installed system. The maser is capable of operation up to ± 60 degrees tilt from the vertical, thus this mounting position gives a maximum sky coverage.

The radiometer, shown in detail in Figure 2, consists of three basic assemblies: the feed-mounted low-noise receiver group (including the TWM, RF switch and modulator, and a transistorized second stage), the standard NRAO 30-Mc receiver-synchronous detector system (reference 1), and the remotely located power and control unit.

The expected sensitivity of the radiometer (assuming no feed-line losses from the antenna to the switch) is given by:

$$\Delta T = \frac{C}{\sqrt{B\tau}} \left[T_a + \underbrace{(L - 1)T_s + LT_r}_{T_{eff}} \right]$$

where:

C = constant dependent upon mode of operation,

B = overall noise bandwidth (predetection),

τ = integration time,

T_a = antenna temperature,

---

* Airborne Instruments Laboratory.

** National Radio Astronomy Observatory.

† Presented at 1963 Nerem Conference; Boston, Massachusetts

L = insertion loss of switch,

T_s = physical temperature of switch,

T_r = effective receiver noise temperature,

T_{eff} = overall effective receiver noise temperature.

The equation makes it clear that the switch loss, its physical temperature, and the effective receiver noise temperature should be kept to a minimum. The use of a low-loss helium-cooled ferrite switch followed by a TWM meets this requirement, and was therefore used. It yielded an overall receiver noise temperature (T_{eff}) of 28°K when measured with a hot and cold load noise generator.

The TWM used a ruby-loaded comb-type slow-wave structure with an active length of 2.6 inches, and oriented with its C-axis at 90 degrees with respect to the DC magnetic field. YIG isolator disks were integrally distributed along the structure to provide unconditional stability. Measured inversion ratios were about 4, yielding a gain of 25 db with an instantaneous bandwidth of 25 Mc at a center frequency of 4995 Mc. Figure 3 is a photograph of the overall maser structure assembly.

The helium-cooled Y-junction circulator switch (reference 2) operates in a low field mode (300 gauss) to facilitate switching. Thus a low $4\pi M_s$ substituted garnet material was used so the field losses would be kept to a minimum. The switch has an insertion loss of about 0.3 db, isolation in excess of 20 db, and a bandwidth of about 240 Mc. It operates at a 20-cps rate and is designed for a minimum of joule losses to conserve liquid helium. (The total joule losses are less than 35 mw.)

The cryogenic system makes use of a specially designed stainless-steel double dewar that can be mounted on an equatorial antenna pedestal. The system provides greater than 24 hours of operation on a single 9 liter charge of liquid helium.

Preliminary observational measurements were made on the overall radiometer system mounted on the NRAO 85-foot antenna. The radiometer has an extremely high degree of stability and is effective in both the total-power mode and the switched mode as shown by the drift curve recording of Virgo A (Figure 4). Record No. 4 shows both the switched and total-power outputs. The total-power record measures the second detector voltage with the radiometer in the switched mode. Record No. 2 is a total-power record measured with the radiometer input switch locked in the antenna position. (Note that the signal-to-noise ratio of the total-power mode is, as expected, twice that measured in the switched mode.)

Both the sensitivity and the stability of the system can be seen in Figure 5, which is a recording of a north-south scan through radio sources No. 36 and 37 (reference 3). The observation is made in the total-power mode with a time constant of 1.5 seconds and a recorder speed of 50 mm/min. The gain stability during this measurement is better than 0.03 db (total record length of 13 minutes).

REFERENCES

1. T. Orhaug and W. Waltman, "A Switched Load Radiometer," Publications of the National Radio Astronomy Observatory, Vol. 1, No. 12, February 1962.

2. J. A. DeGruyl, W. W. Heinz, and S. Okwit, "Helium-Cooled Y-Junction Ferrite Circulator Switch," IEEE Proceedings, June 1963.

3. W. Altenhoff et al., "Messprogramme bei der Wellenlänge 11 cm am 25 m - Radioteleskop Stockert," Veröffentlichungen der Universitäts, Sternwarte zu Bonn, Nr. 59, 1960.

FIGURE 1. 85-FOOT TELESCOPE WITH MASER MOUNTED ON SOUTH FEED SUPPORT LEG

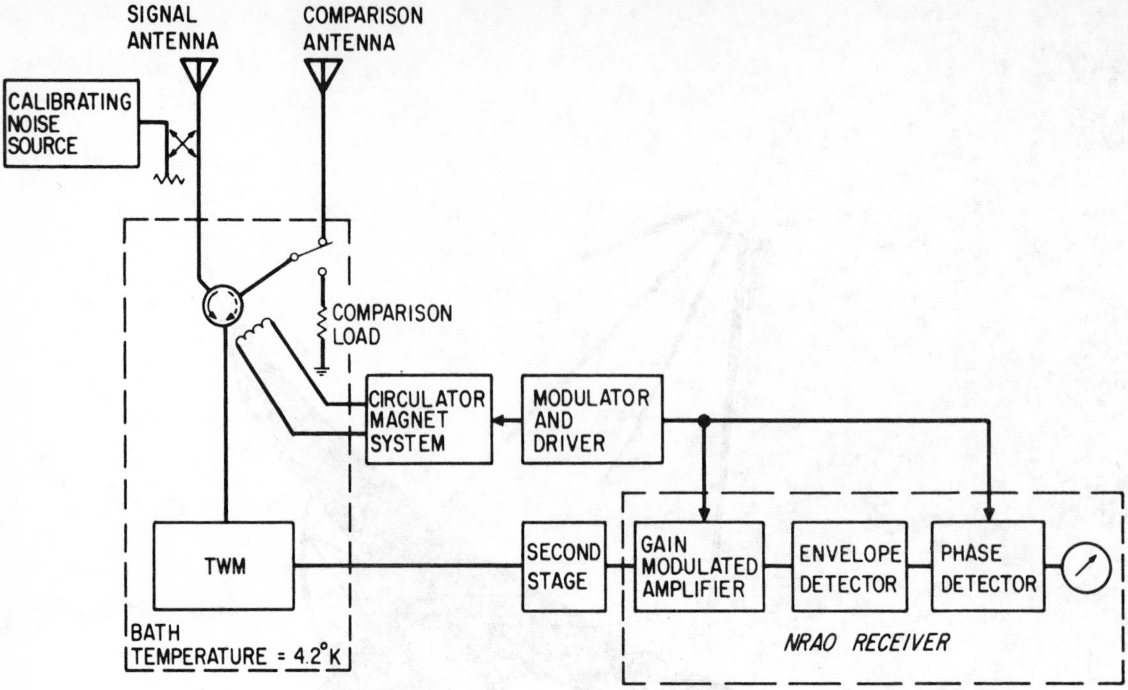

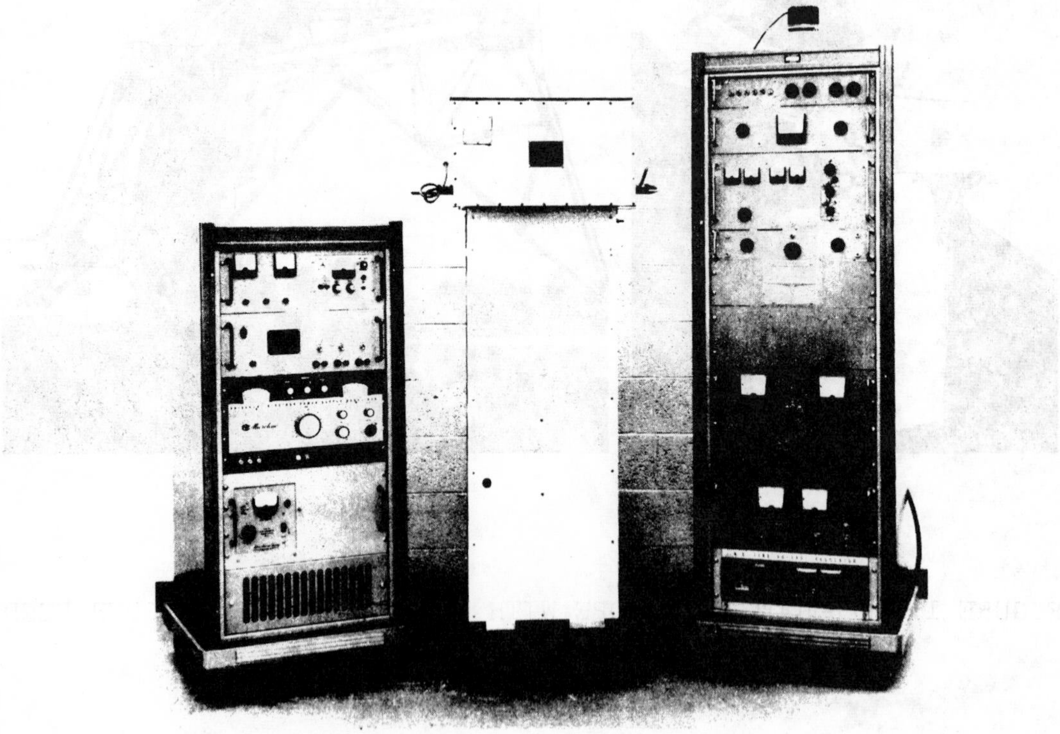

FIGURE 2. RADIOMETER SYSTEM

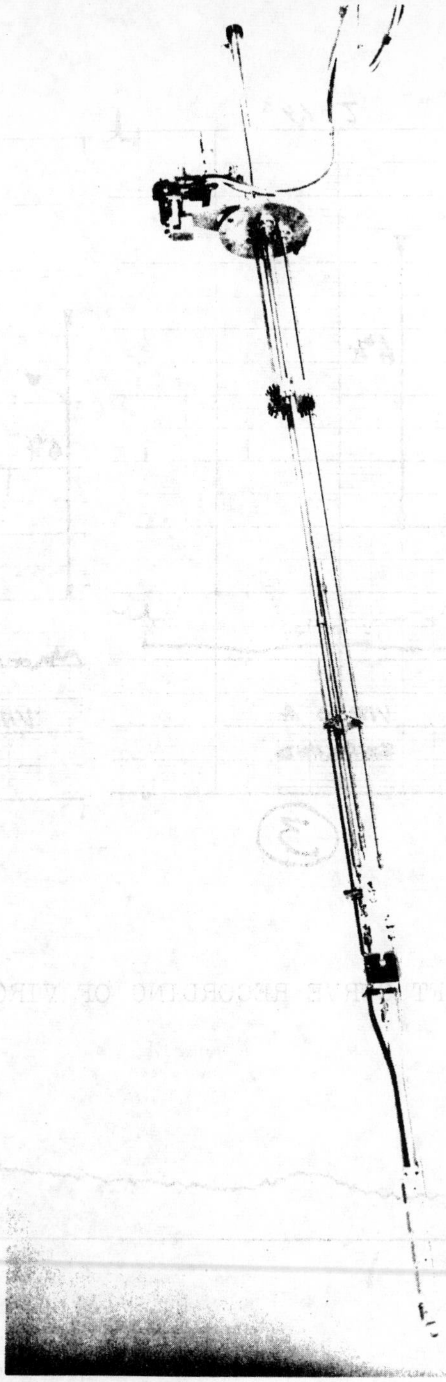

FIGURE 3. MASER SWITCH STRUCTURE

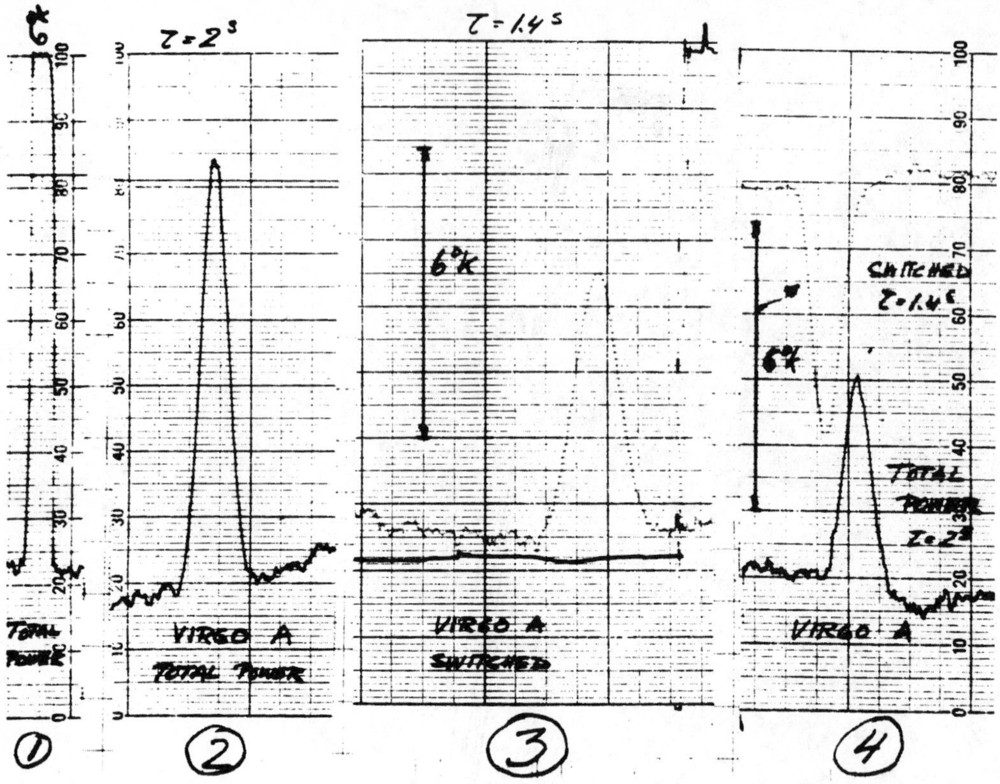

FIGURE 4. DRIFT CURVE RECORDING OF VIRGO A

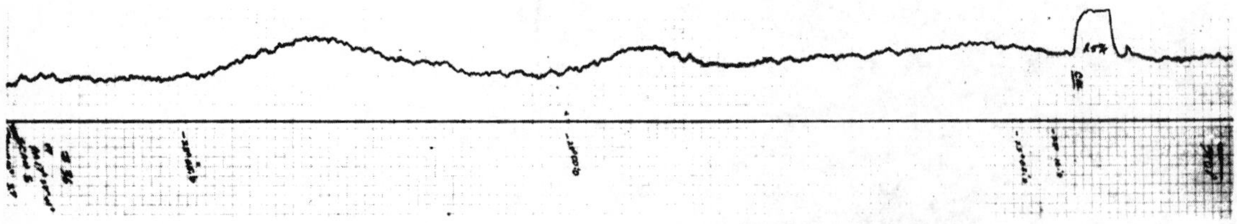

FIGURE 5. RECORDING OF NORTH-SOUTH SCAN THROUGH RADIO SOURCES NO. 36 AND 37

Tunable Millimeter Traveling-Wave Maser Operation*

Prototype sections of a low-noise solid-state maser amplifier have been operated at signal frequencies up to 41 kMc. This K_a-band maser is of the traveling-wave type, has an extremely large tuning range, incorporates ferrite isolators to obtain high gain stability, and uses pump frequencies in the 75 kMc region.

Design Considerations

CW maser operation in the millimeter-wave region is presently dependent upon the availability of high-frequency pump sources. Three-level maser operation in general requires that the pump frequency be greater than twice the signal frequency, *i.e.*, $f_p > 2f_s$. Four-level operation, using push-pull pumping, offers the significant advantages of a relaxed pump frequency requirement ($f_p > f_s$), and higher population inversion ratio for given pump and signal frequencies. Thus, this relaxed pump frequency condition permits the operation of millimeter-wave masers to frequencies almost as high as the frequency of available coherent sources, not considering special techniques.[1,2] To demonstrate this, we have obtained maser action at a signal frequency of 40 kMc, using a pump frequency of only 43 kMc, and an applied magnetic field of 700 oersteds, using push-pull pumped chromium-doped titania as the active maser crystal at 4.2°K.

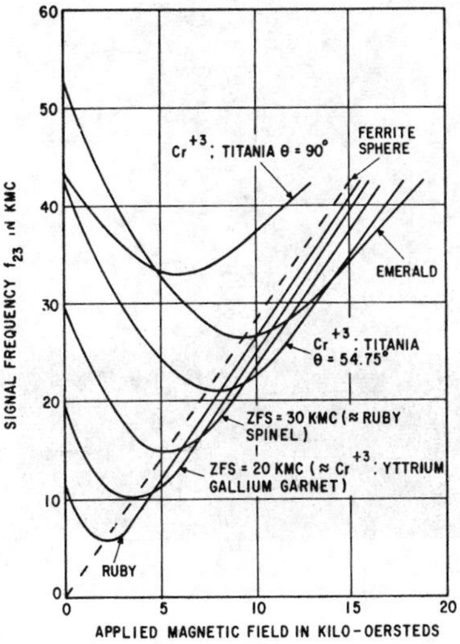

Fig. 1—Comparison of various push-pull-pumped maser materials.

Cr^{3+}-doped crystals have the advantage of symmetry in their energy levels at certain crystal orientations, permitting push-pull pumping over extended signal frequency ranges. Fig. 1 shows signal frequency as a function of applied magnetic field for several Cr^{3+}-doped maser crystals with varying zero-field-splittings (ZFS). As Fig. 1 shows, in the case of Cr^{3+}-doped titania for $\theta \rightarrow 90°$, the presence of the axial (E) term in the Spin Hamiltonian is useful in minimizing magnetic field requirements in the high-field region. The high-field region has the advantages of 1) high gain per unit length, and 2) convenient traveling-wave maser operation, since overlap with a ferrimagnetic isolator material is obtainable by adjusting the ferrite demagnetizing factors (Fig. 1). Cr^{3+}-doped titania[3,4] has the additional attribute of a relatively-high slowing factor, due to its high dielectric constant (greater than 100), without resorting to filter structures. Three-level operation has previously been obtained.[5]

Experimental Results

A two-port traveling-wave maser structure consisting of waveguide loaded with titania, and therefore substantially reduced in size, was matched to standard waveguide over the 26 to 40 kMc band.

Maser action was obtained in the low-magnetic-field region over the entire band from 25 to 40 kMc with pump frequencies from 43 to 47.3 kMc and magnetic fields from 0.7 to 5.2 kilo-oersteds (Fig. 2). The magnetic field was oriented at $\theta = 54.7°$ in the AC plane of the maser crystal, where the two magnetic complexes of Cr^{3+} in TiO_2 are aligned, thereby doubling the db of electronic gain.

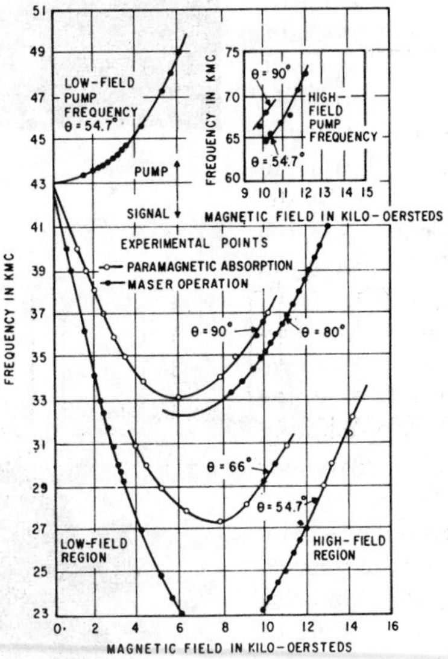

Fig. 2—Experimental operating points.

Population inversion was also obtained using the above crystal orientation at high magnetic fields where higher gains, due to the higher pump frequency, are available. As shown in Fig. 3(a), electronic gains averaging 4.4 db/cm from 23 to 27 kMc were obtained at 4.2°K. The electronic gain increased to 10.5 db/cm at 1.7°K. The measured population inversion correlated well with the calculated value of 2.2 [Fig. 3(b)]. Pump frequencies used were from 64 to 73 kMc.

Traveling-wave maser action over the entire 33.5 to 41 kMc band was obtained using a $\theta = 80°$ crystal, and pump frequencies from 62 to 82 kMc (Fig. 2). Electronic gains

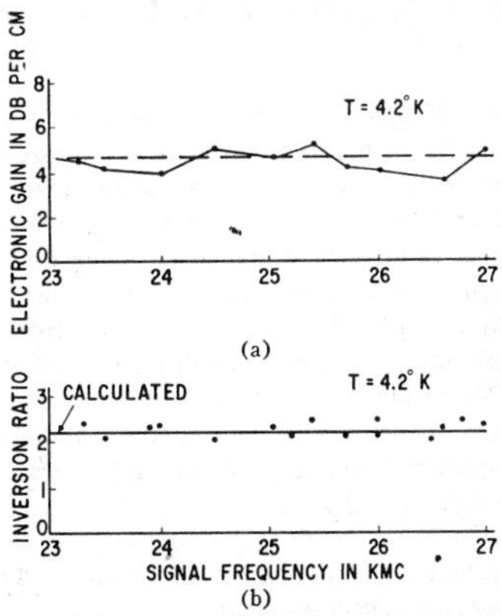

Fig. 3—Electronic gain and population inversion ratio vs signal frequency.

of 6.5 db/cm, and a population inversion ratio averaging 1.5, were obtained at 1.7°K. Ferrite isolators were successfully incorporated into the TWM structure to insure stable operation. The ferrite overlaps the TiO_2 tuning curve from 34 to 42 kMc at liquid helium temperatures. The isolator losses are less than 0.5 db/cm in the forward direction, and over 30 db/cm in the reverse direction.

Conclusion

Stable traveling-wave maser operation has been obtained over very large tuning ranges in K_a-band using Cr^{3+}-doped titania as the active material. The tuning range can be varied by suitably selecting the crystal orientation. The techniques employed are also believed to be applicable at much higher frequencies. Further work is in progress.

F. Arams
B. Peyton
Airborne Instruments Lab.
Deer Park, N. Y.

* Received May 2, 1962; revised manuscript received May 16, 1962. This work was presented at the 1962 Solid-State Circuits Conference, University of Pennsylvania, Philadelphia, Pa., February, 1962, and was supported by the U. S. Navy Bureau of Ships, Washington, D. C., and Aeronautical Systems Center, Wright-Patterson AFB, Ohio.

[1] J. Minkowski, "Cross relaxation effect of Cr and Fe in K_3(Co, Cr, Fe) $(CN)_6$," *Phys. Rev.*, vol. 119, pp. 1577–1578; 1960.
[2] F. Arams, "Maser operation at signal frequencies higher than pump frequency," IRE Trans. on Microwave Theory and Techniques, vol. MTT-9, pp. 68–72; January, 1961.
[3] H. Gerritsen, S. Harrison and H. Lewis, "Chromium-doped titania as a maser material," *J. Appl. Phys.*, vol. 31, pp. 1566–1571; September, 1960.
[4] D. Devor, "Fine Structure Levels and Transition Probabilities of Cr^{3+} in TiO_2 (Rutile)," Hughes Res. Labs., Calif., Res. Rept. No. 148; May, 1960.
[5] H. Gerritsen and H. Lewis, "Operation of a chromium-doped titania maser," *J. Appl. Phys.*, vol. 31, pp. 608–609; March, 1960. Also, E. S. Sabisky and H. J. Gerritsen, "A traveling-wave maser using chromium-doped rutile," Proc. IRE (*Correspondence*), vol. 49, pp. 1329–1330; August, 1961.

A Low-Noise X-Band Radiometer Using Maser*

J. J. COOK†, L. G. CROSS†, M. E. BAIR†, MEMBER, IRE, AND R. W. TERHUNE†

***Summary*—A low-noise *X*-band radiometer, using a ruby maser preamplifier in radio astronomy measurements, is discussed. The radiometer uses a reflection-cavity maser with voltage-gain bandwidth products as high as 300 Mc at 4.2°K. Less than 1 per cent short-term gain instability and dependable performance are obtained. A system noise factor (excluding antenna spillover) of 0.6 db (43°K) has been obtained. The system bandwidth is limited to 8 Mc by the intermediate frequency bandwidth, with maser bandwidths of 20–30 Mc available. RMS noise fluctuations of approximately 0.01°K with a 12-second integration time and 0.007°K with a 42-second integration time are obtained. Gain instability of 0.6 per cent up to 10 minutes and 2 per cent up to 30 minutes has been measured. Electrical and mechanical features as well as measurement and operational techniques are described. Performance data and radio astronomy observations are discussed.**

I. Introduction

THE first successful operation of a ruby maser amplifier at Willow Run Laboratories of the University of Michigan on December 20, 1957[1] stimulated interest in many fields. Since this initial operation, the number of research and development programs in masers and maser systems has greatly increased. Among these programs is the development of reliable, low-noise systems for both active and passive astronomical applications. The system to be described is a modified Dicke system,[2] X-band radiometer specifically designed for use in a long-term radio astronomy research program. It is presently operating on The University of Michigan's 85-foot-diameter radiotelescope (Fig. 1).

The radiometer utilizes a four-level ruby maser preamplifier[3] operating at 8.72 Gc.[4] The maser gain is typically 20–23 db with a voltage-gain bandwidth product of 200 Mc at 4.2°K. Maser bandwidths to 30 Mc and voltage-gain bandwidths to 550 Mc at 4.2°K have been obtained. An equivalent system input temperature of approximately 75°K, including about 30°K caused by antenna spillover and backlobes, has been observed. The remaining 45 ± 5°K results from input-guide noise and a superheterodyne receiver with a noise figure of 9.5 db (including all noise resulting from components following the maser preamplifier). The input-guide

(a)

(b)

Fig. 1—(a) The University of Michigan's 85-foot diameter radio telescope. (b) Detail showing mounting arrangement of packaged maser system, as well as other 2- and 3-cm receivers.

* Received by the IRE, August 31, 1960; revised manuscript received, December 12, 1960. This work was conducted by Project MICHIGAN under Dept. of the Army Contract (DA-36-039-7801) administered by the U. S. Army Signal Corps.

† Willow Run Labs., University of Mich., Ann Arbor.

[1] G. Makhov, C. Kikuchi, J. Lambe, and R. W. Terhune, "Maser action in ruby," *Phys. Rev.*, vol. 109, p. 1399; February, 1958.

[2] R. H. Dicke, "Measurement of thermal radiation at microwave frequencies," *Rev. Sci. Inst.*, vol. 17, p. 268; July, 1946.

[3] C. Kikuchi, J. Lambe, G. Makhov, and R. W. Terhune, "Ruby as a maser material," *J. Appl. Phys.*, vol. 30, p. 1061; July, 1959.

[4] Throughout this paper Gc is used in conformance to the National Bureau of Standard's newly adopted prefixes as recommended by the International Committee on Weights and Measures, accordingly, Gc replaces the former kMc designation.

noise is intended to include all loss noise as well as cavity-wall radiation and spontaneous emission. The system contribution of 45°K was obtained with a maser gain of 23 db and bath temperature of 4.2°K.

The development program was initiated in the fall of 1958 and, following a six-month testing and reliability study on a six-foot van-mounted antenna, was concluded in January, 1960. The system was installed on January 29, 1960 and successfully received the first extraterrestrial radiation on the same day.

II. System Components and Characteristics

A. Physical Description

The radiometer system is shown in simplified block form in Fig. 2. All components to the left of the dashed line are mounted at the apex of the 85-foot antenna and, with the exception of the input guide, are housed in a single weatherproof package, approximately one foot square and four feet long (Fig. 3). The package weighs approximately 250 lbs. The necessary electrical connection into the equipment house is through a system of 20 individually shielded weatherproof cables which are 285 feet long. All electrical power to the antenna-mounted components is dc, a precautionary measure to prevent possible pick-up into signal lines.

The mounting arrangement, along the outside of one of the feed supports, is shown in Fig. 1(b). This position allows the mounting of several other receivers inside the "cone." The dewar orientation is such that the entire antenna positioning range is permissible with a maximum angle, dewar axis to the vertical, of 67°. Refrigerant transfer is accomplished at the apex mount, and no disassembly is required. Maser performance is such that it is unnecessary to reduce the bath temperature, and all performance data are taken at 4.2°K.

B. The Microwave System

The microwave system consists of two major subdivisions: *K*-band pump (18–26 Gc) and *X*-band signal (8.2–12.4 Gc).

The *K*-band pump power is provided by either of two klystrons: the Varian VA 96B or the Raytheon 2K33. The primary requirement of the pump tube is that it provide sufficient power to saturate the ruby crystal. The klystron is housed in its own case to allow forced-air cooling. A ferrite isolator and variable attenuator follow the klystron. The variable attenuator is used to check the degree of saturation. If a 1- or 2-db loss in the pump line causes no maser-gain change, the saturation is sufficient. A 20-db coupler and crystal mount allow monitoring of the pump signal. The remaining system consists of standard bends and straight sections.

The X-band system includes a signal-input line and a comparison-signal line. The Dicke system switching, between the two inputs, is accomplished with a switchable, four-port ferrite circulator. Direct current measurements, in an unmatched system, indicate insertion losses of 0.20 ± 0.05 db and isolations of greater than 25 db. A second (nonswitchable) circulator provides the necessary isolation for a reflection-cavity maser. The input path of this device has a measured insertion loss of 0.12 ± 0.05 db. An additional 0.10-db loss arises from the silver-plated input guide. The total line loss is about 0.45 db.

The amplified maser signal feeds into a balanced mixer using IN23EMR crystals. Local-oscillator power is provided by a stabilized microwave generator with a 10-mw output. Long-term frequency drift is 1 part in 10^6. An electronically controlled variable attenuator and ferrite isolator complete the local-oscillator line.

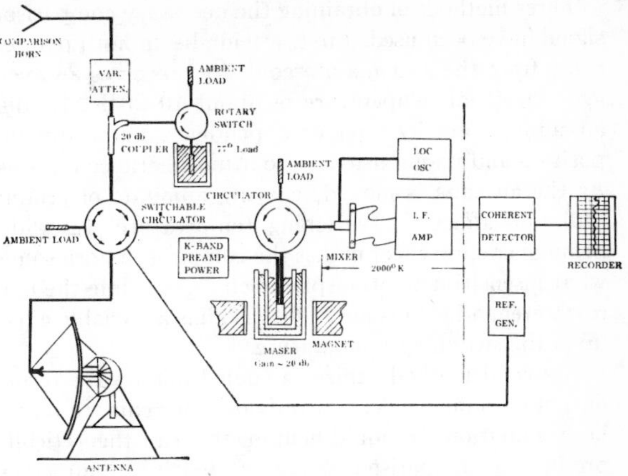

Fig. 2—Basic block diagram of maser radiometer. All equipment to left of dashed line (except input waveguide) is mounted in a single weather-proof package.

Fig. 3—Packaged maser radiometer showing service openings. The complete unit is approximately one foot square and four feet long. It weighs about 250 pounds.

Three methods of obtaining the necessary comparison signal have been used. First, a wide-beam horn pointed away from the antenna at "cold sky" receives an average sky-signal temperature of about 10–20°K. Its disadvantages are its obvious dependence upon antenna position and its insensitivity to atmospheric conditions. As the antenna is moved, varying amounts of ground radiation affect the switching temperature. Its wide-beam averaging effect makes the comparison horn somewhat insensitive to atmospheric changes, while the narrow antenna beam is not. This also has a variable effect upon the switching temperature.

A second method utilizes a cooled microwave termination of sufficient loss to provide approximate black-body radiation. In liquid helium, this can theoretically produce a comparison signal of 4–5°K. Commercial waveguide terminations are not suitable as the absorption characteristics are drastically reduced at liquid-helium temperature. One method, presently under investigation, is the use of a broad-band, matched, dielectrically loaded cavity.

A third method of obtaining a comparison signal is the so-called "double-horn technique." In this scheme, two identical horns are pointed at the antenna surface. By placing these horns a few inches apart, rather large beam separation is possible. In this manner, one can compare two signals originating at discrete points in the sky. Preliminary tests of this technique indicate there is essentially no balancing problem. The two horns see essentially the same spillover and backlobe radiation; therefore, their temperature balance becomes almost independent of antenna motion. Although the narrow beams are quite susceptible to atmospheric changes, such as clouds, etc., their relatively close proximity results in similar effects in each arm.[5]

Regardless of the source of the comparison signal, some device to "balance-out" the two inputs is necessary. This is accomplished with a remotely controlled 0 to 0.3-db attenuator in each line. Physically, a tiny strip of resistance card is inserted into either input as needed. These give a total equivalent-noise-input tuning range of approximately 16°K in each arm.

Calibration of the system is accomplished with two matched waveguide loads, one at ambient temperature and the other in liquid nitrogen. These loads are attached to the two input ports of a rotary, three-port, waveguide switch. The output port feeds, through a 20-db coupler, into the comparison arm. The system is balanced with the switch to ambient; a change to liquid nitrogen produces a signal equivalent to an antenna temperature increase of

$$T_{\text{test}} = 0.01[T_{\text{ambient}} - T_{77,\text{eff}}] \tag{1}$$

where $T_{77,\text{eff}}$ is the temperature equivalent of the liquid nitrogen load, at the switch input.

The cavity assembly (discussed more fully in connection with the maser preamp.) uses a silver-plated ruby cavity.[6] This design yields dependable, stable performance with voltage-gain bandwidth products of over 200 Mc. It has shown experimentally the possibility of products up to 550 Mc.

Closely associated with the waveguide system is the magnet-dewar assembly. The magnet is a permanent alnico magnet having a 1½-inch gap and a field strength of 3850 gauss. Coils are provided to vary the field ±150 gauss. The dewar tip is narrowed to fit into the gap of the externally mounted magnet. Refrigerant capacities are 3.4 and 8.1 liters for liquid helium and liquid nitrogen, respectively. These amounts evaporate completely in about 36 hours in a vertical, stationary dewar; however, during operation a maximum of 17 hours has been obtained.

A liquid-helium level indicator has been provided to allow continuous monitoring of the refrigerant level. The device consists of five carbon resistors spaced at various points along the cavity-assembly waveguide.

C. Associated Electronics

The balanced mixer output is amplified by a 30-Mc amplifier before it leaves the antenna mount. The preamplifier has a bandwidth of 8 Mc, a gain of 30 db, and a noise figure of 1.9 db. The postamplifier has a bandwidth of 10 Mc and a gain of 60 db. The IF output is fed into a selective amplifier and a synchronous detector system. The synchronous detector output is displayed on a recorder. All dc supplies are regulated to at least 1 per cent and a few millivolts ripple. The switchable circulator is driven by a square wave input at 90 cps with a 60-microsecond rise time.

III. The Maser Preamplifier

A. Gain-Bandwidth Requirements

The performance requirements of the preamplifier are determined by the characteristics of the receiver system in which it is used. If we define

$T_i \equiv$ the total input-noise temperature including contributions from sky, antenna, input guide, and preamplifier;

$G \equiv$ power gain of the preamplifier; $\Delta\nu_M =$ bandwidth of the preamplifier;

[5] Concerning the authors' "double-horn technique," see also: M. E. Bair, J. J. Cook, L. G. Cross, and C. B. Arnold, "Recent developments and observations with a ruby maser radiometer," IRE Trans. on Antennas and Propagation, vol. AP-9, pp. 43–49; January, 1961.

This method of comparison has been used successfully in the recent detection of radio radiation from the planet Saturn: J. J. Cook, L. G. Cross, M. E. Bair, and C. B. Arnold, "Radio detection of the planet Saturn," *Nature* (Letters to the Editor), vol. 188, p. 393; October, 1960.

Also in the detection of the first radio radiation from a planetary Nebula: A. H. Barrett, W. E. Howard, F. T. Haddock, J. J. Cook, L. G. Cross, and M. E. Bair, "Measurement of Microwave Radiation at λ3.45 cm from the Planetary Nebula NGC6543," paper presented at the American Astronomical Soc. Meeting, New York, N. Y.; December 28–31, 1960. Further investigation into the use of the "double-horn technique" will be reported as soon as possible.

[6] L. G. Cross, "Silvered ruby maser cavity," *J. Appl. Phys.*, vol. 30, No. 9, p. 1459; 1959.

$T_R \equiv$ noise temperature of one sideband of the receiver; and

$\Delta\nu_R \equiv$ the bandwidth of one sideband of the receiver,

then the effective input temperature is just

$$(T_{IN})_{eff} = T_i + T_R\left[(G-1)\frac{\Delta\nu_M}{2\Delta\nu_R}+1\right]^{-1}. \quad (2)$$

This applies only when $\Delta\nu_M \leqq \Delta\nu_R$. Since in our system $\Delta\nu_M$ was always greater than $\Delta\nu_R$ and $G \gg 1$, (2) can be replaced by the simplier expression:

$$(T_{IN})_{eff} = T_i + \frac{2T_R}{G}. \quad (3)$$

and the figure of merit for the whole system for any given integration time, τ, is

$$\text{Fig. of merit} = F = \frac{2}{\pi}\sqrt{\tau}\Delta T_{RMS} = \frac{T_i}{\sqrt{\Delta\nu_S}} + \frac{2T_{R/G}}{\sqrt{\Delta\nu_S}} \quad (4)$$

where $\Delta\nu_S$ is the net bandwidth of the system and ΔT_{RMS} is the rms value of the system noise output, °K. If $\Delta\nu_S$ was limited by $\Delta\nu_M$ only, where $\Delta\nu_R = \Delta\nu_M$, then minimizing F for any given gain-bandwidth relation would determine the optimum values of G and $\Delta\nu_M$.

For our preamplifier, the following relation applies

$$G^{1/4}\Delta\nu_M \cong C_0 \quad (5)$$

where C_0 is a constant of the maser material. This shall be discussed in Section III, B. Solving then for the optimum gain, with $\Delta\nu_S$ limited only by $\Delta\nu_M$:

$$\text{Optimum } G = 14\frac{T_R}{T_i}. \quad (6)$$

A typical value of C_0 is 70 Mc, corresponding to a voltage gain-bandwidth product, at 20-db gain, of ~220. Using $T_R \sim 1000$°K and $T \sim 50$°K, one would obtain the optimum values $G = 24.5$ db and $\Delta\nu_M = 17.1$ Mc.

However, this optimum point is not at all critical. Fig. 4 shows a plot of F vs preamplifier gain, and it is seen that a wide variation of G with little change in sensitivity is possible. For this reason, G is always chosen to be a little low (20–23 db) to reduce gain instability, and $\Delta\nu_M$ is always more than sufficient to cover the 8-Mc band-pass of the superheterodyne receiver.

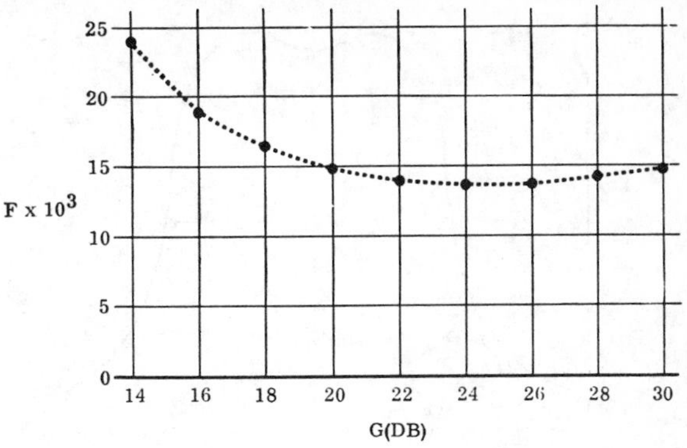

Fig. 4—Plot of radiometer figure of merit vs preamplifier gain for a 2000°K receiver and 50°K input temperature.

B. Theory of Operation

The preamplifier is a reflection-type, resonant-coupled cavity maser using 0.1 per cent ruby at the double-pump operation point ($\theta \cong 54°$). The gain and bandwidth relations for a single-cavity amplifier using nonresonant coupling are just

$$G_0^{1/2} = \frac{\Delta\nu_C + \Delta\nu_m'}{\Delta\nu_C - |\Delta\nu_m'|} \quad (7)$$

$$\Delta\nu_S = \Delta\nu_C - |\Delta\nu_m'| \quad (8)$$

where G_0 is the center gain at the resonant frequency, ν_0, $\Delta\nu_S$ is the $\frac{1}{2}$ power bandwidth, $\Delta\nu_C$ is the coupling bandwidth, and $\Delta\nu_m'$ is the effective magnetic bandwidth. That is,[7]

$$\Delta\nu_C = \frac{\nu_0}{Q_C} \qquad Q_C = \text{external or coupling } Q\text{, and} \quad (9)$$

$$\Delta\nu_m' = \Delta\nu_L + \Delta\nu_m \quad (10)$$

where

$$\Delta\nu_L = \frac{\nu_0}{Q_L} \qquad Q_L = \text{unloaded or loss } Q \quad (11)$$

$$\Delta\nu_m = \frac{\nu_0}{Q_m} \qquad Q_m = \text{magnetic } Q. \quad (12)$$

If one introduces a resonant cavity in front of the maser cavity, the center gain equation is essentially unchanged, functionally; but the bandwidth characteristics are greatly altered. The two resonances will tend to push each other in frequency and the typical double-humped response is obtained, as shown in Fig. 5. The separation of the humps $\Delta\nu_k$ is related to the coupling coefficient k between the two cavities as given by

$$\Delta\nu_k = \nu_0 k. \quad (13)$$

By analyzing a simple equivalent circuit one can obtain the above characteristics and show that the voltage gain bandwidth product is not a constant, but is proportional to $G^{1/4}$; *i.e.*, for high gains

$$(G^{1/2} - 1)\Delta\nu_S \cong 2\Delta\nu_m G^{1/4} \quad (14)$$

or

$$G^{1/4}\Delta\nu_S \cong 2\Delta\nu_m. \quad (15)$$

This dependence has been experimentally verified on this preamplifier over a range of 20–40 db, the voltage-

[7] Here the external and unloaded Q's have the conventional definition in terms of the electromagnetic field, and Q_m is defined in (21).

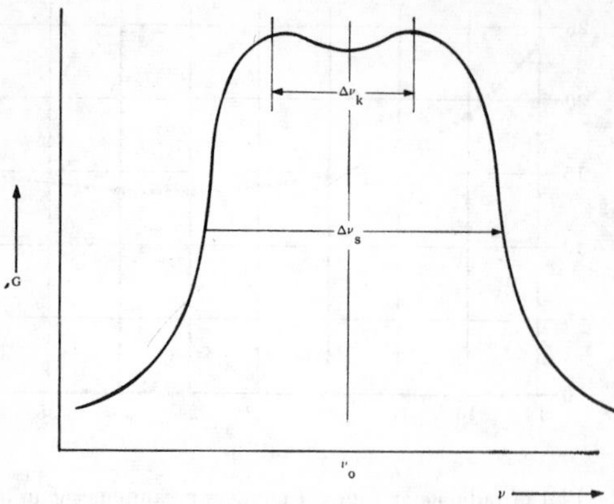

Fig. 5—Gain vs frequency response for the resonant coupled maser cavity.

gain bandwidth product ranging from 200 to 550 Mc.

As stated before, however, the gain instability at high gains has prevented the practical use of gains greater than ~30 db. The gain instability in the high-gain approximation is given by

$$\frac{\delta G}{G} = G^{1/2}\frac{\delta x}{x} \tag{16}$$

where x may be $\Delta\nu_m$, $\Delta\nu_C$ or VSWR. At a gain of 30 db, for instance, $G^{1/2} \cong 32$; hence any variation in the coupling magnetic Q or the VSWR in the waveguide will be amplified by a factor of 32.

The negative magnetic Q obtained is ~200, giving a negative magnetic bandwidth at 8.7 Gc of ~40 Mc under optimum conditions. However, in operation $|\Delta\nu_m'|$ is somewhat less because of the magnetic gain control which is discussed in Section III-C.

The theoretical negative magnetic Q may be obtained from the dynamics of the four-level spin system which determine the paramagnetic properties of ruby. The Zeeman splitting of the ground state of Cr^{+++} in Al_2O_3 shows a symmetry when the angle θ between the applied magnetic field and the crystalline axis is

$$\theta = \arc\cos\frac{1}{\sqrt{3}} \sim 54.7°. \tag{17}$$

The diagram of the energy level vs the magnetic field is shown in Fig. 6(a). Everywhere $\nu_{13}=\nu_{24}$ and $\nu_{12}=\nu_{34}$ and, at $H=3850$ gauss, $\nu_{23}\cong 8.7$ Gc and $\nu_{13}=\nu_{24}\cong 22.3$ Gc, which is a typical operating point for our preamplifier.

The population distribution of electrons among these levels is dependent on the ambient temperature T, the twelve relaxation probabilities ω_{ij} ($i, j=1$ through 4), and the presence of pump power at frequency $\nu_{13}=\nu_{24}$. In Fig. 6(b) and 6(c), the population of the levels is shown without and with pump saturation, respectively. Without saturation the population ratio of any two levels, i and j, is given by the Boltzmann factor

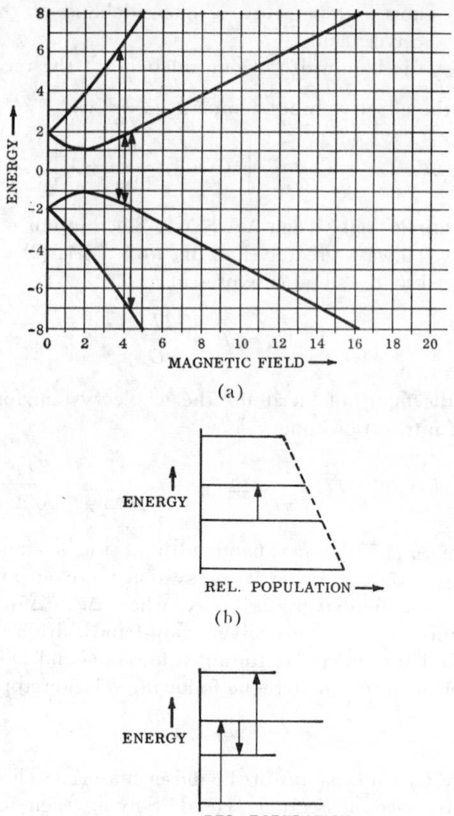

Fig. 6—Electron energy levels in ruby at $\theta=54.7°$ (a) vs magnetic field, (b) at fixed magnetic field without pump, (c) at fixed magnetic field with pump showing electron population changes.

$$\frac{n_i}{n_j} = e^{h\nu_{ij}/kT} \quad \text{where} \quad i > j, \tag{18}$$

but even at 4.2°K, $h\nu \ll kT$ for the frequencies involved, and thus the population difference, in particular for levels 2 and 3, is approximately

$$n_2 - n_3 \cong \frac{N}{4}\frac{h\nu_{23}}{kT} \tag{19}$$

The power absorbed from the cavity at frequency ν_{23} is given by P_{23},

$$P_{23} = h\nu_{23}(n_2 - n_3)\overline{W}_{23}, \tag{20}$$

and the magnetic Q is given by

$$Q_m = \frac{2\pi\nu_{23}\overline{H_{r-f}^2}}{P_{23}}\frac{V_0}{8\pi} \tag{21}$$

where $\overline{W}_{23}$ is the average transition probability over the ruby, H_{r-f} is the microwave magnetic field, and V_0 is the volume of the cavity. Thus, the functional dependence of the magnetic bandwidth $\Delta\nu_m$ is seen to be

$$\Delta\nu_m = (n_2 - n_3)(h\nu_{23})(f) \tag{22}$$

where f is a rather complex function of the cavity mode configuration and the quantum mechanical transition probability. For our mode configuration and crystal orientation, f is close to its maximum value.

Now, for the case of pump saturation $n_1 = n_3$ and $n_2 = n_4$. The resulting population difference in levels 2 and 3 is:

$$(n_2 - n_3) = \frac{N}{4}\frac{h}{kT}\left[\frac{\nu_{23}\omega_{23} - \nu_{14}\omega_{14} + \nu_{12}\omega_{12} - \nu_{34}\omega_{34}}{\omega_{23} + \omega_{14} + \omega_{12} + \omega_{34}}\right] \quad (23)$$

having a maximum negative value, if $\omega_{14} \gg \omega_{23}, \omega_{12}, \omega_{34}$ of

$$(n_2 - n_3)_{\max} = -\frac{N}{4}\frac{h\nu_{14}}{kT} \quad (24)$$

A convenient parameter to measure is the inversion factor I defined as the ratio of negative magnetic Q to positive magnetic Q.

$$I = \frac{|n_2 - n_3|_{\text{saturation}}}{|n_2 - n_3|_{\text{ambient}}}. \quad (25)$$

Eqs. (24) and (19) show the maximum value of I to be

$$I_{\max} = \frac{\nu_{14}}{\nu_{23}} \sim 4 \text{ at } \nu_0 = 8.7 \text{ Gc.} \quad (26)$$

I can be easily calculated from the values of the maser gain with pump on and off, G_1 and G_2, respectively.

$$I = \frac{(G_1^{1/2} - 1)(1 + G_2^{1/2})}{(G_1^{1/2} + 1)(1 - G_2^{1/2})}. \quad (27)$$

We have found that $I = 2.3$, which means that ω_{14} does not predominate, at least at $\nu_{23} = 8.7$ Gc.

C. Physical Description

The cavity and assembly are shown in Fig. 7. The active element is a rectangular parallelopiped of silvered ruby. The size of the silvered ruby for 8.7-Gc operation is 0.7″×0.5″×0.27″, and the signal mode is the (1, 1, 1) mode. In reliability and stability of operation, the silvered-ruby cavity is a significant improvement over the conventional machined-cavity designs that we have investigated. The microwave coupling is provided through slots cut in the silver with a dust cutter which provides a thin stream of air carrying abrasive powder at high velocity. The coupling plate contains a resonant iris operating in a semicoaxial mode because of the insertion of a silver pin. The side of the coupling cavity facing the waveguide is completely open; therefore, it is very heavily coupled to the waveguide. A typical value of $\Delta\nu_C$ for the coupling cavity is 250 Mc.

The cavity and coupling plate are firmly clamped to the waveguide as shown in Fig. 7(a). In this manner, several cavities can be used in the same assembly with a minimum of alteration. The frequency of the coupling cavity is tunable to allow for the change in resonant frequency of the ruby cavity at 4.2°K. This tuning is ac-

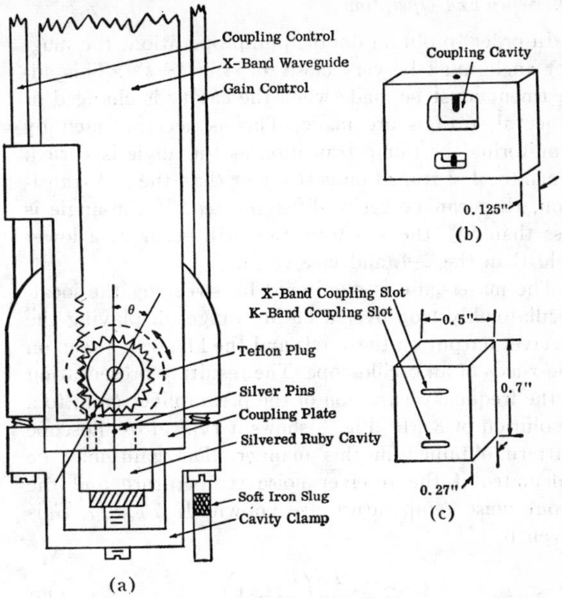

Fig. 7—The maser cavity assembly showing (a) complete assembly, (b) coupling plate containing the coupling cavity, (c) the silvered ruby cavity.

complished by a 5/8-inch diameter, 0.4-inch thick, teflon plug located in the waveguide near the coupling plate. It contains two small pieces of 0.040-inch diameter silver wire. As it is rotated, the silver wire perturbs the resonance field of the coupling cavity and produces a frequency change given by

$$\Delta\nu_0 = 1.2[\cos\theta] \text{ Gc} \quad (28)$$

where θ is as shown in Fig. 7(a). The teflon plug is rotated by means of a rack and pinion arrangement.

The gain of the preamplifier can be varied continuously from 10 to 30 db by the magnetic tuning rod. In this scheme, a small piece (0.125 inch diameter×0.150 inch) of soft iron is soldered into a 1/8-inch stainless steel rod which can be moved up and down. As the iron is moved near the cavity, it produces an inhomogeneity in the magnetic field which lowers the magnetic bandwidth $\Delta\nu_m'$ by broadening the resonance line. The gain-control rod is driven by a 1-rpm motor which advances the rod 1/17 inch per minute. This method of gain control is superior to varying the gain by means of the coupling Q since it does not change the cavity or coupling configuration and thus removes a possible source of instability.

Pump energy is coupled in a manner similar to the signal coupling. There is an abundance of cavity modes at the pump frequency, and saturation can usually be obtained in any of them.

Both signal and pump waveguides are filled with Styrafoam to reduce gain instability caused by a fluctuating liquid-helium level.

D. Setup and Operation

In order to obtain double-pump operation, the magnet angle must be very close to 54.7° ($\pm\frac{1}{2}$°). This adjustment must be made when the cavity is changed or other alterations are made. This is accomplished by monitoring the pump transition as the angle is varied. Since the 1–3 transition is stronger than the 2–4 transition, they can be easily differentiated. If the angle is less than 54°, the 1–3 transition will occur at a lower field than the 2–4, and vice versa.

The maser gain is monitored by sweeping the local-oscillator klystron over a 60-Mc range, displaying the receiver output on the y axis and the klystron sweep on the x axis of an oscilloscope. The resulting presentation is the frequency variation of the preamplifier gain, to a resolution of 8 Mc. Fig. 8 shows a typical oscilloscope pattern obtained in this manner. The gain may be calculated if the receiver noise temperature and the input noise temperature are known. If $T_R \gg T_I$, G is given by

$$G = \frac{T_R}{T_I}\left(\frac{R_2}{R_1} - 1\right). \tag{29}$$

Here R_2 and R_1 are in volts, and the detector is assumed to be operating in the square-law region.

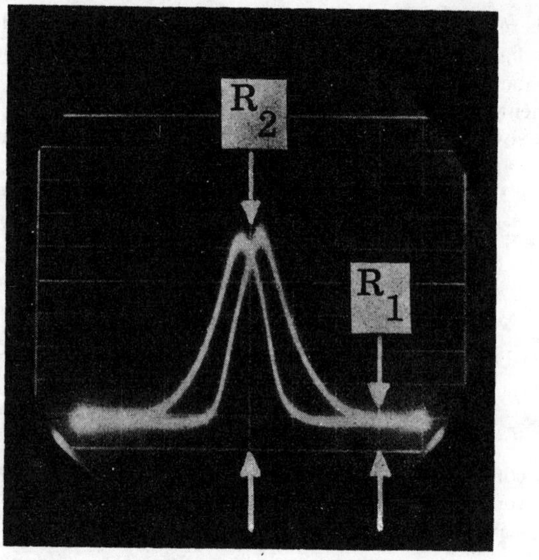

Fig. 8—Noise output of receiver vs local oscillator frequency showing the amplification of the input noise by the maser.

IV. System Performance

A. Threshold Sensitivity

The noise fluctuation, which establishes a lower limit for the sensitivity of a Dicke-system radiometer, arises from internally generated noise and gain instability. The noise contribution of each can be analyzed and their combined rms level taken as a measure of system sensitivity.

If we define a threshold sensitivity, due to internally generated noise, as that signal giving an output equal to the rms noise fluctuations, we get:

$$(\Delta T)_{in} = \frac{\pi}{2}\frac{(T_{in})_{eff}}{\sqrt{\Delta\nu_{ST}}} = \text{rms value of internally generated noise.} \tag{30}$$

Analysis of the gain-variation effect upon the output signal is an extremely complicated problem. Fluctuations throughout the system can occur from vibration, changes in ambient temperature, line voltages, etc., as well as from spurious changes in the components themselves. Assuming that these gain variations are random, they will have a probability density centered about G_0, and a rapidly decreasing frequency spectrum.[8]

One can presumably modulate at such a frequency rate, (f_{mod}), as to make the contribution of these gain variations small. However, there will still be a gain-instability threshold, caused by a nonzero switching signal, given by:

$$(\Delta T)_{GI} = \alpha(\gamma - 1)(|T_{ant} - T_{comp}|)$$
$$= \text{rms value of gain-instability noise.} \tag{31}$$

where γ = the gain-fluctuation factor $= 1 + (\delta G/G_0)$; $\delta G/G_0$ = percentage gain change. The term α depends upon the detection technique. In the case of synchronous detection, α is a rapidly decreasing function of frequency, centered about $\alpha = 1.0$, for gain variations at the modulation frequency, (f_{mod}).

In addition, very low-frequency gain "drift" will result in output changes which follow the drift. The input noise will be amplified by a varying amount; that is, in effect, the equivalent input temperature of (30) will change with maser gain. This type of drift can generally be removed in data reduction by merely adjusting the base line. The maser radiometer system has been affected only slightly by such low-frequency "drift."

Eq. (31) shows the desirability of keeping the temperature contributions of antenna and comparison source as closely balanced as possible. If there are large signals, or if the system cannot be balanced ($|T_{ant} - T_{comp}| > 1$°K), the gain-fluctuation threshold becomes quite large.

Summing the threshold rms noise levels as determined by internally generated noise and gain instability from (30) and (31), the resultant sensitivity threshold becomes

$$(\Delta T)_{rms} = \frac{\pi}{2}\frac{(T_{in})_{eff}}{\sqrt{\Delta\nu_{ST}}} + \alpha(\gamma - 1)(|T_{ant} - T_{comp}|). \tag{32}$$

[8] P. Strum, "Considerations in high sensitivity microwave radiometry," Proc. IRE, vol. 46, pp. 43–53; January, 1958.

B. Noise-Measurement Techniques

The sensitivity threshold of a radiometer has been shown to depend heavily upon the equivalent input temperature. Consequently, it is necessary to develop methods for precise system measurements as well as methods for convenient, approximate measurements.

1) *Precision Noise Measurements:* The circuit for system-noise measurement is shown in Fig. 9. The switchable circulator is dc energized, with the reversing switch thrown to look alternately at T_1 and T_2. The output power level is monitored on a dc microammeter, and the precision 30-Mc attenuator is varied to give an identical output with either T_1 or T_2 as input. If $T_1 > T_2$, we will necessarily add an amount of 30-Mc attenuation (Δ db) when the input is T_1, where:

$$\Delta \text{db} = 10 \log \frac{T_S + T_1}{T_S + T_2} \cdot \qquad (33)$$

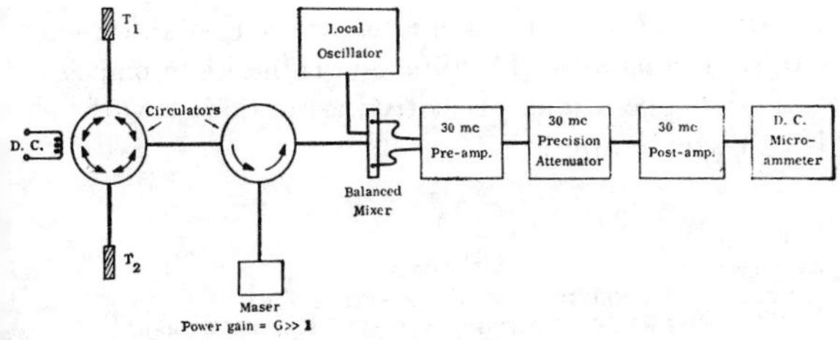

Fig. 9—Block diagram of noise measurement circuit.

In the case of the radiometer system *without maser*, we simply tune the magnetic field off resonance, leaving the system otherwise intact. Since input power of the same level enters the IF amplifiers from both signal and image bands, T_S is one half the excess noise temperature of the receiver and the total equivalent input temperature is $2T_S$.

For the system *with maser*, Δ db is measured as before and T_S obtained from (33). Now, however, input power in the signal band is multiplied by the maser gain (G), whereas the image power is not. T_S is therefore $G/(G+1)$ of the total excess noise temperature of the receiver and to the equivalent input is $T_S(G+1/G)$. Since G is the maser power gain and generally $G \gg 1$, we can quite accurately use a total equivalent input temperature T_S, as given by (33).

2) *Approximate Noise Measurements:* It is advantageous to devise quick checks on system performance which can be made before and during operation. In the case of system-noise temperature, two very convenient approximations have been used. These approximate measurements are adequate for routine checks, and precision methods are required only in special circumstances.

According to (33), the power output ratio between the two input arms is

$$\text{ratio} = \frac{T_S + T_1}{T_S + T_2} = R. \qquad (34)$$

Thus, if we know T_1 and T_2, we can calculate T_S from the ratio taken from an oscilloscope display of the IF postamplifier square-wave output. If we carefully measure T_2 as the total antenna arm input temperature (T_A) in, say, the access position, we need only establish T_1. Experience has shown that a hand over the comparison horn serves as an approximate ambient load. Thus, it becomes quite simple to approximate T_S from:

$$T_S \cong \frac{T_{\text{ambient}} - R(T_A)}{(R-1)} \cdot \qquad (35)$$

A second method, which does not require the antenna to be in the access position, allows a quick approximation of $(T_{\text{in}})_{\text{eff}}$, even during operation. This method, dependent only upon short-term gain stability (a very dependable maser property), utilizes a calibrated test signal. The temperature of the available test signal has been discussed in connection with (1).

The 2°K test signal (T_{test}) will produce a synchronous detector output to the recorder having an off-signal peak-to-peak noise fluctuation, $N = 4(\Delta T)$, and a dc level S due to the signal. We can now calculate $(T_{\text{in}})_{\text{eff}}$ from (30), where $T = \frac{1}{4}$ of the peak-to-peak noise (N).

$$\Delta T = \frac{T_{\text{test}}}{4} \left[\frac{N}{S} \right] \qquad (36)$$

which, when substituted in (30), gives:

$$(T_{\text{in}})_{\text{eff}} = \frac{T_{\text{test}}}{2} \left[\frac{N}{S} \sqrt{\Delta \nu_S T} \right]. \qquad (37)$$

It should be noted that this approximation includes the input temperature, and hence is *not* an *excess* noise measurement.

C. Performance Characteristics

The two most significant characteristics of the radiometer system are its equivalent input temperature and gain stability. The effect of these two parameters upon threshold sensitivity has been discussed [see (32)]. Extensive measurements of these and other operational characteristics have been made and compared with theoretical calculations.

The total system's excess noise temperature T_S may be predicted from the measured performance values:

Ambient temperature, input line loss = 0.45 db: $L_1 = 1.109$

Complete superheterodyne noise figure = 9.5 db; $T = 2000$°K

Cavity radiation and spontaneous emission $\cong$4°K.

We may therefore calculate T_S, dependent only upon maser gain (G), as:

$$T_S = 2000\left(\frac{L_1}{G}\right) + 4(L_1) + 290(L_1 - 1)$$

$$= 2220\left(\frac{1}{G}\right) + 36°\text{K}. \quad (38)$$

This results in a predicted T_S of 58 and 47°K with maser gains of 20 and 23 db, respectively. Actual precision measurements have given values of 70, 57, and 43°K with maser gains of 17, 20, and 23 db, respectively.

The off-source antenna temperature is about 30°K largely because of spillover and backlobe radiation. Conventional horn designs which are 10 or even 20 db down at the dish edge are unsatisfactory for maser radiometer use. The illumination beyond the dish edge adds a variable input noise temperature, negligible even with a 1000°K system, but of great importance as the system temperature is reduced to the maser radiometer range ($T<100$°K). Preliminary studies indicate that it is possible to design a multi-element horn to illuminate the dish in an essentially flat pattern, dropping very rapidly at the dish edges. Such a design is expected to yield an antenna temperature of approximately 10°K, essentially independent of antenna position.

The gain-stability performance of the complete system, taken experimentally with a maser gain of 20 db is approximately

Short term: < 10 minutes: 0.6 per cent
< 30 minutes: 2.0 per cent
Long term: <100 minutes: 5.0 per cent.

The variable-attenuator balance controls are capable of an off-source input signal zeroing to within:

$$T_{\text{ant}} - T_{\text{comp}} \mid < 0.02°\text{K}. \quad (39)$$

This amount of unbalance, together with a system gain instability of 2 per cent, contributes an rms output fluctuation as given by (31) of:

$$\alpha(\gamma - 1)(\mid T_{\text{ant}} - T_{\text{comp}} \mid) < 1.0(0.02)(0.02) = 0.0004°\text{K}. \quad (40)$$

Thus, for present system temperatures, the gain-fluctuation threshold is negligible.

The rms fluctuation due to internally generated noise becomes of primary concern. Theoretically, the threshold is predicted by (30):

$$(\Delta T)_{\text{rms}} = \frac{\pi}{2} \frac{(T_{\text{in}})_{\text{eff}}}{\sqrt{\Delta\nu_S \tau}}$$

where:

$(T_{\text{in}})_{\text{eff}} = T_S + T_{\text{antenna}} \cong 55 + 30 = 85$°K
$\Delta\nu_S$ = bandwidth = 8 Mc (IF limited)
τ = integration time = 2 seconds.

These values result in a threshold sensitivity of:

$$(\Delta T)_{\text{rms}} = \frac{\pi}{2} \frac{85}{\sqrt{16 + 10^6}} = 0.034°\text{K}. \quad (41)$$

Gain instability is such that long integration times are also usable. For example, $\tau = 42$ seconds gives, theoretically,

$$(\Delta T)_{\text{rms}} = \frac{\pi}{2} \frac{85}{\sqrt{336 \times 10^6}} = 0.0073°\text{K}. \quad (42)$$

Actual measurements, based upon a 2°K test signal are in very close agreement with these theoretical predictions. Measurements have given a no signal ($|T_{\text{ant}} - T_{\text{comp}}| < 0.02$°K)$\Delta T_{\text{rms}}$, taken as $\frac{1}{4}$ the peak-to-peak fluctuation, of:

$$(\Delta T)_{\text{rms}} \cong 0.033°\text{K}; \quad \tau = 2 \text{ seconds}$$
$$\cong 0.007°\text{K}; \quad \tau = 42 \text{ seconds}. \quad (43)$$

The latter $(\Delta T)_{\text{rms}}$ output fluctuation was maintained for 16 time constants (11 minutes). Table I summarizes the actual operational sensitivities obtained with a 2°K test-signal input.

TABLE I
SENSITIVITY VS INTEGRATION TIME
UNIVERSITY OF MICHIGAN MASER RADIOMETER

Integration time (τ) (seconds)	$(\Delta T)_{\text{rms}}$; threshold sensitivity ($\frac{1}{4}$ peak-to-peak fluctuation)°K
2	~0.033
12	~0.012
42	~0.007

Maser gain = 20 db: Post-maser noise temperature = 2000°K
Equivalent input temperature = 85°K; system bandwidth = 8 Mc
$\gamma \leqq 1.02$; $(|T_{\text{ant}} - T_{\text{comp}}|) \leqq 0.02$°K

V. RADIO ASTRONOMY OBSERVATION

The final test of any radio astronomy receiver is in the astronomical observations. Several drift curves, representative of the system sensitivity and performance are presented. In this type of observation, wherein the earth's rotation moves the antenna beam past the source, the antenna is stationary relative to the earth, thus eliminating spillover variations. Sources resulting in antenna temperature increases of 35°K to 0.4°K have been observed, using integration times from $\frac{1}{2}$ second to 42 seconds. In all cases, the system is balanced prior to the drift to minimize gain-instability fluctuations. A test-signal calibration is used to measure the antenna-temperature increase caused by the source.

Fig. 10 is a drift curve of the radio source Cassiopeia A, obtained with an integration time of $\frac{1}{2}$ second. No rms fluctuation has been calculated because the operation was relatively insensitive. The peak source con-

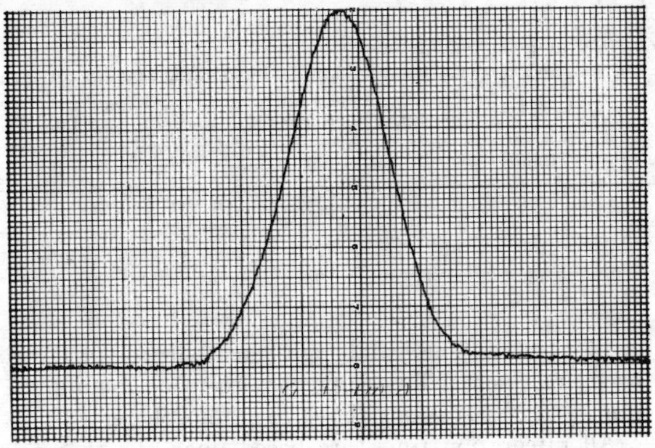

Fig. 10—Drift curve of radio source Cassiopeia A obtained with the maser radiometer (March 10, 1960). Peak antenna temperature increase is about 35°K. Integration time is ½ second.

tribution to antenna temperature is approximately 35°K.

Proceeding to more sensitive system performance, Fig. 11 shows a drift curve of Virgo A (M87, NGC 4486), obtained with a 2-second integration time. The resulting peak antenna-temperature increase was measured as 2.8°K, and the ratio of the signal to the peak-to-peak noise is about 21 to 1. Use of these values in (36) indicates an rms off-source noise fluctuation of 0.033°K; this is in very close agreement with the theoretical prediction of 0.034°K obtained from (41).

The response to Tycho Brahe's Super Nova 1572 is shown in Fig. 12. This figure also shows the calibration signal, in this case 2.05°K. The peak antenna-temperature increase is approximately 0.61°K; integration time is again 2 seconds. The rms value of the noise fluctuation, taken as ¼ of the peak-to-peak, is, in this case, approximately 0.055°K. The theoretical prediction is again about 0.034°K. Because the results are, in general, in excellent agreement with theory, this disagreement is attributed to the least understood variable of the system: the atmospheric effects upon antenna temperature.

Fig. 13 shows the signal from Hydra A, the antenna temperature increase is 0.45°K and the integration time 12 seconds. RMS noise fluctuation is approximately 0.016°K which compares favorably with a theoretical prediction of 0.013°K. Assuming an antenna efficiency of 0.50 (as determined by comparing the results from several strong sources with expected results on the basis of published flux values), the point-source flux from Hydra A at 8.72 Gc (3.45 cm) is $(4.8 \pm 1.4) \times 10^{-26}$ watts/m²/cps.

VI. Conclusion

The performance of this system has shown the maser radiometer to be a dependable, useful addition to radio astronomy equipment. The maser amplifier can be incorporated into a long-term program and engineered to assure reliable, high-sensitivity operation upon installation. With careful design and operation, the ratio of operational to down time has been proven to be as good as a conventional, high-sensitivity, nonmaser receiver.

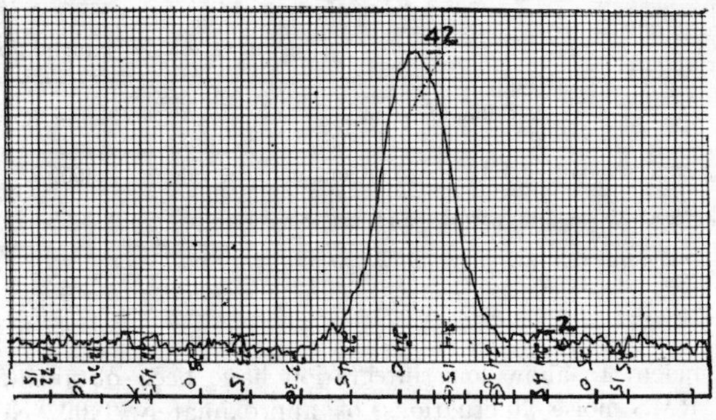

Fig. 11—Drift curve of radio source Virgo A obtained with the maser radiometer (February 25, 1960). Peak antenna temperature increase is 2.8°K. Integration time is 2 seconds.

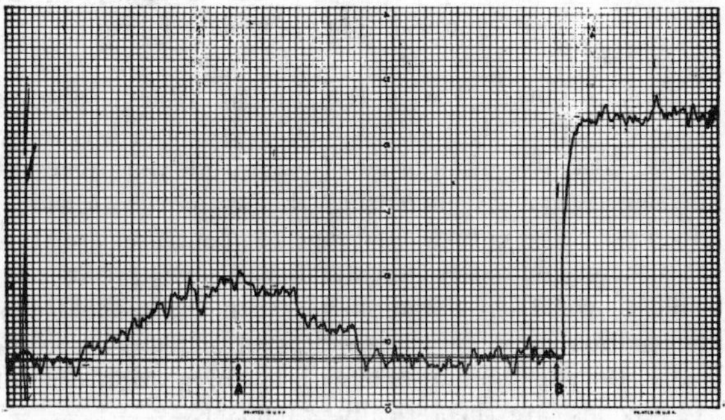

Fig. 12—Drift curve of Tycho Brahe's Super Nova 1572 obtained with the maser radiometer (March 14, 1960). Peak antenna temperature increase is 0.61°K. Test signal is 2.05°K. Integration time is 2 seconds.

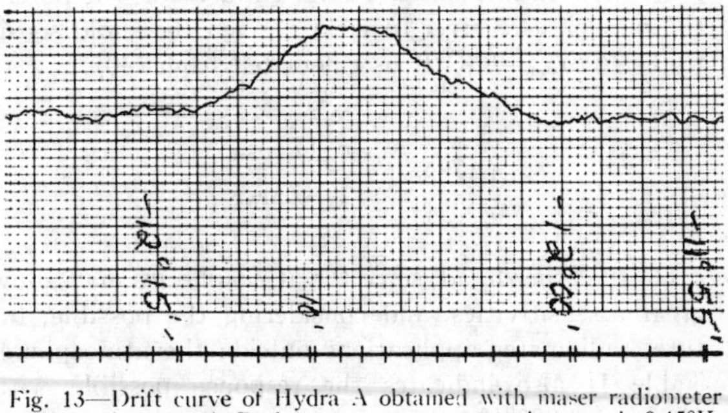

Fig. 13—Drift curve of Hydra A obtained with maser radiometer (March 2, 1960). Peak antenna temperature increase is 0.45°K. Integration time is 12 seconds.

RMS noise fluctuations of approximately 0.01°K with integration times as short as 12 seconds have been obtained for the first time. The faster response, because of the shorter integration time, has great operational significance since it makes it unnecessary to spend many minutes, or even hours, obtaining sensitive observations. Further, the first maser gain stabilities suf-

TABLE II
COMPARISON OF EXISTING AND FUTURE X-BAND RECEIVERS

X-Band System	$(T_{in})_{eff}$(°K)	$\Delta\nu_S$(Mc)	τ (sec) for $(\Delta T)_{rms}=0.02°K$	τ (sec) for $(\Delta T)_{rms}=0.003°K$
Presently existing, broad-band, nonmaser receivers	4000	1000	~100	~4400
Presently existing, narrow-band, maser receiver	75	8	~4.5	~200
Predicted, broad-band, maser receiver	40	100	~0.1	~4.4

ficient to allow long integration have been obtained. RMS noise fluctuations of approximately 0.007°K, with an integration time of 42 seconds, are possible. Improved techniques, such as the use of a cooled-load test signal rather than a noise tube and the "double-horn" comparison technique for sources of small extent (planets, point sources), offer simpler, more reliable operation.

Results obtained with the present system indicate that it is possible to design an even more advanced system, capable of an order-of-magnitude improvement in sensitivity. By increasing the system bandwidth, decreasing the equivalent input temperature, and further increasing maser gain stability, it now appears possible to construct a radiometer with a threshold rms fluctuation of a few thousandths of a degree. Specifically, the rms fluctuations, with an integration time of 12 seconds, are theoretically <0.003°K.

Since atmospheric limitations are, as yet, somewhat unknown, there is some feeling that pushing the radiometer sensitivity below a few thousandths of a degree offers little return. However, the benefit of shorter integration times still exists. Table II illustrates the potential of such a receiver to yield a given threshold sensitivity $(\Delta T)_{rms}=0.02°K$ as calculated from (30):

$$(\Delta T)_{rms} = \frac{\pi}{2} \frac{(T_{in})_{eff}}{\sqrt{\Delta\nu_S \tau}}.$$

On the other hand, since the atmospherics may allow greater sensitivities, and considering the possible, future, radiometer applications outside the atmosphere, Table II also indicates the response possible with $(\Delta T)_{rms}=0.003°K$.

The fast response and high sensitivity of predicted maser receivers will be important to space communications and observations above the atmosphere.

All integration times are based upon the threshold due to internal noise only. Thus, due to gain variations during the extremely long integration times, this sensitivity is improbable with present nonmaser systems.

Future maser receivers will doubtlessly utilize mechanical refrigerators, eliminating much of the troublesome manpower and time requirement of maser operation. Continuous 4.2°K cooling will allow radio astronomy maser receivers to be operated by one man. Also, the constantly refrigerated maser assembly will require essentially no setup adjustment, and routine operation at the flip of a switch is conceivable. Although the present system has been successfully operated by semitrained (in maser operation) radio astronomy personnel, the initial setup has required personnel more experienced in maser work. The predicted continuous cooling and single setup would eliminate this requirement.

ACKNOWLEDGMENT

The authors wish to thank Prof. C. Kikuchi for his guidance and support throughout the program. They wish to express their gratitude to Profs. R. L. Hess and F. T. Haddock, who initiated the program and devoted much time and effort to its support. Special acknowledgment is due A. J. Cote and F. Alred for their technical contributions and assistance throughout the design, construction and installation; C. B. Arnold, G. Latimer and J. Talen for their assistance in the installation and operation; and Drs. A. H. Barrett and W. E. Howard for their supervision of the astronomical observations.

Low-Field *X*-Band Ruby Maser*

A solid-state maser utilizing ruby[1] has been operated at an *X*-band signal frequency of 9540 mc using an *X*-band pump frequency of 10,850 mc. The maser was operated at low magnetic fields (350 gauss) oriented at $\theta = 32°$ to the ruby *C*-axis.

To obtain spin temperature inversion in a three-level maser, it is necessary[2] that either $f_{23}/f_{12} > \tau_{23}/\tau_{12}$ for amplification at frequency f_{12}, or that $f_{12}/f_{23} > \tau_{12}/\tau_{23}$ for amplification at frequency f_{23}, where the three energy levels have been numbered from 1 to 3, and f_{12}, f_{23} and τ_{12}, τ_{23} are the frequencies and spin-lattice relaxation times, respectively, of the two intermediate transitions.

In most three-level ruby masers previously operated,[3,4] these two relaxation times were approximately equal, so that good inversion was obtained by making the idler frequency f_{23} several times the signal frequency f_{12}. However, we, as well as others,[5] found it difficult to obtain this type of "frequency-ratio" maser operation[6] in ruby at low magnetic fields for an *L*-band signal frequency $f_{12} = 800$ to 2000 mc for a large range of magnetic field orientations. Our measurements showed that for θ near 32°, the magnetic absorption in the *L*-band transition increased when pump power was applied. Also, the spin temperature in the idler transition f_{23} becomes more positive when pump power is applied, and, in fact, maser operation at f_{23} is obtained (Fig. 1). Evidently, this is "relaxation-time ratio" operation[6]—that is, τ_{12} is considerably shorter than τ_{23} to overcome the unfavorable frequency ratio $f_{12}/f_{23} \approx 1/6$. Measurements of relaxation times and of the influence of the fourth energy level are being made to investigate this.

* Received by the IRE, May 15, 1959. This work is part of a Ph.D. dissertation, Polytechnic Institute of Brooklyn, Bklyn, N. Y.

[1] G. Makhov, C. Kikuchi, J. Lambe, and R. W. Terhune, "Maser action in ruby," *Phys. Rev.*, vol. 109, pp. 1399–1400; February 15, 1958.

[2] N. Bloembergen, "Proposal for a new type solid-state maser," *Phys. Rev.*, vol. 104, pp. 324–327; October 15, 1956.

[3] R. W. DeGrasse, E. O. Schulz-DuBois, and H. E. D. Scovil, "Three-level solid-state traveling-wave maser," *Bell Sys. Tech. J.*, vol. 38, pp. 305–334; March, 1959.

[4] F. R. Arams and S. Okwit, "Tunable *L*-band ruby maser," Proc. IRE, vol. 47, pp. 992–993; May, 1959.

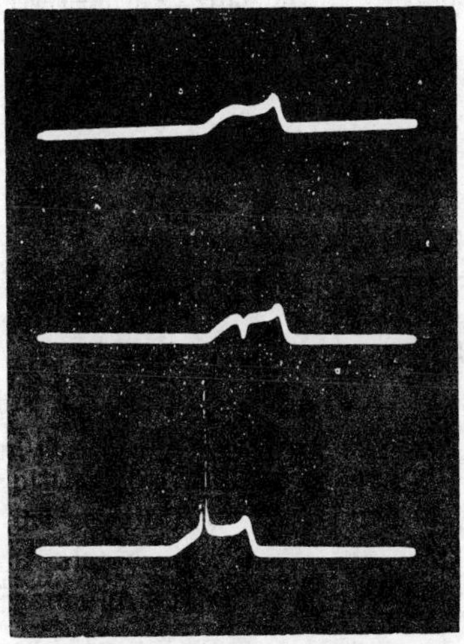

Fig. 1—Oscilloscope display of power reflected from maser cavity as a function of frequency. (a) No pump power. (b) Pump power sufficient to overcome cavity losses. (c) Maser gain with high pump power.

The cavity (operating in the TE_{10} waveguide mode) used a 100-carat ruby crystal having a 0.05-per cent residual chromium content. The measured voltage-gain bandwidth product was 4 mc at a helium bath temperature of 4.2°K. Pump power was approximately 50 milliwatts.

Perhaps the type of operation reported here may find application in millimeter-wave masers using paramagnetic materials with large zero-field splittings. In this application, the relatively low-pump frequency and low-magnetic field requirements of this type of operation may be attractive, even though the achievable gain-bandwidth product will be lower than that for masers using more favorable frequency ratios.

Stimulating discussions with S. Okwit (AIL), M. Birnbaum (Polytechnic Institute of Brooklyn), and S. Shapiro (Harvard University) are gratefully acknowledged.

Frank R. Arams
Airborne Instruments Lab.
Melville, N. Y.

[5] Private communication.

[6] E. O. Schulz-DuBois, H. E. D. Scovil, and R. W. DeGrasse, "Use of active material in three-level solid-state masers," *Bell Sys. Tech. J.*, vol. 38, pp. 335–352; March, 1959.

Operation of a Zero-Field X-Band Maser*

J. E. KING AND R. W. TERHUNE
The University of Michigan, Willow Run Laboratories, Ann Arbor, Michigan
(Received July 10, 1959)

A MASER using iron doped Al_2O_3 has been operated successfully as an amplifier at 12.3 kMc using only very small magnetic fields for tuning. In this case the crystalline electric field splits and mixes the spin states in a manner suitable for three level maser action without a magnetic field present. With other presently used materials, one has to use a large dc magnetic field to obtain a similar situation.

The paramagnetic resonance spectrum of the Fe^{+++} ion in Al_2O_3 has been studied in several laboratories,[1-4] and its energy level diagram for small magnetic fields and $\theta=0°$ (i.e., the c axis aligned with the dc magnetic field) is shown in Fig. 1. A total of six levels is involved as the spin of the Fe^{+++} ion is 5/2. Note that each of the levels is designated as a mixture of spin states. This mixing is a result of interactions with the cubic crystalline electric field and occurs only for ions with a spin of 2 or larger. As a result of this mixing, transitions from the lower two states to the upper two states are allowed even with $\theta=0°$. When θ is varied, the rate of splitting with magnetic field of the pairs of spin states changes.

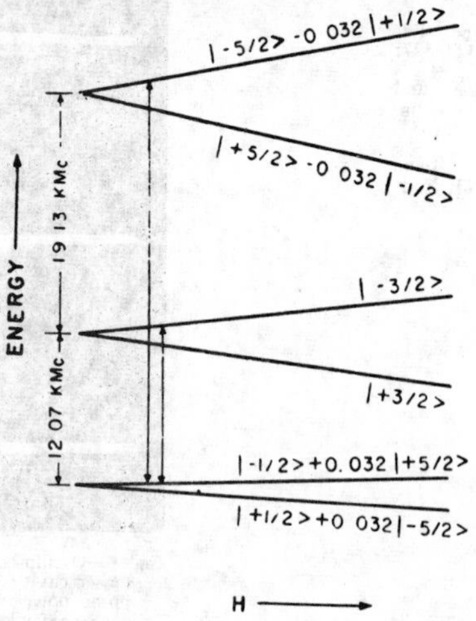

FIG. 1. Energy level diagram for Fe^{+++} ion in Al_2O_3 for small magnetic fields and $\theta=0$.

A small silver-plated rectangular parallelepiped of 0.1% nominal iron-doped Al_2O_3 prepared by Linde was used as a reflection cavity.[5] Cavity modes with excellent loss Q's were obtained at 12.3 and 31.8 kMc. With $\theta=20°$ and $H=120$ gauss the frequencies of the transitions indicated on the energy level diagram matched these cavity resonances.

A QK290 klystron was used to provide 10 mw of pump power at 31.8 kMc. We were able to saturate the 31.8-kMc transition at 4.2° even though the paramagnetic absorption appeared to be very weak. A voltage gain band width product of 15 Mc/sec was obtained at this temperature with a signal frequency of 12.3 kMc.

* This research was supported by Project Michigan (administered by the U. S. Army Signal Corps).

1 L. S. Kornienko and A. M. Prokhorov, J. Exptl. Theoret. Phys. (U.S.S.R) 33, 805–807 (1957).
2 G. S. Bogle and H. F. Symmons, Proc. Phys. Soc. (London) 73, 531 (1959).
3 E. O. Schulz-DuBois (private commuuication).
4 J. W. Meyer (private communication).
5 Lloyd G. Cross (to be published).

Commonwealth of Australia
COMMONWEALTH SCIENTIFIC AND INDUSTRIAL RESEARCH ORGANIZATION

Reprinted from PROCEEDINGS OF THE INSTITUTE OF RADIO ENGINEERS
Vol. 49, No. 2, Page Nos. 573-590, March 1961

Cross-Relaxation Masers*

G. S. BOGLE†

***Summary*—A survey is made of the available ways of using ruby, spinel, rutile and emerald in masers which amplify at frequencies small compared to their zero-field splitting frequencies. Particular attention is paid to means of taking advantage of cross relaxation which, it is shown, can give typically a two-fold improvement in maser performance. Analytic expressions for the energies are given which, to a large extent, remove the need for machine computations in the design of masers of this type.**

I. INTRODUCTION

SINCE the proposal of the three-level solid state maser in 1956,[1] three paramagnetic compounds have been used as working materials, and of these the most generally successful has been ruby.[2] The success of ruby has been due to its high zero-field splitting frequency (11.5 kMc), its high dielectric constant and mechanical strength, and its ready availability in large monocrystals. However, when attempts were made to utilize ruby in *L*-band (about 1400 Mc) masers at low magnetic fields (250 to 500 gauss), anomalous effects were found which prevented maser action,[3,4] and most development work was thenceforward concentrated on a high-field (2000 gauss) mode of operation in which the maser action is particularly good.[5] It will be shown below that cross-relaxation processes[6] (interchanges of energy between neighboring paramagnetic ions) provide an explanation of both the poor action at low fields and the particularly good action at the high field. It will be shown, further, that by a correct choice of conditions the low-field mode can be made to work in a way which derives advantage from cross relaxations.

Paramagnetic resonance data have already been measured for several materials, minerals and gemstones containing Cr^{3+}, which are even more promising than ruby for masers because of their higher zero-field splitting frequencies. A great many such materials no doubt await investigation. It is important to be able to assess

* Received by the IRE, July 18, 1960; revised manuscript received, December 5, 1960.

† Division of Physics, C.S.I.R.O., University Grounds, Sydney, Australia.

[1] N. Bloembergen, "Proposal for a new type solid state maser," *Phys. Rev.*, vol. 104, pp. 324–327; October 15, 1956.

[2] J. Weber, "Masers," *Revs. Modern Phys.*, vol. 31, pp. 681–710; July, 1959.

[3] A. A. Penzias, "Maser Amplifier for 21 cm," Columbia Rad. Lab., New York, N. Y., Fourth Quarterly Progress Rept., pp. 7–9; December, 1958.

[4] G. S. Bogle and F. F. Gardner, "Cross-Relaxation Effects in a Ruby *L*-Band Maser," paper in preparation.

[5] F. R. Arams and S. Okwit, "Tunable *L*-band ruby maser," PROC. IRE, vol. 47, pp. 992–993; May, 1959.

[6] N. Bloembergen, S. Shapiro, P. S. Pershan, and J. O. Artman, "Cross-relaxation in spin systems," *Phys. Rev.*, vol. 114, pp. 445–459; April 15, 1959.

them without having to wait for machine computations of the energy levels such as are now available for ruby, and, to this end, approximate expressions for the energy levels are derived which are sufficiently accurate for maser design in cases where the splittings of the energy levels by the magnetic field are small compared to the zero-field splitting. These expressions, believed to be presented for the first time, are used to discuss the use in low-field masers of the new materials, with emphasis on obtaining assistance from cross relaxation.

In high fields the above approximate methods fail; but, provided that the field is applied along a symmetry axis, the equation for the energy levels may be solved exactly. The solutions are used to derive the field required as a function of amplifying frequency for ruby-like substances in general. The successful high-field ruby L-band maser is an example of a type of cross-relaxation-assisted maser action which is also possible with the new materials. The conditions for its realization are discussed, and it is found that the amplifying frequency is specific to the material concerned.

In what follows, we shall first review maser behavior in the absence of cross relaxation, then discuss the effect of cross relaxation, and finally consider the expected maser performance of the new materials, particularly when advantage is taken of cross relaxation.

II. Maser Action According to the Old Picture

In the old picture[1] of maser action, a system of three energy levels was considered and two types of transition between levels were taken into account. One type was the spin-lattice relaxation transition, in which energy is exchanged between the paramagnetic ions and the lattice thermal vibrations. The associated probability per second is termed w_{ij} where i and j are the participating energy levels. The other type was the radiation-induced transition, in which energy is exchanged between the paramagnetic ions and the electromagnetic field: the transition probability is termed W_{ij}. Cross-relaxation transitions (see below), in which energy is exchanged between paramagnetic ions directly, were not considered.

The method of operation of the three-level maser may be illustrated with the energy levels of Fig. 1, ignoring level 1 for the present time. The system of paramagnetic ions is subjected to a microwave field at the frequency $\nu_{42}=(E_4-E_2)/h$ and of such an intensity that W_{42} is much greater than the w's. In that case the resonance at ν_{42} is saturated and the populations of levels 4 and 2, *i.e.*, n_4 and n_2, are practically equal.[1] This process is described as "pumping the maser at frequency ν_{42}," or simply "pumping ν_{42}."

It can now be shown, if the w's are all of about the same magnitude and $\nu_{32}\gg\nu_{43}$, as in Fig. 1, that $n_4>n_3$. Then if weak radiation at frequency ν_{43} is applied, the system will emit power given by

$$P_{43} = W_{43}(n_4 - n_3)h\nu_{43}. \qquad (1)$$

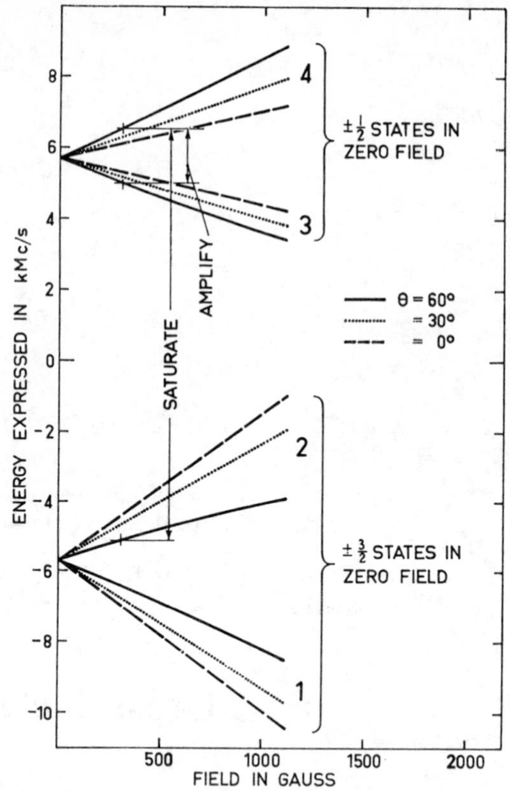

Fig. 1—Energy levels of ruby at low magnetic fields for several angles (θ) between the field and the crystalline axis. The maser saturating and amplifying transitions are indicated for $\theta=60°$.

With suitable circuits is may be possible to make P_{43} greater than the input power so that amplification is achieved.

A useful criterion of merit[2,7] of a maser material in a particular mode of operation is the quantity $-1/Q_M$ which is defined as $(1/2\pi\nu)$ times the ratio of power emitted to energy stored in the maser material.[2] Q_M corresponds to the Q of tuned circuits, but in the maser it is negative because energy is gained instead of lost as in passive circuits. The higher the value of $-1/Q_M$, the higher the maser gain which can be obtained for a given bandwidth. For example, in the case of a cavity maser with voltage-gain $G^{1/2}$ (*i.e.*, power-gain G) and bandwidth Δf, it may be shown that under reasonable practical conditions

$$G^{1/2}\Delta f \simeq 2\nu_s/|Q_M|, \qquad (2)$$

ν_S being the frequency of the signal amplified.[2] By combining (1) and (4) of footnote 7 and adapting the level labels to the present case, it may be shown that

$$-1/Q_M = 4\pi g^2\beta^2|\langle 3|S|4\rangle|^2(n_4 - n_3)/h\Delta\nu, \qquad (3)$$

[7] G. S. Bogle and H. F. Symmons, "Zero-field masers," *Aust. J. Phys.*, vol. 12, pp. 1–20; March, 1959.

where g is the spectroscopic splitting factor,[8] β is the Bohr magneton, $\langle 3|S|4\rangle$ is the matrix element of the spin operator between the states 3 and 4, and $\Delta\nu$ is the width of the transition intensity profile.

In a single material, $\langle i|S|j\rangle$ and $\Delta\nu$ do not vary greatly with mode of operation, so that different modes may be compared principally through their values of $n_4-n_3=\Delta n_{43}$ or, in general, Δn_{ij}. For the maser system under discussion at present, with levels ascending in the order 2, 3, 4 and with pumping at ν_{42} and a signal frequency of ν_{43}, Bloembergen's[1] equation becomes

$$n_3 - n_4 = \Delta n_{34}$$
$$= (hN/3kT)(w_{34}\nu_{43} - w_{23}\nu_{32})/(w_{34} + w_{23}), \quad (4)$$

where $N=n_2+n_3+n_4$. (Note that we are still dealing with a three-level system; the labels have been chosen as 2, 3 and 4 merely to accord better with the discussion later on.) The term $hN/3kT$ also occurs in the expression for n_3-n_4 in thermal equilibrium (*i.e.*, in the absence of pumping), *viz.*:

$$(n_3 - n_4)_0 = \Delta_0 n_{34} = (hN/3kT)\nu_{43}.$$

[The above equations and all similar equations in this paper are only true in the approximation that kT is much larger than the total energy separation of the lowest group of states of the paramagnetic ions (*e.g.*, those of Fig. 1) and much smaller than the energies of excited states (*e.g.*, those responsible for optical absorption). This is a good approximation for many paramagnetic compounds, including ruby, in fields of some thousands of gauss. As a consequence of the approximation there is no need to distinguish between w_{ij} and w_{ji} in writing expressions like those in (4).]

By dividing by $\Delta_0 n_{34}$, and expressing frequencies in terms of the pumping frequency $\nu_p=\nu_{42}$ and the signal (amplifying) frequency $\nu_S=\nu_{43}$, (4) can be put in the simpler form

$$\Delta n_{34}/\Delta_0 n_{34} = 1 - (\nu_p/\nu_S)/(1 + w_{34}/w_{23}). \quad (5)$$

This equation shows clearly how a large ratio of pump to signal frequency is desirable in order to obtain a large negative value of Δn_{34} and secure good maser action.

Because the emphasis is on negative Δn_{34}, and $\Delta_0 n_{34}$ is of course positive, it is customary to define an "inversion ratio" $I=-\Delta n_{34}/\Delta_0 n_{34}$. A higher inversion ratio connotes better maser action.

When account is taken of the fourth energy level E_1, (5) takes a more complicated form which has been given, for example, in (7) of footnote 7. With suitable change of labels, and expressing all frequencies as before in terms of ν_S and ν_p, the following equation is obtained for the inversion when ν_{42} is pumped:

$$I = -\Delta n_{34}/\Delta_0 n_{34}$$
$$= -1 + \frac{\nu_p}{\nu_S}\cdot\frac{w_1 w_{23} + w_{13}w_{12}}{w_1(w_{23} + w_{34}) + w_{13}(w_{12} + w_{14})}, \quad (6)$$

where

$$w_i = \sum_{j\neq i} w_{ij},$$

i taking the value 1 in this case and other values in later equations. It is seen that the predicted maser behavior is essentially the same with four levels as with three; in particular, to obtain a high inversion ratio a high value of ν_p/ν_S is desirable as before.

III. Energy Levels of Cr^{3+}

The energy levels of the paramagnetic Cr^{3+} ion in crystalline solids are derivable from a spin Hamiltonian of the form[8]

$$H = \beta B\cdot g\cdot S + D(S_z^2 - \tfrac{5}{4}) + E(S_x^2 - S_y^2) \quad (7)$$

where g and β are as defined above, B is the magnetic field, S is the spin operator, x, y and z are the axes of symmetry of the crystalline environment of the Cr^{3+} ions, and D and E are constants describing the effect of the crystalline electric field. If its symmetry is trigonal or higher, $E=0$, and z is parallel to the axis of symmetry.[8] It is often the case that the g-tensor is isotropic or may be assumed so with sufficient accuracy for maser design. Then $\beta B\cdot g\cdot S$ may be replaced by $g\beta B\cdot S$, and if at the same time $E=0$, the spin Hamiltonian takes the simpler form

$$H = g\beta B\cdot S + D(S_z^2 - \tfrac{5}{4}). \quad (8)$$

In zero magnetic field, the energy levels determined by (7) are two doublets separated by $2(D^2+3E^2)^{1/2}$ (see Appendix I-Section A); this separation is known as the zero-field splitting.[8] In the special case that $E=0$, the states in zero field are $S_z=\pm\frac{3}{2}$ at D and $S_z=\pm\frac{1}{2}$ at $-D$; and this description of the states is still approximately true when $E\neq 0$, provided that $|E/D|\ll 1$.

When the amplifying frequency is small compared to the zero-field splitting frequency, as it is in the cases to be discussed here, it may be seen from the figures, or from the expressions given below for the energies, that the pumping frequency is comparable to the zero-field splitting frequency. Eq. (6) shows that the population inversion is better the higher the pumping frequency; and later equations, which allow for cross relaxation, will show the same type of dependence. Thus special interest attaches to materials with high zero-field splittings.

Ruby has already been established as an important material for maser design.[2,5,9] Ruby consists of α-Al_2O_3

[8] K. D. Bowers and J. Owen, "Paramagnetic Resonance II," *Repts. Progr. Phys.*, vol. 18, pp. 304–373; 1955.

[9] C. Kikuchi, J. Lambe, G. Makhov, and R. W. Terhune, "Ruby as a maser material," *J. Appl. Phys.*, vol. 30, pp. 1061–1067; July, 1959.

(corundum, or clear sapphire) with a small proportion of the Al^{3+} ions replaced by paramagnetic Cr^{3+}. Its success in maser applications is due to its considerable mechanical robustness and to its high zero-field splitting frequency of 11.5 kMc.[9] From recent paramagnetic studies several other materials are at present known which have similar robustness and even higher splitting frequencies: emerald (beryl, $Be_3Al_2Si_6O_{18}$, containing Cr^{3+}), which has a zero-field frequency of 54 kMc,[10] rutile (TiO_2) containing Cr^{3+}, which has the frequency of 43 kMc,[11] and spinel ($MgAl_2O_4$) containing Cr^{3+}, 30 kMc.[12] Both ruby and emerald have the simpler Hamiltonian (8) with D negative; spinel has the same type of Hamiltonian with the sign of D unknown; rutile has a nonzero value of E and the signs of E and D are not yet known. The signs, however, are unimportant for maser action.[13] In all four substances the g-tensor may be taken as isotropic.

The spin Hamiltonians (7) and (8) each lead to equations[9] for the energies which are in general of the fourth degree for Cr^{3+} and require numerical solution. In the case of the simpler Hamiltonian (8) it is possible to express the energy equation in normalized form by writing $y=W/D$, W being the energy, and $x=g\beta B/D$, and the solutions for y are applicable to any material obeying (8). (W, meaning energy, is not to be confused with W_{ij}, meaning a radiation-induced transition probability.) The direction of the magnetic field needs only to be specified by its polar angle θ relative to the z-axis, since the directions of the x and y axes are not significant in (8). Diagrams and tables of the energy levels and transition probabilities as a function of field strength and direction are given for this case in Weber,[2] Schultz-DuBois[14] and Howarth.[15] (It should be noted that in Weber[2] and Howarth[15], the levels were labeled under the supposition that D in the spin Hamiltonian was positive; the level-labels 1, 2, 3, 4 in those references should be replaced by 4, 3, 2, 1, respectively, to accord with the discussion of ruby maser action presented here.)

In the case of the general Hamiltonian (7), the difficulties of tabulating solutions of the energy equation are much greater: tables would have to be prepared for each value of E/D and would depend on the azimuthal angle ϕ as well as on θ because the directions of the x and y axes are significant in (7). To the author's knowledge, no such tables have yet been published.

The energy levels of ruby are shown for low fields and for $\theta=0°$, 30° and 60° in Fig. 1, and for $\theta=90°$ and up to higher fields in Fig. 2. At fields of a few hundred gauss (Fig. 1) and with θ between 90° and about 20° the transition probabilities[2,14,15] are well adapted for a maser amplifying at ν_{43} and saturated ("pumped") at ν_{42} or ν_{41}. When ν_{43} is 1400 Mc the field required is about 500 gauss at $\theta=0$, varying smoothly to about 250 gauss at $\theta=90°$; and it will be shown that the same is approximately true of substances with higher zero-field splittings than ruby. This type of operation will be referred to as "the low-field mode" of operation, although strictly speaking, it comprises a class of modes each characterized by the value of θ and field used.

At $\theta=90°$ (Fig. 2) the transition probabilities are well adapted for a maser amplifying at ν_{21} and pumped at ν_{31} or ν_{41}. As can be seen from Fig. 2, a field of about 2000 gauss is required for amplification at 1400 Mc with ruby. It will be shown below that even higher fields would be necessary with emerald and spinel. Operation in this mode will be termed "the high-field mode" of operation; it is restricted to values of θ close to 90° since the transition probability between levels 1 and 2 rises to a sharp maximum at 90° and is very weak

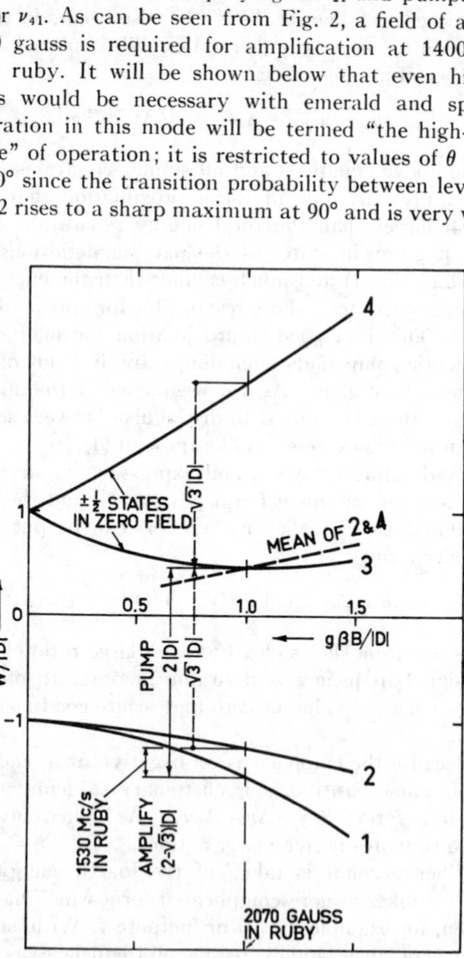

Fig. 2—Normalized energy $W/|D|$ vs normalized field $g\beta B/|D|$ plotted for ruby-like materials. At $g\beta B/|D|=1$, $W_4-W_3=W_3-W_2$, and a cross-relaxation process is possible in which an ion jumps from 4 to 3 while a neighbor jumps from 2 to 3; these are shown as dotted vertical lines. The pumping and amplifying transitions of the cross-relaxation-assisted maser mode are shown. (D is negative, as for ruby and emerald.)

[10] J. E. Geusic, M. Peter, and E. O. Schulz-Du Bois, "Paramagnetic resonance spectrum of Cr^{+++} in emerald," *Bell Sys. Tech. J.*, vol. 38, pp. 291–296; January, 1959.

[11] H. J. Gerritsen, S. E. Harrison, H. R. Lewis, and J. P. Wittke, "Fine structure, hyperfine structure, and relaxation times of Cr^{3+} in TiO_2 (rutile)," *Phys. Rev. Letters*, vol. 2, pp. 153–155; February 15, 1959.

[12] R. Stahl-Brada and W. Low, "Paramagnetic resonance spectra of chromium and manganese in the spinel structure," *Phys. Rev.*, vol. 116, pp. 561–564; November 1, 1959.

[13] Weber, *op. cit.*, p. 710.

[14] E. O. Schulz-Du Bois, "Paramagnetic spectra of substituted sapphires—Part I: ruby," *Bell Sys. Tech. J.*, vol. 38, pp. 271–290; January, 1959.

[15] D. J. Howarth, Properties of ruby as a maser crystal," Royal Radar Establishment, Malvern, Eng., Memo. No. 1525; October, 1958.

between 0° and 80°.[2,14,15] This is the reason why the transition at ν_{21} cannot be used for amplification in the low-field mode: it is well-allowed only when $\theta > 85°$, and then the field required is over 1000 gauss.

The above two modes are the most important modes of operating an L-band maser with ruby and with Cr^{3+} in other compounds where the zero-field splitting is similar to or higher than in ruby. The high-field mode is important because it has been used in the most successful L-band cavity maser yet reported.[5] This had a voltage-gain bandwidth product of nearly 40 Mc. The low-field mode is important, although the best voltage-gain bandwidth product yet achieved appears to be 4 Mc[16] because of the convenience of low magnetic fields.

In discussing these two classes of maser mode it is desirable to have analytic expressions for the energy levels, and it is fortunate that this can be achieved in both cases. At low fields, up to 500 gauss in ruby for example, the term $g\beta B \cdot S$ in the spin Hamiltonian (7) is small compared with the zero-field splitting $2|D|$, so that a series expansion with good convergence can be derived for the energies. This is done in Appendix I. The result, for materials which, like ruby, have $E=0$, is:

$$W_1 = D + \frac{3}{2}\lambda g\beta B\cos\theta + \tfrac{3}{8}\sin^2\theta(g\beta B)^2/D$$

$$W_2 = D - \frac{3}{2}\lambda g\beta B\cos\theta + \tfrac{3}{8}\sin^2\theta(g\beta B)^2/D$$

$$W_3 = -D + \tfrac{1}{2}\lambda g\beta B(1 + 3\sin^2\theta)^{1/2} - \tfrac{3}{8}\sin^2\theta(g\beta B)^2/D$$

$$W_4 = -D - \tfrac{1}{2}\lambda g\beta B(1 + 3\sin^2\theta)^{1/2} - \tfrac{3}{8}\sin^2\theta(g\beta B)^2/D, \quad (9)$$

where $\lambda \equiv D/|D|$. The energies so defined ascend in the order W_1, W_2, W_3, W_4 for negative D (as in ruby, Fig. 1) and descend in the same order for positive D. Subsequent terms are of order $(g\beta B)^3/D^2$ and are not greater than the equivalent of a few Mc in the present case. The corresponding equations for the general Hamiltonian (7) with $E \neq 0$ are more complicated; they are given in Appendix I.

Eq. (9) may be used to calculate the frequencies involved in maser action. A natural situation is one in which the signal frequency ν_{43} is to be held at a given value, and it is desired to know the required value of field as a function of θ. From (9) it is evident that $h\nu_{43} = g\beta B(3\sin^2\theta + 1)^{1/2}$ with an error of order $(g\beta B)^3/D^2$. The numerical formula for the field B in gauss is

$$B = 0.357(2/g)\nu_{43}(1 + 3\sin^2\theta)^{-1/2} \quad (10)$$

where ν_{43} is in magacycles per second. The fractional error in the value of B given by the above equation is at most $(1/4)(h\nu_{43}/2D)^2$, for example 0.5 per cent for ruby when $\nu_{43} = 1440$ Mc. This shows that for substances with higher zero-field splittings than ruby the magnetic field required for L-band maser operation in the low-field mode is practically the same as for ruby. For materials obeying the general spin-Hamiltonian (7), (10) has to be replaced by

$$B = 0.357(2/g)\nu_{43}[\cos^2\theta(1 - 4\sin^2\alpha)^2 + \sin^2\theta(4\cos^4\alpha + 3\sin^2 2\alpha - 4\sqrt{3}\cos^2\alpha\sin 2\alpha\cos 2\phi)]^{-1/2} \quad (11)$$

where θ and ϕ define the direction of the applied magnetic field, and α is given by

$$\tan\alpha = \frac{E\sqrt{3}}{D + \lambda(D^2 + 3E^2)^{1/2}},$$

as shown in Appendix I. For rutile, with $|D| = 0.55$ cm^{-1} and $E = 0.27$ cm^{-1}, the expression under the radical sign in (11) becomes $0.275 + \sin^2\theta(4.09 - 3.94\cos 2\phi)$. It can be seen that the field strength required for L-band operation with rutile in the low-field mode is of the same order of magnitude as with ruby and emerald.

When the field is applied perpendicular to the z-axis of ruby-like materials the energies may be obtained exactly because the secular equation factorizes into two quadratics. The energies are given in (40). Rewriting for the case of negative D and putting $G = g_\perp\beta B$, the levels are

$$W_{4,2} = \tfrac{1}{2}G \pm (D^2 + G^2 + |D|G)^{1/2}$$

$$W_{3,1} = -\tfrac{1}{2}G \pm (D^2 + G^2 - |D|G)^{1/2} \quad (12)$$

labelled to accord with Fig. 2. For the purpose of comparing working materials, it is desirable to have an explicit expression for the field required for a given value of $\nu_{21} = (W_2 - W_1)/h$, which is the amplifying frequency in this mode. Expanding the radicals in W_2 and W_1, and writing $x = g_\perp\beta B/|D|$, one obtains

$$(W_2 - W_1)/|D| = (3/8)x^3 - (15/128)x^5 \cdots.$$

Preserving only the first term in the expansion, the field in gauss required for a given frequency ν_{21} is given by

$$B \simeq 0.31(2/g_\perp)\nu_{21}^{1/3}\nu_{ZF}^{2/3} \quad (13)$$

where ν_{ZF} is the zero-field splitting frequency and ν_{21} is the amplification frequency, and both are expressed in megacycles per second. The fractional error in (13) occasioned by the neglect of the x^5 term in the previous equation is about 0.3 $(\nu_{21}/\nu_{ZF})^{2/3}$, or 10 per cent for ruby and 3 per cent for emerald, both at L-band. From (13), the magnetic field required to operate the high-field mode with emerald, amplifying at about 1400 Mc, is about 5000 gauss. The inconvenience of this high field makes it important to attempt to utilize the low-field mode where the field would be only a few hundred gauss, in spite of the indifferent success of this mode hitherto in ruby.

IV. Effect of Cross Relaxations

The original theory[1] of maser action was shown to be in need of modification when it was found that there was a limiting chromium concentration in a potassium

[16] S. H. Autler, "Tunable L-Band Maser," Lincoln Lab., Lexington, Mass., Quarterly Progress Rept., p. 65; July 15, 1959.

chromicyanide maser, above which the population inversion necessary for maser action could not be obtained.[17] The explanation of this and other effects has been given in terms of cross-relaxation processes.[6,18]

A cross-relaxation process is one in which energy is exchanged directly between neighboring paramagnetic ions. (In contrast, spin-lattice-relaxation processes involve exchange of energy between paramagnetic ions and the lattice vibrations.) The probability of a cross relaxation is greater the closer the neighbors, and so the effect is concentration-dependent. We shall consider the situations in which cross relaxations affect *L*-band maser performance in ruby.

A distinction needs to be drawn between cross relaxations and the more familiar spin-spin relaxations conventionally characterized by the relaxation time T_2. Using Fig. 1 for illustration, a spin-spin relaxation consists typically in one ion jumping from level 1 to 2 while a neighbor does the opposite. This process does not change the level populations and therefore does not affect the maser equations. In contrast, a cross relaxation consists typically in an ion's jumping from level 1 to 2 while a neighbor jumps from 4 to 3. This process does change the level populations and radically affects maser behavior. Unlike spin-spin relaxations, cross relaxations may involve triple or multiple jumps and can occur only in a system of at least three levels with the energy gaps harmonically related.

A. Cross-Relaxation Processes in Ruby at Low Fields

1) *Cross relaxation near $\theta=29°$:* The cross-relaxation process may be illustrated with reference to ruby at low fields (Fig. 1). It may be shown from (9) that near $\theta=29°$, $2(W_4-W_3)=W_2-W_1$. It may be shown by a quantum-mechanical treatment[6] that if a paramagnetic ion in level 1 has two neighbors in level 4 there is a probability that the former will jump up to level 2, while the latter each jump down to level 3, the total energy being conserved in the process. The process is a resonance process, having its maximum probability when the total energy is exactly conserved—*i.e.*, when $2(W_4-W_3)$ is exactly equal to W_2-W_1. Like other resonance processes, it has a "line-width," and this width is of the same order of magnitude as those of the levels themselves (typically 50 Mc in maser materials). The probability of the transition, when "on resonance," depends on the proximity of the neighbors and on the nature of the states of the paramagnetic ion, and is independent of temperature except for the slight temperature-dependence of the lattice dimensions and of the spin Hamiltonian parameters. By contrast, the spin-lattice relaxation times vary rapidly with temperature: in 0.05 per cent ruby, for example, a typical relaxation time has the value 17 μsec at 90°K and 22 msec at 4.2°K.[19] A convincing classical picture of the cross-relaxation process is hard to give; it might be regarded crudely as a phenomenon in which the local magnetic fields of the two ions in state 4, each oscillating at ν_{43}, beat together to form a component at $2\nu_{43}$, which is the correct frequency, ν_{21}, to be absorbed by their neighbor in jumping from level 1 to 2.

As well as the cross-relaxation process just described above, the inverse process of course also occurs, and in the model of footnotes 6 and 18, the latter has the same probability as the former when the equality between $2(W_4-W_3)$ and W_2-W_1 is exact. When the equality is not exact, *i.e.* near but not at $\theta=29°$, the probabilities of the process and its inverse are not precisely equal, but the essential character of the cross-relaxation effect remains the same and this complication will be ignored.

The rate equations for the level populations may now be written in a way analogous to that of Shapiro and Bloembergen,[18] which deals with a two-spin process, whereas the present case is a three-spin process. The method is to write down the rates of change of population of each level and finally to equate them to zero. Following Bloembergen[1] one has, in the absence of cross-relaxation terms, a set of four equations like

$$\frac{dn_i}{dt}=\sum_{j\neq i} w_{ji}\left(n_j-n_i+\frac{Nh\nu_{ji}}{4kT}\right)+\sum_{j\neq i} W_{ji}(n_j-n_i). \qquad (14)$$

W_{ji} is the radiation-induced transition probability between levels i and j, and $W_{ij}\equiv W_{ji}$. The equation is written for a system of four levels, as exemplified by Cr^{3+}.

The contribution of the cross-relaxation processes will now be derived. For a given ion in level 3 at the lattice site α, let us ask what is the probability of a cross-relaxation process in which ion α jumps from level 3 to 4 while simultaneously a neighbor in site β jumps from level 2 to 1 and another neighbor in site γ jumps from 3 to 4. This process is shown diagrammatically in Fig. 3. (We shall disregard the inverse process for the meantime.) The process can occur only if sites β and γ are each filled with paramagnetic ions, and the chance of this is c^2 where c is the concentration of paramagnetic ions in the crystal (usually less than 1 per cent in maser work). If β is filled, the chance that it is correctly filled with an ion in state 2 is n_2/N, where $N=n_1+n_2+n_3+n_4$; and the chance that γ is correctly filled is n_3/N. Thus $c^2n_2n_3/N^2$ is the probability that the appropriate situation exists. Let the probability of a cross-relaxation transition under these circumstances be $w_{\alpha\beta\gamma}$; $w_{\alpha\beta\gamma}$ depends on quantum-mechanical variables and the displacements of β and γ from α. The transition probabil-

[17] S. H. Autler and N. McAvoy, "21-Centimetre solid-state maser," *Phys. Rev.*, vol. 110, pp. 280, 281; April 1, 1958.

[18] S. Shapiro and N. Bloembergen, "Relaxation effects in a maser material, $K_3(CoCr)(CN)_6$," *Phys. Rev.*, vol. 116, pp. 1453–1458; December 15, 1959.

[19] J. H. Pace, D. F. Sampson, and J. S. Thorp, "Spin-lattice relaxation times in ruby at 34.6 kMc/s," *Phys. Rev. Letters*, vol. 4, pp. 18, 19; January 1, 1960.

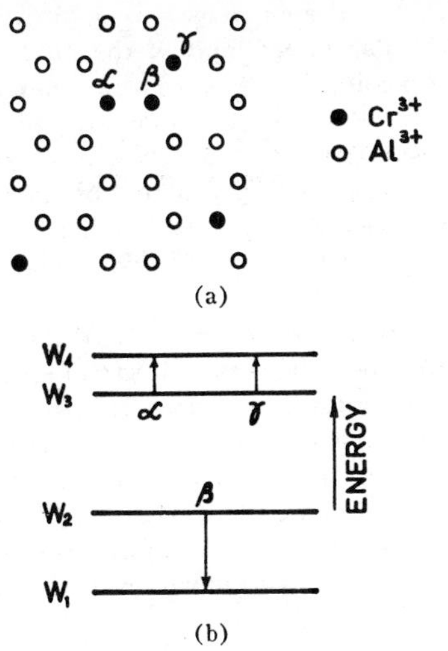

Fig. 3—(a) Sketch of a small region of a ruby crystal showing one of the occasional close groups of paramagnetic ions; and (b) the cross-relaxation process executed by the group when $W_2 - W_1 = 2(W_4 - W_3)$, as in ruby at $\theta = 29°$ in low magnetic fields.

ity associated with these particular sites is then $w_{\alpha\beta\gamma}c^2 n_2 n_3/N^2$, and to dispose of the contribution of site α we must sum over-all neighboring sites β and γ, by replacing $w_{\alpha\beta\gamma}$ by

$$w_\alpha = \sum_{\beta\gamma} w_{\alpha\beta\gamma}.$$

As w_α is not necessarily the same for all sites α, let w_c be its average over unit cell; then the total number of transitions in the crystal becomes

$$n_3 \cdot w_c c^2 n_2 n_3/N^2.$$

In the notation of Shapiro and Bloembergen,[18] $c^2 w_c$ would be called $w_{21,34,34}$. Remembering now the inverse transitions, the net number is seen to be $w_c c^2(n_2 n_3^2 - n_1 n_4^2)/N^2$. The effect of these transitions may now be added to (14), noting that the transition which takes one ion from level 2 takes two from 3, and gives two to 4 and one to 1. Thus the rate equation for level 3, for example, is

$$\frac{dn_3}{dt} = \sum_{j\neq 3} w_{j3}\left(n_j - n_3 + \frac{Nh\nu_{j3}}{4kT}\right) + \sum_{j\neq 3} W_{j3}(n_j - n_3) - 2c^2 w_c(n_2 n_3^2 - n_1 n_4^2)/N^2. \quad (15)$$

This equation, together with the other equations, may now be solved generally by the methods of Shapiro and Bloembergen.[20] However, useful insight into the effect of the cross relaxations may be gained by a qualitative discussion, at any rate for the important case that $c^2 w_c$ is much greater than any w_{ij}. Suppose that it is intended to operate a maser to amplify at ν_{43} by pumping ν_{42} at low fields (Fig. 1) with $\theta = 29°$. Then $W_{42} \gg w_{ij}$, and the other W's are zero, so that no W enters (15). In the steady state $dn_3/dt = 0$, and hence the final term on the right-hand side of (15) is equal to the first. The first is at most of order Nw_{ij}, w_{ij} meaning a typical spin-lattice rate; hence

$$\frac{n_2 n_3^2 - n_1 n_4^2}{N^3} \sim \frac{w_{ij}}{c^2 w_c} \ll 1,$$

which means that $n_2 n_3^2 \simeq n_1 n_4^2$, the fractional difference between them being only of order $w_{ij}/(c^2 w_c)$. The same would be true even if the pumping was done at another frequency, because it would always be possible to choose a dn_i/dt which contained no W, and the above argument could still be applied.

We shall now consider maser action near $\theta = 29°$; it will be seen how cross relaxation introduces an additional constraint on the system. Suppose ν_{42} is pumped with the intention of producing stimulated emission at ν_{43}. The saturation of the resonance at ν_{42} makes n_4 equal to n_2; the cross relaxations make $n_2 n_3^2$ equal to $n_1 n_4^2$: therefore

$$n_3^2 = n_1 n_4.$$

That is, n_3 is the geometric mean of n_1 and n_4. Now consider n_1: it is not being forced into equality with any of the other populations by pumping, and, physically, it would be expected to be the greatest population since it belongs to the lowest level. That is, n_1 is greater than n_3, which is the geometric mean of n_1 and n_4. Therefore n_3 is greater than n_4 and the resonance at ν_{43} remains absorptive. The mathematical solution bears this out. For pumping ν_{42}, and with $c^2 w_c \gg w_{ij}$, the solution of (15) and its companions gives

$$I = \frac{-\Delta n_{34}}{\Delta_0 n_{34}} = -1 + \frac{\nu_{42}}{\nu_{43}} \frac{w_{32} - 2w_{14} - w_{13}}{w_3 + 4w_{12} + 4w_{14}}; \quad (16)$$

this shows that to get a maser effect, *i.e.* a positive inversion, it would be necessary for $2w_{14} + w_{13}$ to be small in comparison with w_{32}. This is a far more stringent requirement on the w_{ij}'s than applies in the absence of cross relaxation [see (6)]. Indeed, (16) shows that it is possible for the absorption coefficient at ν_{43} to be *increased* by pumping, which is found in practice with 0.05 per cent ruby at 4.2°K.[4] This could not happen on the basis of (6).

The situation is altered if the pumping power is applied instead at ν_{41}. Arguing qualitatively, as before, one may observe that the pumping now makes n_1 equal to n_4; the cross relaxations make $n_2 n_3^2$ equal to $n_1 n_4^2$, whence $n_2 n_3^2 = n_4^3$, and so $(n_4/n_3)^2 = n_2/n_4$. As n_2 belongs to a low level, which is not involved in pumping, it might be expected to be larger than n_4, so that, in turn, n_4 would exceed n_3 according to the last equation. Thus there is no obvious influence antagonistic to n_4

[20] Shapiro and Bloembergen, *op. cit.*, p. 4.

being greater than n_3 as required for maser action. In this case the solution of (15) and its companions gives, for $c^2w_c \gg w_{ij}$,

$$I = \frac{-\Delta n_{34}}{\Delta_0 n_{34}} = -1 + \frac{\nu_{41}}{\nu_{43}} \frac{3w_{32} + 2w_{24} + w_{31}}{4w_2 + 4w_{32} + w_3}, \quad (17)$$

showing that maser action should be obtained unless the w_{ij}'s in the numerator were particularly small.

It is interesting now to inquire how this cross-relaxation maser action compares with what would be expected if the concentration c were so low that $c^2w_c \ll w_{ij}$ and the "ordinary" maser equation still applied. Eq. (6) may easily be adapted for pumping at ν_{41} instead of ν_{42} by interchanging the suffices 1 and 2, yielding

$$I = -1 + \frac{\nu_{41}}{\nu_{43}} \cdot \frac{w_2w_{13} + w_{23}w_{21}}{w_2(w_{13} + w_{34}) + w_{23}(w_{21} + w_{24})} \quad (18)$$

as the ordinary maser equation in this case. To compare the inversion ratios in the two cases we need an estimate of the ratios of the w_{ij}'s. Recent work[19] on relaxation rates in ruby at liquid helium temperatures suggests that they are proportional to the magnetic dipole transition probabilities, and, surprisingly, show no dependence on frequency. We shall therefore adopt what might be called a "magnetic dipole model" of relaxation rates by using the magnetic dipole transition probabilities for isotropic radiation. Using the charts given in Howarth,[15] the relaxation rates so calculated for $\theta = 30°$ and for the magnetic field which makes ν_{43} equal to 1400 Mc are, in arbitrary units: $w_{12} = 0.00$, $w_{13} = 1.22$, $w_{14} = 0.26$, $w_{23} = 0.29$, $w_{24} = 1.22$ and $w_{34} = 1.56$. For the cross-relaxation maser, (17), the inversion ratio is 3·1; whereas for the ordinary maser, (18) gives 2·8.

At this point it might be objected that, since the cross-relaxation maser gives only a slight improvement of inversion ratio, and, for other values of the w_{ij}'s, could conceivably give no improvement at all, the term "cross-relaxation-assisted maser" is a misnomer. It is true that on the basis of inversion ratio alone a better description in this case would be "cross-relaxation-compatible maser"; but this compatibility is in itself valuable. If cross-relaxation effects were to be avoided, the concentration would have to be lowered to about ten times below the value of 0.05 per cent commonly used in ruby masers at present, because at 0.05 per cent, the cross-relaxation rate is about twenty times higher than the spin-lattice[4] near $\theta = 29°$ at 4°K. (If the concentration were decreased ten-fold the cross-relaxation rate would decrease one hundred-fold.) Thus masers can work with much higher concentration if their action is compatible with cross relaxation than if it is incompatible, and higher concentration means greater power-handling ability and bandwidth.

Because the cross-relaxation rate at $\theta = 29°$, where the "resonance" condition $2(W_4 - W_3) = W_2 - W_1$ is exact, is many times higher than the spin-lattice relaxation rate, its influence continues to dominate the latter's even when θ is altered to as low as 25° and as high a about 35°.[4] The upper limit of the range is uncertain because of possible interference from a new cross-relaxation process which is "on resonance" at $\theta = 55°$ (see below). As a result of the "29° effect" and the "55° effect," no maser action can be obtained in 0.05 per cent ruby, when ν_{42} is pumped, at any angle between about 25° and 60°.[4] The 55° effect will now be considered.

2) *Cross relaxation near $\theta = 55°$:* At $\theta = 55°$ it follows from (9) that $W_4 - W_3 = W_2 - W_1$ (*cf.* Fig. 1 for $\theta = 60°$), and so a cross-relaxation process is favored in which an ion jumps down from level 4 to 3 while simultaneously a neighbor jumps up from 1 to 2. The discussion of this process may be given along the same lines as that of the 29° process given above, and it turns out that the contribution from cross-relaxation to the rate equation of, say, level 3 is

$$cw_c'(n_1n_4 - n_2n_3)/N$$

[*cf.* (15)]. Here, w_c' is determined by the lattice structure and the quantum-mechanical states of the paramagnetic ion at $\theta = 55°$, and is distinct from the quantity w_c used to describe the 29° process. The cross-relaxation process now tends to equalize n_1n_4 and n_2n_3, and it can be seen qualitatively that if ν_{42} were pumped, equalizing n_2 and n_4, n_1 and n_3 would be equalized as well. This is true not only at $\theta = 55°$, but for a range of angles which extends about ten degrees above and below 55° in pink ruby,[4] and experimentally the effect is to destroy maser action at L-band when the intended amplifying frequency is ν_{43} and the pumping frequency is ν_{42}. The solution of the cross-relaxation equation accords with this observation; we shall not quote it here, but merely observe that it is identical with the solution found when both ν_{42} and ν_{31} are intentionally pumped in an entirely different kind of maser mode called the "double-pumped" or "push-pull" mode.[9] In the latter mode, the angle θ is set as closely as possible to the ideal angle of $\cos^{-1}(1/\sqrt{3})$ or 54.7° where $\nu_{42} = \nu_{31}$; then pumping with a single frequency saturates both transitions, leading to very good inversion at ν_{32}.[9] The push-pull mode requires unusually precise design because, of the two degrees of freedom (field and angle) usually employed in setting up a maser, one is lost. Cross relaxation should be of assistance in the push-pull maser, for even though θ might be different from 54.7° and $\nu_{31} \neq \nu_{42}$, the cross relaxations should maintain both of the conditions $n_1 = n_3$ and $n_2 = n_4$ provided that one of them was maintained by pumping.

To continue with the low-field maser at $\theta = 55°$, we next consider the effect of the cross relaxations when ν_{41} is saturated. Just as with the $\theta = 29°$ case it is found that maser action is now obtainable. Solution of the equations analogous to (15) yields

$$I = -\frac{\Delta n_{34}}{\Delta_0 n_{34}} = -1 + \frac{\nu_{41}}{\nu_{43}} \frac{2w_{23} + w_{24} + w_{31}}{2w_{23} + w_2 + w_3}. \quad (19)$$

At $\theta = 55°$, adoption of the magnetic dipole model for the w_{ij}'s gives (in the same arbitrary units as before) $w_{12}=0.00$, $w_{13}=0.95$, $w_{14}=0.50$, $w_{23}=0.60$, $w_{24}=0.95$ and $w_{34}=1.35$, at the magnetic field necessary to make ν_{43} equal to about 1400 Mc; the pumping frequency is 12.9 kMc. The inversion ratio, from (19), is then 4.0. In the absence of cross relaxation it would be 2.2, from (18). At and near this angle it appears that good maser action should be possible in the presence of cross relaxation.

The angle of 90° is significant as being as unfavorable as possible to the cross-relaxation processes since $\nu_{21} \simeq 0$ at low fields. This angle is also the one used for the only successful low-field L-band maser yet reported[16] which, as mentioned above, had a gain-bandwidth product of 4 Mc, ten times poorer than that of the high-field maser. The inversion obtainable in 0.05 per cent ruby being 2.5 at $\theta = 90°$ in the low-field mode[4] as against 5.2 in the high-field mode (see next paragraph), it is probable that the best possible low-field maser performance has yet to be realized.

B. The High-Field L-Band Maser Mode in Ruby

An unusually high inversion ratio of 5.2 has been measured in ruby at liquid helium temperature at a field of about 2000 gauss perpendicular to the axis.[21] The energy levels are shown in Fig. 2; the levels of which the populations were inverted were 1 and 2, and the pumping transitions were from 1 to 3. At the field used in the measurements, ν_{21}, the monitoring frequency, was 1500 Mc and ν_{31} was about 11.5 kMc.

The high value of the inversion ratio is hard to understand on the basis of the ordinary maser equation, but may be explained in terms of cross relaxation. The ordinary maser equation for this case, obtainable by transposing level-labels in (6), is

$$I = -\frac{\Delta n_{12}}{\Delta_0 n_{12}}$$

$$= -1 + \frac{\nu_{31}}{\nu_{21}} \frac{w_4 w_{23} + w_{24} w_{34}}{w_4(w_{23} + w_{12}) + w_{24}(w_{34} + w_{14})}, \quad (20)$$

and, in the magnetic dipole model of transition probabilities, the values of the w_{ij} are, in arbitrary units, $w_{12}=1.89$, $w_{13}=0.77$, $w_{14}=0.15$, $w_{23}=1.42$, $w_{24}=0.26$ and $w_{34}=1.42$. The inversion is calculated to be only 2.4.

The possibility of a cross-relaxation process in this mode suggests itself when the energy levels for about 2000 gauss are examined. A glance at Fig. 2 shows that $W_4 - W_3$ is nearly equal to $W_3 - W_2$. A cross-relaxation process is therefore possible in which a paramagnetic ion in level 4 jumps to 3 while simultaneously a neighbor jumps from 2 to 3. In the figure, a dotted line is drawn representing $1/2(W_2 + W_4)$; where this crosses the level W_3 the equality of $W_4 - W_3$ and $W_3 - W_2$ is exact. In Appendix II the field for this coincidence is found algebraically, and it is shown to be given by

$$g_\perp \beta B = |D|. \quad (21)$$

It is also shown that the pumping (ν_{31}) and amplifying (ν_{21}) frequencies are given by

$$h\nu_{31} = 2|D|; \qquad h\nu_{21} = (2-\sqrt{3})|D|. \quad (22)$$

Eqs. (21) and (22) are true for any ruby-like Cr^{3+} compound, and they assert that the magnetic field required is that equivalent to half the zero-field splitting-frequency ν_{ZF}, the pumping frequency is equal to ν_{ZF}, and the amplifying frequency is $\nu_{ZF}(2-\sqrt{3})/2$ or 0.134 ν_{ZF}. In the case of ruby, taking $\nu_{ZF} = 11.49$ kMc and $g_\perp = 1.987$,[14] one finds that the ideal magnetic field for the cross-relaxation process is 2065 gauss and the amplification frequency is 1535 Mc. As before, however, the cross-relaxation process can continue to dominate the spin-lattice relaxations even when the "resonance" is not exact. Referring to the 55° cross-relaxation process at low fields, discussed above, we find that it still has an important effect at $\theta = 65°$, at which angle it is "off-resonance" by about 400 Mc. Supposing that a similar latitude applies to the high-field case, it is easy to show, from the energy level curve, that the magnetic field could be about 140 gauss higher or lower than the ideal value of 2065, which means that the amplifying frequency ν_{21} could deviate similarly by ± 200 Mc from the ideal value of 1535 Mc. It is not strictly justifiable to appeal to the low-field 55° case in this way, since the nature of the quantum-mechanical states is not the same as in the high-field case; however, the orders of magnitude of the cross-relaxation line widths should be the same in the two cases.

The above discussion of line widths refers to the standard pink ruby of 0.05 per cent concentration. The type of ruby used in Geusic, *et al.*[21] is not stated; but the writer has little doubt that it was the standard pink ruby, which has been so much used in maser experiments. Hence the cross-relaxation process would be expected to be dominant in the experiments at 1500 Mc,[21] which gave such a high inversion ratio, and also in L-band masers operating at about 1400 Mc.[5]

Having presented reasons for believing that cross-relaxation processes must be occurring, we now examine what effect they would have on maser performance. The cross-relaxation process consists in a paramagnetic ion in level 4 jumping to 3 while simultaneously, a neighbor jumps from 2 to 3 (see Fig. 2), or in the inverse process. By analogy with the low-field 55° case, the contribution to the rate equation for, say, level 3 is

$$2cw_c''(n_2 n_4 - n_3^2)/N.$$

Just as before, if $cw_c'' \gg w_{ij}$ the process tends to equalize $n_2 n_4$ and n_3^2, *i.e.*, makes n_3 the geometric mean of n_2 and n_4. The action when ν_{31} is pumped may now be

[21] J. E. Geusic, E. O. Schulz-Du Bois, R. W. DeGrasse, and H. E. D. Scovil, "Three level spin refrigeration and maser action at 1500 mc/sec," *J. Appl. Phys.*, vol. 30, pp. 1113, 1114; July, 1959.

considered qualitatively. The pumping makes n_3 equal to n_1, so that n_1 is the geometric mean of n_2 and n_4. But, W_4 being so much higher than W_1 ($\nu_{41} \simeq 21.5$ kMc), and level 4 not being directly affected by pumping, n_4 tends to be considerably lower than n_1 so that n_2 must be correspondingly higher than n_1. This implies good maser action at ν_{21}. The solution of the equations analogous to (15), for the case that the cross-relaxation rate cw_r'' is much greater than any spin-lattice relaxation rate w_{ij}, and for saturating the resonance at ν_{31}, is

$$I = -\frac{\Delta n_{12}}{\Delta_0 n_{12}} = -1 + \frac{\nu_{31}}{\nu_{21}}\left(1 + \frac{w_{14} - w_{12}}{w_2 + 2w_{24} + w_4}\right) \quad (23)$$

Substituting the relative values of the w_{ij}'s already quoted, and with $\nu_{31} = 11.5$ kMc and $\nu_{21} = 1.50$ kMc, one obtains an inversion ratio of 4.4, which is in much better agreement with the experimental value of 5.2.[21]

An important question is whether the already good performance of the high-field ruby L-band maser mode would be still further improved by pumping at ν_{41}, 21.5 kMc, instead of at ν_{31}, 11.5 kMc. The solution for this case, with $cw_r'' \gg w_{ij}$, is:

$$I = -\frac{\Delta n_{12}}{\Delta_0 n_{12}} = -1 + \frac{\nu_{41}}{\nu_{21}}\left(1 - \frac{2w_{13} + 4w_{12}}{w_3 + 4w_{24} + 4w_{12}}\right), \quad (24)$$

which, with the w_{ij}'s already given, yields an inversion of 2.7, poorer than that predicted for pumping ν_{31}. Although it is not to be expected that the magnetic dipole model is a perfect guide to the values of the w_{ij}'s, it seems safe to predict that little advantage would be gained by changing to the higher pumping frequency.

V. Use of Working Substances with Higher Zero-Field Splittings than Ruby

Materials known at present in which the zero-field splitting of Cr^{3+} is higher than in ruby are: aluminum acetylacetonate, $Al[(CH_3CO)_2CH]_3$;[8] spinel,[12] $MgAl_2O_4$; rutile,[11] TiO_2; emerald (beryl),[10] $Be_3Al_2Si_6O_{18}$; and cyanite,[22] Al_2SiO_5. The acetyl acetonate is unsuitable for maser work both because its crystals shatter on cooling and because it exhibits six separate Cr^{3+} spectra at low temperatures.[23] Of the others, all exhibit the simple Hamiltonian (8) except rutile, and all have been produced artificially in monocrystalline form except cyanite, which is found as a mineral. Emerald is probably the most expensive of the materials to prepare as large monocrystals, and spinel the cheapest. Spinel contains four differently directed though otherwise equivalent Cr^{3+} sites, and this limits the freedom of orientation in a magnetic field since it is desirable to make the four sites play an equal part in maser action. Rutile contains two differently directed sites, and here the angular freedom is greater; emerald contains only one type of site. The number of different sites in cyanite has not been established by paramagnetic resonance. We shall now discuss the above materials in turn, paying particular attention to the possibility of cross-relaxation-assisted maser action.

A. Emerald: Zero-Field Splitting Frequency 53.6 kMc

To obtain the same kind of assistance from cross relaxation as does ruby in the 2000 gauss perpendicular mode, the frequencies and field would have to be scaled up in the ratio of the zero-field frequencies, *i.e.*, 53.6/11.5 or 4.66. Thus emerald should be a particularly effective maser with a field of 9700 gauss perpendicular to the axis, pumped at a frequency of 53.6 kMc and amplifying at 7200 Mc (*cf.* Fig. 2). The inversion ratio should be about 5, twice as good as if the cross-relaxation assistance were not employed. As an L-band amplifier (say 1400 Mc) emerald could be operated in the same kind of mode as above, *i.e.*, amplifying at ν_{21} (see Fig. 2), and the magnetic field required would then be, from (13), about 5000 gauss. The maser action would not be cross-relaxation assisted and the "ordinary" maser equation would apply, *i.e.*, (20). The pumping frequency, ν_{31}, would be about 50 kMc. Using the magnetic dipole model for the spin-lattice relaxation rates, one obtains an inversion ratio of about 13. In spite of this good inversion ratio, the high magnetic field requirement presents a deterrent to designers, particularly for a traveling wave maser. Hence, it is important to consider the possibilities of the low-field mode.

In low fields, cross-relaxation assistance is present at $\theta = 29°$ or $55°$ when the pumping and amplifying frequencies are respectively ν_{41} and ν_{43} (*cf.* Fig. 1). On the basis of the magnetic dipole model, the spin-lattice relaxation rates are practically the same as for ruby in the low-field applications discussed in Section IV. We shall treat only the 55° mode, which is the more promising. For amplification at 1400 Mc the field is 300 gauss and the pumping frequency 55.0 kMc. The inversion predicted from (19) is 20, as against about half this amount in the absence of cross relaxation.

B. Spinel: Zero-Field Splitting Frequency 29.7 kMc

The Hamiltonian is of the simple type (8), as for emerald and ruby. A disadvantage of the material is that the z-axes of the Cr^{3+} ions are aligned in four different directions, namely the four body-diagonals of the unit cube of the crystal structure. The most attractive application of this material is in a low-field mode, with the magnetic field applied along one of the cube axes. Then the axes of all the ions would be precisely oriented at the angle $\cos^{-1}(1/\sqrt{3})$ or 54.7° which is needed for the cross-relaxation-assisted maser mode at low fields. Operated as an amplifier for 1400 Mc (ν_{43}) the field

[22] O. Deutschbein, "The line emission and absorption of chromium phosphors. III Behaviour at low temperatures and in magnetic fields," *Ann. Physik*, vol. 20, pp. 828–842; 1934. Summarized in P. Pringsheim, "Fluorescence and Phosphorescence," Interscience Publishers, Inc., New York, N. Y., pp. 637–645; 1949.

[23] Bowers and Owen, *op. cit.*, p. 340.

would be 300 gauss, the pumping frequency (ν_{41}) 31 kMc, and the inversion ratio about 12. The ratios of the spin-lattice relaxation rates used in this calculation have been obtained from the magnetic dipole model with the help of the charts given by Howarth.[15] They are very similar to those of ruby in the corresponding mode.

C. Rutile: Zero-Field Splitting Frequency 43 kMc

Rutile presents a case of the more complicated Hamiltonian (7). There are two types of Cr^{3+} position per unit cell with the same Hamiltonian parameters and same z-axis but different x- and y-axes, the x-axis of one type being rotated 90° from that of the other.[11] In seeking a high-field mode analogous to the 2000 gauss perpendicular mode of ruby at L-band, we consider the energy level diagrams of Figs. 4(a), 4(b) and 4(c), next page, for field along the z, x and y directions of the Hamiltonian. (Actually the figures have been drawn for $E=\frac{1}{2}D$, whereas in rutile $E=0.27$ cm^{-1} and $D=0.55$ cm^{-1} with an experimental error presumably of about 0.005 cm^{-1}.[11]) A cross-relaxation-assisted mode is possible with a field of about 4400 gauss in the z-direction [Fig. 4(a)], and this direction has the advantage that the two types of Cr^{3+} ion have identical energies and play an equal part in the maser action. (For field along the x or y direction, only half the Cr^{3+} population could take part in a particular maser mode.)

As shown in Fig. 4(a), the average of W_a and W_d intersects W_c for a field of about 4400 gauss, and the situation is analogous to that in ruby with a perpendicular field of 2000 gauss. If the transition at frequency ν_{cb} is saturated, maser action at ν_{ab} will be cross-relaxation-assisted in the same way as in the ruby L-band maser. In Fig. 4(a) the cross-relaxation transitions are shown as dotted arrows.

The condition for the above-mentioned intersection is worked out in Appendix II. Eq. (45) for $G=g_c\beta B$ is of fourth degree and has to be solved numerically. For the case, $E=\frac{1}{2}D$, closely approximated by rutile, the solution is $G=0.75\ D$, whence $B=4400$ gauss. The pumping (ν_{cb}) and amplifying (ν_{ab}) frequencies are respectively 35 and 5.0 kMc.

To make an estimate of the inversion ratio in this mode it would be necessary to know the magnetic dipole transition probabilities between all the levels. To avoid very tedious computations a semi-quantitative approach will be adopted here. When the secular matrix of the Hamiltonian (7) is written down, following the methods of Bowers and Owen,[8] it is found that the states b and d belong to one sub-matrix and a and c to another. At high fields, a, b, c and d are pure states $|-\frac{3}{2}\rangle$, $|-\frac{1}{2}\rangle$, $|\frac{1}{2}\rangle$, $|\frac{3}{2}\rangle$. As the field is reduced to below the region of $g_z\beta B/D=1$, the states a and c tend to cross in energy, and are strongly mixed by the $S_x^2-S_y^2$ term in the Hamiltonian which produces matrix elements joining a and c. We assume that they are completely mixed, *i.e.*, that $|c,\ a\rangle=(1/\sqrt{2})(|-\frac{3}{2}\rangle\pm|\frac{1}{2}\rangle)$. The states $|b\rangle$ and $|d\rangle$ are also connected by matrix elements, but are not severely mixed since they do not approach closely in energy. These we assume to be completely unmixed, *i.e.*, we take $|b\rangle=|-\frac{1}{2}\rangle$ and $|d\rangle=|\frac{3}{2}\rangle$.

The magnetic dipole transition probabilities are then calculated by standard methods.[8] The labels a, b, c, d are changed to 2, 1, 3, 4, respectively, so that the notation corresponds to that of the high-field mode in ruby, already discussed, and so that (20) and (23) are directly applicable. The spin-lattice relaxation rates, in arbitrary units, are $w_{12}=7/4$, $w_{13}=7/4$, $w_{14}=0$, $w_{23}=1$, $w_{24}=\frac{3}{4}$ and $w_{34}=\frac{3}{4}$. The predicted inversion for cross-relaxation-assisted maser action is then [see (23)] 4.1, whereas without cross relaxation it would be 2.1.

A similar cross-relaxation-assisted mode is possible with the magnetic field in the y-direction [Fig. 4(c)]. Here it is the average of W_a and W_d which crosses W_b. The condition for the intersection, given in (54), is again an equation of fourth degree; the solution for rutile is approximately $g_y\beta B=0.57D$, or $B=3400$ gauss. The pumping frequency, ν_{cb}, and the amplifying frequency, ν_{cd}, are 35 and 8.0 kMc, respectively. Using the same kind of model for spin-lattice relaxation rates as for the z-direction, the inversion is predicted to be 2.2 with cross relaxation as against 0.9 without. The lower inversion ratio in this mode, and the fact that only half the Cr^{3+} population takes part, render it less attractive than the z-direction mode; but this is perhaps offset by the fact that the amplifying frequency is in the familiar X-band.

When the field is in the x-direction a cross-relaxation mode is again possible; but it occurs at a field of about 21,000 gauss in rutile, and the inversion is expected to be low. We shall not discuss this mode further. However, in Appendix II, the general conditions for this mode are discussed, and it is shown that for substances in which $E\ll D/3$ the field requirement is not prohibitive.

In anticipation of the use of substances with small E/D, Appendix II gives explicit expressions for field, and for pumping and amplifying frequencies, in the form of a series expansion up to terms in E^2/D^2, for the x, y and z directions. The author is not aware of any substances which are known to have small E/D and larger zero-field splittings than ruby together with its desirable mechanical and electrical properties; but it can hardly be doubted that such substances will be discovered as soon as a systematic survey of aluminum- and chromium-containing minerals is made.

We next consider the possibility of low-field cross-relaxation action with rutile. The energy levels are given in Appendix I, (30), (31), and (32); and it may be seen that they depend on ϕ, the azimuthal angle describing the field-direction, through $\cos 2\phi$. Thus if the field is applied in the plane $\phi=\pi/4$ for one species of Cr^{3+} ion, $\cos 2\phi=0$ for both species and their energy levels are identical; thus the whole Cr^{3+} population may be used for maser action. We now assume, without loss of generality for maser discussion, that D is positive, and label the levels in the order in which their energies

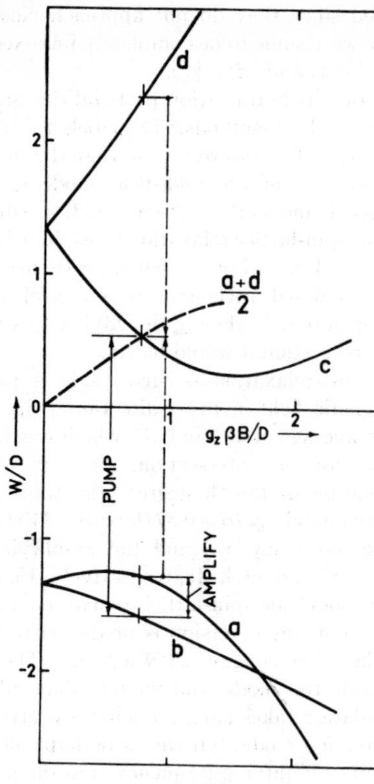

(a)

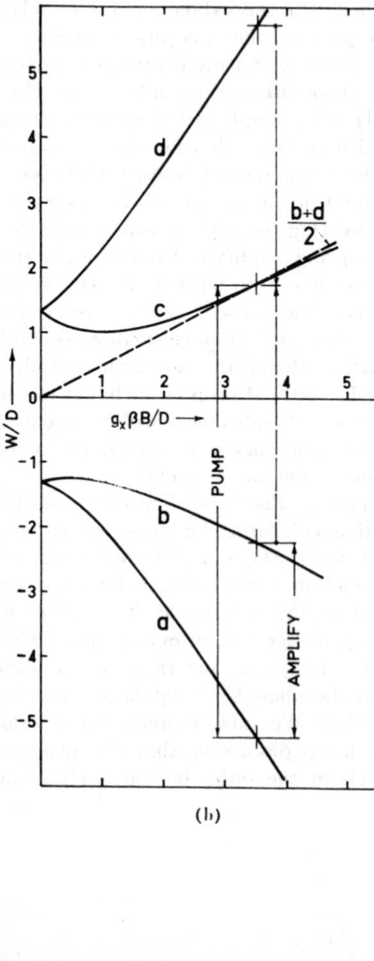

(b)

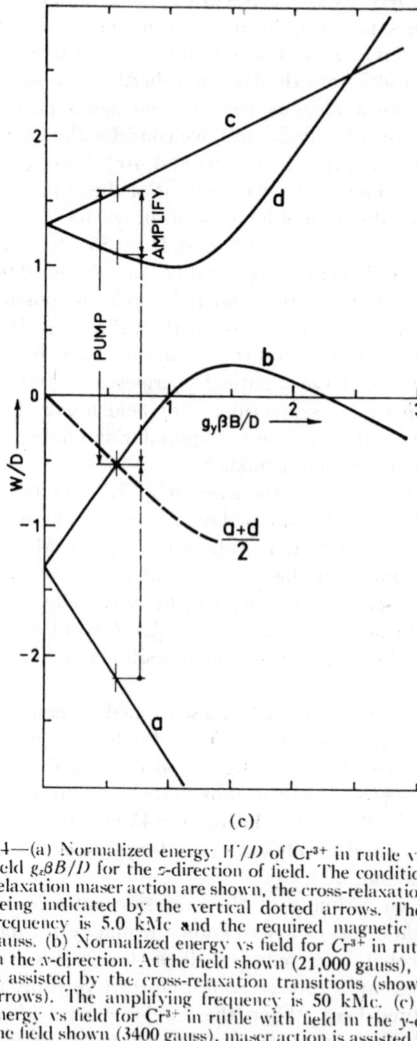

(c)

Fig. 4—(a) Normalized energy W/D of Cr^{3+} in rutile vs normalized field $g_z\beta B/D$ for the z-direction of field. The conditions for cross-relaxation maser action are shown, the cross-relaxation transitions being indicated by the vertical dotted arrows. The amplifying frequency is 5.0 kMc and the required magnetic field is 4400 gauss. (b) Normalized energy vs field for Cr^{3+} in rutile with field in the x-direction. At the field shown (21,000 gauss), maser action is assisted by the cross-relaxation transitions (shown by dotted arrows). The amplifying frequency is 50 kMc. (c) Normalized energy vs field for Cr^{3+} in rutile with field in the y-direction. At the field shown (3400 gauss), maser action is assisted by the cross-relaxation transitions (dotted). The amplifying frequency is 8.0 kMc.

ascend at $\phi=\pi/4$, *viz.*, 1, 2, 3, 4, instead of $-\frac{1}{2}$, $\frac{1}{2}$, $-\frac{3}{2}$, $\frac{3}{2}$ as in the Appendix. Then, substituting Z for $(D^2+3E^2)^{1/2}$, we have

$$W_{4,3} = Z \pm \tfrac{3}{2} G \left[\cos^2\theta(1 - \tfrac{4}{3}\sin^2\alpha)^2 + \tfrac{4}{9}\sin^2\theta\sin^2\alpha(1 + 2\cos^2\alpha)\right]^{1/2}$$

$$W_{2,1} = -Z \pm \tfrac{1}{2} G \left[\cos^2\theta(1 - 4\sin^2\alpha)^2 + \sin^2\theta(4\cos^4\alpha + 3\sin^2 2\alpha)\right]^{1/2}, \quad (25)$$

where α, which describes the extent to which the states are mixed in zero-field, is given by (29). We shall confine attention to the condition that $W_4-W_3=W_2-W_1$, as in the 55° mode in ruby, since that mode is the more promising of the low-field modes. If $W_4-W_3=W_2-W_1$, it follows from (25) that $\cos^2\theta=1/3$, so that $\theta=54.7°$ as in ruby.

The question might now be asked whether, since $\nu_{43}=\nu_{21}$, the amplifying transition is from level 4 to 3 or from level 2 to 1. If E/D were zero we should be dealing with a ruby-like situation: the states 4 and 3 would be quite pure states $|\frac{3}{2}\rangle$ and $|-\frac{3}{2}\rangle$ and the radio-frequency transition probability between them would be zero, so that the amplifying transition could only be between levels 2 and 1. (This case has already been discussed for ruby, with the only difference that levels 1 and 2 were there labeled 4 and 3, and so on, because of the negative sign of D.) For $E/D\neq 0$, the zero-field states may be considerably mixed: for example, in rutile, $\sin\alpha=0.35$ and $\cos\alpha=0.94$, so (Appendix 1) the states of levels 4 and 3 are no longer $|\pm 3/2\rangle$ but $0.94|\pm\frac{3}{2}\rangle+0.35|\mp\frac{1}{2}\rangle$ and the radio-frequency transition probability between them in low fields is of the order of 0.35^2, or one tenth, as strong as the well-allowed transition between 2 and 1. It may be worth while to recall that the effect of the cross relaxations is such that if the resonance at either ν_{43} or ν_{21} becomes emissive, the other does also. Thus in rutile most of the amplification comes from the ν_{21} transitions.

The magnetic field required for a given amplifying frequency may be worked out from either of equations (25), putting $\cos^2\theta=1/3$. For example the second equation gives

$$h\nu_{21} = \sqrt{3}G = \sqrt{3}g\beta B, \quad (26)$$

which, it will be noted, is independent of α and hence of E/D. This gives the formula

$$B = 0.206(2/g)\nu_{21}, \quad (27)$$

B and ν_{21} being in gauss and megacycles per second. Eq. (27) applies not only to rutile, but to any Cr^{3+}-containing compound. For an amplifier for 1400 Mc a field of 290 gauss would be required. The fractional errors in (26) and (27) are similar to that in (10), *i.e.* about $(h\nu_{21}/2Z)^2$ or 0.1 per cent in the above example. Since the states are complicated, we shall not attempt to calculate relaxation rates and the inversion, but observe that the latter should be similar to that already worked out for emerald, *i.e.* of the order of 20. The pumping frequency (ν_{41}) in the above example would be about 45 kMc, from (25). In cases of higher amplifying frequencies ν_S it should be noted that ν_{41} is greater than predicted from (25) by an amount of order ν_S^2/ν_{ZF} [see (33) in Appendix I and the discussion following it].

D. Cyanite: Zero-Field Splitting Frequency 1000 kMc

Cyanite, Al_2SiO_5, containing Cr^{3+} ions was studied by optical absorption methods at low temperatures,[22] and a splitting of the ground level of 33 cm^{-1} or 1000 kMc was found. If sufficient pumping power could be obtained, for example, from an intense infra-red source, cyanite would offer extremely high inversion ratios. The high-field mode is practically out of the question, 30,000 gauss being needed for amplification at L-band. The low-field mode could be used, however, and the field required would be given by (10) or (11).

Application of this material will depend on progress of techniques in the unfamiliar region of 1000 kMc. The pumping radiation would require not only to be sufficiently intense, but also to possess a sharp cutoff at a frequency below the pumping frequency ν_{41} and above ν_{42} and ν_{31} (*cf.* Fig. 1), for pumping at the latter two frequencies, as well as at the former, would interfere with maser action.

E. Gallium Oxide and Yttrium Gallium Garnet: Zero-Field Splitting Frequencies 35.4 and 21.0 kMc Respectively

Measurements on Cr^{3+} in these substances have been reported only very recently.[24,25] The maser applications proposed below should be regarded with some reserve until the number of different Cr^{3+} sites per unit cell has been reported: this information is not stated in references available to the author.

Gallium oxide (β-Ga_2O_3) containing Cr^{3+} has a rutile-like Hamiltonian. Cross-relaxation maser action with an inversion of 3 should be obtained in both the following modes: 1) amplifying at 6.4 kMc with pumping at 28.3 kMc and a field of 2800 gauss along the z-axis of the Hamiltonian; 2) amplifying at 5.3 kMc, pumping at 28.5 kMc, with a 3200 gauss field along the y-axis.

Yttrium gallium garnet ($3Y_2O_3\cdot 5Ga_4O_3$) containing Cr^{3+} has a ruby-like Hamiltonian. It would give cross-relaxation maser action at 2.8 kMc with an inversion of 5 under these conditions: a field of 3800 gauss perpendicular to the magnetic symmetry axis and a pumping frequency of 21.0 kMc.

[24] M. Peter and A. L. Schawlow, "Optical and paramagnetic resonance spectra of Cr^{+++} in Ga_2O_3," *Bull. Am. Phys. Soc.*, vol. 5, p. 158; March, 1960.

[25] S. Geschwind and J. W. Nielsen, "Paramagnetic resonance of Cr^{3+} in yttrium gallium garnet," *Bull. Am. Phys. Soc.*, vol. 5, p. 252; April, 1960.

VI. Conclusion

Although ruby has given good maser performance, a three- or four-fold improvement should be possible with spinel, rutile and emerald. The reason for the good performance of the ruby L-band maser with a 2000 gauss perpendicular field is that cross-relaxation processes are occurring which assist the maser action. The same kind of action can be utilized with the other materials, and should approximately double the maser performance. However, the pumping and amplifying frequencies are specific to the material used. Emerald should give an inversion ratio of about 5 as an amplifier for 7.2 kMc with a pumping frequency of 53.6 kMc, and a field of 9700 gauss; and this is to be contrasted with the inversion of 0.95 which has been obtained with a representative ruby maser amplifying at 6 kMc.[26] It may prove difficult at the present time to obtain sufficient pumping power at the frequency of 53.6 kMc, and perhaps rutile is more promising, offering an amplifying frequency of 5.0 kMc (field: 4400 gauss; inversion ratio: about 4) or 8.0 kMc (field: 3400 gauss; inversion ratio: about 2) depending on the direction of field. The pumping frequency for either case is 35 kMc, which is close to the center of the well-developed 8-mm radar band for which klystrons are commercially available giving continuous power output of 15 watts.[27] This is far more power than is needed to saturate the paramagnetic resonance of rutile at liquid helium temperatures, and indeed would be sufficient at liquid air or even solid carbon dioxide temperatures, where a ruby maser has been successfully operated.[28] Rutile is a very promising material for these temperatures; it should be much easier to pump than ruby since its spin-lattice relaxation time at 77°K is 400 μsec[11] as against 40 μsec for ruby.[19] By comparison with the reported performance of ruby,[28] rutile should give a voltage-gain bandwidth product of about 30 Mc in a cavity maser amplifying at 5 kMc at liquid air temperature. The high dielectric constant of rutile will allow the cavity or traveling wave structure to be small, which will ease the requirements on the magnet used.

For amplifying at the lower microwave frequencies it is important to find maser modes which do not require too high a magnetic field, because a longer wavelength implies a larger structure and therefore a larger magnet pole separation. The ruby 2000 gauss mode for L-band is rather uneconomical in this respect, and spinel and emerald would be even more so in the corresponding mode as they would require 3600 and 5300 gauss, respectively. The better course will be to exploit the low-field modes in the new materials. It has been shown that the failures experienced with ruby in the low-field mode are due to cross-relaxation processes which can be not only avoided but put to good use by a correct choice of orientation and pumping transition. In the case of L-band amplification, spinel, rutile and emerald would require pumping frequencies of 31, 45 and 55 kMc, all with a magnetic field of about 300 gauss, and the maser performance would be about twice as good as in the absence of cross-relaxation.

As far as the improvement of maser action is concerned, cross-relaxation operation is approximately equivalent to push-pull or doubly-pumped operation,[9] which is possible with ruby-like materials at $\theta = 55°$. However, in the push-pull mode the amplifying transition is between levels 2 and 3 which never approach closely: indeed, from (3.4) of Kikuchi, *et al.*,[9] it is readily demonstrable that the lowest possible amplifying frequency is half the zero-field splitting frequency. For example, ruby cannot amplify at a frequency below 5720 Mc in this mode.

Cross-relaxation masers are important, therefore, for achieving high inversion ratios at frequencies low compared to the zero-field splitting frequency of the maser material.

Other applications of cross relaxation have been described by Arams:[29] the most striking is the realization of a maser with signal frequency higher than the pumping. The price for this achievement is a rather low inversion ratio; but important applications may be foreseen in the millimeter-wave region. Chang[30] has described a further case in which the inversion was increased by cross relaxation: this showed that even a process involving as many as four simultaneous spin-flips could affect maser action. It may reasonably be expected that the cross-relaxation phenomenon, though first discovered through its ill effects, will eventually be best known for its beneficial effects on maser action.

Appendix I

Calculation of the Low-Field Energy Levels of a Cr^{3+} Ion Obeying the Hamiltonian

$$g\beta B \cdot S + D(S_z^2 - \tfrac{5}{4}) + E(S_x^2 - S_y^2)$$

In this treatment it is assumed that the g-tensor is isotropic. The energy levels and states are derived exactly for zero field, and the effect on the energies of a small magnetic field obtained by first-order perturbation theory.

[26] E. O. Schulz-Du Bois, H. E. D. Scovil, and R. W. DeGrasse, "Use of active material in three-level solid-state masers," *Bell Sys. Tech. J.*, vol. 38, pp. 335–352; March, 1959.

[27] Klystron type B579, manufactured by Elliott Bros. (London) Ltd., Borehamwood, Hertfordshire, England.

[28] T. H. Maiman, "Maser behavior: temperature and concentration effects," *J. Appl. Phys.*, vol. 31, pp. 222–223; January, 1960.

[29] F. R. Arams, "Maser operation with signal frequency higher than pump frequency," Proc. IRE, vol. 48, p. 108; January, 1960.

[30] W. S. Chang, "Spin-lattice relaxation via harmonic coupling," in "Quantum Electronics," C. H. Townes, Ed., Columbia University Press, New York, N. Y.; 1960.

A. Energies and States at Zero Fields

The Hamiltonian is

$$\mathcal{H} = D(S_z^2 - \tfrac{5}{4}) + E(S_x^2 - S_y^2)$$
$$= D(S_z^2 - \tfrac{5}{4}) + \tfrac{1}{2}E(S_+^2 + S_-^2),$$

where $S\pm \equiv S_x \pm iS_y$.

We now write down the matrix of the Hamiltonian in the representation of the eigenstates of S_z, defined by $S_z|M\rangle = M|M\rangle$. Since S for Cr^{3+} is 3/2, M can take the values $\pm 1/2$, $\pm 3/2$. Proceeding by the methods shown in Bowers and Owen,[31] for example, we obtain for the matrix of $\mathcal{H}$:

$$\begin{array}{c} \\ |\tfrac{3}{2}\rangle \\ |\tfrac{1}{2}\rangle \\ |-\tfrac{1}{2}\rangle \\ |-\tfrac{3}{2}\rangle \end{array} \begin{array}{cccc} |\tfrac{3}{2}\rangle & |\tfrac{1}{2}\rangle & |-\tfrac{1}{2}\rangle & |-\tfrac{3}{2}\rangle \\ \end{array} \begin{bmatrix} D & 0 & E\sqrt{3} & 0 \\ 0 & -D & 0 & E\sqrt{3} \\ E\sqrt{3} & 0 & -D & 0 \\ 0 & E\sqrt{3} & 0 & D \end{bmatrix}, \qquad (28)$$

which can be reduced, by rearrangement of rows and columns, to the following two submatrices:

$$\begin{array}{c|cc} & |\tfrac{3}{2}\rangle & |-\tfrac{1}{2}\rangle \\ \hline |\tfrac{3}{2}\rangle & D & E\sqrt{3} \\ |-\tfrac{1}{2}\rangle & E\sqrt{3} & -D \end{array} \quad \text{and} \quad \begin{array}{c|cc} & |-\tfrac{3}{2}\rangle & |\tfrac{1}{2}\rangle \\ \hline |-\tfrac{3}{2}\rangle & D & E\sqrt{3} \\ |\tfrac{1}{2}\rangle & E\sqrt{3} & -D \end{array}.$$

The identity of the two submatrices shows that results from the $|\tfrac{3}{2}\rangle$, $|-\tfrac{1}{2}\rangle$ manifold can be carried over to the $|-\tfrac{3}{2}\rangle$, $|+\tfrac{1}{2}\rangle$ simply by substituting $|-M\rangle$ for $|M\rangle$.

The secular equation for the energy for either manifold is, in determinantal form,

$$\begin{vmatrix} D - W & E\sqrt{3} \\ E\sqrt{3} & -D - W \end{vmatrix} = 0,$$

whence $W = \pm(D^2+3E^2)^{1/2}$, as already stated in Bowers and Owen.[2]

If $E=0$ it can be seen by inspection of the matrix (28) that the eigenstates are $|\pm\tfrac{3}{2}\rangle$ at energy D and $|\pm\tfrac{1}{2}\rangle$ at $-D$. In defining the states for $E\neq 0$, some attention is needed to the influence of the sign of D, which has been obscured in the expression $(D^2+3E^2)^{1/2}$. Let $\lambda = D/|D|$; then $|\tfrac{3}{2}'\rangle$ must be defined as the state at energy $\lambda(D^2+3E^2)^{1/2}$. Then, as $E\to 0$, $|\tfrac{3}{2}'\rangle \to |\tfrac{3}{2}\rangle$, and the energy approaches its correct value of $\lambda|D|$. Bearing in mind the requirements of normalization and orthogonality, it is evident that the eigenstates of the $|\tfrac{3}{2}\rangle$, $|-\tfrac{1}{2}\rangle$ submatrix may be written as

$$|\tfrac{3}{2}'\rangle = \cos\alpha\,|\tfrac{3}{2}\rangle + \sin\alpha\,|-\tfrac{1}{2}\rangle \text{ at } \lambda(D^2+3E^2)^{1/2}$$
$$|\tfrac{1}{2}'\rangle = \cos\alpha\,|-\tfrac{1}{2}\rangle - \sin\alpha\,|\tfrac{3}{2}\rangle \text{ at } -\lambda(D^2+3E^2)^{1/2}.$$

[31] Bowers and Owen, *op. cit.*, pp. 319–321.

Here α is to be found from the eigenvalue equation,

$$\mathcal{H}|\tfrac{3}{2}'\rangle = W_{3/2}'|\tfrac{3}{2}'\rangle = \lambda(D^2+3E^2)^{1/2}|\tfrac{3}{2}'\rangle,$$

that is

$$\begin{bmatrix} D & E\sqrt{3} \\ E\sqrt{3} & -D \end{bmatrix}\begin{bmatrix} \cos\alpha \\ \sin\alpha \end{bmatrix} = \lambda(D^2+3E^2)^{1/2}\begin{bmatrix} \cos\alpha \\ \sin\alpha \end{bmatrix};$$

or, using the second row of the matrix,

$$E\sqrt{3}\cos\alpha - D\sin\alpha = \lambda(D^2+3E^2)^{1/2}\sin\alpha,$$

whence

$$\tan\alpha = \frac{E\sqrt{3}}{D+\lambda(D^2+3E^2)^{1/2}}. \qquad (29)$$

B. Effect of a Small Magnetic Field

We take as unperturbed states the results of Section A above, namely

$$|\pm\tfrac{3}{2}'\rangle = \cos\alpha\,|\pm\tfrac{3}{2}\rangle + \sin\alpha\,|\mp\tfrac{1}{2}\rangle$$
$$\text{at energy } \lambda(D^2+3E^2)^{1/2}$$

and

$$|\pm\tfrac{1}{2}'\rangle = \cos\alpha\,|\pm\tfrac{1}{2}\rangle - \sin\alpha\,|\mp\tfrac{3}{2}\rangle$$
$$\text{at energy } -\lambda(D^2+3E^2)^{1/2}.$$

The effect of an applied magnetic field B may now be derived by a perturbation treatment,[32] yielding first-order perturbations of order $g\beta B$ and second-order perturbations of order $(g\beta B)^2/(D^2+3E^2)^{1/2}$. The latter, however, are very complicated and we shall be content here with the first-order effect except for the simpler case where $E=0$ in the Hamiltonian (part C). The first-order treatment is applicable with sufficient accuracy to Cr^{3+} in rutile used as an L-band maser, because the zero-field splitting $2(D^2+3E^2)^{1/2}$ is so high.

To obtain the first-order perturbation of energy for the doublet $|\pm\tfrac{1}{2}'\rangle$ one has to write the matrix of the perturbation operator V in the representation of $|+\tfrac{1}{2}'\rangle$ and $|-\tfrac{1}{2}'\rangle$, and solve for its characteristic values.[32]

The perturbation V is expressible in a convenient form by writing

$$V = g\beta B\cdot S = G\cdot S = G_zS_z + \tfrac{1}{2}(G_+S_- + G_-S_+),$$

where

$$G_z = g\beta B_z = g\beta B\cos\theta = G\cos\theta$$
$$G_\pm = g\beta(B_x \pm iB_y) = G\sin\theta e^{\pm i\phi}$$
$$G = g\beta B;$$

then the matrix of V takes the form

[32] E. U. Condon and G. H. Shortley, "The Theory of Atomic Spectra," Cambridge University Press, Cambridge, Eng., pp. 30 ff.; 1951.

$$\begin{array}{c|cc} & |\tfrac{1}{2}'\rangle & |-\tfrac{1}{2}'\rangle \\ \hline |\tfrac{1}{2}'\rangle & G_z(\tfrac{1}{2}\cos^2\alpha-\tfrac{3}{2}\sin^2\alpha) & G_-\cos^2\alpha-G_+\sqrt{3}\sin\alpha\cos\alpha \\ |-\tfrac{1}{2}'\rangle & G_+\cos^2\alpha-G_-\sqrt{3}\sin\alpha\cos\alpha & G_z(-\tfrac{1}{2}\cos^2\alpha+\tfrac{3}{2}\sin^2\alpha) \end{array}$$

and its characteristic values are $+W_{1/2}''$, corresponding to the state $|\tfrac{1}{2}''\rangle$ (which approaches $|\tfrac{1}{2}'\rangle$ as $\theta \to 0$); and $-W_{1/2}''$, corresponding to the state $|-\tfrac{1}{2}''\rangle$, with

$$W_{1/2}'' = \tfrac{1}{2}G\left[\cos^2\theta(1-4\sin^2\alpha)^2+\sin^2\theta(4\cos^4\alpha + 3\sin^2 2\alpha - 4\sqrt{3}\cos^2\alpha\sin 2\alpha\cos 2\phi)\right]^{1/2}. \quad (30)$$

The perturbations of the $|\pm\tfrac{3}{2}'\rangle$ states, found similarly, are $W_{3/2}''$, corresponding to $|\tfrac{3}{2}''\rangle$ (which approaches $|\tfrac{3}{2}'\rangle$ when $\theta \to 0$); and $-W_{3/2}''$, corresponding to $|-\tfrac{3}{2}''\rangle$, with

$$W_{3/2}'' = \tfrac{3}{2}G\left[\cos^2\theta(1-\tfrac{1}{3}\sin^2\alpha)^2 + \tfrac{4}{9}\sin^2\theta\sin^2\alpha(1+2\cos^2\alpha+\sqrt{3}\sin 2\alpha\cos 2\phi)\right]^{1/2}. \quad (31)$$

The angle α which enters (30) and (31) is defined in (29).

Collecting results, the total energies are:

$$W(\pm\tfrac{3}{2}) = \lambda(D^2+3E^2)^{1/2} \pm W_{3/2}'' \quad \text{for } |\pm\tfrac{3}{2}''\rangle$$
$$W(\pm\tfrac{1}{2}) = -\lambda(D^2+3E^2)^{1/2} \pm W_{1/2}'' \quad \text{for } |\pm\tfrac{1}{2}''\rangle. \quad (32)$$

The second-order perturbations will not be given here explicitly for the general case; it would be necessary to solve for the composition of $|\tfrac{3}{2}''\rangle$, $|\tfrac{1}{2}''\rangle$, etc. in the same way as for $|\tfrac{3}{2}'\rangle$, $|\tfrac{1}{2}'\rangle$, etc. in Section A. The second-order perturbation of the energy of $|\tfrac{1}{2}''\rangle$, for example, is[32]

$$\frac{-|\langle\tfrac{1}{2}''|V|\tfrac{3}{2}''\rangle|^2 - |\langle\tfrac{1}{2}''|V|-\tfrac{3}{2}''\rangle|^2}{2\lambda(D^2+3E^2)^{1/2}}, \quad (33)$$

which is a complicated function of α, θ and ϕ of order $(g\beta B)^2/2(D^2+3E^2)^{1/2}$. In the case of rutile operating as an L-band maser at low fields, the frequency-equivalent of this correction is only about $(1400)^2/43{,}000$ or 50 Mc, which should be within the scope of tuning adjustments.

C. Case of the Simpler Hamiltonian $g\beta B\cdot S+D(S_z^2-5/4)$

It is now relatively simple to solve for the states $|\tfrac{3}{2}''\rangle$, $|\tfrac{1}{2}''\rangle$, etc., and the second-order term (33) is found to take the form

$$-3\sin^2\theta(g\beta B)^2/8D. \quad (34)$$

This applies to both $|\tfrac{1}{2}''\rangle$ and $|-\tfrac{1}{2}''\rangle$, while the term for $|\pm\tfrac{3}{2}''\rangle$ has the opposite sign.

Collecting terms from (30), (32) and (34), the energies, up to second order, are found to be:

$$W(\pm\tfrac{3}{2}) = D \pm \tfrac{3}{2}g\beta B\cos\theta + 3\sin^2\theta(g\beta B)^2/8D$$
$$W(\pm\tfrac{1}{2}) = -D \pm \tfrac{1}{2}g\beta B(1+3\sin^2\theta)^{1/2} - 3\sin^2\theta(g\beta B)^2/8D. \quad (35)$$

These are rewritten in (9) in such a way as to maintain a consecutive order of energies whatever the sign of D.

Appendix II

Conditions for Cross-Relaxation-Assisted Maser Action in the "High-Field Mode"

A. Calculation of the Energy Levels

When the spin Hamiltonian has its most general form for Cr^{3+}, namely

$$\mathcal{H} = \beta B\cdot g\cdot S + D(S_z^2 - \tfrac{5}{4}) + E(S_x^2 - S_y^2), \quad (36)$$

the energy levels can be obtained exactly provided that the applied field is along the x, y or z axes.[8]

For the z-direction of field the energy levels are,[33]

$$W_{d,b} = \tfrac{1}{2}G \pm [(D+G)^2+3E^2]^{1/2} = \tfrac{1}{2}G \pm (Z^2+G^2+2DG)^{1/2}$$
$$W_{c,a} = -\tfrac{1}{2}G \pm [(D-G)^2+3E^2]^{1/2} = -\tfrac{1}{2}G \pm (Z^2+G^2-2DG)^{1/2}, \quad (37)$$

where $G=g_z\beta B$ and $2Z$ is the zero-field splitting $2(D^2+3E^2)^{1/2}$. It may be seen by inspection that at very high fields the energy levels ascend in the order a, b, c, d. In Fig. 4(a) these levels are sketched on the assumption that D is positive and $E=\tfrac{1}{2}D$. The figure is therefore closely applicable to rutile, where $D=0.55$ and $E=0.27$ cm^{-1}.

The energy levels for the x- and y-directions may be obtained from (37) by a simple transformation which is given in Bowers and Owen.[34] For field in the x-direction the rule is to replace g_z by g_x, D by $\tfrac{1}{2}(3E-D)$, and E by $-\tfrac{1}{2}(D+E)$. Naturally, the zero-field splitting $2Z=2(D^2+3E^2)^{1/2}$ is invariant under this transformation. The energies become

$$W_{d,b} = \tfrac{1}{2}G \pm [Z^2+G^2+(3E-D)G]^{1/2}$$
$$W_{c,a} = -\tfrac{1}{2}G \pm [Z^2+G^2-(3E-D)G]^{1/2}, \quad (38)$$

where $G=g_x\beta B$. They are sketched in Fig. 4(b).

For field in the y-direction the rule is to replace g_z by g_y, D by $-\tfrac{1}{2}(D+3E)$ and E by $\tfrac{1}{2}(D-E)$, which yields

$$W_{d,b} = \tfrac{1}{2}G \pm [Z^2+G^2-(3E+D)G]^{1/2}$$
$$W_{c,a} = -\tfrac{1}{2}G \pm [Z^2+G^2+(3E+D)G]^{1/2}. \quad (39)$$

These are sketched in Fig. 4(c).

In the important case $E=0$, both (38) and (39) reduce to

$$W_{d,b} = \tfrac{1}{2}G \pm (D^2+G^2-DG)^{1/2}$$
$$W_{c,a} = -\tfrac{1}{2}G \pm (D^2+G^2+DG)^{1/2}, \quad (40)$$

with $G=g_\perp\beta B$. For ruby, where D is negative, the identity of the above levels with those of Fig. 2 is secured by associating a, b, c, d with 1, 2, 3, 4, respectively.

Eq. (40) and Fig. 2 will now be used to discuss cross-relaxation-assisted maser action in ruby in the high-field L-band mode, and analogous action in other materials.

[33] Bowers and Owen, *op. cit.*, p. 335.
[34] *Ibid.*, p. 321.

B. Condition for Cross-Relaxation-Assisted Maser Action in High Fields with Materials Like Ruby

This mode of maser action is exemplified by ruby acting as an L-band amplifier in a perpendicular field of about 2000 gauss (Fig. 2). The results of the following discussion would be the same whatever the sign of D, but for clarity it seems preferable to work in terms of negative D as for ruby (Fig. 2). The energy levels are then, from (40),

$$W_{4,2} = \tfrac{1}{2}G \pm (D^2 + G^2 + |D|G)^{1/2}$$
$$W_{3,1} = -\tfrac{1}{2}G \pm (D^2 + G^2 - |D|G)^{1/2}, \qquad (41)$$

the labels according with Fig. 2.

It has been shown in the text that the cross-relaxation process which benefits the ruby L-band maser requires that $W_4 - W_3 = W_3 - W_2$. This is easily shown from (41) to lead to

$$G = |D|. \qquad (42)$$

In other words, the magnetic field energy is equivalent to half the zero-field splitting. We now calculate the pumping and amplifying frequencies when $G = |D|$. The pumping transition is between the lowest and second-to-highest level, *i.e.*,

$$h\nu_p = W_3 - W_1 = 2(D^2 + G^2 - |D|G)^{1/2} = 2|D|, \qquad (43)$$

which means that the pumping frequency is identical with the zero-field splitting frequency. The amplifying transition is between the two lowest levels, *i.e.*,

$$h\nu_s = W_2 - W_1 = G - (D^2 + G^2 + |D|G)^{1/2} + (D^2 + G^2 - |D|G)^{1/2}$$
$$= |D| - \sqrt{3}|D| + |D| = |D|(2 - \sqrt{3}). \qquad (44)$$

Thus the amplifying frequency is $(1 - \sqrt{3}/2)$, or 0.134, times the zero-field frequency.

C. High-Field Cross-Relaxation Maser Action with Materials Like Rutile

It is shown in the text that cross-relaxation modes are possible with field along the z-, x- and y-axes [Figs. 4(a), (b) and (c)].

1) *Field in the z-direction:* The pumping transition is from level b to c [Fig. 4(a)] and the amplifying from a to b. The cross-relaxation process requires that $W_c = \frac{1}{2}(W_a + W_d)$. Using (37) this condition may be expressed as

$$-G + 3(Z^2 + G^2 - 2DG)^{1/2} = (Z^2 + G^2 + 2DG)^{1/2}, \qquad (45)$$

where $G = g_z\beta B$. Unfortunately this equation is of fourth degree in G, and no analytic solution can be given. If E were small compared with D, which is not the case in rutile, the following solutions would be useful:

$$G = \tfrac{2}{5}D(1 + 45E^2/14D^2 + \cdots) \qquad (46)$$
$$h\nu_{ab} = h\nu_s = 2D(1/5 - E^2/14D^2 + \cdots) \qquad (47)$$
$$h\nu_{cb} = h\nu_p = 2D(4/5 + 8E^2/7D^2 + \cdots), \qquad (48)$$

subsequent terms in the brackets being of order E^4/D^4.

2) *Field in the x-direction:* Two cases occur, one for $E > \frac{1}{3}D$ and the other for $E < \frac{1}{3}D$. In the first case, exemplified by rutile [Fig. 4(b)] the cross-relaxation condition occurs at a very high field, at which the average of W_b and W_d intersects W_c. The pumping transition is from a to c and the amplifying from b to a. The condition for the intersection is, from (38),

$$G = [Z^2 + G^2 - G(3E - D)]^{1/2}, \qquad (49)$$

where $G = g_x\beta B$. It may be noted that G in this equation must be positive. This reduces to

$$G = (D^2 + 3E^2)/(3E - D), \qquad (50)$$

which can only be satisfied if $E > D/3$.

The pumping and amplifying frequencies may be worked out from (38), but we do not quote them here because not only is the required field inconveniently high, but also the ratio of pumping to amplifying frequency is relatively low, and the mode is unsuitable for maser work.

When $E < \frac{1}{3}D$, different levels come into play: the average of W_a and W_c now intersects W_b, and the pumping and amplifying transitions are between b and d, and c and d, respectively. The field required is

$$G = (D^2 + 3E^2)/(D - 3E), \qquad (51)$$

and, as before, only a positive G is meaningful, so that this mode is only possible when $E < \frac{1}{3}D$. When $E \to 0$ this mode approaches that typified by ruby in the 2000 gauss L-band mode, and (51) becomes identical with (42). The amplifying and pumping frequencies are given by

$$h\nu_{dc} = h\nu_s = D[2 - \sqrt{3} + (6 - \sqrt{3})E/D + (24 - 6\sqrt{3})E^2/D^2 + \cdots] \qquad (52)$$
$$h\nu_{db} = h\nu_p = 2Z^2/(D - 3E). \qquad (53)$$

This mode would have practical application only when $E \ll (\frac{1}{3})D$; otherwise the field required would be very high.

3) *Field in the y-direction:* As Fig. 4(c) shows, the average of W_a and W_d intersects W_b at a field somewhat below $G = D$. The pumping transition is from b to c and the amplifying transition from c to d. The condition for the intersection is

$$-G + 3[Z^2 + G^2 - G(3E + D)]^{1/2} = [Z^2 + G^2 + G(3E + D)]^{1/2}, \qquad (54)$$

where $G = g_y\beta B$. Just as for the z-direction, this equation is of the fourth degree in G. To get an approximate treatment the best course is to abandon (54), and to describe the energy levels in terms of a different spin Hamiltonian. It follows from the transformation[34] already used in obtaining (39) that the energy levels for the y-direction of field, that is, the eigenvalues of

$$\mathcal{H} = g_y\beta BS_y + D(S_z^2 - \tfrac{5}{4}) + E(S_x^2 - S_y^2),$$

are identical with the eigenvalues of another Hamiltonian

$$\mathcal{H}' = g_z'\beta BS_z' + D'(S_z'^2 - \tfrac{5}{4}) + E'(S_x'^2 - S_y'^2),$$

where $g_z' = g_y$, $D' = -\frac{1}{2}(D+3E)$ and $E' = \frac{1}{2}(D-E)$. For example, the y-direction energy levels [Fig. 4(c)] of rutile, the published parameters of which are $g_{x/y/z} = 1.97$, $D = 0.55$ and $E = 0.27$ cm^{-1}, could equally well have been calculated as the z-direction levels of a Hamiltonian $\mathcal{H}'$ in which $g_z' = 1.97$, $D' = -0.68$ cm^{-1} and $E' = 0.14$ cm^{-1}. A glance at Figs. 4(a) and 4(c) shows their similarity.

Thus the field requirement and pumping and signal frequencies in the y-direction can be calculated using (46), (47), and (48) already worked out for the z-direction. One more transformation is needed, however: D' has to be replaced by $D'' = -D'$. Then, as a consideration of (37) shows, the energies are reversed in sign and their labeling is brought into correspondence with Fig. 4(a), as is necessary if (46), (47), and (48) are to be applied. After this transformation, of course, the energies are the reverse of the actual y-direction energies; but this does not affect maser considerations.

The equations for the y-direction are thus

$$G = \tfrac{2}{5}D''(1 + 45E'^2/14D''^2 + \cdots) \tag{55}$$

$$h\nu_s = 2D''(1/5 - E'^2/14D''^2 + \cdots) \tag{56}$$

$$h\nu_p = 2D''(4/5 + 8E'^2/7D''^2 + \cdots), \tag{57}$$

where $G = g_y\beta B$, $D'' = \frac{1}{2}(D+3E)$ and $E' = \frac{1}{2}(D-E)$.

Reprinted from the Australian Journal of Physics, Volume 12, Number 1, pp. 1–20, 1959

ZERO–FIELD MASERS

By G. S. Bogle* and H. F. Symmons*†

[*Manuscript received October* 6, 1958]

Summary

Solid state three-level masers operating with zero magnetic field are shown to be feasible and to have advantages over magnetic field masers in many applications. The requirements of the working substance are discussed and it is found that compounds of Cr^{2+}, Fe^{3+}, Ni^{2+}, and Gd^{3+} should be suitable. Diagrams and tables of maser properties of selected compounds are given ; on the basis of present knowledge a number of amplifying frequencies between 120 and 75,000 Mc/s should be available. The range of suitable compounds which has been studied is very small, and should be extended.

I. Introduction

A primary requirement of the three-level maser, which was stated by Bloembergen (1956) in his original proposal of the device, is that non-zero magnetic-dipole transition probabilities should exist between all three of the participating levels. This requirement is not fulfilled when the quantization of angular momentum is pure, since the selection rule $\Delta M=\pm 1$ applies. As a means of breaking down this selection rule, Bloembergen proposed that a paramagnetic salt possessing a Stark splitting due to its internal electric field should be subjected to a magnetic field inclined at an angle to the axis of the crystalline electric field. If the resulting Zeeman splittings are made comparable to the Stark splittings the quantization is very mixed and transitions may in general take place between all levels.

Use has been made of this principle, which one may call magnetic-field mixing, in a number of successful maser oscillators and amplifiers (for example, Scovil, Feher, and Seidel 1957 ; McWhorter and Meyer 1958).

In view of the great interest which has been aroused by the three-level maser it is surprising that no attention seems to have been paid to the possibility of realizing the device without using a magnetic field. It will be shown below that, among the paramagnetic substances already studied, there are several which provide the necessary transitions, between three levels, in zero magnetic field.

Such zero-field masers will not be tunable beyond the line width of the magnetic resonances involved, and so will hardly compete with magnetic-field masers where the profile of a naturally occurring radiation, such as the hydrogen line of radio astronomy, is to be studied. Nevertheless, zero-field masers possess some considerable advantages which may prove paramount in applications

* Division of Physics, C.S.I.R.O., University Grounds, Sydney.

† On leave from the Department of Physics, Otago University, New Zealand.

such as radar, communications, and high-sensitivity paramagnetic resonance experiments, where frequency, as such, is not important. The advantages are :

(1) The necessity for a magnet, which in magnetic-field masers has to fulfil exacting requirements of homogeneity, stability, and working space, is avoided.

(2) The orientation of the crystal loses its primary importance as an energy-determining factor. Thus large monocrystals of paramagnetic material will not be required ; indeed powders could be used, so that unit filling factor could be achieved without difficulty.

(3) As a corollary of (2) it is possible to utilize differently oriented but otherwise equivalent paramagnetic centres in the crystal, whereas in a magnetic-field maser only one type would, in general, be correctly oriented with respect to the field.

(4) Line broadening caused by inhomogeneity of the magnetic field, or of orientation of the crystal axes, is absent.

(5) A superconductor may be employed for the construction of the microwave circuits since no magnetic field is employed.

(6) Complicated or extended microwave structures, limited only by the requirement that they enter a Dewar vessel of reasonable size, may be used.

These advantages lead to great freedom in the design of masers. An attractive example is a travelling-wave maser consisting of a superconducting coaxial line filled with powdered paramagnetic and wound into a coil to permit convenient cooling of a considerable length.

In view of the advantages of zero-field masers we present a compilation of transition probabilities and frequencies calculated for a number of materials which, on the basis of present-day knowledge, are promising as working substances. The grounds for selection will also be given, and this will necessitate a consideration of maser and paramagnetic resonance theory.

II. The Three-level Maser

We refer at this point to Bloembergen's (1956) paper. Bloembergen considers a system with three energy levels $E_3>E_2>E_1$, to which is applied a strong microwave magnetic field at the frequency $\nu_{31}=(E_3-E_1)/h$ and a weak field at the frequency $\nu_{32}=(E_3-E_2)/h$. He gives an expression for the difference in population between levels for the case when all energy level differences are much less than kT. Preserving only terms of order $h\nu/kT$, we may ignore the distinction between w_{ij} and w_{ji}, thus obtaining

$$n_1-n_2=n_3-n_2=\tfrac{1}{3}\cdot\frac{hN}{kT}\cdot\frac{w_{21}\nu_{21}-w_{32}\nu_{32}}{w_{21}+w_{32}+W_{32}}. \quad \ldots\ldots \quad (1)$$

The notation is Bloembergen's : N is the number of paramagnetic centres, the w's are the thermally induced (relaxation) transition probabilities, W_{32} is the transition probability between the levels E_3 and E_2 due to the microwave field $H(\nu_{32})$, and T is the absolute temperature. Without loss of generality one may suppose that $w_{21}\nu_{21}>w_{32}\nu_{32}$, for, if not, the labels 1 and 3 can simply be reversed. Then $n_3 > n_2$, and stimulated emission occurs at the frequency ν_{32}. The power emitted is

$$P_{\text{magn}} = \frac{Nh^2\nu_{32}(w_{21}\nu_{21} - w_{32}\nu_{32})W_{32}}{3kT(w_{21}+w_{32}+W_{32})}. \quad \ldots\ldots\ldots\ldots \quad (2)$$

We now wish to express W_{32} in terms of the exciting field $H(\nu_{32})$, the matrix element $\langle 2 \mid H.S \mid 3 \rangle$, and the width of the magnetic resonance line. At this point we depart from the nomenclature of Bloembergen and use the half-width at half-intensity $\Delta\nu$ instead of the relaxation time T_2. ($\Delta\nu = 1/(2\pi T_2)$.) Then the transition probability takes the form

$$W_{32} = \pi g^2 \beta^2 \mid \langle 3 \mid H.S \mid 2 \rangle \mid^2 / h^2 \Delta\nu = \pi g^2 \beta^2 H(\nu_{32})^2 \mid \langle 3 \mid S_H \mid 2 \rangle \mid^2 / h^2 \Delta\nu, \quad \ldots\ldots\ldots\ldots\ldots\ldots \quad (3)$$

where g is the spectroscopic splitting factor, β the Bohr magneton, and S_H the projection of the spin operator in the direction of $H(\nu_{32})$.

Provided that the field $H(\nu_{32})$ is small, so that $W_{32} \ll w_{21} + w_{32}$, equation (2) shows that the power emitted is proportional to $H(\nu_{32})^2$. One may then define a magnetic quality factor Q_M by the equation

$$\frac{-1}{Q_M} = \frac{\text{power emitted per unit volume}}{2\pi\nu_{32} \times (\text{stored energy per unit volume})}.$$

This definition differs from that of Bloembergen in that unit volume of the paramagnetic is here considered, so that dependence on the volume of any conducting enclosure is avoided. We believe that this definition has the merit of embodying only properties characteristic of the paramagnetic material. Let the further stipulation be made that N shall be the number of paramagnetic centres per unit volume, so that equations (1) and (2) now refer to unit volume. Then

$$-\frac{1}{Q_M} = \frac{4\pi}{3kT} \cdot \frac{Ng^2\beta^2 \mid \langle 3 \mid S_H \mid 2 \rangle \mid^2}{\Delta\nu} \cdot \frac{w_{21}\nu_{21} - w_{32}\nu_{32}}{w_{21}+w_{32}}. \quad \ldots. \quad (4)$$

The concept of magnetic Q is of central importance in any discussion of circuit properties of practical maser amplifiers. In the case of the cavity maser, for example, McWhorter and Meyer (1958) have shown that, under reasonable practical circumstances,

$$G^{\frac{1}{2}}B \doteqdot 2\nu_{32}/\mid Q_M \mid, \quad \ldots\ldots\ldots\ldots\ldots\ldots \quad (5)$$

where G is the power gain, and B is the bandwidth.

As a very different example we shall take a travelling wave coaxial-line structure operating in the principal (*TEM*) mode. The gain per unit length attributable to the magnetic material is

$$G = (1/\mid Q_M \mid)(\nu_{23}/2v)(Z_0/Z) \text{ nepers}, \quad \ldots\ldots\ldots \quad (6)$$

where Z_0 is the intrinsic impedance of the magnetic material, Z is the wave impedance of the filled coaxial line, and v is the group velocity of the wave in the filled coaxial line.

In both cases it is evident that the larger $1/\mid Q_M \mid$ the better the performance, and we shall therefore use it as a figure of merit of paramagnetic materials.

III. Extension of the Maser Equation to Four Levels and Extrapolation to More than Four Levels

The number of paramagnetics with precisely three levels is limited, and in fact the successful masers so far operated have used four or eight levels. In spite of this the equations of a multilevel maser do not appear to have been published. However, some estimate of the influence of extra levels is needed for the assessment of suitability of working substances.

For a four-level maser, we find that, with a natural extension of Bloembergen's notation, the equation analogous to equation (**1**) is

$$n_3-n_2=\frac{1}{4}\cdot\frac{hN}{kT}\cdot\frac{w_4(w_{21}\nu_{21}-w_{32}\nu_{32})+w_{24}(w_{14}\nu_{21}-w_{34}\nu_{32})}{w_4(w_{21}+w_{32})+w_{24}(w_{14}+w_{34})}, \quad \ldots (7)$$

where $w_4\equiv w_{14}+w_{24}+w_{34}$.

If no relaxation transitions exist between the fourth level and the other three, i.e. $w_{14}=w_{24}=w_{34}=0$, the population difference n_3-n_2 turns out to be three-quarters of that given by equation (**1**), which accords with expectation since in this case only $\frac{3}{4}N$ centres are participating in the maser process. The same result is produced in quite a variety of circumstances: (i) if $w_{24}=0$; (ii) if $w_{14}=w_{34}=0$; (iii) if $w_{14}/w_{21}=w_{34}/w_{32}$; (iv) if all the w's are equal.

It may also be seen that the position of the fourth energy level is of no account. However, equation (**7**), like equation (**1**), rests on the assumption that all energy differences are small compared to kT.

Very little is at present known about the values of the relaxation frequencies w. We shall assume here that the effect of extra levels is simply to reduce the working population, so that for an x-level maser,

$$n_3-n_2\doteqdot\frac{1}{x}\cdot\frac{hN}{kT}\cdot\frac{w_{21}\nu_{21}-w_{32}\nu_{32}}{w_{21}+w_{32}}. \quad \ldots\ldots\ldots\ldots (8)$$

The figure of merit then takes the form (cf. equation (**4**))

$$-\frac{1}{Q_M}\doteqdot\frac{4\pi}{xkT}\cdot\frac{Ng^2\beta^2\,|\langle 3\,|\,S_H\,|\,2\rangle|^2}{\Delta\nu}\cdot\frac{w_{21}\nu_{21}-w_{32}\nu_{32}}{w_{21}+w_{32}}. \quad \ldots . (9)$$

IV. Requirements of the Spin and Hamiltonian for Zero-field Masers

In this section we shall discuss what values of spin are required to give three or more energy levels in zero field, and what components must be present in the spin Hamiltonian to provide transitions between the levels. It will be assumed that the nuclear spin is zero; its influence when it is not zero will be discussed in Section VII.

Paramagnetic resonance results are customarily presented in terms of the spin Hamiltonian formalism of Pryce (1950). The ground states of the paramagnetic centres are described in terms of a spin S, and the spin Hamiltonian is a function of spin operators with semi-empirical parameters. Once these are known all paramagnetic properties may be calculated, including those relevant to masers. A particularly useful compilation of spin Hamiltonian parameters has been given in the review article on paramagnetic resonance by Bowers and Owen (1955).

The number of independent states of an ion with spin S is $2S+1$; but, by virtue of Kramers' theorem (1930), the number of distinct energy levels cannot exceed $S+\frac{1}{2}$ for integer-plus-a-half spins. For integer spin the number of levels may be $2S+1$. In either case the full multiplicity allowed by Kramers' theorem may not be realized in crystal fields of high symmetry. Assuming low enough symmetry, the multiplicity is tabulated below as a function of spin:

Spin	1/2	1	3/2	2	5/2	3	7/2
Number of levels ..	1	3	2	5	3	7	4
Example	Cu^{2+}	Ni^{2+}	Cr^{3+}	Cr^{2+}	Fe^{3+}	—	Gd^{3+}

A spin higher than 7/2 is not expected to occur and no examples of spin 3 are known. It is seen that all values of spin except 1/2 and 3/2 are suitable for zero-field masers.

We come next to the required properties of the spin Hamiltonian. By far the commonest form of zero-field Hamiltonian, for $S>\frac{1}{2}$, is

$$\mathscr{H}=D\{S_z^2-\tfrac{1}{3}S(S+1)\}, \qquad (10)$$

where z is an axis of symmetry of the crystalline field. A zero-field maser is out of the question with this Hamiltonian. Since $\mathscr{H}$ commutes with S_z the eigenstates of the energy are simultaneous eigenstates of S_z. The eigenvalues of the Hamiltonian are

$$E_M=D\{M^2-\tfrac{1}{3}S(S+1)\}, \qquad (11)$$

where M is the eigenvalue of S_z. This gives a series of levels, in the order $M=0$, $M=\pm 1$, $M=\pm 2$, . . . for ions with integer spin and in the order $M=\pm 1/2$, $M=\pm 3/2$, $M=\pm 5/2$, . . . for those with integer-plus-a-half spin. The pumping transition for a maser, which must always be a leap-frog transition, that is, one spanning two energy intervals, would here require $\Delta M=\pm 2$. But this is forbidden since the states are pure eigenstates of S_z and the normal selection rule, $\Delta M=\pm 1$, applies.

Fortunately for the zero-field maser, the term in S_z^2, equation (**10**), is quite frequently accompanied by other terms, though generally it remains predominant. The additional terms fall into two classes: those with axial symmetry, viz. S_z^4 and S_z^6; and those with lower symmetry. The axially symmetric terms make no improvement in the situation, for the Hamiltonian after their inclusion still commutes with S_z.

It is to the terms with lower symmetry—rhombic, trigonal, tetragonal, and hexagonal—that one must look in order to realize a zero-field maser. These terms are conventionally expressed as operator functions which transform under rotation in the same way as the spherical harmonics. Most of the terms met with in paramagnetic resonance are given in full in Bleaney and Stevens' (1953) review article (pp. 132, 137, and 150); it is invariably the case that a term with m-fold symmetry contains the operators S_+^m and S_-^m, where

$$S_+\equiv S_x+iS_y, \qquad S_-\equiv S_x-iS_y. \qquad (12)$$

These terms do not commute with S_z, and therefore the eigenstates of the Hamiltonian are not pure eigenstates of S_z, and normal selection rules no longer apply.

In general one may say that any paramagnetic with spin other than 1/2 or 3/2, which has a spin Hamiltonian of rhombic, trigonal, tetragonal, or hexagonal symmetry, is a candidate for a zero-field maser.

There is one exception to the rule. This is the case of perfect cubic symmetry, which has the Hamiltonian (Bleaney and Stevens 1953, p. 137)

$$\mathscr{H}_{\text{cubic}}=\tfrac{1}{6}a\{S_x^4+S_y^4+S_z^4-\tfrac{1}{5}S(S+1)(3S^2+3S-1)\}, \quad \ldots. \quad (13)$$

where a is a numerical coefficient. For all spins less than 3 this Hamiltonian gives fewer than three levels, and for $S=3$ and 7/2 the number of levels is three but the leap-frog transition probability turns out to be zero. It should be emphasized that this is true only of perfect cubic symmetry; $\mathscr{H}_{\text{cubic}}$ in conjunction with other operators has rhombic, trigonal, or tetragonal symmetry and the rule then applies.

V. Line Width and Ultimate Performance

The figure of merit, equation (9), depends on the line width $\Delta\nu$. In a zero-field maser three agencies can contribute to this: (1) the random magnetic fields of the nuclei of the diamagnetic neighbours of the paramagnetic centres; (2) a spread in the values of the spin Hamiltonian coefficients; (3) the fields of the paramagnetic centres themselves. In principle, (1) and (2) can be made small compared to (3) by choosing a host material in which the diamagnetic atoms have small nuclear moments and by obtaining a sufficiently perfect crystal structure. Then performance would depend only on the line width due to paramagnetic spin-spin interaction (3).

Kittel and Abrahams (1953) have calculated the line width for a dilute paramagnetic with a cubic lattice. With some adaptation of their result one obtains

$$\Delta\nu \doteqdot 6g^2\beta^2N\sqrt{\{S(S+1)\}}/h. \quad \ldots\ldots\ldots\ldots\ldots \quad (14)$$

We shall take this to be a fair indication of line width for any lattice, not merely cubic. Then the figure of merit becomes, using (9) and (14),

$$-\frac{1}{Q_M}\doteqdot\frac{2h(w_{21}\nu_{21}-w_{32}\nu_{32})\,|\langle 3\mid S_H\mid 2\rangle|^2}{xkT(w_{21}+w_{32})\sqrt{\{S(S+1)\}}}. \quad \ldots\ldots\ldots \quad (15)$$

The value of $|\langle 3\mid S_H\mid 2\rangle|^2$ will be typically of the order of $(\tfrac{1}{4})S^2$; the number of distinct energy levels, x, is $S+\tfrac{1}{2}$ and $2S+1$ for integer-plus-a-half and integer spins respectively; thus to a rough approximation (15) is independent of spin. Making now the simplifying assumption that $w_{21}\sim w_{32}$, and $\nu_{21}\gg\nu_{32}$, one obtains for the figure of merit

$$-\frac{1}{Q_M}\sim h\nu_{21}/4kT \quad \ldots\ldots\ldots\ldots\ldots\ldots \quad (16)$$

for integer-plus-a-half spin (Kramers degenerate ions). For integer spin the figure of merit is roughly halved.

It is interesting to compare (**16**), which should be valid for a magnetic-field maser as well as for a zero-field maser, with the results of McWhorter and Meyer (1958). In their experiment, $\nu_{21}\sim 6\times 10^9$ c/s, $T=1\cdot 25$ °K, and $S=3/2$. After adjustment for the doubling of multiplicity brought about by the presence of the magnetic field our theory predicts $-1/Q_M \sim h\nu_{21}/8kT$ or 1/35. In fact the experimentally measured figure, derived from the quoted gain-bandwidth product, by the use of equation (**5**), was 1/3300, or about 100 times worse than the ultimate predicted. The factor of 100 is made up in the following way. (*a*) The filling factor of the sample in the cavity was only 10 per cent., which contributes a factor 10. (*b*) The line width (derived from the quoted value of 5×10^{-9} sec for T_2) was 30 Mc/s, whereas that attributable to paramagnetic spin-spin interaction in the working population of 10^{19} per cm^3 was, according to equation (**14**), only 6 Mc/s. This contributes a factor 5. (*c*) The approximation made in deriving equation (**18**), namely, that $\nu_{21} \gg \nu_{32}$, is not justified; in fact $\nu_{32} \doteqdot \frac{1}{2}\nu_{21}$, which contributes a factor 2. The product of these factors is 100. The closeness of this agreement is only accidental, considering the approximations made in deriving equation (**16**).

The significant conclusion from the above comparison is that it is desirable to increase the paramagnetic concentration, or reduce other sources of line width, until the paramagnetic spin-spin width is dominant. The former course—increasing concentration—cannot necessarily be followed with impunity. For example, in their experiments with a 1400 Mc/s maser using dilute potassium chromicyanide, Autler and McAvoy (1958) found that, whereas $\frac{1}{2}$ per cent. crystals ($N\sim 10^{19}$) functioned successfully, 1 per cent. crystals did not. This fact may be understood in terms of the theory of Giordmaine *et al.* (1958). According to this theory, the phonon frequencies near the spin resonances are considerably broadened by interaction with the spins. The phonon width $\Delta\nu_L$ is proportional to $N^{\frac{1}{2}}$, and, for a typical case, $\Delta\nu_L \sim 400$ Mc/s at $N=10^{19}$. It follows that if the resonance at ν_{31} is saturated, as in pumping a maser, the temperature of all phonons in the range $\nu_{31}\pm\Delta\nu_L$ is raised and these will saturate in turn any other spin resonances which they overlap. It is clear that in this model maser action would not occur if $\Delta\nu_L > \nu_{32}$, for then the saturation of ν_{31} would spread to ν_{21} with the result that $n_1=n_2=n_3$. The same failure can occur even if $\Delta\nu_L < \nu_{32}$ because the lattice modes are not expected to show a sharp cut-off at $\nu\pm\Delta\nu_L$.

Since it may not be possible to increase paramagnetic concentration it is probable that the other course, of reducing the width due to diamagnetic neighbours, is the more promising. In most hydrated salts the protons in the water molecules cause a half-width of 20 Mc/s; by substituting heavy water this may be reduced to about 6 Mc/s (Bleaney and Stevens 1953, p. 119). By growing crystals which do not contain water of crystallization even greater improvements may be expected; for example, the diamagnetic neighbour width in dilute $K_3Cr(CN)_6$ crystals is only 3 Mc/s (Bowers 1952).

The other source of width—variation of spin Hamiltonian parameters—is more obscure. For example, it was found by Bleaney and Trenam (1954) that among the diluted ferric alums the ammonium, potassium, and thallium sulphates did not give narrow lines, whereas the rubidium and methylamine sulphates and potassium selenate did.

More experimental data are needed concerning causes of line width in paramagnetic compounds. However, it is reasonable to expect that ways will be found to utilize the full potential figure of merit given by equation (**16**).

To demonstrate the implications of this equation one may propose an example of a cavity maser with a Kramers degenerate working substance ($S=5/2$ or $7/2$) in which $\nu_{21}\sim 20000$ and $\nu_{31}\sim 3000$ Mc/s, $T\sim 2$ °K, $G\sim 30$ dB. From equations (**5**) and (**16**) the bandwidth would be 25 Mc/s. By contrast, the bandwidth so far achieved in a magnetic field maser at the same power gain is only 60 kc/s (McWhorter and Meyer 1958). The example shows that the present view of the maser as essentially a narrow-band device should be revised.

VI. Relaxation Times

The relaxation times for transitions between the three levels affect both the pumping power requirements and the figure of merit of the maser. We shall discuss first the pumping power.

The power absorbed at saturation, P_a, may be found by adapting the treatment of Eschenfelder and Weidner (1953), giving

$$P_a=\frac{N(h\nu)^2 w}{3kT}=\frac{N(h\nu)^2}{6kT}\cdot\frac{1}{\tau}, \qquad \ldots\ldots\ldots\ldots \quad (\mathbf{17})$$

where w is the thermally induced (relaxation) transition probability between the two levels saturated, and τ is the associated spin-lattice relaxation time, which is equal to $1/(2w)$ (see, for example, Andrew 1955, p. 15). The power absorbed in pumping a maser is not correctly given, however, by direct substitution of ν_{31} for ν and w_{31} for w in equation (**17**) because the direct relaxations from level 3 to 1 are supplemented by those passing from 3 to 2 and thence to 1. From the Bloembergen equations we have derived the following general expression valid for three levels

$$P_a=\frac{N(h\nu_{31})^2}{6kT}\cdot\left(\frac{1}{\tau_{31}}+\frac{1}{\tau_{21}+\tau_{32}}\right), \qquad \ldots\ldots\ldots\ldots \quad (\mathbf{18})$$

where $\tau_{ij}=1/(2w_{ij})$.

We now consider the desirable limitations on the relaxation times. We shall use an effective time $\tau=\{1/\tau_{31}+1/(\tau_{21}+\tau_{32})\}^{-1}$; the experimental results available do not warrant a closer examination of the separate times.

The use of liquid helium temperatures is likely to be general since the figure of merit, equation (**16**), is inversely proportional to the absolute temperature. As a typical case, then, one may take $T\sim 1$, $N\sim 10^{19}$, $\nu_{31}\sim 10^{10}$, and $x=4$, whence the power absorbed is about $1/10\tau$ mW/cm³. The volume of working substance will be some tens of cubic centimetres, so that $P_a\sim 1/\tau$ mW. Postulating an upper limit of 1 W, which would evaporate about a litre of liquid helium per hour, one is led to the requirement that τ be a millisecond or longer.

Relaxation times of the order of milliseconds have indeed been measured at liquid helium temperatures (Gorter 1947; Benzie and Cook 1950; Eschenfelder and Weidner 1953 ; Giodmaine *et al.* 1958). It appears to be generally the case that, if a paramagnetic has a long enough relaxation time at room temperature to give observable resonance lines, then it has a relaxation time longer than 1 msec at liquid helium temperatures. We shall therefore assume that to be suitable for a maser a paramagnetic must give observable resonance lines at room temperature.

As Bloembergen (1956) has remarked, the w's may be expected to reflect the Debye (ν^2) phonon spectrum : if so, the figure of merit would contain $(\nu_{21}^3-\nu_{32}^3)/(\nu_{21}+\nu_{32})$. Accordingly we shall assume, for the purpose of this paper, that even if ν_{21} is only a few tens per cent. greater than ν_{32} the substance is a reasonable candidate for a zero-field maser.

VII. Influence of Hyperfine Structure

If the nucleus of a paramagnetic centre has odd mass number it will possess angular momentum and magnetic moment. A magnetic interaction will exist between the nucleus and the paramagnetic electrons, to account for which the term

$$\mathscr{H}_N=A_xS_xI_x+A_yS_yI_y+A_zS_zI_z \quad \ldots\ldots\ldots\ldots \quad (19)$$

must be added to the Hamiltonian, I_x, I_y, and I_z being the components of nuclear spin. An electric quadrupole interaction may also exist but is unimportant for the discussion in hand.

The effect of $\mathscr{H}_N$ is to increase considerably the number of levels. With electronic spin S and nuclear spin I the number of independent states is $(2S+1)(2I+1)$ and, although not all need correspond to distinct energy levels (see, for example, Fig. 8 of the paper by Bleaney and Ingram 1951), the number of levels, that is, x in equation (9), is often nearly an order of magnitude greater than the three required for maser action. The figure of merit is correspondingly reduced. Furthermore, hyperfine-structure masers, with their more closely spaced levels, are more likely to encounter the phonon-width trouble referred to in Section V.

For these reasons we do not regard hyperfine-structure masers as likely to be as important as fine-structure masers (masers with electronic splittings only). Nevertheless, hyperfine-structure masers merit some consideration because they hold the promise of extending the frequency coverage of zero-field masers. The energy splittings caused by $\mathscr{H}_N$ range from A to $(I+\frac{1}{2})A$; A is typically a few hundred Mc/s, and I may be as great as 7/2. Thus the band of frequencies covered is typically from 100 to 1000 Mc/s. We shall give one example of a hyperfine-structure maser in Section XI.

VIII. Eligible Ions

Since it is our aim to focus attention only on the most promising working substances for zero-field masers, we shall now apply rather liberally the disqualifications implied by the preceding sections.

Paramagnetism has been observed in compounds of the five transition groups, the iron, palladium, rare earth, platinum, and actinide groups, which are associated with unpaired electrons in the 3d, 4d, 4f, 5d, and 5f shells respectively.

We shall consider these groups in turn. Most of the available paramagnetic resonance data are collected together in the review article by Bowers and Owen (1955), to which we refer as B & O.

The most thoroughly investigated group is the 3*d*. Most ions in the group give observable spectra at room temperature so that only a few need be disqualified by the relaxation-time criterion, leaving as eligible the ions VO^{2+}, V^{2+}, Cr^{2+}, Mn^{2+} (but not $[Mn(CN)_6]^{4+}$), Fe^{3+} (but not $[Fe(CN)_6]^{3+}$), Ni^{2+}, and Cu^{2+}. Next, the disqualification of ions which possess a large proportion of isotopes with hyperfine structure removes VO^{2+}, V^{2+}, Mn^{2+}, and Cu^{2+}. Those remaining which possess spin 1/2 or 3/2 must be disqualified for providing too few levels: Cr^{3+}, with $S=3/2$ is thus rejected, leaving Cr^{2+} ($S=2$), Fe^{3+} ($S=5/2$), and Ni^{2+} ($S=1$).

The next group, the 4*d* group, provides rather few investigated compounds because chemical stability appears to go hand-in-hand with diamagnetic bonding. Of the compounds investigated, none have spin other than 1/2 or 3/2, so that the entire group is disqualified. The same applies to the 5*d* group (B & O, p. 355).

In the 4*f* or rare earth group relaxation times are generally very short and liquid hydrogen or helium temperatures have had to be employed in order to observe the spectra. The only ions giving observable spectra at room temperature are the iso-electronic Eu^{2+} and Gd^{3+}, which have $S=7/2$. Eu^{2+} is disqualified by its large proportion of isotopes with hyperfine structure (B & O, p. 363). Gd^{3+} has 30 per cent. isotopes with nuclear spin, but the associated hyperfine structure is so small that it eluded for years attempts to resolve it (Low 1956). The four electronic energy levels of Gd^{3+} are each thus effectively single and provide a good basis for a zero-field maser.

In the 5*f* series the behaviour appears to resemble that in the 4*f* series (Bleaney 1955; Hutchison *et al.* 1956), so that very short relaxation times are to be expected. Bleaney (1955) has pointed out that the ions Am^{2+}, Cm^{3+} and Bk^{4+} are expected to behave analogously to Gd^{3+} and Eu^{2+}, with reasonably long relaxation times. However, the expense of these elements and the destruction of crystal structure which their radiations will cause, make it doubtful that they, or any other actinides, will be attractive candidates for zero-field masers and accordingly we shall not consider them further.

It is seen that the promising working substances for zero-field masers are the compounds of no more than four ions: Cr^{2+}, Fe^{3+}, Ni^{2+}, and Gd^{3+}. These will be discussed in detail in Section X.

IX. Transition Probabilities

The transition probability, equation (3), may be expressed in terms of an effective magneton number for the transition p analogous to that used in the description of magnetic susceptibilities. p is defined by

$$p^2H^2=g^2\,|\langle i\,|\,H\cdot S\,|\,j\rangle|^2. \qquad (20)$$

The figure of merit then takes the form (cf. equation (9))

$$\frac{-1}{Q_M}=\frac{4\pi N\beta^2p^2}{xkT\Delta\nu}\cdot\frac{w_{21}\nu_{21}-w_{32}\nu_{32}}{w_{21}+w_{32}}. \qquad (21)$$

If lmn are the direction cosines of H with respect to the axes xyz of the spin Hamiltonian,

$$p^2=l^2p_x^2+m^2p_y^2+n^2p_z^2, \quad \ldots\ldots\ldots\ldots\ldots (22)$$

where $p_x^2=g^2\,|\langle i\,|\,S_x\,|\,j\rangle|^2$, and so on.

It is illuminating to notice that, for a free electron spin with oscillating field applied perpendicular to a steady field, $p^2=g^2\,|\langle -\tfrac{1}{2}\,|\,S_x\,|\,\tfrac{1}{2}\rangle|^2=1$ since $g=2{\cdot}00$. Hence, in general, p^2 denotes the strength of a transition in terms of that for a free spin having the same line width: in other words, p^2 is the strength in free-spin units.

For powdered salts p^2 must be averaged over all directions of H, giving

$$p_{\mathrm{Av}}^2=\tfrac{1}{3}(p_x^2+p_y^2+p_z^2). \quad \ldots\ldots\ldots\ldots\ldots (23)$$

If the spectroscopic splitting factor g were anisotropic, equations (**20**) and (**21**) would require generalization; but for compounds suitable for masers it turns out that g is always nearly isotropic.

X. Maser Properties of Selected Compounds

We shall now consider the suitability of those compounds of Cr^{2+}, Ni^{2+}, Fe^{3+}, and Gd^{3+} which have been studied by paramagnetic resonance. In many cases results have been observed at room temperatures, and the properties deduced from them must be taken only as an indication of what will apply at liquid helium temperatures.

Energies and eigenstates have been calculated from the spin Hamiltonian by standard methods. The eigenstates have been then used to calculate transition probabilities which in the diagrams that follow will be labelled by the value of $p^2=l^2p_x^2+m^2p_y^2+n^2p_z^2$ appropriate to the transition. The information in the diagrams will allow prediction of maser performance in case it should be desired to obtain optimum transition probabilities by mounting crystals of the working substance in a definite orientation in the oscillating fields.

It should be noted, however, that, when there are several differently oriented paramagnetic ions per unit cell of the crystal structure, it is not in general possible to mount crystals so as to use the most favourable component of p^2 for all ions: the spatial average p_{Av}^2 is then a useful guide to performance. Furthermore, one of the characteristic features of zero-field masers is the possibility they provide of using powdered material, which allows structural freedom and good filling factor. Therefore, in the tables of maser properties of specific compounds we shall quote the spatial average.

The ions Cr^{2+} and Ni^{2+} will be treated first. They both lack Kramers degeneracy and have larger splittings and probably shorter relaxation times than Fe^{3+} and Gd^{3+} which are Kramers degenerate.

Cr^{2+}: $S=2$.

Only one compound, $CrSO_4.5H_2O$, has been studied (Ono *et al.* 1954). The results were obtained with undiluted crystals. There are two differently oriented ions per unit cell, each with the Hamiltonian

$$\mathscr{H}=D\{S_z^2-\tfrac{1}{3}S(S+1)\}+E(S_x^2-S_y^2). \quad \ldots\ldots\ldots (24)$$

The g-value is nearly isotropic and equal to $2 \cdot 0$. The energy levels are (B & O, p. 336): $E_1 = -2(D^2+3E^2)^{\frac{1}{2}}$, $E_2 = -D-3E$, $E_3 = -D+3E$, $E_4 = 2D$, and $E_5 = 2(D^2+3E^2)^{\frac{1}{2}}$. The transition probabilities are given in Figure 1.

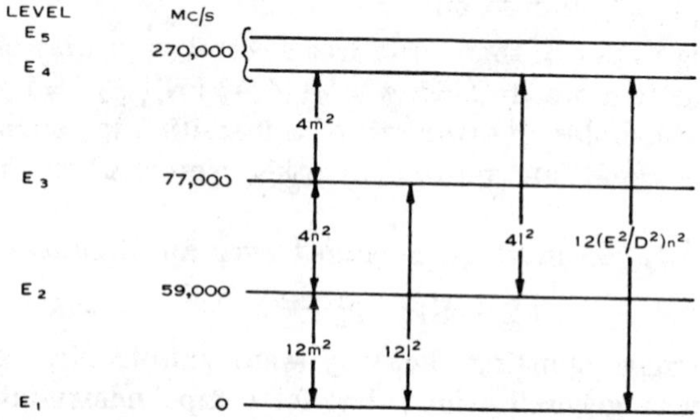

Fig. 1.—Transition probabilities for Cr^{2+} in free-spin units with oscillating field in the direction (lmn). The numerical values of the energy for $CrSO_4.5H_2O$ at room temperature are given; g^2 is taken as 4. For meaning of D and E, see equation (**24**).

The frequencies and spatially averaged transition probabilities are given in Table 1.

From Table 1 it is evident that a very promising possibility exists for a maser amplifying at about 18,000 Mc/s. The higher modes, b and c, may become practicable in the future.

Table 1

MASER PROPERTIES OF Cr^{2+} AND Ni^{2+} SALTS

Salt	Temperature of Measurement (°K)	Pumping Frequency (Mc/s)	Pumping Probability for Powdered Salt (free-spin units)	Amplifying Frequency (Mc/s)	Amplifying Probability for Powdered Salt (free-spin units)	Difference Frequency (Mc/s)
$CrSO_4.5H_2O$	290	(a) 77,000	4	18,000	1·3	59,000
		(b) 270,000	0·01	77,000	4	190,000
		(c) 270,000	0·01	59,000	4	210,000
$K_2Ni(SO_4)_2.6H_2O$ ..	290	115,000	1·7	30,000	1·7	85,000
$(NH_4)_2Ni(SO_4)_2.6H_2O$	90	75,000	1·7	29,000	1·7	46,000
$Tl_2Ni(SO_4)_2.6H_2O$ ..	290	80,000	1·7	6,000	1·7	74,000
$(NH_4)_2Ni(SeO_4)_2.6H_2O$	90	76,000	1·7	27,000	1·7	49,000
$NiSO_4.7H_2O$ ..	290	150,000	1·7	60,000	1·7	90,000

Ni^{2+}: $S=1$.

A number of nickel salts has been studied, and it has been found that where the crystalline environment has trigonal or higher symmetry the spin Hamiltonian provides only two distinct levels (Bleaney and Stevens 1953, p. 144) and so is useless for a zero-field maser. The majority of salts, however, are suitable, exhibiting rhombic symmetry with the same Hamiltonian as that of $CrSO_4.5H_2O$ given above. The g-value is nearly isotropic and equal to $2 \cdot 25$. The energies and transition probabilities are given in Figure 2.

Table 1 gives maser properties of suitable nickel salts (B & O, p. 350). The data refer to undiluted salts ; dilution may alter the frequencies by 20 per cent. In the Tutton salts there are two, and in $NiSO_4.6H_2O$ four differently oriented ions per unit cell.

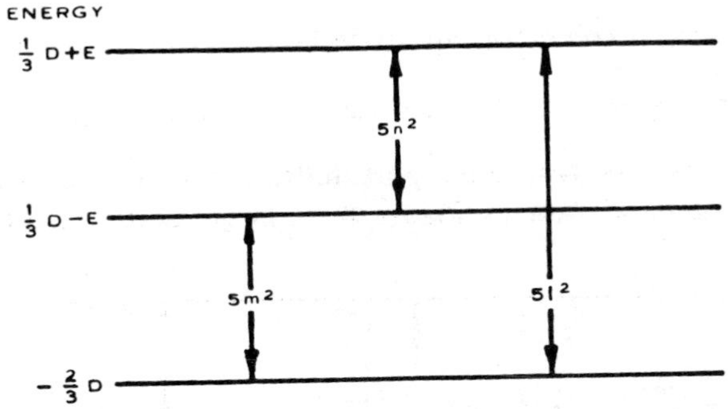

Fig. 2.—Energies and transition probabilities for Ni^{2+} assuming $g^2=5$. The transition probabilities are given in free-spin units and the oscillating field has the direction (lmn). For D and E, see equation (**24**).

It can be seen that a variety of amplifying frequencies is likely to be provided at liquid helium temperatures by nickel salts. The transition probabilities are substantial, being greater than the free-electron probability even for powdered salt.

That paramagnetic resonance has been observed in so few nickel salts is probably because the zero-field splittings for most salts are even greater than those in Table 1. These will constitute a reserve of maser materials for the future as the millimetre wave region develops.

Fe^{3+} : $S=5/2$.

The behaviour of ferric salts hitherto studied is described by the spin Hamiltonian of Bleaney and Trenam (1954) which in zero field takes the form

$$\mathscr{H}=D\left\{S_z^2-\frac{1}{3}S(S+1)\right\}+\frac{1}{6}a\left\{S_\xi^4+S_\eta^4+S_\zeta^4-\frac{707}{16}\right\}+\frac{7}{36}F\left(S_z^4-\frac{95}{14}S_z^2+\frac{81}{16}\right), \quad \ldots\ldots\ldots\ldots (\mathbf{25})$$

where the coordinate system $\xi\eta\zeta$ refers to three mutually perpendicular axes with respect to which the z-axis is the (111) direction. Such a Hamiltonian is to be expected when the environment of the ion is predominantly cubic with cubic axes $\xi\eta\zeta$, with a superposed distortion along the (111) or z-direction such that the resulting symmetry is only trigonal with z as axis. The term in F is usually of small influence.

The term in a, or cubic term, has off-diagonal elements when expressed in the S_z-representation, as may be seen in the matrix given by Meijer (1951). These provide the leap-frog transitions which are necessary for zero-field maser action.

General formulae for the zero-field levels and eigenstates of the Hamiltonian (**25**) have been given by Bleaney and Trenam (1954). The energy levels are doublets at

$$\left.\begin{aligned} E_{1,2}&=\tfrac{1}{3}D-\tfrac{1}{2}(a-F)\pm\tfrac{1}{6}\{(18D+a-F)^2+80a^2\}^{\frac{1}{2}}, \\ E_3&=-\tfrac{2}{3}D+a-F, \end{aligned}\right\} \quad \ldots\ldots (\mathbf{26})$$

and the eigenstates involve trigonometric functions of an angle α defined by

$$\tan\alpha=a\sqrt{20}/\{9D+\tfrac{1}{2}(a-F)\}. \quad \ldots\ldots\ldots\ldots\ldots\ldots (\mathbf{27})$$

From these eigenstates transition probabilities may be calculated, which we present for the general case in Figure 3. The g-value is isotropic and equal to 2·00.

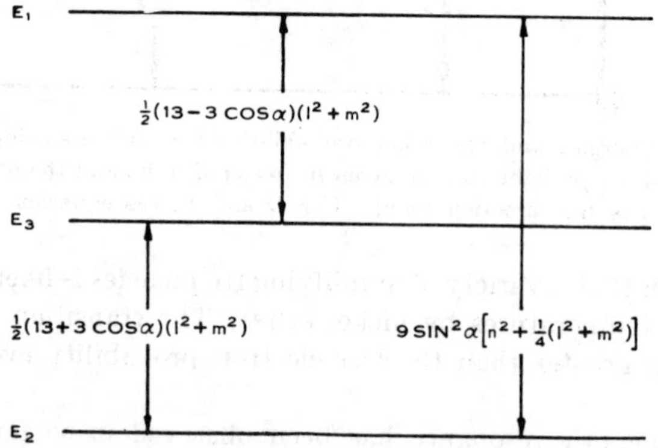

Fig. 3.—Transition probabilities for Fe^{3+} in free-spin units with oscillating field in the direction (lmn), assuming $g^2=4$. The order of levels is appropriate to D positive and predominant. For $E_{1,2,3}$, α, and D, see equations (**25**), (**26**), and (**27**).

Although paramagnetic resonance has been observed in a wide variety of undiluted compounds (B & O, p. 342), the only compounds in which the spectrum of Fe^{3+} has been observed in diluted form (i.e. with high resolution) appear to be the alums (B & O, p. 342), the acetylacetonate (Jarrett 1957), MgO (Low 1957), and Al_2O_3 (sapphire) (Kornienko and Prokhorov 1957 ; Bogle and Symmons, paper in preparation).

Apart from MgO, where the Hamiltonian is purely cubic and need not be considered for a zero-field maser (Section IV), two classes of compounds may be distinguished.

The first class comprises the alums, except methylamine alum, and is characterized by comparable values of D and a, each being a few hundred Mc/s. This class is easy to pump and provides amplifying frequencies from 100 to 1000 Mc/s.

The second class comprises methylamine alum, the acetylacetonate, and sapphire; in these compounds D is some thousands of Mc/s while a remains a few hundred. The pumping transition probability reduces to $(20/9)(a^2/D^2)\{n^2+\frac{1}{4}(l^2+m^2)\}$ for $a \ll D$, which shows that this class is difficult to pump. It provides amplifying frequencies of the order of 10,000 Mc/s.

The maser properties of the above-mentioned compounds are given in Table 2. The methylamine alum is omitted because the pumping probability turns out to be only 0·003 free-spin unit. The acetylacetonate is included in spite of there being no data on the size of a, because the presence of off-diagonal terms is indicated by the failure of the Hamiltonian $D\{S_z^2-\frac{1}{3}S(S+1)\}$ to fit the measurements (Jarrett 1957).

The alums have four differently oriented ions per unit cell, the acetylacetonate two, and sapphire two.

TABLE 2

MASER PROPERTIES OF DILUTE Fe^{3+} AND Gd^{3+} COMPOUNDS

Ion	Diluent	Temperature of Measurement (°K)	Pumping Frequency (Mc/s)	Pumping Probability for Powdered Material (free-spin units)	Amplifying Frequency (Mc/s)	Amplifying Probability for Powdered Material (free-spin units)	Difference Frequency (Mc/s)
Fe^{3+}	$KAl(SeO_4)_2.12H_2O$	20	2,475	0·95	1,020	3·4	1,455
Fe^{3+}	Sapphire ..	4	31,300	0·02	12,030	5·3	19,270
Fe^{3+}	Cobalt acetylacetonate ..	290	17,000	—	6,000	5	11,000
Gd^{3+}	$Sm_2(SO_4)_3.8H_2O$	290	(a) 14,760	2·4	7,370	17	7,390
			(b) 25,040	0·04	10,280	5	14,760
			(c) 17,670	0·04	7,390	8	10,280

Gd^{3+} : $S=7/2$.

The general form of the spin Hamiltonian for gadolinium salts is given by B & O, p. 364. Recasting the Hamiltonian in terms of the b-coefficients, which are normally used to express experimental results, one obtains

$$\mathscr{H}=b_2^0\left\{S_z^2-\frac{1}{3}S(S+1)\right\}+\frac{1}{6}b_2^2(S_+^2+S_-^2)+\frac{1}{60}b_4^0P_4^0+\frac{1}{1260}b_6^0P_6^0+\frac{1}{2520}P_6^6(S_+^6+S_-^6). \quad \ldots\ldots\ldots\ldots\ldots (28)$$

The operators P_4^0 and P_6^0 are rather complicated functions of S_z which are given explicitly by Elliott and Stevens (1953). The only case known not to be described by equation (28) is Gd^{3+} in CaF_2, which has been studied by Ryter (1957). Here the Hamiltonian has cubic symmetry and so does not provide a basis for a zero-field maser (see Section IV).

The dominant term in the Hamiltonian, except for cubic symmetry, is always the first, just as in the case of most iron group compounds. (D of equation (**10**) has the same meaning as b_2^0 of (**28**).) The energy levels are thus approximately those of $b_2^0(S_z^2-\frac{1}{3}S(S+1))$ acting alone, that is, $-5b_2^0$, $-3b_2^0$, b_2^0, and $7b_2^0$, so that the possible maser amplifier frequencies are about $2b_2^0$ and $4b_2^0$.

The Hamiltonian of equation (**28**) presents a generality not found in nature: in compounds so far studied it possesses either hexagonal symmetry, in which case $b_2^2=0$, or else rhombic symmetry, in which case $b_6^6=0$. Nevertheless, no misunderstanding need arise if the energy levels are written down as if all terms in (**28**) were simultaneously present. With the assumption that b_2^0 is the dominant term, the levels are given by the following equations, which are correct to the second degree in b_2^2 and b_6^6:

$$\left.\begin{aligned} E(\pm 7/2)&=7b_2^0+7b_4^0+b_6^0+(7/30)(b_2^2)^2/b_2^0+(2/21)(b_6^6)^2/b_2^0),\\ E(\pm 5/2)&=b_2^0-13b_4^0-5b_6^0+(5/6)(b_2^2)^2/b_2^0-(2/21)(b_6^6)^2/b_2^0,\\ E(\pm 3/2)&=-3b_2^0-3b_4^0+9b_6^0+(31/10)(b_2^2)^2/b_2^0,\\ E(\pm 1/2)&=-5b_2^0+9b_4^0-5b_6^0-(25/6)(b_2^2)^2/b_2^0. \end{aligned}\right\} \quad ..\ (29)$$

The above expressions, except for the term in $(b_6^6)^2$, have in effect been given by B & O, pp. 365 and 368. Although the term in $(b_6^6)^2$ is unimportant for compounds studied hitherto we have included it for the sake of compounds which may be studied in the future.

When one comes to consider transition probabilities it proves desirable, for clarity, to present separate diagrams for the hexagonal and rhombic classes. This is done in Figures 4 and 5 respectively.

Class I. Gd^{3+} with hexagonal Hamiltonian

The only diluted compounds in this class which appear to have been studied in detail are the ethyl sulphate and double nitrate (B & O, p. 367) and the anhydrous chloride (Hutchison, Judd, and Pope 1957). In these salts the pumping transition probabilities are very small, namely, 3×10^{-6}, 6×10^{-5}, and 4×10^{-5} that of a free spin respectively. It is doubtful whether they will ever find application in a zero-field maser and we shall not consider them further.

Class II. Gd^{3+} with rhombic Hamiltonian

The only representative of this class for which data are available appears to be the sulphate octohydrate, which has been studied at room temperature with the corresponding samarium salt as diluent (B & O, p. 367). In this salt $r=b_2^2/b_2^0=0\cdot60$, which is by no means small compared to unity. Consequently the energies and the transition probabilities are not given with sufficient accuracy by equation (**29**) and Figure 4. We have solved the problem numerically in order to obtain the results shown in Figure 6.

Table 2 shows that several possible pumping and amplifying frequencies exist, with substantial transition probabilities. To demonstrate this variety, which is a feature of Gd^{3+} in a rhombic environment, is the main purpose of the entry; no great credence is to be attached to the actual magnitudes since (1) on cooling to liquid helium temperatures b_2^0 may be expected, by analogy with the ethylsulphate (Bleaney *et al.* 1951), to change by about 10 per cent., with the other b's not necessarily changing in proportion; and (2) the diluent will have to be changed from paramagnetic samarium to diamagnetic yttrium. Lanthanum sulphate does not crystallize isomorphously with the gadolinium salt; yttrium sulphate does so, and the Gd^{3+} spectrum has been qualitatively observed in this diluent (Bogle, unpublished data).

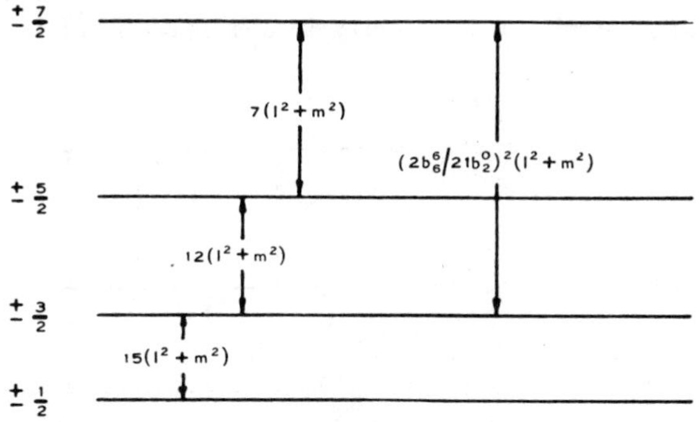

Fig. 4.—Transition probabilities in free-spin units for Gd^{3+} with a hexagonal Hamiltonian and with oscillating field in the direction (lmn). g^2 is taken as equal to 4. For b_6^6 and b_2^0, see equation (**28**). The order of levels is appropriate to b_2^0 positive and dominant.

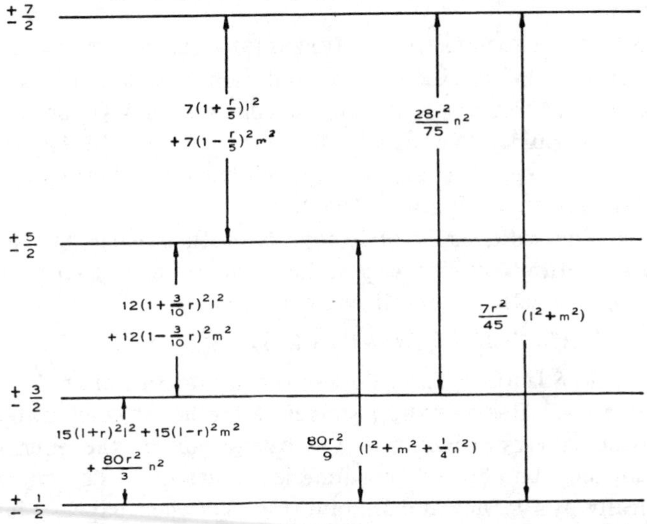

Fig. 5.—Transition probabilities in free-spin units for Gd^{3+} with a rhombic Hamiltonian and with oscillating field in the direction (lmn). g^2 is taken as equal to 4. $r=b_2^2/b_2^0$; for b_2^2 and b_2^0, see equation (**28**). The order of levels is appropriate to b_2^0 positive and dominant.

The conclusion to be drawn from the foregoing discussion is that gadolinium compounds with low symmetry are the most promising for zero-field masers. These have been neglected in the past, probably because both the presence of off-diagonal elements in the Hamiltonian and the frequent occurrence of several directionally inequivalent ions per unit cell have rendered analysis difficult. Some information is already available about the nitrate (Bleaney *et al.* 1951) and the chloride hexahydrate (Dieke and Leopold 1957) which suggests that they will be suitable working substances, with frequencies of similar order to those of the sulphate octohydrate. It can hardly be doubted that a wealth of gadolinium compounds of low symmetry awaits investigation.

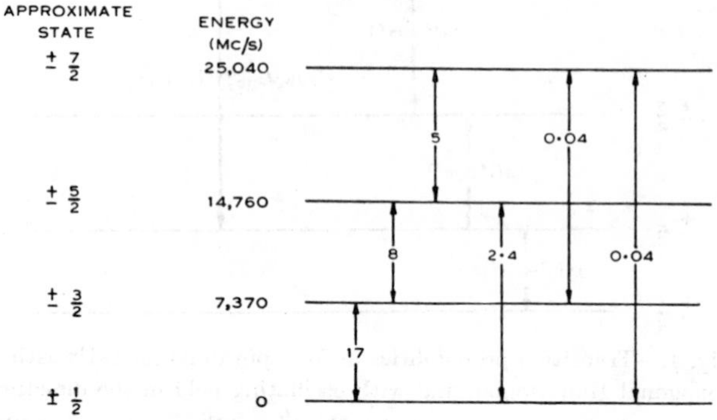

Fig. 6.—Energies and transition probabilities for Gd^{3+} in $Sm_2(SO_4)_3.8H_2O$ at 290 °K. The transition probabilities are averages for a powdered sample and are expressed in free-spin units.

XI. An Example of a Hyperfine-structure Maser

Ions satisfying the relaxation-time criterion (Section VI) and possessing a large proportion of isotopes with nuclear spin are (B & O, pp. 334, 363) V^{2+}, Mn^{2+}, Cu^{2+}, and Eu^{3+}. We choose for our example $(NH_4)_2Mn(SO_4)_2.6H_2O$ diluted with the corresponding zinc salt, which has been thoroughly investigated at 20 °K by Bleaney and Ingram (1951).

Manganese consists entirely of isotope 55 with nuclear spin equal to 5/2 ; the hyperfine-structure coupling is practically isotropic so that in zero field the Hamiltonian is (neglecting a small cubic term)

$$\mathscr{H}=D\{S_z^2-\tfrac{1}{3}S(S+1)\}+E(S_x^2-S_y^2)+AS.I. \quad \ldots\ldots\ldots \quad (30)$$

The electronic spin S is 5/2. The values of the parameters are : $D=830$, $E=150$, and $A=-280$ Mc/s. Because the parameters are all of comparable magnitude the quantization is very mixed and the calculation of the energy levels and eigenstates can only be effected by numerical methods. The energy levels are given numerically by Bleaney and Ingram (Fig. 8 of their paper) ; it may be seen that they extend in a series from 0 to 8500 Mc/s with gaps averaging 400 Mc/s and nowhere exceeding 900 Mc/s.

Expressing transition probabilities in free-spin units as before, one may say that a series of pumping frequencies exists between 4500 and 8500 Mc/s with probabilities of order $(E/D)^2$ or 0·03, and amplifying frequencies between 60 Mc/s and 2000 Mc/s with probabilities of order unity. If a non-resonant microwave structure were used, the salt would provide amplification at 2220, 2160, 2040, 1980, 1920, 1440, 1200, 720, 600, 480, 180, 120 Mc/s, the pumping frequency being required to vary only from 8500 to 7000 Mc/s.

XII. Conclusion

The important fact which has emerged from the search for zero-field maser materials is that even with the few compounds of the eligible ions Cr^{2+}, Fe^{3+}, Ni^{2+}, and Gd^{3+} which have been studied a wide range of frequencies should be available. That the number of known suitable compounds is not greater is simply a consequence of the fact that attention in the past has been concentrated on compounds with properties either inessential or detrimental to zero-field maser action: namely, compounds easily obtainable as large crystals; likely to lead to the discovery of nuclear spins; possessing few inequivalent ions; or characterized by a simple spin Hamiltonian.

There is need for systematic research into that great majority of compounds of the ions named which is as yet untouched. Much of the work may be best pioneered by the classical cavity-resonator technique (fixed frequency and variable magnetic field). The loss of sensitivity occasioned by the necessity, where it exists, to use small crystals should be offset by application of the modern technique of high-frequency field modulation which has proved so simple and sensitive (see, for example, Buckmaster and Scovil 1956; Llewellyn 1957). At the same time direct measurements at zero-field will be needed, since the work of Bleaney, Scovil, and Trenam (1954), one of the few examples of zero-field measurements, has shown that the spin Hamiltonian which fits measurements at fixed frequency and variable field may not correctly predict the zero-field levels. In the case of dilute gadolinium ethyl sulphate the discrepancy amounted to 7 per cent. or 100 Mc/s. The theoretical basis of this anomaly is not yet understood and more experimental data on zero-field splittings are desirable for the solution of this problem as well as for maser design.

When data become available for a large proportion of the stable compounds of suitable ions, it is possible that zero-field masers will be able to supersede magnetic-field masers in the majority of applications.

XIII. References

Andrew, E. R. (1955).—" Nuclear Magnetic Resonance." (Cambridge Univ. Press.)

Autler, S. H., and McAvoy, N. (1958).—*Phys. Rev.* **110**: 280.

Benzie, R. J., and Cooke, A. H. (1950).—*Proc. Phys. Soc.* A **63**: 201.

Bleaney, B. (1955).—*Disc. Farad. Soc.* No. 19: 112.

Bleaney, B., Elliot, R. J., Scovil, H. E. D., and Trenam, R. S. (1951).—*Phil. Mag.* **42**: 1062.

Bleaney, B., and Ingram, D. J. E. (1951).—*Proc. Roy. Soc.* A **205**: 336.

Bleaney, B., Scovil, H. E. D., and Trenam, R. S. (1954).—*Proc. Roy. Soc.* A **223**: 15.

Bleaney, B., and Stevens, K. W. H. (1953).—*Rep. Progr. Phys.* **16**: 108.

Bleaney, B., and Trenam, R. S. (1954).—*Proc. Roy. Soc.* A **223**: 1.

Bloembergen, N. (1956).—*Phys. Rev.* **104**: 324.

Bowers, K. D. (1952).—*Proc. Phys. Soc.* A **65**: 860.

Bowers, K. D., and Owen, J. (1955).—*Rep. Progr. Phys.* **18**: 304.

Buckmaster, H. A., and Scovil, H. E. D. (1956).—*Canad. J. Phys.* **34**: 711.

Dieke, G. H., and Leopold, L. (1957).—*J. Opt. Soc. Amer.* **47**: 944.

Elliott, R. J., and Stevens, K. W. H. (1953).—*Proc. Roy. Soc.* A **219**: 387.

Eschenfelder, A. H., and Weidner, R. J. (1953).—*Phys. Rev.* **92**: 869.

Giordmaine, J. A.. Alsop, L. E., Nash, F. R., and Townes, C. H. (1958).—*Phys. Rev.* **109**: 302.

Gorter, C. J. (1947).—" Paramagnetic Relaxation." (Elsevier Publishing Co.: London.)
Hutchison, C. A., Judd, B. R., and Pope, D. F. D. (1957).—*Proc. Phys. Soc.* B **70**: 514.
Hutchison, C. A., Llewellyn, P. M., Wong, E., and Dorain, P. (1956).—*Phys. Rev.* **102**: 292.
Jarrett, H. S. (1957).—*J. Chem. Phys.* **27**: 1298.
Kittel, C., and Abrahams, E. (1953).—*Phys. Rev.* **90**: 238.
Kornienko, L. S., and Prokhorov, A. M. (1957).—*J. Expt. Theor. Phys.* **33**: 805; (translation: *Soviet Phys. JETP* **6**: 620 (1958)).
Kramers, H. A. (1930).—*Proc. Acad. Sci. Amst.* **33**: 959.
Llewellyn, P. M. (1957).—*J. Sci. Instrum.* **34**: 236.
Low, W. (1956).—*Phys. Rev.* **103**: 1309.
Low, W. (1957).—*Phys. Rev.* **105**: 792.
McWhorter, A. L., and Meyer, J. W. (1958).—*Phys. Rev.* **109**: 312.
Meijer, P. H. E. (1951).—*Physica* **17**: 899.
Ono, K., Koide, S., Sekiyama, H., and Abe, H. (1954).—*Phys. Rev.* **96**: 38.
Pryce, M. H. L. (1950).—*Proc. Phys. Soc.* A **63**: 25.
Ryter, C. (1957).—*Helv. Phys. Acta* **30**: 353.
Scovil, H. E. D., Feher, G., and Seidel, F. (1957).—*Phys. Rev.* **105**: 762.

Duplexing a Solid-State Ruby Maser in an *X*-Band Radar System*

Previous attempts to use maser preamplifiers in conventional pulse radars have been unsuccessful because the leak-through power from standard duplexing circuits can greatly reduce the amplifying characteristic of the maser. The required excess of spin population in the excited state is reduced by strong leak-through signals from the transmitter at the maser amplifying frequency. The purpose of this paper is to describe how this problem was solved for an *X*-band radar having a peak pulse power of 150 kw.

Leak-through power in a conventional TR circuit was minimized by careful selection of components. The peak value varied from 1 to 10 milliwatts, depending on a number of parameters, including frequency and temperature. In addition, pulse-to-pulse variations of up to 25 per cent were observed. A maser gain of 10 db was achieved under these conditions, but it was marginal and subject to fluctuations caused by variations in the leak-through power. The operation of the maser was judged unsatisfactory without further leak-through protection. Laboratory measurements indicated that an additional 30 db of isolation, which reduces the peak leak-through power to less than 10 μw, would allow near-optimum maser performance (25–30-db gain for a pulse repetition rate of 416 PPS and a pulse duration of 2.35 μsec). A direct method of providing the required additional isolation is to use a conventional TR circuit and to insert some RF switching device between the TR tube and the maser. (See Fig. 1.) It is necessary, however, to keep the insertion loss ahead of the maser as low as possible because of the effect such loss has on the noise temperature of the system.

* Received by the IRE, May 21, 1959.

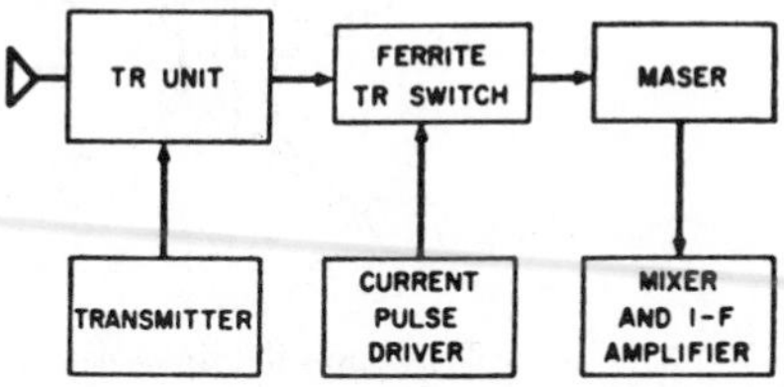

Fig. 1.

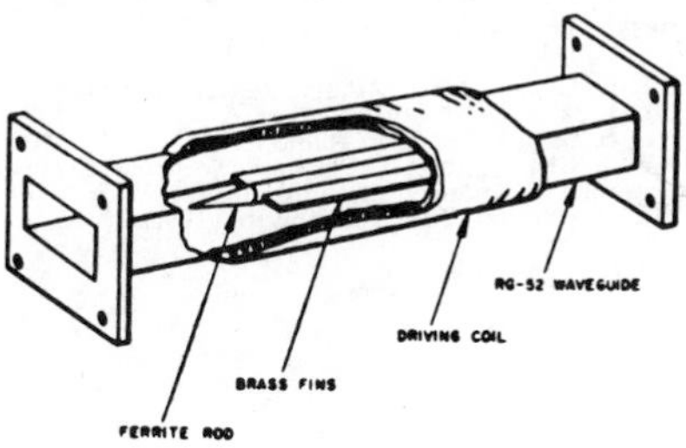

Fig. 2.

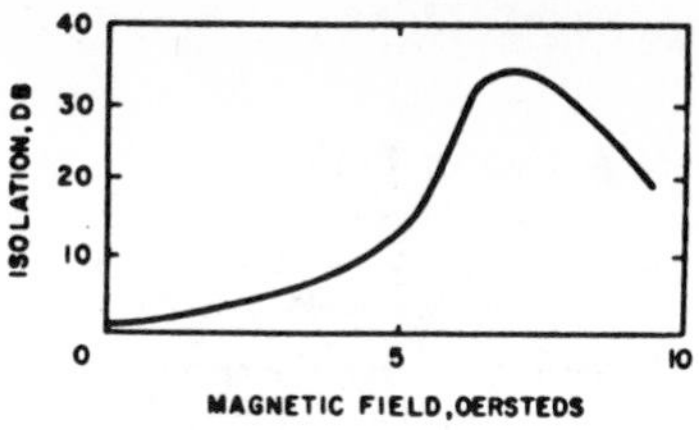

Fig. 3.

The problem of obtaining successful operation of the maser preamplifier in the radar was thus resolved into that of designing a high-speed, electronically operated switch having at least 30 db of attenuation in one state and an absolute minimum of insertion loss in the other state. Since 0.1 db of loss is approximately equivalent to 7°K in noise temperature, the insertion loss of the switch should preferably be no more than a few tenths of a decibel.

Currently available ferrite switches have between 0.5- and 1.0-db loss and require a larger switching pulse than is desired. Consideration of the specific requirements of the TR problem led to the conception and development of a reflective type of ferrite switch having an insertion loss of 0.25 db and an isolation of more than 30 db over a 120-mc band. A cutaway view of the switch is shown in Fig. 2. The isolation provided by the switch as a function of applied dc magnetic field is plotted in Fig. 3. The switch is pulsed to its attenuating condition when the transmitter is on, and it operates with very low loss during the receiving interval. The ferrite rod in the center of the waveguide has a conducting fin that extends from each side parallel to the broad wall. Without a dc magnetic field, the ferrite rod acts essentially as a low-loss dielectric. The tapered ends prevent reflections due to mismatch, and the fins do not disturb the transmission of the normal mode because they are in an equipotential plane. Thus the switch transmits with very low loss. When a longitudinal magnetic field is applied, the wave is converted into a mode which does not propagate through the structure. This results in the creation of a very high reflection at the input, and an attenuation of more than 30 db is obtained over a 120-mc band during the energizing pulse.

With the additional protection provided by the ferrite TR switch, the measured noise temperature of the maser, circulator, mixer, and IF amplifier combined was 65°K. The noise temperature of the over-all receiver, including that due to losses in the ferrite TR switch, the TR tube, waveguide, and rotary joints was 173°K, an excellent value compared with the 1500° to 2500°K noise temperature of a good *X*-band radar receiver without a maser preamplifier.

F. E. Goodwin
Res. Labs.
Hughes Aircraft Co.
Culver City, Calif.

Maser Action in Emerald

F. E. GOODWIN
Hughes Research Laboratories Malibu, California
(Received March 23; in final form, May 24, 1961)

THE paramagnetic resonance spectra of emerald (chromium-doped beryl) have been reported by Geusic *et al.*[1] The stable physical properties and zero-field splitting at 53.6 kMc make this material especially attractive for use in solid-state-maser amplifiers in the millimeter-wave region. Bogle[2] has shown that emerald may also be of importance at X band and L band because of favorable cross-relaxation effects. The spin Hamiltonian of emerald is identical to that for ruby,

$$\mathcal{H}=g\beta\mathbf{S}\cdot\mathbf{B}+D\left[S_z^2-\frac{5}{4}\right],$$

except that the D factor is greater by 4.66. Therefore, the wealth of experimental and computed data available for ruby masers is useful in predicting the operation of emerald masers.[3,4]

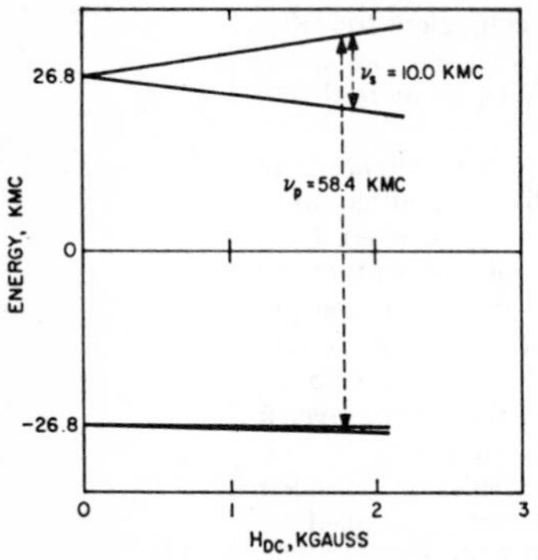

FIG. 1. Energy-level diagram for emerald maser (θ = 90 deg).

This correspondence reports the successful operation of synthetic emeralds in a single-cavity reflection-type maser amplifier operating at 10 kMc. The c axis was oriented at 90 deg with respect to a magnetic field of 1900 gauss and a pump frequency of 58.4 kMc was used (see Fig. 1). The particulars of operation are given in Table I. The expected magnetic $Q(Q_M)$ can be approximated from

$$Q_M=\frac{h\Delta\nu_m}{8\pi\langle\mu^2\rangle(n_2-n_1)F}\cong\frac{kT\Delta\nu_m}{\pi N_0\langle\mu^2\rangle(\nu_p-2\nu_s)F}.$$

For the values given in Table I, $Q_M\cong 180$, which is in approximate agreement with the experiment value:

$$Q_M\cong 2\nu_m/G^{\frac{1}{2}}B\cong 160.$$

The cavity, with dimensions of 0.140×0.280×0.280 in., was constructed of copper and filled with three emerald slabs allowing a TE_{011} resonance. The c axis was in the plane of the crystal slabs and perpendicular to the magnetic field (see Fig. 2). Pump power was introduced into the cavity through the signal iris.

Slabs of beryl were used as seeds on which to grow the emerald material. When the emerald had grown to a thickness of 0.050 in., the samples were removed. As is typical of early growth, these crystals exhibited a number of imperfections, as was evidenced by microscopic twinning and spontaneous nuclei. The filling factor of 80% was a result of these imperfections. The crystal axis exhibited a spread of 3 deg within the sample which caused a broadening of the paramagnetic resonance linewidth to 300 Mc for θ=90 deg and to 500 Mc for θ=55 deg, values five to eight times greater than that for ruby.

TABLE I. Particulars of operation for the emerald maser.

Signal frequency (ν_s)	10.0 kMc
Pump frequency (ν_p)	58.4 kMc
Magnetic field (H_{dc})	1900 gauss
Orientation H_{dc} to c axis	90 degrees
Temperature (T)	4.2°K
Power gain (G)	16 db
Bandwidth (B, 3 db)	20 Mc
Voltage gain bandwidth	126 Mc
Paramagnetic linewidth ($\Delta\nu_m$)	300 Mc
Filling factor (F)	80%
Magnetic Q (expected)	180
Magnetic Q (measured)	160
Concentration (ions/cm³)	2.5×10¹⁹
Average (squared) dipole moment of the maser transition $\langle\mu^2\rangle$	4×10⁻⁴⁰ erg²/gauss²

The maser performance obtained indicates that the broadening of the spectral lines due to microscopic spreading of the c axis does not destroy the maser properties at θ=90 deg; however, preliminary attempts to achieve maser action at θ=55 deg were not successful. Crystals of a longer growth cycle are being synthesized; it is expected that the later samples will be relatively free of polycrystalline effects and will exhibit narrower linewidths and superior maser characteristics.

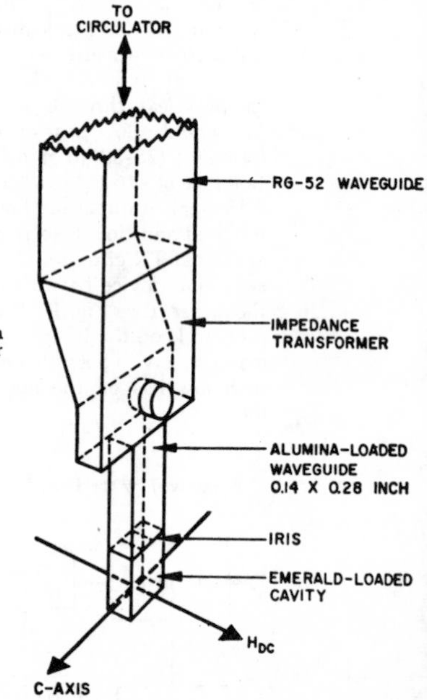

FIG. 2. Configuration of emerald-loaded maser cavity.

The author wishes to thank Dr. R. H. Hoskins for his spectral analysis, G. E. Moss for the development of the experimental maser, and Chatham Research Laboratories for providing the emerald crystals.

[1] J. E. Geusic, Martin Peter, and E. O. Schultz-du Bois, Bell System Tech. J. 38, 291–296 (1959).
[2] G. S. Bogle, Proc. Inst. Radio Engrs. 49, 573–590 (1961).
[3] W. S. Chang and A. E. Siegman, Technical Report No. 156-2, Stanford Electronics Laboratory, Stanford, California, September 30, 1958.
[4] E. O. Schultz-du Bois, Bell System Tech. J. 38, 271–290 (1959).

Dual-Cavity Maser Used in Mars Radar Experiment*

A dual-cavity ruby maser operating at 2388 Mc has been used on an 85-ft diameter paraboloidal antenna at the Goldstone Tracking Station, (a station of the NASA /JPL Deep Space Instrumentation Facility) for planetary radar experiments. In the fall of 1962, a transmitter with 13-kw power output was used to study Venus.[1] Transmitter power was subsequently increased to 100 kw and echoes were received from Mars[2] in January and February, 1963. A Cassegrainian[3] antenna configuration made it possible to achieve a total system temperature of around 40°K (antenna pointed at zenith) as shown in Table I. The detected signal level of the Mars echo was of the order of −180 dbm.

The principal advantage of the multiple cavity maser is the improved gain stability over a single cavity unit operating with the same total gain.

The following relation is readily derived as the ratio of fractional gain variation ($\delta G/G$) for a n-stage maser as compared with a single-stage cavity maser operating with same total gain G_0:

$$\rho_n = \sqrt{n}\, G_0^{(1-n)/2n}. \tag{1}$$

For $n=2$,

$$\rho_2 = \frac{\sqrt{2}}{G_0^{1/4}}\,. \tag{2}$$

For a total gain of 34 db, the improvement factor is around 5. The above equations apply for identical stages with isolation between stages as shown in Fig. 1.

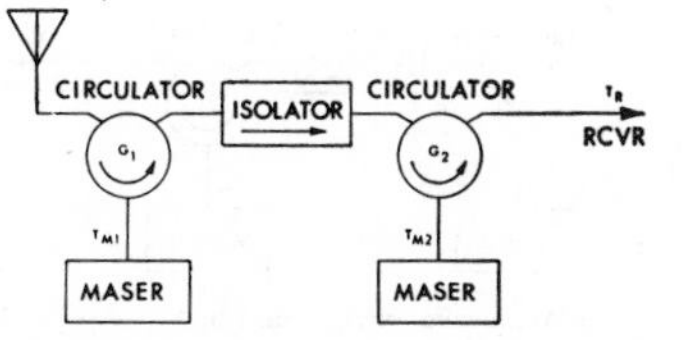

Fig. 1—Microwave circuit for dual cavity maser.

The bandwidth of 2.5 Mc was more than adequate for the radar experiments. Indeed, even with this narrow bandwidth, the black body radiation from Venus was detectable without a switching radiometer; however, the thermal radiation from Mars was much too weak to be discernible.

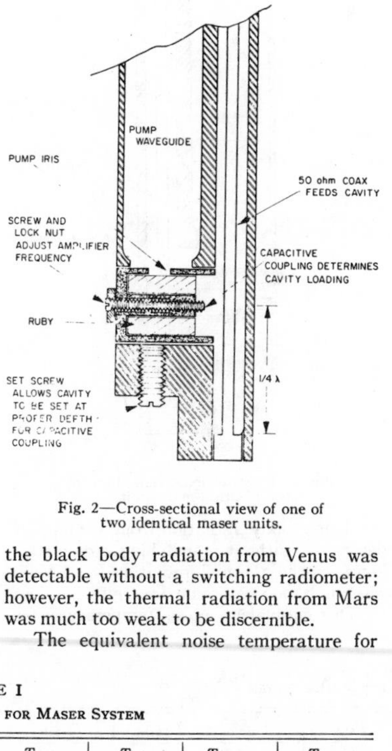

Fig. 2—Cross-sectional view of one of two identical maser units.

The equivalent noise temperature for the dual cavity maser is given by

$$T_s = T_{m1} + \frac{T_{m2}}{G_1} + \frac{T_r}{G_1 G_2}, \tag{3}$$

where

T_s = equivalent system noise temperature and other quantities on the right-hand side of (3) are defined in Fig. 1.

This shows a degradation in noise performance for the dual cavity maser, but the extra term (2nd term is absent for a single cavity maser) can be made negligible for high gain.

Fig. 2 shows a cross-sectional view of one of the two identical stages employed. Liquid helium was kept out of the structure for added stability. Cryogenic fluids were replenished daily, and, with a little care, the maser could be kept in continuous operation for many months.

The authors are grateful to the directors of the Planetary Radar Program, R. Stevens and W. K. Victor, for permission to publish this note separately from the Mars Report,[2] and to W. K. Rose of the Columbia Radiation Laboratory for a fruitful discussion on multiple cavity masers sometime ago.

W. H. Higa
R. C. Clauss
Jet Propulsion Lab.
Pasadena, Calif.

TABLE I

Performance Summary for Maser System

Frequency	Gain	BW	T_m	T_{ant}	$T_{w/g}$	T_{Total}	T_{Bath}
2388 Mc	34 db	2.5 Mc	20°±1	11°±1	8°±1	39°±3°K	4.2°K

* Received March 11, 1963. This paper represents one phase of research carried out at the Jet Propulsion Laboratory, Pasadena, Calif., under contract No. NAS 7-100, sponsored by the National Aeronautics and Space Administration.

[1] R. L. Carpenter and R. M. Goldstein, "1962 JPL Venus radar experiment," *Science*, vol. 139, p. 910; March 8, 1963. See also: W. K. Victor and R. Stevens, "The 1961 JPL Venus radar experiment," IRE Trans. on Space Electronics and Telemetry, vol. SET-8, pp. 84–97; June, 1962.

[2] 1963 JPL Mars Radar Experiment, to be published.

[3] P. Potter, "The application of the Cassegrainian principle to ground antennas for space communication," IRE Trans. on Space Electronics and Telemetry, vol. SET-8, pp. 154–158; June, 1962.

Reprinted from the PROCEEDINGS OF THE IEEE
VOL. 51, NO. 6, JUNE, 1963

Dual-Cavity Maser Used in Mars Radar Experiment*

A dual-cavity ruby maser operating at 2388 Mc has been used on an 85-ft diameter paraboloidal antenna at the Goldstone Tracking Station, (a station of the NASA /JPL Deep Space Instrumentation Facility) for planetary radar experiments. In the fall of 1962, a transmitter with 13-kw power output was used to study Venus.[1] Transmitter power was subsequently increased to 100 kw and echoes were received from Mars[2] in January and February, 1963. A Cassegrainian[3] antenna configuration made it possible to achieve a total system temperature of around 40°K (antenna pointed at zenith) as shown in Table I. The detected signal level of the Mars echo was of the order of −180 dbm.

The principal advantage of the multiple cavity maser is the improved gain stability over a single cavity unit operating with the same total gain.

The following relation is readily derived as the ratio of fractional gain variation ($\delta G/G$) for a n-stage maser as compared with a single-stage cavity maser operating with same total gain G_0:

$$\rho_n = \sqrt{n}\, G_0^{(1-n)/2n}. \tag{1}$$

For $n=2$,

$$\rho_2 = \frac{\sqrt{2}}{G_0^{1/4}}. \tag{2}$$

For a total gain of 34 db, the improvement factor is around 5. The above equations apply for identical stages with isolation between stages as shown in Fig. 1.

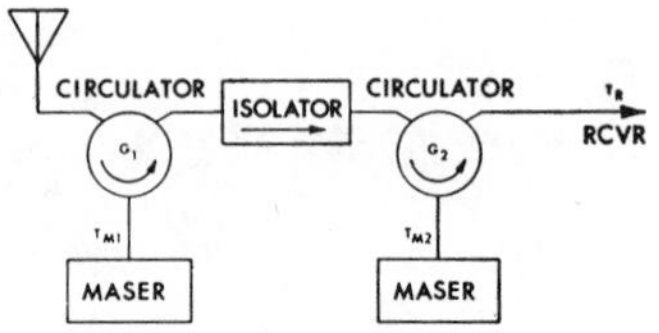

Fig. 1—Microwave circuit for dual cavity maser.

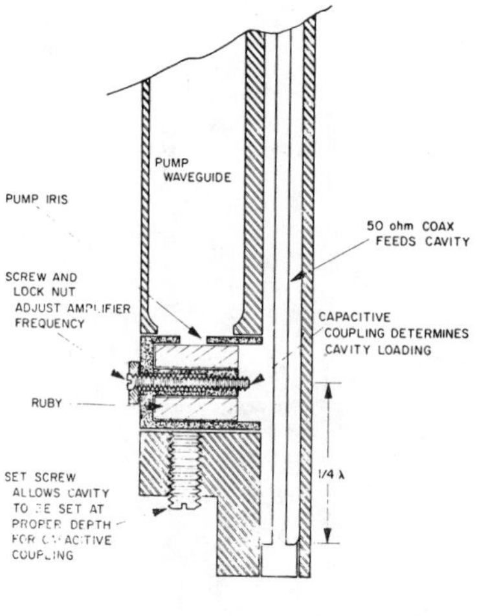

Fig. 2—Cross-sectional view of one of two identical maser units.

The bandwidth of 2.5 Mc was more than adequate for the radar experiments. Indeed, even with this narrow bandwidth, the black body radiation from Venus was detectable without a switching radiometer; however, the thermal radiation from Mars was much too weak to be discernible.

The equivalent noise temperature for the dual cavity maser is given by

$$T_s = T_{m1} + \frac{T_{m2}}{G_1} + \frac{T_r}{G_1 G_2}, \tag{3}$$

where

T_s = equivalent system noise temperature and other quantities on the right-hand side of (3) are defined in Fig. 1.

This shows a degradation in noise performance for the dual cavity maser, but the extra term (2nd term is absent for a single cavity maser) can be made negligible for high gain.

Fig. 2 shows a cross-sectional view of one of the two identical stages employed. Liquid helium was kept out of the structure for added stability. Cryogenic fluids were replenished daily, and, with a little care, the maser could be kept in continuous operation for many months.

The authors are grateful to the directors of the Planetary Radar Program, R. Stevens and W. K. Victor, for permission to publish this note separately from the Mars Report,[2] and to W. K. Rose of the Columbia Radiation Laboratory for a fruitful discussion on multiple cavity masers sometime ago.

W. H. Higa
R. C. Clauss
Jet Propulsion Lab.
Pasadena, Calif.

TABLE I
PERFORMANCE SUMMARY FOR MASER SYSTEM

Frequency	Gain	BW	T_m	T_{ant}	$T_{w/g}$	T_{Total}	T_{Bath}
2388 Mc	34 db	2.5 Mc	20°±1	11°±1	8°±1	39°±3°K	4.2°K

* Received March 11, 1963. This paper represents one phase of research carried out at the Jet Propulsion Laboratory, Pasadena, Calif., under contract No. NAS 7-100, sponsored by the National Aeronautics and Space Administration.

[1] R. L. Carpenter and R. M. Goldstein, "1962 JPL Venus radar experiment," *Science*, vol. 139, p. 910; March 8, 1963. See also: W. K. Victor and R. Stevens, "The 1961 JPL Venus radar experiment," IRE Trans. on Space Electronics and Telemetry, vol. SET-8, pp. 84–97; June, 1962.

[2] 1963 JPL Mars Radar Experiment, to be published.

[3] P. Potter, "The application of the Cassegrainian principle to ground antennas for space communication," IRE Trans. on Space Electronics and Telemetry, vol. SET-8, pp. 154–158; June, 1962.

Reprinted from the PROCEEDINGS OF THE IEEE
VOL. 51, NO. 6, JUNE, 1963

Dual-Cavity Maser Used in Mars Radar Experiment*

A dual-cavity ruby maser operating at 2388 Mc has been used on an 85-ft diameter paraboloidal antenna at the Goldstone Tracking Station, (a station of the NASA /JPL Deep Space Instrumentation Facility) for planetary radar experiments. In the fall of 1962, a transmitter with 13-kw power output was used to study Venus.[1] Transmitter power was subsequently increased to 100 kw and echoes were received from Mars[2] in January and February, 1963. A Cassegrainian[3] antenna configuration made it possible to achieve a total system temperature of around 40°K (antenna pointed at zenith) as shown in Table I. The detected signal level of the Mars echo was of the order of −180 dbm.

The principal advantage of the multiple cavity maser is the improved gain stability over a single cavity unit operating with the same total gain.

The following relation is readily derived as the ratio of fractional gain variation ($\delta G/G$) for a n-stage maser as compared with a single-stage cavity maser operating with same total gain G_0:

$$\rho_n = \sqrt{n}\, G_0^{(1-n)/2n}. \tag{1}$$

For $n=2$,

$$\rho_2 = \frac{\sqrt{2}}{G_0^{1/4}}. \tag{2}$$

For a total gain of 34 db, the improvement factor is around 5. The above equations apply for identical stages with isolation between stages as shown in Fig. 1.

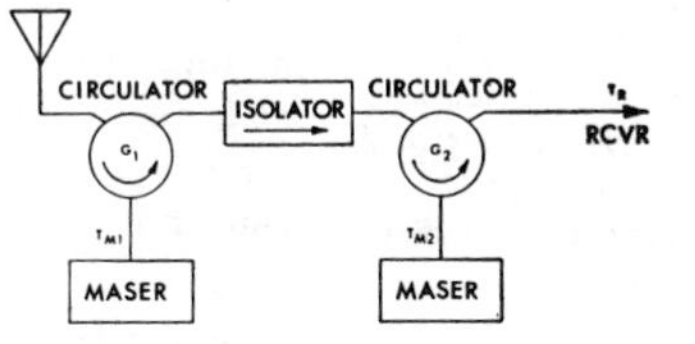

Fig. 1—Microwave circuit for dual cavity maser.

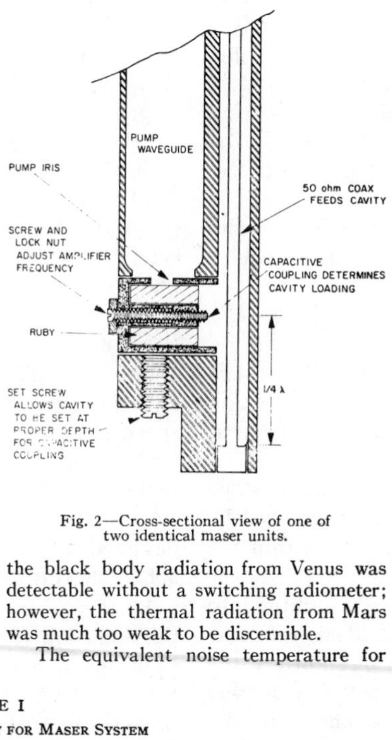

Fig. 2—Cross-sectional view of one of two identical maser units.

The bandwidth of 2.5 Mc was more than adequate for the radar experiments. Indeed, even with this narrow bandwidth, the black body radiation from Venus was detectable without a switching radiometer; however, the thermal radiation from Mars was much too weak to be discernible.

The equivalent noise temperature for the dual cavity maser is given by

$$T_s = T_{m1} + \frac{T_{m2}}{G_1} + \frac{T_r}{G_1 G_2}, \tag{3}$$

where

T_s = equivalent system noise temperature and other quantities on the right-hand side of (3) are defined in Fig. 1.

This shows a degradation in noise performance for the dual cavity maser, but the extra term (2nd term is absent for a single cavity maser) can be made negligible for high gain.

Fig. 2 shows a cross-sectional view of one of the two identical stages employed. Liquid helium was kept out of the structure for added stability. Cryogenic fluids were replenished daily, and, with a little care, the maser could be kept in continuous operation for many months.

The authors are grateful to the directors of the Planetary Radar Program, R. Stevens and W. K. Victor, for permission to publish this note separately from the Mars Report,[2] and to W. K. Rose of the Columbia Radiation Laboratory for a fruitful discussion on multiple cavity masers sometime ago.

W. H. Higa
R. C. Clauss
Jet Propulsion Lab.
Pasadena, Calif.

TABLE I

Performance Summary for Maser System

Frequency	Gain	BW	T_m	T_{ant}	$T_{w/g}$	T_{Total}	T_{Bath}
2388 Mc	34 db	2.5 Mc	20°±1	11°±1	8°±1	39°±3°K	4.2°K

* Received March 11, 1963. This paper represents one phase of research carried out at the Jet Propulsion Laboratory, Pasadena, Calif., under contract No. NAS 7-100, sponsored by the National Aeronautics and Space Administration.

[1] R. L. Carpenter and R. M. Goldstein, "1962 JPL Venus radar experiment," *Science*, vol. 139, p. 910; March 8, 1963. See also: W. K. Victor and R. Stevens, "The 1961 JPL Venus radar experiment," IRE Trans. on Space Electronics and Telemetry, vol. SET-8, pp. 84–97; June, 1962.

[2] 1963 JPL Mars Radar Experiment, to be published.

[3] P. Potter, "The application of the Cassegrainian principle to ground antennas for space communication," IRE Trans. on Space Electronics and Telemetry, vol. SET-8, pp. 154–158; June, 1962.

Reprinted from the PROCEEDINGS OF THE IEEE
VOL. 51, NO. 6, JUNE, 1963

Masers for Radar Systems Applications*

H. R. SENF†, SENIOR MEMBER, IRE, F. E. GOODWIN†, MEMBER, IRE,
J. E. KIEFER†, AND K. W. COWANS‡

Summary—**This paper is intended to provide the systems engineer with a practical introduction to the use of solid-state maser amplifiers in radars. Various environmental problems involved in the successful application of masers are discussed. An elementary survey of reflection-cavity and traveling-wave masers, together with some experimental results are presented. Another section treats the problem of saturation in masers and discusses some of the methods available for protecting masers from the TR leak-through pulses in radar. Progress made in the development of open- and closed-cycle liquid helium cryogenic systems suitable for masers is described. The authors' personal evaluations of the state of the art of ruby masers and closed-cycle helium refrigerators are given in appendixes.**

Introduction

THE PROBLEM of reducing receiver noise has fascinated radar engineers since the earliest days of radar. The value of a reduction in receiver noise, in terms of improvement in detection range, becomes most dramatically apparent when one considers the increase in transmitter power required to achieve a comparable improvement. The results obtained by the combination of a few improvements in the circuits and components used in the front end of the receiver at little or no cost in size, weight, and power might require many hundreds of pounds of additional transmitter equipment.

The search for the ideal radar receiver has progressed through the years with outstanding contributions by many workers, but the end result always fell short of the goal. The maser, meaning "Microwave Amplification by Stimulated Emission of Radiation," has for the first time brought the goal within reach. The results achieved during the past few years with solid-state masers show that the detection range of a radar no longer need be significantly limited by the noise generated within the receiver.

With the advent of the maser we are tempted to speculate that the long quest for the ideal low-noise receiver is approaching an end. It will be shown in the following sections, however, that present-day masers leave many problems for future workers. This is particularly true of important secondary objectives such as simplicity of equipment and flexibility of performance.

System Considerations

The noise in a radar receiver with which the signal must compete in order to be detected is the sum of two parts: that which is generated within the receiver, and that which originates in sources external to the receiver. (In this paper "external" noise is defined as the total noise at the output of the antenna; thus it includes both the "sky" noise as defined by De Grasse, *et al.*,[1] and the integrated atmospheric and earth noise due to the secondary pattern of the antenna.) Throughout the early history of radar, the magnitude of the internal noise was so large in comparison with the external noise that the latter could be neglected without significantly changing the performance of the system. Prior to the advent of masers and parametric amplifiers, the noise temperature of a typical microwave receiver was about 1500°K. The external noise for most radar systems was between 50° and 300° K. Recently, as the result of special care taken in the design of the antenna, the external noise of a *C*-band ground receiving system looking at elevation angles greater than 30 degrees above the horizon in good weather has been reduced to less than 10°K.[1] Further measurements and analyses have shown that external noise for similar antennas and environmental conditions should be less than about 20°K over the frequency band of 1 to 10 kMc (see Fig. 1).[2] For receiving antennas operating outside the earth's atmosphere and not pointing directly toward the earth, sun, or moon, it is expected that external noise will be less than 10°K, throughout the radio frequency range above 1 kMc.[2] Simple calculations based on the radar-range equation show that the detection range of radar for space applications can be increased by as much as three times if the noise generated within the receiver can be reduced so that it is equal to the external noise. The solid-state maser amplifier integrated with a carefully designed antenna has demonstrated the feasibility of achieving this result.

Because of the size, weight, complexity, and operating problems inherent to early maser amplifiers, they have been slow to find applications in practical electronic systems. A maser, to be fully effective, must be placed at or near the feed point of the antenna (see Fig. 2). This arrangement precludes the introduction of internal noise by such components as rotary joints, waveguide runs, switches, etc. Each 0.1 db of loss in such devices placed ahead of the maser will contribute 7°K to the total internal receiver noise, assuming the lossy devices

* Received by the PGMIL, January 17, 1961.
† Hughes Res. Labs., Hughes Aircraft Co., Malibu, Calif.
‡ Aerospace Engrg. Div., Hughes Aircraft Co., Culver City, Calif.

[1] R. W. De Grasse, D. C. Hogg, E. A. Ohm, and H. E. D. Scovil, "Ultra-low and noise measurements using a horn reflector antenna and a traveling-wave maser," *J. Appl. Phys.*, vol. 30, p. 2013; December, 1959.

[2] R. L. Forward and F. Richey, "Effects of external noise on radar performance," *Microwave J.*, vol. 3, pp. 73–80; December, 1960.

are at normal ambient temperatures. The antennas under consideration usually are large dishes mounted on high pedestals with feed horns suspended in positions that are awkward for mounting complex electronic and cryogenic apparatus.

Most of the masers that have been developed to date use rather large double dewars containing liquid nitrogen and liquid helium for the refrigeration system. Typically, these dewars must be refilled with both liquids at least once each day. The logistic problem of supplying the cryogenic fluids at the antenna site, plus the operational problem of transferring the fluids into the maser dewar, have presented two of the most serious obstacles to the use of masers.

Another difficulty with early masers has been the requirement for a large magnet to provide the dc field needed to tune the maser to the desired frequency. The magnet was placed outside the dewar, leading to an "air" gap in the magnetic circuit many times the dimension of the maser material. This gap caused the size and weight of the magnet to be very large.

Together, these problems until recently have limited the application of masers to a few experimental scientific measurements such as radio and radar astronomy.

During the last year or two, important progress has been made toward overcoming many of these obstacles. Several masers using small permanent magnets inside the dewar have been developed. A more compact open helium dewar-maser unit which eliminates the need for liquid nitrogen also has been developed at Hughes. For an X-band receiver, the maser equipment required to be mounted at the feed point occupies only about $\frac{1}{3}$ of a cubic foot, and weighs about 20 lbs. An artist's sketch of an early model of this unit is shown in Fig. 3.

The first models of closed-helium refrigerators for masers for ground systems applications have been developed. These equipments are, as yet, rather large but indicate promise for the use of practical refrigerators for ground applications in the near future.

A compact and relatively efficient closed-helium refrigerator for air- and missile-borne applications is in an advanced state of development. An airborne X-band maser in which the refrigerator and dewar units together will occupy about 1.3 cubic feet and weigh about 60 lbs. is under development at Hughes (see Fig. 4). About $1\frac{1}{2}$ kw of primary power is required to operate the refrigerator for a typical maser.

Until now (and probably for some time in the future), all masers have been custom designed and developed by

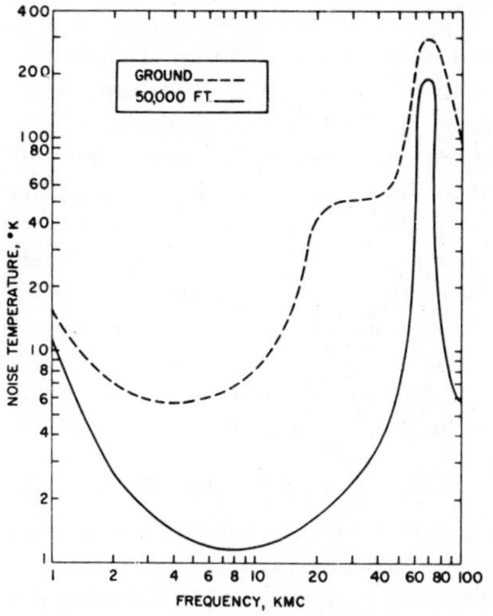

Fig. 1—External noise for ground and airborne antennas (beam 30° above horizon).

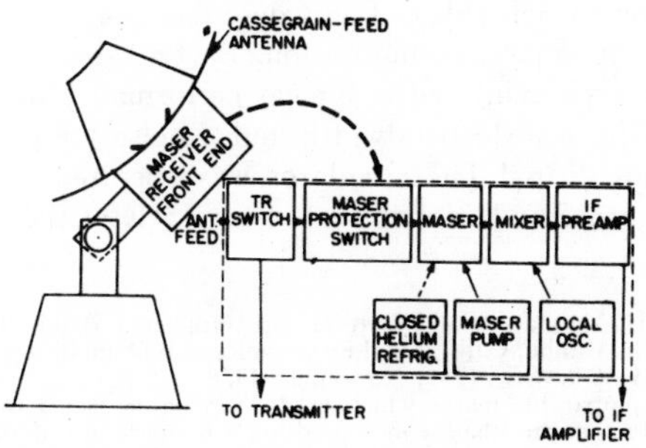

Fig. 2—Typical maser installation for ground radar.

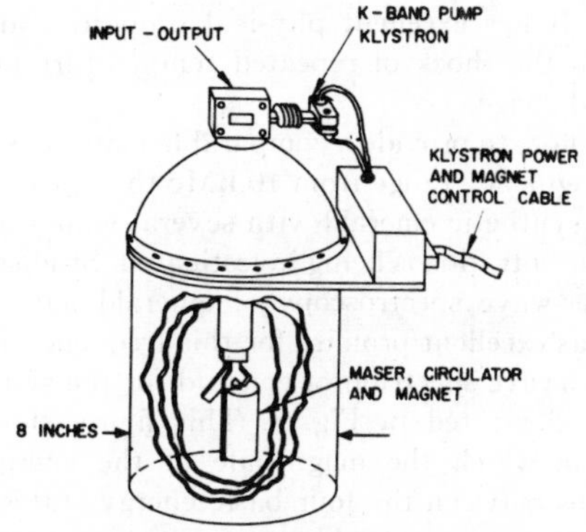

Fig. 3—X-band maser in compact open-helium dewar.

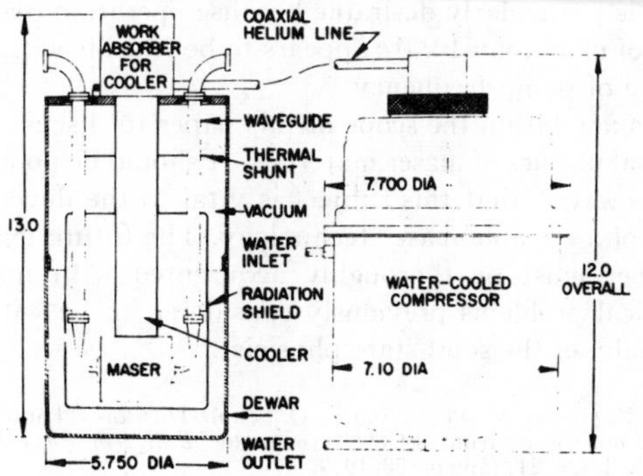

Fig. 4—Maser with integral closed-helium refrigerator.

research engineers. In general, only one of a kind has been made. The same is true of closed-helium refrigerators, and, to a lesser extent, open-helium dewars. Thus, the cost of prototype or experimental masers with closed refrigerators is still very high. The cost and complexity have been justified in the past for a number of critical measurements and specialized applications. During the next few years, as maser techniques are reduced to engineering technology, masers should become practical for an increasing range of system applications.

The authors' personal evaluation of the state of the art of ruby masers and closed-cycle helium refrigerators are given in Appendixes I and II.

Elements of Maser Technology

The problem of developing a maser technology suitable for a variety of systems applications consists of establishing the feasibility of operating over a wide range of frequencies with the necessary gain, bandwidth, tuning range, and stability. All of this must be done with equipment which can be operated continuously without the difficulties of filling the cryogenic system. Another basic element in achieving this capability is that of providing suitable maser materials for the various frequency ranges. Ruby, which is an aluminum oxide crystal with a small percentage doping of chromium ions, has proved to be successful for operation in the frequency range from a few hundred megacycles to 15 kMc. It has excellent physical properties and can withstand the shock of repeated temperature cyclings without damage.

In an effort to provide a comparable material suitable for the frequency range from 10 kMc to approximately 60 kMc, synthetic emerald with several values of chromium concentration is being investigated. Studies of the millimeter-wave spectroscopy of emerald have shown that it has excellent promise for this frequency region.[3] The microwave spectrum of emerald for the symmetric mode is illustrated in Fig. 5. This figure shows the manner in which the magnitude of the energy-level transitions between the four basic energy states of the chromium ion in emerald vary with an externally-applied dc magnetic field. The mode of operation shown is that of a broad-band maser amplifier at 35 kMc. This mode is particularly desirable because operation over a band of more than 1 kMc appears to be feasible without change of pump frequency.

It is not within the scope of this paper to discuss the internal physics of maser materials. It should be pointed out, however, that this subject is vital to the development of a suitable maser technology. The future maser engineer must be thoroughly acquainted with many technical problems previously considered to be within the realm of the solid-state physicist.

[3] J. E. Geusic, M. Peter, and E. O. Schulz-Du Bois, "Paramagnetic resonance spectrum of Cr^{+++} in emerald," *Bull. Am. Phys. Soc.*, ser. II, vol. 4, p. 21; January 28, 1959.

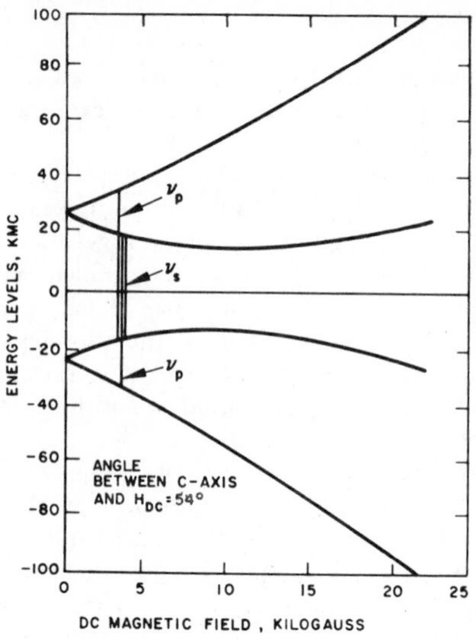

Fig. 5—Microwave spectra of emerald (symmetric model).

A typical maser amplifier consists of a microwave resonator which contains a piece of crystalline maser material. The circuit is resonant both at a signal frequency and at a so-called "pump" frequency. The circuit is cooled to a very low temperature, usually within a few degrees of absolute zero, and placed in a dc magnetic field. A few milliwatts of power are continuously injected into the circuit from the pump oscillator. The maser crystal absorbs and stores energy from the pump. When a signal is applied, it stimulates the emission of some of the stored energy. This energy is released as discrete quanta at signal frequency, each input quantum triggering the emission of many stored quanta. Amplification is obtained by the addition of the emitted energy to the input signal.

Reflection-Cavity Masers

Early masers were constructed in a form usually referred to as a reflection-cavity maser. Two variations of the reflection-cavity maser are shown in Fig. 6. This kind of maser requires a circulator for its operation, since the input and output signals from the maser resonator are present in the same transmission line. The figure on the left side of Fig. 6 describes the basic reflection-cavity maser configuration. Early *X*-band masers of this type exhibited a typical performance of 26-db gain with a 5-Mc bandwidth and a noise temperature of about 25°K.[4] The circulator was operated at room temperature and contributed about 15°K of the noise.[5]

[4] T. H. Maiman, "Solid-State Maser Amplifier X-Band," Hughes Res. Lab., Malibu, Calif., Final Progress Rept. on Signal Corps Contract DA 36-039SC-74951; November, 1958.

[5] A comparable maser which used a circulator cooled to liquid helium temperature had a measured noise temperature of 10°K.

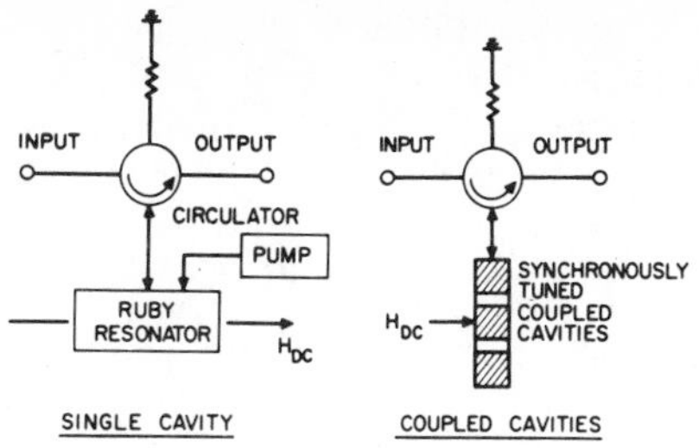

Fig. 6—Reflection-cavity masers.

The figure on the right side of Fig. 6 illustrates a method of broadbanding reflection masers. In this case, the single resonator is replaced by a system of coupled resonators. The amount of improvement which can be obtained in the gain-bandwidth product by this method varies with the absolute gain of the system. For a gain of 26 db, a two-resonator reflection maser has approximately $3\frac{1}{2}$ times the gain-bandwidth of a single-resonator maser.[6] This design is suitable for fixed-frequency systems requiring more gain-bandwidth product than can be achieved in the single-cavity maser.

An important maser engineering problem which already has been solved for some applications is that of replacing the large external electromagnet used in all early research on masers by a small permanent magnet located inside the dewar. Fig. 7 shows an *X*-band maser-dewar unit in which the permanent magnet is placed inside the dewar. This unit was developed at the Hughes Research Laboratories under Signal Corps sponsorship and is one of the first packaged maser units of this type to be delivered to a customer.[5] Fig. 8 shows a close-up of the resonator and the permanent magnet; these are mounted at the bottom of the dewar in liquid helium. This unit combines the advantages of the internal magnet, push-pull pumping, and 100 per cent filling factor. With a low-loss circulator placed outside the dewar at room temperature, the noise temperature of this unit was 25°K and the gain-bandwidth product was 105 Mc. This represented a significant advance for this type of maser at the time it was developed in 1958.

Fig. 9 shows the microwave circuitry of an *X*-band maser with a helium-cooled circulator. This circulator is of the polarization-rotation type. It also can be used to switch the input from the maser to a matched load by reversing the direction of the dc magnetic field. In this way the maser can be protected from the saturating effects of a local pulse signal, such as that obtained in a radar. The noise temperature of this maser amplifier was measured as 10°K. Essentially no noise was contributed by the circulator because of its operating temperature of 4.2°K. Subsequently, miniature cooled *Y*-type circulators that have improved bandwidth

[6] F. E. Goodwin, "One Port and Traveling-Wave Maser Using Coupled Cavities," Hughes Res. Labs., Malibu, Calif., Res. Rept. No. 173; November, 1960.

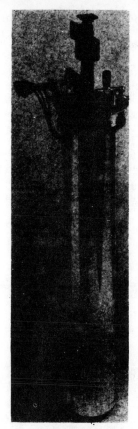

Fig. 7—*X*-band maser-dewar unit.

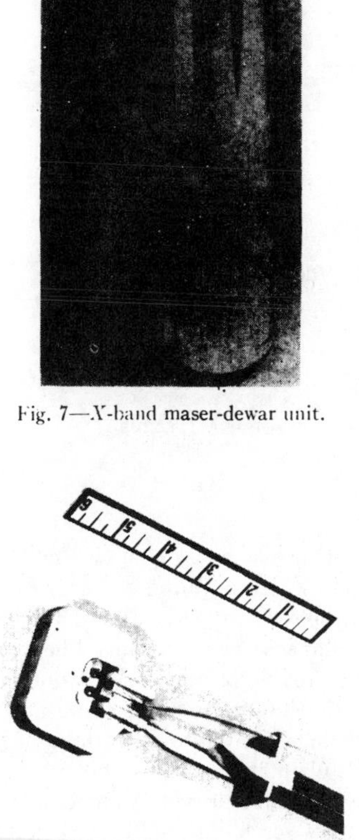

Fig. 8—*X*-band maser resonator and magnet.

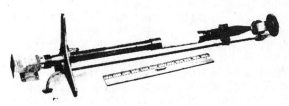

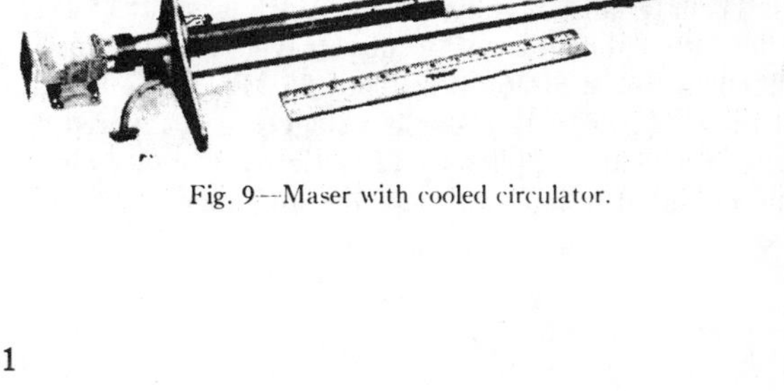

Fig. 9—Maser with cooled circulator.

characteristics and equally low noise have been developed. These will be valuable in making future masers more compact and efficient.

TRAVELING-WAVE MASERS

The traveling-wave maser provides the best solution for systems which require large bandwidth and/or electronic tunability. Fig. 10 illustrates a type of traveling-wave maser circuit that utilizes nonresonant slowing for its operation. The waveguide is filled with maser material; the high dielectric constant of the material causes the wave to propagate more slowly than in an air-filled guide. The slower the wave travels, the more time is available to stimulate emission from the maser material, and thus to amplify the signal.

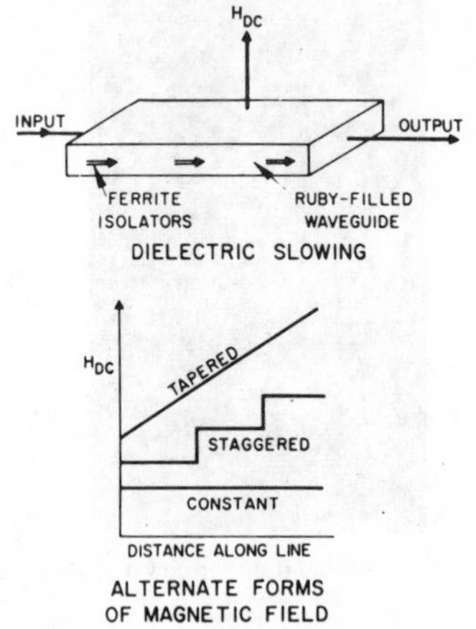

Fig. 10—Nonresonant dielectric slow-wave circuit for masers.

Ferrite isolating elements are shown embedded in the waveguide. These are required to assure that spurious reflections of the forward wave due to any cause are not amplified in the backward direction. The maser material is, in general, capable of amplifying about equally well in both directions. The presence of an amplified backward wave will lead first to variations of gain vs frequency, and ultimately to instability. Well-designed traveling-wave masers provide sufficient attenuation of backward waves so that the circuit remains stable for a short circuit at either the input or output.

The nonresonant, dielectric-loaded slowing circuit has potential for providing large bandwidths at high gains. However, unless the strength of the dc magnetic field is varied, the bandwidth is limited to a fraction of the linewidth of the paramagnetic resonance of the maser material. For ruby this linewidth is about 75 Mc. The 3-db bandwidth of a ruby traveling-wave maser that has a gain of 25 db is about 25 Mc. If the length of the circuit is increased and a staggered or tapered dc magnetic field is applied as a function of distance along the circuit, the bandwidth of the amplifier can be increased. In general, this will also require a variable pump frequency; however, at some frequencies and modes of operating the maser material, considerable bandwidth can be obtained with one pump frequency.

The nonresonant dielectric slowing circuit is not practical for use with ruby or emerald below about 10 kMc because it is too bulky. However, it shows promise for being useful with emerald and ruby in the 10- to 60-kMc band.

Fig. 11 shows two forms of traveling-wave masers which use resonant slowing. The figure at the top of Fig. 11 shows a circuit in which solid resonators of maser material are coupled together to form a band-pass filter structure. This type of circuit is capable of a large slowing factor and thus provides an efficient means for achieving large maser gain in a small structure. This is achieved, however, at the expense of the bandwidth of the structure. Thus, if one wishes to obtain large gain in a small structure, the maximum instantaneous bandwidth that can be achieved, even with staggered tuning of the maser material, is limited to the bandwidth of the structure. The electronic tuning range is similarly limited. This type of circuit should be suitable for use in the frequency band of about 3 to 30 kMc. Above this frequency range, the individual resonators may be too small to fabricate to the necessary precision; for frequencies below 3 kMc, the resonators probably will be too large for practical use.

The center figure of Fig. 11 shows a traveling-wave maser circuit which uses a comb structure. This is a resonant structure with a very large slowing factor. The

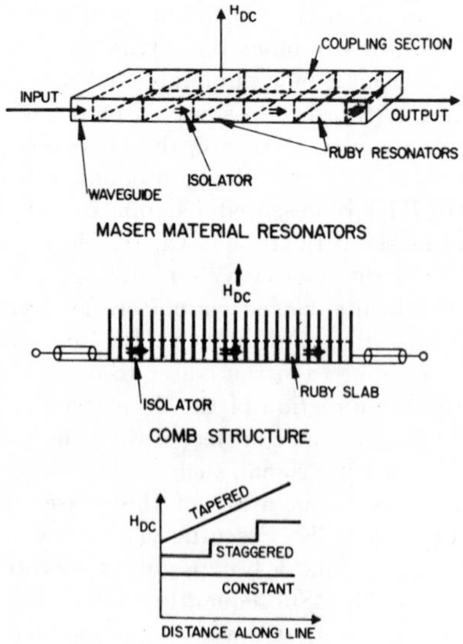

Fig. 11—Resonant slow-wave circuits for masers.

inherent loss of such structures fabricated to date has been somewhat higher than that for structures using coupled ruby resonators. This structure requires the use of a lower bath temperature (1.4°K instead of 4.2°K) to obtain satisfactory net gain per unit length. The Bell Telephone Laboratories have developed this circuit for application in the frequency range of 1 to 6 kMc.[7] A gain of 23 db and a bandwidth of 25 Mc was reported at *C* band. Electronic tuning of this circuit over the bandwidth of the structure has been achieved by varying the magnetic field and the pump frequency.

Maser Saturation and TR Protection

The presence of strong signals at the input to a maser will cause saturation with attendant reduction or complete loss of amplification. This occurs because a strong signal is capable of stimulating all of the excess maser ions stored in the high energy level to fall back to the low energy level. When the strong signal is removed, the maser recovers its gain as soon as the pump can restore the normal number of excess ions in the high energy state. For ruby this recovery time may be as long as 0.1 second. This corresponds to an interval of about 10,000 miles in the radar range. Thus, it is obvious that steps must be taken to prevent these effects in a radar.

The amount of gain reduction caused by a strong signal depends on both the amplitude and duration of the signal. Preliminary measurements indicate that typical radar-like repetitive pulse signals having amplitudes of about 100 microwatts will slightly degrade the gain of ruby masers. Similar pulses at a peak level of about 1 microwatt appear to be tolerable to the maser,[8] although they may produce other undesirable effects in the radar system.

The leak-through pulse from a conventional radar TR circuit is of the order of 1 to 10 milliwatts, and, unless special care is taken, it will be applied directly to the maser input. Thus, for any radar which uses a common antenna for transmitting and receiving, it is necessary to attenuate the TR leak-through pulse by 30 to 40 db in order to assure no degradation of maser performance.

Fig. 12 shows an early form of ferrite switch which was developed for this purpose. This switch is inserted between the TR tube and the maser used in an experimental radar. The driving coil is pulsed while the radar transmitter is on and operates with zero current during the receiving cycle. The normal mode of transmission of the waveguide is suppressed by the application of the dc magnetic field to the ferrite element. This provides more than 30 db of isolation over a 120-Mc band. The

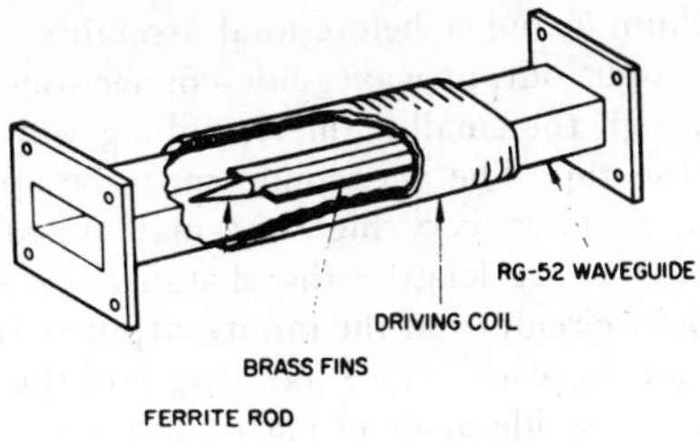

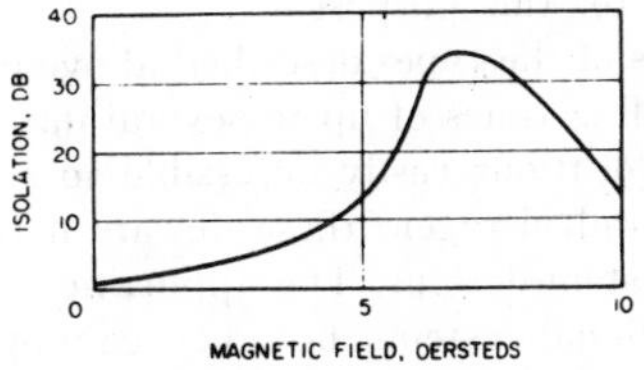

Fig. 12—Ferrite TR switch.

insertion loss during the receiving cycle is less than 0.25 db; thus, an uncooled switch contributes only about 17°K to the noise temperature of the receiver. The maser gain was not affected by the TR pulse during the experimental radar tests mentioned above. It appears reasonable to expect that improved switches, refrigerated if necessary, should contribute negligible noise to the receiver. The helium-cooled, four-port circulator shown in Fig. 9 can be switched to provide TR protection without adding appreciable noise to the receiver.

Cryogenics

Almost all of the solid-state microwave maser amplifiers operated before 1961 have used helium-nitrogen double dewars. The dewar shown in Fig. 7 is a typical example. The inner dewar is fabricated of stainless steel, one of the few practicable materials which is impervious to helium. The outer dewar, which holds the liquid nitrogen, is made of glass. The dewar of Fig. 7 is somewhat larger in diameter than many laboratory-type dewars because it was designed to contain a small permanent magnet to provide the external dc field of the maser. The maser circuitry and magnet (see Fig. 8) are immersed in the reservoir of liquid helium. The long length of the dewar is required to provide sufficient thermal impedance in the thin-walled stainless steel waveguide which connects the cooled maser elements to the input-output port, which is at normal ambient temperature.

An open-helium dewar, which is more suitable for systems use, is shown in Fig. 3. The function of the nitrogen bath of the previous dewar is performed by a radiation shield cooled approximately to liquid nitrogen temperature (77°K) by the helium gas as it escapes from the inner helium reservoir. The helium chamber is a reentrant structure which enables the device to operate in any position. The maser circuitry must be installed

[7] R. W. De Grasse, E. O. Schulz-Du Bois, and H. E. D. Scovil, "The three-level solid-state traveling-wave maser," *Bell Sys. Tech. J.*, vol. 38, pp. 305–334; March 1959.

[8] R. L. Forward, F. E. Goodwin, and J. E. Kiefer, "Application of a Solid-State Ruby Maser to an *X*-Band Radar System," Hughes Res. Labs., Malibu, Calif. Res. Rept. No. 105; June, 1959.

in the helium chamber before final assembly of the dewar. The input-output waveguide connections must be made through the small-diameter tubing which enters through the top. The waveguide must be specifically fabricated to have very high thermal impedance because of its short length; the distance between the cooled maser circuits and the input-output ports is only about 1 foot, instead of the 3-foot length of the previous dewar. A waveguide made of plastic-impregnated fiberglass with a very thin gold layer on the inner surface has been used for this purpose.

Open dewars of the types described above can be designed for holding times of up to several days. For installations in locations easily accessible to supplies of liquid helium and nitrogen, these dewars may provide satisfactory system designs. The application of masers to most operational systems, however, cannot be practically accomplished until suitable closed-helium refrigerators are available.

Other workers in the field have supplied prototype helium refrigerators for masers for use in ground electronic systems. The sizes, weights, and required power, reported for these units indicates that further engineering is needed to make them practicable for some applications. Progress of this nature is certain to occur in the near future.

A compact helium refrigerator for airborne infrared detectors and masers has been developed at the Hughes Aircraft Company. The outline dimensions for a model intended for an airborne maser are shown in Fig. 4. Fig. 13 depicts the flow diagram for this device; a photograph of an early experimental model in which the compressor unit is air cooled is shown in Fig. 14.

Helium gas is compressed to about 30 atmospheres in a two-stage compressor. This gas enters a counter-flow heat exchanger. As indicated in the flow diagram, about one third of the gas is made to enter an adiabatic expansion engine after having been cooled to 80°K. Another one third of the gas is processed similarly by the second adiabatic expansion engine. By these processes, the remainder of the gas is cooled to the critical temperature needed for Joule-Thomson cooling. After a typical cool-down time of less than 1 hour, the output of the Joule-Thomson nozzle is a two-phase mixture consisting of vapor and liquid at 4.2°K, assuming that the pressure in the return system is one atmosphere. This jet flows over a cold plate which is in thermal contact with the maser material and circuit. In this process the liquid helium is changed to a vapor at the same temperature, thus withdrawing 650 calories of heat per liter from the cold plate. The maser circuitry, which is in a vacuum on the other side of the cold plate, must be so designed and connected with the outside world that the total heat flowing into it can be absorbed by the liquid helium being vaporized on the other side of the cold plate. This arrangement requires great care in the design of the waveguides and in provision of adequate radiation shields.

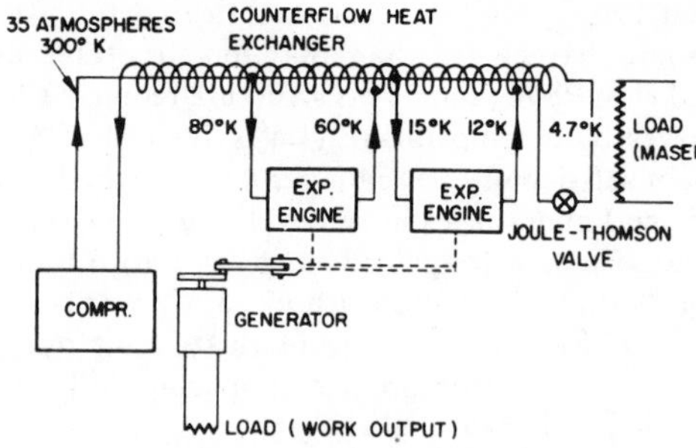

Fig. 13—Flow diagram of closed-helium refrigerator.

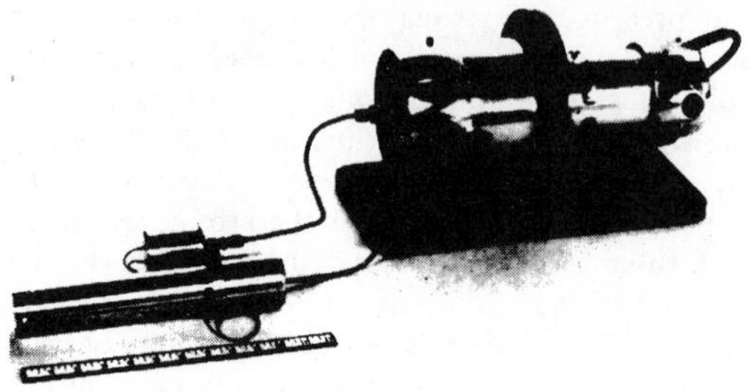

Fig. 14—Closed-helium refrigerator.

The development of an integral helium refrigerator for an airborne maser is in progress at the time of this writing. It is scheduled to be ready for flight test early in 1962.

Conclusions

In the light of the foregoing discussion, it seems reasonable to predict that the low-noise performance capabilities of masers will be of great importance in earth-to-space radar and communications systems. Ground-to-ground communications via satellites and radio and radar astronomy also present potential applications for masers. For many of these systems maser amplifiers should make possible the design of receivers for which the noise generated within the receiver is no longer a significant factor in limiting the detection range.

For the present and near future, the principal system needs and maser performance capabilities lie in the frequency range of several hundred Mc to 10 or 15 kMc. This is the useful band of ruby, which is by far the most fully developed of presently known maser materials.

Within the next few years it appears reasonable to expect that maser materials and techniques will become available for the lower millimeter-wave band. For many earthbound millimeter-wave systems, the very low noise performance of masers probably cannot be fully utilized because the external noise generated in the atmosphere is much greater in this band. However, if millimeter-wave masers can be suitably reduced in complexity, they may play an important role because all other millimeter-wave receiving techniques now available are extremely noisy.

Appendix I

State of the Art of Ruby Masers—1961

The following is the personal estimate of the authors regarding the performance that can be achieved within the present state of the art for ruby masers operated in open cryogenic systems. In general, the numbers given are intended to indicate the order of magnitude of the various detailed performance characteristics suitable for consideration in preliminary system designs. It can be expected that many of the numbers will change significantly during the next few years. However, no attempt is made here to predict these changes.

Frequency Range	400 Mc to 15 kMc
Bandwidth	0.1 to 1.0 per cent of center frequency
Gain	20 to 40 db
Tuning Range	10 to 20 per cent
Noise Temperature	10 to 30°K
Dynamic Range	100 db
Onset of Saturation (low duty cycle pulses)	10^{-5} watts peak
Recovery Time	0.1 second
Weight of Maser-Dewar Unit (excluding pump-power supply)	
1) with permanent magnet in dewar	15 to 50 lbs.
2) with external permanent magnet	100 to 500 lbs.
Weight of Pump-Power Supply	25 to 100 lbs.
Open Helium Dewars	
1) holding time	8 to 35 hours
2) size	0.3 to 2.5 cu. ft.
3) weight	10 to 45 lbs.
4) helium boil-off rate	0.1 to 0.3 liters per hour
5) helium capacity	2 to 10 liters

Appendix II

Tentative Performance for Closed-Cycle Helium Refrigerators

The following are intended as order-of-magnitude predictions of the performance of helium refrigerators in 1962–63 suitable for preliminary planning purposes for future electronic systems which may use masers. They represent the authors' judgment based on rather complete information on cryogenic developments at the Hughes Aircraft Company and limited information on similar work elsewhere.

Refrigerators for Ground Installations

Cooling Capacity at 4.2°K	$\frac{1}{4}$ to 1 watt
Size	3 to 10 cu. ft.
Weight	100 to 500 lbs.
Power Required	1 to 5 kw
Life (between major overhauls)	
1) cryostat	1000 hours
2) compressor	5000 to 10,000 hours

Refrigerators for Air- or Missile-Borne Applications

Cooling Capacity at 4.2°K	$\frac{1}{4}$ to $\frac{1}{2}$ watt
Size	1 cu. ft.
Weight	35 to 50 lbs.
Power Required	1 to 2 kw
Life (between major overhauls)	1000 hours

Acknowledgment

Numerous members of the Technical Staff of the Hughes Aircraft Company have contributed to the work described in this paper. Special credit must be given to Dr. T. H. Maiman and his group, who conducted the basic research on solid-state maser amplifiers under Signal Corps and Hughes sponsorship, and to Dr. H. Barhydt and his group for their work on cryogenics.

MULTILEVEL PULSED-FIELD MASER FOR GENERATION OF HIGH FREQUENCIES*

S. Foner, L. R. Momo, and A. Mayer†
Lincoln Laboratory, Massachusetts Institute of Technology, Lexington, Massachusetts
(Received June 1, 1959)

A proposed[1,2] multilevel pulsed-field ruby maser has been successfully operated at 4.2°K as an oscillator at both 12.61 kMc/sec and 19.15 kMc/sec with a pumping frequency of 12.61 kMc/sec. The results demonstrate the feasibility of generating or amplifying very high frequencies on a pulsed basis by conversion of magnetic field energy, supplied to an inverted spin distribution, into coherent radiation. The principles of operation and characteristics of the maser, and field dependence of spin-lattice relaxation time are discussed.

The pertinent transitions and the energy level diagram of Cr^{3+} in Al_2O_3 for applied fields perpendicular to the c axis[3] are shown in Fig. 1. For simplicity, the $\Delta M = 2$ transition between levels 1 and 3 is saturated[4] at a pump frequency $\nu_3 = \nu_1 + \nu_2$, corresponding to a fixed dc bias field, H_0, above any field where cross relaxation effects[5] may occur, such as at ν_5. The cw three-level maser[6] would operate at $\nu_2 << \nu_3$, when $H = H_0$, with an inverted spin population between levels 2 and 1. If H is now increased to H_i in a time short compared to the spin-lattice relaxation time, oscillation or amplification should be obtainable at any frequency $\nu_i > \nu_2$ for which suitable maser cavity resonances occur. A gain of energy in the ratio of ν_i/ν_2 over the continuous three-level maser is obtained at the expense of energy extracted from the pulsed magnetic field. Wavelengths of about 1 mm would be generated at a field of 100 kilo-oersteds.

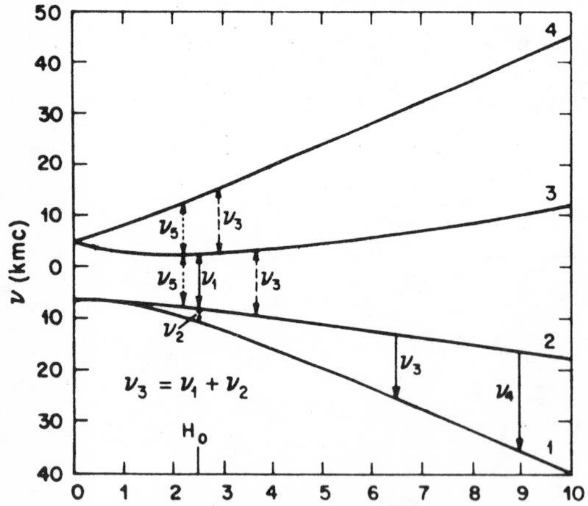

FIG. 1. Energy level diagram for Cr^{3+} in Al_2O_3 with applied field perpendicular to c axis. Operating points for pumping at $\nu_3 = \nu_1 + \nu_2$, and emission at ν_3 and ν_4 are indicated.

The maser reflection cavity, a solid rectangular parallelpiped of ruby,[7] was designed with the two lowest modes (TE_{101} and TE_{102}) occurring at $\nu_3 = 12.61$ kMc/sec and $\nu_4 = 19.15$ kMc/sec, respectively, with undercoupled loaded cavity Q's of about 2000 and 4800, respectively. The pump power and radiated energy were transmitted to and from the single cavity coupling iris by a tapered dielectric transition section attached to K_u-band waveguide. Both the dielectric transition and cavity were coated with a 0.001-in. silver plating in order to assure uniform penetration of the pulsed magnetic field throughout the cavity volume. The pulsed field, H_p, was generated in a solenoid (13 cm length, 7 cm i.d.) by discharge of a 2000-μf variable voltage capacitor bank.[8] A peak field of 9.4 kilo-oersteds was obtained at 1000 volts with a half-period of about 3 milliseconds [see Figs. 2(A), 2(B)]. The maser cavity assembly and surrounding glass Dewars were inserted in the solenoid, and the entire assembly was fixed between the pole faces of an electro-

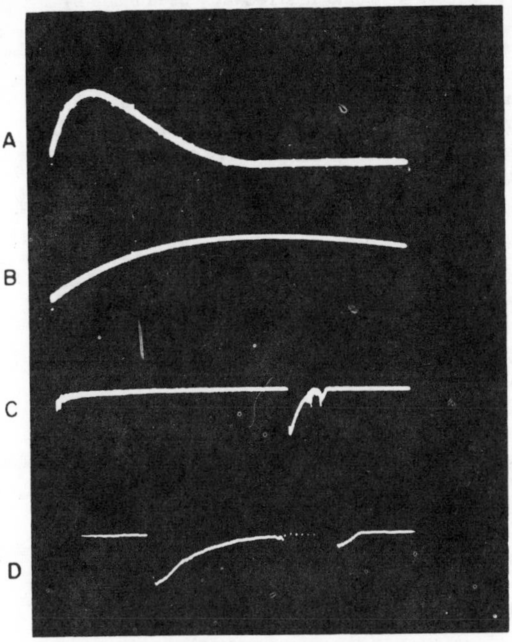

FIG. 2. Oscillograms of pulsed-field maser operation at 4.2°K. (A) Pulsed magnetic field versus time–horizontal time scale 500 μsec/cm. (B) Pulsed magnetic field versus time–horizontal time scale 100 μsec/cm. (C) Envelope detector output showing 19.15-kMc/sec emission of pulsed-field maser–horizontal scale 100 μsec/cm. Emission is obtained during both rise and decay of field pulse. (D) 19.15-kMc/sec emission–horizontal time scale expanded to 20 μsec/cm. An intense burst of radiation occurs at the onset of emission, accounting for the short blank portion of the oscillogram.

magnet. The field orientations were: H_{rf} perpendicular to the c axis, and H_0 perpendicular to both the c axis and to H_p. The mutually orthogonal orientation of H_0, H_p, and the c axis assured that the resultant H was always greater than H_0, and furthermore, that H always remained perpendicular to the c axis. The field dependence of the energy levels therefore remained as indicated in Fig. 1.

The pumping power was gated off within 50 μsec of the start of the pulsed field rise, and oscillations were observed at either ν_3 or ν_4 during the traversal of H_p through the appropriate resonance. Within the accuracy of the pulsed field measurement, emission occurred as predicted from Fig. 1. When the pump power was not turned off, population redistribution between levels 4-3 and 3-2 was observed (see Fig. 1). Typical oscillation characteristics at 4.2°K for the ν_4 mode are shown in Figs. 2(C) and 2(D). The expanded scale of Fig. 2(D) shows the pulsating character[9] of the oscillations, and the sensitive dependence of the emission pulses on the particular magnetic field sweep rate. The number of pulses and total energy output could be controlled by varying the pulsed-field sweep rate–the more rapid traversals resulted in lower peak output, and for a sufficiently fast rise time, no oscillations were observed. In this way it was possible to avoid emission at ν_3 completely, and yet obtain ν_4 emission at the peak of the pulsed field. When only a small portion of the inverted spin system radiated at ν_4, further emission at ν_3 was observed during the field decay. The peak power output at ν_4 was greater than 300 μw, and the integrated output energy for a typical case, e.g., Fig. 2(D), was greater than 0.04 erg. In both cases measurements were made of energy arriving at the crystal detector. Calculations show that a total energy of about 2 ergs would be available in the cavity if complete saturation between levels 1-3 were obtained, and if cavity losses and the spin-lattice relaxation were neglected. A considerable increase in efficiency is expected from an optimized microwave system.

Operation of this particular pulsed field maser would be limited to low magnetic fields if the spin-lattice time varied inversely as some large power of the magnetic field.[10] Measurements of spin-lattice relaxation time in ruby[11] at 4.2°K combined with the present results at ν_4 indicate that such a dependence is not yet dominant. Results of experiments as a function of temperature and field will be presented elsewhere.

An alternate scheme of multiple pumping[1,12] would circumvent most of the spin-lattice time field dependency, and would minimize requirements on the pulsed field system. Spin inversion with $\Delta M = 1$ transitions between levels 1-2, 2-3, and 3-4 in that order may be attained with a relatively small pulsed magnetic field at a reasonable pump frequency ν_j. With appropriate orientations of H_0 and H_p, and with a suitable maser material of large zero-field splitting, emission at a $\Delta M = 2$ or $\Delta M = 3$ transition with $\nu_i \simeq 3\nu_j$ would then permit generation and/or detection and amplification at millimeter wavelengths on a pulsed basis with a rather simple arrangement. For instance, 10^{19} spins radiating at 300 kMc/sec with a repetition rate of only 10 per second would yield an average power of 20 milliwatts—a power somewhat above that presently available (considerably less than 1 μw). If multiple pumping could be employed, pulsed fields of the order of a kilo-oersted would be sufficient.

We are indebted to B. Feldman and J. J. Kelley for valuable assistance, and to Dr. R. H. Kingston, Dr. H. J. Zeiger, and Dr. S. H. Autler for informative discussions.

---

* The work reported in this paper was performed at Lincoln Laboratory, a center for research operated by Massachusetts Institute of Technology with the joint support of the U. S. Army, Navy, and Air Force.

† Present address: Convair, San Diego, California.

[1] S. Foner, Colloque International de Magnétisme de Grenoble, July 2-6, 1958, Contribution No. 32 [J. phys. radium 20, 336 (1959)], and Lincoln Laboratory Quarterly Progress Reports, February 1, 1958 et seq. (unpublished).

[2] An alternate proposal has recently been made by R. H. Hoskins, J. Appl. Phys. 30, 797 (1959).

[3] The energy level diagram is shown for $D<0$ as indicated by recent measurements of Geusic, Peter, and Schulz-du Bois, Bell System Tech. J. 38, 291 (1959).

[4] In principle $\Delta M=3$ pumping may be feasible, and/or spin inversion by a 180 degree pulse or adiabatic fast passage may be employed for higher efficiency.

[5] Bloembergen, Shapiro, Pershan, and Artman, Phys. Rev. 113, 445 (1959).

[6] N. Bloembergen, Phys. Rev. 104, 324 (1956).

[7] Pink ruby (nominally 0.1 % Cr^{3+}) supplied by Linde Air Products Company.

[8] S. Foner and H. H. Kolm, Rev. Sci. Instr. 28, 799 (1957).

[9] Makhov, Kikuchi, Lambe, and Terhune, Phys. Rev. 109, 1399 (1958).

[10] A. H. Cooke, Reports on Progress in Physics (The Physical Society, London, 1950), Vol. 13, p. 276.

[11] Kikuchi, Lambe, Makhov, and Terhune, Project Michigan Report No. 2144-377-T, March, 1959 (unpublished).

[12] A similar proposal has recently been made by A. E. Siegman and R. J. Morris, Phys. Rev. Letters 2, 302 (1959).

Reprinted from JOURNAL OF APPLIED PHYSICS, Vol. 31, No. 4, 742–743, April, 1960

CW Millimeter Wave Maser Using Fe^{3+} in TiO_2*

S. FONER AND L. R. MOMO
Lincoln Laboratory, Massachusetts Institute of Technology, Lexington, Massachusetts
(Received December 21, 1959)

A CW 3-level maser,[1] employing Fe^{3+} ions in a TiO_2 dielectric,[2,3] has been operated at signal frequencies from 26 to 39 kMcps. In contrast with the *pulsed-field* millimeter wave maser,[4] which can use paramagnetic materials with various zero-field splittings, the characteristics of the cw millimeter wave maser material are dictated mainly by technical limitations of available millimeter wavelength pump sources. In this letter, the characteristics of the cw maser are briefly summarized and some of the useful properties of the paramagnetic material are described. Despite the narrow tuning range of the 4-mm wavelength pumping source, maser operation over a wide range of signal frequencies and magnetic fields was attained at 4.2°K. The present results indicate that this maser material will be useful far above and below the frequency range investigated here.

The high dielectric constant of TiO_2 [5] simplified the maser cavity design. Any convenient dimensions of the dielectric assured many suitable modes for both the signal frequency f_s and the pump frequency f_p; the maximum dielectric volume was limited mainly by the available pump power. The cavity was an adjustable rectangular brass box,[6] which contained the dielectric (0.026 in. by 0.15 in. by 0.35 in. for most of the experiments). The dimensions of the rectangular box and the filling factor were not critical. Loaded Q's were a few thousand at both f_p and f_s. The signal and pump waveguide polarizations were mutually orthogonal, and energy was coupled to the cavity through slots. The TiO_2 was oriented so that the c axis was parallel to the rf magnetic field of the f_p waveguide, but the rf field orientations in the multimode dielectric cavity could not be accurately specified. The applied magnetic field H was rotated in a (100) plane.

Pump power[7,8] of 2 to 10 mw was sufficient for maser operation either as an amplifier or as an oscillator at 4.2°K. By carefully adjusting the dimensions of the signal coupling iris, oscillations were observed at f_s. Amplification was then obtained when proper external loading was supplied. With f_p fixed, f_s could be varied over a wide range by simply changing the magnitude of H and the angle θ between H and the c axis. The high density of signal modes permitted almost continuous coverage of f_s from 33.7 to 36.1 kMcps to be obtained by this procedure. As an example, Fig. 1 shows f_s vs θ, where H (approximately 3000 gauss for all the data), θ, and the external loading were varied while f_p was fixed at 70.4 kMcps. By decreasing f_p to 68.4 kMcps, the range of f_s has been increased to 39.2 kMcps at larger values of θ. Maser operation at values of f_s spaced within 300 Mcps of each other was observed over this range. Gain-bandwidth products from 10 to 40×10^6 cps have been measured over the operating range. Signal saturation effects were noted at input powers greater than about 10^{-8} w. Decreased maser operation could be found in a small region near $f_s=f_p/2$, probably because of cross-relaxation effects.[9] Simultaneous amplification at two frequencies separated by about 30 Mcps has been observed for some operating points e.g., Fig. 1, $\theta=-7.2°$. Thus further bandwidth improvements can be expected with larger dielectric cavities or a traveling wave structure.

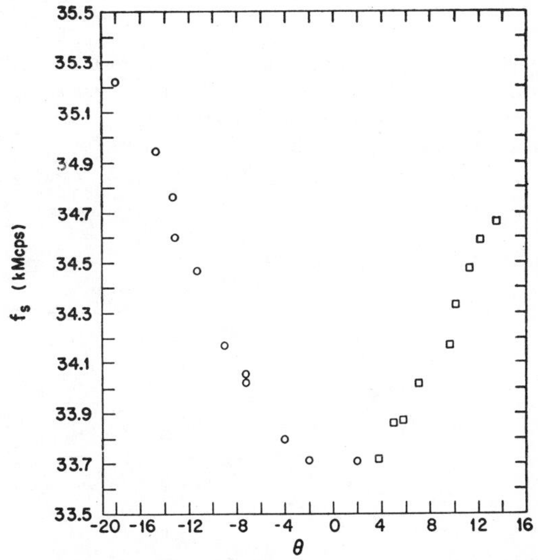

FIG. 1. Maser signal frequency f_s vs θ, the angle between the magnetic field H, and the c axis of the TiO_2 crystal. H was in the (100) plane for this experiment. The pump frequency was 70.4 kMcps, and H was adjusted slightly for the various operating points. Note that the miltimode dielectric cavity permits almost continuous tuning of f_s. The squares and circles correspond to different experiments.

The oscillations showed a pulsating character similar to those described previously.[10,11] The repetition rate could be varied from less than 10^3 per sec to over 2×10^5 per sec by changing pump power, f_s, H, θ, or external loading. Oscillations at more than one frequency are frequently observed, and oscillation could be detected simultaneously at f_s or at frequencies near f_s while amplifying at f_s.[12] Employing f_p near 70 kMcps, oscillations have also been observed for various other energy levels. Oscillations at $f_s\leqslant26.5$ kMcps have been attained at about 4 kilogauss, and a number of other operating points with $H\leqslant16.5$ kilogauss are indicated. Because sufficiently accurate energy level diagrams were not available for these experiments, the maser oscillation characteristics were used to examine feasible regions for maser operation. When f_s was less than the signal waveguide cut-off frequency (21.1 kMcps), evidence of signal oscillations was indirectly indicated by pulsating demands on the pump power.

The maser characteristics of Fe^{3+} in TiO_2 are well suited for operation in the millimeter wavelength region. The high dielectric constant and good mechanical properties permit construction of a small volume, multimode cavity. Tuning of f_s can then be accomplished by varying the magnitude and direction of H. Operation in the 8 mm wavelength region can easily be attained with superconducting solenoid magnets now available,[13] and the small maser cavity will also permit superconducting magnets with ferromagnetic cores[13] to be employed for maser operating points over the entire field range so far investigated. The large zero field splittings of Fe^{3+} in TiO_2, and the large E term[14] in the spin Hamiltonian permit efficient operation over a very wide range of frequencies. The low pumping powers required, and relatively low signal saturation level indicate a long spin-lattice relaxation time for this material. At present, higher operating frequencies appear to be limited by availability of suitable pumping frequency sources.

We wish to thank Dr. Benjamin Lax and Dr. Gerald S. Heller for suggesting this problem, and for encouragement during the course of this work. We also wish to thank Professor W. Low of the Hebrew University, Jerusalem, Israel, for suggesting the possibilities of the paramagnetic material Fe^{3+} in TiO_2, Mr. E. P. Warekois for his valuable assistance in finding a suitable crystal and aid with preparation of maser test samples, and Dr. S. H. Autler for several valuable discussions.

* The work reported in this paper was performed at Lincoln Laboratory, a center for research operated by Massachusetts Institute of Technology with the joint support of the U. S. Army, Navy, and Air Force.

1 N. Bloembergen, Phys. Rev. **104**, 324 (1956).
2 Supplied by the National Lead Company, South Amboy, New Jersey. The starting material contained 0.2% by weight Fe^{3+} (added as Fe_2O_3) in TiO_2. The final concentration of Fe^{3+} is estimated to be from 0.5 to 0.1 of the starting ratio.
3 W. Low (private communication) suggested the use of this particular material.
4 L. R. Momo, R. A. Myers, and S. Foner, J. Appl. Phys. (to be published); S. Foner, L. R. Momo, A. Mayer, and R. A. Myers, "Quantum electronics conference," Shawanga Lodge (September 12–14, 1959) (to be published).
5 $\epsilon=160$ parallel to the c axis, $\epsilon=86$ perpendicular to the c axis at 25°C. See A. von Hippel, *Dielectric Materials and Applications* (The Technology Press of Massachusetts Institute of Technology, p. 302; and John Wiley & Sons, Inc., New York, 1954).
6 The initial cavity design, intended for use with materials of much lower dielectric constant, was similar to that of W. From, 1959 PGMTT National Symposium, Cambridge, Massachusetts (June 1–3, 1959).
7 The pump power was furnished by a Philips Laboratory DX151, kindly loaned to us by the millimeter wave group under the direction of Dr. G. S. Heller.
8 Power measurements were made by J. B. Thaxter and J. McGowan of the millimeter wave group.
9 N. Bloembergen, S. Shapiro, P. S. Pershan, and J. O. Artman, Phys. Rev. **114**, 445 (1959).
10 G. Makhov, C. Kikuchi, J. Lambe, and R. W. Terhune, Phys. Rev. **109**, 1399 (1958).
11 S. Foner, L. R. Momo, and A. Mayer, Phys. Rev. Letters **3**, 36 (1959).
12 The simultaneous amplification and/or oscillation at frequencies near or equal to f_s suggest several possibilities for maser gain stabilization for radiometry. The simultaneous oscillations may also be used as a local oscillator which tracks the nearby maser amplication channel.
13 S. H. Autler, Bull. Am. Phys. Soc. Ser. II, **4**, 413 (1959); Rev. Sci. Instr. (to be published).
14 W. Low, "Symposium on millimeter waves," Polytechnic Institute of Brooklyn, Brooklyn, New York (April 1, 1959).

Reprinted from JOURNAL OF APPLIED PHYSICS, Vol. 31, No. 2, 443, February, 1960

Pulsed Field Millimeter Wave Maser*

L. R. MOMO, R. A. MYERS,† AND S. FONER
Lincoln Laboratory, Massachusetts Institute of Technology, Lexington, Massachusetts
(Received September 10, 1959)

THE frequency range of the previously reported[1] pulsed field ruby maser has been extended to the 70 kMcps range, and the peak output power has been increased, by a factor of about ten, to several milliwatts. These results demonstrate the feasibility of generating pulses of coherent millimeter wavelength radiation with an inverted spin population which extracts energy from a pulsed magnetic field. Operation at 4.2°K extends over a broad band of discrete frequencies with pulsed fields as high as 30 koe. From these observations upper limits of the magnetic field dependence of the spin-lattice relaxation time have been estimated.

In normal operation, the dc biasing field is set at H_0 (see Fig. 1) and levels 1 and 3 are saturated at $\nu_1 = 12.7$ kMcps which corresponds to the TE_{101} mode of the solid ruby cavity. A pulsed magnetic field is then applied to the paramagnetic system, increasing the energy difference between the inverted levels 1 and 2; the pump source is gated off within 10 μsec of the start of the field pulse. Maser oscillations are observed whenever the energy difference ν_{12} corresponds to the frequency of a favorable cavity mode, e.g., ν_2 (TE_{102}) and ν_3 (TE_{103}) in Fig. 1.

Extension of maser operation to the millimeter wave region was attained by systematically increasing the peak pulsed field. Oscillations at the two lowest TE_{10n} modes, 12.7 kMcps and 19.2 kMcps, have been identified; above these frequencies, identification of cavity modes was not feasible. Lower frequency limits were ascertained by means of microwave cutoff filters introduced into the detection system, and the emission frequencies were calculated by comparing the magnitude of the applied field at emission with the energy difference ν_{12}. The highest frequency attained thus far is 75±5 kMcps; operation at higher frequencies has been limited by the available peak magnitude of the pulsed field. As many as 14 different emission frequencies have been observed in the 12 to 70 kMcps range, with up to six distinguishable emission frequencies during a given field traversal.

The size of the single coupling iris has proven a critical variable for the operation of this maser, determining both which modes are observed and the power output. Increased cavity coupling and somewhat greater pump power have increased the earlier reported power[1] by 10 db; peak output power of more than 2.5 mw has been obtained at 12.7 and 19.2 kMcps; and more than 0.025 mw has been detected at about 40 kMcps. The results in the millimeter wave range are underestimated by a large factor because a non-optimum hybrid microwave system of both K_u- and K_a-band components was employed.

During preliminary attempts to obtain inversions of successive levels by adiabatic rapid passage, the biasing dc magnetic field was reduced from H_0 (see Fig. 1) before the pulsed magnetic field was applied. To permit such operation it was, of course, necessary to delay gating off the klystron until the pump transition was traversed. Under these conditions saturation (or, perhaps, partial inversion) of the normal pump transition at H_0 was obtained on a transient basis, and the millimeter wavelength output remained substantially unaffected. In this experiment, millimeter wave maser operation was observed when the biasing dc field was reduced by as much as 700 oe.

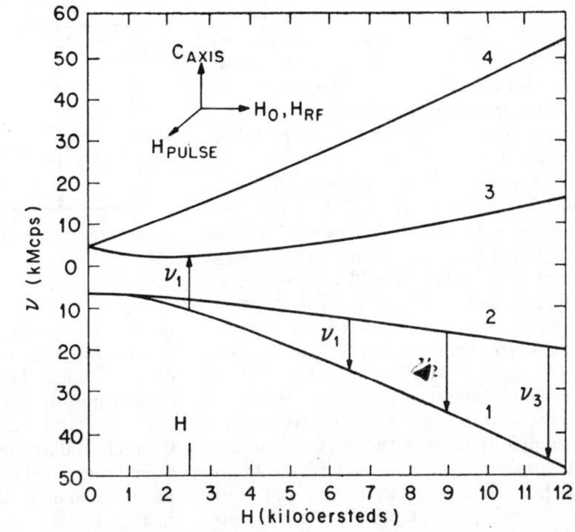

FIG. 1. Energy level diagram for Cr^{3+} in Al_2O_3 for applied field perpendicular to the c axis. Orientation of the magnetic fields with respect to the crystal is indicated in the insert.

Maser oscillations were detected at the peak of pulsed fields as high as 29.2 koe, for which the field rise-time was 600 μsec. This observation requires that any field dependence of the spin-lattice relaxation time in ruby be small, if not entirely negligible, for pulsed fields up to 29.2 koe. Such field dependence has not been extensively studied, either experimentally or theoretically, but it has been suggested[2] that it is of the form

$$1/T_1 = (1+bH^n)/T_0.$$

If this is true, either $bH^n \ll 1$, or n is small. In the latter case, it is possible to show that $n \leqslant 1.1$ for $bH^n \gg 1$ by using our result in conjunction with a value of $T_1 = 25$ msec at 4.2°K and 4 koe obtained by Kikuchi *et al.*[3] In order to investigate the field dependence, more detailed measurements of $T_1(H)$ are being made at high dc magnetic fields.

We are indebted to B. Feldman and J. J. Kelley for valuable assistance, and to Dr. S. Shapiro of the Arthur D. Little Company, Cambridge, Massachusetts, for informative discussions.

* The work reported in this paper was performed at Lincoln Laboratory, a center for research operated by Massachusetts Institute of Technology with the joint support of the U. S. Army, Navy, and Air Force.
† Permanent address: Harvard University, Cambridge, Massachusetts.
[1] Foner, Momo, and Mayer, Phys. Rev. Letters 3, 36 (1959).
[2] J. H. Van Vleck, Phys. Rev. 57, 426 (1940).
[3] Kikuchi, Lambe, Makhov, and Terhune, Project Michigan Report No. 2144-377-T, March, 1959 (unpublished).

70-Gc Maser*

A maser amplifier has been operated at a signal frequency of 70 Gc with pump power supplied at a frequency of 118 Gc. The spin system used for the operation was the iron ion Fe^{3+} in a host crystal of TiO_2 (rutile).

It is generally assumed in the design of masers that it is necessary to have the pump frequency at least twice the frequency of the signal to be amplified. This assumption, on the basis of equal spin lattice transition probabilities, is made to simplify the solutions to the rate equations[1] and is sufficiently accurate for low-frequency maser design. However, in most maser materials, the spin lattice transition probabilities are not exactly equal and in fact, have been shown to vary considerably for different materials. For millimeter-wavelength masers even a slight difference in the transition probabilities will allow a considerable variation in the operating parameters.

For the iron ion Fe^{3+} in a host crystal of TiO_2, the transition probability ω_{13} is greater than the transition probability ω_{35}. By applying the ratio $\omega_{13}/\omega_{35}>1$ to the rate equations, neglecting intermediate levels, we have found that maser amplification at a frequency above 70 Gc should be possible for a pump frequency of 120 Gc. This type of maser operation was reported by Foner, *et al.*,[2] and has been further verified as described in the following experiment.

The 70-Gc maser was constructed in a typical reflection-type spectrometer. The rutile sample itself was the resonant structure. It was mounted in a silver-plated brass cubical box that terminated the signal and pump waveguides and provided a convenient means to position the crystal with respect to the dc magnetic field. The crystal was mounted on the end of a 1-mm diameter

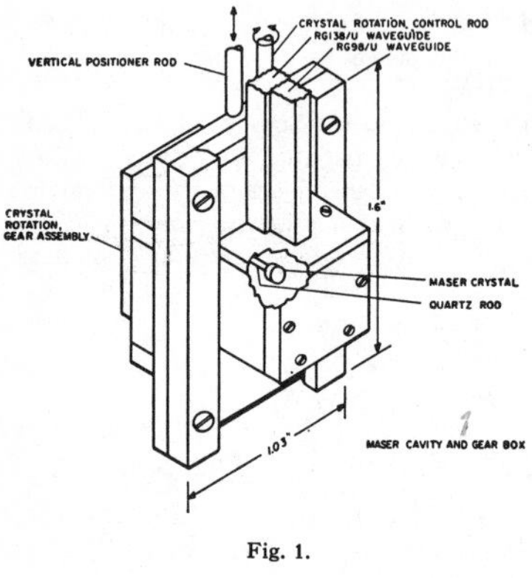

Fig. 1.

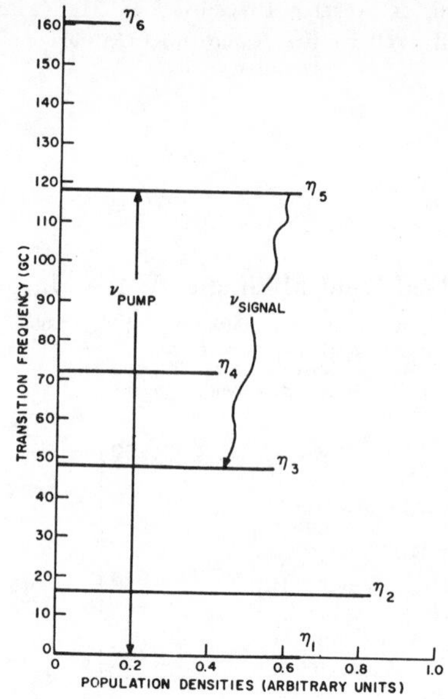

Fig. 2.

quartz rod on a center common to both guides and approximately $\frac{3}{4}\lambda$ from the end of the guides. The rutile sample contained approximately 0.1 per cent substitutional Fe^{3+} ions and was cut cylindrical in shape, 0.1 inch in diameter and 0.04 inch high from a boule supplied by the National Lead Company. A sketch of the assembly is shown in Fig. 1.

The spin energy levels of the iron ion were arranged such that the pump energy was applied at a frequency of ν_{15} equal to 118 Gc. In the presence of a large pumping signal at a frequency ν_{51} and a dc magnetic field of 4.6 kilogauss applied in a direction perpendicular to the [001] crystalline axis ($\phi=0$) and parallel to the [100] axis ($\theta=45°$) the distribution of the spins among the various energy levels at a temperature of 4.2° K will be approximately as shown in Fig. 2.

The gain and bandwidth that was achieved is shown in Fig. 3. The top trace is the video-detected reflected signal power with the pump power off, and the bottom trace is the reflected amplified signal with the pump power on. In this figure, the signal klystron is being swept over a mode of approximately 60 Mc centered at 70 Gc. The gain that has been demonstrated is about 20 db at a bandwidth of approximately 10 Mc.

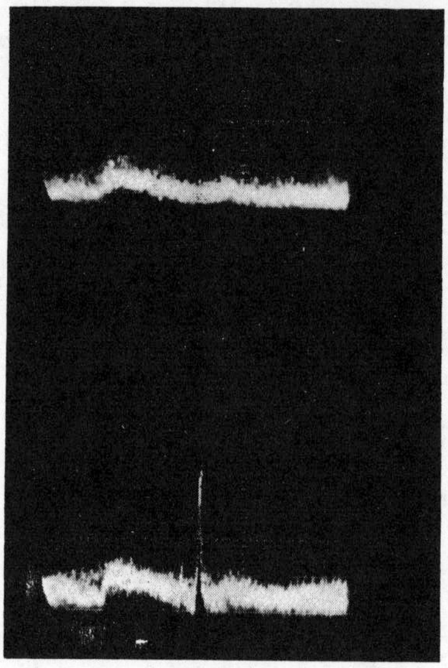

Fig. 3.

In summary, it has been demonstrated that for millimeter-wave maser design it is possible to take advantage of slight differences in relaxation rates and obtain amplification at frequencies more than one half the pump frequency. This advantage increases as the operating frequency increases and will be of considerable consequence for masers in the submillimeter region of the spectrum. It will allow relaxed requirements for maser pump tubes and increase the efficiency of quantum electronic devices in this region.

W. E. Hughes
C. R. Kremenek
Air Arm Div.
Appl. Phys. Group
Westinghouse Electric Corp.
Baltimore, Md.

* Received February 18, 1963; revised manuscript received March 5, 1963. This work was supported by the U. S. Army Signal Research and Development Laboratory, Fort Monmouth, N. J.

[1] N. Bloembergen, "Proposal for a new type solid state maser," *Phys. Rev.*, vol. 104, pp. 324–327; October 15, 1956.

[2] S. Foner, L. R. Momo, J. B. Thaxter, G. S. Heller, and R. M. White, "CW millimeter wavelength maser," in "Advances in Quantum Electronics," Columbia University Press, New York, N. Y., pp. 553–563; 1961.

Reprinted from the PROCEEDINGS OF THE IEEE
VOL. 51, NO. 5, MAY, 1963

Reprinted from JOURNAL OF APPLIED PHYSICS, Vol. 32, No. 12, 2541–2542, December, 1961

A cw Solid State, Push-Pull Maser in the 5 to 6 Millimeter Wavelength Region*

DAVID L. CARTER
Department of Physics, Columbia University, New York, New York
(Received May 1, 1961)

Cw maser oscillation from 49 to 57 kMc was achieved with 0.12% Fe^{3+}-doped rutile, using push-pull pumping at 78.2 kMc. A short experiment on cross-relaxation effects was also performed.

To operate a cw solid-state maser at signal frequencies from 49 to 57 kMc with a pump frequency near 78.2 kMc, Fe^{3+}-doped TiO_2 (rutile) has been used. The maser was operated in the push-pull mode.[1] This operation is indicated in Fig. 1. Pumping radiation is applied simultaneously to transitions 3–5 and 4–6 which are adjusted to the same frequency, and population inversion is obtained in transition 5–4.

For equal relaxation rates between all energy levels this mode of operation has one advantage over ordinary three-level[2] systems in that the pump frequency need not be greater than twice the signal frequency in order to obtain population inversion.

Fe^{3+} in TiO_2 is particularly well suited for millimeter wave masers because it has large zero-field splittings (43.3 and 81.3 kMc), and reasonable relaxation times and linewidths.[3] These zero-field splittings allow one to use moderate values of magnetic field strength to obtain splittings suitable for maser operation in the mm wavelength region. Maser action in Fe-doped rutile at frequencies both higher and lower than those reported here has been achieved by Foner *et al.*[4,5]

In our experiments the signal frequency varied linearly with dc magnetic field strength from 49 to 57 kMc, as the field strength was changed from 7200 to 5500 gauss. The orientation of the magnetic field was held fixed and was 73° from the [110] direction in the (001) plane of the crystal. Figure 1 is a plot of allowed energy as a function of field strength for Fe-doped rutile at the above orientation computed from from the spin Hamiltonian of reference 3. These energy levels predicted the maser operating points to within the paramagnetic resonance linewidth ($\simeq$200 Mc). Also listed in the figure are the maximum values of the computed magnetic dipole moment matrix elements in units of μ_B, the Bohr magneton. From 5500 to 7200 gauss the transitions 3–5 and 4–6 both have the same splittings to within $\frac{1}{2}$% of the average theoretical value of 78.4 kMc. In the experiment it was necessary only to change the field *strength* to obtain maser action over the range of signal frequencies when the pump frequency was held fixed. If the pump frequency was changed by two or three hundred Mc it was necessary to change the magnetic field orientation by a few tenths of a degree to obtain the same range of signal frequen-

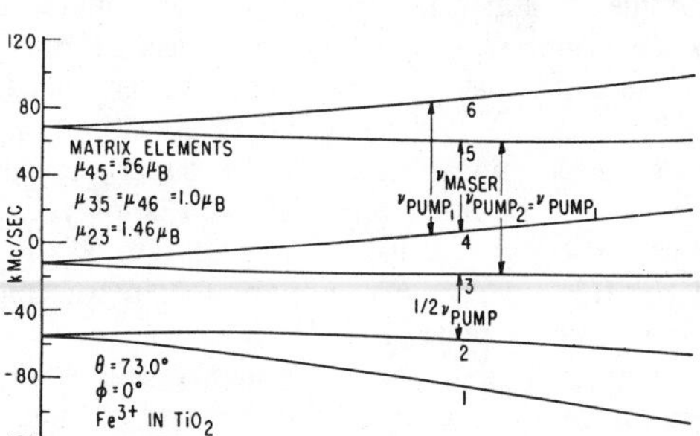

FIG. 1. Energy levels of Fe^{3+} in TiO_2 as a function of magnetic field for the field pointing 73° from the [110] direction in the (001) plane. The matrix elements are the maximum values and μ_B is the Bohr magneton.

* This research was supported in part by the U. S. Air Force and monitored by the Air Force Office of Scientific Research of the Air Research and Development Command.

[1] C. Kikuchi, J. Lambe, G. Makhov, and R. W. Terhune, J. Appl. Phys. **30**, 1061 (1959).

[2] Some three-level masers use idler doping or cross relaxation to improve inversion, and in these cases the restriction of the pump frequency to be greater than twice the signal frequency is removed. See, for example, P. A. Forrester and W. B. Mims, J. Appl. Phys. **32**, 317 (1961).

[3] D. Carter and A. Okaya, Phys. Rev. **118**, 1485 (1960).

[4] S. Foner and L. R. Momo, J. Appl. Phys. **31**, 742 (1960).

[5] S. Foner, L. R. Momo, J. B. Thaxter, G. S. Heller, and R. M. White, *Second International Conference on Quantum Electronics, March, 1961* (to be published).

cies. The range of pump frequencies over which maser action was observed was approximately 78.1 to 78.8 kMc.

Maser action was detected by observing the swept-frequency signal power reflected from the Fe-doped rutile when cw pump power was applied. The rutile was mounted in a cubic copper box 0.6 in., on a side which terminated the two waveguide transmission lines. The rutile was held in position in the box by paraffin or polyfoam. The floor of the box was movable to change microwave coupling and was controlled from outside the cryostat. Both pump and signal guides were 0.074 by 0.148 in. in cross-sectional dimensions. The Fe-doped rutile piece thus mounted provided its own dielectric resonant cavity, as described in reference 3 and by Okaya.[6] The rutile samples used were large enough to accommodate a density of dielectric modes of the order of one every 5 to 20 Mc, dependent upon sample size. These modes had Q's of the order of 10^4 at the pump and signal frequencies when the temperature was below 4.2°K. The doping of the rutile used in the experiments was 0.12% Fe to TiO_2 by weight.[7] Pump power was supplied by a Raytheon QKK 866 reflex klystron which had an available power output of approximately 50 mw at 78.2 kMc. For crystals with a volume of 0.15 cm^3 this power was insufficient to obtain signal gain at 4.2°K, although a decrease in absorption was seen. However, lowering the temperature to 1.6°K increased the spin-lattice relaxation time to give enough saturation of the pump transitions for both maser gain and oscillation. For crystals smaller than $\frac{1}{4}$ of the above volume, the required saturation was easily obtained at both 4.2°K and 1.6°K.

Cw oscillation was observed throughout the signal frequency region. By adjusting coupling parameters, amplitude modulation of the oscillation was produced. It was found that it was very difficult to obtain large enough microwave coupling in the signal resonances to obtain gain stable enough for root-gain-bandwidth measurements. Early measurements were made using video detection with signal power levels of approximately -30 db below a mw. This power was high enough to saturate oscillation and to give the appearance of stable, linear gain. When superheterodyne detection with 10 Mc bandwidth was employed and lower power levels were used, cw oscillation was found at all the frequencies where apparent gain was measured at the higher power levels.

The transition 2–3 has a resonance frequency of $\frac{1}{2}$ the pump frequency over a large range of magnetic fields. Therefore, one might expect cross relaxation[8] to occur between the pump levels and the 2–3 transition; then saturation of levels 2 and 3 would result in saturation of the pump transitions with subsequent inversion of levels 4 and 5. An experiment to test this hypothesis was tried, with a negative result. The magnet was adjusted so that the pump levels and levels 2 and 3 were resonant at the same field for a two-to-one frequency ratio. Then high power was applied to one frequency resonance while the other frequency resonance was monitored for saturation. Other transitions with frequencies equal to $\frac{1}{2}$ pump frequency and which were also coincident in field with the pump transitions were tried without success. It is believed that the negative result was due to the unfavorable ratio of the spin-lattice relaxation time to the cross-relaxation time.

Mims and McGee[9] find three-spin-flip cross-relaxation times of a few milliseconds in ruby with the same spin concentration as the Fe-doped rutile used in our experiment. The nearest neighbor distances in rutile are of the same order as those in ruby and we might therefore conclude that the cross times are of the same order. Pulse-decay measurements, with superheterodyne detection, of the spin-lattice relaxation times at 9680 Mc and 1.4°K for 0.12% Fe-doped rutile yielded values which ranged from 2 msec to somewhat less than 1 msec, dependent upon the transition. From theory[10] and some experiments on various crystals it is to be expected that the spin-lattice time will be the same[11] or shorter[12,13] at millimeter wavelengths than it is at centimeter wavelengths. To this date no experimenters have found an increasing relaxation time with increasing frequency. Therefore, at X band the threefold cross-relaxation effects on a particular resonance line will be greatly reduced by the competing spin-lattice relaxation. At the higher frequencies it is then expected that the spin-lattice process is even more dominant than at X band and that the amount of cross saturation is extremely small.

ACKNOWLEDGMENT

The author would like to thank F. R. Nash for making the X band relaxation measurements and for several illuminating discussions on relaxation phenomena.

[6] A. Okaya, Proc. Inst. Radio Engrs. **48**, 1921 (1960).

[7] These Linde crystals were kindly lent to us by H. Lewis, H. Gerritsen, and E. Sebisky of RCA.

[8] N. Bloembergen, S. Shapiro, P. S. Pershan, and J. O. Artman Phys. Rev. **114**, 445 (1959).

[9] W. Mims and J. McGee, Phys. Rev. **119**, 1233 (1960).

[10] See, for example, R. D. Mattuck and M. W. P. Strandberg, Phys. Rev. **119**, 1204 (1960). This theory, however, does not apply to S state ions.

[11] S. Foner, L. R. Momo, A. Mayer, and R. A. Myers, *Quantum Electronics* (Columbia University Press, New York, 1960), pp. 487–498. This work shows that the relaxation time in ruby is approximately independent of frequency.

[12] J. Castle, P. Chester, and P. Wagner, Phys. Rev. **119**, 953 (1960).

[13] J. Pace, D. Sampson, and J. Thorp, Royal Radar Establishment Memorandum No. 1752 (August, 1960) (unpublished). A comparison of the work of references 12 and 13 shows a decreasing relaxation time with increasing frequency for $K_3Cr(CN)_6$.

† Mims and McGee[9] find three spin flip cross relaxation times of $\simeq 0.1$ msec in ruby at 7 kMc/sec with the same spin concentration used in our experiment. The nearest neighbor distances in rutile are about the same as in ruby. The three-spin-flip process is a second order process and hence its rate is proportional to $(\text{frequency})^{-2}$. Therefore a crude estimate of the cross relaxation time for 0.12% Fe-doped rutile would be $0.1\,(39/7)^2$ msec $= 3$ msec at 39 kMc/sec.

Iron Sapphire Maser with No Magnetic Field*

Maser operation with trivalent iron-doped sapphire in low and medium magnetic fields has been previously reported [1]–[3]. We have recently observed maser action in this material with no magnetic field. Initially, three simultaneous inversions at at 4.2°K were found in a field ≈25 gauss produced by a pair of brass-cored Helmholtz coils for a C-axis orientation of 18°. Two of the maser points were located at 11.878 Gc and 11.978 Gc. The third somewhat smaller inversion appeared on 12.050 Gc. This frequency corresponds to the splitting of the two lower doublets in zero

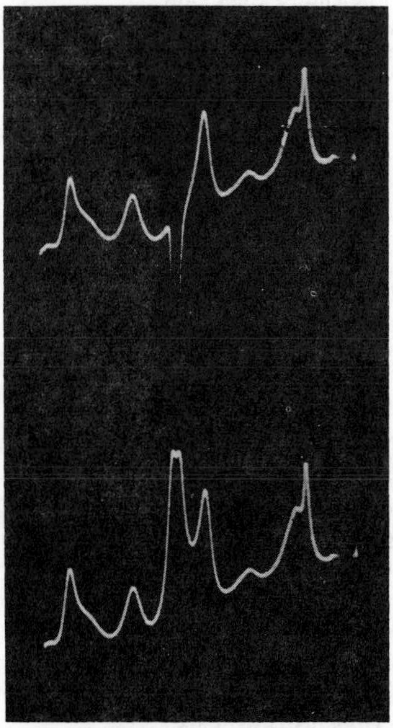

Fig. 1—Iron sapphire double-hump zero-field line absorption (lower). Masering with no magnetic field (upper). Five other cavity modes range from 11.880 Gc to 12.240 Gc.

field of Fe^{3+} in sapphire, while the pump frequency of 31.292 Gc is the separation of the lowest and highest doublet pairs [4], [5]. When the magnetic field was removed completely only the 12.050 signal inversion persisted showing the expected independence of orientation. No hriozontal field outside the dewar tail piece could be detected with an RFL 1890 gaussmeter. We believe this is the first reported microwave maser operation with crystalline field splitting only. The single peak maser line appeared undercoupled and showed a gain-bandwidth product (GBP) of several megacycles. Full pump power could not be applied, however, without producing oscillations. The operating parameters at very low fields which allow identification of the participating spin levels may be obtained from available energy-level plots [6]. For operation with both ion sites magnetically equivalent and arbitrary C-axis orientation relevant parameters have been tabulated [7].

When the signal and pump slots were altered to provide better coupling to the cavity modes the double-hump zero-field line appeared as shown in Fig. 1. The adjusted signal and pump frequencies were 12.040 and 31.30 Gc. Fig. 2 shows an expanded sweep of the no-field maser line operating typically around 30-db gain and a 5-Mc bandwidth. GBP of 165 Mc have been observed at 4.2°K. It is interesting to note that with magnetic fields as low as 5 to 10 gauss the GBP has been increased to ≈250 Mc which the authors believe may not be optimum. These figures are the largest reported to date in the "zero"-field mode of operation with this material. In these latter runs the field was directed at 80° with the crystalline C axis but the inversion was not a sharp function of the angle. The sample of iron sapphire with estimated 10^{19} Fe^{3+} spins was a silver-plated cylinder approximately $\frac{3}{8}$ inch in diameter by $\frac{3}{4}$ inch long. A flattened area $\frac{1}{4}$ inch by $\frac{3}{4}$ inch appropriately slotted allowed coupling to the pump and signal guides through a tuned iris structure described elsewhere [8]. It should be mentioned that a number of other inversions with this cavity were obtained using magnetic fields in the 500-, 1600-to-3000-, and 6000-gauss ranges.

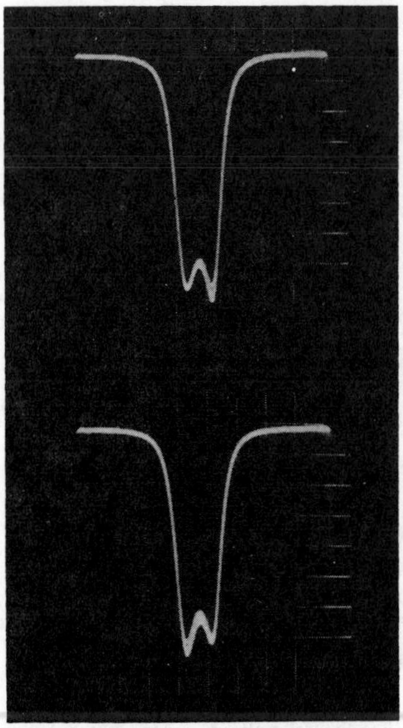

Fig. 2—No-field maser ≈12.04 Gc; gain ≈30 db., bandwidth ≈5 Mc; pump frequency ≈31.30 Gc.

The authors wish to thank Dr. R. C. Pastor and Dr. R. H. Hoskins of the Applied Physics Laboratory, Quantatron, Inc. (now Korad Corporation), for providing the iron sapphire samples and continued interest in these experiments. Thanks are also due J. Minkowski, Carlyle Barton Laboratory. The Johns Hopkins University, and J. O. Artman and J. C. Murphy of the Applied Physics Laboratory for line strength measurements on various samples.

G. E. Friedman
A. W. Nagy
Appl. Phys. Lab.
The Johns Hopkins University
Silver Spring, Md.

Bibliography

[1] L. S. Kornienko and A. M. Prokhorov, "A paramagnetic amplifier and generator, using Fe^{3+} ions in Corundum," *J. Exp. Theoret. Phys.* (USSR), vol. 36, pp. 919–920; March, 1959.

[2] J. E. King and R. W. Terhune, "Operation of a zero-field X-band maser," *J. Appl. Phys.*, vol. 30, pp. 1844–1845; November, 1959.

[3] N. V. Karlov, Yu. P. Pimenov, and A. M. Prokhorov, "Paramagnetic amplifier for the 10-cm band using Fe^{3+} ions in Corundum," *Radio Engrg. and Electronic Phys.* (*USSR*), vol. 5, p. 755; May 1961. (Published by the AIEE).

[4] G. S. Bogle and H. F. Symmons, "Paramagnetic resonance of Fe^{3+} in Sapphire at low temperatures," *Proc. Phys. Soc.* (*London*), vol. 73, pt. 3, pp. 531–532; March, 1959. See also, H. F. Symmons and G. S. Bogle, "On the exactness of the spin-Hamiltonian description of FD^{3+} in Sapphire," *Proc. Phys. Soc.* (*London*), vol. 79, pp. 468–472; March, 1962.

[5] L. S. Kornienko and A. M. Prokhorov, "Electronic paramagnetic resonance of the Fe^{3+} ion in Corundum," *J. Exp. Theoret. Phys.* (*USSR*), vol. 40, pp. 1594–1601; June, 1961.

[6] C. Kikuchi and C. Sims, "Energy Levels at Low Fields for Fe^{3+} in Al_2O_3," Willow Run Laboratories, University of Michigan, Ann Arbor Memo Z-1238; June 24, 1959.

[7] G. A. Sivlina and G. A. Feshchenko, "Fe^{3+} spin levels in Corundum," *Radio Engrg. and Electronic Phys.*, vol. 5, pp. 711–719; May, 1961. (Published by the AIEE.)

[8] A. W. Nagy and G. E. Friedman, "Reflection cavity maser with large gain bandwidth," Proc. IRE (*Correspondence*), vol. 50, pp. 2504–2505; December, 1962.

* Received December 6, 1962. This work was supported by the Bureau of Naval Weapons, Department of the Navy, under Contract NOw-0604-c.

Reprinted from the PROCEEDINGS OF THE IEEE
VOL. 51, NO. 2, FEBRUARY, 1963

Note: Throughout the paper the 5.0 mc bandwidth should be replaced by 6.6 mc. In the middle of the paper replace 165 mc by the words "over 200 mc." In Ref. 4 change FD^{3+} to FE^{3+}.

A No-Field Powder Maser*

The first no-field operation of maser using a monocrystal iron doped sapphire cavity was recently described.[1] Here we report inversion, with no magnetic field, in a powdered sample of this paramagnetic at 4.2°K. Fig. 1 shows the variations in the inverted signal transition (12.03 Gc) with change in coupling to the sample. They indicate potentially useable gain-bandwidth for this mode of operation.

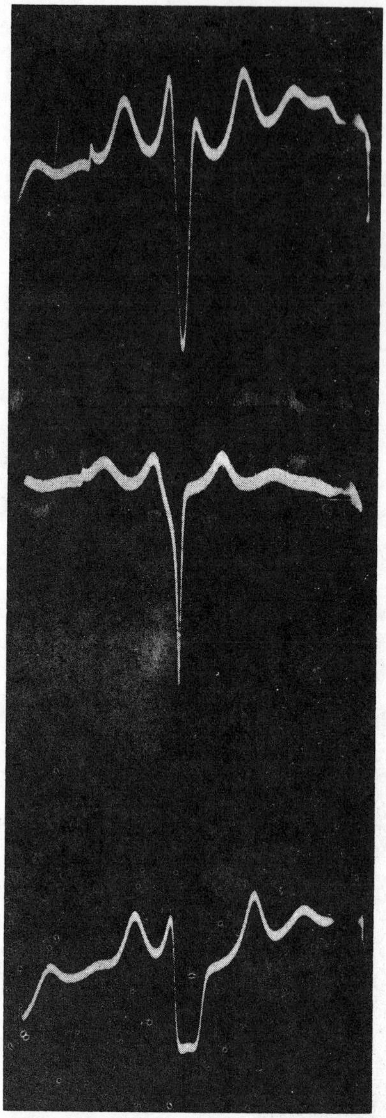

Fig. 1—Inversion in iron sapphire powder with no magnetic field. Variation of gain with coupling ≈3–10 db, bandwidth ≈44 Mc/box. Signal ≈12.03 Gc, pump ≈31.34 Gc.

The sample was prepared by crushing a small cylindrical boule of trivalent iron sapphire which had been previously masered in the no-field mode. The powder was contained within a small teflon box approximately 2.5 cm³ and located at one end of a small plunger-tuned section of rectangular waveguide. The plunger could be adjusted in liquid helium to the desired TE_{10n} operating mode. Signal and pump coupling slots were provided at the end of the guide containing the sample, and coupling to the main signal and pump feeds was made through a tuned iris structure described elsewhere.[2] The teflon container allowed the quantity and packing of powder to be adjusted for the desired tuning and mode of operation.

Although the purpose of this experiment was to demonstrate the feasibility of masering a powder with no magnetic field, we feel that maximum coupling to the powder was not realized with this arrangement. Moreover, it appears that the pumping power was inadequate to achieve, in this particular configuration, full saturation of the pump transition (31.34 Gc).

A no-field powder maser would be limited to operation around the zero-field splitting frequency. However, other suitable zero-field materials with splittings in the higher microwave ranges which have been tabulated[3] offer a choice for possible fixed-frequency applications.

A. W. NAGY
G. E. FRIEDMAN
Applied Physics Laboratory
The Johns Hopkins University
Silver Spring, Md.

* Received May 16, 1963. The work reported here was supported by the Bureau of Naval Weapons, Department of the Navy, under Contract No. NO w-0604-c.

1 G. E. Friedman and A. W. Nagy, "Iron sapphire maser with no magnetic field," PROC. IEEE (*Correspondence*), vol. 51, pp 361–362; February, 1963.

2 A. W. Nagy and G. E. Friedman, "Reflection cavity maser with large gain-bandwidth," PROC. IRE (*Correspondence*), vol. 50, pp. 2504–2505; December, 1962.

3 G. S. Bogle and H. F. Symmons, "Zero field masers," *Aust. J. Phys.*, vol. 12, pp. 1–20; March, 1959.

Reprinted from the PROCEEDINGS OF THE IEEE
VOL. 51, NO. 7, JULY, 1963

PRINTED IN THE U.S.A.

Letters to the Editor

A PARAMAGNETIC AMPLIFIER AND GENERATOR, USING Fe^{3+} *IONS IN CORUNDUM*

L. S. KORNIENKO and A. M. PROKHOROV

Moscow State University

Submitted to JETP editor November 27, 1958

J. Exptl. Theoret. Phys. (U.S.S.R.) **36**, 919-920 (March, 1959)

IN published reports on the construction of quantum-mechanical amplifiers and generators, Gd^{3+} (reference 1) and Cr^{3+} (references 2-8) have been used as the paramagnetic ions. There is also a report of an attempt, as yet unsuccessful, to utilize the ion Ni^{2+} (reference 2) for this purpose.

We have carried out a study of the possibility of constructing a paramagnetic amplifier and generator using the ion Fe^{3+} in corundum. The spectrum of the electronic paramagnetic resonance of the ions Fe^{3+} in the lattice Al_2O_3 has been studied earlier by the authors.[9] The Fe^{3+} ion is in an S state, and has electronic spin $S = 5/2$. In corundum the Fe^{3+} ions form two nonequivalent systems, differing from one another in the direction of the cubic axes of the crystalline electric field. The axes of trigonal symmetry of both systems are parallel. If the trigonal axis of the crystalline electric field is parallel or perpendicular to an externally applied constant magnetic field, then the energy levels of both systems coincide for any magnitude of the magnetic field and arbitrary orientation of the cubic axes. If, however, the trigonal axis of the crystal makes an angle with the direction of the external magnetic field, then the energy levels of both systems coincide only for some definite orientations of the cubic axes of the non-equivalent systems of ions; these orientations can be found by turning the crystal around the trigonal axis until the spectra of the electronic paramagnetic resonances of both systems coincide. In the absence of an external magnetic field the six spin levels of each system are split by the electric field of the crystal into three doublets, the distances between which are 0.39 and 0.62 cm^{-1}. From a comparison of the relative intensities of the spectral lines at 290 and 4.2°K., it was established that the lowest spin doublet is the one which in strong magnetic fields is split into levels characterized by magnetic quantum numbers $M = \pm 1/2$, i.e., the constant, D, in the spin Hamiltonian is positive. For the paramagnetic amplifier levels were used which, if the influence of the cubic components of the crystalline field is neglected, are characterized in the parallel orientation by the quantum numbers $M = -5/2, -3/2, -1/2$. The presence in the crystalline field of a cubic component mixes the states, even in the parallel orientation, as a result of which transitions are allowed between any of the chosen levels. For amplification the levels with $M = -3/2$ and $-1/2$ are used, and the auxiliary radiation induces transitions between the levels with $M = -5/2, -1/2$. The trigonal axis of the crystal made a small angle with the direction of the constant magnetic field. The cubic axes were oriented so that the energy levels of both non-equivalent systems of ions coincided.

Amplification and generation were observed at a temperature of 1.8°K. for a wave-length ~ 3.2 cm. with auxiliary radiation of wave-length ~ 1.2 cm. The magnitude of the constant magnetic field was ~ 1200 Oe.

[1] Scovil, Feher, and Seidel, Phys. Rev. **105**, 762 (1957).

[2] A. L. McWhorter and J. W. Meyer, Phys. Rev. **109**, 312, (1958).

[3] Artman, Bloembergen, and Shapiro, Phys. Rev. **109**, 1392 (1958).

[4] Makhov, Kikuchi, Lambe, and Terhune, Phys. Rev. **109**, 1399 (1958).

[5] Strandberg, Davis, Faughnan, Kyhl, and Wolga, Phys. Rev. **109**, 1988 (1958).

[6] S. H. Autler and N. McAvoy, Phys. Rev. **110**, 280 (1958).

[7] R. H. Kingston, Proc. IRE **46**, 916 (1958).

[8] Zverev, Kornienko, Manenkov, and Prokhorov, J. Exptl. Theoret. Phys. (U.S.S.R.) **34**, 1660 (1958), Soviet Phys. JETP **7**, 1141 (1958).

[9] L. S. Kornienko and A. M. Prokhorov, J. Exptl. Theoret. Phys. (U.S.S.R.) **33**, 805 (1957), Soviet Physics JETP **6**, 620 (1958).

Translated by K. F. Hulme
164

Four-Level K_u-Band Maser*

A four-level push-pull maser[1] using a reflection-type cavity has been built and operated at 15.4 kMc by the authors. The present communication is intended to report the observed performance characteristics of the device and to point out certain design features of general interest.

Linde pink ruby was cut into a rectangular block of dimensions 0.17 by 0.17 by 0.09 inch and coated with silver paint[2] to form a completely filled cavity. The rhombohedral crystal axis was oriented at an angle of 54° 44′ with respect to the dc magnetic field, as required by four-level operation. Coupling holes were provided by removal of circular portions of the silver coating, varying in diameter between 0.05 and 0.09 inch. The cavity thus obtained was soldered with Wood's metal to the side wall of the signal guide approximately $\lambda/4$ from the shorted end, as indicated in Fig. 1.

The pump guide was run along the same side wall of the signal guide and made to terminate at the cavity. The signal coupling mode was TE_{011}; the pump coupling mode was found to be not critical and was probably TE_{013}.

Device performance was quite similar to that observed by others for this particular type of maser. With a pumping power of several milliwatts at 34.7 kMc and a bath temperature of 4.2°K, a stable gain of 26 db was measured in conjunction with a 3-Mc bandwidth corresponding to a gain-bandwidth product $\sqrt{G}\cdot B = 60$ Mc.

A noteworthy feature of the present design is the simplicity of the coupling arrangement between the cavity and the two waveguides. The capacitive tuning screw in front of the cavity shown in Fig. 1 provides for adjustable coupling. This arrangement makes it possible to attach an auxiliary cavity (not shown in Fig. 1) to the opposite wall of the signal guide which resonates at a slightly different frequency and, thus, can be used to increase the bandwidth of the device.

E. J. Schimitschek
E. G. K. Schwarz
W. G. Turnbull
General Dynamics/Astronautics
San Diego, Calif.

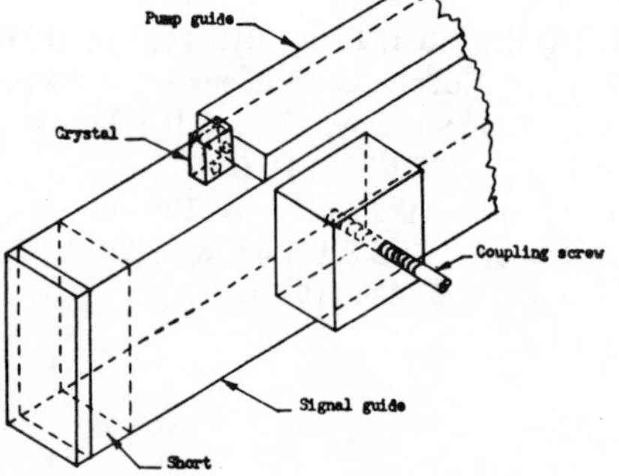

Fig. 1—Maser cavity coupled to waveguides.

* Received November 29, 1962.

[1] G. Makhov, C. Kikuchi, J. Lambe, and R. W. Terhune, "Ruby as a maser material," *J. Appl. Phys.*, vol. 30, p. 1061; July, 1959.

[2] L. G. Gross, "Silvered ruby maser cavity," *J. Appl. Phys.*, vol. 30, p. 1459; September, 1959.

The Potentialities and Present Status of Masers and Parametric Amplifiers in Radio Astronomy*

J. V. JELLEY†

Summary—**The paper reviews the potentialities and present status of maser and parametric radiometer systems in the whole field of radio astronomy, including radar astronomy. A short historical account of the development of the maser is followed by an outline of the objectives of radio-astronomical research, and the radiation mechanisms which arise. After an account of the requirements of the radio astronomer, a detailed discussion is presented of the limitations and relative merits of masers and parametric amplifiers in this field of research.**

The paper includes a compilation of data on existing and planned observatory installations. This data has been gathered from published work and from replies to a questionnaire which was widely circulated by the author; it embraces, it is hoped, most of the currently available information. Finally, there is a brief summary of some of the achievements in astronomy which have resulted directly from the developments and applications of these low-noise devices. A few notes are added, in conclusion, as pointers to the likely trends in the near future.

Historical Introduction

A FEW years ago, when the microwave maser was on the frontiers of physics, there was a vast outburst of activity, both in solid-state University physics departments and in industrial laboratories throughout the world, to explore and develop the potentialities of this then new and exciting field. This activity could hardly have been exaggerated, when it is appreciated that the development of the maser was perhaps the greatest single technological step in radio physics for many years, with the possible exception of the transistor, comparable say with the development of the cavity magnetron during the Second World War.

It is of course natural, in the wake of the recent startling developments in the optical maser field, that the microwave maser has taken second place, is now an established instrument, and the enthusiasm has somewhat abated. It is thus important that the solid-state physicist and radio engineer should not forget what he has created for the radio astronomer! He has been presented with the most sensitive instrument known for the detection of microwave radiation from outer space, the limit of sensitivity being determined primarily by fundamental quantum fluctuation phenomena, and by terrestrial and celestial background radiations, rather than by technological barriers. As we shall see, the over-all system sensitivity of radio-astronomical equipments, in certain limited frequency regions, has been increased by between one and two orders of magnitude. This in turn implies, and it is often the more significant issue in radio astronomy, a great reduction in the integration time for a given yes-no identification of a weak source, the corresponding factor being two, three or even four orders of magnitude.

The object of this review is to present an up-to-date account of the application of masers to radio astronomy, which includes a compilation of the available data on some existing installations, and installations under construction. Although the emphasis is on maser installations, abbreviated accounts of some of the existing and planned parametric amplifier systems is also included, for the parametric amplifier is a serious competitor to the maser, particularly at the lower frequencies, and at observatories where considerations of simplicity, helium supply and cost may prevail.

Although it is not intended to discuss experimental laboratory masers in detail, a brief résumé of the historical steps will now be presented. It was forty-five years ago that Einstein [1], considering the interaction of a quantized atomic system in equilibrium with radiation, showed that there were three basic processes involved, absorption, spontaneous emission and stimulated emission. Under normal conditions in physics the first two processes dominate and stimulated emission is not a significant effect. The significance and importance of stimulated emission, sometimes alternatively known as "induced emission," has, however, been appreciated by workers in spectroscopy and astrophysics for many years and is discussed in text-books on electromagnetic theory, *e.g.*, the work of Heitler [2]. The practical implication of stimulated emission (or negative absorption) as a means of obtaining amplification was, however, appreciated only after a lapse of many years [3], [4]. Finally, in 1955, Townes and his group at Columbia University [4] constructed the first successful maser, the ammonia maser oscillator. This instrument, having a fixed frequency and one which lies close to an H_2O atmospheric absorption band has not, however, been used as yet in radio astronomy.

Disregarding the various forms of solid-state two-level masers, which are only suitable for applications requiring pulsed or intermittent operation, we come to the crucial step in maser development, the proposal by Bloembergen [5] of a three-level solid-state device. This utilizes the energy levels of free electron spins associated with dilute solutions of paramagnetic ions in a crystal lattice, in the presence of a magnetic field. The separation of the levels is determined partly by crystalline electric fields (fixed for a given material) and by an applied magnetic field to obtain Zeeman splitting. Immediately after Bloembergen's theoretical

* Received September 28, 1962.
† Nuclear Physics Division, Atomic Energy Research Establishment, Harwell, Berkshire, England.

paper, vigorous experimental activity flared up in many laboratories. The three-level solid-state maser was soon found to be an instrument of great potentiality. It possesses great flexibility, is tunable, has a reasonable bandwidth for most applications, operates on a continuous basis, possesses an exceptionally low noise figure, is capable of high stability, and has been shown to be reasonably straightforward to design, and to operate on a routine basis. To complete this brief history of the maser, the first three-level laboratory maser was operated at the Bell Telephone Laboratories [6], this being followed by work at the M.I.T. Lincoln Laboratory [7] where the predicted low noise temperatures were first confirmed [8]. Shortly afterwards, an L-band maser was successfully operated at Harvard University [9], this being a specially significant step for the astronomer, who was naturally interested in the possibility of gaining sensitivity at the frequency of the hydrogen line on 1420 Mc. At this stage the number of laboratory masers multiplied at such a rate that reference to further exploratory work would serve no purpose in this review. Readers who wish to gain further knowledge of masers themselves should consult either the standard reference works [10]–[12] or the recent review articles [13], [14].

For various physical and technological reasons, the approximate range over which most masers operate is 1 kMc—100 kMc ($\lambda = 30$ cm to $\lambda = 3$ mm). This region, as we shall see shortly, by a fortuitous set of circumstances, embraces the very region of the extraterrestial radio spectrum where there is a minimum in the sky-temperature diagram and therefore the greatest demand for low-noise receivers in radio astronomy. Although masers have been built to operate outside this range, the problems are the following. At lower frequencies it is difficult to find materials having sufficiently small crystalline field splittings or to obtain adequate population-inversion of the levels. At the higher frequencies it is not easy to find sufficiently large crystalline fields. Added to which are the practical difficulties associated with the necessarily high magnetic fields required, and the purely mechanical problems of the small sizes of the active samples, cavities or other structures.

On the score of sensitivity, the intrinsic noise figure of any maser within the above frequency range is more than adequate for the needs of the astronomer. By more-than-adequate is meant that when the instrument is incorporated into an astronomical radiometer system, the over-all system antenna temperature is determined not by the maser itself but by either, on the one hand, terrestrial and celestial background radiations (*e.g.*, antenna spillover), or by radiation associated with atmospheric absorption or component losses.

Astronomical Research at Radio Wavelengths

During the last decade and a half, the field of radio-astronomy has grown so vast that all but the briefest summary of the situation must be rejected in the present article, and the reader is therefore referred to some of the standard works [16]–[21]. It is sufficient to say that almost all types of astronomical objects emit radio-frequency radiations detectable by existing techniques somewhere within the spectrum, one exception to this being ordinary stars! The following objects thus fall within the domain of passive radio astronomy: the Sun, Solar Corona, some of the Planets, the Moon, bright gaseous Emission Nebulae (within our galaxy), Planetary Nebulae, the Galactic Disk and Galactic Halo (in continuum and at 1420 Mc), Remnants of Supernovae (*e.g.*, the Crab Nebula), some nearby Normal Galaxies, and unusual Extragalactic Objects, such as the Galaxy M87 (with the bright emission "jet") and the so-called "Colliding" Galaxy (Cygnus A). Radar studies have also been included in astronomy and these now extend to Meteors, the Moon, the Sun, and the planet Venus.

The fundamental radiation processes encountered in radio-astronomy fall mainly into three groups, which may be classified under the following headings:

1) True thermal emission, with a continuous spectrum and approximately "black-body" characteristics, *e.g.*,
   a) solid bodies like the Moon and Planets,
   b) hot gaseous bodies such as the Sun, and
   c) tenuous bright Emission Nebulae, with thermal radiation from free-free collision processes in HII regions.
2) Synchrotron radiation, with a continuous spectrum, which results from the circulation of relativistic electrons in magnetic fields (e.g., the Crab Nebula).
3) Monochromatic line emission and absorption from neutral hydrogen in HI regions, both in our Galaxy and from External Galaxies, *i.e.*, the 1420 Mc emission.

Other radiation processes are also involved, but occur only under very restricted conditions; these are cyclotron radiation [77] (nonrelativistic electrons circulating in magnetic fields), Čerenkov radiation [78] and plasma oscillations.

The Astronomical Requirements

With this very brief survey of radio astronomy, what are the requirements posed by the astronomer to the radio engineer, and to what extent has the maser and the parametric amplifier assisted in increasing the sensitivity? At first sight, the low intrinsic noise of these new devices would appear to herald a major revolution in the whole field of radio astronomy. Only in limited frequency bands, however, does the noise temperature of the radiometer itself set the limit to the over-all system noise temperature.

The effective sky-temperature, obtained with directional receiving equipment pointing up to the night-sky zenith in a dry climate on a cloudless night, is shown in Fig. 1. At the lower frequency end of the spectrum, galactic noise is dominant. At the other end of the spectrum, at wavelengths less than about 2 cm, the sky temperature again rises, due to the presence of atmospheric absorption bands from water vapor and oxygen. The sky-temperature diagram thus reveals that there is a fairly broad minimum centered at approximately 4 kMc, which extends over the region from ~2 cm to ~60 cm wavelength. Subsidiary minima also occur around 8 and 4 mm respectively. It is a most fortunate coincidence that masers are at their best performance, and feasible to build and package, in just the wavelength region at which the sky temperatures are lowest and therefore their demand is greatest. It is an even more fortuitous coincidence that the 21-cm hydrogen line should appear in just this same region. Nature has been kind indeed to have placed the HFS splitting in hydrogen at 1420 Mc (21 cm)! Not only does this emission line appear in a spectral region of low background, but it also arises from the most abundant element in the universe which is at the same time the one of greatest interest to the astrophysicist. Moreover, (this is also a remarkable coincidence) the line occurs at such a wavelength that beamwidths ~1° or less may be obtained with parabolic reflectors of quite reasonable size.

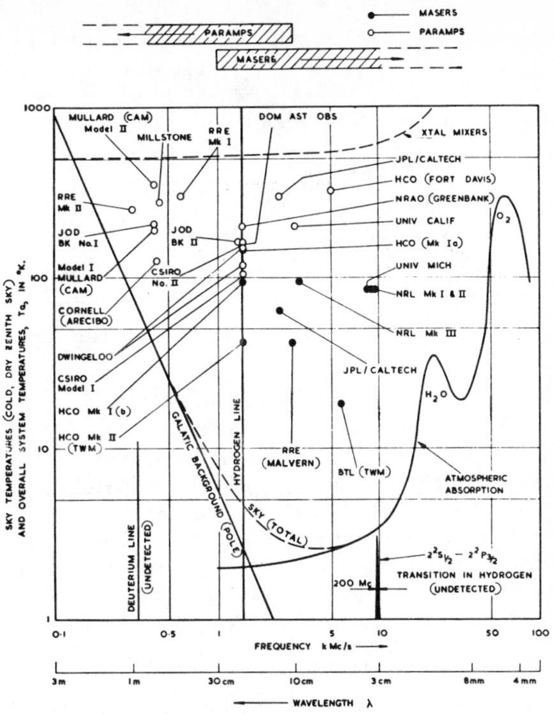

Fig. 1—Sky-temperature as a function of frequency, with plots of the over-all system noise-temperatures (antenna spillover included) of existing and planned low-noise installations.

We see from Fig. 1 that the frequency range which may be covered with masers somewhat overlaps that covered by parametric amplifiers, the overlap region occurring at 20–30 cm wavelength. The relative merits of the two systems will be discussed later.

For the astronomer to gain access to the microwave regions of the spectrum, and he would most certainly like to do this, in order to study individual spectral lines [22] which arise from a variety of molecular transitions in various gases and free radicals which may exist on some of the planets, he must work outside the atmosphere, to eliminate the H_2O and O_2 absorption bands which are shown in Fig. 1. It seems fairly certain then that in due course there will be a demand for tunable tightly packaged masers to operate in sophisticated satellite installations for detailed scrutiny of planetary atmospheres; this work will clearly merge into the infrared fields, where large strides which have been made are increasing the efficiency of detecting equipment [79].

Turning to the lower-frequency regions of Fig. 1, where the galactic background is steeply rising, the situation is not as hopeless as it might at first sight appear. The galactic background, though large, is not in general clumpy, and drift-scans (at a wavelength of, say, 30 cm for which beamwidths ~1° are still attainable) may still reveal the presence of weak "point" sources (*e.g.*, remote galaxies) superimposed on the large background which varies in general relatively slowly. Again, at still lower frequencies, say, 100–300 Mc (λ = 3 m to 1 m), where the single-antenna beamwidths are no longer narrow, the interferometer techniques take over, with multiple antenna systems, such as the Cambridge interferometer [23] and the Mills Cross [24]. Since the switched-lobe interferometer [23] discriminates between "point" and extended sources, the effects of the large galactic background to the left of Fig. 1 can be eliminated, or at least considerably reduced, with this technique; it is thus equally important to develop low-noise equipment in these frequency bands, even though the sky temperatures are high.

Physical, Technical and Operational Limitations

There are a variety of limitations to the applications of masers and parametric amplifiers in radio astronomy, some of these being associated with the instruments themselves, and others with astronomical requirements or operational conditions. Some of these considerations have already been discussed elsewhere [25] and the following is but a brief résumé.

Basic Sensitivity and Bandwidth Limitations

The smallest change in antenna temperature ΔT_a which can be detected at the output of a radiometer, is given by the fluctuation level which is

$$\Delta T_a = T_a/(B\tau)^{1/2} \tag{1}$$

where T_a is the over-all system noise temperature, B the pre-detector bandwidth and τ the post-detector

TABLE I

CONTRIBUTIONS TO T_a FOR THE HARVARD OBSERVATORY MASER

60-ft Dish with Horn Feed (20-db Illumination Taper)

Contributor to Over-all System Temp.	°K	Possible methods to gain improvement	Estimated possible improvement, °K
Spillover (measured)	20	Improved feed; outer antenna screen	14
Switched Circulator (0.35 db)	25	Cool in liquid N_2	5
Maser Circulator (0.35 db)	25	Cool in liquid N_2	5
Cryostat Coax. Cable (0.1 db)	7	Little improvement possible	5
Other Cables Approx.	7	Small gain possible with cooling	5
Spontaneous Emission	2	No improvement possible	2
Second Stage (20-db gain on 900°K)	9	Use of a parametric 2nd Stage	3
Total T_a	95°K		39°K

integration time. It is thus of paramount importance that T_a be reduced to a minimum. For continuum work it is also desirable to have the largest possible value of B. For H-line work, the optimum sensitivity is achieved when B is adjusted to match the line-width of the emission (or absorption). In principle, therefore, for H-line work, a large bandwidth is not required, but in practice, to measure frequency profiles with say a multi-channel system, it is still desirable to have a large value of B available, and to select the channel widths by filters in front of the detector.

τ is usually determined by operational requirements. Often, as for example when taking drift-scans with a pencil-beam receiver, τ is determined by the beam-width of the antenna and the declination of the source, in which case values of τ between 2 sec and 50 sec will be used. In cases where tracking is adopted, much longer values of τ may be accepted, and in extreme cases when looking for threshold signals in crucial experiments (*e.g.*, radar echoes from Venus), τ may be effectively several hours.

In general, regenerative amplifiers with tuned circuit elements, such as cavity masers, have restricted bandwidths. There is thus at the present time great interest in the TWM [15] and distributed-line parametric amplifiers.

Maser Temperature vs System Temperature

In all maser systems constructed so far for astronomical work, the temperature contribution T_0 due to the maser itself (spontaneous emission) is but a small fraction of the total system temperature, T_a in (1), so that in general the full potentialities of the maser cannot as yet be fully exploited. It is partly for this reason that parametric devices, particularly those with cooling, are serious competitors to the maser. To illustrate this point by a specific example Table I shows the breakdown of T_a into its separate components, for the Harvard College Observatory's maser [26], for which the maser proper contributes but 2 per cent to T_a! It is seen how, in this example, it should be possible to affect a substantial improvement in performance, though this would naturally increase costs, complexity and all-up weight.

Stability Limitations

The exceedingly low noise-levels attainable in maser and parametric amplifiers place stringent conditions on the stability requirements for these equipments, conditions far more severe than those demanded in radar and communication installations using these devices. To gain the full advantages of the high sensitivity, the gain fluctuations for the complete receiver have to be reduced to a value equal or lower than ΔT_a in (1). To achieve adequate gain stability has been a major problem in all cases, and in most installations it has been found essential to use either the Dicke comparison system [27], or the variant of this, the "noise-compensated source comparison" system, discussed by a number of authors [28], [29], [25]. An even more refined system in this same general class has recently been investigated [30].

Following the analysis by Drake and Ewen [29], the minimum detectable apparent change in antenna temperature $\Delta T_a'$ for a switched comparison radiometer, in the presence of gain fluctuations of rms value ΔG on a mean gain of G_0, is given by

$$\Delta T_a' = \frac{T_a}{(B\tau)^{1/2}} + \frac{\Delta G}{G_0}\cdot(T_a - T_{ref}) \tag{2}$$

where the first term is the basic fluctuation level given by (1). T_a is the input temperature of the system with the antenna pointing at the source and T_{ref} is the input temperature when the maser is switched to the reference load. From (2) we see that the contribution to $\Delta T_a'$ from gain fluctuations is reduced to a minimum, for a given $(\Delta G/G_0)$, when the noise temperature of the reference source is balanced carefully to that of the antenna temperature.

Since the gain variations $(\Delta G/G_0)$ in general have a random nature, with a distribution which falls steeply with frequency, it follows that the resultant residual gain fluctuations at the output of the synchronous detector decrease with increasing switching frequency. In this connection it is interesting that while, in their first maser, NRL [54] used a switching frequency of 30 cps, and the University of Michigan Observatory [51] one of 90 cps, it was found at Harvard College Observatory [59], that a frequency as low as 3.5 cps was quite adequate in their case.

Antenna Limitations

With the high performance of existing masers, certain limitations are imposed on the design and use of the antenna. The following remarks apply mainly to parabolic "dish" antennas.

Gain and Sensitivity: Since one of the main applications of the maser, at least at the shorter centimeter wavelengths, is in the study of the surface (or cloud) temperatures of the planets, it is important to use a reflector of adequate size so that the beamwidth (λ/a) shall be as small as possible. This is exceedingly important in planetary work, where low physical temperatures ($\sim$100 to 500°K) are combined with small angular size ($\sim$tens of seconds of arc). If T_p is the effective disk temperature of the planet, ω is the solid angle subtended by it at the earth, and Ω is the antenna beamwidth (solid angle), then the effective antenna temperature, in the absence of limb-darkening and other effects, is

$$\Delta T_a \sim T_p \cdot (\omega/\Omega) \tag{3}$$

The short wavelengths and the requirement for narrow beams call for mirrors of good figure in the optical sense, and it is customary to use mesh reflectors for wavelengths $\sim$10 cm upwards, of diameters $\sim$60 feet and higher. There seems little doubt that for wavelengths $\sim$5 cm and below the best performance is obtained with solid-surface antennas, *e.g.*, as at NRL [54]. In practice considerations of windage, engineering problems and costs determine the antenna system.

Spillover and Atmospheric Effects: Insufficient attention seems as yet to have been paid to the problems of antenna spillover. It is clear that sidelobes and direct vision of the ground by the feed-horn contribute a substantial fraction of the total value of T_a. The 20-db illumination taper currently used for the feed-systems appears to be inadequate, and more subtle feeds must be developed; this problem is indeed under study at a number of observatories. The twin-horn-feed comparison system [31] is one method of tackling the problem, while an intrinsically simple and straightforward scheme is to surround the whole antenna with an outer reflector of random figure, so that the spillover collected is but a fraction of the average sky-temperature. This method would lead however to structures of very considerable size, even for a 60-ft telescope.

The atmosphere itself injects detectable radiation into the antenna at 3 cm and shorter wavelengths, from the H_2O absorption bands (Fig. 1), and intermittent clouds are even troublesome at 21 cm. There is no clear-cut solution to this problem and the effects are likely to appear more troublesome when the existing sensitivities are raised still further. The complete solution is to "get into orbit" as soon as possible!

Confusion Limit

Even in the absence of the effects mentioned so far, the useful antenna temperature sensitivity ΔT_a is ultimately limited by "confusion," this limit occurring when the ever-increasing number of weak nonthermal "point" sources (radio "stars") overtakes the more slowly increasing antenna resolution. This, the "confusion limit," has already been discussed in detail [25] and is likely to be approached with some of the more advanced big-dish installations already in existence or about to be commissioned, *e.g.*, the 210-ft instrument at Parkes, New South Wales, Australia [80], and the 300-ft dish at NRAO, Green Bank, West Virginia.

The confusion-limited temperature T_c, following Matthews [25], is given by

$$T_c = KA^{-(2/3)} \cdot \lambda^{[n+(4/3)]} \tag{4}$$

where K is a constant, A the antenna "effective area," and n the index ($\sim$1) in the flux-density spectrum for the point-sources ($S_\lambda \propto \lambda^n$). Inserting known data, calculating K, Matthews obtains the values of T_c shown in Table II.

TABLE II
ANTENNA TEMPERATURE T_c °K AT WHICH CONFUSION BEGINS

	Antenna Diameter in Feet			
λ(cms)	50	90	140	300
30	0.22	0.10	0.055	0.020
10	0.013	0.0060	0.0033	0.0012
3	0.0011	0.00047	0.00026	0.000096

Operational Limitations

The maser, as one of the implements of current astronomy, has a number of limitations which are essentially operational in character, and these may be partly responsible for the rather sparse population of masers at observatories up to the present time. Unlike the parametric amplifier, the maser embraces a number of techniques besides microwave radio, *e.g.*, low-temperature and solid-state, and for observatories at remote sites and with limited resources in funds and adequate staff, a maser installation is undoubtedly more complicated than a parametric system. There is also the question of the availability, storage, transport and handling of liquid helium and, in many countries still, the necessity to recover the helium. Well engineered packaging and the possible development of totally enclosed helium re-cycling systems will considerably ease this problem.

The Maser vs the Parametric Amplifier

Since the parametric amplifier, in a variety of its available forms, has become a serious competitor to the maser, and has indeed already been installed and used with satisfaction at a number of radio observatories, a few general remarks are included for fair assessment of the relative merits of the two types of device. There is no doubt that at all frequences the *intrinsic* sensitivity of a maser is higher than that of any form of parametric amplifier known at the present time. When however the over-all performance of a *system* is considered, the parametric amplifier can become a justifiable competitor. Still however, at the shortest wavelengths, it appears that the maser wins, if we can temporarily disregard what is called above the "operational limitations" of the maser. In the decimeter region, and at higher wavelengths, the parametrics are on the ascendancy. The overlap region, where there is still considerable controversy, lies approximately in the wavelength region $\lambda = 10$ to 30 cm, and this embraces the all important 21-cm band.

The main technological problem with the parametric amplifier is the question of stability, and judging from a variety of reports at the present time, about half the interested groups are still very sceptical of the stability of parametrics for low-level sources at the operationally required integration times, while the other half have been encouraged by the results achieved with practical systems already installed and tested.

Superficially the maser has greater stability than a parametric device, for it is insensitive to pump power under the normal conditions of saturation, and its vital circuitry (the cavity and crystal) are automatically temperature stabilized, being in a bath of very definite temperature (liquid helium at 4.2°K, unless pumped). The other essential parameters of a maser are the magnetic field H and the crystal orientation θ. It is easy however to stabilize H, either by use of a permanent magnet or superconducting solenoid, and θ can be fixed by careful and rigid construction.

The stability problems in a parametric amplifier are predominantly electronic problems, and with sufficient care and sophistication the pump frequency and power level can be adequately stabilized, and the temperature stabilization of the device as a whole is not too difficult, since the dimensions of the unit are fairly small.

In practice, in the overlap region and at the longer wavelengths, the factors which weigh in favor of the parametric amplifier may be listed as follows:

1) No liquid helium required.
2) A parametric installation is considerably lighter than a maser, in consequence of not requiring heavy magnets or exceptionally rigid structures (see Fig. 2).
3) A parametric head amplifier package is smaller than a maser, owing to the absence of a cryostat.
4) As a consequence of 1), less activity is required at the focus of the dish, with consequent saving of useful observing time.
5) The installation of a parametric amplifier is simpler and less expensive than that for a maser.

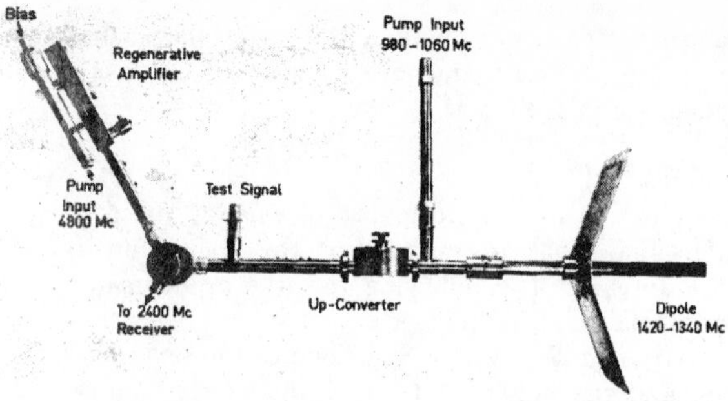

Fig. 2—The two-stage parametric amplifier under development for 1420-Mc work at the Observatory of Leiden. (*Courtesy of the Observatory, Leiden, Holland.*)

The following examples illustrate the importance of these factors. 1) has been a consideration with the CSIRO 210-ft dish at Parkes, NSW, Australia, where the availability of liquid helium is limited, and 2) a factor in the case of the reflector at the Dwingeloo station, Holland. 4) is of considerable importance with large reflectors unless there are special arrangements for working on a platform for extended periods while helium transfers are carried out; a case in point is the 300-ft transit telescope at the NRAO station, Green Bank, West Virginia [71].

Summing up, it would appear that while steady improvements in parametric amplifiers are taking place, including cooling of various components in liquid N_2, the maser is likewise undergoing further development. When TWM's are constructed, with superconducting magnets and compact helium re-cycling systems, it is probable that the maser will succeed at the shorter wavelengths, to provide the ultimate in attainable sensitivity.

The above is a very brief résumé of but a few of the features of the parametric amplifier, and no attempt is made to discuss the relative merits of the different types or to consider such important characteristics as bandwidth, gain, frequency stability and so on.

The general properties of parametric amplifiers may be found in [81]–[85], while some remarks on the application of parametric amplifiers to radar astronomy are presented in [86] and [87].

The performance of several parametric systems is most easily judged from Table IV and Figs. 1 and 10. We see that the parametric systems have a performance very similar to that of masers and in some cases the overlap has occurred, as for example in the case of one of the systems in use at CSIRO, Sydney, Australia

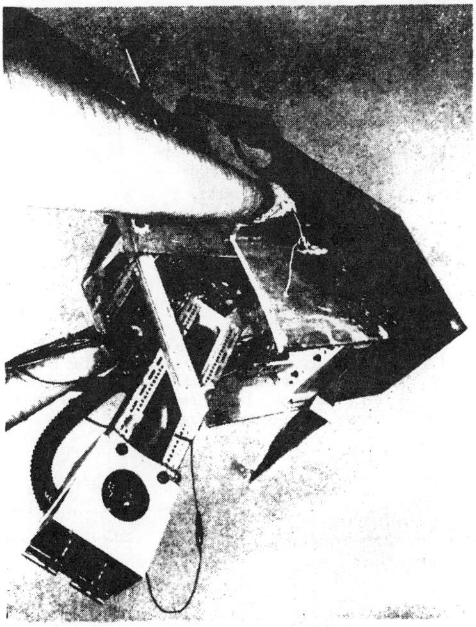

Fig. 3—The original Columbia University/U. S. Naval Research Laboratory X-band maser head at the focus of the NRL 50-ft reflector (1958). The dewar and maser unit were precooled in the laboratory prior to observations. (*Official United States Navy Photograph.*)

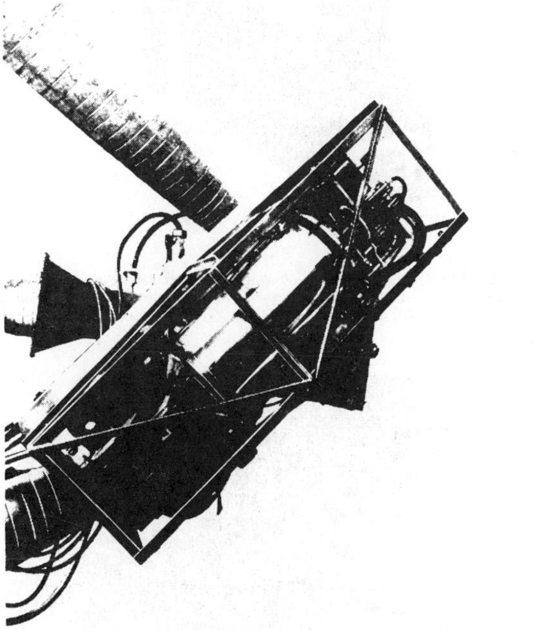

Fig. 4—Harvard College Observatory's 1420-Mc maser package at the focus of the 60-ft reflector at the Agassiz Station at Harvard, Mass., showing the dewar, magnet and other components. (*Courtesy of the Microwave J.*)

Existing Maser and Parametric Installations

The original and main objective of this paper was to present to the reader an up-to-date review of the present status of these devices in their application to astronomy. The number of installations, particularly these using parametric amplifiers, has already become so large that details of individual systems cannot be discussed. Instead it was decided to present the information in graphical and tabular form.

The information contained herein has been gathered from papers and reports, and also from replies to a questionnaire circulated to observatories by the author.

Let us prelude the survey with a few notes on the first installations. The first maser amplifier to be constructed specifically for radio astronomy, and which was mounted at the focus of a large telescope, was the X-band instrument [54] built in the Physics Department at Columbia University and operated as a joint project with the Naval Research Laboratory, Washington (Fig. 3). This enterprise, which was undertaken in 1958, immediately led to a vigorous field of research in weak-source studies in the 3-cm band, with new and fruitful measurements of planetary radiation [18], [37], [88].

This encouraging start, under the leadership of Townes of Columbia and Mayer of NRL, was soon followed up at Harvard where the first operational 21-cm maser was built. This project, also a joint effort, was

Fig. 5—The 60-ft radio telescope at Harvard College Observatory's Agassiz Station, showing the maser unit on its subsidiary declination axis, alongside a smaller unit containing the mixer and IF preamplifier. (*Harvard University Photograph.*)

Fig. 6—The University of Michigan's X-band radiometer package, showing X-band RF circuitry in the near section, and K-band pump circuitry below the dewar (1960). (*University of Michigan Photograph.*)

Fig. 8—The new Columbia University/Naval Research Laboratory packaged S-band twin-cavity maser, at the focus of the 84-ft reflector at the NRL station at Maryland Point. Clearly seen is the feed-horn and also a reference horn pointing direct to the sky (1962). (*Official United States Navy Photograph*).

Fig. 7—The 85-ft radio telescope at the University of Michigan, with maser mounted on the lower leg of the support system. (*University of Michigan Photograph.*)

Fig. 9—A general view of the maser installation of Fig. 7 on the NRL 84-ft radio telescope at Maryland Point (1962). (*Official United States Navy Photograph.*)

initiated by Gold, then of Harvard College Observatory, while the preliminary work was carried out in Bloembergen's group at the Gordon McKay Laboratory at Harvard. This maser, when complete, was installed in October, 1959, at the focus of the 60-ft telescope at the Agassiz station at Harvard, and began to be used for observations in the spring of 1960 (Figs. 4 and 5). This instrument has proved to be a very dependable operational device, and has been used now on a daily routine basis for over two years. Its main contributions have been to continuum and to 21-cm studies of extra-galactic nebulae.

About the same time, the University of Michigan [51] was developing its X-band maser which was later installed at the focus of the Observatory's 85-ft reflector at Dexter, Michigan (Figs. 6 and 7). Beyond this, overlap begins to occur in tracing the history further, but mention should be made of the 2388 Mc maser project by Jet Propulsion Laboratory and Caltech at Goldstone, which played such a decisive role in their CW radar work on the planet Venus [63]. The latest edition to the maser family is the novel twin cavity S-band instrument recently installed on the 84-ft NRL dish at Maryland Point Observatory (See Figs. 8 and 9). This, though a cavity device, has a copious bandwidth and promises to be an effective tool in a frequency band not covered by other installations.

The writer finds it difficult to trace the parallel history of the parametric amplifier in radio astronomy, for the experiments with these devices appear to have been more numerous; it would seem probable that Jodrell Bank (University of Manchester) were at least among the first to use a parametric amplifier in astronomy, in their pulse-radar work on Venus in 1960 [70].

The collected data on existing and planned maser and parametric amplifier installations is presented in Tables III and IV, pp. 38–41, respectively. The numbers in parenthesis correspond to references in the

TABLE III
Maser Installations

Name of Observatory	Naval Research Laboratory			Harvard College Observatory		
Location	Washington, D. C.		Maryland Point	Agassiz Station, Harvard (Mass.)		
References in bibliography	(54) (76) (88)			(58) (59) (26) (62)		
General						
Type of antenna	Solid dish			Kennedy parabolic dish		
Diameter, feet	50		84	60		
Collecting area, m²						
Effective area, m²			150			
Type of feed	Horn		Horn	Horn		
Beamwidth, minutes of arc	Calc. ~8		17	52		
Mounting, altazimuth A, equatorial E	A		E	E		
Frequency bands	X		S	L		
Switching frequency, c.p.s.	30			300	3.5	
Type of radiometer	Comparison horn+switched Dicke system			Cold load+AGS	Cold load+balance	
Maser Installation	Mk. I	Mk. II	Mk. III	Mk. I(a)	Mk. I(b)	Mk. II
Status	O	O (1962)	O	O (1959)	O (1960-)	I
Mounted at focus (F), observatory (O)	F	F	F	F	F	F
Type of maser	Cavity	Cavity	Twin cav.	Cavity	Cavity	TWM
% Cr^{+++} in Ruby	0.05	0.05	1.0	0.05	Same	
Crystal orientation Θ, in degrees	59	55	90	90	"	
Magnetic field, H, Oersteds	3360	3740	2850	2000	"	
Signal frequency, Mc/s	9000	9500	3200	1420	"	~1420
Tuning range, Mc/s	8700 to	10,100	±8	±25	"	
Bandwidth, maser alone, Mc/s	5.5	5.5	16	2.0	"	
Pump frequency, kMc/s	21	23.5	14.26	11.27	"	
Pump power, mW	30	30	~30	Unknown		
Pump frequency stabilization	yes	yes		none	"	
Cavity modes:						
signal	TE (102)	TE (101)	TE (011)	(λ/4) strip resonator	"	
pump	not identified		High mode	TE (012)	"	
Energy levels:						
signal	3→2	3→2	4→3	2→1	"	
pump	1→3	1→3	2→4	1→3	"	
Magnetic Q (negative)	1800	380	~100/cav.	140	"	
Bath temperature, °K	1.4	1.4	1.8	4.2	"	
Is liquid He recovered?	No	No	No	No	No	
Max. angle Dewar tilt	45°	45°		50°		
All-up weight, lbs.			625	200	~250	~500(?)
Gain stabilization	None	None	None	AGS on pump	None	None
Coolants:						
N_2, liters/hours			15/>24	6.2/30		
He, liters/hours	3/(12-15)	3/(12-15)	16/6.5	3.3/16		
Type of input switch	3-port ferrite			None	Y-circulator	Cooled circulator
Type of magnet Perm (P), Boost coils (B), Superconducting (S) Trim (T)	P+B	P+B	P(+T)?	P+T	P+T	P+magnetic shunt tuning
Magnetic tuning, Oersteds				±100	±100	
Special features	First astronomical maser installation. Maser pre-cooled on the ground, He pumped		Twin cavity	First operational hydrogen-line maser installation		Two 9 db TWM sections. Improved horn. Paramp 2nd stage
Performance						
Over-all system noise temp. prior to maser, °K	2190	2190	600	900	900	
Over-all system noise temp. with maser, T_a, °K	85	85	95	148	95	42?
Gain-bandwidth product, Mc/s	10	~50	200	20	20	
Normal gain used, db	20	20	22	20	20	18?
Bandwidth of maser material, Mc/s	200	200		25?	25?	25
Bandwidth of maser unit alone, Mc/s				2.5	2.5	25
Selected pre-detector bandwidth B, Mc/s		5.5	16	1, 0.150, 0.080	1, 0.150, 0.080	25?
Selected normal integration time τ, sec.		5	7	50	50	50
Effective output fluctuation level $\Delta T_a \pm$ °K		0.04	0.013	0.05	0.014	0.0012
Breakdown of T_a				(at B=200 kc)	(at B=1 Mc/s)	(at B=25 Mc)
Antenna spillover (cold zenith sky), °K		20	20	20	20	14?
Circulator+other circuit losses, °K		~21	53	53	39	20
Maser spontaneous emission (calc.), °K		~2	2	2	~2	5
Second-stage noise, °K		~20	20	10	9	3
Other noise sources, °K		22		63	25	
(Origin of this contribution)	ferrite	switch		AGS	(2nd circulator)	
Stability (without switching)	<0.01 db/min.		~5%/hr.	stability	±0.1 db/30 min.	
Stability (with switching)	~ΔT_a for input mis-balance of 0.3°K		~0.03°K per hour	variable	<ΔT_a for ±0.2 db gain change	

Radio Astronomy Observatory Univ. Michigan (Mk. I)	Radio Astronomy Observatory Univ. Michigan (Mk. II)	Goldstone Observatory JPL/Caltech	National Radio Astron. Obs.	Bell Telephone Laboratory	Caltech Radio Obs.	Royal Radar Estab.
Dexter, (Michigan) (31) (50) (51) (32)		Goldstone (Calif.) (63)	Greenbank (W. Va.)	Murry Hill (N. J.) (89) (15)	Owens Valley (Calif.)	Malvern (England)
Parabolic Reflector 85 527 260 Pyramidal horn		Dish 85 527 Shaped beam (Cir. Pol. feed)	Dish 85 527 300	Horn ? Direct to horn	2 Dishes ea. 90 ea. 600 Cyl. horn	2 Dishes ea. 82 490 250 Horns
6 E X 90 Dicke, with twin horn		~3 E S None Total power	~10 (calc.) E C	? Zenith C None Total power	36 E L Interferometer	16 A S Interferometer
Mk. I O F Silvered cav. 0.1 54.7 3850	Mk. II P F Same " " 3950	O F Cavity 0.05 90 2500	P F TWM	E O TWM 0.05 90 ~4000	P TWM 0.03 1993	P F (Cassegrain) TWM 0.05 90 2880
8720 Single frequency 20	9000	2388 ±1 2.5	4995 Fixed	5815 350 25	1300–1440	~3000 290
22.45 70 None	22.80 ?	12.85 30–40 None		18.9–19.5 10 None	11.3	26.4 30
TE (111) Unknown	? ?	TEM TE (11)?		TW ?		
3→2 1→3, 2→4	Same "	2→1 1→3		4→3 2→4		2→1 1→4
200 4.2 No 67° 250 None	? 4.2 No 75? None	~200 4.2 No 250 None		~170? 1.8 No None	2.0 ~300	1.6 Yes None
8.1/17 3.4/17 4-port circ. P+T ±150	P+T ?	7/30 3/30 None P+T	6/24	None E.M.	14.5/? 7.5/?	17/72 S or P
(1) Silvered ruby cavity, (2) Paramp second stage, (3) Twin-horn comparison system at focus, (4) Push-pull pumping (5) Gain controlled by pump power				Lowest over-all sky+system noise temp. observed		
4000 85 220 ~20		64±4 25 20		18.5±0.8		43? 20 or 30
22 8 (I.F. limited) 42(12) 0.0073		2.5 4 ~0.1		60 20 20	20	20–50 50 or 23 1–10
(at B=8 Mc) 30 ~30 4 21 2% (<30 minutes)		(B=2.5, τ=4) 15±4 25±5 4±1 14±3 (Misc. losses)		2±1 (lobes) 3.5±0.2 10.5±2 (maser) Negligible 2.5±0.7 (sky)		30? 9 1 2.5 —
0.0004° for <0.02°K input balance						

TABLE IV

PARAMETRIC AMPLIFIER INSTALLATIONS

Name of Observatory	Mullard Radio Astron. Observatory		Royal Radar Establishment		Radio Observatory Dwingeloo Netherlands			Australian National Radio Astronomy Observatory		
Location	University of Cambridge (England)		Malvern and Defford. (Worcs., England)		Dwingeloo (Netherlands)			Parkes, (NSW), (Australia)		
References to equipment			(96)		(87)			(80) (85) (87) (99)		
General										
Type of antenna	Dish	Cyl. parabolae	2 dishes		Parabolic Reflector			Parabolic Reflector		
Diameter, feet			each 82		82			210		
Collecting area (physical), m^2	42	5500	" 490		500			3200		
Effective area, m^2			" 250							
Type of feed	Dipole	Dipoles+ screen	Horns or Dipoles		Horn			Horn or Dipole		
Beamwidth, minutes of arc.	450	24×216	16		34			13.5 (at 1410 Mc/s)		
Type of mounting, altazimuth (A) equatorial (E)	A	Transit	A		A			A		
Frequency bands, Mc/s	408	408	610	300	L			1410–1420, 3000		
Switching frequency, cps.										
Type of radiometer	Switched receiver	Phase-switch interferometer	Swept-lobe interferometer	Conventional superhet	Model I Straight continuum receiver	Model II Multi-channel hydrogen-line receiver		Model I Continuum receivers	Model II Switched frequency H-line receiver	
Parametric Installation			(Passive Astron)	(Radar)		*Two-Stage Paramp* Stage 1	Stage 2		*Two-Stage Paramp* Stage 1	Stage 2
Status	O	O	O	O	I	P		O	O	
Mounted at focus (F) or observatory (O)	O	O	F	F	F	F		F	F	
All-up weight, if at focus, lbs.			23	23	?			50	34	
Type of amplifier	Electron beam, degenerate	Electron beam, degenerate	Adler tube degenerate	Adler tube degenerate	Quasi-degenerate wide-band	Up-converter	Regenerate amplifier degenerate)	Cavity, degenerate	Cavity up-converter plus	Degenerate amplifier
Parametric element			Electron beam	Electron beam	GaAs diode			Semiconductor diode	Semiconductor diodes	
Manufacturer of parametric element	Zenith	Zenith	English Electric	English Electric	Texas Instr.	Texas Instruments		Hughes	Microwave Associates	Texas Instruments
Pump power stabilization system?	None	None	None	None	Special AGS		Varactor current stabilization		See ref. [100]	
Pump frequency stabilization?	None	None	None	None	Varactor current stabilization				xtal controlled	
Cooling of parametric or other circuit elements	None	None	None	None	None					
Signal frequency, Mc/s	408(404)	408	610	300	1420	1420	2400	1410	1420–1320	2400
Pump frequency, Mc/s	816	816	1220	600	2846	~1000		2820	980–1080	4800
Idler frequency, Mc/s	408	408	610	300	1426			1410		
Output frequency (if different from f_{sig}), Mc/s	—	—	—	—		2400			2400	
Performance										
Over-all system noise temp. prior to installation, °K	1500	2200	--	1500	700			500	800 (single channel)	
Over-all system noise temp. of installation, T_a, °K	190	350	300	250	120			105		160 (over all)
Gain, or conversion gain, db	23	29	20	20	17	1	20	20	1.5	20
Bandwidth of amp. alone, Mc/s	~20	20	20	10	50	150	~5	~25	>300	6
Noise figure of amp. alone, db	≤1.6		≤2.3	1.7	?					
Noise temp. of amp. alone, °K	≤130	~150	200	140	<25	80	41 (150° over all)	25	70	40
System noise temp. on cold load, °K	154	?								
Normal integration time-constant used, τ, sec.	4	2	10	Radar	6			1, 2, 5		20
Effective pre-detector bandwidth used, B, Mc.	2	4	10	10 kc/s	10			10		140 kc/s
Fluctuation level, with above B & τ, ΔT_a, °K	0.07	0.13	0.06					0.015		0.1
Breakdown of system noise temp. T_a:										
(a) Antenna spillover (cold zenith sky) °K	≤2	~60	50?	90	2×20			30		≤30
(b) Circulator+other passive element losses, °K	36 (cables)	110 (feeders)	—	—	2×15			40		20
(c) Parametric amplifier noise temp., °K	130	150	200	130	2×20			25	70	
(d) Second-stage noise, °K	10	13	50	10	10			10		40
(e) Other noise contributions, °K	~15	~15	—	20				—		8
Origin of contribution (e)	(min, sky)	(min, sky)		(feed cable)					Third stage (mixer) noise	
Stability performance without switching	<0.1° in several hours	<10% per day	Not applicable to interferometer	Not applicable to radar			~1:10^3	1°/6 hours	0°.25/1 hour	
Stability performance with switching										
Special features	Power diff. balance adjusted during observations	Two paramps with incoherent pumps				Two-stage amplifier		Stabilized on the reference component of second detector	Pump freq. of up-converter switched for H-work, and tuned for red-shifts	

National Radio Astronomy Observatory		Millstone Radar Obs.	Harvard Radio Astron. Station	Univ. of California	University of Manchester		Dominion Radio Astrophysical Observatory		JPL/Caltech Goldstone Obs.
Green Bank (W. Va.)		Westford (Mass.)	Fort Davis (Texas)	Hat Creek (Calif.)	Jodrell Bank (Cheshire, England)		Penticton (B. C., Canada)		Mojave Desert (Calif.) (63)
Parabolic Reflectors 85 300 Horn	300 3500 ?	Dish 84 500 Horn	Dish 85 530 Horn	Dish 85 526 Horns	Dish 250 ?		Parabolic Reflector 84 515 Horn		Dish 85
38(1420) E Several frequencies Various types	≈10(1420) Transit	125 A 440	~10 E C Total power, switch between antenna and ref. horn	7.0 E S(X, L) (1) Dicke (2) Asym. switch (3) H-line scanning receiver	~35(408) A 408 Radar	Passive astronomy	36 E L H-line scanning receiver (Ewen-Knight)	L	20(2400) E S Lunar Radar
Model I E F	*Model II* E F Electron beam, Adler tube	O On Azimuth deck Up-converter	P F Degenerate	P F 80 Idle band-pass filter	O O Adler tube	30 Regenerative amplifier	*Model I* O F ≈20 Degenerate; Adler tube	*Model II* P F Lower side-band up-converter	O (past) F Non-degenerative
Varactor diode None		Semiconductor diode Microwave Associates None None required None	Semiconductor diode Microwave Associates — — None	Semiconductor diode Microwave Associates 0.1°F temp-stabilization Later development	Electron beam Zenith Corp. Pump level servo-stabilized None None	Varactor diode Pump power supply stabilized None	Electron beam Zenith Corp. Switched AGC Derived from L.O.	Semiconductor diode Sylvania AGS on pump Pound AFC circuit None	Varactor diode Type MA 450
1420 X-band	1420	440 5680 6120 30	5000 10,000	3000 11,000 8000	408 820 412	1389-1420 X-band X-1400	1420±3 2840±6 1420±3	1420 11,000 9580 30	2388 9600 7212
~200	~200	~1000 275±25 ~10 2	~320(?) 200	500 200? 17 80	~200 18 30	800-1200 160 18 10	~1250 155 23 80	? 20-23 >5	1500 300 16 5
		~2 ~200 Unknown Radar	1.5-2.0 10 100 (one sideband) 0.01	~1 up to 20 ?		10	1.0 88 130 30 10 kc or 6 Mc	<2 <200	3.25
						20 100	25 35 88 7	~20	<0.5 db
						±1°K/30 min <±0.2°K/30 min	0.5°K/hour AGC operates on comparison load switch. Stability limited by variations in antenna spillover		over 45 min This amp used as main front end in Lunar Radar

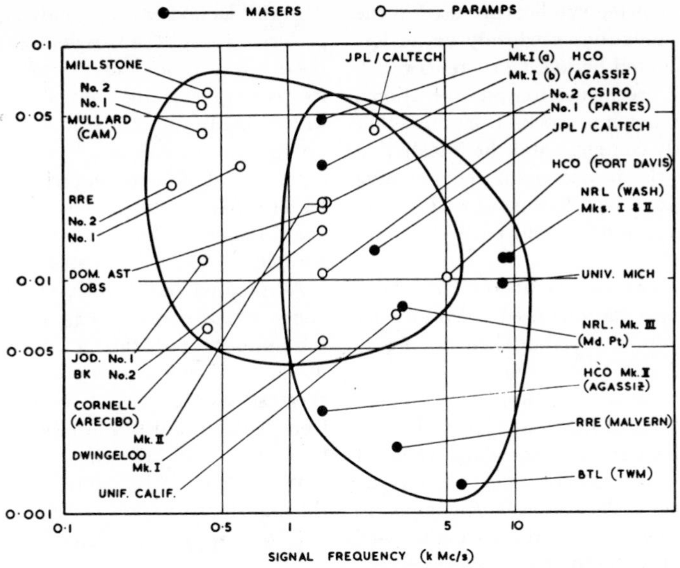

Fig. 10—The "figures of merit" of some existing low-noise radio astronomy installations; Plots of ΔT_a vs f_{sig}. The values of ΔT_a have been calculated from $\Delta T_a = T_a/\sqrt{B\tau}$ and normalized to $\tau = 10$ sec. The values of B are either 1) the operational pre-detector bandwidths (in the case of continuum receivers), or 2) the *available* pre-detector bandwidths (in the case of narrow-band or multichannel H-line receivers.)

TABLE V

SUMMARY OF ASTRONOMICAL WORK

	Observatory / Research Fields	Moon	Planets	Galactic Emission Nebulae	Galactic Continuum	Galactic Hydrogen	Extra-Galactic Continuum	Extra-Galactic Hydrogen	Discrete Sources	Planetary Nebulae	Miscellaneous
1	NRL (Washington and Maryland Point)	86 (Radar)	18, 37, 38 39, 56, 88						88	88	88. Search for 9847 Mc/s line from hydrogen
2	HCO (Agassiz station, Harvard)		40, 46, 47 48, 95				42, 43	44, 45, 41, 94, 91, 92			93. A test of the red-shift relation at 21 cm also Zeeman?
3	Univ. of Michigan (Dexter, Mich.)		49, 53, 52, 103		*		*		*	55	
4	JPL/CALTECH (Goldstone)	* (Radar)	(Radar) 63, 64, 65, 66, 104								
5	Lincoln Lab. MIT (Millstone Radar)	* (Radar)	(Radar) 67, 68, 69								
6	R.R.E. (Malvern, England)	* (Radar)	*, 109		*		*		*		97, 98. Ionosphere research (Radar) -meteors, aurorae, ionosphere incoherent scatter
7	CSIRO (Parkes, NSW, Australia)		*	*	*	*	112, 113	*	107, *		Polarization work, see also [111]
8	Mullard R.A.O. (Cambridge, England)				72, 73		*		74, *		108. Polarization work on galactic background
9	Jodrell Bank (Univ. Manchester, U. K.)	* (Radar)	70								
10	Dom. Ast. Observatory (Penticton. B. C., Canada)				*	*					Zeeman
11	NRAO. Green Bank (W. Va.)		*		*		*	*	*		71, Zeeman
12	Univ. California (Berkeley, Calif.)				*	*	*	*	*		
13	Dwingeloo (Netherlands)					*					
14	CALTECH (Owens Valley, Calif.)		105, 106	*	*	*	*	*	*	*	
15	HCO (Fort Davis, Texas)				*		*		*		
16	Cornell Univ. (Arecibo, Puerto Rico)	* (Radar)	* (Radar + Passive)			*	*	*	*		Solar radar, polarization studies of several types, search for radio emission from near stars, ionospheric radar

bibliography, and the following symbols are used in the "status" column: E, installations used only on an Experimental basis for a limited period. O, systems which have been used, or still are in use, on an Operational basis for extended astronomical work. I signifies that the construction is nearly complete and the installation Imminent, and P that the project is in the Planning stage. References to radar installations are included, though details of the transmitters and pulse-code systems have been excluded.

The over-all system noise temperatures have been plotted on Fig. 1. For installations used in continuum work, the quantity $T_a/(B\tau)^{1/2}$ may be taken as a figure of merit providing the gain fluctuation noise is still smaller. The performances of the various systems on this basis are plotted in Fig. 10 (page 42) in which the figures have been normalized to a standard value of $\tau = 10$ sec. In this plot, for receivers deliberately designed for continuum work, the values of B chosen are those for the pre-detector bandwidths normally used (in general IF limited). For the hydrogen-line receivers, values of B are chosen to correspond to the *available* pre-detector bandwidth (again in general IF limited) even though operationally narrow-pass filters are used in the observations (frequency profile work, etc.).

Achievements to Date

A complete compilation of astronomical work which has been carried out with the new low-noise installations is not the purpose of this paper, and would be too extensive to consider. Instead, a limited number of references have been selected to indicate the diversity of the applications of these devices in radio astronomy. These results, which are presented in Table V (page 42) as references to be found in the bibliography, are all cases in which a maser or parametric amplifier was either essential to the detection or measurement referred to, or at least are cases in which the integration times would have been prohibitive with conventional radiometers. For those cases where specific references are not quoted in Table V, an asterisk indicates the *general* fields of research undertaken.

It is hoped that there are no major omissions in this survey of astronomical work achieved with low-noise amplifiers.

Future Trends

At the present time it would appear that the maser and the paramp will both develop together, with steady improvements in the sensitivities and the bandwidths of both. For meter-wavelength installations, where long-feeder losses and galactic background dominate, it is clear that the parametric amplifier will win. This will even be the case with phase-switched interferometers for which the galactic background is largely eliminated.

In the decimeter range, judging by Fig. 10, the over-all performances of the two devices are comparable, and at the present time (July, 1962), CSIRO is ahead with its paramp systems, at 1420 Mc. The HCO TWM will probably take the lead again, if performance comes up to expectation. At 10-cm wavelength and below, especially at X-band and in the millimeter regions, the maser is likely to remain well ahead in performance, unless fundamentally new developments occur in the parametric field.

As pointed out earlier, the ultimate in sensitivity, above which nothing is gained, is reached by the confusion-limit, and this is already approached in the decimeter bands with the largest reflectors. At the very shortest wavelengths, if we anticipate millimeter work from balloon and satellite-born equipments, the maser has a clear field before it.

What then will be the trends in maser development in the immediate future?

1) The TWM is imminent, and indeed desperately required, for continuum work.
2) Light-weight totally enclosed helium-recycling systems are being developed, this step considerably easing operational problems.
3) For countries with limited helium supplies, it is conceivable that the development of nitrogen-cooled masers is worth while, even though aesthetically this is a retrograde step!
4) The superconducting magnet [57] is also imminent, with its light weight and high field stability. This development will also be significant when packaged millimeter-wave masers evolve, for which high values of magnetic field will be required.
5) The optical pumping [35], [36] of masers is another consideration, one which might lead to simplification, especially if incoherent light sources can be used.
6) Beam-type masers may develop [34], as narrow-band amplifiers, for special studies in the millimeter and sub-millimeter wavelength regions.

Acknowledgment

The author would like to thank all those who assisted him in the preparation of this review, by their generous supply of detailed information through which alone the work was possible.

References

[1] A. Einstein, *Phys. Z.* vol. 18, p. 121; 1917.
[2] W. Heitler, "The Quantum Theory of Radiation," Oxford University Press, New York, N. Y., 3rd ed., pp. 37, 178; 1954.
[3] N. G. Basov and A. M. Prokhorov, *J. Exp. Theoret. Phys.*, vol. 27, p. 431; 1954.
[4] J. P. Gordon, H. J. Zeiger, and C. H. Townes, *Phys. Rev.*, vol. 99, p. 1264; 1955.

[5] N. Bloembergen, *Phys. Rev.*, vol. 104, p. 323; 1956.
[6] H. E. D. Scovil, G. Feher, and H. Seidel, *Phys. Rev.*, vol. 105, p. 762; 1957.
[7] A. L. McWhorter and J. W. Meyer, *Phys. Rev.*, vol. 109, p. 312; 1958.
[8] A. L. McWhorter, J. W. Meyer, and P. D. Strum, *Phys. Rev.*, vol. 108, p. 1642; 1957.
[9] J. O. Artman, N. Bloembergen, and S. Shapiro, *Phys. Rev.*, vol. 109, p. 1392; 1958.
[10] J. R. Singer, "Masers," John Wiley and Sons, Inc., New York, N. Y.; 1959.
[11] G. Troup, "Masers," Methuen and Co., Ltd.; London, England; 1959.
[12] A. A. Vuylsteke, "Elements of Maser Theory," D. Van Nostrand Co., Inc., Princeton, N. J.; 1960.
[13] N. Bloembergen, "Progress in Low Temperature Physics," C. J. Gorter, Ed., North-Holland Publishing Co., Amsterdam, Holland, vol. III, p. 396; 1961.
[14] J. R. Singer, "Advances in electrons and electron physics," 1961.
[15] R. W. de Grass, E. O. Schulz-du Bois, and H. E. D. Scovil, *Bell. Sys. Tech. J.*, vol. 38, p. 305; 1959.
[16] J. L. Pawsey and R. N. Bracewell, "Radio Astronomy," Oxford University Press, New York, N. Y.; 1955.
[17] R. N. Bracewell, "Paris Symposium on Radio Astronomy," Stanford University Press, Calif.; 1959.
[18] J. A. Giordmaine, "Symposium on Radio Astromomy," Indiana Univ., Bloomington, Ind., p. 29; November, 1959.
[19] I. S. Shklovsky, "Cosmic Radio Waves," Harvard University Press, Cambridge, Mass.; 1960.
[20] R. N. Bracewell, "Handbuch der Physik," vol. 54; 1962.
[21] J. L. Pawsey and E. R. Hill, "Cosmic radio waves and their interpretation," *Rept. Prog. Phys.*, vol. 24, p. 69; 1961.
[22] A. H. Barrett, 11th Internatl. Astrophys. Colloquium, Liège, Belgium, paper 16 (proceedings to be published); July, 1962.
[23] J. H. Blythe, *Month. Not. Roy. Astron. Soc.*, vol. 117, p. 652; 1957.
[24] B. Y. Mills and A. G. Little, *Aust. J. Phys.*, vol. 6, p. 272; 1953.
[25] T. A. Matthews, "Quantum Electronics," C. H. Townes, Ed., Columbia University Press, New York, N. Y., p. 256; 1960.
[26] J. V. Jelley and B. F. C. Cooper, "Advances in Quantum Electronics," J. R. Singer, Ed., Columbia University Press, New York, N. Y., p. 619; 1961.
[27] R. H. Dicke, *Rev. Sci. Instr.*, vol. 17, p. 268; 1946.
[28] P. D. Strum, "Considerations in high sensitivity microwave radiometry," Proc. IRE, vol. 46, pp. 43–53; January, 1958.
[29] F. D. Drake and H. I. Ewen, "A broad-band microwave source comparison radiometer for advanced research in radio astronomy," Proc. IRE, vol. 46, pp. 53–61; January, 1958.
[30] T. Orhaug and W. Waltman, *Publs. Natl. Radio Astronomy Observatory*, Green Bank, W. Va., vol. 1, no. 12, p. 179; 1962.
[31] M. E. Bair, J. J. Cook, L. G. Cross, and C. B. Arnold, "Recent developments and observations with a ruby maser radiometer," IRE Trans. on Antennas and Propagation, vol. AP-9, pp. 43–49; January, 1961.
[32] L. G. Cross, *J. Appl. Phys.*, vol. 30, p. 1459; 1959.
[33] "The National Radio Astronomy Observatory," booklet available from NRAO, Green Bank. W. Va; 1962.
[34] F. S. Barnes, "Quantum Electronics," C. H. Townes, Ed., Columbia University Press, New York, N. Y., p. 57; 1960.
[35] J. Brossel, *ibid.*, p. 81.
[36] D. P. Devor, I. J. D'Haenens, and C. K. Asawa, *Phys. Rev. Lett.*, vol. 8, p. 432; 1962.
[37] C. H. Mayer, *Proc. Symp. Physics of the Planets*, 11th Internatl. Colloquium of Inst. Astrophys., Liège, Belgium, survey paper; July, 1962.
[38] L. E. Alsop, J. A. Giordmaine, C. H. Mayer, and C. H. Townes, *Astron. J.*, vol. 63, p. 301; September, 1958.
[39] L. E. Alsop, J. A. Giordmaine, C. H. Mayer, and C. H. Townes, "Paris Symposium on Radio Astronomy," Stanford University Press, Stanford, Calif., p. 69; 1959.
[40] A. E. Lilley, *Astron. J.* vol. 66, p. 290; September, 1961.
[41] M. S. Roberts, *ibid.*, p. 294.
[42] S. J. Goldstein, Jr., *ibid.*, p. 285.
[43] S. J. Goldstein, Jr., *Astron. J.*, vol. 67, p. 171; April, 1962.
[44] N. H. Dieter, *Astron. J.*, vol. 67, p. 217; May, 1962.
[45] *Ibid.*, p. 222.
[46] A. E. Lilley, *Astron. J.*, vol. 66, p. 445; November, 1961.
[47] M. S. Roberts, *ibid.*
[48] M. S. Roberts and G. R. Huguenin, *Proc. Symp. on Physics of the Planets*, 11th Internatl. Colloquium of Inst. Astrophys., Liège, Belgium, paper 56; July, 1962.
[49] J. J. Cook, L. G. Cross, M. E. Bair, and C. B. Arnold, *Nature*, vol. 188, p. 393; October 29, 1960.
[50] J. J. Cook and R. W. Terhune, Willow Run Labs., Willow Run, Mich., Tech. Memo.; May, 1960.
[51] J. J. Cook, L. G. Cross, M. E. Bair, and R. W. Terhune, "A low-noise X-band radiometer using maser," Proc. IRE, vol. 49, pp. 768–778; April, 1961.
[52] M. E. Bair, A. H. Barrett, J. J. Cook, L. G. Cross, and R. W. Terhune, presented at Amer. Astron. Soc. Meeting, Pittsburgh, Pa.; April 18–21, 1960.
[53] W. E. Howard, A. H. Barrett, and F. T. Haddock, *Astron. J.*, vol. 66, p. 287; September, 1961.
[54] J. A. Giordmaine, L. E. Alsop, C. H. Mayer, and C. H. Townes, "A maser amplifier for radio astronomy at X-band," Proc. IRE, vol. 47, pp. 1062–1070; June, 1959.
[55] A. H. Barrett, W. E. Howard, F. T. Haddock, M. E. Bair, J. J. Cook, and L. G. Cross, *Astron. J.*, vol. 66, p. 37; 1961.
[56] L. E. Alsop, J. A. Giordmaine, C. H. Mayer, and C. H. Townes, *Astron. J.*, vol. 63, p. 301; 1958.
[57] S. H. Autler, *Rev. Sci. Instr.*, vol. 31, p. 369; 1960.
[58] J. V. Jelley and B. F. C. Cooper, *Rev. Sci. Instr.*, vol. 32, p. 166; 1961.
[59] B. F. C. Cooper, *ibid.*, p. 202.
[60] B. F. C. Cooper, E. E. Epstein, S. J. Goldstein, Jr., J. V. Jelley, and M. A. Kaftan-Kassim, *Astron. J.*, vol. 65, p. 486; November, 1960.
[61] S. J. Goldstein, Jr., *Astron. J.*, vol. 65, p. 489; November, 1960.
[62] J. V. Jelley, *Microwave J.*, vol. 5, p. 77; February, 1962.
[63] W. K. Victor, R. Stevens, and S. W. Golomb, Jet Propulsion Lab., Calif. Inst. Tech., Rept. No. 32-132; August, 1961.
[64] W. K. Victor and R. Stevens, *Science*, vol. 134, p. 46; 1961.
[65] D. O. Muhleman, *Astron J.*, vol. 66, p. 292; 1961.
[66] D. O. Muhleman, D. B. Holdridge, and N. Block, *Astron. J.*, vol. 67, p. 191; 1962.
[67] R. Price, P. E. Green, T. J. Goblick, R. H. Kingston, L. G. Kraft, G. H. Pettengill, R. Silver, and W. B. Smith, *Science*, vol. 129, p. 751; 1959.
[68] G. H. Pettengill and R. Price, *Planetary & Space Sci.*, vol. 5, p. 70; 1961.
[69] G. H. Pettengill, H. W. Briscoe, J. V. Evans, E. Gehrels, G. M. Hyde, L. G. Kraft, R. Price, and W. B. Smith, *Astron. J.*, vol. 67, p. 181; 1962.
[70] J. H. Thomson, G. N. Taylor, J. E. B. Ponsonby, and R. S. Roger, *Nature*, vol. 190, p. 519; 1961.
[71] H. Hvatum, private communication; July, 1962.
[72] I. I. K. Pauliny-Toth, J. E. Baldwin, and J. R. Shakeshaft, *Month. Not. Roy. Astron. Soc.*, vol. 122, p. 279; 1961.
[73] I. I. K. Pauliny-Toth and J. R. Shakeshaft, *Month. Not. Roy. Astron. Soc.* (to be published).
[74] R. J. Long, J. B. Haseler, and B. Elsmore, *Month. Not. Roy. Astron. Soc.* (to be published).
[75] T. Sato and C. T. Stelzried, "An operational 960-Mc maser system for deep space tracking missions," IRE Trans. on Space Electronics and Telemetry, vol. SET-8, pp. 164–170; June, 1962.
[76] L. E. Alsop, J. A. Giordmaine, C. H. Townes, and T. C. Wang, *Phys. Rev.*, vol. 107, p. 1450; September, 1957.
[77] J. W. Chamberlain, "Physics of the Aurora and Airglow," Academic Press, Inc., New York, N. Y., p. 279; 1961.
[78] J. V. Jelley, "Čerenkov Radiation and Its Applications," Pergamon Press, London, England; 1958.
[79] H. C. Ingrao and D. H. Menzel, *Proc. Symp. on Physics of the Planets*, 11th Internatl. Colloquium of Inst. in Astrophys., Liège, Belgium, paper 18; July, 1962.
[80] H. C. Minnett, "The Australian 210-foot radio telescope," *Sky and Telescope*, vol. 24, p. 184; October, 1962.
[81] H. Heffner, *Microwave J.*, vol. 2, p. 33; March, 1959.
[82] S. Bloom and K. N. Chang, *RCA Rev.*, vol. 18, p. 578; 1957.
[83] H. Heffner, and G. Wade, *J. Appl. Phys.*, vol. 29, p. 1321; 1958.
[84] D. Lennov, *Bell. Sys. Tech. J.*, vol. 37, p. 989; 1958.
[85] B. J. Robinson and J. T. de Jager, *Proc. IEE*, vol. 109, pt. B, no. 45, p. 267; 1962.
[86] F. Wrigley, K. J. Craig, and B. S. Yaplee, presented at the 13th General Assembly, URSI, London, England; September 5, 1960.
[87] J. T. de Jager, "Low Noise Electronics," *Proc. 5th AGARD Avionics Panel Conf.*, Oslo, Norway, Pergamon Press, London, England, p. 266; 1961.
[88] R. Novick, "The Observation of Three Centimeter Radiation from Astronomical Objects with a Ruby Maser," Columbia Radiation Lab., New York, N. Y., Special Tech. Rept., Contract DA-36-039, SC-78330; June 1, 1961.

[89] R. W. de Grasse, D. C. Hogg, E. A. Ohm, and H. E. D. Scovil, *J. Appl. Phys.*, vol. 30, p. 2013; 1959.
[90] M. Ryle, *Proc. Roy. Soc. A*, vol. 211, p. 351; 1952.
[91] N. H. Dieter, *Astron. J.*, vol. 67, p. 313; 1962.
[92] *Ibid.*, p. 317.
[93] N. H. Dieter, E. E. Epstein, A. E. Lilley, and M. S. Roberts, *ibid.*, p. 270.
[94] E. E. Epstein, *ibid.*, p. 271.
[95] M. S. Roberts, *ibid.*, p. 280.
[96] J. S. Hey, *Nature*, vol. 190, no. 4782, p. 1150; 1961.
[97] J. S. Greenhow and C. D. Watkins, *J. Brit. IRE*, vol. 22; December, 1961.
[98] J. S. Greenhow, H. K. Sutcliffe, and C. D. Watkins, *Proc. Internat'l Conf. on the Ionosphere*, London, England; 1962.
[99] B. J. Robinson, "Development of parametric amplifiers for radioastronomy," *Proc. Aust. IRE* (in press).
[100] B. J. Robinson, "On stabilizing the gain of varactor amplifiers," PROC. IRE (*Correspondence*), vol. 48, p. 1648; September, 1960.
[101] J. P. Wild, *Ap. J.*, vol. 115, p. 206; 1952.
[102] "Radio Observatory at Hat Creek, California," *Sky and Telescope*, vol. 24, p. 64; August, 1962.
[103] W. E. Howard, A. H. Barrett, and F. T. Haddock, *Ap. J.* (to be published, see [53]).
[104] G. S. Levy and D. Schuster, *Astron. J.*, vol. 67, p. 320; 1962.
[105] V. Radhakrishnan and J. A. Roberts, *Phys. Rev. Lett.*, vol. 4, p. 493; 1960.
[106] D. Morris, *Proc. Symp. on The Physics of the Planets*, 11th Internat'l Colloquium of Astrophys., Liège, Belgium, paper 55; July, 1962.
[107] F. F. Gardner and J. B. Whiteoak, "Polarization of 20-cm wavelength radiation from radio sources." *Phys. Rev. Lett.* (in press).
[108] R. Wielebinski, J. R. Shakeshaft, and I. I. K. Pauliny-Toth, "A search for a linearly polarized component of the galactic radio emission at 408 Mc/s," *Observatory* (in press).
[109] J. S. Hay, "Observations at 610 Mc/s of the radiation from Jupiter," private communication, 1962.
[110] W. E. Gordon and L. M. LaLonde, "The design and capabilities of an ionospheric radar probe," IRE TRANS. ON ANTENNAS AND PROPAGATION, vol. AP-9, pp. 17–22; January, 1961.
[111] F. J. Kerr, "210-foot radio telescope's first results," *Sky and Telescope*, vol. 24, p. 254; November, 1962.
[112] B. F. C. Cooper and R. M. Price, *Nature*, vol. 195, p. 1084; September 15, 1962.
[113] R. N. Bracewell, B. F. C. Cooper and T. E. Cousins, *Nature*, vol. 195, p. 1288; September 29, 1962.

CORRECTION

A. Okaya and L. F. Barash, authors of "The Dielectric Microwave Resonator," which appeared on pages 2081–2092, of the October, 1962, issue of PROCEEDINGS, have called the following to the attention of the *Editor*:

On page 2086 (31a) should read:

$$R_H = 3.075 \times 10^5 \left(\frac{R_1}{\lambda}\right)^4 \text{ohms.} \qquad (31a)$$

Also (31b) should read:

$$R_E = 7.9 \times 10^2 \left(\frac{R_1}{\lambda}\right)^2 \text{ohms.} \qquad (31b)$$

On page 2091 the first part of (32) should read:

$$\nabla \times E = -\mu \dot{H}, \text{ etc.} \qquad (32)$$

Reprinted from JOURNAL OF APPLIED PHYSICS, Vol. 33, No. 8, 2522–2523, August, 1962

Operation of a Traveling-Wave Maser in a Transverse Field Superconducting Electromagnet*

W. G. NILSEN
Bell Telephone Laboratories, Inc., Murray Hill, New Jersey
(Received January 11, 1962)

A 6-Gc traveling-wave maser has been operated in a novel transverse field superconducting magnet. The magnet produces a uniform field in excess of 4000 Oe over a volume of 1.2×1.5×6 in. The field is directed across the shortest dimension (perpendicular to the direction of propagation) which permits nonreciprocal gain and attenuation. The TWM exhibited net gain in excess of 30 dB with 3-dB bandwidths of about 20 Mc. Gain and bandwidth characteristics were the same as those measured on the same traveling-wave maser in the field of a large laboratory magnet. This indicates a field homogeneity of about ±1 Oe or better in the superconducting magnet over the ruby volume of the maser since greater deviations would result in decreased gain and increased bandwidth.

I. INTRODUCTION

THE requirement for liquid helium temperatures in the operation of practical masers makes the use of superconducting materials for maser magnets very attractive. S. H. Autler[1] studied several types of electromagnets using superconducting wire and devised a switching scheme to make the current persistent. He also operated a cavity maser in a superconducting magnet. The present paper reports on the feasibility of using a superconducting magnet for traveling-wave maser (TWM)[2] applications.

The magnetic field requirements for TWM's are more stringent than for cavity masers. Longer lengths (typically 6 in.) are needed to obtain amplifier gains of practical interest. Further, the magnetic field should be directed perpendicular to the long dimension so that both amplifying and isolating functions can be included in the same slow-wave structure.[2,3]

The superconducting electromagnet developed by P. P. Cioffi[4] seems to be ideally suited to meet the magnetic field requirements of TWM. Superconducting wire is used for the magnetizing coils and high permeability ferromagnetic alloys for the pole faces and low-reluctance return path. In addition, sheets of superconducting material are used as magnetic insulators to prevent fringing from the air gap and the region around the magnetizing coils. The resulting improvement in the efficiency of the magnetic circuit and uniformity of the magnetic field in the air gap makes it possible to reduce the weight and size of the magnet sufficiently so that it can easily be accommodated in a conventional liquid helium Dewar.

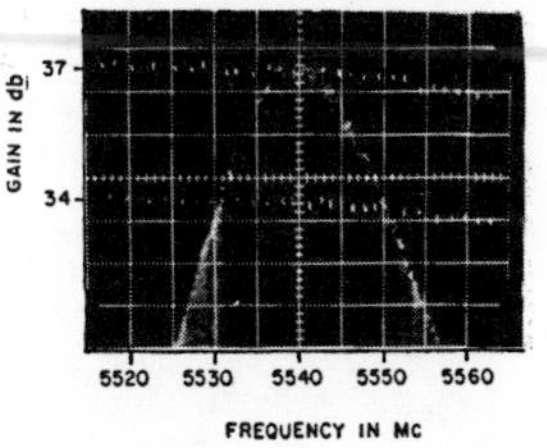

FIG. 1. Gain bandpass of TWM operated in a superconducting magnet. The 3-dB bandwidth is about 19 Mc.

II. EXPERIMENTAL PROCEDURE AND RESULTS

In order to demonstrate the feasibility of using this type of superconducting magnet for TWM, the gain and bandwidth characteristics of a 6-Gc TWM were compared in Cioffi's magnet and in a conventional 12-in. electromagnet known to exhibit a homogeneous magnetic field. The TWM was essentially a more recent version of the one described in reference 2 with a distributed isolator of polycrystalline yttrium iron garnet[5] in place of the original dark ruby isolator. The magnet current was supplied by a conventional regulated power supply. Some series resistance was introduced outside the Dewar to make the supply operate at some convenient voltage and current and to reduce the time constant of the circuit.

Gain and bandwidth measurements were carried out at 4.2°K. Superheterodyne detection was used so that the microwave power level could be kept well below the saturation level of the ruby TWM (about 0.2 μW at the output[3]). The local oscillator was swept at a moderate rate and the output displayed on an oscilloscope against a voltage derived from the L. O. frequency. The voltage pulse which occurs at the output when the signal and L. O. frequencies differ by the 30-Mc intermediate frequency was made quite sharp by inserting a narrow-band filter into the i. f. chain. By slowly sweeping the signal frequency through the instantaneous passband of the TWM, an envelope of spikes is displayed on the oscilloscope, the height of which is proportional to the gain of the amplifier. Gain calibration was obtained through by-passing the TWM at its room temperature input and output and decreasing the attenuation in the microwave path by an appropriate amount. Figure 1 shows the results of such a measurement carried out at

* This work was supported in part by the U. S. Army Signal Corps under Contract DA 36-039-sc-85357.

[1] S. H. Autler, Rev. Sci. Instr. **31**, 369 (1960).
[2] R. W. DeGrasse, E. O. Schulz-DuBois, and H. E. D. Scovil, Bell System Tech. J. **38**, 305 (1959); E. O. Schulz-DuBois, H. E. D. Scovil, and R. W. DeGrasse, *ibid*, 335 (1959).
[3] E. O. Schulz-DuBois, Progress in Cryogenics **2**, 175 (1960).
[4] P. P. Cioffi, J. Appl. Phys. **33**, 875 (1962).
[5] R. W. DeGrasse, J. J. Kostelnick, and H. E. D. Scovil, Bell System Tech. J. **40**, 117 (1961).

a center frequency of 5540 Mc. The net gain is 37 dB and the 3-dB down bandwidth is 19 Mc.

Gain and bandwidth measurements were made in this way at numerous frequencies in the structure pass-band. No evidence was found of either decreased gain or increased instantaneous bandwidth when comparing the data obtained in the superconducting magnet with those in a laboratory 12-in. electromagnet. Such changes would be expected if magnetic field inhomogeneities of more than ±1 Oe in magnitude or ±0.5° in angle were present.

III. CONCLUSION

Superconducting magnets appear to be feasible and practical for operation in conjunction with traveling-wave masers immersed in liquid helium. Most of the desirable magnet properties accrue from Cioffi's use of a magnetic insulator.

The size and weight of the magnet could be reduced by decreasing the cross section of the TWM and by the use of superior superconducting materials such as the recently disclosed niobium zirconium alloy.[6,7]

ACKNOWLEDGMENTS

The author is indebted to P. P. Cioffi for developing and designing the superconducting magnet and for many valuable discussions. The assistance of R. C. Petersen in carrying out the measurements is appreciated.

[6] J. E. Kunzler, Bull. Am. Phys. Soc. **6**, 298 (1961).
[7] T. G. Berlincourt, R. R. Hake, and D. H. Leslie, Phys. Rev. Letters **6**, 671 (1961).

Maser Operation at 96 kMc with Pump at 65 kMc*

Maser operation has been demonstrated at a frequency of 96.3 kMc using a pump frequency of 65.2 kMc. The material used for the maser was the iron ion, Fe^{3+} in a host of TiO_2 rutile. The high dielectric constant and low-loss tangent of the rutile allowed the sample itself to be used as a resonant cavity. The sample size was approximately 4×10^{-4} cubic inches and the Fe/Ti ratio was approximately 10^{-3}.

The spin Hamiltonian[1] in the form of a secular determinant has been programmed into the IBM 7090 computer at Westinghouse and solved as a function of the two angles of orientation (θ, ϕ) and the applied magnetic field, where θ is the angle the magnetic field makes with the [110] crystal axis and ϕ is the angle between the projection of the magnetic field on the (110) plane and the [$\bar{1}$10] crystal axis.

With the solutions obtained by the computer, it was possible to arrange the energy levels as shown in Fig. 1. The configuration allows pumping three transitions simultaneously, *i.e.*, $f_{13} = f_{42} = f_{53} = f_{\text{pump}}$. If the relaxation rates are nearly equal and if $2f_{12} > f_{13}$, then levels 5-4, 3-2 and 5-2 will be inverted and stimulated emission can take place at either f_{54}, f_{32} or f_{52}. Since in this experiment it was desired to have the signal frequency equal to f_{52}, it is necessary to suppress oscillations at f_{54} and f_{32}. This was accomplished simply by making certain that there were no high Q resonant cavities at the frequency f_{54} or f_{32}.

To the author's best knowledge, this is the first time that maser operation has been demonstrated with a pump frequency so much lower than the signal frequency.

Maser oscillations were detected by the use of a 30 Mc IF superheterodyne system with a swept local oscillator covering 250 Mc centered at 96.3 kMc. The detected output of the IF amplifier is shown in Fig. 2 with both sidebands visible in the photograph. The maser could also be made to oscillate simultaneously at two frequencies separated by about 150 Mc. Investigation disclosed that there were two high Q cavities in the rutile which were separated by about 150 Mc; thus, it appears that the oscillations were occurring at these cavities.

The upper trace of Fig. 3 shows the signal power reflected from the crystal and microwave assembly with the pump power on and the crystal positioned so that it is on a paramagnetic resonance at both the signal and pump frequencies. The center trace shows the same conditions except that the pump power has been turned off to show the absorption at the signal frequency due to the paramagnetic resonance. The bottom trace shows the microwave cavities in the rutile when there is no paramagnetic absorption.

From Fig. 3 it can be seen that in order to obtain maximum gain at any one frequency, it will be necessary to reduce the number of resonant cavities and to maximize the coupling to only one cavity. This will be done and a measure of the gain bandwidth product will be made.

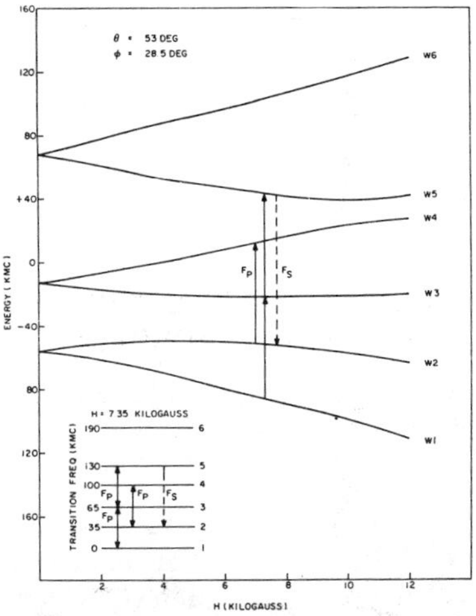

Fig. 1—Energy levels of Fe^{3+} in TiO_2 as a function of magnetic field at $\theta = 53$ and $\phi = 28.5$.

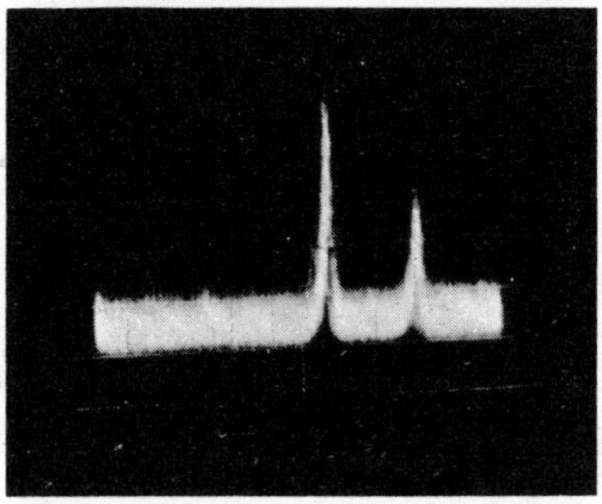

Fig. 2—Maser oscillations at 96.3 kMc with pump at 65.2 kMc: $H = 7.35$ kilogauss, $T = 2.1°$ K, $\theta = 53$ and $\phi = 28.5$.

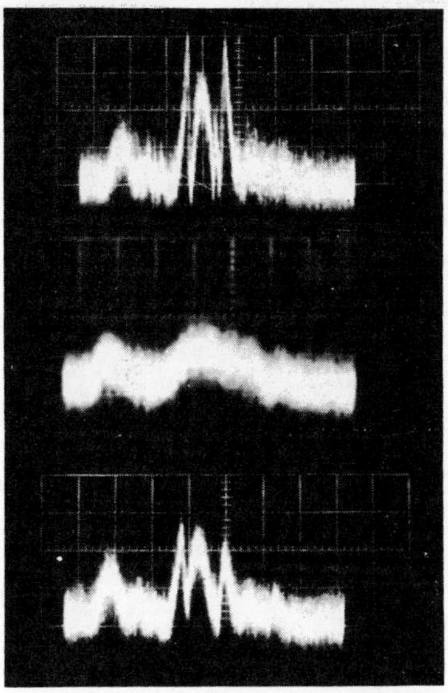

Fig. 3—Reflected microwave power from maser cavity signal mode centered at 96.3 kMc.

ACKNOWLEDGMENT

The author is grateful to all the persons who have helped make this project successful; in particular, I would like to thank T. W. Hollis for his helpful suggestions and J. Hamburger and O. L. Bishop for their help in making the many necessary measurements.

WAYNE E. HUGHES
Westinghouse Electric Corp.
Applied Physics Group
Air Arm Division
Baltimore, Md.

* Received May 16, 1962. This work was supported by the Department of the Air Force, ETL, Aeronautical Systems Division, Dayton, Ohio.

[1] D. L. Carter and A. Okaya, "Electron Paramagnetic Resonance of Fe^{3+} in TiO_2 (Rutile)," Department of Physics, Columbia University, New York, N. Y., September, 1959.

Reprinted from the PROCEEDINGS OF THE IRE
VOL. 50, NO. 7, JULY, 1962

MICROWAVE GENERATION IN RUBY DUE TO POPULATION INVERSION PRODUCED BY OPTICAL ABSORPTION*

D. P. Devor, I. J. D'Haenens, and C. K. Asawa
Hughes Research Laboratories, Malibu, California
(Received April 30, 1962)

Microwave amplification and generation by the stimulated emission of radiation (maser) were observed in ruby as a result of population inversion produced in the ground state of Cr^{3+} by the absorption of the coherent optical emission from a second ruby (optical maser). The maser crystal was oriented in a magnetic field of about 6700 Oe to obtain a transition between a ground ${}^4A_2$ Zeeman sublevel and an excited $\overline{E}({}^2E)$ Zeeman sublevel which would match a spectral component of the output of the optical maser. The arrangement of the experimental apparatus is shown schematically in Fig. 1.

Detection of the interaction of optical and para-

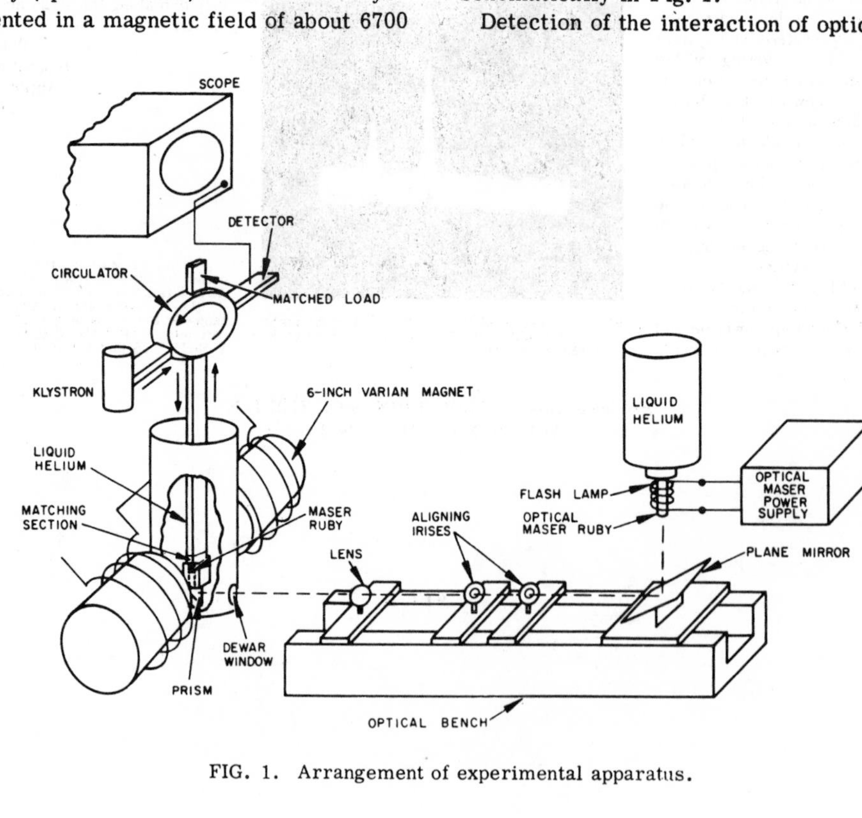

FIG. 1. Arrangement of experimental apparatus.

magnetic transitions in the sharp line spectra of ions in crystalline solids has been accomplished previously through the observation of the effect of the paramagnetism on the optical signals.[1-3] Wieder[1] attempted to directly detect the effect on paramagnetism of depopulation in the $^4A_2$ state in ruby due to the absorption of the R-line fluorescent light. Since the optical spectrum of the ruby optical maser results from R-line emission, the optical maser offered a considerably better optical source (in terms of collimation, spectral purity, and power output) for such an experiment, not only to detect perturbation of the ground-state populations, but also to produce population inversion.

D'Haenens and Asawa[4] havr observed stimulated optical emission in ruby to shift to longer wavelengths from the fluorescent emission. In the present experiment, the optical-maser crystal, initially cooled by conduction to liquid-helium temperature, produced a pump signal of 6934.188 Å (air wavelength) from the $\bar{E}(^2E) \rightarrow \pm\frac{1}{2}(^4A_2)$ transition (spin states correspond to high-field assignments). The optical-maser output was unpolarized.

The separation of the $\bar{E}(^2E)$ and the $\pm\frac{1}{2}(^4A_2)$ states in the maser crystal was taken as the fluorescent wavelength of 6934.082 Å at 4.2°K. The g value of the $\bar{E}$ Kramers' doublet was obtained from the work of Geschwind, Collins, and Schawlow,[2] and the Zeeman structure of the $^4A_2$ ground state was known from the analysis of Chang and Siegman.[5] From their data we calculated that the magnetic field at an angle of 67 degrees, with respect to the crystalline c axis, split the $\bar{E}$ and $^4A_2$ states as shown in Fig. 2(a). At 6700 Oe, the $+\frac{1}{2}(\bar{E}) \rightarrow +\frac{1}{2}(^4A_2)$ transition matched the $\bar{E} \rightarrow \pm\frac{1}{2}(^4A_2)$ component of the optical-maser spectrum, since the latter transition was 0.22 cm^{-1} less than the fluorescent wave number in zero field. The $+\frac{3}{2}(^4A_2) \rightarrow +\frac{1}{2}(^4A_2)$ microwave transition occurred at 22.4 Gc/sec. Figure 2(b) shows a comparison of the fluorescence and optical-maser emission spectra under approximately such conditions. The spectral agreement of the $-\frac{1}{2}(\bar{E}) \rightarrow +\frac{1}{2}(^4A_2)$ transition in fluorescence with the lower energy optical-maser line indicated that the magnitude and orientation of the magnetic field were not particularly critical.

The microwave resonant structure consisted of a section of 0.050- by 0.130-inch waveguide which was beyond cutoff at 22.4 Gc/sec and was partially loaded with a 0.078-inch length of ruby. The structure acted as a ruby-loaded microwave

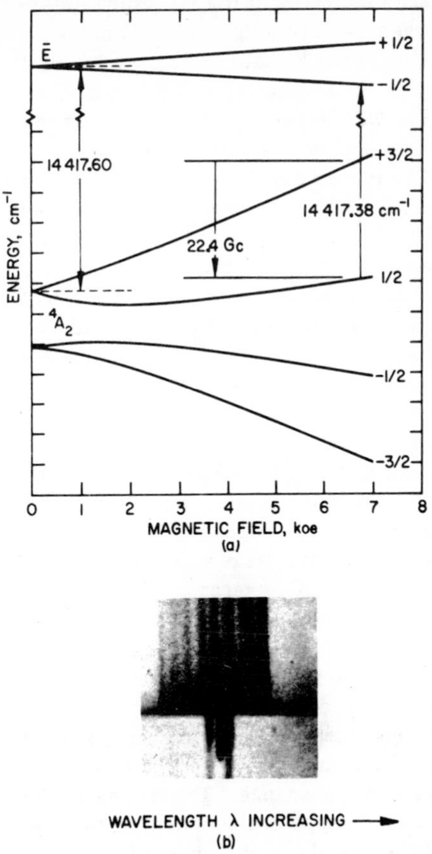

FIG. 2. Comparison of the spectra of ruby in fluorescence and in stimulated emission under conditions suitable for optical pumping. (a) Zeeman structure of Cr^{3+} ruby. The crystalline c axis is oriented at 67 degrees with respect to the magnetic field. The g factor of the $\bar{E}$ state is 0.956, as given by Geschwind et al.[2] (b) Comparison of spectrographs of ruby in fluorescence (upper eight lines) and in stimulated emission at a temperature of 4.2°K. The fluorescence was observed with the c axis at 70 degrees with respect to a magnetic field of 6500 Oe. The short line is the neon reference in ninth order corresponding to $\lambda = 6934.0831$ Å. Spectra were taken with a special Harrison grating.

reflection cavity resonant at 22.4 Gc/sec in a perturbed TE_{011} mode. At liquid-nitrogen temperature, the quality factor Q_0 of this structure, exclusive of magnetic losses and external circuit losses, was about 1600. The filling factor was calculated to be 96%.

The conditions for power gain and/or oscillation in a solid-state maser are given by Bloembergen[6] in terms of the magnetic quality factor Q_m. To overcome the microwave circuit losses, the quality factor Q_0 of the structure must exceed $|Q_m|$ when population inversion is obtained. The population of the $\bar{E}$ state is extremely small at 4.2°K and, consequently, saturation of the $+\frac{1}{2}(^4A_2) \to -\frac{1}{2}(\bar{E})$ pump transition depletes the $+\frac{1}{2}(^4A_2)$ state of one-half the Boltzmann population. The maser crystal was cut from 0.05 wt.% Cr_2O_3:Al_2O_3 ruby, giving a Boltzmann population of 3.06×10^{16} in the $+\frac{1}{2}(^4A_2)$ level. Thus, the absorption of 1.53×10^{16} photons, or 4.39×10^{-3} joule of pump signal, is required for saturation of the $\frac{1}{2}(^4A_2) \to -\frac{1}{2}(\bar{E})$ transition; this amount of energy is orders of magnitude less than that available from the optical maser. Using appropriate data for ruby and the present microwave cavity, the magnetic Q obtained from the saturation of the $\frac{1}{2}(^4A_2) \to -\frac{1}{2}(\bar{E})$ transition is $-Q_m \cong 75$, which is considerably less than the Q_0 of the microwave resonant structure.

The experimental results are shown in Fig. 3. The klystron signal generator was frequency modulated at a repetition rate which allowed us to sample the relative populations of the $^4A_2$ sublevels while the microwave system was being optically pumped. This low effective duty cycle was chosen to avoid microwave saturation effects. The cavity was undercoupled in the absence of paramagnetic resonance. The traces in Fig. 3(a) are recordings of the optical-maser output and a 200-μsec-delayed display of the microwave reflected power. The first klystron sweep shows the ruby sample absorbing at the $+\frac{1}{2}(^4A_2) \to +\frac{3}{2}(^4A_2)$ transition; the second sweep shows the reduction in magnetic losses as $1/Q_m$ goes to zero (or becomes slightly negative) due to depopulation of the $+\frac{1}{2}(^4A_2)$ level; on the third sweep, $1/Q_m$ is sufficiently negative to produce amplification.

In Fig. 3(b) the microwave coupling to the maser crystal was reduced, the optical-maser output was increased, and the klystron power level was the same as that in Fig. 3(a). Figure 3(b) shows simultaneous amplification and oscillation. For the trace in Fig. 3(c) the klystron was turned off and oscillation was produced. The pulsed nature of the oscillation was the same as that observed in microwave-pumped ruby masers by Makhov et al.[7] and Foner et al.[8] The $-\frac{1}{2}(^4A_2) \to +\frac{1}{2}(^4A_2)$ resonance was observed with a small increase in magnetic field. A recording of this resonance, when the optical maser illuminated the maser crystal, showed that the microwave absorption increased markedly [Fig. 3(d)] and thus confirmed the pumping of the $+\frac{1}{2}(^4A_2)$ level.

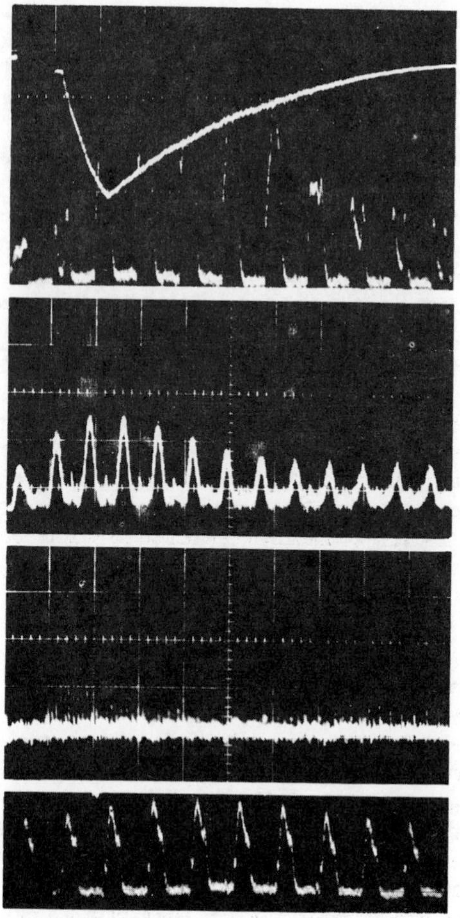

(a)

(b)

(c)

(d)

FIG. 3. Experimental results. (a) Optical-maser output and a 200-μsec-delayed signal of reflected microwave power from the microwave cavity showing amplification at 22.4 Gc/sec. The optical-maser output was about 2.5 joules of which 1 joule was estimated to be incident on the maser crystal. Time scale = 200 μsec/division; input microwave power level ≈50 μW. (b) Simultaneous maser oscillation and amplification. Conditions as in (a) except microwave coupling to the maser crystal was reduced; also, the optical-maser output was increased to about 4 joules of which about 2.8 joules were estimated to be incident on the maser crystal. (c) Maser oscillation observed with no input microwave signal. Time scale = 50 μsec/division. (d) Increased microwave absorption at the $-\frac{1}{2}(^4A_2) \to +\frac{1}{2}(^4A_2)$ transition due to depopulation of the $+\frac{1}{2}(^4A_2)$ level. All conditions were as in (a).

The microwave structure appeared to have two resonant modes separated by 30 or 40 Mc/sec, possibly as a result of the anisotropy of the dielectric constant of sapphire and a slight misalignment of the crystalline *c* axis from the rectangular axis of the cut crystal. The maser was occasionally observed to amplify in both modes simultaneously, although not with equal gain.

With the technique described here, amplification and oscillation at frequencies considerably higher than 22.4 Gc/sec are possible; thus, a brief examination of the energy levels of ruby indicates that amplification at 57 Gc/sec in a magnetic field of 21 000 Oe could be obtained. In addition, the excited state can be selectively populated to allow direct observation of paramagnetic resonance in this state. Furthermore, maser gain was observed for some time after the loss of the liquid helium in the maser Dewar, thus indicating the possibility of operating at temperatures higher than 4.2°K.

The efficacy of the optical maser in an optical-pumping experiment was, to our knowledge, first considered by T. H. Maiman and R. H. Hoskins. Considerable help with the microwave resonant structure was obtained from J. E. Keifer and F. E. Goodwin.

---

*Work supported by the U. S. Army Signal Corps under Contract DA 36-039 SC-87221.

[1]Irwin Weider, Phys. Rev. Letters 3, 468 (1959).

[2]S. Geschwind, R. J. Collins, and A. L. Schawlow, Phys. Rev. Letters 3, 545 (1959).

[3]J. Brossel, S. Geschwind, and A. L. Schawlow, Phys. Rev. Letters 3, 548 (1959).

[4]I. J. D'Haenens and C. K. Asawa (to be published).

[5]W. S. Chang and A. E. Siegman, Stanford Electronic Laboratory, Technical Report No. 156-2, Stanford University, California (unpublished); also as reproduced by J. Weber, Revs. Modern Phys. 31, 681 (1959).

[6]N. Bloembergen, Phys. Rev. 104, 324 (1956).

[7]G. Makhov, C. Kikuchi, J. Lamb, and R. W. Terhune, Phys. Rev. 109, 1399 (1958).

[8]S. Foner, L. R. Momo, and A. Mayer, Phys. Rev. Letters 3, 36 (1959).

Phonon Masers

ATTENUATION OF LONGITUDINAL ULTRASONIC VIBRATIONS BY SPIN-PHONON COUPLING IN RUBY

E. B. Tucker
General Electric Research Laboratory, Schenectady, New York
(Received January 30, 1961)

The attenuation of 9.1-kMc/sec longitudinal ultrasonic vibrations due to spin-phonon interaction has been observed in pink ruby. The value of the magnetoelastic coupling constant has been obtained from the experimental value of the attenuation.

Calculations of the "direct process" spin lattice interaction predict that the coupling involved should be quadrupolar in character[1-3] (i.e., through combinations of operators such as S_z^2, $S_xS_z + S_zS_x$, etc.) for non-S-state ions of the iron group such as Cr^{+++}. For longitudinal waves along the z axis, in this case both the trigonal axis of the ruby and the axis of quantization, the interaction may be represented by a perturbation of the form

$$H' = Ge_{zz}S_z^2,$$

where G is the magnetoelastic coupling constant and e_{zz} is the elastic strain amplitude. The resulting transition probability for a spin to absorb a quantum of energy from the phonon field is

$$G^2 e_{zz}^2 g(\nu) |\langle |S_z^2| \rangle|^2 / 2\hbar^2.$$

$g(\nu)$ is the shape factor for the spin-lattice interaction, the maximum value having been previously determined as $\simeq 10^{-8}$ sec.[4] $\langle |S_z^2| \rangle$ represents the matrix element of the spin operators between the levels involved. Experimental data for the angular variation of the transition probability, determined using saturation techniques similar to those previously described,[4-6] are given in Fig. 1. Theoretical transition probabilities assuming quadrupole coupling have been computed using the ruby calculations of Chang and Siegman.[7] The experimental data agree quite well with the theoretical curves superposed on a background presumed to be due to transverse components, present by virtue of some longitudinal-transverse mode conversion in the crystal. At $\theta = 0°$ the $\pm 1/2$ (high field 1-3) transition is, as expected, not affected by the phonons while the 1-2 and the other 1-3 transition (both pure $\Delta m = \pm 1$) interact only with transverse waves. It has previously been reported that

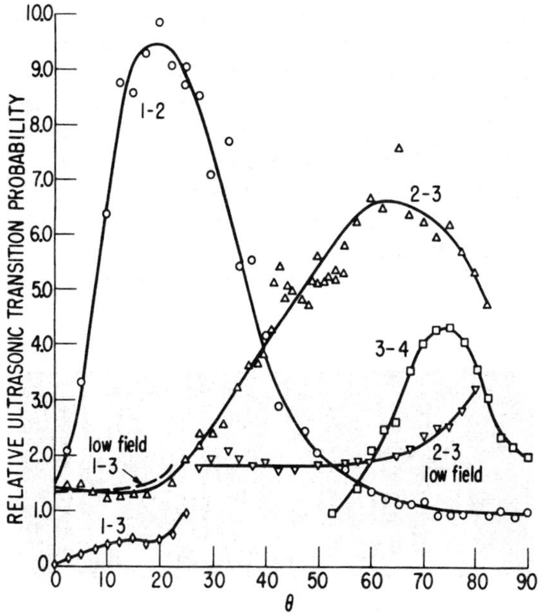

FIG. 1. Angular variation of the ultrasonic transition probability for longitudinal acoustic vibrations along the c axis of pink ruby. The transitions are labeled according to the energy levels involved, with the levels being numbered from the highest (1) to the lowest (4).

Cr^{+++} in ruby obeys the quadrupole selection rules.[8]

The value of the attenuation per centimeter of path is

$$\alpha = G^2 g(\nu) |\langle |S_z^2| \rangle|^2 nh\nu / (2\hbar^2 \rho v^3),$$

where n is the population difference per centimeter between the levels involved, v is the velocity of longitudinal acoustic waves, and ρ is the density of ruby. Since we appear to be justified in taking the theoretical values for $\langle |S_z^2| \rangle$, the determination of a value for G^2 requires an experimental evaluation of α.

The attenuation observation was made using a pulse echo technique similar to that used to determine the attenuation in quartz.[9,10] A double-cavity arrangement,[5] ultrasonic drive and spectrometer cavities, allowed the amplitude of the absorption signal to be monitored while the echo experiment was in progress. The ultrasonic drive cavity was pulsed at a rate of 10 cps using half-microsecond pulses of 90-watt peak power. A superheterodyne detection system was used to monitor the power from the drive cavity through a 3-db directional coupler. The crystals used were in the form of rods 3 mm in diameter, a $1\frac{3}{4}$-cm length of X-cut quartz and a $1\frac{1}{4}$-cm length of Linde pink ruby. The axis of the ruby rod is 25 minutes from being parallel to the c axis. The ends of both quartz and ruby are optically polished flat, and are parallel to within one minute. The bonding material is indium.

Figure 2 illustrates the echo pattern observed

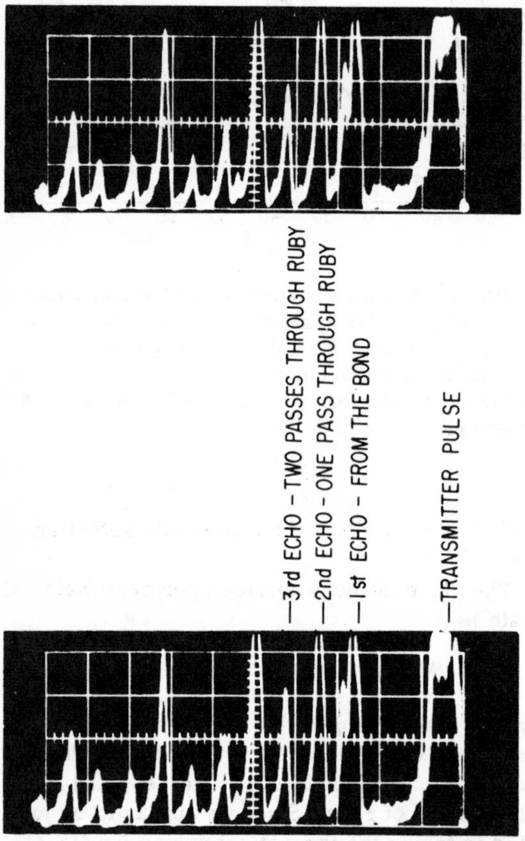

FIG. 2. Echo patterns observed: upper trace with the magnetic field adjusted for resonance at $\theta = 60°$ on the 2-3 transition, and lower trace with the magnetic field just off the resonance value. The origins of the echoes are indicated between the traces.

at 1.5°K. The third echo has traversed the ruby rod four times for a total path length of 5 cm in ruby and $3\frac{1}{2}$ cm in quartz. A longer path length in the ruby would be desirable but, for the particular rod lengths used, echo number four and all succeeding echoes are composites of reflections from the bond and from the end of the ruby. No useful conclusions may be drawn from them. The difference in amplitude of the third echo in the top and bottom trace represents the absorption of phonons by the spin system. The amplitude of the third echo averages 20% lower with the magnetic field at the value required for resonance at $\theta = 60°$ on the 2-3 line compared to its amplitude with the magnetic field just off the resonance value. This transition represents the optimum combination of experimental ultrasonic transition probability and Boltzmann factor. The conclusions below are based on a number of observations made on this transition. Attenuations have also been observed for the 1-2 transition at $\theta = 20°$ and for the 3-4 transition at $\theta = 70°$.

The attenuation observed is 0.2 for the 5-cm path or 0.04 per cm. The corresponding value of G^2 is 1.5×10^{-29} erg^2. If a direct process is assumed for the relaxation process and this value of the coupling constant is assumed to apply to the transverse as well as to the longitudinal waves, the corresponding spin-lattice relaxation time is 0.5 second, assuming Orbach's formula[11]

$$1/T_1 = G^2|\langle|S_z^2|\rangle|^2\omega^2 kT/(2\pi\hbar^2\rho v^5),$$

with $T = 4.2$°K and a velocity (the mean of the longitudinal and transverse velocities) of 9×10^5 cm/sec. There are experimental relaxation-time measurements[12,13] which agree quite well with this figure, while others[14,15] are an order of magnitude lower. In any case the experimental relaxation time results do not show the variation with frequency predicted by this formula.

Attenuations were not observable at $\theta = 0°$ for any of the three absorption lines allowed by the microwave selection rules. Theoretically this is what one expects since none of the transitions should be directly affected by a longitudinal wave. The sensitivity in the present experiment is, however, such that it is not reasonable to draw any conclusions concerning the relative proportions of longitudinal and transverse waves from these results for $\theta = 0°$. The value of the attenuation observed for coherent longitudinal waves should be accurate to better than a factor of two. More accuracy should be obtainable with a judicious choice of rod lengths.

It is a pleasure to acknowledge numerous discussions with Dr. N. S. Shiren and Dr. E. H. Jacobsen, and the loan of the pulser from the latter. T. G. Kazyaka helped take a large part of the data.

---

[1]J. H. Van Vleck, Phys. Rev. 57, 426 (1940).

[2]R. D. Mattuck and M. W. P. Strandberg, Phys. Rev. Letters 3, 369 (1959).

[3]R. D. Mattuck and M. W. P. Strandberg, Phys. Rev. 119, 1204 (1960).

[4]E. B. Tucker, Bull. Am. Phys. Soc. 5, 157 (1960).

[5]E. H. Jacobsen, N. S. Shiren, and E. B. Tucker, Phys. Rev. Letters 3, 81 (1959).

[6]N. S. Shiren, Bull. Am. Phys. Soc. 5, 343 (1960).

[7]W. S. Chang and A. E. Siegman, Stanford Electronic Laboratory Technical Report No. 156-2, 1958 (unpublished).

[8]N. S. Shiren and E. B. Tucker, Phys. Rev. Letters 6, 105 (1961).

[9]E. H. Jacobsen, Phys. Rev. Letters 2, 249 (1959).

[10]H. E. Bömmel and K. Dransfeld, Phys. Rev. Letters 2, 298 (1959).

[11]See, for example, R. L. Orbach, thesis, University of California, 1960 (unpublished).

[12]R. A. Armstrong and A. Szabo, Can. J. Phys. 38, 1304 (1960).

[13]J. A. Giordmaine and F. Nash, Columbia Radiation Laboratory Quarterly Report, June, 1960 (unpublished), p. 17.

[14]C. Kikuchi, J. Lambe, G. Makhov, and R. W. Terhune, J. Appl. Phys. 30, 1061 (1959).

[15]J. H. Pace, D. F. Sampson, and J. S. Thorp, Phys. Rev. Letters 4, 18 (1960).

ERRATA

Page 184, right side of page, second paragraph. Change .04 to .08. Change 1.5×10^{-29} erg^2 to 1.3×10^{-31} erg^2/unit strain^2.

AMPLIFICATION OF 9.3-kMc/sec ULTRASONIC PULSES BY MASER ACTION IN RUBY

E. B. Tucker
General Electric Research Laboratory, Schenectady, New York
(Received April 27, 1961)

The observation of the attenuation of 9.3-kMc/sec ultrasonic pulses by the spin-phonon interaction[1] in ruby implies that amplification should be observable in the same system if the spin population is inverted. We have now observed the amplification of 9.3-kMc/sec pulses of ultrasonic energy in passing through a ruby rod in which the spin system was inverted. This is the first observation of amplification of energy other than electromagnetic in such a system.

The conditions for the observation of maximum gain from the inverted spin system are identical with the conditions for the observation of the maximum attenuation except for the inversion, rather than the normal thermal equilibrium, of the spin system. The published results for attenuation in ruby[1] show that one of the highest ultrasonic interactions occurs, for longitudinal waves, at an angle of 60° between the magnetic field and the ruby c axis ($\theta = 60°$) for the 2-3 transition at high field (3700 gauss for 9.3 kMc/sec). Fortunately, the conditions for use of push-pull pumping[2] (saturation of both the 1-3 and the 2-4 transitions) at a single frequency occur at $\theta = 55°30'$. The actual orientation used for the experiment is a compromise between the above requirements. Since the ultrasonic transition probability is a slow function of angle near $\theta = 60°$, it was found that the best inversion was obtained at an angle of 56° using pump power of 23.3 kMc/sec.

The experimental observations were made using the same methods previously described[1] except that the ruby was contained in a K-band pump cavity. The crystal configuration consists of a $1\frac{1}{2}$-cm X-cut quartz crystal bonded, with indium, to a $1\frac{1}{4}$-cm length of Linde pink ruby (Cr^{+++} in Al_2O_3). Both crystals are in the form of cylindrical rods 3 mm in diameter and the c axis of the ruby is parallel to the rod axis to within $\frac{1}{2}$ degree. The experiments were carried out at 1.5°K.

The traces of Fig. 1 illustrate the effects of the spin system on the first few echoes observed. The echo to the right of the center graticule has made a single return trip through the ruby while the echo to the left of center has made two passes through the ruby. The larger amplitudes of these two echoes in the top picture as compared to the

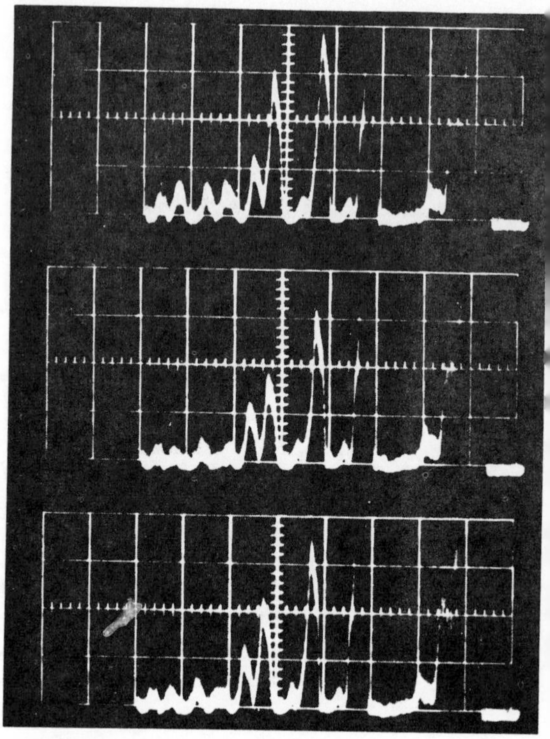

FIG. 1. Echo patterns observed for 9.3-kMc/sec ultrasonic pulse of 0.5-microsecond duration. Large echoes to the right and the left of the center graticule have passed through the ruby once and twice, respectively. Time increases from right to left. Top pictu magnetic field on resonance line and pump on. Cente picture: magnetic field on resonance line, no pump. Bottom picture: magnetic field off resonance line.

bottom trace is due to the amplification through interaction with the spin system. Similarly, the smaller amplitudes of the center trace as compared to the bottom are the result of attenuation due to transfer of energy to the spin system in thermal equilibrium at 1.5°K. The gain observe is 0.12 per centimeter of travel in the ruby.[3] This is somewhat higher than the attenuation of 0.09 per centimeter and is an indication of the efficiency of inversion.

The slower traces of Fig. 2 illustrate much more graphically the magnitude of the effect. The upper picture shows clearly a number of

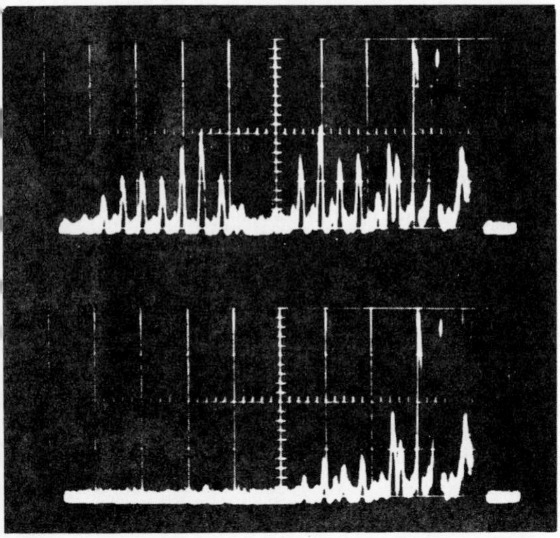

FIG. 2. Echo patterns observed for 9.31-kMc/sec ultrasonic pulse of 0.5-microsecond duration. The change in frequency accounts for the amplitudes of the first few echoes being different from those of Fig. 1. Sweep speed of oscilloscope is about 5 microseconds per centimeter. A round trip through the ruby requires 2.1 microseconds. Time increases from right to left. Top picture: magnetic field on resonance line and pump on. Bottom picture: magnetic field off resonance line.

echoes not visible without the aid of the amplification. From the spacing of these echoes it can be surmised that they are due to pulses which have traveled back and forth in the ruby for as many as eighteen round trips; and that their only traversal of the quartz has been the 3 cm travel to get to the ruby initially and, after the reflections in the ruby, to get back to the transducer end again. Echoes from the bond are almost nonexistent after 10 microseconds. The beating due to phase interference caused by the nonparallel ends and bond as well as crystal inhomogeneities and misalignment is very evident in the top trace of Fig. 2.

The physical perfection required to determine the true propagation characteristics of the quartz-indium-ruby combination is lacking, and hence conclusion of whether or not the gain obtainable from the spin system is sufficient to overcome the system losses is impossible. It is fairly obvious what conditions must be satisfied in order to realize over-all gain, i.e., a phonon maser. Just as in the case of the optical maser[4] the gain from the inverted population must be sufficient to overcome the losses due to attenuation in the materials and reflections at the ends of the cavity, in this case the optically polished ends of the crystals. If one assumes that an attenuation of 0.01 per centimeter (such as is observed in quartz[5]) is attainable in a good ruby crystal, the gain of 0.12 per centimeter is certainly sufficient. For appreciably higher losses either higher spin populations or spin systems with larger magnetoelastic coupling constants, or perhaps both, will be required.

This experimental demonstration of phonon amplification was undertaken after discussions, on the possibility of a phonon maser, with Dr. E. H. Jacobsen and Dr. N. S. Shiren. It is a pleasure to acknowledge their contributions.

---

[1]E. B. Tucker, Phys. Rev. Letters 6, 183 (1961).

[2]C. Kikuchi, J. Lambe, G. Makhov, and R. W. Terhune, J. Appl. Phys. 30, 1061 (1959).

[3]The pictures illustrate amplitudes proportional to voltage whereas the attenuations and gains are referred to power.

[4]A. L. Schawlow and C. H. Townes, Phys. Rev. 112, 1940 (1958).

[5]E. H. Jacobsen (private communication); 0.01 per cm includes end losses for a 3-cm X-cut quartz bar.

Techniques for Solid State Masers

Design Considerations for Circulator Maser Systems*

In its present form the low-noise maser amplifier[1] is a single-port device. That is, the low-level signal enters and the amplified signal leaves the maser by the same port. By connecting a circulator to the single-port maser, maximum gain-bandwidth is obtained, and the maser is isolated from the noise radiated by the receiver.[2] A circulator maser system is shown in Fig. 1. The signal entering through the antenna is directed by the circulator into the maser, and the amplified signal from the maser is directed by the circulator to the receiver.[3]

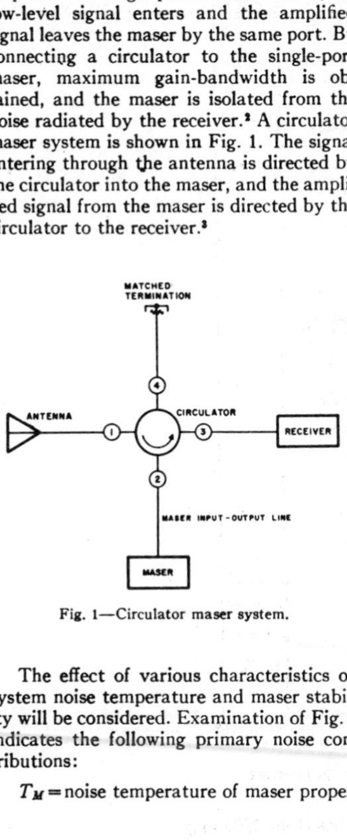

Fig. 1—Circulator maser system.

The effect of various characteristics on system noise temperature and maser stability will be considered. Examination of Fig. 1 indicates the following primary noise contributions:

T_M = noise temperature of maser proper.

T_R = noise temperature[4] of receiver. (Because the receiver is preceded by a maser amplifier, the noise contribution due to T_R becomes T_R/G_M, where G_M is the available maser gain expressed as a power ratio.)

T_{LA} = noise temperature at the antenna terminals due to noise emitted by the matched load which is reflected at the antenna.

T_{LM} = noise temperature at the maser input terminals due to noise emitted by the matched load which is transmitted directly through the circulator because of finite isolation between ports 4 and 2 (L_{42}). For the case of the matched load near room temperature, $T_{LM} = 290/L_{42}$.

T_{RM} = noise temperature at the maser input terminals due to noise emitted by the receiver[5] which is transmitted directly through the circulator because of finite isolation between ports 3 and 2 (L_{32}).

L = all dissipative losses between the antenna and the maser terminals; *i.e.*, the loss in the antenna feed line, the circulator forward loss between ports 1 and 2 (L_{12}), and the loss in the maser input-output transmission line (expressed as available signal power input divided by available signal power output. A loss of 0.1 db yields $L = 1.0233$).

The noise contribution due to L is calculated as follows.[6] The noise factor[7] F_1 of a passive matched network of loss L at a physical temperature T_1 can be shown to be

$$F_1 = 1 + (L - 1)\frac{T_1}{290}. \qquad (1)$$

The noise factor F_{12} of two networks in cascade is

$$F_{12} = F_1 + L(F_2 - 1). \qquad (2)$$

Combining (1) and (2) with the definition for effective noise temperature, $T = (F - 1)290$, the effective noise temperature T_{12} of two cascaded networks is

$$T_{12} = (L - 1)T_1 + LT_2, \qquad (3)$$

where T_2 is the effective noise temperature of network 2.

The general expression for effective maser system noise temperature T_e can now be calculated. The path of the received signal is traced from the receiver back toward the antenna terminals. The noise temperatures are added at the points in the circuit at which they occur. Transformations from point to point through lossy components are calculated using (3).

A simplified form of the resultant expression[8] for effective maser system temperature is written below by assuming that the loss in the maser input-output transmission line is less than 0.4 db.

$$T_e = T_{LA} + (L - 1)T_0 + L\left[T_{RM} + T_{LM} + T_M + \frac{T_R}{G_M}\right], \qquad (4)$$

where all noise temperatures are in ° Kelvin, and T_0 is the physical temperature of the lossy components contributing to L. The fractional error due to the above simplification is under 10 per cent. T_R here is taken to represent the effective receiver noise temperature at the maser output terminals. That is, the losses between the maser output terminals and the receiver are included in T_R by the use of (3).

If L_{32} and L_{42} are approximately 25 db, and if the matched load is at room temperature (290°K), T_{LM} and T_{RM} are each approximately 1°K. If, in addition, the antenna swr is 1.1 or less, T_{LA} is less than 1°K. However, if the antenna swr is higher, the matched termination may have to be refrigerated in order to reduce its noise contribution.

It is, therefore, concluded that for the case where L_{32} and $L_{42} \approx 25$ db and an antenna swr ≈ 1.1, the contributions of T_{LA}, T_{LM}, and T_{RM} become small; letting T_0 equal 290°K, (4) thus becomes

$$T_e = (L - 1)290 + L\left[T_M + \frac{(F_R - 1)290}{G_M}\right]. \qquad (5)$$

The bracketed term in (5) is the effective noise temperature at the maser input terminals. For high-gain masers, this term will be considerably less than 290°K. Under this condition, and if $L < 1.2$ (0.75 db), (5) can be approximated by

$$T_e = 66.7l + [T_M + (F_R - 1)\,290/G_M], \qquad (6)$$

where l is the loss L expressed in decibels. As can be seen, T_e increases by approximately 7°K per 0.1 db of loss for $l < 0.75$ db. For the case where the bracketed term is 6°K, T_e is doubled for $l \approx 0.1$ db.

It is thus seen that the noise due to the dissipative losses in the antenna feed line, the circulator, and the maser input-output line, can be significantly greater than the noise contributed by a high-gain maser.[9] The circulator dissipative loss is likely to be a significant fraction of the losses, particularly at frequencies below 3000 mc.[10]

In addition to the noise considerations above, the question of maser stability must be considered.

Single-port masers will experience variations in gain and may even oscillate, depending upon load conditions, due to the reflec-

* Received by the IRE, January 21, 1958. This work was supported by the Department of Defense.

[1] A. L. McWhorter and J. W. Meyer, "A solid-state maser amplifier," *Phys. Rev.*, vol. 109, pp. 312–318; January, 15, 1958.
H. E. D. Scovil, G. Feher, and H. Seidel, "Operation of a solid state maser," *Phys. Rev.*, vol. 105, pp. 762–763; January 1, 1957.

[2] A. E. Siegman, "Gain bandwidth and noise in maser amplifiers," PROC. IRE, vol. 45, pp. 1737–1738; December, 1957.

[3] In some applications it may be desirable to cascade two single-port maser amplifiers. This may be done by cascading two circulator maser systems, or more simply by modifying the circuit of Fig. 1 by replacing the termination at circulator port 4 with the receiver, and connecting a second maser at port 3. This arrangement would be useful, for example, when a requirement for large bandwidth has resulted in a lower maser gain, in which case the noise contribution due to the receiver becomes substantial.

[4] This receiver noise temperature (T_R) is the effective receiver input noise temperature defined as $(F_R - 1)290$ where F_R is the receiver noise factor expressed as a power ratio. See also, J. Greene, "Noise factor and noise temperature," PROC. IRE, vol. 46, p. 2A; January, 1958.

[5] The noise temperature corresponding to the noise power available *from* the input terminals of a receiver is, in general, not equal to the effective input noise temperature T_R. For example, the input impedance of a crystal mixer acts as a resistive noise generator at room temperature (about 290°K). For a particular RCA 6861 low-noise traveling-wave tube, it was measured to be 470°K at 2700 mc.

[6] It is assumed that the noise power available from the ferrite circulator is equal to that available from a matched resistive network having the same dissipative loss in the direction of propagation that is of interest.

[7] H. T. Friis, "Noise figures of radio receivers," PROC. IRE, vol. 32, pp. 419–422; July, 1944.

[8] Additional noise sources that must be considered, but that are not included in the present discussion, are the dissipative losses in the antenna itself, and the noise temperature seen by the antenna. Since the latter contribution can be substantial, and may be the limiting factor in system sensitivity, extreme refinement in the design of the circulator maser system may be unnecessary in some applications.

[9] A. L. McWhorter and F. R. Arams, "System-noise measurement of a solid-state maser," this issue, p. 913.

[10] C. L. Hogan, "The low-frequency problem in the design of microwave gyrators and associated elements," IRE TRANS. ON ANTENNAS AND PROPAGATION, vol. 4, pp. 495–501; July, 1956.

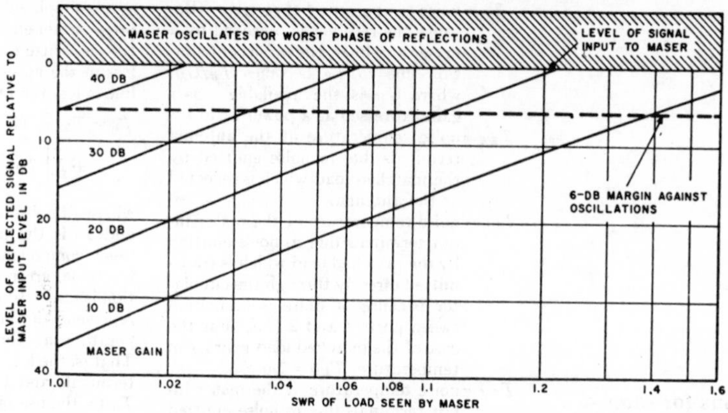

Fig. 2—Effect of load swr and maser gain on maser stability.

tion of some of the amplified signal back into the maser. Fig. 2 is a calculated plot of the level of the reflected amplified signal relative to the input signal as a function of load impedance, expressed in terms of swr. The parameter is maser gain in db. The shaded area represents the conditions of load swr and maser gain for which oscillations may occur. Thus, for a maser gain of 20 db, and for a reflection of arbitrary phase, a 6-db minimum margin to prevent oscillations is obtained by holding the swr to 1.1. The permissible value of swr can be increased by controlling the phase of the reflection or decreasing the oscillation margin.

Reflections from all components of the system will contribute to the swr at the maser terminals. Contributions due to antenna and receiver mismatch may be significant, even though isolated by L_{31} and L_{32}, respectively. For example, it is required that $L_{32}=25$ db in order to reduce a receiver swr of 2 to a value of 1.04 as seen by the maser.

From the above considerations, it can be concluded that the noise and stability requirements for a low-noise circulator maser system are as follows:

Noise

1) The circulator must have a low dissipative loss (a few tenths of a decibel) and an isolation of 25 db or more.
2) The antenna swr should be about 1.1, unless the matched termination of circulator port 4 is refrigerated.
3) The dissipative loss in the maser input-output line and in the antenna feedline must be low.
4) The maser gain should exceed 20 db to reduce the receiver noise contribution to a low value.

Stability

The swr seen by the maser must be low (unless the phases of the reflections are controlled). This in turn requires

1) A low circulator swr.
2) Reasonable antenna and receiver swr in combination with high circulator isolation.

The noise and stability considerations discussed above result in stringent requirements on circulator performance, which become increasingly difficult to realize at the lower microwave frequencies.[10] Fig. 3 shows

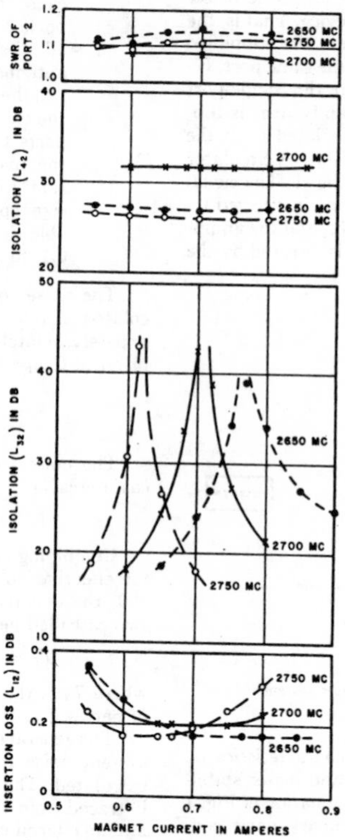

Fig. 3—*S*-band circulator performance.

the measured characteristics (near 2700 mc) of a tunable circulator that was developed for *S*-band maser application. The circulator insertion loss was less than 0.2 db near 2700 mc, and remained below 0.4 db from 2300 to 3150 mc (30 per cent bandwidth). The increase in loss is believed to be due to bandwidth limitations in the hybrid junctions rather than to losses in the ferrite.

Helpful discussions with J. Greene, B. Salzberg, and E. G. Fubini are gratefully acknowledged.

F. R. Arams
G. Krayer
Airborne Instruments Lab., Inc.
Mineola, N. Y.

Proposal for a Maser-Amplifier System Without Nonreciprocal Elements*

A cavity-type solid-state maser[1,2] is intrinsically a regenerative device, so to take full advantage of its low-noise properties[3] one wishes to prevent noise from being fed back from its load; otherwise, the noise temperature of the system cannot be lower than that of the load (presumably a vacuum tube or crystal converter having an effective temperature greater than 290°K). A nonreciprocal device such as a ferrite circulator has been suggested[1] and appears to be the best solution, at least until means are found for using the gyromagnetic properties of the paramagnetic salt to make the maser itself nonreciprocal. However, as masers have been operated at frequencies such as 1380 mc[4,5] and even 300 mc[6] where satisfactory ferrite circulators are not yet available, and because this situation seems likely to continue for some time at low frequencies, a look into the possibility of using cavity masers without circulators seems worth while.

The most direct approach is to introduce attenuation between the maser and its load by some lossless power-dividing network such as a directional coupler. This reduces the noise fed back into the maser by sacrificing gain, but may be useful if enough gain remains (at the desired bandwidth) to overcome the noise from the next amplifier stage.

The system we wish to propose requires two matched masers but involves no loss of gain-bandwidth and is capable in principle of giving a system noise figure equal to that of the masers. As seen in Fig. 1, signal power entering arm 3 of a magic T (this may be coaxial or waveguide, or might be a side-outlet T) divides equally between arms 1 and 2 and is amplified and reflected by the masers. If the masers and the lengths of arms 1 and 2 are adjusted so that the reflected waves are 180° out of phase at the junction, they will combine and go up arm 4 to the receiver. Noise from the receiver also divides between arms 1 and 2, but with 180° phase difference; therefore, the amplified noise returns to the junction in phase, goes up arm 3, and is radiated by the antenna. Ideally the gain, noise, and bandwidth are all the same as for a single maser with an ideal circulator.

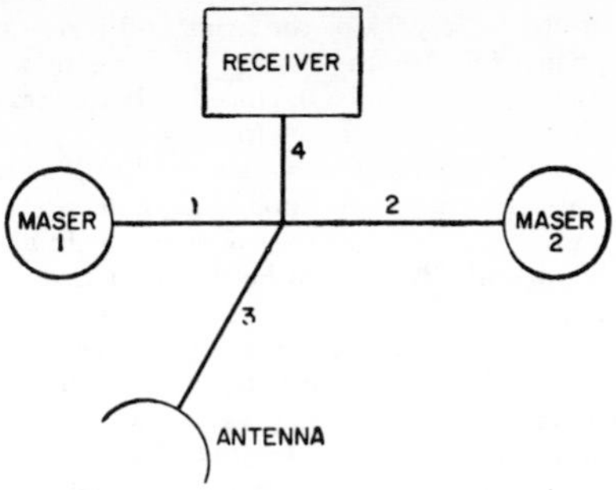

Fig. 1—Balanced amplifier using two one-port masers and a magic T. Arms 1 and 2 differ in length by $\lambda/4$. Variable phase-shifters and attenuators for balancing the bridge are not shown.

Of course, for a number of reasons an actual system will fall short of this performance. Eq. (1) gives the noise temperature, T, of the system

$$T = T_1 + \frac{T_2}{G} + \frac{T_2'}{4}\left(\frac{\epsilon^2}{4} + \phi^2\right) + T_2'GR \quad (1)$$

where

T_1 = the noise temperature of the masers,
T_2 = the noise temperature of the receiver,
T_2' = the temperature of the noise emitted to the maser by the receiver at the signal frequency,
G = the maser gain,
R = the power-reflection coefficient in arm 3,
$\epsilon = G_2 - G_1/G_1$ is the fractional difference in gain between the two masers,
ϕ = the relative phase difference in radians for round trips in arms 1 and 2.

All terms are equivalent noise temperatures at the input of the system and are related to the usual noise figure, F, by $T = 290 (F-1)$. The first term, the noise temperature of the masers, is of the order of 1°K.

The second term is the noise contributed by the receiver. If $G = 20$ db, a receiver noise figure of 6 db makes this term about 9°K.

The third term represents the part of the noise emitted by the receiver which is amplified by the masers and transmitted back to the receivers due to residual unbalance between arms 1 and 2. It is calculated in the Appendix. After the system has been balanced (using a variable phase-shifter and cold attenuator if necessary), any changes will introduce noise. If the maser gains fluctuate by less than ± 1 per cent each, $\epsilon^2/4 < 10^{-4}$ and the noise contribution is less than 0.013°K. The phase unbalance, ϕ, contains contributions α due to variations in the

* Received by the IRE, May 16, 1958. The research in this document was supported jointly by the Army, Navy, and Air Force under contract with Mass. Inst. Tech.

[1] N. Bloembergen, "Proposal for a new solid state maser," *Phys. Rev.*, vol. 104, pp. 324–327; October 15, 1956.

[2] A. L. McWhorter and J. W. Meyer, "Solid-state maser amplifier," *Phys. Rev.*, vol. 109, pp. 312–318; January 15, 1958.

[3] A. L. McWhorter and F. R. Arams, "System-noise measurement of a solid-state maser," PROC. IRE, vol. 46, pp. 913–914; April, 1958.

[4] J. O. Artman, N. Bloembergen, and S. Shapiro, "Three-level solid-state maser at 21 cm," *Phys. Rev.*, vol. 109, pp. 1392–1393; February 15, 1958.

[5] S. H. Autler and N. McAvoy, "21-cm solid-state maser," *Phys. Rev.*, vol. 10, pp. 280–281; April 1, 1958.

[6] R. H. Kingston, "A uhf solid-state maser," PROC. IRE, vol. 46, p. 916; April, 1958.

electrical lengths of the arms and β due to phase shifts in the masers. Passive microwave bridges can be balanced to better than 80 db, corresponding to $\alpha^2=4\times 10^{-3}$, so maintaining $\alpha^2<10^{-4}$ should not be difficult. Variations in β are about $2\Delta\nu/B$ where $\Delta\nu$ and B are the maser's frequency drift and bandwidth. If $B=200$ kc, a maser drift of 1 kc will cause 10^{-2} radians phase shift equivalent to about 0.012°K input noise. It seems that this third term represents a (fluctuating) noise temperature which need not exceed a few hundredths of a degree.

The last term, which may be the most troublesome, is due to noise from the receiver, amplified by the maser but then reflected in arm 3 or at the antenna. With $G=20$ db, a VSWR of 1.02 gives 4.5°K, while 1.05 gives 27°K, and 1.10 gives 104°K. As an untuned antenna may have a VSWR of 1.2 or greater it would probably be necessary to tune it; if the antenna is movable, variations of VSWR with position might complicate matters. The problem of matching the antenna might be eased by using a reasonably good ferrite isolator operating at room temperature; at a given frequency isolators will probably become available before circulators.[7] A perfect isolator inserted in arm 3 would emit no noise toward the junction but would absorb the high-temperature noise ($T_2'G$) traveling toward the antenna, reemitting only 290° noise. An actual isolator would contribute an additional input noise of about 7°K for each 0.1 db of forward attenuation, while imperfect isolation would allow some of the high-temperature noise to reach the antenna.

To summarize, a system noise temperature of 30°K or less (not including antenna noise) should be obtainable. For given values of T_2, T_2', and R there is an optimum gain given by $G_{opt}=T_2/T_2'R$. A low noise figure would be obtained only for the frequency band over which the masers are matched, so it would probably be desirable to make the receiver bandwidth less than that of the masers. We might remark that this type of balanced system could also be useful in connection with other types of low-noise amplifiers such as parametric amplifiers.

The author would like to express his appreciation for helpful discussions with a number of his colleagues, particularly R. H. Kingston, A. L. McWhorter, and J. W. Meyer.

Appendix

We wish to calculate the temperature, T_4, of the noise power reaching the receiver. V_4, the amplitude of the wave generated in arm 4, is proportional to the vector difference between the waves in arms 1 and 2 traveling toward the junction or

$$V_4^2 = \tfrac{1}{2}[V_1^2 + V_2^2 - 2V_1V_2 \cos\phi]$$

where V_1 and V_2 are the amplitudes of the two incoming waves and will be assumed ap-approximately equal; ϕ is their phase difference at the junction and assumed nearly zero.

Then

$$V_4^2 \approx \frac{V_1^2}{2}\left[\left(1-\frac{V_2}{V_1}\right)^2+\phi^2\right]$$

$$\left(\frac{V_2}{V_1}\right)^2 = \frac{G_2}{G_1}$$

where G_2 and G_1 are the power gains of the two masers and if

$$\epsilon = \frac{G_2 - G_1}{G_1}$$

$$\frac{V_2}{V_1} \approx 1 + \frac{\epsilon}{2}, \quad \epsilon \text{ small,}$$

so

$$V_4^2 \approx \frac{V_1^2}{2}\left(\frac{\epsilon^2}{4}+\phi^2\right).$$

Now,

$$V_1^2 \text{ is proportional to } \frac{G_1T_2'}{2},$$

so

$$\frac{T_4}{T_2'} = \frac{G_1}{4}\left(\frac{\epsilon^2}{4}+\phi^2\right)$$

where T_4 is the temperature of the noise power reaching the second stage. Its equivalent temperature at the input is

$$\frac{T_2'}{4}\left(\frac{\epsilon^2}{4}+\phi^2\right).$$

S. H. Autler
Lincoln Lab., M.I.T.
Lexington, Mass.

[7] G. S. Heller and G. W. Catuna, "Measurement of ferrite isolation at 1300 mc," IRE Trans. on Microwave Theory and Techniques, vol. MTT-6, pp. 97–100; January, 1958.

Reprinted from THE REVIEW OF SCIENTIFIC INSTRUMENTS, Vol. 32, No. 2, 202–203, February, 1961

Use of a Y-Type Circulator Switch with a 21-Centimeter Maser Radiometer

B. F. C. COOPER*

Harvard College Observatory, Cambridge 38, Massachusetts

(Received May 18, 1960; and in final form, September 20, 1960)

THE present note describes an adaptation of an L-band Y-type circulator[1] as a Dicke comparison switch for a 21-cm maser radiometer.[2] Although the Y circulator does not appear promising for this application, because of the high magnetic field strength which must be reversed and because of the high VSWR and insertion loss during field reversal, nevertheless, it is the only compact circulator available at this wavelength with low insertion loss and good isolation.

The benefits of a nonreciprocal comparison switch are well known to radiometer designers,[3] and in the case of a regenerative maser the extra isolation which the circulator switch provides between the maser and its source impedances is particularly beneficial.

The present switch has been incorporated into the 21-cm maser radiometer at Harvard Observatory in place of the automatic gain stabilization system which was previously adopted.[2] When the latter system was used, baseline drifts were sometimes observed on the output recorder which could not be ascribed to failure of the gain stabilization per se, but rather to small variations of the radiometer input noise temperature.

This source of baseline drift has been eliminated by adopting the Dicke comparison principle which cancels the effects of gain and noise temperature variations in stages following the comparison switch.

Figure 1 is a block schematic diagram of the radiometer modified to use the circulator switch. The switch alternately connects the input port of the main circulator to the antenna and to a reference load immersed in the liquid helium bath. The effective noise temperatures of the two terminations are equalized by adding noise to the reference arm through a 20-db coupler whose side arm is connected to a continuously running noise lamp through a ferrite modulator (Microwave Engineering Labs., model CL1). The noise temperatures are balanced by controlling the dc current in the modulator. A calibration noise signal may also be injected into the system through an auxiliary 10-db coupler.

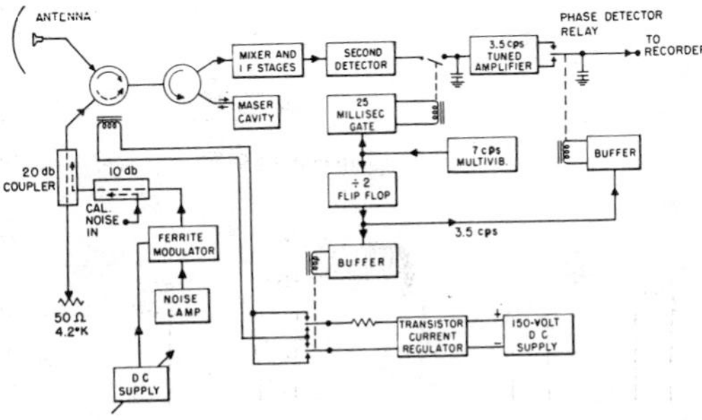

FIG. 1. Harvard College Observatory 21-cm maser using a circulator switch.

The switch is constructed around a Raytheon circulator disk (model CLL11) which has been fitted with a laminated core and a 2400-turn winding. A current of approximately 0.68 amp at 17 v is required in this winding to bias the circulator to the point of minimum insertion loss and maximum isolation. Owing to the long time constant of the winding (~50 msec), special measures have been adopted in the switch control circuits and the output circuits of the radiometer. Power for the switch winding is derived from a 150-v dc supply which is followed by a transistor current regulator. Most of the dc power is dissipated in a series resistor whose presence reduces the circuit time constant to approximately 8 msec. Current is reversed by a double-pole relay with mercury-wetted contacts (Clare HG 3A 1003). Upon reversal of the relay the buildup of switch current in the new direction takes approximately 20 msec to the point where the transistor regulator becomes effective. A relatively low switching rate of 3.5 cps has been adopted to minimize the proportion of time that is occupied by change-over periods.

Since the switch insertion loss is high during these periods, the receiver output consists of 25-msec bursts of room temperature noise sandwiched between 125-msec bursts of low temperature noise from the antenna and the reference source. The change-over noise is blanked out by a relay which is interposed between the second detector and the 3.5-cps tuned amplifier and is opened during change-over periods. A capacitor at the input of the tuned amplifier holds the voltage that existed just prior to the change-over. The tuned amplifier has a high impedance input. Push-pull output is provided so that a single-pole relay may be used as a phase-sensitive output detector.

Total input noise temperature of the radiometer is now approximately 100°K, made up of 70°K due to ohmic losses in the two circulators and the coaxial cables, 20°K from antenna "spillover", and 10°K from the second stage. Recorder fluctuations, referred to the input, are 0.1°K peak to peak for a bandwidth of 1 Mc and integration time of 50 sec, and 0.25°K peak to peak for a bandwidth of 200 kc and integration time of 50 sec. No difficulty is occasioned by the low switching rate of 3.5 cps as the maser gain drifts slowly at a rate never more than 0.05 db/min. In fact, deliberately induced sudden gain changes of 0.2 db produce no noticeable effect in the switched output channel provided the input noise temperature balance is accurate. By the same token, the maser gain changes which may amount to ± 0.2 db during an observation produce no significant baseline shifts.

Astronomical observations made with this instrument will be published elsewhere.

Since the Y-type circulator is now available at frequencies as low as 400 Mc the possibility exists of devising switches similar to the one described for UHF radiometers using parametric amplifiers.

I am indebted to Dr. S. J. Goldstein for many valuable suggestions made during the course of the work described here, and to Mr. W. Weiler for much of the constructional work.

* On leave from the Commonwealth Scientific and Industrial Research Organization, Sydney, Australia.

[1] L. Davis, Jr., V. Milano, and J. Saunders, Proc. IRE **48**, 115 (1960).

[2] B. F. C. Cooper and J. V. Jelley, Proc. Northeast Electronics Research and Engineering Meeting (Boston, 1959); Rev. Sci. Instr. **32**, 166 (1961).

[3] C. H. Mayer, IRE Trans. on Microwave Theory and Tech. **MTT-4**, 24 (1956).

Silvered Ruby Maser Cavity*

LLOYD G. CROSS
The University of Michigan, Willow Run Laboratories, Ann Arbor, Michigan
(Received May 11, 1959)

SHORTLY after ruby was proposed as a maser material,[1] it occurred to us that the metal bonding properties of ruby could be utilized to prepare silver-coated ruby maser cavities. Since then we have constructed several *X*-band cavity masers using rectangular parallelepipeds of ruby coated with a thin layer of metallic silver as the maser cavity. Figure 1 is a photograph of 3 typical cavities.

FIG. 1. *X*-Band silvered ruby cavities.

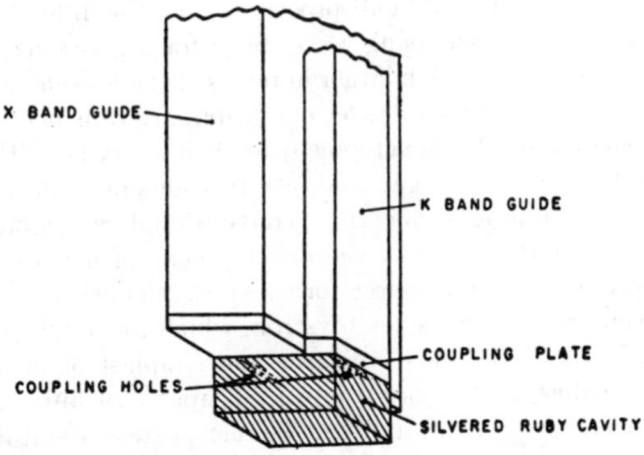

FIG. 2. *X*-Band maser assembly using silvered ruby cavity.

The silvering procedure is quite simple and requires little preparation. After the ruby is cut and ground to the desired cavity dimensions, it is washed in acetone and a very thin coat of silver paint (Hanovia No. 32-A) is applied to the surfaces. The sample is then baked at 700°C for approximately 30 min. Two more coats are applied as before and the treatment is completed. This procedure was suggested by the work done on lavite cavities in this laboratory.[2]

To provide the microwave coupling to the cavity, slots are cut in the silvering with a dust cutter. The dust cutter provides a thin stream of forced air carrying Al_2O_3 dust which removes the silvering quickly and accurately without cutting the ruby. Using this procedure the coupling slots may be cut to any desired geometry, and if a change is required, the slots can be resilvered and cut again.

The resulting loss "Q" for a silvered ruby cavity is very close to the calculated maximum. In a particular case of a cavity of dimensions 0.68×0.5×0.45 in. the loss "Q" for the TM-112 mode was observed to be approximately 4000. Since the loss tangent of ruby is given as 0.0002, the limiting "Q" due to dielectric losses alone is 5000. The silver coating will not flake or chip off and can be scraped off only with difficulty. Repeated temperature cycling from 300 to 4.2°K has shown no observable effect on any of the cavities.

A practical advantage of the silvered ruby cavity over the ordinary machined cavity is the considerable saving in machining time and expense, especially when the cavity design is in the experimental stage. It is also inherently more stable and less lossy than the ordinary metal cavity. These cavities may be soldered to a wave-guide structure in the manner shown in Fig. 2, or, to allow for more versatility, simply clamped to the coupling plate. In this manner several cavities covering a range of frequencies can be used interchangeably with a single wave-guide structure.

The author wishes to acknowledge the encouragement of R. W. Terhune and J. Lambe during the progress of this work.

* This research was supported by Project Michigan (administered by the U. S. Army Signal Corps).
[1] Makhov, Kikuchi, Lambe, and Terhune, Phys. Rev. **109**, 1399 (1958).
[2] J. Lambe and R. Ager, Rev. Sci. Instr. (submitted for publication).

Reprinted from IRE TRANSACTIONS
ON MICROWAVE THEORY AND TECHNIQUES
Volume MTT-9, Number 2, March, 1961

Resonators for Millimeter and Submillimeter Wavelengths*

WILLIAM CULSHAW†, SENIOR MEMBER, IRE

***Summary*—Further considerations on the mm-wave Fabry-Perot interferometer are presented. Computed Q values for parallel metal plate resonators indicate that at spacings around 2.5 cm, values ranging from 60,000 at 3 mm, to 300,000 at 0.1 mm wavelengths are possible. The plates must, however, be quite flat. These results are important for many investigations, and in particular for mm and sub-mm wave maser research. For the aperture per wavelength ratios possible here, diffraction effects should be small. Consideration is given to using curved reflectors or focused radiation in applications where the fields must be concentrated. For this purpose, re-entrant conical spherical resonators are treated in detail, as regards operation in the TEM mode at high orders of interference. Expressions for the Q and shunt impedance are given, and high values are possible at mm and sub-mm wavelengths. Quasi-optical methods of coupling into and out of such a resonator are proposed, and the higher modes possible in such a resonator are considered. Results indicate that it could have application to the mm-wave generation problem, and that it represents a good resonant cavity for solid-state research at mm and sub-mm wavelengths, and for maser applications in particular.**

Introduction

In the region of wavelengths extending downwards from around 1 mm to the long infrared, much important research needs to be done, and many important applications arise. At these wavelengths, conventional cavity resonators become extremely minute, since their dimensions are around one-half wavelength. For some purposes, cavities of larger dimensions, capable of sustaining a number of higher order modes, are possible. This is a difficult procedure, and the difficulties increase with decreasing wavelength for a given size of cavity. Cavities much larger in terms of the wavelength, but which permit mode-free operation, are thus needed. In particular, the development of such a cavity with a suitable interaction gap and new methods of input and output coupling other than conventional waveguides would greatly assist in the development of a primary coherent electronic source for these wavelengths.

Referring to the reflex klystron, which for many purposes is still the most versatile and simplest of microwave tubes, such a cavity must be capable of bunching the electron stream, and hence must possess a suitable interaction gap of small dimensions compared to the wavelength. It also should have a large resonator volume for heat dissipation and a high shunt impedance for efficient electronic interaction. New methods for coupling into and out of the resonator are also necessary. There are other problems, as well, in the design of such tubes for very short wavelengths; another very important one being the provision of an adequate current density at these short wavelengths where the area of the electron beam for efficient interaction with the resonator steadily decreases. This difficulty would certainly be helped by providing larger, more efficient, and more suitable resonators. The required current densities in the resonator gap could possibly be approached with improved cathodes and by the use of suitable magnetic or

* Received by the PGMTT, July 8, 1960; revised manuscript received, October 31, 1960.
† Natl. Bur. of Standards, Boulder Labs., Boulder, Colo.

other focusing devices. In any event, such a resonator development would permit the extension of klystron techniques to shorter wavelengths, and could lead to easier construction techniques and higher powers from tubes presently available at wavelengths extending from 8 mm to around 2.5 mm.

Some progress in this general direction was effected by the development of the dielectric tube resonator.[1] This was used to produce interaction with highly bunched electron beams traveling at relativistic velocities.[2] Such cavities, however, are still not large enough in terms of the wavelength, they do not possess high enough Q values for many purposes, and their use would seem to be limited. Another possibility which seems to possess considerable potential for application in all areas of mm wave research is the mm-wave Fabry-Perot interferometer.[3,4] While this form of resonator is eminently suitable for many purposes, there are other applications, such as the electronic generation problem, or solid-state research, for which a smaller interaction space is desirable. Thus one might make the reflectors spherical and use focused radiation between them. Here diffraction problems arise,[5] and while such a system should resonate at infrared or shorter wavelengths, it may not do so at longer mm wavelengths, unless it is large. In any event, it is difficult to confine the field into linear dimensions even of the order of a wavelength in extent, and such a degree of confinement is not sufficient for the efficient bunching of electron streams as in a klystron. Thus, one must consider the provision of side walls round the interferometer, and a deformation of this into a cavity resonator bounded by two re-entrant cones and a sphere. Such a cavity was considered in the classical paper by Hansen and Richtmeyer[6] on resonators suitable for klystron oscillators, and it has also received considerable attention, particularly by Schelkunoff,[7,8] in the treatment of biconical antennas. At longer wavelengths, other types of resonators proved more suitable. However, at mm and sub-mm wavelengths, such conventional resonators become very small and serious problems arise in heat dissipation, low Q factors, low shunt impedance and in fabrication.

The paper presents a new appraisal of the biconical spherical resonator in the light of the new developments in the mm-wave Fabry-Perot interferometer and the possibility of operating such a biconical resonator at large orders of interference. This would provide a suitable resonator for the purposes discussed above. Features which help this approach considerably are that the coupling into the large biconical resonator is possible by a whole series of regularly spaced coupling holes as in the mm-wave interferometer, and optical methods such as focusing may be used to get the radiation into and out of such a resonator. Such methods seem highly desirable in this wavelength region.

Planar Millimeter Wave Interferometer or Resonator

Fig. 1 shows the mm-wave interferometer as used in transmission measurements.[4] The reflector system may be regarded as a resonant cavity formed by the parallel metal plates and the multiple reflections of plane waves between them. The holes are then exactly analogous to the coupling holes or irises used in microwave cavity resonators, and they provide the means for coupling into and out of the resonance region between the plates, while preserving the large Q value of the metal plate region. For small holes, the loading on the interferometer due to the generator and load impedances is small and can be adjusted by the hole diameter. Side wall losses are essentially absent except for diffraction effects, which can be kept small, and which decrease with decreasing wavelength. This results in a Q for the interferometer which increases directly as the order of interference. Referring to Fig. 1, the field at resonance due to plane waves between the plates with the origin as shown is given by

$$E_y = -2jE_0 \sin (n\pi z/d),$$
$$\eta H_x = 2E_0 \cos (n\pi z/d), \tag{1}$$

where d is the distance between the plates, E_0 is a constant, and $\eta = (\mu/\epsilon)^{1/2}$ is the intrinsic impedance of the medium between the plates in mks units. The energy stored and the mean power lost per unit area of the plates may be deduced from (1), and hence the unloaded Q determined, *viz.*,

$$Q_0 = \lambda/\Delta\lambda = n\pi/(1 - R), \tag{2}$$

where $R = 1 - (8\epsilon\omega/\sigma)^{1/2}$ is the power-reflection coefficient of the metal, ϵ and μ are its permittivity and permeability, usually equal to those of free space, σ is the conductivity, and ω is the angular frequency. In terms of the fringe width Δd between half power points we may write, using the equation $2d = n\lambda$,

$$Q_d = \lambda/\Delta d = 2\pi/(1 - R). \tag{3}$$

[1] R. C. Becker and P. D. Coleman, "The dielectric tube resonator: a device for the generation and measurement of millimeter and submillimeter waves," *Proc. Symp. on Millimeter Waves*, Polytechnic Inst. of Brooklyn, Brooklyn, N. Y., pp. 191–222; March, 1959.

[2] M. D. Sirkis and P. D. Coleman, "The harmodotron—a megavolt electronics millimeter wave generator," *J. Appl. Phys.*, vol. 28, pp. 944–950; September, 1957.

[3] W. Culshaw, "Reflectors for a microwave Fabry-Perot interferometer," IRE Trans. on Microwave Theory and Techniques, vol. MTT-7, pp. 221–228; April, 1959.

[4] W. Culshaw, "High resolution millimeter wave Fabry-Perot interferometer," IRE Trans. on Microwave Theory and Techniques, vol. MTT-8, pp. 182–189; March, 1960.

[5] G. W. Farnell, "Measured phase distribution in the image space of a microwave lens," *Canad. J. Phys.*, vol. 36, pp. 935–943; July, 1958.

[6] W. W. Hansen and R. D. Richtmeyer, "On resonators suitable for klystron oscillators," *J. Appl. Phys.*, vol. 10, pp. 189–199; March, 1939.

[7] S. A. Schelkunoff, "Electromagnetic Waves," D. Van Nostrand Book Co., Inc., New York, N. Y., pp. 285–290; 1943.

[8] S. A. Schelkunoff, "Advanced Antenna Theory," John Wiley and Sons, Inc., New York, N. Y., pp. 32–71; 1952.

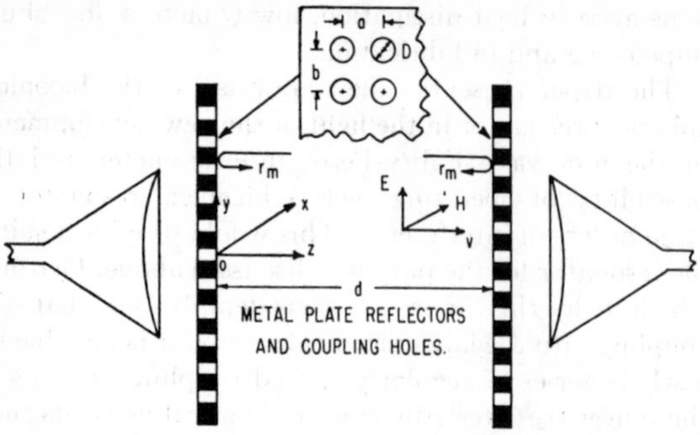

Fig. 1—Millimeter wave Fabry-Perot interferometer.

Since R will be around 0.999 for a metal at these frequencies, (3) shows that the metal plates must be quite flat, within 1/1000 of the operating wavelength.

Table I gives values of Q_0 for wavelengths extending into the submillimeter region and illustrates the great advantages of the Fabry-Perot interferometer, since it would be very difficult, if not impossible, to make conventional cavity resonators for these wavelengths. In contrast to these results, ideally an unloaded Q value of some 9000 would be obtained at 1 mm wavelength with a cylindrical cavity of diameter 0.060 inch operating in the $TE_{01,50}$ mode. This interferometer is thus ideal for many purposes, permitting the use of relatively large structures at these very short wavelengths with freedom from most higher order modes.

TABLE I

Computed Unloaded Q Values for Silver Plates Spaced 2.5 CM Apart in a MM-Wave Interferometer (Conductivity σ Taken as 6.139×10^7 Mhos/M).

λ_{mm}	n	R	Q_0
3.125	16	0.99917	60,300
2.0	25	0.99896	75,300
1.0	50	0.99852	106,500
0.5	100	0.99792	150,000
0.1	500	0.99533	333,900

At suitable terminals, the holes may be regarded as perfect transformers, which enable us to couple into the metal plate resonator, in a uniform and efficient manner. Equivalent circuits for the mm-wave Fabry-Perot interferometer may now be drawn, and are shown in Fig. 2(a) and 2(b) for the transmission and reaction types respectively. The hole size may now be fixed by equating the reflectivity of the bulk metal to that deduced by regarding the hole as a reactive structure on a transmission line.[3] Smaller and larger hole sizes than those given by this criterion correspond respectively to lower and higher values of loading on the interferometer than those given by the matched condition. Such reflectors will have adequate bandwidth for mm-maser and spectroscopy applications, and designs can be optimized for any given wavelength region. The application of the

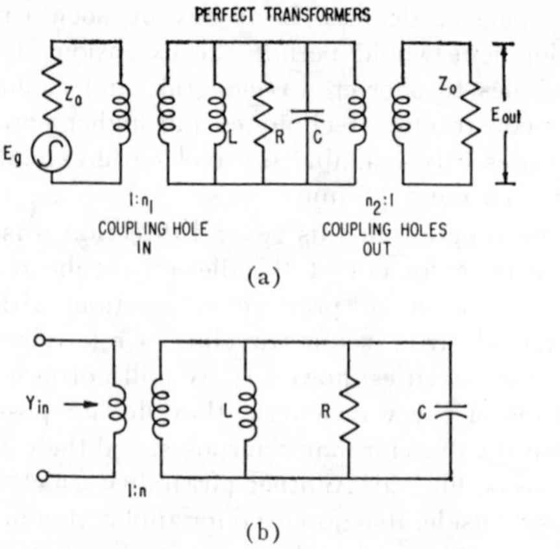

Fig. 2—Equivalent circuits for interferometer. (a) Transmission type. (b) Reaction type.

Fabry-Perot interferometer to the problem of mm-wave masers and spectroscopy is under active development.

Curved or Focused Fabry-Perot Resonators

For some experiments and applications, the planar type of interferometer or resonator is not suitable. Examples of this occur in solid-state research, optical-maser work, and electronic interaction with electric fields. Here, the resonator fields must be concentrated into a smaller volume, and it is natural to consider the use of cylindrical or spherical Fabry-Perot plates and focused radiation to produce concentrated fields in the vicinity of a focus. Such an arrangement might resonate in an analogous way to the plane reflector geometry, and coupling again be effected by a whole series of coupling holes. Fig. 3 shows a possible arrangement for a transmission interferometer employing curved reflectors. Either cylindrical or spherical reflectors could be used with appropriate lenses. The lines showing the concentration of the field and the constant-phase fronts are purely qualitative, but indicate approximately the field distribution between such plates.

The field distribution near the focus of a converging spherical wave has received extensive theoretical study.[9] With the coherent microwave sources and techniques now available, the field distribution in such regions can be experimentally determined. Such work has substantiated the results obtained by applying scalar diffraction theory to this problem when the aperture dimensions are some twenty wavelengths or more in extent,[5] and the regions of interest are close to the axis and somewhat distant from the lens. The literature on this subject is quite extensive, and we shall limit our remarks to those closely connected with the idea of using curved Fabry-Perot resonators.

[9] M. Born and E. Wolf, "Principles of Optics," Pergamon Press, London, Eng. pp. 434–448; 1959.

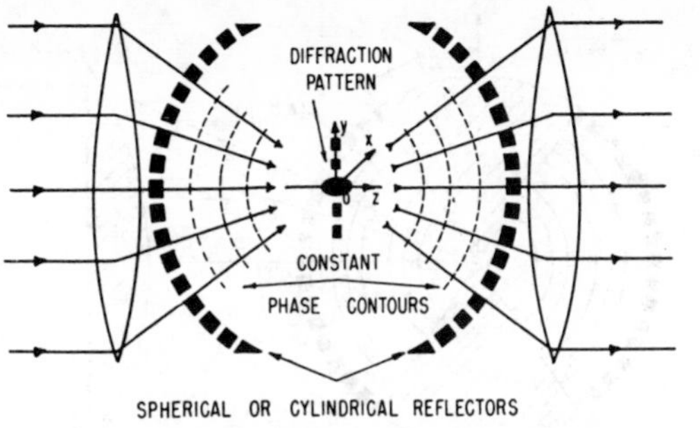

Fig. 3—Focused Fabry-Perot interferometer.

A full treatment of the problem for optics is given in reference 9, and general expressions are derived for the field in the focal region. Referring to Fig. 3, isophotes, or contour lines of intensity $I(p, q)$ near the focus of a converging spherical wave, as well as contours of equal phase, are given. Here $p=\beta z(a/f)^2$, and $q=\beta\rho(a/f)$, where $2a$ is the aperture diameter, f is the focal length, $\beta=2\pi/\lambda$, and $\rho=(x^2+y^2)^{1/2}$ is the radial distance in the focal plane $z=0$. In optics, the intensity distribution is symmetrical about the geometrical focal plane and also about the z axis. Also, the surfaces of constant phase are surfaces of revolution about the z axis. At a distance from the focus, the constant phase surfaces coincide with the spherical wave fronts of geometrical optics but become gradually deformed near the focal region. In the immediate region of the focus, the constant phase surfaces are plane, and on passing through this region, they gradually deform and again become spherical, but with opposite curvature.

In the focal plane $z=0$, the intensity is given by[9]

$$I(0, q) = \left[\frac{2J_1(q)}{q}\right]^2 I_0, \tag{4}$$

where J_1 is the usual Bessel function. This distribution is characteristic of the Airy-ring diffraction pattern in the image plane of an optical lens.[10] Along the z axis, the field intensity is given by

$$I(p, 0) = \left[\frac{\sin p/4}{p/4}\right]^2 I_0. \tag{5}$$

Eqs. (4) and (5) indicate the degree of confinement of the field possible in the focal region for given ratios of f/a. The first zero of $J_1(q)$ is at $q=3.83$; and for $f/a=4$, the radius to the zero of the central ring is 2.5λ. Along the z axis, the first zeros occur for $z=\pm f^2\lambda/2a^2$, and for $f/a=4$, we obtain $z=\pm 8\lambda$.

Farnell[5] discusses the field in the image space of a microwave lens, the main differences from optics arising because of the much smaller aperture to wavelength ratios possible with microwaves. With an optical lens, the field in the focal region is concentrated into smaller volumes and approximations can be used which are not necessarily valid for microwaves. Fig. 4 shows measured contours of constant phase in the image space of a microwave lens. This had a diameter of 50 cm, a focal length around 60 cm, and the wavelength used was 3.22 cm. Contours of constant intensity are also given in reference 5. The same general features discussed above for light optics are evident; there are, however, differences in the shape of the contours. Here the constant phase surfaces and the Airy pattern in the focal plane are slightly curved, the center of curvature being at the lens center as shown. Also the center of curvature of the wave diverging from the focus is at the position of maximum intensity which is not at the focus, but at a point some 2 wavelengths nearer the lens. The center of curvature of the converging wave, however, is at the geometrical image or focus. The deviations are due to the larger angular patterns which occur with microwave lenses, and at shorter mm and sub-mm wavelengths with similar aperture sizes, the optics distribution discussed above would be approached.

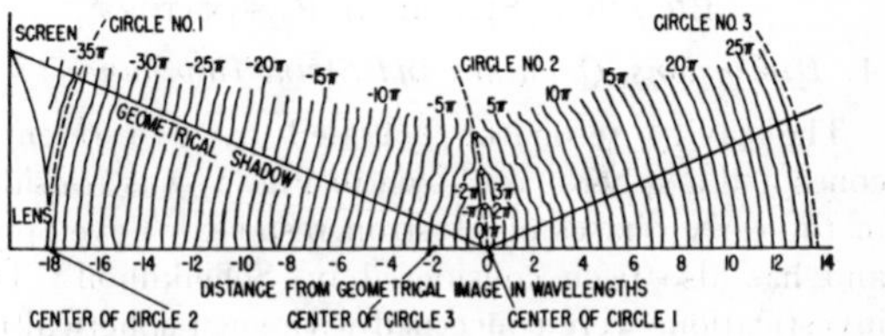

Fig. 4—Measure contours of constant phase in image space of a microwave lens with $R=63$ cm, $a=25$ cm, and $\lambda=3.22$ cm. Phase at geometrical image taken as $\pi/2$ radians. (After G. W. Farnell, *Canad. J. Phys.*, vol. 36, p. 935; 1958.)

Matthews and Cullen[11] have investigated at microwaves a converging spherical wave limited by a rectangular aperture. The approximations used in their analysis correspond to those used in optics, and are therefore valid when the diffraction pattern in the focal region is of small extent. Their deductions and measurements, however, give an interesting physical picture of what happens in the focal region and indicate that there are variations in axial wavelength in the focal region as compared to the free space wavelength. Results in the regions investigated indicated an increase in axial wavelength, or a decrease in the axial propagation constant at small distances either side of the focus. Linfoot and Wolf[12] also deduce that in optics there are regions very near the focus where the nearly plane constant phase surfaces are spaced closer together by a factor $1-a^2/4f^2$ than those in a parallel beam of light of the same wave-

[10] *Ibid.*, pp. 394–397.

[11] P. A. Matthews and A. L. Cullen, "A study of the field distribution at an axial focus of a square microwave lens," *Proc. IEE*, Pt. C., vol. 103, pp. 449–456; July, 1956.

[12] E. H. Linfoot and E. Wolf, "Phase distribution near focus in an aberration-free diffrasion image," *Proc. Phys. Soc.* (*London*), vol. 69, pp. 823–832; November, 1956.

length. There are also regions of rapid phase variation at the nulls of the Airy pattern and along the axis.

We may sum up the possible use of curved reflectors for the mm and sub-mm resonator problem as follows. A spherical or cylindrical converging wavefront limited by an aperture gives a region near the focus where the field is concentrated within distances of a few wavelengths. At optical wavelengths, spherical or cylindrical reflectors placed along appropriate phase contours on either side of the focus should resonate at the appropriate wavelength. As indicated by the work at wavelengths of 3.2 cm, there may be departures from ideal conditions at mm and sub-mm wavelengths, and no such resonance may be possible. The problem in this respect needs further investigation. Such resonator types could thus be useful in optical masers and possibly at very short mm wavelengths, although close attention to the preservation of phase shapes in the focal region when obstacles are inserted would be necessary. Since the field in the focal region is still some wavelengths in extent, such a resonator is not suitable for electron bunching or for harmonic extraction from bunched electron beams.

Biconical Spherical Resonators

A. Dimensions, Q Values and Shunt Impedance

The cavity resonator bounded by two re-entrant cones and a sphere, as shown in Fig. 5, was considered in the early phases of klystron resonator development and has also been considered by Schelkunoff.[7] These investigations were concerned with such spherical resonators of radius equal to $\lambda/4$ or with orders of interference of unity. The feature which makes a new appraisal worthwhile is that such resonators can be operated at higher orders of interference provided facilities exist for coupling into and out of such a resonator in a uniform way and no serious difficulties from higher order modes are encountered. Such a method is that of a whole series of coupling holes as used in the planar Fabry-Perot interferometer. Useful features of such a biconical resonator, especially at mm and sub-mm wavelengths, are that the resonator becomes larger, the Q increases with order of interference, and shunt impedance remains high.

Referring to Fig. 5, if an RF voltage is impressed between the apices of the cones, the principal or TEM mode on such a structure is generated. This has the electric lines coinciding with meridians and the magnetic lines along circles coaxial with the axis as shown. Such a system is equivalent to a transmission line of characteristic impedance given by

$$Z_c = 120 \log \cot (\psi/2), \tag{6}$$

and expressions for the electric and magnetic fields may be obtained.[7] Resonances occur when the radius lq of the spherical boundary is equal to $n\lambda/4$, where n is an integer referred to as the order of interference. Here we consider odd values of n or the case of parallel resonance.

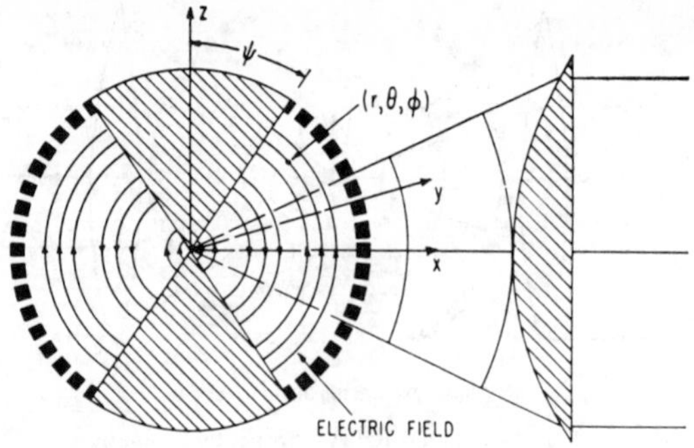

Fig. 5—Biconical spherical resonator and principal TEM mode.

Standing waves then exist in the resonator, and the Q value may be determined for any order n of interference. For equal and opposite cones in the sphere we thus obtain

$$Q_0 = \frac{30\pi^2 n \log \cot (\psi/2)}{R_m[\log \cot (\psi/2) + P \operatorname{cosec} \psi]}, \tag{7}$$

where ψ is the cone angle in Fig. 5 and R_m is the resistive part of the intrinsic impedance of the metal. The parameter P is given by

$$P = \tfrac{1}{2}[C + \log n\pi - Ci(n\pi)], \tag{8}$$

where C is Euler's constant, equal to 0.5772, and the function

$$Ci(x) = \int_\infty^x \frac{\cos t}{t}\, dt, \qquad x > 0. \tag{9}$$

Similarly, the shunt impedance at resonance is given by

$$Z_i = \frac{14400\pi[\log \cot (\psi/2)]^2}{R_m[\log \cot (\psi/2) + P \operatorname{cosec} \psi]} \tag{10}$$

Apart from changes due to the increased order of interference n, (7) and (10) are similar to those given by Schelkunoff.[7]

For $n=1$, Q_0 is a maximum when $\psi = 33.5°$, and is equal to $132/R_m$; hence $Q_0 = 924$ for such a copper resonator at $\lambda = 1$ mm. Also, for $n=1$, Z_i is optimum when $\psi = 9.2°$ and equal to $3.74 \times 10^4/R_m$ ohms; hence for copper $Z_i = 2.6 \times 10^5$ ohms at $\lambda = 1$ mm. It is evident that such a resonator has a high shunt impedance even at short wavelengths, which is a desirable feature for a klystron resonator. However, for $n=1$, the diameter is around 0.020 inch and thus is not very practical. The Q is also low at short wavelengths for this small order of interference.

Fig. 6 shows curves of Q_0 and shunt impedance Z_i for a copper resonator at a wavelength of 1 mm and order of interference $n=41$. As for $n=1$, Q_0 is a maximum when $\psi = 33.5°$. The optimum angle for Z_i depends on n, and is given by

$$P \cot \psi - (2P \operatorname{cosec} \psi)/[\log \cot (\psi/2)] = 1. \tag{11}$$

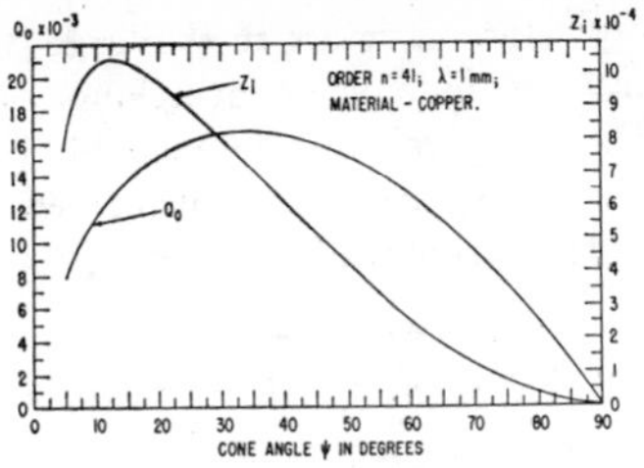

Fig. 6—Unloaded Q values and shunt impedance Z_i of biconical spherical resonator.

Values of Z_i ranging from 75,000 to 100,000 Ω are thus obtained for $n=41$, the diameter of the resonator at $\lambda=1$ mm then being 2 cm. The Q values are also relatively high for this wavelength, ranging up to 16,000. For a klystron resonator, Z_i is the important parameter and must be as high as possible. For other applications a higher Q may be required, and can be obtained by increasing n. Thus for $n=101$ and $\psi=22.5°$, we obtain $Q_0=34{,}200$ and $Z_i=83{,}500$ ohms, with a resonator diameter of 5 cm. The DX 151 Philips klystron for 4 mm wavelengths uses a conventional resonator of diameter 1.6 mm, and height 0.7 mm with a value of Z_i around 77,000 ohms.[13] Such a resonator would thus be extremely small at $\lambda=1$ mm, and Z_i would be reduced to around 38,000 ohms. The advantages of the biconical resonator are thus apparent.

Further computations for $\lambda=0.1$ mm, and $n=401$ are shown in Table II; here the increase in Q should be noted, values of 39,000 now being possible. Due to the increase in R_m at higher frequencies, Z_i decreases but even at $\lambda=0.1$ mm values around 24,000 ohms seem possible. The diameter of this resonator would again be around 2 cm at a sub-mm wavelength of 0.1 mm, an extremely important consideration for many areas of work.

TABLE II

Variation of Q Values and Shunt Impedance Z_i for Biconical Resonators at $\lambda=0.1$ MM and Order of Interference $n=401$

ψ_0	10	13	22.5	33.5
Q_0	26,500	30,200	37,000	39,370
Z_i	24,100	24,400	22,300	17,600

For some purposes the resonator formed by a single re-entrant cone inside a hemisphere, as in Fig. 7, might be useful. Similar considerations apply to this type, and general expressions for Q_0 and Z_i are then

$$Q_0 = \frac{30\pi^2 \, n \log \cot (\psi/2)}{R_m[\log \cot (\psi/2) + P(\operatorname{cosec} \psi + 1)]}, \quad (12)$$

[13] B. B. Van Iperen, "Reflex klystrons for millimeter waves," *Proc. Symp. on Millimeter Waves*, Polytechnic Inst. of Brooklyn, Brooklyn, N. Y., pp. 249–250; March, 1959.

and

$$Z_i = \frac{7200\pi[\log \cot (\psi/2)]^2}{R_m[\log \cot (\psi/2) + P(1 + \operatorname{cosec} \psi)]}. \quad (13)$$

Both Q_0 and Z_i are thus smaller for this resonator, Z_i having around half the value for two re-entrant cones. However, such a resonator could be useful in applications where a number of closely spaced cavities are required.

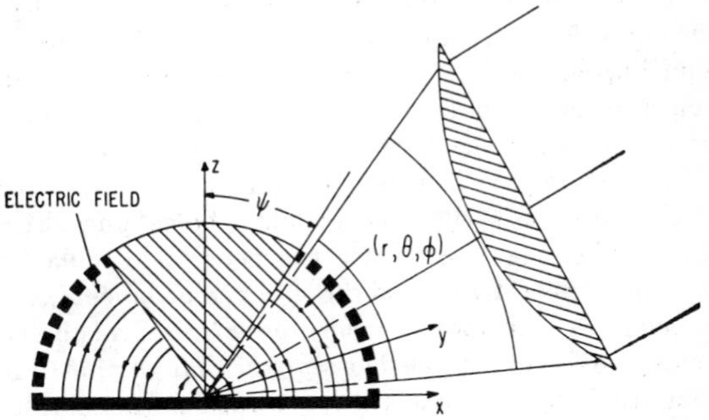

Fig. 7—Hemispherical conical resonator.

B. Coupling Considerations

Ideas on possible forms of coupling into such a resonator arise when it is considered as a distortion of the planar Fabry-Perot interferometer. Hence the design of the whole array of coupling holes will be similar, except now they will be on the surface of the spherical portion and focused radiation must be used as indicated in the figures. The intrinsic impedance of the principal mode is that of free space, *viz*, $E_\theta/H_\phi=\eta$, and the characteristic impedance Z_c may thus be regarded as derived from series and parallel combinations of elemental parallel-plate transmission lines, the number of which are determined by the hole spacings on the spherical surface. Since the number of such holes at fixed spacings around the circle $\theta=$constant on the sphere varies as $\sin\theta$, a resultant Z_c of the form given by (6) is obtained.

From such general considerations, we deduce that the impedance transformations through the equally spaced holes on the spherical surface are identical, since the electric and magnetic walls into which the cavity can be divided give rise to a system of equal parallel-plate transmission lines with intrinsic impedance η. The amplitude transmission coefficients are also identical for all such holes, and since the number of holes around a given latitude varies as $\sin\theta$, and the fields vary as $1/\sin\theta$, the total power transmission from the cavity is the same along each line of latitude. The holes can thus be equally spaced along circles of latitude; some adjustment of the final hole along such a circle will, however, be necessary in general. The same spacings in the θ direction may also be used, but the lines of hole centers need not coincide with lines of longitude.

The biconical resonator may be regarded as a transmission line of length $n\lambda/4$, and of characteristic impedance Z_c given by (6). The impedance across the cone apices for any uniform impedance Z_t over the spherical boundary is then given by

$$Z = Z_c \frac{Z_t + jZ_c \tan \beta l}{Z_c + jZ_t \tan \beta l}, \tag{14}$$

and for $l = n\lambda/4$, $Z = Z_c^2/Z_t$. For a coupling hole system extending over the complete spherical surface, Z_t will be uniform over the surface and may be deduced from the equivalent circuit for such a coupling hole. Thus, the load impedance at the apices can be determined, and hence the degree of loading as compared with the shunt impedance Z_i of the resonator can be deduced.

Another approach which is useful when only a part of the spherical surface has coupling holes, and also in the previous case, is to use the general formulas[7] to determine the Q factor and the shunt impedance Z_i. The impedances transformed from free space through such holes give rise to increased losses over that portion of the spherical boundary concerned, and the external Q values and load impedances can be determined. Thus the result for the increased power loss due to the load coupling will be given by

$$W_L = \tfrac{1}{2} R \int H_\phi H_\phi^* dA, \tag{15}$$

where the limits of integration for ϕ and θ extend over the coupling region on the sphere, and R is the resistive part of the load impedance at the spherical boundary. In this way the effect of various degrees of coupling can be considered and loaded Q values and load impedances determined. A number of coupling holes are thus required, and this approach should be reasonably valid if the area over which energy is coupled into or out of the resonator is large compared with the wavelength; otherwise diffraction effects will be serious. Since such resonators are intended for very short wavelengths this condition can be satisfied.

The coupling may thus be deduced from the equivalent circuit for a single coupling hole in a metal plate, which is shown in Fig. 8. Values of the susceptances are given by the following equations.[14]

$$B_a = \frac{B}{2Y_0} + \frac{|Y_0'|}{Y_0} \tanh\left(\frac{\pi t}{|\lambda_g'|}\right),$$

$$B_b = \frac{|Y_0'|}{Y_0} \operatorname{csch}\left(\frac{2\pi t}{|\lambda_g'|}\right), \tag{16}$$

where in our case $B/2Y_0 = (3a^2\lambda)/(2\pi D^3)$, and

$$\frac{|Y_0'|}{Y_0} = \frac{0.284 a_g^2 \lambda}{D^3}\left[1 - \left(\frac{1.706D}{\lambda}\right)^2\right]^{1/2}, \tag{17}$$

approximately. Here a_g refers to the large dimension of a rectangular waveguide propagating only the dominant mode, and $|\lambda_g'|$ is given in reference 14. For matched conditions in free space, the transformed normalized impedance at the inside wall of the sphere is then given by

$$Z = \frac{B_b^2 + j(B_a + B_b)(B_a^2 + 2B_aB_b + 1)}{(B_a^2 + 2B_aB_b)^2 + (B_a + B_b)^2}. \tag{18}$$

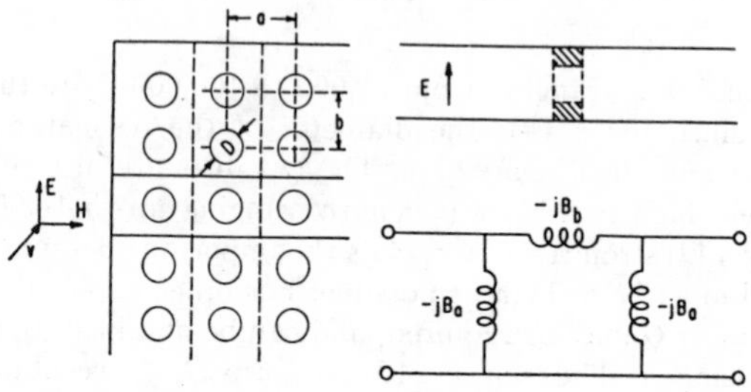

Fig. 8—Perforated metal plate and equivalent transmission line circuit electric wall ——, magnetic wall - - -.

The phase angle of the reflection coefficient at the spherical boundary may thus be determined, and the effect of transformed reactances on the resonance condition investigated for various hole configurations and wall thicknesses. This is important since the resonance condition demands a uniform phase shift over the spherical surface, and the phase changes occurring in regions where there are coupling holes differ from those at a metal wall. However, the phase change for holes in thick walls is not very different from that due to holes in the thinner walls where coupling is effected. This occurs because all holes are circular waveguides excited beyond cut-off, and the reactive contribution to the transformed impedance is close to that due to the hole at the inner surface of the sphere.

Thus, areas other than those used for energy transfer could possibly have thicker walls with holes similar to those in coupling areas. It may also be possible by suitable impedance transformations to have holes only in such coupling regions, with the remaining parts of the metallic spherical surface undisturbed. This would be a more satisfactory arrangement, and while the problem of coupling requires experimental evaluation, it seems clear that it can be done along the lines described.

Higher-Order Modes

So far, we have tacitly assumed the existence of only the principal mode in the biconical resonator, and we must now consider whether difficulties can arise from the higher-order modes which can also exist in it. The problem has been extensively treated by Schelkunoff in his work on antennas.[8] With an impressed RF voltage between the apices of the cones, the modes in question are the transverse magnetic spherical ones with $H_r = 0$.

[14] N. Marcuvitz, "Waveguide Handbook," M.I.T. Rad. Lab. Ser., McGraw-Hill Book Co., Inc., New York, N. Y., pp. 408–412; 1951.

As we have seen, in the biconical region a principal TEM wave exists with the electric field lines terminating normally to the conical surfaces. A continuation of this mode into free space is not possible, and in the case of the biconical antenna, other modes are generated at the spherical boundary between free space and the ends of the cone. The boundary conditions at the spherical boundary between the fields in the antenna region and the fields of spherical TM waves in free space may then be satisfied. Fig. 9 shows the electric field configuration for the first-order TM spherical wave in free space and in the biconical region respectively. The field patterns are quite similar, the difference being the presence of the small loops near the conical conductors which satisfy the boundary conditions for the electric field. The patterns for modes of higher-order are quite similar, except that the number of loops increases. Such field configurations are directly analogous to the electric field patterns of higher-order TM_{0n} modes between parallel plates and arise from appropriate distortions of such plates. If b is the spacing between the plates, the cut-off wavelengths for these modes are given by $2b/n$.

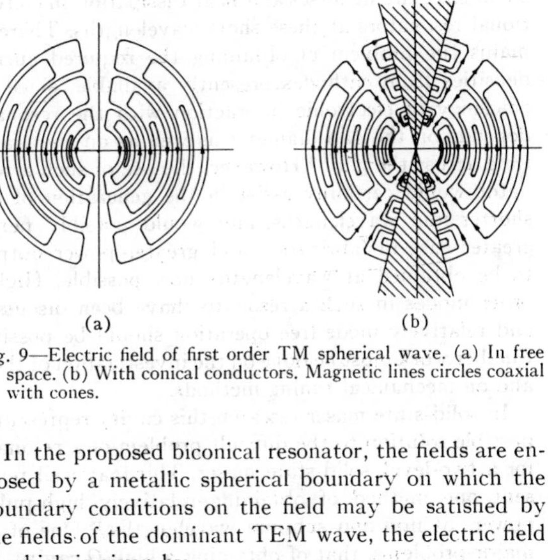

(a) (b)

Fig. 9—Electric field of first order TM spherical wave. (a) In free space. (b) With conical conductors. Magnetic lines circles coaxial with cones.

In the proposed biconical resonator, the fields are enclosed by a metallic spherical boundary on which the boundary conditions on the field may be satisfied by the fields of the dominant TEM wave, the electric field of which is given by

$$E_\theta = j\eta \frac{I_0 \sin \beta(l - r)}{2\pi r \sin \theta}, \qquad (19)$$

where I_0 is the maximum current at $r=l$, and l is the radius of the sphere.[8] Thus, no higher-order modes arise at such a boundary, and this is still true when the coupling holes are present since these are spaced less than $\lambda/2$ apart. The fringing fields at the holes then correspond to non-propagating modes between parallel plates and represent a localized impedance at the spherical boundary. It follows then that no higher-order modes should exist in the resonator when the radius of the input region r_i is very small, or when the cones are pointed. Such higher-order modes may be generated in the input region around the apices of the cones if this is finite in extent, and this must be considered.

Expressions for such fields are given by Schelkunoff[8] and are independent of the angle ϕ. We shall be concerned with θ component of the electric field, which is given by

$$rE_\theta = \frac{\eta V(r)}{2\pi Z_c \sin \theta} + j\frac{\eta}{2\pi}\sum_n \frac{1}{n(n+1)} \frac{d}{d\theta} M_n(\cos\theta) S_n'(\beta r). \qquad (20)$$

Here $M_n(\cos\theta) = \frac{1}{2}[P_n(\cos\theta) - P_n(-\cos\theta)]$, P_n being the Legendre function of order n, and

$$S_n(\beta_r) = A_n Jn_n(\beta r) + B_n Nn_n(\beta r), \qquad (21)$$

where $Jn_n(\beta r)$ and $Nn_n(\beta r)$ are the normalized Bessel functions of the first and second kind, and A_n and B_n are constants determined from the boundary conditions. Values of n over which the summation in (20) is made are determined by the relation

$$M_n(\cos\psi) = 0, \qquad (22)$$

which corresponds to the condition $E_r = 0$ on the conical surfaces. Generally, the values of n are not integral and may be determined from the formula[8]

$$n_m(\psi) = \left[\left(\frac{2m\pi}{\pi - 2\psi}\right)^2 - \frac{1}{4}\right]^{1/2} - \frac{1}{2}, \qquad (23)$$

where $m = 1, 2, 3, \cdots$.

The component E_θ of the electric field must vanish at the spherical boundary for all values of θ, and hence from (20) we must have

$$S_n'(\beta l) = 0, \qquad (24)$$

expressing the resonance condition for any higher-order mode. For perturbations of the input region around the cone apices, the field at a specific input radius r_i may be expanded in terms of the orthogonal properties of Legendre functions and their derivatives; to obtain

$$E_n = \frac{\int_\psi^{\pi-\psi} r_i E_\theta(r_i) \sin\theta \frac{d}{d\theta}(M_n \cos\theta) d\theta}{\int_\psi^{\pi-\psi} \sin\theta \left[\frac{d}{d\theta} M_n(\cos\theta)\right]^2 d\theta}, \qquad (25)$$

where

$$[j\eta S_n'(\beta r_i)]/[2\pi n(n+1)] = E_n. \qquad (26)$$

The values of the constants A_n and B_n in (21) are now determined from (24) and (26) and will be small if the radius r_i is small. Hence for pointed cones in close proximity at the center, operation in the TEM mode without serious excitation of unwanted modes is feasible. This also follows, because $Nn_n(\beta r_i)$ becomes infinite when $r_i \to 0$, and hence B_n must be zero in this case.

As an approximation to the resonance condition we may assume that $E_n = 0$ for small input regions or values of r_i. Then we find from (26) that

$$B_n/A_n = -J'n_n(\beta r_i)/N'n_n(\beta r_i), \quad (27)$$

and hence (24) becomes

$$J'n_n(\beta l)N'n_n(\beta r_i) - N'n_n(\beta l)J'n_n(\beta r_i) = 0. \quad (28)$$

But it follows from (27) that B_n/A_n tends to zero for small values of βr_i, particularly for large values of n. Hence for small perturbations of the input region, the resonance condition for higher modes is given by

$$J'n_n(\beta l) = 0, \quad (29)$$

and we have already noted that the amplitudes of such modes will also be small in this case. Such higher modes would also not exist if $r_i E_\theta(r_i) = 0$ for all θ, which occurs when the apices are joined by a metallic sphere in the input region. Other perturbations can be considered for specific cases, such as for a klystron type resonator, and would have to be investigated. The prime criterion is that the transition of the spherical fields of the TEM mode to those in the input region should be smooth and the field patterns matched as far as is possible. This can be approached by suitable shaping in such regions, and hence mode generation kept small.

Eq. (29) represents the condition for resonance in a higher-order mode, and for the large values of βl applicable here, we may write

$$Jn_n(\beta l) \simeq \sin(\beta l - n\pi/2),$$

and hence

$$J'n_n(\beta l \simeq \cos(\beta l - n\pi/2), \quad (30)$$

which gives the condition for resonance as

$$l = (2m + 1 + n)\lambda/4. \quad m = 1, 2, 3, \cdots. \quad (31)$$

Here n is not an integer in general, and this resonance condition can differ from that required for the principal mode. Thus even though higher-order modes are possible, depending on the shape of the input region between the cones, it may be possible to differentiate against them as regards resonance. We remark again that for small input regions, or perturbations, the amplitudes of such modes will be small and, in general, may be kept small by suitable transitions between the field regions in the resonator.

Conclusions

The basic ideas presented here appear to have considerable promise and significance for future work at mm and sub-mm wavelengths. Some results on a planar type of Fabry-Perot interferometer with high resolution may have already been given.[4] This interferometer represents the solution to the wavemeter problem for this wavelength region. The very high Q values already obtained at 6 mm wavelengths and the increases possible at very short wavelengths indicate its great potential use in all phases of millimeter-wave spectroscopy and maser research. A gaseous maser at a wavelength of 3.4 mm, using such an interferometer as the resonator, is under active development. Applications of this interferometer to solid state masers at sub-mm wavelengths are also feasible. As indicated, the curved reflector or focused type of Fabry-Perot interferometer may find similar applications at very short sub-mm or infrared wavelengths, and it represents an interesting problem for future investigation.

The new developments on the biconical spherical resonator which stem from the Fabry-Perot interferometer investigations appear quite significant. Suitable resonators are needed for electronic generation at mm wavelengths, for solid state masers at mm and sub-mm wavelengths, and for many other areas of research in this important wavelength region. The biconical resonator is a possible solution to this problem. The development of such a klystron resonator at reasonable orders of interference would materially help in the major problems of small size, circuit losses and heat dissipation in conventional resonators at these short wavelengths. There remains the problem of obtaining the required current densities from cathodes presently available, since the efficiency of electronic interaction with the resonator depends on the gap diameter as well as on the transit time across the gap.[13] However, the use of such a resonator would certainly assist in the generation of still shorter mm wavelengths, and would possibly permit greater ease in fabrication and greater power outputs to be obtained at wavelengths now possible. Higher-order modes in such a resonator have been discussed, and relatively mode-free operation should be possible. Further work must be done on the investigation of these, and on mechanical tuning methods.

In solid-state maser research this cavity represents a possible solution to the difficult problem of a resonator for a two-level, solid-state maser. This may well represent one method of obtaining relatively high-pulsed powers at mm and sub-mm wavelengths.[15] One of the major problems, that of obtaining a high Q cavity, appears to be adequately met by the biconical resonator, and for ideal conical geometries inside the sphere, mode troubles should not arise. Specimen shapes would conform to the field geometry at the cone apices or completely fill the cavity with the dc magnetic field suitably oriented along the axes of the cones, or along any other preferred direction. The proposed method of coupling would be extremely desirable in all such areas, since it would eliminate the necessity for long lengths of small waveguide into the low temperature bath. The Q of the cavity would also increase at low temperatures. Similar

[15] J. R. Singer, "Masers," John Wiley and Sons, Inc., New York, N. Y., pp. 71–87; 1959.

remarks apply to the three-level, solid-state maser.

Although further development of these resonators is required, such developments appear feasible in contrast to the present difficulties in applying conventional resonators to mm and sub-mm wavelengths. Such difficulties are very severe and most probably conventional resonators are impractical. There appears to be no reason why the ideas presented here should not be intensively pursued, as the rewards and knowledge to be gained from this virtually unexplored region of the electromagnetic spectrum are very great.

Note added in proof: The biconical spherical resonator has now been operated very satisfactorily by Dr. R. W. Zimmerer at wavelengths around 8 mm. The diameter of the sphere used was 4 inches, and the cone angle Ψ was 45°. Coupling holes after the manner described were used only in areas illuminated by the focused radiation. Both quarter-wavelength and half-wavelength resonances were observed and were the dominant ones. The Q value approaches the theoretical one, and higher mode effects are small.

Acknowledgment

The author would like to acknowledge the assistance and encouragement derived from discussions with his colleagues, and in particular, with Dr. R. C. Mockler.

Helium-Cooled Y-Junction Ferrite Circulator Switch*

During the past few years, effective use has been made of cryogenic temperatures in producing low-noise amplifiers such as masers and, more recently, parametric amplifiers.[1–3] As a result, there has been an ever increasing need for low-loss components, such as ferrite circulators and switches, that are capable of operating at these temperatures.

Low-temperature operation is desirable since by cooling dissipative losses that occur prior to amplification, a significant reduction can be realized in the degrading effect they have on receiver noise performance. The magnitude of this degradation can be determined from

$$T_{ov} = (L-1)T_B + LT_1 \qquad (1)$$

where T_{ov} = over-all effective receiver noise temperature, L = dissipative loss prior to amplification, T_B = physical temperature of the loss (L) and T_1 = original noise temperature of receiver following the loss (L). If $L = 0.5$ db and $T_1 = 10°K$, the degradation is reduced from 36°K to 1.7°K as T_B is reduced from 290°K to 4.2°K. The purpose of this communication is to describe a liquid helium-cooled (4.2°K) low-loss coaxial Y-junction ferrite circulator that is specifically designed to be used as a switch in a 5000-Mc traveling-wave maser-Dicke radiometer system.

A prime consideration in the design of the cooled switch, aside from RF performance, is its thermodynamic characteristics. Since the heat of vaporization of liquid helium is extremely low (about 2.7×10^3 joules per liter), it is necessary from both logistic and economic viewpoints to keep the joule losses to a minimum. (The conductive losses are small compared with the joule losses.) The sources of joule loss in a ferrite circulator switch emanate from 1) I^2R losses from the coils generating the magnetic field and 2) eddy current losses in the circulator ground planes and center conductor due to the switching magnetic field. These losses can be represented by

$$W \approx \underbrace{\frac{K_1 B^2 \rho_1 l^2}{h}}_{\text{coil losses}} + \underbrace{\frac{K_2 B^2 f^2 (t_1 + t_2)}{\rho_2}}_{\text{eddy current losses}} \qquad (2)$$

where B = magnetic induction, l = length of air gap in the magnetic circuit, t_1 and t_2 = thickness of the center conductor and ground planes, respectively, ρ_1 and ρ_2 = resistivity of the coil winding and of the ground planes and center conductor, respectively, h = height of the magnetic field coil, f = switch frequency and K_1 and K_2 = parameters that are a function of the shape of the circulator cross section.

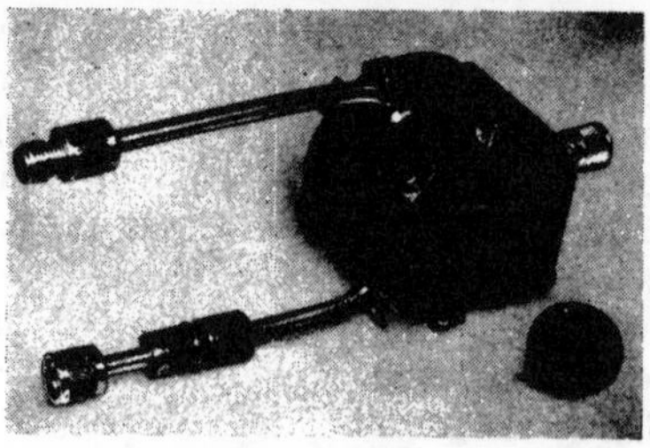

Fig. 1—Packaged circulator switch.

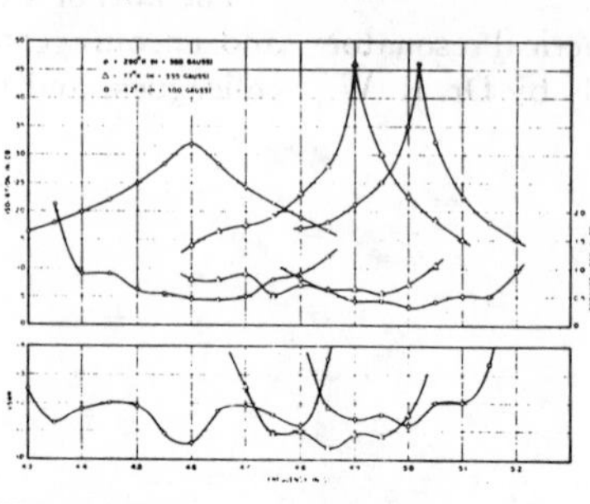

Fig. 2—RF operating characteristics of circulator switch as functions of frequency for bath temperatures of 4.2°K, 77°K and 290°K.

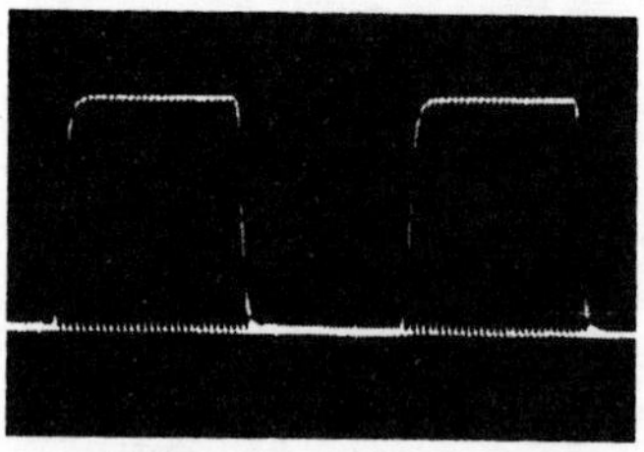

Fig. 3—Oscilloscope trace of helium-cooled circulator being switched at 20 cps (RF being square-wave modulated at 1000 cps).

From (2), the circulator switch shown in Fig. 1 is evolved. It operates in a low magnetic field mode with a magnet that has a small air gap and a low coil resistance. In addition, thin brass sheet stock is used to construct the ground planes and center conductor. This is considered to be a good compromise between mechanical stability, RF loss and eddy current requirements. The total joule loss of the switch operating at 20-cps switching frequency is less than 35 mw, about 10 mw from coil losses and 25 mw from eddy currents.

Since the switch operates in a low field mode (300 gauss), a low $4\pi M_s$ substituted-garnet material is used to eliminate low field losses. The RF operating characteristics of the switch measured at 4.2°K, 77°K and 290°K are shown in Fig. 2. At 4.2°K the switch has an isolation in excess of 45 db, an insertion loss of about 0.3 db and a bandwidth (between 20-db points) of 240 Mc. It is believed that circulator bandwidths approaching an octave can be obtained since no special broad-banding techniques such as dielectric loading and multiple-impedance transformations are used.

At the higher operating temperatures, the optimum operating frequency decreases and the external field requirements increase. This is believed to be caused by a change in the "effective" dielectric constant of the ferrite-loaded strip-line section, due primarily to variations in the mechanical tolerances at different bath temperatures (changing the filling factor). However, good isolation and loss characteristics can be obtained up to room temperature.

The switching characteristics of the circulator at 4.2°K (switched at a rate of about 20 cps) are shown in Fig. 3. Since rise time degrades system sensitivity, it must be kept to a minimum; in Fig. 3 it is 1 msec.

The authors gratefully acknowledge the many helpful discussions with, and suggestions of J. G. Smith.

J. A. DeGruyl
W. W. Heinz
S. Okwit
Airborne Instruments Lab.
Appl. Electronics Dept.
Cutler-Hammer, Inc.
Deer Park, N. Y.

* Received March 15, 1963. This work was supported by the National Radio Astronomy Observatory, Green Bank, W. Va.

[1] M. Uenohara, "An extremely-low-noise 6-Gc nondegenerate parametric amplifier," Proc. IRE (*Correspondence*), vol. 50, pp. 208–209; February, 1962.

[2] C. Blake, L. W. Bowles, E. P. McCurley, and J. A. Nuttal, "Helium cooled parametric amplifier," *Appl. Phys. Letts.* (Submitted.)

[3] H. J. Fink, D. C. Hanson and M. Uenohara, "Varactor diode amplifier at liquid helium temperature," Proc. IEEE (*Correspondence*), vol. 51, p. 246; January, 1963.

Superconducting-Solenoid Traveling-Wave Maser System*

This communication briefly describes an *S*-band traveling-wave maser (TWM) system that operates at 4.2°K and is driven by a lightweight air-core superconducting magnet. A photograph of the system is shown in Fig. 1.

The maser uses a ruby-loaded comb structure similar to the *S*-band TWM reported earlier.[1] The TWM is remotely tunable from 2195 to 2310 Mc, has a stable net gain of about 30 db (Fig. 2), and an instantaneous bandwidth of 18 Mc. Yttrium iron garnet (YIG) isolator disks in the comb structure provide unconditional gain stability. Effective maser noise temperatures were measured over the tuning band using a hot and cold load noise generator. The results of these measurements are shown in Table I.

The superconducting solenoid, which is wound of niobium-zirconium wire, has an extremely large working diameter (7.5 inches), is only 5 inches long, and weighs less than 3 pounds. Fig. 3 is a photograph of the maser and magnet configuration. The magnet can supply stable magnetic fields up to 4320 gauss at a coil current of 6.2 a. The magnetic field that the solenoid supplies to the operating maser is nominally 2500 gauss, and has a field homogeneity better than one part in five thousand over a volume of 4 by 1 by 1 inches. (The 4-inch dimension is perpendicular to the solenoid axis.) The high degree of homogeneity obtained in this relatively short solenoid results from the application of a magnetic loading technique. To obtain the same homogeneity without magnetic loading, a solenoid longer than 25 inches would be required.

Previous work on superconducting magnets for TWM applications consisted of iron-core configurations with field-shaping techniques using the Meissner effect of a superconducting sheet.[2,3] We believe that the solenoid technique described involves less complicated construction procedures and generally yields a lighter magnet. Furthermore, the air-core approach is applicable to masers at frequencies in excess of 10 Gc.

A more detailed description of this system will be submitted for publication at a later date.

Fig. 1—Photograph of over-all traveling-wave maser system.

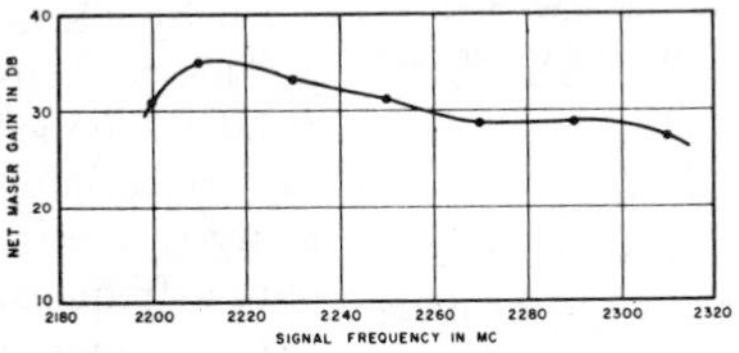

Fig. 2—Net maser gain vs operation frequency measured at 4.2°K bath temperature.

TABLE I

MASER SYSTEM NOISE TEMPERATURE (T_e) MEASUREMENTS*

Signal frequency (Mc)	Net Maser gain (db)	T_e (°K)*	T_2 (°K)	T_m (°K)
2215	36.5	13	10,800	10.3
2240	34.0	11	8,400	7.4
2265	29.5	16	7,550	7.5

* Each T_e measurement is an average of 12 separate readings.

T_e = over all maser receiving system noise temperatures, including second-stage contributions (measurements are within ±2°K),

T_2 = second-stage noise temperature (measured data),

T_m = maser noise temperature, including feed-line contributions (calculated from T_e and T_2).

Fig. 3—Photograph of superconducting solenoid and TWM configuration.

S. OKWIT
K. SIEGEL
J. G. SMITH
Airborne Instruments Lab.
Div. of Cutler-Hammer, Inc.
Deer Park, N. Y

* Received July 1, 1963. This work was supported by the U. S. Air Force, Aeronautical Systems Division, Communications Laboratory.

[1] S. Okwit and J. G. Smith, "Packaged electonically tunable *S*-band traveling-wave maser system," PROC. IRE vol. 50, pp. 1470–1483; June, 1962.

[2] P. P. Cioffi, "Approach to ideal magnetic circuit concept through superconductivity," *J. Appl. Phys.*, vol. 33, pp. 875–879; March, 1962.

[3] W. G. Nilsen, "Operation of a traveling-wave maser in a transverse field superconducting electromagnet," *J. Appl. Phys.*, vol. 33, pp. 2522–2523; August, 1962.

Reprinted from the PROCEEDINGS OF THE IEEE
VOL. 51, NO. 9, SEPTEMBER, 1963

PRINTED IN THE U.S.A.

Broad-Band Impedance Matching into Dielectric-Filled Waveguides*

F. E. GOODWIN†, MEMBER, IRE, AND G. E. MOSS†, MEMBER, IRE

Summary—**The problem of impedance matching between two waveguides filled with different dielectrics is discussed, and the conditions for broad-band matching are determined. Experimental results are presented for standard waveguides matched to guides filled with dielectrics having permittivities ϵ as high as $100\epsilon_0$. Present applications include matching devices for *X*-band coupled-cavity transmission masers which employ ruby and alumina sections ($\epsilon \approx 10\epsilon_0$). Future applications include matching devices for masers utilizing rutile (ϵ as high as $250\epsilon_0$).**

Introduction

IN THE DEVELOPMENT of microwave and millimeter-wave masers, it is necessary to provide means for matching from air-filled waveguides to guides filled with materials having high dielectric permittivities. For practical reasons, the device which makes the transition should be frequency-independent. The most common approach to this problem is to use a uniformly tapered transition; this consists of a tapered waveguide with a dielectric insert having reverse tapers.[1] As a result of preliminary work in which this approach was used, it was concluded that the desired performance could not be achieved reliably with a device of this kind.

These are the types of matching problems which arise in maser circuits. To the best of our knowledge, similar problems have not occurred in more conventional microwave circuits. However, a good matching technique is potentially applicable to a variety of miniaturized microwave circuits, including passive filters and transmission networks.

The maser material most commonly used to date is ruby, which has a tensor permittivity with a magnitude of about 10 ϵ_0. In the *X*-band ruby masers which have been developed at our laboratory, transitions for TE_{01} mode propagation from an air-filled guide to ruby- or alumina-filled guides are required at the input and output of the slow-wave structure. Another maser material which is finding increased application is rutile, doped either with chromium or iron. The permittivity of rutile is also a tensor quantity whose magnitude varies from 80 to 256, depending on the temperature and the angular orientation between the direction of the electric field and the optic axis.[2] The basic slow-wave structure for most rutile masers is simply a continuous waveguide filled with rutile. Since the external RF circuits are air-filled waveguides, the design of rutile masers requires the use of transitions capable of matching two sections of guide in which the permittivity may differ by a ratio of over 250 to 1.

This paper reports a method of obtaining a broad-band RF impedance match into waveguides filled with materials having high dielectric permittivities. An analysis is presented which shows that it is possible to obtain frequency independence at the junction of the two waveguides. Experimental verification is given for matching into alumina-filled and titania-filled waveguides, together with the design principles and construction details.

Analysis

The analytical method takes advantage of the analogy between waveguides and transmission lines. The real part of the reflection at the junction of two waveguides is the same as that predicted at the junction of two transmission lines having the same impedance ratios.[3] The imaginary part of the reflection at the waveguide junction can be represented by a shunt susceptance in the transmission line circuit shown in Fig. 1. The impedance of a waveguide can be defined in many ways, all of which are consistent in that they are proportional to the wave impedance E_y/H_x. When the impedance definition is based on the power and maximum voltage in the waveguide,[4] we have for the fundamental mode

$$Z_1 = \frac{1}{Y_1} = 2\frac{b_1}{a_1}\left(\frac{E_y}{H_x}\right) = 2\frac{b_1}{a_1}\sqrt{\frac{\mu_0}{\epsilon_0}}\frac{\lambda_g}{\lambda_0}$$

$$= 2\frac{b_1}{a_1}\sqrt{\frac{\mu_0}{\epsilon_0}}\frac{1}{\sqrt{\epsilon_1 - \left(\frac{\lambda_0}{2a_1}\right)^2}}$$

$$Z_2 = \frac{1}{Y_2} = 2\frac{b_2}{a_2}\sqrt{\frac{\mu_0}{\epsilon_0}}\frac{1}{\sqrt{\epsilon_2 - \left(\frac{\lambda_0}{2a_2}\right)^2}},$$

* Received August 22, 1962.

† Hughes Research Laboratories, Malibu, Calif.

[1] E. S. Sabisky and H. J. Gerritsen, "Traveling-wave maser using chromium-doped rutile," Proc. IRE (*Correspondence*), vol. 49, pp. 1329–1330; August, 1961.

[2] E. S. Sabisky and H. J. Gerritsen, "Measurements of the dielectric constant of rutile (TiO_2) at microwave frequencies between 4.2° and 300°K," *J. Appl. Phys.*, vol. 33, p. 1450; April, 1962.

[3] G. L. Ragan, "Microwave Transmission Circuits," M.I.T., Rad. Lab. Ser., vol. 9, McGraw-Hill Book Co., Inc., New York, N. Y., p. 54; 1948.

[4] S. A. Schelkunoff, "Electromagnetic Waves," D. Van Nostrand Co., New York, N. Y., p. 319; 1943.

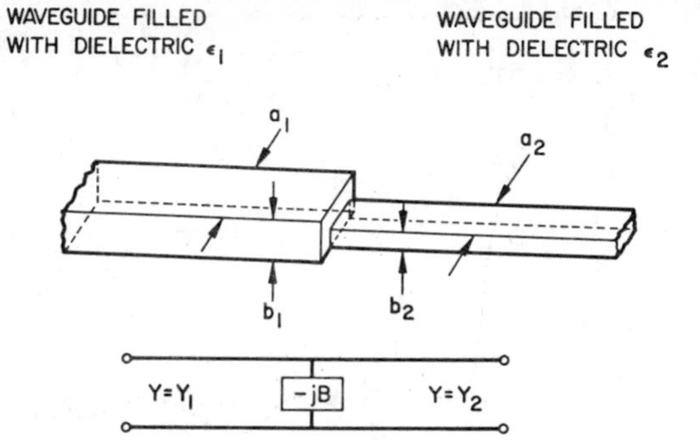

Fig. 1—Junction of two waveguides filled with different dielectrics.

where

$\lambda_0 \equiv$ free space wavelength
$a_1 \equiv$ width of first waveguide
$a_2 \equiv$ width of second waveguide
$b_1 \equiv$ height of first waveguide
$b_2 \equiv$ height of second waveguide
$\epsilon_1 \equiv$ dielectric permittivity of material in first guide
$\epsilon_2 \equiv$ dielectric permittivity of material in second guide
$\lambda_g \equiv$ waveguide wavelength
$-\sqrt{\mu_0/\epsilon_0} = 377\ \Omega$.

To match admittances of the two waveguides, we let $Y_1 = Y_2$; therefore,

$$\frac{a_1}{b_1}\sqrt{\epsilon_1 - \left(\frac{\lambda_0}{2a_1}\right)^2} = \frac{a_2}{b_2}\sqrt{\epsilon_2 - \left(\frac{\lambda_0}{2a_2}\right)^2}.$$

It is obvious from the above equation that for a given ϵ_1 and ϵ_2, the a and b waveguide dimensions may be adjusted to give a match at a particular frequency corresponding to λ_0.

To obtain a frequency-independent match, we must choose

$$b_1 = b_2$$

and

$$\frac{a_1}{a_2} = \sqrt{\frac{\epsilon_2}{\epsilon_1}}.$$

Choosing $b_1 = b_2$ also simplifies the construction of the transition device. The criterion for determining b is that it must be small enough to prevent the TE_{11} mode from propagating and to preserve the TE_{01} mode. The ratio of b to a is $\frac{1}{2}$ for a waveguide filled with an isotropic medium. Since the b dimension does not change, the susceptance of the junction is therefore inductive, and it remains only to match out the reflections from the inductive susceptance $-jB$.

Anisotropy and Birefringence

When a waveguide is filled with a single-crystal paramagnetic material having tensor permittivity, care must be taken to avoid undesirable modes of propagation. For example, a uniaxial crystal with its c-axis oriented at an angle θ with the normal to the broad wall of the filled waveguide will have an effective dielectric constant ϵ_y in the E-plane of the waveguide, determined from the dielectric ellipsoid. Thus, we have for the fundamental mode:

$$\epsilon_y^{-1} = \epsilon_\parallel^{-1}\cos^2\theta + \epsilon_\perp^{-1}\sin^2\theta.$$

To prevent birefringence, the orthogonal mode cannot be allowed; therefore, the b/a ratio of the waveguide for the octave bandwidth condition is determined from

$$\frac{b}{a} < \frac{\epsilon_y}{2\epsilon_x},$$

where

$$\epsilon_x^{-1} \equiv \epsilon_\parallel^{-1}\sin^2\theta + \epsilon_\perp^{-1}\cos^2\theta.$$

Normally, a b/a ratio of $\frac{1}{2}$ is small enough to prevent birefringence in most crystals of interest (other than rutile) over octave bandwidths.

Design and Fabrication of a Transition from Air- to Dielectric-Filled Waveguides

In order to meet the frequency-independent condition, $b_1 = b_2$, the E-dimension of the air-filled waveguide is reduced by either a taper[5] or a series of steps[6] to the height of the dielectric-filled waveguide (Fig. 2). The air-filled waveguide is then joined directly to the dielectric-filled guide, whose width is determined by $a_2 = a_1/\sqrt{\epsilon/\epsilon_0}$. The inductive susceptance is matched by using a circular capacitive stub placed in the air-filled waveguide close to the junction. The optimum location of the stub was found experimentally to be a distance $a/2$ from the dielectric, and the optimum stub diameter was found to be 0.8a (see Fig. 3).

It is essential to obtain a perfect filling factor in the loaded waveguides since relatively minor flaws in the filling factor introduce large susceptances in the guide. One successful technique is to metallize the dielectric material with silver and then to electroform with silver or copper to a nominal thickness to strengthen the part and to permit soldering to appropriate flanges. The losses encountered in dielectric-filled waveguides vary widely, depending upon the quality of the dielectric and the metallizing. Silver-plated alumina has 0.1 db/in of loss at room temperature. Since the dielectric loss accounts for 0.03 db/in, it may be surmised that most of the loss is contributed by the conductive plating.

[5] K. Matsumaru, "Reflection coefficient of E-plane tapered waveguides," IRE Trans. on Microwave Theory and Techniques, vol. MTT-6, pp. 143–149; April, 1958.
[6] L. Young, "Tables for cascaded homogeneous quarter-wave transformers," IRE Trans. on Microwave Theory and Techniques, vol. MTT-7, pp. 233–237; April, 1959.

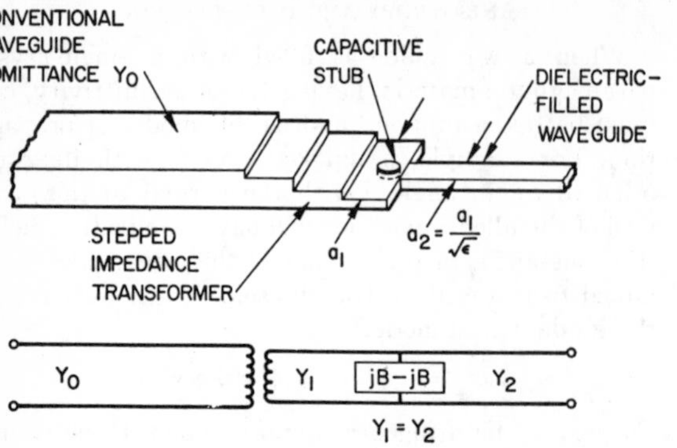

Fig. 2—Junction of a conventional waveguide with one filled with a dielectric.

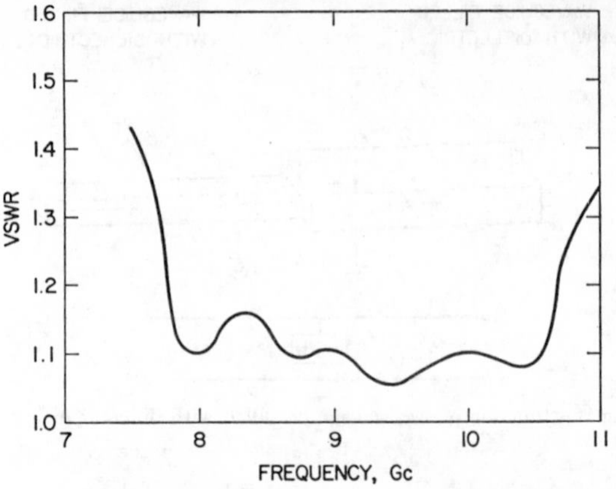

Fig. 5—Typical VSWR vs frequency for transition from an RG-52 to an alumina-filled waveguide.

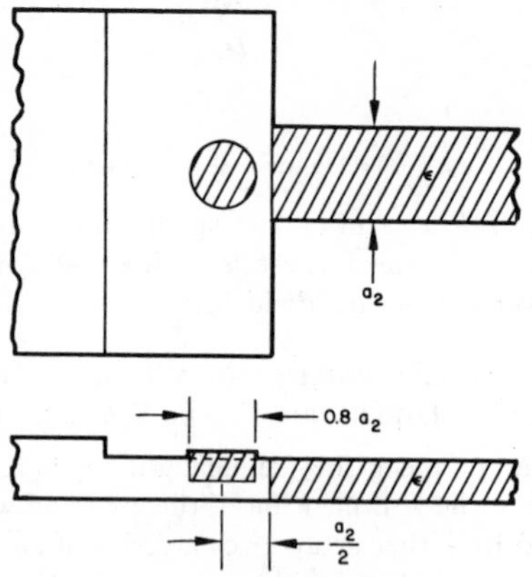

Fig. 3—Matching stub configuration.

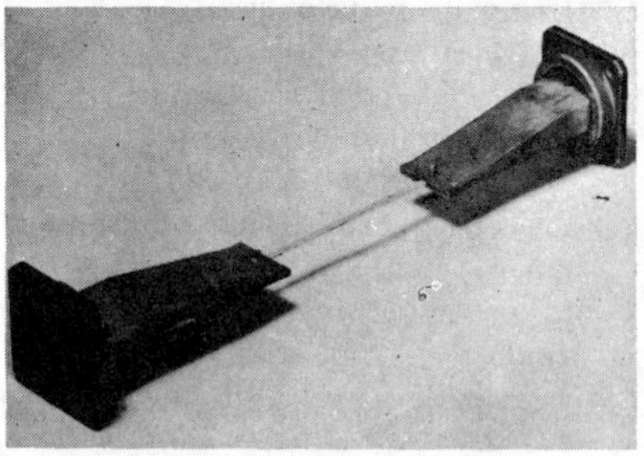

Fig. 6—Transition from an RG-52 to a titania-filled waveguide.

Fig. 4—Transition from an RG-52 to an alumina-filled waveguide and polyiron termination.

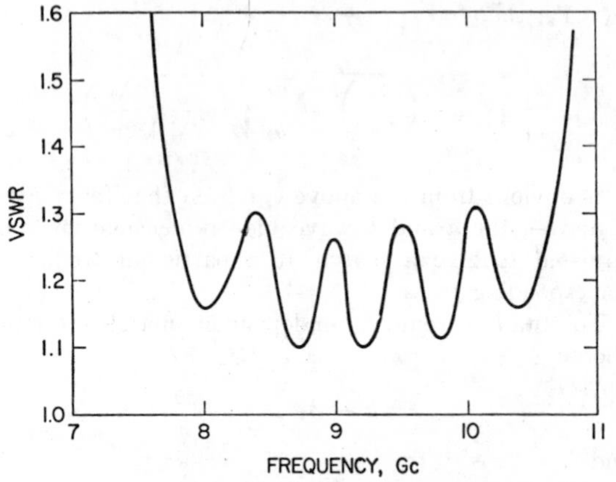

Fig. 7—VSWR vs frequency for transition from an RG-52 waveguide to a titania-filled waveguide.

TABLE I
EXPERIMENTAL RESULTS

Frequency Range, kMc	Dielectric Material	Dielectric Constant	Maximum VSWR	Maximum Loss, db
7.0– 9.0	alumina	9.4	1.16	0.1
8.0–10.6	alumina	9.4	1.16	0.1
7.8–10.7	titania	100.0	1.3	0.4 (includes length of guide)
22.0–25.0	alumina	9.4	1.2	0.2
32.0–38.0	alumina	9.4	1.5	0.5

Experimental Results

The performance of the matching device depends upon the termination of the filled guide. Two termination methods were used in obtaining experimental data. With the ruby- or alumina-filled guides, we used a termination made from a polyiron-filled waveguide, which absorbs the power propagating down the waveguide. Fig. 4 shows the transition to an alumina-filled waveguide and the polyiron termination; the corresponding VSWR is shown in Fig. 5. The rutile-filled waveguide was more difficult to terminate with an absorbing material. Polyiron has an insufficiently high dielectric constant to be well matched to rutile. Titania with a 20 per cent doping of silicon carbide offers promise as an absorbing material for titania- and rutile-filled waveguides and is presently being tested.

For the test data for titania reported here, a second method of terminating the filled waveguide was used. In this method, two transitions are used—one to match into the filled waveguide, and one to match out to the air-filled waveguide and then to a standard termination (see Fig. 6). The titania-filled waveguide is 0.040 in in the *b* dimension and 0.090 in in the *a* dimension. The VSWR plot for this configuration is shown in Fig. 7. Since the measured reflected power is from both transitions, the data in Fig. 7 were those calculated for each transition. Performance data for some typical transitions appear in Table I.

Conclusion

It has been shown that a broad-band RF impedance match from air-filled to dielectric-filled waveguide is possible using an abrupt transition with an appropriate susceptance match. The technique described offers considerable improvement in performance over more conventional dielectric taper transitions, and is easier to fabricate. Immediate application is seen in maser circuits where the waveguide is filled with high dielectric maser material.

Reprinted from IEEE TRANSACTIONS
ON *MICROWAVE THEORY AND TECHNIQUES*
Volume MTT-11, Number 1, January, 1963

Relaxation Phenomena

Electron Spin and Phonon Equilibrium in Masers*

N. BLOEMBERGEN
Harvard University, Cambridge, Massachusetts
(Received January 24, 1958)

TOWNES and co-workers have recently[1] presented experimental evidence indicating that the relaxation rates in paramagnetic salts at temperatures below 4.2°K are not determined by the interaction between the spins and the lattice vibrations, but between the latter and the helium bath. The authors claim that the normally observed relaxation time, e.g., in $KCo(Cr)(CN)_6$, is characteristic of energy transfer between the phonons and the bath, whereas the heat contact between the spin levels and the phonons is a thousand times better. It is the purpose of this Letter to point out that the successful operation of this salt in three-level steady-state masers[2] is incompatible with this assumption about the relaxation rates, regardless of the operating frequencies of the maser.

Let ν_{13} be the saturating frequency, and ν_{23} be the frequency of maser amplification. It has been clear[1] that if the frequency ν_{13} is close enough to either ν_{21} or ν_{23}, the hot phonon band around ν_{13} would overlap one of the other resonances and essentially equalize the populations of all three spin levels.

Consider now the case that the three frequencies are widely spaced and no overlapping of phonon bands occurs. The spin populations of levels 2 and 3 are inverted corresponding to a negative spin temperature and maser action at the frequency ν_{23}. Suppose, however, that the contact with the phonons is good. Then a phonon band around ν_{23} will be heated up. Since the energy levels of a lattice oscillator have no upper bound, the phonon temperature will always remain positive. On the other hand, the spin temperature should be very close to this phonon temperature, because its heat contact is supposed to be so much better than between the phonons around ν_{23} and the bath. The steady-state equilibrium situation would necessarily be one in which the phonon temperature at ν_{23} would be very high and positive and the spin temperature at ν_{23} very high and negative. This means however that the population of spin levels 2 and 3 would be almost equal; whereas for maser action a fairly large difference in population is necessary. It may therefore be concluded that the situation visualized by Townes *et al.* is excluded in paramagnetic salts which allow for successful steady-state maser operation.

The use of the concept "temperature" can be avoided entirely, although we believe it has heuristic value in spite of its lack of rigor in the present context. The problem of the three-level maser and phonon equilibria may be formulated rigorously in terms of six unknowns. The spin populations n_1, n_2, and n_3, and the average lattice oscillator excitation quantum numbers in the three phonon bands $\bar{n}_{ph}(\nu_{23})$, $\bar{n}_{ph}(\nu_{21})$, $\bar{n}_{ph}(\nu_{13})$. Imposition of the steady-state conditions gives five linear equations relating to transport of quanta at the three frequencies. A sixth relation is that $n_1+n_2+n_3$ be equal to the number of paramagnetic ions. The algebraic solution of these six equations confirms the conclusion that n_3-n_2 is very small if the contact betweeen the spins and phonons is better than between phonons and the bath.

In this treatment phonon-phonon collisions have been ignored. They probably are important in practice, and may account for the fact the bottleneck for energy transfer is between the spin levels and phonons in $K_3Co(Cr)(CN)_6$ and other salts.

* This work was carried out at the Ecole Normale Supérieure, Paris, France, while the author held a Guggenheim Fellowship.

[1] Nash, Giordmaine, Alsop, and Townes, Bull. Am. Phys. Soc. Ser. II, **3**, 9 (1958); Giordmaine, Alsop, Nash, and Townes, Phys. Rev. **109**, 302 (1958). See, however, their paragraph headed "Implications of Relaxation Process for Masers," p. 310.

[2] N. Bloembergen, Phys. Rev. **104**, 324 (1956); McWhorter, Meyer, and Strum, Phys. Rev. **108**, 1642 (1957); R. H. Kingston, Proc. Inst. Radio Engrs. (to be published); Artman, Bloembergen, and Shapiro, Phys. Rev. **109**, 1392 (1958).

Cross-Relaxation in Spin Systems*

N. BLOEMBERGEN, S. SHAPIRO, P. S. PERSHAN,† AND J. O. ARTMAN‡
Gordon McKay Laboratory, Harvard University, Cambridge, Massachusetts

(Received November 20, 1958)

The energy transfer between adjacent resonances in nuclear and electron spin systems is analyzed in terms of the overlap of line-shape functions. The procedure is an enlargement on the original proposal of Kronig and Bouwkamp, and consists of taking partial account of off-diagonal elements in the spin-spin interaction, which are omitted in Van Vleck's truncated Hamiltonian. If the frequency of these off-diagonal elements is sufficiently small, they give rise to an additional kind of spin-spin relaxation, observed by Gorter and co-workers. They are also responsible for cross-saturation effects in paramagnetic salts of the type observed by Townes and co-workers. A crucial experiment is described which can be explained by spin-spin interactions, but not by the assumption of a hot-phonon region. Implications of the cross-relaxation for the operation of solid state masers are discussed. Special consideration is given to magnetically dilute substances and inhomogeneously broadened lines. Paradoxically, the latter will usually still undergo a homogeneous steady-state saturation.

1. INTRODUCTION

SINCE Waller's fundamental paper[1] on spin relaxation and Gorter's early experiments,[2] much attention has been paid to the question of thermal equilibrium in magnetic spin systems. Casimir and du Pré[3] postulated the existence of such equilibrium within the spin system to explain the spin-lattice relaxation effects of Gorter and co-workers. Kronig[4] already realized that thermal equilibrium in the whole spin system would only be established if the dipolar interactions between different spins was sufficient to "bridge the gap" between the various spin levels of an individual ion.

With the advent of magnetic resonance techniques, the problem of magnetic relaxation gained new impetus. It was generally recognized that the populations of spin levels which are equally spaced readily attain the Boltzmann ratio, but the establishment of a Boltzmann distribution between spin levels with unequal spacing takes a much longer time. An early illustration[5,6] is the saturation in high magnetic field of one nuclear spin resonance without affecting the other species in the same crystal. The Li^7 and F^{19} spin systems in LiF are better isolated from one another in high fields than they are from the lattice. In magnetic fields below a hundred oersteds, however, they come more readily into equilibrium with one another. Use of this physical phenomenon has been made to reduce the relaxation time of a spin species by giving it the same energy splitting as another species and thus bringing it into contact with another spin system with a shorter spin-lattice relaxation time.[6–8]

It is the purpose of this paper to analyze in some detail the transition region of nearly equally spaced levels. For equal spacing a Boltzmann distribution over the different spin levels is established in a time of the order of T_2. For unequal spacing they come into equilibrium with the lattice first with their respective relaxation times T_1. The Casimir-du Pré hypothesis is not valid in this case. In the intermediate region of approximately equal spacing, different parts of the spin system may come into internal equilibrium in an intermediate time, which we shall call the *cross-relaxation time* and designate by T_{21}. It will be shown that double flip-flops of neighboring spins in which the Zeeman energy is "nearly" conserved are responsible for this effect. The small balance of energy is taken up by the dipolar or internal energy of the spin system.

This raises the important problem of the equilibrium of the Zeeman (and quadrupolar or crystalline splitting) energy on the one hand and the dipolar interaction on the other, which is discussed in a very lucid manner by Abragam and Proctor.[6] These authors assume the existence of a mixing field H^* larger than the local dipolar field H_L. The energy splittings for $H<H^*$ are sufficiently small to allow for a rapid exchange of Zeeman and dipolar energy. Abragam and Proctor do not discuss the dynamics of spin interactions which would give a theoretical justification for the experimental observation of such mixing. One purpose of this paper is to provide a semiquantitative discussion of those processes which transform Zeeman and dipolar energy into each other.

Such processes can also give a quantitative explanation for the cross-saturation effects of adjacent electron

* The research reported in this paper was made possible through support extended Cruft Laboratory, Harvard University, by the National Security Agency.
† National Science Foundation Predoctoral Fellow.
‡ Now at Applied Physics Laboratory, Johns Hopkins University, Silver Spring, Maryland.
[1] I. Waller, Z. Physik **79**, 370 (1932).
[2] C. J. Gorter, *Paramagnetic Relaxation* (Elsevier Publishing Company, Inc., Amsterdam, 1947).
[3] H. B. G. Casimir and F. K. du Pré, Physica **5**, 507 (1938).
[4] R. Kronig and C. J. Bouwkamp, Physica **5**, 521 (1938); **6**, 290 (1939).
[5] R. V. Pound and E. M. Purcell, Phys. Rev. **81**, 279 (1951).
[6] A. Abragam and W. G. Proctor, Phys. Rev. **109**, 1441 (1958).
[7] G. Feher and H. E. D. Scovil, Phys. Rev. **105**, 760 (1957).
[8] H. S. Gutowsky and D. E. Woessner, Phys. Rev. Letters **1**, 6 (1958).

spin resonances reported by Giordmaine and others.[9] Their suggestion of phonon heating over a certain frequency interval is ruled out by a cross-maser experiment described in this paper. The importance of cross-relaxation effects for band width characteristics and low-frequency limits of solid state masers is discussed. Preliminary discussions of these spin-spin interactions have been given.[10]

Finally, these processes are also responsible for the temperature-independent relaxation at intermediate frequencies discovered by de Vryer, Gorter, and others.[11,12] In a recent paper by Verstelle, Drewes, and Gorter[13] an interpretation of those results in terms of the same processes discussed here has been announced.

2. CROSS-RELAXATION TIME

Consider the spin Hamiltonian

$$\mathcal{H}=\mathcal{H}_m+\mathcal{H}_{cr}+\mathcal{H}_{int}, \tag{1}$$

$\mathcal{H}_{cr}$ is the sum of the crystalline field couplings of the individual ions or the quadrupole couplings of the nuclei.

The Zeeman energy in the applied field is given by

$$\mathcal{H}_m=-\sum_i \beta\mathbf{H}\cdot\mathbf{g}_i\cdot\mathbf{S}_i.$$

The interaction between the spins consists of dipolar, pseudodipolar, and exchange terms:

$$\mathcal{H}_{int}=A+B+C+D+E+F, \tag{2}$$

$$A=\sum_{j>i}[A_{ij}+(g_ig_j\beta^2r_{ij}^{-3}+B_{ij})\times(1-3\cos^2\theta_{ij})]S_{zi}S_{zj}, \tag{2a}$$

$$B=\sum_{j>i}[\tfrac{1}{2}A_{ij}+(-\tfrac{1}{4})(g_ig_j\beta^2r_{ij}^{-3}+B_{ij})\times(1-3\cos^2\theta_{ij})](S_{+i}S_{-j}+S_{-i}S_{+j}), \tag{2b}$$

$$C=\sum_{j>i}(-\tfrac{3}{2})(g_ig_j\beta^2r_{ij}^{-3}+B_{ij})\sin\theta_{ij}\times\cos\theta_{ij}e^{-i\phi_{ij}}(S_{+i}S_{zj}+S_{zi}S_{+j}), \tag{2c}$$

$$D=\sum_{j>i}(-\tfrac{3}{2})(g_ig_j\beta^2r_{ij}^{-3}+B_{ij})\sin\theta_{ij}\times\cos\theta_{ij}e^{+i\phi_{ij}}(S_{-i}S_{zj}+S_{zi}S_{-j}), \tag{2d}$$

$$E=\sum_{j>i}\tfrac{3}{4}(g_ig_j\beta^2r_{ij}^{-3}+B_{ij})\sin^2\theta_{ij}e^{-2i\phi_{ij}}S_{+i}S_{+j}, \tag{2e}$$

$$F=\sum_{j>i}\tfrac{3}{4}(g_ig_j\beta^2r_{ij}^{-3}+B_{ij})\sin^2\theta_{ij}e^{+2i\phi_{ij}}S_{-i}S_{-j}. \tag{2f}$$

θ_{ij} and ϕ_{ij} are the polar angles of the radius vector connecting ions i and j with respect to the z-axis.

Consider the simple case of a Kramers doublet with identical spins. Take the z-direction along H. The Zeeman splitting of each individual ion is

$$h\nu_{12}=+g\beta H.$$

It is assumed to be larger than the interaction with other ions. $\mathcal{H}_{int}$ will be treated as a perturbation. The problem, which was already considered by Kronig and Bouwkamp,[4] is to determine the rate at which Zeeman energy and dipolar energy come into mutual equilibrium. Since total energy of the spin Hamiltonian remains conserved, the formulation can also be put in the form: What is the probability that a quantum $h\nu_{12}$ gets absorbed by a rearrangement in the dipolar lattice?

Consider repeated operation of the interaction Hamiltonian. Take products of the type $\cdots(S_{zk}S_{zl})\times(S_{+m}S_{-n})\cdots(S_{+i}S_{zj})\cdots(S_{zp}S_{zq})(S_{+r}S_{-s})$..They turn the spin i in the external field and rearrange the dipolar lattice. It would be difficult to carry through such a high-order perturbation calculation.

A hybrid method between the perturbation calculation and the method of moments[14] is therefore used. Simple first order time-dependent perturbation theory is applied to the terms C and D (and possibly E and F). The repeated effect of the diagonal and semidiagonal terms A and B is absorbed in a line-shape function $g(\nu)$. The transition probability for the Zeeman energy $h\nu_{12}$ of a spin to be converted into dipolar energy is

$$w=(2T_{21})^{-1}=\hbar^{-2}|C|^2N^{-1}g(\nu=0). \tag{3}$$

The characteristic time for this conversion process is called T_{21} to indicate its intermediate position between T_1 and T_2. The shape function $g(\nu)$ has a symmetrical maximum around the frequency ν_{21}. Its second moment around this frequency is given by

$$h^2\langle\Delta\nu^2\rangle=-\frac{\mathrm{Tr}\{[(A+B)\sum_{j>i}S_{zi}S_{+j}-\sum_{j>i}S_{zi}S_{+j}(A+B)]^2\}}{\mathrm{Tr}\{[\sum_{j>i}S_{zi}S_{+j}]^2\}}. \tag{4}$$

This moment has the same order of magnitude as, but is not identical with, the second moments of Van Vleck for transitions induced by an external radio-frequency field.

If the assumption of a Gaussian shape with the correct second moment (4) is made, the cross-relaxation probability becomes for $g_i=g_j$, $S_i=S_j$, $B_{ij}=0$,

$$w=\frac{\hbar^{-2}\times\frac{3}{4}g^4\beta^4S(S+1)\sum_j r_{ij}^{-6}\sin^2\theta_{ij}\cos^2\theta_{ij}}{(2\pi)^{\frac{1}{2}}\langle\Delta\nu^2\rangle^{\frac{1}{2}}}\times\exp\left\{\frac{-g^2\beta^2H^2}{2h^2\langle\Delta\nu^2\rangle}\right\}. \tag{5}$$

The cross-relaxation time T_{21} increases very rapidly as the splitting of the energy levels of an individual ion becomes large compared to the spin-spin interaction. This is the reason why the processes with $\Delta m=\pm2$, caused by the terms E and F are negligible. They would lead to an expression in which the exponent in

[9] Giordmaine, Alsop, Nash, and Townes, Phys. Rev. **109**, 302 (1958).

[10] Shapiro, Bloembergen, and Artman, Bull. Am. Phys. Soc. Ser. II, **3**, 317 (1958). Proceedings of the Symposium on Solid-State Masers, U. S. Army Signal Research and Development Laboratories, Fort Monmouth, New Jersey, June, 1958 (unpublished).

[11] F. W. de Vryer and C. J. Gorter, Physica **18**, 549 (1952).

[12] Smits, Derksen, Verstelle, and Gorter, Physica **22**, 773 (1956).

[13] Verstelle, Drewes, and Gorter, Physica **24**, 632 (1958).

[14] J. H. Van Vleck, Phys. Rev. **74**, 1168 (1948).

the Gaussian is 4 times larger than in (5). Hence their contribution is negligible.

When the splitting approaches zero ($H\rightarrow 0$), the expressions (3) and (4) have to be modified. All terms of the dipolar interaction then become important. Truncation is not permissible. The second moment increases and also the matrix element in Eq. (3) is increased because the E and F terms also contribute. In the case that H is not much larger than the dipolar field, the formula of Kronig-Bouwkamp, who first considered the problem under discussion, should be valid:

$$w=[\langle\Delta\omega^2\rangle_{\text{tot}}]^{\frac{1}{2}}\exp\{-g^2\beta^2H^2/2\hbar^2\langle\Delta\omega^2\rangle_{\text{tot}}\}.$$

It is seen that the cross-relaxation time T_{21} becomes identical with T_2 in the limit $H\rightarrow 0$. If, on the other hand, $T_{21}>T_1$, the Zeeman part and the spin-spin part come separately into equilibrium with the lattice. The hypothesis of Casimir and du Pré is not valid in that case. The interesting region is $T_1>T_{21}>T_2$. In this domain the relaxation phenomena mentioned in the introduction occur.

A warning should be raised against too liberal use of the Gaussian shape, which is so convenient for computational purposes. The value of $g(0)$ may be larger by several orders of magnitude than the Gaussian would predict. Important situations, in which the tails are considerably enhanced, include the case of strong exchange interactions A_{ij} and the case of random paramagnetic dilution. Calculation of the fourth, and higher, moments of $g(\nu)$ shows the enhancement of the tail concomitant with a narrowing at the center.

Interesting new situations arise when three or more levels are considered or when more than one magnetic species is present. Some simple examples are shown in Fig. 1. In Figs. 1(a) and 1(b) the isolated atoms are assumed to have three energy levels. In case 1(a), two of them are closely spaced; in 1(b) one is approximately halfway between the others. They may correspond to a Ni^{++} ion, or nucleus with $I=1$, in an axially symmetric

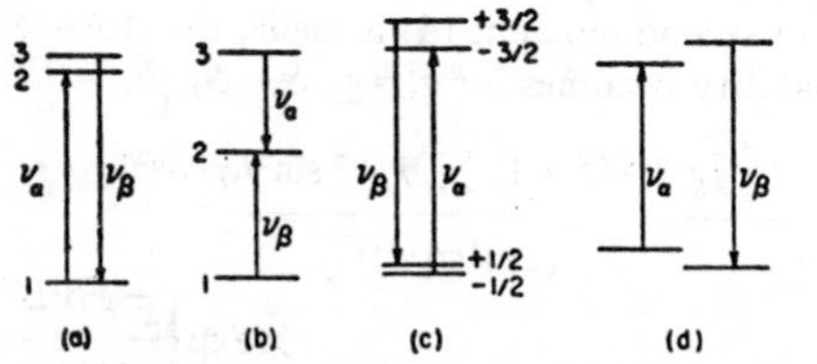

FIG. 1. Some representative situations of double transitions in which the energy is nearly conserved. The α and β transitions take place simultaneously on neighboring spins. (a) Three levels, two of which are closely spaced. Example: the Ni^{++} ion in an axial crystalline field with a small magnetic field. (b) Three levels, with one approximately halfway between the others. Example: Ni^{++} in intermediate field. (c) Two closely spaced pairs of levels. Example: Cr^{+++} or a nucleus with $I=\frac{3}{2}$ in an axial field, with a small magnetic field parallel to the axis. (d) Two Kramers doublets with nearly equal spacing. Example: two Cu^{++} ions with different nuclear spin orientations, or two nuclear spins $I=\frac{1}{2}$ with nearly equal γ in a relatively weak external field.

field with weak or intermediate external magnetic field, respectively. Case 1(c) corresponds to a case with S or $I=\frac{3}{2}$. Case 1(d) corresponds, e.g., to two species $I_\alpha=I_\beta=\frac{1}{2}$, with slightly different gyromagnetic ratios.

The dipolar interaction between the ions may induce transitions in which the sum of Zeeman and crystalline field energies is nearly conserved. These transitions are indicated by the arrows. It should be noted that the two arrows in each case belong to different ions. The balance of energy is again taken up by the spin-spin energy.

The probability per unit time for the process that ion i increases its energy by an amount $h\nu_\alpha$ and ion j decreases its energy by $h\nu_\beta$, the balance of energy $h(\nu_\beta-\nu_\alpha)$ being taken up by the spin-spin interaction of the whole array of dipoles, is then given by

$$w_{ij}=\hbar^{-2}|(E_i,E_j|\mathcal{H}_{ij}|E_i+h\nu_\alpha,\ E_j-h\nu_\beta)|^2g_{\alpha\beta}(\nu=0),\quad\text{(6a)}$$

where $\mathcal{H}_{ij}$ is the interaction between ions i and j.

If m_s is a good quantum number in case 1(d) and the gyromagnetic ratio has the same sign for the two species, the matrix element corresponds to the $\Delta m_s^\alpha=-\Delta m_s^\beta=\pm 1$ transition from the interaction B in Eq. (2) and its square is given by

$$|\mathcal{H}_{ij}|^2=\tfrac{1}{16}(I_\alpha-m_\alpha)(I_\alpha+m_\alpha+1)(I_\beta+m_\beta)$$
$$\times(I_\beta-m_\beta+1)g_i^2g_j^2\beta^4(1-3\cos^2\theta_{ij})^2r_{ij}^{-6}.\quad\text{(7a)}$$

If, however, the gyromagnetic ratios g_i and g_j have opposite sign, the transition which nearly conserves energy has $\Delta m=\pm 2$ and is determined by the E or F term in Eq. (2). This is also true for cases 1(a), (b), and (c), if a magnetic field parallel to the axis of the crystalline field is applied. In the case of Cr^{+++} ion in a small parallel field one has, for example, the transition $m_z^\alpha=\frac{3}{2}\rightarrow\frac{1}{2}$ and $m_z^\beta=-\frac{1}{2}\rightarrow-\frac{3}{2}$.

$$|\mathcal{H}_{ij}|^2=(81/16)g_{\|}{}^4\beta^4r_{ij}^{-6}\sin^4\theta_{ij}.\quad\text{(7b)}$$

The shape function $g_{\alpha\beta}(\nu)$ is calculated by the moment method. The total second moment is

$$h^2\nu_{\alpha\beta}{}^2=-\mathrm{Tr}\{[\mathcal{H}(\textstyle\sum\mathcal{H}_{ij})-(\sum\mathcal{H}_{ij})\mathcal{H}]^2\}/$$
$$\mathrm{Tr}\{[\textstyle\sum\mathcal{H}_{ij}]^2\}.\quad\text{(8a)}$$

The total Hamiltonian $\mathcal{H}$ has to be truncated in a manner appropriate to the particular problem at hand.[15] If m_s is a good quantum number, this truncation is straightforward. The line shape has a maximum at the frequency $\nu_\alpha-\nu_\beta$; $g_{\alpha\beta}(\nu=0)$ will be appreciable, if $h(\nu_\alpha-\nu_\beta)/g\beta$ is not much larger than the local fields.

It is instructive to obtain an estimate of $g_{\alpha\beta}(\nu=0)$ in terms of the observed magnetic resonance lines $g_\alpha(\nu)$ and $g_\beta(\nu)$. The second moments of these shape functions are determined by the expression which results if $\sum\mathcal{H}_{ij}$ in Eq. (8a) is replaced by S_x. The rigorous

[15] Ishiguro, Kambe, and Usui, Physica 17, 310 (1951).

expression (6a) is replaced by

$$w_{ij}=\hbar^{-2}|\mathcal{H}_{ij}|^2\int\int g_\alpha(\nu')g_\beta(\nu'')\delta(\nu'-\nu'')d\nu'd\nu''. \quad (6b)$$

If a Gaussian shape is assumed for $g_\alpha(\nu)$ and $g_\beta(\nu)$ with second moments $(\Delta\nu_\alpha)^2$ and $(\Delta\nu_\beta)^2$, respectively, the integrations in (6b) which represent the overlap between the two resonances can be carried out explicitly. The result is

$$w_{ij}=(2\pi)^{-\frac{1}{2}}\hbar^{-2}|\mathcal{H}_{ij}|^2[(\Delta\nu_\alpha)^2+(\Delta\nu_\beta)^2]^{-\frac{1}{2}} \times\exp\{-(\nu_\alpha-\nu_\beta)^2/2[(\Delta\nu_\alpha)^2+(\Delta\nu_\beta)^2]\}. \quad (8b)$$

This expression is not rigorous and should be used with extreme caution. Equations (6a) and (8a) should be preferred, but $g_{\alpha\beta}(\nu=0)$ is of course not determined by (8a) alone. All higher moments are necessary in principle. The assumption of a Gaussian with the second moment given by Eq. (8a) may still lead to large errors in the tail.

A cross relaxation time T_{21} can be defined by the relation

$$(2T_{21}{}^\alpha)^{-1}=\sum_j w_{ij}p_j{}^\beta. \quad (9)$$

This derivation has physical validity and significance in the range $T_1>T_{21}>T_2$. The right-hand side represents the probability that spin i will absorb a quantum $h\nu_\alpha$, while an arbitray spin j emits a quantum $h\nu_\beta$; $p_j{}^\beta$ represents the probability for a spin j to be in the upper state of a ν_β transition.

It is noteworthy that there is no need for very closely spaced levels. Figure 1(b) shows that the only requirement is that some spacings are nearly equal. If closely spaced levels exist, as in Fig. 1(a), no matrix element between them is required. The Zeeman energy of the $m=\pm1$ levels of Ni^{++} in an axial crystalline field with parallel magnetic field can come into Boltzmann equilibrium with the spin-spin energy via the indicated process.

3. CONSERVATION OF ANGULAR MOMENTUM

In the experiments of Abragam and Proctor, as in other adiabatic (de−) magnetization experiments, the angular momentum of the spin system is not conserved. Nor is it in the processes of Kronig and Bouwkamp or in the $\Delta m=\pm2$ processes considered in the preceding section. For those who are familiar with the magneto-mechanical experiments of Einstein-de Haas and Barnett,[16] the answer is obvious that the balance of angular momentum is transferred to the rigid lattice and appears as a rotation of the whole crystal. Since the question of angular momentum has been raised on more than one occasion, a brief general proof will be given that the transition probabilities which have been derived are correct, even though the question of angular momentum has been ignored.

The coordinate Φ giving the azimuthal orientation of the rigid crystal with respect to a fixed coordinate system is introduced explicitly. The angle ϕ_{ij} measures the azimuthal orientation of the spin pair i and j with respect to a coordinate system attached to the crystal. The z axes of the two systems of reference coincide. Replace ϕ_{ij} in Eqs. (2) by $\phi_{ij}+\Phi$. The angular momentum associated with the rotation of the crystal is represented by the operator $(\hbar/i)(\partial/\partial\Phi)$. The total angular momentum around the z-axis is given by

$$J_z=\sum_j S_{zj}+\frac{\hbar}{i}\frac{\partial}{\partial\Phi}.$$

It can readily be verified that this operator commutes with the Hamiltonian (1):

$$[J_z,\mathcal{H}]=0.$$

The spin angular momentum $\sum_j S_{zj}$ alone does not commute with the dipolar interaction, but total angular momentum is indeed conserved. If the spin system undergoes a transition $\Delta m=+2$, the angular momentum of the crystal changes by $-2\hbar$. The change in rotational energy associated with this change in rotation is negligible because of the very large mass of the crystal. The value of the square of the matrix element $|\mathcal{H}_{ij}|^2$ is not changed by the explicit introduction of Φ and the free rotational wave functions for the crystalline lattice.

4. CROSS-RELAXATION RATE PROCESSES

The rate equations governing the populations of the various spin levels should now be modified to take account of the cross-relaxation of Sec. 2. They will be written down explicitly for the cases of Figs. 1(a) and 1(d). Extension to other, more complicated, situations is straightforward.

Case 1(a).—Let n_1, n_2, and n_3 represent the populations in the three levels. The equilibrium values at the lattice temperature are $n_1{}^0$, $n_2{}^0$ and $n_3{}^0$. The energy difference $h\nu_{21}=E_2-E_1$ is so much larger than the dipolar interaction that no cross-relaxation has to be considered to the ground level E_1. The splitting $h\nu_{32}=E_3-E_2$ is only slightly—say, two to ten times—larger than the dipolar width. Cross-relaxation has to be considered due to the overlap of the ν_{31} and ν_{21} resonances, although their maxima are experimentally well resolved. The populations n_2 and n_3 can now change also by the cross-relaxation processes. Note that the population n_1 is not affected.

$$(\partial n_2/\partial t)_{\text{cross rel}} =-(\partial n_3/\partial t)_{\text{cross rel}}=w[n_3-n_2-(n_3-n_2)_{\text{ad}}] +N^{-1}\sum_j w_{ij}[(n_3n_1-n_2n_1)-(n_3n_1-n_2n_1)_{\text{ad}}].$$

Here w corresponds to the Kronig-Bouwkamp process described by Eq. (3). The w_{ij}, which are given by Eqs. (6) or (8), correspond to the double flips indicated in Fig. 1(a) and their inverses.

[16] C. J. Gorter and B. Kahn, Physica 7, 753 (1940).

The equilibrium value of the population to which the cross-relaxation mechanism tends asymptotically is not given by the Boltzmann distribution at the lattice temperature. The equilibrium value is determined by the requirement that the expectation value of the total spin Hamiltonian (1) changes by the work done during the variation of the external field. The processes are adiabatic in the sense that no heat is transferred to or from the lattice.

In the limit of high temperatures, $kT \gg h\nu_{31}$, the dipolar interaction energy can be defined separately from the Zeeman and crystalline field energy. Let T_l be the lattice temperature, T_z^i the initial "Zeeman temperature" defined by $h\nu_{32}k^{-1}\ln(n_2/n_3)$, T_s^i the initial dipolar temperature, defined by $E_{\rm dip}=\langle \mathcal{H}_{\rm int}^2\rangle/kT_s$, and $T_{\rm ad}$ the final temperature after the spin system has come into internal equilibrium adiabatically. This equilibrium is to be understood in a partial sense, as only those levels participate between which cross-relaxation processes are important.

The usual relations between populations and spin temperature exist.

$$(n_3-n_2)_{\rm ad}=\tfrac{1}{2}(N-n_1)(h\nu_{32})(1/kT_{\rm ad}). \qquad (10)$$

The adiabatic condition can be written

$$-\int MdH_0=\tfrac{1}{4}(N-n_1)(h\nu_{32})^2[(1/kT_z^i)-(1/kT_{\rm ad})] +{\rm Tr}(\mathcal{H}_{\rm int}^2)[(1/kT_s^i)-(1/kT_{\rm ad})]. \qquad (11)$$

In the high-temperature limit, n_1/N may be replaced by $\frac{1}{3}$.

Introduce next the spin-lattice relaxation mechanism and radio-frequency fields at ν_{13} and ν_{23}. The complete rate equations then become, in the same notation as used for three-level masers,[17]

$$\frac{dn_3}{dt}=W_{31}(n_1-n_3)+W_{32}(n_2-n_3) +w_{13}\left(n_1-n_3-\tfrac{1}{3}N\frac{h\nu_{31}}{kT_l}\right) +w_{23}\left(n_2-n_3-\tfrac{1}{3}N\frac{h\nu_{32}}{kT_l}\right) +(w+\tfrac{1}{3}\textstyle\sum_j w_{ij})\left[n_2-n_3-\tfrac{1}{3}N\frac{h\nu_{32}}{kT_{\rm ad}}\right], \qquad (12)$$

$$\frac{dn_2}{dt}=W_{32}(n_3-n_2)+w_{23}\left(n_3-n_2+\tfrac{1}{3}N\frac{h\nu_{32}}{kT_l}\right) +w_{12}\left[n_1-n_2-\tfrac{1}{3}N\frac{h\nu_{21}}{kT_l}\right] -(w+\tfrac{1}{3}\textstyle\sum_j w_{ij})\left[n_2-n_3-\tfrac{1}{3}N\frac{h\nu_{32}}{kT_{\rm ad}}\right]$$

[17] N. Bloembergen, Phys. Rev. **104**, 324 (1956).

This set of equations should, strictly speaking, be supplemented with an equation describing the direct relaxation of the dipolar energy to the lattice. It will turn out that in many applications the details of this process and the exact value of $T_{\rm ad}$ are of no importance.

Case 1(d).—Consider a lattice with N_α ions with two energy levels separated by $h\nu_\alpha$ and N_β ions with two energy levels separated by $h\nu_\beta$, $\nu_\alpha-\nu_\beta \ll \nu_\alpha$. The cross-relaxation processes contribute the following term to the rate equations for the difference in population of the two α-levels and the two β-levels:

$$(\partial\Delta n_\alpha/\partial t)_{\rm cross}=-(\partial\Delta n_\beta/\partial t)_{\rm cross} =-2N_\beta^{-1}\sum_{j=1}^{N_\beta} w_{ij}[(n_\alpha^+n_\beta^- - n_\alpha^-n_\beta^+) -(n_\alpha^+n_\beta^- - n_\alpha^-n_\beta^+)_{\rm ad}]. \qquad (13)$$

In the high-temperature approximation, $kT\gg h\nu_\beta$, Eq. (13) can be put in the form

$$(\partial\Delta n_\alpha/\partial t)_{\rm cross}=-(1/T_{21}^\alpha)\{\Delta n_\alpha-(\Delta n_\alpha)_{\rm ad}\} +(1/T_{21}^\beta)\{\Delta n_\beta-(\Delta n_\beta)_{\rm ad}\},$$

where $(1/T_{21}^\alpha)=(N_\beta/N_\alpha)(1/T_{21}^\beta)$, and $p_j^\beta=\frac{1}{2}$ is substituted in Eq. (9).

The complete rate equations in the presence of spin-lattice relaxation[18] and an applied radio-frequency field at the frequency ν_α become

$$\frac{d(\Delta n_\alpha)}{dt}=-2W_\alpha\Delta n_\alpha-\frac{1}{T_1^\alpha}\left(\Delta n_\alpha-\tfrac{1}{2}N_\alpha\frac{h\nu_\alpha}{kT_l}\right) -\frac{1}{T_{21}^\alpha}\left(\Delta n_\alpha-\tfrac{1}{2}N_\alpha\frac{h\nu_\alpha}{kT_{\rm ad}}\right) +\frac{1}{T_{21}^\beta}\left(\Delta n_\beta-\tfrac{1}{2}N_\beta\frac{h\nu_\beta}{kT_{\rm ad}}\right)$$

$$\frac{d(\Delta n_\beta)}{dt}=\frac{1}{T_1^\beta}\left(\Delta n_\beta-\tfrac{1}{2}N_\beta\frac{h\nu_\beta}{kT_l}\right) +\frac{1}{T_{21}^\alpha}\left(\Delta n_\alpha-\tfrac{1}{2}N_\alpha\frac{h\nu_\alpha}{kT_{\rm ad}}\right) -\frac{1}{T_{21}^\beta}\left(\Delta n_\beta-\tfrac{1}{2}N_\beta\frac{h\nu_\beta}{kT_{\rm ad}}\right) \qquad (14)$$

These rate equations will now be used to interpret a number of relaxation experiments. Although in practice the energy level diagrams are often considerably more complicated than those shown in Fig. 1, Eqs. (12) and (14) for cases 1(a) and 1(d) contain all the essential features. The construction of rate equations for cases

[18] To avoid further nonessential complications, spin-lattice processes in which the two species participate in a coupled fashion, such as those considered by I. Solomon [Phys. Rev. **99**, 559 (1955)], are ignored.

1(b) and 1(c) and for more intricate situations should be straightforward.

5. INTERMEDIATE RELAXATION IN LEIDEN EXPERIMENTS

Paramagnetic dispersion and absorption have been found at intermediate frequencies $(1/T_2)\gg\omega\gg(1/T_1)$. This dispersion is independent of the lattice temperature and may show maxima as a function of an applied dc magnetic field.[11–13] A simple theoretical model, patterned after the treatment of spin-lattice relaxation by Kronig and Gorter,[19] for this new type of relaxation is presented here. A similar explanation has also been announced by the Leiden group.[13]

Let $\Delta H \exp(i\omega t)$ be a small periodic magnetic field in an arbitrary direction. In general the energy levels will shift by $(\partial E/\partial H)\Delta H \exp(i\omega t)$. There is a periodic variation of the populations $\Delta n \exp(i\omega t)$ and a concomitant variation in the magnetic moment. Let us take model 1(a), which applies to the Ni^{++} ion. Substitute the periodic variation on the left-hand sides of Eqs. (12). If $w\gg w_{12}, w_{13}, w_{23}$, the spin-lattice relaxation terms are negligible. The applied field is not at a resonance frequency and hence $W_{31}=W_{32}=0$. The periodic variation of the populations in this region is described simply by

$$i\omega(n_3-n_2)=2(w+\tfrac{1}{3}\textstyle\sum w_{ij})[n_2-n_3-(n_2-n_3)_{\text{ad}}]. \quad (15)$$

The solution is

$$n_3-n_2=(n_3-n_2)_{\text{ad}}(1+i\omega T_{21})^{-1}. \quad (16)$$

Here $T_{21}=\frac{1}{2}(w+\frac{1}{3}\sum w_{ij})^{-1}$ is determined by Eqs. (3) and (6). The population n_1 remains constant.

The susceptibility must now be calculated. The magnetization is given by

$$M=\tfrac{1}{2}(n_3-n_2)(M_{33}-M_{22})+\tfrac{1}{2}(n_3+n_2)(M_{33}+M_{22}) +n_1M_{11}+\text{contributions from off-diagonal elements of the magnetic moment operator.} \quad (17)$$

Only the first term on the right-hand side is frequency-dependent in the range of interest. Its contribution goes to zero as $\omega\gg T_{21}^{-1}$.

The adiabatic value $(n_3-n_2)_{\text{ad}}$ is calculated from the condition that the work done by the variation of the external field is equal to the sum of the changes in Zeeman energy and interaction energy, with the restriction that only effects arising from a variation in n_3-n_2 should be taken into account.

With the relations

$$M_{33}-M_{22}=\frac{\partial(h\nu_{32})}{\partial H},\quad n_3-n_2=\tfrac{1}{3}N\frac{h\nu_{32}}{kT},$$

$$(n_3-n_2)_{\text{ad}}=\frac{\partial(n_3-n_2)}{\partial H_{\text{ad}}}\Delta H \exp(i\omega t), \quad (18)$$

[19] See reference 2, Chap. 4.

Eq. (11) can be put in the differential form

$$\tfrac{1}{6}N\frac{(h\nu_{32})}{kT}\frac{\partial h\nu_{32}}{\partial H}=\left(\frac{\partial}{\partial H}\right)_{\text{ad}}\left[\tfrac{1}{2}\times\tfrac{1}{3}N\frac{(h\nu_{32})^2}{kT}+\frac{\langle\mathcal{H}_{\text{int}}^2\rangle}{kT}\right].$$

This can be further transformed into

$$\left(\frac{\partial}{\partial H}\right)_{\text{ad}}(n_3-n_2)=\frac{\langle\mathcal{H}_{\text{int}}^2\rangle}{\frac{1}{6}N(h\nu_{32})^2+\langle\mathcal{H}_{\text{int}}^2\rangle}\frac{N}{3}\frac{h}{kT}\frac{\partial\nu_{32}}{\partial H}. \quad (19)$$

Combining Eqs. (16), (17), (18) and (19), one finds for the part of the susceptibility which undergoes the intermediate relaxation

$$\chi'-i\chi''=\frac{\langle\mathcal{H}_{\text{int}}^2\rangle\times\frac{1}{6}Nh^2/kT}{\frac{1}{6}N(h\nu_{32})^2+\langle\mathcal{H}_{\text{int}}^2\rangle}\left(\frac{\partial\nu_{32}}{\partial H}\right)^2\frac{1}{1+i\omega T_{21}}. \quad (20)$$

The behavior of χ' as a function of frequency is shown schematically in Fig. 2. The solid curve is for the larger separation of the two levels, the dotted curve has a smaller value of ν_{32}. There is the usual spin-lattice relaxation. For $\omega>T_1^{-1}$ the susceptibility drops to its "adiabatic value." Then the intermediate relaxation of part of this adiabatic susceptibility occurs at $\omega\approx T_{21}^{-1}$. The dispersion is temperature-independent and is a very sensitive function of the separation of the levels because of T_{21}.

Experimentally, the susceptibility is usually plotted at constant frequency *versus* applied dc field. There may easily occur a maximum in this plot, because for certain values of the external field some pairs of levels of the chromium, manganese, and ferric salts may become nearly equidistant. This will make T_{21} about equal to ω^{-1}. For the Cu^{++} ion, which has a Kramers doublet, such a maximum of $\chi'(\omega)$ *vs* H should not occur, in agreement with observation. With the

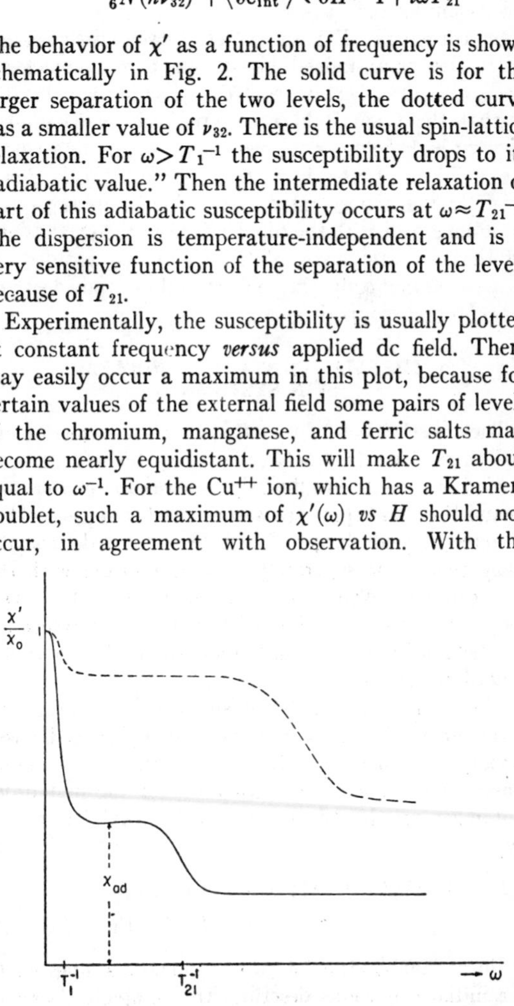

FIG. 2. Qualitative behavior of the real part of the susceptibility in a dilute paramagnetic salt as a function of frequency, showing spin-lattice relaxation and cross-relaxation. The solid curve is for the case where the difference in spacing between the energy levels is slightly larger than the dipolar field; the dotted curve is for the opposite case. There may be several regions of cross-relaxation in systems with many spin levels.

multiple levels of the Cr^{+++}, Mn^{++}, and Fe^{+++} ions, and the presence of several nonequivalent sites in the unit cell, the occurrence of several intermediate relaxation regions is assured. The theory for such multilevel situations can be patterned after the simple case 1(a) given here. The algebra will become quite involved. Since in most experiments polycrystalline powders have been used, an average over all orientations of H with respect to the crystalline fields should be taken. This makes a detailed comparison of published relaxation curves with theory too cumbersome.

Relaxation experiments should be carried out in dilute single crystals. Contributions of individual pairs of levels to the susceptibility may be separated. The experimental data should be plotted *versus* frequency at constant H, because then the energy levels of the ion remain fixed.

In concentrated paramagnetic salts the dipolar interaction may indeed be sufficient to connect all levels with a reasonably short T_{21}, close to the value T_2, so that the Casimir-du Pré hypothesis has validity. In very high fields or for very large crystalline fields, the validity of the hypothesis should break down even for the concentrated salts. The lumping of the crystalline field with the dipolar field in the expressions for the adiabatic susceptibility should be avoided. It is permissible only in polycrystalline powders of concentrated magnetic salts.

6. THERMAL CONTACT IN NUCLEAR SPIN SYSTEMS

The classic experiments on nuclear spin temperature and thermal contact between spin systems have been carried out in lithium fluoride.[6] It was found that the Li and F nuclear spins are well isolated from each other in external fields larger than a few hundred oersteds. They then come separately into equilibrium with the lattice in times of the order of several minutes. However, they come into equilibrium with each other in 6 seconds in a field of 75 oersteds and in less than 0.1 second in a field of 40 oersteds.

The appropriate model of spin levels is case 1(d). Although Li^7 has $I=\frac{3}{2}$ and four equally spaced levels rather than just two, Eqs. (14) can still be used. These two coupled linear equations of the first order will in general give two relaxation times λ^{-1} determined by

$$\{(1/T_1^{\alpha})+(1/T_{21}^{\alpha})-\lambda\}\{(1/T_1^{\beta})+(1/T_{21}^{\beta})-\lambda\} - (1/T_{21}^{\alpha}T_{21}^{\beta})=0. \quad (21)$$

A linear combination of two exponentials adapted to the initial conditions describes the complete decay to the lattice temperature.

The interest here is in the situation that $T_{21}^{\alpha,\beta}\ll T_1^{\alpha,\beta}$. The two spin systems come into adiabatic equilibrium at T_{ad} with a characteristic time $[(T_{21}^{\alpha})^{-1}+(T_{21}^{\beta})^{-1}]^{-1} = N_\beta T_{21}^{\alpha}/(N_\alpha+N_\beta)$. The experiment is carried out in a short time interval, so that subsequent decay to T^l cannot take place.

In agreement with the experimental results, the heat contact should set in rather suddenly below a critical value of the external magnetic field. Equation (8b) indicates that two Gaussian resonances separated by twice their full width at half maximum have a cross-relaxation time of $T_{21}\approx 10^{+4}T_2$. This shows that two well-resolved resonances may indeed mix in a time shorter than T_1. If they are separated by three times their full width, the mixing time is $T_{21}\approx 10^7 T_2$, which will usually be longer than T_1. Substitution of the second-moment values for Li^7 and F^{19} into (8b), with use of Eqs. (7a) and (9), gives $T_{21}=10^{12}$ sec at $H_0=75$ oersteds. This is many orders of magnitude longer than the observed value of 6 seconds. The Gaussian function is of course extremely sensitive to small variations in the effective second moment. It is tempting to invert the procedure and use the observed cross-relaxation time as a measure of the overlap and hence as an exceedingly sensitive tool to measure the line shape far in the wing.

In the case of LiF, for example, the wings will have some bumps. It should be noted that the Zeeman energy is more nearly conserved when two Li^7 nuclei flip $\Delta m_{Li}=2$, for each $\Delta m=-1$ of the F^{19} nuclei. The square of the matrix element $|\mathcal{H}_{ij}|^2$ in Eq. (6a) for these processes is smaller by a factor $(\langle\Delta\nu^2\rangle_{Li}/\nu_{Li}^2) \times[(\nu_F-2\nu_{Li})/\nu_F]^2\approx 3\times 10^{-4}$ for $H_0=75$ oersteds, but this is more than offset by the enormous increase in the Gaussian function, which now has $(\nu_F-2\nu_{Li})^2$ instead of $(\nu_F-\nu_{Li})^2$ in the exponent. The factor in square brackets is included to take account of the partial cancellation of terms in the second-order perturbation calculation, as will be discussed in more detail in Sec. 7. In terms of the moment method one may say that the truncation of $\mathcal{H}$ should not exclude terms $I_{+Li}I_{zj}$. Inclusion of such terms gives rise to small bumps in $g(\nu)$ near the frequency $\nu_F-2\nu_{Li}$. If the approximation of the overlap integral (6b) is used, one finds the value of the cross-relaxation time is 3 seconds, which is in excellent agreement with the experimental value of 6 seconds. At $H_0=40$ oersteds, the cross-relaxation time should be 0.06 second, again in agreement with observation.

Experiments by one of us (P.S.P.) are under way to determine accurately the shape of the overlap as a function of the external field. Cross-relaxation time measurements may also be useful to detect quadrupole background broadening. Similar experiments are also being carried out by various other workers.[20,21]

It can be concluded that all observations on energy transfer between nuclear spin systems are consistent with the theory of spin-spin interaction presented in

[20] R. T. Schumacher, Phys. Rev. **112**, 837 (1958).
[21] M. J. Weber and E. L. Hahn, Bull. Am. Phys. Soc. Ser. II, **3**, 329 (1958).

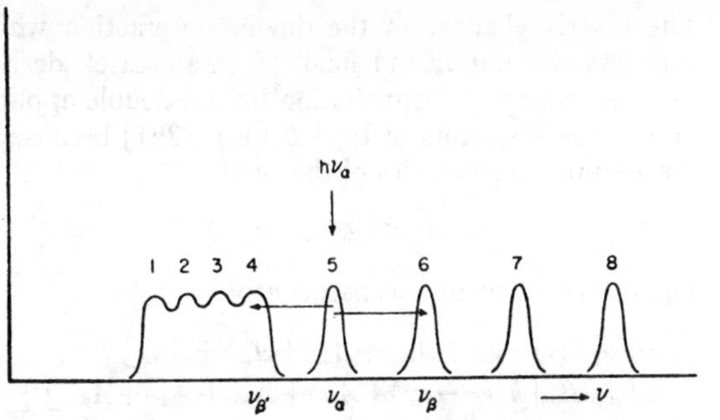

FIG. 3. A reproduction of the resonances in $Cu(NH_4)_2(SO_4)_2 \cdot 6H_2O$ observed by GANT, taken from Fig. 1 of reference 9. Resonance 5 is saturated. The arrows indicate a process of multiple spin flips by which the energy is spread through the structure and cross-saturation occurs. Each arrow represents the simultaneous flip-flop of two spins. The change in Zeeman energy is equal to the length of the arrow. Zeeman energy is conserved for two arrows of equal and opposite length. Four spins are involved in such a process.

this paper. In particular, the discussion of Abragam and Proctor is entirely justified. Their condition that a spin process be adiabatic in the thermodynamic sense can now be made more quantitative:

$$\frac{1}{H_0}\frac{dH_0}{dt} \ll \frac{1}{T_{21}}.$$

This condition is usually not fulfilled if $\gamma H_0 > 5\langle\Delta\omega^2\rangle^{\frac{1}{2}}$. For such high external fields, however, the difference in magnetization in an adiabatic change of H_0 and the constant magnetization in a rapidly changing H_0 is less than 5%.

7. CROSS-SATURATION EFFECTS IN PARAMAGNETIC SALTS

A series of stimulating experiments on paramagnetic resonance saturation and relaxation at liquid helium temperatures in magnetically dilute gadolinium magnesium nitrate, chromium potassium cyanide, and copper ammonium Tutton salt have been reported by Giordmaine, Alsop, Nash, and Townes.[22] Since the most detailed experimental results were obtained on $Cu(NH_4)_2(SO_4)_2 \cdot 6H_2O$, attention will be focused on this salt. There are two nonequivalent Cu^{++} ions in the unit cell and the paramagnetic resonance spectrum consists of sets of four lines, corresponding to the four orientations of the copper nuclear spin. A reproduction of these eight lines as observed by GANT[22] is shown in Fig. 3. The spacing of the hyperfine components in one set was about 100 oersteds. The other set, which had more closely spaced lines, was separated by about 100 oersteds from one hyperfine component in the first set. The full width at half-maximum of each component was 20 oersteds. This width is caused mainly by interactions with proton spins. The dipolar interactions between the copper ions in the diluted salt would give only 3 oersteds. The relaxation time $T_1 = 20$ sec.

The most striking observations were cross-saturation effects, i.e., on steady-state saturation of one of the eight lines, some or all of the others would also show saturation. Furthermore, if one resonance was inverted or saturated by adiabatic rapid passage, it was observed to recover very rapidly in intensity with a characteristic time of $10^{-3}-10^{-4}$ sec$\ll T_1$.

An interpretation of these results is proposed in terms of the spin-spin interactions described by Eqs. (14). This interpretation is very different from the hot-phonon theory proposed by GANT.

It has already been shown in the case of nuclear resonance that the combination of spin-lattice and of cross-relaxation gives rise to two characteristic times given by Eq. (21). In the case that $T_{21} \ll T_1$, these two times are just T_{21} and T_1. The short time, 10^{-4} sec, may be identified with T_{21}. In this time the intensity of a resonance is shared with adjacent resonances and since there are a total of eight resonances, the intensity of a saturated transition results in a time T_{21} to within 15% of its equilibrium value.

The cross-saturation is described by the steady-state solution of Eqs. (14). Note that the ions α and β may be two copper ions in different crystallographic positions or similar Cu^{++} ions with different nuclear orientations. The α Cu^{++} ion is saturated by a resonance field at ν_α with an induced transition probability W_α.

If terms of the order of $h(\nu_\alpha-\nu_\beta)/kT_l$ and $h(\nu_\alpha-\nu_\beta)/kT_{\mathrm{ad}}$ are neglected compared to unity, the steady-state solution of the relative intensity of the α transition may be written in the form

$$\frac{\chi_\alpha''}{\chi_{\alpha,0}''} = 1\bigg/\left[1+2W_\alpha\left(\frac{1}{T_1^\alpha}+\frac{1}{T_1^\beta}\frac{T_{21}^\beta/T_{21}^\alpha}{1+T_{21}^\beta/T_1^\beta}\right)^{-1}\right]. \qquad (22)$$

If $T_{21}^\beta = T_{21}^\alpha \ll T_1$, it is seen that the α resonance is saturated as if it had an effective relaxation time $\{(1/T_1^\alpha)+(1/T_1^\beta)\}^{-1}$.

This relaxation is at the root of the apparent discrepancy between the determination of T_1 from the steady-state saturation experiments by Eschenfelder[23] and the Leiden results[24] on spin-lattice relaxation in dilute chromium salt. In the latter case, one measures the rates $(1/T_1^\alpha)$, $(1/T_1^\beta)$, and $(1/T_1^\gamma)$ for the various spin levels, or averages of these quantities over all orientations in the unit cell and crystallites in the powder. In the steady-state saturation, one measures the much faster rate $\sum_j (1/T_1^j)$, summed over all resonances j which, through cross-relaxation, are also saturated.

[22] See reference 9. This paper will henceforth be referred to as GANT.

[23] A. H. Eschenfelder and R. T. Weidner, Phys. Rev. 92, 869 (1953).

[24] Van der Marel, van den Broek, and Gorter, Physica 23, 361 (1957).

The intensity of the β-resonance showing the cross-saturation is simply

$$(\chi_\beta''/\chi_{\beta,0}'')-1=[(\chi_\alpha''/\chi_{\alpha,0}'')-1]\times(1+N_\beta T_{21}{}^\alpha/N_\alpha T_1{}^\beta)^{-1}. \quad (23)$$

For $N_\alpha=N_\beta$ and $T_{21}{}^\alpha \ll T_1{}^\beta$, the α and β resonances are saturated to the same degree. The β resonance remains unsaturated only when $T_{21}{}^\alpha \geq T_1{}^\beta$.

Is it reasonable to expect cross-relaxation times between 10^{-1} and 10^{-4} sec for the resonances of GANT shown in Fig. 3? A superficial application of Eq. (8b) seems to indicate that the spin-spin cross-relaxation time is longer than T_1. For a separation of the resonances by 100 oersteds and a calculated dipolar width of less than 3 oersteds, Eq. (8b) would give $T_{21}\approx e^{+200}T_2$. This result is an erroneous application of the theory.

The shape of a line in a crystal with random magnetic dilution is not a Gaussian with Van Vleck's value of the second moment. The experimental line shape is narrower in the center and much more intense in the wings as first shown by Abrahams and Kittel.[25] If the magnetic dilution is f, and Z the number of nearest neighbors, the chance for an ion to have a neighboring magnetic ion is Zf. The second-moment contribution of a magnetic nearest neighbor is roughly Z^{-1} times the second moment in the concentrated salt. If $Zf \ll 1$, the situations in which more than one neighboring ion is magnetic may be ignored. An expression replacing Eq. (8) which should approximate the overlap of wings in dilute magnetic materials would be

$$T_{21}\approx (Zf)^{-1}\langle\Delta\nu_\alpha{}^2\rangle_{\rm conc}{}^{-\frac{1}{2}}\exp\left\{\frac{Z(\nu_\alpha-\nu_\beta)^2}{2[\langle\Delta\nu_\alpha{}^2\rangle_{\rm conc}+\langle\Delta\nu_\beta{}^2\rangle_{\rm conc}]}\right\},$$

with $f=10^{-2}$, $Z=8$, $\langle\Delta\nu_\alpha{}^2\rangle_{\rm conc}=\langle\Delta\nu_\beta{}^2\rangle_{\rm conc}=200$ Mc/sec, $\nu_\alpha-\nu_\beta=280$ Mc/sec, this yields $T_{21}\approx 10^3\, T_2{}^{\rm conc}$.

This admittedly very qualitative argument gives order-of-magnitude agreement with the experimental cross-relaxation times. It should be realized that the shape of far wings is not well known and the argument here is that a reasonable shape of the wing can give the required overlap.

A more potent mechanism in the case of eight copper resonances is provided by the observation that quadruple spin flips can exactly conserve the Zeeman energy.

A process of simultaneous double flip-flops is indicated in Fig. 3. Two ions make a downward transition at the frequency ν_α, while ions at frequencies ν_β and $\nu_{\beta'}$ go up. Consider in general four spins α, α', β, β' with $S=\frac{1}{2}$. The effect of nuclear spins and local fields of other spins in the crystal is lumped with the Zeeman energy. The α, α' spins are initially upward, the β, β' spins downward. If all spins are reversed, energy is conserved:

$$\nu_\alpha+\nu_{\alpha'}-\nu_\beta-\nu_{\beta'}=0.$$

[25] C. Kittel and E. Abrahams, Phys. Rev. **90**, 238 (1953).

The matrix element of the dipolar interaction which connects the initial and final "Zeeman-state" derives its most important contribution from a double application of the operators of type B [Eq. (2b)] because of the assumed inequalities of the type

$$|A|<|\nu_\alpha-\nu_\beta|<\nu_\alpha.$$

The matrix element is consequently

$$B_{\alpha\beta}B_{\alpha'\beta'}[h(\nu_\beta-\nu_\alpha)+A_{\alpha\alpha'}+A_{\beta\beta'}+A_{\alpha\beta'}+A_{\beta\alpha'}]^{-1}$$
$$+B_{\alpha'\beta'}B_{\alpha\beta}[h(\nu_{\beta'}-\nu_{\alpha'})+A_{\alpha\alpha'}+A_{\beta\beta'}+A_{\alpha\beta'}+A_{\beta\alpha'}]^{-1}$$
$$+B_{\alpha\beta'}B_{\beta\alpha'}[h(\nu_\alpha-\nu_{\beta'})+A_{\alpha\alpha'}+A_{\beta\beta'}+A_{\alpha\beta}+A_{\alpha'\beta'}]^{-1}$$
$$+B_{\alpha'\beta}B_{\alpha\beta'}[h(\nu_{\alpha'}-\nu_\beta)+A_{\alpha\alpha'}+A_{\beta\beta'}+A_{\alpha\beta}+A_{\alpha'\beta'}]^{-1}.$$

The matrix element vanishes if the dipolar interactions of the type A given by Eq. (2a) are ignored. Then the energy denominators of the first term and the second term, in which the two flip-flops occur in reverse order, would have opposite sign. Similarly, the third and fourth terms would cancel each other. If the $\alpha\beta$ pair and $\alpha'\beta'$ pair are very far apart, the dipolar terms $A_{\alpha\alpha'}$, $A_{\beta\beta'}$, $A_{\alpha\beta'}$, and $A_{\beta\alpha'}$ will be small. They are calculated from Eq. (2a) by allowing a change in quantum number of one constituent, $\Delta S_i=\pm 1$. It is reasonable that the probability for a simultaneous act of two pairs vanishes, if there is no physical interaction between the pairs.

The probability per unit time for the quadruple spin flip is then obtained in the usual way by squaring the matrix element and integrating over a narrow frequency range around the maximum.

The order of magnitude can be estimated by considering the case that $\alpha\beta$ are a pair of nearest neighbors, and so is $\alpha'\beta'$. The distance between the two pairs corresponds to the average distance in the diluted salt. The probability for this initial situation is $(Zf)^2$. It is not necessary to introduce additional factors of $\frac{1}{8}$ to specify $\alpha\beta$, $\alpha'\beta'$ among the eight possible states. The equal spacing between components appears to make double flip-flops possible in most configurations. The probability then becomes

$$w\approx \hbar^{-2}|A|_{\rm dilute}{}^2 g_{\rm max}(\nu)(Zf)^2[|B|_{\rm neighbor}{}^2/h^2(\nu_\alpha-\nu_\beta)^2]^2,$$

or

$$T_{21}\approx (T_2)_{\rm dilute}(Zf)^{-2}|B|_{\rm neighbor}{}^{-4}\; h^4(\nu_\alpha-\nu_\beta)^4.$$

With $Zf=10^{-1}$ and $B_{\rm neighbor}/h(\nu_\alpha-\nu_\beta)\approx\frac{1}{3}$, one finds $T_{21}\approx 10^4 T_2$ in excellent agreement with the observations.

Worded in a different way, the true line shape of each resonance is not Gaussian, but has small bumps which fall just under an adjacent resonance. These side bumps are of a similar nature to those shown by Van Vleck.[14] He omitted these in the truncation of the Hamiltonian for the purpose of calculating the second moment. Here we should not cut off the terms in $S_{+\alpha}S_{-\beta}$ between different ions although we do omit other terms in the dipolar interaction. The bumps in the wing are extremely important, because the interest is in processes which may be more than a million times slower than T_2. The exact values of the cross-relaxation times will be sensitive to the exact positioning of the lines, but values of T_{21} ranging between 10^3T_2 and 10^6T_2 can hardly be avoided. It is believed that this is the most effective mechanism in the copper salt. It explains the rapid transfer of energy to the wing components if the central resonances are saturated and can also account for the asymmetry and partial cross-saturation if a line in the wing is saturated.

The possibility of spin-spin processes had been ruled out by GANT on the basis of the observation that a strong microwave field applied at a frequency between the two resonances does not produce saturation. The assumption hidden in this argument is that the energy would have to be transported from resonance ν_α to ν_β via the small fraction of spins resonating in intermediate fields. The essence of the spin-spin processes is, however, that a jump from resonance $\nu_\alpha \rightarrow \nu_\beta$ can be made, the balance of energy being taken up by a large number of transitions within the resonances ν_α and ν_β, or, even better, as explained in the preceding paragraph, the jump from resonance $\nu_\alpha \rightarrow \nu_\beta$ is accompanied by a simultaneous jump $\nu_\gamma \rightarrow \nu_\delta$, with $\nu_\alpha + \nu_\gamma \approx \nu_\beta + \nu_\delta$.

From a similar viewpoint it may be said that the radio-frequency field, off resonance, still produces transitions at the frequency ν_α, while the balance of energy is again taken up by multiple spin rearrangements. The transition probability for such an induced transition is reduced by a factor $g(\nu-\nu_\alpha)/g_{\max}(0)$. In order to produce saturation of the α-resonance the microwave intensity should be stepped up by a factor 10^6 or more, if applied far away from resonance. Sufficient power cannot be fed into the spin system in the far wings to combat spin-lattice relaxation in the center of the resonance.

It is therefore concluded that spin-spin interactions offer a possible explanation for the cross-saturation effects of GANT. Further discussion of and comparison with their hot-phonon theory will be postponed until the final section.

8. INHOMOGENEOUS BROADENING AND HOMOGENEOUS SATURATION

In sufficiently diluted magnetic substances the line width is usually determined by local variations of nuclear spin arrangements or a distribution of crystalline field parameters. Inasmuch as the dipolar interactions between the ions contribute only a small fraction of the observed second moment, the line is said to have an inhomogeneous broadening.

This type of inhomogeneity should be carefully distinguished from that produced by a gradient in the external fields or by the use of a polycrystalline anisotropic material. In the latter case spins in different parts of the crystal or in different crystallites have different resonant frequencies. Different spin populations in different parts of the resonant curve can only come into equilibrium by spin diffusion in space.[26] This is a very slow process and inhomogeneous saturation—"eating a hole"—occurs readily.[27]

In the former microscopic type of inhomogeneous broadening, adjacent spins will have quite different resonant frequencies. The situation is then more a problem of spin diffusion in the frequency domain rather than in space. The problem can be considered as the cross-effect between two resonances α and β both of which have the same continuous distribution. A qualitative solution can readily be given. Assume that the resonances with a dipolar second moment $\langle\Delta\nu^2\rangle$ are distributed uniformly over a frequency interval $(1/T_2^*)$. Take a frequency ν_α in this distribution. The probability to make a cross-transition to ν_β is of the order of T_2^{-1} if $\nu_\alpha+\frac{1}{2}T_2^{-1}<\nu_\beta<\nu_\alpha+\frac{1}{2}T_2^{-1}$ and is essentially zero outside this interval. The probability that the ν_β of an adjacent spin is indeed in the required interval is T_2^*/T_2. The most probable time to cover a frequency interval T_2^{-1} is therefore $T_2(T_2/T_2^*)$. To diffuse across the whole distribution $(T_2/T_2^*)^2$ steps have to be taken. The time required for an absorbed quantum to diffuse through the inhomogeneous resonance[28] would be T_2^4/T_2^{*3}.

This random step model ignores the existence of quadruple and higher-order spin flips of the type indicated in Fig. 4. Under certain conditions this mechanism may be faster than the diffusion process. If the time $(T_{21})_{\text{multiple}}$ or $T_2^4/(T_2^*)^3$ is shorter than T_1, the inhomogeneous structure will show homogeneous saturation in the steady state. If by a short pulse a small fraction near the center of the structure has been saturated or inverted, this "hole" will be distributed evenly over the entire structure in a time $T_2^4/(T_2^*)^3$, and subsequent return to the lattice temperature will occur in a time T_1. Such effects, depicted in Fig. 4,

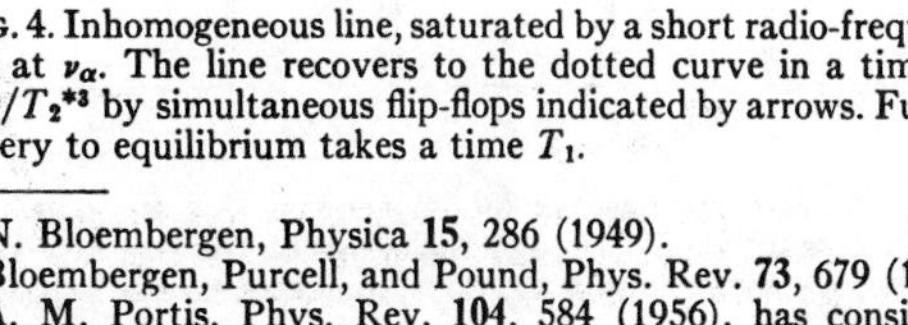

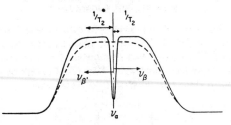

FIG. 4. Inhomogeneous line, saturated by a short radio-frequency pulse at ν_α. The line recovers to the dotted curve in a time $T_{21} \approx T_2^4/T_2^{*3}$ by simultaneous flip-flops indicated by arrows. Further recovery to equilibrium takes a time T_1.

[26] N. Bloembergen, Physica 15, 286 (1949).
[27] Bloembergen, Purcell, and Pound, Phys. Rev. 73, 679 (1948).
[28] A. M. Portis, Phys. Rev. 104, 584 (1956), has considered spin-diffusion in the frequency domain in more detail. His method would give a characteristic time T_2^6/T_2^{*5}. The multiple spin flips will always give an answer shorter than this time, and should then always be taken into account. We are indebted to Professor Portis for correspondence on this point.

have been observed by Bowers and Mims[29] in nickel fluosilicate.

These effects are apparently the same in nature as those which occur between the eight resonances in the copper Tutton salt. The only difference is that there the eight resonances are discrete, while in an inhomogeneous structure a continuous distribution occurs. With the possible exception of extremely dilute magnetic substances (less than 1:10^4), it appears that homogeneous saturation should be the rule rather than the the exception. In the steady-state saturation factor $\gamma^2 H_1^2 T_1 T_2$, the value of T_2 should usually be taken as T_2^*, the inverse of the observed total width. An alternative way of stating this fact is to say that Eq. (22) for the saturation factor has to be used with T_2/T_2^* resonances in parallel.

Finally, the general case of two inhomogeneously broadened structures will be discussed briefly.

Consider two rectangular inhomogeneous resonances A and B. It is tempting to argue that if the center of A is saturated the energy will diffuse to the edge of the A distribution. Then the Gaussian overlap of the true resonance shapes which are represented by the dotted lines will take it to the edge of B whence it will diffuse further. Due to the narrow width of the true resonances, the middle step is very slow. A much faster way can again be devised—e.g., by a sixfold spin flip. The three arrows in Fig. 5 show the three simultaneous flip-flops which conserve energy and transfer one spin from the A to the B resonance.

No attempt will be made here to develop a mathematical theory of random walk with multiple steps. The distribution of splittings will in general not have a rectangular shape. For a Gaussian shape, the random walk theory for an harmonically bound particle may be applied,[30] but multiple steps will again complicate the picture further.

9. A CRUCIAL EXPERIMENT: THE CROSS-MASER EFFECT. FURTHER IMPLICATIONS FOR MASER OPERATION

It has been shown that spin-spin interactions can account satisfactorily for all observations made by GANT. They have used the model of a "hot-phonon" region to explain the results. How can a choice be made between these two different interpretations?

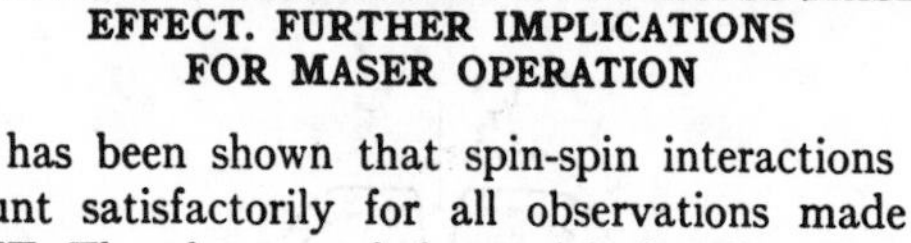

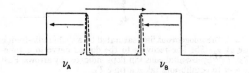

FIG. 5. Two rectangular inhomogeneous line structures. The energy contact is not through the wings of the true line shapes, but through multiple spin flip-flops, indicated by the arrows.

[29] K. D. Bowers and W. B. Mims, Bull. Am. Phys. Soc. Ser. II, 3, 325 (1958).

[30] *Noise and Stochastic Processes*, edited by N. Wax (Dover Publications, New York, 1954), c.f. p. 305.

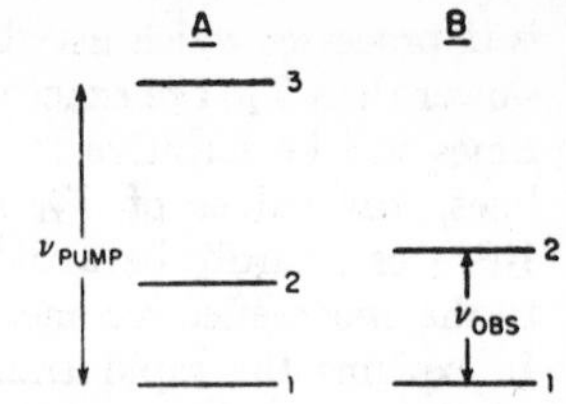

FIG. 6. The simplest energy level diagram required to detect a steady-state cross-maser effect.

In the first place, the experiments on LiF and other nuclear spin systems at room temperature show that spin-spin processes are capable of producing cross-saturation. A "hot-phonon" region is out of the question in this case, as the lattice vibrations are a good thermal reservoir at room temperature. The existence of similar spin-spin processes must therefore be admitted in electron-spin systems. Since they alone can give a satisfactory explanation of the observations, there is no need to invoke a second mechanism.

An attempt has been made to show the existence of cross-saturation effects in dilute $K_3Cr(CN)_6$ at 77°K. At this temperature the spin-lattice relaxation should take place predominantly by Raman processes. Phonons of all frequencies participate and constitute a thermal reservoir without limited heating. Unfortunately, T_1 at 77°K is too short so that no saturation could be obtained.

There is, however, another positive criterion. There is one thing a spin-spin contact can do which hot phonons cannot do. Spin-spin interactions can produce not only cross-saturation, but even cross-maser effects. They can, in other words, establish a contact at negative temperatures.[31] This is already contained in Eq. (23). χ_β'' can be negative, if $\chi_\alpha''<0$, and the last factor is sufficiently close to or larger than unity. This will be true when $N_\alpha \approx N_\beta$, $T_{21}^\alpha \ll T_1^\beta$. The system of energy levels of an harmonic oscillator has no upper bound and such a systen cannot attain negative temperature.[32] The α-system at a negative temperature could therefore heat the phonons at most to an infinite positive temperature. The hot-phonon mechanism could never give $\chi_b''<0$.

A critical experiment would require a salt containing one ion, species α, with three spin levels and another, species β, with two spin levels. The first ion should be made emissive at the frequency ν_α by three-level maser pumping. The $\chi''(\nu_\beta)$ of the well-resolved but nearby resonance ν_β should then be observed, as indicated in Fig. 6.

Unfortunately such a paramagnetic substance is not readily available, and the actual experiment was performed on two nonequivalent Cr atoms in K_3(0.995 Co)(0.005 Cr)$(CN)_6$. The spin levels are sketched in Fig. 7. The magnetic field was applied in the ab plane which contains the z-axes of the crystalline fields for both ions. The magnetic field was near 1080 oersteds

[31] N. F. Ramsey, Phys. Rev. 103, 20 (1956).

[32] J. H. Van Vleck, Suppl. Nuovo cimento 6, 1081 (1957).

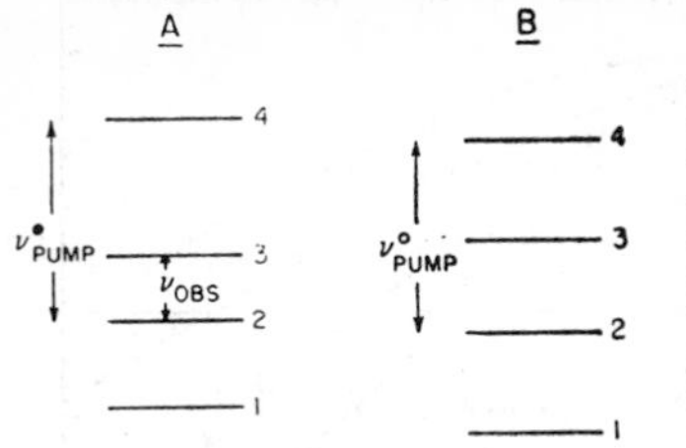

FIG. 7. Energy levels of two nonequivalent Cr^{+++} spins. The transitions indicated correspond to the experimental points in Figs. 8 and 9. It is also possible to observe the ν_{32} transition of B, while saturating either A or B.

and made angles of 4°30′ and 16°30′ with the principal crystal field axes of the two ions. The transition frequencies ν_{32} fell in the L-band, the pump frequencies ν_{24} in the X-band. The maser cavity was tunable at X-band frequency by a sliding coupling diaphragm. A $\lambda_g/4$ section on both sides provided good electrical connection with the fixed guide. Data were taken at 4.2°K on a small crystal to get reliable values for χ''.

The ordinary self-saturation curves of the ions at X-band, i.e., $\chi_A''(\nu_{24})$ *vs* $H_{rf,A}^2(\nu_{24})$ and $\chi_B''(\nu_{24})$ *vs* $H_{rf,B}^2(\nu_{24})$, are shown in Fig. 8. The two ions saturate at different power levels because of the different matrix elements in the two different orientations. These data will be needed in the subsequent analysis.

In Fig. 9 the L-band susceptibility $\chi_A''(\nu_{32})$ of ion A is plotted as a function of power saturation at X-band of ion A (closed points) or ion B (open points). The magnetic field was held fixed at 1087 oersteds. The X-band tuning was changed. The two X-band resonances are 210 Mc/sec apart, the L-band resonances are just resolved at 50 Mc/sec. Note that the "cross-maser" effect is stronger than the "self-maser" effect.

This last situation is no longer true if the L-band resonances are separated further. Figure 10 shows the data, when H_0=1080 oersteds, but makes angles of 10°30′ and 22°30′ with the axes at the two Cr ions in the unit cell. The L-band resonances are now separated by 150 Mc/sec, the X-band resonances by 250 Mc/sec.

Finally, the L-band resonances of ion B have been observed under the same conditions as the data in Fig. 9, except that the magnitude of H_0 was changed by 15 oersteds. These data are represented by curves 1

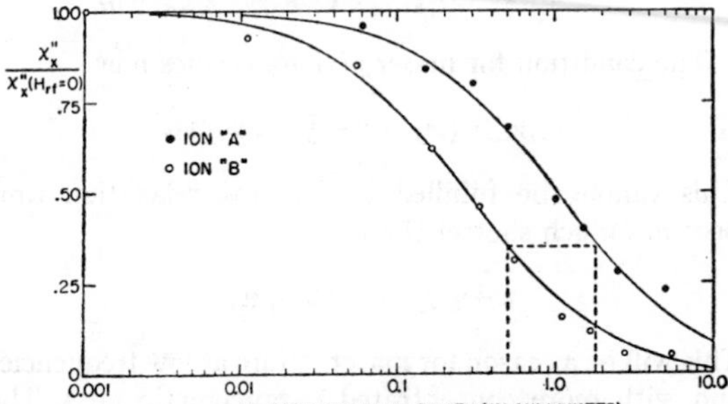

FIG. 8. Self-saturation curves for the X-band transitions of ions A and B. Magnitude and orientation of the field are the same as in Figs. 9 and 11. The solid curves obey the theoretical expression $(1+cH_{rf}^2)^{-1}$.

and 4 in Fig. 11. The data of Fig. 9 are repeated for comparison. For ion B the self-maser effect is stronger than the cross-maser effect.

An interpretation of these data in terms of the hot-phonon theory is now attempted. Cross-maser action may result from cross-saturation between the two X-band resonances. The location of the bottom levels, as illustrated in Fig. 7, is such that none of the frequencies ν_{12}, ν_{13}, ν_{14} lies in the vicinity of the observed transitions. Their existence will be ignored in the following discussion.

At most, ion A can be saturated to the same extent as ion B when $H_B^2(\nu_{24})$ is applied. With the aid of the dotted lines in Fig. 8 the value $H_A^2(\nu_{24})$ is obtained, which would give the same saturation of $\chi_A''(\nu_{24})$. With the self-maser curve in Fig. 9 one can plot the corresponding maser effect given by the crosses and the dotted line. This computed curve practically coincides

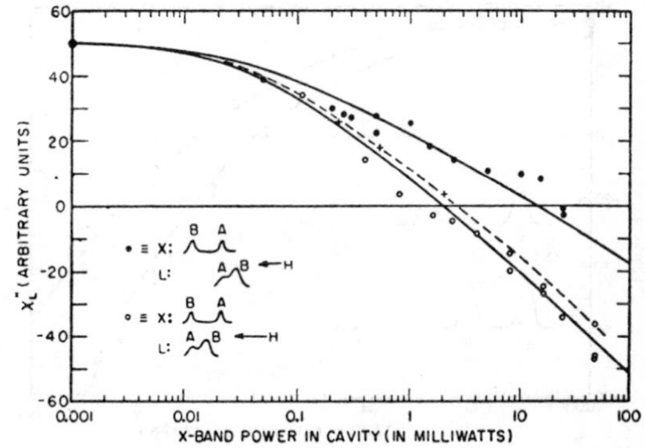

FIG. 9. Self- and cross-maser effects of ion A. Full circles: $\chi_A''(\nu_{32})$ *vs* $H_A^2(\nu_{24})$. Open circles: $\chi_A''(\nu_{32})$ *vs* $H_B^2(\nu_{24})$. The magnetic field of magnitude 1087 oersteds makes angles of 4°30′ and 16°30′ with the crystalline field axes of the two ions. The crosses are points calculated on the basis of maximum phonon interaction at X-band and zero phonon interaction at L-band. The inserts represent the observed line profiles.

with the observed curve for the cross-maser effect. If L-band hot-phonon interaction were admitted, the dotted curve would be pushed towards the axis $\chi''\rightarrow 0$. Then a discrepancy would result. The data of Fig. 9 could be explained by a complete phonon heat interchange between the X-band resonances (210 Mc/sec apart) and no phonon contact between the L-band resonances (50 Mc/sec apart). This explanation is unlikely, but possible.

The data of Fig. 10 show that the cross-maser effect becomes much smaller when the X-band resonances are separated by 250 Mc/sec rather than 210 Mc/sec. This would indicate a drastic decrease from 100% phonon contact at 210 Mc/sec separation to less than 30% contact at 250 Mc/sec.

The situation becomes impossible, however, if we try to explain also the self- and cross-maser effect on ion B, given by curves 1 and 4 in Fig. 11. Again the construction with Fig. 8 is used. If there really is 100% phonon contact at 210 Mc/sec separation between the X-band resonances, the cross effect on ion B should have been much larger and χ'' of curve 1 should have gone through zero at 3 milliwatts instead of 70 milliwatts. The conclusion is that the hot-phonon theory cannot account for all observations of Figs. 8–11.

If the contact by spin-spin interactions is adopted, a quite natural explanation results. Since the X-band resonances are far apart, cross-saturation at X-band is assumed to be small. The contact between the L-band resonances can be estimated from the pair of curves 3 and 4 in Fig. 11 to be about 80%, which is reasonable. If we take the pair of curves 1 and 2, for both of which the X-band resonance of ion A is saturated, one gets 70% for this contact. It is possible that a small cross-saturation at X-band is still present. Presumably this would then also be caused by spin-spin interactions.

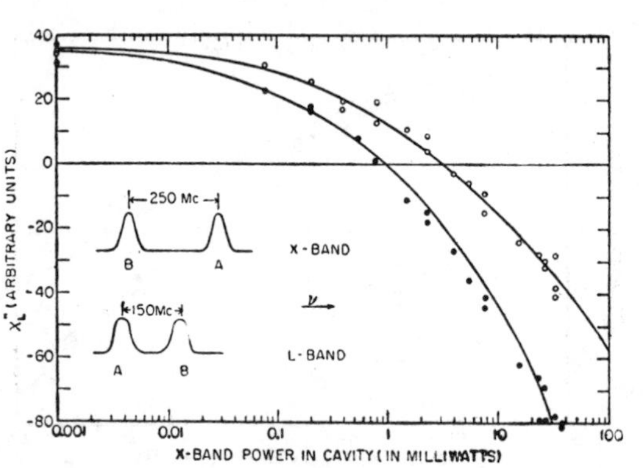

FIG. 10. Self- and cross-maser effects of ion A. Full circles: $\chi_A''(\nu_{32})$ *vs* $H_A^2(\nu_{24})$. Open circles: $\chi_A''(\nu_{32})$ *vs* $H_B^2(\nu_{24})$. The magnetic field of magnitude 1080 oersteds makes angles of 10°30′ and 22°30′ with the crystalline field axes of the two ions. The inserts represent the line profiles as a function of frequency. Due to different values of $\partial\nu/\partial H_0$ for different resonances the observed profiles *vs* H_0 have different widths.

The smaller cross-saturation in Fig. 10 also follows readily from the much reduced overlap of the L-band resonances. It is also clear why the absolute value of the self-maser effect is increased. The L-band A resonance does not have to "drag along" the L-band B resonance to the same extent as in Fig. 9.

Spin-spin interactions alone can account for all observations of Figs. 8–11. Hot phonons do not have to be invoked at all.

The entire resonance at the frequency ν_{32} appears to be inverted. The bandwidth over which a paramagnetic salt in a three-level maser is emissive is equal to the entire width of the observed resonance curve. Even if it has a so-called inhomogeneous line width, the maser effect will be homogeneous. This statement is contrary to one made by GANT. It is of great importance for the operation of a three-level maser. It is, within wide limits, immaterial whether the paramagnetic resonance

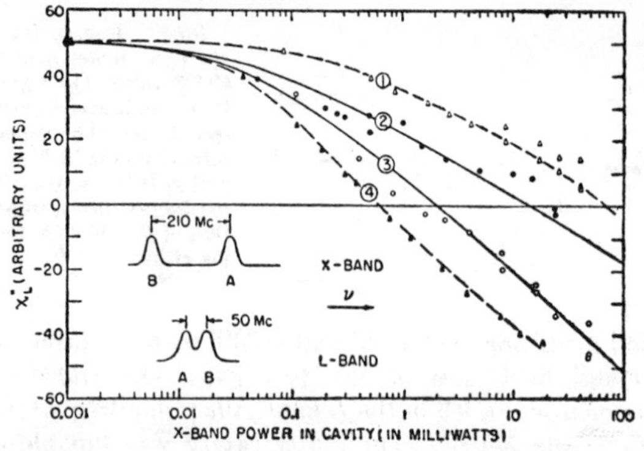

FIG. 11. Self- and cross-maser effects of ions A and B. △ Curve 1: $\chi_B''(\nu_{32})$ *vs* $H_A^2(\nu_{24})$, at $H_0=1072$ oersteds. ● Curve 2: $\chi_A''(\nu_{32})$ *vs* $H_A^2(\nu_{24})$, at $H_0=1087$ oersteds. ○ Curve 3: $\chi_A''(\nu_{32})$ *vs* $H_B^2(\nu_{24})$, at $H_0=1087$ oersteds. ▲ Curve 4: $\chi_B''(\nu_{32})$ *vs* $H_B^2(\nu_{24})$, at $H_0=1072$ oersteds. Curves 2 and 3 are the same as in Fig. 9. The inserts represent the line profiles as a function of frequency. Due to different values of $\partial\nu/\partial H_0$ for different transitions, the observed profiles *vs* H_0 shown in Fig. 9 have a different appearance. The angles between H_0 and the principal axes of the two non-equivalent ions are 4°30′ and 16°30′ for all four curves.

is broadened homogeneously or inhomogeneously on a microscopic scale. The saturation will occur homogeneously over the entire pumping frequency resonance and the salt will amplify over the entire maser frequency resonance.

This statement is in agreement with observations on the band width of a traveling-wave maser,[33] and the observed gain-bandwidth product of various cavity-type masers. It has been pointed out previously[34] by one of us (N.B.) that three-level maser action is incompatible with a dominant interaction with hot phonons. The steady-state condition would then be one of three hot-phonon regions and three saturated resonances.

The lower frequency limit ν_{23} of a three-level maser is set by the overlap of the resonances ν_{13} and ν_{12}. The steady-state solution of Eq. (12) in the limit of heavy pumping $W_{31}\rightarrow\infty$, $n_1-n_3\rightarrow 0$ becomes

$$n_3-n_2=-\frac{1}{3}\frac{hN}{kT}\,\frac{-(w_{32}+w+\frac{1}{3}\sum_j w_{ij})\nu_{32}+w_{21}\nu_{21}}{w_{23}+w_{21}+2(w+\frac{1}{3}\sum_j w_{ij})}.$$

The condition for maser action becomes now

$$w_{21}\nu_{21}\gg(w_{32}+w+\tfrac{1}{3}\textstyle\sum_j w_{ij})\nu_{32}.$$

This cannot be fulfilled if the cross-relaxation time becomes much shorter than T_1:

$$w+\tfrac{1}{3}\textstyle\sum_j w_{ij}\gg w_{21},\ w_{32}.$$

This will be a reason for maser failure at low frequencies and with more concentrated paramagnetic salts. The

[33] Degrasse, Schulz-Dubois, and Scovil, Bell System Tech. J. **38**, 305 (1959).
[34] N. Bloembergen, Phys. Rev. **109**, 2209 (1958).

overlap is of course a very sensitive function of ν_{32} and concentration.

The experimental results of Strandberg *et al.*[35] are also reinterpreted. It is clear from the spacing of energy levels in Fig. 3. of this reference that the cross-saturation effect can account very well for the operation of the S-band maser without invoking hot phonons.

Strandberg[36] has shown that the hot-phonon theory should lead to a different relation between saturation level and incident power. We have found that the steady-state saturation curve of the Cr^{+++} resonance in MgO follows the theoretical curve $(1+\gamma^2 H_{rf}^2 T_1 T_2^*)^{-1}$ with constant $T_1T_2^*$ very well to over 90% saturation. The saturation curves of Fig. 8 point to the same conclusion. The bottleneck for energy transfer in dilute paramagnetic substances is between the spins and the lattice.

In more recent experiments with dilute gadolinium ethylsulphate and chrome alum, Davis, Strandberg, and Kyhl[37] have measured the true spin-lattice relaxation time. The interpretation of the data in this paper is in general agreement with the present conclusions, with the exception of the interpretation of Fig. 4. It was found that the recovery (relaxation) rate of the microwave susceptibility increased rapidly above a certain critical level of monitor power. This should not be ascribed to phonon heating at high monitor power levels, but is probably a consequence of the conventional rate equations. The recovery rate is $(1/T_1)+\gamma^2 H_{\mathrm{mon}}^2 \times g(\nu)$. The measured relaxation is consequently $T_1(1+cH_{\mathrm{mon}}^2)^{-1}$, where c is a constant.

Although it has been shown that phonon heating is neither a necessary nor a sufficient condition for the explanation of relaxation effects in the dilute paramagnetic substances studied, it may well exist on a limited scale. Due to the spin-spin processes the warmed phonon region should be at least as wide as the region of homogeneous spin saturation. Note that the phonon bandwidth is now a consequence rather than a cause of the homogeneous saturation. Suppose a paramagnetic resonance at 3000 Mc/sec in K_3(0.995 Co)(0.005 Cr)$(CN)_6$ has a spin-lattice relaxation time $T_1=10^{-2}$ sec and is saturated over an effective bandwidth of 60 Mc/sec. Suppose further that Raman processes are excluded. Let ΔT be the temperature difference between the phonons in the interior of the crystal with linear dimension $a=0.4$ cm; $c=1.5\times10^5$ cm/sec is the velocity of sound, and η is the heat transfer coefficient at the surface. Equate the power absorbed by spins to the power carried away by the phonons:

$$\frac{1}{4}\left(\frac{h}{kT}\right)Nh\nu T_1^{-1}=\frac{12\pi\nu^2\Delta\nu}{c^3}\frac{2c}{a}\eta k\Delta T.$$

With $N=1.7\times10^{19}$ ions/cc, $\eta=1$ and $T=4$°K and $\nu=3\times10^9$ cps, one finds $\Delta T=0.3$°K. Although this temperature rise is rather small, it indicates that a significant rise in phonon temperature may well occur in concentrated paramagnetic salts, especially when T_1 is also short. The interesting relaxation phenomena found by van der Marel[24,38] in concentrated salts at low temperatures appear to indicate phonon heating.

Recent experiments by Bowers and Mims[29] in nickel fluosilicate show that the acoustical impedance mismatch at the surface measured by η is not important. It makes no difference whether the crystal is cooled by helium vapor or liquid. Perhaps the phonon scattering in real crystals with physical and chemical imperfections is stronger than present theories indicate. Heat conduction experiments by Dransfeld[39] appear to show that the scattering of microwave phonons by electronic spins is not the most important scattering mechanism. Much further work is needed to clear up the phonon aspect of the problem, but in dilute paramagnetic salts above 1°K the phonon heating problem plays a minor role.

10. CONCLUSION

The results obtained in this paper may be summarized as follows:

1. In most dilute paramagnetic substances, in particular in dilute $K_3Cr(CN)_6$, $Cu(NH_4)_2(SO_4)_2\cdot6H_2O$, and $NiSiF_6\cdot6H_2O$, phonon heating plays a secondary role, if any, in the relaxation mechanism.

2. High-order spin-spin interactions, such as multiple simultaneous flip-flops, account for observed cross-saturation and cross-maser effects.

3. These processes determine a "cross-relaxation" time T_{21} which is intermediate between T_1 and T_2.

4. This time T_{21} determines how fast two nearby resonances or two spin systems are brought to the same effective temperature.

5. This time also determines the intermediate-frequency temperature-independent relaxation found by de Vryer and Gorter.

6. The existence and the extent of thermodynamic equilibrium in a multilevel spin system are characterized by a large number of cross-relaxation times.

7. Even so-called inhomogeneously broadened lines will usually show a homogeneous steady-state saturation, unless the inhomogeneity has a macroscopic spatial distribution.

8. Paramagnetic salts used in multiple-level masers are emissive over the full width of the magnetic resonance.

[35] Strandberg, Davis, Faughnan, Kyhl, and Wolga, Phys. Rev. **109**, 1988 (1958).
[36] M. W. P. Strandberg, Phys. Rev. **110**, 65 (1958).
[37] Davis, Strandberg, and Kyhl, Phys. Rev. **111**, 1268 (1958).
[38] Van der Marel, van den Broek, and Gorter, Physica **24**, 101 (1958).
[39] K. Dransfeld, Bull. Am. Phys. Soc. Ser. II, **3**, 325 (1958).

9. The low-frequency limit of such masers is determined by the overlap of adjacent resonances.

ACKNOWLEDGMENTS

The authors wish to acknowledge their indebtedness to Professor J. H. Van Vleck who suggested the rigorous moment formulation for the cross-relaxation effect. They also wish to thank him and Professor E. M. Purcell and Professor R. V. Pound for reading the manuscript. A stimulating conversation with Professor C. P. Slichter on multiple spin processes, which took place several years ago, is remembered with pleasure.

Cross Relaxation in LiF*

P. S. PERSHAN†
Physics Department, Harvard University, Cambridge, Massachusetts

(Received July 31, 1959)

A combined experimental and theoretical study of cross relaxation in LiF has been carried out. In agreement with theory, the cross-relaxation time T_{21} is observed to be strongly anisotropic and field dependent; at 51.7 gauss it goes from 0.025 second in the [100] direction to 7 seconds in the [111] direction. A frequency distribution function analogous to the line shapes for magnetic absorption is measured down to 10^{-4} times the maximum value; for most orientations a Gaussian is an excellent approximation to it.

I. INTRODUCTION

ABRAGAM and Proctor[1] demonstrated that two spins with different resonance frequencies can xchange energy and come into thermal equilibrium ith each other, independent of the lattice, if the ifference in their resonant frequencies is comparable the local fields. This is cross relaxation and Bloembergen, Shapiro, Pershan, and Artman[2] (BSPA) ave given a theory to explain this and several other xperiments.[3–7]

In this paper the cross-relaxation process in LiF is xamined in great detail and a quantitative comparison ith theory is made. Cross relaxation can only be etected when different spins exchange energy with ne another faster than they exchange energy with the ttice; because the spin-lattice relaxation times in iF are a few minutes, the cross-relaxation time T_{21} an be measured over three decades as a function of agnetic field and crystal orientation.

The theory presented in Sec. II is an extension of revious work.[8] in which the author predicted large nisotropies in T_{21}. The experiment, similar to Abragam nd Proctor's T_{21} measurement, is discussed in detail Sec. III. In Sec. IV we discuss the results and show hat for some crystal orientations the absorption lines LiF can be approximated by a single Gaussian nction.

II. THEORY

A. Transition Probability

The simplest cross-relaxation process is when two pins, one Li and one F, make simultaneous opposite flips, the unbalance in Zeeman energy being taken up by the dipole-dipole interaction. For simplicity, we will start with this case although BSPA have shown this is not the mechanism for cross relaxation in LiF at fields above 50 gauss. Assume Li^7 is 100% abundant, although it is actually 92.6%,[9] and ignore its quadrupole moment; in a perfect cubic crystal there should not be a quadrupole interaction and the defects that cause one in a real crystal can be neglected in this experiment. Also assume a rigid lattice with infinite spin-lattice relaxation time T_1; the effect of finite T_1 will be added later.

The Hamiltonian for the system can be written as:

$$\mathcal{H}=\mathcal{H}_0+\mathcal{H}_1+\mathcal{H}_2, \quad (1)$$

where $\mathcal{H}_0$ is the Zeeman terms, $\mathcal{H}_1$ is that part of the dipole-dipole interaction that commutes with the Zeeman terms, and $\mathcal{H}_2$ is the rest of the dipole-dipole interaction. $\mathcal{H}_0+\mathcal{H}_1$ is the truncated Hamiltonian that Van Vleck[10] retains in his moment calculations and $\mathcal{H}_2$ is the nondiagonal terms he discards. If we denote a lithium spin operator by S, a fluorine spin operator by I, and if one prime refers to an interaction between a lithium and a fluorine, two primes to one between two fluorines and no prime between two lithiums, then using the notation of BSPA $\mathcal{H}_1$ and $\mathcal{H}_2$ are given as:

$$\mathcal{H}_1=A+B+A'+A''+B'',$$
$$\mathcal{H}_2=B'+C+C'+D'+E+(B'+C+C'+D'+E)\dagger + \text{other terms of no importance}, \quad (2)$$

where

$$A=\sum_{i,j} A_{ij}S_{zi}S_{zj}; \qquad A_{ij}=\frac{1}{2}\frac{\gamma_{Li}^2\hbar^2}{r_{ij}^3}(1-3\cos^2\theta_{ij}),$$

* The research reported in this document was made possible through support extended Cruft Laboratory, Harvard University, intly by the Navy Department (Office of Naval Research), the Signal Corps of the U. S. Army, and the U. S. Air Force.
† National Science Foundation Pre-Doctoral Fellow.

1 A. Abragam and W. G. Proctor, Phys. Rev. 109, 1441 (1958).
2 Bloembergen, Shapiro, Pershan, and Artman, Phys. Rev. 114, 445 (1959).
3 Robert T. Schumacher, Phys. Rev. 112, 837 (1958).
4 H. S. Gutowsky and D. E. Woessner, Phys. Rev. Letters ,1 6 (1958).
5 Walter I. Goldburg, Bull. Am. Phys. Soc. 4, 165 (1959).
6 S. Shapiro and N. Bloembergen, Phys. Rev. 116, 1453 (1959).
7 Sorokin, Lasher, and Gelles, *Proceedings of the Conference on Quantum Electronics, Bloomingberg, New York, 1959*.
8 P. S. Pershan, Bull. Am. Phys. Soc. 4, 165 (1959).
9 *Handbook of Chemistry and Physics*, edited by C. D. Hodgman (Chemical Rubber Publishing Company, Cleveland, 1954–1955), 394.
10 J. H. Van Vleck, Phys. Rev. 74, 1168 (1948).

$$A'=\sum_{i,j} A_{ij}'S_{zi}I_{zj}: \qquad A_{ij}'=\frac{\gamma_{\mathrm{Li}}\gamma_{\mathrm{F}}\hbar^2}{r_{ij}^3}(1-3\cos^2\theta_{ij}),$$

$$A''=\sum_{i,j} A_{ij}''I_{zi}I_{zj}: \qquad A_{ij}''=\frac{1}{2}\frac{\gamma_{\mathrm{F}}^2\hbar^2}{r_{ij}^3}(1-3\cos^2\theta_{ij}),$$

$$B=\sum_{i,j} B_{ij}(S_{+i}S_{-j}+S_{-i}S_{+j}): \qquad B_{ij}=-\frac{1}{8}\frac{\gamma_{\mathrm{Li}}^2\hbar^2}{r_{ij}^3}(1-3\cos^2\theta_{ij}),$$

$$B'=\sum_{i,j} B_{ij}'S_{+i}I_{-j}: \qquad B_{ij}'=-\frac{1}{4}\frac{\gamma_{\mathrm{Li}}\gamma_{\mathrm{F}}\hbar^2}{r_{ij}^3}(1-3\cos^2\theta_{ij}),$$

$$B''=\sum_{i,j} B_{ij}''(I_{+i}I_{-j}+I_{-i}I_{+j}): \qquad B_{ij}''=-\frac{1}{8}\frac{\gamma_{\mathrm{F}}^2\hbar^2}{r_{ij}^3}(1-3\cos^2\theta_{ij}),$$

$$C=\sum_{i,j} C_{ij}(S_{zi}S_{+j}+S_{+i}S_{zj}): \qquad C_{ij}=-\frac{3}{4}\frac{\gamma_{\mathrm{Li}}^2\hbar^2}{r_{ij}^3}\sin\theta_{ij}\cos\theta_{ij}e^{-i\phi_{ij}},$$

$$C'=\sum_{i,j} C_{ij}'S_{+i}I_{zj}: \qquad C_{ij}'=-\frac{3}{2}\frac{\gamma_{\mathrm{Li}}\gamma_{\mathrm{F}}\hbar^2}{r_{ij}^3}\sin\theta_{ij}\cos\theta_{ij}e^{-i\phi_{ij}},$$

$$D'=\sum_{i,j} D_{ij}'S_{zi}I_{-j}: \qquad D_{ij}'=-\frac{3}{2}\frac{\gamma_{\mathrm{Li}}\gamma_{\mathrm{F}}\hbar^2}{r_{ij}^3}\sin\theta_{ij}\cos\theta_{ij}e^{+i\phi_{ij}},$$

$$E=\sum_{i,j} E_{ij}S_{+i}S_{+j}: \qquad E_{ij}=-\frac{3}{8}\frac{\gamma_{\mathrm{Li}}^2\hbar^2}{r_{ij}^3}\sin^2\theta_{ij}e^{-2i\phi_{ij}}.$$

The terms A, B and A'', B'', etc., are half of their usual values because we choose to sum over each interaction twice.

Consider the following hypothetical experiment. Initially the lithium spin system is at an infinite spin temperature, and the fluorine system is at room temperature in a field of 5000 gauss. Without changing direction, the field is suddenly dropped to H_0, of the order of 50 gauss say, and stays there for a time t when it is raised back to 5000 gauss, again without changing direction. It can be shown[8] that this is equivalent to turning on $\mathcal{H}_2$ for a time t, as in text book examples of standard time-dependent perturbation theory.[11] Treating $\mathcal{H}_2$ by this method, we find the probability per unit time that one lithium "i" and one fluorine "j" have simultaneously flipped is given by

$$W_{m_{\mathrm{Li}}\to m_{\mathrm{Li}}+1;\, m_{\mathrm{F}}\to m_{\mathrm{F}}-1}=\frac{2\pi}{\hbar^2}g_{12}(\omega_{12})|B_{ij}'|^2 \times|\langle m_{\mathrm{Li}}+1, m_{\mathrm{F}}-1|S_{+i}I_{-j}|m_{\mathrm{Li}}m_{\mathrm{F}}\rangle|^2. \quad (3)$$

$g_{12}(\omega_{12})$ is a frequency distribution function which gives the probability that the dipole-dipole interaction can absorb the Zeeman energy left over. We can approximate this function by

$$g_{12}(\omega_{12})=\int_{-\infty}^{\infty} g_{\mathrm{Li}}(\omega)g_{\mathrm{F}}(\omega')\delta(\omega+\omega')P(\omega,\omega')d\omega d\omega'.$$

$g_{\mathrm{Li}}(\omega)$ and $g_{\mathrm{F}}(\omega')$ are the line shape functions obser in the usual absorption experiments, $\delta(\omega+\omega')$ i account for conservation of energy, and $P(\omega,\omega')$ t account of correlations that make it more difficult the local fields to change by large amounts over s distances than over longer distances. Equation can be approximated further by replacing $g_{\mathrm{Li}}(\omega)$ $g_{\mathrm{F}}(\omega')$ by Gaussians with second moments given Van Vleck[10] and setting $P=1$. The result is the Gaus

$$g_{12}(\omega_{12})=\frac{1}{[2\pi(\Delta\omega_{\mathrm{Li}}^2+\Delta\omega_{\mathrm{F}}^2)]^{\frac{1}{2}}}\exp\left[-\frac{1}{2}\frac{(\omega_{\mathrm{F}}-\omega_{\mathrm{Li}})^2}{\Delta\omega_{\mathrm{Li}}^2+\Delta\omega_{\mathrm{F}}^2}\right],$$

where $\omega_{12}=\omega_{\mathrm{F}}-\omega_{\mathrm{Li}}$.

In principle $g_{12}(\omega_{12})$ can be calculated exactly b moment method. However the length of such a calc tion limits us to just the second moment

$$(\Delta\omega)_{12}^2=\frac{1}{\hbar^2}\frac{\mathrm{Tr}|\mathcal{H}_1B'-B'\mathcal{H}_1|^2}{\mathrm{Tr}|B'|^2}.$$

A better approximation than Eq. (5) is to ass $g_{12}(\omega_{12})$ is a Gaussian with second moment given

[11] Leonard I. Schiff, *Quantum Mechanics* (McGraw-Hill Book Company, New York, 1949), first edition, Chap. VIII.

(6) since it takes into account $P\neq 1$. Neglecting ·elations would say the dipole-dipole interaction absorb more energy than it really is able to, dicting cross relaxation at too high fields.

Jeglecting lattice sums like

$$\sum_{i,j,k} A_{ij}'A_{kj}'A_{ik}^2,$$

npared with terms like

$$\sum_{i,j,k} (A_{ij}')^2 A_{ik}^2,$$

. (6) can be evaluated, for the (111) direction, ing $(1/2\pi)[(\Delta\omega)_{12}^2]^{\frac{1}{2}}\approx 11.8$ kc/sec compared to 15 'sec by the overlap integral of Eq. (5). Correlations ke the distribution function narrower by a factor of . Putting numerical values into Eqs. (3) and (5), cross-relaxation time T_{21} can be obtained by a thod to be explained later; the conclusion is $g_{12}(\omega_{12})$ eaked so sharply about $\omega_{12}=0$, even when correla- ns are neglected, that above 40 gauss cross-relaxation es are larger than one minute.

A more likely mechanism for exchange of energy is two Li's flip opposite to one F spin, the Zeeman rgy left over in this process is less than $\frac{1}{3}$ the value the simpler process, the exponent in Eq. (5) is uced by a factor of 10, and the resulting increase in (ω_{12}) more than compensates for the reduction in the trix element accompanying the necessarily higher ler perturbation. Following conventional time- endent perturbation theory, for initial state $|0\rangle$ probability amplitude for final state $|\beta\rangle$ in which o Li's have flipped up and one F down is made up a sum of terms like

$$t)_{ij:kl}=-\frac{1}{\hbar^2}\sum_\alpha B_{ij}'C_{kl}\times\left(\frac{\langle\beta|S_{+i}I_{-j}|\alpha\rangle\langle\alpha|S_{+k}S_{zl}+S_{+l}S_{zk}|0\rangle}{\omega(C_{kl})_{\alpha:0}}+\frac{\langle\beta|S_{+k}S_{zl}+S_{+l}S_{zk}|\alpha\rangle\langle\alpha|S_{+i}I_{-j}|0\rangle}{\omega(B_{ij}')_{\alpha:0}}\right)\times\frac{\exp(i\omega_{\beta:0}t)-1}{\omega_{\beta:0}},\quad(7)$$

ere $\hbar\omega(C_{kl})_{\alpha:0}$ is the energy difference between the tes $|\alpha\rangle$ and $|0\rangle$ that are connected by $C_{kl}(S_{+k}S_{zl}$ $S_{zk}S_{+l})$, similarly for $\hbar\omega(B_{ij}')_{\alpha:0}$. The most naive proach would be to take the absolute value of the uare of a sum of terms given by Eq. (7) and similar nations for other pairs of operators, integrate over a quency distribution and obtain the transition bability. This can't be correct since it would mean three spins which flip do not have to be physically ar one another. In Eq. (7), spin "i" must be near spin "j" but "k" can be anywhere, the resultant transition probability would be too large by a factor N, equal to the number of spins in the crystal.

Since there can only be transitions between states that conserve energy we must consider only those terms in Eq. (7) for which $\omega_{\beta:0}\approx 0$, that is, only those states for which

$$\begin{aligned}\omega(C_{kl})_{\alpha:0}&\approx-\omega(B_{ij}')_{\beta:\alpha},\\ \omega(C_{kl})_{\beta:\alpha}&\approx-\omega(B_{ij}')_{\alpha:0}.\end{aligned}\quad(8)$$

Neglecting the small difference between $\omega(C_{kl})_{\alpha:0}$ and $\omega(C_{kl})_{\beta:\alpha}$ and similarly for $\omega(B_{ij}')_{\alpha:0}$ and $\omega(B_{ij}')_{\beta:\alpha}$, and taking a suitable average, the first approximation to these terms is

$$b_\beta(t)_{ij:kl}=\frac{-1}{\hbar^2}\frac{B_{ij}'C_{kl}}{2}\left(\frac{1}{\omega_{\mathrm{Li}}}+\frac{1}{\omega_{\mathrm{F}}-\omega_{\mathrm{Li}}}\right)\times\{\langle\beta|S_{+i}I_{-j}(S_{+k}S_{zl}+S_{+l}S_{zk})-(S_{+k}S_{zl}+S_{+l}S_{zk})S_{+i}I_{-j}|0\rangle\}\times\frac{\exp(i\omega_{\beta:0}t)-1}{\omega_{\beta:0}}.\quad(9)$$

This probability amplitude is significant only when the three spins which flip are near one another. Taking into account all necessary operators of the form of Eq. (9), the probability per unit time of a transition from $|0\rangle$ to $|\beta\rangle$ is

$$W_{0\to\beta}=\frac{2\pi}{\hbar^2}g_{12}(\omega_{12})|\langle\beta|\mathcal{H}_{12}|0\rangle|^2,\quad(10)$$

where

$$\begin{aligned}\langle\beta|\mathcal{H}_{12}|0\rangle=&\frac{1}{2\hbar}\left(\frac{1}{2\omega_{\mathrm{Li}}}+\frac{1}{\omega_{\mathrm{F}}}\right)\langle\beta|D'E-ED'|0\rangle\\ &+\frac{1}{2\hbar}\left(\frac{1}{\omega_{\mathrm{F}}-\omega_{\mathrm{Li}}}+\frac{1}{\omega_{\mathrm{Li}}}\right)\langle\beta|B'C'-C'B'|0\rangle\\ &+\frac{1}{2\hbar}\left(\frac{1}{\omega_{\mathrm{F}}-\omega_{\mathrm{Li}}}+\frac{1}{\omega_{\mathrm{Li}}}\right)\langle\beta|B'C-CB'|0\rangle,\end{aligned}$$

and neglecting correlations

$$g_{12}(\omega_{12})\approx\frac{1}{\{2\pi[2(\Delta\omega)_{\mathrm{Li}}^2+(\Delta\omega)_{\mathrm{F}}^2]\}^{\frac{1}{2}}}\times\exp\left(\frac{-(\omega_{\mathrm{F}}-2\omega_{\mathrm{Li}})^2}{2[2(\Delta\omega)_{\mathrm{Li}}^2+(\Delta\omega)_{\mathrm{F}}^2]}\right)\quad(11)$$

analogous to Eq. (5).

The second moment of $g_{12}(\omega_{12})$ is rigorously given by

$$\langle(\Delta\omega)_{12}^2\rangle=\frac{1}{\hbar^2}\frac{\mathrm{Tr}|\mathcal{H}_1\mathcal{H}_{12}-\mathcal{H}_{12}\mathcal{H}_1|^2}{\mathrm{Tr}|\mathcal{H}_{12}|^2}.\quad(12)$$

However, it is such a formidable task to just expand this out that no attempt was made to try and evaluate it. From the results of Eq. (6) for the two-spin process, we might expect correlations to cause $(\Delta\omega)_{12}^2$ to be anywhere from $\frac{1}{2}$ to $\frac{3}{4}$ of the second moment in Eq. (11).

When ω_{12} is equal to two or three times the second moment of Eq. (11), g_{12} becomes very sensitive to the value of this moment. Since Van Vleck[10] has shown $(\Delta\omega)_{\text{Li}}^2$ and $(\Delta\omega)_{\text{F}}^2$ to be anisotropic, for a given magnetic field (i.e., constant ω_{12}), g_{12} and T_{21} are also anisotropic. For large enough fields, small changes in linewidths caused by rotating the crystal can cause g_{12} and thus T_{21} to change by a couple of orders of magnitude, because the second moment of g_{12} occurs in the exponent of a Gaussian.

B. Rate Equations and Cross-Relaxation Time

Van Hove[12] and Philippot[13] have shown rigorously that for all but pathological situations rate equations can be written down for a spin system described by the Hamiltonian in Eq. (1). Our treatment of these equations is similar to Schumacher's[3] which is also equivalent to the somewhat different procedure followed in BSPA. Assume the rate of exchange of energy between the Li and F systems is much slower than the time necessary for a Boltzmann distribution to be established in each system separately, (i.e., $T_{21}\gg T_2$). We can then define an Li spin temperature θ and an F spin temperature T, where θ is not equal to T in general.

Let p be the density matrix for the Li spins and P for the F spins. Since the two systems are separately in thermal equilibrium with themselves, p and P are both diagonal. Neglecting the dipole-dipole interaction we have $\langle E_{\text{Li}}\rangle=\text{Tr}\,p\mathcal{H}_0^{\text{Li}}$, $\langle E_{\text{F}}\rangle=\text{Tr}\,P\mathcal{H}_0^{\text{F}}$,

$$p_a=\frac{\langle a|\exp(-\mathcal{H}_0^{\text{Li}}/k\theta)|a\rangle}{\text{Tr}\exp(-\mathcal{H}_0^{\text{Li}}/k\theta)},$$
$$P_b=\frac{\langle b|\exp(-\mathcal{H}_0^{\text{F}}/kT)|b\rangle}{\text{Tr}\exp(-\mathcal{H}_0^{\text{F}}/kT)}. \qquad (13)$$

If $W_{a'b'\to ab}$ is the probability of a transition from a state $a'b'$ to ab, by the principle of detailed balance we have

$$\frac{W_{a'b'\to ab}}{W_{ab\to a'b'}}=\exp\left[\frac{E_{a'}^{\text{Li}}-E_a^{\text{Li}}+E_{b'}^{\text{F}}-E_b^{\text{F}}}{kT_S}\right],$$

where T_S is the equilibrium spin temperature, where

$$\frac{d}{dt}\langle E_{\text{Li}}\rangle=\text{Tr}\mathcal{H}_0^{\text{Li}}\dot{p}=\frac{\partial E_{\text{Li}}}{\partial\theta}\frac{d\theta}{dt}, \qquad (14)$$

and

$$\dot{p}_a=\sum_{a'b'b}p_{a'}P_{b'}W_{a'b'\to ab}-p_aP_bW_{ab\to a'b'}. \qquad (15)$$

[12] L. Van Hove, Physica 21, 517 (1955); Physica 23, 441 (1957).
[13] Jean Philippot, thesis, Université Libre de Bruxelles, 1959 (unpublished).

Combining Eqs. (13), (14), and (15) with simi ones for $\langle E_{\text{F}}\rangle$ and P_β we obtain

$$\frac{d}{dt}\left(\frac{1}{\theta}\right)=-\alpha\left(\frac{1}{\theta}-\frac{1}{T_S}\right)+\beta\left(\frac{1}{T}-\frac{1}{T_S}\right),$$
$$\frac{d}{dt}\left(\frac{1}{T}\right)=-\bar{\alpha}\left(\frac{1}{T}-\frac{1}{T_S}\right)+\bar{\beta}\left(\frac{1}{\theta}-\frac{1}{T_S}\right), \qquad ($$

where if the number of Li and F spins are each N

$$\alpha=\frac{6W}{NS(S+1)(2S+1)^N(2I+1)^N},$$
$$\beta=\frac{1}{2}\frac{\omega_{\text{F}}}{\omega_{\text{Li}}}\alpha,$$
$$\bar{\alpha}=\frac{1}{4}\frac{S(S+1)}{I(I+1)}\alpha,$$
$$\bar{\beta}=\frac{1}{2}\frac{S(S+1)}{I(I+1)}\frac{\omega_{\text{Li}}}{\omega_{\text{F}}}\alpha,$$
$$W=\sum_{ab,a'b'}W_{a'b'\to ab}.$$

Solving Eqs. (16), one of the time constants is infini corresponding to an infinite T_1 for a rigid lattice, t other one is

$$1/T_{21}=\alpha+\bar{\alpha}. \qquad (1$$

From the transition probability given by Eq. (1 and Eqs. (16) and (17)

$$\frac{1}{T_{21}}=\frac{2\pi g_{12}(\omega_{12})}{(\hbar H_0)^2N}[4I(I+1)+S(S+1)]$$
$$\times\left\{\frac{4}{9}S(S+1)\left[\left(\frac{\gamma_{\text{F}}+2\gamma_{\text{Li}}}{2\gamma_{\text{F}}\gamma_{\text{Li}}}\right)^2\sum_{i,j,k}|E_{ij}D_{jk}'|^2\right.\right.$$
$$+\left(\frac{1}{2}\frac{\gamma_{\text{F}}}{\gamma_{\text{Li}}(\gamma_{\text{F}}-\gamma_{\text{Li}})}\right)^2\sum_{i,j,k(i\neq j)}|B_{ij}'C_{jk}'|^2$$
$$+\left(\frac{\gamma_{\text{F}}}{\gamma_{\text{Li}}(\gamma_{\text{F}}-\gamma_{\text{Li}})}\right)^2\sum_{i,j,k}(|B_{ik}'C_{ij}|^2$$
$$\left.+B_{ik}'B_{jk}'|C_{ik}|^2)\right]+\frac{8}{15}[S(S+1)-\tfrac{3}{4}]$$
$$\left.\times\left(\frac{\gamma_{\text{F}}}{2\gamma_{\text{Li}}(\gamma_{\text{F}}-\gamma_{\text{Li}})}\right)^2\sum_{i,k}|B_{ik}'C_{ik}'|^2\right\}, \qquad (1$$

where the last term comes from one Li flipping twic Using $\gamma_{\text{Li}}=2\pi\times1655$ (gauss sec)$^{-1}$, $\gamma_{\text{F}}=2\pi\times40$ (gauss sec)$^{-1}$ and carrying out the lattice sums to th

2nd nearest neighbor, the results in Table I are tained. The last column is that value of H_0 for which e overlap integral approximation [Eq. (11)] predicts $_1=1$ second.

To take the finite spin-lattice relaxation times into count we modify Eqs. (16) as follows,[3]

$$\frac{d}{dt}\left(\frac{1}{\theta}\right)=-\alpha\left(\frac{1}{\theta}-\frac{1}{T_S}\right)+\beta\left(\frac{1}{T}-\frac{1}{T_S}\right)-\frac{1}{T_{1(\mathrm{Li})}}\left(\frac{1}{\theta}-\frac{1}{T_l}\right),$$

$$\frac{d}{dt}\left(\frac{1}{T}\right)=-\bar{\alpha}\left(\frac{1}{T}-\frac{1}{T_S}\right)+\bar{\beta}\left(\frac{1}{\theta}-\frac{1}{T_S}\right)-\frac{1}{T_{1(\mathrm{F})}}\left(\frac{1}{T}-\frac{1}{T_l}\right), \quad (19)$$

here T_l is the lattice temperature, $T_{1(\mathrm{Li})}$ and $T_{1(\mathrm{F})}$ e the Li and F spin-lattice relaxation times, respecvely. The two time constants associated with Eqs. (19) e λ_+ and λ_-; with the aid of Eq. (17) we define

$$\frac{1}{T_{10}}=\lambda_-=\frac{1}{2}\left\{\frac{1}{T_{21}}+\frac{1}{T_{1(\mathrm{F})}}+\frac{1}{T_{1(\mathrm{Li})}}-\frac{1}{T_{21}}\left[1+\frac{2T_{21}}{9}\left(\frac{1}{T_{1(\mathrm{F})}}-\frac{1}{T_{1(\mathrm{Li})}}\right)+T_{21}^2\left(\frac{1}{T_{1(\mathrm{F})}}-\frac{1}{T_{1(\mathrm{Li})}}\right)^2\right]^{\frac{1}{2}}\right\}, \quad (20)$$

$$\frac{1}{\tau}=\lambda_+-\lambda_-=\frac{1}{T_{21}}\left[1+\frac{2T_{21}}{9}\left(\frac{1}{T_{1(\mathrm{F})}}-\frac{1}{T_{1(\mathrm{Li})}}\right)+T_{21}^2\left(\frac{1}{T_{1(\mathrm{F})}}-\frac{1}{T_{1(\mathrm{Li})}}\right)^2\right]^{\frac{1}{2}}.$$

n the limit of $T_{21}\ll T_1$, τ is equal to T_{21}, while if T_{21} infinite $1/\lambda_-=T_{1(\mathrm{Li})}$ and $1/\lambda_+=T_{1(\mathrm{F})}$.

The Li (or F) signal as a function of the time t at H_0 is

$$S=e^{-t/T_{10}}[A+B(1-e^{-t/\tau})]+C, \quad (21)$$

here A, B, and C are determined by the initial onditions, lattice temperature T_l, and H_0.

TABLE I. Numerical results of calculations on cross relaxation in LiF single crystals.

Crystal orientation	$(H_0^2/T_{21}g_{12})$ (gauss/sec)^2	$H_0(T_{21}=1$ sec) (gauss)
100	1.34×10^{11}	104
110	3.88×10^{11}	88
111	1.15×10^{11}	67

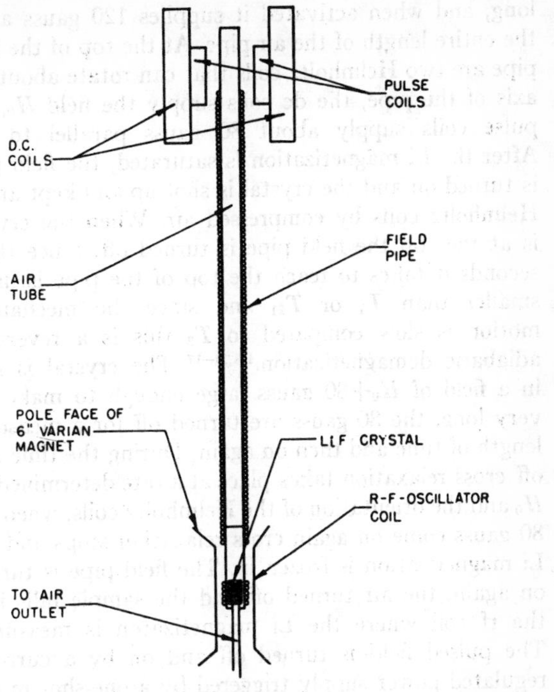

FIG. 1. Experimental arrangement for moving the sample from 4600 gauss to H_0 in which cross relaxation takes place.

III. EXPERIMENT

T_{21} is measured by the same method Abragam and Proctor[1] first used. An LiF crystal is allowed to come into equilibrium with the lattice in a field of 4600 gauss, the Li spins are then saturated and the crystal is quickly moved to a field H_0 of the order of 50 gauss, where cross relaxation takes place. The sample is kept there for a measured length of time and then brought back to 4600 gauss where the Li magnetization is then measured.

Since this is all done fast compared to the spin-lattice relaxation time there can only be nonzero Li magnetization via cross relaxation. The time at the low field is varied and the data fit to Eq. (21). This fit can be made even though the time necessary to move the sample is not really negligible compared to T_1; A, B, and C are functions of various times in the measurement process but care can be taken to make each measurement in exactly the same way so in any one plot of magnetization *vs* time they really are constants. Spin-lattice relaxation times in pure LiF crystals are a couple of minutes long so it is not difficult to do things fast compared with T_1.

This experiment is different from Abragam and Proctor's in the way we move the sample from 4600 gauss to H_0, the apparatus shown in Fig. 1 was constructed for this purpose. The sample is shown in the rf coil used to both saturate and detect the Li magnetization at the bottom of the air tube. The crystal is glued to a plastic piece that has a square cross section, the inside of the air tube is also square which keeps the sample from rotating. The field pipe is a solenoid 80 cm long, and when activated it supplies 120 gauss along the entire length of the air pipe. At the top of the field pipe are two Helmholtz coils that can rotate about the axis of the pipe, the dc coils supply the field H_0, the pulse coils supply about 80 gauss parallel to H_0. After the Li magnetization is saturated, the field pipe is turned on and the crystal is shot up and kept at the Helmholtz coils by compressed air. When the crystal is at the top the field pipe is turned off. Since the 4 seconds it takes to reach the top of the pipe is much smaller than T_1 or T_{21} and since the mechanical motion is slow compared to T_2 this is a reversible adiabatic demagnetization.[1,3,14–17] The crystal is now in a field of H_0+80 gauss large enough to make T_{21} very long, the 80 gauss are turned off for a measured length of time and then on again. During the time it is off cross relaxation takes place at a rate determined by H_0 and the orientation of the Helmholtz coils, when the 80 gauss come on again cross relaxation stops and the Li magnetization is frozen in. The field pipe is turned on again, the air turned off and the sample falls into the rf coil where the Li magnetizaton is measured. The pulsed field is turned off and on by a current-regulated power supply triggered by a one-shot multi-vibrator. The pulse width can be varied from 0.003 second to 24 seconds; longer times can be done manually. Transitients obvseved by a pickup coil and a Tektronix 535 oscilloscope die out in 1 millisecond, and pulse widths are measured this way to better than 3%.

The dc Helmholtz coils have been calibrated with dpph at 70 Mc/sec to better than 1%, they are air cored so the field is strictly proportional to current; current was measured with the same Weston dc ammeter during the experiment and calibration. Homogeneity was better than 0.5% over the sample volume. Field orientation was measured to better than 0.2° by means of marks every degree on the outer circumference of the rotating table holding the coils, it was 50 cm in diameter.

The spins were observed with a Pound-Watkins[18] type spectrometer in which the oscillator section was replaced by one given by Mays, Moore, and Shulman[19] and an extra stage of rf gain was added to improve the *AVC* control at low levels. The oscillation level was adjusted so the Li signal would saturate in approximately 5 seconds, and the frequency was swept so that it took about 10 seconds to go through the line. The output of the spectrometer was fed into a phase sensitive lock-in detector[18] that had a time constant of 0.5 second. The output of the lock-in was recorded on an Esterline Angus recorder. Keeping all other para eters constant the recorded signal is proportional the magnetization immediately before the line swept through. Since proportionality depends on t system being linear an experiment was done to pro linearity. The Li signal was saturated, and, witho moving the sample from the field, we waited a measu length of time before sweeping back and observing t line. When the resultant signal was plotted as a functi of the time waited, it was of the form $(1-e^{-t/T}$ The excellent fit to an exponential is proof the syste really is linear. This is the way we measured T_1 high fields.

In order to fit our data to Eq. (21) we had to ma sure each point in a signal *vs* time plot was measur is exactly by the way. This was done in the followi manner. The line was saturated by sweeping through three times. A radio receiver was tuned to a frequen just off one side of the resonance line, when audio bea were heard in the receiver after the third pass throu the line, a stop watch was started. At 5 seconds t sweep motor was shut off and simultaneously t sample was shot up the tube, where the field pipe w already on. This time was never in error by more tha 0.5 second. It always took 4 seconds for the sample reach the top of the tube, at which time the field pip was turned off and the pulse triggered; this was don in less than one second. The field pulse was observe on an oscilloscope so that within 0.5 second after t 80 gauss came on again, the field pipe was turned o and the sample was falling back to the rf coil. It too 4 seconds to reach the bottom. Within 0.5 second c reaching bottom the sweep motor was turned on agai and the signal was recorded 9 seconds later. Excludin the time during which cross relaxation took place, th entire process lasted 23±2 seconds.

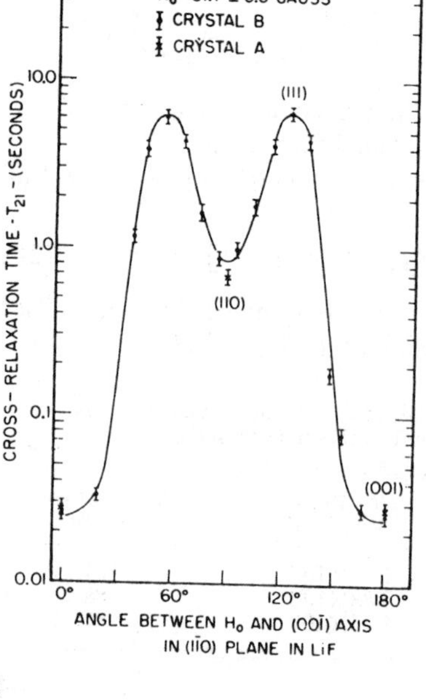

FIG. 2. Cross-re laxation time T_{21} v angle in the (1$\bar{1}$0 plane of LiF, crysta *B*, at 51.7 gauss The cross marks in the [110] and [001] directions are taken from crystal *A*.

[14] R. V. Pound and N. F. Ramsey, Phys. Rev. **81**, 278 (1951).
[15] L. C. Hebel and C. P. Slichter, Phys. Rev. **113**, 1504 (1959).
[16] A. Sachs and E. Turner, thesis, Harvard University, 1949 (unpublished).
[17] A. G. Anderson, Phys. Rev. **115**, 863 (1959).
[18] George D. Watkins, thesis, Harvard University, 1952 (unpublished).
[19] Mays, Moore, and Shulman, Rev. Sci. Instr. **29**, 300 (1958).

Since measurements were reproduceable to within he error expected from the noise of the detection ystem, i.e., less than 5%, we are confident that we vere able to keep A, B, and C constant.

Two crystals were used; both were cut in the form f right circular cylinders, diameter 1 cm and length ' cm. In crystal A the axis of symmetry was the 100], in crystal B it was the [110] axis. Crystal A vas considerably purer than crystal B; this was reflected n the spin-lattice relaxation times,[20] in 4600 gauss T_1(Li) was 8 minutes in crystal A but only 4 minutes n crystal B.

IV. RESULTS

Figure 2 shows the anisotropic behavior of T_{21} oredicted in a previous communication,[8] except for he three points taken from crystal A, it was taken in he $(1\bar{1}0)$ plane of crystal B. The excellent agreement between two crystals with very different spin-lattice relaxation times is evidence that impurities do not play any role in cross relaxation.

The qualitative agreement between the curve in Fig. 2 and the overlap integral approximation is excellent. Cross-relaxation times are longest when the magnetic field is in the [111] direction, this is also the direction in which the absorption lines are narrowest, making g_{12} [Eq. (11)] smallest. T_{21} is shortest in the [100] direction, where the absorption lines are broadest. The similarity between the shape of Fig. 2 in this paper and Fig. 2 in reference 10 is a very clear demonstration of the dependence of T_{21} on linewidths. The anisotropy is so very large, a factor of 500 in 54°, because the probability that energy can be conserved changes rather drastically as the crystal is rotated.

The field dependence of T_{21} is shown in Fig. 3 for

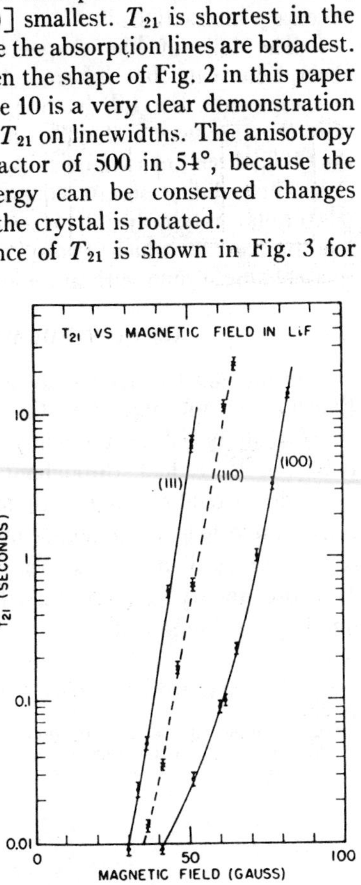

FIG. 3. Cross-relaxation time T_{21} *vs* H_0 for three crystal crystal orientations. The [111] direction was taken on crystal B, the [110] and [100] were from crystal A.

[20] N. Bloembergen, Physica **15**, 386 (1949).

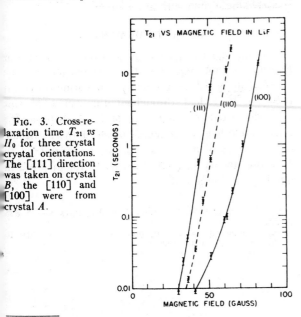

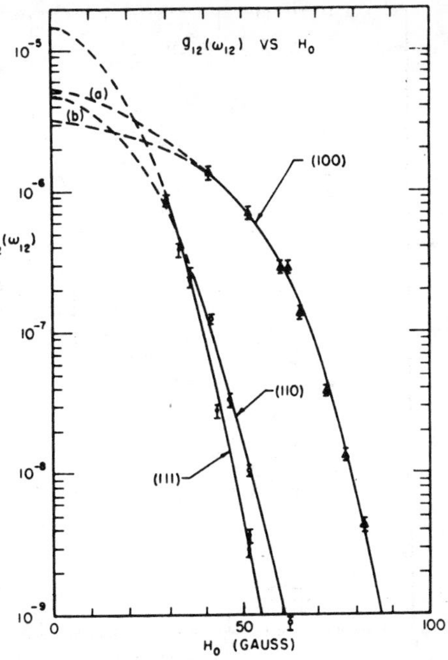

FIG. 4. $g_{12}(\omega_{12})$ *vs* H_0, $\omega_{12}=2\pi 697 H_0$. The curve for the [110] direction is $g_{12}=0.49\times 10^{-5}\exp[-\nu_{12}^2/2(10.3\text{ kc/sec})^2]$, and for the [111] direction $g_{12}=1.4\times 10^{-5}\exp[-\nu_{12}^2/2(8.8\text{ kc/sec})^2]$.

three orientations; the [111] direction was taken on crystal B, the other two curves on crystal A. The fields at which $T_{21}=1$ second are 0.6 to 0.7 times the fields predicted by the overlap integral approximation in Table I. Since this approximation ignored correlations, we expect it to predict too large fields. For the [111] direction the exact calculation of the second moment for the two spin process [Eq. (6)] was 0.8 times the value from the overlap integral for that process. Since the cross-relaxation process we are studying is more complicated than the two-spin model it is to be expected that correlations have a larger effect and 60 to 70% is a reasonable amount.

These results are also consistent with Abragam and Proctor's measurement of $T_{21}=6$ seconds at 75 ± 10 gauss. They paid no attention to orientation so we might assume their measurement yielded the shortest cross-relaxation time for a given field, that should be for the [100] direction where $T_{21}=2$ seconds at 75 gauss and 6 seconds at 79 gauss.

From Fig. 3 and Table I we calculated $g_{12}(\omega_{12})$ as a function of field ($\omega_{12}=2\pi 697 H_0$), and the results are plotted in Fig. 4. The data for both the [111] and [110] could be fit to Gaussians throughout the three decades we were able to measure. However, the results for the [100] direction could not possibly be described by one Gaussian. The Gaussians that describe the tails of $g_{12}(\omega_{12})$ are also good approximations near the center, $\omega_{12}=0$. Since $g_{12}(\omega_{12})$ is normalized to unity

$$\int_{-\infty}^{\infty} g_{12}(\omega_{12})d\omega_{12}=1.$$

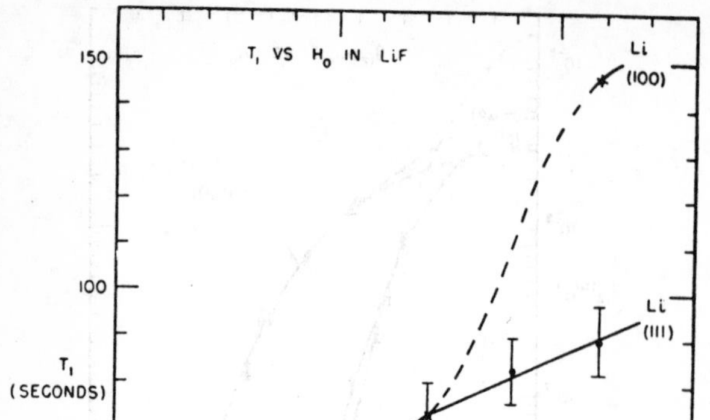

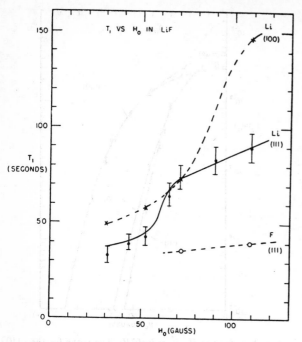

FIG. 5. Spin-lattice relaxation times *vs* H_0 in LiF. For the [100] direction T_1 is given for Li, for the [111] direction T_1 is given for both Li and F, the solid curve is the theoretical function as explained in the text.

Assuming these functions are symmetric about the origin the results are 1.9 for the [111] direction and 0.8 for the [110] direction. In view of the fact that the closest we can get to the center of the line is 0.1 $g_{12}(0)$, the agreement is remarkable. There is every reason to believe the absorption lines have the same qualitative shape as $g_{12}(\omega_{12})$ and thus are also Gaussian in the [111] and [110] direction. In the [100] direction we could not describe $g_{12}(\omega_{12})$ by a Gaussian, however we did make the two extrapolations (a) and (b) that seem to be the limits of reasonable curves; assuming symmetry about the origin the integral from $-\infty$ to $+\infty$ is 1.0 for curve (b) and 1.4 for curve (a), agreement is again excellent.

Curve (b) is very flat and broad near the center and the extrapolation may seem unrealistic. Numerical integration for curve (b) gives

$$[\langle\Delta\omega_{12}^4\rangle]^{\frac{1}{4}}/[\langle\Delta\omega_{12}^2\rangle]^{\frac{1}{2}}=1.26.$$

Van Vleck[10] calculates this same ratio for a simple cubic lattice of spins $\frac{1}{2}$ to be 1.25 in the (100) direction indicating that curve (b) is reasonable.

Watkins[18] observed that in large magnetic fields the spin-lattice relaxation time of Li in LiF is anisotropic.[21]

[21] We are indebted to Dr. A. Redfield for suggesting the investigation of T_1 in low field.

Figure 5 shows T_1 for Li as a function of field for the [100] and [111] orientations of crystal B, and for the [111] direction the T_1 of F is also shown. At 109 gauss the anisotropy is the same as Watkins observed. However, as the field is lowered, it changes considerably and at 71 gauss T_1 is the same for both directions. At this field T_{21} is less than 1 second in the [100] direction and since the F spin-lattice relaxation is more rapid than the Li, the easiest way for the Li's to come into equilibrium with the lattice is by first coming into equilibrium with the F's which then come into equilibrium with the lattice, the apparent T_1 of Li is lowered. In the [111] direction however, T_{21} is more than 10 seconds at 71 gauss and this drop has not yet begun; the slow decrease of the Li T_1 above 70 gauss is not associated with cross relaxation.[22]

Assuming in the absence of T_{21} the T_1's in the [111] direction would continue to decrease along the straight lines they follow above 70 gauss, from Fig. 3 and Eq. (20) we can calculate T_{10} *vs* H_0. The solid curve for Li in the [111] direction is the result. The theoretical curve is an excellent fit to the measured values of T_{10}.

V. CONCLUSIONS

1. The theory of BSPA is correct. Cross-relaxation times can be predicted if one takes into account all the necessary interactions.[23]

2. The tails of line shapes for nuclear magnetic absorption can be inferred from cross-relaxation measurements. For LiF in the [111] and [110] directions they are very well approximated by Gaussians, in the [100] direction a Gaussian is a poor approximation.

3. The validity of rate equations to describe cross relaxation is established. Cross relaxation is an irreversible process in which two-spin systems come into thermal equilibrium with one another.

ACKNOWLEDGMENTS

I would like to express my gratitude to Professor Bloembergen for suggesting this problem and for the benefit I derived from the many stimulating conversations we have had throughout the course of this research. I would also like to thank Dr. Jean Jeener for considerable help in designing much of the electronic equipment used in this experiment. I am grateful to Mr. Guy Boodry and Mr. John Keith for their aid in building my equipment.

[22] E. G. Wikner and E. L. Hahn, Bull. Am. Phys. Soc. 3, 325 (1958).

[23] Quadrupole effects must be taken into account in order to explain the results of reference 3.

Irreversibility in Interacting Spin Systems*

J. PHILIPPOT†
Institute for Fluid Dynamics and Applied Mathematics, University of Maryland, College Park, Maryland
(Received May 11, 1960)

A system whose Hamiltonian is split into two terms $\mathcal{H}=\mathcal{H}_0+\lambda V$ exhibits two types of irreversible processes. The first processes are described by $\mathcal{H}_0$ alone; only the second processes, which result from the pertubation, lead to an increase of the entropy of the system. These processes are illustrated by the examples of free precession and cross-relaxation. General formulas are given for transition probabilities and the expressions, applied to cross-relaxation in LiF, agree with the results obtained by Bloembergen and Pershan.

1. INTRODUCTION

THE master equation describes the evolution of the populations of the eigenstates or group of eigenstates of an unperturbed Hamiltonian $\mathcal{H}_0$ under the influence of a small perturbation λV. The unperturbed Hamiltonian is separable and has a continuous energy spectrum. All the degrees of freedom are mixed in the perturbation λV which causes transitions between the eigenstates of $\mathcal{H}_0$.

The theory of the master equation is based on the existence of a double time scale corresponding to the splitting of the Hamiltonian into a large $\mathcal{H}_0$ and a small perturbation λV. If we follow the evolution of the density matrix ρ, starting from any initial state, we may distinguish two different steps. In the first one, the unperturbed Hamiltonian alone, $\mathcal{H}_0$, has a uniformization effect on the phases of the off-diagonal elements of ρ

$$\rho_{k,l}(t)=\rho_{k,l}(0)\exp[-i(E_k-E_l)t/\hbar]. \quad (1.1)$$

In the second step, as a result of the perturbation λV, and with a time scale depending on the magnitude of λ, the diagonal elements themselves will reach their equilibrium values. Thus, there are in fact two steps in the evolution of the system, and there are also two kinds of irreversible processes. The first class of processes is related to the action of $\mathcal{H}_0$ alone. The second class, which results from the effect of the perturbation, includes the real irreversible processes, in the sense that they lead to an increase of the entropy of the system.

2. EFFECT OF THE UNPERTURBED HAMILTONIAN $\mathcal{H}_0$

A perfect gas without collisions, an harmonic solid, an assembly of independent spins in a constant magnetic field are all examples of systems with a separable Hamiltonian. Borel[1] was the first to study the evolution to homogeneity in space in terms of the velocity distribution in a perfect gas. The case of an harmonic solid has been studied in detail by several authors.[2,3] But the simplest example of this class of irreversible processes is surely the one of an assembly of independent spins.

Consider a set of identical magnetic moments, initially all parallel to the x axis. They are placed in a constant slightly inhomogeneous magnetic field H in the z direction. All magnetic dipoles will precess with some angular velocity $\omega=\gamma H$, where H is the magnetic field at the position of the dipole. To make things simpler, let us suppose that we observe the phenomena in the rotating coordinate system or that the mean value of H over the sample is zero. As a result of the inhomogeneity of the field, there will be a distribution function $g(\omega)$ for the angular velocities ω. The system will thus become rapidly uniform in the angle space, that is the resultant magnetic moment will disappear according

* This research was supported by the U. S. Air Force through the Air Force Office of Scientific Research of the Air Research and Development Command.
† On leave of absence from the University of Brussels, Brussels, Belgium.

[1] E. Borel, *Mecanique Statistique* (Gauthier Villars, Paris, 1925).
[2] G. Klein and I. Prigogine, Physica **19**, 1053 (1953).
[3] P. Mazur and E. Montroll, J. Math. Phys. **1**, 70 (1960).

to the formula

$$\mathbf{M}(t) \sim \int_{-\infty}^{+\infty} g(\omega) e^{i\omega t} d\omega, \quad (2.1)$$

if one introduces a complex x, y plane. The condition for $M(t)$ to vanish at $t=\infty$ is given by Riemann-Lebesgue theorem, that is, it is necessary that the integral

$$\int_{-\infty}^{+\infty} |g(\omega)| d\omega$$

exists.

The interest of this example is that it is so simple. It allows us to understand immediately that there is no contradiction between the reversibility of the equations of motion and the irreversibility of the behavior of certain quantities. Also, it permits us to clarify the meaning of the two paradoxes known as the recurrence paradox (Wiederkehreinwand) and the paradox of the inversion of the velocities (Umkehreinwand). If we wait a very long time, we know that according to Poincaré, the system will come back as near as we want to its initial state. This is of course true, but the corresponding time is so long[4] that it has no physical meaning. Furthermore, it is clear that if we want to predict the evolution for such long times, we have to know exactly the initial positions and velocities, and then we don't have a continuous function $g(\omega)$ but rather a sum of δ functions for which the Riemann-Lebesgue theorem does not hold. On the other hand, if the velocities are reversed, as in spin echo experiments, we come back to the initial situation. It is easily seen that initial situations giving rise to an echo are characterized by the fact that there exists no initial distribution function in the corresponding μ space.[5]

We may summarize as follows the characteristics of this type of irreversible processes:

(1) The system has a large number of degrees of freedom.

(2) Its Hamiltonian is separable and has a continuous spectrum.

(3) There exists no true relaxation time, nor any irreversible equation, but only a characteristic time.

(4) There are as many analytical invariants as initial momenta.

(5) The entropy remains constant.

3. FREE PRECESSION IN INTERACTING SPINS

We consider now a rigid lattice of spins, coupled by a dipole-dipole interaction. It is well known that a system containing a few down spins in an assembly of up spins is described by elementary excitations called spin waves. The interaction between spin waves may be treated in the same way as the interaction between phonons in an anharmonic crystal. This problem shall not be considered here. We shall examine only the situation in which there are nearly as many up as down spins. As an illustration of the previous ideas, we shall study the problem of the free precession signal and the problem of cross-relaxation. We shall see that the first phenomenon, decay of the free precession signal, belongs to the first class of irreversible processes, whereas the second, cross-relaxation, corresponds to an increase of the entropy.

The free precession signal is the Fourier transform of the absorption curve $g(\omega)$. This means that everything happens as if we had an assembly of independent spins with frequency distribution $g(\omega)$. The Hamiltonian of the problem contains the Zeeman part and the dipole-dipole part:

$$\mathcal{H} = -\sum_k \gamma\hbar H_0 S_k^z + \sum_{k<l} v_{kl}, \quad (3.1)$$

where the external magnetic field H_0 is now homogeneous. If we had to deal with the Zeeman part alone, all magnetic moments would precess with the same angular velocity $\omega=\gamma H_0$. The behavior of the whole system would be periodic, with a period $2\pi\omega^{-1}$ equal to the Poincaré recurrence time. Now, the interaction v_{kl} contains a part

$$A_{kl} = (\gamma^2\hbar^2/r_{kl}^3) S_k^z S_l^z (1-3\cos^2\theta_{kl}), \quad (3.2)$$

which is diagonal in the representation in which the z component S_k^z of the individual spin of each nucleus k is diagonal. Let us imagine a model having the Hamiltonian $\mathcal{H}=\mathcal{H}_0+\sum_{k<l} A_{kl}$. We can easily understand the qualitative behavior of the precession signal on the basis of such a model. The precession signal is given by

$$G(t) = \mathrm{Tr}[M_x(t) M_x], \quad (3.3)$$

where $M_x(t)$ is the value of the x component of the magnetic moment operator in the interaction representation

$$M_x(t) = \exp(iAt/\hbar) M_x \exp(-iAt/\hbar), \quad A = \sum_{k<l} A_{kl}. \quad (3.4)$$

Thus

$$G(t) = \sum_{nn'} |M_{xnn'}|^2 \exp[i(A_n - A_{n'})t/\hbar]$$
$$= \mathrm{Tr}(M_x^2) \prod_k \cos(A_{jk}t/\hbar), \quad (3.5)$$

which is the Fourier transform of the absorption curve

$$g(\omega) = \sum_{nn'} |M_{xnn'}|^2 \delta(E_n - E_{n'} - \omega). \quad (3.6)$$

In this model, the precession signal goes to zero with oscillations, but is always positive if the magnetic field coincides with an axis of symmetry of order two of the crystal. We must of course remember that the effect of the flip-flop term B_{kl} has been neglected. Lowe and

[4] P. C. Hemmer, L. C. Maximom, and H. Wergeland, Phys. Rev. 111, 689 (1958).

[5] J. Philippot, Bull. classe sci., acad. roy. Belg. 45, 591 (1959).

Norberg[6] have taken this into account using a power series development in time. The coefficients of t^2 and t^4 are then equal to the second and fourth moments of the absorption curve.

4. CROSS-RELAXATION[7,8]

Let us first consider the transport properties in an assembly of identical spins. We shall admit that we have always nearly as many up as down spins and moreover we shall suppose that up and down spins are "well mixed." That means that we want to exclude very particular situations in which different spin states should be separated in space. In this case, as a result of the diagonal terms in the dipole-dipole interaction (the A_{kl} terms), the static part of the local field, although varying rapidly from one lattice point to another, has a continuous distribution function. This fact results from our assumption of randomness and from the r^{-3} behavior of dipole-dipole interaction. If we try to use the general method of integrating the equations of motion, retaining all terms which are powers of the combination $\lambda^2 t$,[9] a difficulty appears immediately. The calculations are done in the representation where the z components of individual spins are diagonal. But, in order to perform the asymptotic integrations over long times, we have to introduce explicitly a continuous variable for the energy levels. The complexity of the relation between the two representations prevents an exact calculation of this type.

We may describe the processes of energy transfer in the following way. Energy exchange occurs during a time interval $(0,\Delta t)$ between the spins for which the resonance condition in the local field is satisfied. As a result, at time Δt, a new spatial distribution of the local fields is realized for which we shall again make an assumption of randomness. This hypothesis of the persistence of the chaos of the spins is here the analog of the "Stoszzahlansatz." This physical situation is completely different from the one considered by Anderson[10] in his paper on the absence of diffusion in certain random lattices. Anderson considers one up spin in an assembly of down spins, but a fixed energy is associated once and forever to each lattice point. This is the inhomogeneous broadening. Thus, if there is no possibility of conserving energy in a transition at the initial time, a transition shall never occur. When the broadening is of dipolar origin, the local field, or the energy of a spin is a fluctuating quantity as considered by Bloembergen.[11] One could also say that these two distinct situations are characterized by the fact that each spin fixed in space has a frequency distribution with a vanishing or nonvanishing dispersion in the corresponding Gibbs ensemble.

[6] I. T. Lowe and R. E. Norberg, Phys. Rev. **107**, 46 (1957).
[7] N. Bloembergen, S. Shapiro, P. S. Pershan, and J. O. Artman, Phys. Rev. **114**, 445 (1959).
[8] A. Abragam and W. G. Proctor, Phys. Rev. **109**, 1441 (1958).
[9] L. Van Hove, Physica **21**, 517 (1955).
[10] P. W. Anderson, Phys. Rev. **109**, 1492 (1958).
[11] N. Bloembergen, Physica **15**, 410 (1949).

An estimation of the relaxation time may be obtained in this way. Let us consider the pair of spins located at k and l. The probability of finding at k the frequency ω is $g(\omega)$. Assume that there are no correlations and that the probability of finding the frequency ω' at l is $g(\omega')$. The transition probability for a double flip becomes

$$W_{kl}=\frac{1}{4\hbar^2}\int g(\omega)g(\omega')e^{i(\omega-\omega')t}dtd\omega d\omega'|B_{kl}|^2 \quad (4.1)$$

(the temperature dependence has been neglected and I has been chosen $=\frac{1}{2}$). The total transition probability for the spin k is

$$W=\sum_l W_{kl}=\frac{2\pi}{4\hbar^2}\int g^2(\omega)d\omega\sum_l|B_{kl}|^2. \quad (4.2)$$

$(1/\hbar^2)\sum_l|B_{kl}|^2$ is precisely equal to 1/9 of the second moment $M_2=\int\omega^2 g(\omega)d\omega$. Thus we get for the mean lifetime of a Zeeman state the expression

$$T^{-1}=\frac{2\pi}{36}M_2\int g^2(\omega)d\omega. \quad (4.3)$$

If two species of spins with different gyromagnetic ratio γ are present, we have to introduce two distribution functions $g_1(\omega)$ and $g_2(\omega)$. The cross-relaxation time is then given by

$$\frac{1}{4\hbar^2}\int g_1(\omega)g_2(\omega')e^{i(\omega-\omega')t}dtd\omega d\omega'\sum_l|B_{kl}^{(1,2)}|^2 =\tfrac{1}{4}M_2(1,2)\int g_1(\omega)g_2(\omega)d\omega, \quad (4.4)$$

where $M_2(1,2)$ is precisely that contribution to the second moment M_2 which is dropped in the calculation of the line broadening by different spin species.[12] Let us introduce spin temperatures by writing the probability of finding a spin of species 1 with an energy $\pm\hbar\omega$ as

$$g_1^+(\omega)=f_1(\omega)\exp(-\hbar\omega/2kT),$$
$$g_1^-(\omega)=f_1(\omega)\exp(+\hbar\omega/2kT). \quad (4.5)$$

We thus have for the total rate of energy transfer from system 1 to system 2

$$\frac{dE}{dt}(1\rightarrow 2) =\frac{2\pi}{36}NM_2(1,2)\int\hbar\omega f_1(\omega)f_2(\omega) \times\left\{\exp\left[\frac{\hbar\omega}{2k}\left(\frac{1}{T_1}-\frac{1}{T_2}\right)\right]-\exp\left[-\frac{\hbar\omega}{2k}\left(\frac{1}{T_1}-\frac{1}{T_2}\right)\right]\right\}d\omega$$
$$=\int\hbar^2\omega^2 f_1(\omega)f_2(\omega)d\omega\frac{\pi NM_2(1,2)}{36k}\left(\frac{1}{T_1}-\frac{1}{T_2}\right), \quad (4.6)$$

[12] T. H. Van Vleck, Phys. Rev. **74**, 1168 (1948).

where $N=N_1=N_2=$ number of spins of each species. Using the relations

$$\frac{d}{dt}\left(\frac{1}{T_1}\right)=\frac{dE_1}{dt}\bigg/\left(-T_1^2\frac{dE_1}{dT_1}\right), \tag{4.7}$$

$$\frac{dE_1}{dT_1}=\frac{1}{kT_1^2}\frac{\mathrm{Tr}[\mathcal{H}_1^2]}{\mathfrak{N}_1} \tag{4.8}$$

[the index 1 (or 2) refers to system 1 (or 2), $\mathfrak{N}$ is the total number of spin states, here 2^N], we find

$$\frac{d}{dt}\left(\frac{1}{T_1}\right)=-R_{12}\left(\frac{1}{T_1}-\frac{1}{T_2}\right), \tag{4.9}$$

$$\frac{d}{dt}\left(\frac{1}{T_2}\right)=-R_{21}\left(\frac{1}{T_1}-\frac{1}{T_2}\right), \tag{4.10}$$

with

$$R_{12}=\frac{\pi M_2(1,2)}{9\omega_0^2}\int \omega^2 f_1(\omega)f_2(\omega)d\omega,$$

and

$$\frac{R_{21}}{R_{12}}\simeq\left(\frac{\gamma_1}{\gamma_2}\right)^2, \tag{4.11}$$

where we have used the approximation $\mathcal{H}_1\simeq\gamma\hbar H_0\sum_k S_k^z=\hbar\omega_0\sum_k S_k^z$. This gives for this simple case an explicit formula for the coefficients introduced by Schumacher.[13]

5. EXTENSION TO HIGHER ORDERS IN THE PERTURBATION

It happens very often that the expression (4.4) for the transition probability of a cross-relaxation process is vanishingly small compared to higher order terms in the perturbation for which the resonance condition is much more easily satisfied. In other words, we have to calculate the terms which are proportional to the time t but of a higher order in the perturbation. In such processes, the system goes through intermediate states for which the energy is not conserved. We perform this calculation using the interaction representation of the density matrix. We have

$$\mathcal{H}=\mathcal{H}_0+\lambda V,$$

$$\rho_{\mathrm{in}}(t)=\exp(-i\mathcal{H}_0t/\hbar)\rho(0)\exp(i\mathcal{H}_0t/\hbar), \tag{5.1}$$

$$V_{\mathrm{in}}(t)=\exp(-i\mathcal{H}_0t/\hbar)V\exp(i\mathcal{H}_0t/\hbar). \tag{5.2}$$

The equation of motion is

$$i\hbar\partial\rho_{\mathrm{in}}/\partial t=[\lambda V_{\mathrm{in}},\rho_{\mathrm{in}}], \tag{5.3}$$

the formal solution of which is

$$\rho_{\mathrm{in}}(t)=\exp\left(-\frac{i\lambda}{\hbar}\int_0^t V(t')dt'\right)\rho \times\exp\left(+\frac{i\lambda}{\hbar}\int_0^t V(t')dt'\right) \tag{5.4}$$

[13] R. T. Schumacher, Phys. Rev. **112**, 837 (1958).

The exponentials are defined by

$$\exp\left(-\frac{i\lambda}{\hbar}\int_0^t V(t')dt'\right) \equiv 1-\frac{i\lambda}{\hbar}\int_0^t V(t')dt' +\left(-\frac{i\lambda}{\hbar}\right)^2\int_0^t dt'\int_0^{t'}dt''V(t')V(t'')+\cdots. \tag{5.5}$$

When this expression is substituted in (5.4), the terms of a given order in λ are of two types: those coming from the development of one exponential only and those in which the corresponding terms of both exponentials are matched in pairs. These last ones determine the transition probability. Thus the transition probability from state s to state r is given by the term proportional to t in

$$\left[1-\frac{i\lambda}{\hbar}\int_0^t V_{rs}(t')dt' +\left(-\frac{i\lambda}{\hbar}\right)^2\int_0^t dt'\int_0^{t'}dt''V_{rk}(t')V_{ks}(t'')+\cdots\right]\rho_{ss}(0) \times\left[1+\frac{i\lambda}{\hbar}\int_0^t V_{sr}(t')dt' +\left(+\frac{i\lambda}{\hbar}\right)^2\int_0^t dt'\int_0^{t'}dt''V_{sk}(t')V_{kr}(t'')+\cdots\right].$$

When the resonance condition for the λ^2 term is not satisfied, the first nonvanishing contribution is given by

$$\frac{2\pi t}{\hbar^2}\lambda^4\sum_k\left|\frac{V_{rk}V_{ks}}{E_k-E_s}\right|^2\delta\left(\frac{E_r-E_s}{\hbar}\right), \tag{5.7}$$

where the summation over k in the second term is to be

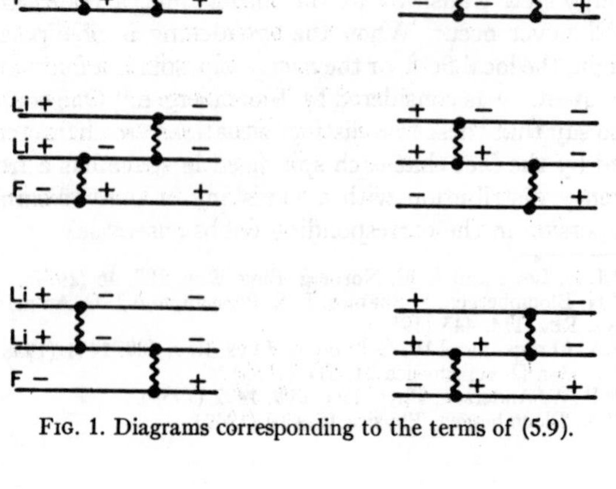

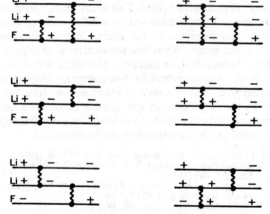

FIG. 1. Diagrams corresponding to the terms of (5.9).

performed over "linked clusters" or "connected diagrams" only. Let us illustrate this using the example of LiF. Pershan[14] has recently shown that for fields of the order of 50 gauss the essential mechanism consists in two Li flips and one opposite F flip. Using Pershan's notations (S denotes a lithium spin operator, I a fluorine spin operator, no prime refers to an interaction between two Li, one prime refers to a LiF interaction, and two primes to two F), we have to evaluate the modulus of

$$\mathcal{V}_{rs}=\frac{1}{\hbar}\left\{\left(\frac{B'C'}{\omega_{\mathrm{Li}}}-\frac{C'B'}{\omega_{\mathrm{F}}-\omega_{\mathrm{Li}}}\right)+\left(\frac{B'C}{\omega_{\mathrm{Li}}}-\frac{CB'}{\omega_{\mathrm{F}}-\omega_{\mathrm{Li}}}\right)+\left(\frac{D'E}{2\omega_{\mathrm{Li}}}-\frac{ED'}{\omega_{\mathrm{F}}}\right)\right\}. \quad (5.9)$$

A connected diagram is associated with each term as shown in Fig. 1.

Neglecting correlations and using the approximation of the overlap of two Gaussian line shapes, one gets for the transition probability

$$W_{rs}=(2\pi/\hbar^2)g_{12}(\omega_{12})|\mathcal{V}_{rs}|^2, \quad (5.10)$$

where

$$g_{12}(\omega_{12})=\frac{1}{\{2\pi[2(\Delta\omega)_{\mathrm{Li}}^2+(\Delta\omega)_{\mathrm{F}}^2]\}^{\frac{1}{2}}}\times\exp\left(\frac{-(\omega_{\mathrm{F}}-2\omega_{\mathrm{Li}})^2}{2[2(\Delta\omega)_{\mathrm{Li}}^2+(\Delta\omega)_{\mathrm{F}}^2]}\right). \quad (5.11)$$

Using the approximation $\omega_{\mathrm{F}}=2\omega_{\mathrm{Li}}$ in (5.9), which is justified if the Gaussian is very narrow, this result coincides with the expression given by Pershan.

The temperature variation is then obtained by replacing the expression for W_{rs} in Schumacher's formula for R_{12}.

ACKNOWLEDGMENTS

We want to express our gratitude to Professor Bloembergen and Professor Prigogine for their interest and to thank Dr. Jeener and Dr. Pershan for many stimulating discussions.

[14] P. S. Pershan, Phys. Rev. 117, 109 (1960).

PHYSICAL REVIEW VOLUME 119, NUMBER 6 SEPTEMBER 15, 1960

Induced and Spontaneous Emission in a Coherent Field. III

I. R. Senitzky
U. S. Army Signal Research and Development Laboratory, Fort Monmouth, New Jersey
(Received November 9, 1959)

The theory developed in the first two articles of this series, dealing with the interaction between the electromagnetic field in a cavity resonator and a number of two-level molecules, is generalized to include a Gaussian spread in the molecular frequency. The center of the molecular frequency distribution coincides with the cavity resonant frequency. There is a coherent driving field in the cavity at the same frequency, and cavity loss is taken into account.

Using the formalism previously developed for a quantum-mechanical field in a lossy cavity, expressions are obtained by means of second-order perturbation theory for the expectation values of the field strength and field energy in the cavity, and of the power loss by the molecules. It is shown that the parts of the field energy resulting from induced and spontaneous emission, respectively, initially increase as the square of the time and approach steady-state values after (different, in general) transient periods, each of which is determined by two time constants: cavity relaxation time and inverse molecular frequency spread. It is also shown that both the induced and spontaneous emission power radiated by the molecules increase initially linearly with the time and approach steady-state values after transient periods. For the induced emission power, the transient period is determined by only one time constant, the inverse molecular frequency spread, while for the spontaneous emission power it is determined both by the inverse molecular frequency spread and the cavity relaxation time. The ratio of induced to spontaneous emission is initially n, and approaches a steady-state value

$$n[\exp(r^2)(1-\mathrm{erf}r)]^{-1},$$

where n is the driving field energy in units of the photon energy, and r is the ratio of the cavity resonance width to molecular frequency spread. The seeming inconsistency of this value with the classical value of the ratio of the Einstein coefficients is discussed.

INTRODUCTION

In the first article of this series,[1] an analysis was made of the interaction between a number of two-level quantum-mechanical systems (hereafter referred to as molecules) and a coherent cavity field, the latter as well as the former being treated quantum-mechanically. The situation considered was that of a lossless cavity, and the molecules were all in resonance with the cavity. Under these two idealizations, neither the induced nor the spontaneous emission approached a steady state. In the second article,[2] a quantum-mechanical formalism was developed for the field of a lossy cavity and applied to the interaction with the molecules. In this case the spontaneous emission approached a steady state after

[1] I. R. Senitzky, Phys. Rev. 111, 3 (1958), hereafter referred to as I.

[2] I. R. Senitzky, Phys. Rev. 115, 227 (1959), hereafter referred to as II.

JOURNAL OF THE PHYSICAL SOCIETY OF JAPAN Vol. 16, No. 4, APRIL, 1961

On the Theory of Cross Relaxation in Maser Materials

By Motokazu HIRONO

Radio Research Laboratories, Kokubunji, Tokyo

(Received December 15, 1960)

A theoretical study of cross relaxation in Maser materials has been carried out based on the moment method. The energy level splittings due to the crystalline electric field and the applied magnetic field are utilized for the computation of the moments of the cross relaxation. If the lattice points are populated at random by paramagnetic ions in highly diluted salts, the second moment is much greater than the overlap integral of the individual ordinary resonance line shapes and to some extent influenced by the orientation of the applied magnetic field. The shape function of the cross relaxation is roughly Gaussian but takes slightly less values in the wings. The cross relaxation in ruby Maser successfully operated at liquid nitrogen temperatures has been briefly discussed.

§ I. Introduction

In a recent paper the theory of cross relaxation in spin systems was developed by Bloembergen, Shapiro, Pershan and Artman[1] (hereafter referred to as BSPA). This paper shows the mechanism of spin-spin relaxation, i.e. the process by which a common spin temperature is achieved. A number of experiments[2)-4)] have verified this theory at least qualitatively

The most fundamental process of cross relaxation is when two spins make simultaneous opposite flips, the balance in Zeeman energy being taken up by the dipole-dipole interaction. The process was treated in several theoretical papers.[1),5),6)] The practical computations in BSPA and in reference 2 were based on replacement of the second moment for cross relaxation with the overlap of individual ordinary line shape functions.

Pershan[5] calculated the second moment for the case of nuclear spins of LiF and showed that the above approximation is useful for concentrated salts to which, however, his consideration is confined. The cross relaxation in highly diluted paramagnetic salts was treated by Kiel[6] in terms of moment method and it was shown that the overlap integral method does not suffice for the diluted salts. In his calculations the effect of the crystalline electric field is neglected. This effect is, however, of fundamental importance for the operation of solid state Masers. In the present paper the rate of cross relaxation is calculated in terms of moment method taking into account the effect of the crystalline electric field in the Maser materials and hence the mechanism of relaxation is essentially different from that of Kiel[6].*

In recent years, the ruby Masers were successfuly operated at liquid nitrogen temperatures by Maiman[7] and Ditchfield.[8] Maiman[7] suggested that the cross relaxation is important for the operation. We briefly examined the process in terms of above mentioned results.

§ 2. General Consideration on Cross Relaxation

Consider the spin Hamiltonian,

$$\mathscr{H}=\mathscr{H}_m+\mathscr{H}_{cr}+\mathscr{H}_{\text{int}} \tag{1}$$

$\mathscr{H}_{cr}$ is the sum of the crystalline field couplings of the individual ions. The Zeeman energy in the applied field is given by

$$\mathscr{H}_m=\sum_i \beta \boldsymbol{H}\cdot \boldsymbol{g}_i\cdot \boldsymbol{S}_i\ .$$

The interaction between the spins are assumed to consist of dipolar and exchange terms:

$$\mathscr{H}_{\text{int}}=\sum \tilde{A}_{ij}(\boldsymbol{S}_i\cdot \boldsymbol{S}_j)+\sum_{j>i}\frac{g^2\beta^2}{r_{ij}^3}\left[(\boldsymbol{S}_i\cdot \boldsymbol{S}_j)-\frac{3}{r_{ij}^3}(\boldsymbol{S}_i\cdot \boldsymbol{r}_{ij})(\boldsymbol{S}_j\cdot \boldsymbol{r}_{ij})\right]$$

where one sort of paramagnetic ions is considered and the usual notations are employed. According to BSPA the interaction energy $\mathscr{H}_{\text{int}}$ can be written in the following forms

$$\mathscr{H}_{\text{int}}=A+B+C+D+E+F \tag{2}$$

$$A=\sum_{j>i}[\tilde{A}_{ij}+g^2\beta^2 r_{ij}^{-3}(1-3\cos^2\theta_{ij})]S_{zi}S_{zj}$$

$$B=\sum_{j>i}[(1/2)\tilde{A}_{ij}-(1/4)g^2\beta^2 r_{ij}^{-3}(1-3\cos^2\theta_{ij})](S_{+i}S_{-j}+S_{-i}S_{+j})$$

$$C=\sum_{j>i}(-3/2)g^2\beta^2 r_{ij}^{-3}\sin\theta_{ij}\cos\theta_{ij}\,e^{-i\phi_{ij}}(S_{+i}S_{zj}+S_{zi}S_{+j})$$

$$D=\sum_{j>i}(-3/2)g^2\beta^2 r_{ij}^{-3}\sin\theta_{ij}\cos\theta_{ij}\,e^{+i\phi_{ij}}(S_{-i}S_{zj}+S_{zi}S_{-j})$$

$$E=\sum_{j>i}(3/4)g^2\beta^2 r_{ij}^{-3}\sin^2\theta_{ij}\,e^{-2i\phi_{ij}}\,S_{+i}S_{+j}$$

$$F=\sum_{j>i}(3/4)g^2\beta^2 r_{ij}^{-3}\sin^2\theta_{ij}\,e^{2i\phi_{ij}}\,S_{-i}S_{-j}$$

where θ_{ij} and ϕ_{ij} are the polar angles of the radius vector connecting ions i and j with respect to the z-axis.

Several types of cross relaxations are considered by BSPA and others. In the following we shall examine the most fundamental processes which proceed through the sets of the neighboring two paramagnetic ions. The probability per unit time for the process that ion

* Some terms are, however, dropped in the equation (9) of Kiel. An exact calculation shows that the concentration independent term of (9) vanishes for $S=I=1/2$, since the term arises from the fact that $\mathscr{H}_{12}$ does not commute with $\sum' C_{p\xi}S_{zp}I_{z\xi}$ and this condition holds except for $S=I=1/2$.

i increases its energy by an amount $h\nu_\alpha$ and ion j decreases its energy by $h\nu_\beta$, the balance of energy $h(\nu_\beta-\nu_\alpha)$ being taken up by the spin-spin interaction of the whole array of dipoles, is given by

$$w_{ij}=\hbar^{-2}|\langle E_i,\ E_j|\mathscr{H}_{ij}|E_i+h\nu_\alpha,\ E_j-h\nu_\beta\rangle|^2 g_{\alpha\beta}(\nu=0)\ . \qquad (3)$$

If m_s is a good quantum number the matrix element is obtained from the term B in (2) and its square is given by

$$|\mathscr{H}_{ij}|^2=\eta g^4\beta^4(1-3\cos^2\theta_{ij})^2 r_{ij}^{-6}$$

where (4)

$$\eta=(1/16)(S-m_\alpha)(S+m_\alpha+1)(S+m_\beta)(S-m_\beta+1)\ .$$

When m_s is not a good quantum number, the expression of η is more complicated, nevertheless it is estimated to be of the order of unity for the cases considered in the following. The shape function $g_{\alpha\beta}(\nu)$ should be calculated by the moment method. The total second moment is

$$h^2\langle\nu_{\alpha\beta}^2\rangle=-T_r\{[\mathscr{H}(\sum\mathscr{H}_{ij})-(\sum\mathscr{H}_{ij})\mathscr{H}]^2\}/T_r\{[\sum\mathscr{H}_{ij}]^2\}\ . \qquad (5)$$

This method was, however, not use by BSPA for practical computation and instead the overlap integral of the line shape function $F(\alpha,\ \beta)$ was used, where

$$F(\alpha,\ \beta)=\iint g_\alpha(\nu')g_\beta(\nu'')\delta(\nu'-\nu'')d\nu'd\nu''\ . \qquad (6)$$

If a Gaussian shape is assumed for $g_\alpha(\nu)$ and $g_\beta(\nu)$ with second moments $\langle\Delta\nu_\alpha{}^2\rangle$ and $\langle\Delta\nu_\beta{}^2\rangle$ (6) is reduced to

$$F(\alpha,\ \beta)=[2\pi\{\langle\Delta\nu_\alpha{}^2\rangle+\langle\Delta\nu_\beta{}^2\rangle\}]^{-1/2}\exp\{-(\nu_\alpha-\nu_\beta)^2/2[\langle\Delta\nu_\alpha{}^2\rangle+\langle\Delta\nu_\beta{}^2\rangle]\}\ . \qquad (7)$$

By the use of the formulae together with excellent insight into the mechanism of elementary reactions, BSPA obtained several important agreement between the theoretical predictions and the experimental results. However, more rigorous mathematical treatment of the shape functions is very desirable to examine the various phenomena in the solid Masers. In the following section we give the estimation of the shape function using the moment method under consideration of the crystalline electric field.

§ 3. Estimation of the Shape Function by the Moment Method

The estimation of the shape function $g_{\alpha\beta}$ by the moment method was carried out by Pershan[5] and Kiel[6] for nuclear spins of LiF and dilute paramagnetic salts respectively. For their calculations, however, the effect of the crystalline electric field was not taken into account. In the following treatment we used a state of C_r^{+++} ion in ruby as a model and hence the influence of the crystalline electric field plays a leading rôle. In the absence of the interaction between paramagnetic ions, the spin Hamiltonian is given by

$$\mathscr{H}_m+\mathscr{H}_{cr}=\beta[g_\parallel H_zS_z+g_\perp(H_xS_x+H_yS_y)]+D[S_z{}^2-S(S+1)]$$

with

$$S=3/2\ .$$

Writing

$$g_\parallel=g_\perp=g \text{ and } D=-\delta\ , \qquad (8)$$

since $g_\parallel\simeq g_\perp$ and D is negative, we obtain the spin Hamiltonian for the ith ion in the case that the magnetic field is parallel to the crystal c axis, as follows:

$$W_i=-\delta(S_{zi}^2-\xi S_{zi})\ ,\quad \xi=g\beta H/\delta\ . \qquad (9)$$

The four energy levels deduced by this expression against magnetic field are shown in Fig. 1.

The total spin Hamiltonian is given by

$$\mathscr{H}=\sum_i W_i+\mathscr{H}_{\text{int}} \,. \tag{10}$$

In order to calculate the moments, we must select the so-called semi-diagonal part of the Hamiltonian, i.e. we take up only that part of the interaction terms that commute with the one-ion energy term $\sum W_i$. This part can be diagonalized simultaneously with the one-ion energy term, so this selection corresponds to the first order perturbation process which was adopted by Ishiguro, Kambe and Usui[9] for the calculation of the moments of the Larmor-lines.

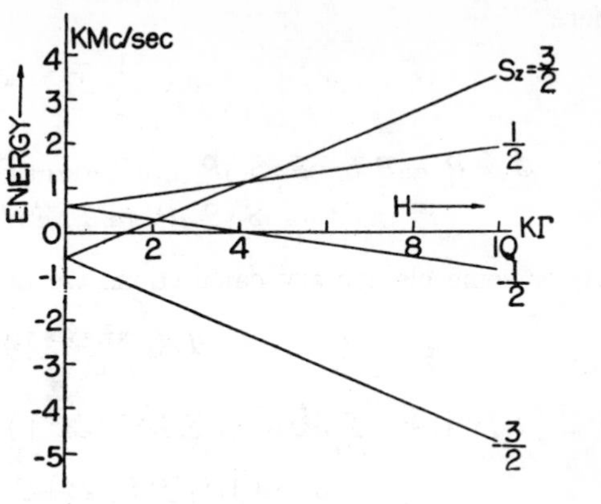

Fig. 1. A model of energy level diagram used for the calculation on the rate of cross relaxation.

The semi-diagonal part of the Hamiltonian may explicitly be written as

$$\overline{\mathscr{H}}=\sum_i W_i+\sum_{j>i}(A_{ij}+B_{ij})S_{zi}S_{zj}+\sum_{j>i}A_{ij}(\overline{S_{xi}S_{xj}}+\overline{S_{yi}S_{yj}}) \tag{11}$$

where

$$\begin{aligned} A_{ij}&=\tilde{A}_{ij}+\frac{g^2\beta^2}{r_{ij}^3}\left(\frac{3}{2}\gamma_{ij}^2-\frac{1}{2}\right), \\ B_{ij}&=-3\frac{g^2\beta^2}{r_{ij}^3}\left(\frac{3}{2}\gamma_{ij}^2-\frac{1}{2}\right) \end{aligned} \tag{12}$$

$$\begin{aligned} \overline{S_{xi}S_{yj}}+\overline{S_{yi}S_{yj}}&=\frac{1}{2}(\overline{S_{+i}S_{-j}}+\overline{S_{-i}S_{+j}}) \\ &=\frac{1}{2}(P_{(3/2)i}P_{(1/2)j}S_{+i}S_{-j}P_{(1/2)i}P_{(3/2)j}+P_{(1/2)i}P_{-(1/2)j}S_{+i}S_{-j}P_{-(1/2)i}P_{(1/2)j} \\ &\quad+P_{-(1/2)i}P_{-(3/2)j}S_{+i}S_{-j}P_{-(3/2)i}P_{-(1/2)j} \\ &\quad+P_{(1/2)i}P_{(3/2)j}S_{-i}S_{+j}P_{(3/2)i}P_{(1/2)j}+P_{-(1/2)i}P_{(1/2)j}S_{-i}S_{+j}P_{(1/2)i}P_{-(1/2)j} \\ &\quad+P_{-(3/2)i}P_{-(1/2)j}S_{-i}S_{+j}P_{-(1/2)i}P_{-(3/2)j}) \end{aligned}$$

where

$$\gamma_{ij}=\cos\theta_{ij} \tag{13}$$

$P_{(3/2)i}$, $P_{(1/2)i}$, $P_{-(1/2)i}$ and $P_{-(3/2)i}$ are the projection operators corresponding to the states $m_i=3/2$, $1/2$, $-1/2$ and $-3/2$ of the i-th ion respectively.

In order to calculate the trace, we select the representation scheme in which each spin is individually space quantized. Thus we have

$$\begin{aligned} P_{(3/2)i}&=(1/6)(S_{zi}+3/2)(S_{zi}^2-1/4)\,, \\ P_{-(3/2)i}&=-(1/6)(S_{zi}-3/2)(S_{zi}^2-1/4)\,, \\ P_{(1/2)i}&=-(1/2)(S_{zi}+1/2)(S_{zi}^2-9/4)\,, \\ P_{-(1/2)i}&=(1/2)(S_{zi}-1/2)(S_{zi}^2-9/4)\,. \end{aligned}$$

Now suppose that one of the two neighboring ions makes $m=1/2\to-1/2$ (α type) transition and the other $m=-3/2\to-1/2$ (β type) transition and the balance of energy $h(\nu_\beta-\nu_\alpha)$ is taken up by the spin-spin interaction.

The operating matrix $\sum\mathscr{H}_{ij}$ in (5) should be replaced by the following expressions

$$\sum_{j>i}\hat{\mathscr{H}}_{ij}=\hat{B}=\sum_{j>i}b_{ij}\Phi_{ij} \tag{14}$$

where

$$b_{ij}=\frac{1}{2}\tilde{A}_{ij}-\frac{1}{4}g^2\beta^2 r_{ij}^{-3}(1-3\gamma_{ij}^2) \tag{15}$$

$$\begin{aligned}\Phi_{ij}=&P_{(1/2)i}P_{-(3/2)j}S_{+i}S_{-j}P_{-(1/2)i}P_{-(1/2)j}+P_{-(1/2)i}P_{-(1/2)j}S_{-i}S_{+j}P_{(1/2)i}P_{-(3/2)j}\\ &+P_{-(1/2)i}P_{-(1/2)j}S_{+i}S_{-j}P_{-(3/2)i}P_{(1/2)j}+P_{-(3/2)i}P_{(1/2)j}S_{-i}S_{+j}P_{-(1/2)i}P_{-(1/2)j}\end{aligned} \tag{16}$$

After some elementary calculations we have

$$Tr\{[\sum_{j>i}\hat{\mathscr{H}}_{ij}]^2\}=3(2S+1)^N\sum_{j>i}b_{ij}^2\ , \tag{17}$$

$$\begin{aligned}-Tr\{[&\overline{\mathscr{H}}(\sum_{j>i}\hat{\mathscr{H}}_{ij})-(\sum_{j>i}\hat{\mathscr{H}}_{ij})\overline{\mathscr{H}}]^2\}\\ &=3(2S+1)^N[\sum_{j>i}b_{ij}^2(2\delta+C_{ij})^2\\ &\quad+\sum_{k\neq(j>i)}\{(5/4)(C_{ik}^2+C_{jk}^2)+(21/8)(A_{ik}^2+A_{jk}^2)\}b_{ij}^2]\end{aligned} \tag{18}$$

where

$$C_{ij}=A_{ij}+B_{ij} \tag{19}$$

and N is the total number of ions in the crystal, and the notation $k\neq(j>i)$ means that k is not equal to j nor i and j is greater than i. In the above expression, terms like

$$\sum_{k\neq(j>i)}C_{ik}C_{jk}b_{ij}^2$$

are neglected compared to the terms like

$$\sum_{j>i}C_{ik}^2 b_{ij}^2\ .$$

Thus we obtain the total second moment using (17), (18) and the equation

$$h^2\langle\nu_{\alpha\beta}^2\rangle=-Tr\{[\overline{\mathscr{H}}(\Sigma\hat{\mathscr{H}}_{ij})-(\Sigma\hat{\mathscr{H}}_{ij})\overline{\mathscr{H}}]^2\}/Tr\{[\Sigma\hat{\mathscr{H}}_{ij}]^2\}\ .$$

For the present case

$$h(\nu_\beta-\nu_\alpha)=2\delta$$

and clearly in the absence of the interaction between ions we have

$$h^2\langle\nu_{\alpha\beta}^2\rangle=(2\delta)^2\ .$$

Thus we get

$$h^2\langle\Delta\nu_{\alpha\beta}^2\rangle=h^2\langle\nu_{\alpha\beta}^2\rangle-(2\delta)^2=M_1+M_2 \tag{20}$$

where

$$\begin{aligned}M_1&=\sum_{j>i}b_{ij}^2C_{ij}^2/\sum_{j>i}b_{ij}^2\\ M_2&=\sum_{k\neq(j>i)}\{(5/4)(C_{ik}^2+C_{jk}^2)+(21/8)(A_{ik}^2+A_{jk}^2)\}b_{ij}^2/\sum_{j>i}b_{ij}^2\end{aligned} \tag{21}$$

and the term

$$\sum_{j>i}4\delta C_{ij}b_{ij}^2$$

is neglected compared with the term

$$\sum_{j>i}C_{ij}^2 b_{ij}^2$$

and $C_{ij}=C_{ji}$ and $A_{ij}=A_{ji}$ are assumed.

In the Maser material, usually the paramagnetic ions are highly diluted with diamagnetic ions. Kittel and Abraham[10] suggested that at least two different types of dilution may be contemplated: namely the lattice points are populated at random by the paramagnetic ions or the effect of dilution were to expand the magnetic lattice uniformly. Let us examine the effect of dilution for these cases.

(i) First suppose that the lattice points are populated at random by paramagnetic ions. Let f be the probability that a lattice site is occupied by a magnetic system. For ruby this is the probability that the Al site is replaced by the Cr ion. By a similar method to Kittel and Abraham[10], M_1 and M_2 are reduced to the following expressions:

$$M_1=\sum_j{}' b_{ij}^2C_{ij}^2/\sum_j{}' b_{ij}^2\,, \tag{22}$$

$$M_2=f[\sum_k{}' \{(5/2)C_{ik}^2+(21/4)A_{ik}^2\}-\sum_j{}' \{(5/2)C_{ij}^2+(21/4)A_{ij}^2\}b_{ij}^2/\sum_j{}' b_{ij}^2 \tag{23}$$

where $\sum_k{}'$ or $\sum_j{}'$ mean sums over all k or j sites, whether or not occupied. From (12), (19) and (15) we have

$$A_{ij}=\tilde{A}_{ij}-(1/3)B_{ij}\,,\quad C_{ij}=\tilde{A}_{ij}+(2/3)B_{ij}$$

$$b_{ij}=(1/2)\tilde{A}_{ij}-(1/6)B_{ij}\,. \tag{24}$$

It is seen that M_1 is independent of the dilution and M_2 is proportional to f. When the exchange interaction is absent $\tilde{A}_{ij}=0$ and we get

$$\begin{aligned} M_1&=(4/9)\sum_j{}' B_{ij}^4/\sum_j{}' B_{ij}^2\,,\\ M_2&=(61/36)f[\sum_j{}' B_{ij}^2-\sum_j{}' B_{ij}^4/\sum_j{}' B_{ij}^2]\,. \end{aligned} \tag{25}$$

According to Van Vleck[11] and Kittel and Abraham[10] the mean square deviation of the frequency from the Larmor value may be written

$$h^2\langle\Delta\nu^2\rangle=[S(S+1)/3]\,f\sum_j{}' B_{ij}^2=(5/4)\,f\sum_j{}' B_{ij}^2 \quad \text{for } S=3/2. \tag{26}$$

It is of interest to note that the first term of M_2 resembles this expression.

For the Maser materials, f is of the order of magnitude of 10^{-3} and hence $h^2\langle\Delta\nu^2_{\alpha\beta}\rangle$ is expressed by M_1 alone.

(a) If the lattice is simple cubic with the applied magnetic field in the (100) direction, we have

$$\sum_j{}' B_{ij}^2=29.9g^4\beta^4d^{-6} \tag{27}$$

and from (20) and (25) it follows that

$$\langle\Delta\nu_{\alpha\beta}^2\rangle=0.091h^{-2}\sum_j{}' B_{ij}^2=2.7h^{-2}g^4\beta^4d^{-6} \tag{28}$$

where d is the distance between nearest lattice sites. It should be noted that the value is to some extent influenced by the direction of the magnetic field.

(b) If the average of the B_{ij}^2 and B_{ij}^4 over the sphere, centered at the i-th ion, with the radius r equal to the distance to the (effective) nearest neighbors the number of which is Z, be denoted by $\overline{B_{ij}^2}$ and $\overline{B_{ij}^4}$ respectively, then we have approximately

$$\sum_j{}' B_{ij}^2\simeq Z\overline{B_{ij}^2}\,,\quad \sum_j{}' B_{ij}^4\simeq Z\overline{B_{ij}^4}\,,\quad \overline{B_{ij}^4}=2.145(\overline{B_{ij}^2})^2\,,\quad \overline{B_{ij}^2}=(9/5)g^4\beta^4r^{-6} \tag{29}$$

and hence from (20) and (25) it follows that

$$\langle \Delta\nu^2_{\alpha\beta}\rangle = 1.7h^{-2}g^4\beta^4r^{-6}\,. \tag{30}$$

If the shape of $g_{\alpha\beta}(\nu)$ is assumed to be Gaussian, we have

$$g_{\alpha\beta}(\nu) = [2\pi\langle \Delta\nu^2_{\alpha\beta}\rangle]^{-1/2}\exp\{-[\nu-(\nu_\beta-\nu_\alpha)]^2/2\langle \Delta\nu^2_{\alpha\beta}\rangle\}\,. \tag{31}$$

In order to compare (31) with (7) we use the following ratio

$$\langle \Delta\nu^2_{\alpha\beta}\rangle/[\langle \Delta\nu_\alpha{}^2\rangle + \langle \Delta\nu_\beta{}^2\rangle] \simeq \langle \Delta\nu^2_{\alpha\beta}\rangle/2\langle \Delta\nu^2\rangle \equiv \lambda^2\,. \tag{32}$$

For the abovementioned case (a) we have

$$\lambda^2 = (28f)^{-1}\,, \tag{33}$$

and for the case (b)

$$\lambda^2 = 0.38(fZ)^{-1}\,. \tag{34}$$

The former is 36 for $f=10^{-3}$ and the latter 48 for $Z=8$ and $f=10^{-3}$. There is some discrepancy between them. However, in any case the calculated moments are much greater than those deduced by the overlap integral of the individual ordinary resonance line shapes.

(ii) Next suppose that the factor f is unity. From (20) and (25) we have

$$h^2\langle \Delta\nu^2_{\alpha\beta}\rangle = (61/36)\sum_j{}' B^2_{ij} - (5/4)\sum_j{}' B^4_{ij}/\sum_j{}' B^2_{ij}\,.$$

(a) For the cubic lattice with the applied magnetic field in (100) direction we have

$$\langle \Delta\nu^2_{\alpha\beta}\rangle = 1.44h^{-2}\sum_j{}' B^2_{ij}$$

and therefore from (32), (26) and (27),

$$\lambda^2 = 0.58\,.$$

(b) If the averages over the sphere are taken as in the case (b) of (i), then we have

$$\langle \Delta\nu^2_{\alpha\beta}\rangle = (1.7Z-2.7)\overline{B^2_{ij}}$$

and therefore for $Z=8$, from (32),

$$\lambda^2 = 0.54\,.$$

Pershan[5] obtained $\lambda^2=(0.8)^2=0.64$, hence our results are nearly equal. If the effect of the dilution changes the location of the magnetic ions as if the magnetic lattice were uniformly expanded, then the ratio λ^2 is constant and $\langle \Delta\nu^2_{\alpha\beta}\rangle$ is proportional to $\langle \Delta\nu^2\rangle$ of Van Vleck.[11] In this case the overlap integral will give a fairly good measure of the cross relaxation.

§ 4. Consideration on the Fourth Moment

In the previous section the shape of $g_{\alpha\beta}(\nu)$ is assumed to be Gaussian. But in principle all higher moments are necessary to determine the exact shape. If we confine our attention to the interval of ν not far from the center, the second and the fourth moment will suffice to outline the shape.

If we write

$$U = \overline{\mathscr{H}}(\Sigma\hat{\mathscr{H}}_{ij}) - (\Sigma\hat{\mathscr{H}}_{ij})\overline{\mathscr{H}}\,,$$

the total fourth moment is given by

$$h^4\langle \nu^4_{\alpha\beta}\rangle = Tr\{[\overline{\mathscr{H}}U - U\overline{\mathscr{H}}]^2\}/Tr\{[\Sigma\hat{\mathscr{H}}_{ij}]^2\}\,.$$

Here we consider the parts of $\langle \Delta\nu^2_{\alpha\beta}\rangle$ and $\langle \Delta\nu^4_{\alpha\beta}\rangle$ which are independent of the dilution f and much greater than the remaining terms for $f \ll 1$. Then we have after some elementary computations,

$$h^4\langle \Delta\nu^4_{\alpha\beta}\rangle = \sum_j{}' b^2_{ij}C^4_{ij}/\sum_j{}' b^2_{ij}\,. \tag{35}$$

For the diluted magnetic lattice mentioned in (i) (a) of section 3, we have

$$\langle \Delta\nu^4_{\alpha\beta}\rangle = 1.35[\langle \Delta\nu^2_{\alpha\beta}\rangle]^2\,,$$

and for the case (i) (b) of section 3

$$\langle \Delta\nu^4_{\alpha\beta}\rangle = 1.44[\langle \Delta\nu^2_{\alpha\beta}\rangle]^2\,.$$

If the shape is Gaussian we should have[11]

$$\langle \Delta\nu^4_{\alpha\beta}\rangle = 3[\langle \Delta\nu^2_{\alpha\beta}\rangle]^2\,,$$

hence in the present case the shape will be roughly Gaussian, but will take slightly less value in the wings.

§ 5. Cross Relaxation Time

According to the discussion of the previous section in terms of the moment method the cross relaxation time is obtained as follows:

From (3), (4) and (31) and considering that

$$\sum_j |\mathscr{H}_{ij}|^2 = f\sum_i{}' |\mathscr{H}_{ij}|^2$$

we have

$$\sum_j w_{ij} = f\cdot\eta\cdot\hbar^{-2}g^4\beta^4 g_{\alpha\beta}(\nu=0)\sum_j{}' (1-3\gamma^2_{ij})^2 r_{ij}^{-6}\,,$$

and from (12) and (26) this expression is reduced to

$$\sum_j w_{ij} = 14\cdot\eta\cdot\langle \Delta\nu^2\rangle\cdot g_{\alpha\beta}(\nu=0)\,,$$

where it should be recalled that $\langle \Delta\nu^2\rangle$ is the second moment of Van Vleck.[11] To see the relation between the results of the moment method and the overlap integral, we use the notation (32), then it follows that

$$\sum_j w_{ij} = 2.8\eta\cdot[2\langle \Delta\nu^2\rangle]^{1/2}\lambda^{-1}\exp\{-(\nu_\alpha-\nu_\beta)^2/4\lambda^2\langle \Delta\nu^2\rangle\}\,. \tag{36}$$

The cross relaxation time T_{21} is obtained by

$$(2T_{21})^{-1} = \sum_j w_{ij}p_j = \frac{1}{4}\sum_j w_{ij}$$

and hence by

$$T_{21} = \left(\frac{1}{2}\sum_j w_{ij}\right)^{-1}. \tag{37}$$

The result of overlap integral is obtained by equating $\lambda=1$ and may agree[2] with some experimental results of the dilute salts of $K_3(C_oCr)(CN)_6$. In general, however, the cross relaxation time with $\lambda=1$ gives far longer times than those required by the experimental results, and it is necessary that λ is greater than unity to satisfy the requirement. In this situation BSPA suggested that the relaxation is mainly taking place through the ions with nearest one neighbor in the diluted salts and showed the formulae

$$T_{21}=(Zf)^{-1}\langle\Delta\nu_\alpha^2\rangle_{\rm conc}^{-1/2}\exp\{Z(\nu_\alpha-\nu_\beta)^2/2[\langle\Delta\nu_\alpha^2\rangle_{\rm conc}+\langle\Delta\nu_\beta^2\rangle_{\rm conc}]\}\ . \qquad (38)$$

This value is obtained from (36) and (37) with

$$\lambda^2=(fZ)^{-1}\ , \qquad (39)$$

namely by equating

$$2(fZ)^{-1}\langle\Delta\nu^2\rangle=2(Z)^{-1}\langle\Delta\nu^2\rangle_{\rm conc}\simeq Z^{-1}[\langle\Delta\nu_\alpha^2\rangle_{\rm conc}+\langle\Delta\nu_\beta^2\rangle_{\rm conc}]$$

and considering that $\eta\sim1$.

Our results (33) and (34) are of the same order of magnitude as the above λ^2, but may be about one third of the latter. The reason that $\lambda\gg1$ seems to be essentially the same as suggested by BSPA. When the value of (34) is adopted we have from (36) and (37)

$$\begin{aligned}T_{21}&=0.21\times(\eta fZ)^{-1}(g^2\beta^2h^{-1}r^{-3})^{-1}\exp\{(\nu_\beta-\nu_\alpha)^2/3.4(g^4\beta^4h^{-2}r^{-6})\}\\&=(\eta fZ)^{-1}(\rho^3/2.5\times10^{11})\exp\{(\nu_\beta-\nu_\alpha)^2\rho^6/9.25\times10^{21}\}\end{aligned} \qquad (40)$$

where ρ denotes the distance of the nearest paramagnetic ions in units of Å. Thus if the lattice points are populated at random by paramagnetic ions the cross relaxation time T_{21} increases very slowly with the decrease of the factor f.

On the other hand if the effect of the dilution changes the location of the magnetic ions as if the magnetic lattice were expanded uniformly, then λ is a constant as shown in the previous section and $\langle\Delta\nu^2\rangle$ is shown to be proportional to the square of the concentration of the paramagnetic ions. Thus we see from (36) and (37) that the cross relaxation time increases very rapidly with the decrease of the concentration of the ions, since $\langle\Delta\nu^2\rangle$ is included in the exponential function.

§ 6. Cross Relaxation in Solid State Masers

We shall evaluate the influence of the cross relaxation on the solid state Masers. First suppose the three level Maser of which the three levels are numbered 1, 2 and 3 from the lowest and n_1, n_2 and n_3 are the spin populations in the three levels as shown in Fig. 2. Let us write $X=2/3\cdot\sum_j w_{ij}$ then the rate equations become, at the steady state,

$$dn_3/dt=W_{13}(n_1-n_3)+S_{32}(n_2-n_3)+w'_{13}(n_1-n_3-\alpha\nu_{31})+w'_{23}(n_2-n_3-\alpha\nu_{32})+X(n_2-n_3)=0\ ,$$

$$dn_1/dt=-W_{31}(n_1-n_3)-w'_{13}(n_1-n_3-\alpha\nu_{31})+w'_{21}(n_2-n_1+\alpha\nu_{12})+X(n_2-n_3)=0\ ,$$

where we introduce such a cross relaxation that $i(1\to2)$ and $j(3\to2)$ transitions simultaneously take place and w'_{ij}, W_{31} and S_{32} denote transition probabilities due to thermal lattice vibrations, strong pumping rf power and signal power respectively, and $\alpha=(1/3)Nh/kT_L$, and it is assumed that $h(\nu_{12}-\nu_{23})/kT_{ad}\simeq0$, with T_L the lattice temperature and T_{ad} the final temperature after the spin system has come into internal equilibrium adiabatically. Using the notations

$$w'_{21}\sim w'_{23}\equiv w'=(2T_1)^{-1}\ ,\quad X=(2T_{21})^{-1}$$

we have from the above equations

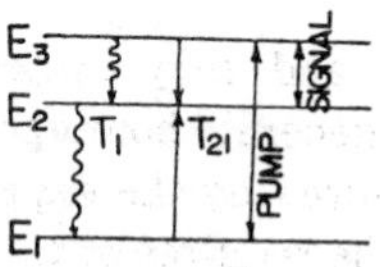

Fig. 2. A three level Maser system used to illustrate the relaxation processes.

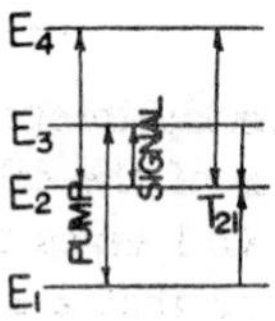

Fig. 3. A push-pull Maser pumping scheme.

$$n_3-n_2=\frac{hN}{6kT}\frac{\nu_{12}-\nu_{32}}{(1+2T_1/3T_{21})+T_1\cdot S_{32}} \tag{41}$$

where $T_L=T_{ad}=T$ is assumed. For the push-pull four level Masers as shown in Fig. 3, in the same way we have

$$n_3-n_2=\frac{Nh}{4kT}\frac{w'_{12}\nu_{12}+w'_{43}\nu_{43}+w'_{14}\nu_{14}-w'_{23}\nu_{23}}{w'_{12}+w'_{43}+w'_{14}+(w'_{23}+2\sum w_{ij})+S_{32}}$$

again using the notations

$$w'_{43}\sim w'_{21}\sim w'_{32}\sim w'_{12}\equiv w'=(2T_1)^{-1}, \quad (3\sum w_{ij})^{-1}=T_{21}, \quad \text{and} \quad w'_{41}/w'\equiv\eta, \quad \text{with} \quad 0<\eta<1,$$

we have

$$n_3-n_2=\frac{hN}{4kT}\frac{(\eta\nu_{41}+2\nu_{12})-\nu_{32}}{(\eta+3)+4\cdot T_1/3T_{21}+2T_1S_{32}} \tag{42}$$

where the cross relaxations are due to simultaneous flips $i(1\to2)$, $j(3\to2)$ and $i(3\to4)$, $j(3\to2)$.

It is well known that the spin-lattice relaxation time T_1 rapidly decreases with the increase of the temperature, but the cross relaxation time T_{21} is independent of the temperature. We see therefore from (41) and (42) that under certain conditions we would obtain a better Maser action in a relatively high temperatures. This presumption was verified by Maiman[7] using the ruby Maser with (nominal) 0.2 percent Cr ions operated at 77°K and further by Ditchfield.[8] The signals were in the X band and the root-gain-bandwidth products were 14 Mc/s and 22 Mc/s respectively. Maiman suggested that the success of the Maser is due to the effective control of the cross relaxation. For their push-pull scheme, the pump frequency ν_p is roughly related to the signal frequency ν_s as follows:

$$\nu_p=1.9\nu_s+5.8 \quad \text{(kMc/s)}.$$

Therefore for $\nu_s=9$ we have $\nu_p=22.9$ and hence

$$\nu_\beta(1\to2)-\nu_\alpha(3\to2)=4.9 \quad \text{(kMc/s)}.$$

It is surprising that the cross relaxation is effective for such a great difference of transition frequencies, therefore a close examination is needed. Maiman measured T_{21} and obtained the following values: $T_{21}=2\times10^{-3}$ sec. and $\sim10^{-6}$ sec for $f=\text{Cr/Al}=$(nominal) 0.2% and 0.6% respectively. In ruby the lattice sites of Al (and hence or Cr) have the near neighbors as shown in the following Table I.

According to Rimai[12] et al, the nearest neighbor is strongly coupled by the exchange interaction and they form rather the molecules and further other antiferromagnetically coupled pairs with smaller exchange constants appear to be present. In addition there is an evidence for the existence of ion pairs coupled by weaker ferromagnetic exchange. These will give rise to different spectrums from the ordinary resonance lines and should probably be omitted from our considerations. Thus we tentatively adopt Z ions at the distance of ρ Å as the effective nearest neighbors and ignor the exchange effect. The real concentrations of Cr are assumed to be one half the nominal.

Fortunately the η and f values do not greatly influence the T_{21} values. We obtain from (40) with $\eta=1$ the values of T_{21} shown in Table II. These values are very rough, however, it may be of interest to note that the values of the first two lines are intermediate of the observed values. It is likely that the cross relaxation would take place in

Table I. Distances and Numbers of the Near Neighbors.

Distance (Å)	2.73	2.81	3.13	3.50	3.78	4.77
Number	1	3	3	6	1	6

Table II. The Cross Relaxation Time T_{21} for the Assumed Nearest Z Neighbors at the Distance ρ.

ρ	Z	$f=10^{-3}$	$f=3\times10^{-3}$
3.50Å	6	3.4×10^{-6} sec	1.1×10^{-6} sec
3.78	1	3.7×10^{-4}	1.24×10^{-4}
4.77	6	$1.4\times10^{+6}$	$4.71\times10^{+5}$

this fashion. Further study is still necessary to confirm the present estimation.

§ 7. Concluding Remarks

The theory of cross relaxation has been discussed on the paramagnetic salts in general use for solid state Masers. To evaluate the rate of cross relaxation, it is necessary to determine the shape function. Under consideration of the crystalline electric field and the applied magnetic field we estimated the shape function in terms of the moment method. The obtained second and fourth moment for the diluted salt show that the shape function is nearly Gaussian but takes slightly less value in the wings. When the paramagnetic lattice sites are randomly populated the second moment is much greater than that deduced by the overlap integral of observed resonance shape functions. This was already suggested by BSPA on the supposition that the cross relaxation takes place mainly through the ions with one nearest neighbor. However our second moment is about one third of that suggested by BSPA and to some extent influenced by the orientation of the applied magnetic field. In this case the cross relaxation time will slowly decrease in proportion to the concentration of the paramagnetic ions.

On the other hand if the effect of the dilution were to expand the magnetic lattice uniformly the cross relaxation time rapidly decreases with the increase of the concentration of the paramagnetic ions.

The cross relaxation in the ruby Maser which is succesfully operated at the liquid nitrogen temperature is briefly discussed. In spite of various unknown factors it is likely that the process is effective also in this case.

Acknowledgements

The author would like to express his gratitude to Dr. Hiroyuki Uyeda director of the Radio Research Laboratories for his constant interest and to Prof. Kenjiro Kambe of the University of Electro-Communications for his valuable discussions. Many thanks are also due to Professor N. Bloembergen of Harvard University and Dr. P. S. Pershan of National Science foundation who read the manuscript and informed him their opinions.

References

1) N. Bloembergen, S. Shapiro, P. S. Pershan and J. O. Artman: Phys. Rev. **114**, 445 (1959).
2) S. Shapiro and N. Bloembergen: Phys. Rev. **116**, 1453 (1959).
3) C. H· Townes: Quantum Electronics (Columbia Univ. Press, New York, 1960) several papers from pp. 293-369.
4) W. B. Mims and J. D. Mc Gee: Phys. Rev. **119**, 1233 (1960).
5) P. S. Pershan: Phys. Rev. **117**, 109 (1960).
6) A. Kiel: Phys. Rev. **120**, 137 (1960).
7) T. H. Maiman: Quantum Electronics (Ed. C. H. Townes) p. 324, Columbia Univ. Press. (1960).
8) C. R. Ditchfield and P. A. Forrester: Phys. Rev. Letters, **1**, 448 (1958). C. R. Ditchfield: Presented at the Solid State Amplifier Conference at Nottingham (Apr. 1960).
9) E. Ishiguro, K. Kambe and T. Usui: Physica, **17**, 310 (1951).
10) C. Kittel and E. Abraham: Phys. Rev. **90**, 238 (1953).
11) J. H. Van Vleck: Phys. Rev. **74**, 1168 (1948).
12) L. Rimai, H. Statz, M. J. Weber and G. A. de Mars.: Phys. Rev. Letter **4**, 125 (1960).

Cross Relaxation Phenomena in Solid State Masers

By S. A. Ahern, P. A. Gould and J. C. Walling
Mullard Research Laboratories, Salfords, Redhill, Surrey

[Received June 20, 1960]

Examination of the potential performance characteristic of a solid state maser to amplify at S-band (3·0 kMc/s band) and pumped at X-band (9·0 kMc/s band) using ruby as the active material (e.g. Chang and Siegman (1958)) suggests that a good performance should be obtained with the applied magnetic field nearly parallel ($0 < \theta < 24°$) to the trigonal axis of the ruby crystal, the pump being applied between levels 2 and 4 and the signal between 3 and 4 (fig. 1).

Fig. 1

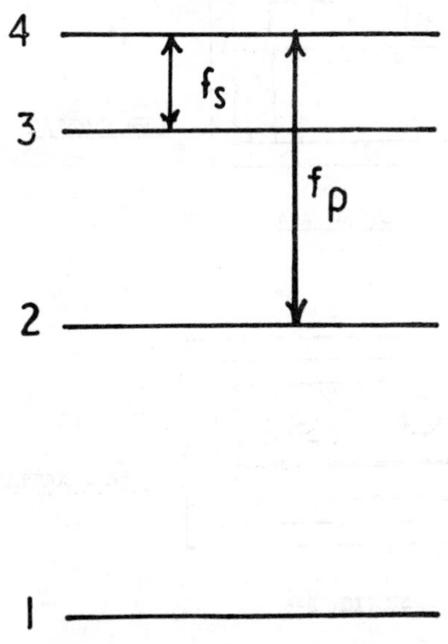

Energy level scheme for $0 < \theta < 24°$.

We have made a detailed examination of the performance of a cavity maser in this region using a strip line cavity resonant in a quarter wave T.E.M. mode at the signal frequency and non-resonant at the pump frequency (fig. 2). A limited amount of signal frequency tuning is obtained by variation of the capacitative loading at the free end of the centre conductor. With this cavity, which is completely filled with ruby containing 0·05% Cr^{3+} and operated at 1·7°K, it has been possible to examine the variation of maser performance with crystal orientation, within the range 2·8–3·2 kMc/s.

Fig. 2

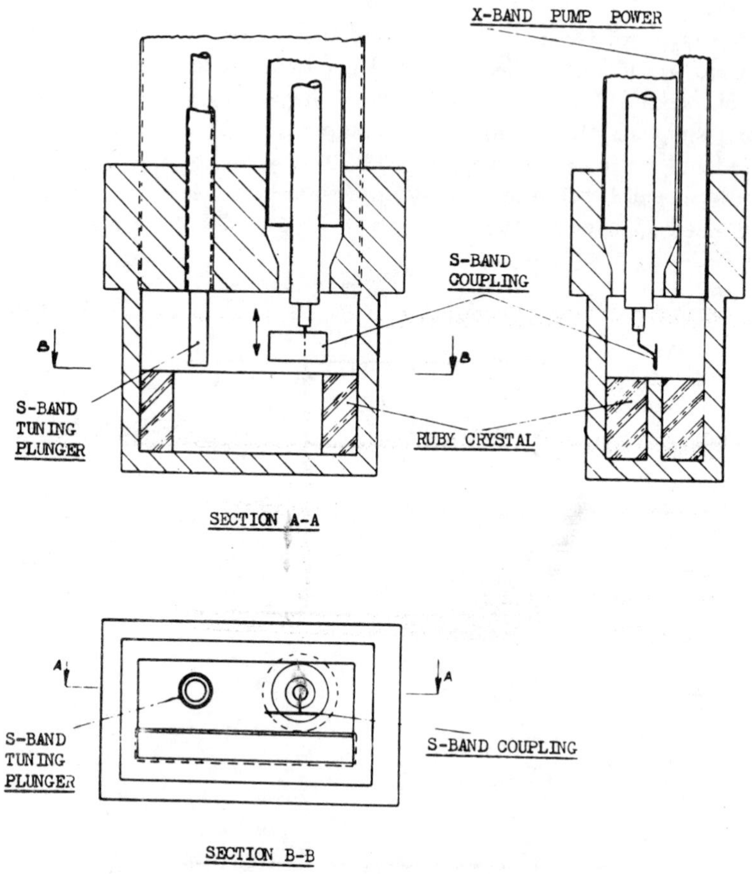

The resonant cavity showing the signal frequency coupling and tuning probes, and the waveguide input for the pump power.

It was found that maser amplification could only be obtained in certain narrow regions shown in fig. 3. Outside these regions no inversion could be obtained.

This appears to be due to cross-relaxation phenomena, two mechanisms being operative:

(i) Cross coupling between 3–2 and 1–4 transitions (fig. 3) which occurs when

$$mf_{32}=nf_{14} \quad \quad (1)$$

Fig. 3

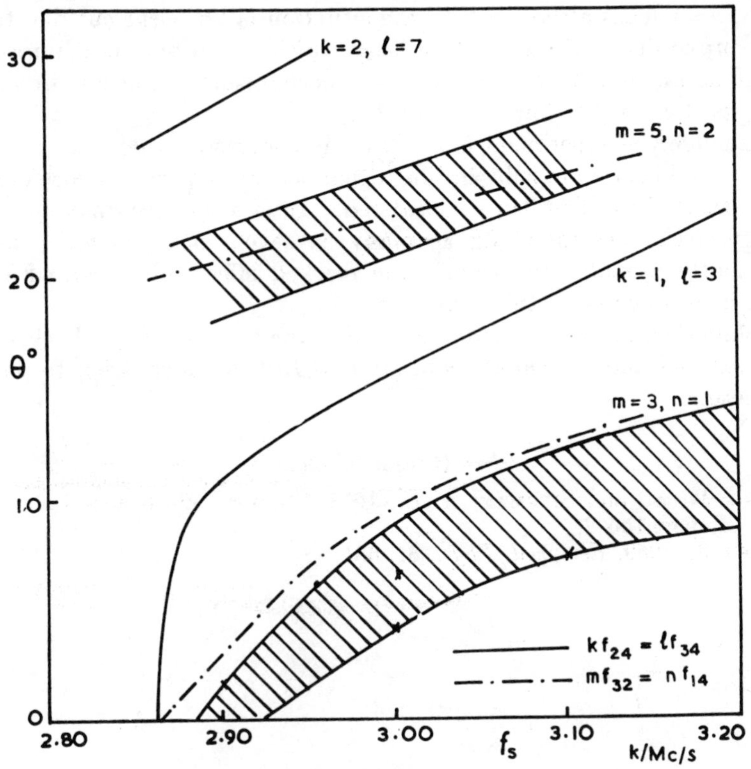

The 'allowed' bands in ruby with the steady magnetic field direction close to the *c*-axis. Amplification occurs in the shaded regions only.

both m and n being integers. The probability of spin–spin interaction of this kind occurring seems likely to be very small unless m and n are small. The effect of this type of cross relaxation will be to produce an increase in the population difference between levels 4 and 3 ($n_4 > n_3$). The loci of points satisfying eqn. (1) have been calculated from the data of Chang and Siegman (1958) for $m=5$, $n=2$ and $m=3$, $n=1$ and are plotted in fig. 2.

(ii) Cross coupling between the 2–4 and 3–4 transitions which occurs when

$$kf_{24} = lf_{34} \quad \ldots \ldots \ldots \quad (2)$$

in which k and l are integers. The effect of this type of cross relaxation will be to produce a decrease in the population difference between levels 4 and 3. In fact, if the cross relaxation probability becomes large then the populations of 3 and 4 are made equal as a result of the pumping. The loci of points satisfying eqn. (2) calculated for $k=1$, $l=3$ and $k=2$, $l=7$ are also plotted in fig. 2.

The upper of the two regions in which maser action was obtained seems to be associated with the $m=5$, $n=2$ locus and the lower region with the $m=3$, $n=1$ locus although here the situation is less clear cut due to the close proximity of the $k=1$, $l=3$ locus which would tend to suppress the maser action due to the $m=3$, $n=1$ mechanism on the low-frequency side—particularly at low values of θ.

Although the experiment is not entirely conclusive it does suggest that maser amplification in ruby in this region occurs as a consequence of cross relaxation of the first type considered. It is surprising that spin–spin energy exchanges involving as many as seven ions ($m=5$, $n=2$) are sufficiently probable to produce the marked effects observed. Further work is in progress on this subject.

Acknowledgment is made to the Director of Mullard Research Laboratories and the Directors of Mullard Ltd. for permission to publish this letter.

References

CHANG, W. S., and SIEGMAN, A. E., 1958, Stanford Electronics Lab. Tech. Report 156–2.
WEBER, J., 1959, *Rev. mod. Phys.*, **31**, 681.

Spin-Spin Energy Transfer and the Operation of Three-Level Masers*

The original experiments on the three level maser[1] demonstrated the importance of the role played by spin-spin energy transfers. These occur whenever there is equality between two energy intervals, whether they belong to the same level scheme or to the level schemes of different spin species present in the material, and they may, by equalizing spin temperatures in the two intervals, profoundly modify the operation of the maser. In the course of recent experiments on paramagnetic relaxation in ruby (Cr^{+++} in Al_2O_3), we have observed a new type of transfer phenomenon which takes place when one energy interval is twice as large as another. This process is independent of temperature in the hydrogen-to-helium range and depends approximately on the square of the concentration. With 0.05 per cent Cr^{+++} the transfer times are of the order of a millisecond, which is long compared with the usual spin-spin times, but considerably shorter than lattice relaxation times at helium temperatures. The experimental evidence indicates that three spins are involved in the energy exchange, as compared with two in the usual type of spin-spin transfer. Consideration of the physical model suggests that this may be only the first in a sequence of higher order processes which become effective as concentration increases.

Spin energy transfers between intervals of different sizes introduces new difficulties and new possibilities in the design of solid state masers. In ruby, for instance, there are eleven ways in which one interval can be twice another (excluding the cases of equal adjacent intervals), and at an arbitrarily chosen setting there is an appreciable chance of working in the vicinity of a two-to-one frequency point. In this case, the two intervals concerned with tend to assume the same spin temperature, resulting in the imposition of a spurious load on the inverted spin group or the accidental cross pumping of levels and the destruction of the negative temperature. We have observed that the transfer effect spreads further to each side of the exact two-to-one setting as the concentration is raised, and it seems likely that this, complemented by higher order processes, may explain some of the difficulties encountered in the attempt to operate masers at higher spin concentrations.

In other circumstances an advantage may be gained by communicating spin temperatures from one interval to another, particularly where the frequencies concerned are near the upper limit of those which can be generated by existing signal sources. For instance, a pumping temperature may be passed from a smaller to a larger gap; in the specially favorable case of $h\nu$ and $2h\nu$ intervals which are adjacent in the same level scheme, a signal at a frequency ν would serve to pump a $3h\nu$ gap. Spin mixing or "double doping" of the host lattice offers more complex possibilities such as two-stage multiplication of the effective pumping frequency, accelerated lattice relaxation, or the transfer of a negative temperature from a smaller to a larger interval. (Ordinary first order spin-spin transfer does not require that both spins belong to the same species, and there seems to be no reason why such a restriction should apply to higher order processes either.)

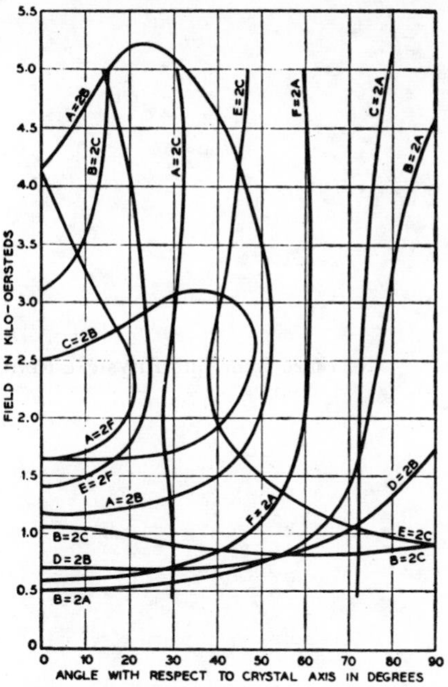

Fig. 1.

Fig. 1 shows angles to the crystal axis and magnetic fields for which there exists a two-to-one ratio between intervals in the ruby level scheme. If we number the ruby levels 1 to 4, starting with the lowest in energy the six intervals are designated by the following letters: A (1, 2), B (2, 3), C (3, 4), D (1, 4), E (1, 3), F (2, 4). The diagram was prepared from level schemes given by E. O. Schulz du Bois,[2] to whom the authors would like to express gratitude for the loan of the original graphs.

W. B. Mims
J. D. McGee
Bell Telephone Labs., Inc.
Murray Hill, N. J.

* Received by the IRE June 25, 1959.

[1] G. Feher and H. E. D. Scovil, "Electron spin relaxation times in gadolinium ethyl sulfate," *Phys. Rev.*, vol. 105, pp. 760–762; January, 1957.

[2] E. O. Schulz du Bois, "Parametric spectra of substituted sapphires," *Bell Sys. Tech. J.*, vol. 38, pp. 271–290; January, 1959.

Reprinted from THE PHYSICAL REVIEW, Vol. 118. No. 1, 129–130, April 1, 1960

Harmonic Spin Coupling in Ruby

J. E. GEUSIC
Bell Telephone Laboratories, Murray Hill, New Jersey
(Received October 19, 1959)

A new mode of maser pumping which makes use of harmonic spin coupling in ruby has been demonstrated. In addition higher order harmonic spin coupling effects in ruby have been found experimentally.

IN ruby a new mode of maser pumping has been demonstrated. This new mode of pumping makes use of harmonic spin coupling in ruby and indicates the possibility of operating a maser with pumping at frequencies lower than the signal frequency. Coupling between spins possessing the same transition frequency has been demonstrated by Feher and Scovil[1]. They found a reduced relaxation time associated with a gadolinium transition if the transition frequency coincides with that of the cerium transition, both ions being simultaneously present in a diamagnetic ethyl sulfate host crystal. Harmonic spin coupling in ruby was found by Mims and McGee.[2] They found an accelerated relaxation rate associated with a resonance transition in ruby whenever orientation and magnitude of the applied magnetic field were such that there was a 1:1, 2:1 or 1:2 ratio between two transition frequencies in the energy level scheme. In addition Mims and McGee[3] suggested that the harmonic spin coupling effect they observed in their relaxation experiments was only the first in a sequence of higher order processes and they further suggested that harmonic spin coupling might be used to advantage for pumping masers at frequencies beyond the range of existing signal sources.

This note contains experimental results which verify the existence of the higher order harmonic spin coupling processes as suggested by Mims and McGee.[3] Also we have demonstrated that harmonic spin coupling processes can be used in maser pumping. Consider four energy levels in ruby with transition frequencies as indicated in Fig. 1(a). For simultaneous observation of essentially all ruby transitions, a ruby sample in the shape of a rod was placed inside a shorted X-band waveguide with a helical transmission line wound on the sample. Signal transmission through the helix permits the study of lower microwave transition frequencies whereas transition frequencies in the

[1] G. Feher and H. E. D. Scovil, Phys. Rev. **105**, 760 (1957).
[2] W. Mims and J. D. McGee, (unpublished).
[3] W. Mims and J. D. McGee, Bell Telephone Laboratories (private communication).

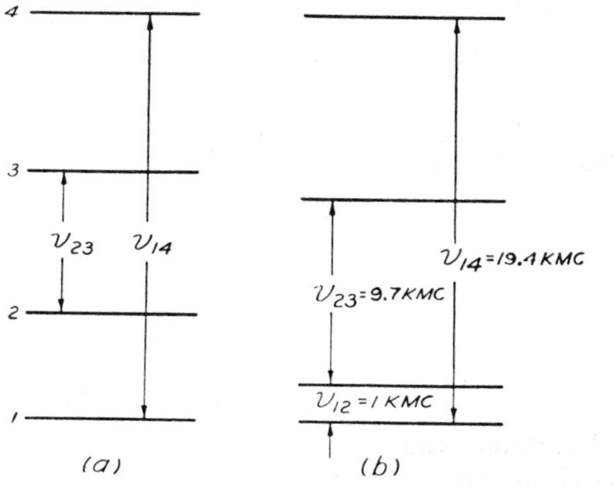

FIG. 1. (a) Typical energy level diagram for ruby. (b) Energy level diagram in ruby for $\theta=90°$ and a magnetic field of 1700 gauss.

X-band range and higher can conveniently be observed by studying the signals reflected from the shorted waveguide. Both methods together allow for a practically continuous coverage of the microwave frequency range. Using this technique, it was observed that if saturating power was applied at ν_{23} then partial or complete saturation of the ν_{14} transition was achieved whenever the condition $\nu_{14}=n\nu_{23}$, with n an integer, was satisfied. In particular for the $\theta=40°$ orientation in ruby effects were seen for $n=3$, 4, and 5 and for the $\theta=90°$ orientation an effect was seen for $n=2$.

For the case of $\theta=90°$ in ruby at a field of 1700 gauss the energy levels are shown in Fig. 1(b). In this operation the complete saturation of the ν_{23} transition at 9.7 kMc/sec produced complete saturation of the ν_{14} transition at 19.4 kMc/sec and spin inversion (emission) at $\nu_{12}=1$ kMc/sec. Normally, if this condition $\nu_{14}=2\nu_{23}$ were not satisfied, pumping at ν_{23} would have produced spin refrigeration (enhanced absorption) rather than spin inversion. The signal frequency region over which maser action by harmonic spin coupling was achieved for $\theta=90°$ in ruby for this mode of operation is shown in Fig. 2. The refrigeration ratio plotted is defined as the ratio of the absorption at ν_{12}, when ν_{23} is saturated, to the absorption at ν_{12}, when the spin system is in thermal equilibrium. Negative refrigeration ratios indicate negative absorption or emission at ν_{12}.

At present the mechanism responsible for harmonic spin coupling in ruby has not been established; however, two possible mechanisms are the direct spin-spin interaction or a spin-phonon-spin process. If the magnetic dipole-dipole interaction is responsible then harmonic spin coupling takes place entirely within the spin system. If, on the other hand, a spin-phonon-spin process is involved then it is imagined that the an-

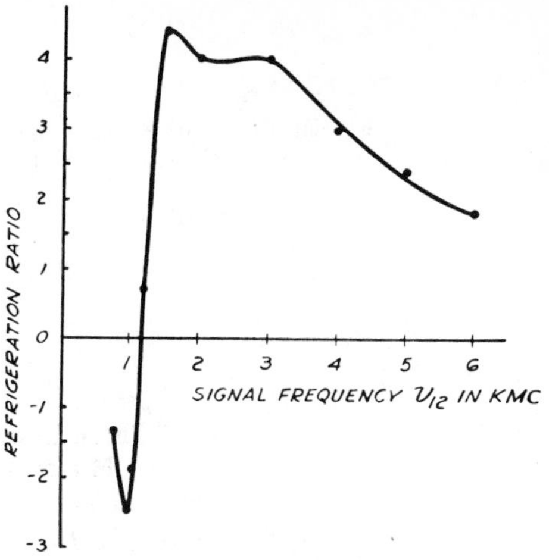

FIG. 2. Plot of the refrigeration ratio versus signal frequency ν_{12} at $\theta=90°$.

harmonic terms in the lattice potential carry out the harmonic or multiplication effects which are coupled to the spins by a phonon-spin interaction. The temperature and concentration dependence[3] of the accelerated relaxation rate observed by Mims and McGee seems to favor the direct spin-spin interaction model at present.

The demonstration of the effects described indicates that one may pump a maser at a frequency lower than the signal frequency by taking advantage of harmonic spin coupling. One would apply pump power at some transition frequency ν_1. By virtue of harmonic coupling, this would lead to saturation at a higher frequency transition $\nu_2=n\nu_1$. Saturation at ν_2 would lead to maser action at a third frequency $\nu_3<\nu_2$ subject to the usual conditions with regard to frequency and relaxation time ratio. This implies the possibility $\nu_3>\nu_1$. It is required in addition, however, that ν_3 is not related in a simple rational ratio to ν_2 or ν_1. This type of maser operation would be of value especially for maser amplification in the millimeter wavelength region where ordinarily submillimeter pump sources would be needed.

The author is indebted to Higa[4] for information about his experimental results prior to publication. Higa studied ruby at the 90° orientation at 1700 gauss with equipment permitting the observation of ν_{12} and ν_{23} only. Disregarding ν_{14}, he expected to find spin refrigeration at ν_{12} upon saturation of ν_{23}. The maser action found instead indicated the presence of an effect which can be identified as harmonic spin coupling.

[4] W. Higa, J. Appl. Phys. (to be published).

Reprinted from JOURNAL OF APPLIED PHYSICS Vol. 30, No. 7, 1113–1114, July, 1959

Three Level Spin Refrigeration and Maser Action at 1500 mc/sec*

J. E. GEUSIC, E. O. SCHULZ-DU BOIS, R. W. DE GRASSE, AND H. E. D. SCOVIL
Bell Telephone Laboratories, Incorporated, Murray Hill, New Jersey
(Received February 27, 1959)

In this Letter, measurements on three level solid state electronic spin systems are reported. It is shown that positive and negative signal spin temperatures, both small compared to the ambient temperature, can be realized through three level excitation. A negative spin temperature indicating population inversion of the signal transition considered can be utilized for signal amplification following Bloembergen's maser proposal.[1] A smaller negative temperature implies more inherent gain and band width per volume of paramagnetic material. An enhancement of the normal population difference can be described by a smaller positive signal spin temperature, hence spin refrigeration. It results in increased absorption of the signal frequency. Refrigeration as applied to interacting nuclear and electronic spin energy levels is known by the work of Overhauser[2] and Feher[3] and it can be applied to nuclear alignment.[4]

The three level scheme of spin refrigeration can easily be treated in general. For brevity, however, let us consider a specific energy evel scheme. Figure 1 represents the energy level diagram of ruby,

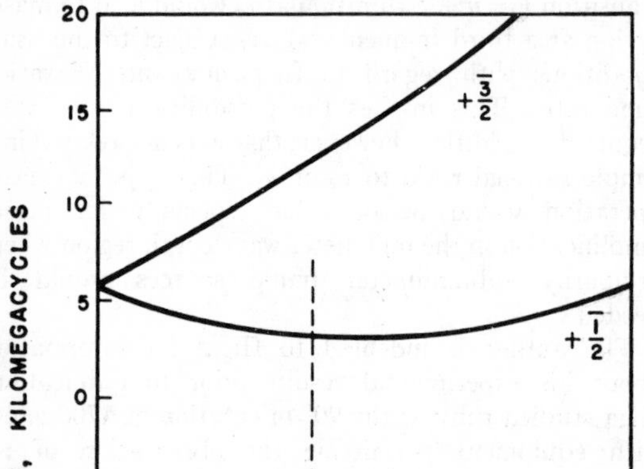

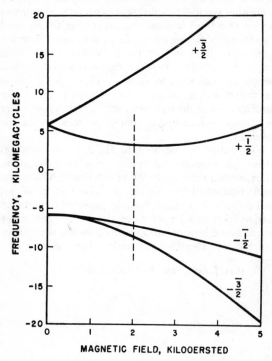

FIG. 1. Energy of Cr^{+++} ions in Al_2O_3 (ruby) with magnetic field applied perpendicular to crystalline symmetry axis.

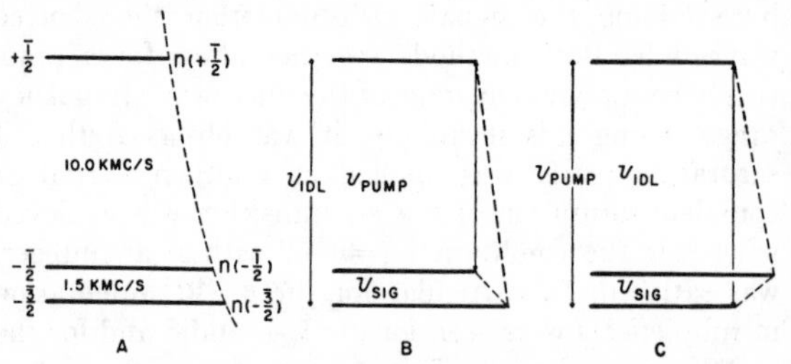

FIG. 2. Energy level diagram and populations at 1.5°K and 2.0 kilogauss (A) in thermal equilibrium, (B) with spin refrigeration, and (C) with maser operation.

that is Cr^{+++} ions in Al_2O_3 (sapphire).[5–7] The abscissa shows applied magnetic field which, for this diagram, is oriented perpendicular to the crystalline symmetry axis.

At about 2 kilogauss, the three lower levels are spaced as shown in Fig. 2(A). All possible transitions are well allowed. In thermal equilibrium, the populations follow a Boltzmann distribution. For a temperature of 1.5°K, the distribution is demonstrated by having the length of each energy line proportional to its population.

Upon saturation of the "pump" transition $-\frac{1}{2}\leftrightarrow+\frac{1}{2}$, the populations change as indicated in Fig. 2(B). We may define a temperature T_{sig} of the signal transition and it is easily shown that

$$\frac{n(-\frac{3}{2})}{n(-\frac{1}{2})}\equiv\exp\frac{h\nu_{sig}}{kT_{sig}}=\frac{\exp\frac{h\nu_{sig}}{kT_{latt}}+\frac{\tau_{sig}}{\tau_{idl}}\exp\frac{h\nu_{idl}}{kT_{latt}}}{1+(\tau_{sig}/\tau_{idl})}. \qquad (1)$$

If the exponential function can be approximated by linear expansion, (1) can be simplified into

$$\frac{T_{sig}}{T_{latt}}=\frac{1+(\tau_{sig}/\tau_{idl})}{1+(\tau_{sig}/\tau_{idl})(\nu_{idl}/\nu_{sig})}. \qquad (2)$$

Refrigeration $T_{sig}<T_{latt}$ takes place since $\nu_{idl}>\nu_{sig}$. Drastic refrigeration effects are achieved by having $\nu_{idl}\gg\nu_{sig}$ and $\tau_{sig}\gg\tau_{idl}$.

For comparison, maser operation in the same three level scheme is illustrated in Fig. 2(C). Note that pump and idler are interchanged with those of the refrigerator. Here

$$\frac{n(-\frac{3}{2})}{n(-\frac{1}{2})}\equiv\exp\frac{h\nu_{sig}}{kT_{sig}}=\frac{\exp\frac{h\nu_{sig}}{kT_{latt}}+\frac{\tau_{sig}}{\tau_{idl}}}{1+\frac{\tau_{sig}}{\tau_{idl}}\exp\frac{h\nu_{idl}}{kT_{latt}}} \qquad (3)$$

with the linearized approximation

$$\frac{T_{sig}}{T_{latt}}=\frac{1+(\tau_{sig}/\tau_{idl})}{1-(\tau_{sig}/\tau_{idl})(\nu_{idl}/\nu_{sig})}. \qquad (4)$$

Maser action depends on temperature inversion $T_{sig}<0$. Strong inversion requires $\nu_{idl} \gg \nu_{sig}$ and $\tau_{sig} \gg \tau_{idl}$.

Experiments have been carried out for the situations shown in Figs. 2(B) and (C). The ruby sample in the shape of a rod is located in a wave guide which supplies the pump power. As a transmission slow-wave structure for the signal frequency, a helix is wound directly on the ruby rod. This arrangement offers the possibility of maser and refrigeration experiments with signal frequencies ranging from 150 mc/sec to 6 kmc/sec.

In a transmission slow-wave structure, the attenuation in ogarithmic scale (db) due to the resonance line is proportional to the population difference, here $[n(-\frac{3}{2})-n(-\frac{1}{2})]$. In the refrigeration experiment with lattice temperature $T_{latt}=1.5$°K and at signal frequency 1.5 kmc/sec, an increase of equilibrium attenuation by a factor 4.0 was observed. With the aid of (1), we find $T_{sig}=0.38$°K and the relaxation time ratio $\tau(-\frac{3}{2}\leftrightarrow-\frac{1}{2})/\tau(-\frac{3}{2}\leftrightarrow+\frac{1}{2})=0.81$. In the maser experiment, strong inversion was observed. The gain is 5.2 times the equilibrium attenuation. Equation (3) yields for this case $T_{sig}=-0.28$°K and $\tau(-\frac{3}{2}\leftrightarrow-\frac{1}{2})/\tau(-\frac{1}{2}\leftrightarrow+\frac{1}{2})=4.1$.

With this maser inversion, short compact unidirectional traveling wave masers appear feasible. At the frequency of the interstellar hydrogen line, such a device would be of interest for radio astronomy purposes. The signal transition is predominantly of circular polarization and hence gives rise to forward and reverse gain at the rate of 3:1. Helium temperature tests of some ferrite materials by F. W. Ostermayer of this laboratory show the feasibility of incorporating ferrite isolation in such a traveling wave maser.

It should be mentioned that a refrigerated spin system will exhibit low noise corresponding to the temperature T_{sig} below lattice temperature when used as attenuator or termination. Although it may seem difficult in practice, spin refrigeration could perhaps be used to cool other macroscopic systems down to T_{sig}. For this, spin-spin interaction might provide an effective coupling mechanism.

In conclusion, we wish to stress the value of spin refrigeration in conjunction with maser experiments. Both measurements together allow the evaluation of relaxation time ratios. Thus they are helpful tools in experiments designed to clarify the mechanisms involved in relaxation of paramagnetics and, at the same time, to find conditions of optimum maser performance, that is, of maximum inversion.

* This work is partially supported by the Signal Corps.

[1] N. Bloembergen, Phys. Rev. **104**, 324 (1956).
[2] A. W. Overhauser, Phys. Rev. **92**, 411 (1953).
[3] G. Feher, Phys. Rev. **103**, 500, 501, 834 (1956).
[4] Beljers, van der Kint, and van Wieringen, Phys. Rev. **95**, 1683 (1954).
[5] A. A. Manenkov and A. M. Prokhorov, J. Exptl. Theoret. Phys. (U.S.S.R.) **28**, 762 (1955).
[6] J. E. Geusic, Phys. Rev. **102**, 1252 (1956).
[7] E. O. Schulz-Du Bois, Bell System Tech. J. **38**, 271 (1959).

Reprinted from JOURNAL OF APPLIED PHYSICS, Vol. 32, No. 2, 317–320, February, 1961

Seesaw Maser Operation

P. A. FORRESTER AND W. B. MIMS
Bell Telephone Laboratories, Inc., Murray Hill, New Jersey
(Received August 9, 1960)

Cross relaxation between adjacent intervals may be used to secure an advantage in maser operation comparable to that obtained by "push-pull" pumping. Equations for the rate of change of populations in a scheme of four levels (A,B,C,D) when AC is pumped and cross relaxation takes place between BC, CD have been formulated, and the steady-state condition corresponding to various assumptions regarding lattice relaxation times is discussed. In an experimental investigation of maser operation based on this scheme and using ruby as the active material, an inversion of 0.9:1 was obtained at a signal frequency of 14.5 kMc when pumping at 24.5 kMc.

AN advantage in maser operation comparable to that obtained by "push-pull" pumping may be secured by utilizing cross relaxation between adjacent intervals of a level scheme. In this way it is possible not merely to combine the lattice relaxation rates of two intervals, but to involve additional lattice relaxation rates in such a manner that they assist in the establishment of an inverted population. This may be illustrated by considering the rate equations for the four-level scheme shown in Fig. 1 when interval AC is pumped and cross relaxation takes place between the equal intervals BC and CD. The small letters a, b, c, and d will be used to denote the populations of levels A, B, C, and D. w_P will denote the probability of a spin making the transition $A\rightarrow C$ or $C\rightarrow A$ under the influence of the pumping field, and w_T will designate the probability of simultaneous transfer of excitation, $B\rightarrow C$, $D\rightarrow C$ or vice versa, resulting from cross relaxation. The probability that the lattice induces a transition $A\rightarrow B$ is written w_{AB}, and is related to the probability w_{BA} for the inverse process by a Boltzmann factor

$$\exp(h\nu_{AB}/kT_L)=w_{AB}/w_{BA}, \tag{1}$$

ν_{AB} being the frequency separation of A, B, and T_L the lattice temperature. w_{AB} and w_{BA} are related to the lattice relaxation time of interval AB by[1]

$$\tau_{AB}^{-1}=w_{AB}+w_{BA}. \tag{2}$$

With the use of this notation and appropriate substitution of suffixes, the equations for the rates of change of populations are:

$$\dot{a}=w_{BA}b-w_{AB}a+w_{CA}c-w_{AC}a+w_{DA}d-w_{AD}a+w_P(c-a); \tag{3}$$

$$\dot{b}=w_{AB}a-w_{BA}b+w_{CB}c-w_{BC}b+w_{DB}d-w_{BD}b+w_T(c^2-bd); \tag{4}$$

[1] K. D. Bowers and W. B. Mims, Phys. Rev. **115**, 285 (195).

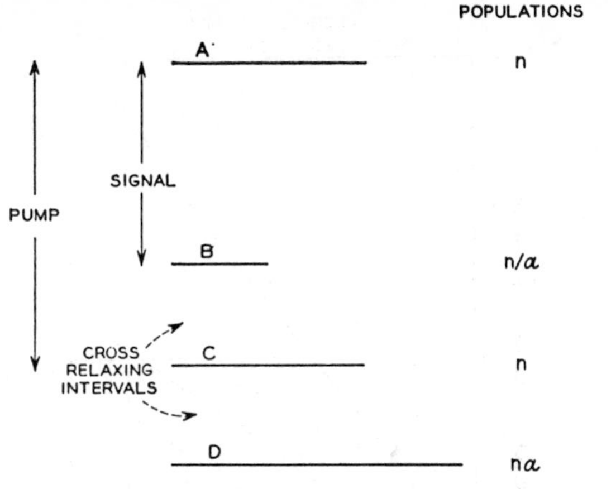

FIG. 1. Four-level scheme with the two lower intervals BC and CD equal. Pumping equalizes the populations of A and C, and cross relaxation establishes the same population ratio α in intervals BC and CD. α is determined by lattice relaxation times, and will usually be >1.

$$\dot{c}=w_{AC}a-w_{CA}c+w_{BC}b-w_{CB}c+w_{DC}d-w_{CD}c-2w_T(c^2-bd)-w_P(c-a); \quad (5)$$

$$\dot{d}=w_{AD}a-w_{DA}d+w_{BD}b-w_{DB}d+w_{CD}c-w_{DC}d+w_T(c^2-bd). \quad (6)$$

The cross-relaxing events $C\rightarrow B$ and $C\rightarrow D$ occur at a rate proportional to c^2, and the opposite events $B\rightarrow C$ and $D\rightarrow C$ at a rate proportional to bd. The term $w_T(c^2-bd)$ gives the net rate of increase of b and d resulting from such events; c is reduced at twice this rate since both cross-relaxing spins make transitions to or from C.

If all transition probabilities were known, the steady state population ratios could be deduced by setting $\dot{a}=\dot{b}=\dot{c}=\dot{d}=0$ and solving any three of Eqs. (3) to (6). We can, however, make a considerable simplification and dispense with the need for knowing w_P and w_T exactly if we assume that in practice they are both several times larger than the lattice transition probabilities. In this case Eq. (3) reduces to $0\simeq w_P(c-a)$ and Eq. (5) reduces to $0\simeq w_T(c^2-bd)$, which correspond ideally to a pumping condition

$$c=a \quad (7)$$

and a cross-relaxing condition

$$c/b=d/c. \quad (8)$$

We may then write down the populations:

$$a=n,\quad b=n/\alpha,\quad c=n,\quad d=\alpha n, \quad (9)$$

where α is the ratio c/b, d/c, which defines a spin temperature T_T in the cross-relaxing intervals by $\alpha=\exp(h\nu_{BC}/kT_T)$. The total number of spins present is $n(2+\alpha+1/\alpha)$, which is approximately equal to $4n$ if $h\nu_{BC}/kT_T\ll 1$. The value of α may now be determined from lattice relaxation probabilities alone. On subtracting Eq. (6) from Eq. (4), we eliminate w_T and obtain

$$\dot{b}-\dot{d}=(w_{AB}a-w_{BA}b)+(w_{CB}c-w_{BC}b)+(w_{DA}d-w_{AD}a)+(w_{DC}d-w_{CD}c)+2(w_{DB}d-w_{BD}b).$$

By inserting the populations [Eq. (9)] in this equation, taking the steady state, and canceling n, we have

$$0=[w_{AB}-(w_{BA}/\alpha)]+[w_{CB}-(w_{BC}/\alpha)]+(w_{DA}\alpha-w_{AD})+(w_{DC}\alpha-w_{CD})+2[w_{DB}\alpha-(w_{BD}/\alpha)]. \quad (10)$$

The lattice relaxation probabilities required for substitution in Eq. (10) may be derived from the corresponding lattice relaxation times by re-expressing Eqs. (1) and (2) in the form

$$w_{AB}=\frac{\exp(h\nu_{AB}/kT_L)}{\tau_{AB}[1+\exp(h\nu_{AB}/kT_L)]},$$

$$w_{BA}=\frac{1}{\tau_{AB}[1+\exp(h\nu_{AB}/kT_L)]}.$$

A further general simplification becomes possible if we assume that $h\nu/kT\ll 1$ in all instances where a fraction of this type appears. Then, if ϵ_{AB} is substituted for $h\nu_{AB}/kT_L$,

$$w_{AB}=(1+\tfrac{1}{2}\epsilon_{AB})/2\tau_{AB}$$

and

$$w_{BA}=(1-\tfrac{1}{2}\epsilon_{AB})/2\tau_{AB}.$$

w_{BC}, w_{CB}, $\cdots$ are given by similar expressions and α, the Boltzmann ratio in the cross-relaxing interval, is $1+\epsilon$, where $\epsilon=h\nu_{BC}/kT_T$. On inserting these approximate values in Eq. (10) and discarding higher powers of ϵ, ϵ_{AB}, $\cdots$ we have

$$\frac{\epsilon_{AB}+\epsilon}{2\tau_{AB}}=\frac{\epsilon_{BC}-\epsilon}{2\tau_{BC}}+\frac{\epsilon_{AD}-\epsilon}{2\tau_{AD}}+\frac{\epsilon_{CD}-\epsilon}{2\tau_{CD}}+\frac{\epsilon_{BD}-2\epsilon}{\tau_{BD}}. \quad (11)$$

It may be noted that $n\epsilon_{AB}$, $n\epsilon_{BC}$, $\cdots$ give the excess populations in the lower levels of the intervals AB, BC, $\cdots$ when in lattice equilibrium, while the corresponding excess populations in the pumped state are $n\epsilon$ for BC, AD, and CD, $2n\epsilon$ for BD, and $-n\epsilon$ for AB. The numerators in Eq. (11) are thus proportional to deviations from lattice equilibrium brought about by pumping. Of the five relaxation times, those belonging to the cross-relaxing intervals may be combined in a single term. Since BC and CD are equal, $\epsilon_{BC}=\epsilon_{CD}=\tfrac{1}{2}\epsilon_{BD}$, and we can rewrite Eq. (11) in the form

$$\frac{\epsilon_{AB}+\epsilon}{2\tau_{AB}}=(\epsilon_{BC}-\epsilon)\left(\frac{1}{2\tau_{BC}}+\frac{1}{2\tau_{CD}}+\frac{2}{\tau_{BD}}\right)+\frac{\epsilon_{AD}-\epsilon}{2\tau_{AD}}. \quad (12)$$

To illustrate the roles of the three resultant relaxation rates, let us consider the special cases which follow.

(*i*) *Rapid relaxation in the outer interval.* $\tau_{AD}\ll$other τ values; then $(\epsilon_{AD}-\epsilon)/2\tau_{AD}=0$ and $\epsilon=\epsilon_{AD}$. Inversion occurs in interval AB with a population difference $b-a=-n\epsilon_{AD}$. If we call AB the signal interval and BC the idler, and denote ν_{AB} and ν_{BC} by ν_{SIG} and ν_{IDL}, the spin temperature in AB is given by

$$T_{\mathrm{SIG}}=-T_L[\nu_{\mathrm{SIG}}/(\nu_{\mathrm{SIG}}+2\nu_{\mathrm{IDL}})]. \qquad (13)$$

This corresponds to the largest inversion attainable in the interval AB by any choice of lattice relaxation parameters.

(*ii*) *Rapid relaxation in the idler interval.* The dominant relaxation rate is $[(1/2\tau_{BC})+(1/2\tau_{CD})+(2/\tau_{BD})]$. $\epsilon=\epsilon_{BC}$, and inversion is still in AB.

$$T_{\mathrm{SIG}}=-T_L(\nu_{\mathrm{SIG}}/\nu_{\mathrm{IDL}}),$$

where the terms have the same meaning as in Eq. (13). The same result is also obtained if

$$\tau_{AB}=\tau_{BC}=\tau_{CD}=\tau_{BD}=\tau_{AD}.$$

(*iii*) *Rapid relaxation in the inner interval.* τ_{AB} is exceptionally short, and the term $[(\epsilon_{AB}+\epsilon)/2\tau_{AB}]$ dominates Eq. (12). Then $\epsilon=-\epsilon_{AB}$, and inversion occurs in BC, AD, CD, and BD. This situation, involving a negative temperature in four intervals and a positive temperature in only one, is not likely to arise in the absence of some special fast-relaxing mechanism in AB.

An over-all qualitative picture can be obtained by visualizing A as an external reference point, and B, C, and D as equally spaced points on a seesaw balanced at C. Populations correspond to vertical heights, the fulcrum C being raised to the height of A by the microwave pump. Cross relaxation establishes a common spin temperature in the intervals connecting B, C and D, and thus ensures that one end of the seesaw rises above C and A if the other is made to fall. The actual angle and direction of tilt is then determined by a balance between lattice relaxation rates, as in Eq. (12). Such an image can be helpful when considering other situations of a similar kind, for instance, a mode of operation with several equal adjacent intervals, or with cross relaxation between harmonically related intervals.[2,3] In the case of there being several equal adjacent intervals, an appropriate number of equally spaced points are marked off along the seesaw and the fulcrum is placed at whichever level is pumped. If harmonic interval relations are involved, the condition of a common spin temperature in the cross-relaxing intervals will still justify representation on a seesaw diagram, but the points will no longer be equally spaced.

The authors have examined seesaw operation at liquid helium temperatures in a ruby specimen containing 0.05% Cr^{3+} ions. The four levels are shown in Fig. 1, BC being made equal to CD by appropriate choice of angle and field settings. AB is designated as the signal interval since it was here that inversion was observed in practice. Fields and frequencies corresponding to the signal, idler, and pump transitions are shown in Fig. 2, with the required angle setting indicated on the upper scale. It may be noted that for this mode of operation the signal frequency may be varied from 12 to 18 kMc with only a 1-deg change of angle.

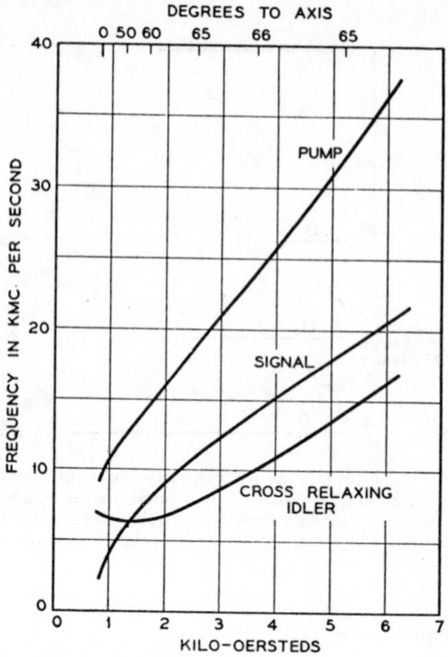

FIG. 2. Field, frequency, and angle setting for $BC=CD$. Transition AB is denoted as the signal since inversion is normally found in this interval. BC and CD are denoted as idler.

Absorption at the signal and idler frequencies was monitored by observing the change in transmission through a helix wound round the cylindrical specimen. The helix was mounted near the end of a shorted circular K-band waveguide, and absorption at the pump frequency was observed in reflection. Provided that the interaction of the microwave field with the spin system is small compared to the transmission loss through the helix, the magnetic resonance signal is directly proportional to the population difference between the two levels, and hence, when $kT\gg h\nu$, to the inverse of the spin temperature.

The measurements were made at an angle $\theta=66.5°$ and 3650 gauss. The signal, idler, and pump frequencies were, respectively, 14.5, 10.0, and 34.5 kMc. The measured inversion, defined as T_L/T_{SIG}, was 0.90 ± 0.05. This value was independent of temperature from 4.2°K to 1.3°K. This corresponds to the idler temperature being $0.77T_L$; a small increase in the idler absorption was observed upon saturating the pump transition, but it

[2] J. E. Geusic, Phys. Rev. **118**, 129 (1960).
[3] W. B. Mims and J. D. McGee, Proc. I. R. E. **47**, 2120 (1959).

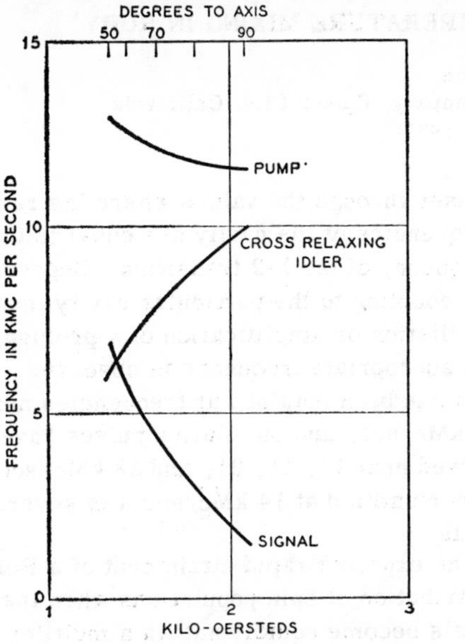

Fig. 3. Conditions for an alternative mode of operation in which $AB=BC$, CD is the signal interval, BD the pump, and AB, BC the idler. The condition $AB=BC$ is also met by another range of settings at higher fields.

was not possible to measure the refrigeration[4] exactly because of the different widths and line shapes of the two idler components.

The importance of relaxation in the outer interval AD is apparent from this result. If the effect of setting CD equal to BC had been merely to accelerate the relaxation in BC,[5] the idler temperature could not fall below T_L, and even under the most favorable circumstances the inversion in the signal interval could not exceed ν_{IDL}/ν_{SIG} or, in our case, 0.69.

In addition to the mode of seesaw operation shown in Figs. 1 and 2, two other modes can be found, both depending on cross relaxation between the upper three levels. The conditions for one of these modes are shown in Fig. 3. A third mode of operation in ruby is also given by $AB=BC$ and covers signal frequencies from 19 kMc upwards. Angular settings range from 0° to 40° and correspond to a relatively low pump transition probability. A survey of the energy level diagrams of other materials which have been successfully used in solid-state masers indicates that the seesaw method should be quite generally applicable, and that, in spite of its being restricted to settings with equal adjacent intervals, there remains a wide choice of possible signal frequencies. Materials containing Fe^{3+} (six levels) or Gd^{3+} (eight levels) offer many alternative modes of operation. Some degree of inversion is to be expected even when the signal interval is almost as large as the pump interval. Indeed, the only alternative is inversion in an interval larger than the pump interval unless, as a result of a unique balance between lattice relaxation probabilities, all the populations are made equal.

Much of the foregoing discussion could be equally well applied to the push-pull pumping scheme for which a very similar analysis can be made. In the push-pull scheme, four levels—A, B, C, and D—are spaced so that $AC=BD$. The pump is applied in this common interval, and inversion is normally observed in BC. If $AC=BD$, then $AB=CD$, and for the purpose of calculating population ratios it is immaterial whether one assumes cross relaxation between AB and CD or the simultaneous pumping of AC and BD to be the dominant mechanism. (A distinction would of course be possible in analogous schemes employing higher order cross-relaxation processes, since one could choose either AC and BD, or AB and CD as the harmonically related intervals.) For the simple push-pull scheme an analysis following the lines of that given here leads to an equation

$$\frac{\epsilon+\epsilon_{BC}}{\tau_{BC}}=(\epsilon_{AB}-\epsilon)\left(\frac{1}{\tau_{AB}}+\frac{1}{\tau_{CD}}\right)+\frac{\epsilon_{AD}-\epsilon}{\tau_{AD}},$$

in place of Eq. (12). If BC is the signal interval and the coupled intervals AB and CD are denoted as the idler, Eqs. (13) and (14) follow for the special cases of rapid lattice relaxation in the outer and in the idler intervals, respectively. In general, the push-pull and seesaw schemes of operation complement one another, and a choice between them may depend on the relative ease with which the required interval relations can be produced in any specific situation.

ACKNOWLEDGMENTS

We should like to thank J. D. McGee and D. H. Olsen for their expert assistance with the experimental work, and J. E. Geusic and E. O. Schulz Du Bois for advice concerning the techniques of helix measurements.

[4] J. E. Geusic, E. O. Schulz Du Bois, R. W. de Grasse, and H. E. D. Scovil, J. Appl. Phys. **30**, 1113 (1959).
[5] G. Feher and H. E. D. Scovil, Phys. Rev. **105**, 760 (1957).

SPIN-LEVEL INVERSION AND SPIN-TEMPERATURE MIXING IN RUBY*

R. H. Hoskins
Research Laboratories, Hughes Aircraft Company, Culver City, California
(Received June 9, 1959)

We have performed experiments on the successive inversion of spin levels of Cr^{+3} in ruby by adiabatic fast passage followed by a pulsed magnetic field. The preliminary results reported here were all obtained at 1.4°K by using a cavity completely filled by solid[1]: 75% clear sapphire, 25% ruby.[2] The pulsed field, in the form of a single sinusoid of period 1.6×10^{-3} sec, was produced by discharging a condenser bank into a Helmholz pair, 3 cm in diameter, located inside the helium Dewar. Peak fields of 18 000 oersteds could be achieved. The experiments to be discussed may be considered to have taken place in a time much shorter than $T_1 \sim 0.1$ sec, the thermal relaxation time.

The energy levels appropriate for the crystal orientation used in one set of experiments are shown in Fig. 1.[3] The experiment is started with a static field H_0 of about 6000 oersteds and the magnetic field is pulsed as shown at the bottom of Fig. 1. An inverting pulse at 9 kMc/sec serves to invert successively the 3-2 and 2-1 transitions[4] as the field is swept down. As the pulsed field reverses direction, stimulated emission of radiation from the 1-2 transition can occur as the field passes through the values where the resonant frequencies of the cavity are equal to the Larmor frequency of the 1-2 transition. Depending upon the coupling to the particular cavity mode, either oscillation or amplification of a probing signal at the appropriate frequency is observed. Amplification has been obtained at frequencies near 14 and 24 kMc/sec, and oscillation pulses have been observed near 14, 18, 24, and 28 kMc/sec. Peak power emitted at 14 kMc/sec was several milliwatts.

The expected rapid attainment of a Boltzmann distribution of spin populations when the energy levels become equidistant[5] in a multilevel spin system such as Cr^{+3} in ruby has been demonstrated directly. Consider the energy-level diagram in Fig. 2.[3] The 9-kMc/sec absorption spectrum obtained with a single sinusoidal field sweep

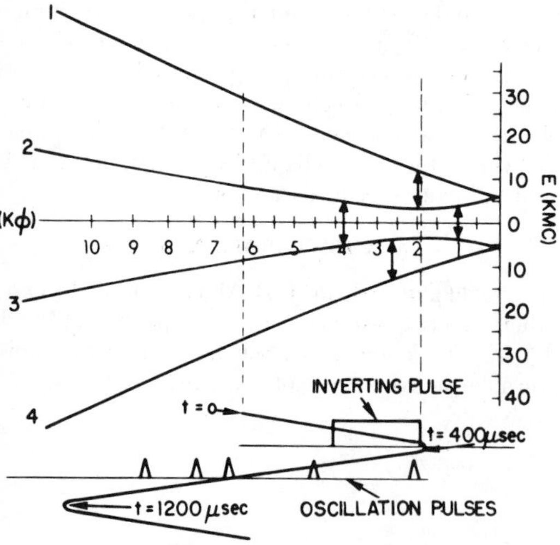

FIG. 1. Energy levels in ruby near 60-degree orientation. The magnetic-field pulse is shown at the bottom of the figure. The levels have been numbered to agree with the matrix element calculations in reference 4; level 1 has the highest energy.

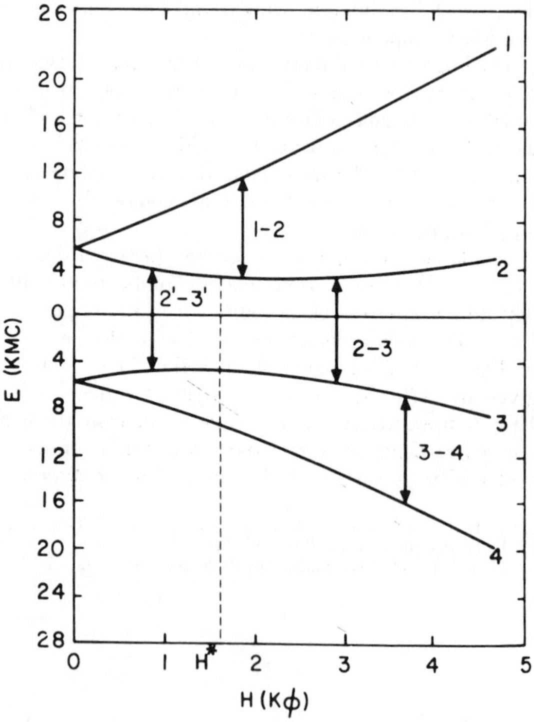

FIG. 2. Energy levels in ruby near 70-degree orientation. The transitions shown are 9 kMc/sec. The levels have been numbered to agree with the matrix element calculations in reference 4; level 1 has the highest energy.

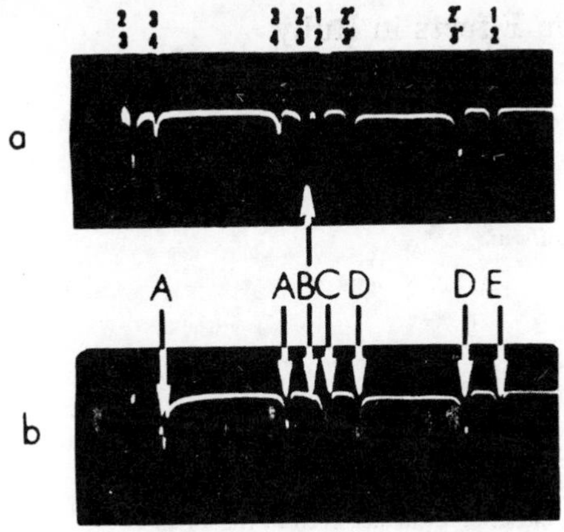

FIG. 3. 9-kMc/sec absorption spectrum in ruby near 70-degree orientation.

having an amplitude of approximately 2000 oersteds starting at an H of approximately 2400 oersteds, is shown in Fig. 3(a). The field initially sweeps upward so that the transitions are traversed in the order 2-3, 3-4, 3-4, 2-3, 1-2, 2′-3′, 2′-3′, 1-2, the total time being 1.6 milliseconds. In Fig. 3(b) a 9-Mc/sec saturating pulse is applied at the time the field first passes through the 2-3 transition. The 3-4 absorption is enhanced because of the fewer number of spins in level 3 (points A). The missing absorption at point B is the return through the 2-3 transition and it shows that this transition is indeed saturated. The 1-2 transition (point C) is seen to be enhanced because of the addition of spins to level 2. Nothing untoward has happened thus far. However, at points D, the 2′-3′ transition, we see that the populations of levels 2 and 3 are no longer equal and have, in fact, been restored in a time $\ll T_1$ to a distribution comparable to that before saturation; furthermore, the 1-2 absorption (point E) is no longer enhanced. The reason is that the field passed through the point indicated by H^* in Fig. 2 where the levels 1, 2, and 3 are equidistant. In this region, spin-spin interaction can set up a Boltzmann distribution between levels 1, 2, and 3 in a time of the order of T_2 which we can estimate from the spin density to be less than one microsecond.

It was found to be impossible to carry out a three-step "staircase"[6] inversion scheme in ruby near the 70-degree orientation because of this mixing. Traversal of enough of the 1-2 transition to allow inversion by fast passage brought the field into close enough proximity to H^* to erase the inversion. Thus, in extending the "staircase" scheme to more than two steps, difficulty may be met not only in cross-relaxation between nearly equal pump transitions,[6] but also in avoiding field regions of equally spaced energy levels. This difficulty may be side-stepped by using a pump frequency that is high compared with the crystal field splitting; in this case, however, a price must be paid in the form of smaller transition probability for the "forbidden" transition.

The author would like to thank Dr. G. Birnbaum and Dr. T. H. Maiman for helpful discussions and C. R. Duncan for technical assistance.

---

* This work was supported in part by the U. S. Army Signal Corps.

[1] T. H. Maiman, Proceedings of the NSIA-ARDC Conference on Molecular Electronics, November, 1958 (unpublished), p. 71.

[2] Linde synthetic ruby; $Cr_2O_3/Al_2O_3 = 0.06\%$ by weight.

[3] D. P. Devor and T. H. Maiman, Hughes Aircraft Company, Quarterly Progress Report DA 36-039 SC-74951, May, 1958 (unpublished).

[4] The 4-3 transition is incidentally inverted in this process. However, the transition probability is low [see W. S. Chang and A. E. Siegman, Stanford Electronics Laboratory Technical Report No. 156-2, September 30, 1958 (unpublished)] and inversion was not complete with the 9-Mc/sec power available (0.5 watt); however, enough inversion was obtained to preclude "staircase" inversion of the 1-3 transition (see reference 6).

[5] For a discussion of this effect, see A. Abragam and W. G. Proctor, Phys. Rev. 109, 1441 (1958), and Bloembergen, Shapiro, Persham, and Artman, Technical Report No. 285, Cruft Laboratory, Harvard University, October 15, 1958 (unpublished).

[6] A. E. Siegman and R. J. Morris, Phys. Rev. Letters 2, 302 (1959).

Reprinted from THE PHYSICAL REVIEW, Vol. 121, No. 4, 997–1000, February 15, 1961

Cross Relaxation and Concentration Effects in Ruby

ROY W. ROBERTS
Melabs, Palo Alto, California

AND

JAMES H. BURGESS
Stanford University, Palo Alto, California

AND

HAROLD D. TENNEY
Melabs, Palo Alto, California

(Received October 13, 1960)

Cross relaxation effects in ruby maser crystals are treated by introduction of a cross relaxation probability in the rate equations. Detailed solutions have been obtained for several specific processes and compared to recent experiments. It is shown that cross relaxation can improve maser performance even in the absence of impurity doping. Pulse experiments at 0.06 and 0.14% chromium ion concentrations in a ruby traveling wave maser are interpreted in terms of a five-spin process in addition to a four-spin process.

I. INTRODUCTION

THE term "cross relaxation" refers generally to the communication of energy between magnetic ions in the crystal. As used in this paper, it refers to the simultaneous transition of two or more ions among their Zeeman energy levels induced by the dipole-dipole interaction. The transition probability then depends on the concentration of paramagnetic ions. Unbalance of Zeeman energy is compensated by a rearrangement of spins in the dipolar system. Since a large change of Zeeman energy requires the relatively improbable cooperation of a large number of ions, the transition probability falls off rapidly around zero unbalance. Thus, at low concentrations, Zeeman energy must be conserved to within a few times the paramagnetic resonance linewidth for a particular cross relaxation process to be important. With increasing concentration this bandwidth broadens until so many processes are allowed that temperature differences within the spin system become impossible. However, there is a region of low concentrations in which individual cross relaxation processes can be observed through their effects on (1) the energy level populations, (2) the effective cw relaxation times, and (3) the transient relaxation times of the paramagnetic system.

Since Bloembergen[1] first pointed out the importance of cross relaxation, many investigators[2–5] have reported experiments in which cross relaxation played an appreciable role, particularly in solid-state maser applications. It has not been generally recognized, however, that cross relaxation may improve maser performance even in cases not involving impurity doping. In the first part of this paper, we discuss several such processes involving three-, four-, and five-spin transitions which correspond to operating conditions in recent maser experiments. Calculated inversion ratios are compared with the experimental results. In the last part of the paper, we describe transient experiments with a ruby traveling-wave maser in which it appears that both a four-spin and a five-spin process are important.

[1] N. Bloembergen, S. Shapiro, P. S. Pershan, and J. O. Artman, Phys. Rev. **114**, 445 (1959).
[2] C. H. Townes in *Quantum Electronics* (Columbia University Press, New York, 1960).
[3] S. Shapiro and N. Bloembergen, Phys. Rev. **116**, 1453 (1959).
[4] W. B. Mims and J. D. McGee, Phys. Rev. **119**, 1233 (1960).
[5] F. Arams, Proc. I.R.E. **48**, 108 (1960).

II. CALCULATION OF CROSS RELAXATION EFFECTS

As has been discussed by Bloembergen and Shapiro,[3] cross relaxation may be incorporated into the framework of the rate equations for the energy level populations. The major condition on the use of the rate equation approach is that the transverse relaxation time T_2 be short enough to prevent large phase coherence effects.[6,7] The form of the cross relaxation term depends on the specific process involved but is based on the assumption of independent occupation probabilities. Thus, in case (a) below, the net rate of increase of population in level 1 is proportional to $n_2^2n_4-n_1n_3^2$. The proportionality constant is taken to be $W'(4/N)^2$, which defines the cross relaxation probability W'. The rate equations for levels 1 and 2 become then

$$\dot{n}_1=-(w_{12}+w_{13}+w_{14})n_1+w_{21}n_2+w_{31}n_3+w_{41}n_4+W'(4/N)^2(n_2^2n_4-n_1n_3^2), \quad (1a)$$

$$\dot{n}_2=w_{12}n_1-(w_{21}+w_{23}+w_{24})n_2+w_{32}n_3+w_{42}n_4+V_{23}(n_3-n_2)-2W'(4/N)^2(n_2^2n_4-n_1n_3^2), \quad (1b)$$

where V_{23} is the transition probability per unit time induced by radiation applied at frequency f_{23}. A factor of 2 multiplies the cross relaxation term in the second equation because each transition changes n_2 by two spins. The cross relaxation term is linearized in the high-temperature approximation by keeping only terms

[6] A. M. Clogston, J. Phys. Chem. Solids **4**, 27 (1958).
[7] J. H. Burgess, J. phys. radium **19**, 845 (1958).

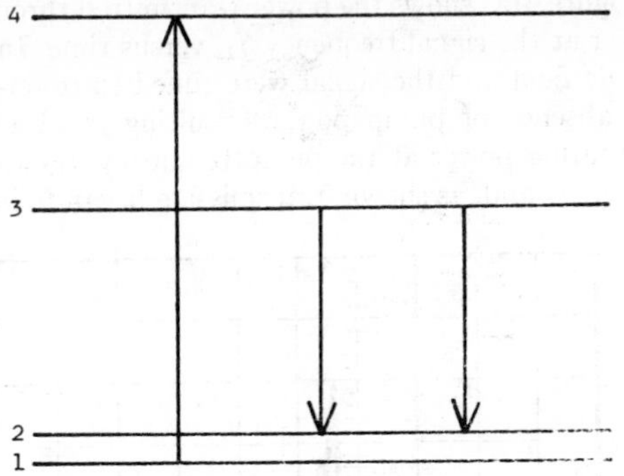

FIG. 1. Energy level diagram for chromium-doped sapphire. $\theta=90°$, $H_{dc}=1675$ oe. Three-spin cross relaxation process indicated by arrows.

involving the first power of $\Delta n_{ij}=n_i-n_j$. The rate equations can then be solved in the usual manner to give the steady-state inversion ratio

$$R_{ij}=-\Delta n_{ij}(V_{ij})/\Delta n_{ij}(0) \tag{2}$$

and the spin temperature

$$T^s_{ij}=-T_L/R_{ij}, \tag{3}$$

where T_L is the lattice temperature.

(a) The energy level diagram shown in Fig. 1 corresponds to ruby with a static magnetic field of 1675 oe applied normal to the C axis ($\theta=90°$). Since the relation $2f_{23}=f_{14}$ is satisfied, the indicated three-spin cross relaxation process conserves Zeeman energy. Transition 2-3 is pumped while the signal is taken at 1-3. In this case $f_s>f_p$. Following the method outlined above and assuming equal spin lattice relaxation times, the inversion ratio is found to be

$$R_{31}=\left[\left(\frac{3f_p}{2f_s}-1\right)\frac{W'}{w}+2-\frac{f_p}{f_s}\right]\bigg/(-2+W'/w), \tag{4}$$

which indicates inversion can be obtained provided $W'/w>2$ even with the signal frequency greater than the pump frequency. These conditions correspond to

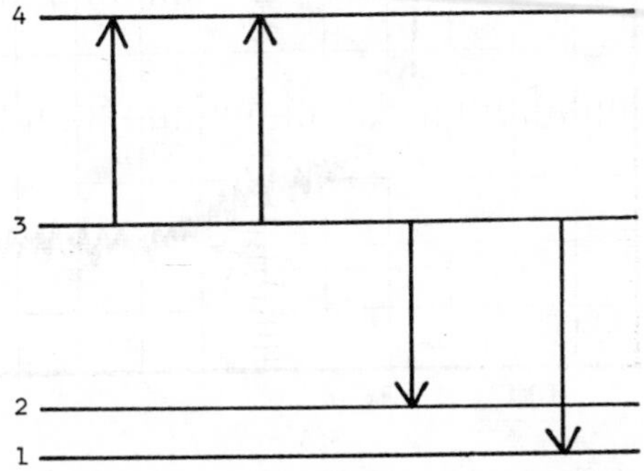

FIG. 2. Energy level diagram for chromium-doped sapphire. $\theta=90°$, $H_{dc}=2750$ oe. Four-spin cross relaxation process indicated by arrows.

those in the experiment of F. Arams[5] at Airborne Instruments Laboratory in which such inversion was observed.

(b) The energy level diagram showing a four-spin cross relaxation process is shown in Fig. 2. The 1-3 transition is pumped and the 1-2 transition is used for the signal. The energy levels satisfy the following relationship: $2f_{34}=f_{13}+f_{23}$. It can be seen that the cross relaxation transition probability will be proportional to $(n_3^4-n_1n_2n_4^2)$. For convenience the proportionality constant will be chosen to be $W'(4/N)^3$. By making the usual high-temperature approximation and assuming all w's equal, the steady-state inversion ratio R is obtained

$$R_{21}=\frac{f_p}{f_s}\frac{4+22W'/w}{8+19W'/w}-1. \tag{5}$$

If the cross relaxation term W'/w is zero, this expression predicts an inversion ratio of 1.48 for a pump frequency of 13.4 kMc and signal frequency of 2.6 kMc. However, experiments performed in this laboratory on a traveling

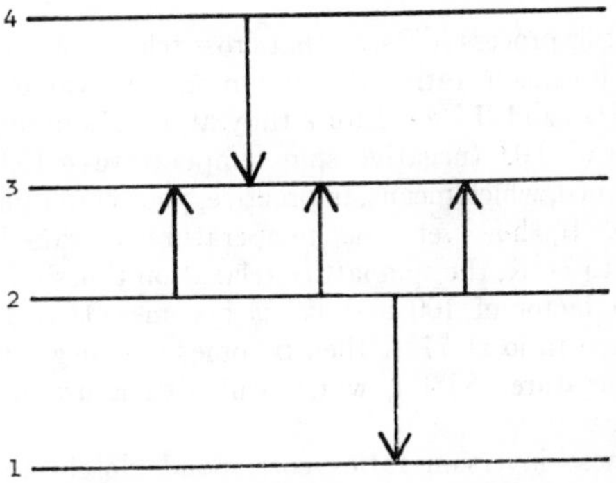

FIG. 3. Energy level diagram for chromium-doped sapphire. $\theta=54°\,44'$, $H_{dc}=3800$ oe. Five-spin cross relaxation process indicated by arrows.

wave maser gave a measured inversion ratio of 4.1. Substituting this value in Eq. (5) gives a value of W'/w of 1.68. These experiments were performed on 0.1% ruby.[8] If cross relaxation effects were not included, this measured inversion ratio would indicate essentially zero idler relaxation time, an unlikely possibility for a homogeneous material.

Examination of the energy level diagram shows that the energy unbalance expressed in megacycles, $\Delta f=2f_{34}-(f_{13}+f_{23})$, is within five linewidths for signal frequencies from 2.6 kMc/sec to 6.0 kMc/sec and goes to zero at approximately 2.65 kMc/sec and 5.95 kMc/sec. These two frequencies correspond to those used in the Melabs traveling wave maser[9] and the Bell Telephone Laboratories[10] traveling wave maser, respectively.

[8] Nominal starting composition. This corresponds to approximately 0.05% chromium ion concentration. The ruby was obtained from Linde Company.

[9] R. Roberts and H. Tenney, unpublished report (1960).

[10] R. DeGrasse, E. O. Schulz-Dubois, and H. E. D. Scovil, Bell System Tech. J. 38, 2 (1959).

(c) The third example of cross relaxation to be considered involves a five-spin process. The energy level diagram shown in Fig. 3 corresponds to the "push-pull" angle for ruby with $\theta=54°\ 44'$ and $H_{dc}=3800$ oe. The energy level separations satisfy the following relationship: $3f_{23}=2f_{12}=2f_{34}$. The 1-3 and 2-4 transitions are pumped and the signal is equal to the 2-3 transition. The cross relaxation-induced transitions for the process shown in Fig. 3 are proportional to $W'(4/N)^4(n_2{}^4n_4-n_1n_3{}^4)$. Because of the degeneracy of the push-pull operating point, two additional five-spin processes occur with the same probability W'. They lead to terms proportional to $W'(4/N)^4(n_4{}^2n_2{}^3-n_3{}^5)$ and $W'(4/N)^4$-$(n_2{}^5-n_3{}^3n_1{}^2)$ in the rate equations. Under the assumed pumping conditions, these two terms and the previous term each reduce to $W'(4/N)^4(n_2{}^5-n_1{}^5)$. The effect is to increase the total cross relaxation probability to $3W'$. The inversion ratio, assuming equal w_{ij}'s, is given by[9]

$$R_{32}=\frac{-1+f_p/f_s}{1+45W'/w}. \qquad (6)$$

For this process it is seen that cross relaxation decreases the inversion ratio. By assuming the values $f_p/f_s=23/10$ and $W'/w=1$ for a ruby at 4.2°K, an inversion ratio of 0.03 (negative spin temperature $=150$°K) is obtained, which means, in practice, poor maser performance. If, however, the temperature is raised from 4.2° to 77°K, the spin lattice relaxation times[11] decrease by a factor of 100 and W'/w becomes 0.01. The inversion ratio at 77°K then becomes 0.9 (negative spin temperature$=85$°K), which will give a useful maser gain.

These inversion ratios correspond closely to those obtained by T. Maiman[12] at Hughes Aircraft Laboratories for a 0.2% ruby and suggest that this process may be more important than the proposed pump-idler coupling which entails an energy unbalance greater than 5 kMc.

III. CONCENTRATION EFFECTS

To check the effects of concentration of chromium ions, a 0.3% ruby[13] was used in a pulsed traveling wave maser at 4.2°K at the operating point of Fig. 2. It was expected that the larger concentration would increase the cross relaxation probability and further enhance the inversion ratio. This did not turn out to be the case. The amount of electronic gain obtained was less than that obtained with the 0.1% crystal. It is evident from this result that the assumption implicit in case (b), that only the four-spin cross relaxation process need be considered, is no longer valid for the 0.3% ruby.

Figure 4(a) shows the power transmitted through the maser at the signal frequency f_{12} versus time. Initially, the dc field and the signal were tuned to resonance in the absence of pump power, resulting in absorption. Saturating power at the pump frequency f_{13} was then pulsed on and, as shown, transmission began to increase

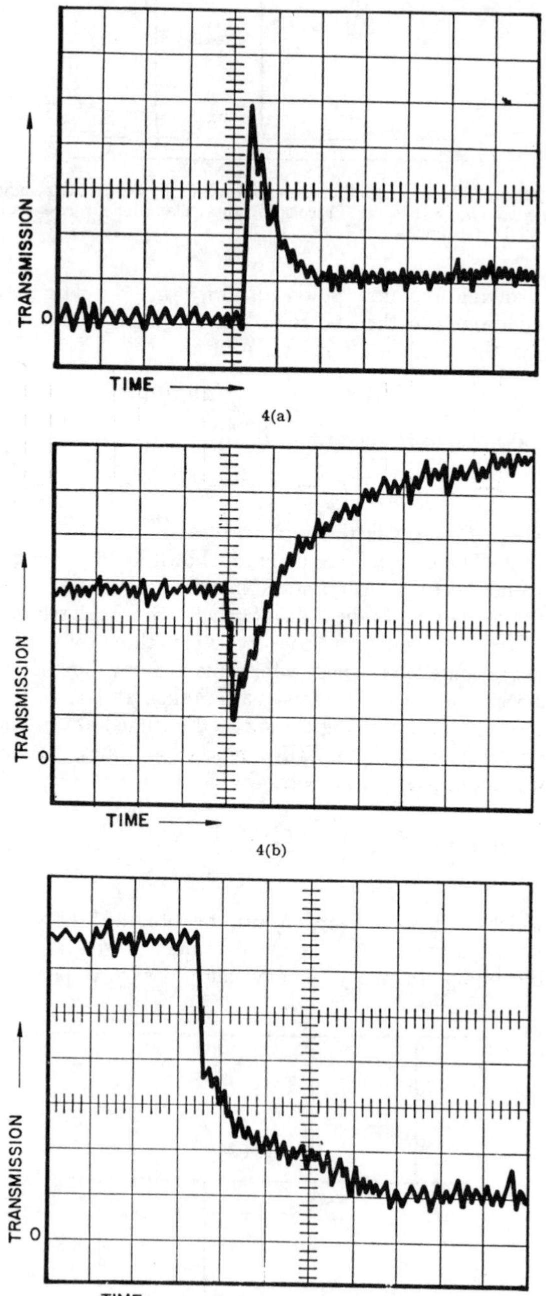

FIG. 4. Signal transmission through the traveling wave maser vs time. (a) 0.3% ruby, f_{13} pulsed on. (b) 0.3% ruby, f_{23} pulsed on. (c) 0.1% ruby, f_{23} pulsed on.

[11] J. C. Gill in *Quantum Electronics* (Columbia University Press, New York, 1960), p. 333.

[12] T. Maiman in *Quantum Electronics* (Columbia University Press, New York, 1960), p. 324.

[13] Starting composition. This corresponds to approximately 0.14% chromium ion concentration.

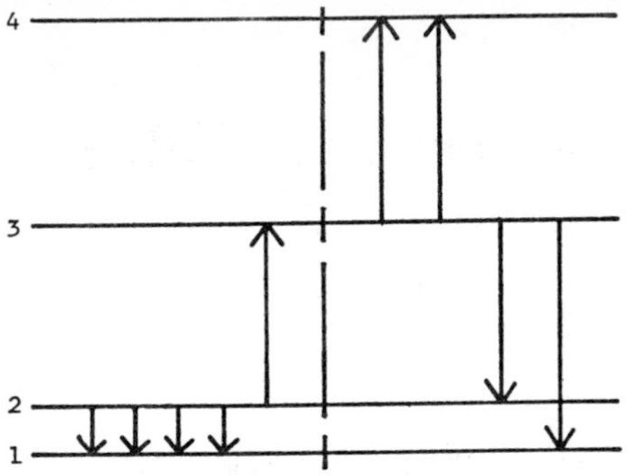

FIG. 5. Energy level diagram for chromium-doped sapphire. $\theta=90°$, $H_{dc}=2750$ oe. Four- and five-spin cross relaxation processes indicated by arrows.

at a very rapid rate, indicating the ruby was becoming emissive. However, before the maximum amount of gain could be realized, another competing mechanism dominated and caused the transmission to reduce to a low steady-state value. The conditions were the same initially in Fig. 4(b). Here saturating power at the idle frequency f_{23} was pulsed on. The transmission decreased sharply and then returned to a higher steady-state value. For comparison purposes, Fig. 4(c) shows the results of the same experiment, pulsing on f_{23}, for the 0.1% ruby. In this case, the transmission decreased considerably and remained at a very low steady-state value.

Inspection of the energy level diagrams corresponding to the point of operation revealed a degeneracy for a five-spin cross relaxation process in addition to the four-spin process already considered. The energy levels satisfy the relationship $4f_{12}=f_{23}$. To determine if this degeneracy would account for the results described above, the rate equations were solved taking into account both cross relaxation mechanisms. The combined processes are shown in Fig. 5. The cross relaxation induced transitions caused by the four-spin process are given by $W_4'(4/N)^3(n_3^4-n_1n_2n_4^2)$ while those resulting from the five-spin process are given by $W_5'(4/N)^4$-$(n_2^5-n_1^4n_3)$. The normal maser case in which the 1-3 transition is saturated will be considered first. The cross relaxation terms are linearized as before. By making the usual high-temperature approximation, and assuming all w's equal, the steady-state inversion ratio is

$$R_{21}=\left[\frac{f_p}{2f_s}-1+\frac{W_4'}{w}\left(\frac{22f_p}{8f_s}-\frac{19}{8}\right)\right]\Big/\left[1+\frac{19W_4'}{8w}+\frac{25W_5'}{8w}\left(3+4\frac{W_4'}{w}\right)\right]. \quad (7)$$

This expression reduces to the normal inversion ratio in the absence of any cross relaxation, $R=-1+f_p/2f_s$ and agrees with Eq. (5) when $W_5'=0$. Since the W_5' term appears in the denominator, it is seen that the five-spin process tends to decrease the inversion ratio in agreement with the experimental results shown in Fig. 4(a).

A similar analysis was carried out for the case in which the idle frequency f_{23} was pulsed on. Proper substitutions and approximations result in the following expression for the inversion ratio,

$$R_{21}=\left[\frac{f_p}{2f_s}+\frac{1}{2}-\frac{W_4'}{w}\left(\frac{3}{8}-\frac{22}{8}\frac{f_p}{f_s}\right)\right]\Big/\left[\frac{20W_5'}{8w}\left(3+\frac{4W_4'}{w}\right)+1-\frac{W_4'}{8w}\right], \quad (8)$$

where f_p is still defined as f_{13} and f_s as f_{12}. In the case of no cross relaxation,

$$R_{21}=-[(f_p/2f_s)+\tfrac{1}{2}]. \quad (9)$$

The inversion ratio and the resultant gain are negative. In the case of $f_p=13.4$ kMc/sec and $f_s=2.7$ kMc/sec, which corresponds to the operating point under consideration, $R=-3$, so that the absorption is expected to triple when saturating power is applied. However, the experimental measurements made on the 0.1% crystal gave an inversion ratio of -5 in this frequency range, indicating that W_4' is not negligible.

From Eq. (8) it can be seen that, as W_5' increases, the inversion ratio approaches zero. Since a five-spin process should depend more strongly on concentration than a four-spin process, W_5' should become important at higher concentrations. This was borne out by measurements made on the 0.3% crystal, which gave smaller negative inversion ratios of from -0.4 to -0.6.

IV. SUMMARY AND CONCLUSIONS

It appears that at low chromium ion concentrations, cross relaxation effects in ruby can be described by specifying one or two specific cross relaxation processes. These effects can be taken into account by adding suitable terms to the rate equations. Solution of the linearized rate equations then allows one to predict qualitatively the effects of the cross relaxation processes on maser performance and the behavior with varying concentration. The optimum concentration for maser action will depend on the particular operating point and the lowest order cross relaxation mechanism for which energy conservation is nearly satisfied. However, as the concentration is increased, so many higher order processes become important that it is impossible to maintain temperature differences in the spin system. This establishes a maximum allowable concentration above which maser amplification is not possible.

V. ACKNOWLEDGMENTS

We would like to thank Dr. J. C. Cromack for many helpful discussions pertaining to this subject. This work was supported in part by the Air Force Cambridge Research Center.

Maser Operation at Signal Frequencies Higher than Pump Frequency*

FRANK R. ARAMS†, SENIOR MEMBER, IRE

Summary—**Methods using harmonic spin coupling for operating solid-state masers with signal frequencies higher than the pump frequency are discussed. Expressions for the population inversion ratios are presented, and the maximum signal-to-pump-frequency ratios are calculated.**

Experimental data is presented on a ruby maser which is operated using the symmetrical method. Amplification was obtained at signal frequencies from 10,320 to 10,740 Mc, using pump frequencies ranging from 9580 to 9670 Mc.

An experiment in which maser operation is obtained simultaneously at two frequencies is described.

SOLID-STATE masers are ordinarily operated with the pump frequency two to ten times the signal frequency. This relationship—a relatively high pump frequency—permits good spin-population inversion (and hence satisfactory gain-bandwidth products) at the signal frequency.[1]

A major obstacle to the development of masers with very high signal frequencies has been the lack of availability of satisfactory pump power sources in the millimeter-wave and submillimeter-wave regions. One approach toward circumventing the unavailability of satisfactory millimeter pump sources has been the pulsed maser. With the pulse technique, transient maser amplification of signals up to 70 kMc has been obtained.[2]

Because transient methods have obvious disadvantages, there is a need for a continuous-wave maser in which the pump frequency is kept as low as possible relative to the signal frequency.

One method of keeping the pump frequency low is the method used in the "X-X maser." In this maser, the pump frequency is only about 15 per cent higher than the signal frequency.[3] This method of operation can probably be used in the millimeter-wave region by using maser materials which have suitably large zero-field splittings—for example, emerald, and Cr^{+++} or Fe^{+++} doped titania.

As the signal frequency is raised higher and higher, it becomes increasingly desirable to use a pump frequency lower than the signal frequency. Several methods for achieving continuous-wave maser operation with a signal frequency higher than the pump frequency will be discussed in this paper. Operating data on a maser operating in such a manner will be given.

The low-pump-frequency maser operation discussed here involves spin-coupling of transitions that are equal in frequency or harmonically related. In the harmonic-spin-coupling process, simultaneous spin flips cause energy transfer between transitions that are harmonically related in frequency; all, or almost all, of the Zeeman energy of the spin system is conserved.[4–8] Saturation of the lowest-frequency transition by applied pump power will result in a simultaneous saturation effect in the harmonically related transition. This spin-coupling mechanism will alter the spin population distribution between the energy levels in such a manner that a negative temperature is obtained at a signal frequency higher than the pump frequency.

The Symmetrical Method

A maser material is required having four (or more) energy levels. Let these energy levels be numbered from 1 to 4 in order of increasing energy, and let the notation f_{ij} represent the frequency corresponding to the energy difference between the ith and the jth levels. An operating point (in terms of magnetic field strength and orientation with respect to the crystal C-axes) is chosen at which $f_{14}=2f_{23}$. The method of operation is as follows.

The spin population distribution among the various levels before application of pump power is approximately as shown in Fig. 1(a). The f_{23} transition is saturated by means of pump power from an external pump source at frequency f_{23}. The saturation of the f_{23} transition will result in the simultaneous saturation (at least partial) of the f_{14} transition through the mechanism of harmonic spin coupling. Thus, the spin populations of

* Received by the PGMTT, July 15, 1960. This work is part of a doctoral dissertation at the Polytechnic Inst. of Brooklyn, Brooklyn, N. Y.

† Airborne Instruments Lab., Cutler-Hammer, Inc., Melville, L. I., N. Y.

[1] N. Bloembergen, "Proposal for a new type solid-state maser," *Phys. Rev.*, vol. 109, pp. 324–327; October 15, 1956.

[2] S. Foner, L. Momo, A. Mayer, and R. Myers, "Pulsed field millimeter wave maser," in "Quantum Electronics," Columbia University Press, New York, N. Y., p. 487; 1960.

[3] F. R. Arams, "Low field X-band ruby maser," Proc. IRE, vol. 46, p. 1373; August, 1959.

[4] N. Bloembergen, S. Shapiro, P. Pershan, and J. O. Artman. "Cross-relaxation in spin systems," *Phys. Rev.*, vol. 144, pp. 445–459; April 15, 1959.

[5] W. H. Higa, "Excitation of an L-band ruby maser," in "Quantum Electronics," Columbia University Press, New York, N. Y., p. 298; 1960.

[6] J. E. Geusic, "Harmonic spin coupling in ruby," *Phys. Rev.*, vol. 118, pp. 129–130; April 1, 1960.

[7] W. S. C. Chang, "Spin lattice relaxation via harmonic coupling," in "Quantum Electronics," Columbia University Press, New York, N. Y., p. 346; 1960.

[8] W. B. Mims and J. McGee, "Spin-spin energy transfer and the operation of three-level masers," Proc. IRE, vol. 47, p. 2120; December, 1959.

levels 2 and 3 have been equalized to the average value of their equilibrium populations. The same will be true of levels 1 and 4. The spin population distribution, assuming that all spin-lattice relaxation times are equal, is shown in Fig. 1(b). Note that a negative temperature is obtained in the f_{12} transition.[5,6]

The negative temperature at f_{12} and the saturated f_{23} transition combine to produce a negative temperature at a frequency f_{13}, which is higher than the pump frequency f_{23}. In terms of the spin populations of the various energy levels, since $n_2 > n_1$, and $n_2 = n_3$, it follows that $n_3 > n_1$, so that maser action can be obtained at f_{13}. Thus, a way has been found to obtain operation with a signal frequency higher than the pump frequency. Maser amplification can thus be obtained simultaneously at two signal frequencies, f_{12} and f_{13}, which are related by the expression $f_{sig_1} + f_{pump} = f_{sig_2}$. (This circumstance will be discussed further later on.)

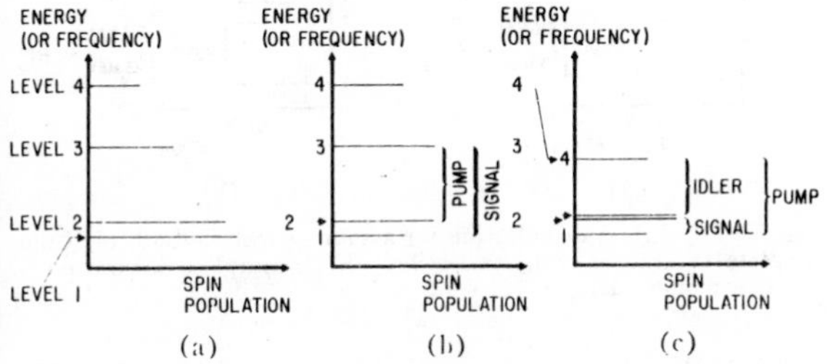

Fig. 1—Population distribution in symmetrical method. (a) Thermal equilibrium, pump power off. (b) Pump power (at f_{23}) on. (c) Analogous three-level technique illustrating that f_{34} is idler transition.

Comparison of this symmetrical method with the standard Bloembergen three-level maser[1] shows that f_{34} plays the role of the idler transition, and that Fig. 1(b) is analogous to the Bloembergen three-level maser technique if we think of the f_{23} transition as the degenerate intermediate energy level; this is shown in Fig. 1(c) and is verified by the following analysis.

Analysis:

We can solve for the steady-state (negative) population difference, $\Delta n_{13} = n_1 \; n_3$, using the usual linearized rate equations[1] and the conditions $n_2 = n_3$ caused by pump saturation and $n_1 = n_4$ caused by saturation by second-harmonic spin coupling. A more general procedure is to add to each of the standard rate equations one term representing the spin coupling between the harmonically related transitions. (All other possible simultaneous multiple spin-flip processes are neglected.) Let w_c be the harmonic-spin-coupling transition probability; w_{ij}, the spin-lattice transition probability between the ith and jth energy levels; and n, the order of the spin-coupling harmonic. The condition $n_1 = n_4$ is not used, since the degree of saturation of the f_{14} transition will depend upon the parameter w_c/w_{ij}. For $w_c/w_{ij} = \infty$, the results are identical with those calculated for the first method. The two pertinent rate equations (since we are pumping between levels 2 and 3) are

$$\frac{dn_1}{dt} = -w_{12}\left[\Delta n_{12} - \frac{Nh}{4kT_0} f_{12}\right] - w_{13}\left[\Delta n_{13} - \frac{Nh}{4kT_0} f_{13}\right] - w_{14}\left[\Delta n_{14} - \frac{Nh}{4kT_0} f_{14}\right] - w_c\left|\Delta n_{14} - n\Delta n_{23}\right| \quad (1a)$$

$$\frac{dn_4}{dt} = w_{14}\left[\Delta n_{14} - \frac{Nh}{4kT_0} f_{14}\right] + w_{24}\left[\Delta n_{24} - \frac{Nh}{4kT_0} f_{24}\right] + w_{34}\left[\Delta n_{34} - \frac{Nh}{4kT_0} f_{34}\right] + w_c\left|\Delta n_{14} - n\Delta n_{23}\right|. \quad (1b)$$

In these equations N is the total spin population, h is Planck's constant, k is Boltzmann's constant, and T_0 is the bath temperature. The form of the harmonic spin coupling terms in (1) is obtained by linearizing (for second-harmonic) terms of the form[4] $(n_2^2 n_4 - n_3^2 n_1.)$ For all w_{ij} equal, we obtain for the steady-state

$$\Delta n_{13} = -\frac{Nh}{4kT_0} \cdot \left[\frac{w_{ij}(f_{23} - 2f_{13}) + w_c\left[\left(\frac{n+1}{2}\right)f_{23} - f_{13}\right]}{2w_{ij} + w_c}\right]. \quad (2)$$

For $w_c/w_{ij} = \infty$, this reduces to

$$\Delta n_{13} = -\frac{Nh}{4kT_0}\left(\frac{f_{34} - f_{12}}{2}\right). \quad (3)$$

This expression is independent of n and has the same form as that for a standard Bloembergen three-level maser, which for all w_{ij} equal is

$$\Delta n_{signal} = -\frac{Nh}{4kT_0}\left(\frac{f_{idler} - f_{signal}}{2}\right). \quad (4)$$

Hence, it is evident that f_{34} and f_{12} act as the idler and signal transitions, respectively [Fig. 1(c)], and that we wish to maximize f_{34}.

Taking (2), normalizing it to the Boltzmann thermal equilibrium population difference $(\Delta n_{13})_0$, and rewriting it in terms of the signal frequency, f_{13}, and pump frequency, f_{23}, we obtain

$$\frac{\Delta n_{13}}{(\Delta n_{13})_0} \equiv \frac{T_0}{T_{s13}} = 1 - \frac{\left(n + 1 + 2\frac{w_{ij}}{w_c}\right)\frac{f_{23}}{f_{13}}}{2\left(1 + 2\frac{w_{ij}}{w_c}\right)} \quad (5)$$

where T_{s13} is the spin temperature of the f_{13} transition. T_0/T_{s13} must be negative in order to obtain amplification, and the obtainable gain is proportional to T_0/T_{s13}. As (5) shows, for $n > 1$, amplification can be obtained with a signal frequency f_{13} larger than the pump frequency f_{23}.

Using (5) we solve for the maximum ratio of signal-frequency-to-pump-frequency, with n and w_c/w_{ij} as parameters, by setting $T_0/T_{s_{13}}$ equal to zero. The results are shown in Table I. As can be seen, for $w_c/w_{ij}=\infty$, the maximum ratio of signal-frequency-to-pump-frequency is 1.5 for $n=2$, and 2.0 for $n=3$. The maximum signal frequency is seen to be dependent upon w_c/w_{ij}. This is intuitively reasonable, because the f_{14} (second-harmonic) transition is not saturated for finite w_c/w_{ij}. As expected, the maximum ratio increases with n. It is seen that w_c/w_{ij} need not be very high to permit maser amplification at frequencies higher than the pump frequency. However, because w_c is an implicit function of n, it may be difficult to achieve high signal-frequency-to-pump-frequency ratios. To maximize w_c/w_{ij}, it is desirable to go to as low a bath temperature as possible, since w_c is independent of and w_{ij} is proportional to bath temperature. This parameter—the ratio of the w's—can also be changed by varying the concentration of the paramagnetic ion in the maser crystal.

TABLE I
SYMMETRICAL METHOD: MAXIMUM RATIO OF SIGNAL FREQUENCY TO PUMP FREQUENCY

	$w_c/w_{ij}=\infty$	10	4	2	1
$n=2$	1.5	1.33	1.17	1.0	0.83
3	2.0	1.75	1.5	1.25	1.0
4	2.5	2.17	1.83	1.5	1.17
n	$\frac{n+1}{2}$	$\frac{n+1.2}{2.4}$	$\frac{n+1.5}{3}$	$\frac{n+2}{4}$	$\frac{n+3}{6}$

Eq. (5) also shows that the inversion improves as the signal-frequency-to-pump-frequency ratio is decreased. In fact, it continues to increase even when the signal frequency becomes lower than the pump frequency. When the signal frequency is less than the pump frequency, the energy-level arrangement could be called harmonic push-pull pumping (Fig. 2). Thus, even when the signal is less than the pump frequency, the improved inversion (and hence increased gain-bandwidth product) makes the harmonic-coupling technique attractive in comparison with the standard three-level Bloembergen maser technique.

ALTERNATIVE SYMMETRICAL METHOD

Suppose the energy levels are arranged in such a manner that $f_{14}=2f_{23}$ (as previously), but $f_{34}<f_{12}$ (rather than $f_{34}>f_{12}$, as previously). It is still possible to obtain maser amplification at a signal frequency (now f_{24}) higher than the pump frequency (f_{23}). Here, f_{12} is the idler transition. Thus, just as in the standard Bloembergen three-level maser, maser operation can be obtained with the idler transition higher in energy than the signal transition, or vice versa.

THE ASYMMETRICAL METHOD

In this method, we again require four (or more) energy levels numbered from 1 to 4 in order of increasing energy. We chose an operating point at which $f_{24}=2f_{12}$. The method of operation is as follows (see Fig. 3).

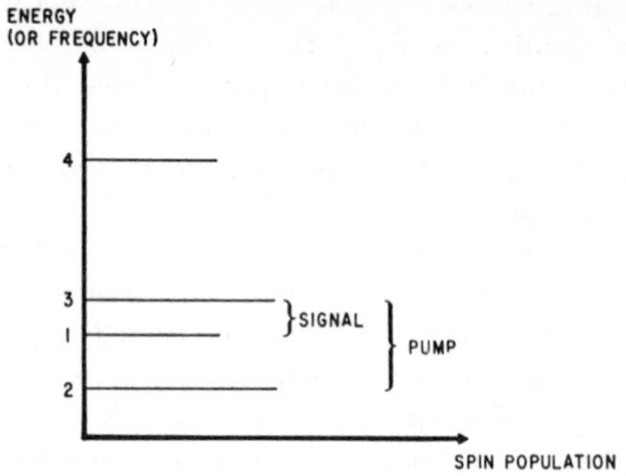

Fig. 2—Population distribution for harmonic push-pull pumping.

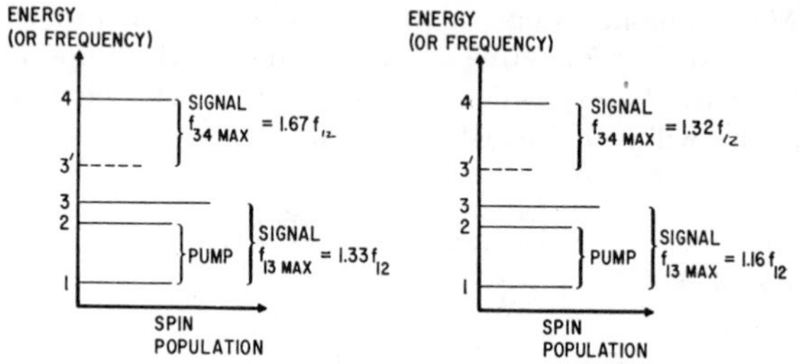

(a) (b)

Fig. 3—Population distribution for asymmetrical method. (a) Complete saturation of f_{24} transition. (b) Incomplete saturation of f_{24} transition $w_c/w_{ij}=10$; $n=z$.

The f_{12} transition is saturated by means of pump power from an external pump source at frequency f_{12}. The harmonic spin-coupling mechanism results in the simultaneous saturation (at least partial) of the f_{24} transition. The populations of levels 1, 2, and 4 will be essentially equalized to their average value. The spin population distribution will then be as shown in Fig. 3(a).

A negative temperature can be obtained at a signal frequency f_{13} (and f_{23}) or f_{34}, depending upon the location of energy level 3. The signal frequency f_{13} will be, and the signal frequency f_{34} may be, higher than the pump frequency f_{12}.

Analysis:

We can solve for the steady-state (negative) population differences, Δn_{13} and Δn_{34}, using the usual linearized rate equations and the saturation condition $n_1=n_2=n_4$.

Again, the more general procedure is to add the harmonic spin-coupling terms to the rate equations. In the steady state, assuming that all w_{ij} are equal, we obtain for the population inversion ratios,

$$\frac{T_0}{T_{s_{13}}}=1-\frac{\left(n+2+4\frac{w_{ij}}{w_c}\right)\frac{f_{12}}{f_{13}}}{3+8\frac{w_{ij}}{w_c}} \qquad (6)$$

and

TABLE II

ASYMMETRICAL METHOD: MAXIMUM RATIO OF SIGNAL FREQUENCY TO PUMP FREQUENCY

	$w_c/w_{ij}=\infty$		10		4		2	
	f_{13}	f_{34}	f_{13}	f_{34}	f_{13}	f_{34}	f_{13}	f_{34}
$n=2$	1.33	1.67	1.16	1.32	1.0	1.0	0.86	0.71
3	1.67	2.33	1.42	1.84	1.2	1.4	1.0	1.0
4	2.0	3.0	1.74	2.37	1.4	1.8	1.14	1.29
n	$\frac{n+2}{3}$	$\frac{2n+1}{3}$	$\frac{n+2.4}{3.8}$	$\frac{2n+1}{3.8}$	$\frac{n+3}{5}$	$\frac{2n+1}{5}$	$\frac{n+4}{7}$	$\frac{2n+1}{7}$

$$\frac{T_0}{T_{s34}} = 1 - \frac{(2n+1)\dfrac{f_{12}}{f_{34}}}{3 + 8\dfrac{w_{ij}}{w_c}}. \tag{7}$$

The maximum ratios of signal-frequency-to-pump-frequency as functions of n and w_c/w_{ij} for the asymmetrical method are shown in Table II. The maximum signal-to-pump ratio is different for the f_{13} and f_{34} transitions, being 1.33 and 1.67, respectively, for second-harmonic spin coupling, and 1.67 and 2.33, respectively, for third-harmonic spin coupling. Eqs. (6) and (7) also show that, as in the symmetrical method, harmonic spin coupling significantly improves maser operation over the three-level Bloembergen maser, even when the signal frequency is lower than the pump frequency.

The population ratio of the pump transition f_{14} was calculated assuming that the f_{12} transition is saturated by externally applied pump power. We obtain

$$\frac{T_0}{T_{s14}} = \frac{8 - \dfrac{4}{n+1}}{8 + 3\dfrac{w_c}{w_{ij}}} \tag{8}$$

for the dependence of the degree of saturation of the f_{14} transition upon the w_c/w_{ij} parameter. As expected, $T_0/T_{s14} \to 0$ for $w_c/w_{ij} \to \infty$. How incomplete saturation of the spin-coupled second-harmonic transition reduces the maximum signal frequency is shown in Fig. 3(b). The reduction in population of level 4 combines with an increase of the level 1 and 2 populations to yield only a limited frequency range where inverted populations are obtainable.

THE PUSH-PUSH MASER

This may be considered as a special case of the asymmetrical method with $n=1$. Since $f_{12}=f_{24}$, both transitions are saturated directly by the applied pump power.[9] The population inversion ratios can be obtained directly from (6) and (7) by setting $w_c/w_{ij}=\infty$ and $n=1$. The result shows that the push-push maser produces a significant improvement in population inversion ratio over the three-level Bloembergen maser. However, maser operation at a signal frequency higher than the pump frequency can be obtained for unequal spin-lattice relaxation times only.

EXPERIMENTAL DATA

Continuous-wave maser operation with the signal frequency about 1000 Mc higher than the pump frequency was successfully achieved using the symmetrical method. By using the four energy levels in ruby (chromium-doped aluminum oxide), maser amplification was first obtained at $f_{13}=10{,}590$ Mc, using a pump frequency of $f_{23}=9595$ Mc. The magnetic field of 1675 oersteds was oriented at 90 degrees to the ruby C-axis. The energy levels used are indicated in Fig. 4; they were so arranged that $f_{14}=2f_{23}$.

We established experimentally that the f_{14} transition is saturated because of the pump power applied at frequency f_{23}, and that the frequency ratio need not be exactly integral.[10] It was possible, using a constant pump frequency of $f_{23}=9650$ Mc, to saturate the f_{14} transition over a 600-Mc frequency range (centered near 19,300 Mc) with an optimized magnetic field.

The experimental result that the second-harmonic, f_{14}, transition can be saturated over a range of frequencies with constant pump frequency, is attributable in part to the fact that the frequency of the f_{23} transition varies very little with magnetic field (Fig. 4), changing by less than 40 Mc per 100 oersteds in the region of interest.

The experimental setup consisted of a doubly resonant tunable cavity operating in the TE_{10} waveguide mode. The ruby crystal had a nominal 0.05-per cent residual chromium content. The pump power was 8 milliwatts at a liquid helium bath temperature of 4.2 degrees K. To ascertain that the saturation of the f_{14} transition was primarily caused by harmonic spin coupling, we measured the second-harmonic power output of the pump power source in the 18 to 26 kMc range and found it to be less than 1 microwatt.

A voltage-gain bandwidth product of 11 Mc was measured at a liquid helium bath temperature of 4.2 degrees K. It is expected that larger gain-bandwidth products can be obtained, since the ruby occupied only a small portion of the cavity. The filling factor is estimated to be 50 per cent. The spin population inversion ratio was also measured, and was found to be -0.37.

[9] "Solid-State Research," MIT Lincoln Lab. Quarterly Progress Rept., p. 65; July 15, 1959.

[10] F. R. Arams, "Maser operation with signal frequency higher than pump frequency," PROC. IRE, vol. 47, p. 108; January, 1960.

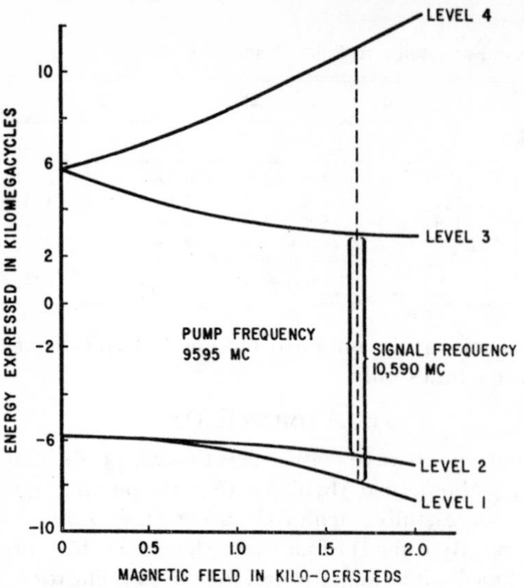

Fig. 4—Energy levels used in ruby in symmetrical method experiment.

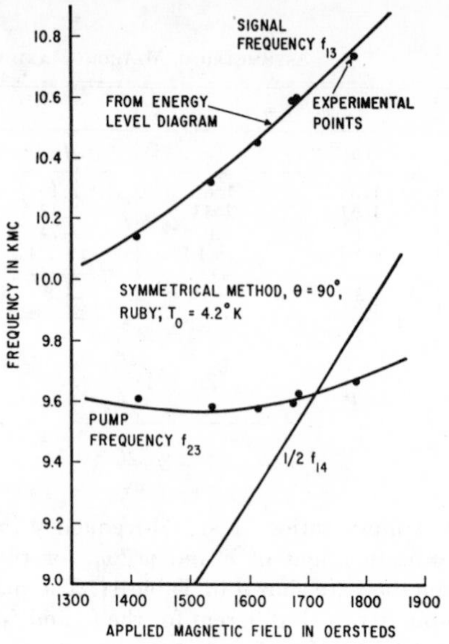

Fig. 5—Frequency tuning range of ruby maser using symmetrical method.

The tuning range was 420 Mc with optimized pump frequency and magnetic field and a liquid helium bath temperature of 4.2 degrees K. Maser amplification was obtained over the 10,320- to 10,740-Mc range, using pump frequencies ranging from 9580 to 9670 Mc. The data are plotted in Fig. 5. The tuning range obtained is also of interest in view of the frequency difference between the pump frequency f_{23} and $\frac{1}{2}f_{14}$, but it is consistent with the observed wide-range harmonic saturation of f_{14} previously described. A greater tuning range should be obtainable at 1.5 degrees K.

An attempt was also made at obtaining maser operation using the asymetrical method. The orientation of 60° between ruby C-axis and applied magnetic field is of particular interest, since the harmonic relationship $f_{24}=f_{12}$ is maintained over a wide range of frequencies,[8] that is, a pump frequency $f_{12}=8.3$ to 12.7 kMc, and a signal frequency $f_{34}=10$ to 15 kMc. Q improvement was observed, but inversion has not yet been obtained, indicating the possibility that additional factors (such as other spin-flip processes) may need to be included that were not considered in the present analysis.

Two-Frequency Maser Operation

In the symmetrical method, a negative spin temperature was obtained at two frequencies simultaneously. One of these is at a relatively low frequency, designated f_{s1}. The second frequency f_{s2} is numerically related to f_{s1} via the pump frequency f_p—that is, $f_{s2}=f_{s1}+f_p$.

A triply resonant cavity experiment was set up, and it was possible to obtain maser amplification at f_{s1} and f_{s2} simultaneously. Operating conditions were: magnetic field = 1650 gauss at 90 degrees to the ruby C-axis; $f_p = 9600$ Mc; $f_{s1}=1005$ Mc; and $f_{s2}=10,605$ Mc. When the liquid helium bath temperature was reduced to 1.5 degrees K, maser action was obtained at f_{s1} and f_{s2}, simultaneously. Maser action would get better or worse at both frequencies concurrently as adjustments—such as angular orientation and magnetic field strength—were being made.

The condition $f_{s2}=f_p+f_{s1}$ used here is also used in the parametric amplifier up-converter. In that application, p-n junction diodes or ferromagnetic materials are used, and the input is at frequency f_{s1}, the output is at frequency f_{s2}, and the obtainable power gain is equal to the frequency ratio f_{s2}/f_{s1}.

In the experimental double-frequency maser setup, no interaction between the f_{s1} and f_{s2} signals was observable except when the input power level approached saturation. An input signal at f_{s1} did not affect the f_{s2} output, and vice versa. It is concluded that the absence of coherence between the f_{12} and f_{13} transitions prevents the realization of a maser amplifier up-converter.

Conclusions

Several methods for obtaining CW maser operation with a signal frequency higher than the pump frequency were analyzed. Performance data on the symmetrical method were presented. This maser was tuned over a 420-Mc range. Using the methods described, millimeter-wave masers having pump frequencies lower than signal frequencies should become available in the foreseeable future.

Acknowledgment

The author wishes to thank Professor Milton Birnbaum of the Polytechnic Institute of Brooklyn, Brooklyn, N. Y. for valuable advice and discussions.

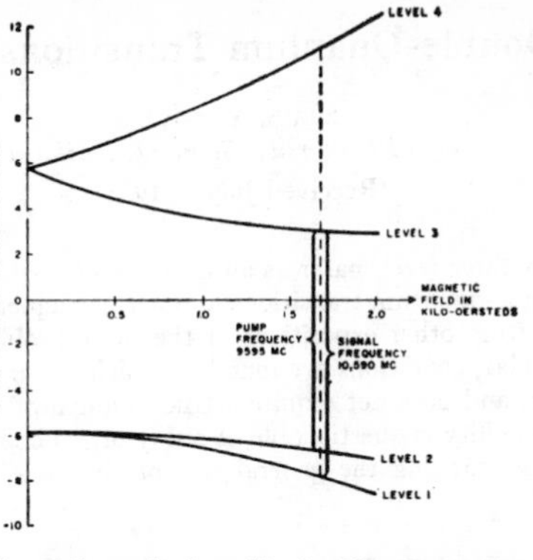

Fig. 1—Energy levels used in obtaining maser operation at a signal frequency higher than the pump frequency.

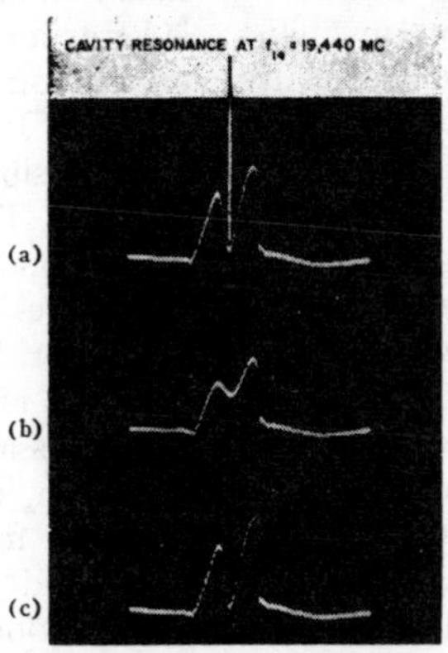

Fig. 2—Oscilloscope display of power reflected from maser cavity as a function of frequency. (a) Magnetic field off, pump power off; (b) magnetic field on, pump power off; (c) magnetic field on, pump power on at 9650 mc, showing saturation.

Maser Operation with Signal Frequency Higher than Pump Frequency*

An X-band solid-state maser utilizing the four Zeeman levels in ruby has been successfully operated with a signal frequency (10,590 mc) higher than the pump frequency (9595 mc). The method of operation depends upon the mechanism of harmonic spin-coupling[1,2] which is closely allied to the cross-relaxation mechanism treated by Bloembergen, *et al.*[3]

Continuous-wave operation was obtained at a magnetic field of 1675 oersteds oriented at 90 degrees to the ruby C axis. The energy level diagram is shown in Fig. 1, where the energy levels are numbered in order of increasing energy. For essentially the same operating conditions, anomalous excitation of a maser with signal frequency $f_{12} \approx 1000$ mc using a pump at $f_{23} \approx 9650$ mc had previously been reported by Higa[1] and Geusic.[2] The explanation for the anomalous operation is given in terms of harmonic spin-coupling between the f_{23} and f_{14} transitions, since $f_{14} = 2f_{23}$ for this operating point.

* Received by the IRE, October 28, 1959. This work is part of a doctoral dissertation at Polytechnic Inst. of Brooklyn, Brooklyn, N. Y.

[1] W. H. Higa, "Anomalous Excitation of a Solid-State Maser," presented at the Conf. on Electron Tube Res., Mexico City, Mexico, June 24, 1959; to be published in *Proc. Conf. Quantum Electronics—Resonance Phenomena*, Columbia University Press, New York, N. Y.

[2] J. E. Geusic, "Maser Action in Ruby in the Frequency Range 800 to 9000 Mc, and Harmonic Spin Coupling in Ruby," presented at the Conf. on Electron Tube Res., Mexico City, Mexico; June 24, 1959.

[3] N. Bloembergen, S. Shapiro, P. Pershan, and J. O. Artman, "Cross-relaxation in spin systems," *Phys. Rev.*, vol. 144, pp. 445–459; April 15, 1959.

Solution of the rate equations shows that f_{34} acts as the idler in this type of operation.

We have established experimentally that the f_{14} transition is saturated due to the pump power applied at frequency f_{23} (Fig. 2). Furthermore, the frequency ratio need not be exactly integral. It was possible, using a constant pump frequency of $f_{23} = 9650$ mc, to saturate the f_{14} transition over a 600-mc frequency range (centered near 19,300 mc) with optimized magnetic field.

The negative temperature at f_{12} and the saturated f_{23} transition combine to obtain a negative temperature at a frequency f_{13} that is 1000 mc higher than the applied pump frequency f_{23}. This was verified experimentally, and strong CW maser amplification and oscillations were obtained.

The experimental setup consisted of a doubly-resonant tunable cavity, operating in the TE_{10} waveguide mode. The ruby crystal had a 0.05 per cent residual chromium content. The pump power was 8 milliwatts at a liquid helium bath temperature of 4.2°K. To be sure that the saturation of the f_{14} transition was primarily due to harmonic spin-coupling, the second-harmonic power output of the pump power source in the 18- to 26-kmc range was measured and was found to be less than 1 microwatt. Further measurements, such as gain-bandwidth product and tuning range, are in progress.

Harmonic spin coupling and cross-relaxation effects play an important role in masers and have relaxation times normally short compared with spin-lattice relaxation times.[4,5] Higher-order cross-relaxation effects[6] are probably responsible for transient maser action reported in hyperfine structure of $Cu(NH_4)_2(SO_4)_2 \cdot 6H_2O$ with a signal frequency 200 mc higher than the pump frequency.[7] In addition to the presently-described mode of operation, other interesting schemes for maser operation can be obtained,[8] in which harmonic spin-coupling effects are of importance. By taking advantage of this mechanism, it can be expected that CW millimeter-wave maser amplifiers using low-frequency pump sources (and frequency ratios higher than 2) will become available in the foreseeable future.

Stimulating discussions with Prof. M. Birnbaum, Polytechnic Institute of Brooklyn, are gratefully acknowledged. The author also wishes to thank Prof. A. E. Siegman for discussions and an advance copy of the paper by Chang.[5]

Frank R. Arams
Airborne Instruments Lab.
Melville, L. I., N. Y.

[4] S. Shapiro and N. Bloembergen, "Relaxation Effects in a Maser Material, $K_3(CoCr)(CN)_6$," Cruft Lab., Harvard University, Cambridge, Mass., Tech. Rept. No. 306; June, 1959.

[5] W. S. C. Chang, "Spin-Lattice Relaxation via Harmonic Coupling," *Proc. Conf. Quantum Electronics—Resonance Phenomena*, Bloomingburg, N. Y., September 14, 1959; to be published by Columbia University Press, New York, N. Y.

[6] P. Sorokin, G. Lasher, and I. Gelles, "Cross-Relaxation and Maser Pumping by a Quadruple Spin Flip Mechanism," *Proc. Conf. Quantum Electronics—Resonance Phenomena*, Bloomingburg, N. Y., September 14, 1959; to be published by Columbia University Press, New York, N. Y.

[7] F. R. Nash and E. Rosenvasser, "Cross-Relaxation and Maser Action in $Cu(NH_4)_2(SO_4)_2 \cdot 6H_2O$," *Proc. Conf. Quantum Electronics—Resonance Phenomena*, Bloomingburg, N. Y., September 14, 1959; to be published by Columbia University Press, New York, N. Y.

[8] F. R. Arams, "Low-field X-band ruby maser," Proc. IRE, vol. 46, p. 1373; August, 1959.

Reprinted from THE PHYSICAL REVIEW, Vol. 113, No. 6, 1538–1544, March 15, 1959

Role of Double-Quantum Transitions in Masers*

SHAUL YATSIV†
Stanford University, Stanford, California
(Received July 7, 1958)

A generalized treatment of a three-level maser as an example of double-irradiation experiments is based on a previous analysis of multiple-quantum transitions in nuclear magnetic resonance. The emphasis in the present treatment, as distinct from other expositions of the same problem, is on the role of the double-quantum transitions. In particular, conditions are found in which the maser operation is mainly governed by the double-quantum process and does not require a true "pumping" stage. Such a case is realizable in practice but its technical applicability is questionable. A study of the behavior of various transitions in this example is instructive for understanding the general role of the double-quantum transitions in double-resonance experiments.

SEVERAL workers[1,2] have observed that Bloembergen's original theory[3] of the three-level maser requires a generalization to include the effects of double-quantum transitions. Such transitions involving simultaneous double-quantum jumps are frequently encountered when a quantum-mechanical system is subject to two different radiation fields. In these cases double-quantum processes are superposed on the ordinary single-quantum transitions and should, therefore, modify the expressions for the transition probabilities obtained with the assumption of pure single-quantum processes. This generalization was elegantly discussed by Javan,[1] who calculated the time dependence of the state amplitudes under the combined influence of the radiation fields and a collision-type relaxation process. His method gives better physical insight than the more compact but essentially equivalent density matrix formulation. On the other hand, his model for the relaxation processes is not sufficiently refined to treat a general multilevel system involving several independent relaxation parameters.

The present note, being the outcome of an independent formulation, is concerned with the role of double-quantum transitions in double-irradiation experiments. In the analysis, the special case of the three-level maser will be used as an example. Particular attention is paid to physical conditions that make the double-quantum process relatively more important than the single-quantum transition. In the following discussion we assume that a quantum-mechanical system with discrete energy levels interacts simultaneously with two radiation fields of widely different frequencies. The two radiation fields are capable of inducing ordinary single-quantum transitions in two different energy intervals. A double-quantum process can take place only if these intervals have a common energy level, so that only three levels are considered. Since the interesting results as regards the relative importance of single- and double-quantum transitions are indepenent of the nature of the system or of its interaction with the radiation fields, any operator related to these properties is kept in as general form as possible. Henceforth, the quantum-mechanical system will be referred to as "the system." It is in contact with a "thermal bath" which is responsible for the relaxation processes in the various intervals. The interaction energy $\hbar G$ of the system with the thermal bath is considered as a perturbation on the eigenstates of the energy operators $\hbar E$ of the system and $\hbar F$ of the thermal bath. However, since the energy spectrum of the thermal bath is practically continuous, it is necessary to have recourse to Dirac's perturbation theory in following the time development of the distribution matrix σ of the system. This was done by Bloch and Wangness[4] in formulating a general theory of relaxation. Their methods and notation are followed in the present work which is also closely related to a previous analysis[5] of multiple-quantum transitions in nuclear magnetic resonance.

Let the energies of the three levels, expressed in units of angular frequency, be a, b, and c, where $a>b>c$ and $a-b\neq b-c$ (Fig. 1), In the ordinary operation of a three-level maser the transition $c-a$ is saturated with radiation of frequency $\omega_1\approx a-c$. This saturation may lead to inversion of the population difference in one of the subintervals $a-b$ or $b-c$. Let us arbitrarily assume that this inversion takes place in the latter interval so that the population of the level b is higher than that of c. Applying a second radiation field with frequency $\omega_2\approx b-c$ will induce stimulated emission in this interval. The system serves primarily as a frequency converter: it absorbs radiation energy at one frequency and releases part of it as an induced emission at a lower frequency. Emission can also be induced by a different mechanism which is of a double-quantum nature. For instance, a transition from b to a occurs when a quantum with frequency ω_1 is absorbed and a quantum with frequency ω_2 is simultaneously emitted. This is accompanied by the inverse process which is weighted down

* Supported in part by the joint program of the Office of Naval Research and the U. S. Atomic Energy Commission.
† On leave from the Hebrew University of Jerusalem, Israel.
[1] A. Javan, Phys. Rev. **107**, 1579 (1957).
[2] A. M. Clogston, J. Phys. Chem. Solids 4, 271 (1958); P. W. Anderson, J. Appl. Phys. **28**, 1049 (1957).
[3] N. Bloembergen, Phys. Rev. **104**, 324 (1956).
[4] R. K. Wangness and F. Bloch, Phys. Rev. **89**, 728 (1953); F. Bloch, Phys. Rev. **102**, 104 (1956); F. Bloch, Phys. Rev. **105**, 1205 (1957). Hereafter referred to as I, II, and III, respectively.
[5] S. Yatsiv, preceding paper [Phys. Rev. **113**, 1522 (1959)].

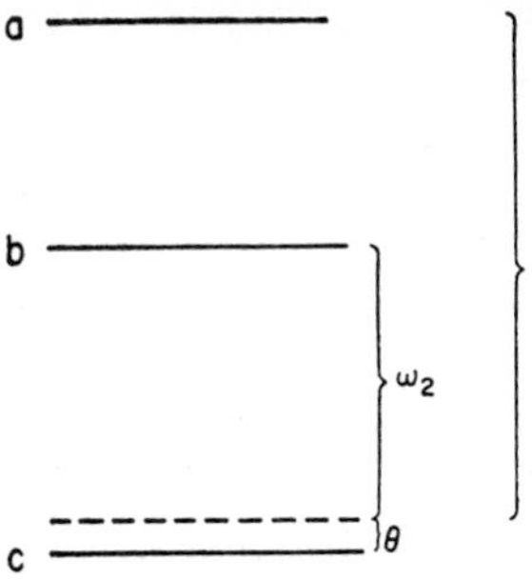

FIG. 1. Diagram of 3-level system.

by the population ratio of the levels b and a so that a net absorption takes place at the frequency ω_1 and a net emission at ω_2. It should be noted that in the double-quantum process the population of the level c does not change through a direct interaction with the radiation field. It will be shown further that the emission accompanying the pure double-quantum process is possible in either of the two subintervals $a-b$ or $b-c$, in contradistinction to the situation in the ordinary operation of a maser.

In the following formulation the two radiation fields have frequencies $\omega_1 \approx a-c$ and $\omega_2 \approx b-c$. This is necessary to obtain continuous induced emission at the frequency ω_2. However, the general results, and in particular the results for conditions where the double-quantum process predominates, apply with only formal modification to the case where two radiations induce transitions in any two of the intervals $a-b$, $b-c$, $a-c$. The equations determining the distribution matrix σ are based upon the treatment presented in Secs. 1 and 2 of II. The notation used there will be followed in the present treatment, with g and g' denoting any two of the nondegenerate energy levels a, b and c.

Following Eqs. (2.47) and (2.48) in II, the distribution matrix can be written in the form

$$\sigma = \sigma_0 + \chi, \tag{1}$$

where σ_0, given by

$$\sigma_0 = \zeta e^{-\beta g} \delta_{gg'}, \quad (\beta = \hbar/kT;\ \zeta = [\textstyle\sum_g e^{-\beta g}]^{-1}) \tag{2}$$

is the solution in the absence of radiation fields, and χ satisfies the equation

$$\frac{d}{dt}(g|\chi|g') + i(g|[E_0+E_1, \chi]|g') + i(g|[E_1,\sigma_0]|g') - (g|\Gamma(\chi)|g') = 0, \tag{3}$$

with

$$(g|\Gamma(\chi)|g') = \textstyle\sum_p [2e^{\beta p}\Gamma_{gg'}{}^p (g+p|\chi|g'+p) - (\Gamma_{gg}{}^p + \Gamma_{g'g'}{}^p)(g|\chi|g')], \tag{4}$$

derived from Eq. (2.44) of II. In the present case, $\hbar E_0$ is the energy of the system in the absence of radiation and has the eigenvalues $\hbar a$, $\hbar b$ and $\hbar c$. $\hbar E_1$ is the interaction energy of the system with the radiation fields and has the form

$$E_1 = D_1 e^{i\omega_1 t} + D_1^* e^{-i\omega_1 t} + D_2 e^{i\omega_2 t} + D_2^* e^{-i\omega_2 t}. \tag{5}$$

D_1 and D_2 are time-independent operators otherwise unspecified, whose form depends on the nature of the interaction. The term $(g|\Gamma(\chi)|g')$ in (4) represents the interaction of the system with the thermal bath, leading to the relaxation processes. The coefficients $\Gamma_{gg'}{}^p$ are defined in Eq. (2.45) of II.

The conditions upon which Eq. (3) is based are given in (2.33) of II and can be rewritten in the form

$$(|D_1|, |D_2|, 1/T_1, 1/T_2) \ll (\omega_1, \omega_2, \omega^*, 1/\beta), \tag{6}$$

where T_1 and T_2 represent orders of magnitude of quantities with properties of "longitudinal" and "transversal" relaxation times,[6] related to the various intervals on hand. The characteristic frequency ω^* is defined and discussed in Sec. 3 of I. For systems embedded in a solid matrix, it indicates the frequency where the phonon spectrum attains its maximum. Assuming that this spectrum has a Debye distribution and for temperatures well below the Debye temperature of the matrix material, one finds approximately $\omega \approx 3kT/\hbar \approx 4\times 10^{11}\, T$ rad/sec which satisfies the inequality (6) for all practical purposes.

The specific condition for which we wish to solve Eq. (3) require as additional assumptions that the matrix elements $(c|D_1|a) = (a|D_1^*|c)^*$ and $(c|D_2|b) = (b|D_2^*|c)^*$ are different from zero, and that the frequencies ω_2 and ω_2 are sufficiently close to their respective resonances so that the condition

$$(|\omega_1 - (a-c)|,\ |\omega_2 - (b-c)|) \ll (\omega_1, \omega_2) \tag{7}$$

is satisfied.

A quantity which is relevant to maser operation is the time-average power exchange between the system and the radiation field. A convenient expression for this power is

$$P = N\hbar \lim_{t\to\infty} \frac{1}{t} \int_0^t \langle \dot{E}_1 \rangle dt. \tag{8}$$

In other words, the power exchange with a sample containing N individual systems is equal to the time average of the statistical expectation value, $\langle\ \rangle$, of the operator $\hbar E_1$. A proof of the validity of the definitation (8) is due to Halbach and is presented in Appendix I.

With the explicit form (5) for E_1, Eq. (8) becomes

$$P = N\hbar \lim_{t\to\infty} \frac{1}{t} \int_0^t \{ i\omega_1(\langle D_1\rangle e^{i\omega_1 t} - \langle D_1^*\rangle e^{-i\omega_1 t}) + i\omega_2(\langle D_2\rangle e^{i\omega_2 t} - \langle D_2^*\rangle e^{-i\omega_2 t})\} dt$$

$$= -N\hbar \lim_{t\to\infty} \frac{2}{t} \int_0^t \mathrm{Im}\{\omega_1 \langle D_1\rangle e^{i\omega_1 t} + \omega_2 \langle D_2\rangle e^{-i\omega_2 t}\} dt. \tag{9}$$

The only nonvanishing contribution to (9) arises

[6] F. Bloch, Phys. Rev. 70, 460 (1946).

from the part $\langle D_1\rangle_{-\omega_1}$ of $\langle D_1\rangle$ that varies as $e^{-i\omega_1 t}$, and the part $\langle D_2\rangle_{-\omega_2}$ of $\langle D_2\rangle$ that varies as $e^{-i\omega_2 t}$. Since D_1 and D_2 are independent of one another, the expressions for the power exchange at the two frequencies are

$$P_{\omega_1}=-2N\hbar\omega_1\,\mathrm{Im}[\langle D_1\rangle_{-\omega_1}e^{i\omega_1 t}],$$
$$P_{\omega_2}=-2N\hbar\omega_2\,\mathrm{Im}[\langle D_2\rangle_{-\omega_2}e^{i\omega_2 t}]. \qquad (10)$$

To facilitate the solution of Eq. (3), it is convenient to expand χ in the form

$$\chi=\sum_{n_1,n_2}\chi_{n_1\omega_1+n_2\omega_2}e^{i(n_1\omega_1+n_2\omega_2)t}, \qquad (11)$$

with coefficients $\chi_{n_1\omega_1+n_2\omega_2}$ that are independent of the time. The periodic form of (11) implies that transient solutions are disregarded. Since χ is Hermitian, the coefficients in (11) satisfy the relation

$$\chi_{n_1\omega_1+n_2\omega_2}=\chi^*{}_{-n_1\omega_1-n_2\omega_2}. \qquad (12)$$

As a result of conditions (7), only a few of the matrix-elements of Eq. (3) need be considered. All the others can be neglected in a way similar to that involved in the derivation of Eqs. (3.7), (3.11)–(3.13) in II. Substituting expression (11) for χ into Eq. (3) leads to a set of relations between the matrix elements of $\chi_{n_1\omega_1+n_2\omega_2}$. Each of these relations consists of mutually independent constituents, characterized by their specific time dependences. As a result, every relation can be split into separate smaller equations relating only components with the same time dependence. Conditions (6) and (7) then ensure that the matrix elements $(g|\chi_{n_1\omega_1+n_2\omega_2}|g')$ approximately satisfying the resonance condition

$$g'-g\cong n_1\omega_1+n_2\omega_2 \qquad (13)$$

are considerably larger than any of the others. Neglecting matrix elements that do not satisfy Eq. (13), one arrives at the following equations and their complex conjugate for the "resonance" matrix elements:

$$(\omega_2-\omega_1+a-b-i\Gamma_{ab})(a|\chi_{\omega_2-\omega_1}|b)$$
$$+(a|D_1^*|c)(c|\chi_{\omega_2}|b)-(a|\chi_{-\omega_1}|c)(c|D_2|b)=0, \qquad (14)$$

$$(-\omega_1+a-c-i\Gamma_{ac})(a|\chi_{-\omega_1}|c)$$
$$-(a|\chi_{\omega_2-\omega_1}|b)(b|D_2^*|c)$$
$$+(a|D_1^*|c)[\chi(c)-\chi(a)+\sigma_0(c)-\sigma_0(a)]=0, \qquad (15)$$

$$(\omega_2+c-b-i\Gamma_{cb})(c|\chi_{\omega_2}|b)+(c|D_1|a)(a|\chi_{\omega_2-\omega_1}|b)$$
$$+(c|D_2|b)[\chi(b)-\chi(c)+\sigma_0(b)-\sigma_0(c)]=0, \qquad (16)$$

$$\sum_p[e^{\beta p}\chi(g+p)-\chi(g)]\Gamma_{gg}{}^p$$
$$=\mathrm{Im}(g|[\chi_{-\omega_1},D_1]+[\chi_{\omega_2},D_2^*]|g), \qquad (17)$$

with

$$\sigma_0(g)=\zeta e^{-\beta g},\quad \chi(g)=(g|\chi_0|g). \qquad (18)$$

Equations (17) relate the dynamic equilibrium population changes of the various levels under the combined influence of the radiation fields and the relaxation processes.

Introducing the notation

$$(c|D_1|a)(a|\chi_{-\omega_1}|c)=\mathrm{Re}_1+iI_1,$$
$$(b|D_2^*|c)(c|\chi_{\omega_2}|b)=\mathrm{Re}_2+iI_2, \qquad (19)$$

leads to the following explicit form of Eq. (16):

$$\sum_p[e^{\beta p}\chi(a+p)-\chi(a)]\Gamma_{aa}{}^p=I_1, \qquad (20)$$

$$\sum_p[e^{\beta p}\chi(b+p)-\chi(b)]\Gamma_{bb}{}^p=-I_2, \qquad (21)$$

$$\sum_p[e^{\beta p}\chi(c+p)-\chi(c)]\Gamma_{cc}{}^p=-I_1+I_2. \qquad (22)$$

A further condition, $\mathrm{Tr}\chi=0$, arises from the normalizing condition $\mathrm{Tr}\sigma=1$ and the definition (1). The number of relations imposed by Eqs. (20)–(22) and by $\mathrm{Tr}\chi=0$ is not overabundant since the three equations are independent as seen from the relation

$$\sum_{pg}[e^{\beta p}\chi(g+p)-\chi(g)]\Gamma_{gg}{}^p=0, \qquad (23)$$

which holds for any set of values $\chi(g)$, in virtue of the relation

$$\Gamma_{gg}{}^p=e^{-\beta p}\Gamma_{g+p,\,g+p}{}^{-p}. \qquad (24)$$

The latter relation is given in Eq. (2.46) of II for $g=g'$. It expresses the fact that the probability ratio for the system to gain or lose an energy quantum hp through relaxation processes is given by $e^{-\beta p}$. The frequencies $\Gamma_{gg}{}^p$, defined in Eq. (2.45) of II, are positive since the operator G is Hermitian. In most practical applications the inequality $\beta p\ll 1$ is amply satisfied so that Eqs. (20)–(23) can be rewritten in an approximate form where $e^{\mp\beta p}$ is replaced by unity. It should be noted, however, that this approximation is justifiable only for determining the small deviations $\chi(g)$ from the equilibrium distribution $\sigma_0(g)$. If used for determining the quantities $\sigma_0(g)$ themselves, it would have led to an unrealistic uniform population distribution, to begin with. Introducing accordingly the notation

$$\Gamma_{aa}{}^{c-a}\cong\Gamma_{cc}{}^{a-c}=1/R_1,\quad \Gamma_{aa}{}^{b-a}\cong\Gamma_{bb}{}^{a-b}=1/R_3,$$
$$\Gamma_{cc}{}^{b-c}\cong\Gamma_{bb}{}^{c-b}=1/R_2, \qquad (25)$$

and considering Eqs. (20)–(22) as representing relations in a circuit diagram, with the potentials $\chi(g)$, the currents I_i, and the resistances R_i (Fig. 2), one arrives at the following solution for the voltages $\chi(a)-\chi(c)$ and $\chi(c)-\chi(b)$:

$$\chi(a)-\chi(c)=TI_2-T_{ac}I_1, \qquad (26)$$

$$\chi(c)-\chi(b)=TI_1-T_{cb}I_2. \qquad (27)$$

The quantities

$$T_{ac}=\frac{R_1(R_2+R_3)}{R_1+R_2+R_3},\quad T_{cb}=\frac{R_2(R_1+R_3)}{R_1+R_2+R_3},$$
$$T=\frac{R_1R_2}{R_1+R_2+R_3}, \qquad (28)$$

are positive and have the dimensions of time as follows from the definitions (25).

Being particularly concerned with the relative importance of the single- *versus* double-quantum transition probability, we shall assume that the resonance condition for the double-quantum process is satisfied at all times. This is expressed by

$$a-b+\omega_2-\omega_1=0, \tag{29}$$

which, together with the identity $\omega_2-\omega_1+a-b=(\omega_2+c-b)+(-\omega_1+a-c)$, leads to

$$-\omega_1+a-c=-(\omega_2+c-b)=\theta. \tag{30}$$

The quantity θ measures the frequency deviations of ω_1 and ω_2 from their respective single-quantum resonance values. With these notations and results the solution of Eqs. (14)–(17) is carried out in Appendix II.

Expressions (10) for the power exchange at the two frequencies ω_1 and ω_2 can be considerably modified by using definitions (1), (11), and (19), and the properties of σ_0 and $\chi_{n_1\omega_1+n_2\omega_2}$ previously described. This leads to

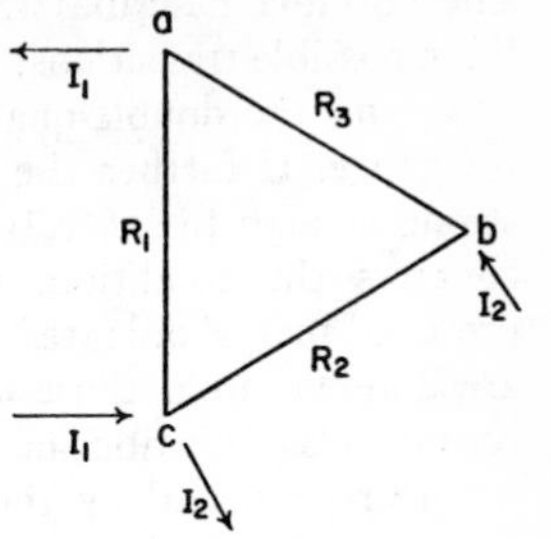

FIG. 2. Equivalent circuit diagram for $\beta p \ll 1$.

$$P_{\omega_1}=-2N\hbar\omega_1\,\mathrm{Im}[(c|D_1|a)(a|\chi_{-\omega_1}|c)]=-2N\hbar\omega_1 I_1, \tag{31}$$

$$P_{\omega_2}=-2N\hbar\omega_2\,\mathrm{Im}[(c|D_2|b)(b|\chi_{-\omega_2}|c)]=2N\hbar\omega_2 I_2. \tag{32}$$

With the values of I_1 and I_2 derived in Appendix II, these expressions take the form

$$P_{\omega_1}=\frac{2N\hbar\omega_1|d_1|^2\left\{\sigma_0(c)-\sigma_0(a)+\dfrac{|d_2|^2[\sigma_0(b)-\sigma_0(c)](T+\Gamma^{-1}+w\theta^2)}{\Gamma_2+|d_1|^2\Gamma^{-1}+|d_2|^2T_{cb}+w\theta^2(\Gamma\Gamma_1+|d_2|^2)}\right\}}{\Gamma_1+|d_2|^2\Gamma^{-1}+|d_1|^2T_{ac}+w\theta^2(\Gamma\Gamma_2+|d_1|^2)-\dfrac{|d_1d_2|^2(T+\Gamma^{-1}+w\theta^2)^2}{\Gamma_2+|d_1|^2\Gamma^{-1}+|d_2|^2T_{cb}+w\theta^2(\Gamma\Gamma_1+|d_2|^2)}}, \tag{33}$$

$$P_{\omega_2}=\frac{2N\hbar\omega_2|d_2|^2\left\{\sigma_0(c)-\sigma_0(b)+\dfrac{|d_1|^2[\sigma_0(a)-\sigma_0(c)](T+\Gamma^{-1}+w\theta^2)}{\Gamma_1+|d_2|^2\Gamma^{-1}+|d_1|^2T_{ac}+w\theta^2(\Gamma\Gamma_2+|d_1|^2)}\right\}}{\Gamma_2+|d_1|^2\Gamma^{-1}+|d_2|^2T_{cb}+w\theta^2(\Gamma\Gamma_1+|d_2|^2)-\dfrac{|d_1d_2|^2(T+\Gamma^{-1}+w\theta^2)^2}{\Gamma_1+|d_2|^2\Gamma^{-1}+|d_1|^2T_{ac}+w\theta^2(\Gamma\Gamma_2+|d_1|^2)}}, \tag{34}$$

where $d_1=(c|D_1|a)$, $d_2=(b|D_2|c)$ and $w=(\Gamma\Gamma_1\Gamma_2+\Gamma_1|d_1|^2+\Gamma_2|d_2|^2)^{-1}$, with $\Gamma=\Gamma_{ab}$, $\Gamma_1=\Gamma_{ac}$ and $\Gamma_2=\Gamma_{cb}$. The expression in curly brackets in the numerator of both equations represents effective population differences between the corresponding energy intervals. The deviation of these differences from the Boltzmann population distribution is due to the presence of the second radiation field. When $d_2=0$ in (33) and $d_1=0$ in (34), both expressions reduce to the ordinary power absorption at the respective intervals.

DISCUSSION

We shall examine Eq. (34) for the power exchange at the lower frequency ω_2. At this frequency the quantum-mechanical system can emit induced radiation under favorable circumstances. However, most of the results are equally applicable to the expression (34) for the power exchange P_{ω_1}. The quantity θ defined in (30) is a convenient parameter in discussing the relative contributions of single- and double-quantum transitions to the power exchange. For that purpose we consider separately two ranges of values for θ.

A. θ Comparable to or Smaller than the Natural Line Widths

$$\theta \lesssim (\Gamma,\Gamma_1,\Gamma_2). \tag{35}$$

In this region the quantity $w\theta^2$ in (34) satisfies the relation

$$w\theta^2 \lesssim 1/|\Gamma|, \tag{36}$$

where $|\Gamma|$ represents the order of magnitude of the quantities Γ, Γ_1, and Γ_2. Consequently, it is not difficult to show that the expression (34) for $\theta=0$ is not appreciably different from its value for $\theta\neq 0$. In the latter case Eq. (34) becomes

$$P_{\omega_2}=\frac{2N\hbar\omega_2|d_2|^2\left\{\sigma_0(c)-\sigma_0(b)+\dfrac{|d_1|^2[\sigma_0(a)-\sigma_0(c)](\Gamma^{-1}+T)}{\Gamma_1+|d_2|^2\Gamma^{-1}+|d_1|^2T_{ac}}\right\}}{\Gamma_2+|d_1|^2\Gamma^{-1}+|d_2|^2T_{cb}-\dfrac{|d_1d_2|^2(\Gamma^{-1}+T)^2}{\Gamma_1+|d_2|^2\Gamma^{-1}+|d_1|^2T_{ac}}}. \tag{37}$$

This formula describes the power exchange when all three possible transitions, i.e., the single-quantum $c-b$, $c-a$, and the double-quantum transition $b-a$ are on resonance. If further the radiation of frequency ω_1 is strong enough to saturate the transition $c-a$, one encounters the conditions under which Bloembergen's proposed maser[3] operates. However, the present results are different from those of Bloembergen in that they contain also contributions of a pure double-quantum nature represented by the terms containing Γ^{-1}. It is true that in solids one generally finds $|T|\gg|\Gamma^{-1}|$, where $|T|$ and $|\Gamma|$ stand for the orders of magnitude of (T_{ac},T_{cb},T) and $(\Gamma,\Gamma_1,\Gamma_2)$, respectively. In that case saturation is reached with values of d_1 and d_2 considerably smaller than $|\Gamma|$. With such small values of d_1 and d_2 one can neglect the terms containing Γ^{-1} in (35) so that

$$P_{\omega 2}=\frac{2N\hbar\omega_2|d_2|^2\{\sigma_0(c)-\sigma_0(b)-[\sigma_0(c)-\sigma_0(a)]TT_{ac}^{-1}\}}{\Gamma_2+|d_2|^2(T_{cb}-T^2T_{ac}^{-1})}. \tag{38}$$

This expression is seen to be equivalent to Eq. (4) in Bloembergen's article[3] by taking account of the different notation. The quantities w_{ij} employed in Eq. (1) of his article are equal to the quantities $R_{1,2,3}^{-1}$ in the approximation $\beta p\ll 1$ used in both treatments. In this approximation the following relations are found to hold:

$$w_{31}=w_{13}=\frac{1}{R_1}=\frac{T_{cb}-T}{T_{ac}T_{cb}-T^2},\quad w_{12}=w_{21}=\frac{1}{R_2}=\frac{T_{ac}-T}{T_{ac}T_{cb}-T^2},$$

$$w_{23}=w_{32}=\frac{1}{R_3}=\frac{T}{T_{ac}T_{cb}-T^2}. \tag{39}$$

The denominators are all positive definite as is evident from the definitions (28).

Equation (38) represents a genuine absorption process as long as the numerator is positive. But, when the relation

$$[\sigma_0(c)-\sigma_0(a)]T>[\sigma_0(c)-\sigma_0(b)]T_{ac} \tag{40}$$

is satisfied, the effective population difference of the levels c and b is opposite in sign to the usual Boltzmann population difference and an induced emission takes place. In that case, Eq. (39) gives the power emitted at the frequency ω_2. For large values of $|d_2|^2$, this power attains a maximum

$$P_{\omega 2}(\max)=\frac{2N\hbar\omega_2\{[\sigma_0(c)-\sigma_0(b)]T_{ac}-[\sigma_0(c)-\sigma_0(b)]T\}}{T_{ac}T_{cb}-T^2}. \tag{41}$$

Such conditions, however, imply saturation of the transition $b-c$ and are seldom encountered in practice.

For nonviscous fluids, where the relation $|T|\approx|\Gamma|^{-1}$ holds and for arbitrary large values of d_1 and d_2, the more general expression (37) applies. The distinctive properties of this expression, as compared with a treatment that ignores the double-quantum effects, lies in the terms containing Γ^{-1}. The terms $|d_1|^2\Gamma^{-1}$ and $|d_2|^2\Gamma^{-1}$ indicate a shift in the resonance frequency of the double-quantum transition and will be discussed further in the next section. The term appearing in conjunction with the time T in the circular brackets modifies the effective population difference and the saturation properties of the signal as a result of the double-quantum effects. In general, however, it is difficult to make in this region a clear distinction between the contributions of transitions of different multiplicity. Such distinction is easily recognized for sufficiently large values of θ as discussed in the next section.

B. θ Large Compared to the Line Width

In this region, which is of particular interest in the present treatment, θ^2 is large compared with $|d_1|^2|\Gamma||T|$ and $|d_2|^2|\Gamma||T|$, and the driving field represented by d_1 is large compared to the line width $|\Gamma|$;

$$\theta^2\gg(|d_1|^2+|d_2|^2)|\Gamma||T|;\quad |d_1|>|\Gamma|. \tag{42}$$

The fact that $|\Gamma||T|\gtrsim 1$ implies also the less stringent condition

$$\theta^2\gg|d_1|^2+|d_2|^2, \tag{43}$$

which together with the second part of (42) indicates that the two single-quantum transitions $c-a$ and $c-b$ are far off their respective resonance frequencies. This fact and the assumed magnitude of d_1 will be shown to insure that the double-quantum transition predominates over the off-resonance value of the single-quantum transitions.

Considerable simplification of Eq. (34) can be carried out by dividing the numerator and denominator of the right-hand side by θ^2 and expanding each of them in powers of θ^{-2}. With condition (42) determining which terms can be neglected, Eq. (34) becomes

$$P_{\omega 2}=\frac{2N\hbar\omega_2|d_1d_2|^2\theta^{-2}[\sigma_0(a)-\sigma_0(b)]\Gamma}{\Gamma^2+(|d_1|^2-|d_2|^2)^2\theta^{-2}+|d_1d_2|^2\theta^{-2}(T_{ac}+T_{cb}-2T)\Gamma}. \tag{44}$$

The distinctive property of this expression is that, since $\sigma_0(a)-\sigma_0(b)$ is a negative quantity, it represents power emission which does not require a pumping process. This emission is due to a pure double-quantum transition as borne out by the fact that $P_{\omega 2}$ vanishes when either d_1 or d_2 is zero. The system undergoes a transition from b to a by a simultaneous absorption of a quantum with frequency ω_1 and emission of another with frequency ω_2. This process is accompanied by its inverse: emission at ω_1 and absorption at ω_2, but this inverse process is weighed down by the population ratio of the levels b and a. The term $(|d_1|^2-|d_2|^2)^2\theta^{-2}$ in the denominator of (44) is the square of a frequency shift of the double-quantum resonance, similar to that encountered in Eq. (2.33) of reference 5. Here it appears isolated, that is, unassociated with the deviation of $\omega_1-\omega_2$ from its exact double-quantum resonance value, only because this deviation was chosen zero at the outset [Eq. (29)]. The inequality (43) indicates that this shift is much smaller than θ and we shall assume that it does not become larger than the line width $|\Gamma|$ and, therefore, can be ignored.

In solids, where $|T|\gg|\Gamma|^{-1}$, and also for $\theta^2\gg|\Gamma|^3|T|$ it is possible to saturate the double-quantum transition by meeting the condition

$$|d_1d_2|^2\gg\theta^2\Gamma(T_{ac}+T_{cb}-2T)^{-1} \tag{45}$$

without violating conditions (42) or the assumption that the frequency shift $(|d_1|^2-|d_2|^2)\theta^{-1}$ is smaller than the line width $|\Gamma|$. The power emitted then approaches a maximum value

$$|P_{\omega_2}(\max)|=\frac{2N\hbar\omega_2[\sigma_0(b)-\sigma_0(a)]}{T_{ac}+T_{cb}-2T}, \tag{46}$$

which is comparable with favorable cases described in Eq. (41) for the ordinary operation of masers. Such conditions, however, are difficult to achieve in practice.

It is easy to show that in the absence of radiation with frequency ω_1 ($d_1=0$) the off-resonance power absorption of a single-quantum transition at ω_2, subject to conditions (42), is considerably weaker than the double-quantum emission (44) when $d_1=0$. This explains the distinct double-quantum nature of the approximate expression (44). Such relations do not hold for the power exchange at ω_1 under the same conditions since they are not symmetric with respect to d_1 and d_2. In fact, conditions (42) do not restrict the smallness of d_2 so that the off-resonance single-quantum absorption need not be negligible compared with the double-quantum absorption. However, with the added assumption $|d_2|>|\Gamma|$, Eq. (33) can be modified in a way similar to the derivation of (44) so as to give

$$P_{\omega_1}=\frac{2N\hbar\omega_1|d_1d_2|^2\theta^{-2}[\sigma_0(b)-\sigma_0(a)]\Gamma}{\Gamma^2+(|d_2|^2-|d_1|^2)\theta^{-2}+|d_1d_2|^2\theta^{-2}(T_{ac}+T_{cb}-2T)\Gamma} \tag{47}$$

for the power absorbed at the frequency ω_1 via the double-quantum transition. Only a formal modification is required to apply Eqs. (44) and (47) to any pure double-quantum process in the same energy level pattern. In particular, when the two radiation fields are near resonance for transitions in the two subintervals $a-b$ and $b-c$, the two corresponding equations will describe a genuine power absorption in a double-quantum transition from c to a. The restriction of unequal spacing of the two intervals may then be lifted and the resulting formulas will describe a double-quantum transition with *unequal* frequencies in a equidistant pattern of levels (Fig. 3). In the double-quantum transitions described by Eqs. (44) and (47), an amount of energy $\hbar(\omega_1-\omega_2)$ is disposed of by the relaxation processes and transformed into heat. This is essentially the only heating source in this mode of operation because both single-quantum transitions are far off their respective resonance frequencies. On the other hand, in the ordinary "population inversion" mode, additional heating arises from the saturation of the transition $c-a$, i.e., the pumping stage. There, unused energy is dissipated as a direct relaxation from c to a which bypasses the level b and reduces the pumping efficiency.

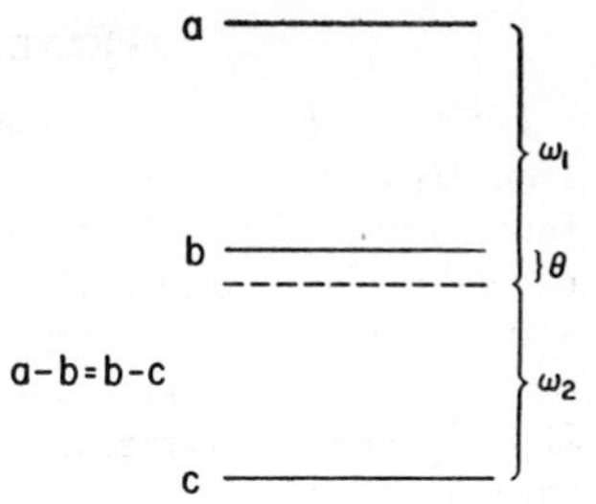

FIG. 3. Equidistant pattern of levels.

It is doubtful whether the double-quantum mode of operation described in this section finds practical applications in the microwave region. The requirement $|d_1|>|\Gamma|$ is too severe for most solid-state masers where the value of $|\Gamma|$ is typically large. In the radiofrequency range, however, an induced emission of the type described by Eq. (44) can be effectively carried out. For example, free radical systems exist in which an electron is coupled to the nucleus by an interaction proportional to $(\mathbf{I}\cdot\mathbf{S})$ and where the lines are relatively narrow.[7] In a dc magnetic field that is too small to decouple the spins of the electron and nucleus, one finds energy intervals whose matrix elements are suitable for double-quantum power emission. There are a few advantages to using a pure double-quantum process for frequency conversion: The choice of suitable systems is not limited by the scarcity of materials in which a useful population inversion can be produced. Furthermore, either of the two subintervals in a three-level arrangement can serve for double-quantum emission as compared with only one in the usual operation. On the other hand, Eq. (38) shows that any drift in the frequency ω_1 or random fluctuations of d_1 will be transformed into a corresponding frequency drift or amplitude variation of the emitted power at ω_2.

ACKNOWLEDGMENTS

It is a pleasure to express my gratitude to Professor F. Bloch for encouragement and many clarifying discussions. Many thanks are due also to Dr. K. Halbach, Dr. B. Herzog, and Dr. M. Mandel for reading the manuscript and for helpful suggestions.

[7] Pake, Weissmann, and Townsend, Discussion Faraday Soc. No. 19, 147 (1955).

APPENDIX I

Let $\hbar(H+E_1)$ represent the total energy of the system. $\hbar H$ is the combined energy of the system and thermal bath in the absence of radiation and does not depend explicitly on the time. $\hbar E_1$ describes the interaction energy of the system with the radiation field. If $\hbar E_1$ consists of periodic functions as, for instance, in Eq. (5), the time-average power exchange of the system with an external radiation field can be defined as

$$P=\lim_{t\to\infty}\frac{\hbar N}{t}\int_0^t \frac{d}{dt}\langle H+E_1\rangle dt. \quad \text{(A1.1)}$$

Here, N is the number of individual systems in the sample, $\langle\Omega\rangle=\mathrm{Tr}(\Omega\rho)$ is the statistical expectation value of the operator Ω, and ρ is the density matrix of the entire system including the bath. Equation (A1.1) defines the required average rate of change in the energy content of the combined system.[8] From the definitions given above, it follows that

$$\frac{d}{dt}\langle H+E_1\rangle=\mathrm{Tr}\{\dot{\rho}(H+E_1)\}+\mathrm{Tr}(\rho\dot{E}_1), \quad \text{(A1.2)}$$

since $\dot{H}=0$ by the assumption. But

$$\mathrm{Tr}\{\dot{\rho}(H+E_1)\} = -i\,\mathrm{Tr}\{[H+E_1,\rho](H+E_1)\}=0, \quad \text{(A1.3)}$$

since $\dot{\rho}=-i[H+E_1,\rho]$. Thus

$$\frac{d}{dt}\langle H+E_1\rangle=\mathrm{Tr}(\rho\dot{E}_1)=\langle\dot{E}_1\rangle, \quad \text{(A1.4)}$$

which leads to Eq. (8) of the text.

APPENDIX II

The following simplified notation is introduced to facilitate the solution of Eqs. (14)–(17):

$$\Gamma_{ab}=\Gamma,\quad \Gamma_{ac}=\Gamma_1,\quad \Gamma_{cb}=\Gamma_2, \quad \text{(A2.1)}$$

$$(c|D_1|a)=d_1,\quad (b|D_2|c)=d_2. \quad \text{(A2.2)}$$

Using further the notation (19), Eqs. (26) and (27) and the value θ of the matrix element $(a|\chi_{\omega_2-\omega_1}|b)$ derived from Eq. (14), one is led to the following modification of Eqs. (15) and (16):

$$[\theta-i(\Gamma_1+|d_2|^2\Gamma^{-1})](a|\chi_{-\omega_1}|c)+id_1^*d_2^*\Gamma^{-1}(c|\chi_{\omega_2}|b) +d_1^*[T_{ac}I_1-TI_2+\sigma_0(c)-\sigma_0(a)]=0, \quad \text{(A2.3)}$$

$$[-\theta-i(\Gamma_2+|d_1|^2\Gamma^{-1})](c|\chi_{\omega_2}|b)+id_1d_2\Gamma^{-1}(a|\chi_{-\omega_1}|c) +d_2[T_{cb}I_2-TI_1+\sigma_0(b)-\sigma_0(c)]=0. \quad \text{(A2.4)}$$

Multiplying Eq. (A2.3) by d_1 and Eq. (A2.4) by d_2 and solving for the unknown quantities Re_1, I_1, Re_2, I_2, defined in (19), one arrives at

$$\mathrm{Re}_1=\theta[(\Gamma\Gamma_2+|d_1|^2)I_1-|d_1|^2I_2]w, \quad \text{(A2.5)}$$

$$\mathrm{Re}_2=\theta[|d_2|^2I_1-(|d_2|^2+\Gamma\Gamma_1)I_2]w, \quad \text{(A2.6)}$$

$$I_1=\frac{-|d_1|^2\left\{\sigma_0(c)-\sigma_0(a)+\dfrac{|d_2|^2[\sigma_0(b)-\sigma_0(c)](T+\Gamma^{-1}+w\theta^2)}{\Gamma_2+|d_1|^2\Gamma^{-1}+|d_2|^2T_{cb}+w\theta^2(\Gamma\Gamma_1+|d_2|^2)}\right\}}{\Gamma_1+|d_2|^2\Gamma^{-1}+|d_1|^2T_{ac}+w\theta^2(\Gamma\Gamma_2+|d_1|^2)-\dfrac{|d_1d_2|^2(T+\Gamma^{-1}+w\theta^2)^2}{\Gamma_2+|d_1|^2\Gamma^{-1}+|d_2|^2T_{cb}+w\theta^2(\Gamma\Gamma_1+|d_2|^2)}}, \quad \text{(A2.7)}$$

$$I_2=\frac{|d_2|^2\left\{\sigma_0(c)-\sigma_0(b)+\dfrac{|d_1|^2[\sigma_0(a)-\sigma_0(c)](T+\Gamma^{-1}+w\theta^2)}{\Gamma_1+|d_2|^2\Gamma^{-1}+|d_1|^2T_{ac}+w\theta^2(\Gamma\Gamma_2+|d_1|^2)}\right\}}{\Gamma_2+|d_1|^2\Gamma^{-1}+|d_2|^2T_{cb}+w\theta^2(\Gamma\Gamma_1+|d_2|^2)-\dfrac{|d_1d_2|^2(T+\Gamma^{-1}+w\theta^2)^2}{\Gamma_1+|d_2|^2\Gamma^{-1}+|d_1|^2T_{ac}+w\theta^2(\Gamma\Gamma_2+|d_1|^2)}}, \quad \text{(A2.8)}$$

with

$$w=(\Gamma\Gamma_1\Gamma_2+\Gamma_1|d_1|^2+\Gamma_2|d_2|^2)^{-1}. \quad \text{(A2.9)}$$

This is used in Eqs. (33) and (36) of the text.

[8] It may seem questionable whether the operator E_1 should be included in the definition of this energy content. For the present case, however, the question is irrelevant since the contribution of the periodic operator E_1 to Eq. (A1.1) can be shown to be zero.

Maser Action in Ruby by Off-Resonance Pumping*

Strong microwave maser action has been obtained in ruby by pumping in the far wings of the pump transition as much as 1400 Mc from its center frequency. In a systematic investigation of the variation of population inversion with pump frequency, several anomalous inversion peaks were observed as the applied pump frequency was moved from the pump transition line center into the wings. For a fixed signal frequency of 1055 Mc, population inversion was maintained for a variation in pump frequency of 2500 Mc.

The investigation was made at 4.2°K for pink ruby (nominally 0.06 per cent Cr^{+++} by weight) whose C axis was oriented at 90° to the applied magnetic field. The experimental structure was similar to that of Geusic, *et al.*[1] This structure permits the direct determination of the population inversion ratio by measuring the magnetic emission (pump on) and magnetic absorption (pump off) over a range of signal frequencies.

Constant Pump Frequency Measurements: A number of measurements were made of the population inversion ratio while keeping the pump frequency constant, and varying the signal frequency f_{12} from 800 to 3400 Mc. (The notation f_{xy} refers to the frequency spacing between energy levels x and y numbered in order of increasing energy.) The incident pump power was kept constant near 200 mw. The applied magnetic field was changed for each signal frequency to correspond to the value required for normal three-level maser operation. Fig. 1 shows the population inversion ratio as a function of signal frequency for a fixed pump frequency $f_p = 12{,}465$ Mc. In addition to the peak at $f_{12} = 2150$ Mc, which corresponds to normal three-level maser operation, two new, relatively strong, inversion peaks are noticed at lower signal frequencies. Another inversion peak is observed near $f_{12} = 3000$ Mc. This operating

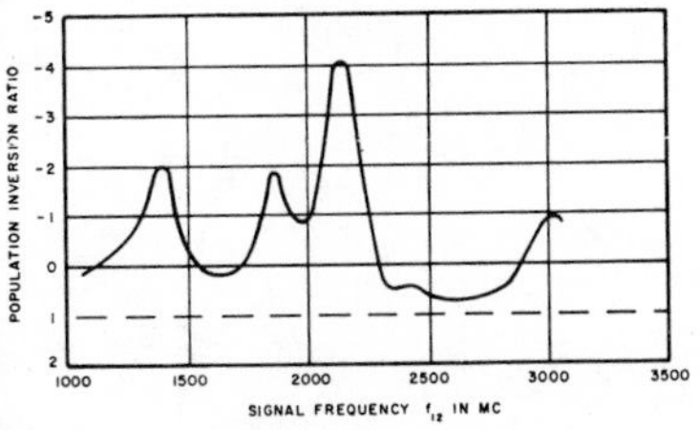

Fig. 1—Population-inversion ratio as a function of signal frequency for a fixed pump frequency $f_p = 12{,}465$ Mc.

point, where $f_p \approx f_{34}$, was shown to give significant gain in a traveling-wave maser.[2]

Constant Signal Frequency Measurement: An interesting measurement of population-inversion ratio as a function of pump frequency was obtained for a fixed signal frequency $f_{12} = 1055$ Mc. The applied magnetic field was kept fixed at its optimum value for normal three-level maser operation. Inversion was maintained for pump frequencies from 9600 to 12,100 Mc—a 2500-Mc range corresponding to more than 40 line widths (Fig. 2). The central peak corresponds to normal three-level operation ($f_p = f_{13}$). The inversion peak at $f_p = 9700$ Mc corresponds to $f_p = f_{23}$, which causes saturation of the f_{14} line via harmonic spin-coupling[3–5] since $f_{14} = 2f_{32}$ here. The refrigeration valley at 8700 Mc is due to $f_p = f_{34}$, and can be accounted for by harmonic spin-coupling ($f_{14} = 2f_{23}$). A strong anomalous inversion peak is observed at $f_p = 11{,}730$ Mc.

These and other measurements are summarized in Fig. 3, where pump frequency is plotted as a function of signal frequency f_{12}. The inversion *peaks* from the various measurements are shown as solid points. We have superimposed lines corresponding to the computed energy levels for ruby.[6] Inversion was obtained at pump frequencies removed as much as 1400 Mc (23 line-widths) from the f_{13} (or any other) resonance line.

In order to interpret the observed anomalous inversion peaks, other theoretical lines corresponding to pump frequencies equal to 1) $f_{13} + f_{12}$ and 2) $f_{34} + f_{12}$ have been superimposed on Fig. 3. The fit between these lines and the experimentally observed inversion peaks is very good. Calculation of the expected inversion, on the basis of a Lorentzian line shape[7] for the pump transition, accounts for the small inversion ratio obtained between the peaks. The anomalous

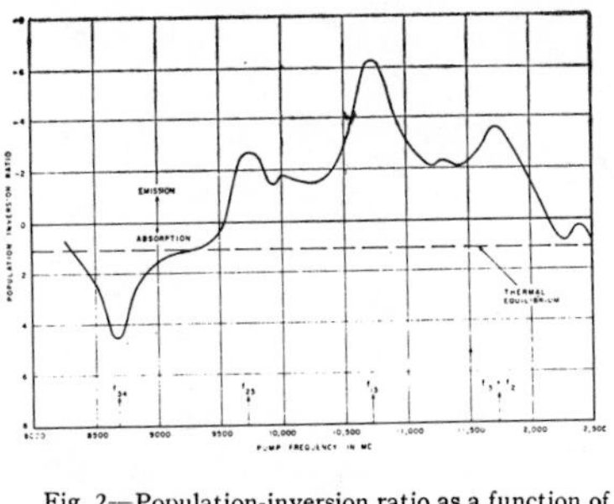

Fig. 2—Population-inversion ratio as a function of pump frequency for fixed signal frequency $f_{12} = 1055$ Mc and fixed magnetic field.

peaks correspond very closely to frequencies at which there is a high probability of multiple spin-flip processes that conserve Zeeman energy and involve several energy levels. We believe these processes to be similar in nature to cross-relaxation processes discussed by Bloembergen *et al.*,[8] for LiF, and analyzed by Van Vleck for crystals with two magnetic species.[9] The predominant, simultaneous triple spin-flip processes corresponding to the anomalous peaks are:

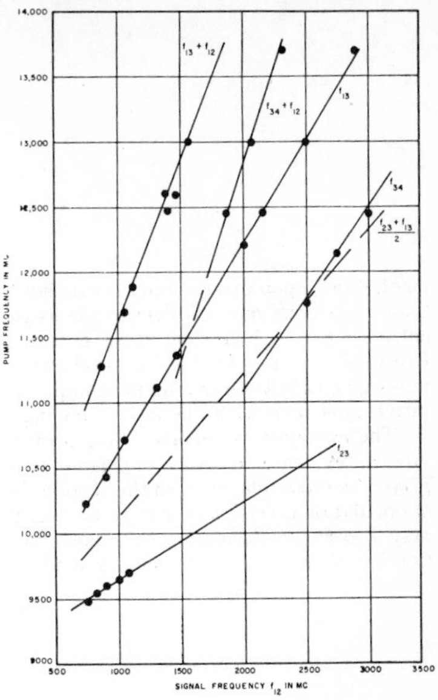

Fig. 3—Inversion peaks and their correlation with computed energy levels and anomalous lines $f_p = f_{13} + f_{12}$ and $f_p = f_{34} + f_{12}$.

For $f_p = f_{13} + f_{12}$, a downward spin-flip at the off-resonance pump frequency, and upward spin-flips from level 1 to 3 and 1 to 2. For $f_p = f_{34} + f_{12}$, a downward spin-flip at the off-resonance pump frequency and upward spin-flips from level 3 to 4, and 1 to 2. These spin-flips are the most probable at that frequency in the wings where energy transfer can occur to the line *centers* while conserving Zeeman energy. A phenomenological treat-

* Received by the IRE, May 4, 1961; revised manuscript received, June 5, 1961. This is part of a Doctoral Dissertation performed at the Polytechnic Institute of Brooklyn, N. Y. The support of the Airborne Instruments Lab., Melville, N. Y., is gratefully acknowledged.

[1] J. Geusic, E. Schulz-DuBois, R. DeGrasse, and H. Scoril, "Three-level spin refrigeration and maser action at 1500 Mc/sec," *J. Appl. Phys.*, vol. 30, pp. 1113–1114; July, 1959.

[2] S. Ahern, private communication. Also, J. Walling and P. A. Gould, Mullard Res. Labs., Salfords, Surrey, Eng. Rept. 2312; December, 1960.

[3] F. Arams, "Maser operation at signal frequencies higher than pump frequency," IRE TRANS. ON MICROWAVE THEORY AND TECHNIQUES, vol. MTT-9, pp. 68–72; January, 1961.

[4] W. H. Higa, "Excitation of an *L*-band ruby maser," in "Quantum Electronics," Columbia University Press, New York, N. Y., p. 298; 1960.

[5] J. E. Geusic, "Harmonic spin coupling in ruby," *Phys. Rev.*, vol. 118, pp. 129–130; April, 1960.

[6] W. S. Chang and A. E. Siegman, "Characteristics of Ruby for Maser Applications," Electron Devices Lab., Stanford Univ., Stanford, Calif., Tech. Rept. 156-2, Figs. 14, 15; September 30, 1958. Also J. Weber, "Masers," *Rev. Mod. Phys.*, vol. 31, pp. 681–710; July, 1959.

[7] C. Kittel and E. Abrahams, "Dipolar broadening of magnetic resonance lines in magnetically diluted crystals," *Phys. Rev.*, vol. 90, pp. 238–239; April, 1953.

[8] N. Bloembergen, S. Shapiro, P. Pershan, and J. Artman, "Cross-relaxation in spin systems," *Phys. Rev.*, vol. 114, pp. 445–459; April, 1959.

[9] J. H. Van Vleck, "Dipolar broadening of magnetic resonance lines in crystals," *Phys. Rev.*, vol. 74, p p1168–1183; November, 1948.

ment, based upon inclusion in the rate equations of the cross-relaxation terms, shows the enhancement in inversion to be expected. Reasonable values for the cross-relaxation times give calculated results in semiquantitative agreement with the measurements.

The experiments reported here provide further evidence of the important role played by cross-relaxation in the attainment of population inversion in masers. Such data may also yield information on cross-relaxation line shape (since the magnetic field can be held constant) and higher-order spin-flip processes that give fine structure. By using a pulsed pump it may be possible to measure the relaxation times of various competing energy transfer processes.[10,11] Furthermore, the maser technique described here appears to be a sensitive tool for studying spin-spin processes and the behavior of paramagnetics in the far wings where the line susceptibility is decreased by orders of magnitude.

F. Arams
Airborne Instruments Lab.
Melville, N. Y.
M. Birnbaum
Polytechnic Institute of Brooklyn
Brooklyn, N. Y.

[10] K. Bowers and W. Mims, "Paramagnetic relaxation in nickel fluos licate," *Phys. Rev.*, vol. 115, pp. 285–295; July, 1959.

[11] W. Mims and J. McGee, "Cross relaxation in ruby," *Phys. Rev.*, vol. 119, pp. 1233–1237; August, 1960.

Reprinted from the PROCEEDINGS OF THE IRE
VOL. 49, NO. 9, SEPTEMBER, 1961

SPIN-LATTICE RELAXATION FROM STATE OF NEGATIVE SUSCEPTIBILITY*

S. A. Collins, Jr.,† R. L. Kyhl, and
M. W. P. Strandberg
Department of Physics,
Department of Electrical Engineering and
Research Laboratory of Electronics,
Massachusetts Institute of Technology,
Cambridge, Massachusetts
(Received December 29, 1958)

A state of negative magnetic susceptibility has been demonstrated in potassium chromicyanide by using a 180° pulse technique. The spin-lattice relaxation from this state has been observed in the time domain, and the complex susceptibility shows no change in slope as it passes through zero.[1]

Negative paramagnetic susceptibility has been demonstrated in nuclear magnetic resonance with the use of both rapid passage[2] and 180° pulse techniques.[3] Negative electron paramagnetic susceptibility has been produced in the three-level maser[4] and in the two-level maser by means of rapid passage.[5,6] The feasibility of generating a negative susceptibility in semiconductors by using spin-echo techniques has also been demonstrated.[7] We have produced negative electron magnetic resonance susceptibility by means of a 180° pulse. The working material was $K_3Co(CN)_6$ containing 0.1% Cr^{3+}. The $-\frac{1}{2}\rightarrow+\frac{1}{2}$ transition at 9000 Mc/sec in a field of 3150 gauss, oriented parallel to the crystalline c-axis, was used.

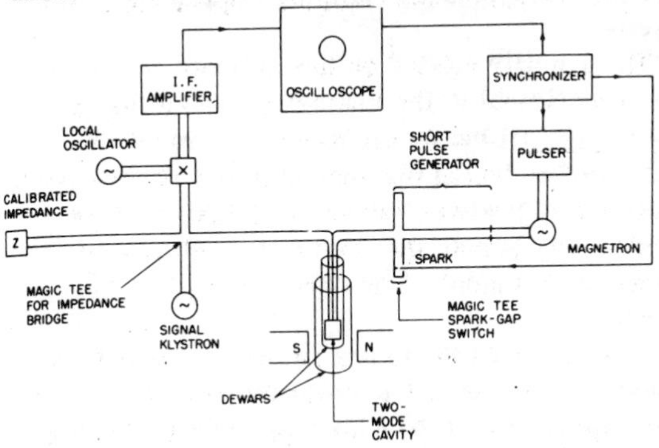

FIG. 1. Block diagram of equipment.

The equipment has been described elsewhere.[8] The general arrangement is shown schematically in Fig. 1. A microwave pulse, roughly 10 mμsec in duration, is generated from energy stored in a cavity formed from a length of waveguide excited by an 0.5-μsec magnetron pulse. One end of the waveguide is opened by firing a spark which unbalances a magic tee "bridge" by changing a plane of reflection. The sample is placed in a cavity that possesses two degenerate, orthogonal modes. The mode to which the short pulse is applied has a very low Q (roughly 30). The other mode, which has a high Q, is used to observe the magnetic resonance of the sample. In order to use a small measuring signal, a superheterodyne detection system (30-Mc/sec i.f.)

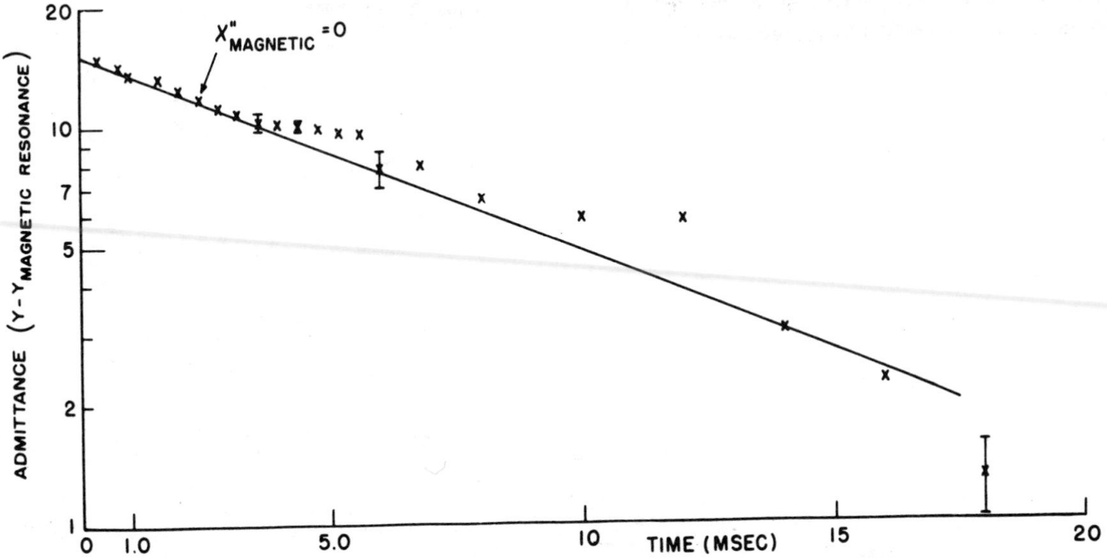

FIG. 2. Semilogarithmic plot of a quantity proportional to magnetic susceptibility *versus* time.

is used. An impedance bridge is used to measure the instantaneous complex impedance of the cavity.

The quantity plotted on the ordinate in Fig. 2 is proportional to the magnetic susceptibility. The cavity filling factor was not determined. The point at which the susceptibility passes from negative to positive values is indicated. It is interesting to note that there is no change in slope at this point. The observed T_1 is 8.65 msec.

As a check on the tuning of the cavity and magnetic field and on the correct interpretation of the experiment, it was also possible to display the complex reflection coefficient of the cavity on an oscilloscope by means of auxiliary equipment that is not shown in Fig. 1 (i.e., a high-speed Smith-chart plotter).

To our understanding, a simple relaxation process uncomplicated by anomalous phonon effects is to be expected in crystals that are as dilute as this at 4.2°K. This result indicates that spin spectral diffusion[9] and the effect of the other levels do not strongly influence the simple decay of the susceptibility. That anomalies can occur in less dilute crystals can be seen, since others,[10] using saturation techniques, obtain for this crystal with 0.5% Cr^{3+} a T_1 of 0.2 sec, independent of spin quantum numbers. Presumably, these measurements have determined a lattice-bath relaxation time rather than a true spin-lattice relaxation time.[11] Thus, measurements of the associated relaxation time from a state of negative magnetic susceptibility shed new light on spin-lattice relaxation processes in paramagnetic crystals.[12]

*This work was supported in part by the U. S. Army (Signal Corps), the U. S. Air Force (Office of Scientific Research, Air Research and Development Command), and the U. S. Navy (Office of Naval Research).

†Now with Sperry Gyroscope Company, Great Neck, New York.

[1]Research on Paramagnetic Resonances, Third Quarterly Progress Report, Signal Corps Contract DA36-039-sc-74895, January - April 1958. (The complete research report, of which this work is only a part, has been unduly delayed, and will be presented later.)

[2]Bloembergen, Purcell, and Pound, Phys. Rev. 73, 679 (1948).

[3]E. L. Hahn, Phys. Rev. 80, 580 (1950).

[4]Scovil, Feher, and Seidel, Phys. Rev. 105, 762 (1957); Strandberg, Davis, Faughnan, Kyhl, and Wolga, Phys. Rev. 105, 447 (1957).

[5]Feher, Gordon, Buehler, Gere, and Thurmond, Phys. Rev. 109, 221 (1958).

[6]Chester, Wagner, and Castle, Phys. Rev. 110, 281 (1958).

[7]J. P. Gordon and K. D. Bowers, Phys. Rev. Lett. 1, 368 (1958).

[8]Research on Paramagnetic Resonances, First Quarterly Progress Report, Signal Corps Contract DA36-039-sc-74895, July - October 1957 (unpublished).

[9]A. M. Portis, Phys. Rev. 104, 584 (1956).

[10]A. L. McWhorter and J. W. Meyer, Phys. Rev. 109, 312 (1958).

[11]M. W. P. Strandberg, Phys. Rev. 110, 65 (1958).

[12]Similar results were reported by Castle, Chester, and Wagner at the Molecular Electronics Symposium held at the Statler-Hilton Hotel, Washington, D. C., November 13-14, 1958.

COMMUNICATION No. 321a, reprinted from: Physica 26 (1960) 133.

B. BÖLGER *) **and B. J. ROBINSON** **). — *Paramagnetic relaxation rates determined by pulsed double resonance experiments.*

Summary

The relaxation rates for synthetic ruby and $K_3Cr(CN)_6/K_3Co(CN)_6$ are determined for various Cr concentrations, magnetic field conditions and temperatures. In some cases it is possible to measure directly the cross relaxation rate. It is concluded that as the temperature is raised the Cr concentration in these salts can be increased without losing maser action.

1. *Introduction.* During the development of a three level maser [1][2], some double resonance experiments have been carried out to obtain more information about the mechanisms governing the establishment of spin-spin and spin-lattice equilibrium. Pulsed double resonance experiments were carried out on substances with magnetic dilutions for which negative spin temperatures could be obtained and at higher concentrations for which this was not possible. According to the views of Bloembergen *e.a.* [3]) multiple spin flips with a total energy change of the order of the spin-spin interaction energy are effective in establishing a spin-spin equilibrium, thus preventing maser action. The rate at which such multiple spin flips take place is called the cross relaxation rate U_{cr}. To allow prediction of maser action the magnitude of U_{cr} has to be compared with the spin-lattice relaxation rates U_{ij} between levels i and j.

2. *Experimental method.* When carrying out a double resonance experiment on a multilevel spin system, saturation of one of the transitions („pump" transition) will influence the population difference of another, the „signal", transition. Finding the exact magnitudes and directions of the magnetic field $\boldsymbol{H}$ for which saturation of the pump transition influences the signal absorption most, which we shall call the „operating points", may present some difficulties. A quick method to locate the operating points is provided by pulse modulating the pump power at a repetition rate lower than the relaxation rates; near an operating point the signal absorption

*) Now at Philips Scientific Apparatus Department, Eindhoven, Nederland.
**) Radiophysics Laboratory, C.S.I.R.O., Sydney, Australia.

will also become modulated, and the largest modulation will occur at its centre.

With the arrangement of fig. 1, using an unmodulated 1420 MHz signal, the time behaviour of the signal absorption was displayed on the oscilloscope

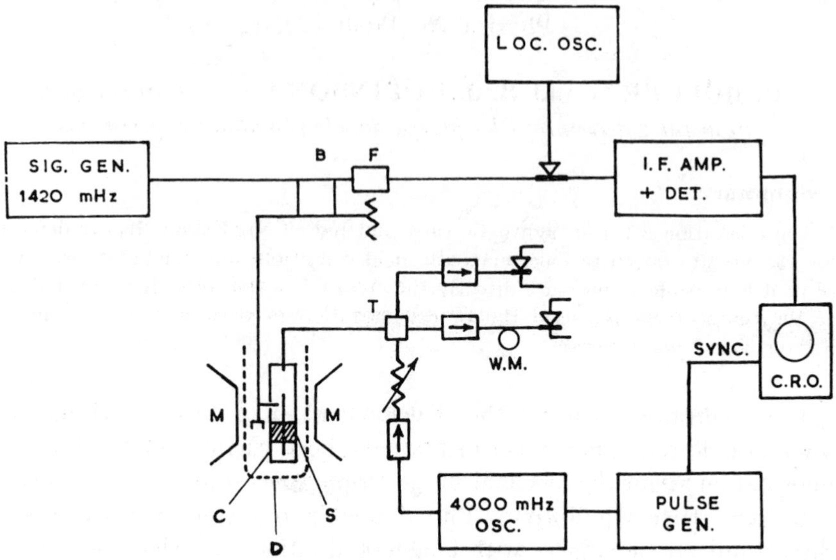

Fig. 1. Apparatus for experiments with two different frequencies. B bridge element (hybrid) for 1420 MHz; F low pass filter; T Magic Tee for 4000 MHz; C dual resonance cavity; S sample; D dewar; M magnet.

(Tektronix type 532). This had its time base synchronized to the pump modulation, and the trace was photographed. Examples of the resulting modulation of the signal are shown in fig. 2. Two methods were used to determine the time constants τ of the recovery of the absorption after the pump power was switched off. The first was to measure the deviation of the signal from its equilibrium value as a function of time and plot this on a

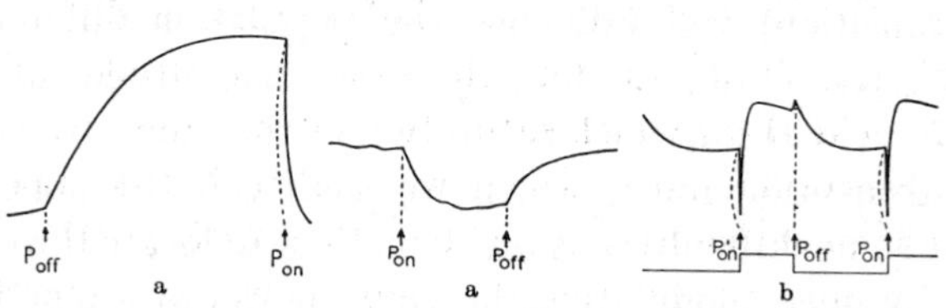

Fig. 2. Signal absorption as a function of time for a pulse modulated pump power P.
a) $K_3Cr(CN)_6/K_3Co(CN)_6$ *b*) Ruby operating point R_1

single logarithmic scale, as shown in fig. 3. The second, a much faster but somewhat less accurate method, was by trying to identify the recorded curve with one out of a set of exponential curves with different time constants, drawn on a glass plate. One then needs to know only the time scale of the record, which was obtained by photographing the graticule of the oscilloscope and noting the setting of its calibrated timebase.

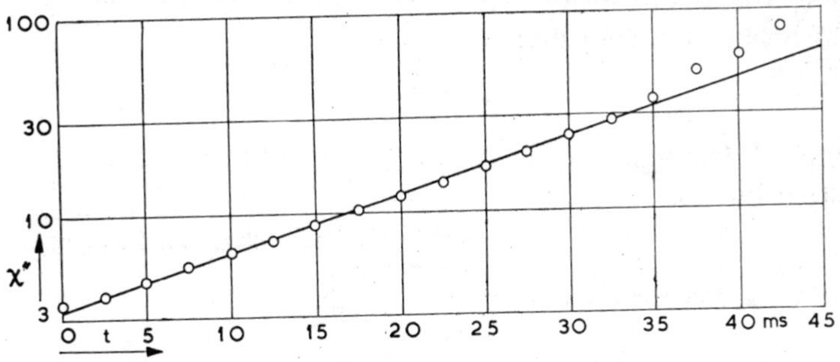

Fig. 3. $K_3Cr(CN)_6/K_3Co(CN)_6$. Time behaviour of χ'' after a pulse of pump power.

3. *Results on* $K_3Cr(CN)_6/K_3Co(CN)_6$. Measurements were performed on $K_3Cr(CN)_6$ diluted with $K_3Co(CN)_6$ for different chromium concentrations, among which one sample, *A*, contained 0.035% Cr to Co and another sample, *B*, 0.1% Cr to Co. The measurements described here were performed with a signal frequency of 1420 MHz and a pump frequency of 3850 MHz.

The chemical analysis of the chromium content was performed by the method described by Dean [4]) and by röntgen fluorescence spectrography *). The values of the magnetic field and its direction for four operating points are given in table I, the energy levels being numbered from the lowest. The results of the steady state maser experiments, as described in [1]), are also given.

TABLE I

Data of operating points in $K_3Cr(CN)_6/K_3Co(CN)_6$.
Pump 3850 MHz (1–3 tr.); Signal 1420 MHz.

Operating point	I	II	III	IV
Signal transition	1–2	2–3	2–3	1–2
Magnetic field (oersted)	480	680	1170	1280
$\angle$ ***H*** to *a*-axis (in *ac*-plane)	11°	25°	14°	3°
$\lim_{P_{pump}\to\infty} Q_m^{-1}/(Q_m^{-1})_{P_{pump}=0}$:				
A Cr/Co = 0.035%	−1.23	−1.05	−0.90	−1.3
B Cr/Co = 0.1%	0	0	0	0
C Cr/Co = 0.05%	≈ −1	0	0	≈ −1
For sample *A*				
U_{23}/U_{12}	4.6	1/3.1	1/2.3	5.7
τ_{off} (ms) at 1.4°K	44.7	26.1	33.4	29.0

In the last row the values of the recovery times τ_{off} of the signal transitions, when the pump power was switched off, are presented for sample *A* at

*) We are very much indebted to Mr. J. de Vries of the N.V. Philips' Gloeilampenfabrieken for performing this analysis.

1.4°K. The relaxation time as a function of temperature at operating point I was determined for both samples. The results are given in fig. 4. For both samples we may take $\tau \sim T^{-3,3}$ between 6°K and 20°K but below this range the temperature dependences differ. For sample A we found at liquid helium temperatures

$$\tau_A = 62/T \text{ ms.} \tag{1}$$

For sample B the values of τ_B in this temperature range can be very well represented by

$$1/\tau_B = 1/\tau_A + 1/31 \text{ ms}^{-1}. \tag{2}$$

This curve has been drawn in fig. 4.

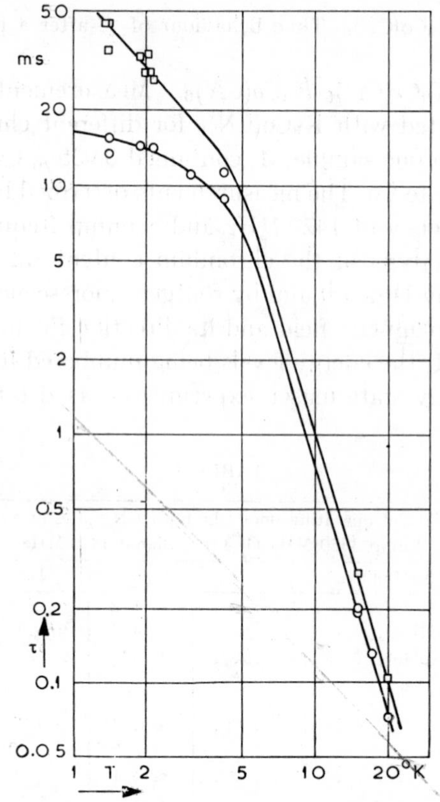

Fig. 4. τ_{off} as a function of T for $K_3Cr(CN)_6/K_3Co(CN)_6$.
□ τ_{off} sample A ○ τ_{off} sample B

It was checked whether the pulse length of the pump modulation had any influence on the characteristic times. For sample B, at nearly all temperatures investigated, the pump pulse was varied between 1 ms and 100 ms. The recovery time of the signal τ_{off} was found not to depend on the pulse length, although there was a slight indication of a decrease below about 4 ms pulse length.

4. *Results on synthetic ruby*. Synthetic ruby, Al_2O_3 with a small amount of Cr_2O_3, has proved to be a suitable maser material. The zero field splitting corresponds to a frequency of 11593 MHz with no rhombic component present and with an isotropic *g*-value of 2.00. In fig. 3 of [1]) some of the loci of the transitions in $\boldsymbol{H}$ space are shown ($\boldsymbol{H}$ in *ac*-plane), the levels again being numbered from the lowest.

For the 1–2 transition at 1430 MHz it is possible to use the 1–3 transition at 10.7 kMHz as a pump frequency. An operating point occurs for $\boldsymbol{H} = 430$ Oe at 23° to the *c*-axis of the crystal; this point will be denoted by R_{I}. Another operating point investigated, R_{II}, was obtained with $\omega_p/2\pi = 8500$ MHz for the 1–3 transition and $\omega_s/2\pi = 1430$ MHz for the 2–3 transition with $\boldsymbol{H} = 2100$ Oe at 21° to the *c*-axis.

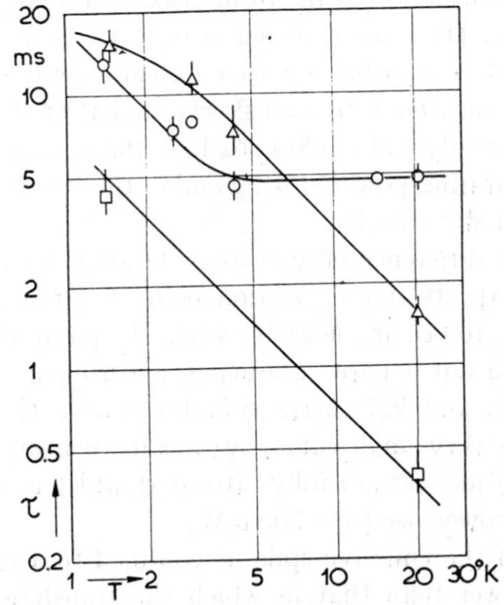

Fig. 5. Characteristic times of signal absorption for ruby.
△ τ_{off} pump 8.5 kMHz point R_{II}
○ τ_{off} pump 10.7 kMHz point R_{I}
□ decay time spike (pump 10.7 kMHz)

With a ruby of a nominal ratio of Cr : Al = 1 : 200 it was not possible to obtain an emissive condition for the signal transitions, and all resonances saturated homogeneously when applying the pump power. For Cr : Al = 1 : 1000 emission was obtained at operating point R_{II} whilst this was not the case at point R_{I} for the same crystal. The experiments described in the following were carried out on this last ruby.

A. Pump frequency 8500 MHz. Operating point R_{II}. In fig. 5

the recovery time of the signal, τ_{off}, is plotted as a function of temperature. It is seen that it is close to $22/T$ ms. The temperature dependence appears to become less at the lower temperature range. For this operating point emission was observed.

B. Pump frequency 10.7 kMHz. Operating point R_{I}. For the 1–2 transition at R_{I} the absorption observed was much stronger than for the 2–3 transition at R_{II}, in agreement with a calculation using the matrix elements.

However, on applying the saturating field, only a brief pulse of emission, lasting a few milliseconds, was obtained. This can be seen in figure 2*b* where the 10.7 kMHz oscillator is pulsed on for 13 ms every 40 ms, as indicated on the lower trace. The upper trace shows the signal reflected from the cavity at 1430 MHz, emission from the (unpolished) ruby causing a decrease in the reflection (downwards deflection) for the undercoupled cavity used. When the 10.7 kMHz oscillator is switched on, there is a short pulse of emission, followed by an increase in the absorption to above its equilibrium value. This was observed at both 1.4°K and 20°K. The time constant has been plotted in fig. 5. Other measurements then showed that subsequently the absorption decreased slowly, and after about 1 s (at 1.4°K) it had fallen to a steady value close to half the equilibrium absorption. Even with high saturating powers ($\gg$ 200 mW) the steady state absorption could not be further decreased.

As the population difference only decreased to half the equilibrium value at 1430 MHz one expects the absorption at the 2–3 transition (9270 MHz), the idling frequency, to become negative when the pump is fully saturating. We therefore carried out a triple frequency experiment and observed the signals at 1430 MHz and 9270 MHz simultaneously. The 2–3 signal was seen to decrease to a very small value, but not to turn negative, indicating that the pump transition was not fully saturated, which is surprising because of the large pump power used ($\gg$ 200 mW).

The occurrence of the emissive spike is confined to a region of the field and its angle narrower than that in which the transferred modulation is visible. Also the spike decay time is a sensitive function of field and angle, being a minimum exactly at the operating point and increasing by a factor four 2.5° further from the crystal axis, in which direction it became equal to τ_{off} and the spike started to disappear. Rotating $\boldsymbol{H}$ towards the axis made the spike disappear without changing the decay time. Increasing $\boldsymbol{H}$ from the value at R_{I} increased the spike decay time; decreasing $\boldsymbol{H}$ from R_{I} made the spike disappear.

The characteristic time τ_{off} of the signal at 1430 MHz is plotted in fig. 5 as a function of temperature in the range from 20.4°K to 1.4°K. One observes τ_{off} in that range to be a constant above 4°K, while below 4°K a T^{-1} law is followed.

5. *Discussion of the pulse measurements.* *A*. Discussion of the results on $K_3Cr(CN)_6/K_3Co(CN)_6$. One expects to find three time constants for sample *A*. Only one was found, as is evident from fig. 3. The deviations from the straight line in that figure are due to a time constant of about 80 ms in the apparatus. We will now relate the relaxation rates to the recovery times observed by assuming that the fourth level does not take part in the relaxation processes. The time dependent equations for the level populations are then easily solved and one finds for the reciprocal of the two time constants left (1–2 signal and 1–3 pump transition) (cf. ref. [5]) p. 23):

$$\lambda_{1,2} = \bar{V}_{12} + \bar{V}_{13} + \bar{V}_{23} \pm \pm \sqrt{\bar{V}_{12}^2 + \bar{V}_{13}^2 + \bar{V}_{23}^2 + \bar{V}_{12}\cdot\bar{V}_{13} + \bar{V}_{12}\cdot\bar{V}_{23} + \bar{V}_{13}\bar{V}_{23}} \quad (3)$$

where $\bar{V}_{ij} = (U_{ij} + U_{ji})/2 + W_{ij}$ and W_{ij} is the induced transition rate.

This expression can be simplified when it is possible to expand the root, and one then finds with $\bar{V}_{12}/\bar{V}_{23} = r$ and $\bar{V}_{13}/\bar{V}_{23} = R$:

$$\lambda_1 = \bar{V}_{23}\frac{Rr + r + R}{2(1 + R + r)} \quad (4)$$

$$\lambda_2 = 2\bar{V}_{23}(1 + R + r) - \lambda_1.$$

For the time behaviour after removing the pump power ($W_{ij}=0$) we can try to identify the reciprocal rise time observed with λ_1 or with λ_2. Inserting the values found by steady state measurements at 1.4°K for U_{12}, U_{23} (as derived in [1]) to be $U_{12} = 0.65\ s^{-1}$ and $U_{23} = 2.65\ s^{-1}$) and $\lambda = 10^3/44\ s^{-1}$ for operating point I of sample *A*, results in a negative value of *R* if λ_1, and in $R = 3.1$ if λ_2 is the reciprocal recovery time observed.

Only the last solution is acceptable, so we find:

$$\bar{U}_{12} = 0.6\ s^{-1};\ \bar{U}_{23} = 2.6\ s^{-1};\ \bar{U}_{13} = 8.1\ s^{-1}$$

and $\lambda_1 = 1.2\ s^{-1}$ for $T = 1.4$°K. The values of *U* when plotted as a function of ω on a double logarithmic scale lie on a straight line corresponding to $U \sim \omega^{2,6}$. This proportionality should not be taken too seriously as the matrix elements of the spin operators for the different transitions do enter. The expected frequency dependence for equal matrix elements is ω^2. From these experiments no information is obtained about relaxation rates involving the fourth level.

During the pump pulse, λ_2 is large, while λ_1 approaches the limit $\lambda_{1_{\text{pulse}}} = (\bar{U}_{12} + \bar{U}_{23})/2$, which equals $1.6\ s^{-1}$. The time constant $1/\lambda_{1_{\text{pulse}}}$ characterizes the time it takes to establish a stationary population of level 2, the pump transition being saturated. The time constant was probably as long as this, for it took about one second for the maser to start amplifying after applying the pump power.

The reason for working with the particular concentrations used was that for sample A maser action was obtained, while this was not the case for sample B (cf. table I). This indicates that for A the spin lattice relaxation rates determine the individual level populations while in sample B the spin system comes to equilibrium through cross relaxations in a time shorter than a critical value determined by the spin lattice relaxation times.

When cross relaxations become important two situations may arise. In the first $U_{\mathrm{cr}} \gg U_{ij_{\max}}$ (the largest U_{ij} present at that temperature) and the time behaviour of the population difference of the signal transition is essentially determined by $U_{ij_{\max}}$. The second situation may be met with when the cross relaxation rate forms a bottleneck for the energy transfer, but is still fast enough to prevent maser action. This occurs when (see [3]) and [5]))

$$\overline{U}_{\mathrm{cr}}\omega_{kl} > \overline{U}_{im}\omega_{lm} - \overline{U}_{kl}\omega_{kl} \tag{5}$$

where $k \rightarrow l$ is the signal transition and ω_{kl} its frequency and

$$\overline{U}_{\mathrm{cr}} < U_{ij_{\max}}. \tag{6}$$

τ_{off} is mainly determined by $\overline{U}_{\mathrm{cr}}$.

As the U_{ij}'s are temperature dependent, while this is not the case for U_{cr}, these conditions may be fulfilled at one temperature, but at a lower temperature the first situation, or at a higher one, maser action may be expected. We suggest that in the measured temperature range below 4°K the second situation exists for sample B with $U_{\mathrm{cr}} \approx 10^3/31\ \mathrm{s}^{-1}$ (see eq. (2)).

Above this temperature an inverted difference in populations of transition 1–2, or at least a non-equilibrium situation in the spin system, seems also to be possible for sample B. At temperatures much lower than those used in the measurements τ_{off} is excepted to increase again (situation 1). Condition (6) can be fulfilled by assuming that at least one of the relaxation rates from the fourth level towards the three levels just considered is fast. Theoretically this is expected to be U_{14}.

B. Discussion of the results on the ruby. The recovery times τ_{off} observed at the operating point R_{I} (pump 10.7 kMHz) can be explained in the following way. Relation (5) holds for the whole temperature range measured, but below 4°K we have $U_{\mathrm{cr}} > U_{ij_{\max}}$. As $U_{ij_{\max}} \sim T$, condition (6) may be fulfilled at a higher temperature; this appears to be the case above 4°K, with $U_{\mathrm{cr}} \approx 10^3/5\ \mathrm{s}^{-1}$.

As emission was observed for operating point R_{II}, the inequality (5) does not hold. Cross relaxations appear to become important in the lower temperature range. The spike behaviour is not quite understood. If only three levels are concerned, relaxation processes will not increase the absorption above its equilibrium value. However, this could be explained if there were cross relaxations involving the fourth level. Since $\tau_{\mathrm{spike}} \sim T^{-1}$ a lattice relaxation rate to this fourth level would then have to be the determining factor.

6. *Conclusion.* The foregoing results show that, due to the temperature independence of U_{cr}, it is possible to use magnetically more concentrated material for the construction of a three level maser at higher temperatures than would have been possible at lower temperatures. This explains why some experimenters [6]) obtained no maser action at helium temperatures, but did so at hydrogen and at liquid air temperatures.

Under some conditions it is shown that U_{cr} can be measured directly.

The authors wish to thank Prof. C. J. Gorter for his stimulating interest and advice, and Mr. J. M. Noothoven van Goor for his help with the measurements. This work was the result of a collaboration between the „Stichting voor Fundamenteel Onderzoek der Materie (F.O.M.)", the „Stichting Radiostraling van Zon en Melkweg", the Philips Research Laboratories and the Radiophysics Laboratory of C.S.I.R.O., Australia.

REFERENCES

1) Bölger, B., Robinson, B. J. and Ubbink, J., Commun. Kamerlingh Onnes Lab., Leiden No. 319*c*; Physica **26** (1960) 1.
2) Bölger, B. and Robinson, B. J., Commun. Suppl. No. 114*i*; Arch. Sci. (Genève) **11** (1958) 187.
3) Bloembergen, N., Shapiro, S., Pershan, P. S. and Artman, J. O., Phys. Rev. **114** (1959) 445.
4) Dean, J., Anal. Chem. **30** (1958) 977.
5) Bölger, B., Thesis Leiden (1959).
6) Bogle, G. S., private communication.

COMMUNICATION N°. 322b, reprinted from:
Physica 26 (1960) 761.

B. BÖLGER*). — *On the power transfer between paramagnetic spins and crystal lattice I.*

Summary

The determination of the heat contact η between a system of paramagnetic spins and the crystal lattice is discussed. The relation between the transient and the steady state method is shown to depend on the degree of internal spin equilibrium. The temperature and field dependences of η for concentrated salts as determined previously by the relaxation method are still unexplained. The influence of spin-spin interactions is considered, but can explain said dependences only when strong spin-spin interactions are present. The failure of the hot phonon theory for concentrated salts is explained on the base of the broadness of the spin spectrum over which energy exchange with the lattice vibrations can take place.

The formulae used in the relaxation and the saturation method are for linear systems shown to become identical by a suitable transformation.

1. *Introduction.* The magnetization of a paramagnetic system will not follow instantaneously a change in the applied magnetic field. This is partly due to a finite power transfer between a system of paramagnetic spins and the external degrees of freedom. The approach to equilibrium can be characterized by the so called spin-lattice relaxation time τ_1, when spin-spin relaxation is neglected.

With the usual method of paramagnetic relaxation to determine τ_1, one measures the differential susceptibility $\mathrm{d}\boldsymbol{M}/\mathrm{d}\boldsymbol{H}$ with a small alternating magnetic field $\Delta\boldsymbol{H}$ of frequency ω parallel to $\boldsymbol{H}$. By using a formula derived by Casimir and du Pré [1]) τ_1 can then be obtained from the χ' or the χ'' *vs* ω plots.

$$\chi(\omega)/\chi_0 = (1 - F) + F/(1 + i\omega\tau_1)$$
$$F = (C_H - C_M)/C_H \qquad (1)$$

where χ_0 is the static susceptibility, C_H the specific heat at constant magnetic field $\boldsymbol{H}$ and C_M that at constant magnetization. The theories and results of measurements by this method were surveyed and discussed by Gorter [2]), while more recent experiments were published a.o. by Kramers, Bijl and Gorter [3]) and Van der Marel, Van den Broek and Gorter [4])[5])[6]).

*) Now at Philips' Scientific Equipment Department, Eindhoven, Nederland.

A second method to determine relaxation times presents itself by using paramagnetic resonance. An alternating magnetic field $\boldsymbol{h}$ with a frequency ω will induce transitions between two Zeeman levels E_i and E_j ($E_i - E_j = \hbar\omega_{ij}$), with level populations n_i en n_j, at a rate

$$W_{ij} = \tfrac{1}{4}g^2\beta^2 \, |\langle i| \, \boldsymbol{h}\cdot\boldsymbol{S} \, |j\rangle|^2 \, g(\omega - \omega_{ij}) \tag{2}$$

where g is the factor of Landé, β the Bohr magneton, $\boldsymbol{S}$ the spin operator and $g(\omega - \omega_{ij})$ the normalized shape function of the transition. The power absorbed by a sample containing N magnetic ions is

$$P_m = (n_i - n_j) \, \hbar\omega_{ij} W_{ij} = \frac{N}{2S+1} \, \frac{(\hbar\omega_{ij})^2}{kT_L} \, \frac{W_{ij}}{1 + 2W_{ij}\tau_1} \tag{3}$$

where T_L is the lattice temperature of the sample. The last equality has sometimes been used to determine τ_1 by way of paramagnetic resonance, but will be shown to hold under certain restrictions only. When measuring P_m as a function of W_{ij}, one expects curves for P_m and $1/\chi'' \propto W_{ij}/P_m$ *vs* h^2 as shown in fig. 1. The slope of $1/\chi''$ *vs* h^2 is proportional to $T\tau_1$. Measurements by this method were published a.o. by Eschenfelder and Weidner [7]). Their results deviated strongly from those obtained by the relaxation method.

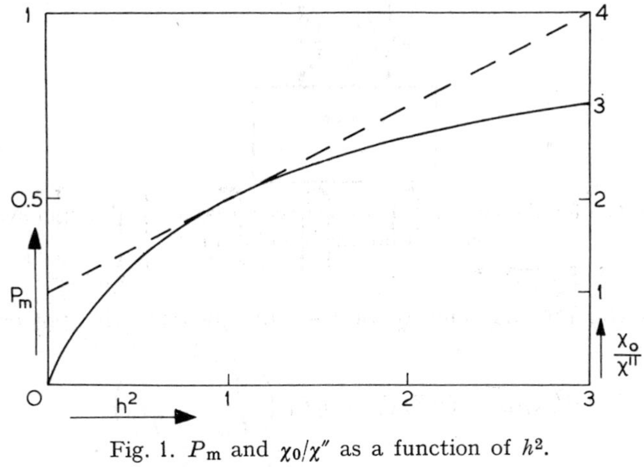

Fig. 1. P_m and χ_0/χ'' as a function of h^2.
——— P_m ----- χ_0/χ''

In the following we shall reconsider the assumptions made in both methods, and also some of the theories concerning τ_1 with the intention of using the results in following experimental papers (see also [8])).

2. *The power balance between a paramagnetic spin system and the crystal lattice.* If during a paramagnetic resonance experiment the spin system

is in equilibrium at a temperature T_S and the lattice at a temperature T_L the situation may be represented by the block diagram of fig. 2. For the absorbed power, due to all transitions, we may write $P_m = QW/T_S$. The distribution of the spins over their energy levels will be described by the density matrix

$$\rho_S(E_i) = (\exp - E_i/kT_S)/(\Sigma_i \exp - E_i/kT_S)$$

where E_i are the eigenvalues of the spin Hamiltonian $\mathscr{H}_{sp}$ in which spin-spin interactions are included. Due to the lattice vibrations, transitions will be induced between spin levels i and j at a rate of say U_{ij}. For the total power transferred from the spin system in equilibrium at T_S to the lattice we have:

$$P_{tr} = \Sigma_{i>j} \hbar\omega_{ij}[U_{ij}\rho_S(E_i) - U_{ji}\rho_S(E_j)] = \eta T_L\left(\frac{1}{T_L} - \frac{1}{T_S}\right), \tag{4}$$

where the last equality serves to define the power transfer parameter η.

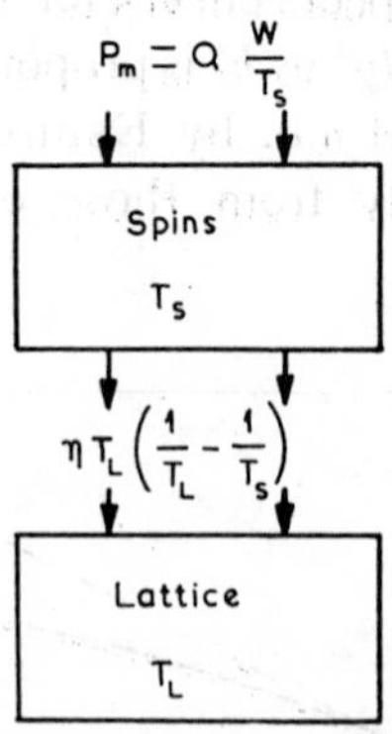

Fig. 2. Model for the energy balance between a lattice and a spin system each in internal equilibrium.

When U_S is the internal energy of the spin system, the power balance becomes:

$$dU_S/dt = QW/T_S - \eta T_L\left(\frac{1}{T_L} - \frac{1}{T_S}\right). \tag{5}$$

For the steady state solution of this equation one obtains

$$T_S = T_L + QW/\eta = T_L(1 + P_0/\eta) \tag{6}$$

where $P_0 = QW/T_L$ equals the power that would have been absorbed in case of a very good spin-lattice heat contact ($\eta \to \infty$). The absorbed power for a finite η will be:

$$P_m = QW/(T_L + QW/\eta) = P_0/(1 + P_0/\eta). \tag{7}$$

If (3) were valid, the value of τ_1 determined by steady state measurements would have been, (by comparing (3) and (7))

$$\tau_{1st} = Q/2\eta T_L = N(\hbar\omega)^2/2(2S+1)k\eta T_L. \tag{8}$$

The spin-lattice relaxation time, however, is not defined by (3), but as the time characterizing the decay of a perturbation in the magnetization component parallel to $\boldsymbol{H}$. We thus have to take the transient solution of (5) realizing that, when $\boldsymbol{H}$ is kept constant,

$$\frac{dU_S}{dt} = C_H \frac{dT_S}{dt} = \frac{b + CH^2}{T_S^2}\frac{dT_S}{dt} \tag{9}$$

where C is the Curie constant. When after $t = 0$ the induced transition rate has the value W, and at $t=0$ the spin temperature is $T_S(0)$, we have from (9) and (5)

$$\frac{1}{T_S(t)} - \frac{\eta}{QW + \eta T_L} = \left\{\frac{1}{T_S(0)} - \frac{\eta}{QW + \eta T_L}\right\} e^{-(QW+\eta T_L)t/(b+CH^2)}. \tag{10}$$

If $W = 0$ we thus find for the relaxation time

$$\tau_1 = (b + CH^2)/\eta T_L. \tag{11}$$

The ratio between the relaxation times as found by the steady state method using formula (5) and by the transient method with $W = 0$, is with respect to (8) and (11)

$$\tau_{1tr}/\tau_{1st} = \tfrac{2}{3}\, S(S+1)\,(2S+1)\gamma^2\, \frac{(b/c + H^2)}{\omega^2}. \tag{12}$$

At a high magnetic field ($H^2 \gg b/C$) the relation $\omega = \gamma H$ holds, and this factor becomes 1, 4, 10, 20, 35 for $S = \frac{1}{2}, 1, \frac{3}{2}, 2, \frac{5}{2}$ respectively.

The reason for the difference between τ_{1st} and τ_{1tr} for $S > \frac{1}{2}$ is found in the derivation of the equation (3) which was obtained by considering the relaxation probability at the saturated transition only, while one actually has to consider the total power transfer between spin system and lattice as in formula (5) leading to (7).

The steady state measurements thus determine directly a value of η to be called η_{st} by using (7). The relaxation measurements determine τ_1, and by use of (11), where internal spin equilibrium is presupposed a value of η, called η_{rel}, is derived.

3. *The connection between τ_1 and η_{st}* depends on the degree of internal equilibrium in the spin system. This is in part established by multiple spin flips which do redistribute the level populations to a Boltzmann ratio, but which have a total energy change smaller than the spin-spin interactions. These processes with a rate U_{cr} (cf. [8]), were named cross relaxations by Bloembergen *e.a.* [9]).

From the double resonance measurements, described in [10]), followed, that we have to distinguish between three situations as to the degree in which internal spin equilibrium is established during a time τ_1.

1) The cross relaxation rates are negligible compared with the spin lattice relaxation rates, *i.e.* $U_{cr} \ll U_{ij}$.

In general the saturation and relaxation measurements will not give the same results. When there are more resonance lines, each one may have a different value of U_{ij}.

Examples are $K_3Cr(CN)_6/K_3Co(CN)_6$, sample A of which the U_{ij}'s are computed in [10]) and ruby at operating point R_{II} [10]). The variation of the occupation of the different energy levels as a function of time depends on the initial conditions and is in general not according to a simple exponential. The relaxation method yields an average relaxation time, which together with the behaviour of $\boldsymbol{M}$ under saturation conditions, can be calculated with the method described by Lloyd and Pake [11]).

Generally there is not a simple relation between τ_1 and η_{st}. In the case of $S = \frac{1}{2}$, we may also have $\eta_{rel} \neq \eta_{st}$, if there are ions with different g-values in a unit cell, or if the resonance line is broadened inhomogeneously, that is to say for a spatially distributed inhomogeneity.

2) The cross relaxation rates are of the same order of magnitude as those between spins and lattice, *i.e.* when (5) and (6) of [10]) are valid. At some resonance lines it is possible to measure by saturation directly U_{cr}, as this may be the rate determining η_{ij} for that transition. An example is the ruby at operating point R_I above 4°K in reference [10]).

3) Complete spin equilibrium, *i.e.* $U_{cr} \gg U_{ij_{max}}$. The transition to this situation is demonstrated by the behaviour of τ_{off} for the ruby, operating point R_I, near 4°K in reference [10]). In general this situation is expected to be realized in concentrated salts, at not too high a temperature and magnetic field. The energy transfer between spins and lattice can be described by the scheme used in section 2. Saturation and relaxation experiments are expected to yield the same value of η, as in both experiments the spin system is presumably in internal equilibrium, so that

$$\eta_{tr} = \eta_{st} = (b + CH^2)/T_L\tau_{1_{tr}}.$$

Which of the three situations is realized depends on the magnetic concentration (which influences U_{cr} and more or less U_{ij}), the vector $\boldsymbol{H}$ (with an influence on U_{cr} and U_{ij}) and the temperature (which influences U_{ij}). Transitions between the three situations are demonstrated in [10]).

As for the relation between $\tau_{1_{tr}}$ and η_{st} it is seen that for none of the three situations (8) is satisfied. This relation was derived by making use of (3), in analogy with nuclear resonance ($b \approx 0$).

4. *The temperature and field dependence of* η. Surveys of the theories on this subject have been given in references [2]) [8]). Waller [12]) indicated, that

with regard to the excitation of the lattice vibrations, two essentially different processes have to be distinguished: the direct process in which the energy of the spin transition is used to create or absorb only one phonon, and the indirect or Raman process in which two phonons play a rôle. Kronig [13]) and Van Vleck [14]) have shown that the perturbation lattice-orbit-spin is the predominant one. Two terms have to be distinguished in the perturbation calculation, an adiabatic term in which the contribution of the spin energy to the energy denominator (difference between orbital ground state and next higher orbital level) is negligible, and a non-adiabatic term in which this spin energy has to be taken into account.

With $E_i > E_j$ and taking p_{ij} as the quantum number of the normal mode of vibration of the lattice at frequency ω_{ij}, we find for the direct processes for the ratio of the probability of phonon creation to that of phonon destruction

$$\frac{U_{ij}}{U_{ji}} = \frac{p_{ij}+1}{p_{ij}} \qquad (13)$$

and, as the spin-lattice perturbation contains the lattice modes linearly, $U_{ij} \propto T_L$ for $\hbar\omega_{ij} \ll kT_L$. We may write then for the part of η due to the direct processes with (4)

$$\eta_d = \Sigma_{i>j}\, \eta_{ij_d} = \Sigma_{i>j}\, (\hbar\omega_{ij})^{\alpha+1}\, |\langle i|\mathscr{H}_1'(\boldsymbol{S})|\, j\rangle|^2 \qquad (14)$$

where $\langle i|\mathscr{H}_1'(\boldsymbol{S})|j\rangle$ contains the matrix elements of the spin operators in U_{ij}. The exponent α equals 3 for the adiabatic terms (a factor ω^2 due to the density of the normal modes of the lattice and ω due to the Boltzmann factor) and $\alpha = 5$ for the non-adiabatic terms. From formulae (4) and (13) one expects η_d to be independent of temperature.

The indirect process entails U_{ij} independent of ω_{ij} but with a strong temperature dependence due to the fact that two phonons play a rôle, and those with energies near kT_L mainly determine η_{ind} because of their abundance ($\eta_{ind_{ad}} \propto T_L^6$ and $\eta_{ind_{nad}} \propto T_L^8$ for T_L far below the Debije temperature.)

Formula (14) may be written as a diagonal sum, so that the adiabatic terms become

$$\eta_{d_{ad}} \propto Tr[[\mathscr{H}_1' \cdot \mathscr{H}_{sp}]\mathscr{H}_{sp}]^2. \qquad (15)$$

The non-adiabatic terms would require the calculation of a sixth moment. The advantage of expressing η in an invariant form is that one can easily take the spin-spin interactions into account by including them in $\mathscr{H}_{sp}$ although it may be a tedious process to calculate the higher moments of the spin-lattice perturbation. If no spin interaction were present, η would be independent of the magnetic concentration c and if there are no crystalline field splittings either we would find $\eta = 0$ for $\boldsymbol{H} = 0$. With interactions, however, the energy splittings $\hbar\omega_{ij}$ in (4) and (14) for $\boldsymbol{H} = 0$ are mainly determined by the dipolar or exchange interactions (or crystalline field splittings) and thus η becomes a function of c. To compare some of the available experimental data with the theory we give in table I the exponents β and δ in

$$\eta_{rel} \propto c^{\varepsilon}(b/C + pH^2)^{\delta/2}\, T^{\beta} \tag{16}$$

for $c = 1$ and $\boldsymbol{H}$ not too large and ε in the limit of $\boldsymbol{H} \to 0$ as found approximately by the relaxation methods at helium temperatures [3] [4] [5] and [6].

The theoretical values, to be derived in the following section, are also given.

TABLE I

		ε	δ	β	$\delta + \beta$
Exp.	$FeNH_4$-alum	1.3–1.5	0	4–4.5	4–4.5
	CrK-alum	1.2	2	1.9	4
	$MnNH_4$-tutton salt	1.1	2	4.1	6
	$CuK_2Cl_4.2H_2O$	—	0	4	4
	CuK-tutton salt	neg.	2	2	4
Theory	dir. ad. terms	1–2	4	0	4
	dir. non-ad. terms	3–?	6	0	6
	ind. ad. terms	1	2	6	8
	ind. non-ad. terms	1	2	8	10

5. *The influence of spin-spin interactions on* η. The heat transfer between spin and lattice systems is in the theory of Kronig and Van Vleck essentially a single spin process. However, the spin-spin interactions mix the spin operators of an ion with those of its neighbours causing the Heisenberg operator $\boldsymbol{S}(t)$ to have higher frequency components than expected from the single spin spectrum. Temperley [15] suggested therefore the possibility that multiple spin jumps, with emission of a phonon at the sum energy, play an important rôle.

If for the direct process the largest quanta, which still contribute appreciably to the power transfer, become of the order of kT_L, it is not allowed to expand the exponentials in (4) and for $T_S \approx T_L$, η_d will be strongly temperature dependent. With increasing T_S the probability for an ion to have neighbours in a higher energy state, increases. Thus η_d will be enhanced and will depend on T_S. However, the ratio of η at large T_S to η at small T_S is not expected to be very large (about a factor 2 to 4).

In the limit of $T_S \to \infty$, η_d becomes independent of T_L as the transfer is governed by spontaneous emission of phonons. This is a general consequence of (4) and (13).

Temperley made a rough calculation of the influence of spin-spin interactions, which, however, can be carried out exactly by using the diagonal sum method.

Considering the formulae (14) and (15) for η, we see that, as $\mathscr{H}_{\text{sp}}$ contains also the spin-spin interactions, the adiabatic terms in η_{d} can contain four spin processes at most, and the non-adiabatic terms six spin processes. Both terms are affected by exchange interactions. The indirect process is affected by interactions between two spins only and may be influenced by the exchange if $S > \frac{1}{2}$ or by exchange between inequivalent ions if $S = \frac{1}{2}$, for instance. The relaxation rates U_{ij} of the individual transitions were calculated by perturbation theory and have to be averaged over the resonance line shape $g(\omega - \omega_{ij})$ of the transition involved. To calculate η in (4) using these U_{ij}'s would mean that we have to compute the truncated moments in for instance (15), assuming that the dipole-dipole interactions are not strong enough to produce transitions between the Zeeman levels. The Temperley effect can be calculated by taking the full untruncated moments. These calculations are lengthy, but for the case that $S = \frac{1}{2}$ and that only the component S_x is important in the relaxation process, we can use the results of [16]) and [17]), supposing $\boldsymbol{H} \,//\, z$-axis. When calculating the values of η for one gramion one finds for the truncated case in a simple cubic crystal lattice with $\boldsymbol{H} \,//\, (001)$-axis,

$$\eta_{\text{d}_{\text{ad}}} \propto \langle\omega^4\rangle_{\text{av}} = \omega_{\text{L}}^4 + 6\omega_{\text{L}}^2\omega_{\text{d}}^2 + 3\omega_{\text{d}}^4(0.742 + 0.07/c) + c'(\pi/2)\,\omega_{\text{ex}}^2\omega_{\text{d}}^2 \quad (17)$$

with

$$\omega_{\text{d}}^2 = \langle|\omega - \omega_{\text{L}}|^2\rangle_{\text{av}} = 7.5c\gamma^4\hbar^2 d^{-6} \quad (18)$$

where ω_{L} is the Larmor frequency, d is the lattice constant, c the magnetic concentration, and $c' = c$ for $c > 1/z$ and $c' \approx 0$ for $c < 1/z$, z being the number of neighbours an ion has an exchange interaction with. It is seen that at lower concentrations ($c < 0.1$) the term with $1/c$ in (17) is important. Further we have

$$\eta_{\text{ind}} \propto \omega_{\text{d}}^2 + \omega_{\text{L}}^2. \quad (19)$$

For the Temperley effect we take the untruncated moments as calculated by Miss Wright [18]).

$$\eta_{\text{d}_{\text{ad}}} \propto \omega_{\text{L}}^4 + 20\omega_{\text{L}}^2\omega_{\text{d}}^2 + \tfrac{100}{3}\omega_{\text{d}}^4(3c'\omega_{\text{ex}}^2/\omega_{\text{d}}^2 + 2.5). \quad (20)$$

It is seen that the term with ω_{d}^4 has become more important by a factor of about 34, while this factor is about 64 for the term with $\omega_{\text{ex}}^2\omega_{\text{d}}^2$.

For the non-adiabatic processes one finds:

$$\eta_{\text{d}_{\text{nad}}} \propto \omega_{\text{L}}^6 + 50\omega_{\text{L}}^4\omega_{\text{d}}^2 + 15\omega_{\text{L}}^2\langle\Delta\omega^4\rangle_{\text{av}} + \langle\Delta\omega^6\rangle_{\text{av}} \quad (21)$$

where $\langle\Delta\omega^4\rangle_{\text{av}}$ is the last term of (20) and

$$\langle\Delta\omega^6\rangle_{\text{av}} = \left(\frac{10}{3}\right)^3 \omega_{\text{d}}^6 \left[2\cdot 10^{-3}\cdot\left(\frac{\omega_{\text{ex}}}{\omega_{\text{d}}}\right)^4 + 0.424\left(\frac{\omega_{\text{ex}}}{\omega_{\text{d}}}\right)^2 + 1.5\right]. \quad (22)$$

Concentration dependent terms such as in (17) ought to be added to (20) and (21). For the indirect process the untruncated η becomes

$$\eta_{\text{ind}} \propto \omega_L^2 + \tfrac{10}{3}\omega_d^2. \qquad (23)$$

To calculate the relaxation times we need the specific heat

$$C_H = \frac{b + CH^2}{T^2} = \frac{C}{\gamma^2 T^2}\left[\frac{5}{3}\omega_d^2\left(1 + 2.55\frac{\omega_{ex}^2}{\omega_d^2}\right) + \omega_L^2\right]. \qquad (24)$$

It is better to use the measured values, however.

Miss Wright used for the exchange interaction the following expression

$$\mathscr{H}_{ex} = A\,\Sigma_{i>j}\frac{\gamma^2\hbar^2}{r_{ij}^3}\,\boldsymbol{S}_i\cdot\boldsymbol{S}_j.$$

To convert A to the mostly used exchange constant J, the following relations are given for a simple cubic crystal and $S = \frac{1}{2}$.

$$J = 2A^2\hbar^2\omega_d^2/30 = \hbar^2\omega_{ex}^2/2.12. \qquad (25)$$

As $T\tau_{...} = (b + CH^2)/\eta_{...}$, where τ has the same index as η, we see that for $\omega_L = 0$, $\omega_{ex} = 0$ and for concentrations higher than about 0.1

$$\tau_{d_{ad}} \propto c^{-1}$$
$$\tau_{d_{nad}} \propto c^{-2} \qquad (26)$$
$$\tau_{ind} \propto c^0$$

while for c smaller than about 0.1 we expect

$$\tau_{d_{ad}} \propto c^0.$$

The values of $T\tau$ (scale arbitrary) due to the various processes for different concentrations and exchange interactions have been plotted in fig. 3 and fig. 4. As the measurements of Van der Marel [4][5]) gave τ as a function of $\boldsymbol{H}$, we also plotted τ and not η *vs* $\boldsymbol{H}$ on a double logarithmic scale, for easier comparison.

Of the graphs for $T\tau_{ind}$ (fig. 3), only curve E, with $p = 0.5$ for $\omega_{ind} = 0$, has a resemblance to those observed experimentally. For larger exchange interactions p becomes larger, which does not tally with the experimental data. However, one has to keep in mind that exchange between inequivalent ions influences η and that in second order the S_z component may be important. The second and fourth moment of S_z depend strongly on the exchange.

The concentration dependence of $T\tau_{d_{ad}}$ is displayed in fig. 3; curves A, B and C for $c = 1$, $1/5$ and $1/50$ respectively. As $\omega_d^2 \propto c$, the abscissa in this figure is concentration dependent.

The observed concentration dependences of η_{rel} (cf. table I), are intermediate between those calculated for the indirect and adiabatic direct processes and so are the temperature dependences.

The curves E and F for $T\tau_{d_{ad}}$ (fig. 4) are seen to be nearly horizontal up to $(\omega_L/\omega_d)^2 \approx 10$ and not to increase like curve D ($\omega_{ex} = 0$). This is due to the exchange interactions, the influence of which on the spin specific heat is larger than on the fourth moment. The increase of curve D with ω_L is much less than observed experimentally and there has to be a mechanism, which makes η less dependent on ω_L. Neither larger exchange nor larger dipole interactions make the factor by which $T\tau_{d_{ad}}$ initially increases, larger.

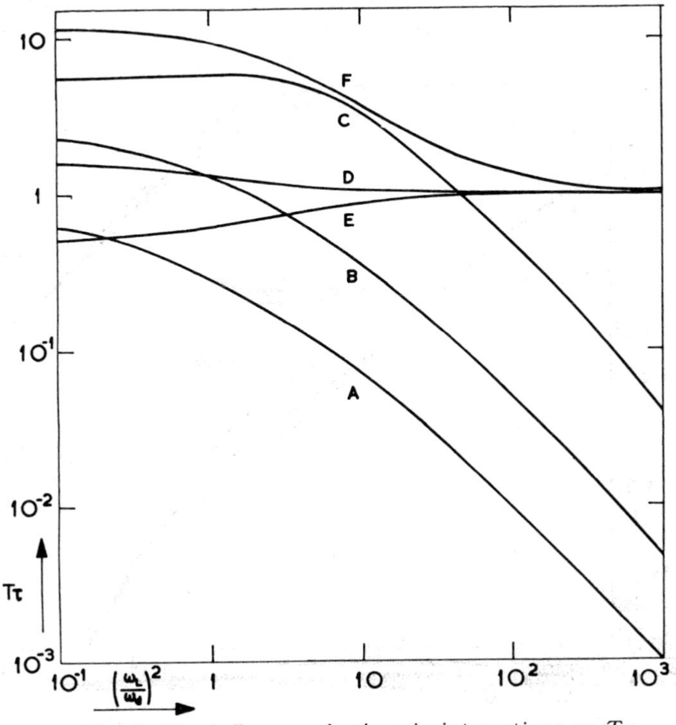

Fig. 3. The influence of spin-spin interactions on $T\tau$.

A. $T\tau_{d_{ad}}$ $c = 1$ } trunc. $\omega_{ex} = 0$
B. $T\tau_{d_{ad}}$ $c = 1/5$ } trunc. $\omega_{ex} = 0$
C. $T\tau_{d_{ad}}$ $c = 1/50$ } trunc. $\omega_{ex} = 0$
D. $T\tau_{ind}$ trunc.
E. $T\tau_{ind}$ untr. $\omega_{ex} = 0$
F. $T\tau_{ind}$ untr. $\omega_{ex}/\omega_d = 3$

It is found in this section that the Temperley effect does exist but, as has been stressed by Van Vleck [14]) previously, it is not as large as Temperley suggested.

The spectrum of the phonons, which the spin system is able to excite is according to the foregoing not simply that of the resonance line at ω_L with a half width ω_d when $S = \frac{1}{2}$, but a spectrum with peaks at multiples of ω_L. Apart from the peak at ω_L all other peaks at multiples of the Larmor frequency will be broadened by exchange interactions. When $S > \frac{1}{2}$ the situation becomes even more involved as the perturbation $\mathscr{H}_1'(\boldsymbol{S})$ has non-zero matrix elements for nearly all single ion transitions.

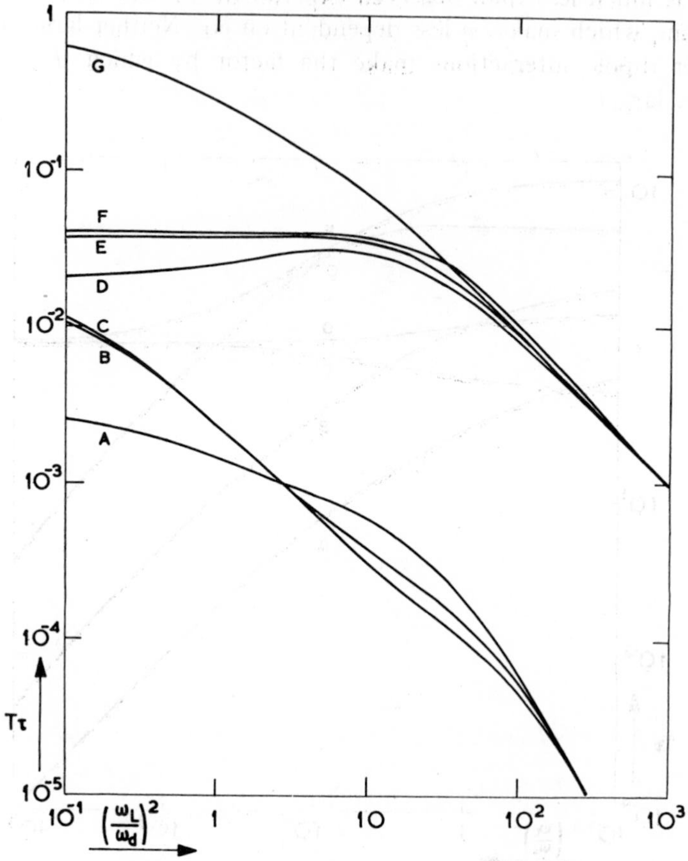

Fig. 4. The influence of spin-spin interactions on $T\tau_d$; $c = 1$

A. $(\omega_{ex}/\omega_d)^2 = 0$
B. $(\omega_{ex}/\omega_d)^2 = 3$ } $T\tau_{d_{nad}}$ untrunc.
C. $(\omega_{ex}/\omega_d)^2 = 9$

D. $(\omega_{ex}/\omega_d)^2 = 0$ untr.
E. $(\omega_{ex}/\omega_d)^2 = 3$ untr.
F. $(\omega_{ex}/\omega_d)^2 = 9$ untr. } $T\tau_{d_{nad}}$
G. $(\omega_{ex}/\omega_d)^2 = 0$ trunc.

For these reasons the number of phonons on speaking terms with the spin system will be substantially increased when spin-spin interactions become important and this is one of the reasons of the failure of the hot phonon theory [19]) for more concentrated salts.

The temperature dependence of η. If the largest quanta which still contribute appreciably to the power transfer become of the order of kT_L it is not allowed to expand the exponentials in (4) and η becomes strongly temperature dependent. The upper limit of this temperature dependence is obtained by integrating (4) over ω_{ij}, assuming the matrix elements of $\mathscr{H}_1'(\boldsymbol{S})$ in U_{ij} to be independent of ω_{ij}. This results in $\eta \propto T^{\alpha+1}$ and so a T^4 law for the adiabatic and a T^6 law for the non-adiabatic terms. Assuming other spectra for $\langle i|\mathscr{H}_1'(\boldsymbol{S})|j\rangle$ would result in η to be made up of terms of the form (16) with $\delta + \beta = \alpha + 1$. Strong interactions, normally not present in the spin system, are necessary for this procedure to be valid at higher temperatures, but might be found locally in the crystal (exchange pockets).

Comparison with the results of the relaxation measurements (cf. tabel I) suggests that for $FeNH_4$- and CrK-alum the adiabatic terms are important and for $MnNH_4$ tutton salt the non-adiabatic ones. That different terms play a rôle for Fe^{+++} and Mn^{++} may be due to the fact that for Fe^{+++} the spin-orbit interaction is of the normal $\boldsymbol{L}\cdot\boldsymbol{S}$ type, but for Mn^{++} of the tensor type [20]).

This section was intended mainly to illustrate the possibility for obtaining temperature and field dependences of η, other than those expected by previous theories, and corresponding with those observed.

6. *The influence of an inhomogeneously distributed power transfer constant.* The values of η may differ from ion to ion, and when saturating this would result in a spatially inhomogeneous distribution of the spin temperature over the sample.

A closer comparison can be made between the relaxation and the saturation measurements than by comparing averages of τ_1 and η_{st} only.

By the relaxation method the dependence of χ on frequency is measured and fitted to a curve of the form (1). For many salts this cannot be achieved with a single value of τ_1, and a distribution of relaxation times has to be assumed (cf. [5])). Such a distribution has of course an influence on the form of the saturation graphs ($1/\chi''$ *vs* h^2, fig. 1).

Suppose that the fraction $f(\eta)\,\mathrm{d}\eta$ of the N ions has a value of the power transfer between η and $\eta + \mathrm{d}\eta$. Normalizing $f(\eta)$ we can rewrite eq.(1), using (11), as

$$\frac{\chi(\omega) - \chi_0}{\chi_0 F} + 1 = \int_0^\infty \frac{f(\eta)\,\mathrm{d}\eta}{1 + i\omega(b + CH^2)/\eta T_L} \tag{27}$$

The radio frequency power absorbed by the sample is obtained by averaging (7) over the whole crystal.

$$P_m = P_0 \int_0^\infty \frac{f(\eta)\,\mathrm{d}\eta}{1 + P_0/\eta} \tag{28}$$

The expression for P_m/P_0 is seen to be identical to (27) when we substitute $P_0 = i\omega(b + CH^2)/T_L$.

To obtain (1) by starting from (5) with $W = 0$, one may contain ΔH and the temperature amplitude ΔT as the variables instead of the procedure followed in [2]). The formulae then obtained are identical with those for the stationary solution of (5) when we identify:

$$\begin{aligned} &\text{relaxation-formulas} \leftrightarrow \text{saturation-formulas} \\ &(\chi(\omega) - \chi_0)/\chi_0 F + 1 \leftrightarrow P_{\mathrm{m}}/P_0 \\ &i\omega(b + CH^2)/T_{\mathrm{L}} \leftrightarrow P_0 \\ &(1/T_{\mathrm{L}} - 1/T_{\mathrm{S}})H_{\mathrm{c}}/F\Delta H \leftrightarrow (1/T_{\mathrm{L}} - 1/T_{\mathrm{S}}) \end{aligned} \tag{29}$$

This procedure becomes more interesting when terms have to be added to (5), due for instance to cross relaxations towards impurities with temperature T_i or terms due to spin diffusion. Also certain boundary conditions may have to be fulfilled (cf. Bloembergen [21])), an example of which will be presented later. It is straightforward to show that this transformation can be performed when the added terms and the additional boundary conditions are homogeneous linear functions of or linear operators on $(1/T_{\mathrm{L}} - 1/T_{\mathrm{s}})$ and $(1/T_{\mathrm{L}} - 1/T_i)$. These variables namely all contain a factor $H_{\mathrm{c}}/\Delta HF$ in the relaxation formulae, but not in the saturation formulae (see third substitution (29)). By representing the saturation graphs by an analytical expression, the corresponding plots for $\chi'(\omega)$ and $\chi''(\omega)$ can thus be derived.

7. *Conclusion.* The power transfer η is the parameter directly measured by steady state methods, while the relaxation time τ is determined by transient methods. The relaxation between τ and η has been shown to depend on the degree of internal equilibrium. The Temperley effect cannot explain the temperature and field dependences of τ as determined by the relaxation method, except for very large spin interactions which are normally not present.

A dependence of η on magnetic dilution enters through the spin-spin interactions and through a concentration dependence of the crystalline electric field.

Because of spin-spin interactions the number of phonons with which the spin system can exchange energy, is largely increased. This is one of the reasons for the failure of the hot phonon theory for the concentrated salts.

Comparison with experiment has to be made to decide whether the conclusions reached at in section 2 are sufficient to remove the discrepancies between the relaxation times measured by Eschenfelder and Weidner and those by Van der Marel *e.a.* In a following paper the transformation will be applied to some of the measured saturation graphs. The author is indebted to Prof. C. J. Gorter for his stimulating interest and many suggestions and to J. M. Noothoven van Goor and W. J. Caspers for their help and interest in this research.

This work was a part of the research program of the "Stichting voor Fundamenteel Onderzoek der Materie (F.O.M.)"

REFERENCES

1) Casimir, H. B. G. and Du Pré, F. K., Physica **5** (1938) 507; Commun. Kamerlingh Onnes Lab., Leiden, Suppl. No. 85*a*.
2) Gorter, C. J., Paramagnetic Relaxation, Elsevier Publ. Co. Amsterdam (1947).
3) Kramers, H. C., Bijl, D. and Gorter, C. J., Physica **16** (1950) 65; Commun. No. 280*a*.
4) Van der Marel, L. C., Van den Broek, J. and Gorter, C. J., Physica **24** (1958) 101; Commun. No. 310*a*.
5) Van der Marel, L. C., Thesis Leiden (1958).
6) Van den Broek, J., Van der Marel, L. C. and Gorter, C. J., Physica **25** (1959) 371; Commun. No. 314*c*.
7) Eschenfelder, A. H. and Weidner, R. T., Phys. Rev. **92** (1953) 869.
8) Bölger, B., Thesis Leiden (1959).
9) Bloembergen, N., Shapiro, S., Pershan, P. S. and Artman, J. O., Phys. Rev. **114** (1959) 445.
10) Bölger, B. and Robinson, B. J., Physica **26** (1960) 133; Commun. No. 321*a*.
11) Lloyd, J. P. and Pake, G. E., Phys. Rev. **94** (1954) 579.
12) Waller, I., Z. Phys. **79** (1932) 370.
13) Kronig, R., Physica **6** (1939) 33.
14) Van Vleck, J. H., Phys. Rev. **57** (1940) 426.
15) Temperley, H. N. V., Proc. Camb. Phil. Soc. **35** Pt. II (1939) 256.
16) Van Vleck, J. H., Phys. Rev. **74** (1948) 1168.
17) Kittel, C. H. and Abrahams, E., Phys. Rev. **90** (1953) 238.
18) Wright, A., Phys. Rev. **76** (1949) 1827.
19) Gorter, C. J., Van der Marel, L. C. and Bölger, B., Physica **21** (1955) 103; Commun. No. 109*c*.
20) Pryce, M. H. L., Phys. Rev. **80** (1950) 1107.
21) Bloembergen, N., Physica **15** (1949) 386; Commun. No. 277*a*.

Relaxation Time Measurements in Ruby by a dc Magnetization Technique*

SHIH-YU FENG† AND N. BLOEMBERGEN
Gordon McKay Laboratory of Applied Science, Harvard University, Cambridge, Massachusetts
(Received 5 December 1962)

Relaxation-time measurements by observation of the recovery of the z component of the dc magnetization have been carried out in ruby. Harmonic cross-relaxation processes, involving two, four, and five spins, have been identified. The cross-relaxation time for the five-spin process is found to be proportional to $f^{-2.6}$, where f = Cr:Al atom ratio. The spin-lattice relaxation time is proportional to f^{-1} for small f, but decreases faster at higher concentrations. The temperature dependence as T^{-1} or T^{-2} can be explained by a model of cross relaxation between single ions and exchange coupled pairs. The magnetic field dependence is small.

I. INTRODUCTION

THE observation of the time-dependent z component of the dc magnetization as a measure of the relaxation time(s) in spin systems was introduced about ten years ago.[1,2] A high-power microwave pulse saturates the magnetic resonance in the sample. The induced emf in a pickup coil, mounted outside the cavity, is proportional to the time derivative of the dc magnetization. The output of an integrating amplifier directly records the relaxation behavior of M_z^{dc}. The time dependence of this quantity is governed by the rate equations. The population of the ith spin level is given by[3]

$$dn_i/dt=\sum_j W_{ij}(n_j-n_i)+\sum_j(-w_{ij}n_i+w_{ji}n_j)$$
$$+\sum_{jkl} w_{ij,kl}N^{-1}(n_jn_l-n_in_k)$$
$$+\sum_{nklmn} w_{ij,kl,mn}N^{-2}(n_jn_ln_n-n_in_kn_m)+\cdots. \quad (1)$$

The last two terms represent cross-relaxation processes[4] in which two and three spins jump simultaneously. Higher order cross-relaxation terms should be added. The first term on the right-hand side of Eq. (1) represents the transitions induced by the externally applied microwave field. The second term represents the ordinary spin-lattice relaxation processes. The equations can be linearized in the populations n_i in the high-temperature approximation, $h\nu_{ij}\ll kT$. The sum of the populations in the four-spin levels of the Cr^{3+} ions in ruby is, of course, fixed by the number of Cr^{3+} ions, N. Transient solutions of Eqs. (1) will, therefore, consist of a linear combination of three exponential functions with three characteristic times. The dc magnetization M_z is determined by the diagonal matrix elements and the populations in each level,

$$M_z^{dc}(t)=\sum_{i=1}^{4}\langle i|M_z|i\rangle n_i(t). \quad (2)$$

Experimental data often allow the distinction of two characteristic times. The faster time can be identified with temperature-independent cross-relaxation processes. The slower time sometimes has the order of magnitude of the w_{ij}^{-1}, the inverse of the spin-lattice transition probabilities. This is, however, not always the correct interpretation. In particular, it is not correct for ruby, where the slower time is found to depend on the Cr^{3+} concentration.

The following section will describe the experimental method and the results. The observed signals $M_z(t)$ can be matched with approximate solutions of the rate equations. The resulting values of the spin-lattice and cross-relaxation times have been determined as a function of the relative concentration f of Cr^{3+} ions, the temperature, and the external magnetic field. In the final section the results are compared with those of several other workers,[5–11] who observed the saturation or pulsed recovery of the microwave components of magnetization in ruby. Good agreement with these other data and with existing theoretical models is obtained.[12–15]

* This research was supported by the Office of Naval Research, the Signal Corps of the United States Army and the United States Air Force.
† Present address: Central Research Department, E. I. du Pont de Nemours & Company, Wilmington, Delaware.
[1] R. W. Damon, Rev. Mod. Phys. **25**, 239 (1953).
[2] N. Bloembergen and S. Wang, Phys. Rev. **93**, 72 (1954).
[3] N. Bloembergen, in *Progress in Low Temperature Physics*, edited by C. J. Gorter (North-Holland Publishing Company, Amsterdam, 1961), Vol. 3, p. 369.
[4] N. Bloembergen, S. Shapiro, P. S. Pershan, and J. O. Artman, Phys. Rev. **114**, 445 (1959).
[5] J. E. Geusic, Phys. Rev. **118**, 129 (1960).
[6] W. B. Mims and J. D. McGee, Phys. Rev. **119**, 1233 (1960).
[7] R. A. Armstrong and A. Szabo, Can. J. Phys. **38**, 1304 (1960).
[8] J. H. Pace, D. F. Sampson, and J. S. Thorp, Proc. Phys. Soc. (London) **76**, 697 (1960).
[9] J. C. Gill, Nature **190**, 619 (1961); Proc. Phys. Soc. (London) **79**, 58 (1962).
[10] G. S. Bogle and F. F. Gardner, Australian J. Phys. **14**, 381 (1961).
[11] P. L. Donoho and R. B. Hempill, in Proceedings of the Eighth Conference on Low-Temperature Physics, London, 1962 (unpublished).
[12] N. Bloembergen and P. S. Pershan, in *Advances in Quantum Electronics*, edited by J. S. Singer (Columbia University Press, New York, 1961), p. 373; J. H. Van Vleck, *ibid*. p. 388.
[13] J. C. Gill and R. J. Elliott, in *Advances in Quantum Electronics*, edited by J. S. Singer (Columbia University Press, New York, 1961), p. 399.
[14] M. Hirono, J. Phys. Soc. Japan **16**, 766 (1961).
[15] A. Kiel, Phys. Rev. **120**, 137 (1960).

II. EXPERIMENTAL METHOD AND RESULTS

Figure 1 is the block diagram of the experimental system. The klystrons were *V*-58 and 2*K*33 in the *X* band and the *K* band, respectively. All amplifiers employed have a flat response to very low frequencies, because the relaxation times are of the order of 100 msec. Figure 2 shows the relative positions of the cavity, the ruby crystal, and the pickup coil. A second coil, away from the sample and connected in opposite sense with respect to the first one, compensates for any undesired pickup from time-varying stray magnetic fields. The integrator not only converts dM_z/dt to M_z, but also improves the signal-to-noise ratio by narrowing the effective bandwidth. The experimental error in the data is estimated to be 5% in case of concentrated samples and about ten times higher in case of very dilute samples.[16]

Figure 3 shows a typical relaxation signal before and after integration, in the absence of cross relaxation. Only one characteristic time can be distinguished. During saturation of the spin transition at ν_{ij}, this time may be identified approximately with τ, where $\tau^{-1}=2W_{ij}+w_{ij}+w_{ji}$. The relaxation at the end of the microwave pulse may be identified with $T_1=\frac{1}{2}w_{ij}^{-1}$. Rigorously there should be three characteristic times which are combinations of all w_{kl}'s in the limit of extreme dilution. The observed signal is, however, satisfactorily described by a single exponential, characteristic of the relaxation behavior of a two-level system. The interpretation will be given in Sec. III.

At certain particular values of crystal orientation and the magnetic dc field H_0, however, cross-relaxation signals were observed as shown in Fig. 4. This case, where the field $H_0=2990$ G, makes an angle of 21° with the trigonal axis, is identified as a five-spin cross-relaxation process. The four-spin states can still be labeled approximately by the magnetic quantum-quantum numbers m_s, which are good quantum numbers if H_0 is parallel to the trigonal axis. Although the energy of the spin system is conserved in the simultaneous transitions of five spins indicated in Fig. 4(b), the dc magnetization changes by about nine Bohr magnetons, $-5(-3/2)+3(-1/2)+2(3/2)=+9$.

The application of microwave power initially tends to equalize the population of the state $m_s=-1/2$ and $-3/2$. This causes a decrease in the total magnetic quantum number. As the population in the states $m_s=-3/2$ increases, a cross-relaxation process proportional to $n_{-3/2}{}^5-n_{-1/2}{}^3n_{3/2}{}^2$ becomes effective. The total magnetic quantum number increases rapidly and the change in dc magnetization reverses sign. This "cross-over" effect is very striking, as a comparison of Fig. 4 with Fig. 3 shows. Finally, after the microwave power is cut off, the signal $M_z(t)$ recovers exponentially to its initial value.

A theoretical description of the signal may be obtained by approximating the rate equations (1) in the following way: The presence of level 2 with $m=+1/2$ is ignored. It does not take part in the cross-relaxation process and its influence on the spin-lattice relaxation is neglected. The populations of levels 1, 3, and 4, with approximate quantum numbers $m_s=-1/2$, $-3/2$, and

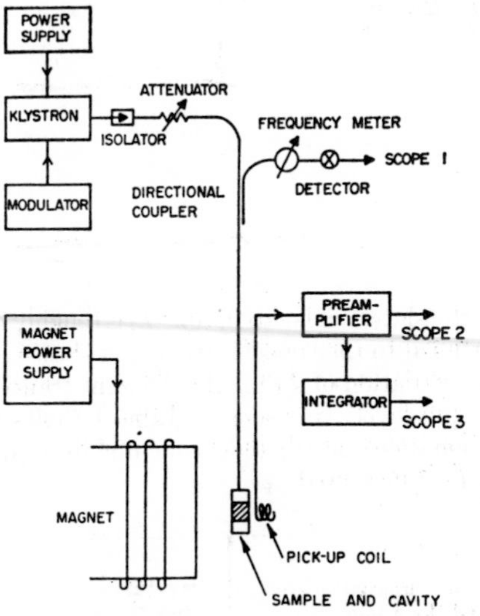

FIG. 1. Block diagram of equipment to measure the relaxation of the longitudinal component of magnetization.

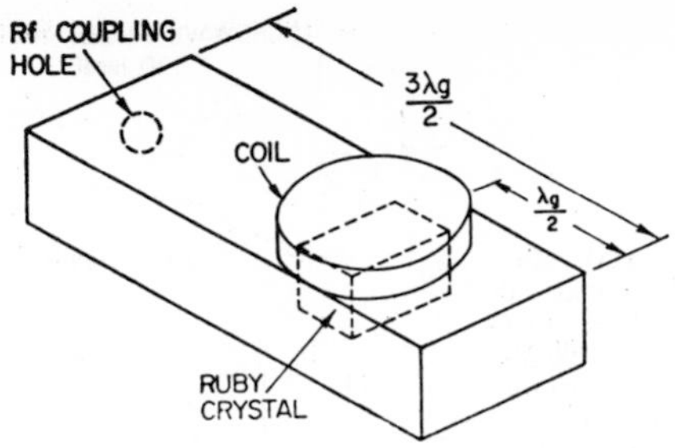

FIG. 2. Cavity, ruby crystal, and the pickup coil.

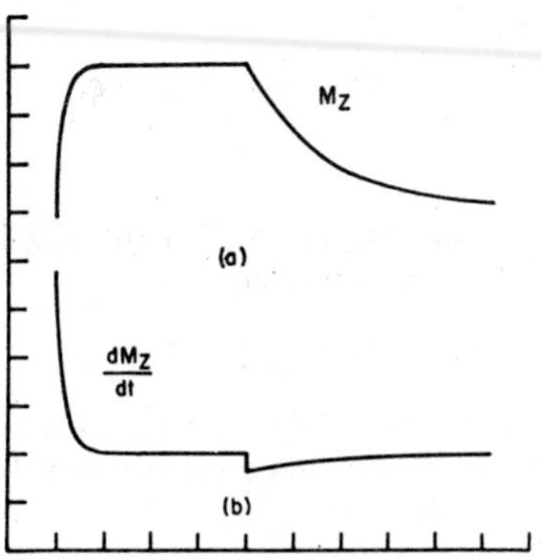

FIG. 3. Sketch of signal at 3025 G, 8400 Mc/sec, 4.2°K, $H_{dc}\|c$ axis, concentration 0.08%, (a) after integration, (b) before integration.

[16] Further details about the experimental equipment may be found in S. Feng, Ph.D. thesis, Harvard University, 1962 (unpublished).

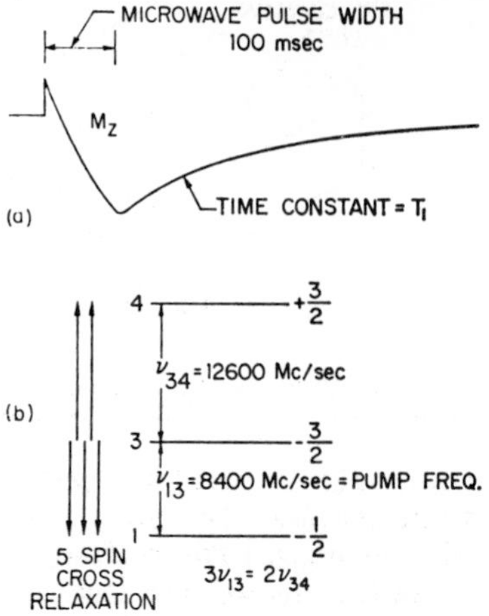

FIG. 4(a). Integrated signal for $\theta=21°$, $H_{dc}=2990$ G, 4.2°K, $\nu_0=8400$ Mc/sec, concentration 0.04%. (b) The corresponding energy levels.

$+3/2$, respectively, satisfy the relation $n_1+n_3+n_4=\frac{3}{4}N$. The rate equations (1) then reduce to a set of two independent equations. During the strong saturating microwave pulse these may be written in the form,

$$\dot{n}_1-\dot{n}_3=-\frac{n_1-n_3}{\tau}-\frac{8}{38}\frac{3(n_1-n_3)-2(n_3-n_4)}{T_{21}}, \quad (3)$$

$$\dot{n}_3-\dot{n}_4=\frac{n_1-n_3}{2\tau}-\frac{7}{38}\frac{2(n_3-n_4)-3(n_1-n_3)}{T_{21}}, \quad (4)$$

where $\tau=\frac{1}{2}W_{13}^{-1}$ is the characteristic time under the radiation and T_{21} is the cross-relaxation time. The spin-lattice relaxation term is neglected since its rate is slow compared with the other two processes during the pulse. When the microwave pulse is cut off, the rate equations may be written as

$$\dot{n}_1-\dot{n}_3=\frac{n_1-n_3-(n_1^0-n_3^0)}{T_1}-\frac{8}{38}\frac{3(n_1-n_3)-2(n_3-n_4)}{T_{21}}, \quad (5)$$

$$\dot{n}_3-\dot{n}_4=-\frac{n_3-n_4-(n_3^0-n_4^0)}{T_1}-\frac{7}{38}\frac{2(n_3-n_4)-3(n_1-n_3)}{T_{21}}. \quad (6)$$

The set of Eqs. (3) and (4), or (5) and (6), can be solved exactly, and the time dependence of M_z,

$$M_z(t)=[-\tfrac{1}{2}n_1(t)-\tfrac{3}{2}n_3(t)+\tfrac{3}{2}n_4(t)]\beta$$

is thus determined. If the nun rical values $T_{21}=2\times10^{-2}$ sec, and $T_1=0.2$ sec are chosen, and a calculated value $\tau=0.5\times10^{-3}$ sec, one finds

$$M_z(t)=-0.49\exp(-2000t)+3.3\exp(-7.94t) \quad (7)$$

during the microwave pulse, and

$$M_z(t)=-2.86\exp(-5t)+0.03\exp(-50t) \quad (8)$$

after the microwave pulse. The solutions reproduce the shape of the observed signal in Fig. 4 satisfactorily.

Other cross-relaxation signals were observed for four-spin and two-spin processes, shown in Figs. 5 and 6. They can be analyzed in a similar manner.

For the most dilute crystal ($f=0.04\%$) the cross-relaxation signal was observed only in the vicinity of the harmonic point. But for higher concentrations, such a signal was observed over a very wide range of crystal orientations. Figure 7 shows the orientation dependence of the cross-relaxation time T_{21}, which is independent of temperature for the five-spin process mentioned above. The concentration dependence is as $f^{-2.6}$ at the harmonic point.[5–7] For the most concentrated crystal (0.55%) many cross-relaxation processes are always present and no dependence on the orientation was found.

Size dependence was not found at 0.55% concentration. The two samples were cut from the same host crystal. They were 195 and 2055 mg in weight each. This rules out phonon-heating phenomena. A true spin-lattice interaction is measured.

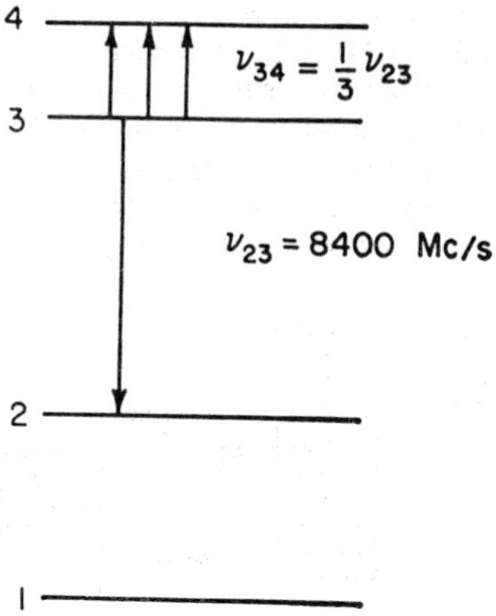

FIG. 5. Energy levels and the 4-spin cross-relaxation process at $H_{dc}=1020$ G, $\theta=73°$, $\nu_0=8400$ Mc/sec.

The spin-lattice relaxation time T_1 is roughly inversely proportional to the concentration f, as shown in Fig. 8.

Some variation of T_1 for the different transitions between spin levels is observed. Table I shows that the relaxation time is nearly independent of the frequency at which T_1 is measured.

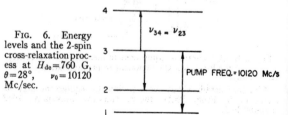

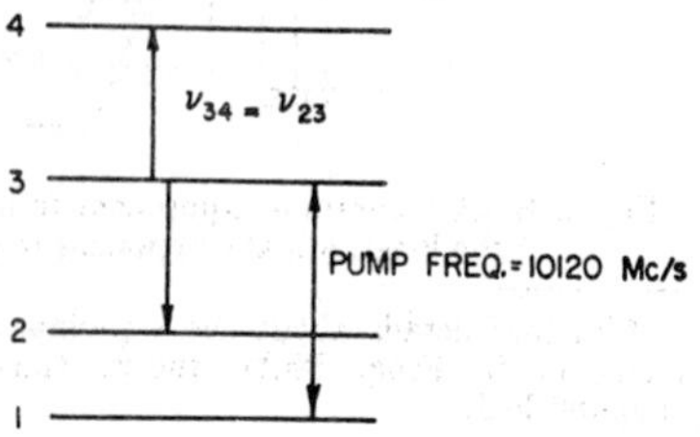

FIG. 6. Energy levels and the 2-spin cross-relaxation process at $H_{dc}=760$ G, $\theta=28°$, $\nu_0=10120$ Mc/sec.

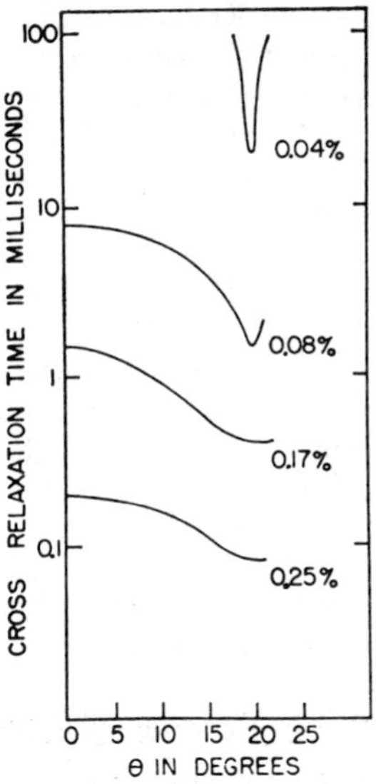

FIG. 7. Change of the cross-relaxation time with orientation at various concentrations.

The temperature dependence of the relaxation time is more interesting, as shown in Fig. 9. At low concentrations, T_1 is inversely proportional to the temperature T, and at high concentrations, T_1 is inversely proportional to T^2. At some intermediate concentration T_1 goes as T^{-1} at lower temperatures and as T^{-2} at higher temperatures. Both K- and X-band measurements show essentially the same temperature dependence.

III. DISCUSSION AND COMPARISON WITH THEORY

The experimental results described above corroborate earlier findings of cross-relaxation effects in ruby near harmonic points.[5–7,10] Mims and McGee found that a three-spin process had a concentration dependence T_{21} proportional to $f^{-2.4}$, whereas we find for the five-spin process a $f^{-2.6}$ dependence.

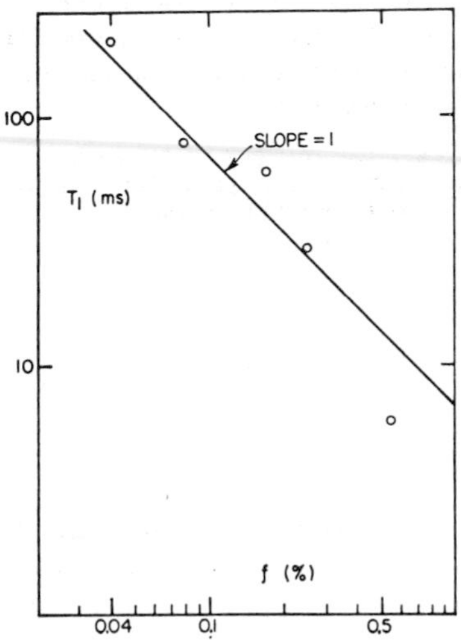

FIG. 8. Change of spin-lattice relaxation time T_1 with concentration f.

TABLE I. Spin-lattice relaxation times for various lines at 4.2°K.

Line	Relaxation times (msec)	Frequency
1–3	200	X band
1–3	100	X band
2–3	80	X band
3–4	100	X band and K band
1–4	120	K band
2–4	120	K band

Basic theoretical considerations show that, in the limit of very small concentration with random distribution of the magnetic ions, an n-spin cross-relaxation process should have a concentration dependence f^{-n+1}. This prediction is confirmed by more elaborate calculations of Hirono.[14] Armstrong and Szabo[7] and Kiel[15] arrived at similar conclusions.

It should be noted that the concentration range over which the pure five-spin process could be followed is very small. It is apparent from Fig. 7 that many competing mechanisms should be considered for concentrations $\geq 0.1\%$. The deviation from the theoretical f^{-4} dependence is not to be regarded as serious. Perhaps the experimental data indicate a slight preference for clustering of the Cr^{3+} ions instead of a completely random distribution.

The longer characteristic time, identified with a spin-lattice relaxation time T_1, is found to be dependent both on temperature and on concentration. At low temperature the concentration dependence is approximately as f^{-1}, as shown in Fig. 8. At low concentration T_1 is proportional to T^{-1}, while at high concentration it goes as T^{-2}. This behavior is shown in Fig. 9. These results are in excellent agreement with the much more extensive

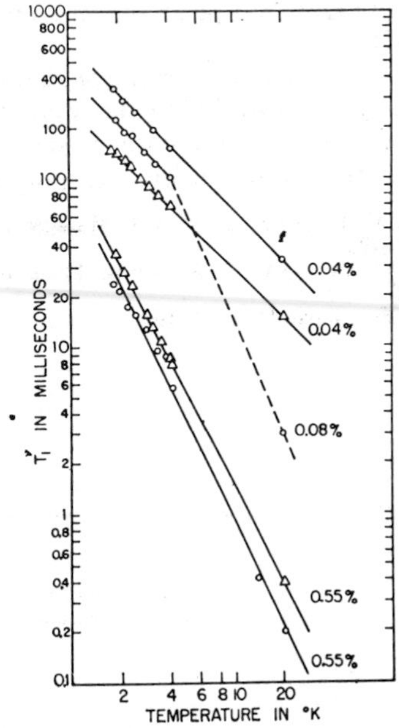

FIG. 9. Dependence of T_1 on temperature at different concentrations ○: 8400 Mc/sec, △: 23 000 Mc/sec.

measurements of Gill.[9] He, as well as Statz[17] and coworkers, also found that the relaxation time of resolved resonance lines originating in excited multiplet states of ion pairs is several orders of magnitude shorter than the values for single ion lines.

The interpretation of the combined temperature and concentration dependence of the relaxation time of single ions has been discussed by several authors.[9,12,13] There is rapid cross relaxation between the single-ion spin levels and those of excited spin multiplets of ion pairs. The latter relax fast via a Finn-Orbach-Wolf[18] mechanism to the singlet ground state of the ion pair. There is a distribution of splittings between the multiplet and singlet in the ion pair depending on the distance between the two Cr^{3+} ions. A reasonable distribution of multiplet splittings in the ion pair states can account for all observed features. In very dilute materials the direct spin-lattice relaxation process becomes dominant. This process is proportional to T^{-1} and independent of concentration.

The magnetic field dependence of T_1 appears to be very small. No difference has been detected on the same resonance observed at X and K band shown in Table I. Pace, Sampson, and Thorp[8] have found that values of T_1 at 34600 Mc/sec are somewhat shorter, perhaps by a factor two, than those measured at X band in rubies of the same concentration.

In the more concentrated rubies the absence of a magnetic field or frequency dependence can be understood, if the explanation given above for relaxation in these specimens is adopted. Neither the cross-relaxation time to the ion pair states, nor the relaxation from the excited ion pair states to the ground state are field dependent. Since Fig. 8 shows that T_1 is concentration dependent down to the lowest concentrations used, this may explain the absence of the field dependence in these experiments. Gill found that T_1 depends on concentration even at $f=0.01\%$.

At very low concentrations the direct spin-lattice relaxation process may dominate.[11,19] In this case the transition probabilities between states which are not Kramers' conjugates are expected to have w_{ij} proportional to ν_{ij}^2. Transitions between Kramers pairs, e.g., $m_s \rightarrow \frac{1}{2} \rightarrow -\frac{1}{2}$, should have probabilities w proportional to ν_{ij}^4. These should, however, be very small, since these processes can only occur in higher approximation.[20]

Orbach[21] suggested that the zero-field splitting may explain the approximately constant value of T_1 for transitions between the spin quartet levels, if the magnetic field is varied between 0 and 5000 G. The three characteristic times have been determined for the rate equations (1), in which only terms with w_{ij} connecting $|m_s|=3/2 \rightarrow 1/2$ levels have been kept. If these w_{ij} are assumed to be proportional to ν_{ij}^2, the result is indeed that the average relaxation rate is essentially independent of H_0 below 4000 G and increases approximately linear with H_0 to 15 000 G. This is also compatible with the observations of Pace *et al.* in high fields, and those of Gill and us in fields below 4000 G.

IV. CONCLUSIONS

The observation of the relaxation behavior of the dc component of magnetization can be carried out successfully in rather dilute paramagnetic spin systems at liquid-helium temperature. The method has the advantage of simplicity. The microwave system can be rudimentary. The only requirement is sufficient intensity to saturate a resonance line. It should be feasible to accomplish this in an untuned transmission line. The relaxation behavior at many different field strengths and different spin transitions can thus be studied rather rapidly.

The experimental results corroborate earlier findings about the temperature concentration and magnetic field dependence of the spin-lattice relaxation time in ruby. Higher order harmonic cross-relaxation processes are also readily detected. The "crossover" of the M_z magnetization shown in Fig. 4 is a special feature of the present technique, which aids in the identification of cross-relaxation processes.

The general characteristics of the experimental observations are well explained by existing theories. The implications for the operation of ruby masers which prompted many of the experimental relaxation studies have been discussed elsewhere.[3,10,12]

[17] H. Statz, L. Rimai, M. J. Weber, and G. A. DeMars, Suppl. J. Appl. Phys. **32**, 218S (1961).

[18] C. B. P. Finn, R. Orbach, and W. P. Wolf, Proc. Phys. Soc. (London) **77**, 261 (1961).

[19] Y. Nisida, J. Phys. Soc. Japan **17**, 1519 (1962).

[20] R. Orbach, Proc. Phys. Soc. (London) **77**, 821 (1961).

[21] R. Orbach (private communication). The authors are indebted to Professor Orbach for several helpful discussions.

Spin–Lattice Relaxation of Chromium Ions in Ruby

By J. Ç. GILL

Royal Radar Establishment, Malvern, Worcs.

MS. received 28th July 1961

Abstract. Measurements have been made of the spin–lattice relaxation of single chromium ions and of certain chromium–chromium pairs in ruby. Pairs whose energy levels are split by 'exchange' interactions equivalent to a few degrees K relax much more rapidly than the single ions. There is some evidence that the phonons participating in the relaxation have energies equal to certain of the splittings. Modulation of the 'exchange' interaction by the lattice vibrations provides a possible means of relaxation at low temperatures. In sufficiently concentrated crystals (containing at least 0·21% Cr) a rapid transfer of excitation is observed between the pairs and the single ions. The relaxation via the pairs then accounts in order of magnitude for that of the single ions. The coupling to the observed pairs is too weak to explain the concentration-dependent relaxation of the single ions in more dilute crystals.

§ 1. INTRODUCTION

IT HAS been suggested that pairs or larger clusters of paramagnetic ions might be responsible for the concentration-dependent spin–lattice relaxation in some magnetically dilute crystals (e.g. Bowers and Mims 1959, Van Vleck 1960). The pairs are assumed to relax rapidly, perhaps as a result of 'exchange' interaction, and to convey to the lattice energy reaching them by spin–spin transfer from the single ions. Some support for the proposal has come from recent studies of chromium pairs in ruby. A short account has been given (Gill 1961) of the measurement of the relaxation of the pairs from the recovery of their microwave absorption lines after saturation. It was found that at temperatures less than 77 °K the pairs commonly relax one or two orders of magnitude faster than do the single ions. Evidence that they relax rapidly at much higher temperatures is provided by measurements of line-width by Statz, Rimai, Weber, de Mars and Koster (1961).

Further measurements of relaxation in ruby are described below. Possible mechanisms of 'pair' relaxation are discussed. The extent to which the pairs might account for the relaxation of the single ions is also considered.

§ 2. EXPERIMENTAL DETAILS

Measurements were made using a conventional 9500 Mc/s cavity spectrometer with superheterodyne detection. Spectra were recorded either with a pen recorder, using a slowly varying direct magnetic field without other modulation, or photographically from an oscilloscope trace, with 50 c/s modulation of the magnetic field. Slight adjustment of the operating frequency was made automatically to compensate for drifts and to ensure that only the absorptive part of the complex susceptibility was detected. Relaxation times were measured by a method similar in principle to that of Bowers and Mims. The recovery of an absorption line could be recorded photographically after saturation by a pulse of resonant radiation. The pulse duration was usually 10μsec, but could be increased if necessary.

Table 1 gives details of seven ruby specimens that were studied. The crystals were grown by a flame-fusion method. Chromium concentrations were measured either spectrographically (specimens 1 to 5) or from the microwave spectra. Ferric ions (about 30 parts per million) were also detected.

Table 1

Details of Ruby Specimens

Specimen No.	1	2	3	4	5	6	7
Atomic Cr/Al ratio (%)	0·76	0·38	0·21	0·12	0·08	0·03	0·01

§3. SPECTRA AND ENERGY LEVELS OF CHROMIUM PAIRS

Lines due to chromium–chromium pairs were detected in the paramagnetic resonance spectra of the six most concentrated crystals. Examples are given in figure 1. The 'pair' lines were less intense than the single-ion lines by factors proportional to, and of the same order as, the Cr/Al ratios. This would happen if the pairs arose from a random distribution of chromium ions amongst the available lattice sites.

The 'pair' spectrum is complex and an exhaustive analysis has not been attempted. An analysis of the 15·74 Gc/s spectrum, in which clustering of the lines from different pairs is pronounced and facilitates their identification, has been made by Statz, Rimai, Weber, de Mars and Koster. They find appreciable anti-ferromagnetic 'exchange' even between relatively widely separated ions. The parameter J in the isotropic interaction $J\mathbf{S}_1.\mathbf{S}_2$ ranges from 390 cm^{-1}, for nearest-neighbour pairs, to about 0·5 cm^{-1} for eleventh nearest neighbours. Following these authors, a spin Hamiltonian for a pair of ions S_1, S_2 may be written

$$H = g\beta\mathbf{H}\,.\,(\mathbf{S}_1+\mathbf{S}_2)+D\{S_{1z}{}^2+S_{2z}{}^2-\tfrac{2}{3}S(S+1)\}$$

$$+J\mathbf{S}_1\,.\,\mathbf{S}_2+\frac{g^2\beta^2}{r^3}\left\{\mathbf{S}_1\,.\,\mathbf{S}_2-3\frac{(\mathbf{S}_1\,.\,\mathbf{r})(\mathbf{S}_2\,.\,\mathbf{r})}{r^2}\right\}$$

$$+\text{anisotropic exchange terms.} \qquad (1)$$

The last terms arise, via the spin–orbit coupling λ, from exchange splitting in excited orbital levels (e.g. Bleaney and Bowers 1952, Moriya 1960). If Δ is the energy of these levels, the greatest anisotropic exchange terms are of the order $J\lambda/\Delta$, and may be ignored in this case if J is not greater than a few cm^{-1}(λ/Δ is approximately 3×10^{-3}).

If J is much greater than D, the energy levels form multiplets characterized by effective spins S'. Microwave transitions are observed between levels belonging to the same S' multiplet. Levels with S' equal to 3, 2 and 1 lie respectively $6J$, $3J$ and J above the ground singlet, and give rise to lines whose intensities vary as $A\exp(-6J/kT)$, $A\exp(-3J/kT)$ and $A\exp(-J/kT)$, where A is the factor

$$(1/kT)\{7\exp(-6J/kT)+5\exp(-3J/kT)+3\exp(-J/kT)+1\}^{-1},$$

T is the temperature, and kT is much greater than D.

The determination of J from the temperature variation is difficult. The pair lines are very weak in the more dilute crystals, and are so numerous that they tend to coalesce if the concentration is increased. The measurement would be better made using a frequency higher than 9500 Mc/s. Attention has been concentrated mainly on the more prominent lines *a*, *b*, *c*, *d* and *e* of figure 1. These are well separated from the single-ion lines and evidently come from pairs in which J is at least comparable with D. In order to simplify the spectrum as much as possible, measurements were made with the

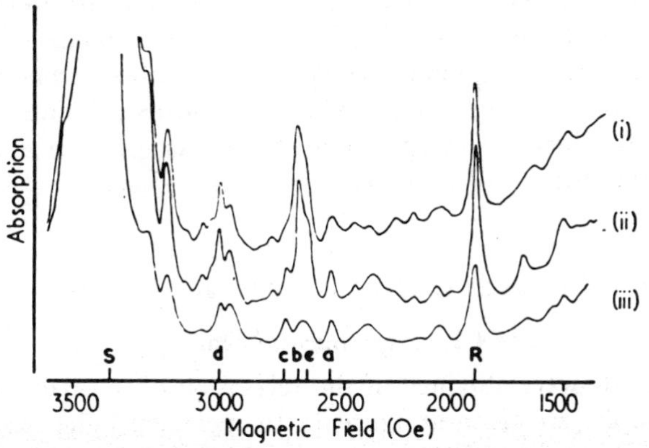

Figure 1. Spectra of pairs of chromium ions in ruby: (i) T = 52 °K, (ii) 11 °K, (iii) 1·4 °K (frequency 9460 Mc/s, magnetic field parallel to crystal axis, chromium concentration 0·21%). The $+\frac{1}{2} \leftrightarrow -\frac{1}{2}$ single-ion transition gives rise to line S near 3400 Oe. Line R is due to single ions in a small fragment of crystal with axis perpendicular to the magnetic field.

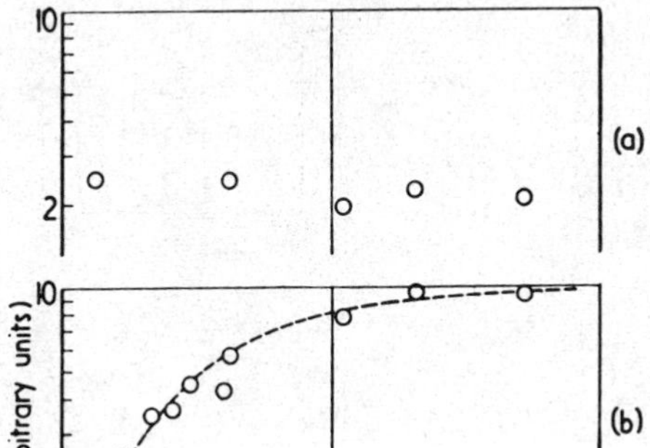

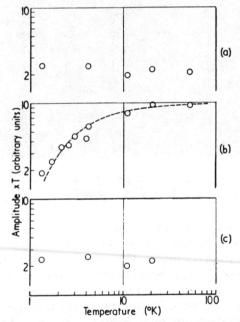

Figure 2. Temperature-dependence of lines *a*, *b* and *c*. The broken line shows the variation expected for levels with $S' = 3$, 4·5 deg K above the ground state.

magnetic field parallel to the crystal axis. Figure 2 shows the temperature-dependence (omitting the factor $1/kT$) measured for specimen 3 by comparing the amplitudes of lines *a*, *b* and *c* with that of the reference line R. It is apparent that line *b* originates in excited levels; states with $S' = 3$, 4·5 ± 0·5 deg K above the ground state (i.e. with

$J = 0{\cdot}5\ \text{cm}^{-1}$), fit the data satisfactorily. The line is probably due to transitions between states ($S' = 3$, $M_z' = -1$) and ($S' = 3$, $M_z' = 0$). The neighbouring line *e* could not be measured accurately, but from figure 1 it clearly comes from states of only slightly lower energy. Lines *a* and *c*, on the other hand, come from much lower levels, probably within 1 deg K of the ground state. Line *d* was too close to other pair lines for accurate measurement of amplitude. The measured lines appeared representative, in temperature variation and relaxation behaviour, of those observed at liquid helium temperatures. In the liquid hydrogen range many additional weak lines were seen, coming presumably from other pairs with splittings at least as great as 4 deg K. Confusion between adjacent lines prevented their accurate measurement.

§ 4. Relaxation of the ion-pairs

4.1. *Experimental results*

Satisfactory records were obtained of the relaxation of ion-pairs in specimens 2, 3, 4 and 5. Two examples are given in figure 3. In specimen 1 the relaxation times were less than the limit, about 5 μsec, set by the recovery of the receiver. Pair lines in the

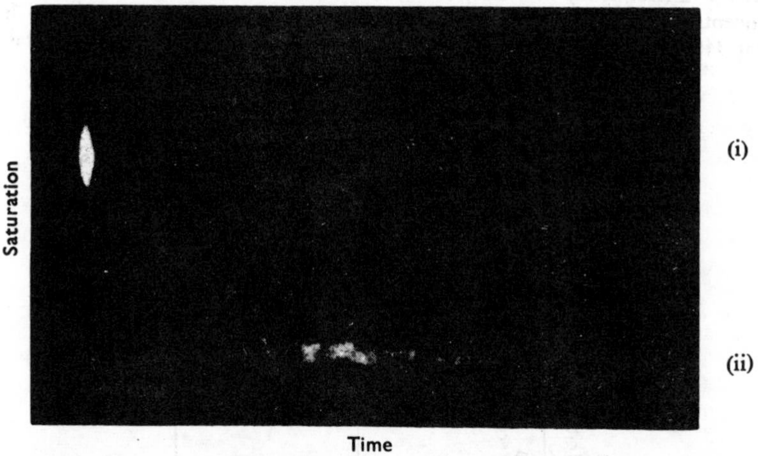

Figure 3. Relaxation of ion-pairs. (i) line *d*, $T = 1{\cdot}4$ °K, concentration 0·08%, time-base duration 11·5 msec; (ii) line *b*, 20·4 °K, concentration 0·21%, time-base 0·48 msec.

other crystals were too weak for measurement. Care was taken to ensure that the microwave power used in observing the recovery did not itself cause saturation, and consequent reduction of the recovery time.† The recovery could usually be described adequately by a single relaxation time. Small deviations from an exponential law apparent during the early stages of the recovery of lines *b* and *e* in specimen 4, but not in specimen 5, were attributed to spin–spin relaxation between the two lines. Line *d*, belonging to a group of almost coincident pair lines, behaved similarly. In such cases relaxation times were measured from the later stages of the recovery. Other anomalies were noticed in the relaxation of pair lines lying close to the single-ion lines, including line *d* in specimens 2 and 3. When the pulse power (or duration) was increased much beyond that needed to saturate the pair line, an additional and longer time-constant was seen at the

† It was found that some of the helium-temperature results reported previously (Gill 1961) had been slightly affected by saturation.

end of the recovery. Saturation of the fringes of the single-ion line was apparently being observed.

Figure 4 shows the relaxation times measured for lines *a*, *b* and *d*. A few times measured for lines *c* and *e* at liquid helium temperatures were similar to those for lines *a*

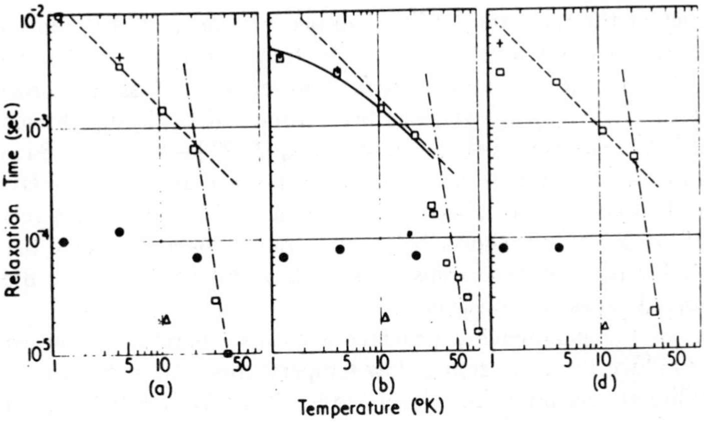

Figure 4. Relaxation times measured from pair lines *a*, *b* and *d*. Chromium concentrations: +, 0·08%; □, 0·12%; •, 0·21%; △, 0·38%. Variations of relaxation time as T^{-1} (– – – – – –), T^{-7} (–·–·–·–·–) and as $\{1-\exp(-3\cdot8°/T)\}$(———) are indicated.

and *b* respectively. Records for helium temperatures usually gave times consistent within ± 10%. Results for higher temperatures are less accurate; at temperatures greater than 25 °K they may be in error by as much as ± 50%.

4.2. *Interpretation*

As the temperature is reduced, the relaxation of the pairs in specimens 2 and 3 becomes temperature-independent, but varies rapidly with concentration. The limits approached by the relaxation in the different pair lines are similar in order of magnitude; measurement of fifteen lines of specimen 3, observed at fields ranging from 1000 to 3200 Oe, gave times all between 50μsec and 200μsec. In such cases the recovery is evidently due to the transfer of excitation from the pairs to the single ions by temperature-independent spin–spin processes. The thermal capacity of the single ions is so much greater than that of the saturated 'pair' levels that the recovery of the latter in this way is virtually complete. The transfer is presumably similar to the 'general cross-relaxation' between single ions, described by Mims and McGee (1960). Temperature-independent relaxation times of the same order as the limiting 'pair' times were in fact measured from the beginning of the recovery of the single-ion line (table 2, § 5.1).

The relaxation times of lines *a* and *b* in specimen 4 are not significantly different from those in specimen 5. Spin–spin transfer thus appears to be small, and the recovery may be attributed mainly to spin–lattice relaxation. It is significant that general cross-relaxation was not apparent in the relaxation of the single ions in these crystals. In specimen 4 line *d* shows evidence of spin–spin relaxation, perhaps to neighbouring pair lines.

At low temperatures the spin–lattice relaxation presumably takes place through single-phonon processes. The expected rapid decrease of relaxation time as Raman processes assume importance is observed at temperatures above 20 °K.

4.3. *Discussion*

The tendency of the relaxation in line b to become constant at the lowest temperatures is explicable (without invoking spin–spin transfer) in terms of separate single-phonon transitions to and from an intermediate lower level. A similar process, but involving an intermediate upper level, has been discussed by Finn, Orbach and Wolf (1961), and leads to relaxation times varying as $\{\exp(E/kT)-1\}$, where E is the phonon energy. In the present case it is easily shown that one might expect relaxation times proportional to $\{1-\exp(-E/kT)\}$, becoming constant for $kT \ll E$. The levels giving rise to line b have $S' = 3$, and it is shown below that transitions are possible between these and the $S' = 1$ levels. For these transitions we have E equivalent to 3·8 deg K, with which the observed times are consistent.

Modulation of the parameter J provides a means whereby the lattice vibrations might possibly induce the relaxation at low temperatures. An approximate expression for the probability of relaxation from level i to level j is (Waller 1932, Al'tshuler 1956)

$$P_{ij}{}^{D} = \frac{8\pi^3}{3h^4}\frac{r^2}{\rho v^5}\frac{E_{ij}{}^3}{\{1-\exp(-E_{ij}/kT)\}}\sum_{q=x,y,z}|\langle i|(dU/dq)|j\rangle|^2 \qquad (2)$$

where E_{ij} is the energy difference $E_i - E_j$, ρ is the density of the crystal, v is an average value for the velocity of sound, r is the distance between the ions of the pair, and U is the interaction whose modulation by displacements in direction q brings about the relaxation. If J is sufficiently small for anisotropic exchange to be negligible, the interaction dU/dq may be identified with $(dJ/dr)(\mathbf{S}_1 . \mathbf{S}_2)$. This operator would be diagonal with respect to the eigenstates of the pair (from equation (1)) were it not for the anisotropy of the crystal field and the dipole–dipole terms. When J is much greater than D, the greatest off-diagonal elements of $\mathbf{S}_1 . \mathbf{S}_2$ are of the order D/J and couple certain states whose effective spins S' differ by 2. Adjacent S' multiplets have opposite symmetry with respect to interchange of $\mathbf{S}_1$ and $\mathbf{S}_2$ and are not coupled by $\mathbf{S}_1 . \mathbf{S}_2$. Elements between states within the same multiplet are of higher order in D/J. Small matrix elements arise in a similar manner from the dipole–dipole coupling.

On substituting in expression (2) $\rho = 4$ g cm^{-3}, $v = 6\times10^5$ cm sec^{-1}, $r = 5$ Å, $D = 0{\cdot}2$ cm^{-1}, $E = 5J$, and $\langle i|\mathbf{S}_1 . \mathbf{S}_2|j\rangle = D/J$, a value $(dJ/dr) = 13$ cm^{-1} Å^{-1} is found to lead to relaxation times of 2 msec at 4·2 °K (the required dJ/dr is independent of J, provided that J is much greater than D). Such a value does not appear unlikely. According to Statz, Rimai, Weber, de Mars and Koster, a temperature change that alters the lattice dimensions by 0·1% causes a ten to fifteen per cent change in J, for pairs with $J \sim 0{\cdot}5$ cm^{-1} and $r \sim 5$ Å. From this one finds dJ/dr to be between 10 and 15 cm^{-1} Å^{-1}.

Relaxation of the pairs through modulation of the crystal fields, in the manner proposed by Van Vleck (1940) to account for the relaxation of the single ions, is also possible. The appropriate matrix elements connecting pair states with S' differing by 2 are of the same order as those between the single-ion states. For single-phonon relaxation one therefore expects the pair relaxation to be faster than that of the single ions by a factor approximately $(E_p/E_s)^2$, where E_p, E_s are the relevant phonon energies, assumed small compared with kT. For the lines observed at liquid helium temperatures this factor is unlikely to be much greater than 10. Since the Van Vleck process leads to single-ion relaxation times of 10 seconds at 4·2 °K (Mattuck and Strandberg 1960), it is clear that it is not sufficient to account for the observed relaxation of the pairs.

The mechanism of Raman relaxation is less clear. The measured relaxation times are typically about 100μsec at 30 °K; in lines *a* and *d* the variation with temperature is approximately as T^{-7}, and in line *b* more nearly as T^{-3}. An expression for Raman relaxation through modulation of J is

$$P_{ij}^{R} = \frac{\pi^3}{18}\frac{r^4}{\rho^2 v^{10}}\int_0^\infty |\langle i|\mathrm{M}|j\rangle|^2\, \nu^6 e^{-h\nu/kT} d\nu \tag{3}$$

where ν is the frequency of the absorbed phonon. It is assumed that $E_{ij} \ll kT \ll k\theta$, where θ is the Debye temperature. The operator M contains a term $(d^2J/dr^2)(\mathbf{S}_1 \cdot \mathbf{S}_2)$, which has matrix elements independent of ν and leads to a T^{-7} variation of relaxation time, and also terms arising from $(dJ/dr)(\mathbf{S}_1 \cdot \mathbf{S}_2)$ by second-order perturbation. In the temperature range of interest these have matrix elements of the form $\langle i|\mathbf{S}_1 \cdot \mathbf{S}_2|k\rangle\langle k|\mathbf{S}_1 \cdot \mathbf{S}_2|j\rangle(dJ/dr)^2(E_{jk}/h^2\nu^2)$, where the intermediate state k is one of the spin levels of the ground orbital state, and give relaxation times proportional to T^{-3}. However, equation (3) yields the observed times only when impossibly large values are assumed for d^2J/dr^2 (2000 cm^{-1} Å^{-2}) or dJ/dr (3000 cm^{-1} Å^{-1}). Possibly the Van Vleck mechanism is of importance in the Raman relaxation, though the order-of-magnitude difference between the pair and single-ion relaxation times is then difficult to explain. A difference might conceivably arise from the splitting of excited orbital levels (cf. Mattuck and Strandberg 1960, equation (73)).

§ 5. RELAXATION OF THE SINGLE IONS

5.1. *Measured Relaxation Times*

The recovery in the more concentrated crystals is modified by cross-relaxation between different transitions in the manner described by Mims and McGee. Its effects are considered later. 'Phonon heating', of the type considered by Van Vleck (1941), appeared to be unimportant. One would expect any restriction of the relaxation rate, if too few lattice modes were available to remove energy from the crystal, to lead to an increase of relaxation time with concentration. A decrease with concentration was in fact usually observed. There is also the possibility, in the more dilute crystals, of measuring a recovery due largely to 'spin diffusion' within an inhomogeneously saturated line. 'Hole-burning', however, was not observed in lines displayed using 50 c/s modulation of the magnetic field, and no difference was found between the relaxation after saturation in a constant field, and that seen after using a suitable pulse in the presence of field modulation to saturate the whole line. Bloembergen, Shapiro, Pershan and Artman (1959) have shown that inhomogeneous saturation would not be expected in crystals of the present dilution in the absence of macroscopic irregularities.

One expects the recovery of the four-level Cr^{3+} system to be described by

$$\{A(\infty)-A(t)\} = \{A(\infty)-A(0)\}\{a \exp(-t/\tau_a)+b \exp(-t/\tau_b)+c \exp(-t/\tau_c)\} \tag{4}$$

where $A(t)$ is the absorption at time t. In the absence of cross-relaxation the three times τ_a, τ_b, τ_c characterize the spin–lattice relaxation. If rapid cross-relaxation occurs between two transitions, one of the times τ_a becomes shorter than the rest and decreases indefinitely as the rate of cross-relaxation increases. The other times τ_b, τ_c may at first decrease, but should approach constant values when 'thermalization' of the affected transitions is rapid compared with the spin–lattice relaxation. When general cross-relaxation affects all four levels, two of the times τ_a, τ_b should decrease indefinitely and τ_c alone approach a constant value.

Because of this the time-constant measured from the last (detectable) part of the recovery had been adopted as the spin–lattice relaxation time. The duration of the saturating pulse could be increased if necessary to aid measurement of components of small amplitude and long time-constant. Figure 5 shows the times measured for the

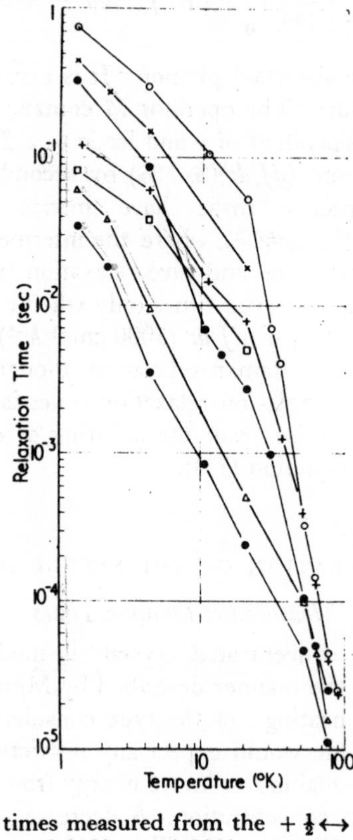

Figure 5. Relaxation times measured from the $+\frac{1}{2} \leftrightarrow -\frac{1}{2}$ single-ion line. Chromium concentrations: ○, 0·01%; ×, 0·03%; +, 0·08%; □, 0·12%; ●, 0·21%; △, 0·38%; ⊕, 0·76%.

$+\frac{1}{2}$ to $-\frac{1}{2}$ transition, with the magnetic field parallel to the crystal axis. Most of the measurements were made on specimens of dimensions 5 mm × 5 mm × 2 mm. The use of the last part of the recovery ensured that the receiver output measured was a linear function of the saturation, even when the paramagnetic absorption was not much less than the cavity losses. A rapid initial recovery due to general cross-relaxation was apparent in specimens 2 and 3. Approximate 'thermalization times' are given in table 2. The effects of the four-spin process $3 \times (+\frac{1}{2} \leftrightarrow -\frac{1}{2})$, $1 \times (-\frac{3}{2} \leftrightarrow +\frac{3}{2})$ were not detected.

Table 2

'Thermalization' times

Specimen	1	2	3	4–7
Measured time (μsec)	<5	15	150	>20000

In specimen 1 thermalization appeared to be complete before the 10μsec saturating pulse ended. Three components were identified in the recovery in specimens 2 and 3. In these cases, therefore, the longest time-constant, τ_c, was measured without ambiguity. In more dilute crystals no more than two components could be resolved. The results of Armstrong and Szabo (1960) at 2920 Mc/s suggest that τ_c was then probably not measured. In the recovery of the $+\frac{1}{2} \leftrightarrow -\frac{1}{2}$ transition in a 0·015% crystal at 1·6 °K, these authors observed a component with a very long time-constant (12 seconds) when cross-relaxation allowed the population of the $+\frac{3}{2}$ level to be disturbed. Otherwise the recovery proceeded mainly by transitions between $+\frac{1}{2}$ and $-\frac{1}{2}$ levels, and the last part of the recovery detected yielded a time-constant similar to those given in figure 5 for specimens 6 and 7. Thus it is likely that no direct comparison is possible between the times measured for specimens 4 to 7, and those for specimens 1 to 3. In particular, the unexpectedly long times exhibited by specimens 3 at liquid helium temperatures do not imply that 'phonon heating' occurred, although its possibility cannot be excluded entirely.

5.2. *Discussion*

Except at the highest temperatures, where Raman processes are dominant, the relaxation of the single ions is concentration-dependent and is more rapid than predicted in the theoretical analyses of Van Vleck (1940) and Mattuck and Strandberg (1960). Cross relaxation does not provide an explanation. The decrease of relaxation time with increasing concentration is apparent in dilute crystals, in which cross relaxation is negligible, and also in the most concentrated crystals, in which thermalization is rapid in comparison with spin–lattice relaxation. Further, it occurs over a wide range of temperature, whereas cross relaxation is essentially independent of temperature.

If the relaxation of the pairs is responsible, the single-ion relaxation times τ_s should be related to the 'pair' times τ_p very approximately by

$$\frac{1}{\tau_s} = \frac{1}{N_s}\sum \frac{N_p}{(\tau_p+\tau_t)} \tag{5}$$

where N_s, N_p are the populations of the pair and single-ion levels, and a transfer time τ_t characterizes the spin–spin processes that convey the excitation between a pair transition and the single ions. The sum includes all pair levels that participate in the relaxation. Where the ions are distributed randomly, the number of pairs of any given type is approximately c times the number of single ions, if the Cr/Al ratio c is much less than unity. Since a pair has four times as many energy levels as a single ion, the average value of N_p is then $\frac{1}{4}cN_s$, leading to rates $1/\tau_s$ that vary at least as rapidly as the concentration. In a more rigorous treatment it would be necessary to increase the measured times τ_p, before substitution in (5), to allow for the effects of saturating several pair lines simultaneously. This would tend to increase τ_s. On the other hand a factor tending to decrease it should also be introduced, since the energy released to the lattice in a pair transition is likely to be greater than that of a single-ion transition.

In the most concentrated crystals, τ_t sets the limit to the pair relaxation time observed at low temperatures. In specimens 1, 2 and 3, for temperatures below 20 °K, τ_t is much less than the measured values of τ_p. Substituting $\tau_t = 0$ and $\tau_p = 2$ msec (at 4·2 °K) in (5), the single-ion times measured for specimens 1 and 2 (about 4 and 8 msec respectively) are obtained if perhaps 250 pair lines are assumed to participate in the relaxation. Rather fewer lines are needed to account for the relaxation in specimen 3. At least forty lines with effective coupling to the single ions were distinguishable in the restricted range of the spectrum (0 to 3800 Oe) accessible to the available spectrometer. It is to be expected from the symmetry of the corundum lattice that in many of these lines there are contributions from three or six usually inequivalent types of pair, whose spectra become identical when the magnetic field is parallel to the crystal axis. It is thus likely that enough lines are available to account for the single-ion relaxation in these specimens.

The absence of any obvious 'phonon heating' is then not surprising. If many pairs take part in the relaxation, the energy is released into a wide range of lattice modes, most of which have relatively high frequency, and is removed from the crystal without difficulty.

The single-ion relaxation times for specimens 1 and 2 vary approximately as T^{-2}. The variation of N_p/τ_p for the excited levels of the pairs provides a possible explanation. For example, relaxation between S' multiplets gives times τ_p respectively proportional to $\{1-\exp(-5J/kT)\}$, $\{1-\exp(-3J/kT)\}$, and $\{\exp(5J/kT)-1\}$ for lines from $S' = 3$, $S' = 2$ and $S' = 1$ levels. Combining these with the appropriate populations of the pair levels (from §3), and assuming for convenience that the values of τ_p become similar when kT is large compared with J, a variation of τ_s approximately as T^{-2} in the range $0{\cdot}8J < kT < 5J$ is obtained. The pairs with $J \sim 0{\cdot}5$ cm^{-1} may thus account for the T^{-2} law at helium temperatures. It is not known whether a similar explanation is possible at higher temperatures.

The relaxation in more dilute crystals is less easily explained. Even in specimens 4 and 5 there is little spin–spin transfer between the single ions and the pair lines for which measurements were made. Effective transfer probably takes place only to pair lines that lie within a few line-widths of each single-ion line. Pairs of the type measured, in which J is at least comparable with D, give rise to lines which are not concentrated near the single-ion lines. The proportion of such pairs able to affect the single ions is therefore likely to be small, and can hardly account for their relaxation. The absence of any critical dependence of single-ion relaxation on the direction of the magnetic field (except where there is cross-relaxation between the single ions) provides further evidence that chance coincidences with pair lines are not of great importance.

If ion-pairs are to account for the relaxation in these crystals, one must suppose that the effective pairs are those in which the exchange interaction is so weak that the pair and single-ion lines almost coincide. It remains to be seen whether pairs with such small exchange can relax sufficiently rapidly to affect the single ions appreciably. Although pair lines clustered round the single-ion lines are apparent in the spectra, spin–spin transfer prevents measurement of their spin–lattice relaxation by the present method. Calculation of the relaxation time is not yet possible, since the relevant values of J, r and dJ/dr are unknown (also one cannot ignore the possibility that the division into single ions and rapidly relaxed pairs is not valid for ions sufficiently far apart to have the required small J). It is perhaps significant that a variation of relaxation time as T^{-1} is observed in specimens 4 to 7 between 1·4 °K and 20 °K. This indicates that the relaxation process involves phonons with energies smaller than kT throughout this temperature range.

§ 6. CONCLUSIONS

The most important conclusions would appear to be:

(i) Chromium–chromium pairs are observed with exchange splittings of a few cm^{-1}. Their relaxation is much more rapid than that of the single ions, and there is evidence that it involves phonons of energy equivalent to the splittings. Modulation of an isotropic exchange interaction provides a possible mechanism for the low-temperature relaxation.

(ii) In crystals containing more than 0·21% of chromium, there is sufficient spin-spin coupling for the relaxation of the pairs to account for the order of magnitude of the single ion relaxation.

(iii) In less concentrated crystals, pairs of the type studied are not sufficiently coupled to the single ions to account for their relaxation.

ACKNOWLEDGMENTS

I have pleasure in acknowledging help from discussions in particular with Dr. R. J. Elliott and Dr. R. Orbach. I should also like to thank Mr. R. A. Mostyn, of the Chemical Inspectorate, Royal Arsenal, Woolwich, for analysing the ruby specimens. This paper is published with the permission of the Controller, H.M. Stationery Office.

REFERENCES

Al'tshuler, S. A., 1956, *Bull. Acad. Sci. U.R.S.S.*, **20,** 1207.
Armstrong, R. A., and Szabo, A., 1960, *Canad. J. Phys.*, **38,** 1304.
Bleaney, B., and Bowers, K. D., 1952, *Proc. Roy. Soc.* A, **214,** 451.
Bloembergen, N., Shapiro, S., Pershan, P. S., and Artman, J. O., 1959, *Phys. Rev.*, **114,** 445.
Bowers, K. D., and Mims, W. B., 1959, *Phys. Rev.*, **115,** 285.
Finn, C. B. P., Orbach, R., and Wolf, W. P., 1961, *Proc. Phys. Soc.*, **77,** 261.
Gill, J. C., 1961, *Nature, Lond.*, **190,** 619.
Mattuck, R. D., and Strandberg, M. W. P., 1960, *Phys. Rev.*, **119,** 1204,
Mims, W. B., and McGee, J. D., 1960, *Phys. Rev.*, **119,** 1233.
Moriya, T., 1960, *Phys. Rev.*, **120,** 91.
Statz, H., Rimai, L., Weber, M. J., de Mars, G. A., and Koster, C. F., 1961, *J. Appl. Phys.* (Suppl.), **32,** 218S.
Van Vleck, J. H., 1940, *Phys. Rev.*, **57,** 426.
—— 1941, *Phys. Rev.*, **59,** 724, 730.
—— 1960, *Quantum Electronics* (New York: Columbia University Press), p. 392.
Waller, I., 1932, *Z. Phys.*, **79,** 370.

Spin–Lattice Relaxation Times in Ruby at 34·6 Gc/s

By J. H. PACE, D. F. SAMPSON and J. S. THORP

Royal Radar Establishment, Malvern, Worcs.

MS. received 1st *April* 1960, *in revised form* 20th *May* 1960

Abstract. Measurements of spin–lattice relaxation time in ruby have been made at 34·6 Gc/s by a pulse saturation method at temperatures from 1·4° to 90°K. With weak concentrations the values for the first-order transitions (e.g. 22 msec at 4·2°K) are of the same order of magnitude as those reported at lower frequencies, and the variation of relaxation time with temperature is in fair agreement with theory. A successive increase in relaxation time with the order of the transition, pronounced at 1·4°K, decreases with increasing temperature, and at about 77 °K a common value of about 44 μsec is obtained for all transitions. The main effects of increasing concentration are to reduce the relaxation time and alter its temperature dependence.

---

§ 1. Introduction

The importance of measurements of spin–lattice relaxation times T_1 in paramagnetic materials has grown recently because of the rapid developments in the maser field. Although several theories have been proposed (e.g. Van Vleck 1940, Al'tshuler 1956, Gill 1959, unpublished) the physical basis of the relaxation process is not clearly understood, and the formulation of a general theory applicable to a range of materials awaits the accumulation of more experimental data. Specific problems occur, however, which demand knowledge of relaxation times and their dependence on certain parameters. Two examples are the extension of maser techniques for amplification or oscillation to the short millimetre wavelength region (Foner, Momo and Mayer 1959), and the operation of lower frequency masers at elevated temperatures (Ditchfield and Forrester 1958) with increased bandwidth and power handling capacity. In the former case the magnitude and frequency dependence of the relaxation time are important, and in the latter the effects of temperature and concentration. This paper describes measurements of the spin–lattice relaxation time in synthetic ruby made at 34·6 Gc/s with the object of investigating these effects. The temperature and concentration ranges covered were 1·4° to 90°K and 0·03%Cr to 0·78% Cr respectively, using the fixed polar angle $\theta = 90°$. The concentration is defined as the ratio of weights of chromium and aluminium oxide. Ruby was selected because it is known to be a suitable material for many maser applications and the frequency was chosen, bearing in mind the current interest in millimetre wavelength masers, as being the highest at which sufficient microwave power and components were easily obtainable. Preliminary results have already been reported by the authors Pace, Sampson and Thorp (1960).

§ 2. Apparatus and Technique

2.1. *General Features*

A pulse saturation method was used in which the transition studied was saturated by a short pulse, recovery to thermal equilibrium being observed by measuring the absorption of a low power, c.w. monitoring signal of the same frequency (cf. Davis, Strandberg and Kyhl 1958).

The general arrangement of the equipment followed conventional lines. The low temperature assembly however was a straight silver-plated cupro-nickel waveguide (inside dimensions 0·280 in. × 0·140 in., wall thickness 0·005 in.) terminated by a removable plane plunger on which the specimen was mounted. Use of this system removed difficulties of cavity tuning on cooling, permitted large samples to be used, and enabled the whole structure to be made easily removable for sample changing at helium temperatures. It also led to a small structure, a particularly valuable feature at high magnetic fields where space in the gap is restricted. Magnetic fields of up to 16 000 gauss over a 4·5 cm gap were provided by a Newport Instruments Type D electromagnet. These were uniform to at least 1 in 10^4 over a volume of about 2 cm cube, and field stabilities of the same order were readily obtained using a bank of batteries to drive the electromagnet. Additional coils enabled low frequency field modulation to be supplied when required.

2.2. *Microwave System*

The microwave arrangement, shown in figure 1, consisted of a waveguide bridge, a low power monitor source, a high power pulsed source, and a superheterodyne receiver.

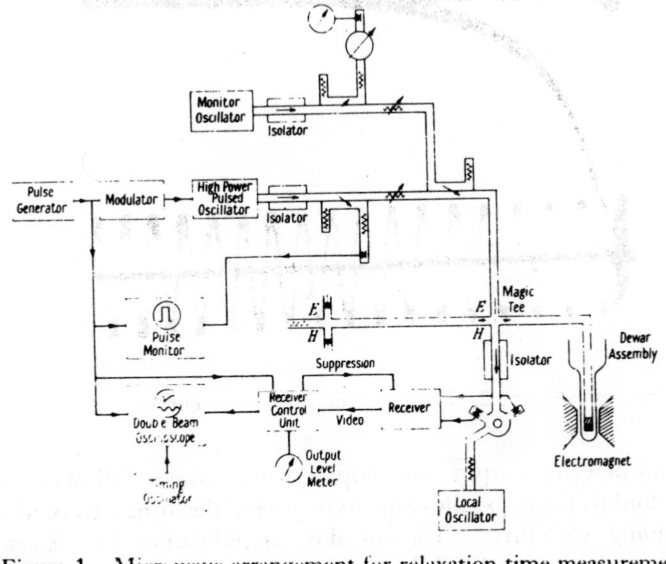

Figure 1. Microwave arrangement for relaxation time measurement.

One arm of the bridge was the low temperature assembly described above. Balance was obtained when off magnetic resonance by adjusting the *E–H* tuner in the other arm for cancellation of reflected power into the balanced mixer.

When absorption occurred in the sample, i.e. on magnetic resonance, the bridge became unbalanced and a signal proportional to the degree of absorption was fed into the receiver.

The bridge input consisted of two signals mixed in a 6 dB directive feed, viz: (i) a low power, c.w. monitoring signal, variable between 1 μW and 10 μW to allow for sensitivity changes, supplied from a VX.5023 reflex klystron and (ii) a high power pulse, generated by an Elliott Type B.579 floating drift tube klystron. The latter valve was pulsed by a hard valve modulator driven by a pulse generator, and produced pulses variable in length from 50 μsec to 500 μsec at pulse repetition frequencies up to 25 c/s. The maximum pulse power available was 6 watts peak. With a pulse duration of 200 μsec the minimum power required for saturation was 60 mw at 1·4 °K.

The frequency of measurement was determined by the fixed frequency of the drift tube klystron, 34·6 kMc/s, to which the monitor oscillator was tuned. It was unnecessary to stabilize the monitor oscillator because with the samples used, whose line widths were not less than about 30 gauss, saturation occurred if the pulse frequency was within $\pm$ 50 Mc/s of the absorption frequency.

The receiver was of conventional design, employing a second VX.5023 as the local oscillator. An intermediate frequency bandwidth of 10 Mc/s allowed operation without frequency stabilization or automatic frequency control. The overall gain to the second detector was 110 dB at 45 Mc/s and the total noise factor, including the mixer, was 15 dB. The recovery time to maximum sensitivity, after suppression during the saturating pulse, was 5 μsec.

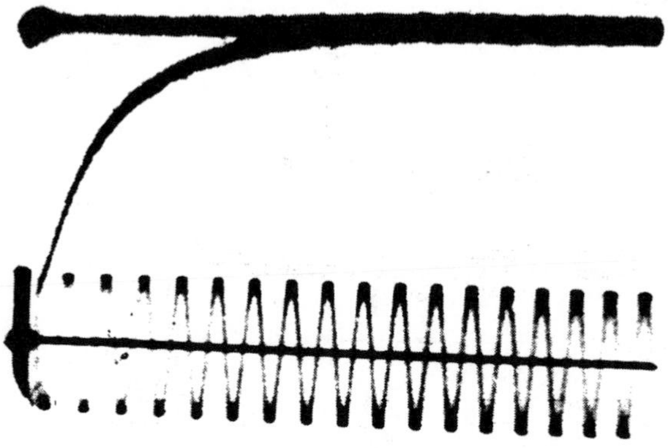

Figure 2. Presentation of recovery curve.

The second detector output was coupled via a cathode follower to one trace of a Cossor double beam oscilloscope type 1049, the other trace displaying a sinusoidal timing waveform. Use of d.c. amplification in the oscilloscope sinabled the maximum and minimum levels of absorption to be displayed independent of the form and duration of the recovery curve. A facility for emultaneous interruption of the timing waveform and the drive pulse to the modulator enabled the maximum absorption level to be displayed independently. In this way a composite photographic record was taken showing (*a*) the recovery curve, (*b*) the maximum absorption level in the absence of the saturating pulse superimposed on this, and (*c*) the timing waveform (figure 2); the value of relaxation time could be derived from this. The overall accuracy of the measurements was estimated to be within about ±10%, and the minimum measurable relaxation time, set by the receiver recovery, was about 10 μsec.

§ 3. Relaxation Times for Low Chromium Concentration

The primary factor governing the orientation chosen was the need to assess ruby as a material for pulsed field maser experiments. In these use of the maximum available relaxation time would reduce the complexity of the circuitry required. Since it was known from the work of Bloembergen *et al.* (1959) that cross relaxation processes can be very important and that they reduce relaxation times a position was selected at which these would be negligible. This orientation was with the *c* axis of the crystal perpendicular to the d.c. magnetic field, $\theta = 90°$ (cf. Mims 1959). The first measurements were made on a sample of nominal concentration 0·1% Cr as it was known that crystals of this concentration had been successfully used in three level masers. (Analysis subsequently showed that this crystal contained 0·03% Cr). Figure 3 shows the energy level diagram at $\theta = 90°$ together with possible transitions at 34·6 Gc/s. The measured relaxation times are given in the table.

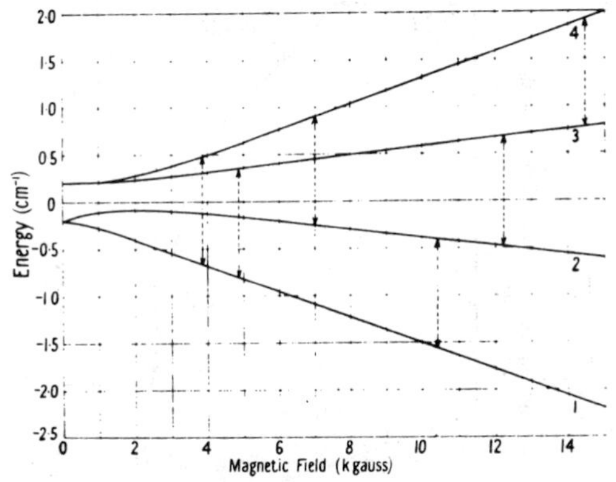

Figure 3. Energy level diagram for ruby at $\theta = 90°$ showing 34·6 **Gc/s** transitions.

Relaxation Times (msec) in Nominal 0·1% Cr Ruby

34·6 Gc/s, $\theta = 90°$

Transition	1·4°K	4·2°K	10·1°K	20·3°K	56°K	77°K	90°K
3–4	60	21	16	4	0·086	—	0·016
2–3	64	16	10	8	0·083	0·045	0·015
1–2	59	22	10	6	0·10	0·044	0·017
2–4	147	54	12	10	0·16	0·049	—
1–3	100	56	—	12	0·13	—	—
1–4	296	—	—	—	0·12	—	—

The conclusions which may be drawn from these results will now be discussed.

3.1. *Variation of Relaxation Time with Frequency*

The measured value of T_1 at 4°K for the 1–2 transition is 22 msec. As far as comparison with previous measurements can be made this is of the same order as those reported at 7·2 Gc/s (Mims†) and 9·3 Gc/s (Gill and Harvey 1958, unpublished) and 24 Gc/s (Kikuchi *et al.* 1959). It therefore appears that over this range the spin–lattice relaxation time does not vary appreciably with frequency. No general theoretical rule for the frequency dependence can be made, since this is determined by the material and the coupling mechanism. It may be noted however that a variation as $(\text{frequency})^{-2}$ or $(\text{frequency})^{-4}$, predicted by Van Vleck for chromium alum, is not found.

3.2. *Variation of Relaxation Time with Temperature*

The effect of temperature on the relaxation time of the 1–2 transition is shown in figure 4. In the range of temperature from 1·4° to 20°K the relaxation time is approximately inversely proportional to temperature. This behaviour is similar to that reported in ruby at 9·3 Gc/s (Harvey 1958, unpublished)

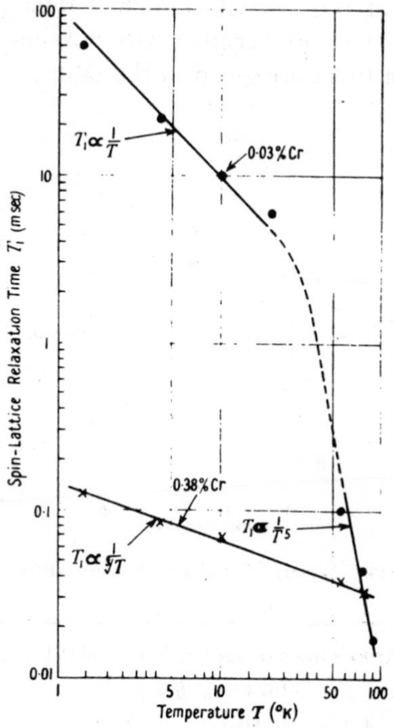

Figure 4. Variation of relaxation time with temperature (1–2 transition, $\theta = 90°$).

and in potassium chromicyanide in the helium range when cross relaxation effects are negligible (Shapiro and Bloembergen 1959): it would be expected if relaxation were due to a direct exchange of energy between the spin system and lattice phonons. Between 20° and 56°K this relation breaks down, and above 56°K the rapid decrease in relaxation time with increasing temperature is consistent with the predominance of Raman effects; preliminary observations

† Paper given at Radio-frequency Spectroscopy Conference, Oxford, 1959.

suggest that the variation is as $(\text{temperature})^{-5}$. This is not quite so rapid as the $(\text{temperature})^{-7}$ suggested by the Van Vleck model. For the other transitions a broadly similar temperature dependence was found.

3.3. *Relaxation Times for Transitions of Different Order*

At 1·4°K the relaxation times associated with the different transitions are not equal, and the second- and third-order transitions have significantly longer relaxation times than the first-order transitions although the recovery curves remain substantially single exponentials. This is contrary to predictions based on the Van Vleck model, but a recent development of Al'tschuler's theory (Gill 1959, unpublished) has shown that different relaxation times for the various transitions are to be expected if the relaxation process is governed by near-neighbour interaction and gives close agreement with experiment. As the temperature is increased the difference between the relaxation times for the various transitions decreases, and a common value is reached at about 77°K. The occurrence of this common value has previously been observed in ruby at 77°K at 9·3 Gc/s (Gill 1959, unpublished) and is presumably a consequence of the different relaxation process occurring at higher temperatures.

§ 4. Effects due to Increased Concentration

It is found that the relaxation time for a given transition is a function of the concentration of paramagnetic centres and the temperature. Ruby samples of known concentration were available only in small sizes, and measurements were therefore confined to the strong first-order transitions. The concentration range covered was from 0·02% Cr to 0·38% Cr.

4.1. *Behaviour at Fixed Temperatures*

At helium temperatures the relaxation time decreases with increasing concentration N. The results at 1·4°K are shown in figure 5 (lower curve) and can be expressed approximately by $T_1 \propto N^{-2}$. A similar concentration dependence has also been observed at 4·2°K and 9·3 Gc/s (de Grasse *et al.* 1959). It may be noted that a concentration dependence is not predicted by theories based on the Van Vleck model, but is a consequence of theories based on near neighbour interaction.

At 77°K the effect of concentration is much smaller (figure 5, upper curve) and is approximately given by $T_1 \propto N^{-0 \cdot 1}$. This result is of importance in connection with the operation of three level masers at nitrogen temperatures, because it implies that a higher concentration can be used—thereby increasing both the inherent bandwidth and the power handling capacity of the maser—without undue increase in the pump power requirement.

4.2. *Relaxation Time–Temperature Dependence*

The dependence of relaxation time on temperature has already been discussed for a low concentration sample (figure 4, upper curve). The curve is characterized by two regions over which $T_1 \propto T^{-1}$ and $T_1 \propto T^{-5}$ respectively. As the concentration is increased this behaviour changes and at concentrations above about 0·3% Cr, a smooth variation from 1·4° to 90°K is found (figure 4, lower curve). It is found that, approximately, $T_1 \propto T^{-1/3}$ and it is thus clear that a different relaxation process occurs. This slow variation suggests that, with the correct material, maser action should be possible at relatively high temperatures.

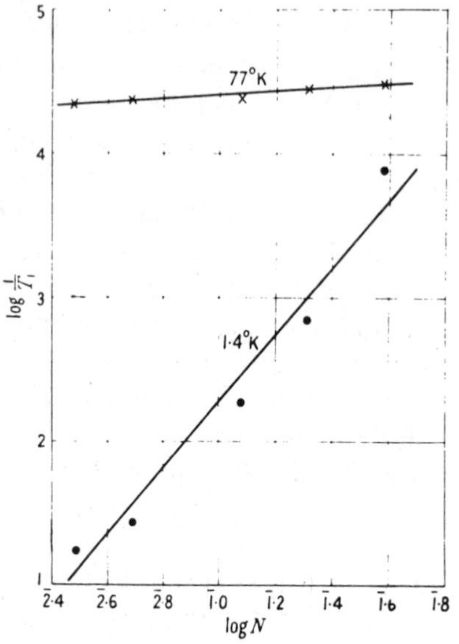

Figure 5. Variation of relaxation time with concentration (1–2 transition, $\theta=90°$).

It is interesting to note that somewhat similar concentration effects have been observed in other materials. In nickel fluosilicate Bowers and Mims (1959) found that in the helium range there was a general tendency for the relaxation times to be less temperature dependent at high concentrations while in potassium chromicyanide Shapiro and Bloembergen (1959) have shown that the smaller relaxation times observed at high concentrations can be explained by the growing importance of cross relaxation.

§ 5. Very High Concentration

One sample was available with a chromium concentration of 0·78% Cr. In preliminary observations on this sample it was found that at 77°K a simple exponential recovery curve was obtained. This gave a relaxation time of about 30 μsec, as would be expected from the foregoing results. At helium temperatures, however, the recovery curve had a fast initial rise (corresponding to a relaxation time of about 15 μsec) followed by a much slower rise (corresponding to a 20 msec relaxation time). A similar effect at 9 Gc/s has been reported (de Grasse *et al.* 1959) and the results suggest that the fast recovery is due to effects within the spin system while the slow recovery is at a rate comparable with the relaxation time for a dilute sample.

§ 6. Conclusions

Using a given polar angle, $\theta=90°$, the spin–lattice relaxation time in ruby at 34·6 Gc/s has been shown to depend on the temperature, the transition, and the chromium concentration. Comparison with results obtained at lower frequencies suggest that the relaxation time is substantially independent of frequency. At low concentrations the temperature variation found agrees broadly with predictions based on the Van Vleck model; the remaining observations can best be explained by assuming that the dominant mechanism in the relaxation process is near neighbour interaction.

Because of the long relaxation times obtainable ruby appears to be a promising material for pulsed field masers intended to amplify or oscillate at millimetre wavelengths. At lower microwave frequencies it appears that improvements are to be gained in the operation of masers at elevated temperatures by using ruby with high chromium concentration.

Acknowledgments

We wish to record our thanks to Dr. D. J. Howarth, Royal Radar Establishment, Malvern, for supplying the data given in figure 3, to the Chemical Inspectorate, Woolwich, for the analysis of the samples, and to colleagues in the Laboratory for helpful discussions.

This paper is published by permission of the Controller, Her Majesty's Stationery Office.

References

Al'tshuler, S. A., 1956, *Bull. Acad. Sci. U.S.S.R. (Phys. Ser.)*, **20**, (11), 1207.
Bloembergen, N., Shapiro, S., Pershan, P. S., and Artman, J. D., 1959, *Phys. Rev.*, **114**, 445.
Bowers, K. D., and Mims, W. B., 1959, *Phys. Rev.*, **115**, 285.
Davis, C. F., Strandberg, M. W. P., and Kyhl, R. L., 1958, *Phys. Rev.*, **111**, 1268.
de Grasse, R. W., Geusic, J. E., Shulz-Dubois, E. O., and Scovil, H. E. D., 1959, 9th *Interim Report on Microwave Solid State Devices*, Bell Telephone Laboratories.
Ditchfield, C. R., and Forrester, P. A., 1958, *Phys. Rev. Lett.*, **1**, 448.
Foner, S., Momo, L. R., and Mayer, A., 1959, *Phys. Rev. Lett.*, **3**, 36.
Kikuchi, C., Lambe, J., Makhow, G., and Terhune, R. W., 1959, *J. Appl. Phys.*, **30**, 1061.
Pace, J. H., Sampson, D. F., and Thorp, J. S., 1960, *Phys. Rev. Lett.*, **4**, 18.
Shapiro, S., and Bloembergen, N., 1959, *Phys. Rev.*, **116**, 1453.
Van Vleck, J. H., 1940, *Phys. Rev.*, **57**, 426.

REPRINTED FROM THE
PROCEEDINGS OF THE PHYSICAL SOCIETY, VOL. LXXVII, p. 257, 1961

Spin-Lattice Relaxation Times in Sapphire and Chromium-doped Rutile at 34·6 Gc/s

BY J. H. PACE, D. F. SAMPSON AND J. S. THORP
Physics Department, Royal Radar Establishment, Malvern

MS. received 15th August 1960

Abstract. The paper describes measurements made at 34.6 Gc/s on synthetic sapphire (Fe^{3+} in Al_2O_3) and chromium-doped rutile (Cr^{3+} in TiO_2) in the temperature range 1.4°K to 56°K. Spin–lattice relaxation times of up to 5 milliseconds at helium temperatures are reported. The main features of the temperature dependence of the relaxation times show a broad similarity with the results previously reported by the authors for ruby, but there are insufficient data to show whether the relaxation times are substantially independent of frequency as was found for ruby.

MEASUREMENTS of spin–lattice relaxation times in ruby, made by a pulse saturation method at 34·6 Gc/s, have recently been reported by the authors (Pace, Sampson and Thorp 1960a). These were undertaken to assess the suitability of ruby for maser operation at millimetre wavelengths and it was shown that because of the long relaxation times available it appeared to be a promising material. This note describes corresponding measurements made on synthetic sapphire (Fe^{3+} in Al_2O_3) and chromium-doped rutile (Cr^{3+} in TiO_2) both of which possess some advantages as alternative materials. In ruby the chromium ion has a spin of $s=3/2$ and the zero field splitting is 11·59 Gc/s. In sapphire, however, iron has a spin of $s=5/2$ and the zero field splitting of 31·2 Gc/s is considerably larger; the resulting spectrum of six levels affords both a wider choice of transition and the possibility of low field maser operation (Bogle and Symmons 1959a). Chromium in rutile has a spin of $s=3/2$ as in ruby, giving a spectrum only four levels, but the zero field splitting of 43·3 Gc/s (Gerritsen *et al.* 1959) is of the same order as that of sapphire and the exceptionally high value of the dielectric constant enables unplated samples to resonate as multimode cavities of reasonable Q (Foner and Momo 1960).

To obtain estimates of the maximum available relaxation times orientations were chosen so that cross-relaxation effects (Bloembergen *et al.* 1959) were minimized. Convenient orientations fulfilling this condition were ($\theta=90°$, $\phi=0°$) for sapphire, at which the spectra for the two non-equivalent ions in the unit cell coincide, and ($\theta=90°$, $\phi=0°$) for the chromium-doped rutile; the energy level diagrams for these orientations are shown in Figs 1 and 2 respectively. A limited number of samples of known concentration were available and measurements were made on a sapphire crystal containing 0·03% Fe and a rutile crystal containing 0·07% Cr, both of which gave line widths of about 20 gauss. Analysis for impurities has not yet been completed. In the sapphire, however, no lines

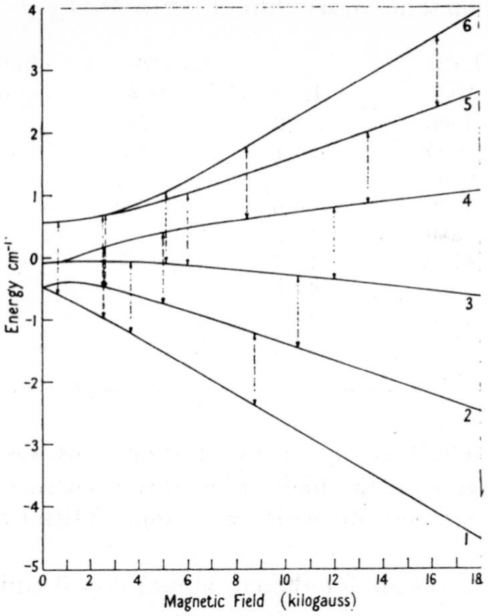

Fig. 1. Energy level diagram for sapphire at $\theta = 90°$, showing 34·6 Gc/s transitions.

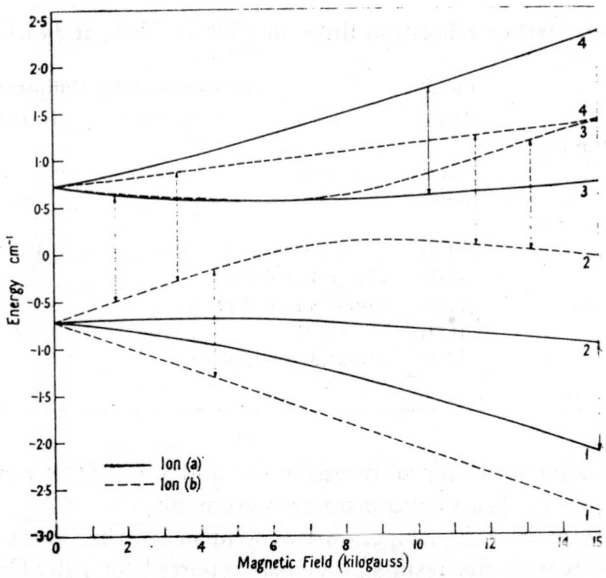

Fig. 2. Energy level diagram for chromium-doped rutile at $\theta = 90°$, $\phi = 0°$, showing 34·6 Gc/s transitions.

other than those due to iron were found; in the rutile some very weak lines were detected which were well removed from those due to chromium. As in the previous measurements the overall accuracy was estimated to be to within ±10% and the minimum measurable relaxation time, set by the receiver recovery, was about 10 microseconds. The observed relaxation times for the sapphire sample are given in Table 1.

Table 1. Relaxation times in sapphire, Fe^{3+} in Al_2O_3; $\theta = 90°$; 34·6 Gc/s.

Transition	Field (Oe)	Relaxation time (milliseconds) 1·4°K	4·2°K	10·1°K	20·2°K
4–5	13500	4·0	1·8	0·77	0·45
3–4	11900	4·1	1·6	0·80	0·55
2–3	10500	4·1	1·5	0·80	0·55
1–2	8800	4·0	2·0	0·80	0·50
3–6	4850	11·2	—	—	0·9
2–3	4750	13·5	—	—	0·9
1–3	3550	12·5	—	—	1·1
2–5	2800	11·7	—	—	—
2–6	2350	13·2	—	—	—

At and above 56°K the relaxation time for all transitions was less than 10 microseconds. Measurements on the high order lines occurring below 4850 oersted were restricted because their intensities were some 20 dB less than those of the first-order transitions.

The corresponding results for the chromium-doped rutile crystal are given in Table 2.

Table 2. Spin–lattice relaxation times of Cr^{3+} in TiO_2 at 34·6 Gc/s, $\theta = 90°$.

Transition		Field O(e)	Relaxation time (milliseconds) 1·4°K	4·2°K	10·1°K	20·3°K
	Ion (*a*)					
1–2		15000	6·0	4·5	2·2	0·6
3–4		10300	4·7	2·5	2·0	0·6
	Ion (*b*)					
2–3		13100	5·6	2·5	1·6	0·6
1–2		4400	about 4 at 4·2°K			
2–3		1700	about 3 at 4·2°K			
2–4		11600	3·9	2·1	1·4	0·6
2–4		3400	about 3 at 4·2°K			

Again the relaxation times for all transitions at and above 56°K were less than 10 microseconds and the low field transitions were weak.

The main features of the temperature dependence of the relaxation times show a broad similarity with the results previously reported for ruby (Pace, Sampson and Thorp 1960 b). In sapphire the relaxation time varies approximately as $(\text{temperature})^{-1}$ up to about 10°K, in agreement with theory (Van Vleck 1940); this effect has also been found in potassium chromicyanide (Shapiro and Bleombergen 1959) and in nickel fluosilicate (Bowers and Mims 1959) when cross-relaxation effects are negligible. In the chromium-doped rutile the relaxation time varies approximately as $(\text{temperature})^{-1/2}$ up to 10°K; the departure from a $(\text{temperature})^{-1}$ law is probably due to the rather high chromium content and is similar to the temperature variation found in the higher concentration ruby samples previously studied. In both materials the transition to a region where the relaxation time varies at least as rapidly as (temperature)$^{-5}$ occurs at about 20°K; this is considerably lower than the corresponding temperature for ruby and suggests that high temperature maser operation (Ditchfield and Forrester 1958) would be unlikely. Some relaxation time measurements at lower frequencies have been reported. In sapphire Bogle and Symmons (1959b) using a pulse saturation method found that $T_1 = 7 \pm 2$ milliseconds at 4·2°K and 9 Gc/s in a sample containing 0·005% Fe; in rutile Gerritsen *et al.* (1959) using a c.w. saturation method obtained a value of 40 milliseconds at 4·2°K and 23·7 Gc/s for a sample containing 0·12% Cr. At present there are insufficient data on the variation of the spin–lattice relaxation times with concentration to deduce from the above results and the 34·6 Gc/s measurements whether the relaxation times are substantially independent of frequency as was previously found for ruby. However, the fact that relaxation times of up to 5 milliseconds at 34·6 Gc/s can be obtained at helium temperatures in material giving useful line widths suggests that both sapphire and chromium-doped rutile would be promising materials for millimetre wavelength masers.

Acknowledgment

This paper is published by permission of the Controller, Her Majesty's Stationery Office.

References

Bloembergen, N., Shapiro, S., Pershan, P. S., and Artman, J. D., 1959, *Phys. Rev.*, **114**, 445.
Bogle, G. S., and Symmons, H. F., 1959 a, *Aust. J. Phys.*, **12**, 1.
—— 1959 b, *Proc. Phys. Soc.*, **73**, 531.
Bowers, K. D., and Mims, W. B., 1959, *Phys. Rev.*, **115**, 285.
Ditchfield, C. R., and Forrester, P. A., 1958, *Phys. Rev. Letters*, **1**, 448.
Foner, S., and Momo, L. R., 1960, *J. Appl. Phys.*, **31**, 742.
Gerritsen, H. J., Harrison, S. E., Lewis, H. R., and Wittke, J. P., 1959, *Phys. Rev. Letters*, **2**, 153.
Pace, J. H., Sampson, D. F., and Thorp, J. S., 1960 a, *Phys. Rev. Letters*, **4**, 18.
—— 1960 b, *Proc. Phys. Soc.*, **76**, 697.
Shapiro, S., and Bloembergen, N., 1959, *Phys. Rev.*, **116**, 1453.
Van Vleck, J. H., 1940, *Phys. Rev.*, **57**, 426.

Materials, Preparation, Spectra

Solid State Maser Materials

L. G. VAN UITERT

Bell Telephone Laboratories, Inc.,
Murray Hill, New Jersey

Abstract

A number of the factors that are considered in selecting materials for solid state maser applications and the methods of growing useful crystals are discussed. Tabulations of data concerning materials which have been made to operate in (a) the microwave and (b) the optical region of the spectrum are given.

INTRODUCTION

The term "maser" is an acronym for the phrase "microwave amplification by the stimulated emission of radiation" (1). By common usage it is employed to denote oscillators as well as amplifiers that operate by stimulated emission. The microwave and the related optical devices that fall into this category do not differ in principle. However, the term "laser" (2) ("light amplification by the stimulated emission of radiation") is often employed to denote the latter. The microwave masers are the first devices to operate with noise temperatures below 20°K. Since masers (in general) make use of molecular or atomic transitions, they can act as oscillators or amplifiers at much higher frequencies than have been obtained by other means. Maser action was first obtained by Gordon et al. using ammonia gas as the active medium. (1) The output was in the microwave region (at about 24,000 Mc). Later, Javan et al. demonstrated that continuous maser action could be obtained in the optical region (at about 11,500 A) using a mixture of neon and helium (3,4).

The solid state three level maser was proposed by Bloembergen (5) and first operated by Scovil et al. (6) in the microwave region (at 9,000 Mc). The active medium was lanthanum ethyl sulfate into which gadolinium and cerium had been incorporated. Maiman was the first to report maser action in the optical region (2). He obtained coherent oscillations in ruby at a wavelength of about 0.7 μ. A number of attempts have been made to operate liquid masers. As yet there has been no reported success.

The masers that have been constructed employing crystals as the active media have considerably greater power handling capacity and bandwidth and operate with much lower noise temperatures than the gas masers. These advantages are desired in amplifying devices. However, oscillators designed to generate carrier frequencies should have a very narrow band output. Hence the gas masers may be more suitable for this purpose. While there are obviously strong interests in both the solid state and the gas masers, there is little preparative chemistry required in constructing the latter. For this reason, the present review has been limited to the solid state maser materials. Since the separations in energy of the spin states involved in microwave transitions are relatively small, the narrow transition linewidths (about 100 Mc) obtained in a single crystal are required for suitable operation in the microwave region. In the optical region, where transitions between orbital states are involved, the energy gaps are roughly 10^5 times those for microwave transitions. Here glasses (which have broad emission lines) can be used for some pulse applications, but the narrow linewidths found in crystals are still necessary to obtain the continuous operation required in communication circuits.

A number of methods of maser operation are indicated in Figure 1. Microwave devices have been built employing two level (7,8), three level (6,9,10), and four level (11,12) schemes. Two level operation is indicated by Figure 1a. The crystals employed in this method of operation contain relatively free electrons. Examples are silicon doped with phosphorus (7) (which is an electron donor) or quartz which has electrons trapped in F centers (8). The application of a magnetic field across the crystal aligns part of the electrons with the field and part against the field. At thermal equilibrium a

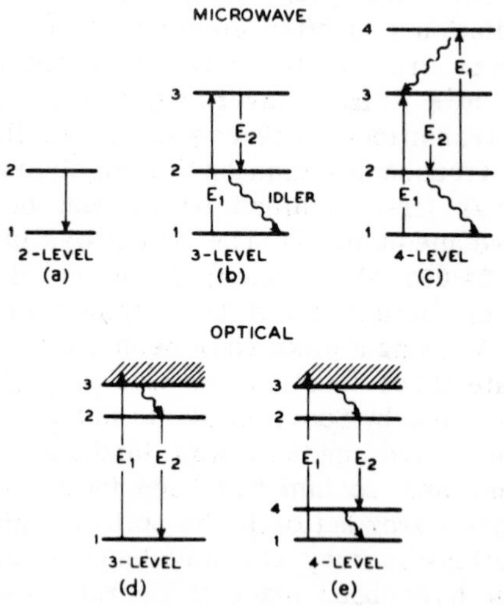

Fig. 1. Energy level schemes for maser operation.

greater number of spins will be in the state with lower energy. By sweeping the magnetic field through resonance in the presence of a strong rf field, an inversion in the populations of the two levels is realized. Maser action can be obtained over part of the period required for the system to relax to the equilibrium condition. The two level devices only operate part of the time and, therefore, are of limited interest as communication devices.

Continuous maser operation is obtained employing a three level scheme (Fig. 1b). Pumping at a frequency corresponding to E_1 can be employed to provide an inverted population between levels 3 and 1. In a typical solid state device, photons of energy (E_1) cause up or down transitions of electrons (between levels 1 and 3 of the active ion) with equal probability per electron. Saturation is achieved when the pump signal is strong enough to equalize the populations in these levels. Under operating conditions, this results in level 3 having a greater population than level 2. Hence, when a photon having an energy equal to the difference between levels 3 and 2 (E_2) traverses the crystal, it has a greater probability of stimulating a down transition from level 3 to level 2 (with the subsequent release of a similar photon) than of being absorbed. Normal spin-lattice interactions return the electrons from level 2 to level 1. The latter nonmaser transition is called the idler transition.

It is often desirable to speed up the spin-lattice relaxation process for the idler transition and thereby decrease the recovery time of the device. Scovil et al. (6) accomplished this by choosing an orientation of their lanthanum ethyl sulfate crystal wherein the Zeeman splitting of the ground state doublet of Ce^{3+} was equal in energy to the gap for the idler transition of Gd^{3+}. Under these circumstances, and due to the relatively high concentration of Ce^{3+}, cross relaxation interactions between Ce^{3+} and Gd^{3+} decreased the idler relaxation time by a factor of 10. Also, Er^{3+}, Co^{2+}, Ti^{3+} and in some cases Fe^{3+} can be used to decrease the relaxation time of the idler transition.

Makhov (11) suggested and Minkowski (12) showed that a comparable effect could be obtained by orienting a crystal of corundum containing chromium (pink ruby) so that the transitions 1 to 3 and 2 to 4 of Cr^{3+} were equal in energy (as shown in Fig. 1c). Thus, electrons terminating their maser transitions in level 2 (as discussed in connection with Fig. 1b) could be excited to level 4. This helps to deplete level 2 while increasing the availability of electrons to level 3 through spin-lattice relaxation from level 4.

Maser action in the optical region was first proposed by Schawlow and Townes (13) and first observed by Maiman (2) using pink ruby. This material operates as a three level maser (Fig. 1d). A xenon arc flash lamp was employed to excite Cr^{3+} by pumping into its strong absorption bands in the visible region. The excited electrons relax from the broadband region (3 in Fig. 1d) through interaction with the lattice to the metastable state (2) and subsequently returned to the ground state through spontaneous or stimulated emission. It is generally desirable to employ a pumping scheme of the above type in the optical region since the useful high intensity lamps are broad-band and, hence, supply (on the average) relatively little energy at each frequency.

For three level operation to the successful, strong pumping is required to deplete the ground state to the extent that level 2 has a greater population. This difficulty can be avoided by using four level operation (Fig. 1e). When the emission transition is to a normally empty level (4) which lies above the ground state, a favorable population distribution is relatively easy to obtain.

MICROWAVE MASER MATERIALS

Continuously operating traveling wave (14) structures are of particular interest for microwave communication systems. Pulsed and continuously operating cavity masers are of technical interest but do not have the bandwidth or stability of the traveling wave structures. In principle, a considerable variety of crystals containing paramagnetic ions can be employed in these devices. In practice, however, the selection is limited by the following considerations.

1. The host structure should provide a noncubic environment for the paramagnetic ion in which the latter has a suitable zero field splitting. The electronic states of the paramagnetic ions tend to become pure states in magnetic fields that are large in comparison to the zero field splitting. In the pure states, the transitions are subject to the selection rule $\Delta m = \pm 1$ which prevents pumping from level 1 to level 3 in the three level scheme shown in Figure 1b. Hence, a zero field splitting that is larger than the maser transition is desirable.

2. The paramagnetic ions involved should occupy equivalent lattice sites. Preferably, these should be unique positions in the crystal or positions whose point symmetries are reciprocally related. It is possible to align a crystal so that ions in two nonequivalent lattice sites will have the same spectrum. However, this limits the number of crystal orientations that may be employed. In any case, each paramagnetic ion should produce the same spectrum. In hydrates, for example, they can produce multiple spectra or spectra with broad lines as a result of variations in the environment due to the nonidentical orientation of the H_2O molecules. In structures such as $NaY(WO_4)_2$ (where Na^+ and Y^{3+} ions are distributed randomly in lattice sites) the spectral lines are also broadened by the resulting random electrostatic influences.

3. The atoms composing the host structure should have low nuclear magnetic moments (15). Otherwise they will interact with the paramagnetic ion to produce hyperfine structure. This increases the number of transitions possible and, hence, increases the pumping power required to produce a suitable inversion in population.

4. The paramagnetic ions involved should consist principally of isotopic forms which have a nuclear magnetic moment of zero. This

is also to avoid hyperfine structure. Further, the paramagnetic ions should have at least three low lying levels which have separations comparable to microwave frequencies when subjected to a suitable combination of crystalline and magnetic fields. Their spectroscopic splitting factors should be close to 2 and isotropic. This indicates a weak spin-orbital interaction, hence, a reasonably long spin-lattice relaxation time (16). The ions Cr^{3+}, Fe^{3+}, and Gd^{3+} fulfill these requirements and have been successfully used in maser devices. It may be possible to obtain maser action employing Ni^{2+}. However, in the materials containing this ion that have been studied to date, inhomogeneous line broadening (and, hence, the required pump power) is excessive. This may be associated with the g value of Ni^{2+} which is generally in excess of 2. Ions such as V^{2+}, Mn^{2+}, or Co^{2+} are of limited interest since they have nuclear magnetic moments. The ground states of the rare earth ions (other than those which are S states and, hence, have an orbital angular momentum of zero) are in general split into doublets that have large energy separations. These separations are in excess of the energies corresponding to the output frequencies of the microwave pumps which generate sufficient power to provide an inverted population while working against the very short relaxation times of the rare earths. This is due to a relatively strong spin-orbit coupling in the rare earth ions.

5. The host structure should be hard, nonfragile, and chemically stable. It should not suffer phase transitions, strains, or physical damage upon going to very low temperatures; it should be susceptible to growth as large, well-formed single crystals.

Each of the above requirements does not pose a serious problem by itself. However, the combination of requirements severely limits the useful materials to a relatively few host structures and paramagnetic ions. The materials listed in Table I have been employed as the active elements in experimental devices employing three level operation. The relaxation times given are for the maser transitions at 4.2°K. In general, the recovery time of the device decreases with the relaxation time; however, the pumping power required for operation increases as the relaxation time decreases. Additional data on a number of these compounds and other materials for which the EPR spectra have been determined have been tabulated by Gerritsen (38).

PREPARATION OF MATERIALS

Lanthanum ethyl sulfate (a in Table I) is grown by the slow evaporation of the saturated solution at or near to room temperature. The crystal is neither hard nor chemically stable. Further, it must be handled with great care to avoid cracking on cooling. It is remarkaable that maser action was obtained in this, the first maser material, at 9000 Mc; a frequency that is much larger than the zero field splitting of the material. This was made possible by the incorporation

TABLE I. Active Elements in Experimental Devices Employing Three Level Operation

Compound	Maser action, ref.	Structure	N[a]	Dielectric const.	Zero field splitting, kmc	EPR data, ref.	Approx. relaxation time 4.2°K, msec[b]	Ref.
(a) $La(C_2H_5SO_4)_3 \cdot 9H_2O$	6	Hexagonal			3.39	17	0.03 m	18
$Gd_{0.0005}Ce_{0.002}$			2		2.50			
					1.40		0.003 i	19
(b) $K_3Co(CN)_6:Cr_{0.005}$	9	Monoclinic	2	5	5.1	21	50 est.[c]	20
	20							
(c) $Al_2O_3:Cr_{0.0005}$	10	Hexagonal	1	9—11	11.5	22	50	14
(d) $Al_2O_3:Fe$	23	Hexagonal	1	9—11	19.2	24	3	24
					11.8			
(e) $TiO_2:Cr$	25	Tetragonal	2	130—260	43.3	28	2.5	29
	26			(ref. 26)				
	27							
(f) $TiO_2:Fe$	30	Tetragonal	2	130—260	81.3	31	0.1 est.	30
					43.3			
(g) $Be_3Al_2Si_6O_{18}:Cr_{0.005}$	32	Hexagonal	1	6	53.7	33	1 est.	34
(h) $CaWO_4$:	35	Tetragonal	1	12	17.9	35	0.02	35
$Gd_{0.0003}Er_{0.0003}$					10.4			
					4.6			
(i) $ZnWO_4:Cr_{0.005}$	36	Monoclinic	1	12	51.64	36	1	36
(j) $ZnWO_4:Fe_{0.005}$	36	Monoclinic	1	12	61	37	0.5 est.	36
					77			

[a] The number of nonequivalent sites occupied by the paramagnetic ion.
[b] Here m is the maser transition; i the idler transition; the relaxation times are 3 times longer at 1.5°K.
[c] 0.2 sec. at 1.25°K.

of Ce^{3+} to speed up the idler transition. Thus, the first experimental maser not only operated under difficult circumstances but was made to do so by a rather sophisticated means.

Potassium cobalticyanide (b) is grown by slowly cooling the saturated aqueous solution or by evaporation. Both trivalent cobalt and trivalent chromium are strongly bonded to the cyanides. Cobalt has no unpaired electrons under these conditions while chromium has its usual three. This material has been used in cavity masers at 2800 and 1400 Mc at temperatures below 2°K. It is difficult to cool without cracking and is toxic.

The corundum crystals (c) employed in microwave devices are grown by the Verneuil flame fusion technique (3,9). In this process, a very fine Al_2O_3 powder is fed through an oxy-hydrogen flame onto a pedestal or mounted seed rod at about 2050°C. By suitably controlling the furnace conditions, the powder is caused to melt before it strikes the seed, add to the molten surface on the seed, and cool to form part of the crystal as the process continues. This process is illustrated in Figure 2a. Pink ruby (principally supplied by the Linde Co.) is the most widely used maser material. It is suitable for devices at frequencies ranging up to 11,000 Mc. However, it suffers from one limitation: the Cr^{3+} ions tend to cluster at relatively low concentrations (40). The resulting spin-spin coupling between Cr^{3+} ions reduces the inversion and, hence, the gain that can be obtained. It is considerably more difficult to incorporate Fe^{3+} into

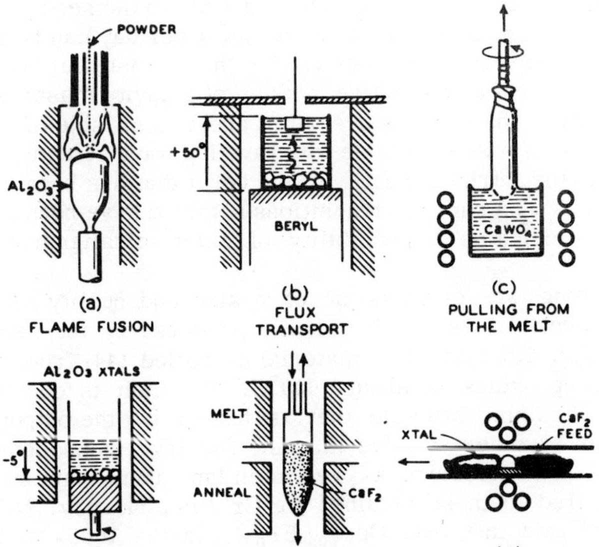

Fig. 2. Methods of growing maser crystals.

corundum than Cr^{3+} due to the ease with which iron is reduced at the melting point of Al_2O_3.

Rutile (TiO_2) containing limited amounts of Cr^{3+} (e) or Fe^{3+} (f) can also be grown by the flame fusion technique. The boules so obtained are dark due to the presence of reduced titanium but can be oxydized by annealing in air or oxygen. Rutile has a very high dielectric constant varying from 130 to 260 with orientation at 4.2°K (26). This presents a number of unresolved engineering problems in using this material at frequencies below 10,000 Mc in comb-type traveling wave structures. Sabisky and Gerritsen (26) and Arams and Peyton (27), however, have been able to construct traveling wave masers operating in the 10,000- and 30,000-Mc region, respectively, employing this material. Foner et al. (30) have operated cavity masers employing rutile containing Fe^{3+} in the 4- and 8-mm wavelength region. Here they feel that the high dielectric constant of rutile simplifies some of their cavity design problems.

Beryl (g), suitable for microwave applications, can be grown by transport methods employing V_2O_5 as a flux (Fig. 2b) (41). In this method, beryl—which is denser than V_2O_5 at 1000°C—is placed in a platinum crucible with small amounts of aluminum oxide, beryllium oxide, and chromium oxide, and/or iron oxide. The crucible is then placed in the upper part of a pot furnace, heated to about 1000°C, and filled with V_2O_5 (which melts at about 650°C). A natural beryl seed plate is then suspended in the upper part of the flux. Under the indicated conditions, the upper part of the flux is somewhat cooler than the lower part; as a consequence the beryl dissolves into the V_2O_5 at the bottom of the crucible and adds to the seed plate at the top. Growth rates of from 10 to 50 mils per day can be obtained. The Cr^{3+} has a linewidth of about 100 Mc in this material (42). Goodwin employed beryl as the active medium of a cavity maser operating 24,000 Mc (32). The process described above is capable of producing beryl crystals of a size suitable for traveling wave structures. However, to date the intrinsic quality of the beryl that has been measured is not certain. The pumping transitions obtained have been relatively broad. This indicates a possibility of axial misalignments in the crystals.

Calcium tungstate crystals (f) of a size and quality suitable for microwave applications can be readily prepared by the Czochralski technique (Fig. 2c) (43). The material is pulled (44) from a melt of the component oxides at about 1600°C. The melt is contained in a rhodium or iridium crucible that is heated by the output of an rf generator or by other suitable means. The inversions obtained for Gd^{3+} in this host structure as well as in lanthanum ethyl sulfate are small compared to those obtained for Cr^{3+} in pink ruby. Nilsen (35) has obtained gain in $CaWO_4:Gd_{0.0003}Er_{0.0003}$ in the 1000- to 2000-Mc range employing a traveling wave structure, but a practical device has not been constructed to date. The Er^{3+} plays much the same role in this material as does Ce^{3+} in the lanthanum ethyl sulfate. A number of other divalent tungstates and molybdates which have the same structure as $CaWO_4$ can be prepared (45) by the Czochralski technique. These materials are of interest for optical as well as microwave maser devices.

Zinc tungstate (g) is also prepared (46) by the Czochralski technique. A platinum crucible susceptor is employed in this case, since the melting point of the material is at about 1050°C. Inversions are shown by $ZnWO_4{:}Cr_{0.005}$ that are comparable to those obtained for pink ruby (at its optimum chromium content) at 1500 Mc (36). However, the volume content of Cr^{3+} (or the spin density) is much higher. This should enable structures to be built which may have larger gain bandwidth products. Of interest as potential maser materials are $MgWO_4$, $CdWO_4$, and a number of rare earth tantalates having the same structure as $ZnWO_4$. The crystals $MgWO_4$ and $CdWO_4$ that are suitable for EPR studies can be grown from a $Na_2W_2O_7$ flux by slow cooling (47).

OPTICAL MASER MATERIALS

Optical oscillators and amplifiers that are capable of operating continuously are of interest for communication systems because of the large absolute bandwifth that they may afford. There may be a gain of one to two orders of magnitude over the present microwave systems in the number of channels that a carrier signal may handle. Further, since the divergence of a coherent beam of electromagnetic energy varies inversely with its frequency, power loss in propagating over a long distance is much less for optical frequencies than for microwave frequencies. Hence, optical masers are of interest for space communications. Pulse-operated oscillators are capable of delivering large bursts of power (14 Mw have been reported) (48). The light sources used for pumping optical masers are relatively simple in comparison to the klystrons employed for pumping microwave masers; however, they are much less efficient. The FT524 helical xenon flash lamp is commonly employed to excite maser action on a pulse basis and a compact arc xenon lamp or a high-pressure mercury arc lamp on a continuous basis. The outputs of these lamps are indicated in Figure 3.

The primary requirements for an optical maser material are: first, that it fluoresce with a suitably high intensity and narrow emission linewidth under the operating conditions employed; and, second, that the material should be of a suitable optical quality. The choice of materials for optical masers that (hopefully) operate continuously with a relatively low power input is limited by the following considerations.

1. The host material should be a single crystal of optical quality, free from gross defects, inclusions, and light scattering centers. It should also be hard and chemically stable so that it can take a highly polished finish. Due to the large absolute bandwidths of the optical maser transitions, the generation of hyperfine structure (as

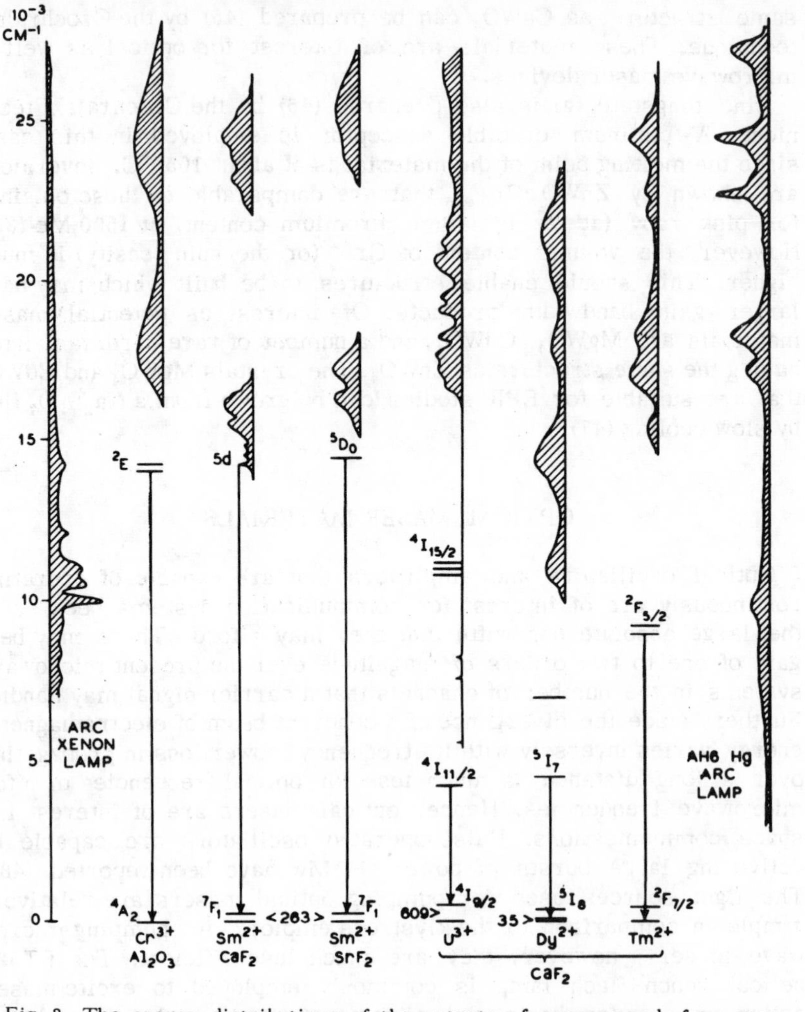

Fig. 3. The energy distributions of the outputs of a xenon and of a mercury arc lamp are shown. The absorption bands and maser transitions of the indicated materials are also given. The positions in energy of a number of terminal states of the maser transitions are also indicated.

a result of the presence of ions with nuclear magnetic moments in the material) is not the problem that it is at microwave frequencies.

2. The fluorescing ions should occupy equivalent positions in the host structure. Random electrostatic effects—due to nonequivalent ions distributing themselves in identical sites—should be avoided. Under these conditions, the spectrum produced by the fluorescing ions should show the minimum linewidths and detail consistent with the site symmetry. In general, the higher the site symmetry, the more degenerate the electronic states and, hence, the fewer the transitions that should be observed in fluorescence. It often happens,

however, that a given transition is highly favored in a noncubic environment.

3. The same environment is not optimum for every ion that is capable of fluorescing. The ligand field can have a marked effect on brightness. For example, Cr^{3+} is known to fluoresce in environments where it replaces Al^{3+}, Ga^{3+}, or Mg^{2+}; but not in many others. The rare earth ions with atomic numbers close to that of Gd^{3+} fluoresce as hydrates, a greater number fluoresce as fluorides, and all of them fluoresce as oxides. In the oxides, the intensity of emission of a given rare earth ion tends to increase with its binding energy (49,50), particularly when the emission of the ion is not enhanced by processes taking place in the host structure. Thus, at least to where the excited states of the fluorescing ions become excessively perturbed (51), conditions that afford a reduction in interaction distance and a higher site symmetry should result in brighter fluorescence (50).

4. The concentration of the fluorescing ion can also be important. In the case of ruby, where the maser transitions are to the ground state, an excessive concentration of Cr^{3+} can make it difficult to obtain a suitable population inversion for the single ion maser transition. The aggregation of Cr^{3+} ions at high concentrations also leads to the production of additional spectral lines within a few hundred angstrom units of those for the single ions. The satellite lines are produced by interactions between neighboring Cr^{3+} ions which split their energy levels (52). The strongest of these satellite lines terminate on states that are unoccupied at very low temperatures and, hence, provide the possibility of four level operation (53). Energy absorbed by the individual Cr^{3+} ions in ruby is in part transferred to the paired ions and acts to increase the intensity of the above satellite lines. This makes it possible to excite all of the ion pairs while only exciting a small part of the unpaired Cr^{3+} ions. Maser action has been produced employing these satellite lines (54,55).

In the case of the rare earth ions, where crystal field effects are less important, the opposite effect often occurs wherein the overall emission spectrum becomes simpler upon increasing concentration. This is due to the sequential quenching of emission from the several metastable states of the rare earth ions involved, proceeding (in general) from the levels that lie higher in energy to those that lie lower in energy as concentration increases (51). The quenching interactions that occur between rare earth ions are dependent upon the structure of the host crystal and the orbital angular momenta of the occupied electronic states, as well as the dispostions of the energy levels of the ions (56).

5. Processes wherein energy is captured by the host structure and transported to incorporated rare earth ions may also be of interest. This has been demonstrated to occur for Sm^{3+} in $CaWO_4$ (59) by Kroger (57). Excitation in the region of the absorption edge of a host crystal provides a direct means of exciting incorporated rare earth ions by a preferred charge transfer as well (58). In general,

excitation processes which involve the absorption edge of the host crystal have proved unsatisfactory since color centers are readily produced in the crystals under these conditions. It is preferable to employ crystals whose absorption edges are well above the excitation frequency or excitation frequencies that are well below the absorption edge of the host crystal. Excitation is then dependent upon the absorption characteristics of the fluorescing ions themselves, or of these ions in combination with other paramagnetic species which have been incorporated into the host crystal. Examples of the former are Cr^{3+} in pink ruby (2), U^{3+} in CaF_2 (59), and Nd^{3+} in $CaWO_4$ (60); and Ce^{3+} plus Tb^{3+} in CaF_2 and Tb^{3+} plus Eu^{3+} in tungstates and molybdates are examples of the latter.

Garrett and W. Kaiser (61) obtained a quantum efficiency of about 0.2 for Tb^{3+} in CaF_2 over a wide range of excitation frequencies. They also found that when both Ce^{3+} and Tb^{3+} were incorporated (in the 1% concentration range) the same overall quantum efficiency was obtained for the emission of Tb^{3+} when exciting in the broad absorption band of Ce^{3+} which lies in the 2300- to 3100-A region. This indicates that the efficiency of energy transfer from Ce^{3+} to Tb^{3+} is close to 100%. The d-absorption bands of Ce^{3+} (due to 4f to 5d transitions) lie above the metastable level of Tb^{3+} (approximately 20,700 cm^{-1}) in CaF_2 (see Fig. 4). In the scheelites (e.g., $CaWO_4$) these bands extend well below the metastable level of Tb^{3+}. As a result, Ce^{3+} strongly quenches Tb^{3+} (and many other ions) in the tungstates.

The ability of Tb^{3+} to enhance the fluorescence of Eu^{3+} in the tungstates, molybdates (62), and many other compounds is due to the fact that—unlike the d bands of Ce^{3+} which vary in position with the ligand field—the metastable (f electron) level of Tb^{3} always lies above that of Eu^{3+} (approximately 17,300 cm^{-1}). Further, these ions have energy gaps of over 11,000 cm^{-1} between their metastable levels and the closest lower lying levels (see Fig. 4). When energy transfer from Tb^{3+} to Eu^{3+} occurs, the difference in energy between the two metastable levels is given up to the host structures, producing phonons. If (as for Eu^{3+}) the effective gap between the metastable level and the lower lying levels of the rare earth ions is large, the metastable level is relatively undisturbed by the increased phonon activity. Where the gap is small, the more usual effect is to quench emission altogether (5,6).

OPERATION

A list of crystals and glasses that have produced maser action along with the approximate wavelength of the resulting signals is presented in Table II. References to the spectral data for the active ions and the maser operation conditions are also given. The glasses are of technical interest and may find uses in high power applications. However, the rare earth ions occur in a variety of sites in

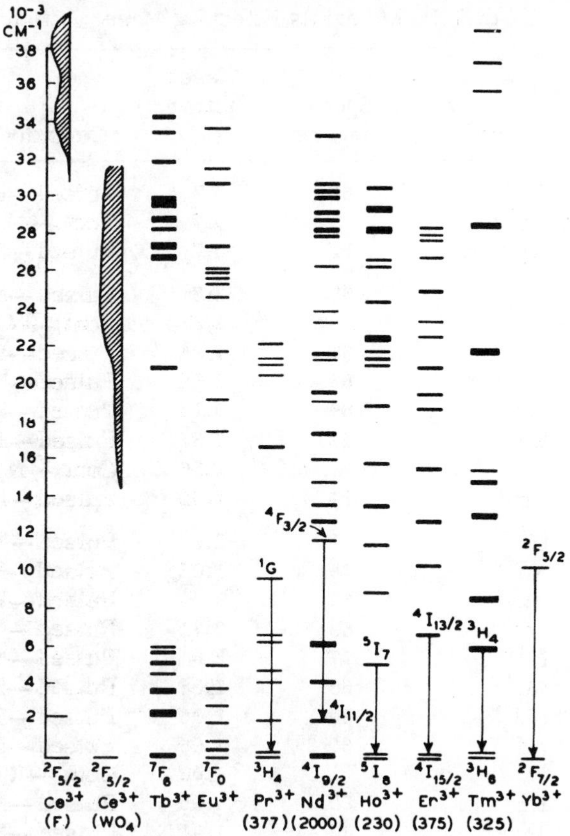

Fig. 4. The absorption bands, energy levels, and maser transitions for a number of trivalent rare earth ions are shown. The positions in energy of the terminal states of a number of the maser transitions are indicated in parentheses below the columns.

these amorphous media and, hence, have multiple spectra and broad absorption and emission lines.

Rare earth ions which have strong d-absorption bands as well as narrow emission lines are highly favored as the active ions in the fluorides (see Fig. 3). Since the 4f to 5d transitions are allowed dipole transitions, their oscillator strengths are usually two or three orders of magnitude greater and their radiative lifetimes shorter than those for the 4f orbital transitions. A comparison of the radiative lifetimes of allowed and nonallowed transitions of Sm^{2+} can be obtained from $CaF_2:Sm^{2+}$ and $SrF_2:Sm^{2+}$. The quantum efficiency of Sm^{2+} obtained by pumping the lower d band of this ion in these host crystals is close to 1 (69). However, in CaF_2 the emission is from a low lying level of the d band of Sm^{2+} while in SrF_2 it is from the $^5D_0$ state of Sm^{2+} (see Fig. 3). The measured lifetime in CaF_2 is about 2×10^{-6} sec, while that in SrF_2 is about 1×10^{-2} sec (69). The

TABLE II. Materials Effecting Maser Actions

Lattice	Ion	Spectrum, ref.	Maser action, μ	Conditions	Ref.
Al_2O_3	Cr^{3+}	63	0.7	Pulsed—RT	2
	Cr^{3+}		0.7	Cont.—N_2	64
	Cr^{3+} pair	52	0.7	Pulsed—N_2	54
CaF_2	U^{3+}	65	2.6	Pulsed—N_2	59
			2.6	Cont.—N_2	66
	Nd^{3+}	67	1.06	Pulsed—RT	67
	Ho^{3+}	68	2.05	Pulsed—N_2	68
	Sm^{2+}	69	0.71	Pulsed—H_2	70
	Dy^{2+}	71	2.36	Pulsed—N_2	71
			2.36	Cont.—N_2	71–73
	Tm^{2+}	74	1.12	Pulsed—H_2	75, 76
SrF_2	U^{3+}	77	2.6	Pulsed—N_2	77
	Nd^{3+}	68	1.06	Pulsed—RT	68
	Tm^{3+}	68	1.91	Pulsed—RT	68
	Sm^{2+}	69	0.71	Pulsed—N_2	78
BaF_2	U^{3+}	77	2.6	Pulsed—N_2	79
	Nd^{3+}	68	1.06	Pulsed—RT	68
LaF_3	Nd^{3+}	80	1.06	Pulsed—RT	80
$CaWO_4$	Nd^{3+}	60	1.06	Pulsed—RT	60
			1.06	Cont.—RT	81
	Pr^{3+}	82	1.05	Pulsed—N_2	82
	Tm^{3+}	83	1.91	Pulsed—N_2	83
	Ho^{3+}	84	2.05	Pulsed—N_2	84
	Er^{3+}	85	1.61	Pulsed—N_2	85
$SrWO_4$	Nd^{3+}	68	1.06	Pulsed—RT	68
$CaMoO_4$	Nd^{3+}	68	1.06	Pulsed—RT	68
$SrMoO_4$	Nd^{3+}	68	1.06	Cont.—N_2	68
$PbMoO_4$	Nd^{3+}	68	1.06	Pulsed—RT	68
$Na_{1/2}La_{1/2}MoO_4$		68	1.06	Pulsed—RT	68
Glass	Nd^{3+}	86	1.06	Pulsed—RT	86
Glass	Yb^{3+}	87	1.01	Pulsed—N_2	87

ions with strong d bands include U^{3+}(59), Sm^{2+}(70), Dy^{2+}(71), and Tm^{2+} (75,76). The d bands are not always the most effective place to pump, however. Maser action for U^{3+} in CaF_2 is produced more efficiently by pumping its $^4I_{15/2}$ levels (at about 11,000 cm^{-1}) (66). As shown in Figure 3, these levels lie in the strong emission region of the xenon lamp. A threshold for continuous operation of 350 w and an output of 0.150 w for an 800-w input have been obtained (88).

The efficiency with which maser action is produced can be strongly influenced by the position in energy of the terminal state of the maser transition relative to the ground state. The greater this gap (ΔE_t) the lower the population of the terminal state at thermal equilibrium. When the terminal state is empty, a relatively small population in the metastable level may permit maser action. The ΔE_t is about 2000 cm^{-1} for Nd^{3+} in $CaWO_4$, 609 cm^{-1} for U^{3+} in CaF_2, and less than 400 cm^{-1} for the other ions that have taken part in maser action (see Figs. 3 and 4). The fact that $CaWO_4$:Nd has shown continuous maser action at room temperature (81) may be attributed to the low thermal population of the 2000-cm^{-1} level. The threshold for continuous operation at 90°K (employing a high-pressure mercury arc lamp) was about 600 w and at room temperature about 1200 w. At 90°K an output in excess of 0.2 w was obtained for a 1600-w input using a rod with silvered ends (89) and 0.5 w using a rod with dielectric coated ends (68). The 600-w threshold of Nd^{3+} may in part be due to the line character and low oscillator strengths of its absorption transitions in comparison to those for the d bands of Sm^{2+}, Dy^{2+}, or Cr^{3+}. The threshold would be lower if a greater part of the lamp emission occurred at the absorption frequencies of Nd^{3+}.

The ΔE_t for Dy^{2+} in CaF_2 is only 35 cm^{-1}. However, this material has been made to operate continuously at 77°K with considerable efficiency. A threshold for continuous operation of about 100 w and outputs as high as 0.3 w with an 800-w input have been obtained employing a compact air-cooled xenon arc lamp (73). This exceptional behavior may be attributed to the coincidence of the lower d band of Dy^{2+} with a strong output region of the xenon lamp (88).

In Al_2O_3 Cr^{3+} operates as a ground state ($\Delta E_t = 0$) maser (2). The crystal must be pumped strongly to obtain a suitable excess population in its metastable state. As a result, the usual rod form has only been made to operate on a pulse basis. When the Cr^{3+} content of the ruby rod is relatively high, sheathing it with clear Al_2O_3 helps to focus the excitation into the active volume of the crystal. This can reduce the input threshold by a significant amount (90). A much greater reduction in input threshold has been obtained by end pumping through a sapphire trumpet which is an integral part of the rod. The trumpet arrangement affords an increase in efficiency of a factor of about 15. Under these circumstances, continuous maser operation was obtained with an 850-w input to a special high-pressure mercury-xenon arc lamp. With a 930-w input, the maser beam had a measured power of 0.004 w (64).

CRYSTAL PREPARATION

The threshold for maser operation in ruby increases with increasing strain and with decreasing homogeneity. Olt (91) has described the procedures employed at the Linde Co. to improve rubies grown by flame fusion for optical maser applications. They have obtained their best results using disc growth techniques which employ a very low temperature gradient across the boule. As previously mentioned, additional improvements have been made by using sapphire overlays on the maser rods and by growing a sapphire trumpet on one end of a maser rod.

Maser action has also been obtained using ruby crystals which were grown from the flux. The process for growing these crystals was developed by Remeika of these laboratories in 1955. Remeika is responsible for much of the recent development of crystal growth by flux techniques. A typical run is as follows (see Fig. 2d) (92). A platinum crucible (6 in. diam by 10 in. deep) is filled with a mixture consisting of 750 g of Al_2O_3, 400 g of B_2O_3, 2 g of Cr_2O_3, and 5000 g of PbO; covered with a platinum lid and heated in a vertical furnace to 1300°C. The pot is mounted on a rotating stand in a position such that when the furnace is at temperature the top of the resulting melt (which is then about 4 in. deep in the pot) is about 5° hotter than the bottom. The temperature is held at 1300°C for about 5 hr to effect solution of all of the oxides in the melt. During this period the pot is continuously rotated 30 revolutions in one direction (at about 1 rps), stopped and then rotated 30 revolutions in the other direction to effect stirring. At the end of this period the rotation is stopped and the temperature is slowly lowered (at less than 5° per hour) to affect crystallization. The down gradient in temperature encourages nucleation and growth at the bottom of the pot. Rhombohedral crystals that are about 1.5 cm in their longest direction are readily produced under the above conditions. Excellent optical quality is obtained. An added advantage is gained in that the slow growing faces of the crystal are almost perfectly parallel. Nelson has obtained excellent maser characteristics under pulsed conditions using silvered natural faces of a flux grown crystal as reflecting surfaces (93).

The alkaline earth fluorides are the principal host structures employed for rare earth ions in their lower valence states. The cations are accommodated in sites which provide eight nearest neighbor fluorine ions in a cubic arrangement. This environment provides the highest site symmetry for the cations and the shortest interaction distance between the anions and the rare earth ion to be found in the halides. When trivalent rare earth ions are incorporated into these materials, some form of charge compensation is required. This can occur in three ways (94-96). Only one-half of the centers of the cubes defined by the F^- lattice in MF_2 are occupied by M^{2+} ions. When an M^{3+} ion is introduced, an extra F^- ion can occupy an adjacent cube center. This produces a fourfold symmetry about the 100 axis of the crystal. A second means of compensating for the added charge on the M^{3+} ion is by introducing an O^{2-} ion in place of an F^- ion. This produces a threefold symmetry about the 111 axis of the crystal (97). In sites remote from the M^{3+} ions, F^- ions may also occur. Each of these arrangements produces a different spectrum. In the case of uranium, the undesirable U^{4+} species also occurs in the crystal if oxygen is present. By avoiding the incorporation of oxygen into the crystals and annealing, the spectra can be reduced to that for the ions occurring in the fourfold positions. The hexagonal rare earth fluorides MF_3 are also of interest, particularly where high M^{3+} concentrations are desired.

Guggenheim (98) has developed a process for producing high-quality alkaline earth fluorides and lanthanum fluoride by the Bridgeman-Stockbarger technique (99) (Fig. 2e). In preparing an MF_2 compound, the alkaline earth chloride is slowly heated from 500 to 1200°C in an HF atmosphere. Platinum containers and tubing are employed in this as well as the remainder of the process. The resulting fluoride is loaded into a straight wall platinum crucible with a conical tip. A cap with an inlet and an outlet tube is then welded on. The resulting unit can be evacuated or have a controlled atmosphere. The latter is generally used, preferably as a He and HF mixture. The crucible is then brought to a temperature well above the melting point of the fluoride and slowly lowered through a sharp thermal gradient into an annealing furnace whose temperature is below the melting point of the fluoride. When the crystal is entirely within the annealing furnace, the latter is slowly cooled to room temperature. Where divalent ion species such as Sm^{2+}, Dy^{2+}, and Tm^{2+} are desired, they are conveniently obtained by subjecting the crystals containing the trivalent ions to γ-radiation (100—102). In preparing rare earth fluorides for feed materials, the oxides are converted directly to fluorides by sintering in HF at about 1250°C.

Guggenheim has also adapted the molten zone techniques (103) commonly employed in the zone refining and doping of germanium to the growth of fluorides (104) (see Fig. 2f). For example, a CaF_2 seed crystal is placed at one end of a horizontal graphite boat, and the remainder of the boat is filled with CaF_2 feed. The rare earth fluoride to be introduced into the growing crystal is added in the region shared by the seed and the loose CaF_2. The graphite boat is then mounted in a horizontal quartz tube that can be caused to move slowly in one direction. A hot zone is supplied by rf coupling to the graphite. Part of the seed is melted in the hot zone at the start. As the boat travels through this zone, the loose CaF_2 melts and transfers to the seed crystal. The rare earth fluoride in the molten zone generally distributes itself quite evenly throughout the resulting crystal.

In the tungstates and molybdates which have the scheelite structure, the M^{2+} ions occur in 8-fold positions. Trivalent rare earth ions can replace M^{2+} ions in these materials either by two M^{3+} ions and an M^{2+} site vacancy replacing three M^{2+} ions, or an M^+ plus and M^{3+} ion replacing two M^{2+} ions. The random distribution of lattice vacancies over the M^{2+} sites in effect produces a variable site symmetry which results in the presence of extra spectral lines (105). This difficulty is alleviated by incorporating the M^+ ions into the structure. At high M^+ plus M^{3+} concentrations, however, the resulting random Coulombic effects can produce line broadening.

The growth of tungstates or molybdates by the Czochkalski technique must be carried out with considerable care (44,45). Crystals grown from the flux (47) are a preferred source of material for pulling from the melt. Materials prepared by coprecipitation from reagent grade nitrates and ammonium tungstate or molybdate can also be very suitable. They should be washed thoroughly and calcined at 1000 and 1300°C to eliminate solvent, ammonia, and excess WO_3 or MoO_3 prior to their use in crystal growth. The rare earth ion may be added as the alkali metal rare earth tungstate or molybdate. Crystals can be pulled conveniently at a rate of 1/2 in./hr while rotating. A close control on temperature is desirable to avoid inhomogeneities in the concentration of the active ion. The grown crystal should be annealed for several hours at a temperature not too far below its melting point to eliminate straings and lattice imperfections.

ACKNOWLEDGMENTS

The author wishes to thank G. D. Boyd, C. G. B. Garrett, J. E. Geusic, H. Guggenheim, L. F. Johnson, S. K. Kurtz, W. G. Nilsen, D. F. Nelson, J. P. Remeika, H. E. D. Scovil, W. J. Tabor, and A. Yariv for permission to cite their unpublished results and for helpful discussions.

References

1. Gordon, J. P., H. J. Zeiger, and C. H. Townes, Phys. Rev., 95, 282 (1954); 99, 1264 (1955).

2. Maiman, T. H., Brit. Commun. Electron., 7, 674 (1960); Nature, 187, 493 (1960).

3. Javan, A., in Quantum Electronics, C. H. Townes, ed., Columbia Univ. Press, New York, 1960, p. 564.

4. Javan, A., W. R. Bennett, Jr., and D. R. Herriot, Phys. Rev. Letters, 6, 106 (1961).

5. Bloembergen, N., Phys. Rev., 104, 324 (1956).

6. Scovil, H. E. D., G. Feher, and H. Seidel, Phys. Rev., 105, 762 (1957).

7. Feher, G., J. P. Gordon, E. Buehler, E. A. Gere, and C. D. Thurmond, Phys. Rev., 109, 221 (1958).

8. Chester, P. F., P. E. Wagner, and J. G. Castle, Phys. Rev., 110, 281 (1958).

9. McWhorter, A. L., and J. W. Meyer, Phys. Rev., 109, 312 (1958).

10. Makhov, G., C. Kikuchi, J. Lambe, and R. W. Terhune, Phys. Rev., 109, 1399 (1958).

11. Makhov, G., Bull. Am. Phys. Soc., 4, 21 (1959).

12. Minkowski, J. M., Phys. Rev., 119, 1577 (1960).

13. Schawlow, A. L., and C. H. Townes, Phys. Rev., 112, 1940 (1958).

14. DeGrasse, R. W., E. O. Schulz-Dubois, and H. E. D. Scovil, Bell. Syst. Tech. J., 38, 305 (1959).

15. For a tabulation of nuclear magnetic moments and isotropic abundances, see G. E. Pake; Solid State Physics, Vol. 2, F. Seitz and D. Turnbull, eds., Academic Press, New York, 1956.

16. Singer, J. R., Masers, Wiley, New York, 1960.

17. Bleaney, B., H. E. D. Scovil, and R. S. Trenam, Proc. Roy. Soc. (London), A223, 15 (1954).

18. Feher, G., and H. E. D. Scovil, Phys. Rev., 105, 760 (1957).

19. Scovil, H. E. D., private communication.

20. Artman, J. O., N. Bloembergen, and S. Shapiro, Phys. Rev., 109, 1399 (1958).

21. Baker, J. M., B. Bleaney, and K. D. Bowers, Proc. Phys. Soc. (London), B69, 1205 (1956).

22. Geusic, J. E., Phys. Rev., 102, 1252 (1956).

23. Korienko, L. S., and D. A. M. Prokhorov, Soviet Phys. JETP, 9, 649 (1959).

24. Korienko, L. S., and A. M. Prokhorov, Soviet Phys., JETP, 6, 620 (1958).

25. Gerritsen, H. J., and H. R. Lewis, J. Appl. Phys., 31, 608 (1960).

26. Sabisky, E. S., and H. J. Gerritsen, Proc. Inst. Radio Engs., 49, 1329 (1961); J. Appl. Phys., 33, 1450 (1962).

27. Abrams, F. R., and B. Peyton, Solid State Circuits Conf. Digest Univ. of Penn., Feb. 1962, and Proc. Inst. Radio Engs., 50, (1962).

28. Gerritsen, H. I., S. E. Harrison, H. R. Lewis, and J. P. Wittke, Phys. Rev. Letters, 2, 153 (1959).

29. Geusic, J. E., Solid State Maser Research, U. S. Army Signal Corp. Contract No. DA 36-039 SC85357, First Quarterly Rept., Sept. 20, 1960.

30. Foner, S., L. R. Momo, J. B. Thaxter, G. S. Heller, and R. M. White, in Advances in Quantum Electronics J. R. Singer, ed., Columbia Univ. Press, New York, 1961, p. 553.

31. Carter, D. L., and A. Okaya, Phys. Rev., 118, 1485 (1960).

32. Goodwin, F. E., J. Appl. Phys., 32, 1624 (1961).

33. Geusic, J. E., Martin Peter, and E. O. Schulz-DuBois, B.S.T.J., 38, 291 (1959).

34. Geusic, J. E., private communication.

35. Nilsen, W. G., Solid State Maser Research, U. S. Army Signal Corp. Contract No. DA 36-039 SC85357, 2nd Quarterly Rept., December 20, 1960.

36. Kurtz, S. K., and W. G. Nilsen, Phys. Rev., 128, 1586 (1962).

37. Peter, M., L. G. Van Uitert, and J. B. Mock, in Advances in Quantum Electronics, J. R. Singer, ed., Columbia Univ. Press, New York, 1961.

38. Gerritsen, H. J., Appl. Opt., 1, 37 (1962).

39. Vernenil, A. V. L., Ann. Chim. Phys. Ser., 3, No. 8, 20 (1904).
40. Tabor, W. J., Solid State Maser Research, First and Second Quarterly Reports, U. S. Army Signal Corps, Contract DA 36-039 SC85357 Sept. and Dec. 1960; also, S. K. Kurtz 4th Quarterly Rept., June 1961.
41. Linares, R. C., A. A. Ballman, and L. G. Van Uitert, J. Appl. Phys., 33, 3209 (1962).
42. Kurtz, S. K., and W. G. Nilsen, private communication.
43. Czochralski, J., Z. Physik Chem., 92, 219 (1918).
44. Nassau, K., and L. G. Van Uitert, J. Appl. Phys., 31, 1508 (1960).
45. Preziosi, S., R. R. Soden, and L. G. Van Uitert, J. Appl. Phys., 33, 1893 (1962).
46. Van Uitert, L. G., and S. Preziosi, J. Appl. Phys., to be published.
47. Van Uitert, L. G., and R. R. Soden, J. Appl. Phys., 31, 328 (1960).
48. McClung, R. J., and R. W. Hellwarth, Abstracts 2, No. 1, Electrochemical Soc. Spring Meeting, Los Angeles, May 1962.
49. Van Uitert, L. G., and R. R. Soden, J. Chem. Phys., 36, 517 (1962).
50. Van Uitert, L. G., J. Chem. Phys., 37, 981 (1962).
51. Van Uitert, L. G., J. Electrochem. Soc., 107, 803 (1960).
52. Schawlow, A. L., D. L. Wood, and A. M. Clogston, Phys. Rev. Letters, 3, 271 (1959).
53. Schawlow, A. L., in Quantum Electronics, C. H. Townes, ed., Columbia Univ. Press, New York, 1960.
54. Schawlow, A. L., and G. E. Devlin, Phys. Rev. Letters, 6, 96 (1961).
55. Wieder, I., and L. R. Sarles, Phys. Rev. Letters, 6, 95 (1961).
56. Van Uitert, L. G., and S. Iida, J. Chem. Phys., 37, 986 (1962).
57. Kroger, F. A., Some Aspects of the Luminescence of Solids, Elsevier, New York, 1948.
58. Van Uitert, L. G., R. R. Soden, and R. C. Linares, J. Chem. Phys., 36, 1793 (1962).
59. Sorokin, P. P., and M. J. Stevenson, Phys. Rev. Letters, 5, 557 (1960).
60. Johnson, L. F., and K. Nassau, Proc. Inst. Radio Engs., 49, 1704 (1961).
61. Garrett, C. G. B., and W. Kaiser, private communication.
62. Van Uitert, L. G., and R. R. Soden, J. Chem. Phys., 36, 1289 (1962).
63. For relevant data see P. Pringsheim, Fluorescence and Phosphore Science, Interscience, New York, 1949.
64. Nelson, D. F., and W. S. Boyle, Appl. Opt., 1, 181 (1962).
65. Galkin, L. N., and P. P. Feofilov, Doklady Akad. Nauk SSSR, 114, 745 (1957); Soviet Phys. Dok., 2, 255 (1957).
66. Boyd, G. D., R. J. Collins, S. P. S. Porto, A. Yariv, and W. A. Hargraves, Phys. Rev. Letters, 8, 269 (1962).

67. Johnson, L. F., J. Appl. Phys., 33, 756 (1962).
68. Johnson, L. F., J. Appl. Phys., to be published.
69. (a) Wood, D. L., and W. Kaiser, Phys. Rev., 126, 2079 (1962). (b) W. Kaiser, C. G. B. Garrett, and D. L. Wood, Phys. Rev., 123, 766 (1961).
70. Sorokin, P. P., and M. J. Stevenson, IBM J. Res. Develop., 5, 56 (1961).
71. Kiss, Z. J., and R. C. Duncan, Proc. Inst. Radio Engs., 50, 1531 (1962).
72. Johnson, L. F., Proc. Inst. Radio Engs., 50, 1691 (1962).
73. Yariv, A., Proc. Inst. Radio Engs., 50, 1699 (1962).
74. Kiss, Z. J., Phys. Rev., 127, 718 (1962).
75. Boyd, G. D., and L. F. Johnson, private communication.
76. Kiss, Z. J., and R. C. Duncan, Proc. Inst. Radio Engs., 50, 1532 (1962).
77. Porto, S. P. S., and A. Yariv, Proc. Inst. Radio Engs., 50, 1543 (1962); H. A. Bostick and J. R. O'Connor, Proc. Inst. Radio Engs., 50, 219 (1962).
78. Sorokin, P. P., M. J. Stevenson, J. R. Lankard, and G. D. Petit, Phys. Rev., 127, 503 (1962).
79. Porto, S. P. S., and A. Yariv, Proc. Inst. Radio Engs., 50, 1542 (1962).
80. Johnson, L. F., and H. Guggenheim, to be published.
81. Johnson, L. F., G. D. Boyd, K. Nassau, and R. R. Soden, Proc. Inst. Radio Engs., 50, 213 (1962).
82. Yariv, A., S. P. S. Porto, and K. Nassau, J. Appl. Phys., 33, 2519 (1962).
83. Johnson, L. F., G. D. Boyd, and K. Nassau, Proc. Inst. Radio Engs., 50, 86, (1962).
84. Johnson, L. F., G. D. Boyd, and K. Nassau, Proc. Inst. Radio Engs., 50, 87, (1962).
85. Kiss, Z. J., and R. C. Duncan, Proc. Inst. Radio Engs., 50, 1531 (1962).
86. Snitzer, E., Phys. Rev. Letters, 7, 444 (1961).
87. Etzel, H. W., H. W. Gandy, and R. J. Ginther, Appl. Opt., 1, 534 (1962).
88. Yariv, A., private communication.
89. Boyd, G. D., private communication.
90. Devlin, G. E., J. McKenna, A. D. May, and A. L. Schawlow, Appl. Opt., 1, 11 (1962).
91. Olt, R. D., Appl. Opt., 1, 25 (1962).
92. Remeika, J. P., private communication.
93. Nelson, D. F., private communication.
94. Feofilov, P. P., Doklady Akad Nauk., SSSR, 99, 731 (1954).
95. Bleaney, B., P. M. Llewellyn, and P. A. Jones, Proc. Phys. Soc. (London), A69, 856 (1956).
96. Yariv, A., Proc. 1st Int. Conf. on Paramagnetic Resonance, Jerusalem, July, 1962.
97. Sierro, J., J. Chem. Phys., 34, 2183 (1961).

98. Guggenheim, H., to be published.
99. Bridgman, P. W., Proc. Am. Acad. Arts Sci., 60, 303 (1925); D. C. Stockbarger, Rev. Sci. Instr., 10, 205 (1939).
100. Prizibram, K., Irradiation Colors and Luminescence, Pergamon Press, London, 1956.
101. Feofilov, P., Opt. i Spektroskopiya, 1, 992 (1956).
102. O'Connor, J. R., and H. A. Bostick, J. Appl. Phys., 33, 1868 (1962).
103. Pfann, W. G., Zone Melting, Wiley, New York, 1958.
104. Guggenheim, H., J. Appl. Phys., 32, 1337 (1961).
105. Johnson, L. F., private communication.

DISCUSSION

H. F. MATARÉ (Bendix): Would you care to comment on the role of the magnetic field and the striking difference between the microwave maser and the optical maser? In the case of ruby, you need the magnetic field to align the pump and maser frequency for a specific crystallographic axis, but in the optical maser you have such broad band pumping that you do not need this. But the noise figure is very high (50,000 kT) for the optical maser so it is not very suitable for communication purposes. Yet, there may be other possibilities in the optical range.

L. G. VAN UITERT: In the microwave region magnetic fields are employed to split the Kramers doublets of chromium in ruby, for example, and to adjust the frequencies at which the microwave transitions occur. At zero applied field chromium only has two low lying energy states (Kramers doublets). In the presence of a suitable magnetic field these are split producing four states, thus permitting three and four level maser action. The optical masers operate at frequencies approximately 10^5 times those of the microwave masers. Hence, the application of a magnetic field has a relatively negligible effect percentagewise on the frequencies at which the transitions between energy states occur.

Spontaneous emission (or noise) increases exponentially with frequency. Hence, the noise generated by an optical maser is far greater than that obtained in a microwave maser. However, the bandwidth and directionality of the former is also far greater. The choice between the two depends upon the application.

P. H. KECK (Texas Instruments): Have you any data for threshold, especially for neodymium-doped tungstate? The threshold data reported in the literature cover a very wide range. Do you have any comment on what the minimum threshold might be?

L. G. VAN UITERT: As discussed in the text, Johnson has reported a threshold for continuous operation of calcium tungstate containing neodymium of 1200 w at 300°K and 600 w at 77°K. These results were obtained employing a mercury arc lamp in a confocal setup. Yariv obtained a threshold for continuous operation of calcium fluoride containing divalent dysprosium of 100 w at 77°K employing a xenon arc lamp under similar conditions. Pulsed thresholds of less than 1 joule have been obtained on calcium tungstate containing neodymium employing a helical xenon lamp. This is a much less efficient arrangement than the confocal setup. Hence, one can expect to obtain still lower pulse thresholds if one improves the efficiency of the apparatus.

M. E. LASSER (Philco Corp.): In your discussion of cross relaxation processes you stated that cerium quenches the fluorescence of many of the other rare earths. It appears from your curves that when neodymium and cerium are incorporated in the tungstates, the neodymium metastable level lies below the cerium levels. If this is the case then I do not see why the cerium does not pump the neodymium.

L. G. VAN UITERT: The 5d bands of trivalent cerium are shown to extend into the infrared region in Figure 4. I was not able to ascertain just how far down in energy the weaker 5d band extends. However, we have found that when cerium is incorporated into the tungstates, even at the 1 mole-% level, no fluorescence in the infrared is seen from the other rare earth ions. In calcium fluoride the 5d bands of cerium lie above the metastable levels of most rare earth ions. In this environment cerium may transfer energy to other rare earth ions or may not affect them one way or the other.

Paramagnetic Spectra of Substituted Sapphires—Part I: Ruby*

By E. O. SCHULZ-DU BOIS

(Manuscript received September 29, 1958)

The paramagnetic resonance properties of Cr^{+++} ions in Al_2O_3 (ruby) were investigated theoretically and experimentally in order to obtain information necessary for the application of this material as active material in a three-level solid-state maser (3LSSM). Numerically computed energy levels, together with their associated eigenvectors, are presented as a function of applied magnetic field for various orientations of the magnetic field with respect to the crystalline symmetry axis. A more detailed discussion is devoted to energy levels, eigenvectors and transition probabilities at angles 0°, 54.74° and 90°, where certain simple relations and symmetries hold. Paramagnetic spectra for signal frequencies between 5 and 24 kmc are shown; agreement between computed and measured resonance fields is satisfactory.

I. INTRODUCTION

Among the paramagnetic salts that have been used as active materials in three-level solid-state masers (3LSSM),[1, 2, 3] ruby shows rather desirable properties. While maser action of this material has been achieved at microwave signal frequencies of 3 to 10 kmc,[4] it should be possible to cover more than the whole centimeter microwave range. Perhaps even more important from a practical point of view are the bulk physical properties. Extremely good heat conductivity at low temperatures allows handling of relatively high microwave power dissipation. Industrial growth of large single crystals by the flame fusion technique and machinability with diamond tools make it possible to fabricate long sections of ruby to very close tolerances, a necessity in travelling-wave maser (TWM) development. Also, ruby can be bonded to metals, thus allowing a high degree of versatility in maser structural design. While the use of ruby in 3LSSM, in particular in nonreciprocal TWM, will be described

* This work is partially supported by the Signal Corps under Contract Number DA-36-039 sc-73224.

in forthcoming papers by members of Bell Telephone Laboratories, this paper is intended to give some background on paramagnetic resonance behavior of ruby.

In general, the paramagnetic resonance properties of an ion in a crystal can be completely described by a spin Hamiltonian containing a relatively small number of constants. In the case of ruby, these include the spectroscopic splitting factors parallel and perpendicular to the crystalline axis, $g_{\parallel}$ and $g_{\perp}$, the total spin $S = 3/2$ and the sign and magnitude of $2D$, the zero field splitting. Nuclear interactions can be neglected since the most abundant isotope, Cr^{52}, is nonmagnetic ($I = 0$) whereas the magnetic isotope, Cr^{53}, ($I = 3/2$) has small abundance (9.5 per cent) and leads to negligible line broadening only. Taking this into account, one can even predict on the basis of the total spin and the crystalline symmetry surrounding the Cr^{+++} ion that no other terms can occur in the spin Hamiltonian.

However, in order to predict operating conditions of this or other materials in a 3LSSM, it is necessary to know the separation of energy levels for supplying the proper pump and signal frequencies, the order of magnitude of the associated transition probabilities and perhaps other circumstances, such as coincidence of transition frequencies, which, by spin-spin interaction, may lead to shortening of the associated relaxation times (self-doping condition). In this paper, this information is evaluated by the formalism of the spin Hamiltonian and, at least in part, compared with experiment. The data presented graphically are intended to form an "atlas" of the ruby paramagnetic resonance properties. In the paper which follows, some general viewpoints are presented on modes in which paramagnetic materials can be operated as active materials in a 3LSSM. In further papers, paramagnetic spectra of other substitutional ions such as Co^{++} and Fe^{+++} in sapphire will be presented in order to furnish sufficient information to find coincidences of transition frequencies of Cr^{+++} with Co^{++} or Fe^{+++} lines resulting in reduced relaxation times (impurity-doping condition).

For a derivation of the method of spin Hamiltonians, reference should be made to such review articles as those by Bleaney and Stevens[5] and Bowers and Owen.[6] Knowledge of the associated formalism is perhaps desirable but not necessary for utilization of the results reported in this paper. Briefly, the spin Hamiltonian describes the energy of a paramagnetic ion arising from interaction with host crystal environment and applied magnetic field. Obeying quantum laws, the ion can exist in one of several states associated with discrete energy levels. Transitions between such states can occur if the energy balance ΔE is supplied to or extracted from the ion. Given some probability for radiative transitions, these can be induced by applying a magnetic field of radio frequency $\nu = \Delta E/h$ (h = Planck's constant). If there are more transitions to the higher state, net absorption will be observed such as is normally observed with a spectrometer. If there are more transitions to the lower state, stimulated emission of energy will be observed such as is utilized for amplification in a 3LSSM.

II. THE SPIN HAMILTONIAN

The spin Hamiltonian of Cr^{+++} in Al_2O_3 was first published by Manenkov and Prokhorov[7], and later by Geusic[8] and Zaripov and Shamonin.[9] It was given in the form

$$\mathcal{H} = g_{\parallel} H_z S_z + g_{\perp}(H_x S_x + H_y S_y) + D[S_z^2 - \tfrac{1}{3}S(S+1)]. \qquad (1)$$

The effective spin $S = 3/2$ is identical with the true spin. All Cr^{+++} ions in the crystal lattice show identical paramagnetic behavior, with the magnetic z-axis being the same as the trigonal symmetry axis of the crystal. The best values for the constants seem to be

$$2D = -2D' = -0.3831 \pm 0.0002 \text{ cm}^{-1} = -11.493 \pm 0.006 \text{ kmc},$$

$$g_{\parallel} = 1.9840 \pm 0.0006,$$

$$g_{\perp} = 1.9867 \pm 0.0006.$$

While it is customary in spectroscopy to express energy in units of cm^{-1} omitting a factor hc (h = Planck's constant, c = velocity of light), units of kmc are used simultaneously, omitting a factor of $10^9\, h$, because this allows direct interpretation in observed spectra.

In particular, the negative sign of D was obtained by Geusic.[8] He deduced this from the fact that $g_{\parallel} < g_{\perp}$, since in less than half-filled d-shell ions, such as Cr^{+++}, the spin-orbit coupling term λ is positive, and D is given by $2D = \lambda(g_{\parallel} - g_{\perp})$. Sign and magnitude of D are in agreement with results of low-temperature static susceptibility measurements by Bruger.[10] In this work also, the negative sign of D was confirmed by comparing the relative intensities of two lines at liquid nitrogen and helium temperatures.

The spin Hamiltonian (1) can more conveniently be written in spherical coordinates:

$$\mathcal{H} = g_{\parallel} H \cos\theta S_z + \tfrac{1}{2} g_{\perp} H \sin\theta (e^{-i\varphi} S_+ + e^{i\varphi} S_-) - D'[S_z^2 - \tfrac{1}{3}S(S+1)]. \qquad (2)$$

Here $S_\pm = S_x \pm iS_y$. In both representations (1) and (2) the crystalline axis was chosen to be the z-axis. While the choice of reference system is immaterial to obtaining eigenvalues (energy levels), this choice shows up in the associated eigenvectors. The eigenvectors have no direct physical interpretation; they must be evaluated in order to obtain transition probabilities. The transition probabilities most naturally obtained from eigenvectors of the Hamiltonian (2) are those which correspond to excitation by RF magnetic fields whose polarization is either linear and parallel to, or circular and perpendicular to, the *crystalline axis.*

In 3LSSM design, however, it seems more appropriate to analyze the performance in terms of RF magnetic fields whose polarization is either linear and parallel to, or circular and perpendicular to, the *applied field.* The corresponding eigenvectors and transition probabilities can, of course, be obtained from those belonging to the Hamiltonian (2) by a 4-by-4 transformation matrix. But it is more efficient to obtain them directly through a transformation of the original spin Hamiltonian (1) or (2) into a coordinate system with the z-axis parallel to the applied field. The result of this transformation is

$$\begin{aligned}\mathcal{H} = {} & (g_\parallel \cos^2\theta + g_\perp \sin^2\theta)\beta H S_z \\ & - D'(\cos^2\theta - \tfrac{1}{2}\sin^2\theta)[S_z^{\,2} - \tfrac{1}{3}S(S+1)] \\ & - D'\tfrac{1}{2}\cos\theta\sin\theta[e^{-i\varphi}(S_zS_+ + S_+S_z) + e^{i\varphi}(S_zS_- + S_-S_z)] \\ & - D'\tfrac{1}{4}\sin^2\theta(e^{-2i\varphi}S_+^{\,2} + e^{2i\varphi}S_-^{\,2}).\end{aligned} \tag{3}$$

III. ENERGY LEVELS AND EIGENVECTORS

From the Hamiltonian $\mathcal{H}$ (3), its energy eigenvalues W are found numerically by solving the fourth-order secular equation

$$\begin{gathered}\| \langle n \mid \mathcal{H} - W \mid m\rangle \| = 0, \\ n, m = 3/2, 1/2, -1/2, -3/2.\end{gathered} \tag{4}$$

The eigenvalues W are functions of H and θ, but not of φ since, because of the symmetry of the Hamiltonian, rotation about the z-axis does not change the physical situation. On the following plots (left-hand sections of Figs. 1 through 11) diagrams of energy levels W (in units of kmc) are shown as a function of applied field H (in units of kilogauss). Plots are given for angles θ from 0° to 90° in steps of 10° and, in addition, for 54.74°.

Also, by change of scales, dimensionless eigenvalues $y = W/D'$ are shown as functions of the dimensionless quantity $x = G/D'$, where

$$G = (g_\parallel \cos^2\theta + g_\perp \sin^2\theta)\beta H.$$

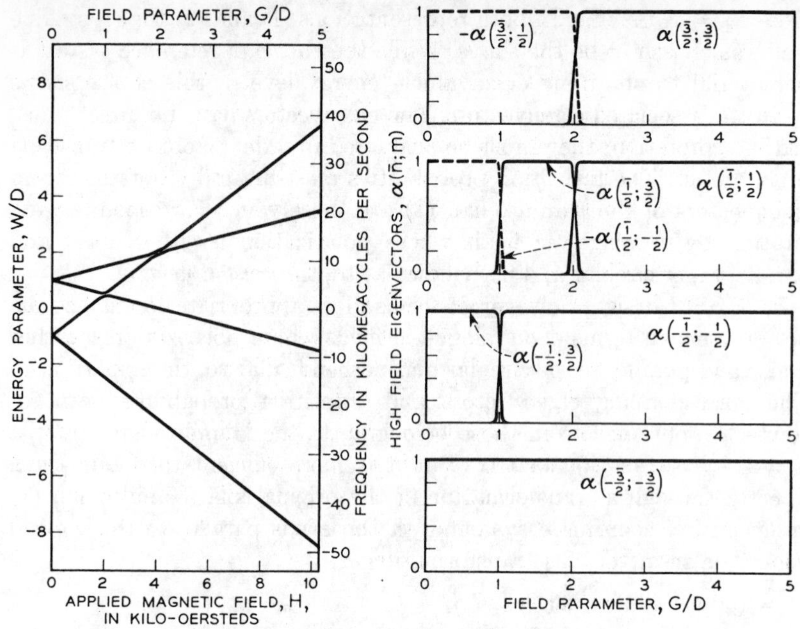

Fig. 1 — Energy levels and eigenvectors of the Cr^{+++} paramagnetic ion in ruby at angle $\theta = 0°$ between crystalline symmetry axis and applied magnetic field.

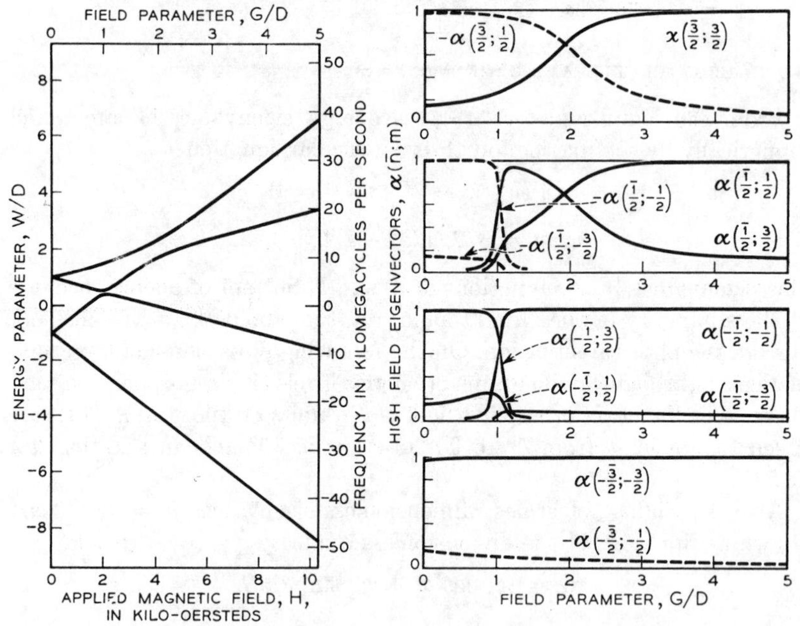

Fig. 2 — Energy levels and eigenvectors at 10°.

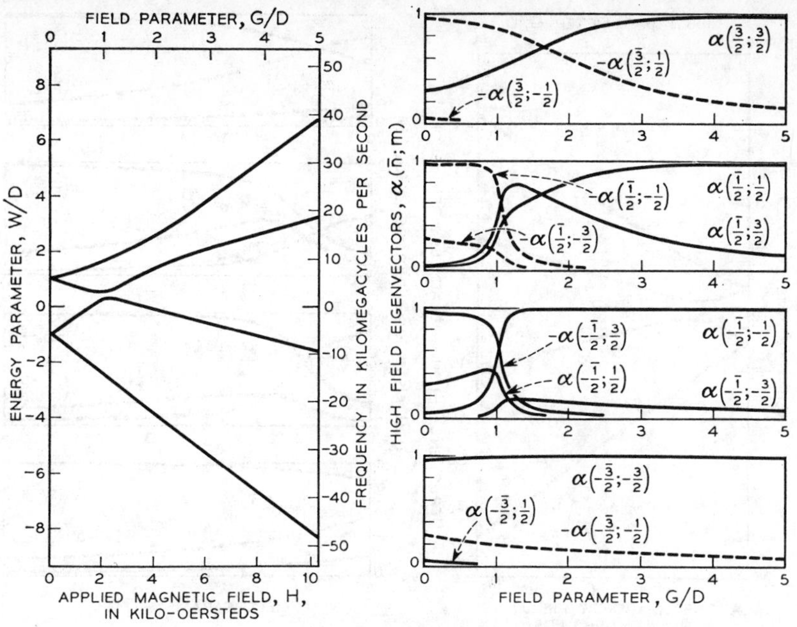

Fig. 3 — Energy levels and eigenvectors at 20°.

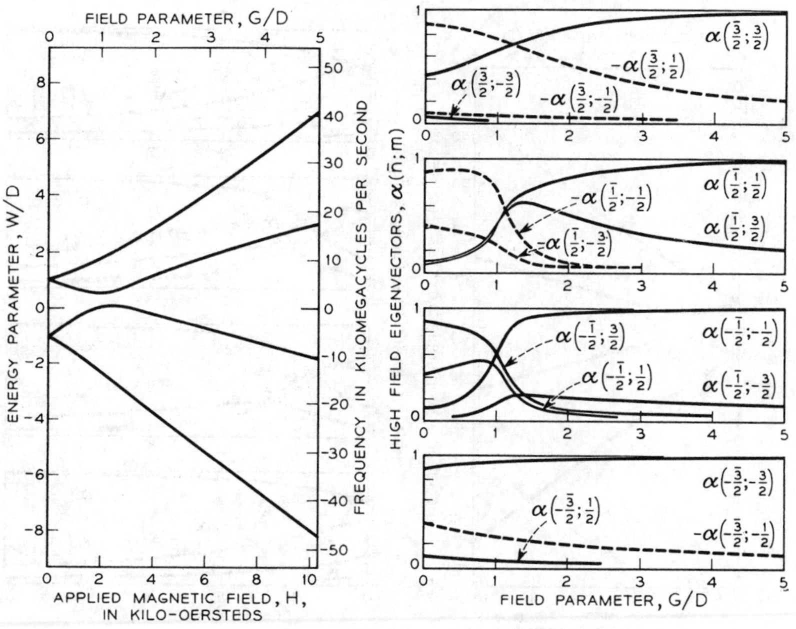

Fig. 4 — Energy levels and eigenvectors at 30°.

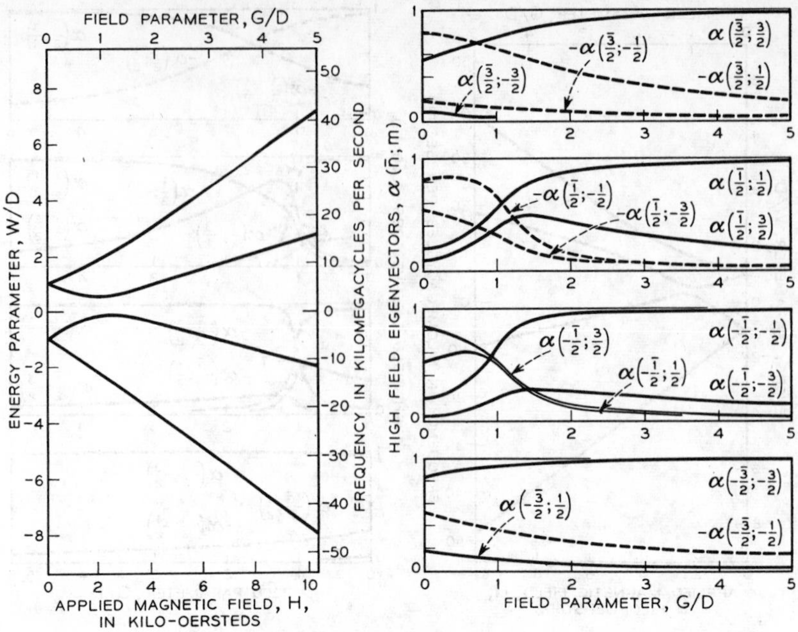

Fig. 5 — Energy levels and eigenvectors at 40°.

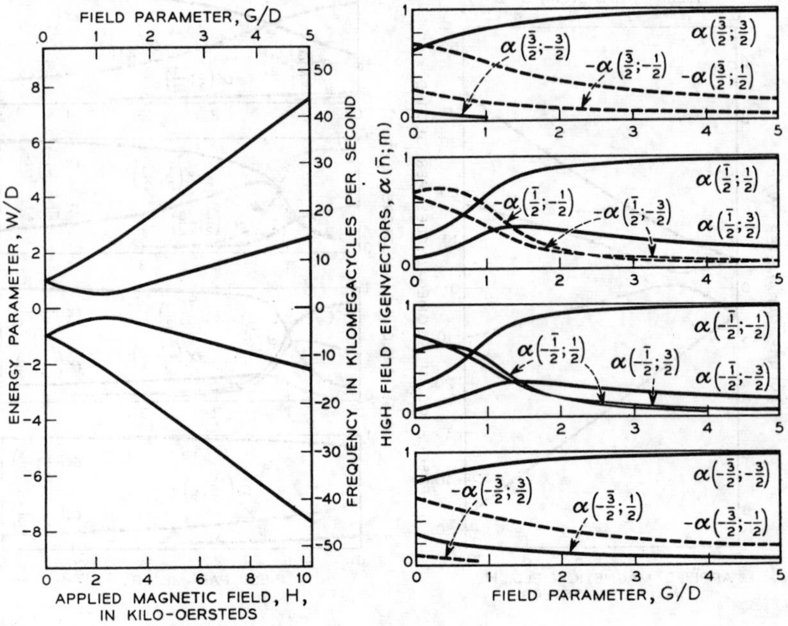

Fig. 6 — Energy levels and eigenvectors at 50°.

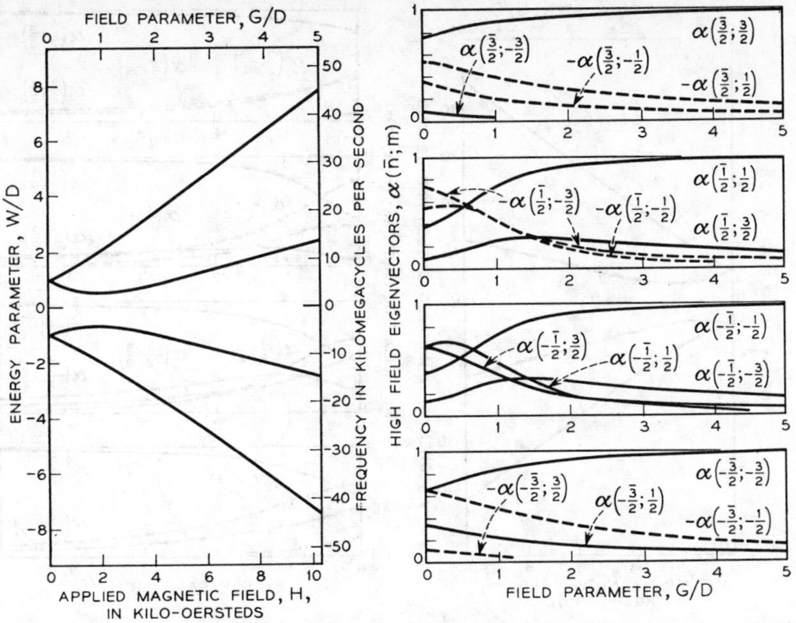

Fig. 7 — Energy levels and eigenvectors at 54.7°.

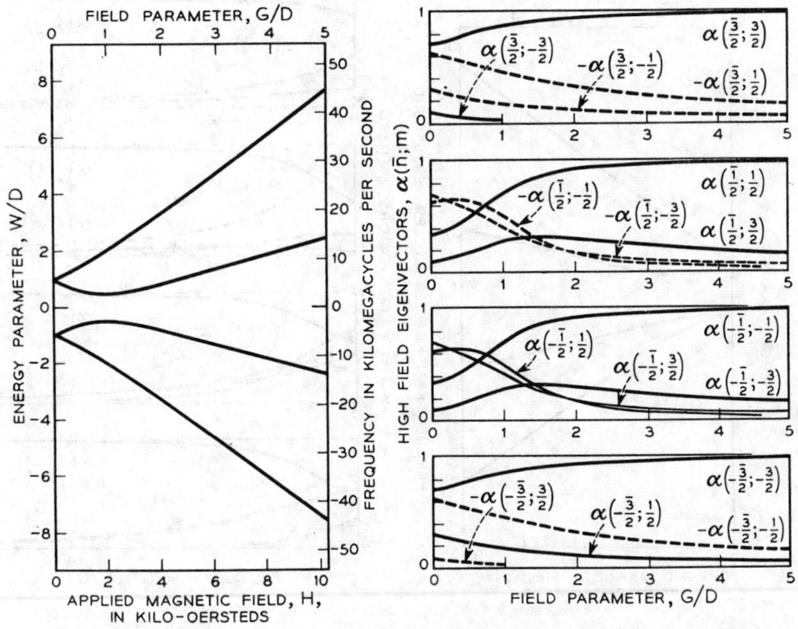

Fig. 8 — Energy levels and eigenvectors at 60°.

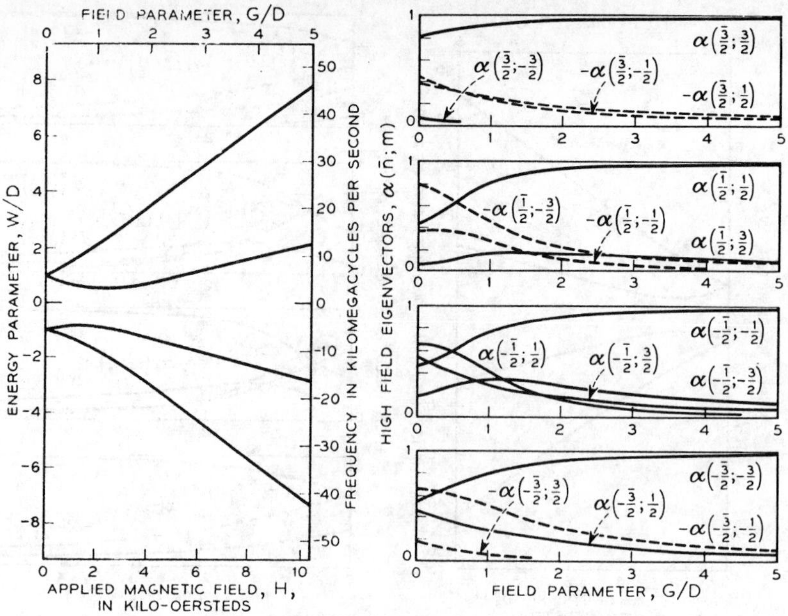

Fig. 9 — Energy levels and eigenvectors at 70°.

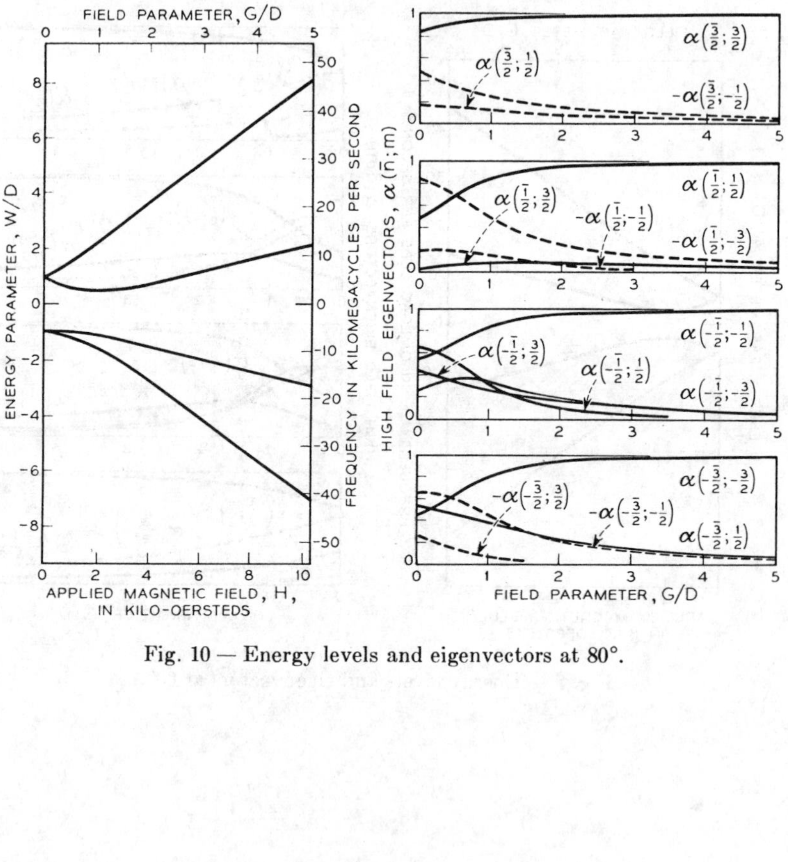

Fig. 10 — Energy levels and eigenvectors at 80°.

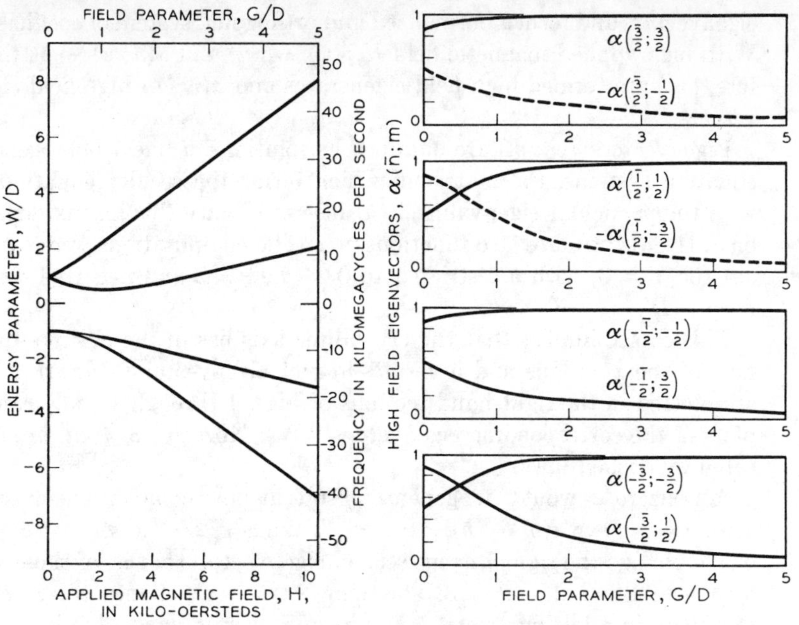

Fig. 11 — Energy levels and eigenvectors at 90°.

This dimensionless representation facilitates computations and reveals more clearly symmetries and singular relations in the energy level scheme. It also permits the use of the same diagrams for ions having the same Hamiltonian but different zero field splitting $2D$. Similar energy level diagrams were computed by P. M. Parker[11] for the case of nuclear spin resonance with nuclear quadrupole splitting present which is described by the same type of Hamiltonian.

As a convenient way to identify the energy levels W, a quantum number $\bar{n}$ ranging from $-\frac{3}{2}$ to $+\frac{3}{2}$ is used *in order of increasing energy.* Thus $W(-\frac{3}{2})$ is the lowest, $W(\frac{3}{2})$ the highest energy level. It is easily shown that, for all angles θ and $x = 0$, $y(-\frac{3}{2}) = y(-\frac{1}{2}) = -1$ and $y(\frac{1}{2}) = y(\frac{3}{2}) = 1$. As a matter of mathematical curiosity, it may be mentioned that, irrespective of θ at $x = 1$, $y(\frac{1}{2}) = 1/2$.

The eigenstates $|\,\bar{n}\rangle$ (using Dirac's "ket" notation) associated with energy levels $W(\bar{n})$ can be expanded in the form

$$|\,\bar{n}\rangle = \sum_{m=-3/2}^{3/2} \alpha(\bar{n}; m)\,|\,m\rangle. \tag{5}$$

Here, $|\,m\rangle$ are eigenstates of a Zeeman Hamiltonian $\mathcal{H} = g\beta HS_z$. The $\alpha(\bar{n}; m)$ are amplitudes of eigenvector components or, more briefly, eigenvectors and form a normalized and orthogonal system of coefficients. With high applied magnetic field H, $|\bar{n}\rangle \rightarrow |n\rangle$ and $\alpha(\bar{n}; n) \rightarrow 1$; therefore, $|m\rangle$ are termed high-field eigenstates and $\alpha(\bar{n}; m)$ high-field eigenvectors.

Eigenvectors $\alpha(\bar{n}; m)$ are obtained as solutions of linear homogeneous equation systems, the matrix of which forms the secular equation (4) with the particular eigenvalue $W(\bar{n})$ inserted. Since this matrix depends on φ, the $\alpha(\bar{n}; m)$ are also functions of φ. The computations were carried out for $\varphi = 0$, with θ restricted to $0 < \theta < \pi/2$ and negative sign of $D = -D'$.

This choice implies that the crystalline axis lies in the positive quadrant of the x-z plane and it results in real eigenvectors $\alpha(\bar{n}; m)$. These are plotted in the right-hand sections of Figs. 1 through 11, adjacent to plots of the corresponding eigenvalues $W(\bar{n})$. Negative $\alpha(\bar{n}; m)$ are indicated by dashed lines.

A nonzero φ would, in general, result in new complex eigenvectors $\alpha'(\bar{n}; m) = [\exp i(m - \bar{n})\varphi]\alpha(\bar{n}; m)$. Taking $\pi/2 < \theta < \pi$ or $\varphi = \pi$ would change the sign of every second eigenvector, that is, of those with $m = n \pm 1$ and $m = n \pm 3$. The same is true for a change of sign of D, but then, in addition, every $\bar{n}$ and m and energy eigenvalue has to be replaced by its negative. It is obvious that such transformations do not change the physical situation as far as transition probabilities are concerned.

IV. TRANSITION PROBABILITIES

There are several ways in which transition probabilities could be evaluated and plotted. One way would be to consider transitions induced by radiation of given polarization. With eigenvectors belonging to the Hamiltonian (3), the obvious RF magnetic field polarizations to consider are those with RF H-field linear and parallel to, or circular and perpendicular to, the applied field. But transitions due to any other polarization could be evaluated as well. Perhaps more natural from a theoretical point of view would be an evaluation of the maximum transition probability. This requires a particular—in general—elliptical, polarization for excitation, which of course should be evaluated, too. All polarizations orthogonal to this (which in general are elliptical as well), and which describe a plane in space having complex components, are associated with zero transition probability. Taking into account these different viewpoints and the six transitions which are possible between four energy levels, it appears that an unrealistically high number of graphs would be necessary to describe the transition probabilities properly.

Furthermore, in maser design it is usually sufficient to know the order of magnitude of transition probabilities of particular lines, because often other factors may be more important. Therefore, no plots of transition probabilities are presented. On the other hand, enough of the pertinent formalism is given below so that any transition probability can be evaluated from the eigenvectors plotted.

Following essentially Bloembergen, Purcell and Pound,[12] with slight generalization, the transition probability w describing the rate of transitions per ion from a lower state $\bar{n}$ to a higher state $\bar{n}' > \bar{n}$ is given by

$$w_{\bar{n}\to\bar{n}'} = \frac{1}{4}\left(\frac{2\pi g\beta H_1}{h}\right)^2 g(\nu - \nu_0) \mid \langle \bar{n}' \mid S_1 \mid \bar{n} \rangle \mid^2. \tag{6}$$

Here H_1 is the amplitude of the exciting RF magnetic field, $g(\nu - \nu_0)$ is a normalized function describing the line shape $\int g(\nu - \nu_0)\, d\nu = 1$, and S_1 is a spin operator reflecting the polarization of the inducing RF magnetic field. If the RF magnetic field is described by the real parts of $H_x = H_1 a e^{i\omega t}$, $H_y = H_1 b e^{i\omega t}$, $H_z = H_1 c e^{i\omega t}$ with "complex direction cosines" a, b, c accounting for elliptical polarization,

$$a^*a + b^*b + c^*c = 1,$$

then

$$S_1 = a^*S_x + b^*S_y + c^*S_z\,. \tag{7}$$

Matrix elements for S_1 occurring squared in (6) are linear combinations of the following three:

$$\langle \bar{n}' \mid S_z \mid \bar{n} \rangle = \sum_{m=-3/2}^{+3/2} m\alpha(\bar{n}'; m)\alpha(\bar{n}; m), \tag{8}$$

$$\langle \bar{n}' \mid S_+ \mid \bar{n} \rangle = \sum_{m=-3/2}^{+1/2} [S(S + 1) - (m + 1)m]^{1/2}\alpha(\bar{n}'; m + 1)\alpha(\bar{n}; m), \tag{9}$$

$$\langle \bar{n}' \mid S_- \mid \bar{n} \rangle = \sum_{m=-1/2}^{+3/2} [S(S + 1) - (m - 1)m]^{1/2}\alpha(\bar{n}'; m - 1)\alpha(\bar{n}; m). \tag{10}$$

The square root in (9) and (10) takes on the values $\sqrt{3}$, 2 and $\sqrt{3}$. For example, with linear polarization in the z-direction, $H_z = H_1 \cos \omega t$ and $S_1 = S_z$. For circular polarization perpendicular to the z-direction,

$H_x = (1/\sqrt{2})H_1 \cos \omega t$, $H_y = \pm(1/\sqrt{2})H_1 \sin \omega t$ and $S_1 = (1/\sqrt{2})S_{\pm}$. For linear polarization in the x direction, $H_x = H_1 \cos \omega t$ and $S_1 = S_x = \frac{1}{2}(S_+ + S_-)$. Similarly, in the y direction $H_y = H_1 \cos \omega t$ and $S_1 = S_y = (1/2i)(S_+ + S_-)$.

The expression (7), or more correctly, the associated matrix element, can be interpreted as a scalar product of (a^*, b^*, c^*) with $\langle \bar{n}' \mid S \mid \bar{n} \rangle$. It should be noted that, in general, all components can be complex. As a consequence of this interpretation, the maximum transition probability occurs if H_{rf} or (a, b, c) is parallel in space and conjugate complex in phase to $\langle \bar{n}' \mid S \mid \bar{n} \rangle$. Since for real eigenvectors the matrices (8), (9), (10) are all real, it follows that $\langle \bar{n}' \mid S_x \mid \bar{n} \rangle$ and $\langle \bar{n}' \mid S_z \mid \bar{n} \rangle$ are real, whereas $\langle \bar{n}' \mid S_y \mid \bar{n} \rangle$ is imaginary. Thus, for all ruby lines, the polarization for maximum transition probability will be a linear combination of H_x and H_z components with an H_y component in quadrature. In a similar fashion, a set of complex direction cosines can be found which causes the scalar product of (a^*, b^*, c^*) with $\langle \bar{n}' \mid S \mid \bar{n} \rangle$, and hence the transition probability, to vanish. These vectors (a, b, c) describe a plane orthogonal to the vector for maximum transition probability.

It should be noted that frequently the complete formula (6) is not used to evaluate and compare transition probabilities. Instead, usually only the squared matrix element $| \langle \bar{n}' \mid S_1 \mid \bar{n} \rangle |^2$ is computed and this is then compared with a simple standard transition. The obvious standard is the transition $-1/2 \to +1/2$ of an $S = 1/2$ Zeeman doublet induced by circular polarization. This is described, in our notation, by $| \langle +1/2 \mid (1/\sqrt{2})S_+ \mid -1/2 \rangle |^2 = 1/2$. Accordingly, transitions involving a squared matrix element of order 1 or greater are considered strong, while perhaps 1/100 is typical of weak transitions.

V. SPECIAL CASES

5.1. $\theta = 0°$.

The energy levels are parts of straight lines $y = 1 \pm \frac{1}{2}x$, $-1 \pm \frac{3}{2}x$ with change of slope for some of them at $x = 1$ and 2. Eigenvectors are ± 1 and 0 only, again joined for some levels at $x = 1$ and 2. The minus sign of eigenvectors at 0° has no significance; it is only used to preserve continuity to neighboring angles.

At $\theta = 0°$ and $x < 2$, the labeling of energy levels by high field quantum numbers *in order of increasing energy* is perhaps not the usual one. In this paper, however, it seems appropriate because, with this terminology, in going from $\theta = 0°$ to other orientations, the notation of states stays the same. It may be pointed out that energy levels defined in this fashion should be considered as continuous functions of applied field without cross-overs (see Fig. 1). The reason is that any off-diagonal perturbation will indeed prevent levels from intercepting by perturbation theory arguments.

Only three transitions are allowed:

$$0 < x < 1: \langle +\tfrac{3}{2} \mid S_+ \mid +\tfrac{1}{2}\rangle^2 = 4$$

$$\langle +\tfrac{3}{2} \mid S_- \mid -\tfrac{1}{2}\rangle^2 = \langle +\tfrac{1}{2} \mid S_+ \mid -\tfrac{3}{2}\rangle^2 = 3,$$

$$1 < x < 2: \langle +\tfrac{3}{2} \mid S_+ \mid -\tfrac{1}{2}\rangle^2 = 4$$

$$\langle +\tfrac{3}{2} \mid S_- \mid +\tfrac{1}{2}\rangle^2 = \langle +\tfrac{1}{2} \mid S_+ \mid -\tfrac{3}{2}\rangle^2 = 3,$$

$$2 < x: \quad \langle +\tfrac{1}{2} \mid S_+ \mid -\tfrac{1}{2}\rangle^2 = 4$$

$$\langle +\tfrac{3}{2} \mid S_+ \mid +\tfrac{1}{2}\rangle^2 = \langle -\tfrac{1}{2} \mid S_+ \mid -\tfrac{3}{2}\rangle^2 = 3.$$

It is interesting to note that, for $0 < x < 2$, one transition requires opposite polarization from the others. This was verified in an experiment. Resonance absorption was measured for this and another transition in a propagating comb-type slow-wave structure having regions of predominantly circular polarization. Reversal of applied magnetic field results in drastic increase of one and reduction of the other line.

5.2. $\theta = 54.74°$, $\cos^2 \theta = 1/3$.

For this angle, the fourth-order secular equation reduces to a biquadratic one. The four eigenvalues are $y = \pm[1 + \frac{5}{4}x^2 \pm (3x^2 + x^4)^{1/2}]^{1/2}$. This implies an up-down symmetry $y(-\bar{n}) = -y(\bar{n})$. The closest approach of the two middle eigenvalues is $y(+\frac{1}{2}) - y(-\frac{1}{2}) = 1$ at $x = 1$. A similar symmetry relation holds for eigenvectors $\alpha(-\bar{n}; -m) = (\bar{n}m/|\bar{n}m|)\alpha(\bar{n}; m)$. As a consequence, some transition probabilities for linear polarization are identical, namely

$$\langle -\tfrac{1}{2} \mid S_z \mid -\tfrac{3}{2}\rangle = \langle +\tfrac{3}{2} \mid S_z \mid +\tfrac{1}{2}\rangle$$

and

$$\langle +\tfrac{1}{2} \mid S_z \mid -\tfrac{3}{2}\rangle = -\langle +\tfrac{3}{2} \mid S_z \mid -\tfrac{1}{2}\rangle.$$

The analogous is not true for other polarizations.

5.3. $\theta = 90°$.

The secular equation can be factorized into two quadratic equations with the solutions

$$y(\tfrac{3}{2}) = \frac{x}{2} + (1 + x + x^2)^{1/2},$$

$$y(\tfrac{1}{2}) = -\frac{x}{2} + (1 - x + x^2)^{1/2},$$

$$y(-\tfrac{1}{2}) = \frac{x}{2} - (1 + x + x^2)^{1/2},$$

$$y(-\tfrac{3}{2}) = -\frac{x}{2} - (1 - x + x^2)^{1/2}.$$

Each state contains only two eigenvectors, namely $\alpha(\bar{n};\, n)$ and $\alpha(\bar{n}; n \pm 2)$. In addition, $\alpha(\bar{n}; n) = \alpha(\overline{n \pm 2}; \bar{n} \pm 2)$ and $\alpha(\bar{n}; n \pm 2) = -\alpha(\overline{n \pm 2};\, n)$. As a result, transition probabilities between adjacent

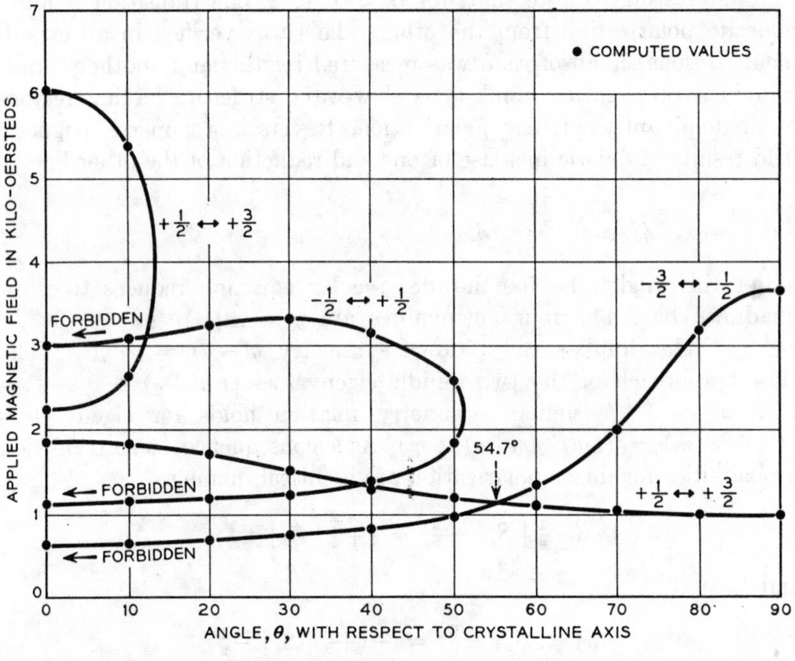

Fig. 12 — Paramagnetic resonance spectrum of Cr^{+++} ions in ruby at signal frequency 5.18 kmc.

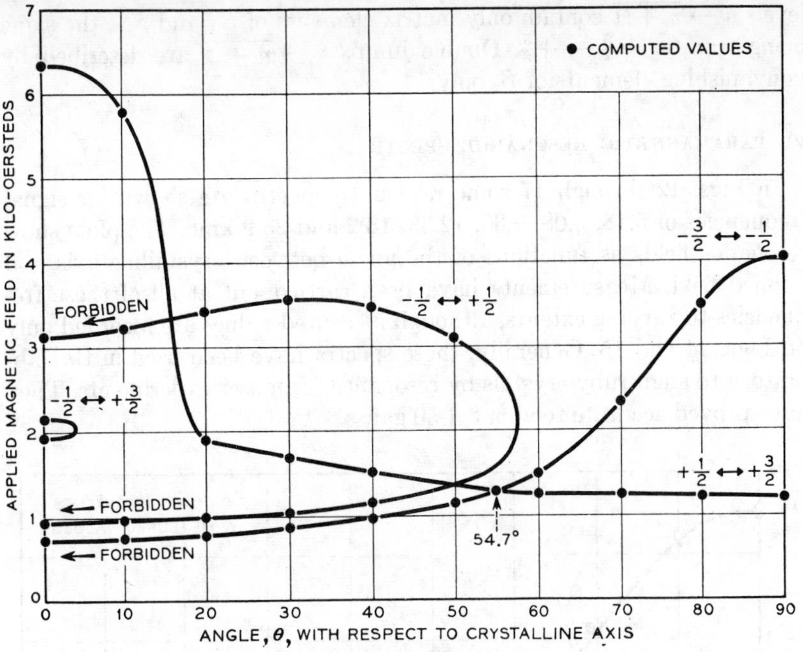

Fig. 13 — Resonance spectrum at 6.08 kmc.

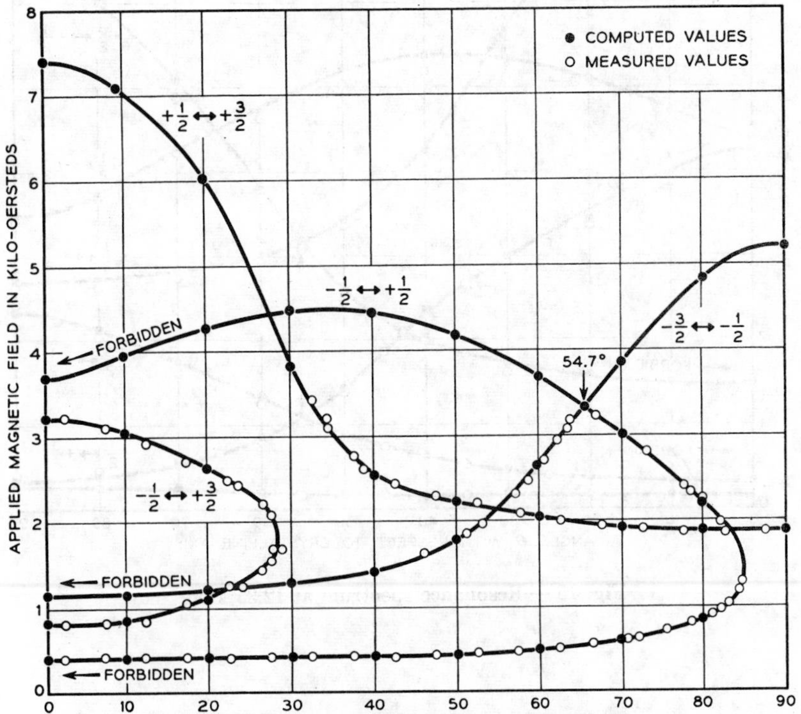

Fig. 14 — Resonance spectrum at 9.30 kmc.

levels $\bar{n} \rightarrow \overline{n+1}$ contain only matrix elements of S_+ and S_-, the same being true for $-\frac{3}{2} \rightarrow +\frac{3}{2}$. Double jumps $\bar{n} \rightarrow \overline{n+2}$ are described by nonvanishing elements of S_z only.

VI. PARAMAGNETIC RESONANCE SPECTRA

In Figs. 12 through 17 some resonance spectra are shown for signal frequencies of 5.18, 6.08, 9.30, 12.33, 18.2 and 23.9 kmc. The plots show resonance fields as functions of the angle between crystalline axis and applied field. Measurements have been carried out at all of these frequencies to varying extents, although measured values are recorded only on Figs. 14 and 15. Generally, these spectra have been used in the laboratory to align ruby crystals by resonance for maser experiments. They have proved accurate to about ±50 gauss.

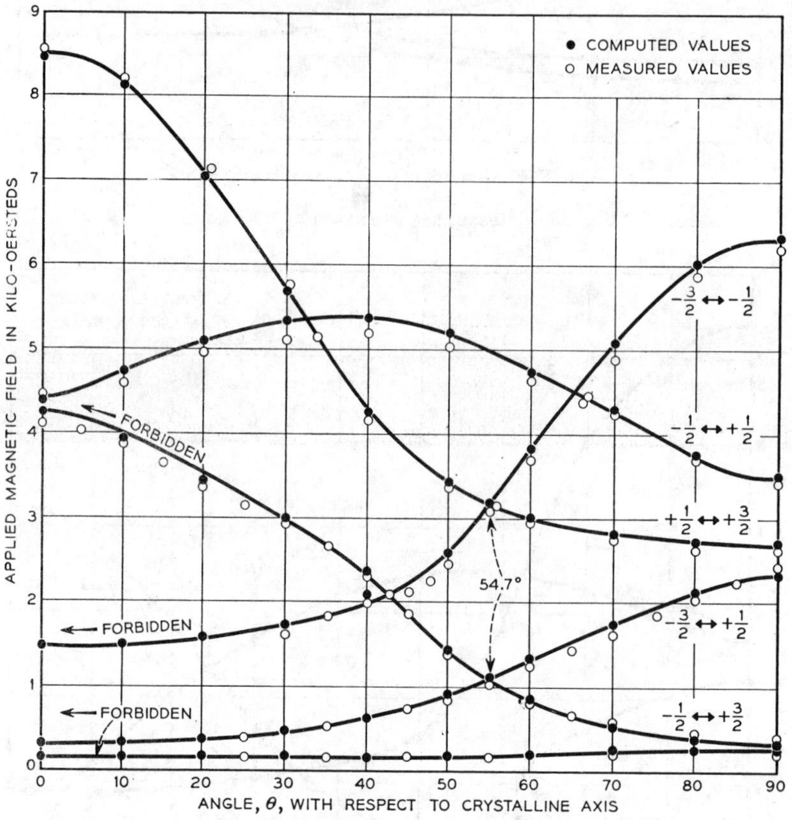

Fig. 15 — Resonance spectrum at 12.33 kmc.

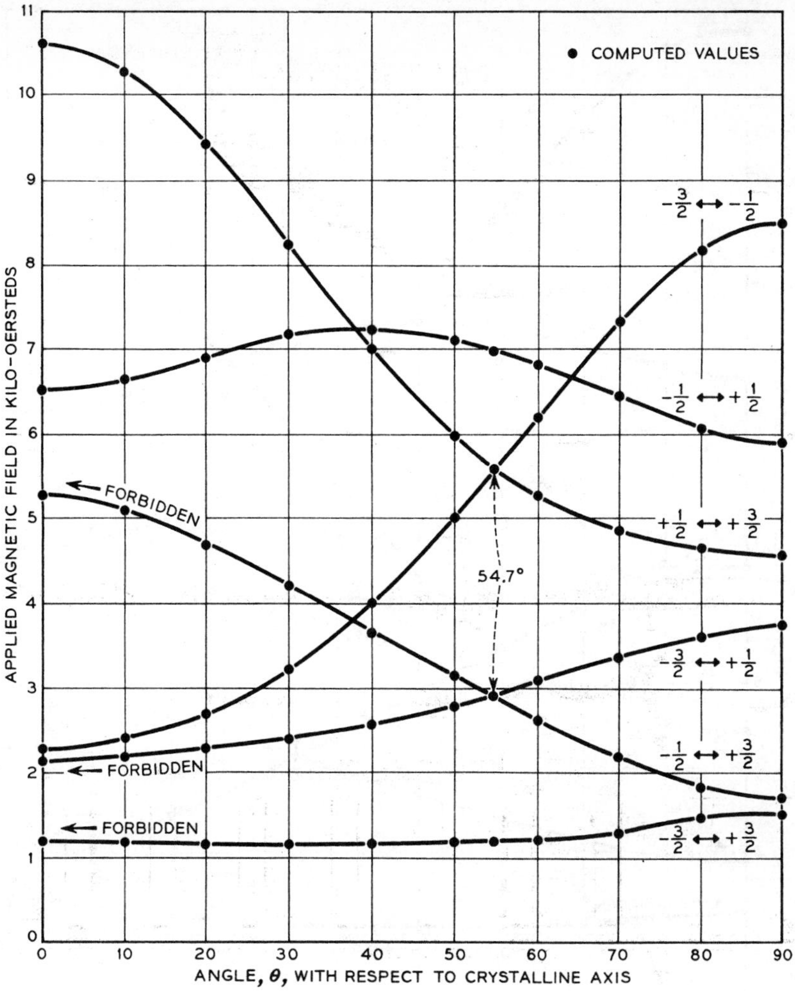

Fig. 16 — Resonance spectrum at 18.2 kmc.

Measurements at 9.3 kmc are an extension of Geusic's work[4] and confirm his results. Results at 12.33 kmc show some discrepancy between theory and experiment, which, however, is believed to be caused by inadequate magnetic field measuring equipment used in an experiment designed for other purposes. As a general rule, the spectra show two looping lines if $\nu < 2D$. Lines marked "forbidden" are strictly forbidden at 0° only. Usually, however, they can be followed quite close to 0° by

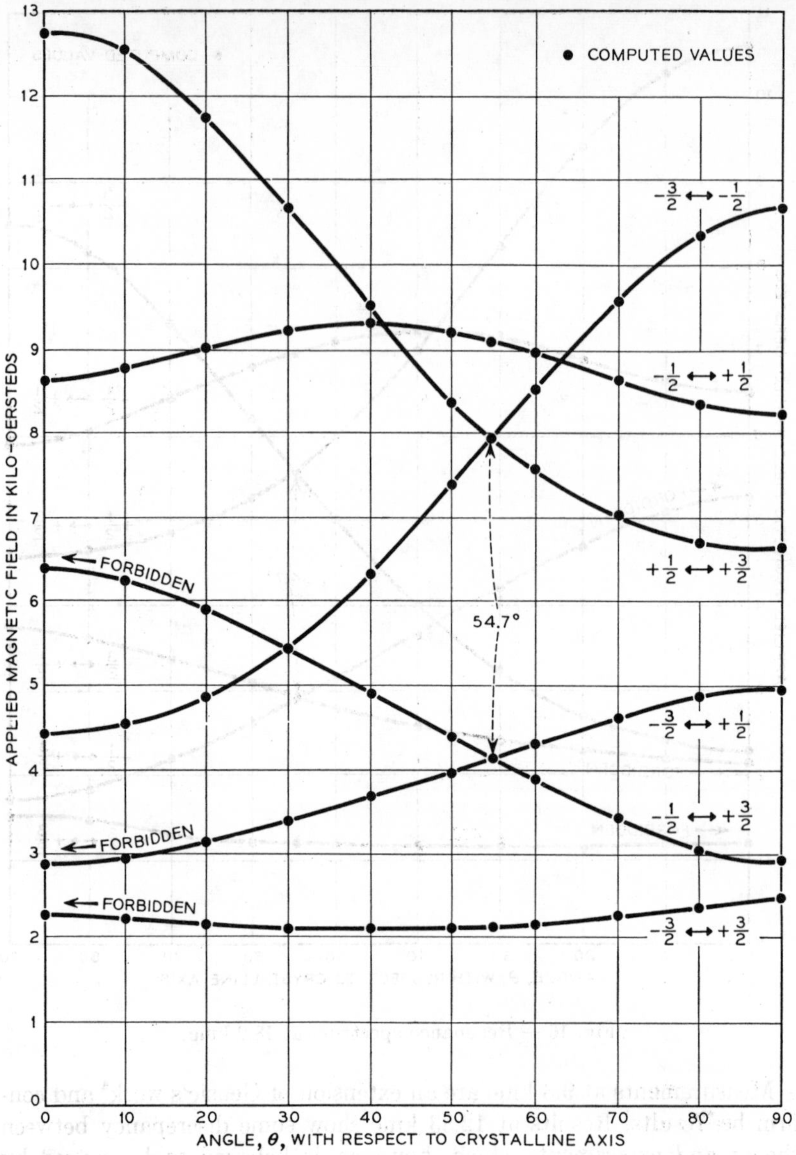

Fig. 17 — Resonance spectrum at 23.9 kmc

use of more sensitivity in the spectrometer. An exception is the line shown on the graphs having the lowest resonance field at 0° if $\nu < \frac{6}{5}D'$. It has the second lowest resonance field if $\frac{6}{5}D' < \nu < \frac{3}{2}D'$ and the third lowest if $\frac{3}{2}D' < \nu < 3D'$. It originates between $-\frac{3}{2}$ and $+\frac{3}{2}$ eigenstates at 0° and is more strongly forbidden than the other forbidden lines; hence it usually ceases to be measurable at about 30°.

For reasons of symmetry, all lines approach 0° and 90° with zero slope $dH/d\theta$. Experimentally, it has been found that most lines are rather narrow at 90° and similarly at 0°, whereas they broaden in proportion with $dH/d\theta$. This behavior is expected from crystalline imperfections if these can be interpreted as fluctuations throughout the crystal of the direction of the crystalline axis.

VII. ACKNOWLEDGMENT

The author wishes to thank many colleagues at Bell Telephone Laboratories for suggestions in the course of this study. He is particularly indebted to H. E. D. Scovil and J. E. Geusic. Miss M. C. Gray programmed and supervised the numerical calculations.

REFERENCES

1. Bloembergen, N., Proposal for a New-Type Solid-State Maser, Phys. Rev., **104,** October 15, 1956, p. 324.
2. Scovil, H. E. D., Feher, G. and Seidel, H., Operation of a Solid-State Maser, Phys. Rev., **105,** January 15, 1957 p. 762.
3. Scovil, H. E. D., The Three-Level Solid-State Maser, Trans. I.R.E., **MTT-6,** January 1958, p. 29.
4. Makhov, G., Kikuchi, C., Lambe, J. and Terhune, R. W., Maser Action in Ruby, Phys. Rev., **109,** February 15, 1958, p. 1399.
5. Bleaney, B. and Stevens, K. W. H., Paramagnetic Resonance, Rep. Prog. Phys., **16,** 1953, p. 107.
6. Bowers, K. D. and Owen, J., Paramagnetic Resonance II, Rep. Prog. Phys., **18,** 1955, p. 304.
7. Manenkov, A. A. and Prokhorov, A. M., J. Exp. Theor. Phys. (U.S.S.R.), **28,** 1955, p. 762.
8. Geusic, J. E., Phys. Rev., **102,** June 15, 1956, p. 1252; also Ph.D. dissertation, Ohio State Univ., 1958.
9. Zaripov, M. and Shamonin, I., J. Exp. Theor. Phys. (U.S.S.R.), **30,** 1956, p. 291.
10. Bruger, K., Ph.D. dissertation, Ohio State Univ., 1958.
11. Parker, P. M., J. Chem. Phys., **24,** 1956, p. 1096.
12. Bloembergen, N., Purcell, E. M. and Pound, R. V., Relaxation Effects in Nuclear Magnetic Resonance Absorption, Phys. Rev., **73,** April 1, 1948, p. 679.

Paramagnetic Resonance Spectrum of Cr^{+++} in Emerald*

By J. E. GEUSIC, MARTIN PETER and E. O. SCHULZ-DU BOIS

(Manuscript received October 6, 1958)

Paramagnetic resonance for the Cr^{+++} ion in emerald has been observed at X-band (8.2 to 12.4 kmc), K-band (18 to 26.5 kmc) and M-band (50 to 75 kmc). From spectra observed at these frequencies, the spectroscopic splitting factors $g_{\|}$, $g_{\perp}$ and D have been determined. The large value of D observed suggests the possible use of emerald as an active material in relatively high microwave-frequency solid-state masers.

I. INTRODUCTION

Survey articles by Bleaney and Stevens[1] and Bowers and Owens[2] list paramagnetic resonance data for crystals containing ions of the transition groups. A careful study of these tabulated data reveals that most of the crystals studied are hydrated or contain several magnetically nonequivalent ions and, therefore, discourages the use of many of these crystals in a practical three-level solid-state maser (3LSSM).

The present study was undertaken with a view to investigating crystals doped with paramagnetic ions which possess good chemical stability and which might be expected to have energy-level schemes suitable for extending the design of solid-state masers to higher microwave frequencies. In this article, paramagnetic resonance spectra of emerald (Cr-doped beryl) are reported. The large zero field splitting observed for the Cr^{+++} ion in this crystal might suggest emerald as a possible material for use in the design of solid-state masers for high microwave-frequency applications.

II. CRYSTAL STRUCTURE AND SPIN HAMILTONIAN OF EMERALD

The structure of beryl[3, 4, 5] is hexagonal with two molecules of ($Be_3Al_2Si_6O_{18}$) per unit cell. In the crystal, SiO_4 tetrahedra share oxygens

* This work is partially supported by the Signal Corps under Contract Number DA 36-039 sc-73224.

to form Si_6O_{18} rings, with each Al linked to six Si_6O_{18} rings. In the lattice, all Al sites are identical and the symmetry at each Al site includes a three-fold axis parallel to the hexagonal or c-axis of the crystal. In emerald, it is found that Cr substitutionally replaces Al in the beryl lattice and is present as Cr^{+++}.

For the Cr^{+++} ion in such a crystalline electric field of three-fold symmetry, it is well known[1] that the paramagnetic resonance spectrum is described by a spin Hamiltonian of the form

$$\mathcal{H} = \beta[g_{\parallel}H_zS_z + g_{\perp}(H_xS_x + H_yS_y)] + D[S_z^2 - \tfrac{1}{3}S(S + 1)], \quad (1)$$

with $S = \frac{3}{2}$ and with the z-axis taken parallel to the three-fold symmetry axis which in emerald is the c-axis. In the preceding paper[6] the energy levels of the spin Hamiltonian above were discussed for arbitrary values of the parameters $g_{\parallel}$, $g_{\perp}$ and D and for arbitrary orientation of the magnetic field H with the z-axis. The notation of the previous paper is adopted for labeling the energy levels of (1). The energy levels are labeled $W(\bar{n})$ where $\bar{n}$ is used to enumerate the levels in order of their energy and is just the high magnetic field quantum number which takes on the values $-\frac{3}{2}, \cdots, +\frac{3}{2}$. For example, $W(-\bar{\frac{3}{2}})$ represents the lowest energy level and $W(\bar{\frac{3}{2}})$ represents the highest energy level.

III. EXPERIMENTAL WORK

Initial paramagnetic resonance measurements of Cr^{+++} in a single emerald crystal were made at 9.309 kmc. The spectrometer used for these X-band measurements is similar in design to that described by Feher.[7] At 9.309 kmc and magnetic fields which were available, the spectrum of Cr^{+++} in emerald consisted of a single anisotropic line. The effective g-value, $g^e(\theta)$, of this line is plotted in Fig. 1 as a function of θ, where θ is the angle between the magnetic field H and the c-axis of the crystal. The extreme values of g^e at 9.309 kmc. are $g^e(0°) = 1.973 \pm 0.002$ and $g^e(90°) = 3.924 \pm 0.004$. This line was identified (taking the sign of D negative) as the transition $W(\bar{\frac{1}{2}}) \rightarrow W(\bar{\frac{3}{2}})$. The fact that $g^e(90°) \cong 4$ suggests that at 9.309 kmc the frequency of observation is much less than the splitting of the energy levels of (1) in zero field. Under the condition that ν, the frequency of observation, is small compared to the zero field splitting, a perturbation expression for the g^e of the $W(\bar{\frac{1}{2}}) \rightarrow W(\bar{\frac{3}{2}})$ transition is given by

$$g^e = [g_{\parallel}^2 + (4g_{\perp}^2 - g_{\parallel}^2) \sin^2 \theta]^{1/2} \left[1 - \tfrac{1}{2}\left(\frac{g_{\perp}\beta H}{2D}\right)^2 F(\theta)\right], \quad (2)$$

where

$$F(\theta) = \frac{3 \sin^2 \theta(\sin^2 \theta - \frac{1}{3})}{\sin^2 \theta + \frac{1}{3}}.$$

Specialization of (3) to $\theta = 0°$ and $\theta = 90°$ gives

$$g^e(0°) = g_\parallel,$$

$$g^e(90°) = 2g_\perp \left[1 - \tfrac{3}{4}\left(\frac{g_\perp \beta H}{2D}\right)^2\right],$$

from which it is seen that the zero field splitting $|2D|$ can be computed from measurements of $g^e(90°)$ at two frequencies small compared to $|2D|$. Measurements at 23.983 kmc gave $g^e(90°) = 3.814 \pm 0.004$. From the measurements of $g^e(0°)$ and $g^e(90°)$ at X-band and $g^e(90°)$ at K-band, the constants in (1) were found to be

$$g_\parallel = 1.973 \pm 0.002,$$

$$g_\perp = 1.97 \pm 0.01,$$

$$2D = -52.0 \pm 2.0 \text{ kmc}.$$

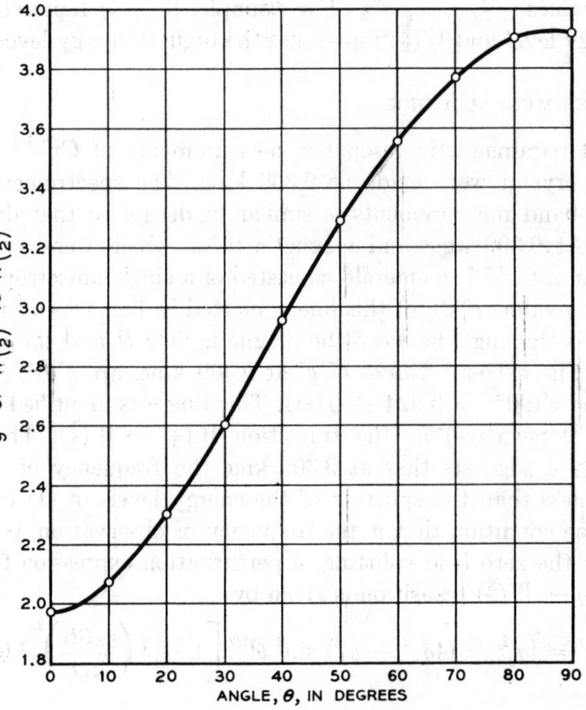

Fig. 1 — Variation of the effective g-value, g^e, of the $W(\frac{1}{2}) \rightarrow W(\frac{3}{2})$ transition at 9.309 kmc.

In order to establish the sign of D, the intensity of the $W(\frac{1}{2}) \rightarrow W(\frac{3}{2})$ line of Cr^{+++} in emerald was compared at two temperatures with the intensity of the same line of Cr^{+++} in ruby. The measurements were carried out with both crystals simultaneously mounted in the X-band spectrometer using temperatures of 78°K and 1.6°K, respectively. The variation of line intensity with temperature can be predicted from Boltzmann statistics if the sign of D is known. Computations were carried out, therefore, on this variation, assuming positive and negative signs of D for both ruby and emerald. The results of these calculations and of the measurement are summarized in Table I. It thus can be concluded that the sign of D for both emerald and ruby is negative.

In order to obtain $2D$ more accurately, measurements were made on Cr^{+++} in emerald at M-band. The millimeter wave paramagnetic resonance spectrometer used was constructed by one of the authors (M. Peter); a block diagram is shown in Fig. 2. Microwave power for this spectrometer is generated by free-running backward wave oscillators (BWO's). Three such BWO's are used to cover the frequency range of 48 to 82 kmc. No resonant cavity is employed in this spectrometer; instead, the sample is situated in "straight" waveguide so that the remarkably wide tuning range of the BWO's can be used. The sensitivity of this spectrometer is comparable to those at low microwave frequencies employing resonant cavities. This is because the loss of sensitivity due to the absence of a cavity is compensated for by higher microwave susceptibility and higher filling factors at these frequencies.

At M-band and for $\theta = 0°$, the two allowed transitions are, in our notation, $W(-\frac{1}{2}) \rightarrow W(\frac{3}{2})$ and $W(-\frac{3}{2}) \rightarrow W(\frac{1}{2})$; they are illustrated in Fig. 3. Both these transitions merge at zero field with the transition frequency being $|2D|$. Both transitions were studied as a function of magnetic field, as shown on Fig. 4. By following them to zero field, the value of the zero field splitting was determined to be $|2D| = 53.6 \pm 0.1$ kmc. From these X-band, K-band and M-band measurements, the best values for the constants in the spin Hamiltonian (1) for

TABLE I

$$\text{Ratio } R = \frac{I_{\text{ruby},\ 1.6°K}}{I_{\text{ruby},\ 78°K}} \times \frac{I_{\text{emerald},\ 78°K}}{I_{\text{emerald},\ 1.6°K}}$$

Computed with sign of D for			Measured R_{exp}
Emerald	Ruby	R_{theor}	
negative	negative	1.8	
negative	positive	2.6	
positive	negative	0.5	1.9 ± 0.1
positive	positive	0.7	

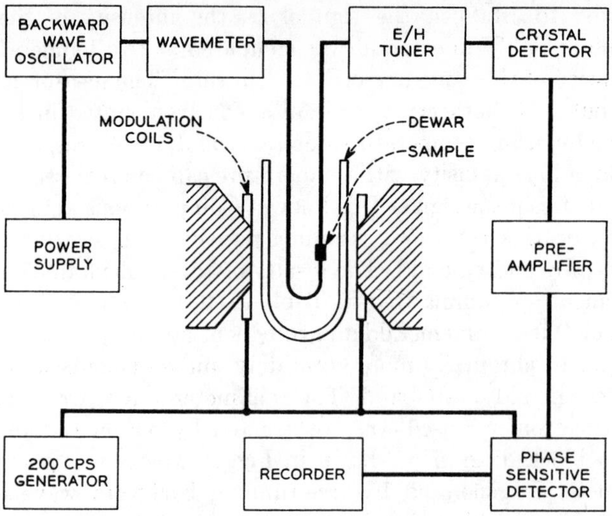

Fig. 2 — Block diagram of the M-band spectrometer.

Cr^{+++} in emerald are

$$2D = -53.6 \pm 0.1 \text{ kmc},$$

$$g_{\parallel} = 1.973 \pm 0.002,$$

$$g_{\perp} = 1.97 \pm 0.01.$$

This value of $2D$ for Cr^{+++} in emerald is, to date, the largest zero field splitting which has been reported for the Cr^{+++} ion in any crystal. Measurements on spin lattice relaxation times in this crystal are planned.

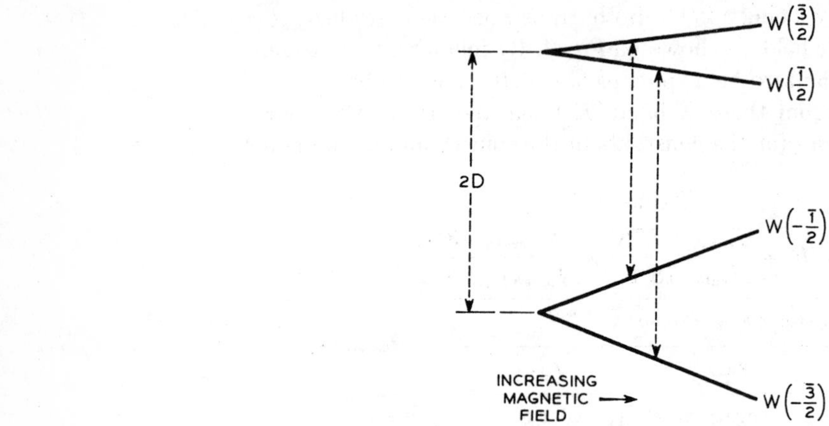

Fig. 3 — Energy level diagram of Cr^{+++} in emerald with applied magnetic field parallel to crystalline axis.

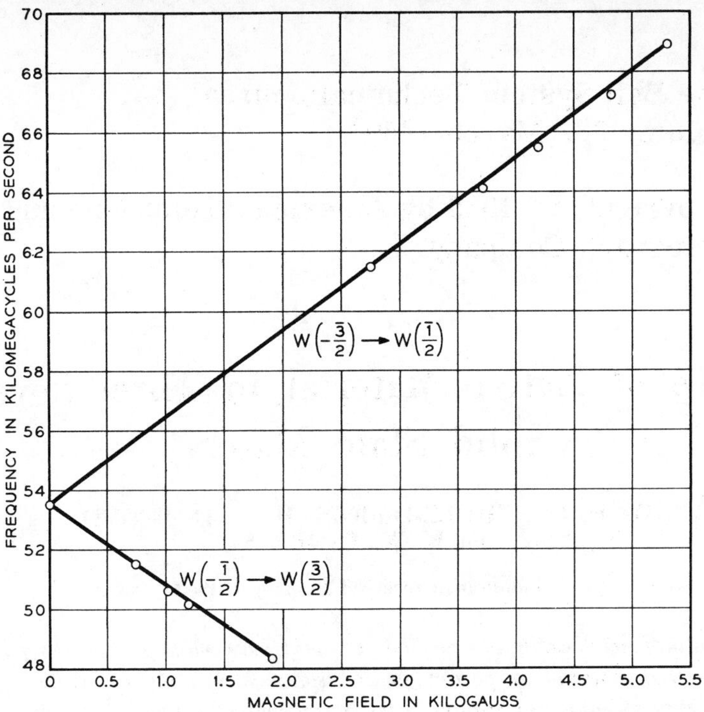

Fig. 4 — Plot of frequencies associated with transitions $W(-\frac{1}{2}) \rightarrow W(\frac{3}{2})$ and $W(-\frac{3}{2}) \rightarrow W(\frac{1}{2})$ at low applied magnetic fields and $\theta = 0°$.

IV. ACKNOWLEDGMENTS

The authors wish to thank H. E. D. Scovil for suggestions throughout the course of the work. We are indebted to S. Geschwind and D. Linn for making the *K*-band measurements, and to J. B. Mock for valuable assistance with the *M*-band measurements.

REFERENCES

1. Bleaney, B. and Stevens, K. W. H., Paramagnetic Resonance, Rep. Prog., Phys. **16,** 1953, p. 107.
2. Bowers, K. D. and Owen, J., Paramagnetic Resonance II, Rep. Prog. Phys., **18,** 1955, p. 304.
3. Bragg, W. L. and West, J., Proc. Roy. Soc. (London), **A111,** 1926, p. 691.
4. Bragg, W. L., *Atomic Structure of Minerals*, Cornell Univ. Press, Ithaca, N. Y., 1937.
5. Wyckoff, R. W. G., *The Structure of Crystals*, The Chemical Catalog Co., New York, 1931.
6. Schulz-DuBois, E. O., this issue, pp. 271–290.
7. Feher, G., Sensitivity Considerations in Microwave Paramagnetic Resonance Absorption Techniques, B.S.T.J., **36,** March 1957, p. 449.

The Bell System Technical Journal
Volume 38, March 1959

Use of Active Material in Three-Level Solid State Masers*

By E. O. SCHULZ-DuBOIS, H. E. D. SCOVIL,
and R. W. DeGRASSE

(Manuscript received January 2, 1959)

The three-level excitation method for solid state masers, including some background material on paramagnetic resonance, is reviewed. With respect to the experimental application of the maser material, two cases can be distinguished. In the first, maser action is based mainly on a favorable relaxation time ratio in signal and idler transitions. It is shown that the relaxation time ratio can be changed artificially by a doping technique. Experimental evidence is presented for two such doping techniques, one self-doping, the other impurity doping. In the second case, maser action is based primarily on a favorable frequency ratio of signal and idler transitions. Maser experiments using this approach are described. In addition, excitation of unidirectional gain and attenuation by circular polarization is discussed. Properties of practical isolator materials are surveyed; they include high-concentration paramagnetic and polycrystalline ferrimagnetic materials.

I. INTRODUCTION

In 1956, Bloembergen[1] proposed a three-level excitation scheme for obtaining microwave amplification by stimulated emission of radiation in paramagnetic solids, or three-level solid state *maser* (3LSSM) for short. It is superior to many other microwave amplifiers in that its noise contribution to an amplified signal should be virtually negligible compared to other noise sources in a system. The principal advantage of a solid state maser over a gaseous maser is that the amplified bandwidth should be of the order of megacycles, a magnitude sufficient for many communication applications. In contrast to the two-level solid state masers, its gain factor should be constant in time.

* This work was supported in part by the U. S. Army Signal Corps under Contract DA-36-039 sc-73224.

Experimental work has confirmed the theoretical predictions. It has been shown that microwave energy can be extracted from paramagnetics by stimulated emission.[2,3,4] If the circuit employed consists of a microwave resonant cavity, the energy extracted can be used to maintain either oscillations or amplification depending on the choice of the coupling parameter. Three paramagnetic salts have been used as active materials. These are gadolinium ethyl sulfate,[2] potassium chromicyanide[3] and ruby.[4] Gain and bandwidth obtained are in agreement with theoretical expectations. Noise measurements have indicated that maser noise is of the magnitude expected.

More recently, traveling wave masers (TWM) have been developed, as described in the accompanying paper.[5] A TWM is a transmission device which can be designed to be nonreciprocal. That is, power traveling from the input to the output is amplified while power traveling the opposite direction is attenuated. A nonreciprocal TWM offers several advantages over a cavity-type maser. Among these are greater gain stability, larger instantaneous bandwidth and the possibility of electronic tuning over a wider frequency range. Gain stability is of great practical importance because in many applications, gain fluctuations deteriorate the system's performance in the same way as noise.

In this paper, the active materials aspect of 3LSSM is treated. Viewpoints are presented on how a given paramagnetic spectrum can be used efficiently in maser applications. Two typical modes of operation are described for active maser materials. Properties of both are evaluated and illustrated by experimental results obtained with gadolinium ethyl sulfate and ruby. Also, those material aspects are discussed which are relevant to nonreciprocal behavior.

II. PARAMAGNETIC RESONANCE IN CRYSTALS

Consider a dilute concentration of paramagnetic ions placed in a diamagnetic host crystal. Obeying quantum laws, each ion can exist in one of several energy states. The number of such states is $2S + 1$, where S is the effective spin associated with the ion. The energy of any state stems from two contributions. One is Zeeman energy, that is, magnetostatic interaction of an applied magnetic field with the magnetic moment of unpaired electrons within the paramagnetic ion. The other is electrostatic in nature and leads to "zero field splitting", that is, separation of energy levels in the absence of an external magnetic field. This latter interaction takes place between the electrostatic field due to neighbors of the ion considered and the electronic charge present in the orbital states of the ion. It is apparent that this zero field energy will reflect

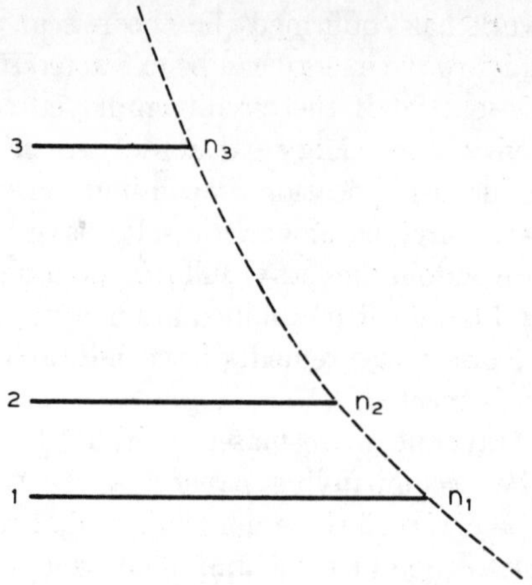

Fig. 1 — Three-level system in thermal equilibrium.

the geometry of the ion environment. As a rule, energy levels are about equally spaced if the magnetic energy outweighs the zero field energy. The spacing is rather unequal in the other extreme.

Fig. 1 shows a three-level scheme which may be part of a scheme of more levels. It is assumed that all three transitions between these are reasonably probable. This can be ascertained by calculations or, preferably, by direct observation of the transitions. A transition from E_i to E_j is excited by radiation of frequency $\nu_{ij} = (E_i - E_j)/h$, where h is Planck's constant. Experimentally, absorption of power at this frequency is observed.

If the ions are in thermal equilibrium with the crystal lattice, the average numbers of ions found in each state are related by Boltzmann's distribution law

$$n_i/n_j = e^{-(E_i - E_j)/kT_0}. \tag{1}$$

Here k is Boltzmann's constant and T_0 the absolute temperature of the lattice. This distribution is indicated in Fig. 1, where the length of each line representing an energy level is made proportional to its population. The thermal contact between ions and lattice occurs through relaxation processes which, to some degree, may be described by a relaxation time τ_{ij}. This time may be visualized as the average time of ions in state i before relaxing to state j. In thermal equilibrium, as many ions must go from i to j as go in the opposite direction. With the help of (1), we thus find

$$\tau_{ij}/\tau_{ji} = n_i/n_j = e^{-(E_i - E_j)/kT_0}. \tag{2}$$

This equation indicates that the relaxation time is shorter for ions in a higher state. For present purposes, this result as based on Boltzmann theory may be sufficient. It might be mentioned, however, that, following Einstein, the situation of (2) can be described by the concept of spontaneous transitions.[6] These occur only in the downward direction and thereby enhance this relaxation rate. In still another, more modern treatment,[7] the inequality of the two relaxation times in (2) follows directly by taking into account the quantum nature of lattice vibrations or radiation field.

With transitions excited by radiation of frequency ν_{ij}, the rate of transitions is described by the transition probability w_{ij}. The transition probability due to applied radiation is the same for upward and downward transitions, $w_{ij} = w_{ji}$. The energy absorbed from the exciting field is one quantum $h\nu_{ij}$ per transition. The power absorbed per unit volume is therefore

$$P_{ij} = h\nu_{ij}w_{ij}(\rho_j - \rho_i). \tag{3}$$

Here i denotes the higher state and ρ denotes the density of ions in each particular state. Power is emitted rather than absorbed if the densities are "inverted," $\rho_i > \rho_j$.

The transition probability can be written[8]

$$w_{ij} = \frac{1}{4}\left(\frac{2\pi}{h}\right)^2 g(\nu - \nu_{ij})\,|\mathbf{H}_{rf}{}^* \cdot \boldsymbol{\mu}_{ij}|^2. \tag{4}$$

Here $g(\nu - \nu_{ij})$ is a normalized function describing the line shape as a function of frequency, $\int g(\nu - \nu_{ij})d\nu = 1$; the line is centered at ν_{ij}. $\mathbf{H}_{rf}$ is the exciting rf magnetic field and $\boldsymbol{\mu}_{ij}$ is the magnetic dipole moment associated with the transition from state i to j. Bold face symbols are used to indicate vector (and tensor) quantities. The asterisk (*) denotes the conjugate complex, that is, a quantity having the opposite time dependence. Using Dirac's bracket notation, this dipole moment is defined quantum-theoretically by

$$\boldsymbol{\mu}_{ij} = g\beta \langle j \mid \mathbf{S} \mid i \rangle = \boldsymbol{\mu}_{ji}{}^*. \tag{5}$$

Here g is the spectroscopic splitting factor, a number usually close to 2, β is the Bohr electronic magneton, $\mathbf{S}$ is the vector spin operator whose components are S_x, S_y and S_z. It should be pointed out that both $\mathbf{H}_{rf}$ and $\boldsymbol{\mu}_{ij}$ are varying in time like $\exp(i\omega_{ij}t)$. This implies the possibility of phase differences between the components of $\boldsymbol{\mu}_{ij}$ or the components of $\mathbf{H}_{rf}$. An important example is that of circular polarization. With respect to some reference system, $\boldsymbol{\mu}_{ij}$ has components μ_x and μ_y equal in amplitude but 90° out of phase. Such a transition is excited by the corresponding circularly polarized RF magnetic field, but not by circular polarization of the opposite sense. This property can be used to give nonreciprocal gain and attenuation in the same way as the gyromagnetic behavior of ferrites is utilized in unidirectional passive devices.

Since w_{ij} is proportional to the incident power, the absorption can be described, on a macroscopic scale, by the imaginary part χ'' of susceptibility, where χ'' is independent of power at low power levels. It is a tensor defined by

$$P_{ij} = \tfrac{1}{2}\omega_{ij}\mu_0 \mathbf{H}_{\text{rf}}^* \cdot \chi_{ij}'' \cdot \mathbf{H}_{\text{rf}} . \tag{6}$$

By comparison with (3) and (4) we find

$$\mathbf{H}_{\text{rf}}^* \cdot \chi_{ij}'' \cdot \mathbf{H}_{\text{rf}} = \frac{\pi}{\mu_0 h} g(\nu - \nu_{ij})(\rho_j - \rho_i)\mathbf{H}_{\text{rf}}^* \cdot \boldsymbol{\mu}_{ij}\boldsymbol{\mu}_{ij}^* \cdot \mathbf{H}_{\text{rf}} . \tag{7}$$

This representation shows the tensor character of χ''_{ij}. The properties of the tensor with respect to polarization of $\mathbf{H}_{\text{rf}}$ in space and phase are described by the dyadic product $\boldsymbol{\mu}_{ij}\boldsymbol{\mu}_{ij}^*$. This also shows that this tensor is degenerate. Instead of three nonvanishing eigenvalues it has only one, namely $|\mu_{ij}|^2$ with the associated eigenvector. The eigenvector represents the polarization of the magnetic moment $\boldsymbol{\mu}_{ij}$ with respect to space and phase. Magnitude and polarization of $\boldsymbol{\mu}_{ij}$ in (5) can be calculated in a standard quantum theoretical fashion. Maximum transition probability occurs if $\boldsymbol{\mu}_{ij}$ and $\mathbf{H}_{\text{rf}}$ have the same polarization, which in general will be elliptical.

As an example, we give the numerical values of imaginary part χ'' of susceptibility for a particular transition in ruby.[8] This transition occurs between $-\frac{3}{2}$ and $-\frac{1}{2}$ states (see Fig. 2) at a field of 3.97 kilo-oersted applied perpendicular to the crystalline axis. Its transition frequency is 5.85 kmc. It is the same line whose inversion is discussed below and which is employed in the TWM described in the accompanying paper.[5] We compute the quantities χ_+'' and χ_-'', which are the values of χ'' for excitation with circular polarization. The circular polarization is defined in an x–y plane where the z-direction coincides with the applied dc magnetic field. The magnitude of χ_+'' is defined by

$$|\chi_+''| = (\mathbf{H}_{\text{rf}+}^* \cdot \chi'' \cdot \mathbf{H}_{\text{rf}+})/(\mathbf{H}_{\text{rf}+}^* \cdot \mathbf{H}_{\text{rf}+}) \tag{7a}$$

and similarly for χ_-''.

The ruby crystal is the commercial "pink sapphire" produced by Linde Company. The chromium content of 0.05 per cent substituting for aluminum indicated by the manufacturer was verified by chemical

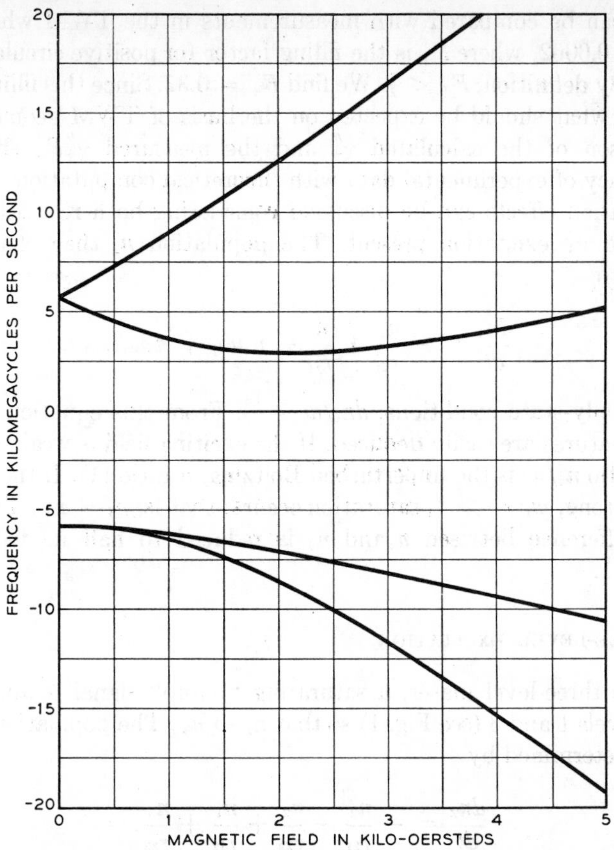

Fig. 2 — Energy-levels of Cr^{+++} in ruby as function of magnetic field applied perpendicular to crystalline symmetry axis.

analysis.[9] We thus have $\rho_0 = 2.35 \times 10^{19}$ Cr^{+++} ions cm^{-3}. For the density difference

$$\rho_{-3/2} - \rho_{-1/2} \approx \frac{\rho_0}{2S+1} \frac{h\nu}{kT}$$

we find, at $T = 1.6°K$, $\rho_{-3/2} - \rho_{-1/2} = 1.04 \times 10^{18}$ cm^{-3}. Assuming a Lorentzian line shape, at the line center $g(0) = 2/\pi\Delta\nu$, where $\Delta\nu = 6 \times 10^7$ sec^{-1} is the measured full line width at half intensity. Using the eigenvectors evaluated in Ref. 8 and (5), we find $|\mu_+|^2 = 5.08 \times 10^{-40}$ erg^2 $oersted^{-2}$ and $|\mu_-|^2 = 0.57 \times 10^{-40}$ erg^2 $oersted^{-2}$. The resulting numbers for susceptibility by circular excitation are $\chi_+'' = 0.0166$ and $\chi_-'' = 0.0018$, respectively.

This can be compared with measurements in the TWM which yield $\chi''_+ F_+ = 0.0062$, where F_+ is the filling factor for positive circular polarization. By definition, $F_+ < \frac{1}{2}$. We find $F_+ = 0.37$. Since this filling factor is about what should be expected on the basis of TWM geometry, the comparison of the calculated χ''_+ and the measured $\chi''_+ F_+$ shows the consistency of experimental data with theoretical computation.

Saturation effects can be discussed considering both relaxation processes and RF excitation present. The population n_1 then changes according to

$$\frac{dn_i}{dt} = -\frac{n_i}{\tau_{ij}} + \frac{n_j}{\tau_{ji}} - n_i w_{ij} + n_j w_{ij}. \tag{8}$$

With steady-state conditions, $dn_i/dt = 0$. From this equation, the following features are easily deduced. If the exciting field is weak, $w_{ij}\tau_{ij} \ll 1$, the ratio n_i/n_j is the unperturbed Boltzmann ratio (1). If the exciting field is strong, $w_{ij}\tau_{ij} \gg 1$, saturation occurs; that is, $n_i = n_j$. The Boltzmann difference between n_i and n_j is reduced to half its value with $w_{ij}\tau_{ij} = 1$.

III. THREE-LEVEL EXCITATION

In the three-level maser, a saturating "pump" signal is applied between levels 1 and 3 (see Fig. 1) so that $n_1 \rightarrow n_3$. The population n_2 then will be determined by

$$\frac{dn_2}{dt} = -\frac{n_2}{\tau_{21}} - \frac{n_2}{\tau_{23}} + \frac{n_1}{\tau_{12}} + \frac{n_3}{\tau_{32}}.$$

Applying steady state conditions and relations like (2),

$$\frac{n_2}{n_1} = \frac{1 + \dfrac{\tau_{12}}{\tau_{23}}\dfrac{n_3}{n_1}\exp\left(\dfrac{h\nu_{32}}{kT}\right)}{\exp\left(\dfrac{h\nu_{21}}{kT}\right) + \dfrac{\tau_{12}}{\tau_{23}}}, \tag{9}$$

where, with the pump transition saturated, $n_3/n_1 = 1$. Under this condition, the equation indicates that it would be rather accidental if $n_2/n_1 = 1$. If $n_2/n_1 > 1$, stimulated emission could be obtained at ν_{21}. This situation is indicated in Fig. 3. If $n_2/n_1 < 1$, that is, $n_3/n_2 > 1$, maser action could be obtained at ν_{32}.

For further discussion, let us identify arbitrarily ν_{21} *or* ν_{32} with the signal frequency ν_{sig}, and the other frequency with idler frequency ν_{idl}.

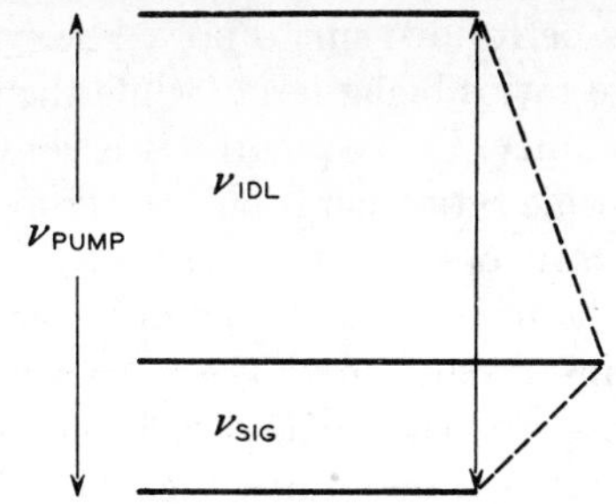

Fig. 3 — Energy-level scheme to demonstrate maser action.

In analogy to (1), we may introduce a spin signal temperature T_{sig} by

$$\frac{n_i}{n_j} = e^{-(h\nu_{sig}/kT_{sig})}, \tag{10}$$

where i is the upper state and j the lower state of the signal transition. Also, we expand the exponential functions in (9) and (10) to the linear term. This is frequently justified under experimental conditions. Even where it is not, the resulting simpler equations show the qualitative features more clearly. We find

$$\frac{T_{sig}}{T_0} = \frac{1 + \frac{\tau_{sig}}{\tau_{idl}}}{1 - \frac{\tau_{sig}}{\tau_{idl}}\frac{\nu_{idl}}{\nu_{sig}}}. \tag{11}$$

We may define as "inversion" the quantity $-T_0/T_{sig}$. It is easily measured in a TWM as the ratio of gain with saturating pump power to attenuation without pump power, both expressed in decibels. To obtain large gain and bandwidth from a given number of ions in a crystal at T_0, the inversion should be as large as possible or the negative T_{sig} should be as small as possible. This suggests that it would be desirable for

$$\tau_{sig}/\tau_{idl} \gg 1 \tag{12}$$

and

$$\nu_{idl}/\nu_{sig} \gg 1. \tag{13}$$

In most experiments performed up to now, however, maser action was based on one of these ratios being large, while the other was not appreciably different from unity. Consequently, it is convenient to distinguish between "relaxation time ratio operation" of 3LSSM, where (12) is satisfied, and "frequency ratio operation", where (13) is satisfied. Both modes of operation will be discussed in more detail below.

Before entering this discussion, however, let us now consider two interesting refinements of (11). The first is concerned with saturation of the signal transition. It will determine the upper limit of the dynamic range of a maser amplifier. For this, a transition probability w_{sig} at the signal frequency ν_{sig} is introduced. Instead of (11) we then find

$$\frac{T_{sig}}{T_0} = \frac{\left(1 + \frac{\tau_{sig}}{\tau_{idl}}\right)\left(1 + w_{sig}\frac{\tau_{sig}\tau_{idl}}{\tau_{sig} + \tau_{idl}}\right)}{1 - \frac{\tau_{sig}}{\tau_{idl}}\frac{\nu_{idl}}{\nu_{sig}}}. \tag{14}$$

The numerator shows that, in saturating a maser signal, the applied RF field has to overcome the shunted signal and idler relaxation times. Thus, in general, the maser signal saturates at a higher power level than the same line in the absorbing state. If both relaxation times are appreciably different, this shunted value is essentially the shorter of the two. The difference in saturation levels is drastic, therefore, if the idler relaxation time is short compared to the signal relaxation time.

The other refinement considered is the effect of incomplete saturation of the pump transition. Such considerations are important with the application of very high pump frequencies. For a description of incomplete saturation, a pump temperature T_{pump} is defined analogously to the signal temperature in (10). The resulting modification of (11) is

$$\frac{T_{sig}}{T_0} = \frac{1 + \frac{\tau_{sig}}{\tau_{idl}}}{1 - \frac{\tau_{sig}}{\tau_{idl}}\frac{\nu_{idl}}{\nu_{sig}}\left(1 - \frac{\nu_{pump}}{\nu_{idl}}\frac{T_0}{T_{pump}}\right)}. \tag{15}$$

The denominator shows that, with comparatively high pump frequencies, appreciable inversion can be achieved with slight saturation of the pump transition. Suppose a certain inversion results from complete saturation ($T_{pump} \to \infty$) at pump frequency ν_{pump}. With the relaxation time ratio unchanged, the same inversion occurs with pump frequency $\nu'_{pump} = a\nu_{pump}$($a$ is a number greater than unity) and pump temperature $T'_{pump} =$

$aT_0/(a-1)$. For example, with $\nu'_{pump} = 2\ \nu_{pump}$, this requires $T'_{pump} = 2\ T_0$. In this sense, pump frequency can be traded for pump saturation.

IV. RELAXATION TIME RATIO OPERATION

We have defined this operation by $\tau_{sig}/\tau_{idl} \gg 1$, while ν_{idl}/ν_{sig} is not specified but not too far from unity. From (11), we thus find

$$T_{sig}/T_0 = -\nu_{sig}/\nu_{idl}. \tag{16}$$

Following the discussion of (14), a particularly attractive property of this operation is that the inverted signal transition saturates at a rather high power level in proportion to the idler relaxation time. By the same token, after a very strong signal resulting in saturation of the signal transition, the amplifying condition is restored in a short time, of the order of the idler relaxation time.

Unfortunately, experimental data about relaxation times are rather scarce. Usually, our experiments have yielded relaxation time ratios close to one; only in exceptions have they been as high as five. Also, there is no adequate theory of relaxation processes that would enable one to compute conditions leading to large relaxation time ratios. This difficulty was bypassed by Scovil and Feher using a technique of impurity doping.[2] We explain this technique by considering the effect of concentration on relaxation times.

At very low concentrations, ions do not interact with each other. The individual resonance lines are narrow, but slightly displaced with respect to each other, as a result of random local fields. The observed over-all line is "inhomogeneously" broadened.[10] In this range, line width and relaxation time should be independent of concentration. With higher concentration, spin-spin interaction comes into play in two ways: (a) the dc magnetic field associated with neighboring spins produces addition inhomogeneous broadening; (b) the RF magnetic field associated with spins during relaxation type transitions leads to "homogeneous" broadening in excess of the inhomogeneous. This can be visualized as a resonant coupling between spins which results in a broader line of identical frequency for every ion. The homogeneous broadening increases proportionally to ion concentration. Gadolinium ethyl sulfate as a maser material is used in a range where homogeneous broadening outweighs the inhomogeneous broadening effects by about a factor of two. This is the case with a concentration of 0.5 per cent gadolinium in a diamagnetic host crystal of lanthanum ethyl sulfate. Some measurements in this concentration range in our laboratory have indicated a rather strong dependence of relaxation time on concentration. A typical value found is a reduction in relaxation time by a factor of 10 upon doubling the ion concentration. This applies to the pump relaxation time, too, indicating a rather strong concentration dependence of pump power required to saturate the pump transition. In practice, one uses as high an ion concentration as is compatible with the pump power which is available and which can be dissipated in the cryostat, in order to have maximum gain and bandwidth per volume of maser material.

In the doping technique, an additional transition is used, whose frequency coincides with that of the idler transition and whose dipole moment is similar to that of the idler. Spin-spin interaction will then be effective at the idler frequency, which can be regarded as due to an effective increase of ion concentration. As a result, the idler relaxation time is shortened considerably. On the basis of the figure given above, a reduction in relaxation time by a factor of 10 might be expected for an effective doubling of ions in the idler transition. It should be pointed out, however, that at lower ion concentrations such as are typical of inhomogeneous broadening, no doping effects are observed. In this range, the idler relaxation time is essentially unaffected by the doping transition.

The doping transition may be one between other levels in the same ion energy level scheme. We call this case "self-doping condition." Alternatively, the doping condition can be provided by a transition of another ion spectrum within the same crystal lattice. This case we call "impurity doping condition." An advantage of this latter case is the free choice of impurity concentration which allows one to control the strength of doping action.

We will illustrate this type of operation by describing the use of gadolinium in a crystal of hydrated lanthanum ethyl sulfate containing cerium as an additional impurity. Fig. 4 shows part of a measured spectrum of a crystal containing 0.5 per cent gadolinium and 0.2 per cent cerium. Resonance fields for a signal frequency of 6.298 kmc are plotted versus the angle between applied magnetic field and crystalline axis. Experimentally, doping conditions are found at crossover points of lines in an observed spectrum. The energy-level diagrams indicating the doping conditions at points A and B in Fig. 4 are shown in Fig. 5. Relaxation times were measured by the saturation method. With uncluttered $-\frac{3}{2} \leftrightarrow -\frac{1}{2}$ and $-\frac{1}{2} \leftrightarrow +\frac{1}{2}$ lines, the relaxation times are nearly the same. At point A, the $-\frac{1}{2} \leftrightarrow +\frac{1}{2}$ relaxation time τ_{idl} is reduced by a factor of 5. The effect is comparatively small because the $+\frac{5}{2}$ and $+\frac{7}{2}$

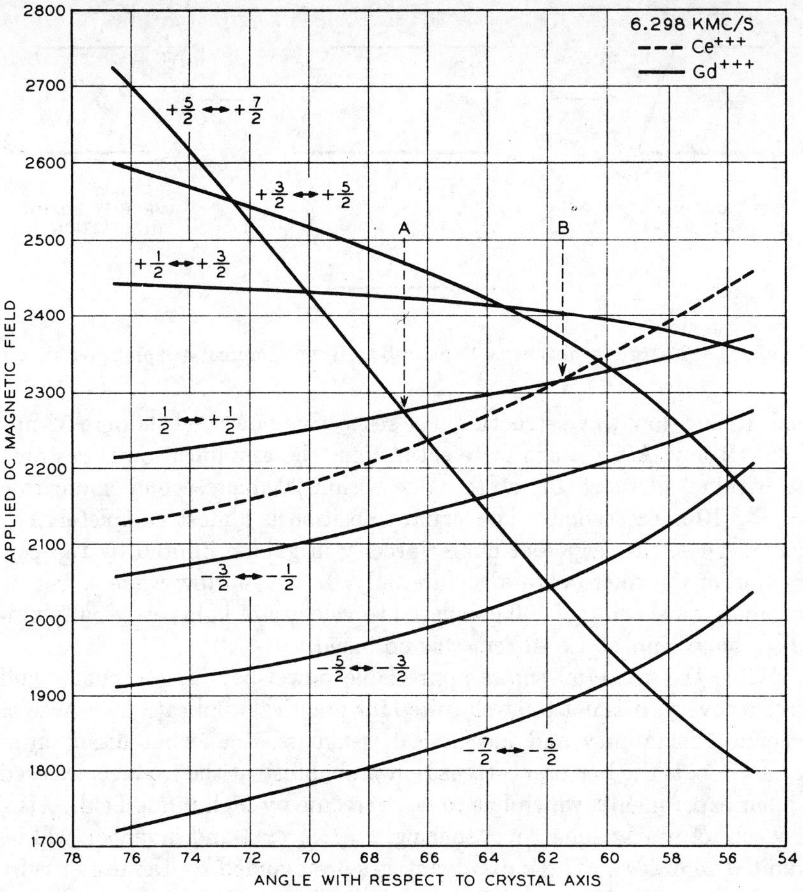

Fig. 4 — Part of measured paramagnetic resonance spectrum of lanthanum ethyl sulfate containing gadolinium and cerium.

levels are not very populated at 1.5°K. As should be expected from (11) with a frequency ratio $\nu_{idl}/\nu_{sig} = 0.94$, the measured inversion obtained by applying pump power to the $-\frac{3}{2} \leftrightarrow +\frac{1}{2}$ transition was $-T_0/T_{sig} = 0.5$. At point B, reduction in τ_{idl} was by a factor 10. In agreement with this, inversion observed was $-T_0/T_{sig} = 0.8$. Possibly the near cross-over of $+\frac{3}{2} \leftrightarrow +\frac{5}{2}$ is helpful in achieving the large reduction of τ_{idl}. For it was found that strong doping was effective even when idler and doping frequency differed by as much as 100 mc, i.e., more than the line width (30 mc). Further tests showed saturation of the inverted signal at about 10 times the saturating power required for the absorption sig-

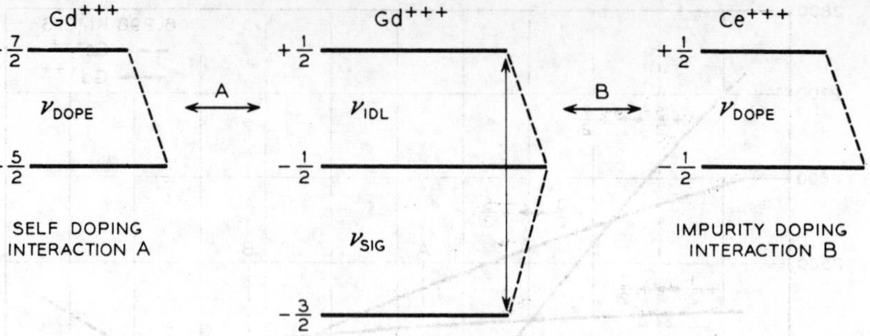

Fig. 5 — Energy-level scheme to describe self- and impurity-doping conditions.

nal. In our slow-wave structure, the respective power levels were 32 mw and 3.2 mw. After a complete saturation, the amplification is restored to within $\frac{1}{8}$ of its steady-state value within 20 microseconds indicating $\tau_{\text{idl}} \approx 10$ microseconds. The signal transition is almost completely circular. Thus, the degree of nonreciprocity in gain is limited by the perfection of the microwave structure only. In a test slow-wave structure exhibiting a slowing of 100 compared to velocity of light, essentially unidirectional gain of 4.5 db/cm was obtained.

While this material shows appreciable power-handling capacity and fast recovery, it is not too well suited for practical application because of chemical instability and mechanical weakness. Somewhat disadvantageous, too, is the low pump-transition probability at the frequencies used in our experiments, which has to be overcome by high pump fields. Also, because of nearly equal level spacing, $\nu_{\text{idl}}/\nu_{\text{sig}} \approx 1$ and inversion will be limited to order 1. These disadvantages are avoided by the use of ruby at the expense of somewhat lower gain, lower signal saturation and slower recovery.

V. FREQUENCY RATIO OPERATION

Equation (11) suggests that inversion can always be achieved by a sufficiently large ratio $\nu_{\text{idl}}/\nu_{\text{sig}}$ independent of $\tau_{\text{sig}}/\tau_{\text{idl}}$. From a practical point of view, there are limits to this approach. For a given signal frequency, the highest useful ratio $\nu_{\text{idl}}/\nu_{\text{sig}}$ is restricted by pump power sources available at high microwave frequencies. Depending on the power requirements, this limit lies presently between perhaps 35 and 100 kmc, unless optical, incoherent power sources could be utilized. Also, one would like to use for practical masers only such operations where the relaxation time ratio τ_{sig}/τ_{idl} is at least not below unity. If this is satisfied, one might expect an inversion of order

$$-T_0/T_{sig} \approx \nu_{idl}/2\nu_{sig} . \qquad (17)$$

The inversion could be improved with a more favorable relaxation time ratio.

For our experiments with frequency ratio operation at low signal frequencies, the energy-level diagram of ruby[8, 11, 12] was used with magnetic field applied perpendicular to the crystalline symmetry axis. This diagram is shown in Fig. 2. Use of the perpendicular orientation is suggested by the observation that all lines are reasonably narrow (of order 60 mc in 0.05 per cent ruby) and correspondingly intense at this orientation and that all possible transitions are reasonably probable. For a signal frequency of about 5.8 kmc, two transitions are available. One is between $+\frac{1}{2}$ and $+\frac{3}{2}$ levels at about 1.0 kilogauss. With a pump frequency of about 15 kmc between either $-\frac{3}{2}$ or $-\frac{1}{2}$ and $+\frac{3}{2}$, no inversion was observed but only saturation of the signal. This indicates an unfavorable relaxation time ratio of about $\tau_{sig}/\tau_{idl} = 0.7$. The other signal transition occurs between $-\frac{3}{2}$ and $-\frac{1}{2}$ levels at a field of 3.97 kilogauss. The $-\frac{3}{2} \leftrightarrow +\frac{1}{2}$ transition is used for pumping at a frequency of about 18.5 kmc. The inversion found is $-T_0/T_{sig} = 0.95$. Thus, the relaxation time ratio $\tau_{sig}/\tau_{idl} = 1.45$ favors this maser operation.

Both relaxation times are rather long, of the order $\frac{1}{10}$ second. Consequently, gain saturation at the output sets in at a fairly low level of 6 microwatts c.w. output power in our structure. The power level of saturation can be appreciably higher in pulsed operation. This can be understood by considering the energy stored in the inverted spin system. As long as pulses repeat in a time shorter than the relaxation time, it is only the average power which determines the saturation behavior. Thus, with a 10^{-3} duty cycle, saturation was observed at peak power of 6 mw.

VI. OPTIMIZATION OF MASER MATERIAL OPERATION

From the preceding discussion, it is apparent that the distinction of relaxation time ratio operation and frequency ratio operation is somewhat artificial. This classification is justified, however, because both cases offer viewpoints for the experimental approach to maser operation. They allow one to predict maser action with a reasonable chance of success from the knowledge of the energy-level diagram only. In the relaxation time ratio operation, the respective ion concentrations are the only critical parameters whose effect has to be investigated experimentally. They have to be compatible with the doping effect and pump power available. In the frequency ratio operation, similarly, maser action is assured if the line is homogeneously broadened, if the pump power available is sufficient for saturation and if the relaxation time ratio is not too unfavorable. It is clear that an ideal maser material should exhibit both a large frequency ratio ν_{idl}/ν_{sig} within practical limits set by available pump power sources *and* a large relaxation time ratio τ_{sig}/τ_{idl}. To accomplish the first, paramagnetic materials with high zero field splitting are required. To accomplish the second, another similar spectrum of a different ion or ion site within the same host crystal could be used for doping the idler relaxation time. This approach requires a rather intimate knowledge of the involved paramagnetic spectra, but there is little doubt that more ideal maser materials will be found as development continues.

VII. NONRECIPROCAL ATTENUATION

The development of unilateral TWM depends on the availability of elements exhibiting nonreciprocal attenuation. In contrast to conventional ferrite nonreciprocal devices, which operate at room temperature and at a magnetic field adjusted for optimum performance of the device, the nonreciprocal behavior in the TWM must be achieved at a low temperature and at a field dictated by the maser operation. Two practical solutions have been found so far, while others may appear useful in the future.

The first approach uses the same paramagnetic material as that supplying maser gain, but with positive signal temperature. Experimentally it was established that the pump power used in the ruby TWM (of order 100 mw) is not sufficient to saturate the pump transition of a higher concentration (0.9 per cent) ruby. At the signal frequency, only very slight reduction in attenuation was observed. Thus it is possible to place low- and high-concentration materials together into the same structure, with one exhibiting gain and the other attenuation. Suppose a forward wave in the structure produces right circular polarization in one region, left circular in another. Both gain and isolator materials interact with right circular polarization only. Thus, we place gain material in the right circular region so that it amplifies the forward wave. Isolator material in the left circular region does not interact with the forward wave. A reverse wave, however, produces the opposite senses of circular polarization. This can easily be verified by the observation that, aside from absorption, a reversal of direction of propagation is equivalent to a change in sign of time. Thus, the right circular polarization of the reverse wave interacts with the isolator material, but not with the gain material. Ideally, pure forward gain and pure reverse attenuation should result. In practice, the reverse-to-forward ratio of attenuation has an upper limit, C, the circularity of the signal transition, which then will be further reduced by variation of the degree of circular polarization in the microwave structure. The same applies to the forward-to-reverse ratio of gain. For the ruby signal transition discussed before, $C = |\chi''_+|/|\chi''_-| = 8.95$.

One obvious advantage of using the same paramagnetic ion for amplification and for isolation is that the resonance condition will always occur at the same magnetic field. The isolator will automatically track the amplifying material with electronic tuning. One disadvantage is that pump power will be absorbed by the isolator. It is not saturated at the pump frequency and therefore absorbs a major fraction of the pump power.

This difficulty could be avoided by using a different paramagnetic material as isolator. In practice, this approach may be rather difficult because the resonance line considered should occur at a magnetic field given by the maser operation and, in addition, it should exhibit high circularity.

The other approach is to use ferrimagnetic materials. Investigations on the resonance behavior of ferrimagnetic materials at liquid helium temperature are being carried out by F. W. Ostermayer of Bell Telephone Laboratories. While he shall report his results in detail, we mention some typical features. Three ferrimagnetic polycrystalline materials have shown useful resonance properties at helium temperature. They are yttrium iron garnet, yttrium gallium iron garnet and nickel zinc ferrispinel. From a room temperature line width usually below 50 oersteds, the helium temperature line width is of the order of 1000 oersteds for these materials. The strength of the resonance absorption decreases accordingly. Still, the resonance absorption is very strong compared to gain or attenuation due to paramagnetics. Therefore the ferrite volumes used in a TWM are extremely small. The resonance field can be shifted to the field required for the maser action within a range set by the saturation magnetization by shaping the ferrite sample. The shape follows from the demagnetizing factors, which in turn are calculated from Kittel's[13] resonance condition.

Two such isolators have been tested as parts of a TWM. One used 0.020-inch diameter spheres of yttrium gallium iron garnet and was used in conjunction with the maser operation of gadolinium ethyl sulfate described before. The applied field of about 2.1 kilogauss provided resonance conditions for both the active material and the isolator. Reverse-to-forward attenuation at helium temperature was better than 30. The other is a rectangular slab of nickel zinc ferrispinel with 0.010- by 0.020-inch cross section having the length of the maser slow wave structure. Its resonance field is sufficiently close to that of the $-\frac{3}{2}$ to $-\frac{1}{2}$ line in ruby at 5.85 kmc and with crystalline symmetry axis perpendicular to the applied magnetic field. Maser operation using this line is described above. At helium temperature, the ratio of reverse to forward attenuation in the nickel zinc ferrispinel isolator is better than 10. In both cases, the isolator reverse attenuation is adjusted to exceed the forward maser gain slightly. Due to the large ferrimagnetic line width, no great care has to be taken to have the maser magnetic field coincident with the field of the resonance isolator. By the same token, tracking over reasonably wide bands by electronic tuning is not difficult. A decisive advantage of ferrimagnetic isolation is the small interaction of the ferrimagnetic material with the pump frequency. Also, the figure of merit favors this type of isolation, so that it appears as the more attractive possibility.

VIII. SUMMARY

The use of active materials in three-level solid state masers has been discussed. Experimental data have been presented for two typical paramagnetic salts used as active materials in masers. Maser action in these materials can be analyzed in terms of two important modes of operation that make use of either a favorable ratio of signal to idler relaxation time or a favorable ratio of idler to signal frequency. It has been pointed out that more ideal maser materials can be developed that combine the advantages of both modes of operation. Some mention has been made of the use of paramagnetic and ferrimagnetic materials for low-temperature isolators. While the experimental results warrant the use of some materials presently available in practical traveling-wave masers, appreciably improved characteristics can be expected from better materials yet to be developed. The application of active and isolator materials to a traveling-wave maser is treated in the accompanying paper.

REFERENCES

1. Bloembergen, N., Proposal for a New-Type Solid State Maser, Phys. Rev., **104,** October 1956, p. 324.
2. Scovil, H. E. D., Feher, G. and Seidel, H., Operation of a Solid State Maser, Phys. Rev., **105,** January 1957, p. 762.
3. McWhorter, A. L. and Meyer, J. W., Solid State Maser Amplifier, Phys. Rev., **109,** January 15, 1958, p. 312.

4. Makhov, G., Kikuchi, C., Lambe, J. and Terhune, R. W., Maser Action in Ruby, Phys. Rev., **109**, February 15, 1958, p. 1399.
5. DeGrasse, R. W., Schulz-DuBois, E. O. and Scovil, H. E. D., this issue.
6. Einstein, A., Phys. Zeit, **18**, 1917, p. 121.
7. Fermi, E., Rev. Mod. Phys., **4**, 1932, p. 87; Rosenfeld, L., Ann. Inst. Henri Poincare, **1**, 1931, p. 25; Heitler, W., *Quantum Theory of Radiation*, 2nd Ed., Oxford Univ. Press, New York, 1944.
8. Schulz-DuBois, E. O., Paramagnetic Spectra of Substituted Sapphire—Part I: Ruby, B.S.T.J., **38**, January 1959, p. 271.
9. Wood, D. L., private communication.
10. Portis, A. M., Phys. Rev., **91**, 1953, p. 1071.
11. Manenkov, A. A. and Prokhorov, A. M., J. Exp. Theor. Phys. (U.S.S.R.), **28**, 1955, p. 762.
12. Geusic, J. E., Phys. Rev., **102**, 1956, p. 1252.
13. Kittel, C., Phys. Rev., **71**, 1947, p. 270.

Reprinted from THE BELL SYSTEM TECHNICAL JOURNAL
Vol. XXXVIII, No. 1, January, 1959

Paramagnetic Resonance Spectrum of Cr^{+++} in Emerald*

By J. E. GEUSIC, MARTIN PETER and E. O. SCHULZ-DU BOIS

(Manuscript received October 6, 1958)

Paramagnetic resonance for the Cr^{+++} ion in emerald has been observed at X-band (8.2 to 12.4 kmc), K-band (18 to 26.5 kmc) and M-band (50 to 75 kmc). From spectra observed at these frequencies, the spectroscopic splitting factors $g_{\parallel}$, $g_{\perp}$ and D have been determined. The large value of D observed suggests the possible use of emerald as an active material in relatively high microwave-frequency solid-state masers.

I. INTRODUCTION

Survey articles by Bleaney and Stevens[1] and Bowers and Owens[2] list paramagnetic resonance data for crystals containing ions of the transition groups. A careful study of these tabulated data reveals that most of the crystals studied are hydrated or contain several magnetically nonequivalent ions and, therefore, discourages the use of many of these crystals in a practical three-level solid-state maser (3LSSM).

The present study was undertaken with a view to investigating crystals doped with paramagnetic ions which possess good chemical stability and which might be expected to have energy-level schemes suitable for extending the design of solid-state masers to higher microwave frequencies. In this article, paramagnetic resonance spectra of emerald (Cr-doped beryl) are reported. The large zero field splitting observed for the Cr^{+++} ion in this crystal might suggest emerald as a possible material for use in the design of solid-state masers for high microwave-frequency applications.

II. CRYSTAL STRUCTURE AND SPIN HAMILTONIAN OF EMERALD

The structure of beryl[3, 4, 5] is hexagonal with two molecules of ($Be_3Al_2Si_6O_{18}$) per unit cell. In the crystal, SiO_4 tetrahedra share oxygens

* This work is partially supported by the Signal Corps under Contract Number DA 36-039 sc-73224.

to form Si_6O_{18} rings, with each Al linked to six Si_6O_{18} rings. In the lattice, all Al sites are identical and the symmetry at each Al site includes a three-fold axis parallel to the hexagonal or c-axis of the crystal. In emerald, it is found that Cr substitutionally replaces Al in the beryl lattice and is present as Cr^{+++}.

For the Cr^{+++} ion in such a crystalline electric field of three-fold symmetry, it is well known[1] that the paramagnetic resonance spectrum is described by a spin Hamiltonian of the form

$$\mathcal{H} = \beta[g_{\parallel}H_zS_z + g_{\perp}(H_xS_x + H_yS_y)] + D[S_z^2 - \tfrac{1}{3}S(S + 1)], \quad (1)$$

with $S = \frac{3}{2}$ and with the z-axis taken parallel to the three-fold symmetry axis which in emerald is the c-axis. In the preceding paper[6] the energy levels of the spin Hamiltonian above were discussed for arbitrary values of the parameters $g_{\parallel}$, $g_{\perp}$ and D and for arbitrary orientation of the magnetic field H with the z-axis. The notation of the previous paper is adopted for labeling the energy levels of (1). The energy levels are labeled $W(\bar{n})$ where $\bar{n}$ is used to enumerate the levels in order of their energy and is just the high magnetic field quantum number which takes on the values $-\frac{3}{2}, \cdots, +\frac{3}{2}$. For example, $W(-\bar{\frac{3}{2}})$ represents the lowest energy level and $W(\bar{\frac{3}{2}})$ represents the highest energy level.

III. EXPERIMENTAL WORK

Initial paramagnetic resonance measurements of Cr^{+++} in a single emerald crystal were made at 9.309 kmc. The spectrometer used for these X-band measurements is similar in design to that described by Feher.[7] At 9.309 kmc and magnetic fields which were available, the spectrum of Cr^{+++} in emerald consisted of a single anisotropic line. The effective g-value, $g^e(\theta)$, of this line is plotted in Fig. 1 as a function of θ, where θ is the angle between the magnetic field H and the c-axis of the crystal. The extreme values of g^e at 9.309 kmc. are $g^e(0°) = 1.973 \pm 0.002$ and $g^e(90°) = 3.924 \pm 0.004$. This line was identified (taking the sign of D negative) as the transition $W(\bar{\frac{1}{2}}) \rightarrow W(\bar{\frac{3}{2}})$. The fact that $g^e(90°) \cong 4$ suggests that at 9.309 kmc the frequency of observation is much less than the splitting of the energy levels of (1) in zero field. Under the condition that ν, the frequency of observation, is small compared to the zero field splitting, a perturbation expression for the g^e of the $W(\bar{\frac{1}{2}}) \rightarrow W(\bar{\frac{3}{2}})$ transition is given by

$$g^e = [g_{\parallel}^2 + (4g_{\perp}^2 - g_{\parallel}^2)\sin^2\theta]^{1/2}\left[1 - \tfrac{1}{2}\left(\frac{g_{\perp}\beta H}{2D}\right)^2 F(\theta)\right], \quad (2)$$

where

$$F(\theta) = \frac{3\sin^2\theta(\sin^2\theta - \frac{1}{3})}{\sin^2\theta + \frac{1}{3}}$$

Specialization of (3) to $\theta = 0°$ and $\theta = 90°$ gives

$$g^e(0°) = g_{\parallel},$$

$$g^e(90°) = 2g_{\perp}\left[1 - \tfrac{3}{4}\left(\frac{g_{\perp}\beta H}{2D}\right)^2\right],$$

from which it is seen that the zero field splitting $|2D|$ can be computed from measurements of $g^e(90°)$ at two frequencies small compared to $|2D|$. Measurements at 23.983 kmc gave $g^e(90°) = 3.814 \pm 0.004$. From the measurements of $g^e(0°)$ and $g^e(90°)$ at X-band and $g^e(90°)$ at K-band, the constants in (1) were found to be

$$g_{\parallel} = 1.973 \pm 0.002,$$

$$g_{\perp} = 1.97 \pm 0.01,$$

$$2D = -52.0 \pm 2.0 \text{ kmc}.$$

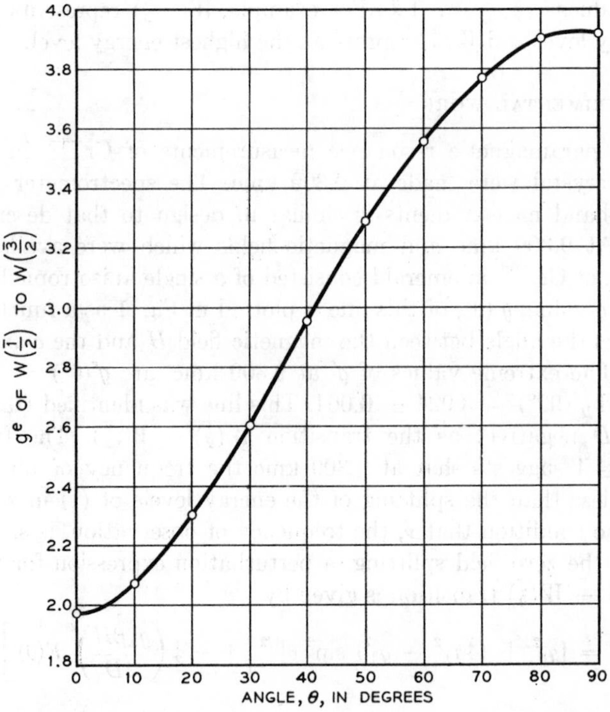

Fig. 1 — Variation of the effective g-value, g^e, of the $W(\frac{1}{2}) \rightarrow W(\frac{3}{2})$ transition at 9.309 kmc.

In order to establish the sign of D, the intensity of the $W(\frac{1}{2}) \rightarrow W(\frac{3}{2})$ line of Cr^{+++} in emerald was compared at two temperatures with the intensity of the same line of Cr^{+++} in ruby. The measurements were carried out with both crystals simultaneously mounted in the X-band spectrometer using temperatures of 78°K and 1.6°K, respectively. The variation of line intensity with temperature can be predicted from Boltzmann statistics if the sign of D is known. Computations were carried out, therefore, on this variation, assuming positive and negative signs of D for both ruby and emerald. The results of these calculations and of the measurement are summarized in Table I. It thus can be concluded that the sign of D for both emerald and ruby is negative.

In order to obtain $2D$ more accurately, measurements were made on Cr^{+++} in emerald at M-band. The millimeter wave paramagnetic resonance spectrometer used was constructed by one of the authors (M. Peter); a block diagram is shown in Fig. 2. Microwave power for this spectrometer is generated by free-running backward wave oscillators (BWO's). Three such BWO's are used to cover the frequency range of 48 to 82 kmc. No resonant cavity is employed in this spectrometer; instead, the sample is situated in "straight" waveguide so that the remarkably wide tuning range of the BWO's can be used. The sensitivity of this spectrometer is comparable to those at low microwave frequencies employing resonant cavities. This is because the loss of sensitivity due to the absence of a cavity is compensated for by higher microwave susceptibility and higher filling factors at these frequencies.

At M-band and for $\theta = 0°$, the two allowed transitions are, in our notation, $W(-\frac{1}{2}) \rightarrow W(\frac{3}{2})$ and $W(-\frac{3}{2}) \rightarrow W(\frac{1}{2})$; they are illustrated in Fig. 3. Both these transitions merge at zero field with the transition frequency being $|2D|$. Both transitions were studied as a function of magnetic field, as shown on Fig. 4. By following them to zero field, the value of the zero field splitting was determined to be $|2D| = 53.6 \pm 0.1$ kmc. From these X-band, K-band and M-band measurements, the best values for the constants in the spin Hamiltonian (1) for

TABLE I

$$\text{Ratio } R = \frac{I_{\text{ruby},\ 1.6°\text{K}}}{I_{\text{ruby},\ 78°\text{K}}} \times \frac{I_{\text{emerald},\ 78°\text{K}}}{I_{\text{emerald},\ 1.6°\text{K}}}$$

Computed with sign of D for			Measured R_{exp}
Emerald	Ruby	R_{theor}	
negative	negative	1.8	1.9 ± 0.1
negative	positive	2.6	
positive	negative	0.5	
positive	positive	0.7	

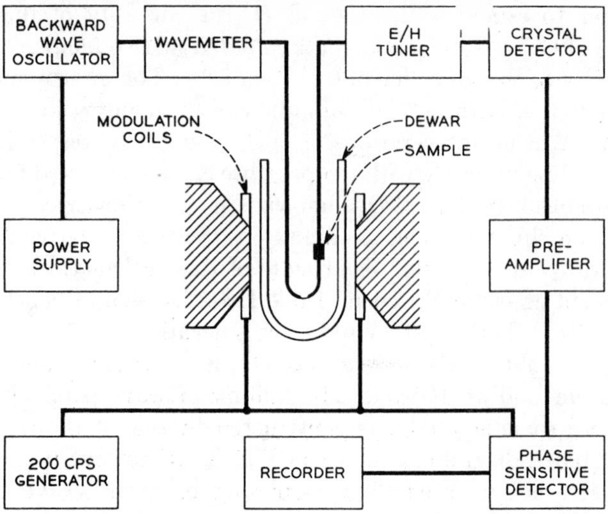

Fig. 2 — Block diagram of the M-band spectrometer.

Cr^{+++} in emerald are

$$2D = -53.6 \pm 0.1 \text{ kmc},$$
$$g_{\parallel} = 1.973 \pm 0.002,$$
$$g_{\perp} = 1.97 \pm 0.01.$$

This value of $2D$ for Cr^{+++} in emerald is, to date, the largest zero field splitting which has been reported for the Cr^{+++} ion in any crystal. Measurements on spin lattice relaxation times in this crystal are planned.

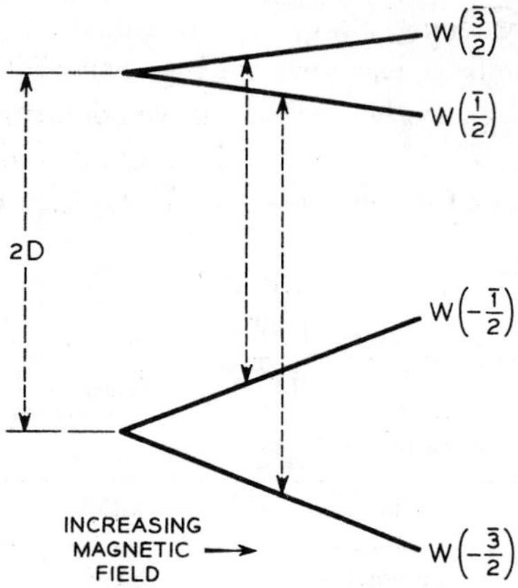

Fig. 3 — Energy level diagram of Cr^{+++} in emerald with applied magnetic field parallel to crystalline axis.

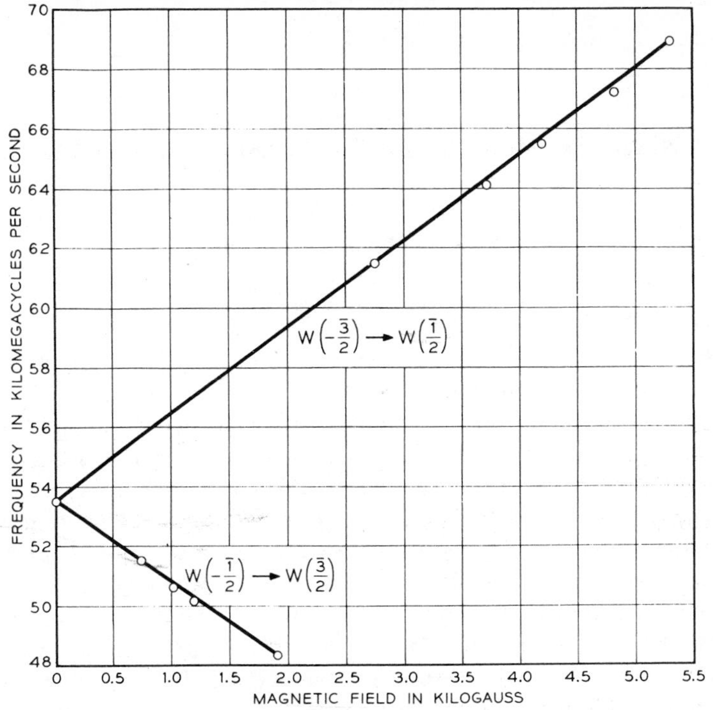

Fig. 4 — Plot of frequencies associated with transitions $W(-\frac{1}{2}) \rightarrow W(\frac{3}{2})$ and $W(-\frac{3}{2}) \rightarrow W(\frac{1}{2})$ at low applied magnetic fields and $\theta = 0°$.

IV. ACKNOWLEDGMENTS

The authors wish to thank H. E. D. Scovil for suggestions throughout the course of the work. We are indebted to S. Geschwind and D. Linn for making the K-band measurements, and to J. B. Mock for valuable assistance with the M-band measurements.

REFERENCES

1. Bleaney, B. and Stevens, K. W. H., Paramagnetic Resonance, Rep. Prog., Phys. **16,** 1953, p. 107.
2. Bowers, K. D. and Owen, J., Paramagnetic Resonance II, Rep. Prog. Phys., **18,** 1955, p. 304.
3. Bragg, W. L. and West, J., Proc. Roy. Soc. (London), **A111,** 1926, p. 691.
4. Bragg, W. L., *Atomic Structure of Minerals*, Cornell Univ. Press, Ithaca, N. Y., 1937.
5. Wyckoff, R. W. G., *The Structure of Crystals*, The Chemical Catalog Co., New York, 1931.
6. Schulz-DuBois, E. O., this issue, pp. 271–290.
7. Feher, G., Sensitivity Considerations in Microwave Paramagnetic Resonance Absorption Techniques, B.S.T.J., **36,** March 1957, p. 449.

REPRINTED FROM THE
PROCEEDINGS OF THE PHYSICAL SOCIETY, VOL. LXXIII, p. 937, 1959

A New Class of Materials for Bloembergen-type Masers

BY B. BLEANEY
Clarendon Laboratory, Oxford

MS. received 6th February 1959

THE operation of a maser of the type proposed by Bloembergen (1956) requires a paramagnetic salt with more than two electronic levels, where there are allowed transitions between levels which are not necessarily consecutively spaced in energy. In general, this has been achieved by the use of a substance where the initial degeneracy of the levels has been lifted by crystal field interactions. For the desired transitions to have adequate intensity it is then necessary that the initial splitting (expressed in frequency units) should be of the same order of magnitude as the applied frequencies. The purpose of this note is to point out that there exists another class of substances where there are four levels degenerate in zero field, which have a linear Zeeman effect, but are not necessarily equally spaced when a magnetic field is applied, and where there are allowed transitions which are not limited to those between adjacent energy levels.

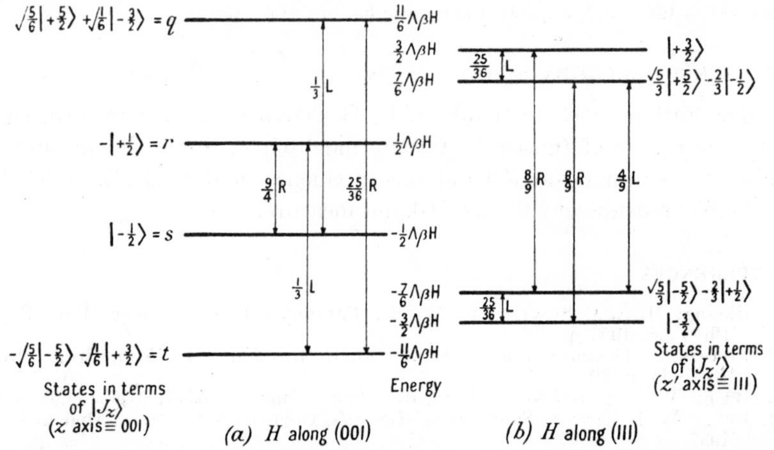

Energy levels and allowed transitions within the quartet of levels which form the ground state of an f^1, $^2F_{5/2}$ ion subjected to a cubic (tetrahedral) crystal field, and to a magnetic field (*a*) parallel to an 001 axis, (*b*) parallel to a 111 axis. The symbols R, L denote the sense required when circularly polarized radiation is used to excite the various transitions. The states are given in terms of $|J_z\rangle$, with the z axis along 001 and 111 respectively. Λ is the Landé g-factor ($=\frac{7}{6}$ for f^1, $^2F_{5/2}$).

As a simple example we will take the case of an ion with one f-electron subjected to a cubic (tetrahedral) crystal field whose strength is small compared with that of the spin orbit coupling. This is a situation which could be obtained with a Ce^{3+} ion, $4f^1$, $^2F_{5/2}$, in a suitable crystalline matrix. The ground state of this ion is $J=5/2$, and under the action of a cubic field it splits into a doublet and a quartet, the latter being lower in energy if the cubic field is that due to 4 or 8 charges, as in a tetrahedron or cube. Under the conditions:

spin orbit coupling $\gg$ cubic field splitting $\gg$ Zeeman energy,

the quartet state has a linear Zeeman effect with the splitting shown in the figure when the magnetic field H is directed along one of the cube axes. It will be seen that the levels are not equally spaced and that there are four allowed transitions of which only one is between adjacent levels. These transitions can be induced by an oscillatory field normal to H; the oscillatory field can be either linearly polarized or circularly polarized, but if it is circularly polarized then the sense is different for different transitions. In the diagram transitions which require circularly polarized radiation of the same sense as that generally needed for electrons are labelled R, while those transitions which require the opposite sense are labelled L. Although the system has cubic symmetry, the spacing of the levels is not independent of orientation, and the effect of placing the steady field along the 111 axis is shown in the figure, (*b*). The level spacing is different and there are now five allowed transitions instead of four; the sense of the circularly polarized radiation required for these transitions is again given by the labels, R, L. The relative transition probabilities of the various transitions are shown in the figure for both directions of H; the designation of the states in terms of J_z (z axis $\equiv$ 001 and 111 respectively) is also shown. The unusual circular polarization properties suggest that these substances may be of use in novel gyrator applications.

For an arbitrary direction of the magnetic field H, with direction cosines (l, m, n) to the cubic axes, the energy levels are given by the equation (where Λ is the Landé g-factor)

$$(W/\Lambda\beta H)^2 = (65/36) \pm \frac{1}{9}\{270(l^4+m^4+n^4)-74\}^{1/2}. \qquad \ldots\ldots(1)$$

The maximum and minimum values (1 and 1/3) of $(l^4+m^4+n^4)$ occur for the two special cases shown in the figure, so that these correspond to the extremes of variation of the energy levels. For the cones of directions such that $l^4+m^4+n^4=9/10$, the levels are equally spaced. Though a detailed calculation has not been made, it can readily be seen that all six transitions between the various levels will be allowed for an arbitrary direction of H (including the special directions where the levels are equally spaced).

The situation outlined above is not peculiar to an f^1, ${}^2F_{5/2}$ ion, though the actual numbers are, but may hold for any state designated by Γ_8 in Bethe's (1929) notation. Thus it would occur also for a d^5 ion ($S=5/2$), where the cubic field splitting is much greater than βH; this would correspond exactly to the case above, with $\Lambda=2$ (instead of 7/6 for f^1, $2F_{5/2}$). Unfortunately, the cubic field splitting of d^5 ground states is usually less than $0{\cdot}1\ \mathrm{cm}^{-1}$, so that the theory developed here is applicable only to rather small magnetic fields. The same difficulty holds for a $4f^7$ ion, where under certain (rather unusual) conditions a Γ_8 state can be lowest in energy. Inspection of Bethe's tables show, however, that Γ_8 quartets occur in all the rare earth ions with Kramers' degeneracy since these have ground states with $J \geqslant 5/2$. Of particular use are likely to be ions of the second half of the lanthanide group, where both J and Λ are largest so that large Zeeman effects can be obtained with small fields. It is also fortunate that the ions with Γ_8 quartet states are the trivalent ions with even atomic number, most of whose isotopes have zero nuclear spin and hence no hyperfine structure.

The problem of obtaining a suitable ion with a Γ_8 quartet as the ground state is that of finding a crystal with cubic symmetry and suitable ratio of the fourth and sixth degree parameters. This problem is being examined theoretically by Dr. B. R. Judd, but two cases where a Γ_8 state is certainly lowest are the ions Ce^{3+}, Sm^{3+} ($J=5/2$) in a cubic (tetrahedral) field. Unfortunately, these have rather small Landé factors ($\Lambda=6/7$ for Ce^{3+}, 2/7 for Sm^{3+}). One of the few sets of rare earth compounds with overall cubic symmetry is the sequioxides (La_2O_3 etc.) but these have a very complicated structure and it is unlikely that the local symmetry at a lanthanon ion site is cubic. The same is true of the garnets which are being investigated in this laboratory by Dr. W. P. Wolf. The most promising materials at present appear to be CaF_2 (and its isomorphs CdF_2, SrF_2, BaF_2, $SrCl_2$), ThO_2 and MgO, in all of which trivalent ions have been observed to give spectra with cubic symmetry when prepared in certain ways. Baker, Hayes and Jones (1959) have observed the resonance spectrum of Er^{3+} ions with cubic symmetry in CaF_2; unfortunately in this case the ground state is a doublet, but its high g-value (6·78) indicates that Er^{3+}, $4f^{11}$, $J=15/2$, $\Lambda=6/5$; and the ions Nd^{3+}, $4f^3$, $J=9/2$, $\Lambda=8/11$; Dy^{3+}, $4f^9$, $J=15/2$, $\Lambda=4/3$; Yb^{3+}, $4f^{13}$, $J=7/2$, $\Lambda=8/7$, are likely to be of greatest use when economy of magnetic field is desired.

A suitable spin Hamiltonian for Γ_8 states is considered in the following note (Bleaney 1959).

References

Baker, J. M., Hayes, W., and Jones, D. A., 1959, *Proc. Phys. Soc.*, **73**, 942.
Bethe, H. A., 1929, *Ann. Phys., Lpz.*, **3**, 133.
Bleaney, B., 1959, *Proc. Phys. Soc.*, **73**, 939.
Bloembergen, N., 1956, *Phys. Rev.*, **104**, 324.

REPRINTED FROM THE
PROCEEDINGS OF THE PHYSICAL SOCIETY, VOL. LXXIII, p. 939, 1959

The Spin Hamiltonian of a Γ_8 Quartet

BY B. BLEANEY
Clarendon Laboratory, Oxford

MS. received 6*th February* 1959

THE Zeeman effect of a Γ_8 quartet state in a special case is analysed in the preceding note (Bleaney 1959). It is clear that such effects cannot be represented by a spin Hamiltonian of the normal kind, though it would be useful to find a spin Hamiltonian to represent this situation, using an effective spin $S=\frac{3}{2}$ since there are four levels. Some time ago Dr. A. Abragam pointed out to the writer that it must be possible to find an appropriate spin Hamiltonian using, for example, matrix elements of the form $H_xS_x^3$ etc. To have cubic symmetry, be invariant under inversion through the origin, and give a linear Zeeman effect the spin Hamiltonian must then be of the form

$$\mathscr{H}=g\beta(H_xS_x+H_yS_y+H_zS_z)+f\beta(H_xS_x^3+H_yS_y^3+H_zS_z^3). \quad \ldots\ldots(1)$$

The matrix elements of this Hamiltonian are then in 1 : 1 correspondence with those of the Zeeman operator $\Lambda\beta\mathbf{H}\cdot\mathbf{J}$ (where Λ is the Landé g-factor in the notation of Elliott and Stevens (1953) within the quartet manifold considered in the preceding note, provided we make the following correspondence between the states: either $(q, r, s, t) \equiv (-\frac{3}{2}, +\frac{1}{2}, -\frac{1}{2}, +\frac{3}{2})$ or $(q, r, s, t) \equiv (+\frac{1}{2}, -\frac{3}{2}, +\frac{3}{2}, -\frac{1}{2})$, These form two alternative orders in which the states (designated by $|S_z\rangle$, with the z axis $\equiv$ 001 cubic axis) can be chosen to correspond with the levels q, r, s, t, whose designation in terms of $|J_z\rangle$ is shown in the figure of the preceding note. (The phases shown are chosen so as to obtain a 1 : 1 correspondance between all matrix elements of $\mathscr{H} = \Lambda\beta\mathbf{H} \,.\, \mathbf{J}$ and of the spin Hamiltonian (1)). These two correspondences are completely equivalent alternatives, but the values of g, f are naturally different for the two cases: the former requires $g = 23\Lambda/18$, $f = -10\Lambda/9$, the latter $g = 25\Lambda/6$, $f = -2\Lambda$.

The off-diagonal matrix elements of the spin Hamiltonian (1) are rather tedious to calculate, but their general nature can be seen from equation (2), which is a less elegant form of (1):

$$\mathscr{H} = g\beta H_z S_z + f\beta H_z S_z^3 + \beta[\tfrac{1}{2}g + \tfrac{1}{4}f\{3S(S+1)-2\}](H_+S_- + H_-S_+) - (3f\beta/8)S_z(H_+S_- + H_-S_+)S_z + \tfrac{1}{8}f\beta(H_+S_+^3 + H_-S_-^3). \quad \ldots\ldots (2)$$

The off-diagonal matrix elements are those between $|S_z = M\rangle$ and $|M \pm 1\rangle$ arising from S_+, S_-; and between $|M\rangle$ and $|M \pm 3\rangle$, arising from S_+^3, S_-^3. The only element of the latter kind is that between the states $|+\frac{3}{2}\rangle$ and $|-\frac{3}{2}\rangle$, and it is this element which is responsible for the ambiguity noted above for the special case considered in the previous note. This is a general feature of the spin Hamiltonian (1), and arises from the fact that the operators with off-diagonal matrix elements generate new states in the cyclic sequence

$$|+\tfrac{3}{2}\rangle \to |+\tfrac{1}{2}\rangle \to |-\tfrac{1}{2}\rangle \to |-\tfrac{3}{2}\rangle \to |+\tfrac{3}{2}\rangle.$$

By a double cyclic permutation in which the state $|+\frac{3}{2}\rangle$ becomes $|-\frac{1}{2}\rangle$, etc., one finds that the system can again be represented by the spin Hamiltonian (1)

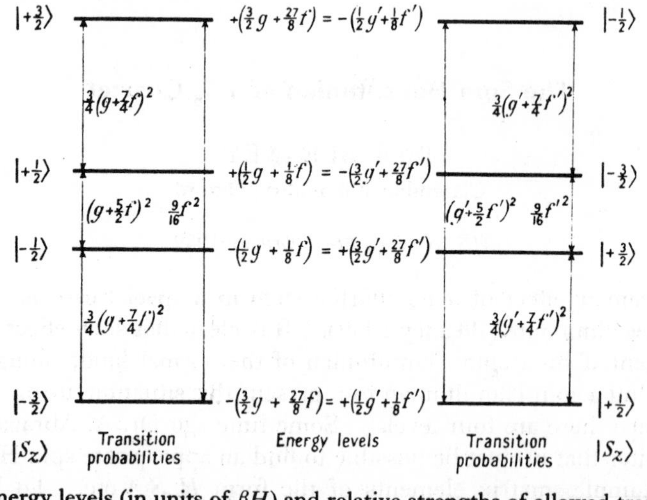

Spin states, energy levels (in units of βH) and relative strengths of allowed transitions when H is along the z axis of the spin Hamiltonian (1). The two alternative representations are shown to the right and to the left. It will be seen that the special cases $g + 7f/4 = 0$, $g + 5f/2 = 0$ (and similarly for g', f') correspond to certain transitions having zero probability; in each of these cases a simpler spin Hamiltonian can be found.

but with new values of the parameters g', f' such that $12g = -40g' - 91f'$, $3f = 4g' + 10f'$. The correspondence between the alternative representations is shown in the figure, which gives the energy levels both in terms of g, f and of g', f' for the special case when the steady magnetic field H is along an 001 axis.

The relative intensities of the allowed transitions when the steady magnetic field is along the z axis are also shown in the figure. These transitions can be induced by an oscillatory magnetic field in the 001 plane, but if circularly polarized radiation is used the sense required is different for various transitions. The sense is readily found by observing whether the operator which generates a state of higher energy is associated with $H_+ = H_x + iH_y$ or with $H_- = H_x - iH_y$.

If the steady field is in an arbitrary direction whose direction cosines are (l, m, n) with respect to the cubic axes, the energy levels are given by equation (3)

$$(W/\beta H)^2 = \tfrac{1}{4}(5\gamma^2 + 3\delta^2) \pm \gamma[\gamma^2 + \tfrac{1}{2}\delta^2\{9(l^4 + m^4 + n^4) - 3\}]^{1/2} \quad \ldots\ldots (3)$$

where $\gamma = g + 7f/4$, $\delta^2 = f(g + 5f/2)$. If the axes are rotated so that H lies along the z' axis of a new coordinate system (x', y', z') where the spin components are now S_z', S_+', S_-' the spin Hamiltonian is found to contain terms in $S_+'^2$, $S_-'^2$. Thus, in general, transitions will be allowed between every pair of levels (here it must be remembered that the spin Hamiltonian for the oscillatory field will also contain such terms). This includes the special directions for H satisfying the relation

$$l^4 + m^4 + n^4 - 3/5 = 2\delta^2/25\gamma^2 \quad \ldots\ldots (4)$$

where the levels are equally spaced. The cases where H is along 001 or 111 are exceptions where some transitions have zero intensity.

There are three special cases for particular ratios of $f : g$ giving δ or $\gamma = 0$, where the angular variation of the energy levels vanishes. These are:

(*a*) $f = 0$. This is a trivial case, since it corresponds to the terms in S_x^3 etc., vanishing;

(*b*) $g + 5f/2 = 0$. In this case the levels are again equally spaced; transference to the alternative g', f' system shows that it corresponds to $f' = 0$, so that in this system the S_x^3 etc. terms would vanish;

(*c*) $g + 7f/4 = 0$. For this case also $g' + 7f'/4 = 0$, and the levels degenerate into two doublets with energy $W/\beta H = \pm 3g/7$.

Inspection of the figure shows that in these special cases some of the transitions have zero intensity, corresponding to the fact that in each case a simpler spin Hamiltonian exists of the form $\mathcal{H} = g\beta \mathbf{H} \cdot \mathbf{S}$, with $S = \tfrac{3}{2}$ in cases (*a*), (*b*) and $S = \tfrac{1}{2}$ in (*c*).

The spin Hamiltonian (1) is subject to the same limitations as applied to the f^1, ${}^2F_{5/2}$ case considered in the previous note. It is valid only under the condition $E \gg \beta H$, where E is the energy separation between the quartet levels and other levels. The behaviour af the susceptibility is also of interest. At temperatures such that $E \gg kT \gg \beta H$ the susceptibility is isotropic and follows Curie's law $\chi = Np^2\beta^2/3kT$ (apart from a temperature independent term), with $p^2 = \tfrac{5}{8}(5\gamma^2 + 3\delta^2)$ The susceptibility will not be isotropic at temperatures such that $\beta H \sim kT$, and the saturation moment will vary with the direction of the external field, being proportional to the lowest root of equation (3).

If the ion has a non-zero nuclear spin, there will be a hyperfine structure which is also anisotropic. For a rare earth ion, to the approximation that the magnetic hyperfine interaction can be represented by a term $a\mathbf{I} \cdot \mathbf{J}$, and that all matrix elements of the hyperfine structure can be neglected except those within the quartet manifold, one can replace J_x by $(gS_x + fS_x^3)/\Lambda$, etc. This should apply both to the magnetic hyperfine structure and the nuclear electric quadrupole interaction. The latter is not zero in a Γ_8 quartet even with cubic symmetry. This can be verified by considering the quantity $3J_z^2 - J(J+1)$ of the f^1 ion discussed in the preceding note; it has the value $+8$ for the states q, t and -8 for the states r, s, so that the quadrupole interaction could be determined directly by measurements in a strong magnetic field.

Acknowledgments

The writer is indebted to a number of people in the Clarendon Laboratory for helpful discussion; in particular to Dr. B. R. Judd, who derived equation (3); and to Professor C. A. Hutchison, whose unpublished results on $[(CH_3)_4N]_2NpCl_6$ drew my attention to this problem.

References

Bleaney, B., 1959, *Proc. Phys. Soc.*, **73**, 937.
Elliott, R. J., and Stevens, K. W. H., 1953, *Proc. Roy. Soc.* A, **218**, 553.

"CORRIGENDUM TO BE PRINTED IN OCTOBER ISSUE"

The Spin Hamiltonian of a Γ_8 *Quartet*, by B. Bleaney (*Proc. Phys. Soc.*, 1959, **73**, 939).

Equation (2) *should read*

$$\mathcal{H} = g\beta H_z S_z + f\beta H_z S_z^3 + \beta[\tfrac{1}{2}g + \tfrac{1}{8}f\{3S(S+1)-2\}](H_+S_- + H_-S_+)$$
$$- (3f\beta/8)S_z(H_+S_- + H_-S_+)S_z + \tfrac{1}{8}f\beta(H_+S_+^3 + H_-S_-^3). \quad \ldots\ldots (2)$$

P. 941, 9 lines from the bottom. The value of p^2 in the susceptibility *should read*

$$p^2 = \tfrac{3}{4}(5\gamma^2 + 3\delta^2).$$

The author is indebted to Mr. H. Hutchinson of Mullard Research Laboratories for drawing his attention to these errors.

Zero-Field Splitting of the Cr^{3+} Ground State in YGa and YAl Garnet

J. W. Carson and R. L. White
Hughes Research Laboratories, Malibu, California
(Received January 9, 1961)

THE Cr^{3+} ion has been the subject of considerable investigation in recent years, occasioned largely by its potential as a maser material. We report here on the paramagnetic resonance spectra of Cr^{3+} in the diamagnetic gallium and aluminum garnets, $Y_3Ga_5O_{12}$ and $Y_3Al_5O_{12}$. The measurements were made at 35 kMc, at 300° and 77°K, on oriented single crystals having about 3% of the Ga (or Al) sites occupied by Cr^{3+} ions. The Cr^{3+} enters predominantly a site of sixfold cubic coordination with a slight trigonal distortion along the crystal (and local) [111] direction. It is the trigonal distortion which gives rise to the zero-field splitting ($2D$) of the ground state spin quartet into two doublets. Davis and Strandberg[1] have worked out thoroughly the theory of the Cr^{3+} ion in such a site, and our data were fully compatible with their theory both as to absorption positions and relative intensity. The parameters resulting from our measurements are summarized in Table I.

For the YGa garnet, the room temperature results agree with those reported by Geschwind and Nielsen.[2] The sign of the temperature dependence of the zero-field splitting differs for the two kinds of garnets. The explanation of this is not obvious. X-ray diffraction pictures of the YAl garnets indicated a considerable degree of strain. At room temperature the $g_{\parallel}$ and $2D$ were the same for all the aluminum garnets (within experimental error), but $2D$ at 77°K varied from 15.5 to 15.7 kMc among the samples examined. Annealing at 1200°C for 24 hr produced no detectable change in $2D$ at 300° or 77°K for any of these samples.

Table I. Summary of zero-field splitting $2D$ and $g_{\parallel}$ for Cr^{3+} in $Y_3Ga_5O_{12}$ and $Y_3Al_5O_{12}$.

Garnet	300°K $g_{\parallel}$	300°K $2D$	77°K $g_{\parallel}$	77°K $2D$
YGa	1.98	21.0 kMc	1.98	20.9 kMc
YAl	1.98	15.3 kMc	1.98	15.7 kMc

The difference in zero-field splitting of the Cr^{3+} ion in the two types of garnets is strongly dependent on the exact positions of the oxygen neighbors, and accurate crystal parameter information is not available on these two garnets. However, the work of Abrahams and Geller[3] indicates that the oxygen octahedron in grossalurate (an aluminum garnet) is appreciably more regular than that of yttrium iron garnet. Since the Ga^{3+} ion is very similar in size to the Fe^{3+} ion, one is tempted to extrapolate these results to predict that the oxygen octahedron is more regular in $Y_3Al_5O_{12}$ than in $Y_3Ga_5O_{12}$. This conclusion is in agreement with the reduced zero-field splitting in $Y_3Al_5O_{12}$ observed in these experiments.

[1] C. F. Davis, Jr. and M. W. P. Strandberg, Phys. Rev. **105**, 447 (1957).
[2] S. Geschwind and J. W. Nielsen, Bull Am. Phys. Soc. **5**, 252 (1960).
[3] S. C. Abrahams and S. Geller, Acta. Cryst. **11**, 437 (1958).

JOURNAL OF APPLIED PHYSICS VOLUME 32, NUMBER 5 MAY, 1961

Cross-Doping Agents for Rutile Masers*

P. F. CHESTER†
Westinghouse Research Laboratories, Pittsburgh 35, Pennsylvania

(Received December 27, 1960)

The EPR spectra of nonstoichiometric rutile and rutile doped with tantalum, niobium, and cerium have been examined at helium temperatures. Ta^{4+} and Nb^{4+} have short spin-lattice relaxation times and appear to be suitable for cross doping in maser applications.

INTRODUCTION

IN the three-level maser[1] and in proposals for four-level[2,3] and continuously operating two-level masers,[4] it is desired to decrease the spin-lattice relaxation time T_1 between a given pair of spin states. One method of achieving this is to "cross dope" the host crystal with a second paramagnetic ion having a short T_1 and a transition degenerate with the appropriate transition of the maser ion.[5-7] In view of the importance of chromium- and iron-doped rutile as maser materials, cross-doping agents for rutile are of interest. The present paper describes some results obtained with tantalum, niobium, and cerium doping and also with departures from stoichiometry. The measurements were made using a reflection type superheterodyne spectrometer operating near 9 kMc in the temperature range from 1.5°–50°K.

NIOBIUM DOPING

The EPR spectrum of a carefully oxidized sample[8] of niobium-doped rutile was examined at 4.2°K. It is interpreted in terms of Nb^{4+} ($S=\frac{1}{2}$; Nb^{93}, 100% abundant, $I=9/2$) substituting for Ti^{4+} with two sites per unit cell. The spin Hamiltonian appropriate to this case is[9,10]

$$\mathcal{H}=\beta(g_zH_zS_z+g_xH_xS_x+g_yH_yS_y)+A_zS_zI_z+A_xS_xI_x+A_yS_yI_y+\tfrac{3}{2}P_z[I_z^2-\tfrac{1}{3}I(I+1)]+(P_x-P_y/2)(I_x^2-I_y^2)-g_n\beta_nH\cdot I.$$

TABLE I. Resonance parameters for niobium in rutile.

Direction of H	g	$A\times10^4$ cm^{-1}
c	1.948	2.1
110	1.981	8.0
$1\bar{1}0$	1.973	$\leqslant$1.8

With $H//110$ and $H//c$, the spacing of the hyperfine lines was regular within the resolution of the experiment. The terms involving P were, therefore, neglected in obtaining the principal values of g and A given in Table I. In the $1\bar{1}0$ direction, the hyperfine structure was not resolvable. With $H//c$ the over-all width of the pattern, which is illustrated in Fig. 1, was ~25

FIG. 1. Spectrum of niobium in rutile at 4.2°K $H//c$ axis.

* This work supported in part by the U. S. Air Force, under contract.
† Present address: Central Electricity Research Laboratories, Leatherhead, Surrey, England.
[1] N. Bloembergen, Phys. Rev. **104**, 324 (1956).
[2] G. Makhov, Bull. Am. Phys. Soc. 4, 21 (1959).
[3] P. E. Wagner, Westinghouse Research Rept. 403FF200-R1, May, 1959.
[4] D. I. Bolef and P. F. Chester, IRE Trans. **MTT-6**, 47 (1958).
[5] G. Feher and H. E. D. Scovil, Phys. Rev. **105**, 760 (1957).
[6] E. O. Schulz-duBois, H. E. D. Scovil, and R. W. DeGrasse, Bell System Tech. J. **38**, 335 (1958).
[7] J. M. Minkowski, Phys. Rev. **119**, 1577 (1960).
[8] Grown by flame fusion at M.I.T. and kindly loaned to the author by Dr. H. P. R. Frederikse.
[9] K. D. Bowers and J. Owen, Repts. Progr. in Phys. **18**, 304 (1955).
[10] B. Bleaney, K. D. Bowers, and D. J. E. Ingram, Proc. Roy. Soc. (London) **A228**, 147 (1955).

FIG. 2. Spectrum of tantalum in rutile at 4.2°K $H//c$ axis.

gauss, while with $H//110$ it was ~90 gauss. When the magnetic field was not along a principal axis, a set of nine lines was observed in between the 10 hyperfine lines. These are attributed to normally forbidden transitions, ($\Delta m_n = \pm 1$), allowed because of the niobium quadrupole interaction. Similar lines have been seen in the resonance of Cu^{2+} by Bleaney *et al.*[10]

The main features of the present spectrum were observed to remain unchanged up to about 25°K. Above this temperature, the hyperfine structure gradually disappeared and the line narrowed and became dispersive. At the same time the microwave coupling was observed to change markedly. This behavior is attributed to the onset of electronic conduction.

An attempt was made to measure T_1 by the field-sweep inversion method[11] at 1.4°K. The line could not be inverted and the relaxation time appeared to be about 70 μsec. Thus, with H not too far from the c axis (to keep down the over-all width of the spectrum), niobium should be a satisfactory cross-doping agent in rutile masers.

TANTALUM DOPING

The tantalum-doped rutile, nominally 0.05 at.% Ta, was grown by the National Lead Company. A sample cut straight from the boule and a sample oxidized in a stream of oxygen at 750°C for six hours showed identical spectra, which are interpreted in terms of Ta^{4+} ($S=\frac{1}{2}$; Ta^{181}, 100% abundant, $I=9/2$) substituting for Ti^{4+}. The spin Hamiltonian is the same as that for niobium. In the case of tantalum, however, the hyperfine structure was only resolvable with $H//c$ and the effects of the tantalum quadrupole moment were clearly important. The spectrum with $H//c$ is shown in Fig. 2. Because of the poor resolution, it was not possible to obtain accurate values for A and P. The values for A in Table II are only approximate. The over-all width of the spectrum at any orientation was less than 35 gauss.

The main features of the spectrum were observed to remain unchanged up to about 10°K, above which temperature the hyperfine structure disappeared, the line narrowed and became dispersive, and the microwave coupling changed markedly. At 1.4°K the spin-lattice relaxation time appeared to be about 100 μsec.

In order to test the suitability of tantalum for cross doping, experiments were carried out on two different rutile crystals doped with both chromium and tantalum. The first crystal contained nominally 0.05 at.% chromium and 0.1 at.% tantalum. It appeared to be electrically conducting even at 2°K and no relaxation data could be obtained. The second crystal contained nominally 0.05 at.% chromium and 0.05 at.% tantalum. This appeared to be slightly lossy at 4.2°K but not sufficiently to interfere with relaxation measurements. The 3–4 transition[12] of the Cr^{3+} ion was examined at 4.2°K with H in the plane formed by the c axis and a 110 axis. The values of T_1 obtained are given in Table III, where θ is the angle between H and the 110 axis. The decrease in T_1 of the chromium 3–4 line as it is made to approach the tantalum line can be seen in Fig. 3. The effect does not extend much beyond ±100 oe from coincidence. The results are not completely satisfactory, however, since T_1 at $\theta = 15.3$ is about four times shorter than in rutile doped only with chromium, probably a result of the (albeit low) conductivity of the sample. Presumably, this could be rectified by decreasing the tantlaum content or increasing the chromium content. It should also be noted that the Ta+Cr-doped crystals were visibly inhomogeneous in composition.

It would seem that tantalum is indeed a suitable cross-doping agent for $Cr:TiO_2$ masers, but further work needs to be done on homogeneous crystals of greater Cr:Ta ratios with the actual values of H and θ that would be used in a maser application.

TABLE II. Resonance parameters for tantalum in rutile.

Direction of H	g	$A\times 10^4$ cm^{-1}
c	1.945	~2.7
110	1.979	<2.5
$1\bar{1}0$	1.979	<2.5

CERIUM DOPING

The cerium-doped rutile, nominally 0.1 at% cerium, was also grown by flame fusion.[13] Unlike the niobium-

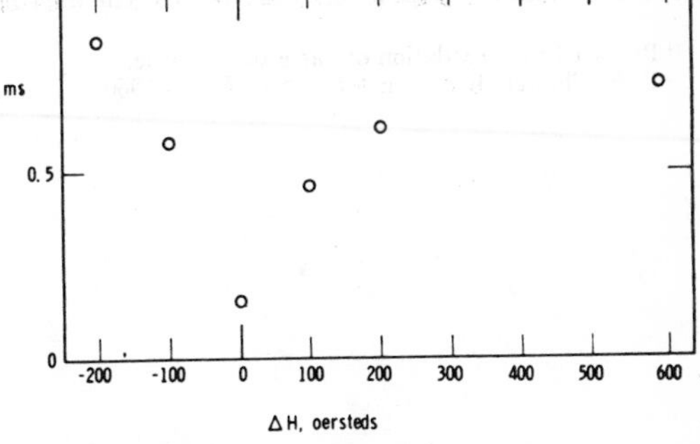

FIG. 3. Relaxation time of chromium 3–4 line as function of proximity to tantalum line. Temperature 4.2°K.

[11] J. G. Castle, P. F. Chester, and P. E. Wagner, Phys. Rev. **119**, 953 (1960).

[12] Numbering the energy levels in order of increasing energy.

[13] National Lead Company, South Amboy, New Jersey.

TABLE III. Spin-lattice relaxation time of the chromium 3–4 line as a function of proximity to the tantalum line.

θ deg	H oe	T_1, msec
0	3910	0.74
9.3	3500	0.64
10.8	3400	0.47
12.0	3305	0.16[a]
13.7	3200	0.59
15.3	3100	0.85

[a] Coincidence with the tantalum line.

and tantalum-doped crystals, it was not blue in color. No spectrum that could be attributed to Ce^{3+} was observed down to 1.4°K. Presumably the cerium is present as Ce^{4+} substituting for Ti^{4+}.

In an attempt to change the valence state of the cerium, a sample was heated in vacuum for 24 hr at 1000°C. This produced a blue coloration and two spin resonance spectra at helium temperatures. An extensive and complicated set of lines extends from $g \sim 2.05$ to $g \sim 1.75$. This spectrum is very similar to that observed in strongly reduced rutile. The second spectrum corresponds to a center with $S=\frac{1}{2}$ on two sites each having the following characteristics:

Direction of H	g
c	3.86_6
110	2.06_3
110	4.39_4

This center is tentatively identified as Ce^{3+} on a titanium site. The relaxation time at 4.2°K was found to be ~ 4 msec with $H//110$, and ~ 1 msec with $H//c$.

NONSTOICHIOMETRIC RUTILE

The spin resonance of slightly oxygen-deficient rutile[14] has already been reported[15] and is characterized by a moderate relaxation time, 12 msec at 2.16°K. At greater degrees of reduction, where the sample has a deep transparent blue color (in a thickness of 1 mm), the spectrum changes character and a single, motionally narrowed line is observed. The relaxation time of this line is less than 100 μsec at 2.16°K. To test the usefulness of this line for cross doping, a sample of chromium-doped rutile (nominally 0.1 at.% Cr^{3+}) was subjected to varying degrees of reduction and its relaxation behavior subsequently examined.

Heating in a vacuum of 10^{-5} mm Hg for 24 hr at temperatures up to 1000°C did not introduce the motionally narrowed line but rather an untidy group of lines centered about the same g value. The relaxation time of this group appeared to be about the same as that of the Cr^{3+}, a few milliseconds at 4.2°K. Coincidence with the 1–2 line or the 3–4 line of the Cr^{3+} spectrum produced no noticeable reduction in relaxation time of the Cr^{3+} lines.

Heating a sample in hydrogen for 15 min at 850°C resulted in an opaque crystal with an untidy spectrum very similar to that of the vacuum-reduced samples. Relaxation measurements on the "oxygen-deficient" spectrum of this sample gave $T_1 \sim 250$ μsec at 1.4°K. However, it was found that T_1 for the 1–2 line and 3–4 line of Cr^{3+} was now about 70 μsec, irrespective of proximity to the oxygen deficient spectrum. Presumably there is sufficient electronic conductivity in this sample for the relaxation to be dominated by a process involving conduction electrons. Such a process would be expected to become less effective at higher fields such that the Zeeman energy exceeded the thermal energy of the electrons. It would seem that the oxygen-deficient spectrum is not as useful for cross doping as tantalum or niobium.

[14] Prepared by reoxidation of "as-grown" rutile.
[15] P. F. Chester, Bull. Am. Phys. Soc. 5, 72 (1960).

CONCLUSIONS

Tantalum and niobium appear to be suitable cross-doping agents for securing a short spin-lattice relaxation time in masers using rutile as the host crystal. Initial tests on rutile doped with chromium and tantalum are encouraging. Cerium does not appear to enter rutile as Ce^{3+}. Departure from stoichiometry, although it may result in a spectrum with short spin-lattice relaxation time, presents the problem of nonfrequency-selective cross relaxation.

ACKNOWLEDGMENTS

The author wishes to thank Clinton C. Brooks and J. R. Sutter for assistance in making the measurements.

Reprinted from JOURNAL OF APPLIED PHYSICS SUPPLEMENT, Vol. 32, No. 10, 2233–2236, October, 1961

Electron Spin Resonance in Semiconducting Rutile*

P. F. CHESTER
Westinghouse Research Laboratories, Pittsburgh 35, Pennsylvania, and Central Electricity Research Laboratories, Leatherhead, Surrey, England†

The ESR spectra of oxygen-deficient and doped rutile have been investigated at liquid helium temperatures. Niobium and tantalum are shown to give rise to the donors Nb^{4+} and Ta^{4+} rather than Ti^{3+}. The spectrum of reduced rutile depends on the method of reduction. Reasons for this are discussed. Under certain circumstances, involving hydrogen reduction, a particularly simple spectrum is observed. This degenerates and is replaced by a single line as the temperature is raised. A similar effect is obtained by increasing the concentration of centers. Possible assignments are discussed. Vacuum reduction results in distinctly different spectra which persist to higher temperatures. Resistivity measurements indicate a higher activation energy, by a factor of three, for vacuum-reduced samples.

ALTHOUGH a great deal of work has been carried out on the semiconductivity of oxygen-deficient and doped rutile,[1–5] we cannot yet say with certainty which of the models proposed for the donor center is the correct one, nor are we sure of the role of Ti^{3+} in the conduction process. Recently,[6,7] the further possibility of polaron states and/or bands has been recognized. Since the Ti^{3+} ion and some of the proposed donor centers are paramagnetic, it is to be expected that measurements of electron spin resonance (ESR) would give additional, and perhaps decisive, information.

This expectation has been fulfilled in the case of doped rutile. Results published in another connection on niobium and tantalum doping[8] show that, at low temperatures, the effect is not the stabilization of Ti^{3+}, as had previously been assumed. Instead, the donors Nb^{4+} and Ta^{4+} are formed. Gerritsen and Lewis[9] similarly have shown that vanadium enters as V^{4+}, but with a much larger ionization energy. It is now apparent that, at low temperatures, a distinction must be drawn between oxygen-deficient rutile and rutile doped with pentavalent impurities.

* This work was supported in part by the U. S. Air Force under contract.
† Present address.
[1] References to earlier work are given in the review article by F. A. Grant, reference 2.
[2] F. A. Grant, Revs. Modern Phys. **31**, 646 (1959).
[3] D. C. Cronemeyer, Phys. Rev. **113**, 1222 (1959).
[4] H. P. R. Frederikse and W. R. Hosler, N.B.S. Report 6585, November 1, 1959.
[5] L. E. Hollander and Patricia L. Castro, Phys. Rev. **119**, 1882 (1960).
[6] H. P. R. Frederikse, Conference on Compound Semiconductors, Schenectady, New York, June, 1961, and International Semiconductor Conference, Prague, 1960.
[7] T. Holstein (private communication).
[8] P. F. Chester, J. Appl. Phys. **32**, 866 (1961).
[9] H. J. Gerritsen and H. R. Lewis, Phys. Rev. **119**, 1010 (1960).

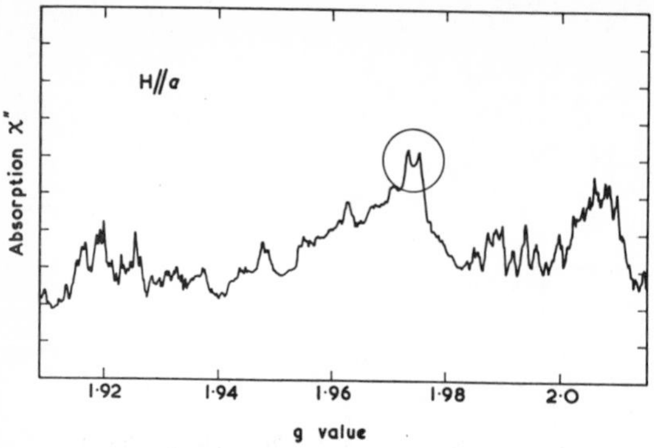

FIG. 1. Spectrum of Linde "as grown" rutile, $H \parallel a$, 2.0°K. The circled portion corresponds with the A spectrum.

The situation in oxygen-deficient rutile is not so simple. In the present work,[10] a number of samples have been examined with an X-band spectrometer in the liquid helium temperature range. ESR spectra are observed which, under certain conditions, are particularly simple in form.[11] An unexpected complication, however, was the discovery that the spectra observed, and by implication the defect structures responsible for them, depend strongly on the method of sample preparation.

Starting materials for the present work were commercial single-crystal boules[12] grown by flame fusion using an oxy-hydrogen flame. In the "as grown" condition, without deliberate oxidation, the Linde material had a resistivity of a few tenths ohm cm[13] and was an opaque blue-black color in a thickness of 1 mm. The spectrum of this material, for one orientation, is shown in Fig. 1. It extends over more than 250 oe and clearly indicates a high degree of disorder in the crystal. This material was not investigated in detail. Attention was concentrated on samples of higher resistivity and greater internal order as outlined below.[10]

Samples with resistivities in the range 10 to 40 ohm cm were prepared in two ways. The first was to heat Linde "as grown" material in air at about 625°C for $2\frac{1}{2}$ hr. The second was to cut directly from National Lead "as supplied" boules which had been partially reoxidized in air at 1100°C after growth. All the samples so prepared were a pale greyish-blue color in a thickness of 1 mm. They showed the same ESR spectrum which was investigated in detail. This spectrum, which we shall denote "A," corresponds closely with the circled portion in Fig. 1. It appears that, of all the centers contributing to the resonance in Linde "as grown" material, only the A centers survive the process of partial reoxidation. It should be noted however that the A centers themselves can be removed, as far as ESR is concerned, by complete oxidation.

At 4.2°K with the magnetic field H in the (001) plane, the A spectrum consists of two, three, or four lines depending on the angle ϕ between H and an a axis. The appearance of these lines, which are individually about 1 oe in width, is shown for a Linde specimen in Fig. 2. With $H \| c$, a single line, 1 oe wide, is observed. No other lines are observed at any orientation in the range 500 to 8400 oe. The observed g values are well described by the relation: $g^2 = g_x^2 \cos^2\theta_x + g_y^2 \cos^2\theta_y + g_z^2 \cos^2\theta_z$, where θ_x, θ_y, and θ_z are the angles made by H with the magnetic axes x, y, and z. There are four sites per unit cell, each having $S = \frac{1}{2}$, $g_x = 1.974$, $g_y = 1.977$, and $g_z = 1.941$.[14] The four z axes coincide and lie along the crystal c axis. The x axes make angles of $\pm 26°$ with the crystal a axes. This fourfold multiplicity rules out an assignment to Ti^{3+} ions on normal titanium sites. Attempts were made, with H carefully aligned along the c axis, to detect hyperfine structure. Although a pattern of satellite lines, accounting for a few percent of the total absorption, was observed, they were asymmetrically disposed about the center line and could not be interpreted in terms of hyperfine interaction with single nuclei of Ti^{47} or Ti^{49}. The spin-lattice relaxation time of the A spectrum with $H \| c$ was found to be 0.012 sec at 2.16°K in a Linde sample.

It is apparent from Fig. 2 that the intensities of the lines are not symmetric about the midpoint of the pattern, as would be expected from four crystallographically equivalent sites. This appears to be due to the presence of another line, on the low-field side of the A spectrum, whose g value is independent of ϕ. The asymmetry was somewhat less at 1.3°K and increased markedly as the temperature was raised above 4.2°K, as shown in Fig. 3.

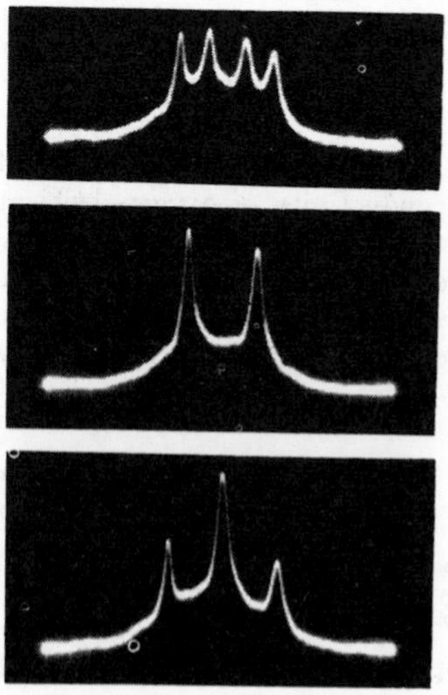

FIG. 2. The A spectrum observed in partially reoxidized Linde rutile, $H \perp c$, 2.16°K. Sweep 18.5 oe, field increasing from left to right. Top: $\phi = 9°$. Center: $\phi = 0°$. Bottom $\phi = 18°$.

[10] A full account is contained in Westinghouse Scientific Paper No. 908 C 901-P3.

[11] P. F. Chester, Bull. Am. Phys. Soc. **5**, 72 (1960).

[12] One from the Linde Company, 30 East 42nd Street, New York **17**, New York, two from the National Lead Company, P. O. Box **58**, South Amboy, New Jersey.

[13] Unless otherwise stated, all resistivities refer to the c axis and room temperature.

[14] This value was confirmed by a measurement at 19.66 kMc.

It appears that the *A* spectrum degenerates with increasing temperature and that a new line, to be denoted "*B*" and which is present to some extent at 1.3°K, grows out of it.

It was observed that the National Lead samples showed a greater asymmetry and less sharp lines than the Linde sample. This may be connected with the fact that the latter contained about 100 times as much aluminium impurity (0.1%).

The *A* spectrum was also found to be present, although it accounted for only a small fraction of the total absorption, in a sample[15] prepared by reduction in a mixture of hydrogen and argon to a resistivity of about 60 ohm cm.

Since the temperature dependence of the *A* spectrum and the emergence of the *B* spectrum were suggestive of a thermally activated conduction process, attempts were made to increase the concentration of centers and thereby to increase the "hopping" rate. Four samples having a deep clear blue color were prepared, one by reoxidation of Linde "as grown" material in air for 3 hr at 450°C (giving $\rho_c=0.82$ ohm cm) and three by heating National Lead "as supplied" material in oxygen at a few mm pressure for 8 hr at 825°C (giving in two cases $\rho_c=0.76$ and 0.78 ohm cm, respectively). At 4.2°K these samples showed a single line spectrum with axial symmetry about the crystal *c* axis. The parameters of this spectrum, which will be denoted "*C*," are: $g_{\parallel}=1.941$ and $g_{\perp}=1.976$. These values correspond closely with those of the *B* spectrum. The *C* spectrum was not

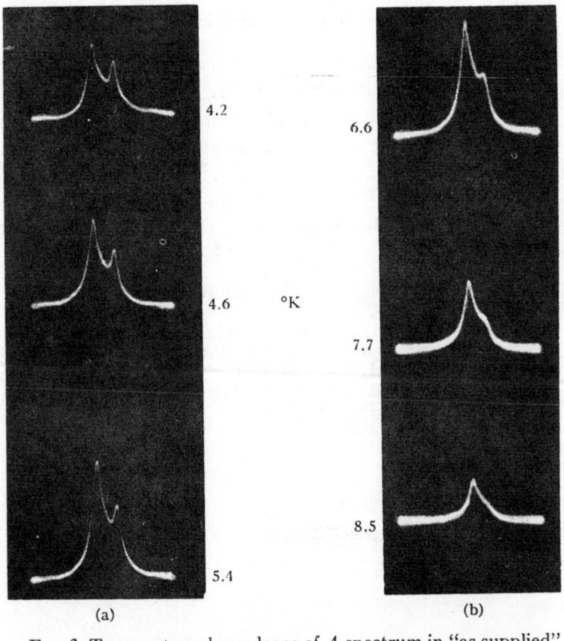

FIG. 3. Temperature dependence of *A* spectrum in "as supplied" National Lead rutile, $H \parallel 110$. Sweep ~30 oe, field increasing from left to right. The scale of absorption at different temperatures is not constant.

[15] Kindly loaned by L. E. Hollander.

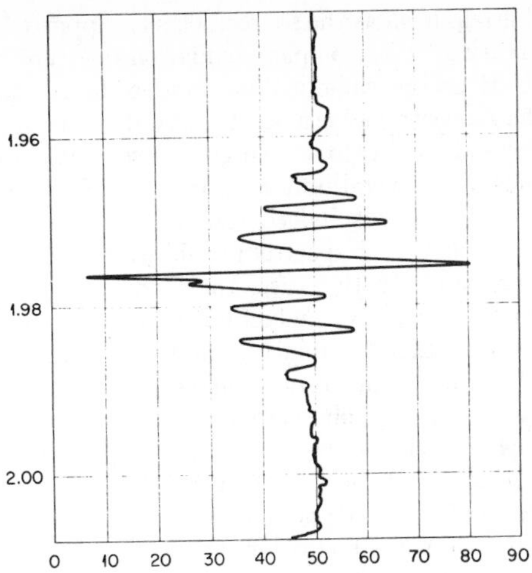

FIG. 4. Derivative spectrum of vacuum-reduced, 10-ohm cm sample, $H//[110]$, 4.4°K.

equally "clean" in all the samples. In the best case ($\rho_c=0.76$ ohm cm), the linewidth was measured as a function of temperature and orientation. With $H\parallel c$ it was 1.9 oe and nearly independent of temperature, while with $H\perp c$ it decreased from 3.8 oe at 2.3°K to 1.8 oe at 17.8°K. The spin-lattice relaxation time was found to be about 100 μsec at 2°K. The center responsible for the *C* spectrum appears, therefore, to be partly mobile. Its hopping frequency at 10°K is of the order of 10^8 sec^{-1}. A careful comparison shows that the *C* spectrum is not centered on the *A* spectrum. This rules out simple exchange between the four stationary sites of the *A* spectrum.

At the present stage, a definitive interpretation of the above spectra cannot be made. The most obvious assignment of the *A* spectrum is to an interstitial site occupied by Ti^{3+} (with or without a lattice polarization) or by a self-trapped electron. There are four interstitial sites in the unit cell, each enclosed by a distorted octahedral arrangement of oxygen atoms, which differ only in the orientations of their principal axes in the (001) plane. These axes make angles of about ±31° with the *a* axes. Another possible assignment, already discussed,[11] is that of Ti^{3+} (with or without a lattice polarization) on a titanium site that is perturbed by an oxygen vacancy in a next-nearest neighbor position in the (001) plane. A third possible assignment is to an unidentified center whose presence is due to the incorporation of hydrogen in the rutile lattice. It is known[16] from infrared measurements that significant quantities of hydrogen can be taken up to form O–H bonds which then constitute defects in the rutile structure. It may be significant that the *A* spectrum has so far been observed only in samples prepared in hydrogen. The absence of hyperfine structure rules out atomic hydrogen or the

[16] B. H. Soffer, M.I.T. Laboratory for Insulation Research, Tech. Report 140, August, 1959.

O–H group itself as the source. This is supported by the observation[16] that complete oxidation does not remove the O–H groups while it does remove the *A* spectrum.

The *B* spectrum, because of its axial symmetry, must correspond either to a center whose wave function extends over several unit cells or to a mobile center. If the *A* spectrum is indeed due to a weakly trapped polaron, then the *B* spectrum could well correspond to a polaron band. In this case, the *C* spectrum might be assigned to 'impurity' conduction—perhaps involving the *A* sites. Another possibility is that the transition from the *A* to the *C* spectrum is linked with the change in optical absorption observed by Cronemeyer[3] between 3 and 4 ohm cm (*a* axis). The *a* axis resistivities of the samples showing the *C* spectrum were about 2.7 ohm cm, while those of the samples showing the *A* spectrum were in excess of 40 ohm cm.

In an attempt to produce a series of samples of graduated resistivity to explore the transition from the *A* to the *C* spectrum, a series of samples of National Lead material were first oxidized in pure oxygen at 600°C for 8 hr (which removed the *A* spectrum) and then reduced in vacuum for 24 hr at temperatures in the range 600° to 1150°C. Resistivities ranged from 80 to 2 ohm cm (*c* axis). Unexpectedly, none of the samples showed the simple *A* or *C* spectra. The 600° samples showed only weak resonances. With $H\perp c$, the others showed similar spectra, each consisting of a central peak at $g=1.975$, whose position was roughly independent of ϕ, together with an irregular pattern of large satellites, whose appearance was markedly dependent on ϕ, extending over about 70 oe. No measurements were made with $H\|c$. The structure and extent of these spectra remained unchanged up to at least 30°K in a 5-ohm cm sample and to at least 20°K in a 10-ohm cm sample. Although there is not enough data at present for an accurate description of these centers, it is clear that they differ markedly from the *A* center produced by partial reoxidation of "as grown" material and are more strongly bound. This latter point was confirmed by resistivity measurements below room temperature on one partially reoxidized sample (National Lead "as supplied," 10 ohm cm) and two vacuum-reduced samples (10 and 5 ohm cm). Below 30°K the activation energies observed were 0.01, 0.028, and 0.034 ev, respectively.

The central line in Fig. 4, with $H\perp c$, is very similar to the B spectrum of Fig. 3. If they can in fact be proved to be the same, the *B* spectrum would have to be regarded as the fundamental spectrum of reduced rutile, and logically attributed to mobile or spatially extensive polaron states.

The results outlined above show clearly that "oxygen-deficient" rutile of a given resistivity has a defect distribution which is dependent on the method of reduction. Although the defect structure of rutile is by no means well understood, one can see how the method of preparation can enter. Straumanis *et al.*[17] have recently shown that the TiO_2 phase boundary is at $TiO_{1.983}$. Beyond this point, according to Hurlen[18] and Andersson *et al.*,[19] one can expect the condensation of oxygen vacancies and their elimination in the formation of planes of interstitial titanium. The defect structure remaining after partial reoxidation will then depend on the relative diffusivities of the defects. This, in turn, is likely to depend on impurities (e.g., nitrogen) in the reoxidizing atmosphere[20] or in the crystal (aluminium is likely to be particularly important here). The possible role of hydrogen has already been discussed.

Since the magnetic and electrical properties of the various possible defects are by no means identical, it is essential for the understanding of the low temperature conductivity of "reduced rutile" that the defect structure be known and controlled. Room temperature resistivity is not a sufficient specification. In this connection the diagnostic value of ESR has been demonstrated.

ACKNOWLEDGMENTS

The experimental work in this paper was carried out at the Westinghouse Research Laboratories and it is a pleasure to thank T. Holstein and E. I. Blount for many informative and stimulating discussions there. The interpretation was carried out in part at the Central Electricity Research Laboratories, where the work is continuing, and the author is grateful to the C.E.G.B. for the opportunity to present this paper.

[17] M. E. Straumanis, T. Ejima, and W. J. James, Acta Cryst. **14**, 493 (1961).

[18] Tor Hurlen, Acta. Chem. Scand. **13**, 365 (1959).

[19] S. Andersson, B. Collén, U. Kuylenstierna, and A. Magnéli, Acta Chem. Scand. **11**, 1641 (1957).

[20] V. I. Arkharov and G. P. Luckin, Doklady Akad. Nauk. S.S.S.R. **83**, 837 (1952).

Reprinted from JOURNAL OF APPLIED PHYSICS, Vol. 31, No. 9, 1566–1571, September, 1960

Chromium-Doped Titania as a Maser Material*†

H. J. GERRITSEN, S. E. HARRISON, AND H. R. LEWIS
RCA Laboratories, Princeton, New Jersey
(Received March 4, 1960; and in final form May 16, 1960)

A discussion of the paramagnetic properties of Cr^{3+} in TiO_2 is given with particular reference to its use in solid-state masers. Energy level diagrams are included for magnetic fields in the (110), (1$\bar{1}$0), (001), and (100) planes.

I. INTRODUCTION

IN the short time since Bloembergen[1] first suggested the possibility of producing a cw solid-state maser, amplifiers using this principle have been operated at frequencies ranging from 300[2] to 39 000 Mc.[3] A large variety of circuits have been employed in these amplifiers including those which use resonant cavities to strengthen the coupling of the radiation to the paramagnetic ions and those which use slow wave structures for the same purpose. However, the most important element in a device of this kind is the paramagnetic material and to date little choice has been available for this component. By far the largest number of masers have employed chromium as the paramagnetic ion in a host lattice of either $K_3Co(CN)_6$ or Al_2O_3. Gadolinium ethyl sulphate[4] has also been used in a maser, but has relatively poor properties for this application. Iron-doped alumina has been used in at least one amplifier and is principally of interest because it can be used in a zero-field device.[5] This article describes in detail the properties of a new maser material, chromium-doped titania,[6] which has already been used to extend the frequency range of masers and which should in addition lead to improved amplifiers at the lower frequencies.

II. HOST LATTICE (TiO_2)

Titania is a very hard crystal (7–7½ mohs) with a Debye temperature of 758°K at 4°K.[7] It withstands large temperature changes with no apparent damage. Its crystal structure[8] (Fig. 1) is tetrahedral (D_{4h}), and the c axis can be found conveniently by using polarized light. The dielectric constant of titania is rather large and varies slowly with frequency. At 9 kMc[9] it is 91 perpendicular to the c axis. Measurements of dielectric constant have recently been made at 23 kMc by Magid and Sabisky, at RCA Laboratories: the result is 88 perpendicular to the axis at room temperature, increasing to 121 at 77°K. Large changes in the dielectric constant of titania may be made by adding small amounts of certain metal ions to the lattice.[10a] However, the addition of about 1% chromium or iron does not radically alter its dielectric properties. Large single crystals of "pure" titania can be obtained from Linde Air Products and the National Lead Company. These samples normally contain about 0.005% iron, an amount easily detectable by paramagnetic resonance. This can lead to some confusion in analyzing the spectrum of samples intentionally doped with other paramagnetic ions.

III. CHROMIUM IN TITANIA

While pure titania is fairly translucent and slightly yellow, titania containing 0.075% chromium by weight is black. Even slabs 0.030 in. thick are quite opaque and the crystal axis must be found by x-ray analysis. The paramagnetic spectrum of this material is easily observed at room temperature; the absorption lines are strong and relatively narrow (~60 Mc) so that the hyperfine structure due to the 9% of isotope Cr^{53}, with nuclear spin of $\frac{3}{2}$, is easily detected in unenriched samples. A minor practical difficulty in observing the spectrum is caused by the large dielectric constant of

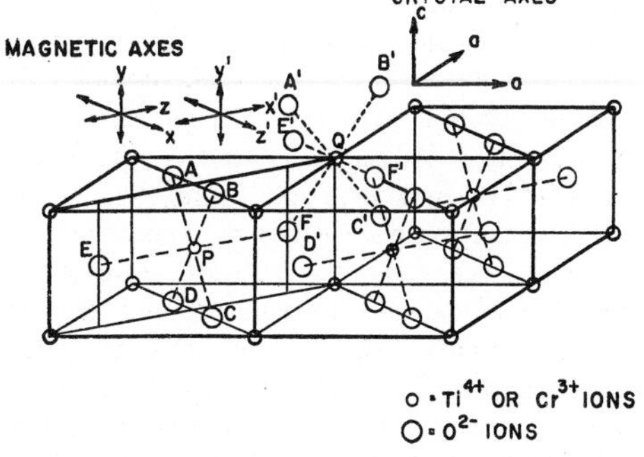

FIG. 1. Crystal structure of TiO_2 and its magnetic axes.

* Partially supported by U. S. Army (Signal Corps).

† Energy levels at 10° intervals in these planes as well as transition-probabilities along the axes can be obtained from the authors.

[1] N. Bloembergen, Phys. Rev. **104**, 324 (1956).

[2] R. H. Kingston, Proc. I.R.E. **46**, 916 (1958).

[3] S. Foner and L. R. Momo, Lincoln Laboratory Rept. M82-16 (December 11, 1959).

[4] H. E. D. Scovil, G. Feher, and H. Seidel, Phys. Rev. **105**, 762 (1957).

[5] R. W. Terhune and I. E. King, Information Note 2, Project Michigan (1959).

[6] H. J. Gerritsen, S. E. Harrison, H. R. Lewis, and J. P. Wittke, Phys. Rev. Letters **2**, 153 (1959). J. Sierro, K. A. Müller, and R. Lacroix, Arch. sci. (Geneva) **12**, 122 (1959).

[7] P. M. Keesom and N. Pearlman, Phys. Rev. **98**, 1539(A) (1955).

[8] R. W. C. Wyckoff, *Crystal Structures Handbook* (Interscience Publishers, Inc., New York, 1958).

[9] J. G. Powles and W. Jackson, Proc. Inst. Elec. Engrs. (London) **96**, 383 (1949).

[10] (a) Ia. M. Ksendzov, Acad. Sci. U.S.S.R. **22**, 3 (1958); (b) B. Marinden and A. Magneli, Acta Chem. Scand. **11**, 1635 (1957).

titania, which has the effect of making even very small samples significantly perturb cavity fields. One way of avoiding this difficulty is to mount samples in waveguide without using a cavity. The material itself acts as a resonant structure and a movable plunger behind the sample can be used to adjust the coupling. The theory of this kind of resonant structure has been studied by O. Okaya[11] at Columbia University.

An analysis[6] of the paramagnetic resonance spectrum (Figs. 2–4) of titania containing 0.075% by weight of chromium shows that trivalent chromium ions substitutionally replace titanium ions in the lattice. The local crystal field at the chromium ions is orthorhombic and has the symmetry D_{2h}. The appropriate Hamiltonian[12] is then

$$H=\beta H\cdot g\cdot S+DS_z^2+E(S_x^2-S_y^2)+AI\cdot S.$$

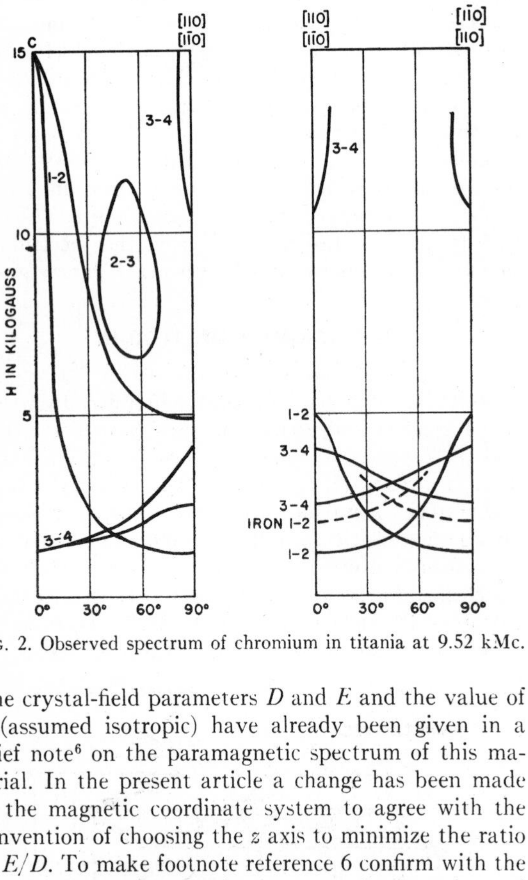

FIG. 2. Observed spectrum of chromium in titania at 9.52 kMc.

The crystal-field parameters D and E and the value of g (assumed isotropic) have already been given in a brief note[6] on the paramagnetic spectrum of this material. In the present article a change has been made in the magnetic coordinate system to agree with the convention of choosing the z axis to minimize the ratio of E/D. To make footnote reference 6 confirm with the present choice, the y and z axes must be interchanged and the value of D and E must be transformed to refer to the new coodinate system. In order to make reading easier, reference will also be made to the crystal axes wherever it seems important. The direction cosines of the new coodinate system with respect to the crystal axes, and the appropriate values of D, E, and g are

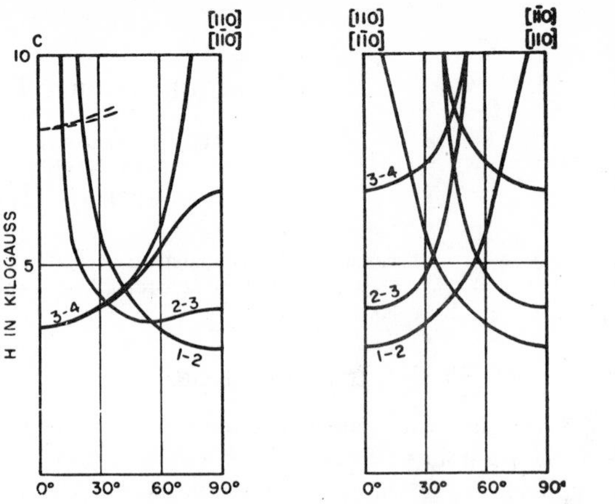

FIG. 3. Observed spectrum of chromium in titania at 23.8 kMc.

given in Table I. The crystal field parameters are quite insensitive to temperature change. There are two titanium (or chromium ions) per unit cell and these are related by a 90° rotation about the y axis. The sign of D was determined by observing absorption intensity ratios at 4.2° and 1.4°K. As is well known, a change in the sign of D inverts the energy levels but leaves them otherwise unchanged. Generally speaking, this is of little importance for materials like ruby where the zero-field splitting is small, but may be quite significant in chromium-doped titania where even at low fields some levels are separated by energies of the order of kT at 4.2°K. In choosing the sign of E, the convention of labeling the axes as xyz according to increasing ratio of $|D/E|$ was followed. Because of the particular arrangement of the two systems of magnetic axes, the absolute sign of E could not be determined.

According to susceptibility measurements on powdered rutile with iron and chromium concentrations of 1% and higher[13] it seems that those ions are mainly in the 4^+ state when replacing titania in the lattice.

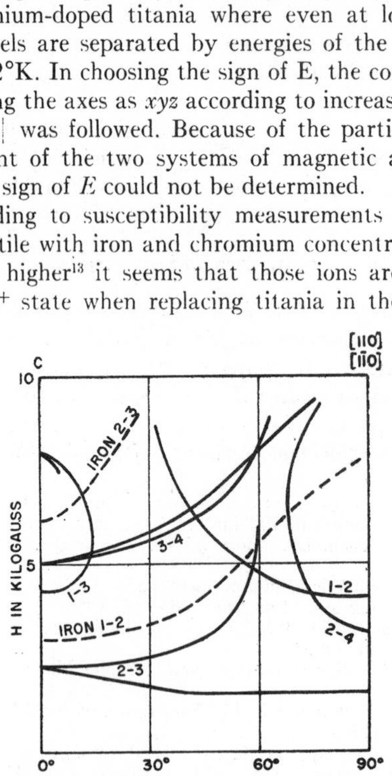

FIG. 4. Observed spectrum of chromium in titania at 34.0 kMc.

[11] O. Okaya (private communication).

[12] K. D. Bowers and J. Owen, Repts. Progr. Phys. 18, 304 (1955).

[13] P. W. Selwood and Lorraine Lyon, Discussions Faraday Soc. 8, 227 (1950),

TABLE I. Magnetic axes and crystal field parameters of Cr^{3+} in TiO_2.

	a	a	c	
				$D=-0.68\ cm^{-1}(\pm 0.005)$
x	$-\sqrt{2}/2$	$\pm\sqrt{2}/2$	0	$E=-0.14\ cm^{-1}(\pm 0.005)$
y	0	0	1	$g=1.97(\pm 0.01)$
z	$\pm\sqrt{2}/2$	$+\sqrt{2}/2$	0	$A=0.0015\ cm^{-1}(\pm 0.0002)=45$ Mc
				Zero field splitting $=2(D^2+3E^2)^{\frac{1}{2}}=43.3(\pm 0.2)$ kMc

However, two recent publications[10] bring forward experimental and theoretical evidence that both chromium and iron do replace Ti^{4+} in the lattice but themselves remain in the 3+ valence state. Theoretically this should be the most favorable configuration from energy considerations, because all three ionic radii involved are rather closely the same, while Cr^{4+} and Fe^{4+} with their much smaller radii would introduce large strains in the lattice.

In order to determine how much chromium is in a valence state different from 3+, two sets of experiments were carried out. One was to see whether any extra lines which would be due to chromium in a valence state other than 3+ could be detected. The experiments were done at 4.2°K, because Cr^{4+}, if present, would have short spin lattice relaxation times and thus broad lines, except at low temperature. The search was made at frequencies ranging from 9 to 57 kMc and indeed extra lines were observed, but all of them were 1% or less the intensity of the main Cr^{3+} spectrum. Part of those lines could be identified as iron 3+ and part tentatively as Cr^{3+} in a different lattice position, perhaps with an oxygen vacancy nearby. The zero field splitting for the latter ions is 36.5 (+0.1) kMc at 77°K as compared to 43.3 kMc for the abundant Cr^{3+}. More work is needed, however, to determine the symmetry and constants in the Hamiltonian for this small fraction. All those weak lines were also observed at 77°K. Because it is quite well possible that all the lines due to Cr^{4+} fall outside our frequency magnetic field range, a second method was applied. Careful measurements were done of the magnetic Q at liquid air for five resonances along the three magnetic axes. These values agreed within 10% with Q values computed for those resonances, assuming all the chemically determined Cr to be in the 3+ valence state. Ten different dielectric resonances were used and the mode pattern in each of them could be fairly well determined by comparing calculated transition probabilities with the intensities of the five resonance lines. The spread in the results was about 10%, so that practically all of the chromium in the rutile contributes to the observed spectrum.

TABLE II. Characteristics of maser crystals doped with chromium.

	$K_3Co(CN)_6$	Al_2O_3	TiO_2
Zero field splitting (kMc)	5.1	11.4	43.3
Maximum signal frequency[a] (kMc)	9	20	72
Maximum operating field[a] (kgauss)	3	7.5	28
Pump frequency range[b] (kMc)	4.5–20	10–45	30–180
Relaxation time at 4.2°K[c] (m-sec)	50	10–50	40
Relaxation time at 78°K[c]	very short	0.2–1.0	0.5
Dielectric constant at 300°K	5	8–10	85 160 (and about 50% higher at 4°K)
Concentration in wt % of paramagnetic ions for a 20-gauss linewidth	0.5	0.05	0.1
Ions per unit cell	2	1	2

[a] This is an approximate number based on the field at which the transition probability for the pump decreases to about 10% of its maximum value.
[b] In the case of titania, a more practical limit may be imposed by magnetic field requirements. If the magnetic field is limited to 10 kgauss, the maximum signal frequency for TiO_2 is 50 kMc and the pump range is 30–120 kMc.
[c] The relaxation times of titania were measured using the cw method and are subject to appreciable error because of the difficulty in calculating H_{rf} within a high dielectric sample in a resonant cavity.

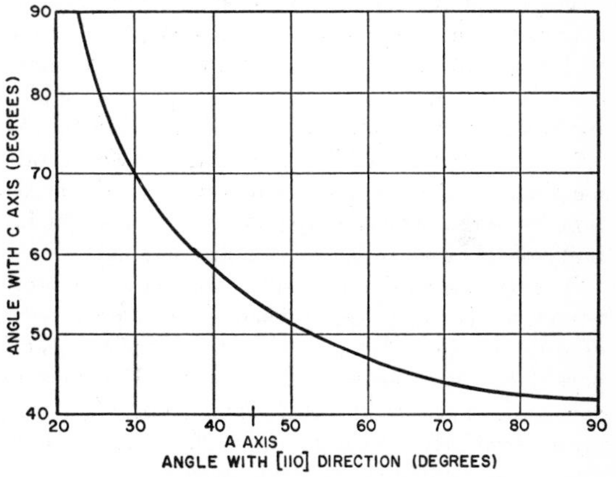

FIG. 5. Orientations for push-pull operation of chromium in titania masers.

IV. CHROMIUM-DOPED TITANIA AS A MASER MATERIAL

Titania doped with chromium has a number of properties which make it important as a maser material (Table II). Because of its large zero field splitting, 43.3 kMc, it can be used in amplifiers operating at frequencies up to 50 kMc with magnetic fields under 10 kgauss. If this field limitation is lifted, higher signal frequencies can be obtained. A maser has been operated at a signal frequency of 23 kMc[14] using a pump at 50 kMc and it should not be difficult to construct an amplifier at the first atmospheric "window" (approx 35 kMc). Moreover, the zero-field splitting is not so large that pump power becomes a problem. For example, a 9 kMc maser[14] was pumped with a Philips DX-184 klystron operating at 34 kMc. This device had a gain-bandwidth product of 25 Mc at 4.2°K and performance was limited by oscillation. Klystrons providing sufficient pump power are also available at higher frequencies

[14] H. J. Gerritsen and H. R. Lewis, Quantum Electronics Conference, Bloomingsburg, New York, September, 1959.

to exploit fully the high-signal-frequency possibilities of this material.

The relaxation times of titania are much like those of ruby in both absolute value and temperature dependence. Thus operation at temperatures above 4.2°K should be possible for titania. The very high dielectric constant of titania has some interesting device implications. In the 9-kMc maser reported above a sample 0.25×0.75×0.1 in. was used. Because of the high dielectric constant, this sample formed a resonant cavity operating in a very high mode. Thus cavity resonances at the signal frequency were spaced at intervals of about 10 Mc and it was possible to make several of these resonances simultaneously emissive. This suggests that by using a somewhat larger sample, cavity resonances can be made to overlap at the signal frequency to produce an electronically tuneable cavity maser.

Alternatively, the high dielectric constant can be used to advantage in a traveling wave maser. If a waveguide is entirely filled with dielectric, a slowing factor equal to $(\epsilon)^{\frac{1}{2}}$ is obtained. In the case of titania this may be sufficient slowing for a practical amplifier. In addition the less tangent of chromium-doped rutile is only about 5.10^{-5} at 77° and 4°K. The advantages of this arrangement are very broad tuneable bandwidth and an exceptionally simple structure. Experiments to test the feasibility of this kind of application are planned.

A direct comparison of ruby and chromium-doped titania at low frequencies where both can be used is of some interest. To date only the titania maser reported has been operated at 9 kMc. The measured gain-bandwidth product of 25 Mc was obtained using a rather primitive circuit in which the cavity coupling was not adjustable. A new device with variable coupling is under construction and should give a better idea of the ultimate capabilities of the amplifier. Many ruby masers have been built and the design of these devices has reached a fairly sophisticated state. For example, workers at the University of Michigan have reported a gain-bandwidth product of 500 Mc in a 9-kMc device operated at 4.2°K.[15]

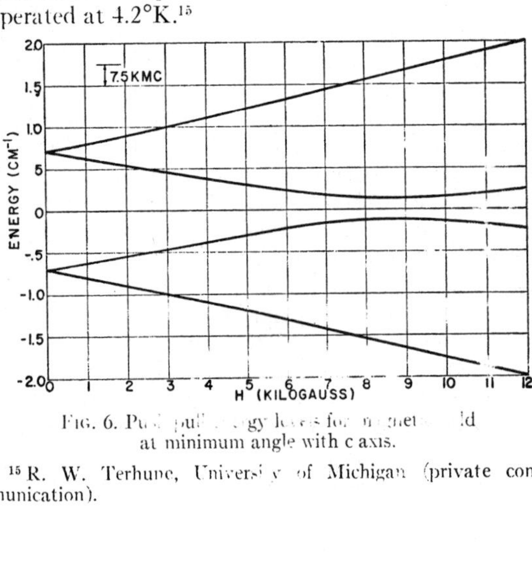

FIG. 6. Push-pull energy levels for magnetic field at minimum angle with c axis.

[15] R. W. Terhune, University of Michigan (private communication).

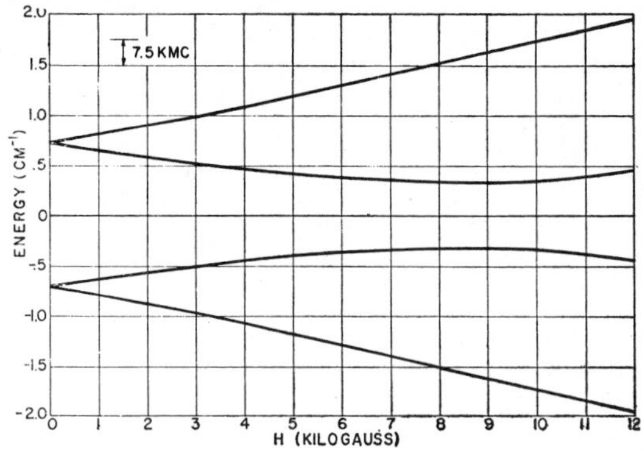

FIG. 7. Push-pull energy levels along *a* axis.

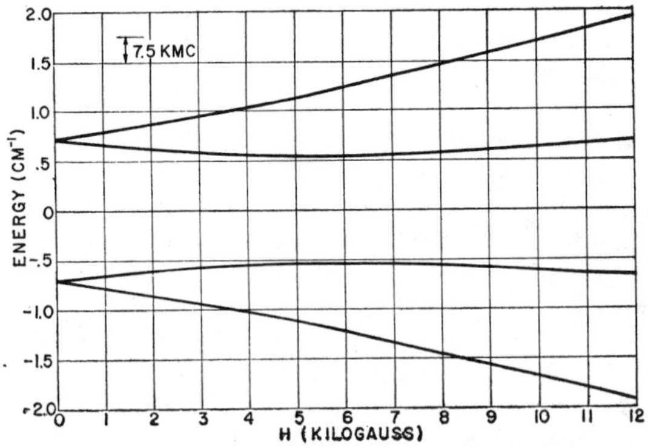

FIG. 8. Push-pull energy levels for magnetic field at maximum angle with c axis.

The possibility that chromium-doped titania can equal and even surpass this figure is suggested by the following argument. The density of chromium ions in rutile is twice the density of chromium ions in ruby in crystals with equal line width (50 Mc). This advantage of rutile just compensates for its disadvantage of two ions per unit cell. Consequently one expects the magnetic Q of chromium-doped rutile to be lower than that of ruby because it can be pumped at a higher frequency. Moreover, rutile can be operated in orientations where the two ions per unit cell are identical. In this case its magnetic Q is further reduced by 50% and consequently its bandwidth can be increased.

Both ruby and chromium-doped titania can be operated in either the push-push or the push-pull mode[16,17] to increase inversion. Because titania is orthorhombic, a variety of energy levels suitable for push-pull operation can be found while in ruby only one energy level diagram is available for this purpose. On the other hand, it should be easier to orient ruby than titania to obtain push-pull operation. The crystal orientations for push-pull operation of chromium-doped titania are given by

[16] Lincoln Lab., Quarterly Progr. Rept. July, 1959 (unpublished).

[17] C. Kikuchi, J. Lambe, G. Makhov, and R. W. Terhune, J. Appl. Phys. 30, 106 (1959).

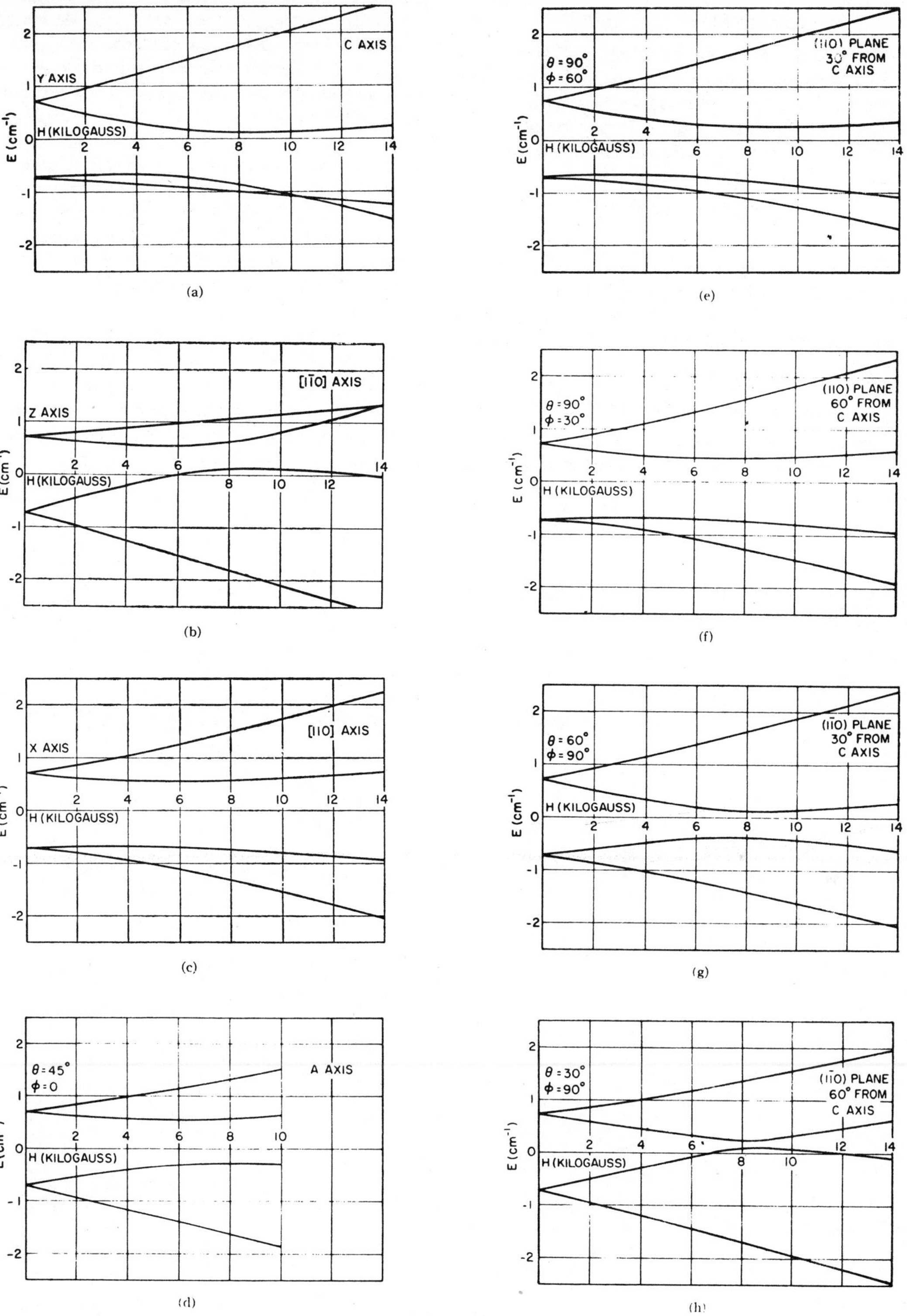

Fig. 9. Energy levels of Cr^{3+} in TiO_2.

the relation[17]

$$\cos 2\phi = (D/E)[1-(2/3\sin^2\theta)],$$

where θ and ϕ are the polar coodinates. Figure 5 is a plot of this relation relative to the c axis of the crystal.

Figures 6–8 show representative push-pull energy level diagrams of titania. Figure 7 may be of special interest since it combines push-pull operation with an orientation in which all ions are identical.

ACKNOWLEDGMENTS

The authors express their thanks to I. Bernal for his assistance in the study of the paramagnetic resonance spectra and to Macy Heller for his help in the construction of equipment and data taking. We have also profited from discussions with A. Okaya of Columbia University.

APPENDIX

Energy Levels of Cr^{3+} in TiO_2

The energy levels which follow are given in two distinct notations. On the left side of each graph the appropriate spherical coordinates of the magnetic field relative to the magnetic axes are stated. Although these axes have been chosen to conform with convention, they are not particularly well suited to this crystal. For example, the two ions per unit cell are related to one another by a rotation about the y magnetic axis. Therefore, the plane in which the two ions are identical is not simply stated in spherical coordinates in the magnetic system. For this reason, the energy level diagrams have also been labeled with orientations relative to the crystal axes. This designation appears on the right-hand side of each graph. For example, the plane in which the two ions are identical is the ac plane in this notation.

In using these diagrams one should remember that a single graph applies to one of the two nonequivalent ions. The energy levels for the second ion are found by looking at the graph appropriate for a magnetic field rotated 90° about the y (or c) axis from the actual field. [See Figs. 9(a)–9(h).]

Two-Level Maser Materials*

R. H. Hoskins
Research Laboratories, Hughes Aircraft Company, Culver City, California
(Received January 27, 1959)

THE purpose of this note is to comment upon some advantages of paramagnetic ions in ionic crystals as materials for two-level solid-state masers. It has been suggested[1] that the true spin lattice relaxation time for paramagnetic ions in ionic crystals may be much shorter than that measured by cw saturation methods, thereby precluding inversion of the electron spin population by adiabatic rapid passage.[2] It has been found in this laboratory that such inversion may be readily achieved by a method similar to that described by Chester, Wagner, and Castle.[3] Inversion by adiabatic rapid passage of $\Delta m=1$ spin transitions has been observed for Cr^{+++} in Al_2O_3, $K_3CO(CN)_6$, and $La_2Mg_3(NO_3)_{12}\cdot 24H_2O$ and for Gd^{+++} in $La_2Mg_3(NO_2)_{12}\cdot 24H_2O$ at liquid helium temperatures. The relaxation time of the inverted state, of the order of 10^{-2} sec at liquid He temperatures, was found to be in rough agreement with that measured by cw microwave methods.

A two-level solid-state maser employing ruby[4] as the paramagnetic material has been operated at X band at liquid helium temperatures. Spin population inversion was easily achieved by sweeping the magnetic field through the resonance in a time of about 50 microseconds while an inverting microwave pulse of approximately 500 milliwatts was applied. Upon returning the magnetic field to resonance, either oscillation or amplification of a small probing signal was observed depending upon the size of the inverting pulse, the cavity coupling, and the elapsed time after the inverting pulse. No attempt was made to provide the stability of the inverting pulse necessary for stable operation of the device as a low noise amplifier. The repetition rate was limited by the relaxation time to about 10 sec^{-1}.

The crystalline field splitting of the magnetic energy levels inherent in ionic crystals may be used to advantage in lessening magnetic field requirements of two-level solid-state masers. At X band, for example, two-level maser operation in ruby was obtained in an external field of only 500 gauss. The extensions to higher microwave frequencies are obvious and attempts to effect systematic changes in crystal field parameters[5] are under way in this laboratory.

The limitation on the repetition rate of two-level masers imposed by the long thermal relaxation time is a serious disadvantage. An alternative scheme would make use of the multiple energy levels of materials commonly used for three-level masers. Referring to the energy level diagram[6] for Cr^{+3} in Fig. 1, suppose that it is desired to amplify at X band, corresponding to ν_{43}, and that the magnetic field is fixed at H_0. If the magnetic field is pulsed down to H_0' such that $\nu_{42}'=\nu_{43}$, inversion of the spin population of levels

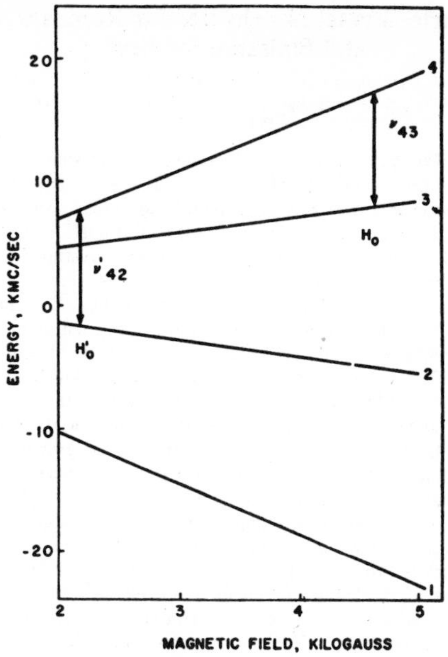

FIG. 1. Energy levels of Cr^{+3} in $K_3Co(CN)_6$ near $H_0 \perp a$ axis.

3 and 2 would result if a pulse of microwave power of frequency ν_{43} having sufficient power to saturate the ν_{42} transition were applied. The field is then returned to H_0 and amplification could be obtained. The advantage of obtaining inversion by this method rather than by adiabatic rapid passage is that the system need not return completely to thermal equilibrium before being reactivated and the repetition rate might be much faster than T_1^{-1}. The same inversion technique could be applied for generation of higher microwave frequencies.

We wish to thank Dr. T. H. Maiman and Dr. G. Birnbaum for helpful discussions and C. Duncan for technical assistance.

* Supported in part by the U. S. Army Signal Corps.
[1] Giordmaine, Alsop, Nash, and Townes, Phys. Rev. **109**, 302 (1958).
[2] F. Bloch, Phys. Rev. **70**, 460 (1946).
[3] Chester, Wagner, and Castle, Phys. Rev. **110**, 281 (1958).
[4] Linde pink sapphire, 0.1% nomial Cr^{+++} concentration.
[5] Hoskins, Trigger, and Pastor, J. Chem. Phys. (to be published).
[6] D. P. Devor and T. H. Maiman, Hughes Aircraft Company, Quarterly Progress Report DA 36-039 SC-74951 (February, 1958).

Single-Crystal Molybdates for Resonance and Emission Studies

G. VAN UITERT, F. W. SWANEKAMP, AND S. PREZIOSI
Bell Telephone Laboratories, Inc., Murray Hill, New Jersey
(Received February 23, 1961)

OXIDES that can be readily grown as large single crystals, and into which rare-earth as well as transition-metal ions can be incorporated, are of considerable interest for microwave and optical maser studies. To this end, conditions for growing a number of molybdate compositions have been investigated.

Lead molybdate, which has the scheelite structure, can be pulled as a clear, slightly yellow crystal by the modified Czochralski technique wherein the crystal is rotated while being pulled. In structure and properties it is related to calcium tungstate, which has been discussed in more detail elsewhere.[1,2] The melting point of lead molybdate is 1075°C, well within the temperature range of ordinary resistance furnaces and platinum crucibles. Large disks of this material are readily grown by nucleation on a platinum wire or by growth from a suspended seed crystal under low-temperature-gradient conditions. Such conditions can be obtained by working, with the molten material held in a platinum crucible in the upper part of a pot furnace, through a hole which is about $\frac{1}{4}$ to $\frac{1}{2}$ the diameter of the crucible.

Rods similar to those previously reported for calcium tungstate[3] are readily grown under high-temperature-gradient conditions, such as are obtained when the melt is contained by a platinum crucible susceptor which is heated directly by rf induction and without surrounding shielding. Rare earths as well as transition metal ions are readily incorporated into lead molybdate under these conditions. When Eu^{3+} is incorporated, part of it is reduced to Eu^{2+}, giving a red color to the crystal. However, this discoloration can be removed by oxidizing the Eu^{2+}. This is accomplished by annealing at 700°C in oxygen. The fluorescent intensity of Eu^{3+} is about the same before and after annealing. This indicates that the fraction of europium originally in the reduced state is small.

The absorption edges of the molybdates are at longer wavelengths than those of the corresponding tungstates. That for $PbMoO_4$ is at about 3700 A.[1] This is responsible for its slightly yellow color. $PbMoO_4$ shows a bright green band fluorescence at liquid-nitrogen temperature under short-wave or long-wave ultraviolet excitation. Trivalent praseodymium can be excited by 3660-A excitation in this material, while in $CaWO_4$ it is only excited by short-wave ultraviolet or direct radiation into the absorption bands of Pr^{3+}. The latter lie at about 4500, 4700, and 5900 A. The fluorescence of Pr^{3+} in $PbMoO_4$ produced by 3660-A excitation is due to the close proximity of the absorption edge to the exciting frequency in this material. The absorption edge of $CaWO_4$, in contrast, is at about 2500 A.

As in the tungstates,[4] trivalent dysprosium fluoresces strongly in lead molybdate when present at about 1 mole % of the lead content and excited by a 3660-A spotlamp. This is largely due to direct radiation into an absorption band of dysprosium which lies about the same wavelength as the peak in the lamp radiation.

Zinc molybdate melts at 900°C. It can be pulled, under high-temperature-gradient conditions, as a clear, water-white crystal from a mixture of the component oxides. Rare-earth ions as well as transition-metal ions can be incorporated into this material. The amounts of the rare earths entering the structure are small, but can be easily detected by their visible fluorescence.

A number of akali-metal–rare-earth molybdates can be grown as single crystals in the form of thin micalike sheets under low-as well as high-temperature-gradient conditions. Cesium-europium molybdate, $CsEu(MoO_4)_2$, for example, can be pulled or grown upon a wire or seed below the surface of a melt containing equal mole parts of $CsEu(MoO_4)_2$ and Cs_2MoO_4 at about 1050°C. These materials show the characteristic rare-earth fluorescence.

[1] F. A. Kröger, *Some Aspects of the Luminescence of Solids* (Elsevier Publishing Company, Inc., New York, 1947).
[2] L. G. Van Uitert and R. R. Soden, J. Appl. Phys. **31**, 328 (1960).
[3] K. Nassau and L. G. Van Uitert, J. Appl. Phys. **31**, 1508 (1960).
[4] L. G. Van Uitert, J. Electrochem. Soc. **107**, 803 (1960).

Paramagnetic Resonance Spectra of f^3 Ions in a Cubic Site*

G. VINCOW† AND W. LOW
Department of Physics, The Hebrew University, Jerusalem, Israel

(Received January 23, 1961)

The paramagnetic resonance spectra of Nd^{3+} and U^{3+} in the cubic field of CaF_2 have been investigated at 3 cm at 20°K. In the case of Nd^{3+} transitions within the lowest quartet $\Gamma_8^{(2)}$ and possibly in the next higher quartet $\Gamma_8^{(1)}$ have been observed. The angular behavior conforms with that predicted by Bleaney's formulism of the spin Hamiltonian of a Γ_8 state. In the case of U^{3+} there are considerable deviations of the experimental g values from the calculated ones. It is suggested that these deviations are caused by the stronger cubic field.

The efficiency of the thermal conversion from axial to cubic site is discussed. Additional lines suggest a new axial center along the [111] direction.

I. INTRODUCTION

In this paper we present the results of an investigation of the paramagnetic resonance spectra of trivalent neodymium and trivalent uranium ions in the cubic sites of single crystals of calcium fluoride. Spectra of these ions in an axial site have been reported briefly by Bleaney *et al.*[1] The cubic field spectra of the f^3 system are of particular interest in that they can be used as a check on the recently proposed spin Hamiltonian of a Γ_8 state.[2]

Single crystals of calcium flouride showing the cubic-site spectra of neodymium were grown by the Stockbarger process as reported by Dvir and Low.[3] The crystals containing uranium and neodymium were obtained from R. W. H. Stevenson of the University of Aberdeen. These showed axial-site spectra exclusively.

All measurements reported here were made at 20°K and 3-cm wavelength.

II. SPECTRUM OF NEODYMIUM IN A CUBIC SITE

In a cubic field the ground state of the f^3 configuration ($^4I_{9/2}$) is split into two Γ_8 quartets and one Γ_6 doublet. Neglecting nuclear effects, the Hamiltonian for the problem is given by

$$\mathcal{H}=g\beta(\mathbf{J}\cdot\mathbf{H})+B_4{}^0O_4{}^0+B_4{}^4O_4{}^4+B_6{}^0O_6{}^0+B_6{}^4O_6{}^4, \quad (1)$$

where $O_n{}^m$ are operators having the same transformation properties as the corresponding spherical harmonics. $B_n{}^m$ are crystal field coefficients which can be determined from paramagnetic resonance or optical absorption spectra. In the cubic field case the relation

$$B_4{}^0O_4{}^0+B_4{}^4O_4{}^4+B_6{}^0O_6{}^0+B_6{}^4O_6{}^4 = B_4{}^0(O_4{}^0+5O_4{}^4)+B_6{}^0(O_6{}^0-21O_6{}^4)$$

holds.

Evaluation of the matrices using Stevens' operator techniques[4] yields the following energy levels:

$$\begin{aligned}\Gamma_6&: 28c-182.5d,\\ \Gamma_8{}^{(1)}&: 12.18c+151.0d,\\ \Gamma_8{}^{(2)}&: -26.18c-59.5d,\end{aligned} \quad (2)$$

where c and d refer to the fourth- and sixth-order contribution of the crystal field potential, respectively.

For a point-charge model of an eight-coordinated CaF_2 crystal, these can be calculated explicitly to be

$$\begin{aligned}c&=(50/3)(Z_{\rm eff}e^2/R^5)\beta_{9/2}\langle r^4\rangle,\\ d&=50(Z_{\rm eff}e^2/R^7)\gamma_{9/2}\langle r^6\rangle,\end{aligned} \quad (3)$$

where $\beta_{9/2}$ and $\gamma_{9/2}$ are multiplicative factors[5] and $Z_{\rm eff}$ is the effective charge.

For all values of c and d the lowest energy is given by $\Gamma_8{}^{(2)}$. The predicted transitions and relative intensity within the two quartets along the [100] directions are given in Table I.

The angular dependence as well as the transition probabilities can be calculated using Bleaney's formalism of the spin Hamiltonian of a Γ_8 state[2] (provided the cubic field splitting is larger than the Zeeman energy):

$$\mathcal{H}=g\beta(H_xS_x+H_yS_y+H_zS_z) +f\beta(H_xS_x{}^3+H_yS_y{}^3+H_zS_z{}^3), \quad (4)$$

where f and g are constants related to Λ, the Lande g factor.

The angular dependence of the energy levels of the quartet can be expressed in terms of the parameters f and g and the direction cosines l, m, n as[2]

$$(W/\beta H)^2=\tfrac{1}{4}(5\gamma^2+3\delta^2) \pm\gamma\{\gamma^2+\tfrac{1}{2}\delta^2[9(l^4+m^4+n^4)-3]\}^{\frac{1}{2}}, \quad (5)$$

where $\gamma=g+(7/4)f$, and $\delta^2=f(g+5f/2)$.

---

* Supported in part by the U. S. Office of Scientific Research, Air Research and Development Command, through its European Office.

† Israel Ministry of Culture and Education Scholar. This award was under the auspices of the Institute of International Education.

[1] B. Bleaney, P. M. Llewellyn, and D. A. Jones, Proc. Phys. Soc. (London) **69**, 858 (1956).

[2] B. Bleaney, Proc. Phys. Soc. (London) **73**, 939 (1959).

[3] M. Dvir and W. Low, Proc. Phys. Soc. (London) **75**, 136 (1960).

[4] K. W. H. Stevens, Proc. Phys. Soc. (London) **65**, 209 (1952); see also W. Low, *Paramagnetic Resonance in Solids* (Academic Press, Inc., New York, 1960), Tables VII(a) and (b) and Tables IX(a) and (b).

[5] W. Low, Proc. Phys. Soc. (London) **75**, 136 (1960), Table X.

TABLE I. Predicted transition within the Γ_8 quartet along the [100] direction.

	g value	Transition	Relative intensity
$\Gamma_8^{(2)}$	2.24	$0.8722\|-\frac{5}{2}\rangle-0.4892\|+\frac{3}{2}\rangle \rightarrow 0.8722\|+\frac{5}{2}\rangle-0.4892\|-\frac{3}{2}\rangle$	2.0
	1.15	$0.8722\|\pm\frac{5}{2}\rangle-0.4892\|\mp\frac{3}{2} \rightarrow 0.05410\|\mp 9/2\rangle-0.2981\|\mp\frac{1}{2}\rangle+0.9530\|\pm\frac{7}{2}\rangle$	4.4
	4.54	$0.05410\|+9/2\rangle-0.2981\|+\frac{1}{2}\rangle+0.9530\|-\frac{7}{2}\rangle \rightarrow 0.05410\|-9/2\rangle-0.2981\|-\frac{1}{2}\rangle+0.9530\|+\frac{7}{2}$	0.075
$\Gamma_8^{(1)}$	1.63	$0.8722\|-\frac{5}{2}\rangle-0.4892\|+\frac{3}{2}\rangle \rightarrow 0.8722\|+\frac{5}{2}\rangle-0.4892\|-\frac{3}{2}\rangle$	1.1
	0.789	$0.8722\|\pm\frac{5}{2}\rangle-0.4892\|\mp\frac{3}{2} \rightarrow 0.05410\|\mp 9/2\rangle-0.2981\|\mp\frac{1}{2}\rangle+0.9530\|\pm\frac{7}{2}\rangle$	2.02
	4.05	$0.05410\|+9/2\rangle-0.2981\|+\frac{1}{2}\rangle+0.9530\|-\frac{7}{2}\rangle \rightarrow 0.05410\|-9/2\rangle-0.2981\|-\frac{1}{2}\rangle+0.9530\|+\frac{7}{2}\rangle$	0.044

The transition probability is easily calculated from $|\langle\Psi_i|gS_z+fS_z^3|\Psi_j\rangle|^2$, with i and j taking the values 1, 2, 3, 4 of the four eigenvectors Ψ corresponding to the solution of matrix (4).

Investigation of the cubic field spectrum is complicated by the presence of the axial field spectra with the many hyperfine levels of the two odd isotopes of neodymium. We have observed two lines along the [100] direction, one at $g=2.26\pm0.02$ and a less intense line at $g=1.10\pm0.05$. Both these lines showed an anisotropic angular dependence.

Along the [110] direction, lines were predicted at $g=1.46$, 1.70, 4.85, and 3.16 with relative intensities in the ratio of 2.02:1.43:0.047:0.0024, respectively. A line was detected along this direction with $g=1.45\pm0.01$ and approximate full width at half maximum of 75 gauss. An overlapping weak shoulder observed on the low-field end of this line could be identified with the predicted line at $g=1.70$ and has the approximate g value (allowing for overlap) of 1.6.

The angular variation of the transition corresponding to the g value 2.26 along the [100] direction is given in Table II.

The detection of lines associated with the higher energy quartet $\Gamma_8^{(1)}$ and doublet is complicated because of the many hyperfine lines from the axial spectrum. Values of g were calculated for the higher energy quartet along various directions. Along the [111] direction, no axial neodymium lines should interfere with the predicted line at $g=1.63$. A very weak and wide line was observed along this axis at $g=1.55\pm0.03$, which we tentatively attribute to the $\Gamma_8^{(2)}$ quartet. No line was observed which could be identified with the Γ_6 doublet for which an isotropic line with $g=8/3$ is predicted.

Approximately 20% of the trivalent neodymium in the crystal investigated was in a cubic site.

The optical spectrum of these crystals is now being investigated by one of us (W.L.) at liquid helium temperatures. Preliminary results show differences in the linewidth between the two crystals. The well-annealed crystal of Nd containing only axial sites has much sharper optical absorption lines.

III. SPECTRUM OF URANIUM IN A CUBIC SITE

In a heat-treated crystal of uranium, two extremely weak lines were observed along the [110] direction which can be associated with cubic sites. The g values are 1.57 and 1.62, and the relative intensities are about 1.5:1. The line width taken between points of maximum slope is approximately 50 gauss for both lines.

For a pure $^4I_{9/2}$ ground state of uranium, the calculated g values are the same as for neodymium. The above values should be compared with the predicted g values of $g=1.46$ and $g=1.70$ with calculated relative intensities of 1.4:1. The angular variation of these lines was observed in the (001) plane. Both lines move down in field when the angle is varied from the [110] direction towards the [100] direction. The angular variation of the $g=1.57$ line is in semiquantitative agreement with the predicted variation; however, the $g=1.62$ line is predicted to move up in field. We are, therefore, not certain regarding the origin of the $g=1.62$ line.

The discrepancy between the calculated and observed g factors could arise from the partial breakdown of Bleaney's spin Hamiltonian for the case when the spin-orbit coupling is of the same order as the cubic field splitting. The increased cubic field splitting is expected for $5f$ electrons which are not as well shielded and take part in the chemical bonding. Evidence for the greater extension of the wavefunction is found by observation of the fluorine hyperfine structure in the axial spectrum in this crystal. The optical spectrum, moreover, shows linewidths more than 20 times the width of the neodymium spectrum even at liquid helium temperatures, indicative of stronger interactions with the surrounding lattice.

The longer relaxation times of the U^{3+} spectrum as compared with the Nd^{3+} spectrum is further evidence

TABLE II. Angular variation of the $0.8772|-\frac{5}{2}\rangle-0.4892|+\frac{3}{2}\rangle \rightarrow 0.8722|+\frac{5}{2}\rangle-0.4892|-\frac{3}{2}\rangle$ transition in the $\Gamma_8^{(2)}$ quartet.

Angle	g calculated	g experimental ±0.02
0°	2.24	2.26
10°	2.16	2.15
30°	1.675	1.68
45°	1.46	1.45

of larger crystal field splittings in the U^{3+} case. An additional influence, but probably of smaller magnitude, is the breakdown of Russell-Saunders coupling which is expected to be larger for uranium.

IV. THERMAL TREATMENT OF CRYSTALS

Several attempts were made to convert the neodymium and uranium crystals from axial into cubic sites by the use of the thermal method of Friedman and Low.[6] In the case of neodymium, no spectral lines arising from cubic sites were detected, thus indicating a maximum limit of the conversion of 10%. Extended heating at 1200°C, as well as reduction of the quenching time to 5 min produced no discernible effects.

Application of the same method to uranium crystals resulted in a loss of the characteristic red color of trivalent uranium and the production of either opaque or transparent colorless crystals. Use of a quartz container instead of the graphite crucible[6] led to no significant change in results. No trace of the axial resonance lines was observed, nor were any new lines detected. Apparently a valence transformation had been effected. The fact that no new resonances are observed from the resultant valence state finds confirmation in the investigations of Llewellyn[7] who heat-treated a crystal of $CaF_2:U^{3+}$ in a reducing atmosphere (H_2) and observed a loss of red color and presumably the conversion to divalent uranium. No resonance was observed.

The time of heat treatment was shortened to a few hours and the temperature decreased to 1000°C in order to preserve the trivalent uranium. Both of these modifications should result in a reduced efficiency of conversion. In a crystal heated for 2 hr at 1000°C and quenched in 5 min, about $\frac{1}{2}$% of the uranium was converted to a cubic site.[8]

In a nonheated crystal no cubic lines were observed, and the upper limit of uranium in a cubic site was $\frac{1}{4}$%.

In view of these experiments we tentatively propose that there is a great difference in conversion efficiency between S-state and non-S-state ions. Further, in the case of non-S-state ions, it is probably the rate of lowering through the thermal gradient and not the annealing process which is predominant in determining the point symmetry. It has been previously suggested that S-state ions, because of the symmetric charge distribution, tend to preserve the cubic point symmetry.[9] These experiments seem to give some additional support for this suggestion.

V. ADDITIONAL AXIAL SPECTRA IN THE Nd^{3+} CRYSTAL

In a crystal of Nd containing predominantly axial sites, a number of weak lines were observed with angular variation differing from those associated with the cubic site and the previously investigated axial site. The angular variation indicates that these lines arise from Nd in a new axial site. The site proposed is one in which the excess F^- ion occupies the position at the center of the cube of fluorine ions sharing a corner with the cube containing the Nd ion. Although such a F^- ion is $\sqrt{3}$ times the distance from the rare-earth ion, as in the usual axial site (along the cubic axes), there are $\frac{4}{3}$ as many possible positions. A detailed analysis in the Nd case is made difficult by the presence of the 48 hyperfine lines of the usual axial field spectrum. The trivalent cerium and gadolinium ions are more promising cases of investigation, and in both crystals a number of weak anisotropic lines in the spectrum have been reported previously.[3,10]

ACKNOWLEDGMENT

We are grateful to Dr. R. W. H. Stevenson of the University of Aberdeen for supplying us with some of the doped CaF_2 cyrstals.

[6] E. Friedman and W. Low, J. Chem. Phys. **33**, 1275 (1960).

[7] P. M. Llewellyn, thesis, Oxford University, Cambridge, England, 1956.

[8] In one particular crystal the conversion efficiency was unaccountably much higher. Unfortunately, on repeating the procedure on the same crystal the valence was changed.

[9] W. Low, Phys. Rev. **105**, 801 (1957).

[10] W. Low, Phys. Rev. **109**, 265 (1958).

Reprinted from Journal of Applied Physics, Vol. 31, No. 8, 1508, August, 1960

Preparation of Large Calcium-Tungstate Crystals Containing Paramagnetic Ions for Maser Applications

K. Nassau and L. G. Van Uitert
Bell Telephone Laboratories, Inc., Murray Hill, New Jersey
(Received April 25, 1960)

The technique of pulling single crystals from the melt[1] has been applied to calcium tungstate, both pure and containing rare earth additions. This appears to represent the first clearly successful application of the Czochralski method to multiple oxide systems. This method seems to have been used in the case of pure oxides only for V_2O_5 by Boros,[2] who gives no experimental details. The Kyropoulos technique (growth below the surface of a melt from a rotating seed) has been used for potassium niobate by Miller[3] and barium titanate by Linares,[4] using K_2CO_3 and BaF_2, respectively, as flux. In the present work no flux was used, and continuous pulling produced crystals up to 7 in. in length and up to $\frac{1}{2}$ in. in diam, essentially free from visible defects.

Calcium-tungstate crystals containing rare earth ions are of interest for maser applications.[5,6] Masers employing traveling wave structures in particular require long rods of these materials.

Previous methods used to obtain crystals of calcium tungstate have included growth from the flux[5,7,8] and applications of the Bridgman-Stockbarger[9] and the Verneuil (flame fusion) processes.[9,10] Hydrothermal growth has also been used.[11] Large single crystals have proven to be difficult to obtain by these methods, while the pulling technique employed below appears to impose no limitation as to size, even when appreciable rare earth additions are present.

In the present work, a rhodium crucible was heated directly by rf induction. Crystals were rotated during growth at 12 rpm and pulled at rates of up to 3 in./hr. Seed crystals were not essential, as growth initiated readily on a platinum wire. Small pieces so obtained are then tied to a platinum rod to grow larger crystals. Calcium tungstate grown from the flux as well as commercial luminescent grade material were used, both pure and in combination with flux-grown[5] $Na_{0.5}re_{0.5}WO_4$, where re has included elements such as cerium, europium, gadolinium, terbium, dysprosium, and erbium. Rare earth concentrations as high as 4 formula % are readily incorporated. Other alkali rare earth tungstates, or pure rare earth tungstates, undoubtedly will incorporate readily. It seems likely that at least in the case of low concentrations some sodium is lost.

In the experimental apparatus used, single crystals were readily grown at temperatures near 1600°C. Some annealing was helpful both to prevent cracking of the thicker crystals and to remove the slight discoloration sometimes observed. The latter is believed to originate from slight reduction due to limited access of atmospheric oxygen during growth. The crystals obtained are usually perfectly transparent and fluoresce brightly under ultraviolet illumination. Figure 1 shows a calcium-tungstate crystal containing 0.3% dysprosium and grown as described above. The diameter is nonuniform, due to lack of temperature control during growth. Preliminary results indicate the feasibility of growth in several crystallographic directions. It appears that the maximum dimensions that can be attained are limited only by the sizes of the crucible and pulling mechanism.

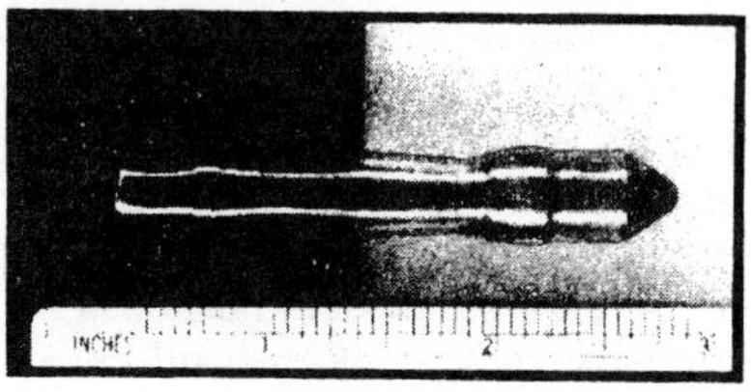

Fig. 1. Calcium-tungstate single crystal containing 0.3% dysprosium pulled from the melt.

The authors wish to acknowledge the assistance of K. E. Benson and F. W. Swanekamp of these Laboratories in the early phases of this work. The flux-grown material was prepared by R. R. Soden and the photograph taken by S. Preziosi.

[1] W. D. Lawson and S. Nielsen, *Preparation of Single Crystals* (Academic Press, Inc., New York, 1958), p. 10 ff.
[2] J. Boros, Z. Physik **126**, 721 (1949).
[3] C. E. Miller, J. Appl. Phys. **29**, 233 (1958).
[4] R. C. Linares, J. Phys. Chem. (to be published).
[5] L. G. Van Uitert and R. R. Soden, J. Appl. Phys. **31**, 328 (1960).
[6] C. F. Hempstead and K. D. Bowers, Phys. Rev. **118**, 131 (1960).
[7] L. G. Sillen and A. L. Nylander, Arkiv. Kemi, Mineral. Geol. **17A**, No. 4 (1943).
[8] I. N. Anikin, Doklady Akad. Nauk. S.S.S.R. **110**, 645 (1956).
[9] S. Zerfoss, L. R. Johnson, and O. Imber, Phys. Rev. **75**, 320 (1949).
[10] R. K. Verma, G. N. Sirkar, and S. Chaterjee, J. Sci. Ind. Research (India) **13A**, 516 (1954).
[11] R. A. Laudise (to be published).

(*Reprinted from Nature, Vol.* 191, *No.* 4791, *pp.* 901–902, *August* 26, 1961)

A New Technique for the Production of Synthetic Corundum

LARGE crystals of corundum have been grown for many years by the flame-fusion process originated by Verneuil[1]. Crystals coloured by small amounts of chromium, titanium, vanadium and other transition metal oxides are used in the gem industry and as jewel bearings and gramophone styli. The recent interest in ruby (chromium-doped corundum) as a paramagnetic material for use in masers and lasers has directed attention to the imperfections of the flame-fusion crystals. In particular, the inhomogeneity of chromium distribution in the crystals, the excessive residual strain and gross lattice imperfections detract from their usefulness in micro-wave and optical devices. Alternative methods of growth capable of giving better quality crystals are therefore of considerable interest for research in solid-state physics.

The hydrothermal growth of corundum has been accomplished (ref. 2 and Butcher, J., private communication, Hirst Research Centre of the General Electric Co., Ltd.), but considerable difficulties are involved in the production of good-quality crystals. It is necessary, for example, to work under conditions of high temperature and pressure where serious attack of conventional autoclave materials is experienced. The development of autoclaves of new design with heat-resisting alloys and inert metal liners is necessary, and the process is not yet suitable for the consistent production of large crystals.

Frémy and Feil[3] in 1877 produced small flakes of corundum from solution in lead oxide, but no further attempts to develop this method are recorded, and presumably after the success of Verneuil in 1890 the incentive to synthesize ruby was largely removed. The fluxed-melt technique for crystal growing has, in recent years, been revived for the laboratory production of comparatively large crystals of several inorganic oxide materials, for example, barium titanate, yttrium iron garnet and calcium tungstate[4].

Good-quality crystals of corundum, pure and doped with transition metal oxides, have now been produced from solution in lead fluoride. The process is carried out in a platinum crucible heated in a conventional laboratory furnace. The crystals are produced by spontaneous nucleation on slow cooling as hexagonal plates up to 2–3 cm. across. The thickness of the plates is largely dependent on the initial conditions of cooling, and in favourable circumstances they measure up to 1 cm. along the *c*-axis.

The crystals grow as truncated trigonal trapezohedra bounded by (0001) and $(10\bar{1}1)$ type faces, but $(10\bar{1}2)$ faces are occasionally observed. The surfaces of the latter appear roughened and they evidently disappear if the duration of growth is sufficiently prolonged. The $\{10\bar{1}2\}$ faces are thus more commonly observed on thick crystals, which require more growth perpendicular to the *c*-axis for these faces to grow out.

There is some tendency for the incorporation of lead fluoride in planes parallel to (0001); but many good-quality clear crystals, free from obvious faults, are obtainable.

The incorporation of high concentrations of paramagnetic ions can be readily achieved by this technique, and the products have the additional advantage of being strain-free.

E. A. D. White

Central Research Laboratories,
Hirst Research Centre,
General Electric Co., Ltd.,
Wembley.

[1] Verneuil, *C.R. Acad. Sci., Paris*, **135**, 791 (1902); *Ann. Chim.* (France), **3**, 20 (1904).

[2] Laudise, R. A., and Ballman, A. A., *J. Amer. Chem. Soc.*, **80**, 2655 (1958).

[3] Frémy, E., and Feil, C., see Smith, Herbert, *Gemstones* (Methuen, London, 1958).

[4] See White, E. A. D., *Quart. Rev. Chem. Soc.*, **15**, 1 (1961).

Reprinted from JOURNAL OF APPLIED PHYSICS, Vol. 33, No. 9, 2908–2909, September, 1962

Zinc Tungstates for Microwave Maser Applications

L. G. VAN UITERT AND S. PREZIOSI
Bell Telephone Laboratories, Incorporated, Murray Hill, New Jersey
(Received May 7, 1962)

The monoclinic tungstates,[1] $MgWO_4$, $ZnWO_4$, and $CdWO_4$ which contain Fe^{3+} and other transition metal ions are of interest for microwave maser studies. The preparation of single crystals of these materials by flux growth methods has been previously described.[2] Zero-field splittings of Fe^{3+} and Cr^{3+} in crystals grown by this method have been measured by Peter.[3,4]

We have found that large single crystals of zinc tungstate, pure and with transition metal ions incorporated, can be readily prepared by the Czochralski technique[5] wherein crystals are pulled from the melt while being rotated. In these experiments a suitable melt was obtained by heating a platinum crucible susceptor containing the component oxides of the crystal to about 1000°C employing an rf induction generator. A typical melt might contain the following ratio of components 0.998 ZnO, 0.0005 Fe_2O_3, 0.005 Li_2O, and 1.00 WO_3. The excess of lithium over that required to compensate for the presence of Fe^{3+} or Cr^{3+} assures its presence in the crystal in stoichiometric amounts. This simplifies the spectra obtained.

These crystals are grown in slab form with a thickness of about $\frac{1}{2}$ of the width when pulled along the axis lying in the (010) plane. When pulled parallel to the (010) axis cylindrical rods are obtained. The latter axis is less desirable, however, due to a relatively easy cleavage in the (010) plane. Crystals pulled in the former orientations appear to be quite stable to thermal shock. Pulled crystals, which have not been annealed, have been cooled to liquid helium temperature without resulting damage.

S. K. Kurtz and W. G. Nilsen of these Laboratories have found the pulled crystals to be of interest for maser applications in the 50 kMc region as well as at lower frequencies. The zero-field splittings for Fe^{3+} in zinc tungstate lie close to 60 and 75 kMc and that for Cr^{3+} lies close to 50 kMc. Preliminary inversion and absorption measurements on the Cr^{3+}-doped $ZnWO_4$ indicate that it compares favorably with ruby. A further property of interest is a distinctly faster recovery time for the signal transition as compared with ruby.

The authors wish to thank S. K. Kurtz and W. G. Nilsen for permission to cite their results.

[1] For structure, see R. O. Keeling, Jr., Acta Cryst. **10**, 209 (1957).
[2] L. G. Van Uitert and R. R. Soden, J. Appl. Phys. **31**, 328 (1960).
[3] M. Peter, Phys. Rev. **113**, 801 (1959).
[4] M. Peter, L. G. Van Uitert, and J. B. Mock, *Advances in Quantum Electronics*, edited by J. R. Singer (Columbia University Press, New York, 1961), p. 435.
[5] J. Czochralski, Z. physik. Chem. **92**, 219 (1918).

Single Crystal Tungstates for Resonance and Emission Studies

L. G. Van Uitert and R. R. Soden
Bell Telephone Laboratories, Incorporated, Murray Hill, New Jersey
(Received May 27, 1959)

A number of single crystal tungstates have been prepared for paramagnetic resonance and emission studies. Compositions such as monoclinic $MgWO_4$, $ZnWO_4$, $CdWO_4$, and tetragonal $CaWO_4$, $SrWO_4$, and $BaWO_4$ containing paramagnetic ions of the transition and rare earth series have been prepared. They were grown by dissolving the constituent oxides into an equimolar mixture of Na_2WO_4 and WO_3 at 1100 to 1250°C and cooling at 2 to 3°C per hour to 700°C.

These crystals offer the advantages of one environment for the paramagnetic ions present, freedom from strain (hardness equal to that of iron), absence of random ordering effects, minimal effects from nuclear magnetic moments, and chemical stability. Large zero field splitting are observed in the monoclinic crystals, making them of interest for studies at high microwave frequencies. The tetragonal compositions are promising at the lower microwave frequencies and have shown very narrow resonance lines. Line widths as low as 1.5 Mc have been obtained in $CaWO_4$:Mn.

$Na_{0.5}Y_{0.5}WO_4$ crystals, which have the scheelite structure, were also grown. Random ordering effects of monovalent sodium and trivalent yttrium, however, result in a nonhomogeneous electrostatic environment throughout the crystals and hence cause broad paramagnetic resonance lines.

INTRODUCTION

The divalent metal ion tungstates have been of interest for their luminescent properties for some time.[1] They also provide a number of outstanding host lattices for paramagnetic ions for resonance studies. Two classes of tungstate crystals are of particular interest: the monoclinic compounds $MgWO_4$, $ZnWO_4$, and $CdWO_4$, which are isomorphous with $MnWO_4$, $FeWO_4$, $CoWO_4$, $NiWO_4$, and $CuWO_4$; and the tetragonal compounds $CaWO_4$ (scheelite), $SrWO_4$, $BaWO_4$, and $PbWO_4$, which are isomorphous with $Na_{0.5}R_{0.5}WO_4$ where R is yttrium, lanthanum, and the rare earths in their trivalent states.

In the past the monoclinic crystals mentioned above have been grown by crystallization from a sodium chloride melt.[2] Only small crystals have been obtained by this procedure, since the solubilities of these compounds are quite low in sodium chloride. The maximum furnace temperature that may be used with this solvent is limited by the vaporization of the NaCl and of the additives such as $NiCl_2$ and $CoCl_2$ and by the attack of the container by chloride ions.

Others[3] have grown sodium lanthanum tungstates and related rare earth crystals from Na_2WO_4 with comparable success. Calcium tungstate has been grown by the above methods and also as large crystals by the Bridgeman technique.[4]

CRYSTAL GROWTH

Na_2WO_4 was studied as a possible solvent for growing divalent metal tungstate crystals. It was found that this compound offers considerable advantage over NaCl

[1] F. A. Kröger, *Some Aspects of the Luminescence of Solids* (Elsevier Publishing Company, Inc., New York, 1948).
[2] A. Geuther and E. Forsburg; Ann. Chem. Liebigs **120**, 270 (1861).
[3] L. G. Sillen and A. L. Nylander, Arkiv Kemi Mineral Geol. **17A**, No. 4 (1943).
[4] Zerfoss, Johnson, and Imbers, Phys. Rev. **75**, 320 (1949).

in that it melts at 692°C, as compared to 800°C for NaCl; it has an ion in common with the salts to be crystallized from it, and hence there is relatively less chance for entrapping solvent during crystal growth; and it can be taken to much higher temperatures without suffering from volatilization of the components present or attack of the container. The growth of large divalent metal ion tungstate crystals is facilitated by the addition of WO_3 to the solution. This results in the conversion of $WO_4^{=}$ ions to $W_2O_7^{=}$ ions thus reducing the effective $WO_4^{=}$ concentration in solution allowing for increased solubility of the divalent metal ion tungstate. For this reason an equimolar mixture of Na_2WO_4 and WO_3 was used as the solvent. The melting point of the resulting composition ($Na_2W_2O_7$) is about the same as that of Na_2WO_4.

Satisfactory results were obtained by slowly cooling molten mixtures consisting of 60 to 75 mole % $Na_2W_2O_7$ and other components sufficient to form 25 to 40 mole % of a divalent metal ion tungstate in solution. The melts were compounded from as pure sources of material as were commercially available. These were the reagent grade nitrates of the group 2 and transition metal ions, reagent grades of Na_2WO_4, ZnO, and CdO, Amend cp tungstic anhydride; and rare earths, and Y_2O_3 from the Lindsay Chemical Company.

Crystals of monoclinic $MgWO_4$, $ZnWO_4$, and $CdWO_4$ containing additions of from 0.001 to 5.0% of the metal atoms present of one or more of the transition metal ions or rare earths have been grown in sizes up to 0.5 cm in diameter and 1 cm in length. Specimens of tetragonal $CaWO_4$ (scheelite) $SrWO_4$, $BaWO_4$ and $Na_{0.5}Y_{0.5}WO_4$ containing similar additions but somewhat smaller in size have also been grown. In each case the required components were melted together in platinum crucibles at 1100 to 1250°C. The melts were cooled at about 2.5°C per hour to approximately 700°C and then furnace cooled. The $Na_2W_2O_7$ is removed from the resulting crystals by washing with concentrated sodium hydroxide solution. This treatment converts water insoluble $Na_2W_2O_7$ to soluble Na_2WO_4 without harming the desired product. The trivalent metal ions enter the divalent metal tungstate lattice by Na^+M^{3+} pairs replacing $2M^{2+}$ ions.

The distributions of additions which impart color to the media can be estimated visually. The pure forms of the crystals prepared indicate that $MgWO_4$ is a clear light blue-green, (iron impurities are responsible for the yellow color generally attributed to this material); $ZnWO_4$ is transparent but tends toward a white opalescence in the thicker section; $CdWO_4$ is a clear light greenish yellow, and the pure tetragonal crystals are clear and colorless and have high indices of refraction. In $MgWO_4$, for example, an addition of nickel to the extent of 0.5% of the metal atoms present produces a crystal with an amethyst yellow color. As little as 0.05% of the metal atoms present of cobalt provides a strong blue color. When both nickel and cobalt are present in the above concentrations, the crystal is pea green. Crystals of this type grown under the previously given conditions show green centers wrapped in blue outside layers, indicating that the nickel is more concentrated in the center of the crystal. The distributions of a number of the rare earths in the tetragonal crystals are also detectable by color variations. Ce, Nd, and Er color the crystals, Ho gives the crystals a pink color under a fluorescent light, Sm and Eu emitted red under 2537 A ultraviolet light, etc.

DISCUSSION

It is desirable that a material for paramagnetic resonance studies provide but one type of lattice site for the paramagnetic ions. The tungstates under discussion fulfill this condition.[5,6]

The materials which have tetragonal crystal structures such as that found in $CaWO_4$ (schellite) are of particular interest as host lattices for paramagnetic ions which can show favorable Zeeman splittings. The zero field splitting for gadolinium in calcium tungstate is $4\frac{1}{2}$ times that found for it in lanthanum ethyl sulfate, which implies that it can operate as a maser material at considerably higher frequencies.* Compounds with the scheelite structure are also of interest at high microwave frequencies, since certain rare earth ions that can be accommodated in its structure can show large changes in resonance frequency for small changes in magnetizing fields.[7]

Materials with monoclinic crystal structures such as $MgWO_4$:Fe exhibit large zero field splittings.[8] The low symmetry electric fields acting on the paramagnetic ions present in this material can cause resonances to occur at millimeter wavelengths in the absence of an applied magnetic field. M. Peter found that the line width for iron in $MgWO_4$ was less than 100 Mc under these conditions.

It is highly desirable that line broadening effects, other than the interaction with neighboring paramagnetic ions that have been added, should not be present. When line widths greater than the minimum obtainable values are required, they may then be realized by increasing the concentration of the paramagnetic ions present, thus gaining in moment for a desired line width. Strains in soft materials may have marked line broadening effects; hence, it is of considerable interest to employ carefully grown crystals of hard materials. The tungstates are comparable in hardness to iron (about 5.5 on Moh's scale).

---

[5] For structure of $CaWO_4$ see Wycoff, *The Structure of Crystals* (The Chemical Catalog Company, Inc., New York, 1931) p. 285.

[6] R. O. Keeling, Jr., Acta Cryst. **10**, 209 (1957) (for structure of $NiWO_4$).

* To operate a maser at high frequencies a large magnetic field is usually required. However, as the interaction with the magnetic field increases beyond the zero field splitting, the pumping transition becomes increasingly forbidden.

[7] For example see K. D. Bowers and J. Owens, Repts. Progr. in Phys. **18**, 304 (1955).

[8] M. Peter, Phys. Rev. **113**, 801 (1959).

Additional line broadening effects can be related to the nuclear magnetic moments of neighboring ions and random ordering, particularly of ions with different valence states. Calcium tungstate is exceptional in that its constituent ions have very low nuclear magnetic moments throughout. The isotopes which have nuclear magnetic moments occur to the extent of 0.13% in calcium, 14% in tungsten, and 0.04% in oxygen. Further, the moments possessed by these isotopes are quite small in comparison to the values possessed by atoms such as aluminum, sodium, and fluorine.

Measurements made by C. F. Hempstead[9] of these Laboratories on samples of $Na_{0.5}Y_{0.5}WO_4$ and $CaWO_4$, both containing Gd and having the scheelite structure, show large differences in line width although these crystals were prepared under the same conditions. The line width observed in $CaWO_4$ was less than 6 Mc (as low as $1\frac{1}{2}$ Mc was measured for very dilute manganese in $CaWO_4$). The line width for Gd observed in $Na_{0.5}Y_{0.5}WO_4$, in comparison, was approximately 600 Mc. This marked increase may be attributed to the effects of random ordering of Na^+ and Y^{3+} in the 8-fold sites in the scheelite structure and in some degree to the arger nuclear magnetic moments of Na^+ and Y^{3+}. When the ordering of these is completely random, the odds are roughly 10 to 1 that the electric fields resulting from variable arrangements of Na^+ and Y^{3+} in the nearest 8-fold sites about those containing Gd^{3+} will be different. By comparison, when Na^+ and Gd^{3+} are randomly distributed in $Ca_{0.99}Gd_{0.005}Na_{0.005}WO_4$, the odds are less than 1 to 100 that anything but Ca^{2+} will be located in the nearest 8-fold sites to Gd^{3+}. Thus, it is possible that the effects of random ordering are decreased by a factor of as much as 1000 in the $CaWO_4$.

Calcium tungstate can be considered nearly ideal as a host lattice for the study of many paramagnetic ions. The chemical stability of this compound and the tungstates of Mg, Zn, and Cd as compared to water soluble salts is also of considerable advantage. The $SrWO_4$ and $BaWO_4$ compositions offer one possible advantage over $CaWO_4$ for applications involving optical transitions in that the former do not show a broad band luminescence under 2537 A excitation as do $CaWO_4$ and the other tungstates discussed.

[9] C. F. Hempstead and K. D. Bowers (to be submitted to Phys. Rev).

ACKNOWLEDGMENTS

We wish to thank K. D. Bowers for his very helpful discussions on the properties of paramagnetic materials, and M. Peter and C. F. Hempstead for permission to cite their line width measurements.

Papers on Solid State Masers Not Listed Elsewhere

Reprinted from JOURNAL OF APPLIED PHYSICS, Vol. 28, No. 9, 1049–1053, September, 1957

The Reaction Field and Its Use in Some Solid-State Amplifiers

P. W. ANDERSON
Bell Telephone Laboratories, Inc., Murray Hill, New Jersey
(Received May 22, 1957)

It is shown that the theory of the maser can be simply presented in terms of the concept of the radiation reaction field. This is the radiation field produced in a cavity or wave guide by the presence of the sample's electromagnetic moment. Its reaction back on the sample causes coherence effects such as those called "superradiance" by Dicke.

Two amplifiers using the radiation reaction field in different ways from the usual solid-state maser are discussed. One of them takes advantage of the nonlinearity of the equations of motion to make a modulated coupling between two cavity modes by means of a sample with three energy levels such as is used in Bloembergen's maser. The resulting amplifying mixer behaves the same as (but is different in principle from) Suhl's ferromagnetic amplifier. A second type of amplifier employs the reaction field to destroy the circular polarization of a paramagnetic resonance. It is then possible to make an amplifier from this using the principle of the subharmonic generator.

I. INTRODUCTION

IN microwave spectroscopy some effort is usually expended in making the coupling between the microwave circuitry and the sample being investigated sufficiently weak. Only then can one be sure of measuring the properties of the sample alone. However, recently a number of cases in which the weak coupling condition is not satisfied have become interesting. The most famous of these is the "maser"[1,2] which as we shall see can be discussed in terms of the regenerative effects of the reaction of the sample's radiation on it. Similar effects have been discussed by Dicke under the name of "superradiance."[3,4]

It is our purpose here to outline a straightforward way of discussing these phenomena which we shall call the method of the "reaction field." We shall then show how this may be used in two new solid-state amplifiers.

In this method we divide the problem conceptually into two parts. First, we consider the sample in an arbitrary electromagnetic field, and solve its general quantum-mechanical equations of motion in the form (for instance)

$$i\hbar\dot{\rho}(t)=[\rho(t),H]-\frac{i\hbar(\rho-\rho_0)}{\tau}, \qquad (1)$$

where ρ is the density matrix and we choose a particularly simple form for the relaxation term (a simplification having no particular bearing on further developments). The Hamiltonian H contains the interaction with an arbitrary time-varying field. Second, we conceptually solve Maxwell's equations in the given cavity or wave guide, with the currents or magnetic moments present in the sample acting as driving terms. The solution will give the field at the sample; and in principle all that is now necessary is to make the two calculations self-consistent. Since Maxwell's equations are linear, what we expect to find is that the field of the sample is proportional to some constant times the moment of the sample: i.e., H contains a term proportional to ρ. This of course makes the quantum-mechanical equations nonlinear.

In practice, the above procedure is not particularly useful unless some simplifying conditions are valid. The most important is that the coupling, while large, must not be so large as to appreciably mix different unperturbed cavity modes. If this condition is satisfied, one can in principle act as though the field and response in the sample are uniform, since they are at least proportional. The cavity, however, need not be a small perturbation on the sample in any sense.

It is convenient if we may also assume that demagnetizing and depolarizing fields are small compared to the radiation fields. This excludes the ferromagnetic case, and while it is instructive to note that radiation fields can be of importance in Suhl's devices,[5] it is probably true that these are not conveniently described by the present analysis.

II. ELECTROMAGNETIC THEORY OF THE REACTION FIELD[6]

Let us for definiteness study the magnetic resonance case. The equation of motion (1) may be exemplified by the particularly simple form for a paramagnet with no fine structure splittings:

$$\dot{M}=\gamma(M\times H)-\left(\frac{M-M_0}{\tau}\right), \qquad (2)$$

where the term in bold face parentheses is a simplified relaxation term which we can modify at will. Now it is only necessary to find H as a function of M by solving

[1] Gordon, Zeiger, and Townes, Phys. Rev. **99**, 1264 (1955).
[2] N. Bloembergen, Phys. Rev. **104**, 324 (1956).
[3] R. H. Dicke, Phys. Rev. **93**, 99 (1954).
[4] N. Bloembergen and R. V. Pound, Phys. Rev. **95**, 8 (1954) have discussed these phenomena from a point of view similar to ours.
[5] H. Suhl, Phys. Rev. **106**, 384 (1957).
[6] Much of this section evolved during conversations with H. Suhl.

Maxwell's equations in a cavity. M, like any vector field, can be divided into transverse and longitudinal parts:

$$M=M_t+M_l \quad \nabla\times M_l=0 \quad \nabla\cdot M_t=0. \tag{3}$$

If we substitute into Maxwell's equations, we see that they divide neatly into transverse and longitudinal parts:

Transverse:

$$-\nabla^2E=-\frac{1}{c^2}(\partial^2E/\partial t^2)-\frac{4\pi}{c}(\nabla\times\dot{M}_t)$$

or,

$$\nabla^2E-\frac{(\partial^2E/\partial t^2)}{c^2}=\frac{4\pi}{c}j_m, \tag{4}$$

where $j_m=\nabla\times M_t$ is the effective current sheet equivalent to the magnetic moment of the sample: this is the source of the radiation field. From the solution of (4) one derives the radiation field to insert into the equation of motion (2):

$$\nabla\times H_r=\frac{1}{c}\dot{E} \quad (\nabla\cdot H_r=0). \tag{5}$$

Now for the longitudinal part. Let

$$H=H_r+H_d \quad H_d=\nabla\varphi.$$

Then

$$\nabla^2\varphi=-4\pi\nabla\cdot M_l$$

determines H_d. As we see, H_d is the solution of a purely magnetostatic problem. For paramagnetics under most circumstances H_d is negligible in effect; H_r is not, for large samples near a cavity resonance.

Solution of Eq. (4) near a particular cavity resonance can rather simply be shown to lead to the reaction field

$$H_r=\frac{4\pi}{2Q(\omega/\omega_n-1)+i}Q\eta M_t=KM_t, \tag{6}$$

defining K, the "reaction field constant."[7] Here Q is the cavity Q due to losses of various kinds, η is the usual filling factor, and ω_n is the cavity resonant frequency. We see that, if $\omega\simeq\omega_n$, H_r is of the order $Q\eta$ bigger than a typical demagnetizing field. Since Q can be 10^4 and η as large as $\frac{1}{2}$ or so, this may be a large factor. At cavity resonance H_r is imaginary which as we shall see leads to an added loss; but off-resonance the reaction field is reactive and acts like a demagnetizing field.

III. REACTION-FIELD COUPLING IN MANY-LEVEL SYSTEMS

Let us now study the effect of the reaction field on many-level systems to which equations of motion of the type (1) apply. First we shall study the two-level system with and without an inverse population difference, and then consider the three-level system and show how nonlinear coupling between different natural frequencies of the sample may arise.

The equations of motion (1) for a two-level system are:

$$\dot{\rho}_{11}+\left(\frac{\rho_{11}-\rho_{11}^{(0)}}{\tau}\right)=-i[\rho_{12}V_{21}-V_{12}\rho_{21}]$$

$$\dot{\rho}_{22}+\left(\frac{\rho_{22}-\rho_{22}^{(0)}}{\tau}\right)=-i[\rho_{21}V_{12}-V_{21}\rho_{12}] \tag{7}$$

$$\dot{\rho}_{12}+\frac{\rho_{12}}{\tau}=-i(\rho_{11}-\rho_{22})V_{12}.$$

Here we have written all energy matrix elements V in frequency units, and we are using the interaction representation in which the time-dependence due to the unperturbed Hamiltonian has been transformed out, and the matrix elements V are assumed to have the correct time dependence. (This does not preclude frequency shifts, which of course may occur; any such shifts will show up by ρ having an extra time-dependence.) The usual steady-state theory gives

$$\rho_{11}-\rho_{22}=\frac{(\rho_{11}-\rho_{22})^0}{1+4|V_{12}|^2\tau^2}, \tag{8}$$

while

$$\rho_{12}=-iV_{12}\tau(\rho_{11}-\rho_{22}). \tag{9}$$

Let us now study what a reaction field does in (7). Since the dipole moment

$$\mathbf{M}=nTr(\rho\boldsymbol{\mu}), \tag{10}$$

where μ is the dipole moment matrix and n the density of spins (or electric dipoles),[8] the dipole moment moving at frequency ω_{12} must be given by

$$\mathbf{M}(\omega_{12})=n\boldsymbol{\mu}_{21}\rho_{12} \tag{11}$$

and the reaction field (6) leads to an interaction potential

$$\begin{aligned}V_{12}&=\mu_{12}H_r\\&=n\mu_{12}^2K\rho_{12},\end{aligned} \tag{12}$$

where K is a constant of the form given in Eq. (6). Let us for brevity write a new reaction-field constant

$$R_{12}=\frac{V_{12}}{\rho_{12}}=n\mu_{12}^2K_{12}. \tag{13}$$

Now Eqs. (7) become

$$\dot{\rho}_{12}+\frac{\rho_{12}}{\tau}=-iR_{12}\rho_{12}(\rho_{11}-\rho_{22}) \tag{14}$$

[7] In circuit problems this is often referred to as the radiation mpedance.

[8] All of our calculations are true practically unchanged for electric dipoles. However, conservation rules, electric dipole line-broadening, and the large number of molecular levels all combine to make reaction field devices less practicable in the electric case.

and

$$\frac{d}{dt}(\rho_{11}-\rho_{22})+\frac{(\rho_{11}-\rho_{22})-(\rho_{11}-\rho_{22})^0}{\tau}=-4|\rho_{12}|^2 I(R_{12}). \qquad (15)$$

Equation (15) shows us that the imaginary part of R is the absorptive part. If 1 is the lower level, the last term must be always positive (energy must always be given to the resistances surrounding the sample) so that $I(R_{12})$ is negative. This may be expressed by

$$Re[iR_{12}(\rho_{11}{}^0-\rho_{22}{}^0)]>0. \qquad (16)$$

The first equation of the pair, (14), contains within it the maser effect. Namely, if $\rho_{11}-\rho_{22}$ has the normal sign, the right-hand side is negative and ρ_{12} decreases if excited even more rapidly than $1/\tau$ because of R. However, if $\rho_{22}>\rho_{11}$ with ρ_{11} the lower state, the term on the right slows the decay of ρ_{12}, and if

$$R_{12}\Delta\rho>(1/\tau), \qquad (17)$$

which is the same as the usual maser condition,[1,2,4] we get maser oscillations, with energy being fed into the external circuit. Our analysis is in fact very close to that of references 2 and 4.

The method of achieving $(n_2-n_1)>0$ differs from one maser to another; all schemes have in common that coherence effects only occur in the simple 2-level scheme —i.e., that only one off-diagonal density matrix element enters the problem. In such a two-level system the reaction-field idea has only the advantage that it is somewhat simpler to insert the circuit reaction and look for unstable oscillations than to try to calculate the impedance the sample presents to the cavity.

In the three-level scheme, however, the reaction can play an essential physical role. We shall make no attempt to exhaust the possibilities of the effect in the three-level scheme, but shall simply exhibit one non-

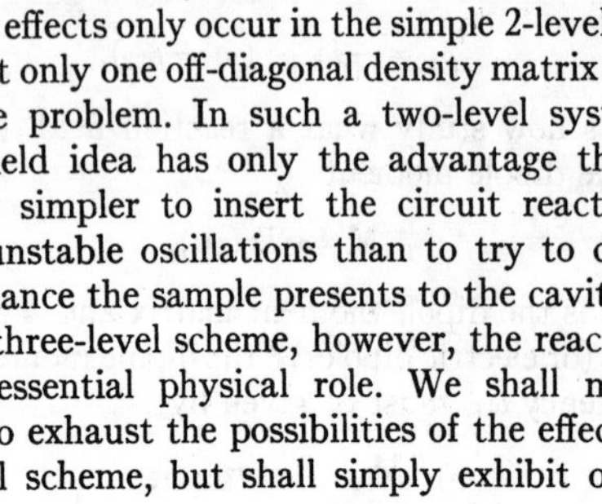

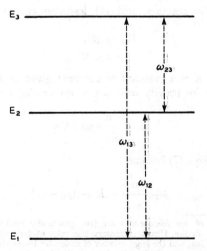

FIG. 1. Energy levels and frequencies in the three-level scheme.

linear oscillating device which uses coherence between different levels in an essential way. Consider a sample with three energy levels 1, 2, and 3, with 1 the lowest (see Fig. 1). Typical paramagnetic salts having such levels all connected by matrix elements are mentioned by Bloembergen.[2]

Let us write out one typical diagonal equation of motion and two off-diagonal ones.

$$\frac{d}{dt}(\rho_{11}-\rho_{11}{}^0)+\frac{\rho_{11}-\rho_{11}{}^0}{\tau}=i(\rho_{12}V_{21}-\rho_{21}V_{12}) +i(\rho_{13}V_{31}-\rho_{31}V_{13}), \qquad (18)$$

$$\begin{aligned}\dot{\rho}_{12}+\frac{\rho_{12}}{\tau}&=i(\rho_{11}-\rho_{22})V_{12} +i(\rho_{13}V_{32}-V_{13}\rho_{32}),\\ \dot{\rho}_{32}+\frac{\rho_{32}}{\tau}&=i(\rho_{33}-\rho_{22})V_{32} +i(\rho_{31}V_{12}-V_{31}\rho_{12}).\end{aligned} \qquad (19)$$

The interesting terms in (19) are those like $\rho_{13}V_{32}$ and $V_{13}\rho_{32}$, which physically describe Raman-like processes such as excitation from 1 to 2 with excitation from 3 to 1 and emission of a quantum $\hbar\omega_{32}$.

The kind of physical system we intend to study is the following. We drive with a large signal at the frequency ω_{13} with a "pumping" interaction V_{13}. There appears to be good reason to avoid radiation reaction at the frequency ω_{13}. We then look for unstable oscillations at the frequencies ω_{12} and ω_{23} in the event that cavities are coupled by radiation reaction to these two frequencies. Thus we have the usual solution (8), (9), for ρ_{13} and $\rho_{11}-\rho_{33}$,

$$\rho_{13}=-iV_{13}\tau(\rho_{11}-\rho_{33}), \qquad (20)$$

and we hope that $\rho_{11}-\rho_{33}$ is *not* saturated; while we introduce reaction fields at ω_{12} and ω_{23}:

$$\begin{aligned}V_{12}&=R_{12}\rho_{12},\\ V_{23}&=R_{23}\rho_{23}.\end{aligned} \qquad (21)$$

We are asking for the condition for initiation of unstable oscillations; for this reason, just as in Eq. (14) of the two-level maser, we can take the populations as given. In the Bloembergen maser, one relies on the revised populations ρ_{11}, etc. due to saturation for the effect; we, on the other hand, shall find that we prefer the populations to be normal, and study coherence effects of the off-diagonal elements. If we insert the steady-state equation for ρ_{13}, (20), the complete coupled equations for ρ_{12} and ρ_{23} are

$$\begin{aligned}\dot{\rho}_{12}+\frac{\rho_{12}}{\tau}-i(\rho_{11}-\rho_{22})R_{12}\rho_{12} &=-iV_{13}\rho_{32}[1+iR_{23}{}^*\tau(\rho_{11}-\rho_{33})]\\ \dot{\rho}_{32}+\frac{\rho_{32}}{\tau}+i(\rho_{22}-\rho_{33})R_{23}{}^*\rho_{32} &=-iV_{31}\rho_{12}[1-iR_{12}\tau(\rho_{11}-\rho_{33})].\end{aligned} \qquad (22)$$

A particular set of conditions* under which these equations can be unstable is the following: let us assume the population differences unperturbed and that level 2 is about half-way between 1 and 3. Let us also set $R_{23}^*=-R_{12}=-R$, that is detune modes ω_{23} and ω_{12} in opposite directions (the imaginary parts taken equal for convenience).† Let $\rho_{11}-\rho_{33}=\Delta\rho$, the population difference of the outside levels. Then (42) becomes

$$\dot{\rho}_{12}+\frac{\rho_{12}}{\tau}-i\frac{\Delta\rho}{2}R\rho_{12}=-iV_{13}\rho_{32}(1-iR\tau\Delta\rho),$$
$$\dot{\rho}_{32}+\frac{\rho_{32}}{\tau}-i\frac{\Delta\rho R\rho_{32}}{2}=-iV_{31}\rho_{12}(1-iR\tau\Delta\rho). \quad (23)$$

We search for a solution,

$$\rho_{12}=\rho_{12}^0e^{\lambda t},$$
$$\rho_{32}=\rho_{32}^0e^{\lambda t},$$

and λ is a solution of the secular equation,

$$\lambda+\frac{1}{\tau}-i\frac{\Delta\rho R}{2}=\pm|V_{13}|(iR\tau\Delta\rho-1). \quad (24)$$

λ can have a positive real part, and thus be unstable, if

$$\frac{1}{\tau}+\frac{R^i\Delta\rho}{2}<|V_{13}\tau|(R^r\Delta\rho). \quad (25)$$

The meaning of (25) physically is that the right-hand side represents a nonlinear coupling to the ρ_{13} "pump" matrix element by means of the reactive part R^r of the reaction field—a mechanism such as is used in Suhl's ferromagnetic amplifiers—while the left side contains the two types of losses which must be overcome, namely cavity losses R^i as well as $1/\tau$. Clearly we must compromise by detuning the cavity until $R^r\gg R^i$. Figure 2 shows a plot of (25) as a relation between R^r and R^i, as well as the impedance circle for R, showing the domain of instability.

Optimization of (25) leads, by simple algebra, to the condition

$$4|V_{13}\tau|^2=\frac{4}{(2\pi Q\eta)(\gamma M_z^e\tau)}, \quad (26)$$

where

$$n\mu\Delta\rho=M_z^{\text{eff}}.$$

In the case envisioned by Bloembergen[2] in which the three levels are well scrambled, $V_{13}\tau\simeq[H_1/(\Delta H)_{\frac{1}{2}}]$. Assuming conditions roughly comparable to those he suggested for Ni fluosilicate, except that by one means or another we must make T_1 not much longer than T_2, we get

$$\left|\frac{H_1}{\Delta H_{\frac{1}{2}}}\right|^2=\frac{4\Delta H_{\frac{1}{2}}}{(2\pi Q\eta)(\chi H_0)} \quad (27)$$

which is not impossible to satisfy. Note that $H_1^2 \propto ((\Delta H)^3/\chi)\propto n^2$ if dipolar broadening is important so that low concentration is useful. (We cannot go to the exchange narrowing region because exchange broadens ω_{13}.)

From a practical point of view this device has the following advantages:

(1) Saturation is avoided; hence higher temperatures are more easily available.

(2) We do not rely on particular relaxation time relationships.

(3) Power available seems nearly unlimited.

The disadvantage in relation to Bloembergen's maser and Suhl's devices[5] is the large power requirement. The chief interest in our device is theoretical, as a bridge between the Bloembergen maser and the nonlinear ferromagnetic amplifiers of Suhl's type, although it operates more nearly on the latter principle. However, one cannot predict the technical future; in particular, the ferromagnetic device may have unexpected noise sources.

IV. A SECOND TYPE OF PARAMAGNETIC RESONANCE AMPLIFIER

The device just discussed will not work in concentrated salts where the $\Delta m=1$ selection rule is obeyed

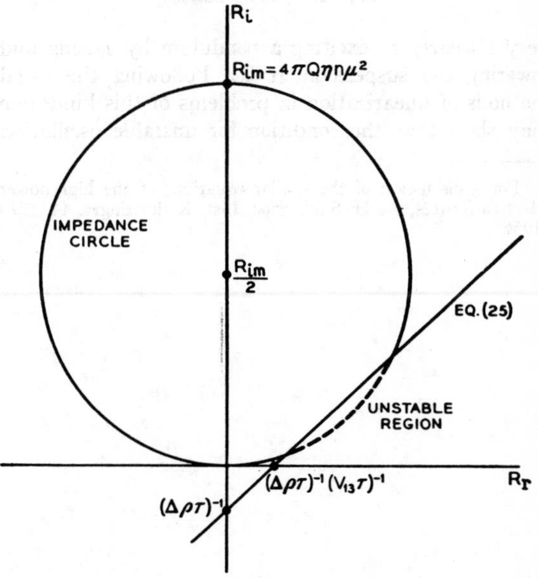

FIG. 2. "Impedance circle" for the reaction field constant R. The line is the instability condition of Eq. (25), and oscillation occurs if the circle crosses this line.

* *Note added in proof.*—A. Javan, Phys. Rev. (to be published) has discovered an entirely different regime of instability of the same set of equations (22). I am indebted to C. H. Townes for communication and discussion of these results.

† It is not inconceivable to make these the same cavity mode affecting two different sample frequencies.

and exchange narrowing is present. The following device can use such salts and is therefore of some interest, although its power requirement is rather high. For this reason and because it seems of less general interest, we shall discuss it only briefly.

In this scheme we take advantage of another similarity of the reaction field to a demagnetizing field: namely, that it may be linearly polarized, and thus may cause the usual circular polarization of paramagnetic resonance to become elliptical. With an external field H_z and such a reaction field H_{rx} the equation of motion $\partial \mathbf{M}/\partial t=\gamma \mathbf{M}\times \mathbf{H}$ becomes

$$\dot{M}_x=\gamma M_y H_z - M_x/\tau,$$

$$\dot{M}_y=-\gamma M_x H_z - \frac{M_y}{\tau}+\gamma M_z H_{rx}. \tag{28}$$

We write the reaction field

$$H_{rx}=K_r M_x - K_i M_y,$$

where K_r+iK_i is a reaction-field constant like that in (6).

Now (28) with a constant $H_z=H_0$ has an elliptically polarized resonant solution at

$$\omega_0=\gamma[H_0(H_0-K_r M_z)]^{\frac{1}{2}}. \tag{29}$$

Because of the elliptical polarization, M_z changes at a rate $2\omega_0$. Thus it is not surprising that one can drive this resonance by applying a modulation at frequency $2\omega_0$ to H_z:

$$H_z=H_0+H_1 \cos 2\omega_0 t \tag{30}$$

very similarly to exciting a pendulum by raising and lowering the suspension at 2ω. Following the usual methods of linearization in problems of this kind[9] one may show that the condition for unstable oscillation (and thus for useful amplification) is

$$\frac{\gamma^2 H_1}{4\omega_0} K_r M_z \geq \frac{1}{\tau}+\frac{\gamma K_i M_z}{2}. \tag{31}$$

Optimizing this condition to obtain the lowest possible driving power, we get, with $\omega_0 \simeq \gamma H_0$, $M_z=\chi H_0$, $1/\tau=\Delta\omega=\gamma\Delta H$,

$$H_1^2 \geq \frac{8H_0 \Delta H}{\pi Q \eta \chi}. \tag{32}$$

For DPPH at frequencies of X-band and one degree Kelvin, this implies $H_1 \sim 40$ oe if $Q\eta \sim 4\times 10^3$, which is rather large. The condition is easier at lower frequencies. The conditions on K_r and K_i are such that the sample loss is only doubled by coupling to the cavity, while the frequency of the sample resonance is shifted about 10%, and the cavity is detuned by the order of 1%.

V. DISCUSSION

These ideas started in the form of a question: what is the relationship between Bloembergen's maser and the nonlinear mixer-amplifier which is exemplified by Suhl's devices?[5] In both devices, one inserts a local oscillator signal at a frequency $\omega=\omega_1+\omega_2$, where ω_1 and ω_2 are possible frequencies of the system; it then amplifies at one of the lower frequencies.

One was tempted to think of the Bloembergen device as the quantum analog of the other, which appears essentially classical in principle. However, we found, as Sec. III shows, that the coherence effects which operate in the mixer-amplifier also exist in the three-level system used in Bloembergen's maser. Thus we are able to use this system with its radiation reaction fields as a nonlinear element coupling two sample frequencies to a "pump" at a higher frequency. This effect is apparently completely different in principle from the usual maser, and also seems to be a unique kind of nonlinear element.

I should like to acknowledge helpful discussions with A. M. Clogston, as well as those with H. Suhl already mentioned.

[9] For a discussion of the similar equations of the high-power effect in ferrites, see H. Suhl, Proc. Inst. Radio Engrs. 44, 1270 (1956).

Thermodynamics and Statistical Mechanics of a Three-Level Maser*

WILLIAM A. BARKER†
Argonne National Laboratory, Argonne, Illinois

(Received December 16, 1960; revised manuscript received June 26, 1961)

The three "spin" states of a maser are treated as individual chemical species. It is assumed that these three species are in thermal equilibrium with the lattice at temperature T but that they are not necessarily in chemical equilibrium with one another. The principle of minimum entropy production is used to derive an equation of reaction equilibrium from which the steady-state behavior of the system with a microwave pump may be completely described. In addition to the population distribution, which is in agreement in first order with the results obtained by solving the rate equations, explicit expressions are obtained for the internal energy, heat capacity, and entropy. The calculations are extended to include spontaneous emission and cross-relaxation as well as the usual thermal relaxation mechanisms.

I. INTRODUCTION

CONSIDER N paramagnetic impurity ions in a diamagnetic crystal placed in an external magnetic field. Let us suppose that the interaction between the spin magnetic moment of each ion and the combined magnetic and crystal field gives rise to three unequally spaced levels: E_i $(i=1,2,3)$. Spin lattice relaxation mechanisms are "thermalizers." That is, they tend to bring the system to a Boltzmann distribution at the lattice temperature T. These are denoted in the customary way by the thermal transition probabilities w_{ij} $(i,j=1,2,3)$ where $w_{ij}=w_{ji}\exp[(E_i-E_j)/kT]$. Time-varying magnetic fields of the proper frequencies are "equalizers." That is, they induce transitions between pairs of levels which tend to equalize (or saturate) the population distribution. The radiative induced transition probabilities are specified in the usual way by W_{ij} $(i,j=1,2,3)$ where $W_{ij}=W_{ji}$. Competition between the thermal and radiative transition probabilities leads to a steady-state population distribution, denoted by n_i. The power output, gain-bandwidth product, noise-temperature, and other performance features of a three-level maser may be calculated once the n_i are known. The conventional method used to calculate the n_i is by solution of the rate equations and normalization condition:

$$\frac{dn_i}{dt}=\sum_j (n_jw_{ji}-n_iw_{ij})+\sum_j W_{ij}(n_j-n_i)=0, \quad (1)$$

$$N=\sum_{i=1}^{3} n_i. \quad (2)$$

It is the purpose of this paper to analyze the problem of a three-level maser from the point of view of statistical mechanics and irreversible thermodynamics. This approach yields results which are consistent with those obtained by a solution of the rate equations. In addition it enables one to calculate related thermodynamic quantities such as the internal energy, heat capacity, and entropy, and to describe in detail what happens to the "pump" power. The theory may be readily extended to include spontaneous emission and cross-relaxation.

II. STATISTICAL MECHANICS AND IRREVERSIBLE THERMODYNAMICS OF A THREE-LEVEL MASER

A. Statistical Mechanics

We divide the N paramagnetic ions into three chemical species corresponding to the three energy values, E_i. We assume that these three chemical species are in thermal equilibrium with the lattice at temperature T but they are not necessarily in chemical equilibrium with one another. The total partition function for a single ion with spin energy E_i may be written as the product of z_i and z_l, where $z_i=\exp-E_i/kT$ and z_l is a factor associated with all other contributions to the energy of the ion. We assume z_l is the same for all three chemical species and focus our attention on the partial partition function z_i. The corresponding partition function[1] for n_i identical ions of energy E_i is

$$Z_i=[\exp(-E_i/kT)]^{n_i}/n_i!. \quad (3)$$

The free energy F_i associated with the ith species is given by

$$F_i=-kn_iT\ln Z_i=-kn_iT\ln z_i+kT\ln n_i! =n_iE_i+kT\ln n_i!. \quad (4)$$

The internal energy, entropy, and chemical potential for the ith species may be found from F_i as follows:

$$U_i=-T^2(\partial/\partial T)(F_i/T)=n_iE_i, \quad (5)$$

$$S_i=-(\partial F_i/\partial T)_{n_i}=-k\ln n_i!, \quad (6)$$

$$\mu_i=(\partial F_i/\partial n_i)_T=E_i+kT\ln n_i. \quad (7)$$

The expression for μ_i is obtained with the aid of Stirling's approximation,

$$\ln n_i!\simeq n_i\ln n_i-n_i. \quad (8)$$

* Based on work performed under the auspices of the U. S. Atomic Energy Commission.
† On leave from St. Louis University, St. Louis, Missouri, during the summer of 1960.

[1] L. D. Landau and E. M. Lifschitz, *Statistical Physics* (Addison-Wesley Publishing Company, Reading, Massachusetts, 1958), p. 120.

B. Irreversible Thermodynamics

Let B_i denote the ith chemical species and consider the following "chemical" reactions among these species.

$$\begin{aligned}&(1)\quad B_1 \rightleftarrows B_2,\\ &(2)\quad B_2 \rightleftarrows B_3,\\ &(3)\quad B_1 \rightleftarrows B_3,\\ &(4)\quad B_1 + h\nu_{31} \rightleftarrows B_3.\end{aligned} \tag{9}$$

The first three reactions are thermal relaxation processes in which the lattice supplies or receives energy from the paramagnetic spin system. The last reaction represents a radiative transition induced by the presence of a time varying electromagnetic field of frequency $\nu_{31} = (E_3 - E_1)/h$.

We define the chemical affinities A_j ($j = 1,2,3$) and the differential degrees of advancement $d\xi_k$ ($k = 1,2,3,4$) as follows:

$$\begin{aligned}A_1 &\equiv \mu_2 - \mu_1,\\ A_2 &\equiv \mu_3 - \mu_2,\\ A_3 &\equiv \mu_3 - \mu_1,\end{aligned} \tag{10}$$

$$\begin{aligned}d\xi_1 &\equiv d_1 n_1 = -d_1 n_2,\\ d\xi_2 &\equiv d_2 n_2 = -d_2 n_3,\\ d\xi_3 &\equiv d_3 n_1 = -d_3 n_3,\\ d\xi_4 &\equiv d_4 n_1 = -d_4 n_3.\end{aligned} \tag{11}$$

In Eq. (11), $d_k n_i$ means the change in n_i due to the kth reaction,

$$dn_i \equiv \sum_{k=1}^{4} d_k n_i. \tag{12}$$

We assume the validity of the Gibbs relation when the system is not necessarily in thermodynamic equilibrium:

$$TdS = dU - \textstyle\sum_i \mu_i dn_i + dW. \tag{13}$$

We set $dW = 0$ on the assumption that the sample volume and static magnetic field are held constant. With the aid of Eqs. (10)–(12), Eq. (13) may be rewritten as follows:

$$TdS = dU + \sum_{j=1}^{3} A_j d\xi_j + A_3 d\xi_4. \tag{14}$$

The internal entropy production associated with the irreversible relaxation processes is

$$d_i S/dt = (1/T) A_j (d\xi_j/dt). \tag{15}$$

The $d\xi_j/dt$ and the A_j are related as follows:

$$\begin{aligned}d\xi_1/dt &= d_1 n_1/dt = n_2 w_{21} - n_1 w_{12} \simeq (N/3kT) w_{21} A_1,\\ d\xi_2/dt &= d_2 n_2/dt = n_3 w_{32} - n_2 w_{23} \simeq (N/3kT) w_{32} A_2,\\ d\xi_3/dt &= d_3 n_1/dt = n_3 w_{31} - n_1 w_{13} \simeq (N/3kT) w_{31} A_3,\\ d\xi_4/dt &= d_4 n_1/dt = (n_3 - n_1) W_{13} \simeq (N/3kT) W_{13}(A_3 - h\nu_{31}).\end{aligned} \tag{16}$$

Two approximations are made in obtaining the right-hand side of Eq. (16) from Eq. (10):

$$A_j \ll kT \quad \text{and} \quad h\nu_{ij} \ll kT. \tag{17}$$

Combining Eqs. (15) and (16), we have

$$\begin{aligned}d_i S/dt &\simeq (N/3kT^2)[w_{21} A_1^2 + w_{32} A_2^2 + w_{31} A_3^2]\\ &\simeq (N/3kT^2)[w_{21} A_1^2 + w_{32}(A_1^2 - 2A_1 A_3 + A_3^2)\\ &\qquad + w_{31} A_3^2].\end{aligned} \tag{18}$$

The second form for Eq. (18) follows from the fact that the A_j are not independent:

$$A_2 = A_3 - A_1. \tag{19}$$

In thermodynamic equilibrium $d_i S/dt = 0$. It follows from Eqs. (18), (10) and (7) that $A_1 = A_2 = A_3 = 0$, $\mu_1 = \mu_2 = \mu_3$, and $n_i/n_j = \exp[(E_j - E_i)/kT]$, which is the normal Boltzmann distribution.

In the presence of a radiative "pumping" field, A_3 is held fixed at a nonzero value:

$$A_3 = sh\nu_{13}, \quad 0 \leqslant s \leqslant 1. \tag{20}$$

Equation (20) may be used as the defining equation for s, the saturation parameter. It may be readily interpreted with the help of Eqs. (7) and (10).

$$n_1/n_3 = \exp[h\nu_{31}(1-s)/kT]. \tag{21}$$

When $s = 0$, there is no "pumping" field and we have the Boltzmann distribution. When $s = 1$, the "pumping" field completely saturates levels 1 and 3 for which $n_1 = n_3$. If Eq. (21) is expanded and only the linear term is retained, s is seen to be the same as the parameter defined by Overhauser[2]:

$$s = 1 - (n_1 - n_3)/(N_1 - N_3), \tag{22}$$

where the N_i's represent the normalized Boltzmann population distribution. In the presence of the constraint on the system represented by $A_3 \neq 0$, the principle of minimum entropy production requires that

$$(\partial/\partial A_1)(d_i S/dt) = 0. \tag{23}$$

Carrying out the indicated differentiation on the second form of Eq. (18) leads to the condition

$$w_{21} A_1 = w_{32} A_2. \tag{24}$$

This is equivalent to the equation of reaction equilibrium

$$\mu_2 = f_1 \mu_1 + f_2 \mu_3, \tag{25}$$

where

$$f_1 \equiv w_{21}/(w_{21} + w_{32}) \quad \text{and} \quad f_2 \equiv w_{32}/(w_{21} + w_{32}). \tag{26}$$

This is one of the principal results of this paper. In conjunction with the normalization condition $\sum_i n_i = N$, it enables one to calculate the normalized population distribution of the three-level maser in terms of the saturation parameter, the relaxation rates, the energy

[2] A. W. Overhauser, Phys. Rev. 92, 411 (1953).

level separations, and the lattice temperature. From Eqs. (7) and (24), it follows, for example that

$$n_3/n_2=\exp[(f_1 s h\nu_{31}-h\nu_{32})/kT]. \quad (27)$$

If we take the linear term in the expansion of Eq. (27), the population difference is

$$n_3-n_2=\frac{Nh}{3kT}\left[\frac{s\nu_{31}w_{21}-\nu_{32}(w_{21}+w_{32})}{w_{21}+w_{32}}\right]. \quad (28)$$

In the limit of complete saturation, $s=1$, Eq. (28) yields a well-known consequence[3] of the rate equations.

C. Internal Energy, Heat Capacity, and Entropy

It is now a simple matter to compute the internal energy, heat capacity, and entropy of a three-level maser.

$$U=\sum_{i=1}^{3} U_i=\sum_{i=1}^{3} n_i E_i, \quad (29)$$

$$C_H=(\partial U/\partial T)_H, \quad (30)$$

$$S=\sum_i kn_i(1-\ln n_i)=Nk-k\sum_i n_i \ln n_i. \quad (31)$$

Thus

$$U(s=1)=\frac{N}{3}(\nu_{31}+\nu_{21})$$

$$-\frac{Nh^2}{9kT}(\nu_{21}-\nu_{32})\left(\frac{\nu_{21}w_{21}-\nu_{32}w_{32}}{w_{21}+w_{32}}\right), \quad (32)$$

$$U(s=0)=\frac{N}{3}(\nu_{31}+\nu_{21})-\frac{2Nh^2}{9kT}(\nu_{21}^2+\nu_{21}\nu_{32}+\nu_{32}^2), \quad (33)$$

$$C_H(s=1)=\frac{Nh^2}{9kT^2}(\nu_{21}-\nu_{32})\left(\frac{\nu_{21}w_{21}-\nu_{32}w_{32}}{w_{21}+w_{32}}\right)+\Phi(T), \quad (34)$$

$$C_H(s=0)=\frac{2Nh^2}{9kT^2}(\nu_{21}^2+\nu_{21}\nu_{32}+\nu_{32}^2). \quad (35)$$

In Eq. (34), $\Phi(T)$ is added to take into account the temperature dependence of the thermal relaxation rates.

$$\Phi(T)=-\frac{Nh^2}{9kT}(\nu_{21}-\nu_{32})\left(\nu_{21}\frac{\partial f_1}{\partial T}-\nu_{32}\frac{\partial f_2}{\partial T}\right). \quad (36)$$

If the thermal relaxation rates increase linearly with temperature, a not unreasonable assumption, then $\Phi(T)=0$.

From Eqs. (32) and (33), if $w_{21}=w_{32}$, we find that the internal energy of a fully saturated maser *exceeds* that of an unsaturated maser by $\frac{1}{6}N(h\nu_{31})^2/kT$.

From Eqs. (34) and (35), if $w_{21}=w_{32}$, we find that the heat capacity of a saturated maser is *less* than that of an unsaturated maser by $\frac{1}{6}Nk(h\nu_{31}/kT)^2$.

For the special case of $s=1$ and $w_{21}=w_{32}$,

$$S(s=1)-S(s=0)\simeq\tfrac{1}{6}Nk\ln\left[\frac{N}{3}\left(\frac{h\nu_{31}}{kT}\right)^2\right]. \quad (37)$$

It is not surprising that the entropy of the paramagnetic spin system in thermodynamic equilibrium is less than that of the saturated system. The entropy is a maximum for the equilibrium state provided the energy is held constant, a condition which is clearly not met when a radiation field is pumping energy into the system.

D. Power Absorption

It is instructive to inquire what happens to the power P_{13}, absorbed by the maser system:

$$P_{13}=(n_1-n_3)h\nu_{13}W_{13}\simeq\frac{N}{3}\left(\frac{h\nu_{13}}{kT}\right)(1-s)W_{13}. \quad (38)$$

A fraction s of this power increases the internal energy of the maser without an increase in temperature. This is represented by the last term on the right-hand side of Eq. (14):

$$-A_3\frac{d\xi_4}{dt}=s(n_1-n_3)h\nu_{13}W_{13}\simeq\frac{N}{3}\left(\frac{h\nu_{13}}{kT}\right)s(1-s)W_{13}. \quad (39)$$

The balance, $(1-s)P_{13}$, increases the temperature of the sample without an increase in the internal energy of the spin system. If the maser material is kept at constant temperature T, this power boils off some of the liquid helium or liquid nitrogen coolant. In the steady state the rate of increase in internal energy is exactly compensated by the power lost due to thermal relaxation. This latter is represented by

$$T\left(\frac{d_iS}{dt}\right)_{\min}=\frac{N}{3kT}(sh\nu_{13})^2\left(w_{31}+\frac{w_{21}w_{32}}{w_{21}+w_{32}}\right). \quad (40)$$

By equating Eqs. (39) and (40) for the steady state, we find an explicit expression for the saturation parameter:

$$s=\frac{W_{13}(w_{32}+w_{21})}{W_{13}(w_{32}+w_{21})+w_{31}w_{21}+w_{31}w_{32}+w_{21}w_{32}}. \quad (41)$$

This result may also be obtained by using Eq. (22) as the definition for s and solving the rate equations with the linear approximation to the Boltzmann factor.[4] As the saturation is increased to higher levels, less of the power absorbed is used to increase the sample temperature (or boil the coolant) and more is used to increase

[3] See, for example, J. Weber's review article on masers, Revs. Modern Phys. 31, 681 (1959).

[4] W. A. Barker, Argonne National Laboratory Report 6390, June, 1961 (unpublished).

the internal energy of the maser system. In the limit of $s=1$, when $W_{13}\gg w_{ij}$, we see from Eqs. (38)–(41) that

$$P_{13}=\frac{N}{3kT}(h\nu_{13})^2\left(w_{31}+\frac{w_{32}w_{21}}{w_{32}+w_{21}}\right)=T\left(\frac{d_iS}{dt}\right)_{\min}. \quad (42)$$

E. Spontaneous Emission and Cross Relaxation

In maser systems spontaneous emission[5] and cross-relaxation[6] processes may be important. The foregoing theory may be extended to take these mechanisms into account. In addition to the thermal relaxation probabilities w_{ij} let us consider a spontaneous emission probability A_{21} and a cross-relaxation probability w_{2123}. A_{21} tends to deplete the population of level 2 and increase the population of level 1 by emission of a photon. It is important to note that the relation

$$w_{21}+A_{21}=w_{12}\exp(h\nu_{21}/kT) \quad (43)$$

is now required to produce a Boltzmann distribution among the energy levels of the maser system in the absence of external constraints. w_{2123} tends to bring the populations of levels 1 and 2 into equilibrium with the populations of levels 2 and 3. It is important to bear in mind that w_{2123} is appreciable only if $\nu_{21}-\nu_{32}$ is small.

Spontaneous emission as well as nonradiative thermal relaxation is now understood to be included in the reaction

$$(1)\quad B_1\rightleftarrows B_2. \quad (44)$$

Cross-relaxation may be taken into account by adding a fifth "chemical" reaction to Eqs. (9):

$$(5)\quad B_2\rightleftarrows B_1+B_3. \quad (45)$$

And to Eqs. (10) and (11), we must therefore add another chemical affinity and differential degree of advancement:

$$A_5\equiv(\mu_3-\mu_2)+(\mu_1-\mu_2), \quad (46)$$

$$d\xi_5\equiv d_5n_2=-d_5n_1-d_5n_3. \quad (47)$$

The relationship between the $d\xi_j/dt$ and the A_j is now more complicated than that specified by Eqs. (16). The first of Eqs. (16) now has an added term due to spontaneous emission:

$$d\xi_1/dt=d_1n_1/dt=n_2w_{21}-n_1w_{12}+n_2A_{21} \simeq(N/3kT)(w_{21}+A_{21})A_1. \quad (48)$$

An additional equation is required to describe the specified cross-relaxation effect.

$$d\xi_5/dt=(w_{2123}/N)(n_1n_3-n_2^2) \simeq(Nw_{2123}/9kT)[A_5+h(\nu_{21}-\nu_{32})] \simeq Nw_{2123}A_5/9kT. \quad (49)$$

[5] T. Maiman, Nature 187, 493 (1960) and Phys. Rev. Letters 4, 564 (1960).

[6] N. Bloembergen, S. Shapiro, P. S. Pershan, and J. O. Artman, Phys. Rev. 114, 445 (1959).

The right-hand sides of Eqs. (48) and (49) are obtained from Eq. (10) and the approximations of Eqs. (17) and in addition explicit use is made of Eq. (43) and of the fact that $\nu_{21}-\nu_{32}$ is small. The rate of internal entropy production now has two additional terms:

$$\frac{d_iS}{dt}=\frac{N}{3kT^2}[(w_{21}+A_{21})A_1^2+w_{32}A_2^2+w_{31}A_3^2+\tfrac{1}{3}w_{2123}A_5^2]$$
$$+\frac{N}{3kT^2}(w_{21}+A_{21})A_1^2+w_{32}(A_1^2-2A_1A_3+A_3^2)+\tfrac{1}{3}w_{2123}(A_3^2-4A_1A_3+4A_1^2)]. \quad (50)$$

The second form of Eq. (50) makes use of the interrelationship among the chemical affinities:

$$A_5=A_2-A_1=A_3-2A_1. \quad (51)$$

In thermodynamic equilibrium $d_iS/dt=0$ again leads to the Boltzmann distribution. On the other hand if A_3 is held fixed at a nonzero value to represent the radiation "pump" field, then the principle of minimum entropy production requires that $(\partial/\partial A_1)(d_iS/dt)=0$. This now leads to a more general condition:

$$(w_{21}+A_{21}+\tfrac{2}{3}w_{2123})A_1=(w_{32}+\tfrac{2}{3}w_{2123})A_2, \quad (52)$$

which is equivalent to the equation of reaction equilibrium

$$\mu_2=\mu_1f_1'+\mu_3f_2', \quad (53)$$

where

$$f_1'\equiv(w_{21}+A_{21}+\tfrac{2}{3}w_{2123})/(w_{21}+A_{21}+w_{32}+\tfrac{4}{3}w_{2123}),$$
$$f_2'\equiv(w_{32}+\tfrac{2}{3}w_{2123})/(w_{21}+A_{21}+w_{32}+\tfrac{4}{3}w_{2123}). \quad (54)$$

Since Eq. (53) is precisely of the same form as Eq. (25), all the previous results derived for thermal relaxation mechanisms may now be extended to include spontaneous emission and cross relaxation by using the following simple prescription:

$$w_{21}\rightarrow w_{21}+A_{21}+\tfrac{2}{3}w_{2123},$$
$$w_{32}\rightarrow w_{32}+\tfrac{2}{3}w_{2123}. \quad (55)$$

III. CONCLUSION

It has been shown in this paper that the principle of minimum entropy production leads to an equation of reaction equilibrium which may be used in a statistical mechanical formulation to calculate the population distribution of a three-level maser. The mechanisms considered include thermal relaxation effects, spontaneous emission, and cross-relaxation. The approximations made are

(1) $h\nu_{ij}\ll kT,\quad i\neq j=1, 2, 3;$

(2) $sh\nu_{13}\ll kT$

(3) $f_2'sh\nu_{13}\ll kT$ } $(A_j\ll kT)$, (56)

(4) $\nu_{21}-\nu_{32}\simeq 0$ (cross-relaxation).

Inasmuch as s and f_2' are less than or equal to unity, approximations (2) and (3) are less restrictive than (1). The results for the population distribution agree with those obtained from the rate equations in first order when approximation (1) is also made.

The new features of this paper include explicit calculations of the internal energy, heat capacity, entropy, saturation parameter, and minimum entropy production of a three-level maser. The spontaneous emission and cross relaxation mechanisms introduced tend to reduce the value of the saturation parameter from its value given in terms of w_{ij} and W_{13} alone. Since w_{2123} is appreciable when $\nu_{21}-\nu_{32}$ is small, this cross relaxation mechanism has an interesting effect on the maser's internal energy and heat capacity as can be seen by an inspection of Eqs. (32)–(35) inclusive. As s goes from 0 to 1, the internal energy of a three level maser is increased by $(2Nh^2/9kT)(\nu_{21}^2+\nu_{21}\nu_{32}+\nu_{32}^2)$ whereas the associated heat capacity is decreased from its equilibrium value of $(2Nh^2/9kT^2)(\nu_{21}^2+\nu_{21}\nu_{32}+\nu_{32}^2)$ to zero.

ACKNOWLEDGMENTS

The author wishes to express his gratitude to the Argonne National Laboratory for their sponsorship of this research and in particular to Dr. Lester Guttman, Dr. Oliver Simpson, and Dr. Bernard Smaller for helpful suggestions.

CALCULATION OF THE NORMALIZED POPULATION DISTRIBUTION OF MULTILEVEL MASER SYSTEMS BY THE INSPECTION METHOD

BY

J. D. KEATING[1] AND WILLIAM A. BARKER[1]

ABSTRACT

A method has been devised, and examples given, for determining the normalized steady state population distribution, n_i, of multilevel maser systems, "by inspection" of the system energy-level diagram. Using this method, it is also possible to determine from inspection, such other parameters as the population differences, saturation parameter, *pump* power absorbed, spin temperature, and *signal* power output. The method includes consideration of thermal relaxation transitions and radiation-induced transitions, and is not restricted to the linear approximation to the exponential Boltzmann relationship. Within the restrictions stated, this method is valid for the same conditions for which the *rate equations* are valid. Possible extensions of the method to more general cases and to machine computations are indicated.

I. INTRODUCTION

In studying the characteristics of any multilevel maser system the most commonly used approach is to determine the steady state energy-level population distribution, n_i, by solution of the *rate equations*. For a system of many levels which includes all possible thermal and radiation-induced transitions, the algebraic solution, although not difficult, becomes very tedious and time consuming.

A method has been devised for determining the normalized population distribution, n_i, "by inspection" of the system energy-level diagram.

---

[1] Research Division, McDonnell Aircraft Corporation, St. Louis, Mo.

Throughout this paper. generalized rules of the inspection method are set in *italics* and apply to any multilevel maser subject to the following restrictions:

(a) Steady state conditions, that is, $\frac{dn_i}{dt} = 0$.

(b) $\gamma H_{pump} T_2 << 1$ (**1, 2**).[2] (This condition assures the validity of the rate equations.)

(c) Spontaneous emission and cross relaxation are neglected.

Likewise, all numbered equations except those marked with an asterisk apply to the general case as defined above.

To demonstrate the application of the method, two examples within the above restrictions are developed and presented as the method is explained:

Example I: A 4-level maser, in which $(E_i - E_j) << kT$ is illustrated and discussed in Section II-*B*.

Example II: A 3-level maser, in which $(E_i - E_j)$ may have any value, is illustrated and discussed in Section IV-*C*.

II. NORMALIZED POPULATION DISTRIBUTION

A. The Physical Relations

The number of spins in level i is denoted by n_i. The thermal relaxation probability for a spin to go from level j to level i is denoted by w_{ji}, and $W_{ji} = W_{ij}$ is the radiation-induced transition probability for a spin to go between level i and level j.

The normalization equation or conservation relation relating the n_i's, is

$$N = \sum_{i=1}^{\beta} n_i, \tag{1}$$

where N is equal to the total number of spins in the β-level system.

Thermal equilibrium between levels of the system implies a relationship between w_{ij} and w_{ji} given by

$$\frac{w_{ji}}{w_{ij}} = \frac{N_i}{N_j} = e^{-(E_i - E_j)/kT}, \quad j \neq i \tag{2}$$

where E_i is the energy of ith level, k is the Boltzmann constant, T is the lattice temperature in degrees Kelvin, and N_i is the Boltzmann distribution population for level i.

In order to illustrate the discussions which follow, a particular 4-level maser system, Example I, described by the diagram in Fig. 1, will be used as an example. Also, the w_{ji} will be referred to as a *relaxation* and will imply a thermal relaxation transition from the jth to the ith energy level where,

[2] The boldface numbers in parentheses refer to the references appended to this paper.

by convention, we take $j > i$. The W_{ij} will be referred to as a *pump* or as a *signal* and will imply a radiation-induced transition from the ith to the jth energy level.

Equation 2 can be simplified by making use of the following relationships from Example I:

$$\Delta = \frac{E_3 - E_1}{kT} = \frac{E_4 - E_2}{kT}; \qquad \delta = \frac{E_2 - E_1}{kT} = \frac{E_4 - E_3}{kT}.$$

In this specific case, as in many cases, the values of $(E_i - E_j)$ are small with respect to kT. The linear approximation,

$$e^X \approx 1 + X, \qquad X << 1 \tag{3}$$

can be made and the exponential forms of Eq. 2 can be eliminated.

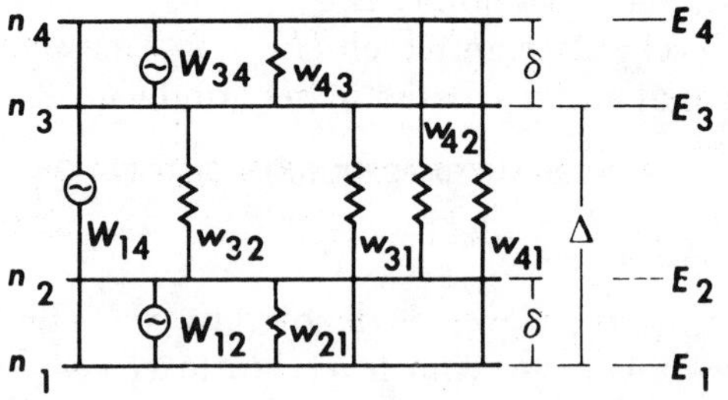

FIG. 1. Energy level diagram of a typical four-level maser system showing appropriate thermal relaxation and radiation induced transitions (Example I).

B. Solution by Inspection

The solutions sought are of the form

$$n_i = \frac{\mathcal{N}^{(i)}}{D}, \tag{4}$$

where the $\mathcal{N}^{(i)}$ and D are a numerator and denominator, respectively, each of which contains the same terms, X_r, but, in general, different coefficients. The terms, X_r, consist of the products of $(\beta - 1)w_{ji}$'s and/or W_{ij}'s and each term has a coefficient D_r or $\mathcal{N}_r^{(i)}$ which may involve some linear combination of the $(E_i - E_j)$. Hence,

$$\mathcal{N}^{(i)} = \sum_r \mathcal{N}_r^{(i)} X_r; \qquad D = \sum_r D_r X_r. \tag{5}$$

The normalized population distributions, n_i, of the maser system depicted by the energy-level diagram of Fig. 1 may be determined by inspection of the diagram in the manner now to be described. Quantities generated in the process are tabulated in Table I.

First, *all possible combinations of the products of the* w_{ji} *and/or* W_{ij} *taken*

TABLE I.

Terms and Term Coefficients for the Normalized Energy-Level Populations of the Four-Level Maser System of Fig. 1. Boltzmann Distribution Terms are Indicated by Brackets [ ].

1	2	3	4	5	6	7	8	9	10
No. (r)	Term (X_r)	$N_r^{(1)}/N$	$N_r^{(2)}/N$	$N_r^{(3)}/N$	$N_r^{(4)}/N$	D_r	$\frac{N_r^{(1)} - N_r^{(2)}}{N}$	$\frac{N_r^{(3)} - N_r^{(4)}}{N}$	$\frac{N_r^{(1)} - N_r^{(4)}}{N}$
1	$w_{21}w_{31}w_{41}$	1	$1 - \delta$	$1 - \Delta$	$1 - \Delta - \delta$	$4 - 2\Delta - 2\delta$	δ	δ	$\Delta + \delta$
2	$w_{21}w_{31}w_{42}$	1	$1 - \delta$	$1 - \Delta$	$1 - \Delta - \delta$	$4 - 2\Delta - 2\delta$	δ	δ	$\Delta + \delta$
3	$w_{21}w_{31}w_{43}$	1	$1 - \delta$	$1 - \Delta$	$1 - \Delta - \delta$	$4 - 2\Delta - 2\delta$	δ	δ	$\Delta + \delta$
4	$w_{21}w_{32}w_{41}$	1	$1 - \delta$	$1 - \Delta$	$1 - \Delta - \delta$	$4 - 2\Delta - 2\delta$	δ	δ	$\Delta + \delta$
5	$w_{21}w_{32}w_{42}$	1	$1 - \delta$	$1 - \Delta$	$1 - \Delta - \delta$	$4 - 2\Delta - 2\delta$	δ	δ	$\Delta + \delta$
6	$w_{21}w_{32}w_{43}$	1	$1 - \delta$	$1 - \Delta$	$1 - \Delta - \delta$	$4 - 2\Delta - 2\delta$	δ	δ	$\Delta + \delta$
7	$w_{21}w_{41}w_{43}$	$1 - \delta$	$1 - 2\delta$	$1 - \Delta - \delta$	$1 - \Delta - 2\delta$	$4 - 2\Delta - 6\delta$	δ	δ	$\Delta + \delta$
8	$w_{21}w_{42}w_{43}$	$1 - \delta$	$1 - 2\delta$	$1 - \Delta - \delta$	$1 - \Delta - 2\delta$	$4 - 2\Delta - 6\delta$	δ	δ	$\Delta + \delta$
9	$w_{21}w_{31}W'_{14}$	1	$1 - \delta$	$1 - \Delta$	1	$4 - \Delta - \delta$	δ	$-\Delta$	0
10	$w_{21}w_{31}W'_{34}$	1	$1 - \delta$	$1 - \Delta$	$1 - \Delta$	$4 - 2\Delta - \delta$	δ	0	Δ
11	$w_{21}w_{32}W'_{14}$	1	$1 - \delta$	$1 - \Delta$	1	$4 - \Delta - \delta$	δ	$-\Delta$	0
12	$w_{21}w_{32}W'_{34}$	1	$1 - \delta$	$1 - \Delta$	$1 - \Delta$	$4 - 2\Delta - \delta$	δ	0	Δ
13	$w_{21}w_{41}W'_{34}$	1	$1 - \delta$	$1 - \Delta - \delta$	$1 - \Delta - \delta$	$4 - 2\Delta - 3\delta$	δ	0	$\Delta + \delta$
14	$w_{21}w_{42}W'_{34}$	1	$1 - \delta$	$1 - \Delta - \delta$	$1 - \Delta - \delta$	$4 - 2\Delta - 3\delta$	δ	0	$\Delta + \delta$
15	$w_{21}w_{43}W'_{14}$	$1 - \delta$	$1 - 2\delta$	1	$1 - \delta$	$4 - 4\delta$	δ	δ	0

TABLE I (*Continued*)

16	$w_{21}W'_{14}W'_{34}$	1	$1-\delta$	1	1	$4-\delta$	δ	0	0
17	$w_{31}w_{32}w_{41}$	$1-\Delta+\delta$	$1-\Delta$	$1-2\Delta+\delta$	$1-2\Delta$	$4-6\Delta+2\delta$	δ	δ	$\Delta+\delta$
18	$w_{31}w_{32}w_{42}$	$1-\Delta+\delta$	$1-\Delta$	$1-2\Delta+\delta$	$1-2\Delta$	$4-6\Delta+2\delta$	δ	δ	$\Delta+\delta$
19	$w_{31}w_{32}w_{43}$	$1-\Delta+\delta$	$1-\Delta$	$1-2\Delta+\delta$	$1-2\Delta$	$4-6\Delta+2\delta$	δ	δ	$\Delta+\delta$
20	$w_{31}w_{41}w_{42}$	$1-\Delta$	$1-\Delta-\delta$	$1-2\Delta$	$1-2\Delta-\delta$	$4-6\Delta-2\delta$	δ	δ	$\Delta+\delta$
21	$w_{31}w_{42}w_{43}$	$1-\Delta$	$1-\Delta-\delta$	$1-2\Delta$	$1-2\Delta-\delta$	$4-6\Delta-2\delta$	δ	δ	$\Delta+\delta$
22	$w_{31}w_{32}W'_{14}$	$1-\Delta+\delta$	$1-\Delta$	$1-2\Delta+\delta$	$1-\Delta+\delta$	$4-5\Delta+3\delta$	δ	$-\Delta$	0
23	$w_{31}w_{32}W'_{34}$	$1-\Delta+\delta$,	$1-\Delta$	$1-2\Delta+\delta$	$1-2\Delta+\delta$	$4-6\Delta+3\delta$	δ	0	Δ
24	$w_{31}w_{41}W'_{12}$	1	1	$1-\Delta$	$1-\Delta-\delta$	$4-2\Delta-\delta$	0	δ	$\Delta+\delta$
25	$w_{31}w_{42}W'_{12}$	1	1	$1-\Delta$	$1-\Delta$	$4-2\Delta$	0	0	Δ
26	$w_{31}w_{42}W'_{14}$	$1-\Delta$	1	$1-2\Delta$	$1-\Delta$	$4-4\Delta$	$-\Delta$	$-\Delta$	0
27	$w_{31}w_{42}W'_{34}$	$1-\Delta$	$1-\Delta$	$1-2\Delta$	$1-2\Delta$	$4-6\Delta$	0	0	Δ
28	$w_{31}w_{43}W'_{12}$	1	1	$1-\Delta$	$1-\Delta-\delta$	$4-2\Delta-\delta$	0	δ	$\Delta+\delta$
29	$w_{31}W'_{12}W'_{14}$	1	1	$1-\Delta$	1	$4-\Delta$	0	$-\Delta$	0
30	$w_{31}W'_{12}W'_{34}$	1	1	$1-\Delta$	$1-\Delta$	$4-2\Delta$	0	0	Δ
31	$w_{32}w_{41}w_{42}$	$1-\Delta$	$1-\Delta-\delta$	$1-2\Delta$	$1-2\Delta-\delta$,	$4-6\Delta-2\delta$	δ	δ	$\Delta+\delta$
32	$w_{32}w_{41}w_{43}$	$1-\Delta$	$1-\Delta-\delta$	$1-2\Delta$	$1-2\Delta-\delta$	$4-6\Delta-2\delta$	δ	δ	$\Delta+\delta$
33	$w_{32}w_{41}W'_{12}$	1	1	$1-\Delta+\delta$	$1-\Delta-\delta$	$4-2\Delta$	0	2δ	$\Delta+\delta$

TABLE I (*Continued*).

34	$w_{32}w_{41}W_{34}$	$1-\Delta+\delta$	$1-\Delta-\delta$	$1-2\Delta$	$1-2\Delta$	$4-6\Delta$	2δ	0	$\Delta+\delta$
35	$w_{32}w_{42}W_{12}$	1	1	$1-\Delta+\delta$	$1-\Delta$	$4-2\Delta+\delta$	0	δ	Δ
36	$w_{32}w_{42}W_{14}$	$1-\Delta$	1	$1-\Delta+\delta$	$1-\Delta$	$4-3\Delta+\delta$	$-\Delta$	δ	0
37	$w_{32}w_{43}W_{12}$	1	1	$1-\Delta+\delta$	$1-\Delta$	$4-2\Delta+\delta$	0	δ	
38	$w_{32}w_{43}W_{14}$	$1-\Delta$	1	$1-\Delta+\delta$	$1-\Delta$	$4-3\Delta+\delta$	$-\Delta$	δ	0
39	$w_{32}W_{12}W_{14}$	1	1	$1-\Delta+\delta$	1	$4-\Delta+\delta$	0	$-\Delta+\delta$	0
40	$w_{32}W_{12}W_{34}$	1	1	$1-\Delta+\delta$	$1-\Delta+\delta$	$4-2\Delta+2\delta$	0	0	$\Delta-\delta$
41	$w_{32}W_{14}W_{34}$	$1-\Delta+\delta$	1	$1-\Delta+\delta$	$1-\Delta+\delta$	$4-3\Delta+3\delta$	$-\Delta+\delta$	0	0
[42	$w_{41}w_{42}w_{43}$	$1-\Delta-\delta$	$1-\Delta-2\delta$	$1-2\Delta-\delta$	$1-2\Delta-2\delta$	$4-6\Delta-6\delta$	δ	δ	$\Delta+\delta$]
43	$w_{41}w_{42}W_{34}$	$1-\Delta$	$1-\Delta-\delta$	$1-2\Delta-\delta$	$1-2\Delta-\delta$	$4-6\Delta-3\delta$	δ	0	$\Delta+\delta$
44	$w_{41}w_{43}W_{12}$	$1-\delta$	$1-\delta$	$1-\Delta-\delta$	$1-\Delta-2\delta$	$4-2\Delta-5\delta$	0	δ	$\Delta+\delta$
45	$w_{41}W_{12}W_{34}$	1	1	$1-\Delta-\delta$	$1-\Delta-\delta$	$4-2\Delta-2\delta$	0	0	$\Delta+\delta$
46	$w_{42}w_{43}W_{12}$	$1-\delta$	$1-\delta$	$1-\Delta$	$1-\Delta-\delta$	$4-2\Delta-3\delta$	0	δ	Δ
47	$w_{42}w_{43}W_{14}$	$1-\Delta-\delta$	$1-\delta$	$1-\Delta$	$1-\Delta-\delta$	$4-3\Delta-3\delta$	$-\Delta$	δ	0
48	$w_{42}W_{12}W_{34}$	1	1	$1-\Delta$	$1-\Delta$	$4-2\Delta$	0	0	Δ
49	$w_{42}W_{14}W_{34}$	$1-\Delta$	1	$1-\Delta$	$1-\Delta$	$4-3\Delta$	$-\Delta$	0	0
50	$w_{43}W_{12}W_{14}$	$1-\delta$	$1-\delta$	1	$1-\delta$	$4-3\delta$	0	δ	0
51	$W_{12}W_{14}W_{34}$	1	1	1	1	4	0	0	0

(β − 1) at a time are written down. Phenomenologically, Eq. 1 requires that all levels of the system be coupled together in each term, and hence, some of these combinations must be eliminated. In the case of Example I, with nine transition probabilities (six thermal transitions plus three radiation-induced transitions), there are 84 different combinations possible. Only 51 terms of these 84 combinations will fulfill the normalization condition and they are tabulated in column 2 of Table I.

The *combinations which must be eliminated from the total possible for the system will fall into one or both of the following categories:*

(a) One (or more) of the β levels of the system is not present in the index subscripts of the term (for example, Fig. 2a).

(b) Two levels of the system are connected by more than one type of transition process in the term (for example, Fig. 2b).

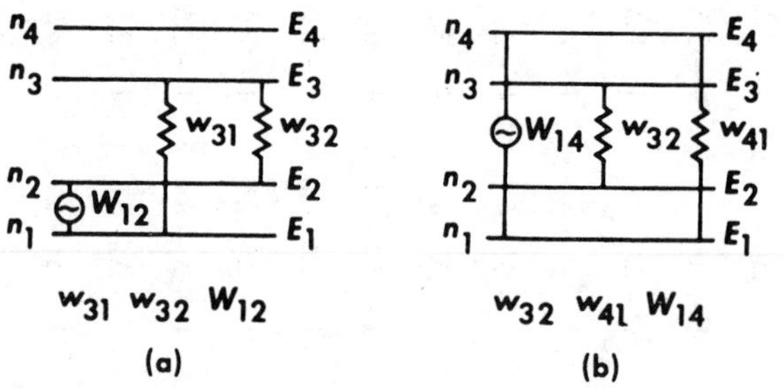

FIG. 2. Examples of combinations of the transition probabilities of Fig. 1 which are excluded because they do not fulfill the requirements of the normalization equation, $\sum_{i=1}^{\beta} n_i = N$.

Hence, excluded terms can be eliminated "by inspection."

The coefficients, $N_r^{(i)}$ and D_r for each term in the numerators and the denominator must now be determined. *The term coefficients $N_r^{(i)}/N$ for the numerator of n_i are all set equal to unity except for terms which have an intermediate level coupled, by a thermal relaxation, to a higher level which is coupled to the first level. In this case, the population of the first level differs from unity by a factor $e^{-\alpha}$, where α is the energy difference between the intermediate level and the higher level through which it is coupled to the first level. If two intermediate levels are so coupled to the first level, the first level population becomes $(e^{-\alpha_1})(e^{-\alpha_2})$.* The difference of a particular value of $N_r^{(1)}/N$ from unity may be thought of as being the result of *effective* competitive relaxations from an upper level, when one relaxation couples or *effectively* couples to the first level. This competitive relaxation results in the population of the first level differing from unity by a factor $e^{-\alpha}$.

The terms which have a nonunity value for $N_r^{(1)}/N$ may be determined "by inspection" to fall into one or more of the following categories:

(a) The term indicates two or more relaxations downward from the same level. One of these relaxations couples directly to the first level (for example, Fig. 3a, where $\alpha = \delta$) or couples to another lower level which couples to the first level (for example, Fig. 3b, where $\alpha = \delta$). The value of $N_r^{(1)}/N$ will then differ from unity by a factor $e^{-\alpha}$. If there are more than two intermediate levels as in Fig. 3c, α's would be established for each such intermediate level and applied as indicated in the preceding paragraph (for example, $\alpha_1 = \delta$, $\alpha_2 = \Delta$).

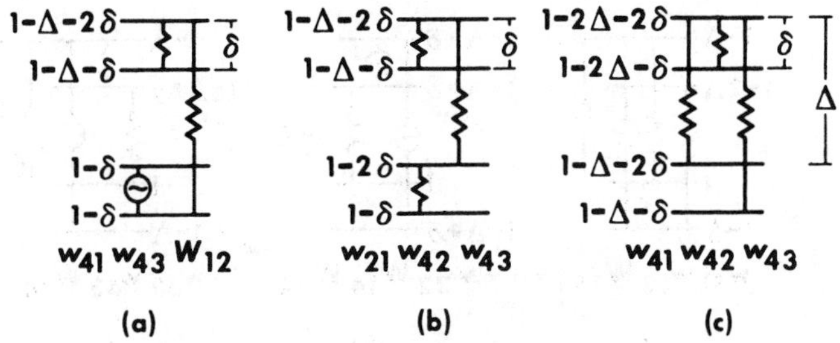

FIG. 3. Examples of terms in the normalized population distribution of a four-level maser system which have two or more relaxations downward from the same level.

(b) An effective multiple relaxation from the same level is indicated by a radiation-induced transition between two levels from which there are relaxations (for example, Fig. 4a and 4b, with $\alpha = \Delta$ and $[\Delta - \delta]$, respectively). The renormalized value of $N_r^{(1)}/N$ is then determined as in (a) above.

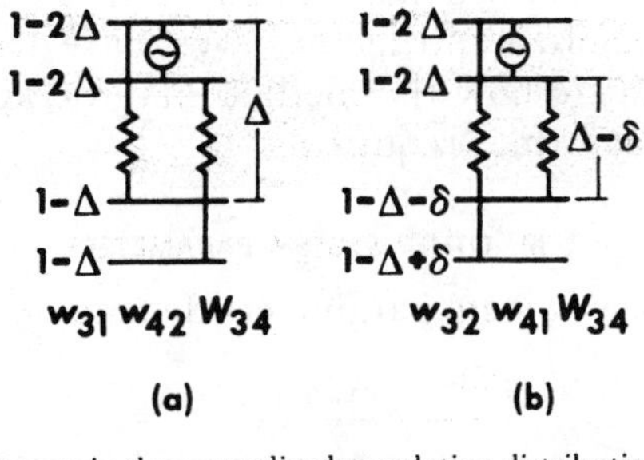

FIG. 4. Examples of terms in the normalized population distribution of a four-level maser system which have *effective* multiple relaxations downward from the same level.

(c) An intermediate level is coupled to the first level through a higher level by having the higher level coupled to the first level by a radiation-induced transition (for example, Fig. 5a, 5b, and 5c, with $\alpha = \Delta$, $[\Delta - \delta]$ and Δ, respectively). The value of $N_r^{(1)}/N$ again differs from unity by a factor which is determined as in (a) above.

The coefficient for each term in the numerator for n_1 is listed in column 3, Table I, under the heading $N_r^{(1)}/N$.

The transition probabilities in a given term indicate the ratios of the $N_r^{(i)}/N$ to each other, since a w_{ji} implies a Boltzmann relationship (Eq. 2), between the populations of levels i and j, while W_{ij} implies an equalization of the populations of levels i and j. The value of the coefficient of the rth term in D is

$$D_r = \sum_{i=1}^{\beta} N_r^{(i)}/N. \tag{6}$$

The coefficients in columns 4, 5, 6, and 7 of Table I are filled in accordingly for Example I.

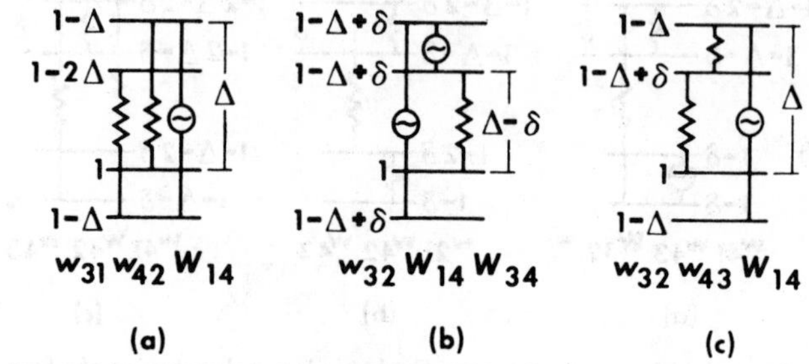

FIG. 5. Examples of terms in the normalized population distribution of a four-level maser system having both a thermal relaxation and a radiation-induced transition downward from the same level.

Table I can be used with Eqs. 4 and 5 to obtain the normalized population distribution. It can be shown that a simpler form of Table I may be constructed in which all the $N_r^{(1)}/N$ are set equal to unity and the ratios of the $N_r^{(i)}/N$ to one another are maintained. This is valid for the linear approximation to the Boltzmann factor. We have written Table I in the present form to indicate how the method may be applied to cases where the exact exponential form is required.

III. OTHER SYSTEM PARAMETERS

A number of maser system parameters depend on

$$\frac{N_r^{(i)} - N_r^{(j)}}{N}, \qquad i \neq j$$

which can be obtained by the method indicated, and which, for the specific example considered here are tabulated in columns 8, 9, and 10 of Table I. These values are necessary to determine the population differences, $(n_i - n_j)$; $i \neq j$. The *saturation parameter* (3) s_{ij}, defined as

$$s_{ij} \equiv 1 - \frac{n_i - n_j}{N_i - N_j}; \qquad 0 < s_{ij} < 1, \tag{7}$$

and the power input and output, P_{ij}, are expressed in terms of these population differences. Using Eq. 4 we can get the following expression:

$$(n_i - n_j) = \frac{\mathcal{N}^{(i)} - \mathcal{N}^{(j)}}{\mathcal{N}} \times \frac{\mathcal{N}}{D} = \frac{\mathcal{N}^{(i)} - \mathcal{N}^{(j)}}{D}. \tag{8}$$

The quotient indicated by Eq. 8 can be obtained from Table I "by inspection." The first order approximation of the quotient is a consequence of the linear approximation, Eq. 3. The terms in the numerator of the quotient described by Eq. 8 may be divided into two groups: (1) those resulting in a Boltzmann distribution of energy-level populations and containing only relaxations, w_{ji}, and (2) those which do not result in a Boltzmann distribution of energy-level populations and hence contain at least one *pump* or *signal*, W_{ij}. The expression for $(n_i - n_j)$ can be shown to be of the form

$$(n_i - n_j) = \frac{\mathcal{N}}{\beta}(A_{ij} - R_{ij}) \tag{9}$$

where: A_{ij} = contribution due only to Boltzmann distribution terms

$= \dfrac{\mathcal{N}_r^{(i)} - \mathcal{N}_r^{(j)}}{\mathcal{N}}$ for any one Boltzmann distribution term; and

R_{ij} = *remainder* or contribution due to non-Boltzmann distribution terms.

The remainder, R_{ij}, will be of the form

$$R_{ij} = \frac{\sum_{\phi} (A_{ij} - K_\phi) X_\phi}{\sum_{r=1}^{51} X_r} \tag{10}$$

in which X_ϕ is a term or combination of w_{ji} and W_{ij} representing only a non-Boltzmann distribution of energy-level populations, and K_ϕ is the coefficient for X_ϕ in the numerator $(\mathcal{N}^{(i)} - \mathcal{N}^{(j)})/\mathcal{N}$, where

$$\frac{\mathcal{N}^{(i)} - \mathcal{N}^{(j)}}{\mathcal{N}} = -\sum_{r=1}^{51} K_r X_r.$$

All of the parameters in Eq. 9 for $(n_i - n_j)$ can therefore be written down "by inspection."

Combining Eqs. 7 and 9 and referring to Table I, we can write

$$s_{14} = \frac{R_{14}}{(\Delta + \delta)} = \frac{R_{14} kT}{h\nu_{14}} \tag{11*}$$

where ν_{14} is the frequency corresponding to the energy difference between levels 1 and 4. Hence, s_{14} may easily be written "by inspection."

The *power absorbed* from the *pump* field, P_{14}, is expressed by

$$P_{14} = (n_1 - n_4)h\nu_{14}W_{14}. \qquad (12)^*$$

Another useful and convenient form of the expression for power absorbed is in terms of R_{14}.

$$P_{14} = \frac{Nh\nu_{14}W_{14}}{4}\left[\frac{h\nu_{14}}{kT} - R_{14}\right]. \qquad (13)^*$$

Hence, P_{14} may be written "by inspection" using columns 10 and 2 of Table I.

The *spin temperature*, $T_{M(ij)}$, associated with levels i and j is defined by

$$\frac{n_i}{n_j} \equiv \exp\left(h\nu_{ij}/kT_{M(ij)}\right), \qquad j > i, \qquad (14)$$

and is a parameter of the nonequilibrium population ratio, while T, the lattice temperature, is a parameter of the equilibrium or Boltzmann population ratio as in Eq. 2. If, as before, we assume $h\nu_{ij} << kT_{M(ij)}$ then we can use the linear approximation (3), and Eq. 14 becomes, after rearranging,

$$T_{M(ij)} = \frac{h\nu_{ij}n_j}{k(n_i - n_j)}, \qquad j > i. \qquad (15)$$

The *spin temperature* may then be written "by inspection."

Another useful parameter of a maser system is the *power emitted*, P_E. In the case considered here, P_E is composed of two components since we are considering two detection fields, characterized by W_{12} and W_{34}. Hence, we can write

$$P_E = P_{21} + P_{43} = (n_2 - n_1)h\nu_{12}W_{12} + (n_4 - n_3)h\nu_{34}W_{34}. \qquad (16)^*$$

Here we see that in order for P_{21} and P_{43} to be positive it is necessary that n_2 be greater than n_1 and that n_4 be greater than n_3, respectively. The power emitted may be expressed in terms of the spin temperatures associated with the detection frequencies by combining Eqs. 15 and 16*:

$$P_E = -\left(\left[\frac{h\nu_{12}}{kT}\right]^2 W_{12}n_2\frac{T}{T_{M_{(12)}}} + \left[\frac{h\nu_{34}}{kT}\right]^2 W_{34}n_4\frac{T}{T_{M_{(34)}}}\right). \qquad (17)^*$$

In the special case of the system represented by Fig. 1, where $\nu_{12} = \nu_{34}$, Eq. 17* can be written as

$$P_E = -\left[\frac{h\nu_{12}}{k}\right]^2\left[\frac{W_{12}n_2}{T_{M_{(12)}}} + \frac{W_{34}n_4}{T_{M_{(34)}}}\right]. \qquad (18)^*$$

The contributions to P_E of the two terms of Eq. 18* are positive only when the spin temperatures are negative. This is equivalent to saying that there will only be power emitted at the detection frequency when there is an inversion of the system-level populations corresponding to the detection frequency.

IV. EXTENSIONS OF THE INSPECTION METHOD

A. The β-Level Maser

In the particular 4-level maser system considered in the previous sections only three radiation fields, exemplified by three W_{ij}'s were considered. There is, however, no limit imposed by the inspection method of solution on the number of transition probabilities which may be considered. In fact, considering the ease with which the solution may be written down by following the procedure outlined in the second section, it may be advisable in many instances to consider a general system of the appropriate number of levels and all possible independent transition processes. The maximum number of thermal relaxation transition probabilities, $X_{\beta(max.)}$, for a β-level system in a general case is the number of combinations of β things taken two at a time,

$$X_{\beta(max)} = \binom{\beta}{2} = \frac{\beta!}{(2!)(\beta - 2)!}. \tag{19}$$

There will be a like number, Y_β, of radiation-induced transition probabilities. The total number of transition probabilities, T_β, for a β-level system, considering only thermal and radiation-induced transitions, will be

$$T_\beta = X_\beta + Y_\beta. \tag{20}$$

In the general case, when $X_\beta = Y_\beta =$ (maximum),

$$T_{\beta(max)} = \beta(\beta - 1). \tag{21}$$

Then for a total of T_β transition probabilities there will be Z_β combinations taken $(\beta - 1)$ at a time.

$$Z_\beta = \binom{T_\beta}{\beta - 1} = \frac{(X_\beta + Y_\beta)!}{(\beta - 1)!\,(X_\beta + Y_\beta - \beta + 1)!} \tag{22}$$

and when $X_\beta = Y_\beta =$ (max)

$$Z_{\beta(max)} = \frac{[\beta(\beta - 1)]!}{(\beta - 1)!\,(\beta^2 - 2\beta + 1)!} \tag{23}$$

Of these Z_β possible combinations there will be some which are excluded by reason of the fact that they do not couple the β-levels of the system. Z_β^* will be defined as the number of Z_β which are not excluded.

For nongeneral cases in which all possible w_{ji} and W_{ij} are not considered, the values for Z_β and Z_β^* will be less than for the general case since T_β will be less than the maximum.

Table II shows values of Z_β and Z_β^* for some typical values of β and T_β.

TABLE II.—*Effective Number of Terms for Several β-level Maser Systems.*

β	X_β	Y_β	T_β	Z_β	Z^*_β	General Case
3	3	2	5	10	—	
3	3	3	6	15	12	✓
4	6	3	9	84	—	
4	6	6	12	220	~~124~~ 128	✓
5	10	10	20	4,845	2,000	✓
6	15	3	18	8,568	—	
6	15	15	30	142,506	41,472	✓

Notice that in the nongeneral cases of Table II, the value of Z^*_β is not indicated since it is determined by the specific W_{ij}'s and w_{ji}'s which are considered. The expression for Z^*_β for a general case, when all possible thermal and radiation-induced transition processes are considered, is shown by Hobbs (**4**) to be

$$Z^*_\beta = 2^{(\beta-1)}\beta^{(\beta-2)}. \tag{24}$$

B. Machine Computation

Consideration of Table II leads one to conclude that the analysis of maser systems of more than four energy levels will be extremely tedious, even by the simplified techniques of the "inspection method," due to the large number of terms to be written down. However, the simplified rules for constructing the desired solutions which have been described in the preceding section can easily be translated into instructions in suitable language for automatic machine computation. With the assistance of machine computation, analysis of extremely complex systems (for example, greater than four energy levels) becomes feasible. Furthermore, machine computational techniques can easily be applied to the optimization of any multilevel maser system. Some further references to machine analysis of maser systems and similar problems are contained in the accompanying paper (**5**) in this JOURNAL.

C. Solution when $(E_i - E_j)/kT$ Is Not Small

It should also be noted that the inspection method of solution is in no way limited to the accuracy imposed by the linear approximation to the

TABLE III.—*Relative Contributions of Terms of the Four-Level Maser System in Fig. 1 to the Power Emitted.*

Relative Contribution	Term No.
2Δ	26
Δ	29, 49
$\Delta - \delta$	9, 11, 22, 36, 38, 39, 41, 47

exponential shown in Eq. 3. The exact exponential form of the solution can be written using the inspection method with no more difficulty than that required to write the approximate solution. This is done explicitly in Table IV for the three-level maser system of Example II, Fig. 6. The exact solution so obtained can then be expanded in a series to any degree of approximation desired.

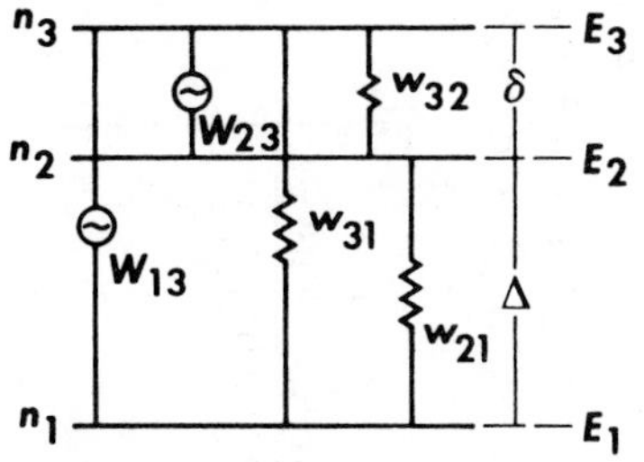

FIG. 6. A typical three-level maser system energy-level diagram (Example II).

D. Identification of Critical Parameters

The tabulation of data resulting from the inspection method of solution provides a method for observing all of the pertinent coefficients in a compact array so that any term or group of terms which contributes to a particular effect is easily seen in proper perspective. As an illustration, let us consider the following example.

Consider Example I. We know from the preceding section that the detection power emitted, P_E, is a maximum when the saturation due to pumping, s_{14}, is unity, that is, when $n_1 = n_4$. From Eq. 11* and Table I, we can see that only those terms for which $(\mathcal{N}_r^{(4)} - \mathcal{N}_r^{(1)})/\mathcal{N}$ is zero can contribute to a P_E which is positive. Furthermore, from Eqs. 15 and 18* it can be seen that of the terms of Table I for which $(\mathcal{N}_r^{(4)} - \mathcal{N}_r^{(1)})/\mathcal{N}$ is zero, only those for which $(\mathcal{N}_r^{(2)} - \mathcal{N}_r^{(1)})/\mathcal{N}$ and/or $(\mathcal{N}_r^{(4)} - \mathcal{N}_r^{(3)})/\mathcal{N}$ is a positive quantity, will result in a positive P_E. Recalling that, in this case, $\nu_{12} = \nu_{34}$, we can see from Table I that term No. 26 contributes more than any other term to detection power emitted. The relative contributions of the various terms to P_E is shown in Table III.

Note that terms 15, 16, 50, and 51 do not contribute to detection power emitted even though the coefficient $(\mathcal{N}_r^{(4)} - \mathcal{N}_r^{(1)})/\mathcal{N}$ is zero for these terms. The varying relative contributions to P_E indicated in Table III leads one to conclude that some thermal relaxation transitions are more favorable to a large detection power emission than are other transitions. Specifically, the relaxations which are common to terms 15, 16, and 50, which have no contribution, are w_{21} and w_{43}, while the term which contributes most, term No. 26, contains w_{31} and w_{42}. It follows, then, that any process which will increase the values of w_{31} and/or w_{42} with respect to w_{21} and w_{43} will result in improved performance of the maser system. Such a process might be the addition of selected impurities which have energy-level separations

TABLE IV.—*Terms, Term Coefficients, and Normalized Energy-Level Populations of the Three-Level Maser System of Fig. 6. Boltzmann Distribution Terms are Indicated by Brackets [ ].*

Term No. (r)	Term (X_r)	$N_r^{(1)}/N$	$N_r^{(2)}/N$	$N_r^{(3)}/N$	D_r
1	$W_{13}W_{23}$	1	1	1	3
2	$W_{13}w_{32}$	$e^{-\delta}$	1	$e^{-\delta}$	$1 + 2e^{-\delta}$
3	$W_{13}w_{21}$	1	$e^{-\Delta}$	1	$2 + e^{-\Delta}$
4	$W_{23}w_{31}$	1	$e^{-(\Delta+\delta)}$	$e^{-(\Delta+\delta)}$	$1 + 2e^{-(\Delta+\delta)}$
5	$W_{23}w_{21}$	1	$e^{-\Delta}$	$e^{-\Delta}$	$1 + 2e^{-\Delta}$
[6	$w_{31}w_{32}$	$e^{-\delta}$	$e^{-(\Delta+\delta)}$	$e^{-(\Delta+2\delta)}$	$e^{-\delta} + e^{-(\Delta+\delta)} + e^{-(\Delta+2\delta)}$]
7	$w_{31}w_{21}$	1	$e^{-\Delta}$	$e^{-(\Delta+\delta)}$	$1 + e^{-\Delta} + e^{-(\Delta+\delta)}$
8]	$w_{32}w_{21}$	1	$e^{-\Delta}$	$e^{-(\Delta+\delta)}$	$1 + e^{-\Delta} + e^{-(\Delta+\delta)}$]
—	$W_{13}w_{31}$	(Excluded; see Section B)			
—	$W_{23}w_{32}$	(Excluded; see Section B)			

$$n_1 = N\left[\frac{(W_{13}W_{23} + W_{13}w_{21} + W_{23}w_{31} + W_{23}w_{21} + w_{31}w_{21} + w_{32}w_{21}) + e^{-\delta}(W_{13}w_{32} + w_{31}w_{32})}{\begin{array}{l}3W_{13}W_{23} + (1 + 2e^{-\delta})(W_{13}w_{32}) + (2 + e^{-\Delta})(W_{13}w_{21}) + (1 + 2e^{-(\Delta+\delta)})(W_{23}w_{31}) \\ + (1 + 2e^{-\Delta})(W_{23}w_{21}) + (e^{-\delta} + e^{-(\Delta+\delta)} + e^{-(\Delta+2\delta)})(w_{31}w_{32}) \\ + (1 + e^{-\Delta} + e^{-(\Delta+\delta)})(w_{31}w_{21} + w_{32}w_{21})\end{array}}\right]$$

$$n_2 = N\left[\frac{(W_{13}W_{23} + W_{13}w_{32}) + e^{-\Delta}(W_{13}w_{21} + W_{23}w_{21} + w_{31}w_{21} + w_{32}w_{21}) + e^{-(\Delta+\delta)}(W_{23}w_{31} + w_{31}w_{32})}{\begin{array}{l}3W_{13}W_{23} + (1 + 2e^{-\delta})(W_{13}w_{32}) + (2 + e^{-\Delta})(W_{13}w_{21}) + (1 + 2e^{-(\Delta+\delta)})(W_{23}w_{31}) \\ + (1 + 2e^{-\Delta})(W_{23}w_{21}) + (e^{-\delta} + e^{-(\Delta+\delta)} + e^{-(\Delta+2\delta)})(w_{31}w_{32}) + (1 + e^{-\Delta} + e^{-(\Delta+\delta)})(w_{31}w_{21} + w_{32}w_{21})\end{array}}\right]$$

$$n_3 = N\left[\frac{(W_{13}W_{23} + W_{13}w_{21}) + e^{-\delta}(W_{13}w_{32}) + e^{-(\Delta+\delta)}(W_{23}w_{31} + w_{31}w_{21} + w_{32}w_{21}) + e^{-\Delta}(W_{23}w_{21}) + e^{-(\Delta+2\delta)}(w_{31}w_{32})}{\begin{array}{l}3W_{13}W_{23} + (1 + 2e^{-\delta})(W_{13}w_{32}) + (2 + e^{-\Delta})(W_{13}w_{21}) + (1 + 2e^{-(\Delta+\delta)})(W_{23}w_{31}) \\ + (1 + 2e^{-\Delta})(W_{23}w_{21}) + (e^{-\delta} + e^{-(\Delta+\delta)} + e^{-(\Delta+2\delta)})(w_{31}w_{32}) + (1 + e^{-\Delta} + e^{-(\Delta+\delta)})(w_{31}w_{21} + w_{32}w_{21})\end{array}}\right]$$

corresponding to ν_{31} and ν_{42} but not to any other frequencies of the maser system. The thermal relaxation times for transitions between levels 3 and 1 and between levels 4 and 2 would then be shortened with the resultant increase in transition probabilities w_{21} and w_{43} with respect to all of the other w_{ji}'s.

These conclusions are fairly readily reached as a consequence of the tabulation involved in the inspection method of solution, whereas they would probably have been most difficult to obtain from the usual form of the solution of the rate equations.

V. VERIFICATION OF SOLUTION

The solutions for both examples of Table I and Table IV were verified by direct substitution to determine that they satisfy:

1. The rate equations

$$\frac{dn_i}{dt} = \sum_{j=1}^{\beta} n_j w_{ji} - n_i \sum_{j=1}^{\beta} w_{ij} + \sum_{j=1}^{\beta} (n_j - n_i) W_{ij},$$

$$i = 1, 2, \ldots, \beta; \quad j \neq i. \tag{25}$$

2. The normalization equation, Eq. 1.

The verification of the solution of two examples does not constitute a rigorous mathematical proof of the "inspection method." However, the general rules are put on a sound mathematical basis by the proof presented in the accompanying paper (5) in this JOURNAL.

VI. CONCLUSION

The method described in the foregoing sections greatly simplifies and expedites the determination of the normalized population distribution for a multilevel maser system and many useful system parameters which are based on these population distributions.

The results obtained by the inspection method are identical to those obtained by the customary method of solution of the rate equations. The rules for writing down the solution by inspection have a basis in physical principles which makes the applications and extensions of the method to more general systems reasonable. Consequently, the method may be applied with ease to general cases involving any possible combination of thermal and radiation-induced transitions, with simplifying assumptions and exclusions made after the solution has been written down and examined rather than before the solution has been attempted. Solutions by the inspection method may be written in the exponential form of the Boltzmann relationship if so desired.

The present method which provides a solution equivalent to the solution from rate equations written as a function of thermal relaxation transitions and radiation-induced transitions only, appears to be extendable to include cross relaxations and spontaneous relaxations. Essentially, then, the only real limitations of the inspection method of solution are the same as those of the simultaneous equation method of solution of the steady state problem, namely that $\gamma H_{pump} T_2 << 1$.

The inspection method is valuable not only as a labor saving device but also as a means for providing physical insight into those mechanisms which improve maser performance. Hence, it is feasible to investigate a variety of more complex systems in much greater detail than heretofore, especially in view of the adaptability of the method to machine computation.

Acknowledgments

The authors wish to thank L. E. Follis for carrying out some of the preliminary calculations and for helpful suggestions. The interest, encouragement and suggestions of Dr. A. E. Lombard, Jr., are also very much appreciated.

REFERENCES

(1) A. M. CLOGSTON, *J. Phys. Chem. Solids*, Vol. 4, p. 271 (1958).

(2) S. SHAPIRO AND N. BLOEMBERGEN, in "Quantum Electronics," edited by C. H. Townes, New York, Columbia University Press, 1960, p. 370.

(3) W. A. BARKER, "Thermodynamics and Statistical Mechanics of a Three Level Maser," ANL Report No. 6390, Argonne National Laboratory, Lemont, Illinois, 1961.

(4) E. W. HOBBS, private communication.

(5) E. W. HOBBS, "Proof of a Combinatorial Formula in the Theory of Multilevel Maser Systems," JOUR. FRANKLIN INST., Vol. 274, p. 270 (1962).

Reprinted from JOURNAL OF APPLIED PHYSICS, Vol. 28, No. 7, 800–805, July, 1957

Effects of Radiation Damping on Spin Dynamics*

STANLEY BLOOM
RCA Laboratories, Princeton, New Jersey
(Received March 7, 1957)

When a two-state quantum system, capable of making radiative transitions, is driven by a high-frequency field, there occur damping effects due to the reaction of the sample to its own radiated field. This damping, which becomes important for high-Q rf structures and for samples of large dc susceptibilities, is here analyzed classically for a simple prototype system—a magnetic spin system obeying the Bloch equations. These equations are augmented to include the radiation-damping torques and are then solved for the four cases of usual interest. Firstly, for steady-state slow passage, radiation damping broadens and lowers the absorption and dispersion signals. Secondly, for adiabatic fast passage, damping causes the dispersion signal to dip at the line center and causes the otherwise absent absorption signal to become finite. However, if the radiation damping field becomes larger than the rf driving field a complete adiabatic inversion is shown to be no longer possible. Thirdly, the conditions for the occurrence of delayed power peaks of the free-precession signal are discussed. Fourthly, for the case of the driven nonsteady state, the stimulated emission may, for large radiation damping, become quite large if the system is driven from an initially "negative temperature" condition.

I. INTRODUCTION

WHEN a spin system is driven by an rf magnetic field, there occur reaction effects due to the coupling between the spin system and its own radiated field. If the rf structure supporting the applied field has a large Q or if the spin sample has a large static susceptibility, then these radiation damping effects will have a pronounced influence upon the response of the spin system to the applied field. For example, as was recently pointed out by Bruce, Norberg, and Pake,[1] the absorption and dispersion signals in slow-passage magnetic resonance experiments will change shape appreciably when radiation damping becomes important.

Bloembergen and Pound[2] have treated the problem of radiation damping from the point of view of a single coupled system—the spin sample plus the rf structure. Thus in addition to the Bloch equations, their formalism includes coupling equations relating the parameters of the rf structure to the total field seen by the spin sample.

In such a formulation the physical picture is somewhat obscured by the lumping of the radiation damping field and the applied driving field into a single rf field. The analysis can be compacted if, instead, one treats,

* This work was carried out under Signal Corps Contract DA36–039–sc–73031. See Project Reports July-September, 1956 and October-December, 1956.

[1] Bruce, Norberg, and Pake, Phys. Rev. **104**, 419 (1956).

[2] N. Bloembergen and R. V. Pound, Phys. Rev. **95**, 9 (1954).

not the single coupled system, but rather the spin system alone and merely augments its Bloch equations with terms due to the radiation damping field. The phase of this damping field is determined by the phase of the transverse component of the magnetization, and the amplitude of the damping field is proportional to the size of this component. The proportionality factor can then easily be found by a conservation-of-energy argument.

Using such an approach we determine the behavior of the spin system for the following important cases: (a) steady-state slow passage (which is the case treated in reference 1 by a different method), (b) adiabatic fast passage, (c) free precession with spin-spin de-phasing, (d) time-dependent behavior with a resonant driving field. Although the analysis is carried out for a magnetic spin system as a simple prototype, the results are general and apply—with an appropriate re-interpretation of symbols—to any two-state quantum system connected by radiative transitions.[3,4]

Problems in radiation damping should gain increased practical importance because of the current work being done on solid-state Masers[5,6]—devices which employ high-Q cavities and paramagnetic samples with high spin densities.

II. BLOCH EQUATIONS WITH RADIATION DAMPING

As shown in Fig. 1, we consider a macroscopic moment M, per unit volume of sample, acted upon by a large dc magnetic field H_0 in the z direction and by a small oscillating field $2H_1 \cos\omega t$ in the x direction. It is assumed that all of the individual spins composing M see the same dc field H_0, i.e., that there is no inhomogeneity broadening. The three components of the magnetization are

$$M_x = M \sin\theta \cos\phi;\quad M_y = -M \sin\theta \sin\phi;\quad M_z = M \cos\theta. \quad (1)$$

The component of magnetization in the $x-y$ plane is $M \sin\theta$. Because of its rotation it produces a rotating radiation-damping field H_r—which for brevity we shall refer to as the "*ringing*" field. This ringing field lags the rotating $M \sin\theta$ by 90° and has the magnitude

$$H_r = kM \sin\theta, \quad (2)$$

where k is a proportionality constant which we shall later see is dependent upon the rf structure enclosing the spin sample. It is assumed that the rf structure is at the sample resonance and has a resonance width sufficiently large that the ringing field can instantly follow the magnetization.[2] The three components of

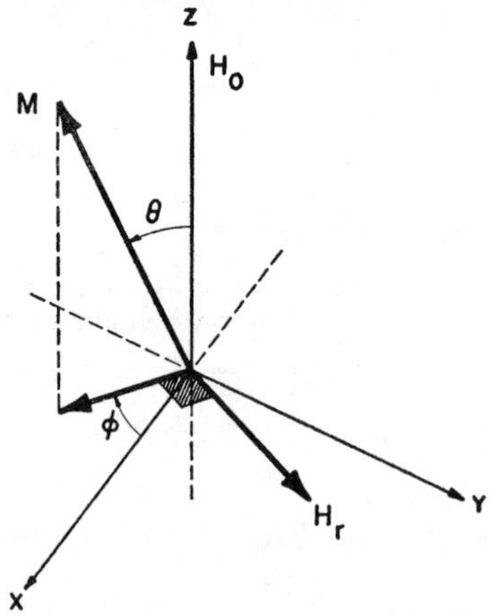

FIG. 1. The macroscopic moment M is inclined at the angle θ to the dc field H_0. An oscillating driving field, $2H_1 \cos\omega t$, is applied along the x axis. To include the effects of radiation damping, the transverse component $M \sin\theta$ is considered. It rotates in the x-y plane and produces a radiation-damping field H_r which is proportional to $M \sin\theta$ and which lags it by 90°.

the total magnetic field are

$$\begin{aligned} H_x &= H_1 \cos\omega t + H_r \sin\phi, \\ H_y &= -H_1 \sin\omega t + H_r \cos\phi, \\ H_z &= H_0, \end{aligned} \quad (3)$$

where the oscillating driving field has been resolved into two oppositely rotating fields of amplitude H_1 and only the synchronous component has been retained.

The torque equations, including the spin-lattice (or, thermalizing) and the spin-spin (or, de-phasing) relaxation times, T_1 and T_2, respectively,[7] are

$$\begin{aligned} \frac{d}{dt}M_{x,y} &= \gamma(\mathbf{M}\times\mathbf{H})_{x,y} - M_{x,y}/T_2, \\ \frac{d}{dt}M_z &= \gamma(\mathbf{M}\times\mathbf{H})_z - (M_z - M_0)/T_1, \end{aligned} \quad (4)$$

where γ, the gyromagnetic ratio, is assumed positive and M_0 is the thermal equilibrium value of M_z. On introducing the new variables

$$\begin{aligned} u &\equiv M_x \cos\omega t - M_y \sin\omega t = M \sin\theta \cos(\omega t - \phi), \\ v &\equiv -M_x \sin\omega t - M_y \cos\omega t = -M \sin\theta \sin(\omega t - \phi), \end{aligned} \quad (5)$$

and on using Eqs. (1), (2), and (3), we obtain from Eqs. (4) the following, which are the Bloch[8] equations augmented by terms (in r) due to the radiation damping:

[3] S. Bloom, J. Appl. Phys. **27**, 785 (1956).
[4] Feynman, Vernon, and Hellwarth, J. Appl. Phys. **28**, 49 (1957).
[5] Combrisson, Honig, and Townes, Compt. rend. **242**, 2451 (1956).
[6] N. Bloembergen, Phys. Rev. **104**, 324 (1956); Scovil, Feher, and Seidel, Phys. Rev. **105**, 762, (1957).

[7] As has been pointed out by Redfield [Phys. Rev. **98**, 1787 (1955)], with large rf fields the energy of alignment in these fields may be large compared to the energy of typical spin-spin interaction, and that then the simple phenomenological concept of a "T_2" relaxation time breaks down.
[8] F. Bloch, Phys. Rev. **70**, 460 (1946).

$$du/d\tau+\beta u+\delta v=-ruM_z, \quad (6a)$$

$$dv/d\tau+\beta v-\delta u+M_z=-rvM_z, \quad (6b)$$

$$dM_z/d\tau+\alpha M_z-v=\alpha M_0+r(u^2+v^2), \quad (6c)$$

where

$$\tau\equiv\gamma H_1 t;\quad \alpha\equiv 1/\gamma H_1 T_1;\quad \beta\equiv 1/\gamma H_1 T_2$$

$$\delta\equiv(\omega_0-\omega)/\gamma H_1;\quad \omega_0=\gamma H_0;\quad r\equiv k/H_1.$$

If the spin sample is enclosed by coils or by a cavity, the ringing factor k can be found from a conservation-of-energy argument as follows. The energy density of the system is $\mathbf{M}\cdot\mathbf{H}=H_0M_z+H_1u$, and so the power radiated per unit volume of sample, by ringing alone, is $P_r=H_0(\dot{M}_z)_{\text{ring}}$. By Eq. (6c) this power is $P_r=\omega_0 k\times(u^2+v^2)=\omega_0 k(M\sin\theta)^2=\omega_0 H_r^2/k$. On the other hand, if V_c is the volume of the cavity and Q is its quality factor, the losses due to the oscillating field $2H_r$ are given by $P_{\text{cav}}=\omega_0 V_c(2H_r)^2/8\pi Q$. This power must equal V_sP_r were V_s is the volume of the spin sample. Thus

$$k=2\pi Qf, \quad (7)$$

where f is the filling factor.

III. SOLUTIONS OF THE BLOCH EQUATIONS

A. Steady-State Slow Passage

With $d/d\tau=0$, the steady-state slow passage solutions of Eqs. (6) are

$$u=\frac{\delta M_z}{\delta^2+(\beta+rM_z)^2},\quad v=-\frac{M_z(\beta+rM_z)}{\delta^2+(\beta+rM_z)^2}, \quad (8)$$

with M_z given by the real root of

$$r^2M_z^3+(2r\beta-r^2M_0)M_z^2+(\delta^2+\beta^2+\beta/\alpha-2r\beta M_0)M_z=M_0(\delta^2+\beta^2). \quad (9)$$

Far from saturation, $1/\alpha\beta\ll 1$ and Eq. (9) yields

$$M_z=M_0.$$

The complex susceptibility, referred to the applied driving field, is

$$\chi_{H1}=e^{-i\omega t}(M_x-iM_y)/2H_1=(u+iv)/2H_1=\chi'_{H1}-i\chi''_{H1}$$

which, by Eqs. (8), gives

$$\chi'_{H1}=\tfrac{1}{2}\omega_0\chi_0T_2\cdot\frac{(\omega_0-\omega)T_2}{(\omega_0-\omega)^2T_2^2+(1+k\omega_0\chi_0T_2)^2},$$
$$\chi''_{H1}=\tfrac{1}{2}\omega_0\chi_0T_2\cdot\frac{1+k\omega_0\chi_0T_2}{(\omega_0-\omega)^2T_2^2+(1+k\omega_0\chi_0T_2)^2}. \quad (10)$$

These results are equivalent to those obtainable from the voltage representation used by Bruce *et al.*[1] [their Eq. (12)]. Because of ringing, the absorption line-breadth is increased from T_2^{-1} to $T_2^{-1}+k\omega_0\chi_0$.

If, however, the susceptibility is referred to the *total* rf field seen by the spin sample, then

$$\chi_{HT}=\frac{M_x-iM_y}{2(H_x-iH_y)}=\frac{u+iv}{2(H_1+kv-iku)}.$$

This leads to the usual Bloch values

$$\chi'_{HT}=\tfrac{1}{2}\omega_0\chi_0T_2\cdot\frac{(\omega_0-\omega)T_2}{(\omega_0-\omega)^2T_2^2+1},$$

$$\chi''_{HT}=\tfrac{1}{2}\omega_0\chi_0T_2\cdot\frac{1}{(\omega_0-\omega)^2T_2^2+1}.$$

From Eq. (10) we see that the absorption on resonance is given by $\chi_{H_1}''=(\omega_0\chi_0T_2/2)(1+k\omega_0\chi_0T_2)^{-1}$. For a maser, in which the static susceptibility χ_0 has been made negative, the start-oscillation condition is $\chi''_{H1}\rightarrow-\infty$, or

$$k|\chi_0|\omega_0T_2\geq 1$$

which is the same result as Eq. (2) of reference 5.

B. Adiabatic Fast Passage

In the case of adiabatic fast passage the system is taken through a succession of quasi-steady states by varying the dc field from one side of resonance (H_0

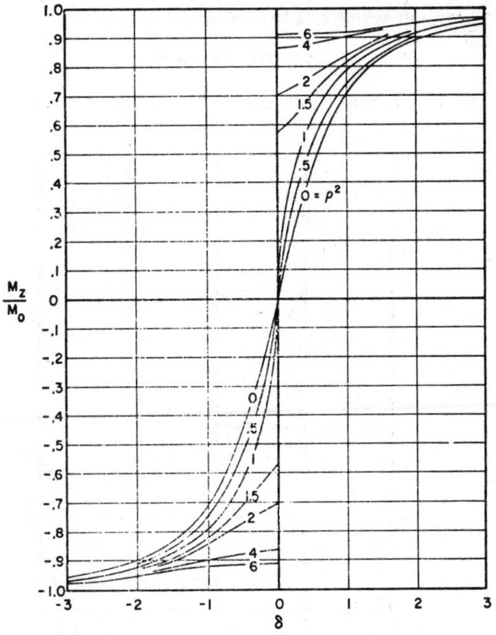

FIG. 2. The z component of magnetization, $M_z/M_0=\cos\theta$, for the case of adiabatic fast passage, as a function of the frequency deviation δ, for various values of the ringing parameter ρ^2. For negligible radiation damping, the curve is given by $\delta(1+\delta^2)^{-\frac{1}{2}}$. For large damping ($\rho^2>1$), a smooth adiabatic inversion of the magnetization is not possible.

$=\omega/\gamma$) to the other. This passage through resonance must be done in a time long compared to $1/\gamma H_1$, yet short compared to T_1 and T_2. Thus, with $\alpha\approx\beta\approx 0$ and with M being approximated by M_0, Eqs. (6) give

$$\frac{u}{M_0}=\frac{\delta\cos\theta}{\delta^2+(\rho\cos\theta)^2};\quad \frac{v}{M_0}=-\frac{\rho\cos^2\theta}{\delta^2+(\rho\cos\theta)^2},\tag{11}$$

where

$$\rho\equiv rM_0=kM_0/H_1\tag{12}$$

and the tipping angle θ is found from the equation

$$u^2+v^2=(M_0\cos\theta)^2/(\delta^2+\rho^2\cos^2\theta)=(M_0\sin\theta)^2,$$

or

$$\sin^2\theta=\{\rho^2+\delta^2+1-[(\rho^2+\delta^2+1)^2-4\rho^2]^{\frac{1}{2}}\}/2\rho^2.\tag{13}$$

The z component of magnetization, $M_z/M_0=\cos\theta$, computed from Eq. (13), is shown in Fig. 2 for various values of the ringing parameter ρ^2. On resonance ($\delta=0$), $\cos\theta=0$ if $\rho\leq 1$ and $\cos\theta=\pm(1-\rho^{-2})^{\frac{1}{2}}$ if $\rho\geq 1$, the positive sign holding for $\delta=0^+$ the negative for $\delta=0^-$. The meaning of this discontinuity is clear from Eq. (2), which we rewrite as

$$H_r/H_1=\rho\sin\theta.$$

For $\rho<1$, a smooth adiabatic inversion of M_z is possible, the ringing field H_r being always smaller than the driving field H_1. However, when $\rho>1$, H_r and H_1 are out of phase but equal in magnitude at resonance and so an adiabatic passage from one side of $\delta=0$ to the other is no longer possible. In this case *there is a maximum tipping angle which can be reached adiabatically:*

$$\theta_{max}=\cos^{-1}(1-\rho^{-2})^{\frac{1}{2}}$$

and motion beyond this angle is no longer steady-state.

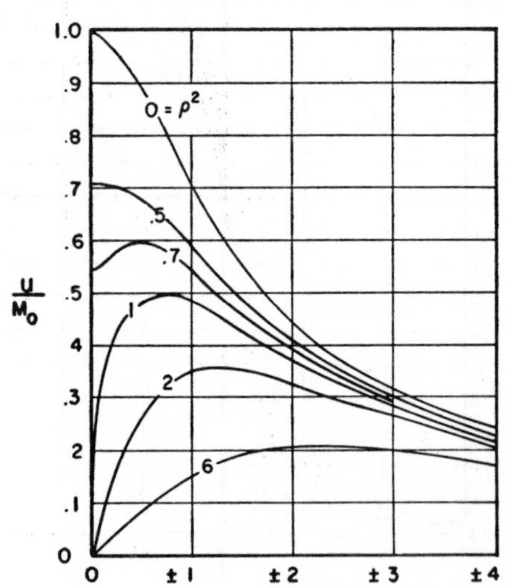

FIG. 3. The dispersion signal, u/M_0, for adiabatic fast passage. For negligible radiation damping, the curve is given by $(1+\delta^2)^{-\frac{1}{2}}$. For increasing radiation damping, the signals dip at resonance, finally reaching zero for $\rho^2>1$.

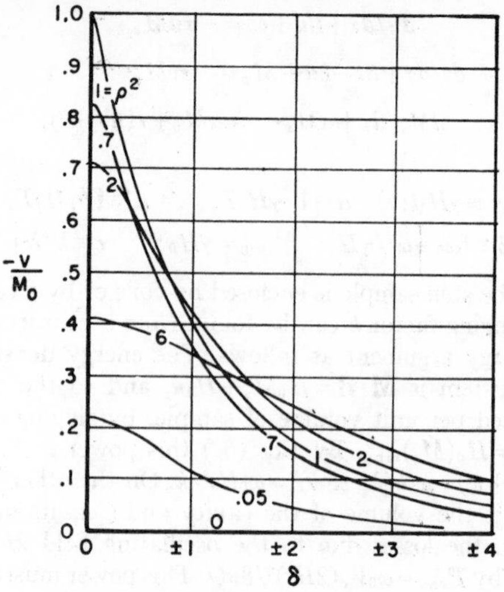

FIG. 4. The absorption signal, $-v/M_0$, for adiabatic fast passage. For negligible radiation damping, the absorption is zero. But as damping increases, the absorption signal may reach values comparable to the dispersion signal.

The dispersion (u) and absorption (v) signals given by Eqs. (11) are plotted in Figs. 3 and 4. The dispersion values at resonance are $u/M_0=0$ if $\rho\geq 1$ and $u/M_0=(1-\rho^2)^{\frac{1}{2}}$ if $\rho\leq 1$. The absorption values at resonance are $-v/M_0=\rho^{-1}$ if $\rho\geq 1$ and $-v/M_0=\rho$ if $\rho\leq 1$. As the ringing increases, *the centers of the dispersion curves decrease*[9] and finally reach zero when $\rho=1$. Although the absorption is zero when radiation damping is neglected, as ρ increases the absorption becomes appreciable.

C. Effects of Spin-Spin Relaxation on Free Precession

For free precession, i.e., radiation following the removal of the driving field, H_1 is set equal to zero. Equations (6) then reduce to

$$\begin{aligned}dH_r/dt+H_r/T_2+\gamma kH_rM_z=0,\\ dM_z/dt+(M_z-M_0)/T_1-\gamma H_r^2/k=0,\end{aligned}\tag{14}$$

where use has been made of the fact that $(u^2+v^2)^{\frac{1}{2}}=M\sin\theta=H_r/k$. If we neglect spin-lattice relaxation, these nonlinear equations can be solved in closed form. This is a physically meaningful approximation, as T_1 for certain systems is much larger than the spin-spin relaxation time T_2. Thus with $T_1=\infty$, the solution of

[9] Radiation damping is possibly the explanation of the dispersion-signal line shapes reported by G. Feher (Electron Tube Research Conference, Boulder, Colorado, June, 1956). The dispersion signal from paramagnetic lithium-doped silicon was measured using the adiabatic fast passage technique. The number of active spins was successively increased by allowing the sample to partially thermalize in a dc magnetic field for successively longer intervals of time. Following each such exposure, the dispersion signal was recorded as a function of the swept dc field. As the exposure time was increased, $\rho\propto M_0$ increased and the dispersion exhibited a dipping at the line center.

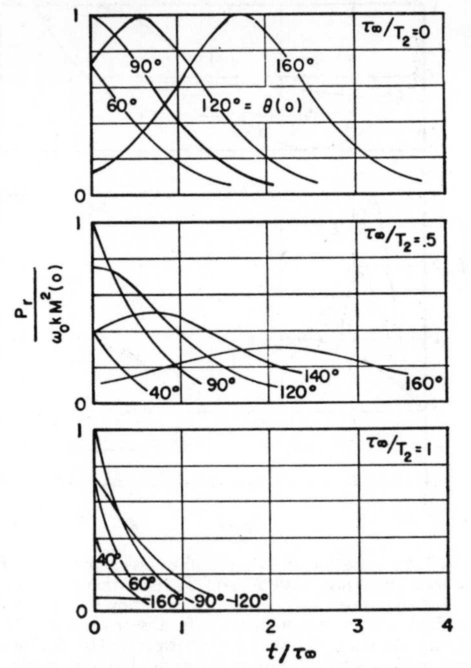

FIG. 5. If the rf driving field H_1 is cut off after the magnetization has been driven to the value $M(0)$ through the angle $\theta(0)$, then the subsequent free-precession power per cc, P_r, varies with time as shown. A necessary condition that this power exhibit a delayed peak is that the radiation damping be strong enough, and/or the spin-spin relaxation time T_2 be long enough, that $\tau_\infty/T_2 \leq 1$.

Eqs. (14) is found to be

$$M_z(t) = (\gamma k\tau)^{-1}\tanh(t-t_m)/\tau - (\gamma k T_2)^{-1},$$
$$H_r(t) = (\gamma\tau)^{-1}\operatorname{sech}(t-t_m)/\tau,$$

in which t_m is determined by

$$\exp(2t_m/\tau) = \frac{1-[(\tau/T_2)+(\tau/\tau_\infty)\cos\theta(0)]}{1+[(\tau/T_2)+(\tau/\tau_\infty)\cos\theta(0)]},$$

and the *radiation-damping relaxation time* τ is related to its value in the absence of spin-spin relaxation,

$$\tau(T_2=\infty) \equiv \tau_\infty = 1/\gamma k M(0),$$

by the relation

$$\tau_\infty/\tau = [(\tau_\infty/T_2)^2 + 2(\tau_\infty/T_2)\cos\theta(0)+1]^{\frac{1}{2}}.$$

Here $t=0$ is the instant of cutoff of the driving field H_1, the tipping angle then having the value $\theta(0)$ and the total magnetization the value $M(0)=M_z(0)/\cos\theta(0)$.

The ringing power, $P_r=\omega_0 H_r^2/k$, reaches a peak value of $\omega_0 k M^2(0)(\tau_\infty/\tau)^2$ at time t_m. With $T_2\neq\infty$, t_m is *not* the instant when M_z is zero. This radiation peak will occur after cutoff, i.e., $t_m\geq 0$, provided $-\cos\theta(0)\geq\tau_\infty/T_2$. Thus for there to be *delayed* power peaks, not only must the magnetization be first driven beyond the transverse plane by H_1, but also the spin-spin time T_2 must be sufficiently long that $\tau_\infty/T_2\leq 1$. The ringing power P_r, normalized to its value for $T_2=\infty$, is shown in Fig. 5 as a function of time, for various cutoff angles $\theta(0)$ and for three values of the relaxation time ratio τ_∞/T_2. The quantities t_m/τ and τ_∞/τ are shown in Figs. 6 and 7.

As an illustrative example, consider the case of electron spin resonance in phosphorous-doped silicon. The spin-lattice relaxation time T_1 is long, of the order of seconds,[10] for a spin density of $N\approx 5\times 10^{16}$ per cc at 2°K. Thus, for $Q\approx 2\times 10^4$, $f\approx 1/10$, and $T_2\approx 10^{-7}$ sec,

$$\tau_\infty/T_2 = 1/\gamma k M(0) T_2 = KT/(2\pi Q f\omega_0 N\mu^2 T_2)$$

has the value $\tau_\infty/T_2\approx 1$, and so delayed power peaks should almost be observable. The maximum ringing power per cc, $P=\omega_0 k M^2(0)$, occurring just after a 90°

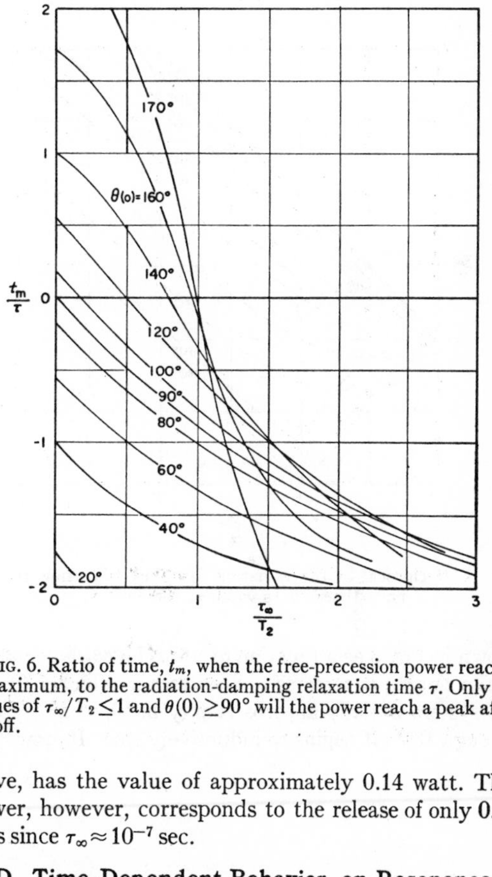

FIG. 6. Ratio of time, t_m, when the free-precession power reaches a maximum, to the radiation-damping relaxation time τ. Only for values of $\tau_\infty/T_2\leq 1$ and $\theta(0)\geq 90°$ will the power reach a peak after cutoff.

drive, has the value of approximately 0.14 watt. This power, however, corresponds to the release of only 0.14 ergs since $\tau_\infty\approx 10^{-7}$ sec.

D. Time-Dependent Behavior, on Resonance

Here we consider the effect of radiation damping on the time behavior of the spin system when the driving field $2H_1\cos\omega t$ is on resonance. Thus $\delta=0$, and $u=0$ is seen to be a solution of Eqs. (6). By Eq. (5) this corresponds to

$$\phi=\omega_0 t\mp\pi/2,$$
$$v=\mp M\sin\theta.$$

[10] G. Feher and R. C. Fletcher, Bull. Am. Phys. Soc. 1, 125 (1956).

Equations (6b) and (6c) thus give, if we neglect relaxation effects by taking $T_1=T_2=\infty$,

$$d\theta/dt=\pm\gamma H_1-\gamma k M_0\sin\theta.$$

This equation is solved for the initial conditions in which M is along $H_0(\theta=0)$, or opposite to $H_0(\theta=\pi)$. The solution is

$$\rho\sin\theta=\frac{\pm\rho^{-1}(1-\rho^2)^{\frac{1}{2}}\sin\Omega-\cos\Omega+1}{\pm\rho^{-1}(1-\rho^2)^{\frac{1}{2}}\sin\Omega-\cos\Omega+\rho^{-2}},\qquad(15)$$

where $\Omega\equiv\gamma H_1 t(1-\rho^2)^{\frac{1}{2}}$ and $\rho=kM_0/H_1$. The stimulated-emission power per unit volume is, since $u=0$,

$$P=H_0\dot{M}_z=H_0M_0d(\cos\theta)/dt,$$

where $\theta(t)$ is obtained from Eq. (15). This power is

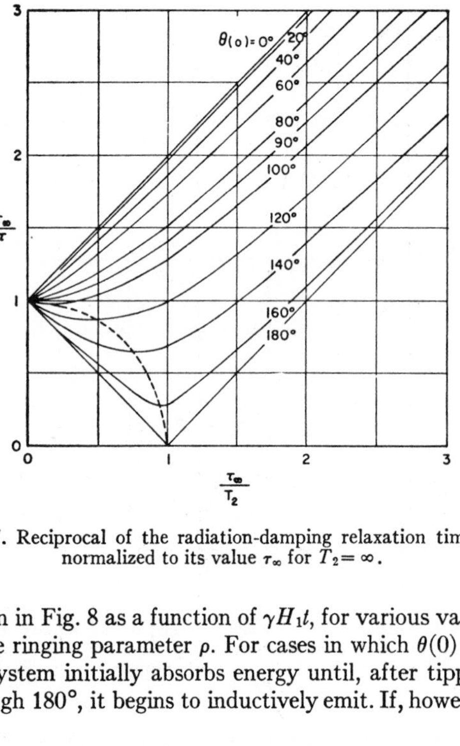

FIG. 7. Reciprocal of the radiation-damping relaxation time τ, normalized to its value τ_∞ for $T_2=\infty$.

shown in Fig. 8 as a function of $\gamma H_1 t$, for various values of the ringing parameter ρ. For cases in which $\theta(0)=0$, the system initially absorbs energy until, after tipping through 180°, it begins to inductively emit. If, however,

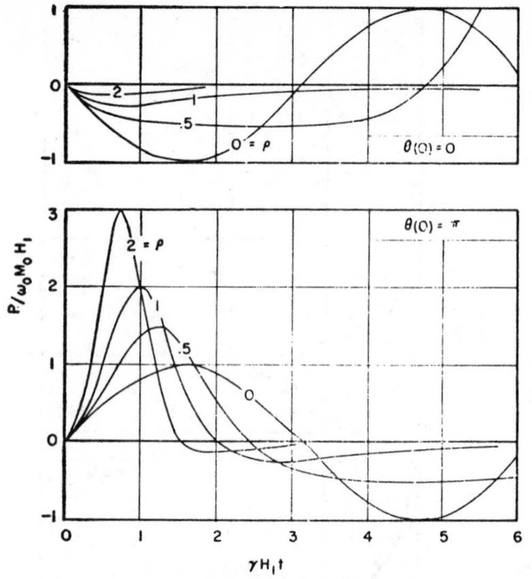

FIG. 8. Time variation of the induced-emission power, as affected by radiation damping, with T_1 and T_2 relaxation processes neglected. For the upper figure, the magnetization starts parallel to the dc field and the system initially absorbs energy. For the lower figure, the magnetization starts antiparallel to H_0 ("negative temperature" condition) and the system initially emits. This emission increases with the ringing parameter ρ and may become quite large. For negligible radiation damping, the power varies sinusoidally.

the radiation damping is large enough (i.e., $\rho\geq1$), the magnitization cannot tip to 180° because the tipping torque due to the driving field is being over-compensated by the damping. For cases in which $\theta(0)=\pi$, corresponding to a "negative temperature" condition, the spin system initially radiates, until, after reaching 0°, it begins to absorb. The driving field H_1 is enhanced by the ringing field H_r and together these tip the magnetization up toward 0° more rapidly than in the absence of radiation damping. Thus, the stimulated emission can become quite large.

ACKNOWLEDGMENTS

The author has enjoyed helpful discussions with Dr. J. P. Wittke and Mr. L. E. Norton.

SUSCEPTIBILITY OF THE THREE-LEVEL MASER

A. M. CLOGSTON

Bell Telephone Laboratories, Inc., Murray Hill, N.J.

(*Received* 28 *August* 1957)

Abstract—The quantum-mechanical equations of motion of a three-level maser, including the off-diagonal terms, are solved approximately to obtain the susceptibility χ presented by the paramagnetic material at the frequency $(1/h)(E_3-E_2)$. The effect of the cavity reaction at the frequency $(1/h)$ (E_2-E_1) is considered. The line shape is shown to be drastically altered for large-amplitude driving fields.

1. INTRODUCTION

THE great interest that has arisen in recent months in the field of maser oscillation and amplification has resulted in a variety of theoretical treatments of the dynamics of maser operation.[1–4] One particularly systematic way of approaching the maser consists in describing the response to a radiation field of the solid or gas involved by means of a frequency-dependent susceptibility. The ammonia maser, a two-level system, has been discussed in this way by GORDON *et al.*[1] If the susceptibility χ is written in the usual way as $\chi'-i\chi''$, where χ' describes the in-phase and χ'' the out-of-phase response of the system, the maser principle can be expressed by the statement that χ' and χ'' have the opposite sign to that encountered in a passive system. The negative value of χ'' presented to the radiation field counteracts the losses present in the electromagnetic system and thereby leads to regenerative amplification or oscillation. In the case of the ammonia maser, the change of sign arises, of course, from the experimental arrangements that permit only excited NH_3 molecules to interact with the radiation field. Another form of maser, based on three quantum levels, has been proposed by BLOEMBERGEN.[2] In this case a strong driving or pumping field is applied resonant with the outer pair of levels and is effective in so changing the equilibrium populations of the levels that an inverted susceptibility appears across one of the inner pair of levels. We shall calculate this susceptibility in the following sections, using an analysis that includes the effect of off-diagonal components of the density matrix. A similar approach has been used by ANDERSON[3] and JAVAN.[4] The results generally agree with those of BLOEMBERGEN, but they permit a discussion of certain questions not touched upon in his work. We are able to show, for instance, that the susceptibility offered by one pair of levels is usually unaffected by the cavity reaction on the other pair.* Another result is a saturation of the susceptibility that appears at high levels of the pumping field. This effect is also described by JAVAN.[4]

2. EQUATIONS OF MOTION

Let us consider the three-level quantum-mechanical system shown in Fig. 1, where the energy levels are E_1, E_2, and E_3 in order of ascending energy. We shall describe this system in terms

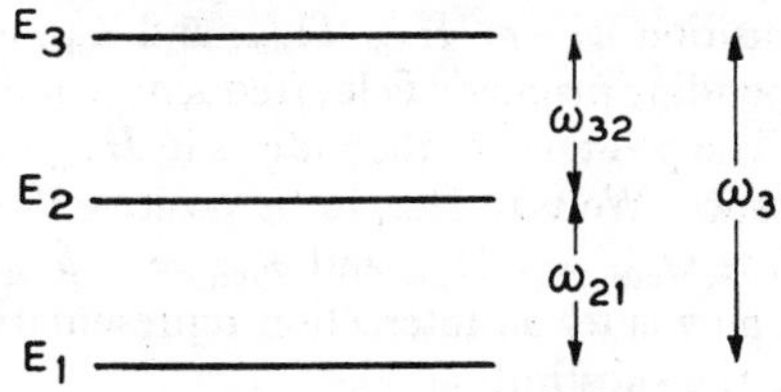

FIG. 1. Energy level scheme.

of its density matrix ρ_{nm}, where n and m run from one to three. The equations of motion for ρ_{nm},

* ANDERSON[3] describes a case in which the cavity reaction is important.

including relaxation terms, are

$n = m$

$$\dot{\rho}_{nn} = \sum_k (W_{kn}\rho_{kk} - W_{nk}\rho_{nn}) + \frac{1}{i\hbar}\sum_k (V_{nk}\rho_{kn} - \rho_{nk}V_{kn}) \quad (1)$$

$n \neq m$

$$\dot{\rho}_{nm} = -\frac{1}{\tau_{nm}}\rho_{nm} + \frac{1}{i\hbar}(E_n - E_m)\rho_{nm} + \frac{1}{i\hbar}\sum_k (V_{nk}\rho_{km} - \rho_{nk}V_{km}). \quad (2)$$

In these equations the terms W_{kn} are transition probabilities between the various levels and are subject to the restrictions of detailed balancing

$$0 = (W_{kn}\rho_{kk}{}^0 - W_{nk}\rho_{nn}{}^0) \quad (3)$$

where $\rho_{nn}{}^0$ represents the components of ρ_{nm} in thermal equilibrium. The quantities $\tau_{nm} = \tau_{mn}$ are relaxation times associated with the off-diagonal components of ρ_{nm}. The elements V_{nk} constitute a perturbation matrix existing because of the presence of electromagnetic fields. We suppose that there are three plane-polarized fields, separated in frequency, and interacting with the transitions $1 \to 3$, $1 \to 2$, and $2 \to 3$. The matrix components V_{nm} may then be written

$$V_{nm} = -\mu_{nm}H_{nm}\cos(\Omega_{nm}t - \phi_{nm}) \quad (4)$$

where μ_{nm} is the dipole moment associated with the transition $n \to m$. H_{nm}, Ω_{nm}, and ϕ_{nm} are the corresponding magnetic field, frequency, and phase angle. The positions of the indices in H_{nm} have no significance. We take Ω_{nm} to be positive if $n > m$ and place $\Omega_{mn} = -\Omega_{nm}$ and $\phi_{mn} = -\phi_{nm}$. Let us now enter an interaction representation by making the substitution

$$\rho_{nm} = \sigma_{nm}\exp(-i\omega_{nm}t) \quad (5)$$

where

$$\omega_{nm} = \frac{1}{\hbar}(E_n - E_m).$$

Equations (1) and (2) become respectively

$$\dot{\sigma}_{nn} = \sum_k (W_{kn}\sigma_{kk} - W_{nk}\sigma_{nn}) - \sum_k \left\{\frac{H_{nk}}{2i\hbar}\right\}\Big[\mu_{nk}\sigma_{kn}\exp\{i[(\Omega_{kn} - \omega_{kn})t - \phi_{kn}]\} - \sigma_{nk}\mu_{kn}\exp\{-i[(\Omega_{kn} - \omega_{kn})t - \phi_{kn}]\}\Big] \quad (6)$$

$$\dot{\sigma}_{nm} = -\frac{1}{\tau_{nm}}\sigma_{nm} - \sum_k \left\{\frac{H_{nk}}{2i\hbar}\right\}\mu_{nk}\sigma_{km}\exp\{i[(\Omega_{kn} - \omega_{kn})t - \phi_{kn}]\} - \left\{\frac{H_{km}}{2i\hbar}\right\}\sigma_{nk}\mu_{km}\exp\{-i[(\Omega_{km} - \omega_{km})t - \phi_{km}]\}. \quad (7)$$

We next proceed by making the substitutions

$$A_{nk} = \frac{1}{2\hbar}H_{nk}\mu_{nk}\exp(i\phi_{nk}) \quad (8)$$

$$\sigma_{nk} = \lambda_{nk}\exp[-i(\Omega_{nk} - \omega_{nk})t] \quad (9)$$

and then obtain, keeping only the secular terms,

$$0 = \sum_k (W_{kn}\lambda_{kk} - W_{nk}\lambda_{nn}) + i\sum_k (A_{nk}\lambda_{kn} - \lambda_{nk}A_{kn}) \quad (10)$$

$$\left[-i(\Omega_{nm} - \omega_{nm}) + \frac{1}{\tau_{nm}}\right]\lambda_{nm} = i\sum_k (A_{nk}\lambda_{km} - \lambda_{nk}A_{km}) \quad (11)$$

with the condition that

$$\Omega_{31} = \Omega_{32} + \Omega_{21}. \quad (12)$$

Expressions (10) and (11) represent six equations in the six independent components of the density matrix λ_{nm} and could be solved in general. However, we proceed in the next section under somewhat specialized conditions.

3. COMPONENTS OF THE DENSITY MATRIX

We shall assume that the diagonal elements of the density matrix are essentially controlled by a large radio-frequency magnetic field causing transitions between levels 1 and 3 and that this field is in resonance with these levels, so that

$\Omega_{31} = \omega_{31}$. Writing out explicitly four of the six equations contained in (10) and (11), we have

$$-(W_{12}+W_{13})\rho_{11}+W_{21}\rho_{22}+W_{31}\rho_{33}+ +i(A_{13}\lambda_{31}-\lambda_{13}A_{31}) = 0 \quad (13)$$

$$-(W_{21}+W_{23})\rho_{22}+W_{12}\rho_{11}+W_{32}\rho_{33} = 0 \quad (14)$$

$$-(W_{31}+W_{32})\rho_{33}+W_{13}\rho_{11}+W_{23}\rho_{22}- -i(A_{13}\lambda_{31}-\lambda_{13}A_{31}) = 0 \quad (15)$$

$$\lambda_{13} = i\tau_{13}A_{13}(\rho_{33}-\rho_{11}) \quad (16)$$

since it is obvious that $\lambda_{nn} = \sigma_{nn} = \rho_{nn}$. Certain second-order terms have been dropped in these equations. Equation (15) is not independent of equations (13) and (14), but we may use the additional relation $\rho_{11}+\rho_{22}+\rho_{33} = 1$, together with equations (13), (14) and (16), to obtain

$$(\rho_{33}-\rho_{22}) = \frac{(\rho_{33}^0-\rho_{22}^0)+\frac{1}{\hbar^2}H_{13}^2|\mu_{13}|^2\tau_{13}T_e}{1+\frac{1}{\hbar^2}H_{13}^2|\mu_{13}|^2\tau_{13}T} \quad (17)$$

$$(\rho_{22}-\rho_{11}) = \frac{(\rho_{22}^0-\rho_{11}^0)-\frac{1}{\hbar^2}H_{13}^2|\mu_{13}|^2\tau_{13}T_e}{1+\frac{1}{\hbar^2}H_{13}^2|\mu_{13}|^2\tau_{13}T} \quad (18)$$

$$(\rho_{33}-\rho_{11}) = \frac{(\rho_{33}^0-\rho_{11}^0)}{1+\frac{1}{\hbar^2}H_{13}^2|\mu_{13}|^2\tau_{13}T}. \quad (19)$$

If a set of relaxation times T_{nm}, consistent with equation (3), are defined by

$$W_{nm} = \frac{1}{T_{nm}}\rho_{mm}^0, \quad (20)$$

then the quantities T and T_e are given by*

$$T = \frac{\frac{1}{T_{12}}\rho_{11}^0+\frac{1}{2}\left(\frac{1}{T_{12}}+\frac{1}{T_{23}}\right)\rho_{22}^0+\frac{1}{T_{23}}\rho_{33}^0}{\frac{1}{T_{13}T_{12}}\rho_{11}^0+\frac{1}{T_{12}T_{23}}\rho_{22}^0+\frac{1}{T_{13}T_{23}}\rho_{33}^0} \quad (21)$$

$$T_e = \frac{1}{2}\cdot\frac{\frac{1}{T_{12}}(\rho_{11}^0-\rho_{22}^0)+\frac{1}{T_{23}}(\rho_{33}^0-\rho_{22}^0)}{\frac{1}{T_{13}T_{12}}\rho_{11}^0+\frac{1}{T_{12}T_{23}}\rho_{22}^0+\frac{1}{T_{13}T_{23}}\rho_{33}^0}. \quad (22)$$

If the remaining two equations contained in (11) are written out explicitly, we have

$$\left[i(\Omega_{32}-\omega_{32})+\frac{1}{\tau_{21}}\right]\lambda_{21}+iA_{31}\lambda_{23} = iA_{21}(\rho_{11}-\rho_{22})+iA_{23}\lambda_{31} \quad (23)$$

$$\left[i(\Omega_{32}-\omega_{32})+\frac{1}{\tau_{23}}\right]\lambda_{23}+iA_{13}\lambda_{21} = iA_{23}(\rho_{33}-\rho_{22})+iA_{21}\lambda_{13} \quad (24)$$

where we have set $(\Omega_{21}-\omega_{21}) = -(\Omega_{32}-\omega_{32})$ as follows from the assumption $\Omega_{31} = \omega_{31}$. These are the basic equations of the three-level maser. We note first that the free oscillation of the off-diagonal components of the density matrix are coupled in the presence of the pumping field H_{13}. The coupling clearly arises from the fact that ρ_{23} can beat with H_{13} to produce a frequency that excites ρ_{21}, and similarly ρ_{21} can beat with H_{13} to excite ρ_{23}. Next we see that this set of coupled equations is driven by the signal fields H_{12} and H_{23} in a way depending on the population difference of the corresponding levels. Finally, the equations are driven by terms arising from a beat between the signal fields and the oscillation of ρ_{13}.

The quantities $(\rho_{11}-\rho_{22})$, $(\rho_{33}-\rho_{22})$, and λ_{13} have already been found. We may proceed then to solve equations (23) and (24) simultaneously, with the result

* Definition of an effective time T_e has also been considered by LLOYD and PAKE.[6]

$$\lambda_{21} = \frac{i\left[i(\Omega_{32}-\omega_{32})+\frac{1}{\tau_{23}}\right][A_{21}(\rho_{11}-\rho_{22})+A_{23}\lambda_{31}]+A_{31}[A_{23}(\rho_{33}-\rho_{22})+A_{21}\lambda_{13}]}{\left[i(\Omega_{32}-\omega_{32})+\frac{1}{\tau_{21}}\right]\left[i(\Omega_{32}-\omega_{32})+\frac{1}{\tau_{23}}\right]+|A_{13}|^2} \quad (25)$$

$$\lambda_{23} = \frac{i\left[i(\Omega_{32}-\omega_{32})+\dfrac{1}{\tau_{12}}\right][A_{23}(\rho_{33}-\rho_{22})+A_{21}\lambda_{13}]+A_{13}[A_{21}(\rho_{11}-\rho_{22})+A_{23}\lambda_{31}]}{\left[i(\Omega_{32}-\omega_{32})+\dfrac{1}{\tau_{21}}\right]\left[i(\Omega_{32}-\omega_{32})+\dfrac{1}{\tau_{23}}\right]+|A_{13}|^2} \tag{26}$$

We have now obtained all components of the density matrix and can proceed to evaluate the susceptibilities.

4. SUSCEPTIBILITIES

Let us now characterize the physical situation as follows. The paramagnetic sample is in a resonant cavity in the presence of three radio-frequency fields. One of these is the pumping field H_{13}. The second field, H_{23}, will be a signal field introduced into the cavity from an external source. The response of the sample to the signal field will produce an oscillating dipole moment M_{12} between levels 1 and 2. This dipole will create a third field, H_{12}, in the cavity in a way determined by the cavity "susceptibility" $\chi_c = \chi_c'-i\chi_c''$. That is

$$M_{12} = \chi_c' H_{12}\cos(\Omega_{21}\tau-\phi_{21})+ +\chi_c'' H_{12}\sin(\Omega_{21}\tau-\phi_{21}) \tag{27}$$

where χ_c can be shown in a standard way to be given by

$$\frac{1}{\chi_c} = \sum_n \frac{4\pi F_n[\omega^2-i(\omega\omega_n/Q_n)]}{(\omega_n{}^2-\omega^2)+i(\omega\omega_n/Q_n)} \simeq \sum_n \frac{4\pi F_n\omega}{2(\omega_n-\omega)+i(\omega_n/Q_n)}. \tag{28}$$

Here the sum is carried over all modes of the cavity, with ω_n, Q_n, and F_n (the filling factor) being characteristics of a particular mode. Expressed in terms of the density matrix, M_{12} is given by

$$M_{12} = N(\rho_{12}\mu_{21}+\rho_{21}\mu_{12}) = N[\lambda_{12}\exp(i\Omega_{21}\tau)\mu_{21}+\lambda_{21}\exp(-i\Omega_{21}\tau)\mu_{12}] \tag{29}$$

where N is the number of spins per unit volume. From equations (27) and (29) we find with a little manipulation

$$(\chi_c'+i\chi_c'')A_{21} = \frac{N|\mu_{12}|^2}{\hbar}\lambda_{21}. \tag{30}$$

Similarly, if the susceptibility of the sample offered to the signal field by transitions between levels 2 and 3 is $\chi = \chi'-i\chi''$, we find

$$(\chi'-i\chi'')A_{23} = \frac{N|\mu_{23}|^2}{\hbar}\lambda_{23}. \tag{31}$$

If λ_{21} and λ_{23} are substituted from equations (25) and (26) into equations (30) and 31), there are obtained two homogeneous equations in A_{21} and A_{23}. Placing the determinant of the coefficients equal to zero, one obtains an equation for the susceptibility χ

$$\chi = \chi_{32}\left[i\left\{\frac{d_{21}+rb}{d_{21}d_{32}+b}\right\}+\frac{b\left\{\dfrac{1+Rd_{21}}{d_{21}d_{32}+b}\right\}\left\{\dfrac{1+rd_{32}}{d_{21}d_{32}+b}\right\}\chi_{12}}{\chi_c{}^*-i\left\{\dfrac{d_{32}-Rb}{d_{21}d_{32}+b}\right\}\chi_{12}}\right] \tag{32}$$

where we make the following definitions:

$$d_{21} = 1-i(\Omega_{21}-\omega_{21})\tau_{12}$$

$$d_{32} = 1+i(\Omega_{32}-\omega_{32})\tau_{23}$$

$$R = \frac{\tau_{13}(\rho_{11}-\rho_{33})}{\tau_{12}(\rho_{11}-\rho_{22})},\quad r = \frac{\tau_{13}(\rho_{11}-\rho_{33})}{\tau_{23}(\rho_{33}-\rho_{22})}$$

$$b = \frac{1}{4\hbar^2}H_{13}{}^2|\mu_{13}|^2\tau_{12}\tau_{23}$$

$$\chi_{12} = \frac{1}{\hbar}N|\mu_{12}|^2\tau_{12}(\rho_{11}-\rho_{22})$$

$$\chi_{32} = \frac{1}{\hbar} N|\mu_{23}|^2\tau_{23}(\rho_{33}-\rho_{22}).$$

Equation (32) is the most general expression for the susceptibility of a three-level maser. The susceptibility, together with the characteristics of the microwave cavity at the frequency Ω_{32}, determine all the important properties of the maser except its noise behavior.

5. APPROXIMATE EQUATION FOR THE SUSCEPTIBILITY

We shall next consider a special set of conditions, appropriate to the operation of a three-level maser, which allows equation (32) to be considerably simplified. Suppose first that the various energy differences are small enough compared with the operating temperature so that one may write approximately

$$\left.\begin{aligned} \rho_{11}^0-\rho_{22}^0 &= \frac{E_2-E_1}{3kT} \\ \rho_{11}^0-\rho_{33}^0 &= \frac{E_3-E_1}{3kT} \\ \rho_{22}^0-\rho_{33}^0 &= \frac{E_3-E_2}{3kT}. \end{aligned}\right\} \quad (33)$$

Let us also assume that $T_{12} \ll T_{13}$ or T_{23}, a circumstance that can be realized in the manner reported by Scovil *et al.*[5] In that case, equation (18) indicates that very closely

$$(\rho_{11}-\rho_{22}) = (\rho_{11}^0-\rho_{22}^0). \quad (34)$$

From equation (19) and the definition of b, we find

$$(\rho_{11}-\rho_{33}) = \frac{(\rho_{11}^0-\rho_{33}^0)}{1+4b(T/\tau)} \quad (35)$$

where we have assumed all the off-diagonal relaxation times equal to τ. From equations (34) and (35) there is found

$$R = \frac{E_3-E_1}{E_2-E_1}\cdot\frac{1}{1+\dfrac{4T}{\tau}b}. \quad (36)$$

It is also easily shown that

$$r = \frac{R}{1-R} \quad (37)$$

and

$$(\rho_{33}-\rho_{22}) = (\rho_{11}^0-\rho_{22}^0)(1-R). \quad (38)$$

A slight rearrangement of equation (32) gives

$$\chi = i\chi_{32}\left(\frac{d_{21}+rb}{d_{21}d_{32}+b}\right)\times \left[1+\frac{b\left(\dfrac{1+Rd_{21}}{d_{21}d_{32}+b}\right)\left(\dfrac{1+rd_{32}}{d_{21}+rb}\right)}{\dfrac{i\chi_c^*}{\chi_{21}}+\left(\dfrac{d_{32}-Rb}{d_{21}d_{32}+b}\right)}\right]. \quad (39)$$

We now subject the second term in brackets in equation (39) to a close examination based on the following considerations:

(*a*) We shall be interested in the susceptibility χ only for Ω_{32} fairly close to ω_{32} and for Ω_{21} correspondingly close to ω_{21}.

(*b*) The cavity susceptibility χ_c will be controlled by the cavity mode whose resonance is closest to Ω_{21} and is found from equation (28) to be

$$\chi_c = \frac{2(\omega_0-\Omega_{21})}{4\pi F\omega_0}+i\frac{1}{4\pi FQ}. \quad (40)$$

We assume typical values of $F = \frac{1}{10}$ and $Q=5000$. If $\omega_0 \simeq \Omega_{21}$, we shall say that the resonance is close. There must always be a cavity resonance near ω_{32} in any useful maser. If there is no resonance closer to Ω_{21}, and if the level separations are such that $|\Omega_{21}-\omega_0| > \omega_0$, we shall say that the resonance is remote.

(*c*) We assume that the energy difference (E_2-E_1) corresponds to a frequency in the neighborhood of 24,000 Mc/s and that the working temperature is a few degrees absolute. Then $(\rho_{11}^0-\rho_{22}^0) \simeq \frac{1}{10}$. If the spin density is about 10^{20} and τ about 10^{-8} sec, we find $\chi_{12} \simeq 10^{-2}$.

The detailed analysis allows one to conclude that the second term may be neglected under the following conditions:

(*a*) If ω_0 is remote and $1-R>0$

(*b*) If ω_0 is close, $1-R > \frac{1}{10}$, and

$$\frac{\tau}{T} < 4\left(\frac{E_2-E_1}{E_3-E_2}\right)10^{-4}.$$

The condition on R avoids some complications in

the behavior of χ at low levels of the pumping field, but leaves available the interesting range. In essence, the second term, may be neglected if ω_0 is remote, and may still be neglected if ω_0 is close, provided τ/T is small enough. With these restrictions, we write for the susceptibility

$$\chi = i\chi_{12}\frac{(1-R)(1+i\Delta)Rb}{(1+i\Delta)^2+b} \tag{41}$$

where we have placed $\Delta = (\Omega_{32}-\omega_{32})\tau = -(\Omega_{21}-\omega_{21})\tau$ and assumed $|\mu_{23}|^2 = |\mu_{12}|^2$. In this approximation, χ no longer depends upon the cavity susceptibility. The real and imaginary parts of $\chi = \chi'-i\chi''$ may be easily found from equation (41) to be

$$\frac{\chi'}{\chi_{12}} = \frac{\Delta[(1-R)+(3R-1)b+(1-R)\Delta^2]}{(1+b-\Delta^2)^2+4\Delta^2} \tag{42}$$

$$\frac{\chi''}{\chi_{12}} = \frac{(1+b)(1-R+Rb)+(1-R-Rb)\Delta^2}{(1+b-\Delta^2)^2+4\Delta^2}. \tag{43}$$

If b is set equal to zero in equations (41), (42), and (43), the susceptibilities then correspond to BLOEMBERGEN's original results.

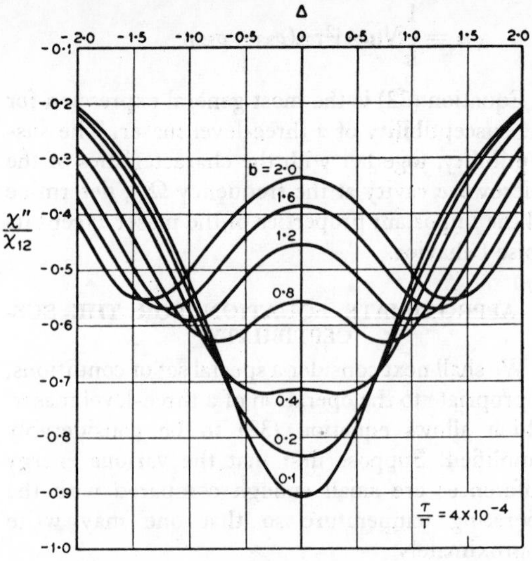

FIG. 3. Imaginary part of the normalized susceptibility as a function of $\Delta = (\Omega_{32}-\omega_{32})\tau$, for $\tau/T = 4\times10^{-4}$ and various values of $b = |(1/2\hbar)H_{13}\mu_{13}\tau|^2$.

In Figs. 2–6 we have plotted a series of susceptibility curves calculated from equations (42) and (43). These curves show the dependence of χ'/χ_{12} and of χ''/χ_{12} upon $\Delta = (\Omega_{32}-\omega_{32})\tau$ and are plotted

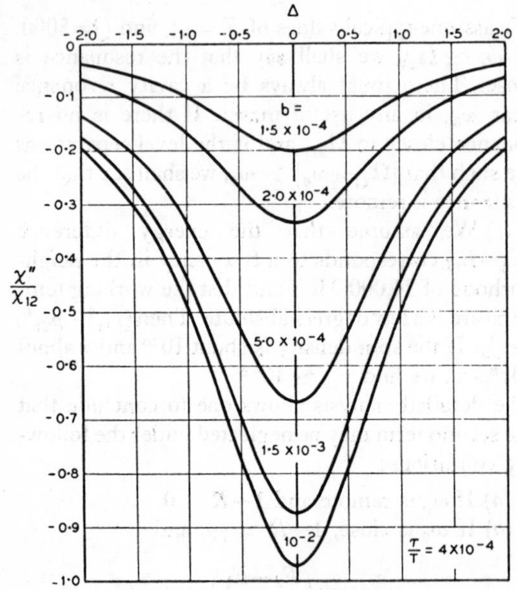

FIG. 2. Imaginary part of the normalized susceptibility as a function of $\Delta = (\Omega_{32}-\omega_{32})\tau$, for $\tau/T = 4\times10^{-4}$ and various values of $b = |(1/2\hbar)H_{13}\mu_{13}\tau|^2$.

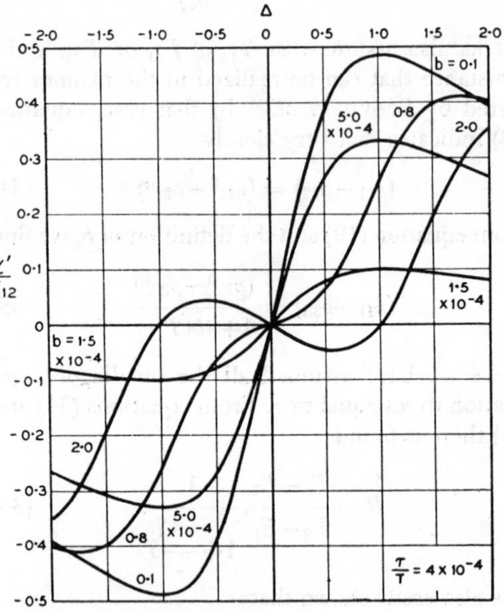

FIG. 4. Real part of the normalized susceptibility as a function of $\Delta = (\Omega_{32}-\omega_{32})\tau$, for $\tau/T = 4\times10^{-4}$ and various values of $b = |(1/2\hbar)H_{13}\mu_{13}\tau|^2$.

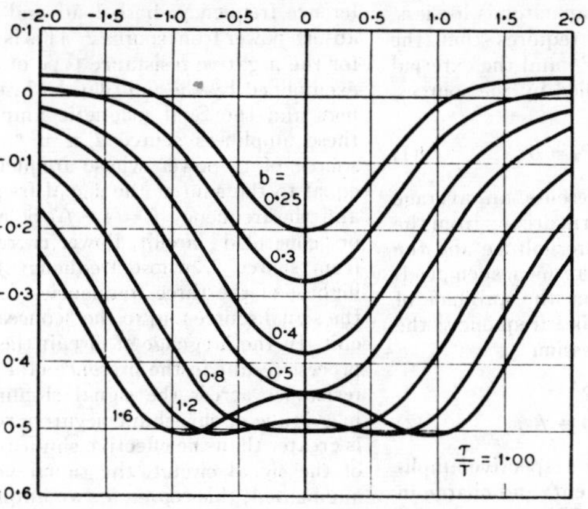

FIG. 5. Imaginary part of the normalized susceptibility as a function of $\Delta = (\Omega_{32} - \omega_{32})\tau$, for $\tau/T = 1{\cdot}00$ and various values of $b = |(1/2\hbar)H_{13}\mu_{13}\tau|^2$.

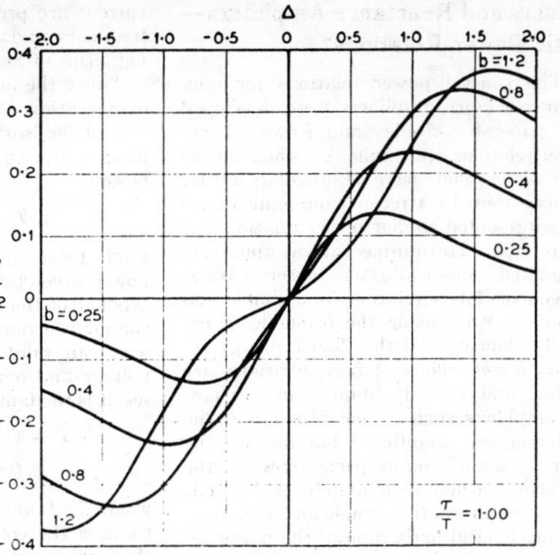

FIG. 6. Real part of the normalized susceptibility as a function of $\Delta = (\Omega_{32} - \omega_{32})\tau$, for $\tau/T = 1{\cdot}00$ and various values of $b = |(1/2\hbar)H_{13}\mu_{13}\tau|^2$.

for various values of $b = |\tau/2\hbar H_{13}\mu_{13}|^2$. Two extreme values have been chosen for the ratio of off-diagonal to diagonal relaxation times. In Figs. 2, 3, and 4, we have chosen $\tau/T = 4\times10^{-4}$; the condition of validity for equation (41) is then met for ω_0 either close or remote provided b is greater than $1{\cdot}2\times10^{-4}$. Figs. 2 and 3 show the imaginary part of the susceptibility, while the real part is shown in Fig. 4. In Figs. 5 and 6, we take $\tau/T = 1$; the curves are then valid only for ω_0 remote and $b > \frac{1}{4}$. The imaginary part of the susceptibility is presented in Fig. 5 and the real part in Fig. 6.

These curves exhibit the increasing negative value of χ'' as the pumping signal specified by b is increased. The most striking feature of the curves is the splitting of the line into a doublet when b becomes sufficiently large. This behavior has been discussed by JAVAN[4] and is illustrated in Fig. 2 of his paper. The effect has also been discussed by AUTLER and TOWNES[7] in connection with the molecule OCS. The splitting of the line is necessarily accompanied by an anomalous behavior of the real part of the susceptibility as may be seen in Figs. 4 and 6.

Acknowledgements—The author would like to acknowledge many helpful discussions with P. W. ANDERSON and H. SUHL. In particular he would like to thank A. JAVAN for the opportunity of examining his paper prior to its publication.

REFERENCES

1. GORDON J. P. ZEIGER H. J. and TOWNES C. H. *Phys. Rev.* **99**, 1264 (1955).
2. BLOEMBERGEN N. *Phys. Rev.* **104**, 324 (1956).
3. ANDERSON P. W. *J. Appl. Phys.* **28**, 1049, (1957).
4. JAVAN A. *Phys. Rev.* To be published.
5. SCOVIL H. E. D., FEHER G. and SEIDEL H. *Phys. Rev.* **105**, 762 (1957).
6. LLOYD J. P. and PAKE G. E. *Phys. Rev.* **94**, 579 (1954).
7. AUTLER S. H. and TOWNES C. H. *Phys. Rev.* **100**, 703 (1955).

Masers and Reactance Amplifiers—Basic Power Relations*

The general power relations for nonlinear reactance amplifiers were developed in a paper by Manley and Rowe.[1] These power relations are simple, but the analysis from which they were obtained is rather sophisticated. In a recent communication,[2] Weiss presented similar power relations for the related quantum-mechanical amplifiers designated generically as Masers. Weiss derived the latter relations in a simple and elegant way by using the principle of detailed balancing and the Planck energy relation $E=hf$. These power relations are fundamental not only to quantum-mechanical amplifiers such as the Maser and the Suhl magnetic amplifier,[3] but also to the older "classical" counterparts known as the dielectric and magnetic amplifiers. For this reason, an alternative simple and nonquantum-mechanical derivation of the power relations given by Manley and Rowe is desirable. Such a derivation is presented here.

Consider a nonlinear capacitance modulator consisting of a lossless device, whose charge vs voltage characteristic is nonlinear, in series with two sources and a load circuit. For the latter elements assume the following: each of the source voltages is sinusoidal with characteristic frequencies f_1 and f_2, respectively. To avoid the degenerate case for which the sum and difference frequencies coalesce with the harmonic frequencies, f_1 and f_2 are assumed incommensurable. The internal source impedances are significant only at their respective source frequencies. The load circuit impedance is significant only at the combination frequency $f_3=(mf_2\pm nf_1)$, where m and n may be any of the integers 1, 2, 3, $\cdots$. The load circuit voltage is thus also sinusoidal with characteristic frequency f_3.

The voltage applied to the nonlinear capacitor is the sum of the load voltage and the two source voltages minus the corresponding internal source-impedance voltage drops. Since these voltages are all sinusoidal and since the charge vs voltage characteristic of the capacitor is nonlinear, the resultant charge is periodic and representable in general by a dc term and a series of sinusoidal terms in the fundamental and harmonics of f_1 and f_2 and in all possible sum and difference combinations of f_1 and f_2. The amplitudes and phases of these terms are functions of the specific nonlinear device characteristic and of the amplitudes and phases of the three voltages, but not of the frequencies. These conclusions are reached directly if the nonlinear characteristic is represented, as it can be, by a power series in the voltage. The common steady-state current is the time derivative of the charge and therefore is representable by a similar series. The amplitudes of the terms in the current are proportional to the product of frequency and amplitude of the corresponding terms in the charge.

Since the nonlinear capacitor is lossless, conservation of energy requires that the sum of the load power, P_3, and the external powers, P_1 and P_2, supplied by the sources, be zero.

$$P_1+P_2+P_3=0. \tag{1}$$

Each term in (1) represents an average power, given by the dc term arising from the product of the appropriate voltage and the common current. The dc term in such products can only arise from the product of voltage and current of like frequency; the result is the familiar expression

$$P=(VI/2)\cos\phi$$
$$=f(\pi VQ\cos\phi)=fw, \tag{2}$$

where V, I, and Q are the respective amplitudes of the voltage, current, and charge in the corresponding terms of frequency f, and ϕ is the phase angle between voltage and current or charge. The quantity w is the energy per cycle; it is analogous to the quantity Nh in the Weiss paper.[2]

From (2) the expressions for the external energy per cycle supplied by each source and for the load are

$$w_1=(\pi V_1Q_1\cos\phi_1)=P_1/f_1$$
$$w_2=(\pi V_2Q_2\cos\phi_2)=P_2/f_2$$
$$w_3=(\pi V_3Q_3\cos\phi_3)=P_3/f_3,$$
$$f_3=mf_2\pm nf_1. \tag{3}$$

The result of combining (1) and (3) is

$$f_1(w_1\pm nw_3)+f_2(w_2+mw_3)=0. \tag{4}$$

As observed earlier, the amplitudes and phases of the charge components are functions only of the nonlinear device characteristic and of the amplitudes and phases of the three voltages. However, the load voltage and current or charge are connected by the load circuit impedance, which is a function of f_3. Therefore the charge amplitudes and phases in (3) are also functions of f_3. Since f_3 is a linear combination of f_1 and f_2 and not a function of their ratio, the only admissible solution of (4) is the set

$$w_1\pm nw_3=0$$
$$w_2+mw_3=0. \tag{5}$$

By using (3), (5) can be rewritten as

$$-P_3/(mf_2\pm nf_1)=P_2/mf_2=\pm P_1/nf_1. \tag{6}$$

Eq. (6) is the Manley-Rowe power relation for a load circuit responsive only to the sum or difference frequency $f_3=(mf_2\pm nf_1)$. The minus sign before P_3 indicates that the load absorbs power. If the load is responsive only to the sum frequency, both sources supply power to the load. When the load is arranged to absorb no power, $P_3=P_2=P_1=0$. Thus there can be no interchange of power between the sources unless an absorbing load is present. The ratio of the power absorbed by the load to the power supplied by source 1 is $-(P_3/P_1)=1+(mf_2/nf_1)$. This is the theoretical stable gain obtained by a lossless dielectric or magnetic amplifier. Such an amplifier consists of a signal source of frequency f_1, an rf power source of frequency f_2, and a sum-frequency load circuit whose output is subsequently demodulated.

If the load is responsive only to the difference frequency, both load and source 1 absorb power from source 2. This is the basis for the negative resistance type of amplifier exemplified by the multilevel Maser amplifiers and the Suhl magnetic amplifier. In these amplifiers source 2 is a "pumping" source of rf power whose frequency f_2 is equal to the sum of the signal frequency f_1 and the frequency $f_3=(f_2-f_1)$ of a built-in or "concealed" circuit. Power is transferred from source 2, whose frequency f_2 is the highest of the three frequencies f_1, f_2, f_3 to the signal source and to the "concealed" circuit. In the language of circuit theory, this process results in the presence of a negative resistance across the signal circuit. If the magnitude of this shunt negative resistance is greater than the effective shunt resistance of the signal circuit, the signal voltage is augmented; this represents an amplification of the signal. If the magnitude of the shunt negative resistance is less than the effective shunt resistance of the signal circuit, oscillation can occur.

If the load consists of two circuits in series, one responsive only to the sum frequency $f_+=(mf_2+nf_1)$ and the other responsive only to the difference frequency $f_-=(mf_2-nf_1)$, (6) becomes

$$(P_1/nf_1)+(P_+/f_+)-(P_-/f_-)=0$$
$$(P_2/mf_2)+(P_+/f_+)+(P_-/f_-)=0. \tag{7}$$

When $n=m=1$, (7) becomes identical with the power relations developed by Weiss for the four-level Maser.

The general Manley-Rowe power relations can be obtained simply by considering the load as a series of circuits, each responsive only to a single combination frequency and including enough circuits to account for all possible sum and difference frequencies. For the case of two sources and 2 m load circuits, (4) remains the same except that the coefficients of f_1 and f_2 each contain $(2m+1)$ terms in the w's. If there is only one source and m (harmonic) load circuits, (4) simplifies to the form $f_1\cdot(w_1+\text{sum of } w_m\text{'s})=0$. Further extension to multiple sources and loads is straightforward.

Although the foregoing derivation was developed specifically for a lossless nonlinear capacitor, the method is equally valid for a lossless nonlinear inductor. The results in both cases are identical; the power relations involve only the source and load frequencies and are independent of the specific characteristics of the nonlinear device.

I am indebted to my colleagues, Dr. E. G. Fubini and E. W. Sard, for helpful discussion.

BERNARD SALZBERG
Airborne Instruments Laboratory, Inc.
Mineola, N. Y.

* Received by the IRE, August 16, 1957.

[1] J. M. Manley and H. E. Rowe, "Some general properties of nonlinear elements—Part I. General energy relations," PROC. IRE, vol. 44, pp. 904–913; July, 1956.

[2] M. T. Weiss, "Quantum derivation of energy relations analogous to those for nonlinear reactances," PROC. IRE, vol. 45, pp. 1012–1013; July, 1957.

[3] H. Suhl, "Proposal for a ferromagnetic amplifier in the microwave range," *Phys. Rev.*, vol. 106, pp. 384–385; April 15, 1957.

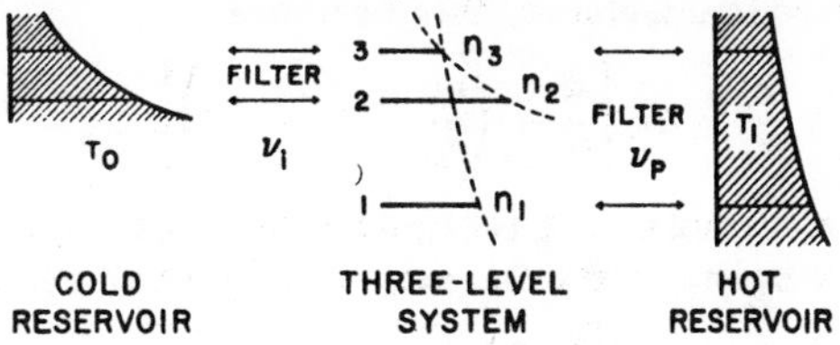

FIG. 1. Three-level system in thermal contact with two heat reservoirs.

THREE-LEVEL MASERS AS HEAT ENGINES*

H. E. D. Scovil and E. O. Schulz-DuBois
Bell Telephone Laboratories,
Murray Hill, New Jersey
(Received January 16, 1959)

The purpose of this note is to demonstrate that three-level masers[1,2] can be regarded as heat engines. The principal conceptual difference between these and conventional heat engines is that in the 3-level maser one is concerned with the discrete energy levels of a particle's internal energy whereas in a conventional heat engine one is concerned with the continuous spectrum of energies associated with external motion of the working substance. In treating a 3-level maser as a prototype of heat engine, a particular advantage is, in our opinion, the resulting conceptual simplicity. Especially, it is easily shown that the limiting efficiency of a 3-level maser is that of a Carnot engine.

Consider the system shown in Fig. 1. A three-level system is assumed with all transitions allowed and with no appreciable relaxation processes. The usual 3-level maser terminology is introduced by correlating transition 1 ⟶ 3 with pump frequency ν_p, 1 ⟶ 2 with signal frequency ν_s, and 2 ⟶ 3 with idler frequency ν_i. As a further convention, the length of each energy level line is drawn proportional to its population.

The levels 1 and 3 are in thermal contact, through a filter passing frequencies in the vicinity of ν_p and rejecting frequencies in the vicinity of ν_i and ν_s, with a heat reservoir at temperature T_1. The temperature is indicated in the figure by showing schematically the Boltzmann distribution of this heat reservoir. Levels 2 and 3 are in thermal contact with a reservoir at a lower temperature T_0 through a filter which passes frequencies in the vicinity of ν_i but rejects those close to ν_p and ν_s.

Experimentally, the high-temperature reservoir might be realized by a gas noise lamp and the filter by a wave guide cutting off the lower frequencies. For practical purposes, however, the single mode present in a wave guide does not provide good thermal contact. The assumed coupling situation to the low-temperature reservoir, on the other hand, was closely approximated by experimental conditions in some maser experiments.[3] There, the idler transition of the gadolinium three-level system was coupled, through spin-spin interaction at frequency ν_i, to a transition of the same frequency of cerium ions within the same crystal. Thus, through the resultant short spin-lattice relaxation time, good thermal contact to the lattice heat reservoir at T_0 was established.

In the system described, for each quantum $h\nu_p$ supplied by the hot reservoir, the energy $h\nu_i$ is passed to the cold reservoir. The smaller quantum $h\nu_s$ can be extracted at the signal transition if maser action prevails, that is if $n_2/n_1 \geq 1$. Thus the efficiency of this idealized system in maser operation is

$$\eta_M = \nu_s/\nu_p. \qquad (1)$$

From the Boltzmann factors involved, we find

$$\frac{n_2}{n_1} = \frac{n_2}{n_3}\frac{n_3}{n_1} = \exp\left(\frac{h\nu_i}{kT_0}\right) \times \exp\left(-\frac{h\nu_p}{kT_1}\right). \qquad (2)$$

After rearrangement, this becomes

$$\frac{n_2}{n_1} = \exp\left[\frac{h\nu_S}{kT_0}\left(\frac{\nu_p}{\nu_S}\,\frac{T_1 - T_0}{T_1} - 1\right)\right]. \quad (3)$$

In this formula, one recognizes the maser efficiency η_M and the efficiency of the Carnot cycle,

$$\eta_c = (T_1 - T_0)/T_1. \quad (4)$$

Using these, the condition for maser action is

$$\eta_M \leq \eta_c. \quad (5)$$

This may be regarded as another formulation of the second law of thermodynamics. Maser efficiency equals that of a Carnot engine if the signal transition is at the verge of inversion, $n_2 - n_1 \to +0$ or $T_{\rm sig} \to -\infty$.

As any heat engine, this system should be reversible so that it acts as a refrigerator. This is indeed the case. Suppose a quantum $h\nu_s$ is applied to the signal transition. It causes an ion to go from state 1 to 2. The ion may further jump to state 3 if the energy $h\nu_i$ is supplied by the cold reservoir. The cycle is finally completed when the ion returns from state 3 to state 1 while the energy $h\nu_p$ is communicated to the hot reservoir. In this process, energy is extracted from the idler transition, that is from the cold reservoir, so that it is refrigerated. The scheme outlined here, however, requires the signal transition to be absorptive. Otherwise the first step, application of $h\nu_{\rm sig}$ to the signal transition, would not have been possible. Thus the refrigeration scheme is possible if $n_2/n_1 \leq 1$. Again, the limiting efficiency of the refrigerator is that of a Carnot engine and it is realized with $n_2 - n_1 \to -0$ or $T_{\rm sig} \to +\infty$.

It seems probable at this time that generation of microwaves through thermal excitation by two temperatures will be possible experimentally. Such a scheme should be very attractive for high microwave signal frequencies. Refrigeration experiments, on the other hand, as applied to interacting nuclear and electronic spin systems have been suggested by the theoretical work of Overhauser.[4] A thermodynamical analysis of the Overhauser effect has been given by Brovetto and Cini[5] and Barker and Mencher.[6]

Finally, we should like to point out that the possibility of treating masers as heat engines sets a fundamental distinction between these and parametric amplifiers. Three-level masers are capable of operating with noise-like excitation in all three transitions. Parametric amplification requires some phase coherence, that is, monochromatic excitation is necessary for at least one of the three frequencies involved. This statement excludes heat as the source of energy for parametric amplification.

---

*This work is partially supported by the Signal Corps.

[1]N. G. Basov and A. M. Prokhorov, J. Exptl. Theoret. Phys. U.S.S.R. 28, 249 (1955) [translation: Soviet Phys. JETP 1, 184 (1955)].

[2]N. Bloembergen, Phys. Rev. 104, 324 (1956).

[3]Scovil, Feher, and Seidel, Phys. Rev. 105, 762 (1957).

[4]A. W. Overhauser, Phys. Rev. 92, 411 (1953).

[5]P. Brovetto and G. Cini, Nuovo cimento 11, 618 (1954).

[6]W. A. Barker and A. Mencher, Phys. Rev. 102, 1023 (1956).

Reprinted from the PROCEEDINGS OF THE IEEE
VOL. 51, NO. 1, JANUARY, 1963

Masers and Millimeter Waves*

FRANK S. BARNES†, MEMBER, IRE

***Summary*—The characteristics of a number of different kinds of masers are reviewed to estimate their usefulness in the region between one and a tenth millimeter. An estimate of the maximum power output for these systems is made and compared with the output to be expected from mixing two optical signals in a nonlinear dielectric and on a photocathode. Additionally, the noise characteristics of maser amplifiers are briefly reviewed for this region of the spectrum.**

INTRODUCTION

THIS PAPER reviews some of the characteristics of masers for application to the region between one and a tenth of a millimeter. At the risk of being made obsolete by a major new development, an attempt is made to estimate what the limitations on the power output of maser oscillators and the noise temperature of maser amplifiers will be for operation in this portion of the frequency spectrum. For the purpose of characterizing maser systems along these lines, it is most convenient to classify them by the method used to invert the population. The three most common schemes for obtaining an inverted population are: 1) the sorting of the molecules in a beam into high and low energy states with an unhomogeneous electric or magnetic field, 2) the pumping of molecules into the upper level of a multiple level energy system with electromagnetic radiation above the frequency of the maser oscillator, and 3) the excitation of an atomic system by electron bombardment.

In all these systems, the fundamental conditions for maser oscillation is that the power radiated by the atomic or molecular system is greater than the power lost. The power radiated by the atomic or molecular system is equal to the difference in the population of the two energy states of interest times the transition probability p_t times the quantum of energy radiated per atoms, or

$$P_r = (N_{n+1} - N_n) P_t hf, \tag{1}$$

where h is Planck's constant and f is the transition frequency. The condition for oscillation in terms of the loaded Q of the resonant structure, Q, its volume V, the matrix element μ, and interaction time with the radiation field t, are given by [37]

$$N_{n+1} - N_n \geq \frac{3hV}{2\pi\mu^2 Q}\left(\frac{\sin^2\delta}{\delta^2} - t^2\right)^{-1}, \tag{2}$$

where $\delta = (\omega - \omega_0)t/2$, ω is frequency of oscillation, and ω_0 is the natural transition frequency.

For the case of a beam maser at resonance, (2) reduces to

$$N_{n+1} - N_n \geq \frac{3hV}{4\pi^2\mu^2 Q T_0^2}, \tag{3}$$

where T_0 is the flight time of a molecule through the resonant structure.

For a radiation pumped gas or solid state maser, (2) reduces to

$$N_{n+1} - N_n \geq \frac{3h\Delta f V}{2\pi^2\mu^2 Q}, \tag{4}$$

where Δf is the natural linewidth of the transition.

The power output from a maser oscillator is given by the product nhf where n is the number of photons leaving the maser per second. In order to obtain this power output, excited atoms or molecules must be supplied to the system at a rate greater than n by an amount corresponding to the losses of the system. As may be seen from Table I, this rate is very large for a watt of power and approximately a thousand times greater than for an optical system with the same capabilities. It is the problem of supplying this very large number of excited atomic or molecular systems per second which leads to much of the difficulty in obtaining substantial amounts of power from maser systems in the millimeter wave region.

TABLE I

PHOTON ENERGIES VS WAVELENGTH

Wavelength	Frequency	Energy of a Photon HF: joules	Energy of a Photon HF: ev	Minimum Number of Photons per Second for One Watt of Power
10 mm	3×10^{10} cps	1.98×10^{23}	1.24×10^{4}	5×10^{22}
1 mm	3×10^{11} cps	1.98×10^{22}	1.24×10^{3}	5×10^{21}
0.1 mm	3×10^{12} cps	1.98×10^{21}	1.24×10^{2}	5×10^{20}
6.9×10^{4}mm	4.35×10^{14}cps	2.87×10^{19}	1.8	3.5×10^{18}

* Received June 11, 1962.
† Electrical Engineering Department, University of Colorado, Boulder, Colo.

Beam Masers

A beam maser similar to that shown in Fig. 1 will probably prove to be one of the simplest ways of obtaining a small amount of coherent power in the region near a tenth millimeter. The molecules are admitted through a cluster of small tubes at the left to form a beam with half intensity points between 10 and 30°. The molecules in the higher of the two energy states of interest are then focused toward the beam axis by a large inhomogeneous electric field. The molecules in the lower of the two energy states are bent radially outward between the rods of the focuser and trapped. Classically, the focuser may be thought of as inducing an average dipole moment in the rotating molecule and then applying a force to it whose sign is determined by its orientation. The resonant structure, which in this case is a millimeter wave version of a Fabry-Perot interferometer, provides a means for inducing the transition and coupling the power out [6]-[8], [18], [38].

The output power for a system of this kind is limited by the speed with which molecules can be pumped through the system and the density of molecules which can be tolerated while maintaining a mean free path which is comparable to the length of the beam. For NH_3 operating pressures are limited to less than 10^{-5} mm of Hg by the cross section for the interaction between the rotational energy levels. This cross section is appreciably larger than the cross section for kinetic scattering. For other gases the pressure limitation is of the same order of magnitude. Although considerably higher pumping speeds are available with very large diffusion pumps or liquid helium cold traps, a limit of about 10^4 liters per second is reasonable for simple experimental setups. At a pressure of 10^{-5} mm of Hg this speed corresponds to 4×10^{18} molecules per second. Of these molecules only 2 or 3 per cent are usually in the energy state of interest and the focuser is generally less than 20 per cent efficient. Thus, for the kinds of vacuum pumps which are easy to obtain we would expect the maximum available power from a beam maser at one millimeter to be on the order of one microwatt. About 10^{-9} watts have been obtained at lower frequencies thus far. Although this is not much power, I believe it is more than we presently have available in the region between 0.5 and 0.1 millimeters.

Table II shows a number of molecular beam maser systems which are being considered in various laboratories. Of these, an HCN maser has been operated by D. Marcuse of the Bell Telephone Laboratories at 3.4 mm [26].

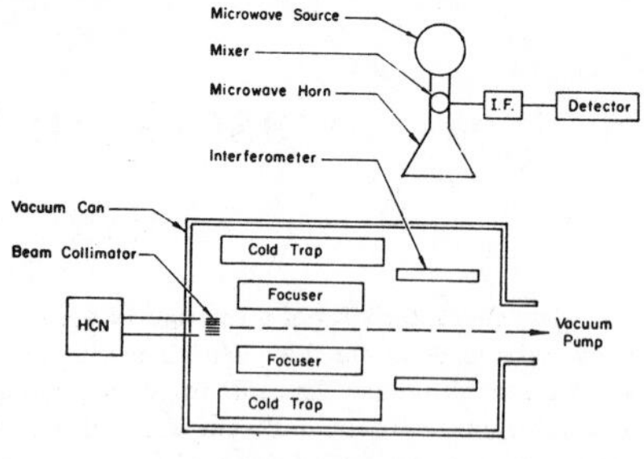

Fig. 1—Beam maser.

TABLE II

Possible Molecules for Beam Masers

Molecule	Transition	Wavelength	Estimated Minimum Starting Current (molecules/sec)
HCN*	$J=1\leftrightarrow0$	3.4 mm	3.3×10^{12}
NH_3*	$J=2\leftrightarrow1$	0.252 mm	1.5×10^{13}
CH_3F†	$J=2\leftrightarrow1$	2.95 mm	1.7×10^{13}
CH_3CN†	$J=5\leftrightarrow6$	2.72 mm	3.3×10^{12}
CH_3NC†	$J=4\leftrightarrow5$	3.00 mm	3.2×10^{12}
ND_3‡	$J=2\leftrightarrow1$	0.485 mm	4.0×10^{13}
HF‖	$J=1\leftrightarrow0$	0.24 mm	

* Barnes [6].
† Newman, [2].
‡ V. E. Derr, J. J. Gallagher, and M. Lichtenstein, *Proc. of 15th Ann. Symp. on Frequency Control*, Atlantic City, N. J., June 1, 1961; U. S. Army Signal Research and Development Lab., Ft. Monmouth, N. J.
‖ M. E. Zhabetinskii and V. F. Zolin, *Radio engrg. and electronics*, vol. 11, pp. 289–299; 1959.

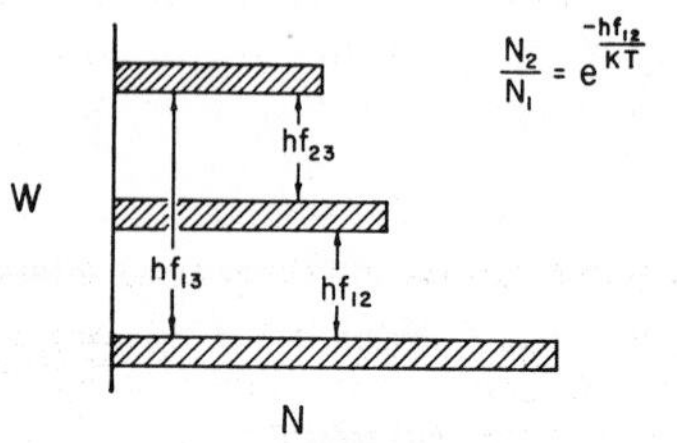

Fig. 2.

Optically Pumped Masers

In the radiation pumped maser the population inversion is usually obtained by supplying power at a frequency corresponding to a transition between two energy levels with a greater energy separation than those corresponding to the maser signal. For example, in Fig. 2 a large amount of power may be applied at a frequency f_{13}. Since the transition probability for absorption and induced emission is the same, the effect is to transfer atomic or molecular systems from state one to state three. Depending on the relative decay rates from states three to two and two to one, we can make either $n_3>n_2$ or $n_2>n_1$ [5], [10], [35], [41].

The maximum efficiency with which we can convert a quantum of energy at the pump frequency f_{13} to a quantum of energy at signal frequency f_{23} with this scheme is given by the ratio of f_{23} to f_{13}. Unfortunately, our nearest sources of a substantial amount of power to pump a maser operating in the submillimeter wave region are at optical or near infrared frequencies. Thus, the maximum efficiency of our systems is limited to something between one and a tenth per cent. It should be noted that this limit on the power conversion efficiency is the same as that given by the Manley Rowe relations for a lossless reactance and applies to multiple energy level schemes as well as three level systems.

A second difficulty with this scheme for inverting the population is in finding a material with an appropriate energy level system. A desirable energy level system would be somewhat similar to that shown for Cs in Fig. 3 except that a broader absorption band would be preferred for the upper level [12]. In this system the optical pumping transition from $6S_{1/2}$ level to the $8P_{1/2}$ level is allowed while the transition from $6S_{1/2}$ state to the $8S_{1/2}$ state is forbidden. This allows the use of a relatively broad spectrum of a strong ultraviolet line in He for pumping power without increasing the population in the terminal $8S_{1/2}$ state. In the idealized system it is also desirable to have both a strong pumping source available and the terminal state well separated from the ground state so that the thermal equilibrium density of excited atomic or molecular systems is negligible. And finally, it is desirable to have a decay rate from the terminal to the ground state which is much faster than the decay rate from the upper maser level. It is the decay rate from the terminal state in these multiple energy level systems which places a major limitation on the maximum power output. The decay rate from the upper level to the terminal state determines the line width and thus the minimum population difference which is required to get maser oscillation. In gas vapor such as Cs this line width is usually determined by Doppler broadening, and in solids it is usually the inhomogeneities of the crystal field.

Radiation pumped masers which have been proposed include a gas maser using the transition at 518 kMc between the sodium *D* lines [9], and two solid state masers using cyclotron resonance levels and impurity band levels [24] in semiconductors.

Of these schemes the sodium *D* lines seem to offer the most hope for a substantial amount of power output. The cyclotron resonance maser should have the advantage of being tunable over a wide range of frequencies by varying the external magnetic field, and an output power as large as a milliwatt may be obtainable. Substantially larger output powers for the two solid state masers will be difficult to obtain because of the low pumping power efficiency, and the heat transfer problems brought about by the cryogenic temperatures required for operation.

Gas Masers

A third scheme for creating a population inversion is by means of electron bombardment in a gas discharge. In a gas discharge the electron temperature is often greater than the temperature of the gas atoms or molecules. If the electron bombardment cross section for exciting an atom to an upper energy level is larger than that for a lower state, it is possible to get a population inversion. This situation may occur in neon, helium, oxygen and other gas discharges. In some cases the population inversion can also be enhanced by mixing two or more gases as in the case of the He-Ne maser shown in Fig.4 [22], [23]. In this case the excitation of the 2*s* states in Ne are increased by the transfer of energy from 2^3s state in He and both the 2^3s state in He and the 2*s* states in Ne have larger electron excitation cross sections than the 2*p* states. The maser action takes place between the 2*s* states and 2*p* states of the Ne.

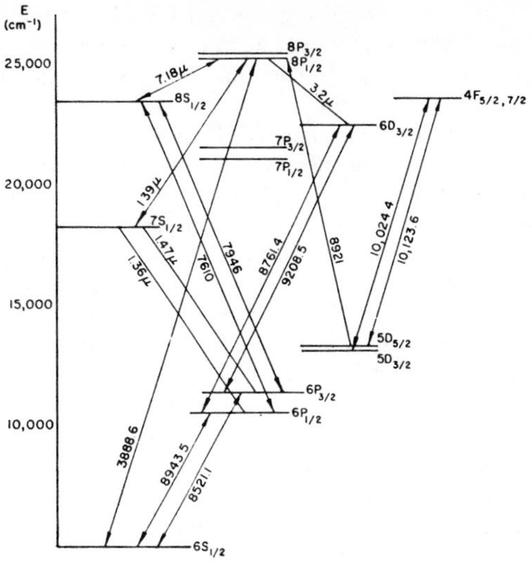

Fig. 3—Energy levels and transitions of cesium [12].

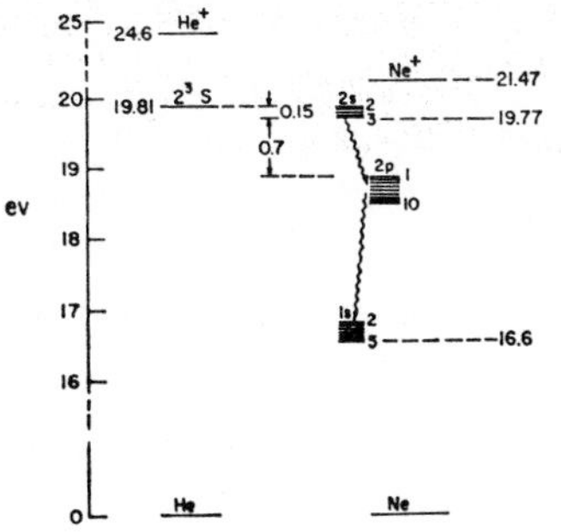

Fig. 4—Energy level diagram of He and Ne atoms [23].

The principle difficulty with the use of schemes of this type to obtain maser action at submillimeter wave frequency is finding a material with appropriately spaced energy levels, such that the upper level has a significantly larger electron excitation cross section than the lower one. Additionally, atoms in the lower energy level must decay much more rapidly than from the upper level. Although there appears to be no really fundamental limits on the power output of gas discharge masers of this type other than the volume of gas required, there are both materials problems and many practical difficulties in obtaining a high power maser.

Other schemes for obtaining population inversions include subharmonic pumping [4], [13], [14] and large pulsed magnetic fields [28]; however, space will not permit even a brief description of these systems.

A fourth and promising method for generating submillimeter waves is by beating two optical maser signals together in a nonlinear medium. Three schemes which have been proposed for doing this include mixing in a nonlinear dielectric such as ADP or KDP, mixing with a photocathode, and mixing with a point contact semiconductor diode.

Of these, the efficiency of the mixing in a nonlinear dielectric is limited to the ratio of the signal to pumping frequency by the Manley Rowe relations. Additionally, the results obtained for harmonic generation indicate that practically we should expect a power output which is down by an additional factor of 10^2 to 10^5 depending on the optical efficiency of the coupling system [17], [25]. Thus, with an efficiency of 10^{-5} or less this scheme does not appear to be particularly attractive for power generation; however, it may prove useful for an electronically tunable low noise parametric amplifier.

One of the most promising schemes for power generation seems to be the use of an optical maser beam to excite a photocathode as shown in Fig. 5. The photocathode behaves as a square law mixer [15], [27]. It emits a beam which has a density modulated component at the difference frequency between the two optical signal frequencies as shown below.

$$
\begin{aligned}
I &= K(E_1 + E_2)^2 \\
&= KE_0^2 \Big\{ 1 + \cos\left[(\omega_2 - \omega_1)t + \frac{y}{c}(\omega_2 \sin\theta_2 + \omega_1 \sin\theta_1) \right] \\
&\quad + \cos\left[(\omega_2 + \omega_1)t + \frac{y}{c}(\omega_2 \sin\theta_2 - \omega_1 \sin\theta_1) \right] \\
&\quad + \tfrac{1}{2}\cos\left[2\omega_2\left(t + \frac{y \sin\theta_2}{c}\right)\right] \\
&\quad + \tfrac{1}{2}\cos\left[2\omega_1\left(t + \frac{y \sin\theta_1}{c}\right)\right]\Big\} \qquad (5)
\end{aligned}
$$

The density modulated beam is accelerated and energy at the difference frequency is coupled out with a Cerenkov coupler. With an S_1 photocathode surface one should be able to obtain about a 10 per cent photon to electron conversion efficiency and at the frequency of the ruby laser 100 mw of input power should yield about 5 ma of beam current. The interaction impedance for a Cerenkov coupler may be made as large as 1000 Ω and thus with $\frac{1}{4}$ of the beam current at the difference frequency, about 1.5 mw of submillimeter wave power out may be obtained for 100 mw of optical power in. Possible improvements in the efficiency of this system could be made by using a velocity jump amplifier to amplify the difference frequency component of the current and appreciably larger beam currents should be easily obtainable. Other slow wave structures should also be useful for coupling power out of the beam. The principle advantage of this proposed system over other microwave tubes for generating millimeter waves is that it simplifies the problem of obtaining a bunched beam.

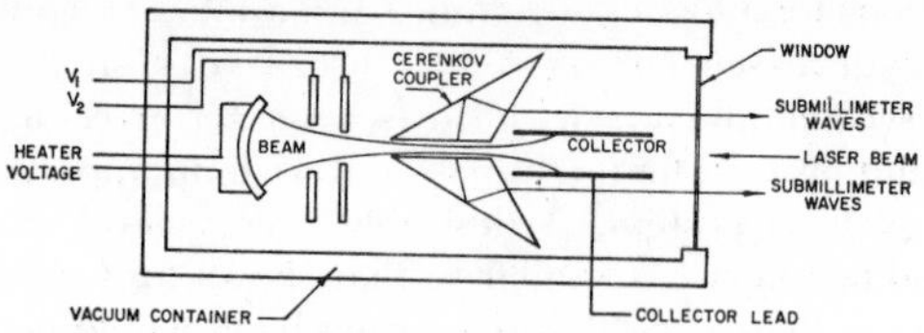

Fig. 5.

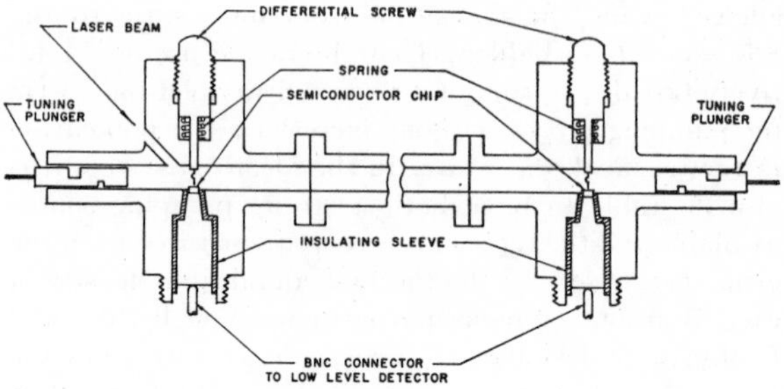

Fig. 6.

The last scheme[1] proposed for generating millimeter wave power is with a point contact diode as shown in Fig. 6. The amount of difference frequency power generated by this method will be small and it is difficult to estimate because of the unknowns in the characteristics of the diodes. However, because of the constructional simplicity of the system, it should be useful in detecting the difference frequency between optical maser systems.

Maser Amplifier Noise

The noise figure for a reflection cavity maser amplifier with large gains is given by [39], [41]

$$F = \left[1 + \frac{Q_1}{Q_0}\right]\left[1 - \frac{P_N(T_m)}{P_N(T)}\right], \qquad (6)$$

where Q_1 is the Q of the coupling to the cavity Q_0 is the unloaded Q of the cavity,

$$P_N(T) = \frac{hf}{e^{hf/kT} - 1} \quad \text{and} \quad P_N(T_m) = \frac{hf}{e^{hf/kT_m} - 1}.$$

T_m is a negative temperature which is defined to measure the extent of the population inversion as given below.

$$T_m = -\frac{hf}{k} n \left(\frac{N_{n+1}}{N_n}\right). \qquad (7)$$

In the limit of $|T_m|$ large and $kT \gg hf$, (6) reduces to

$$F = 1 + \frac{hf}{kT}, \qquad (8)$$

[1] This scheme came to my attention from the Philco Electronics Defense Group in Palo Alto, Calif., and has been made to work at lower microwave frequencies both there and at the Bell Telephone Laboratories.

which gives an effective noise temperature for the amplifier $T_e = hf/k$. At 1 mm $T_e = 14.4°K$. As we go to higher frequencies and systems where a few photons may be measured the significance of this effective noise temperature has been questioned for amplifying a coherent signal. I. R. Senitzky [36] shows that assumptions on spontaneous emission from which this limiting noise temperature was derived do not hold for a coherent signal, and he obtains an effective noise temperature

$$T_e = \left(\frac{4}{Bt}\right)\frac{hf}{k},$$

where B is the inverse of the cavity relaxation time and t is the interaction time for the molecule with the radiation field. For beam masers the noise reduction factor Bt will be about the same as for lower frequencies, but more important. For solids and gases we would expect t to decrease with frequency and thus low noise temperatures will be more difficult to obtain as the frequency increases. A. Yariv indicates that a maser system can approach the characteristics of the best possible amplifier for those situations where one has a large number of quanta, and phase information is important. For the cases when only a few quanta are available, an ideal quantum counter appears to be a better detector than an ideal maser.

Acknowledgment

The author wishes to express his appreciation to his colleagues for numerous helpful discussions and in particular, W. Turner and M. Petroff. Additionally, he wishes to express his appreciation to the University Council on Research and the National Engineering Science Company for their financial support.

Bibliography

[1] I. D. Abella and H. Z. Cummins, "Thermal tuning of ruby optical masers," *J. Appl. Phys.*, vol. 32, pp. 1177–1178; June, 1961.

[2] J. B. Newman, "Advances in Quantum Electronics," J. R. Singer Ed., Columbia University Press, New York, N. Y.; 1961.

[3] L. E. Alsop, J. A. Giordmaine, C. H. Townes and T. C. Wang, "Measurement of noise in a maser amplifier," *Phys. Rev.*, vol. 107, pp. 1450–1451; September, 1957.

[4] F. R. Arams, "Maser operation at signal frequencies higher than pump frequency," IRE Trans. on Microwave Theory and Techniques, vol. 9, pp. 68–72; January, 1961.

[5] J. Artman, N. Bloembergen, and S. Shapiro, "Operation of a 3-level solid state maser at 1,000 Mc/s," *Phys. Rev.*, vol. 109, pp. 1392–1393; February, 1958.

[6] F. S. Barnes, "The feasibility of building beam type masers in the millimeter and submillimeter wave range," in "Quantum Electronics," Columbia University Press, New York, N. Y., pp. 57–65; 1960.

[7] F. S. Barnes, "Operating characteristics of an ammonia beam maser," Proc. IRE, vol. 47, pp. 2085–2098; December, 1959.

[8] N. G. Basov and A. M. Prokhorov, "The Theory of a Molecular Oscillator and a Molecular Power Amplifier," Discussions of the Faraday Society, no. 19, p. 96; 1955.

[9] S. M. Bergmann, "Submillimeter wave maser," *J. Appl. Phys.*, vol. 31, pp. 275–276; February, 1960.

[10] N. Bloembergen, "Proposal for a new type solid state maser," *Phys. Rev.*, vol. 104, pp. 324–327; October, 1956.

[11] G. D. Boyd and J. P. Gordon, "Confocal multimode resonator for millimeter through optical wavelengths maser," *Bell Sys. Tech. J.*, vol. 40, pp. 489–508; March, 1961.

[12] H. Z. Cummins, I. D. Abella, O. S. Heavens, N. Knable, and C. H. Townes, "Alkali vapor infrared masers," in "Advances in Quantum Electronics," J. R. Singer, Ed., Columbia University Press, New York, N. Y.; 1961.

[13] J. Fontana, R. Pantell, and R. Smith, "Harmonic generation by means of multiple quantum transitions," in "Advances in Quantum Electronics," Columbia University Press, New York, N. Y.; 1961.

[14] J. Fontana, R. H. Pantell, and R. Smith, "Harmonic generation using the ammonia inversion transition," Proc. IRE (*Correspondence*), vol. 50, pp. 469–470; April, 1962.

[15] A. T. Forrester, R. A. Gudmundsen and P. O. Johnson, "Photoelectric mixing of incoherent light," *Phys. Rev.*, vol. 99, pp. 1691–1700; September, 1955.

[16] A. G. Fox and T. Li, "Resonant modes in a maser interferometer," *Bell Sys. Tech. J.*, vol. 40, pp. 453–488; March, 1961.

[17] P. A. Franken, A. E. Hill, C. W. Peters, and G. Weinreich "Generation of optical harmonics," *Phys. Rev. Lett.*, vol. 7, pp. 118–119; August 15, 1961.

[18] J. P. Gordon, H. J. Zeiger, and C. H. Townes, "Molecular microwave oscillator and new hyperfine structure in the microwave spectrum of NH_3," *Phys. Rev.*, vol. 95, pp. 282–284; July, 1954.

[19] J. Gordon and L. White, "Noise in maser amplifiers—theory and experiment," Proc. IRE, vol. 46, pp. 1588–1594; September, 1958.

[20] J. C. Helmer, "Maser oscillators," *J. Appl. Phys.*, vol. 28, pp. 212–215; February, 1957.

[21] J. C. Helmer, "Maser noise measurement," *Phys. Rev.*, vol. 107, pp. 902–903; August, 1957.

[22] A. Javan, "Possibility of production of negative temperature in gas discharges," *Phys. Rev. Lett.*, vol. 3, pp. 87–89; June 15, 1959.

[23] A. Javan, W. R. Bennett, and O. R. Herriott, "Population inversion and continuous optical maser oscillation in a gas discharge containing a He-Ne mixture," *Phys. Rev. Lett.*, vol. 6, pp. 106–110; February, 1961.

[24] B. Lax, "Cyclotron resonance maser," in "Advances in Quantum Electronics," J. R. Singer, Ed., Columbia University Press, New York, N. Y.; 1961.

[25] P. D. Maker, R. W. Terhune, M. Nisenhoff, and C. M. Savage, "Effects of dispersion and focusing on the production of optical harmonics," *Phys. Rev. Lett.*, vol. 8, pp. 21–22; January 1, 1962.

[26] D. Marcuse, "Maser oscillation observed from HCN maser at 88.6 kMc," Proc. IRE (*Correspondence*), p. 1706; November, 1961.

[27] B. J. McMurty and A. E. Siegman, "Photomixing experiments with ruby optical maser and a traveling-wave microwave phototube," *Appl. Optics*, vol. I, pp. 51–53; January, 1962.

[28] C. R. Momo, R. A. Myers, and S. Foner, "Pulsed field millimeter wave masers," *J. Appl. Phys.*, vol. 31, p. 443; February, 1960.

[29] M. Muller, "Noise in a molecular amplifier," *Phys. Rev.*, vol. 106, pp. 8–12; April, 1957.

[30] B. M. Oliver, "Signal-to-noise ratios in photoelectric mixing," Proc. IRE (*Correspondence*), vol. 49, pp. 1960–1961; December, 1961.

[31] J. F. Proter, "Rare earth salts for use in infrared quantum counter," in "Advances in Quantum Electronics," J. R. Singer, Ed., Columbia University Press, New York, N. Y., pp. 595–601; 1961.

[32] "Quantum Electronics, A Symposium," C. H. Townes, Ed., Columbia University Press, New York, N. Y.; 1960.

[33] A. F. Schawlow and C. H. Townes, "Proposal to extend maser to infrared," *Phys. Rev.*, vol. 112, pp. 1940–1949; December, 1958.

[34] R. N. Schwartz and C. H. Townes, "Interstellar and interplanetary communications by optical masers," *Nature*, vol. 190, pp. 205–208; April 15, 1961.

[35] H. Scovil, G. Feher, and H. Seidel, "Operation of a solid state maser," *Phys. Rev.*, vol. 105, pp. 762–763; January, 1957.

[36] I. R. Sentzky, "Noise in a coherent signal maser amplifier," in "Advances in Quantum Electronics," J. R. Singer, Ed., Columbia University Press, New York, N. Y., p. 538; 1961.

[37] K. Shimoda, "Theory of Masers for Higher Frequencies," *Sci. Papers Inst. Phys. Chem. Research (Tokyo)*, vol. 55, pp. 1–6; March, 1961.

[38] K. Shimoda, T. C. Wang, and C. H. Townes, "Further aspects of maser theory," *Phys. Rev.*, vol. 102, pp. 1308–1321; June, 1956.

[39] M. L. Stitch, "Maser amplifier characteristics for transmission and reflection cavities," *J. Appl. Phys.*, vol. 29, pp. 782–789; May, 1958.

[40] M. W. P. Strandberg, "Inherent noise of quantum mechanical amplifiers," *Phys. Rev.*, vol. 106, pp. 617–620; May, 1957.

[41] G. Troup, "Masers," Methuen Co. Ltd., London; 1959.

[42] A. A. Vuylsteke, "Elements of Maser Theory," D. Van Nostrand Co., Inc., Princeton, N. J.; 1960.

[43] A. Yariv, "Advances in Quantum Electronics," J. R. Singer, Ed., Columbia University Press, New York, N. Y., p. 519; 1961.

THE OPTIMUM LINE WIDTH FOR THE TRANSITION USED IN A REFLECTION CAVITY MASER AMPLIFIER

By G. J. Troup*

[*Manuscript received April* 8, 1959]

Summary

The line width of the amplifying transition in a reflection cavity maser is shown to have an optimum value, which will give maximum amplification bandwidth at a fixed gain. Difficulties associated with achieving the optimum line width in practice for the paramagnetic maser are briefly discussed.

I. Introduction

The bandwidth of a resonant cavity maser amplifier at a fixed gain depends upon the line width of the amplifying transition and is always considerably less than this line width (Gordon, Zeiger, and Townes 1955 ; Gordon and White 1958 ; Stich 1958). It will be shown below that, for a given reflection cavity maser system, there is an optimum transition line width which will give maximum amplification bandwidth at constant gain. The value of the optimum line width is a function of various amplifier parameters (frequency, filling factor for the active medium, etc.), of the dipole moment for the transition, and of the concentration of excess molecules in the emissive condition. (Molecule will be used throughout as a generic term.)

In order to take full advantage of the low noise input temperature of a maser amplifier, it must be operated at a gain of the order of 20 dB if followed by a conventional microwave receiver (see, for example, Wittke 1957). At such gains, reported cavity maser bandwidths are narrow ; for example, Morris, Kyhl, and Strandberg (1959) report a bandwidth of 4 Mc/s at $\sim$9000 Mc/s with a gain of 20 dB, actually a vast improvement on previously reported masers (for example, McWhorter and Meyer 1958 ; Autler and McAvoy 1958). Bandwidth increase is desirable, and the knowledge of the optimum transition line width is therefore useful.

Moreover, any limitation of the concentration of excess upper-state molecules in a maser also limits the obtainable bandwidth, and operation of the system at optimum line width may then be the only method of bandwidth increase. This is important in the case of the three-level paramagnetic maser (Bloembergen 1956), for the device cannot be placed in an emissive condition when the concentration of paramagnetic ions exceeds a certain value. One is led to the idea that the maximum bandwidth obtainable with a Bloembergen cavity maser will

* Weapons Research Establishment, Salisbury, S. Aust.

occur when the concentration of active centres is close to the limiting value and operation at optimum line width is used. A prediction of the ultimate bandwidth obtainable from a Bloembergen system then becomes possible, but this will not be undertaken here.

II. The Reflection Cavity Maser

Only the reflection cavity maser is considered, since it is superior in all respects (noise factor, bandwidth at a fixed gain, etc.) to the transmission cavity amplifier (Gordon and White 1958). Maser performance depends upon the " molecular Q " Q_m, which is defined by

$$-Q_m=\frac{2\pi f\times \text{Average energy stored in the cavity}}{\text{Average power emitted in the cavity}}. \quad \ldots\ldots (1)$$

Here, f is the resonant frequency of the cavity, taken as equal to the frequency of amplification and to the central frequency of the molecular response.

It can be shown (e.g. Strandberg 1957) that Q_m is of the form

$$|Q_m|=(K\delta/N^*), \quad \ldots\ldots\ldots\ldots\ldots\ldots (2)$$

where δ is the line width of the amplifying transition, N^* is the number density of the excess molecules in the emissive state, and K is a constant for the particular molecules and amplifier system. K includes the square of the dipole moment for the amplifying transition and the filling factor for the active medium in the cavity. (This last is the ratio of the field energy coupled to the molecules to the total field energy stored in the cavity.)

Subject to certain assumptions, the gain G of the reflection cavity maser can be written

$$G\simeq(|Q_m|+Q_L)^2(|Q_m|-Q_L)^{-2}, \quad \ldots\ldots\ldots\ldots (3)$$

where Q_L is the loaded Q of the cavity. The assumptions are:

(i) that the gain has a reasonably high value (>10, say);

(ii) that the cavity has a high unloaded Q, so that the loaded Q is determined mainly by the external coupling to the cavity (McWhorter and Meyer 1958).

The bandwidth B of the reflection cavity maser, after some manipulation of the results of Gordon and White (1958) and of Stich (1958) (which are identical), can be written

$$B\simeq\delta[(|Q_m|/Q_L)-1][1+(\delta\,|Q_m|/f)]^{-1}, \quad \ldots\ldots\ldots\ldots (4)$$

where f is the centre frequency of the molecular response and of the cavity resonance, as previously; a Lorentz line shape is assumed for the transition. The amplification bandwidth B is seen to be always less than the line width δ, both because of the factor $[(|Q_m|/Q_L)-1]$, which may be regarded as the gain-dependent term (see equation (3)), and because of the form of the remainder of the expression.

III. Optimum Line Width for the Reflection Cavity Maser

From equation (2), any alteration in the line width δ will alter the molecular Q, and hence (equation (3)) the gain. However, the gain can be kept constant by suitably adjusting the loaded Q of the cavity. Then only the terms $\delta[1+(\delta\,|\,Q_m\,|/f)]^{-1}$ need be considered to determine whether the transition line width has an optimum value at constant gain. Using equation (2), the expression governing the bandwidth is rewritten as

$$\delta[1+(\delta\,|\,Q_m\,|/f)]^{-1}=b=\delta[1+(K\delta^2/N^*f)]^{-1}. \quad \ldots\ldots \quad (5)$$

N^*, the concentration of excess emissive molecules, is taken as constant for the amplifier system. Differentiation of this expression with respect to δ then shows that b has a maximum value

$$b_{\text{max.}}=\tfrac{1}{2}(K/N^*f)^{-\frac{1}{2}}, \quad \ldots\ldots\ldots\ldots\ldots\ldots\ldots \quad (6)$$

when

$$\delta=(K/N^*f)^{-\frac{1}{2}}=2b_{\text{max.}}.$$

Hence the amplification bandwidth of a given reflection cavity maser system can be given a maximum value by the adjustment of the line width of the amplifying transition to an optimum value.

Two conditions must be fulfilled before the optimum line width can be realized. Firstly, alteration of the line width must not alter N^*, the concentration of excess emissive molecules, i.e. the efficiency of excitation must remain constant. Secondly, any method used to alter the line width must not affect the magnitude of the dipole moment for the amplifying transition (contained in the factor K). This last requirement is not unrealistic. In the case of the three-level paramagnetic maser, the energy levels are mixtures of states, dependent on the strength and direction of a steady magnetic field: the use of magnetic field inhomogeneity to increase the line width might therefore affect the dipole moment of the amplifying transition.

For completeness, an important practical case is considered next. When paramagnetic ions are diluted in a host lattice, the transition line width can be directly proportional to the concentration of the ions, N (Bogle and Symmons 1959). Since N^*, the concentration of excess ions in the emissive state, will also be directly proportional to the total ionic concentration N, the molecular Q can be a constant, independent of the line width (equation (2)). If variation of the line width is then carried out solely by variation of the ionic concentration, equation (5) shows that the best width is the broadest obtainable; for

$$\left.\begin{aligned} b\rightarrow(f/|\,Q_m\,|) \text{ as } \delta\rightarrow\infty,\\ \text{i.e. as } N\rightarrow\infty, \end{aligned}\right\} \quad \ldots\ldots\ldots\ldots \quad (7)$$

since δ/N is a constant.

Equations (6) and (7) show that the cavity maser amplification bandwidth is influenced by the concentration of excess emissive molecules. Therefore, limiting this concentration also limits the bandwidth at constant gain. The fact that operation of the Bloembergen maser cannot be achieved when the concentration of paramagnetic ions reaches a certain critical value (Autler and McAvoy 1958; Giordmaine *et al.* 1958) indicates that adjustment of the transition line width may become an important method of bandwidth increase (see also Bogle and Symmons 1959).

IV. Practical Considerations for Paramagnetic Masers

The actual realization of the optimum line width for a given maser system may not be easy. Increasing the effective line width for paramagnetic transitions might be done relatively simply, by the use of magnetic-field inhomogeneity. Decreasing the line width is more difficult, since this will involve changing the maser crystal in some way—for example, by using special isotopes to reduce hyperfine broadening. It is desirable to work with a substance in which the line width is less than the optimum width for a given maser system, but which will still give a low molecular Q when the line width is increased. Much research into the causes of line widths of paramagnetic ions in crystals still needs to be done; in many cases the line widths are considerably in excess of calculated spin-spin widths (Bogle and Symmonds 1959).

V. Conclusion

It has been shown that there is an optimum line width for the transition used in a cavity maser, such that the amplification bandwidth is a maximum at a fixed gain. The realization of this optimum line width may be difficult in practice, since the line width must be variable without changing any other amplifier parameters.

VI. Acknowledgments

The author is indebted to Dr. G. S. Bogle and Dr. H. F. Symmons for the communication of their paper (Bogle and Symmons 1959) prior to publication. The present paper is published with the permission of the Chief Scientist, Australian Department of Supply.

VII. References

Autler, S. H., and McAvoy, N. (1958).—*Phys. Rev.* **110**: 280.

Bloembergen, N. (1956).—*Phys. Rev.* **104**: 324.

Bogle, G. S., and Symmons, H. F. (1959).—*Aust. J. Phys.* **12**: 1.

Giordmaine, J. A., Alsop, L. E., Nash, F. R., and Townes, C. H. (1958).—*Phys. Rev.* **109**: 302.

Gordon, J. P., and White, L. D. (1958).—*Proc. Inst. Radio Engrs., N.Y.* **46**: 1588.

Gordon, J. P., Zieger, H. Z., and Townes, C. H. (1955).—*Phys. Rev.* **99**: 1264.

McWhorter, A. C., and Meyer, J. W. (1958).—*Phys. Rev.* **109**: 312.

Morris, R. J., Kyhl, R. L., and Strandberg, M. W. P. (1959).—*Proc. Inst. Radio Engrs., N.Y.* **47**: 80.

Stich, M. L. (1958).—*J. Appl. Phys.* **29**: 782.

Strandberg, M. W. P. (1957).—*Phys. Rev.* **106**: 617.

Wittke, J. P. (1957).—*Proc. Inst. Radio Engrs., N.Y.* **45**: 291.

THE OPTIMUM LINE WIDTH FOR A REFLECTION CAVITY MASER*

By G. J. Troup†

Introduction

It has been pointed out previously (Troup 1959, hereinafter referred to as I) that there is an optimum line width for the transition used in a reflection cavity maser and that this optimum line width gives maximum bandwidth for a given gain. However, it was not explicitly deduced in I that this optimum line width actually gives the maximum value of $(\text{Gain})^{\frac{1}{2}}\times$Bandwidth product for a given cavity maser system. This note makes the appropriate deduction.

The Line Width for Maximum $(Gain)^{\frac{1}{2}}\times$Bandwidth Product

Commencing with equation (3) of I, we have that the gain G of a reflection cavity maser is given to a good approximation by

$$G\simeq(|Q_m|+Q_L)^2(|Q_m|-Q_L)^{-2}, \quad \ldots\ldots\ldots\ldots \quad (1)$$

where Q_L is the loaded Q of the cavity and $|Q_m|$ is the modulus of the negative molecular Q.

The bandwidth B of a reflection cavity maser, assuming a Lorentz line shape for the amplifying transition, is given by (equation (4) of I)

$$B\simeq\delta[(|Q_m|/Q_L)-1][1+\delta|Q_m|/f]^{-1}, \quad \ldots\ldots\ldots \quad (2)$$

where δ is the line width of the amplifying transition and f is the centre frequency of both cavity and molecular responses.

Using equations (1) and (2), we get

$$G^{\frac{1}{2}}B\simeq\delta[(|Q_m|/Q_L)+1][1+\delta|Q_m|/f]^{-1}. \quad \ldots\ldots\ldots\ldots \quad (3)$$

* Manuscript received April 29, 1960.

† Weapons Research Establishment, Salisbury, S. Aust.

Now for reasonably large gains ($G>10$ say) $|Q_m|\simeq Q_L$, so that

$$G^{1/2}B\simeq 2\delta(1+\delta\,|Q_m|/f)^{-1}. \qquad (4)$$

Now the molecular Q, Q_m, is of the form (equation (2) of I)

$$|Q_m|=K\delta/N^*, \qquad (5)$$

where K is a constant for the particular active material and cavity system, and N^* is the number density of excess molecules in the emissive state.

Using equation (5), we rewrite equation (4) as

$$G^{1/2}B\simeq 2\delta[1+(K\delta^2/N^*f)]^{-1}. \qquad (6)$$

Differentiation of this expression with respect to δ shows that $G^{1/2}B$ has a maximum value

$$(G^{1/2}B)_{\text{max.}}=(K/N^*f)^{-1/2}, \qquad (7)$$

when $\delta=(K/N^*f)^{-1/2}=\delta_{\text{opt.}}$. The quantity $\delta_{\text{opt.}}$ is identical with the value of δ deduced in I to give maximum bandwidth at a given gain. This means that suitable adjustment of the transition line width δ, keeping all other parameters constant, can maximize the $(\text{Gain})^{1/2}\times$Bandwidth product.

Conclusion

In the paramagnetic maser, the simplest way of adjusting δ is clearly to use a magnetic field deliberately made inhomogeneous. This of course requires that $\delta<\delta_{\text{opt.}}$ initially. The discovery of the narrowness of the lines of Fe^{3+} in Ti_2O_3 (Butcher and Gill 1959; Low 1960) makes the technique described above particularly applicable to this material. Moreover, Townes *et al.* at Columbia have obtained a $(\text{Gain})^{1/2}\times$Bandwidth product of 250 Mc/s at 4500 Mc/s using ruby (Cr^{3+} in Al_2O_3) as the active medium, by the use of magnetic field inhomogeneity (Butcher and Gill 1959). This latter result is taken as experimental confirmation of the existence of an optimum line width for a given maser system. It also confirms that the use of an inhomogeneous magnetic field is a practicable way of adjusting the line width.

Note added in Proof.—Maiman (1960) has come to the same conclusions regarding optimum line width, and has pointed out some of the consequences for paramagnetic masers.

The author is indebted to Dr. J. E. Houldin, Physics Department, Chelsea Polytechnic, London, for encouraging the submission of this note for publication. Permission to publish has been granted by the Chief Scientist, Research and Development Branch, Department of Supply, Australia.

References

Butcher, P. N., and Gill, J. C. (1959).—Report on the Conference on Quantum Electronics, New York September 1959: Royal Radar Establishment Memorandum No. 1667.

Low, W. (1960).—Paramagnetic substances suitable for maser operation in the millimeter range. "Proceedings of the Symposium on Millimeter Waves." p. 45. (Polytechnic Institute of Brooklyn Press: New York.)

Maiman, T. H. (1960).—Temperature and concentration effects in a ruby maser. *In* "Quantum Electronics." (Ed. C. H. Townes.) p. 324. (Columbia Univ. Press.)

Troup, G. J. (1959).—*Aust. J. Phys.* **12**: 218.

Negative L and C in Solid-State Masers*

R. L. KYHL†, MEMBER, IRE, R. A. McFARLANE‡, MEMBER, IRE, AND M. W. P. STRANDBERG§, FELLOW, IRE

Summary—**The analysis of solid-state cavity masers is extended to include the reactive component of the paramagnetic resonance. This reactance is inverted (in opposition to Foster's reactance theorem). A two-cavity network makes use of this negative frequency dependence of reactance to obtain a broad-band flat-topped amplifier response. In verification of this theory a ruby maser has been built which has a 95-Mc bandwidth at 14-db gain and operates at 9000 Mc and 1.5°K. This performance is comparable to that of published, tapered magnetic field traveling-wave masers. General network limitations on cavity maser amplifiers are derived. Broadbanding techniques that have been published for parametric amplifiers are essentially equivalent. The tuning of the broad-band amplifier is critical. The same performance can be achieved in a unilateral transmission maser by using circularly polarized cavities, but the problem of circuit design and tuning with the increased number of parameters has thus far prevented successful operation.**

* Received February 19, 1962; revised manuscript received, May 1, 1962. This work was supported in part by the U. S. Army Signal Corps under Contract DA36-039-sc-87376, the Air Force Office of Scientific Research, and the Office of Naval Research.

† Department of Electrical Engineering and Research Laboratory of Electronics, Massachusetts Institute of Technology, Cambridge, Mass.

‡ Bell Telephone Laboratories, Inc., Murray Hill, N. J. Formerly with Research Lab. of Electronics, M.I.T.

§ Fulbright Lecturer, University of Grenoble, France, 1961–1962; on leave from the Dept. of Physics and Research Lab. of Electronics, M.I.T.

I. Introduction

The STIMULATED emission behavior of the active material in a solid-state maser can be characterized satisfactorily by its contribution to the complex electric or magnetic susceptibility of the material. (Beam masers are somewhat more complicated in this respect.) Typically this susceptibility shows a sharp resonance at a frequency corresponding to the quantum transition involved. The imaginary component of the susceptibility is, of course, responsible for the maser gain, but the real, or reactive, component must also be present. In narrow-band systems this reactance may be masked by the larger reactive effects of the microwave cavity or circuits. As larger gains and bandwidths are obtained with better substances and design configurations, the reactive component must be taken into consideration to obtain a correct analysis of the circuit behavior. When the population distribution between the quantum levels is inverted to achieve maser amplification, both components of the susceptibility reverse sign. The resulting frequency dependence of reactance corresponds to the situation that would obtain in conventional circuit analysis if the symbols

L and C could be assigned negative values.[1]

This report describes the construction and successful operation of one scheme for utilizing the negative L and C properties of inverted populations to achieve improved gain-bandwidth performance from a cavity maser. We call this "reactance compensation." Other efforts in this direction have been reported.[2] The same combination of negative R, L, and C appears in parametric amplifiers, although for entirely different reasons.[3]

This analysis will be entirely classical, although quantum phenomena are important in determining the susceptibilities that we take as our point of departure.

Large-signal nonlinearities may be safely ignored at the signal levels for which masers are useful. Saturation effects at the signal frequency are adequately treated by permitting slow time variation of the susceptibility.

The pumping mechanism by which the inverted population is achieved does not enter the discussion, although it should be recognized that the circuit performance will be affected by failure to achieve inversion over the entire volume of the active material.

II. Basic Theory

We introduce a simplified model for detailed calculations. A resonant cavity containing a substance showing quantum-mechanical resonance absorption can be well represented near resonance by the equivalent circuit of Fig. 1. The series circuit represents the cavity resonance (including any nonresonant susceptibilities of the material), and the parallel circuit represents the resonance susceptibility of the material. There are several approximations and pitfalls in this model. The cavity must, of course, have a single isolated high-Q resonance.

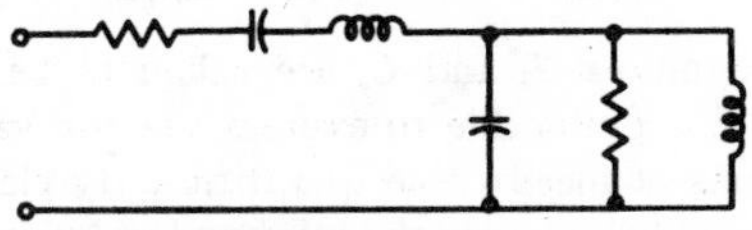

Fig. 1—Equivalent circuit for cavity containing resonant susceptibility.

[1] R. L. Kyhl, "Negative L and C in solid-state masers," Proc. IRE (*Correspondence*), vol. 48, p. 1157, June, 1960; *Errata*, vol. 49, p. 519, February, 1961.

[2] J. J. Cook, L. G. Cross, M. E. Bair, and R. W. Terhune, "Low-noise X-band radiometer using maser," Proc. IRE, vol. 49, pp. 768–778; April 1961. See also Goodwin and Moss.[17]

[3] H. Seidel and G. F. Herrmann, "Circuit aspects of parametric amplifiers," 1959 IRE WESCON Convention Record, pt. 2, pp. 83–91.

G. L. Matthaei, "Study of optimum wide-band parametric amplifiers and up-converters," IRE Trans. on Microwave Theory and Techniques, vol. MTT-9, pp. 23–38; January, 1961.

A. G. Little, "Wide-band single-diode parametric amplifier using filter techniques," Proc. IRE, vol. 49, pp. 821–822; April, 1961.

G. Schaffner and F. Voorhaar, "A nondegenerate S-band parametric amplifier with wide bandwidth," Proc. IRE, vol. 49, pp. 824–825; April, 1961.

M. Gilden and G. L. Matthaei, "A nearly optimum wide-band degenerate parametric amplifier," Proc. IRE, vol. 49, pp. 833–834; April, 1961.

The representation of the quantum-mechanical resonance by a single degree of freedom needs justification, since there are, in fact, at least 10^{14} active ions all resonating near the frequency range that is of interest. Some of the subtleties of this view are discussed in Appendix I and a more complete discussion is presented elsewhere.[4] The resulting simplification in Fig. 1 can be used to represent a Lorentz-shaped line. In many cases of interest the observed line shape is more nearly Gaussian, with the resulting reduction of absorption or emission (but not reactance) in the wings of the line. Notwithstanding these criticisms, it is felt to be best to analyze the simplest possible circuit that exhibits the phenomena in which we are interested.

Other simple choices of circuit could have been made with a suitable shift in reference plane, including the dual of Fig. 1.[4] The present choice fits well intuitively with the use of a paramagnetic crystal such as ruby for which the permeability near resonance (Lorentzian line shape) is given by

$$\mu = \mu_0\left[1 - \frac{j\chi_{\max}''}{1 + jT_2\Delta\omega}\right] \tag{1}$$

where $\chi_{\max}''$ is the peak value of the absorptive component of the magnetic resonant susceptibility. The full linewidth is $2/T_2$, and $\Delta\omega$ represents the deviation from center frequency.

This equation "describes" the parallel circuit and part of the series inductance of Fig. 1. The remainder of the series inductance is to be associated with RF magnetic fields in parts of the cavity that do not contain active material. Alternatively, one could define an effective susceptibility $\chi_{\text{eff}}'' = f\chi_{\max}''$, where f is a filling factor. The circuit model presents an open circuit far from cavity resonance. We might have preferred a short circuit, but our choice will be shown to be convenient later. As is customary for microwave circuits, the impedance level is left arbitrary.

We now introduce an inverted-population, stimulated-emission situation by suitable "pumping" of the active material. We then have

$$\mu = \mu_0\left[1 + \frac{j\chi_{\max}''}{1 + jT_2\Delta\omega}\right] \tag{2}$$

and the equivalent circuit of Fig. 2. The $-L$ and $-C$ in Fig. 2 express the fact that the dependence of reactance on frequency is the reverse of the usual case. These results derive from the solution of the equation of motion for the quantum-mechanical system in question. In the case of paramagnetic resonance, the Bloch equations[5]

[4] R. L. Kyhl (paper being prepared for publication).

[5] F. Block, "Nuclear induction," *Phys. Rev.*, vol. 70, pp. 460–474; October 1 and 15, 1946. See Section III.

show that, for every solution for the macroscopic magnetization vector, there is another solution in the same applied fields with the direction of magnetization reversed. This indicates an inverted population distribution among the magnetic sublevels, and also a reversal of both in-phase and out-of-phase magnetic currents. Bloch's analysis provides additional insight into the result that could have been obtained by substituting a negative population difference in the susceptibility formula.[6] Feynman[7] has shown that the Bloch analysis can be extended to other quantum-mechanical transitions by replacing the magnetization vector with a state vector in an abstract space. If the discussion is confined to linear systems, the same result can be obtained from the general relations between real and imaginary parts of a complex response function.[8]

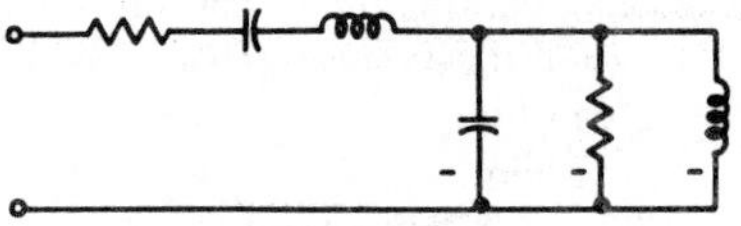

Fig. 2—Equivalent circuit for cavity containing inverted resonant susceptibility.

III. Elementary Properties of $-L$ and $-C$

The use of the negative L and C notation does not require any modification of the fundamental circuit equations. Interpretation requires a little care. For example, a resonant circuit composed of $+L$, $+C$, and $-R$ is unstable; but the combination of $-L$, $-C$, and $-R$ is stable. It becomes unstable with heavy loading, that is, with tight coupling to a resonant circuit.

Perhaps the most peculiar formal property of negative L and C circuits is negative stored energy. There is no real paradox because the devices that exhibit this property have additional stored energy that is available for maser amplification, and the total energy in the system remains positive. Total storage of energy in a network is associated with frequency dependence of reactance. By combining elements with negative stored energy and elements with positive stored energy one might hope to obtain improved frequency response.

It is not really necessary to introduce these new symbols. The circuit of Fig. 3(a) is equivalent to the circuit of Fig. 3(b) which has only negative R. However, since the negative R of the maser is found only in conjunction with the negative L and C, it is felt that the introduction of additional concepts is justified.

[6] A. M. Clogston, "Susceptibility of the three-level maser," *J. Phys. Chem. Solids*, vol. 4, pp. 271–277; 1958.

[7] R. P. Feynman, F. L. Vernon, Jr., and R. W. Hellwarth, "Geometric representation of the Schrödinger equation for solving maser problems," *J. Appl. Phys.*, vol. 28, pp. 49–52; January, 1957.

[8] J. R. Macdonald and M. K. Brachman, "Linear-system integral transform relations," *Rev. Mod. Phys.*, vol. 28, pp. 393–422; October, 1956.

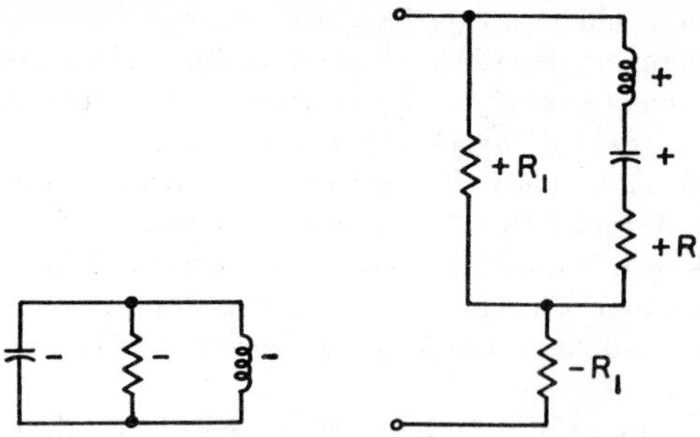

Fig. 3—Negative R synthesis of negative L and C.

IV. Reactance Compensation

If the series impedance in Fig. 2 is very low, the circuit of Fig. 4 suggests itself. Here, except for the series circuit, cancellation of the reactance as well as greatly increased bandwidth can be achieved. The equivalent circuit of Fig. 4 corresponds physically to two cascaded cavities with resonant permeability in the second cavity, as shown in Fig. 5. For use as a maser the circuit of Fig. 5 would be used with a circulator as in conventional cavity masers. Section VIII of this report presents experimental results from a circuit of this type. Ignoring cavity losses we calculated the theoretical voltage gain curves shown in Figs. 6–8. In Section V general network theory is extended to this stituation.

From the circuit of Fig. 4 (but with cavity losses omitted) synchronously tuned at ω_0, we have near resonance

$$\begin{aligned} Y_1 &\cong 2j(\omega - \omega_0)C_1 \\ Z_2 &\cong 2j(\omega - \omega_0)L_2 \\ Y_3 &\cong -G_3 - 2j(\omega - \omega_0)C_3. \end{aligned} \tag{3}$$

Here the symbols G_3 and C_3 are taken to be positive numbers. It is preferable to express the equivalent circuit in terms of measurable quantities. By elementary circuit analysis we derive the midband voltage gain

$$\mathcal{G}^{1/2} = \frac{G_3Z_0 + 1}{G_3Z_0 - 1} \tag{4}$$

in terms of the characteristic impedance of the transmission line. The various coupling coefficients are involved. For $G_3Z_0 < 1$, the circuit is unstable. The paramagnetic (full) linewidth between half-power points is given by

$$\Delta\omega_{\text{para}} = G_3/C_3. \tag{5}$$

The magnetic Q, defined, as is customary, in terms of stored energy in the cavity fields and power dissipated by the paramagnetic material, is given by

$$Q_M = -\omega_0 L_2 G_3. \tag{6}$$

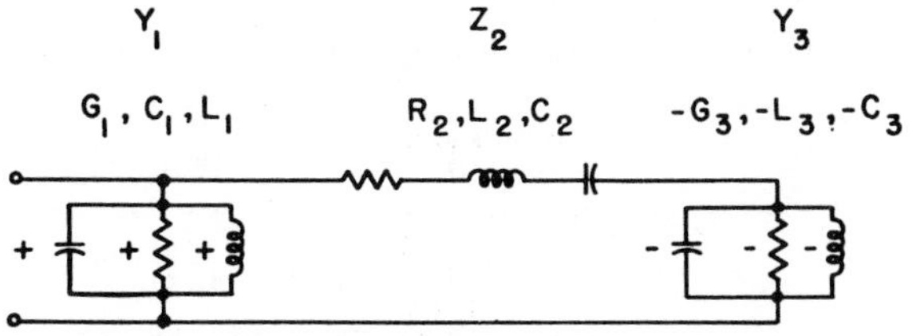

Fig. 4—Two-cavity reactance-compensation circuit.

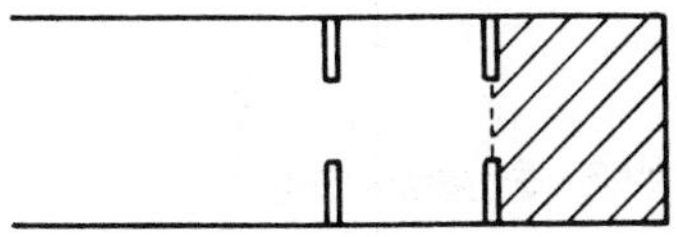

Fig. 5—Two-cavity reactance-compensation configuration.

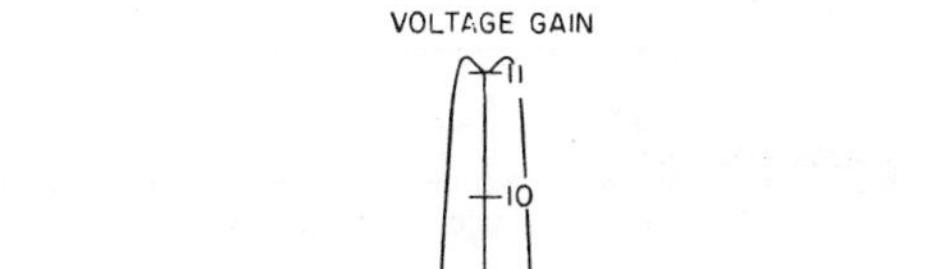

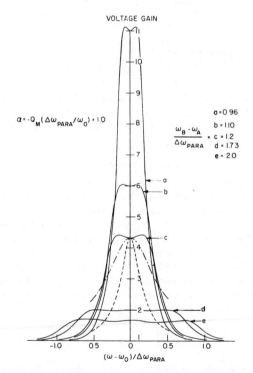

Fig. 6—Theoretical voltage gain-bandwidth curve, $\alpha=1.0$. Curve *c* can be compared with dot-dash curve: single cavity with infinite-bandwidth ruby; and with dashed curve: single cavity with actual ruby.

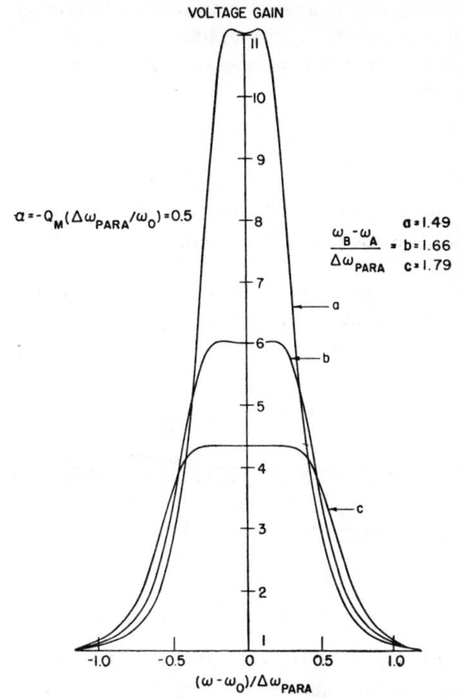

Fig. 7—Theoretical voltage gain-bandwidth curve, $\alpha=0.5$.

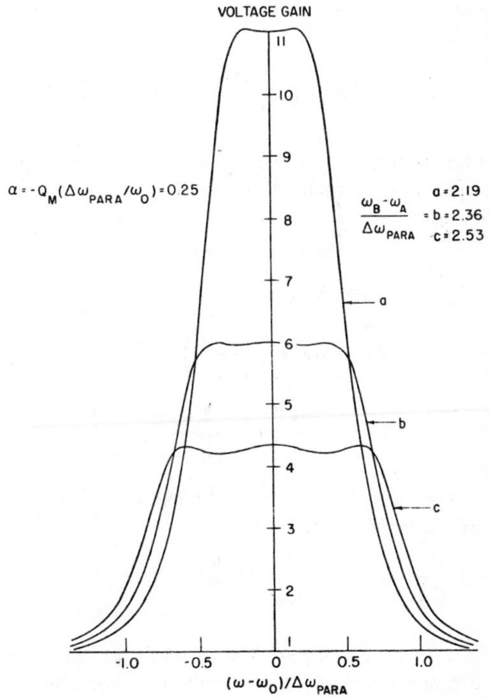

Fig. 8—Theoretical voltage gain-bandwidth curve, $\alpha=0.25$.

Historically this definition was introduced when paramagnetic reactance was negligible compared with cavity reactance. For amplification we take Q_M to be negative. In terms of the resonance susceptibility we find that

$$Q_M = -\frac{1}{|\chi_{\max}''|} \tag{7}$$

for unity filling factor. In general the equality holds if $\chi_{\max}''$ is the effective susceptibility, which includes a filling factor.

The coupling between the two cavities produces a split in resonant frequencies in the absence of paramagnetic resonance.

$$\omega_B - \omega_A = \frac{1}{\sqrt{C_1 L_2}} \cdot \tag{8}$$

If we normalize this splitting by comparing it with the paramagnetic linewidth, we obtain a circuit coupling parameter that is given by

$$\left(\frac{\omega_B - \omega_A}{\Delta\omega_{\text{para}}}\right) = \frac{C_3}{G_3\sqrt{L_2 C_1}} \cdot \tag{9}$$

Finally we calculate the ratio of the electromagnetic energy storage at resonance in the filled cavity to the energy storage in the equivalent circuit that represents the paramagnetic resonance. This ratio is called α. It is an indication of the possibility of significant reactance compensation. We shall see that α should be as small as possible.

$$\alpha = \frac{L_2 G_3^2}{C_3} = -Q_M\left(\frac{\Delta\omega_{\text{para}}}{\omega_0}\right) = +\frac{\Delta\omega_{\text{para}}}{\chi_{\max}''\omega_0} \cdot \tag{10}$$

In terms of $\mathcal{G}^{1/2}$, α, and $(\omega_B - \omega_A)/\Delta\omega_{\text{para}}$, the equivalent circuit may be recharacterized, as shown in Fig. 9. In this figure

$$Y_1 = \frac{j}{\alpha Z_0}\left(\frac{\Delta\omega_{\text{para}}}{\omega_B - \omega_A}\right)^2\left(\frac{\omega - \omega_0}{\frac{1}{2}\Delta\omega_{\text{para}}}\right)$$

$$Z_2 = j\alpha Z_0\left(\frac{\omega - \omega_0}{\frac{1}{2}\Delta\omega_{\text{para}}}\right) \tag{11}$$

$$Y_3 = -\frac{1}{Z_0}\left[1 + j\left(\frac{\omega - \omega_0}{\frac{1}{2}\Delta\omega_{\text{para}}}\right)\right] \tag{12}$$

and the turns ratio n of the ideal transformer is such that $Z_{aa} = n^2 Z_{bb}$, with

$$n^2 = \left(\frac{\mathcal{G}^{1/2} - 1}{\mathcal{G}^{1/2} + 1}\right) . \tag{13}$$

Numerical calculations were made for values of α in the range achievable with pink ruby completely filling the cavity and operating at 9 kMc at 4.2°K and 1.5°K. For each choice of gain the cavity splitting was chosen to optimize the flatness of the top of the band-pass curve. Results are shown in Figs. 6–8. Fig. 10 shows the result of detuning the magnetic field. In practice a 1-gauss shift of the magnetic field makes a significant change in band shape.

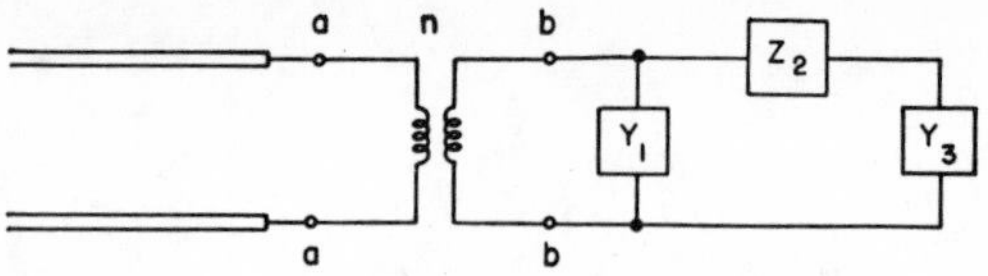

Fig. 9—Modified two-cavity reactance-compensation circuit.

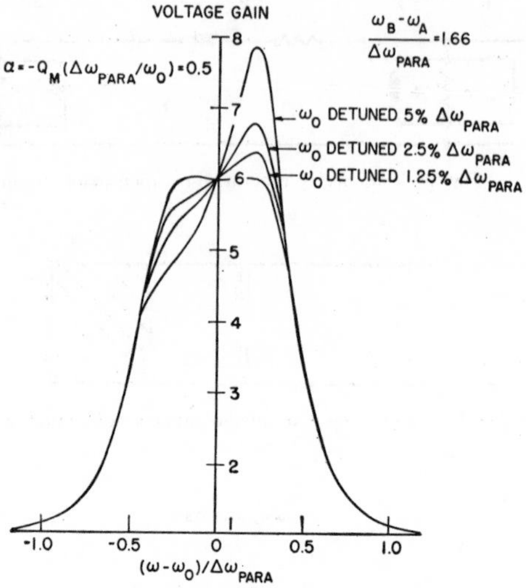

Fig. 10—Change of voltage-gain curve with detuning of resonance susceptibility.

V. General Network Theorems

Consider Fig. 11, the generalization of the circuit of Fig. 4, in which an arbitrary network is used to adjust the gain curve of the maser cavity.

The gain will be represented by the reflection coefficient, Γ, at the terminals. Because G is negative, $|\Gamma| \geq 1$. The corresponding low-pass problem with positive G was solved by Fano.[9] Our development will closely parallel his analysis. The simpler problem shown in Fig. 12 was analyzed by Bode[10] who gave the familiar relation for the low-pass network

$$\frac{1}{\pi}\int_0^\infty \ln\frac{1}{|\Gamma|}\,d\omega \leq \frac{G}{C} \cdot \tag{14}$$

The equality holds when Γ has no zeros in the right half-plane.

The low-pass equivalent of Fig. 11 is shown in Fig. 13. There are two general relationships in this case. As

[9] R. M. Fano, "Theoretical limitations on the broadband matching of arbitrary impedances," *J. Franklin Inst.*, vol. 249, pp. 57–84, January, 1950; vol. 249, pp. 139–154, February, 1950.

[10] H. W. Bode, "Network Analysis and Feedback Amplifier Design," D. Van Nostrand Company, Inc., New York, N. Y., ch. 6; 1945.

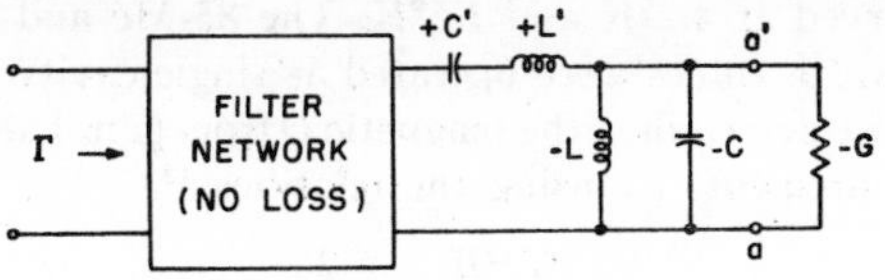

Fig. 11—Generalized reactance compensation circuit.

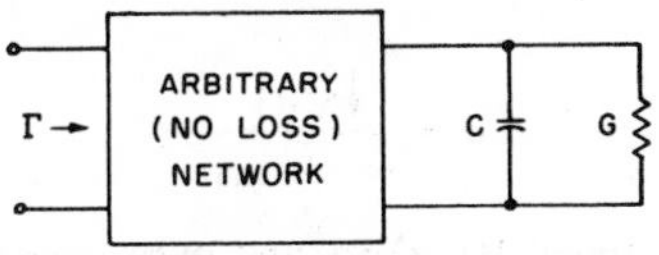

Fig. 12—Network for Bode Theorem.

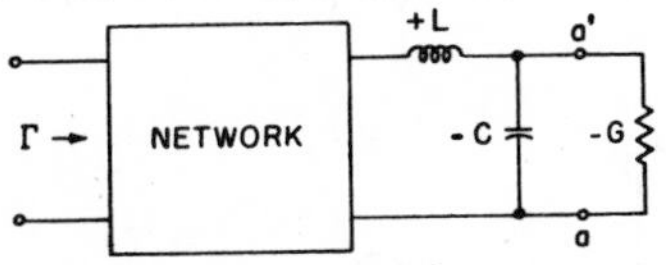

Fig. 13—Low-pass equivalent of reactance-compensation circuit.

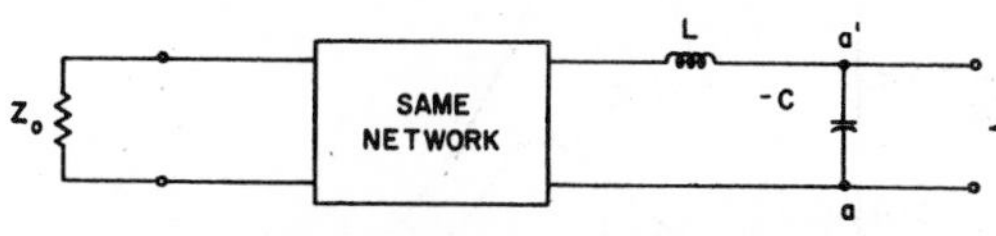

Fig. 14—Circuit for definition of Γ'.

shown in Appendix II, they are

$$\frac{1}{\pi}\int_0^\infty \ln|\Gamma|\,d\omega = -\frac{G}{C} + \sum \lambda_p - \sum \lambda_z \tag{15}$$

$$\frac{1}{\pi}\int_0^\infty \omega^2 \ln|\Gamma|\,d\omega$$

$$= \frac{G^3}{3C^3} + \frac{G}{LC^2} - \frac{1}{3}\sum \lambda_p^3 + \frac{1}{3}\sum \lambda_z^3. \tag{16}$$

The λ's are defined in terms of the circuit of Fig. 14. Here, Γ' is defined relative to $+G$, and the λ's are the values of complex $s = j\omega$ at which Γ' has poles and zeros in the right half-plane. Relations (15) and (16) differ from the ones given by Fano in the following ways:

1) When G becomes negative the $|\Gamma|$ is inverted. Compare (14) with (15) and (16).
2) There are appropriate sign changes caused by $-C$.
3) The presence of $-C$ permits the presence of both poles and zeros of Γ' in the right half-plane. Indeed the network is not stable without at least one pole to make the right side of (15) positive.

We now transform the expressions to the high-frequency maser case. The network is modified to shift center frequency from zero to ω_0. Then $\mathcal{G}^{1/2}$ is substituted for $|\Gamma|$. We go from a single-sided integral from zero frequency upward to an integral over the full bandwidth of the gain curve, although the limits are still 0 to ∞. This introduces a factor of 2 on the right. The L and C above (16) are *not* the same as L_2 and C_3 in (3). The correspondence must be made on the basis of $Y(\omega)$ or $Z(\omega)$. This introduces another factor of 2. For the band-pass case,

$$\frac{1}{\pi}\int_0^\infty \ln \mathcal{G}^{1/2}\,d\omega \cong -\Delta\omega_{para} + 2(\lambda_p - j\omega_0) \tag{17}$$

$$\frac{1}{\pi}\int_0^\infty (\omega - \omega_0)^2 \ln \mathcal{G}^{1/2}\,d\omega$$

$$\cong \frac{2}{3}\left(\frac{\Delta\omega_{para}}{2}\right)^3 + \left(\frac{\Delta\omega_{para}}{2}\right)^2 \omega_0\chi_{max}'' - \frac{2}{3}(\lambda_p - j\omega_0)^3. \tag{18}$$

The expressions are now approximate because we have ignored the pass band at negative frequencies and also the negative-frequency poles, as in fact we have already done in (1) and (2). We have dropped the summations because (as is shown in Appendix III) in a properly designed maser there are no zeros—just one pole of Γ' in the right quadrant. The network has lost some generality in the shift because the gain curve must presumably be symmetric about the center frequency ω_0 in order to correspond with the low-pass formulas. This is not a serious restriction and may not be completely necessary. The situation does not merit too close an inspection in any case, since in a practical microwave maser there are other cavity resonances and other resonant susceptibilities that are ignored here.

Eqs. (17) and (18) give the general limitations on gain and bandwidth for a single crystal, Lorentzian line-shape maser—that is, single crystal in the sense that the active material is describable by a single set of elements in an equivalent circuit. A long, thin crystal for use in a traveling-wave structure does not fit into this category. (See also Appendix I and Section IX.) It is clear from (17) that the circuit design should maximize $(\lambda_p - j\omega_0)$ for best performance; however, $(\lambda_p - j\omega_0)$ cannot be made arbitrarily large because of the restriction of (18). Since G is never less than 1 for the circuit in question, both integrals must remain positive to preserve stability. Eq. (17) gives little insight into possible gain-bandwidth figures until λ_p has been evaluated. This can be done in some particular cases. If the maser amplifier is to be a high-gain, narrow-band one, then we may set the second integral (18) equal to zero. We may then solve for λ_p and substitute in (17) so that, in the narrow-band limit, we obtain

$$\frac{1}{\pi}\int_0^\infty \ln \mathcal{G}^{1/2}\,d\omega = \Delta\omega_{para}\left[\left(1 + \frac{3\chi_{max}''\omega_0}{\Delta\omega_{para}}\right)^{1/3} - 1\right]$$

$$= \Delta\omega_{para}[(1 + 3/\alpha)^{1/3} - 1]. \tag{19}$$

It is seen that for poor filling factors or weak resonances $(\alpha > 3)$ the gain-bandwidth product is linear in $1/\alpha$. For strong resonance and filling factor near unity $(\alpha < 3)$ the gain-bandwidth product may become arbitrarily large, but only as the cube root of $(1/\alpha)$.

Another interesting situation is the square response with constant gain over a bandwidth of $\Delta\omega$ and unity gain outside. The integrals of (17) and (18) can be evaluated directly to give

$$\frac{\chi_{max}''\omega_0}{\Delta\omega_{para}} = \frac{1}{\alpha} = \left(\frac{\Delta\omega}{\Delta\omega_{para}}\frac{\ln \mathcal{G}^{1/2}}{\pi}\right) + \left(\frac{\Delta\omega}{\Delta\omega_{para}}\frac{\ln \mathcal{G}^{1/2}}{\pi}\right)^2$$

$$+ \frac{1}{3}\left(\frac{\Delta\omega}{\Delta\omega_{para}}\frac{\ln \mathcal{G}^{1/2}}{\pi}\right)^3\left[1 + \left(\frac{\pi}{\ln \mathcal{G}^{1/2}}\right)^2\right]. \tag{20}$$

Although such an ideal response cannot be obtained with a finite network, (20) gives some idea of what can be accomplished with broad-band operation. For example, if we wish to achieve a voltage gain of 23, ($\ln \mathcal{G}^{1/2} = \pi$) and a bandwidth equal to a typical ruby bandwidth of 60 Mc, we need an α of 3/8 or less, which is entirely possible at low temperature.

It should be recognized that $1/\alpha$ is not a complete figure of merit for maser materials because it only tells what can be achieved relative to the natural linewidth, and, other things being equal, a broader linewidth will give broader band operation so that $\Delta\omega_{para}/\alpha$, or $(\chi_{max}''\omega_0)$, is nearer to a true figure of merit.

VI. Verification—Experimental Determination of Optimum Ruby-Chromium Concentration

A ruby maser at 9000 Mc was built to demonstrate the operation of reactance compensation. The design was, in other respects, a conventional three-level cavity maser operated at liquid-helium temperature. One of the most important factors in achieving large gain-bandwidth operation is the choice of optimum ruby concentration. Our selection was from several boules of Linde Company synthetic ruby.

The paramagnetic linewidth of Cr^{3+} in Al_2O_3 increases with Cr^{3+} concentration, and has a residual value of approximately 42 Mc at vanishingly small concentrations.[11] As the linewidth $\Delta\nu_{para}$ is more easily measured than the density of paramagnetic centers N, it was used as an indication of the relative Cr^{3+} concentrations in the several ruby samples examined. The value of χ_{max}'' depends on $N/\Delta\nu_{para}$ for a fixed inversion ratio, and it is apparent that there should be some optimum value for N which would make χ_{max}'' as large as possible without going to unduly high concentrations in which deleterious effects, such as cross relaxation, can decrease the achievable inversion.[12]

Five samples with linewidths from 67 Mc to 220 Mc were measured. Of these only the three lowest concentration materials exhibited significant inversion when pumped. Fig. 15 shows the value of $1/|Q_M|$ which were observed at 4.2°K and 1.5°K. The 85-Mc and 106-Mc linewidth rubies were operated as single-cavity masers, and we determined the magnetic Q from gain-bandwidth measurements by using the relations [13]

$$\frac{\mathcal{G}^{1/2}B}{\Delta\nu_{para}} = \frac{2}{1+\alpha} \tag{21}$$

and

$$\alpha = \frac{|Q_M|}{\omega_0/\Delta\omega_{para}}.$$

The 67-Mc linewidth data are only approximate, as values of magnetic Q have been estimated from the measurements of the compensated amplifier performance.

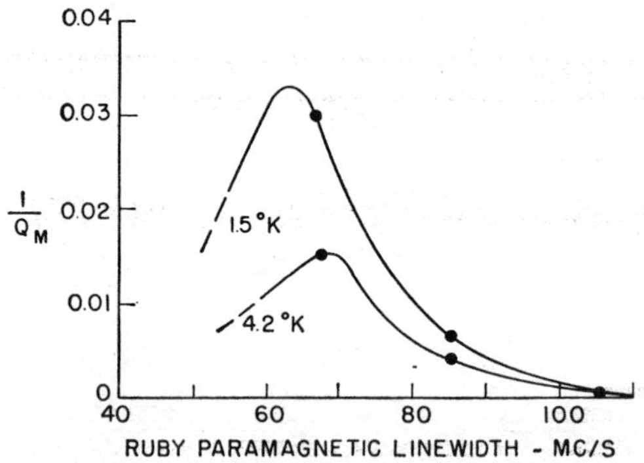

Fig. 15—Experimental ruby magnetic Q vs paramagnetic linewidth for the samples used in this work.

Clearly, the available population difference for the signal transition decreases very rapidly as the Cr^{3+} concentration is increased beyond some optimum value. The change with temperature was only a factor of approximately 2 for the lowest concentration material studied. In the absence of cross-relaxation processes this should be nearer 3. We conclude that the 67-Mc linewidth material is still slightly high in concentration, the optimum apparently being near a linewidth of 60 Mc. Unfortunately, data for samples of lower concentration were not available. In the low-concentration limit $1/Q_M$ must be proportional to concentration.

A change in line shape from Gaussian for low concentration to Lorentzian at high concentration was observed as the Cr^{3+} concentration was increased and the linewidth varied from 67 Mc to 223 Mc. (The linewidths quoted are half-power absorption full widths.)

VII. Cavity Design

The amplifier was designed to operate at a signal frequency near 9 kMc with a pump frequency of 23 kMc; operation is in the push-pull pumping mode. This

[11] "Research on Paramagnetic Resonances," Res. Lab. of Electronics, M.I.T., Cambridge, Mass., Eleventh Quarterly Progress Rept. on Signal Corps Contract DA36-039-sc-74895, pp. 1–3, May 15, 1960; Tenth Quarterly Progress Rept., *op. cit.*, pp. 17–27, February 15, 1960.

[12] T. H. Maiman, "Maser behavior: temperature and concentration effects," *J. Appl. Phys.*, vol. 31, pp. 222–223; January, 1960.

[13] M. W. P. Strandberg, "Unidirectional paramagnetic amplifier design," Proc. IRE, vol. 48, pp. 1307–1320; July, 1960.

required that the c axis of the crystal make an angle of 54.7° with the dc magnetic field.

To achieve the highest possible filling factor, we used the ruby crystal to entirely fill the fixed tuned microwave cavity that resonated in the TE_{101} mode at 9 kMc. It was, therefore, convenient to cut the ruby crystal as shown in Fig. 16. The H_{rf} was everywhere perpendicular to H_0, which gives strong coupling. The crystal was pumped at a higher mode cavity resonance. A number of resonances were present at 23 kMc, but it was not necessary that one of these coincide exactly with the push-pull pump frequency since saturation of both pump transitions is achievable through cross relaxation for the 67-Mc linewidth material under approximately push-pull pumping conditions. The cavity was formed by enclosing the ruby with two pieces of O.F.H.C. copper, as shown in Fig. 17, and brazing them together in a hydrogen atmosphere. The resulting block was cut down to provide a continuous 0.007–in wall of copper around the ruby, and signal and pump coupling irises were machined out.

The compensation cavity was made in a similar fashion, but contained polycrystalline sapphire (Wesgo Type A-300), a high-density, low-loss material having a dielectric constant of 10 at X band. The large coupling aperture to the signal waveguide lowers the resonant frequencty of this cavity approximately 10 per cent, and this must be considered in the calculation of the cavity dimensions. The size of the aperture between the cavities was adjusted with each concentration to provide for the separation of the normal-mode resonant frequencies indicated for the desired operating performance.

A movable knife-edge in front of the signal aperture in the sapphire cavity provided a very fine control of the cavity center frequency, and an adjustable capacitive post in the waveguide was used as a loading control to vary the amplifier gain. The individual cavities and the coupled system are shown in Fig. 18.

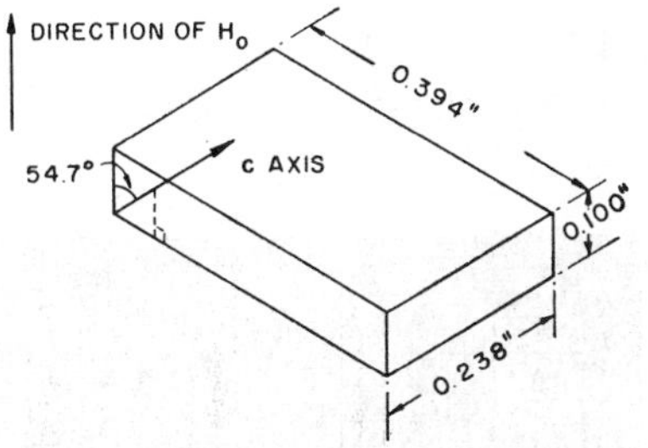

Fig. 16—Ruby crystal dimensions.

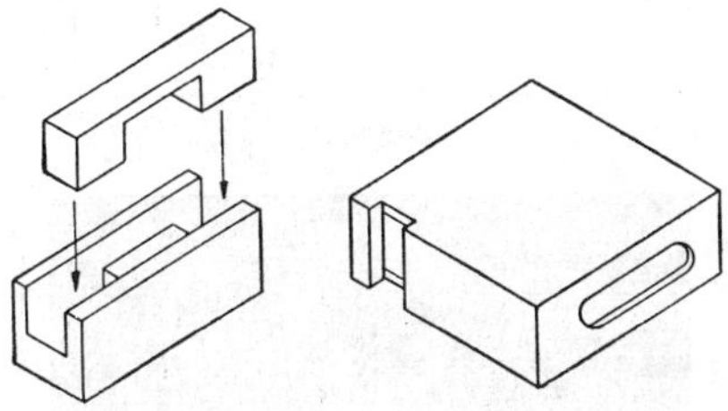

Fig. 17—Assembly procedure for copper-clad ruby cavity.

Fig. 18—Two-cavity assembly with cover block containing pump guide removed. Enlarged views of the two cavities are shown above.

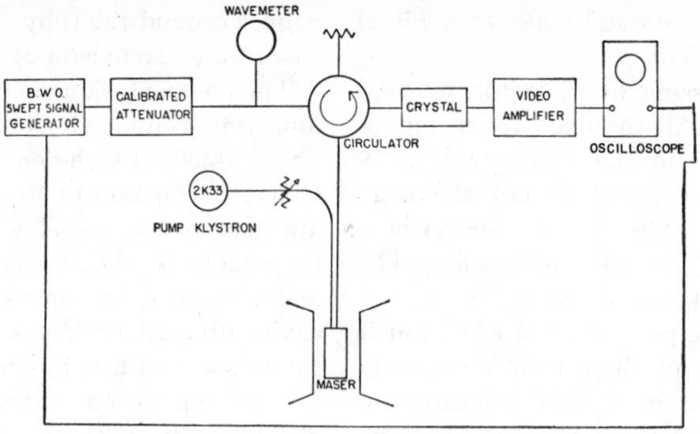

Fig. 19—Schematic drawing of test system.

TABLE I
SINGLE-CAVITY MEASUREMENTS

Paramagnetic Linewidth (mc)	Temperature (°K)	Center Frequency (mc)	$\mathcal{G}^{1/2}B$ (mc)	α	$\|Q_M\|$
85	4.2	9300	53	2.2	240
	1.5	9300	70	1.43	155
106	4.2	9100	8	24.5	2100

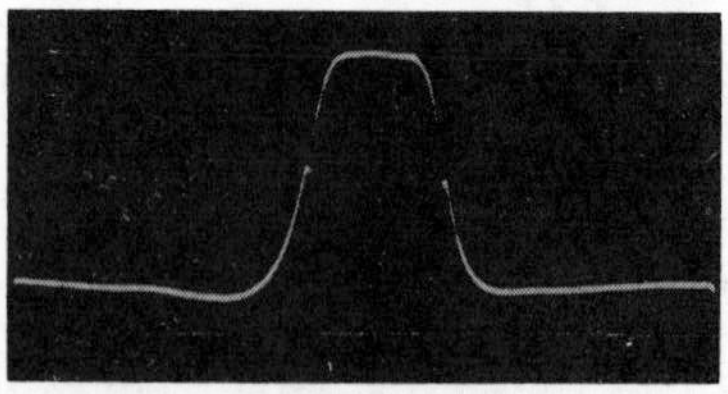

Fig. 20—Experimental power-gain curve at 4.2°K; ruby linewidth, 85 Mc; 55-mc bandwidth.

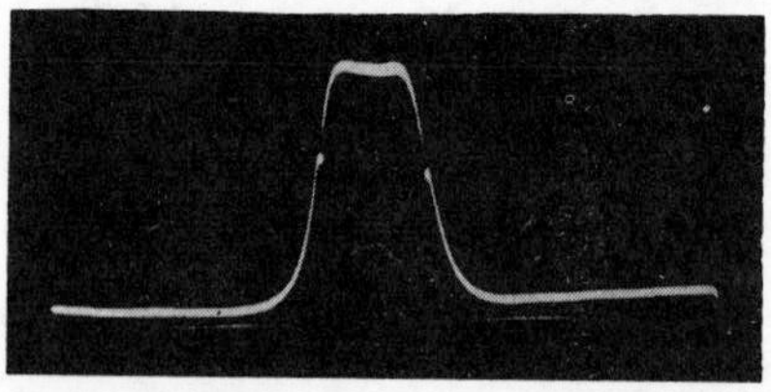

Fig. 21—Experimental power-gain curve at 1.5°K; ruby linewidth, 85 Mc; 48-mc bandwidth.

VIII. AMPLIFIER OPERATION

The test system is shown in Fig. 19. A broad-band swept oscillator was used as a signal source, and gain measurements were determined by means of a precision calibrated attenuator. To avoid amplifier saturation, we maintained output signals below -20 dbm. Sufficient video gain was available for oscilloscope presentation of the band-pass characteristics.

The pump klystron supplied 20 mw of power, and it was determined during the measurements that this was at least 3 db in excess of that required to saturate the pump transition. Significantly lower pump power was required for the low-concentration ruby.

Results

The single-cavity $\mathcal{G}^{1/2}B$ measurements made on the 85-Mc and 106-Mc materials are summarized in Table I. The values of α given in Table I for the 85-Mc linewidth material will be compared with the performance data of the same material in the compensated amplifier.

The 85-Mc linewidth ruby was operated in the double-cavity configuration at 4.2°K and 1.5°K with a circuit-coupling parameter of 1.06 which represents a separation of 90 Mc between the normal cavity modes. Fig. 20 shows the band-pass characteristic obtained at 4.2°K. Midband gain was 7.4 db, and the half-power bandwidth was 55 Mc. For a value of $\alpha=2.2$ as determined above, the theoretical bandwidth is approximately 70 Mc at this gain. Fig. 21 shows the amplifier performance at 1.5°K. The gain was 10.6 db, and the bandwidth was 48 Mc. The theory predicts a bandwidth of 70 Mc for a value of $\alpha=1.43$.

The results for the 67-Mc linewidth ruby are substantially better. They are summarized under a variety of design conditions at 9 kMc, in Table II. The value of α was not measured in a single-cavity maser for the 67-Mc ruby. The assumed values of α which best fit observed two-cavity operation were $\alpha=0.5$ at 4.2°K and 0.25 at 1.5°K. The observed and theoretical band-pass curves are shown in Fig. 22 for the 9-db and 14-db gain cases. The quantity (f_B-f_A)/linewidth is under experimental control, but, as can be seen from Table II, the

TABLE II
RESULTS OF MEASUREMENTS FOR 67-MC LINEWIDTH RUBY

Temperature (°K)	Gain (db)	Bandwidth (mc)	f_B-f_A (mc)	Measured: Bandwidth / Linewidth	Measured: f_B-f_A / Linewidth	Theoretical: Bandwidth / Linewidth	Theoretical: f_B-f_A / Linewidth
4.2	14	50	120	0.75	1.8	1.02	1.72
1.5	14	95	155	1.4	2.3	1.54	2.45
1.5	12	108	169	1.6	2.5	—	2.58
1.5	9	122	171	1.8	2.55	2.30	2.90
1.5	∼6	145	200	2.2	3.0	—	3.46

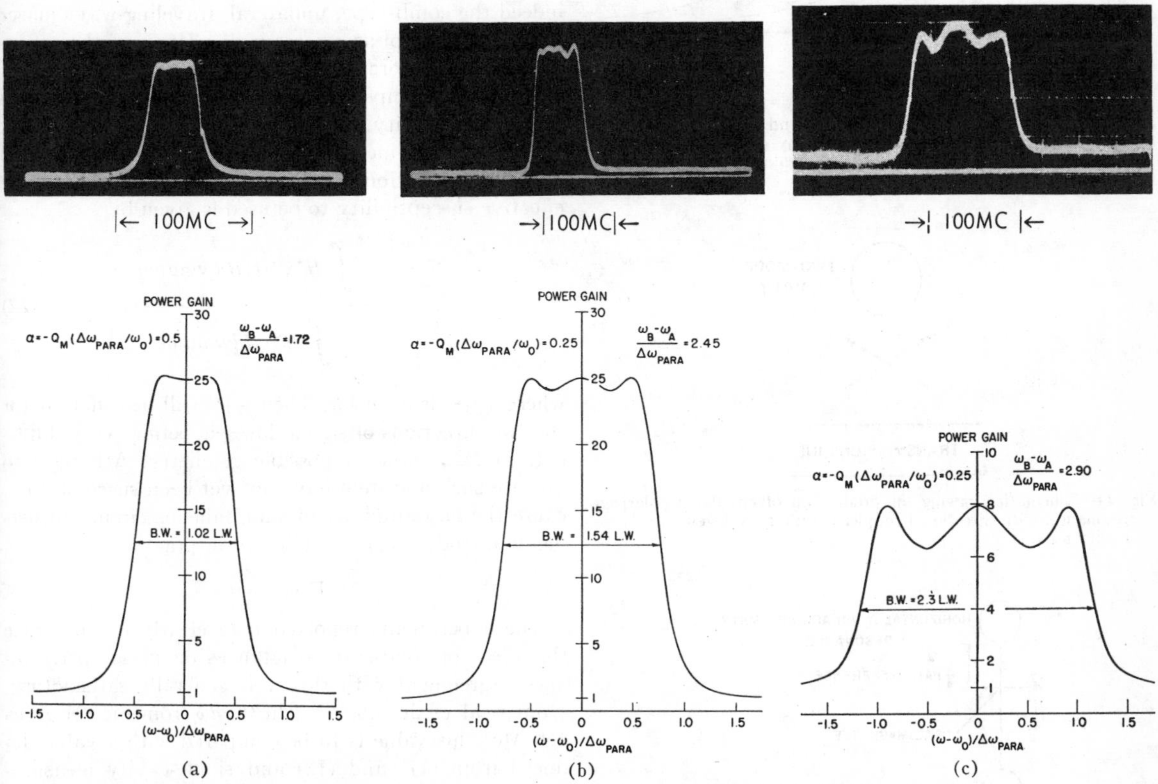

Fig. 22—(a) Experimental and theoretical power-gain curve for 67-Mc linewidth ruby maser. T=4.2°K; gain, 14 db. (b) Experimental and theoretical power-gain curve for 67-Mc linewidth ruby maser. T=1.5°K; gain, 14 db. (c) Experimental and theoretical power-gain curve for 67-Mc linewidth ruby maser. T=1.5°K; gain, 9 db.

value used for the calculations was not precisely the value used in the experimental measurements of bandwidth and gain.

Fig. 23 (next page) summarizes all of the measurements on the compensated amplifier and shows the necessary normal-mode splitting to achieve the flattest frequency response at a specified voltage gain, with α as a parameter. The single-cavity measurements on the 85-Mc linewidth material are substantiated here. For the 67-Mc line-width ruby at 1.5°K, the chosen value of $\alpha=0.25$ for the theoretical calculations appears to be slightly less than that actually obtained during operation.

IX. EXTENSION TO CIRCULARLY POLARIZED CAVITIES

If the coupling of the quantum-mechanical transition to the electromagnetic field is circularly polarized, and if a cavity that can be driven in a circularly polarized mode is used, nonreciprocal gain can be achieved without the use of circulators.[14] These conditions can be partially met. With typical magnetic fields and crystal orientations as used in masers, paramagnetic resonance is elliptically polarized with the ratio between right- and left-hand circularly polarized components being

[14] Strandberg, *op. cit.*, p. 1309.

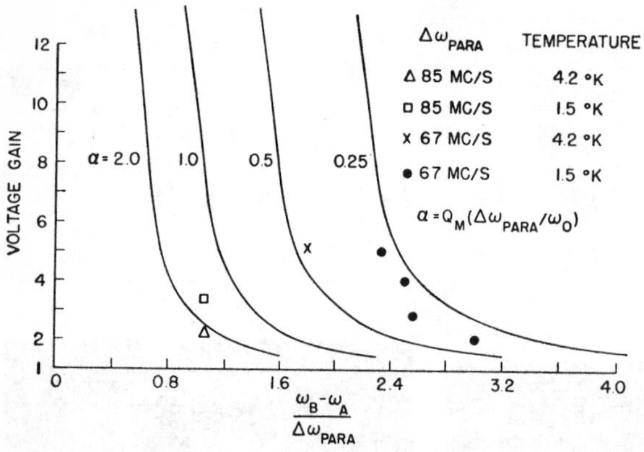

Fig. 23—Summary of experimental results and theory: voltage gain plotted against cavity coupling with ruby quality as a parameter. Optimum flatness of the top of the gain curve is assumed in the design.

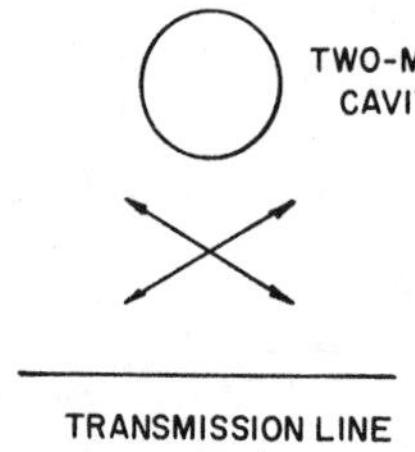

Fig. 24—Schematic drawing for production of circularly polarized resonance, with directional-coupler coupling to degenerate-mode cavity used.

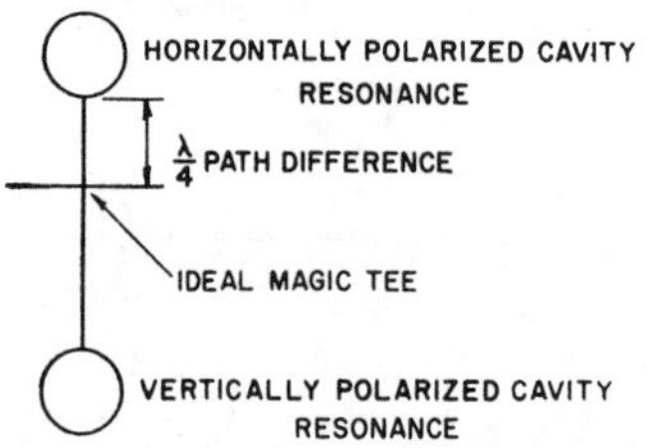

Fig. 25—Equivalent circuit of circularly polarized resonance.

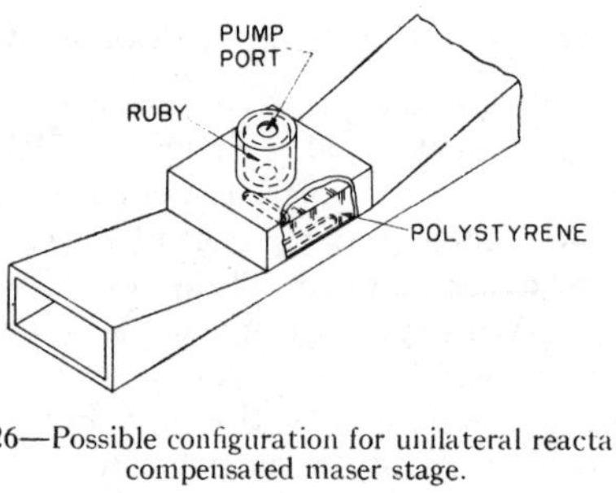

Fig. 26—Possible configuration for unilateral reactance-compensated maser stage.

strongly dependent on operating conditions.[14,15] In order to obtain circularly polarized cavity modes, it is necessary to have a cavity with two degenerate modes which is coupled, as shown in Fig. 24, by using directional-coupler coupling.[16] A useful equivalent circuit for analysis is shown in Fig. 25.

A signal in one port of the two-port circuit produces a circularly polarized mode of one sense of rotation; a signal in the other port produces the opposite sense of rotation. The resulting fields will be circularly polarized in some parts of the cavity and will more generally be elliptically polarized. Such structures can be cascaded; indeed the comb-type, unilateral, traveling-wave maser can be thought of as a cascade of a large number of individual resonators.

Reactance compensation, in principle, can be applied to unilateral cavity systems. The transmission coefficient will obey the same conditions that have been derived above for reflection coefficients in simple cavities. The effective susceptibility to be used is given by

$$\chi_{\text{eff}}'' = \frac{\int H^* \chi''(r) H d \text{ volume}}{\int H^* \cdot H d \text{ volume}}, \tag{22}$$

where $\chi''(r)$ is a tensor. Then χ_{eff}'' will be different for the two directions of signal flow—hopefully very different. Fig. 26 shows a possible geometry. Attempts to operate such a system have not yet been successful because the large number of simultaneous circuit adjustments introduces great difficulty in practice.

X. Discussion

The experiments reported here clearly demonstrate the effect of solid-state reactances on maser performance. Agreement with theory is generally satisfactory. Numerical evaluation of $\int \ln \mathcal{G}^{1/2} d\omega$ from Fig. 21 gives 460 Mc; this value is to be compared with a value deduced from (17) and (18) and single-cavity measurements of 720 Mc. The discrepancy is undoubtedly the result of our neglect of cavity losses, although departure from the Lorentzian line shape is a factor.

A considerable increase in bandwidth has been obtained over the maximum value that is possible with a single cavity.

No noise-figure measurements were made, but the same effective noise temperature should prevail as for other maser designs. Careful construction should keep cavity losses low enough to avoid serious adverse noise contribution.

[15] W. S. Chang and A. E. Siegman, "Characteristics of ruby for maser applications," Stanford Electronics Labs., Stanford, Calif., Tech. Rept. 156-2; September 30, 1958. (Reprinted January 30, 1959.)

[16] M. Tinkham and M. W. P. Strandberg, "The excitation of circular polarization in microwave cavities," Proc. IRE, vol. 43, pp. 734–738; June, 1955.

Some work carried out elsewhere has indicated that improved gain-bandwidth results from putting active ruby in the reactance-compensation cavity.[17] Some simple numerical calculations made here indicate the opposite when the active material in both cavities has identical resonance behavior.

It is too early to say whether reactance compensation in the form described here will be useful in maser development. A small number of cascaded, reactance-compensated, unilateral cavity units, presumably including some unilateral, reverse-attenuation elements, and possibly stagger-tuning of the paramagnetic resonance, can in principle match or exceed the performance of other designs, including traveling-wave devices. The decision as to the actual circuit to be used will be made on the basis of practical considerations. Here it must be admitted that the adjustment of reactance-compensated circuits is critical. A slight change in cavity loading will produce either a single narrow-gain curve or two sharp gain peaks, as illustrated in Fig. 27. Additional change in loading in either direction leads to instability. The traveling-wave maser that is broad-banded by means of tapered magnetic field to provide tapered paramagnetic resonance[18] frequency may well be simpler to operate. At present, solid-state reactance effects are not ordinarily taken into account in traveling-wave maser design.[20] One of the advantages of traveling-wave masers is the possibility of tuning the operating frequency by adjusting the magnetic field without the necesssity of retuning the structure. Use of reactance-compensation schemes, to achieve a flat gain-response, for example, would seriously interfere with this flexibility.

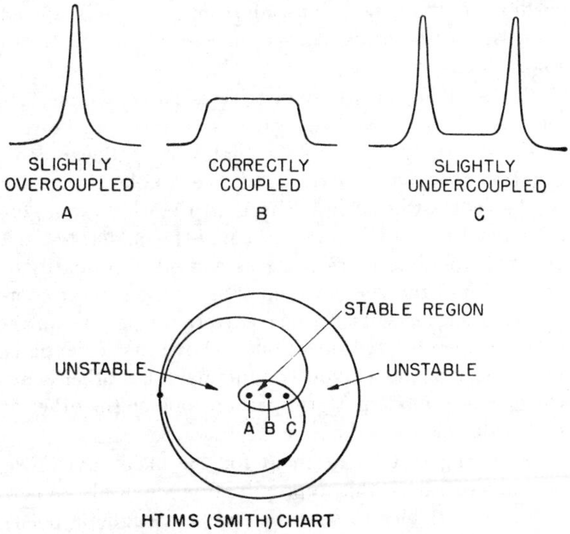

Fig. 27—Impedance behavior of reactance-compensated maser, showing effect of coupling adjustment (the HTIMS Chart is used[19]).

In any case, the inverted reactance behavior will be a factor in the analysis of any solid-state maser for which large filling factors are used.

Appendix I

Circuit Representation of Paramagnetic Resonance

The perturbation formula for initially lossless cavities[21]

$$\Delta Z = j\omega \frac{\int d\,\text{volume}\,[H^*\Delta\mu H + \mathcal{E}^*\Delta\epsilon\mathcal{E}]}{|I|^2} \tag{23}$$

yields the desired formula immediately. Setting

$$\Delta\mu = -\frac{j\chi_{\max}''}{1 + jT_2\Delta\omega}$$

and factoring it out of the integral, we obtain

$$\Delta Z = \omega\left(\frac{\chi_{\max}''}{1 + jT_2\Delta\omega}\right)\frac{\int d\,\text{volume}\,H^*H}{|I|^2}. \tag{24}$$

If we combine (24) with the impedance of the cavity near resonance and assume that $\int d\,\text{volume}\,H^*H/|I|^2$ is constant over the frequency range of interest (which requires use of the series resonance form for the cavity), we have an expression of the form

$$Z = R + jx(\Delta\omega) + \left(\frac{\omega\chi_{\max}''}{1 + jT_2\Delta\omega}\right)\cdot\text{constant} \tag{25}$$

which describes the equivalent circuit of Fig. 2. This derivation, although qualitatively correct, creates difficulties. The use of a perturbation expression is valid since $\Delta\mu$ is indeed small for all maser materials that are now available. However, the constancy of $\int |H|^2\,d\,\text{volume}/|I|^2$ is open to question. The frequency range for the validity of the expression is not clear, and it is by no means obvious how to proceed in the case of more complex cavity networks. By the method of expanding the cavity fields in the set of orthonormal modes of the uncoupled cavity, several authors have shown that the admittance or impedance of an air-

[17] F. E. Goodwin and F. W. Moss, Hughes Aircraft Co., Culver City, Calif. (private communication, November 12, 1959).

[18] S. Okwit and J. G. Smith, "Traveling-wave maser with instantaneous bandwidths in excess of 100 Mc," Proc. IRE (*Correspondence*), vol. 49, p. 1210; July, 1961.

[19] R. L. Kyhl, "Plotting impedances with negative resistance components," IRE Trans. on Microwave Theory and Techniques, vol. MTT-8, p. 377; May, 1960.

[20] R. W. DeGrasse, E. O. Schultz-DuBois, and D. Scovil, "The three-level solid state traveling-wave maser," *Bell Sys. Tech. J.*, vol. 38, pp. 305–334; March, 1959.

[21] B. Lax, "Frequency and loss characteristics of microwave ferrite devices," Proc. IRE, vol. 44, pp. 1368–1386; October, 1956. Only trivial modifications of the equations are required.

filled cavity can be expressed in the form[22]

$$Y = \sum_i \frac{\text{constant}_i}{(\omega - \omega_i)} \qquad (26)$$

in which the complex ω_i represents both the infinite set of complex natural resonance frequencies of the cavity with the input coupling aperture short-circuited (open-circuited in the case of the corresponding impedance formula) and also a dc term $\omega_i = 0$. The corresponding equivalent circuit is shown in Fig. 28.

For well-separated resonances it is common to truncate the circuit, lumping the reactances of all terms except one into Y_0 (as shown in Fig. 29) to obtain the simple circuit that is valid in the neighborhood of one of the resonances. If there are two closely spaced resonances in the cavity, one can similarly approximate the admittance behavior in the neighborhood of the pair of resonances by the equivalent circuit of Fig. 30(a) which, by algebraic manipulation, can be converted into the equivalent forms of Fig. 30(b)–(d). If it is possible to choose a new reference plane in an input transmission line, the circuits can be reduced to the still simpler forms of Fig. 30(e) and (f).

The extension of the general expression (26) to include other dynamic variables, such as electric or magnetic polarizations, is to be expected and is demonstrated in another paper.[4] The present problem concerns the truncation of the expression for practical analysis.

Out of the essentially infinite number of degrees of freedom introduced by the sample, how many must be retained to give an acceptably accurate equivalent circuit? For an empty cavity, all but one or two of the resonance frequencies occur outside the frequency range that is of interest. However, all of the resonances of the material itself, associated with a particular paramagnetic transition, occur in the relevant frequency interval. Clearly the overwhelming majority must represent spatial patterns of the magnetization which are very complicated and which, therefore, couple weakly, if at all, to the incident field. In order to make the problem tractable we must introduce simplifying assumptions. We have assumed that

1) The material shall be homogeneous in the sense that all portions show the same paramagnetic resonance frequency and linewidth. There is then a direct relation between the cavity-field pattern and the polarization pattern. Clearly, a radical violation of this assumption leads to chaos. We are not attempting to analyze tapered magnetic-field situations.
2) The cavity-field pattern shall be assumed not to be influenced by the material. All maser materials have small resonance susceptibilities. They are large enough to radically change network impedances, but they represent only a small perturbation on μ or ϵ. Large nonresonant susceptibilities, such as the dielectric constant of the ruby, are considered to be part of the cavity system.
3) As the final step we assert that the cavity-field patterns remain constant over the frequency range of interest, being, in fact, just the mode pattern for the particular isolated cavity resonance in question. This is a commonly made assertion but is not necessarily a good one.

Combining these three assumptions, we conclude that a single new variable is capable of describing the state of magnetic or electric polarization of the material in the frequency range of interest. If the line shape is Lorentzian, then this new variable satisfies a harmonic type of equation of motion and, when coupled with the cavity field equations, produces just one additional normal mode of the coupled system. The validity of the equivalent circuits in Fig. 30 follows directly. (The difficulty with a Gaussian line shape is that the polarization vector obeys no simple equation of motion. The case of a cavity filled completely with a uniform linear medium and having a Gaussian resonance can be solved numerically and leads to an infinite set of normal modes for each cavity mode.)

The next higher approximation is based on the fact that the fields in a cavity near resonance can be represented with considerable accuracy by a linear combination of *two* field patterns.[4] For example, these may be the field patterns for a "short" at the window and for an "open" at the window. For small- or moderate-sized coupling windows these patterns will differ primarily in the region of the window, and thus another linear combination suggests itself—one pattern being the difference between the two mentioned above and essentially the pattern of the window fringing field, the other being the ordinary mode pattern, perhaps one or the other of the modes mentioned above.

Returning to the argument for the filled cavity, we see that to match this approximation we need *two* new dynamic variables to describe the paramagnetic polarization. This is enough to describe the class of acceptable equivalent circuits. We give a physically intuitive sample in Fig. 31.

The values of the parameters in the chosen equivalent circuit can, in principle, be determined from a solution for the normal modes of the system. It is much better for the experimenter to relate the circuit parameters to the physically measurable behavior of the structure, as was done in Section IV. For this reason the choice,

[22] J. C. Slater, "Microwave Electronics," D. Van Nostrand Company, Inc., New York, N. Y., p. 74; 1950.
K. Kurokawa, "The expansion of electromagnetic fields in cavities," IRE Trans. on Microwave Theory and Techniques, vol. MTT-6, pp. 178–187; April, 1958.

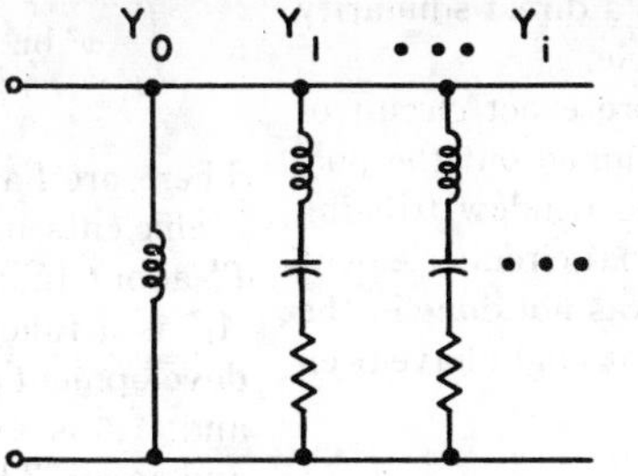

Fig. 28—Conventional equivalent circuit for normal-mode expansion of cavity impedance.

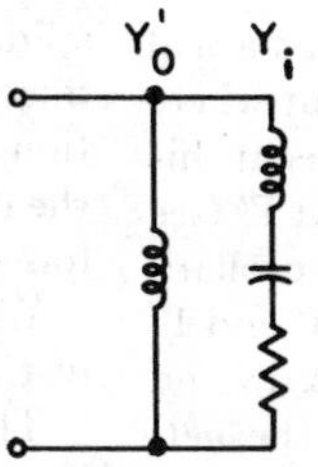

Fig. 29—Approximate circuit near an isolated resonance.

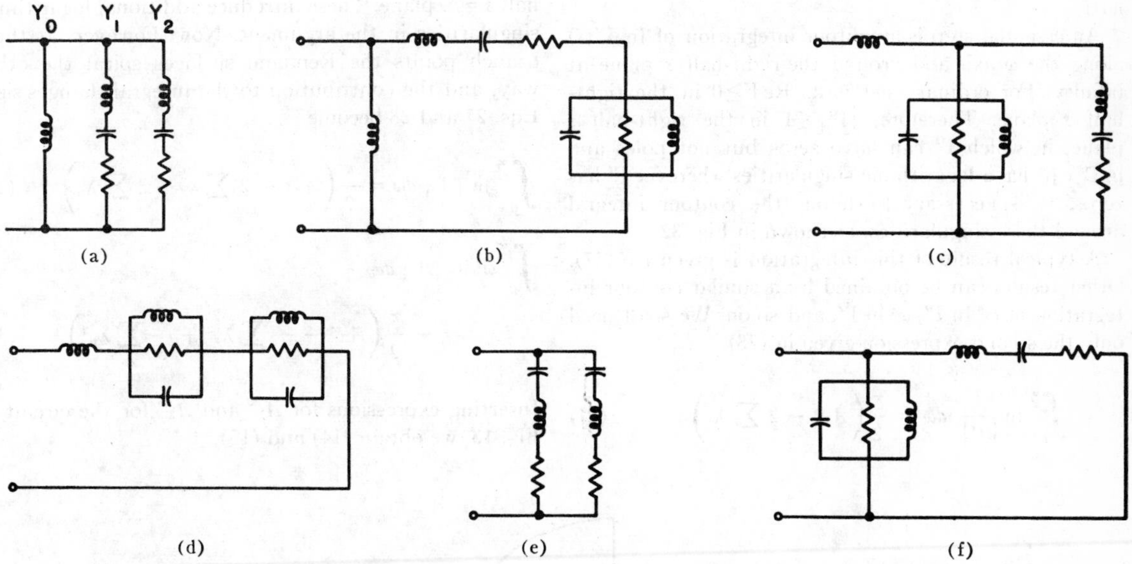

Fig. 30—Forms of approximate equivalent circuits near a pair of isolated resonances. (e) and (f) have the reference plane chosen to simplify the representation.

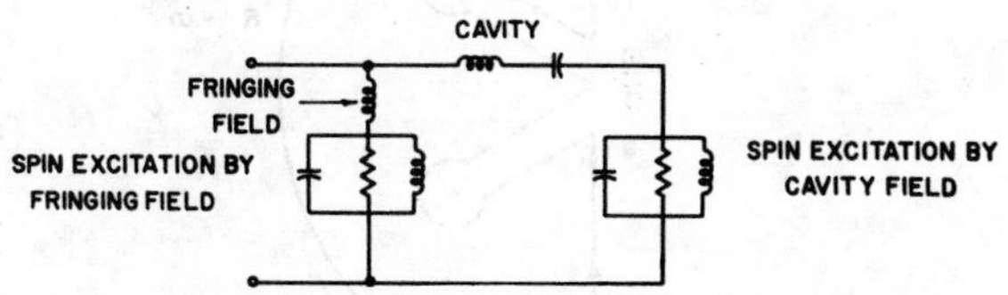

Fig. 31—Equivalent circuit for single ruby-filled cavity, including the action of the window-coupling field on the ruby resonance.

when possible, of a circuit that bears a direct similarity to the structure is extremely desirable.

Our analysis does not use the more exact circuit of Fig. 31. If we had intentionally machined out the portion of the ruby in the region of the window fringing field, the introduction of the additional circuit element would have been unnecessary. This was not done in the experiments, although it appears that it might have been a good idea.

APPENDIX II

EXTENSION OF FANO'S ANALYSIS TO THE $-L$ AND $-C$ SITUATION

We do not need to repeat the entire mathematical analysis of Fano,[9] but it is necessary to point out where changes or modifications must be made. He began his analysis by investigating the reflection coefficient Γ' (see Fig. 14). Then he argued that $|\Gamma'| = |\Gamma|$ as a corollary of the reciprocal nature of the network where Γ and Γ' are defined by the positive G equivalents of Figs. 13 and 14. The impedance levels at the two ports of the network do not influence the result directly, if it is understood that the Γ's are defined in terms of the respective conductances, $+G$ on the right and a chosen Z_0 on the left.

An essential step is a contour integration of $\ln \Gamma'(s)$ along the ω axis and around the right-half s plane at infinity. For ordinary networks $\text{Re}\, Y \geq 0$ in the right-half s plane. Therefore, $|\Gamma'| \leq 1$ in the right-half s plane, in which Γ' can have zeros but not poles and $\ln \Gamma'$ can have logarithmic singularities wherever Γ' has zeros. It is necessary to detour the contour integral around these singularities, as shown in Fig. 32.

A typical result of this integration is given by (27). Other results can be obtained by a similar contour integration of $\omega^2 \ln \Gamma'$, $\omega^4 \ln \Gamma'$, and so on. We shall need only the second expression given in (28).

$$\int_0^\infty \ln \frac{1}{|\Gamma|}\, d\omega = \frac{\pi}{2}\left(A_1^\infty - 2 \sum_z \lambda_z\right) \tag{27}$$

$$\int_0^\infty \omega^2 \ln \frac{1}{|\Gamma|}\, d\omega = -\frac{\pi}{2}\left(A_3^\infty - \frac{2}{3} \sum_z \lambda_z^3\right). \tag{28}$$

These are Fano's equations (21) and (22).[9] The A's are coefficients in a Laurent expansion of the argument $\ln \Gamma'$ about infinity. A major point of the theory is that A_1^∞ is a function of *only* the first element of a ladder development of the entire network, starting at the right, and A_3^∞ is a function of *only* the first two elements, and so on. This is not at all obvious; the proof is given by Fano.[9] The λ's are the values of s at the logarithmic singularities in the right half-plane. There are no residues at these points, but they form branch points of a spiral-staircase nature for the logarithmic function. Successive Riemann surfaces have values of the function differing by $2\pi j$ at all points. The contribution of the detour out and back to the contour integral is therefore $2\pi j\lambda$.

We are now able to make the necessary modifications in the theory.

The argument for $|\Gamma| = |\Gamma'|$ is still valid, for reciprocity is not related to the sign of C. Changing the sign of G results in the inversion of $|\Gamma|$. The new factor in the problem is the presence of poles of Γ' in the right-half $s = j\omega$ plane. These introduce additional logarithmic singularities in the argument. Now, however, at these branch points the Reimann surfaces spiral the other way, and the contribution to the integral changes sign. Eqs. 27 and 28 become

$$\int_0^\infty \ln |\Gamma|\, d\omega = \frac{\pi}{2}\left(A_1^\infty - 2 \sum_z \lambda_z + 2 \sum_p \lambda_p\right) \tag{29}$$

$$\int_0^\infty \omega^2 \ln |\Gamma|\, d\omega = -\frac{\pi}{2}\left(A_3^\infty - \frac{2}{3} \sum_z \lambda_z^3 + \frac{2}{3} \sum_p \lambda_p^3\right). \tag{30}$$

Inserting expressions for A_1^∞ and A_3^∞ for the circuit of Fig. 13, we obtain (14) and (15).

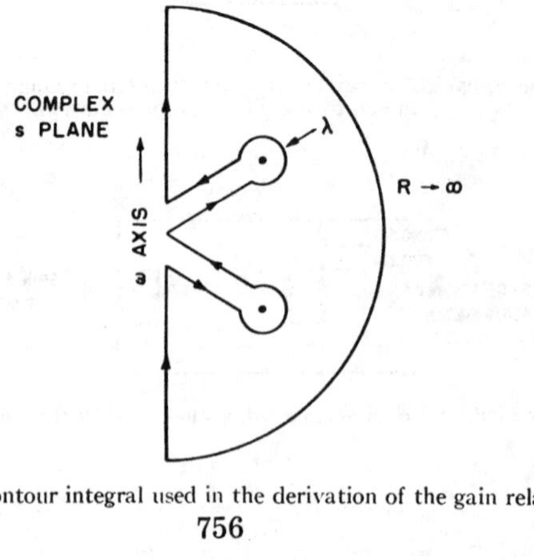

Fig. 32—Contour integral used in the derivation of the gain relations.

Appendix III

Optimum Pole-Zero Configuration

It can be shown that the low-pass circuit that we have been using must have just *one* pole of Γ' in the right-half s plane because the network starts with a single negative element. A plausibility argument may be made as follows: Looking in at aa' (Fig. 14) in the absence of the negative capacitance we see that Y will have a positive real part in the right half-plane and thus neither poles nor zeros. Now by adding $-sC$ to the admittance, we add a simple pole at ∞ but none in the right half-plane. However, far enough to the right in the half-plane, the real part must become arbitrarily large and negative. There must be at least one point on the positive real s-axis where $Y=-1$, and at this point there is a pole of Γ'. To show the absence of any additional poles of Γ', we consider the locus of Re $Y=-1$ in the right half-plane. This contour cannot cross the imaginary axis, and it cannot form loops or be multiply connected because there are no singularities. All that Im Y can do along this locus is behave monotonically, going to infinity at $s=\pm\infty$. Hence, there are no other points where $Y=-1$, and no other poles of Γ'.

Critics may object that this is a strange argument to make about a circuit that is only claimed to be a valid representation over a small frequency range, but the behavior of the structure should approximate the behavior of the idealized network in this frequency range.

A number of zeros of Γ' are possible, however. We should maximize $(\lambda_p-\Sigma\lambda_z)$ in (15) and keep $(\lambda_p^3-\Sigma\lambda_z^3)$ below a fixed limit in order to keep the expression in (16) positive. Now

$$[\lambda_p^3 - \sum \lambda_z^3] = [\lambda_p - \sum \lambda_z] \cdot\left[\lambda_p^2 + \lambda_p(\sum \lambda_z) + (\sum \lambda_z^2) + \frac{(\sum \lambda_z)^3 - \sum \lambda_z^3}{(\lambda_p - \sum \lambda_z)}\right]. \quad (31)$$

This expression is to be minimized while $(\lambda_p-\Sigma\lambda_z)$ is maximized, hence the last expression in brackets is to be minimized. All terms are positive—it takes a little algebra to show that $(\Sigma\lambda_2)^3-\Sigma\lambda_z^3$ is positive. Therefore, for best gain-bandwidth performance, $\Sigma\lambda_z=0$, and there are no zeros in the right half of the s plane.

Acknowledgment

The authors would like to express their appreciation to Dr. T. Ogawa of Doshida University, Kyoto, Japan, for his assistance with these experiments.

Reprinted from the PROCEEDINGS OF THE IRE
VOL. 50, NO. 7, JULY, 1962

Comments on Frequency-Pulling of Maser Oscillators*

C. H. TOWNES
Columbia University, New York, New York
(Received May 14, 1957)

THE frequency of oscillation of a beam-type maser oscillator is "pulled" from the resonance frequency v_0 of the molecules by the tuning of the cavity an amount[1]

$$v-v_0=Q/Q_l(v_c-v_0)f(n), \tag{1}$$

where v_c is the resonance frequency of the cavity, Q and Q_l are the quality factors for the cavity and molecular resonance, respectively (and inversely proportional to their resonance widths), and $f(n)$ is a function of the order unity which depends on n, the number of molecules entering the cavity per second. For a beam of uniform velocity, $f(n)$ decreases monotonically with increasing n.[1] For a Maxwellian distribution of velocities, Helmer and Lamb[2,3] have shown that $v-v_0$ initially increases with increasing n, and then decreases. This result may be surprising at first consideration, and experimental results[3] have not confirmed this initial increase in $v-v_0$. We shall discuss its physical origin, and indicate a possible reason why it was not observed.

When n is very small, most of the microwave energy delivered to the cavity may come from a relatively small group of rather slow molecules, since they stay in the cavity a long time, and the probability of transition for weak fields is proportional to the square of this time, or inversely to the square of the velocity. These slow molecules have a resonance which is sharper than that for faster molecules, and hence give the equivalent of a larger effective Q_l. As n is increased, faster molecules yield a larger fraction of the energy, and the effective value of Q_l may be considered to have decreased. Such an effect can be demonstrated mathematically.

Assume that there are two groups of molecules entering the cavity with velocities v_1 and v_2 and abundance n_1 and n_2, respectively. A treatment similar to that of Helmer and Lamb shows that if the oscillating field in the cavity is very weak, then the change in pulling with increasing field strength in the cavity is proportional to

$$p=-\frac{1}{v_1^2}\left\{\frac{n_1/n_2+(v_1/v_2)^3}{n_1/n_2+v_1/v_2}-\frac{3[n_1/n_2+(v_1/v_2)^4]}{5[n_1/n_2+(v_1/v_2)^2]}\right\}, \tag{2}$$

where a negative value of p indicates less pulling.

Now if v_1/v_2 is neither fairly large nor fairly small, p is negative for all values of n_1/n_2, showing that for two velocity groups which are not very different the pulling always decreases with increasing n. However, if v_1/v_2 is either large or small, then p may become positive for particular values of n_1/n_2. Thus for $v_1/v_2=\frac{1}{2}$, p is always negative. For $v_1/v_2=\frac{1}{10}$, p is negative for n_1/n_2 either very large or very small (i.e., for molecules of essentially a single velocity). However, for n_1/n_2 in the range between 1/10 and 1/100, p is positive, indicating more pulling with increasing power (still under the assumption that the power is rather small).

A continuous distribution of velocities, such as a Maxwellian distribution, is of course more complicated, but must evidently contain groups of molecules with rather widely different velocities if the pulling is to initially increase with increasing numbers of molecules. For an actual maser, scattering of the molecular beam and the limited solid angle accepted by the cavity tend to decrease the effectiveness of the very slow molecules of the Maxwellian distribution. These effects, and the importance of the very slow molecules in determining theoretical behavior of pulling, are presumably the reasons why no increase in the pulling has actually been observed.

* Work supported jointly by the Signal Corps, the Office of Naval Research, and the Air Force Office of Scientific Research.

1 Shimoda, Wang, and Townes, Phys. Rev. 102, 1308 (1956).
2 W. E. Lamb and J. C. Helmer, Stanford University Microwave Laboratory Technical Report No. ML-311 (1956).
3 J. C. Helmer, J. Appl. Phys. 28, 212 (1957).

Reprinted from JOURNAL OF APPLIED PHYSICS, Vol. 31, No. 4, 740–741, April, 1960

Spontaneous Emission from an Inverted Spin System

AMNON YARIV
Bell Telephone Laboratories, Incorporated, Murray Hill, New Jersey
(Received December 16, 1959)

THIS paper summarizes the results of calculations made in an attempt to explain the origin of the observed modulation effects in two-level maser experiments.[1,2]

In a spontaneously oscillating spin system any transverse magnetization, which couples rf power out of the spin system, is due to the presence of a transverse rf field, which is in turn induced by the transverse magnetization. Any consideration of the dynamics of the spin system or the build-up of the radiation field must consequently treat the two systems simultaneously.

Our analysis uses a model first formulated by Bloembergen and Pound,[3] except that our problem is inherently nonlinear[4] and we cannot make the simplifying assumption $M_z=\text{const}$, which linearizes the equations of motion, and are forced to have recourse to an IBM 704.

The physical situation is that of an inverted, homogeneously broadened, magnetization of amplitude M_0 placed inside a microwave cavity which can support a circularly polarized transverse magnetic field. If we take the spin precession frequency γH_0 to be equal to the cavity resonant frequency $(LC)^{-\frac{1}{2}}$, assume that no external power is fed into the cavity, and that the spin lattice relaxation time T_1 is infinite, we can write a set of three nonlinear simultaneous differential equations.

$$\frac{2j\omega}{T_R|M_0\gamma|}M_1+\frac{2}{T_R|M_0\gamma|}\frac{dM_1}{dt}+Q\frac{dH_1}{dt}+\omega H_1=0, \tag{1}$$

$$\frac{dM_1}{dt}-j\gamma M_zH_1+\frac{M_1}{T_2}=0, \tag{2}$$

$$\frac{dM_z}{dt}=\text{Im}[\gamma M_1{}^*H_1]. \tag{3}$$

Equations (1)–(3) appear in a slightly different form in footnote 3. M_1 and H_1 are complex and are defined by

$$M_x+jM_y=M_1e^{j\omega t} \tag{4}$$

and

$$H_x+jH_y=H_1e^{j\omega t}, \tag{5}$$

where M_x, M_y, H_x, and H_y are the transverse components of the magnetization and magnetic field, respectively. γ is the magnetogyric ratio. T_R is the radiation damping time defined by

$$T_R=(2\pi\eta|\gamma M_0|Q)^{-1}.$$

η is the sample filling factor, Q is the loaded "Q" of the cavity. T_2 is the spin-spin relaxation time which for a homogenous Lorentizian line is given by

$$T_2=2/\gamma\Delta H=2/\Delta\omega,$$

where ΔH is the separation in gauss between the half power points. $M_1{}^*$ is the complex conjugate of M_1. Since M_z, H_1, and M_1 are functions of time. Equations (1)–(3) constitute a set of nonlinear differential equations. The solution was carried out with

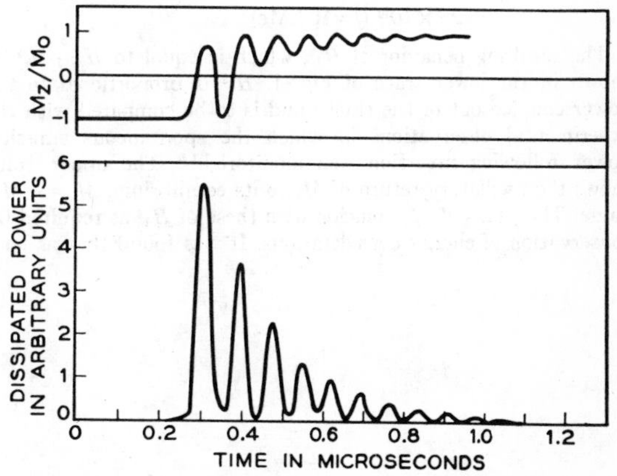

FIG. 1. Upper trace: $M_z(t)/M_0$ vs t following spin inversion at $t=0$. $M_0=5\times10^{-4}$. Lower trace: $(H_i{}^2+H_r{}^2)/M_0{}^2$ which is proportioned to the power coupled out of the cavity is shown as a function of the time following the spin inversion, $M_0=5\times10^{-4}$.

the aid of an IBM 704. For numerical purposes it was necessary to consider the following set of equations which are the real and imaginary parts of Eqs. (1)–(3)

$$aM_r+b\frac{dM_i}{dt}+Q\frac{dH_i}{dt}+\omega H_i=0, \tag{6}$$

$$-aM_i+b\frac{dM_r}{dt}+Q\frac{dH_r}{dt}+\omega H_r=0, \tag{7}$$

$$\frac{dM_i}{dt}+|\gamma|M_zH_r+CM_i=0, \tag{8}$$

$$\frac{dM_r}{dt}-|\gamma|M_zH_i+CM_r=0, \tag{9}$$

and

$$\frac{dM_z}{dt}+|\gamma|M_rH_i-|\gamma|M_iH_r=0, \tag{10}$$

where

$$M_1=M_r+jM_i,$$

$$H_1=H_r+jH_i,$$

$$a=\frac{2\omega}{T_R|M_0\gamma|}=4\pi\omega\eta Q,$$

$$b=\frac{2}{T_R|M_0\gamma|}=4\pi\eta Q,$$

and

$$c=1/T_2.$$

Since we are dealing with an inverted magnetization, our first boundary condition is $M_z(0) = -M_0$. This constitutes an unstable equilibrium and some mechanism is necessary to trigger the spontaneous emission. This could be either some residual transverse magnetization or some cavity current present at $t=0$. We used the residual current for a trigger and put $H_r(0) = 0.1M_0$. The magnitude of $H_r(0)$ was found to have little effect on the subsequent behavior of the magnetization.

The values of ω, Q, and M_0 were chosen to approximate the experimental conditions prevailing at the two-level maser experiment performed by Chester, Wagner, and Castle of Westinghouse.[2] These are

$$M_0 = 5\times10^{-4} \text{ gauss } (10^{18} \text{ spins at } 4.20\text{K}),$$
$$Q = 10\,000,$$

and

$$\omega = 2\pi\times10^{10} \ (f = 10 \text{ kMc}).$$

The resulting behavior of H_1^2, which is equal to $H_r^2+H_i^2$, is shown in the lower trace of Fig. 1. H_1^2 is proportional to the power coupled out of the cavity and is to be compared with the experimental observations in which the spontaneous emission power following inversion was monitored.[1,2] The upper trace shows the oscillatory return of M_z to its equilibrium, $M_z = +M_0$, value. The peaks of M_z coincide with these of H_1^2 as required by conservation of energy considerations. It was found that as long as $T_r < T_2$ which is the start oscillation condition for a two-level maser oscillator, T_2 had a negligible effect on the shape of the curves and could be assumed to be infinite. The behavior of H_1^2 bears a close resemblance to the experimental results—especially those of the Westinghouse Group.[2] A significant difference remains—the time interval between power peaks in Fig. 1 is ~0.1 μsec while the observed results give ~1 μsec. This difference may be due to the actual inhomogenous nature of the line, in contrast to the homogenous line assumed in our analysis. The envelope curve, traced through the successive oscillation peaks, decays with a characteristic time corresponding to the cavity Q, i.e.,

$$T_{\text{envelope}} \approx Q/\omega.$$

This feature is retained regardless of the magnitude of M_0. The interval between peaks depends on M_0. This dependence is not very strong and using a value of M_0 which is smaller by a factor of 15 than that used in Fig. 1 yielded a value of ~0.3 μsec which is closer to the experimentally observed values.

The author is indebted to J. P. Gordon for some helpful discussions and to Miss J. Liu for carrying out the numerical computation.

[1] G. Feher, J. Gordon, E. Buehler, E. Gere, and C. Thurmond, Phys. Rev. **109**, 221 (1958).
[2] P. F. Chester, P. E. Wagner, and J. G. Castle, Jr., Phys. Rev. **110**, 281 (1958).
[3] N. Bloembergen and R. V. Pound, Phys. Rev. **95**, 8 (1954).
[4] A. Yariv, J. R. Singer, and J. Kemp, J. Appl. Phys. **30**, 265 (1959).

Reprinted from THE PHYSICAL REVIEW, Vol. 109, No. 1, 221–222, January 1, 1958

Spontaneous Emission of Radiation from an Electron Spin System

G. FEHER, J. P. GORDON, E. BUEHLER, E. A. GERE, AND C. D. THURMOND
Bell Telephone Laboratories, Murray Hill, New Jersey
(Received November 4, 1957)

IT was pointed out by Combrisson, Honig, and Townes[1] that under certain conditions energy which has been stored in a spin system may be spontaneously and coherently radiated into a resonant cavity at the Larmor precession frequency of the spins. In this note we wish to report the direct observation of such an emission.

If the magnetization which appears in a spin system in thermal equilibrium in an applied dc magnetic field H_0 is inverted by a 180° rf pulse or an adiabatic fast passage, the energy W put into the system is $W=gN\mu^2H_0^2/kT$, where N is the total number of spins, μ is the Bohr magneton, and g is the electronic g value. The condition for spontaneous reradiation of this energy is[1]

$$N\geq kTV_c\Delta H\langle H_v^2\rangle_{\text{Av}}/(4\pi Q_L\mu^2H_0\langle H_s^2\rangle_{\text{Av}}),$$

where Q_L and V_c are the loaded Q and volume of the cavity, ΔH is the full width at half maximum of the spin resonance line, and $\langle H_s^2\rangle_{\text{Av}}$ and $\langle H_v^2\rangle_{\text{Av}}$ are the squares of the microwave fields averaged over the sample and cavity respectively. In previous experiments[1] phosphorus donors in silicon were used, but the above condition was not satisfied, and hence spontaneous oscillations were not observed.

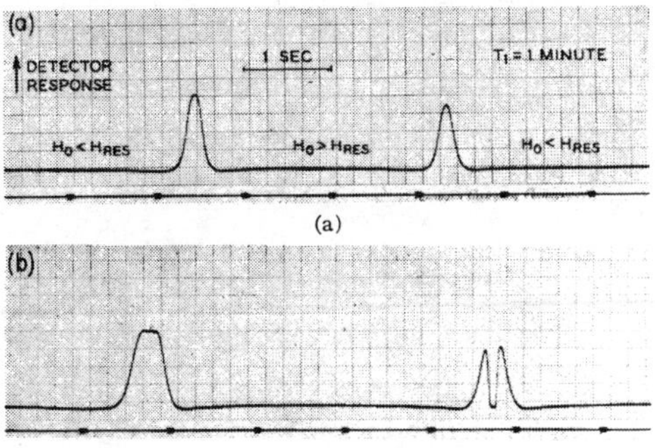

(a)

(b)

FIG. 1. Adiabatic fast passage through one phosphorus hyperfine line in silicon-28 at 1.2°K and ~9000 Mc/sec. In Fig. 1(a) the dc magnetic field was on for less than the relaxation time; the resulting small magnetization did not satisfy the oscillation condition. In Fig. 1(b) the oscillation condition was satisfied. Note that as a result of the emission the magnetization at the center of the line is destroyed.

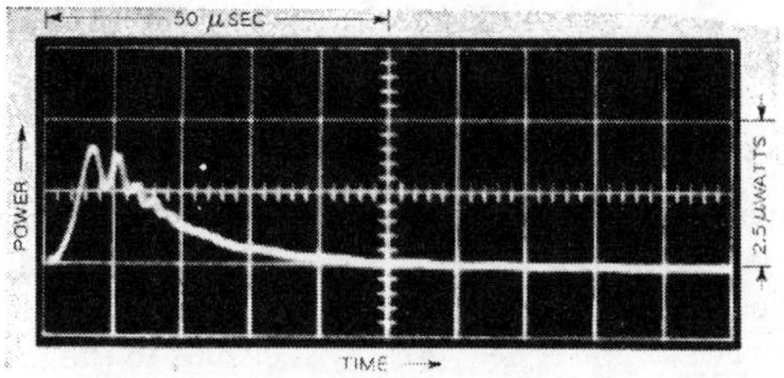

FIG. 2. Power output delivered by the spin system with the microwave oscillator turned off. The area under the curve agrees with calculated energy stored previously in the spin system.

In the present experiments, the spin resonance, which is inhomogeneously broadened by hyperfine interactions of the donor electrons with the Si^{29} nuclei,[2] was narrowed from 2.7 oersteds in width to 0.22 oersted through the use of a crystal of isotopically purified silicon[3] [estimated final isotopic purity (99.88±0.08)% Si^{28}]. As a result the oscillation condition was easily satisfied.

The sample used in this experiment had a volume of about 0.3 cm³ and a phosphorus concentration of 4×10^{16} atoms/cm³. Its relaxation time at the operating temperature of 1.2°K was one minute; however, this can be greatly reduced by shining light on the sample[4] or otherwise injecting carriers into it. The cavity was resonant at ~9 kMc/sec, and its loaded Q at 1.2°K was ~20 000.

In Fig. 1 we show the observed signals under adiabatic fast passage conditions. In Fig. 1(a) the oscillation condition *is not* satisfied. Going slowly from a magnetic field below resonance to one above, the magnetization of the sample is inverted and its energy increased. If we now slowly reduce the field to below resonance before the spins relax appreciably, we return the magnetization to its equilibrium value. In Fig. 1(b) the oscillation condition *is* satisfied. The trace shows

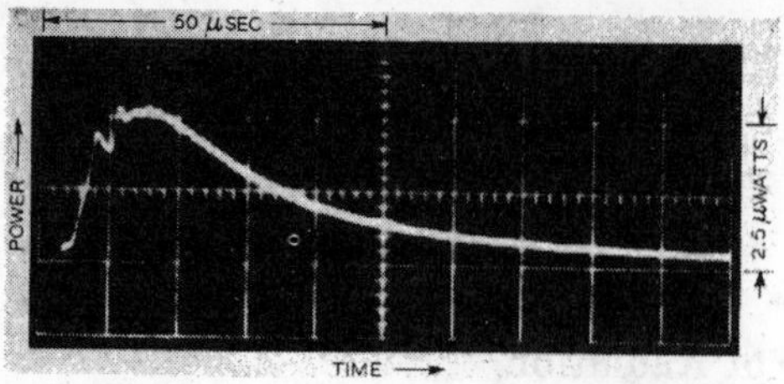

FIG. 3. Same as Fig. 2 with a large magnetization. The spin system was equilibrated at 8000 oersteds before letting it oscillate at 3000 oersteds.

that the magnetization near the center of the line is destroyed through reradiation which occurs during the first passage.

This immediate emission may be avoided conveniently either by decreasing Q_L or by increasing ΔH during the first passage. We increased ΔH by introducing a field inhomogeneity which was removed after the magnetization was turned over. Then we turned off the microwave signal generator and returned the magnetic field to resonance. Figure 2 shows the pulse of microwave power delivered by the spins to the cavity at this time. The maximum amplitude of the rf field in the cavity during the pulse was of order ΔH. This limit is imposed since the negative susceptibility of the sample decreases at greater field strengths. After the spontaneous oscillation was over, the residual magnetization could be detected by turning on the signal klystron and again observing a fast passage signal. It was found that the magnetization associated with the central portion of the line had inverted itself during the oscillation. The observed energy output obtained from the area under the curves of Figs. 2 and 3, and corrected for the cavity coupling (reflection coefficient $=0.94$), corresponded roughly to that given up by the spin system. By equilibrating the magnetization at a higher field, a larger output was obtained, as shown in Fig. 3.

The traces of Figs. 2 and 3 show a superimposed amplitude modulation which gradually diminishes, and has a frequency of approximately the line width. The exact origin of this effect is not clear at present. It presumably arises from an interference between different spin packets within the line.

We wish to thank Mr. M. Kowalchik for his assistance in preparing the sample.

[1] Combrisson, Honig, and Townes, Compt. rend. **242**, 2451 (1956).

[2] Fletcher, Yager, Pearson, and Merritt, Phys. Rev. **95**, 844 (1954).

[3] We are indebted to the Isotope Division, Oak Ridge, Tennessee, for supplying us with 5 grams of an equal-mole mixture of Si and SiO_2 ($99.98\pm0.02\%$ Si^{28}). This was purified by us by making use of an aluminum reduction step, followed by a solution-precipitation step with molten tin. This procedure permitted 90% of the silicon to be recovered as fusible crystallites. This material was subsequently zone refined and doped with phosphorus to the desired concentration.

[4] G. Feher and R. C. Fletcher, Bull. Am. Phys. Soc., Ser. II **1**, 125 (1956).

Super-Radiation and Super-Regeneration*

C. GREIFINGER† AND G. BIRNBAUM‡

Summary—**The transient behavior of a two-level spin system coupled to an electric circuit is investigated by using the equations of Bloembergen and Pound.[1] The equations are solved, in the limit where the circuit ringing time is very short compared with all other characteristic times, for two cases: 1) the spin-lattice and spin-spin relaxation times both infinite, with an externally applied driving field, and 2) the spin-lattice relaxation time infinite but the spin-spin relaxation time finite, in the absence of an external field. In case 1), it is shown that the motion of an initially inverted magnetization under the action of an applied signal consists roughly of two stages: in the first stage, the effect of radiation damping is unimportant and the motion of the system is determined principally by the applied signal via the ordinary Bloch equations, whereas in the second stage, the motion is essentially the same as if the applied signal had been turned off and only radiation damping were present. In case 2), it is shown that a delayed peak in the emitted radiation should be observed under certain conditions. The delayed peak condition is identical with that derived by Bloom. Curves are presented showing the peak power and the time at which the delayed peak occurs as functions of the relevant parameters. In connection with the ordinary maser behavior of a two-level spin system, it is shown that for values of the parameters typical of steady-state maser amplification, the effects of radiation damping should be unimportant. Finally, systems are examined for which the radiation damping time is much shorter than all other characteristic times (super-regenerative systems). It is indicated how such systems might be operated as one-shot multivibrators or as linear amplifiers. For the latter type of operation, an expression for the gain is derived which is found to be similar to that encountered in ordinary circuit theory.**

INTRODUCTION

In this paper we investigate, in connection with possible maser application, the transient behavior of a two-level spin system which has been put into an excited state. The equations of Bloembergen and Pound,[2] which are the Bloch equations modified by the inclusion of additional terms to describe the interaction between the radiating magnetization and the electric circuit containing the sample, are the starting point of our treatment. Bloembergen and Pound have shown, in particular, that this interaction can give rise to spontaneous coherent radiation by the sample, and they obtain an approximate expression for the spontaneous decay of the magnetization under conditions where T_1, the spin-lattice relaxation time, and T_2, the spin-spin relaxation time, may be considered infinite. We here extend their treatment to two additional cases of interest: 1) to the decay, under the action of an externally applied signal, of a magnetic spin system for which T_1 and T_2 may be considered infinite, and 2) to the spontaneous decay of a magnetic spin system for which T_1 may be considered infinite but for which T_2 is finite.

These cases have been considered independently by Bloom[3] in a broader investigation of the effects of radiation damping on the dynamics of a spin system. In his analysis, however, the coupling between the spin system and the electric circuit is approximated by augmenting the Bloch equations with terms proportional to the transverse component of the magnetization, representing the radiation damping field. We start from the Bloembergen and Pound equations, which describe the coupled system, and show that they reduce to such a formulation of the problem, in first approximation, provided that the circuit ringing time is short enough. If the circuit ringing time is comparable with or greater than the radiation damping time, the coupling between the spin system and circuit cannot be considered in this simple way and such a formulation is no longer valid. In addition, we discuss in greater detail, with a view toward possible maser application, some of the physical implications of the results.

SPIN-LATTICE AND SPIN-SPIN RELAXATION TIMES INFINITE

The Bloembergen and Pound equations of motion describing the complete system (Fig. 1) consisting of magnetic material in a constant magnetic field H_0 in the z-direction and two crossed coils parallel to the x and y directions, respectively, may be written:

$$\frac{K}{L}\frac{dM^+}{d\tau} + \frac{di^+}{d\tau} + \frac{\tau_R}{\tau_c} i^+ + \omega_c^2\tau_R^2 \int_0^\tau i^+ \, d\tau = \frac{\tau_R}{L} V^+, \quad (1)$$

$$\frac{dM^+}{d\tau} = -j\gamma\tau_R M^+ H_0 - M^+ \frac{\tau_R}{T_2} + j\gamma\tau_R M_z K' i^+, \quad (2)$$

$$\frac{dM_z}{d\tau} = -Im\,(\gamma\tau_R K' M^{+*} i^+) - (M_z - M_0)\frac{\tau_R}{T_1}. \quad (3)$$

We have taken the two electrical circuits in Fig. 1 to have identical circuit constants $L_x = L_y = L$, $C_x = C_y = C$, and $R_x = R_y = R$, where R includes the circuit, generator, and detector resistances. This circuit arrangement allows rotating fields to be produced. $M^+ = M_x + jM_y$ is the component of the magnetic moment per unit volume transverse to the steady field H_0, written as a com-

* Manuscript received by the PGED, September 18, 1958; revised manuscript received, February 9, 1959. This work was supported in part by the U. S. Army Signal Corps.

† The RAND Corp., Santa Monica, Calif. Formerly at Res. Labs., Hughes Aircraft Co., Culver City, Calif.

‡ Res. Labs., Hughes Aircraft Co., Culver City, Calif.

[1] N. Bloembergen and R. V. Pound, "Radiation damping in magnetic resonance experiments," *Phys. Rev.*, vol. 95, pp. 8–12; July, 1954.

[2] *Ibid.*, p. 9.

[3] S. Bloom, "Effects of radiation damping on spin dynamics," *J. Appl. Phys.*, vol. 28, pp. 800–805; July, 1957.

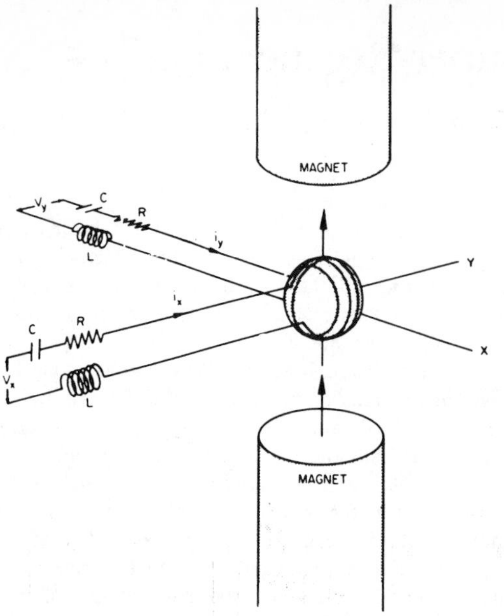

Fig. 1—Arrangement of electrical circuits and paramagnetic substance.

plex function. The x and y components, V_x and V_y, of the driving force have been written as the real and imaginary parts of one complex function, $V^+ = V_x + jV_y$. The currents in the two circuits have similarly been written in terms of $i^+ = i_x + ji_y$. K and K' are geometrical factors, K being the ratio of the transverse component of the magnetic field produced at each coil to the current in that coil, and K' being essentially the mutual inductance between each electrical circuit and the "circuit" formed by the (rotating) magnetization. K and K' are related to each other by $KK' = 4\pi L\xi$, ξ being the sample filling factor. M_0 is the magnetization per unit volume appropriate for a constant magnetic field H_0, $\tau_c = Q_L/\omega_c$ is the ringing time of the circuit without sample, $Q_L = \omega_c L/R$, $\tau_R = (2\pi\xi M_0 Q_L \gamma)^{-1}$ is the radiation damping time, and $\tau = t/\tau_R$ is the time in units of τ_R. In the expression for τ_R, γ is the ratio of the angular frequency of free precession of the magnetization in a constant magnetic field to the field.

We first consider the case where the spin-lattice relaxation time, T_1, and the spin-spin relaxation time, T_2, are both infinite. It is assumed that the magnetization is initially at 180° with respect to the applied field. In practice, the magnetization may be inverted either by adiabatic fast passage or by a 180° pulse. Because of practical limitations, the magnetization will, in general, not be at exactly 180°, but tipped from 180° through some small angle δ_0. As the subsequent analysis for T_2 finite will show, if the initial angle is not exactly 180° and if the magnetization and circuit are resonant near the same frequency, the state may not be a stable one. Under certain conditions, the transverse component of the magnetization, however small, will induce a signal in the circuit, and the reaction of the induced signal on the magnetization will cause the system to radiate away all its energy in a time of the order of a few τ_R (radiation damping). A 180° state may be achieved by changing the resonant frequency of the circuit or of the magnetization immediately after the magnetization is inverted, *e.g.*, by detuning the circuit or pulsing the magnetic field. If the resonant frequencies of circuit and magnetization are separated by a few line widths, the voltage induced in the circuit by the transverse component of the magnetization will see essentially infinite impedance. Consequently, no current will be induced in the circuit; *i.e.*, there will be no radiation damping field and the equations of motion for the magnetization will be the ordinary Bloch equations. These equations show that after a time of the order of a few T_2, the transverse component of the magnetization becomes negligibly small. Therefore, if we wait for a time of this order after inverting the system, we will have essentially an exact 180° state. We can then return the circuit and magnetization to the same frequency and apply a small external signal. All of this, of course, must occur in a time short compared with T_1, since in this time the energy stored in the spin system is returned to the lattice.

After the system has been prepared in the manner described above, and in a time short compared with T_1, a steady signal is applied at the resonant frequency (which is assumed to be the same for the circuit and the magnetization). The subsequent motion of the magnetization vector is governed by the Bloembergen and Pound equations.

The equations are most easily treated by the usual procedure of transforming to a coördinate system rotating with angular frequency $\omega_0 = \gamma H_0$ (Fig. 2). Thus we set

$$i^+ = i(\tau)e^{-j\omega_0\tau_R\tau}, \tag{4a}$$

$$M^+ = M(\tau)e^{-j\omega_0\tau_R\tau}, \tag{4b}$$

$$V^+ = V(\tau)e^{-j\omega_0\tau_R\tau}, \tag{4c}$$

where $i(\tau)$, $M(\tau)$, and $V(\tau)$ are complex quantities. If we now set $V(\tau) = V_0(\tau)\, e^{j\chi}$, where V_0 is a real function and χ is a phase factor, and substitute (4) into (1), (2), and (3), we obtain, after some manipulation,

$$2\frac{M}{M_0} + \frac{1}{M_z}\frac{dM}{d\tau} = j\gamma H_1 \tau_R e^{j\chi} \tag{5}$$

where H_1 is defined by

$$K'\frac{V_0}{R} = K' i_0 \equiv H_1 \tag{6}$$

and represents the field produced at the sample by the applied signal only. In deriving (5), we have neglected terms of relative order $1/\omega_0\tau_R$ and τ_c/τ_R. Eq. (5) is therefore not valid if the circuit ringing time is comparable with or greater than the radiation damping time.

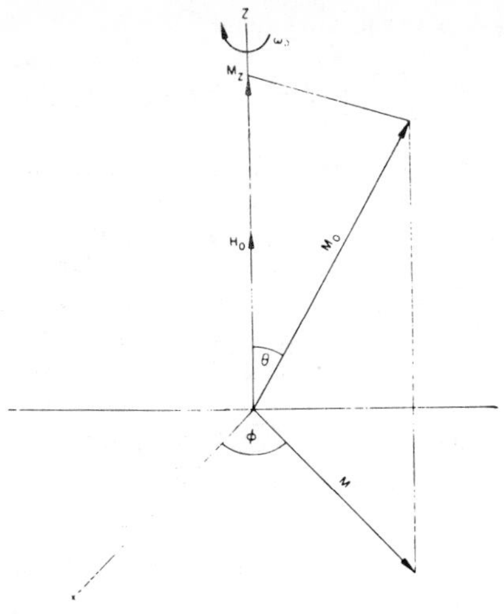

Fig. 2—Vector representation of the magnetization in polar coordinates. Axes are rotating with angular frequency ω_o with respect to fixed set of axes.

If we transform to polar coordinates, (Fig. 2), writing $M_z = M_0 \cos\theta$, $M = M_0 \sin\theta\, e^{i\phi}$, the real and imaginary parts of (5) yield the two coupled equations

$$2\sin\theta + \frac{d\theta}{d\tau} = -\gamma H_1 \tau_R \sin(\chi - \phi) \tag{7a}$$

and

$$\tan\theta \frac{d\phi}{d\tau} = \gamma H_1 \tau_R \cos(\chi - \phi). \tag{7b}$$

If the magnetization vector is initially at 180° (or 0°) the transverse component of the magnetization is that induced by the applied RF field and is therefore perpendicular to this field. The solution for ϕ is then[4]

$$\chi - \phi = \pm\frac{\pi}{2} \tag{8}$$

and the θ-equation becomes[5]

$$\frac{d\theta}{d\tau} = \pm\gamma H_1 \tau_R - 2\sin\theta, \tag{9}$$

the minus sign applying when the magnetization is initially at 180° (stimulated emission) and the plus sign when the magnetization is initially at 0° (absorption). If the magnetization has already been tipped through some angle when the RF field is applied, the initial phase angle, $\chi - \phi_0$, between applied field and the already existing transverse component of magnetization will be some arbitrary angle. Eqs. (7a) and (7b) show that, unless this angle is $\pm\pi/2$, $\chi - \phi$ will not remain constant; *i.e.*, a "dragging" occurs between the applied field and the transverse component of magnetization. This must be taken into account when one considers the effect of noise on such a system, since noise consists essentially of a series of pulses of uncorrelated phase applied with arbitrary phase to the already rotating magnetization.

Let us consider the case where the magnetization is initially at 180°. The first term on the right-hand side of (9) is the external driving field, while the second term expresses the effect on the system of radiation damping. We thus see that, to terms of relative order $1/\omega_0\tau_R$ and τ_c/τ_R, the applied field and the radiation field act independently on the system. The radiation field simply gives rise to an additional driving term, a term proportional to the transverse component of the magnetization and 90° out of phase with it.

The solution of (9) is

$$\tan\frac{\theta}{2} = \frac{1}{\gamma H_1 \tau_R}\left(K_0 \operatorname{ctnh}\frac{K_0\tau}{2} - 2\right) \tag{10}$$

where

$$K_0 = [4 - (\gamma H_1 \tau_R)^2]^{1/2}. \tag{11}$$

In many systems of interest, $\gamma H_1 \tau_R \ll 1$. Let us examine (10) when this condition holds, in the two limiting cases; $t \ll \tau_R$ and $t \gg \tau_R$. For $t \ll \tau_R$, (10) becomes

$$\delta \equiv \pi - \theta = \gamma H_1 t, \tag{12}$$

which is the ordinary Bloch solution in the absence of radiation damping. For $t \gg \tau_R$, (10) reduces to

$$\tan\frac{\theta}{2} = \frac{4}{\gamma H_1 \tau_R} e^{-2t/\tau_R}. \tag{13}$$

This should be compared with the solution of the Bloembergen and Pound equations for the case of free radiation damping, *viz*:

$$\tan\frac{\theta}{2} = \tan\frac{\theta_0}{2} e^{-2t/\tau_R} \tag{14}$$

where θ_0 is the initial angle between the magnetization and the positive z-axis. Eqs. (13) and (14) are identical if we set $\delta_0 \equiv \pi - \theta_0 = \gamma H_1 \tau_R/2$.

Eqs. (12)–(14) indicate that the motion of an initially inverted magnetization under the action of an applied signal may be thought of as consisting roughly of two separate stages. In the first stage, until the magnetization has been tipped through an angle $\gamma H_1 \tau_R/2$, the effect of radiation damping may be neglected, and the motion of the system is determined principally by the applied signal. In the second stage, as the magnetization tips beyond an angle $\gamma H_1 \tau_R/2$, radiation damping takes over, and the subsequent motion of the system is essentially the same as if the applied signal had been turned off and only radiation damping were present. Of course, if the applied signal is turned off in a time $t < \tau_R/2$, the mag-

[4] Eq. (7b), of course, does not apply when $\theta = 0$ or π, and, in fact, the angle ϕ has no meaning for these values of θ. In practice, of course, thermal fluctuations make it extremely unlikely that the magnetization will be at exactly 180° at the instant the external signal is applied.

[5] Our equations and results differ from Bloom's by a factor of 2 in all terms containing the effects of the radiation damping field because we have treated the case of crossed RF coils rather than that of a single coil. Our results apply to a single coil if everywhere we replace $\tau_R/2$ by τ_R.

netization tips only through an angle $\gamma H_1 t$ before radiation damping takes over.

Spin-Lattice Relaxation Time Infinite, Spin-Spin Relaxation Time Finite

We next consider the spontaneous decay (no external driving field) of a system for which T_1 is infinite but T_2 is finite. We assume that the system is initially at an angle δ_0 and we examine the subsequent motion of the magnetization, taking into account the effects of radiation damping and of a finite T_2.

The analysis proceeds as in the case of $T_2 = \infty$, with the following changes. Instead of using (4b), we let

$$M^+ = M(\tau)e^{-i\omega_0\tau_R\tau-(\tau_R/T_2)\tau}. \tag{15}$$

Then, instead of (7), we obtain the two coupled equations

$$\frac{dM_z}{d\tau} = 2\frac{|M|^2}{M_0}e^{-(2\tau_R/T_2)\tau}, \tag{16a}$$

$$2\frac{M}{M_0} + \frac{1}{M_z}\frac{dM}{d\tau} = 0. \tag{16b}$$

The solution of (16a) and (16b) is

$$|M| = \frac{M_0}{2}C\operatorname{sech} C(\tau - \tau_m)e^{(\tau_R/T_2)\tau} \tag{17}$$

where

$$C = \left[4 - 4\frac{\tau_R}{T_2}\cos\delta_0 + \frac{\tau_R^2}{T_2^2}\right]^{1/2}. \tag{18}$$

The value of τ_m is given by

$$\tau_m = \frac{1}{C}\operatorname{sech}^{-1}\left(\frac{2\sin\delta_0}{C}\right) \tag{19}$$

where the positive value of sech^{-1} is to be taken if $\tau_R/2T_2 < \cos\delta_0$, while the negative value is to be taken if $\tau_R/2T_2 > \cos\delta_0$. We have chosen the direction of H_0 to be the positive z-direction as before.

By substituting (17) into (16a), we find that the power, $P = d/dt\,(M_z V H_0)$, radiated by the sample at any time t after the cutoff of the applied signal is

$$P = \frac{M_0VH_0}{2\tau_R}C^2\operatorname{sech}^2 C(\tau - \tau_m), \tag{20}$$

V being the volume of the spin sample. It follows from (20) that when $\tau_m > 0$, *i.e.*, when $\tau_R/2T_2 < \cos\delta_0$, the radiated power exhibits a delayed peak at time $t_m = \tau_m\tau_R$; but when $\tau_m < 0$, the power decreases monatonically from its value at $t = 0$. Thus a delayed peak in the emitted radiation can be observed only if $\tau_R/2T_2 < 1$,[6] and if the magnetization is not initially tipped at too large an angle. The larger the initial angle δ_0, the sooner the peak power will occur, finally occurring at $t = 0$ when $\cos\delta_0$ becomes equal to $\tau_R/2T_2$. In Fig. 3, τ_m is plotted as a function of δ_0 for a number of values of $\tau_R/2T_2$.

[6] The same delayed peak condition is derived by Bloom, *op. cit.*, in whose notation it reads $\tau_\infty/T_2 < 1$.

The peak power has the value

$$P_{max} = \frac{M_0VH_0}{2\tau_R}\left[\left(4 - 4\frac{\tau_R}{T_2}\cos\delta_0 + \frac{\tau_R^2}{T_2^2}\right)\right]. \tag{21}$$

If $\tau_R/2T_2 \ll 1$, the peak power has the value $2M_0VH_0/\tau_R$, independent of the initial angle (or of when the peak occurs), whereas if $\tau_R/2T_2$ is not negligible compared with unity, the peak power increases as the initial angle increases. On the other hand, if $\tau_R/2T_2 > 1$, no delayed power peak can be observed, whatever the initial angle δ_0. In this case, the radiated power has its largest value $P(0) = (2M_0VH_0/\tau_R)\sin^2\delta_0$ at $t = 0$, and thereafter decreases monotonically to zero. In Fig. 4 we have plotted P_{max} in

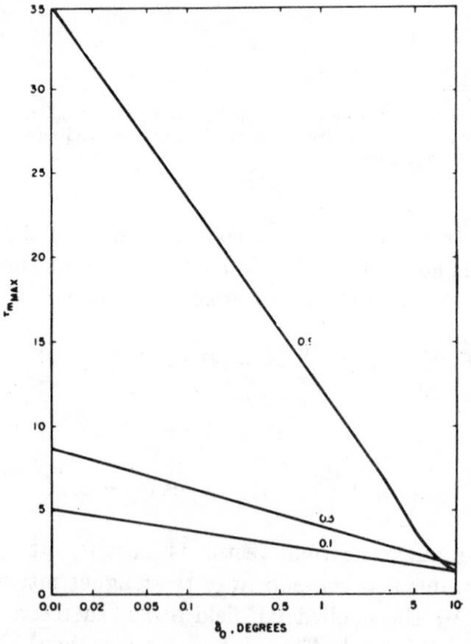

Fig. 3—Time, in units of τ_R, at which delayed peak occurs as a function of tipping angle δ_0 for a number of values of $\tau_R/2T_2$.

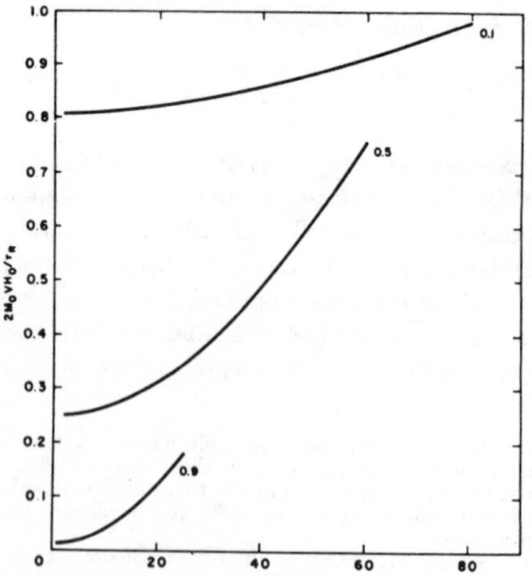

Fig. 4—Delayed peak power, in units of $2M_0VH_0/\tau_R$, as a function of tipping angle δ_0 for a number of values of $\tau_R/2T_2$.

units of $(2M_0VH_0/\tau_R)$, as a function of δ_0 for a number of values of $\tau_R/2T_2$.

Using (17), we may now solve (16b) for M_z. The result is

$$M_z = \frac{M_0}{2}\left[C \tanh C(\tau - \tau_m) - \frac{\tau_R}{T_2}\right]. \quad (22)$$

From (22) and (18), it follows that the asymptotic value of M_z is

$$M_z(\infty) = \frac{M_0}{2}\left[\left(4 - 4\frac{\tau_R}{T_2}\cos\delta_0 + \frac{\tau_R^2}{T_2^2}\right)^{1/2} - \frac{\tau_R}{T_2}\right], \quad (23)$$

whereas from (17) and (15) the asymptotic value of M^+ is

$$M^+(\infty) = 0. \quad (24)$$

Finally, the total energy radiated by the system is

$$W = [M_z(\infty) - M_z(0)]VH_0. \quad (25)$$

The general behavior of such a system may be deduced from an examination of (23)–(25). In the first place, it is seen from (24) that the final state of the system is either a 180° state or a 0° state; *i.e.*, the system keeps radiating as long as there is any transverse component of magnetization. Let us now examine (23) in the two limiting cases, $\tau_R/2T_2 \gg 1$ and $\tau_R/2T_2 \ll 1$.

If $\tau_R/2T_2 \gg 1$, then

$$M_z(\infty) \cong -M_0 \cos\delta_0 = M_z(0). \quad (26)$$

We thus obtain the result that if T_2 is much shorter than $\tau_R/2$, the transverse (radiating) component of the magnetization is removed before the system has had a chance to radiate away any energy. The final state of the system is therefore a 180° state, with the z-component of the magnetization unchanged. This is precisely the behavior the system would exhibit in the absence of radiation damping.

On the other hand, if $\tau_R/2T_2 \ll 1$, then $M_z(\infty) \cong M_0$; *i.e.*, the system radiates away all its energy before any transverse component of magnetization can be removed. The final state is therefore a 0° state with the length of the magnetization vector unchanged. This is just the motion of a system undergoing free radiation damping with T_2 infinite.

For intermediate values of $\tau_R/2T_2$, the final state of the system will be either a 180° or a 0° state, with $M_z(\infty)$ lying between the asymptotic values for the limiting cases. For a given value of the ratio τ_R/T_2, whether the final state is a 180° or a 0° state is determined by the initial angle δ_0. As can be seen from (23), there is a critical angle δ_c given by $1/\cos\delta_c = \tau_R/T_2$ such that, for $\delta_0 < \delta_c$, a 180° final state results, while for $\delta_0 > \delta_c$, a 0° final state results. Of course, if $\tau_R/T_2 < 1$, the final state will always be a 0° state, whatever the value of δ_0.

A rather interesting aspect of the over-all motion of a two-level system appears in an examination of the energy radiated by such a system after the removal of the tipping pulse. In Fig. 5 we have plotted, as a function of initial tipping angle, the fraction radiated away after the re-

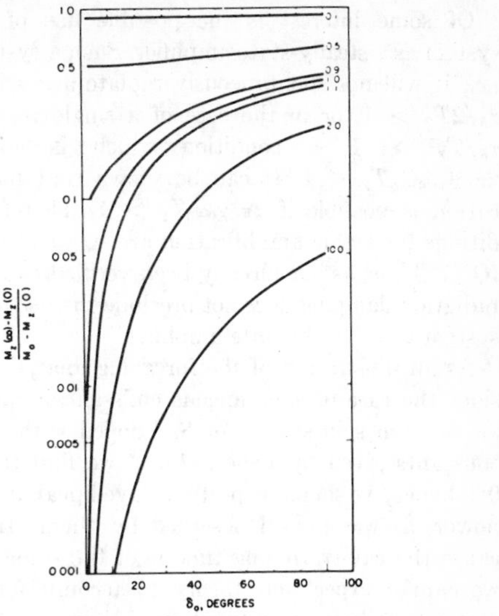

Fig. 5—Fractional energy radiated following tipping pulse as a function of tipping angle δ_0 for a number of values of $\tau_R/2T_2$.

moval of the tipping pulse, of the residual energy stored in the system. The curves are plotted for a number of values of $\tau_R/2T_2$ ranging from 0.1 to 10. It is seen that, for $\tau_R/2T_2 > 1$, the fractional energy radiated is quite small, independent of the initial angle. For example, if $\tau_R/2T_2 = 10$, the system radiates away less than five per cent of the remaining energy even if the initial angle is as great as 90°. Such a system might well be termed stable. The effects of radiation damping on the system are negligible and its motion is governed by the ordinary Bloch equations. The system will be essentially in equilibrium with an applied signal which has been on for a time of the order of a few T_2. After the signal has been turned off, the system will ring for a time of the order of a few T_2, radiating away only a small fraction of its energy before coming to equilibrium.

It is interesting to note that the conditions just described, namely a large value of $\tau_R/2T_2$ and an initial angle of 90°, are those characteristic of spin-echo experiments.[7]

On the other hand, if $\tau_R/2T_2 \sim 1$ (or smaller), the system radiates away an appreciable fraction of its energy, even if the initial angle is very small. For the case $\tau_R/2T_2 = 0.5$, for example, it is seen that the system will radiate away at least one half of its energy for an initial angle that is arbitrarily close to zero. This type of system might be called super-regenerative or super-radiant. Here, after a time of the order of a few τ_R, the system disgorges an appreciable fraction of its energy in the form of a pulse of radiation lasting a few τ_R. Such a system will run away from an applied signal, its motion after a few τ_R being governed primarily by radiation damping.

[7] E. L. Hahn, "Spin echoes," *Phys. Rev.*, vol. 80, pp. 580–594; November 15, 1950.

Of some interest is the possible use of a two-level system as a steady-state amplifier. Such a system is stable, *i.e.*, it will not spontaneously radiate away its energy, if $\tau_R/2T_2 > 1$, or in the case of a single resonant circuit $\tau_R/T_2 > 1$, a condition which is equivalent to $2\pi\xi\chi_0\omega_0 Q_L T_2 < 1$. It can be shown that maser amplification is possible if $2\pi\xi\chi_0\omega_0 T_2 > 1$. Therefore the conditions for stable amplification are $(Q^{-1}_0) < 2\pi\xi\chi_0\omega_0 T_2 < (Q^{-1}_L)$. Thus, as has already been verified experimentally,[8] radiation damping does not preclude the use of a two-level system as a steady-state amplifier.

As an illustration of the foregoing analysis, let us consider the case of spontaneous emission of radiation from an electron spin system of Si^{28} doped with P. Using the constants given by Feher, *et al.*,[9] we find that $\tau_R/T_2 \sim 0.3$; hence, we should expect a delayed peak in the radiated power, as was indeed observed by them. However, because the cavity ringing time is of the same order as τ_R, we cannot expect our theory to account for the details of power radiated as a function of time.

Super-Regeneration

Of some practical interest, also, are super-regenerative systems, in particular, systems with $\tau_R/T_2 \ll 1$. Suppose that we start with such a system in a metastable state and displace it from 180° through a small angle $\delta_0 = \gamma H_1 t_s \ll 1$ by means of a weak external signal of duration $t_s < \tau_R/2$. If we now allow the system to radiate freely, it will radiate away all its energy by virtue of its super-regenerative nature, with the peak of the radiation pulse occurring, from (18), (19), and (20), at a time

$$t_m = \tau_R \tau_m \cong \frac{\tau_R}{2} \ln \frac{1}{\delta_0}. \tag{26'}$$

The system, therefore, acts very much like a one-shot multivibrator. Suppose, on the other hand, that we quench the radiation (*e.g.*, by detuning the cavity) after a time $T \ll t_m$. In this case, the system radiates away only a small fraction of its energy and returns to the metastable state where the cycle may now be repeated. The average power radiated per cycle is

$$\bar{P} = \frac{1}{T_c} [M_z(T) - M_z(0)] V H_0 \tag{27}$$

where $1/T_c$ is the repetition rate. Now, for the case under consideration, $\delta_0 = \gamma H_1 t_s \ll 1$, $\tau_m \cong 1/2 \ln 1/\delta_0 \gg 1$, and $T/\tau_R \ll \tau_m$. Under these conditions, (27) reduces to

$$\bar{P} \cong \frac{M_0 V H_0}{T_c} \delta_0^2 e^{4T/\tau_R}. \tag{28}$$

On the other hand, the power supplied to the cavity by the input signal is $P_c = \omega_0 V_c H_1^2/8\pi$, where V_c is the volume of the cavity. Since $\delta_0^2 \sim H_1^2$, the average radiated or output power is proportional to the input power. In this mode of operation, then, a super-regenerative system might be operated as a linear amplifier. The system, of course, remains active only for a time of the order of T_1, the time it takes the spins to come to thermal equilibrium with the lattice, after which time the magnetization must be inverted again.

We know from our previous discussion that, for a system in a super-regenerative state, radiation damping takes over when the magnetization tips beyond an angle of about $\gamma H_1 \tau_R/2$. Therefore, if the signal to be amplified lasts a time $t_s \geq \tau_R/2$, we must replace δ_0 in (28) by $\gamma H_1 \tau_R/2$. The gain of the amplifier, $G = \bar{P}/P_c$, is then given by

$$G \simeq \frac{\tau_R}{T_c} e^{(4T/\tau_R)}, \tag{29}$$

where T now is measured from $\tau_R/2$ to the quenching of the radiation. This expression for the gain of a super-radiant system operated in this mode is similar to that given by Chester and Bolef[10] from apparently purely circuit considerations. We note, however, that they appear to use the circuit as the "flywheel," for their amplifier; *i.e.*, the build-up time is the characteristic time of the circuit, whereas we use the super-radiant spin system as the "flywheel," with the build-up time as the radiation damping time characteristic of the sample. This would imply that they have considered systems for which $\tau_c \geq \tau_R$. For such systems, as has been pointed out, our analysis is no longer valid.

[8] P. F. Chester, P. E. Wagner, and J. G. Castle, Jr., "Two-level solid-state maser," *Phys. Rev.*, vol. 110, pp. 281–282; April 1, 1958.

[9] G. Feher, J. P. Gordon, E. Buehler, E. A. Gere, and C. D. Thurmond, "Spontaneous emission of radiation from an electron spin system," *Phys. Rev.*, vol. 109, pp. 221–222; January 1, 1958.

[10] R. F. Chester and D. I. Bolef, "Super-regenerative masers," Proc. IRE, vol. 45, pp. 1287–1289; September, 1957.

FIELD-SWEPT MASER OSCILLATION

James C. Kemp
Department of Physics, University of Oregon, Eugene, Oregon
(Received May 1, 1961)

Recently Singer and Wang[1] (SW) have put forth an analysis which purportedly describes the behavior of a very wide variety of maser oscillators. An experimental verification was offered, based on a pulsed maser oscillation waveform from the present writer's work.[2]

The purposes of the present note are as follows: (1) To show that our waveforms, on one of which SW based their Fig. 1, show large qualitative and quantitative discrepancies from their predicted radiation envelope structure. For this purpose we will first discuss their main Eq. (8) and show how its solution (SW Fig. 2) differs from our waveforms. Our reason for the discrepancies is that our oscillator was of the "field-swept" type, in which emission occurs as the Zeeman field value H_0 is swept through resonance, giving a radiation envelope determined largely by the H_0 sweep rate and showing a modulation due, we believe, to a mechanism unrelated to that invoked by SW. (2) To summarize our own analysis[2] of the oscillator behavior, which we feel conforms adequately with our waveforms. In particular our asymptotic form [Eq. (2) below] for relatively fast sweep and weak oscillation will be seen to agree quantitatively within experimental limits, and qualitatively in all details, with an appropriate sample (Fig. 3) from a series of oscillograms.[2] We hope this note will help explain waveforms seen in other paramagnetic maser oscillators involving H_0 sweep.

As for the nature of the SW solution, the nutation-angle substitution[3] $\theta = \int_0^t 2\hbar\mu H(t')dt'$ in their Eq. (8), with $pE \rightarrow \mu H$ and N_e constant, the relevant case, gives $\ddot{\theta} + \tau^{-1}\dot{\theta} + (\tau\tau_\gamma)^{-1}\sin\theta = 0$, the simple damped-pendulum equation, where $\tau = 2Q/\omega$ = cavity ringing time and τ_γ = radiation damping time.[4] This writer noted previously[3] (see also Yariv[5]) that even with $\theta(0) \sim \pi$ (initial inverted state), in the pertinent case the radiation amplitude $H = \gamma^{-1}\dot{\theta}$ is given adequately by $\exp(-t/\tau) \times \sin[t/(\tau\tau_\gamma)^{1/2}]$ after the first "cycle" or two. The resulting emission would have mean duration of order τ and would show roughly uniform 100% modulation with period of order $\overline{(\tau\tau_\gamma)^{1/2}/2\pi}$. In our experiments[2] $\tau \cong 0.6\,\mu$sec. Our observed durations depended on the sweep rate, and ranged[2] from 7 μsec (fastest sweep) to 500 μsec (slowest sweep), with representative values 500, 15, and 90 μsec, respectively, for Figs. 1, 2,

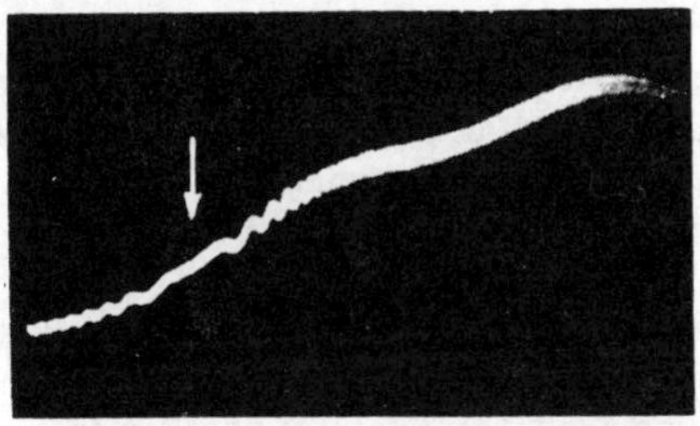

FIG. 1. Field-swept maser oscillation, displaying emission envelope $|H(t)|$. Slow sweep, $dH_0/dt = 800$ gauss/sec. $\beta \cong 0.001$; $\tau_\gamma \cong 0.1\,\mu$sec. Trace length 200 μsec. Fractional Zeeman energy release ~70%. Shown here is the rising portion of the envelope, which decays to the right. The thickness of the trace in the upper part is not noise but unresolved rapid modulation. The arrow is believed in the vicinity of passage through the line-center resonance ($t = 0$), though this point was not localized experimentally. Equation (2) of text is not applicable.

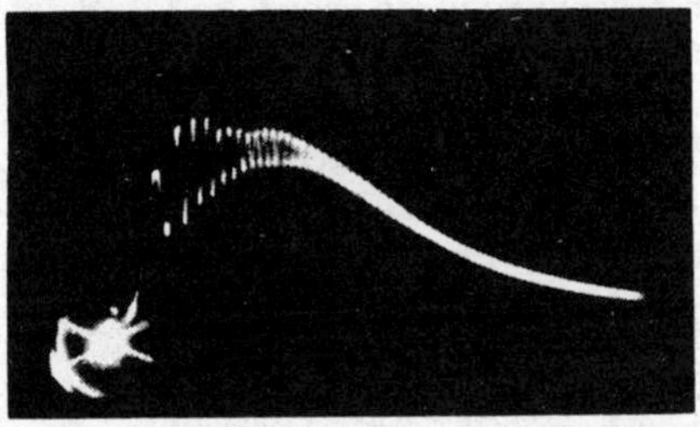

FIG. 2. Field-swept emission. $dH_0/dt = 2\times10^4$ gauss/sec. $\beta \cong 0.03$; $\tau_\gamma \cong 0.1\,\mu$sec. Trace length 30 μsec. Owing to the fast sweep, in spite of about 50% Zeeman energy release the modulation pattern is surprisingly like that of Eq. (2) except for average shallowness. Period of fifth modulation cycle $T_5 = 1.2\,\mu$sec (theor) = 0.8 μsec (exp).

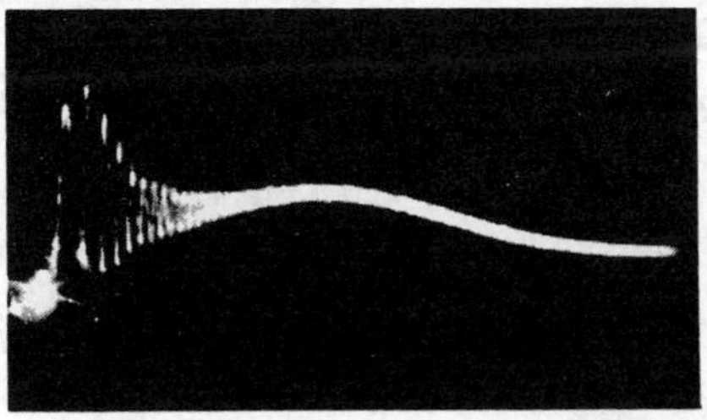

FIG. 3. Field-swept emission. $dH_0/dt = 4\times10^3$ gauss/sec. $\beta \cong 0.03$; $\tau_\gamma \cong 0.6\,\mu$sec. Trace length 200 μsec. Energy release ~30%. $T_5 = 2.8\,\mu$sec (theor) = 4.0 μsec (exp). Equation (2) well describes this plus seven other oscillograms in reference 2, with moderate to rapid sweep and not too strong oscillation.

and 3 shown in this note. Our waveforms show, rather than uniform 100% modulation, a modulation with frequency increasing indefinitely with time, after sweep through resonance, with a percent depth that depends strikingly on the sweep rate.

The possibility of observing two-level paramagnetic maser oscillation showing the pendulum-like behavior[6] expected from a static-H_0 analysis[1,3] was investigated by the writer.[2] We concluded that, when one induces oscillation by the common procedure of sweeping the field H_0 into or through resonance, at least in our apparatus it was impossible to establish oscillation conditions "suddenly" enough to allow emission to occur with essentially static parameters (the field H_0). Emission with H_0 varying in time linearly through resonance was then studied systematically, and was the subject of our work,[2] which we now summarize.

Our theoretical treatment[2] of the field-swept case starts with the coupling equation between a complex radiation field amplitude H and a complex transverse magnetization M. For sweep through resonance rapid enough to allow only a small fractional Zeeman energy release, such that $M_z \cong -M_0$ holds, the spin-dynamic equations are soluble explicitly for arbitrary $H(t)$ and $\Delta H_0(t) = H_0(t) - \omega/\gamma$. We choose $\Delta H_0 = \gamma^{-1}\alpha t$, where α is a constant sweep rate. We assume a Lorentz line of width $(T_2^*)^{-1}$ and, for convenience,[7] that $T_2^* \cong \tau$. One gets

$$\frac{d^2H}{dt^2}+\left(\frac{2}{\tau}-i\alpha t\right)\frac{dH}{dt}+\frac{1}{\tau}\left(\frac{1}{\tau}-\frac{1}{\tau_\gamma}-i\alpha t\right)H=0, \qquad (1)$$

which is readily transformable to Weber's equation.[8] The pertinent solution, in terms of a Weber's function of imaginary order, is

$$H = K\exp(i\alpha t^2/4 - t/\tau)D_{i/\beta}[-(1+i)(\alpha/2)^{1/2}t],$$

with K = const. From asymptotic forms[2,8] we find, for moderate to rapid sweep,

$$|H(t)| \cong A(t)\left[1+\frac{1}{\beta^{1/2}\alpha^{1/2}t}\sin(\tfrac{1}{2}\alpha t^2+\phi)\right], \qquad (2)$$

where ϕ varies slowly and $\beta = \alpha\tau\tau_\gamma$ is a dimensionless sweep rate. This form described the radiation envelope for $\beta \gtrsim 1/8\pi \cong 0.04$ and $t \gtrsim (2\pi/\alpha)^{1/2}$. $|H(t)|$ rises monotonically during the interval about passage through resonance ($t=0$). $A(t)$, giving the gross shape, rises to simple maximum at roughly $t_1 = \beta^{-1}(2\tau_\gamma/\tau)^{1/3}\tau$, and then decays, asymptotically like $\exp(t/\tau - 1/\beta^2\alpha t^2)$. The sine term gives an amplitude modulation, with fractional depth about 100% (for $\beta \sim 1/8\pi$) initially, but decreasing in percentage as $1/t$, and increasing indefinitely in frequency with t.

The modulation mechanism described by (1) and (2) inherently involves the time-varying H_0, which continually tends to throw the magnetization into the wrong phase, with respect to the radiation field, for oscillation buildup. Modulation due to this mechanism should vanish for vanishingly slow sweep.[9]

Figures 1-3 are from the writer's experimental field-swept oscillator,[2] and display $|H(t)|$. Relevant measured parameters were: $\tau \cong 0.6\,\mu$sec; $T_2^* \cong 0.8\,\mu$sec. τ_γ and $dH_0/dt = \gamma^{-1}\alpha$ were adjustable, respectively, over the ranges 0.1-0.8 μsec and 0.8-40 kilogauss/sec, giving a β range 0.001-0.06. Equation (2) should apply best to Fig. 3. The linearization $M_z \cong -M_0$ of Eq. (1) holds reasonably for Fig. 3 but marginally for Fig. 2. In spite of small β, and nonlinearity, even Fig. 1 has some features in common with Eq. (2). Modulation appears most marked just when Eq. (2) applies. The predicted period $T_n = (\pi/n\alpha)^{1/2}$ from (2), of the nth modulation period to appear, is correct within 50% for T_5 in Figs. 2 and 3. For the expected emission duration T, a useful rough estimate[2] is $2(\tau\tau_\gamma)^{1/2}\beta$, yielding reasonable values 500, 20, and 50 μsec for Figs. 1, 2, and 3, respectively.

We have shown that the maser oscillator emission envelope had in our case a structure dependent almost entirely on the field sweep. Though a simple pendulum-like energy exchange between cavity and emitting sample, described by the "general analysis" of SW, is a basic process,[2] it had nothing to do with our case, with either fast or slow H_0 sweep.

---

[1] J. R. Singer and S. Wang, Phys. Rev. Letters 6, 351 (1961).

[2] J. C. Kemp, thesis, University of California, Berkeley, 1960 (unpublished). The relevant portion is available as a University of California Report AFOSR-TN-60-509, issue 275, E.R.L., Berkeley, 1960 (unpublished).

[3] J. C. Kemp, J. Appl. Phys. 30, 1451 (1959). Though this paper covered the rather fundamental "pendulum nutation" mechanism (discussed earlier, without the nonlinearity, in reference 4), the possible role of H_0 sweep in actual experiments was not then appreciated. Adding line broadening to the static-parameter (static H_0) emission problem was discussed in this reference, in reference 5, and further in reference 2 (thesis only), and gives a possible lengthening of emission duration and a modulation frequency which can be smaller on the aver-

age but cannot increase with t over the envelope.

[4]N. Bloembergen and R. V. Pound, Phys. Rev. 95, 8 (1954). $\tau_\gamma^{-1} = \gamma M_0 Q/\mu_0 V$ (mks units[2]), where γ = magnetogyric ratio, M_0/V = available magnetization per unit cavity volume. In SW notation, $\tau_\gamma^{-1} = 4\pi N_e \gamma p Q$ or $4\pi N_e \gamma \mu Q$.

[5]See A. Yariv, J. Appl. Phys. 31, 740 (1960), who omitted a minor approximation (reference 2 Report, Appendix) leading to the pendulum equation, but gave a computer solution justifying our statement that the solution is quite like an exponentially decaying sinusoid.

[6]An unpublished waveform of P. F. Chester, P. E. Wagner, and J. G. Castle, Jr., Scientific Paper 6-94439-8-P4, Westinghouse Research Laboratories, Pittsburgh, Pennsylvania, 1958 (unpublished), p. 10, taken without H_0 sweep, shows the characteristic 100% almost uniform modulation, in my knowledge the only observed such case.

[7]It happened that $T_2^*/\tau \cong 1$ in our experiments. The mathematics can easily accommodate the more general case.

[8]E. T. Whittaker and G. N. Watson, Modern Analysis (Cambridge University Press, New York, 1935), 4th ed., pp. 347-351.

[9]Sweep-rate dependence of modulation depth was also noted by S. Foner, L. R. Momo, and A. Mayer, Phys. Rev. Letters 3, 36 (1959).

Reprinted from JOURNAL OF APPLIED PHYSICS, Vol. 30, No. 9, 1451–1452, September, 1959

Theory of Maser Oscillation*

JAMES C. KEMP
Department of Electrical Engineering, University of California, Berkeley 4, California
(Received April 9, 1959)

AT least two observers[1,2] have reported on the amplitude-modulated nature of the signal from an inverted spin system undergoing maser oscillation or coherent spontaneous emission. Attempts that have been made[3] to explain this phenomenon have not been entirely convincing. Bloembergen and Pound[4] treated the case of small departures of the magnetization from the equilibrium direction, $M_z \approx +M_0$, for which the result is a simple damped oscillation of the xy-plane components of the magnetization. Yariv, Singer, and Kemp,[5] showed that the case $M_z \approx -M_0$ (inverted state) gives only exponential buildup of the signal, provided the oscillation condition $\tau_r < T_2$ is satisfied, where $\tau_r = \mu_0 V/\gamma M_0 Q$; the so-called radiation damping time. Here V = cavity volume, M_0 = net available magnetization at temperature T, Q = cavity Q, γ = magnetogyric ratio, μ_0 = permeability of free space. The units used in this paper are in the mks system. $M_0 Q/\mu_0 V$ is a steady-state cavity field that would be induced by a magnetization vector of magnitude M_0 precessing in the xy plane; τ_r would be the nutation time for spins under the influence of this field. Homogeneous broadening was assumed, T_2 being the reciprocal homogeneous line width. For an inhomogeneously broadened system the behavior with either $M_z \approx +M_0$ or $-M_0$ is comparable to that for homogeneous broadening: a monotonic buildup results for the inverted case providing the oscillation condition is satisfied, T_2 being the inhomogeneous reciprocal line width.

It is clear that we are dealing here with large-amplitude nutations of the magnetization vector, and the behavior is essentially nonlinear. The nature of this oscillation is brought out if we first neglect line-broadening mechanisms and treat these later by perturbation techniques. We represent the cavity dominant mode by series R, L, and C, and a voltage $ve^{j\omega_0 t}$, where v is a time-varying voltage proportional to M_x, the xy-plane component of the magnetization. In treating the spin-dynamic problem we work in the usual rotating frame, rotating about $+z$, that is, about the dc field H_0, with angular velocity $\omega_0 = \gamma H_0$. It is easy to see that, if the magnetization $\mathbf{M}_0$ lies initially in the xz plane at a small angle from the $-z$ direction, a reaction field $\mathbf{H}_1$ arises along the y axis proportional to the cavity-circuit current amplitude i, and that this phase relationship is maintained: $\mathbf{M}_0$ nutates about $\mathbf{H}_1$, toward the xy plane, and H_1 grows. Since M_x is slowly varying compared to the rf frequency ω_0, the cavity current remains essentially in phase with the inducing voltage, which is in quadrature with the xy component of the magnetization $\mathbf{M}$ as viewed in a stationary frame. Due to spin dephasing the magnitude of $\mathbf{M}$ varies, but $\mathbf{M}$ remains in the xz plane: This is obvious for homogeneous broadening. Under inhomogeneous broadening, this follows if we assume that the Zeeman frequencies of individual spins spread according to a symmetric distribution function $g(e)$, where $\int_0^\infty g(e)de = 1$, and $e = |\omega - \omega_0|$, the departure from line-center frequency. The dynamic equations for a single spin are

$$\begin{aligned}\dot{M}_z &= \omega_1 M_x \\ \dot{M}_x &= eM_y - \omega_1 M_z \\ \dot{M}_y &= -eM_x\end{aligned} \tag{1}$$

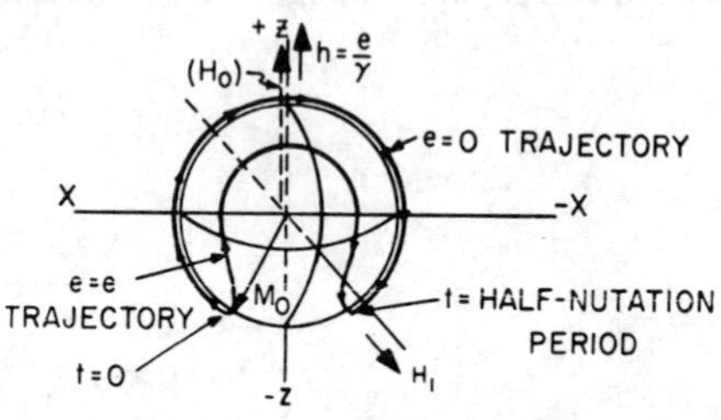

FIG. 1. Comparison of spin-trajectories of $e=0$ spin and $e\neq 0$ spin.

where $\omega_1 = \gamma H_1$. The simultaneous substitutions $e \to -e$, $M_y \to -M_y$ leave these equations unchanged, so that it is seen that M_y components cancel out in pairs over a symmetric distribution.

Now if the ringing time $\tau = 2L/R = 2Q/\omega$ of the circuit, as well as the shortest characteristic time of the spin system, that is τ_r (considered $\ll T_2$), is long compared with one rf period, energy conservation gives

$$\tfrac{1}{2}Li^2 + \int_0^t Ri^2 dt' = -H_0 \int_1^\infty M_z(e,t) g(e) de \tag{2}$$

for inhomogeneous broadening. Note that i is the amplitude of the cavity current. Using $\omega_1 = \gamma H_1 = \gamma i K_2^{-1}$, where K_2 is a constant, differentiating (2), and using $\dot{M}_z = \omega_1 M_x$, we get

$$\frac{d\omega_1}{dt} + \frac{1}{\tau}\omega_1 = -\frac{\gamma\omega_0}{LK_2^2}\int_0^\infty M_x(e,t) g(e) de. \tag{3}$$

Now in terms of the nutation angle $\theta = \theta(0) + \int_0^t \omega_1 dt'$, which gives the position in the xz plane of spins with $e=0$ only,

$$\frac{d^2\theta}{dt^2} + \frac{1}{\tau}\frac{d\theta}{dt} = -\frac{\gamma\omega_0 M_0}{LK_2^2}\int_0^\infty \frac{M_x(e,t)}{M_0} g(e) de. \tag{4}$$

To evaluate the constant on the rhs, note that K_2 is the steady-state current that would produce unit H_1. But the stored cavity energy is $\frac{1}{2}\mu_0 H_1^2 V = \frac{1}{2}Li^2$, so $K_2 = (\mu_0 V/L)^{\frac{1}{2}}$, and (4) reads

$$\frac{d^2\theta}{dt^2} + \frac{1}{\tau}\frac{d\theta}{dt} = -\frac{1}{\tau\tau_r}\int_0^\infty \frac{M_x(e,t)}{M_0} g(e) de. \tag{5}$$

If the line width T_2^{-1} goes to zero, that is if $g(e)$ becomes a delta function, we have pure rotation of the magnetization in the xz plane, and

$$\frac{d^2\theta}{dt^2} + \frac{1}{\tau}\frac{d\theta}{dt} + \frac{1}{\tau\tau_r}\sin\theta = 0 \tag{6}$$

which is the simple pendulum equation with a damping term. The solution without damping can be written in terms of a Jacobian elliptic function, but for $\theta \lesssim 160°$, we have closely, since the third harmonic is less than 10%,

$$\theta \cong \phi \cos\frac{\pi}{2K}\frac{t}{(\tau\tau_r)^{\frac{1}{2}}} = \phi\cos\Omega t \tag{7}$$

where $\pi/2K \cong 1 - \frac{1}{16}\phi^2$, K being the complete elliptic integral of the first kind, and $\phi = \theta(0)$. For large nutation angles, e.g.

$\phi \sim 160°$, the period is of the order of twice that for small ϕ. The observed signal is proportional to the magnitude of the current i or field H_1

$$|\gamma H_1| = |d\theta/dt| \cong \Omega |\sin \Omega t| \quad (8)$$

and the interval between peaks of the observed signal is $T = \pi/\Omega$. A mean value is $T \cong 4(\tau\tau_r)^{\frac{1}{2}}$.

Actually ϕ falls off due to the damping term, and treating the damping as a perturbation in (6), using (7) but assuming ϕ slowly varying, we can estimate the number of cycles needed to reduce ϕ from $\sim\pi$ to $<\pi/4$, that is, to traverse the region of large nutation. This is of the order of $(\tau/\tau_r)^{\frac{1}{2}}$. Thus the duration of the nonlinear oscillation is of the order of 8τ. For $Q \sim 10\,000$, $8\tau \sim 2.5$ μsec. For $\tau_r \sim 0.1$ μsec, this gives $T \sim 0.7$ μsec, and something like three large-amplitude peaks would be seen, followed by a linear decay period $M_z \approx +M_0$, during which the amplitude of the peaks falls off exponentially.

Now allowing the line width to be finite but small, spin dephasing can be treated as a perturbation for the inhomogeneous case by expanding $M_x(e,t)$ in Eq. (5) in even powers of e (symmetry of the distribution prevents odd powers). For small e^2 it is possible to solve the dynamic Eqs. (1). Having solved these to first order in e^2 for arbitrary $\omega(t) = d\theta/dt$, the resultant $M_x(e,t)$ is inserted in (5) and θ is expanded in the even moments of the line, $\theta = \theta_0 + (\tau\tau_r/T_2^2)\theta_2 + \cdots$, where $T_2^{-2} = \int_0^\infty e^2 g(e) de$. Ignoring damping terms, θ_0 is just the solution of Eq. (6), and the second-order equation (in θ_2) turns out to be a Hill's equation with driving term. Some strenuous arithmetic shows that to a good approximation for $\phi \leq 160°$,

$$\theta_2 \cong \sin\phi(1-\cos\Omega t) - \tfrac{1}{2}\sin\phi \frac{t}{(\tau\tau_r)^{\frac{1}{2}}} \sin\Omega t \quad (9)$$

with initial conditions $\theta_0(0) = \phi$, $\theta_2(0) = 0$. Actually

$$\theta \cong \theta_0 + (\tau\tau_r/T_2^2)\theta_2$$

is the nutation angle of $e=0$ spins, under the influence of the current due to the induced voltage of the whole spin distribution. It is possible to go back from (9) to the spin dynamics and trace the trajectories of spins on the surface of a sphere, as in Fig. 1, which is a qualitative sketch of the paths of an $e=0$ and an $e \neq 0$ spin. A little attention to the effect of the dephasing field $h = e/\gamma$ reveals that spins tend to return to coincidence at the extremes $\theta = \pm\phi$ of a nutation cycle, in a manner akin to the rephasing in spin echoes; this is consistent with the periodic nature of the first term in (9). It can be shown that the second term, in $t \sin\Omega t$, corresponds to a progressive fanning out of the end points of the spin trajectories in the xz plane, due to the fact that the nutation frequencies are different. This is a second-order dephasing effect and the minimum time necessary for destruction of the magnetization would seem to be at least of the order of $[\pi T_2^2/(\tau\tau_r)^{\frac{1}{2}}]$, which is typically several times T_2. Actually if we imagine T_2 and τ_r as slowly varying quantities as spins on the wings of the line are lost from coherence, we can show that, if for example initially $T_2 = 10\tau_r$, the actual dephasing time for the spins in the central third of the line—these being sufficient to sustain oscillation—is some ten times $\pi T_2^2/(\tau\tau_r)^{\frac{1}{2}}$, where T_2 and τ_r are the initial values. This follows since both T_2 and τ_r are roughly inversely proportional to the number of spins remaining in coherence. With these considerations in mind we can describe the oscillation in terms of effective or average values of τ_r and the inhomogeneous T_2, both some several times the initial or theoretical values, and adjusted to fit the observed wave forms.

The picture would be different assuming purely homogeneous broadening. In this case the magnetization would be essentially destroyed in a time of the order of T_2, once the nutation amplitude ϕ through damping is reduced appreciably from its initial value $\sim\pi$; typically, scarcely more than one cycle of oscillation would be visible.

The wave forms shown by Feher[1] and Chester[2] are thus explainable as due to large-amplitude nutation of the magnetization, and indicate that the homogeneous T_2 is at least some few microseconds in both cases. In Feher's picture the large-amplitude peaks are followed by monotonic decay. This can be explained by noting that if through cumulative dephasing the net magnetization is reduced to the point where the oscillation condition $\tau_r < T_2$ is no longer fulfilled, the latter portion of the process will be nonoscillatory. In this case, the available Zeeman energy is of course not used up, and the spin system is left partly excited. Although the observed signal is roughly a damped full-wave rectified sine wave, the "valleys" in the signal will not appear to drop to zero due to finite band width of the detection system.

I wish to thank J. R. Singer for suggesting this problem, and A. Yariv, E. L. Hahn, and A. Portis for helpful discussion.

* This research was supported by the U. S. Air Force through the Air Force Office of Scientific Research of the Air Research and Development Command under Contract No. AF 49(638)-102.

1 Feher, Gordon, Buehler, Gere, and Thurmond, Phys. Rev. 109, 221 (1958).
2 Chester, Wagner, and Castle, Phys. Rev. 110, 281 (1958).
3 I. Senitzky, Phys. Rev. Letters 1, 167 (1958).
4 N. Bloembergen and R. U. Pound, Phys. Rev. 95, 8 (1954).
5 Yariv, Singer, and Kemp, J. Appl. Phys. 30, 265(L) (1959).

ERRATA

First Paragraph, Pg. 772, should read: condition is satisfied, T_2 being replaced by the inhomogeneous reciprocal line width, T_2*.

Third Paragraph, Pg. 773, 8th line, T_2^2 should read $T_2{*}^2$ and $T_2{*}^{-2}$.
15th line, T_2^2 should read $T_2{*}^2$

First Paragraph, Second Column, 5th line, T_2 should read T_2*.
6th, 9th, 11th, 12th, 15th lines should read T_2* instead of T_2.

Third Paragraph, Second Column, 7th line, should read T_2*, instead of T_2.

ADDENDUM

It has come to light that H_0 field-sweep was present in the experiments of Feher et al and in some of the experiments of Chester, Wagner, and Castle. Amplitude modulation "wiggles" in this case are due not to the static-field pendulum nutation mechanism, discussed here, but to a field sweep effect -- see J. C. Kemp, Phys. Rev. Letters, 7, 21 (1961).

A Double Pumping Scheme Applicable to Low-Frequency Masers*

Two multiple level pumping schemes have been used successfully to improve the performance of paramagnetic masers. One is termed "push-pull" pumping[1] and the other "push-push" pumping.[2] Another possible scheme for increasing maser performance, which might be called "parallel" pumping, is suggested here.

The energy level configuration for the parallel pumping scheme assumes the form shown in Fig. 1.

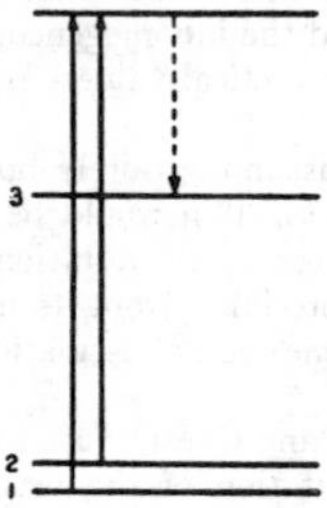

Fig. 1.

It is seen that this scheme employs pumping transitions between levels 1 and 4, and 2 and 4. The essential point is that levels 1 and 2 are sufficiently close together to be pumped by the same cavity mode and klystron mode.

Assuming that induced emission is to occur between levels 4 and 3, the difference of populations of levels 4 and 3 achieved in this case is calculated by making use of the dynamic equations of the spin system:

$$\frac{dn_i}{dt} = -n_i \sum_{j=1}^{4} w_{ij} + \sum_{j=2}^{4} n_j w_{ji} + \sum_{j=1}^{4} (n_j - n_i) W_{ji} \quad i = 1, 2, 3, 4 \quad j \neq i \qquad (1)$$

and the conservation equation:

$$N = \sum_{i=1}^{4} n_i. \qquad (2)$$

Here n_i is the population of the ith level; N is the total number of active spins; w_{ij} is the thermal relaxation transition probability of the $i \leftrightarrow j$ transition,

$$w_{ji} = w_{ij} \exp \frac{hf_{ij}}{kT}, \quad j > i,$$

where f_{ij} is the resonant frequency of the $i \leftrightarrow j$ transition; and W_{ij} is the induced transition probability of the $i \leftrightarrow j$ transition

$$W_{ji} = W_{ij}.$$

Assuming steady-state operation, *i.e.*,

$$\frac{dn_i}{dt} = 0 \quad i = 1, 2, 3, 4 \qquad (3)$$

and solving (1) and (2) simultaneously, we obtain, under the assumptions of small signal and large pumping:

$$(n_4 - n_3)_1 = \frac{Nh}{4kT} \frac{w_{32} f_{32} + w_{31} f_{31} - w_{43} f_{43}}{w_{34} + w_{23} + w_{13} + W_{43}} . \qquad (4)$$

Repeating this analysis with $W_{14} = 0$, one has:

$$(n_4 - n_3)_2 = \frac{Nh}{4kT} \frac{w_{31}(w_{21} f_{32} - w_{41} f_{43}) + (w_{41} + w_{31} + w_{21})(w_{32} f_{32} - w_{43} f_{43})}{w_{31}(w_{41} + w_{21}) + (w_{41} + w_{31} + w_{21})(w_{43} + w_{32} + W_{43})} . \qquad (5)$$

The power emitted by the paramagnetic crystal is given by:

$$P_{43} = (n_4 - n_3) h W_{43} f_{43}. \qquad (6)$$

Straightforward algebraic manipulation shows that for a given maser system

$$(P_{43})_1 > (P_{43})_2.$$

The actual improvement in performance is dependent on the relaxation times which are characteristic of particular transitions. Under the reasonable assumption of equal relaxation times an improvement by approximately a factor of two may be expected.

The parallel pumping scheme is of particular importance when low frequency operation of the ruby maser is desired. Such operation is conveniently obtained at large values of polar angle and low magnetic field. There, the energy level configuration is essentially that shown in Fig. 1.[3] For example, gain bandwidth products in excess of 40 mc at 4.2°K have been obtained at the following operating point: $\theta = 90°$, $H = 750$ gauss, $f_p = 14.0$ kmc, $f_s = 4.08$ kmc. This suggests a gain bandwidth product of at least 100 mc at 1.25°k.

J. E. King
A. Birko
G. Makhov
Willow Run Labs.
The University of Michigan
Ann Arbor, Mich.

* Received by the IRE, May 25, 1959. This research was supported by Project Michigan (administered by the U. S. Army Signal Corps).

[1] G. Makhov, C. Kikuchi, J. Lambe, and R. W. Terhune, "Stimulated Microwave Emission in Ruby," presented at Internatl. Conf. on Solid State Physics and Its Applications to Electronics and Telecommunications, Brussels, Belgium; June, 1958.

[2] J. W. Meyer, "Multiple or Regenerate Mode Pumping of Solid State Masers," Lincoln Lab., M.I.T., Lexington, Mass., Quart. Prog. Rept., p. 71; November, 1958.

[3] W. S. Chang and A. E. Siegman, "Characteristics of Ruby for Maser Applications," Stanford Electronics Lab. Tech. Rept. No. 156-2; September 30, 1958.

Reprinted from JOURNAL OF APPLIED PHYSICS, Vol. 33, No. 1, 202–204, January, 1962

On the Problem of Pulsed Oscillations in Ruby Maser*

GEORGE MAKHOV
Institute of Science and Technology, The University of Michigan, Ann Arbor, Michigan
(Received June 22, 1961)

It is shown by means of a semiquantitative nonlinear analysis that elementary interaction between an inverted electron spin system and a resonant cavity does not give rise to the pulsed mode of operation of the ruby maser oscillator. It is suggested that the additional nonlinearity necessary for the existence of such a mode resides in the "distant ENDOR," the interaction between the chromium electrons and the Al^{27} nuclei.

THE existence of the pulsed mode of operation of the ruby maser oscillator[1] has been attributed by Statz and DeMars[2] to time-dependent interaction between the inverted population of the electron-spin systems of the paramagnetic substance and the resonant cavity. It has come to this writer's attention that conclusions contained in reference 2 are based solely on analog computer solutions of nonlinear differential equations describing the interaction between the spin system and the cavity. A semiquantitative analysis of these equations shows the computer solutions to be in error, and consequently the conclusions of reference 2 concerning the nature of pulsed oscillations to be incorrect.

The equations in question, as derived by Statz and DeMars, and also independently by this writer[3] are of the form:

$$\begin{aligned} dx/dt &= -c_1xy+c_2(x_0-x) \\ dy/dt &= c_3xy-c_4y, \end{aligned} \tag{1}$$

where x is the population difference, and y is the magnetic energy in the cavity. The coefficients c_1, c_2, c_3, and c_4, and the constant x_0 are functions of material and circuit parameters, of temperature, and of excitation. Definitions of these quantities may be found in reference 2. For the purposes of the present analysis it is sufficient

* This work was conducted by Project MICHIGAN under a Department of the Army contract administered by the U. S. Army Signal Corps.

[1] C. Kikuchi, J. Lambe, G. Makhov, and R. Terhune, J. Appl. Phys. **30**, 1061 (1959).

[2] H. Statz and G. DeMars, *Quantum Electronics* (Columbia University Press, New York, 1960), p. 530.

[3] G. Makhov, Conference on Electron Tube Research, Mexico City, 1959.

to establish that c_2 is the inverse of spin-lattice relaxation time T_1, and c_4 is inversely proportional to the cavity Q.

In order to account for pulsed oscillations these equations must admit periodic solutions. Furthermore, in order to be in agreement with experimental data, there must occur a transition from the periodic to the aperiodic mode, as the magnitude (but not the sign) of one or more coefficients is changed. It is shown below that neither condition is satisfied by Eqs. (1).

The system of equations (1) is of second order and hence Liapunoff's stability criterion is applicable.[4] There are two singular points: a focus or a node at

$$x_1=c_4/c_3 \qquad y_1=(c_3c_2/c_1c_4)(x_0-x_1) \tag{2}$$

and a saddle point at

$$x_2=x_0 \qquad y_2=0. \tag{3}$$

Only the former singularity is of interest insofar that the latter merely determines the condition of dynamic equilibrium in the absence of signal field. Of course, the condition

$$x_2>x_1$$

must be satisfied in order for oscillations to occur.

The first-order terms of the Taylor expansion about x_1,y_1 are computed to be

$$a=-c_3c_2/c_4 \qquad b=-c_1c_4/c_3 \qquad c=(c_3^2c_2/c_1c_4)(x_0-x_1) \qquad d=0. \tag{4}$$

These quantities are coefficients of the linearized equations of (1).

The characteristic equation is of the form

$$\lambda^2-\lambda(a+b)+(ad-cb)=0. \tag{5}$$

Substitution of (4) into (5) yields

$$\lambda^2+(c_3c_2/c_4)x_0\lambda+c_3c_2(x_0-x_1)=0. \tag{6}$$

The coefficient of the linear term in λ is positive for all positive values of c_3, c_2, and c_4. Hence, the singularity is stable. Further examination of Eq. (6) shows that for all practical operating conditions, the singular point is a focus. This implies that the solution tends towards (x_1, y_1) in an oscillatory manner. This behavior corresponds to the *c-w* mode of the oscillator.

It is now inquired whether there exist closed trajectories in the *x-y* plane about (x_1, y_1). It will be recalled that, experimentally, transitions from the *c-w* mode to the pulsed mode are most easily effected by changing the cavity Q. In terms of the coefficients of Eqs. (1) this corresponds to changing c_4. The singularity, however, remains stable for all positive values of c_4; negative values of c_4 would imply negative cavity Q. Hence, the phenomenon of bifurcation, i.e., transformation of a stable focus into an unstable focus surrounded by a stable limit cycle, which might account for the observed behavior of the maser oscillator, is not to be expected.

The above reasoning does not preclude the existence of an arbitrary number of limit cycles about (x_1, y_1). A general proof of nonexistence of such limit cycles is very difficult. Bendixon's theorem fails to yield any useful information in the present case. The following reasoning, however, based on experimental evidence, shows that Eqs. (1) do not have limit cycles in the region of the *x-y* plane important to the operation of the maser oscillator.

From the physical point of view, the only limit cycles that may be reached from the point $(x_1, 0)$ must be situated between this point and (x_1, y_1). However, the existence of such limit cycles will not permit the trajectory to approach the singular point, i.e., aperiodic behavior would be impossible unless the initial conditions were adjusted so as to place the starting point $(x_1, y>0)$ inside the first limit cycle. This is clearly in contradiction with experimental evidence, since transition between the two modes is obtained without a change in initial conditions. Furthermore, the introduction of a microwave bias, or for that matter, of a noise bias corresponding to a nonzero value of the initial condition on y, fails to produce a transition from pulsed to *c-w* mode. It appears, therefore, safe to conclude that Eqs. (1) do not admit periodic solutions which may account for the pulsed mode of operation of the maser oscillator. They do, however, account adequately for the *c-w* mode.

This analysis is readily extended to transients encountered in optical masers.[5] Decaying oscillation pulses observed by Sorokin and Stevenson[6] in the case of uranium doped calcium fluoride bear a striking resemblance to transients of the *c-w* mode of the ruby maser.[7]

It may be stated in support of the above considerations that analog and digital computer solutions of Eqs. (1) carried out at this laboratory failed to reveal periodic solutions demonstrated in reference 2. Furthermore, there exists ample experimental evidence that the pulsed mode of operation of the ruby maser oscillator does not arise from an elementary interaction between the spin system and the cavity as suggested in reference 2. The most pertinent experimental results to this end appear to be the absence of the pulsed mode in the case of maser oscillator using more heavily doped (0.2% Cr) ruby, and the transition between the *c-w* and the pulsed

[4] N. Minorski, *Nonlinear Mechanics* (Edwards Brothers, Inc., Ann Arbor, Michigan, 1947).

[5] H. Statz, C. Luck, C. Shafer, and M. Clifton, Quantum Electronics Conference, Berkeley, California, 1961.

[6] P. D. Sorokin and M. J. Stevenson, Quantum Electronics Conference, Berkeley, California, 1961.

[7] In reference 5 it has been indicated that earlier computer solutions were inaccurate, and that small additional nonlinearities are required to have undamped oscillation pulses.

modes effected by magnetic resonance of Al^{27} nuclei.[8,9] These results provide an indication that the mechanism responsible for the pulsed mode is contained in the paramagnetic materials and bears a connection with ENDOR interactions existing in ruby.[9,10] Accordingly, it is thought that the pulsed mode can be accounted for if the first of the Eqs. (1), the spin system equation, is supplemented by a function of the population difference; the second of Eqs. (1), the cavity equation, remains unchanged. In other words, the modified equations are of the form:

$$\begin{aligned} dx/dt &= -c_1xy+c_2(x_0-x)+c_5f(x) \\ dy/dt &= c_3xy-c_4y. \end{aligned} \tag{7}$$

The singular point of interest is now located at

$$\begin{aligned} x_1' &= c_4/c_3 \\ y_1' &= (c_3/c_1c_4)[c_2(x_0-x_1)+c_5f(x_1)]. \end{aligned} \tag{8}$$

The pertinent characteristic equation, obtained as previously, is

$$\lambda^2+\left\{\frac{c_3}{c_4}[c_2x_0+c_5f(x_1')]-c_5\frac{df(x)}{dx}\bigg|_{x=x_1'}\right\}\lambda +c_3[c_2(x-x_0)+c_5f(x_1')]=0. \tag{9}$$

Here, the coefficient of the linear term in λ may be positive, zero, or negative, depending on the relative magnitudes of the two terms of opposite sign comprising it. Thus, one may expect, respectively, stable, neutrally stable, and unstable behavior. The first corresponds to the *c-w* mode of the oscillator; the second is essentially impossible to obtain in practice; and the third corresponds to the pulsed mode.

Further examination of the coefficient of the linear term in λ provides an indication as to the nature of the function $f(x)$. In order to induce instability, $f(x)$ must have positive slope. Experiment shows that the transition from the *c-w* to the pulsed mode is effected by decreasing the cavity Q, which corresponds to a proportional increase in the coefficient c_4. This suggests that $df(x)/dx$ must increase with x. An elementary example of such a function is the power function $f(x)=x^n$. It is shown below that satisfactory agreement with experiment is obtained if one chooses $n=1+\epsilon$, where ϵ is a small positive number. With the reasonable assumption of $x_0=2x_1$, the ordinate of the singularity is given by

$$y_1'=\frac{c_3}{c_1c_4}(c_2x_1'^{(1+\epsilon)}). \tag{10}$$

It is now recalled that in the case of Eqs. (1), the corresponding quantity y_1 was given by

$$y_1=(c_2c_3/c_1c_4)x_1. \tag{11}$$

This quantity is both measured and computed to be of the order of 10^{-6} ergs. Comparing Eqs. (10) and (11), one can conclude that in order for y_1' to be in agreement with experiment, the second term on the right-hand side of Eq. (10) must be of this order of magnitude or smaller. This implies that $c_2>c_5$, or that the rate of the process responsible for the second term is slower than spin-lattice relaxation. This process is thought to be the interaction between the chromium electrons and the distant aluminum nuclei, or "distant ENDOR." Relaxation time associated with this interaction is of the order of ten seconds.[8,9] Letting $c_5=0.1$ sec^{-1}, $c_2=10$ sec^{-1}, $x_1=10^{18}$, and choosing $\epsilon=1/9$, one has for y_1':

$$y_1'=2\cdot10^{-6}\approx y_1$$

as required. The coefficient of the linear term in λ, given in the present case by

$$c_2-c_5\epsilon x_1'^{\epsilon}$$

is computed to be approximately -90. Thus, the system is unstable, and the oscillator will operate in the pulsed mode. In order to obtain aperiodic operation, cavity Q must be increased; or pumping must be increased; or ϵ must be decreased. The first two conditions are known to be in agreement with experiment; no applicable data is available at the present time which may permit an evaluation of the third condition.

The choice of $f(x)$ made above was, of course, quite arbitrary. It is known, however, that the interaction between the chromium electrons and aluminum nuclei increases rapidly as the polarizations of the two systems become comparable. This suggests that in the case of the maser oscillator this interaction affects the pumping, rather than the signal transition. As emission occurs, the population difference in the latter decreases, and the polarization of the former increases. This leads to a decrease in the intensity of electron nuclear interaction with decrease in signal transition population difference x. This reasoning appears to indicate that the representation of $f(x)$ over a limited range as a monotonically increasing function of x has reasonable validity. In reality, this function is undoubtedly much more complicated. Currently, it is being attempted to determine $f(x)$ experimentally. A detailed study of the dynamic behavior of the ruby maser oscillator will be published in the near future.

The author wishes to thank Margaret M. Spencer and Dennis Sinnett for obtaining computer solutions to Eqs. (1), and Arnold Birko for competent technical assistance.

[8] G. Makhov, R. Terhune, J. Lambe, and L. Cross, J. Appl. Phys. **31**, 936 (1960).
[9] G. Makhov, Conference on Electron Tube Research, Seattle, Washington, 1960.
[10] J. Lambe, N. Laurance, E. McIrvine, and R. Terhune, Phys. Rev. **142**, 1161 (1961).

Effect of Nuclear Polarization on the Behavior of Solid State Masers*

G. Makhov, L. G. Cross, R. W. Terhune, and J. Lambe†
Willow Run Laboratories, The University of Michigan, Ann Arbor, Michigan
(Received January 15, 1960)

COWEN, Schafer, and Spence[1] have shown that the saturation of the electron spin transitions of the Cr^{+++} ions in ruby produces significant polarization of the Al_{27} nuclei. Other investigators[2,3] have detected a similar effect in a variety of paramagnetic materials. Recently, we have observed what amounts to the inverse of this effect, i.e., that the application of rf power at or near frequency of the quadrupole resonance of the aluminum nuclei in ruby produced a marked change in the electron-spin resonant absorption under saturation conditions.[4] This communication deals with the effect of this interaction on the behavior of solid-state maser.

In the basic experiment, a two-turn coil was wound about a ruby sample containing nominally 0.1% chromium. This assembly was placed in a doubly resonant microwave cavity and located in the dc magnetic field in such a manner that the axis of the coil was perpendicular to the direction of the field, and the polar angle was approximately 60°. With the system cooled to 4.2°K, a K-band microwave pump was used to saturate the 1–3 transition, and stimulated emission at X-band frequency was obtained in the 3–2 transition. Subsequent application of rf power at 4.5 Mc produced an increase in the gain of the maser amplifier, and resulted in a change of mode of operation of the maser oscillator. The effect was most pronounced at the resonant frequency of the free aluminum nuclei; however, at higher levels of rf power substantial interaction was obtained over a band extending from 500 kc to 20 Mc. Typically, power levels required to produce a detectable effect were of the order of 10 mw on resonance, and about an order of magnitude higher off resonance.

Comparing the performance of the maser amplifier with rf power on and off, as shown in Figs. 1(a) and 1(b), respectively, we may calculate the change in the magnetic Q due to the change in polarization of aluminum nuclei. The dependence of gain of the maser amplifier on the magnetic Q is given by

$$G=\left(\frac{1}{Q_c}-\frac{1}{Q_L}+\frac{1}{|Q_m|}\right)^2\Big/\left(\frac{1}{Q_c}+\frac{1}{Q_L}-\frac{1}{|Q_m|}\right)^2,$$

where Q_c is the coupling Q, Q_L is the loss Q, and Q_m is the negative magnetic Q. In our setup, Q_c and Q_L are typically 10^3. By using this value, we compute the decrease in Q_m caused by the application of rf to be approximately 20%. This change in magnetic Q was observed under conditions of partial saturation of the pumping transition.

The effect of decreased nuclear polarization on the behavior of the maser oscillator is shown in Fig. 2. The application of rf power tended to make the transient of the cw mode of the oscillator [Fig. 2(a)] less damped, and led eventually to the relaxation mode of operation [Fig. 2(b)]. The use of high rf power levels tended to diminish, or even reverse the effect.

It should be noted that the transient form of the interaction can be observed without the use of rf power. When maser action is initiated by bringing the dc magnetic field rapidly to the appropriate value, there results a transient during which the amplifier gain rises quickly to a high value, then decays slowly to a lower steady-state value. The time constant of the transient is of the order of seconds. The existence of the transient cannot be ascribed to spin-lattice relaxation, since T_1 for cooled ruby is of the order of 0.1 sec. Rather, it appears to result from the relaxation of polarization of aluminum nuclei.

Subsequent experiments have indicated that the application of rf power does not affect thermal relaxation processes to any perceptible degree. Rather, it can be thought of as added pumping, resulting in an increase in the magnetic Q. The degree of enhancement of the punping process is of the order of change in the degree of nuclear polarization, estimated to be about 1% under

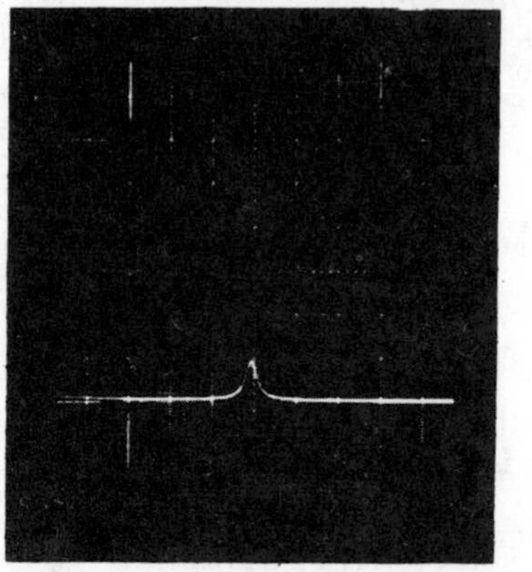

(a)

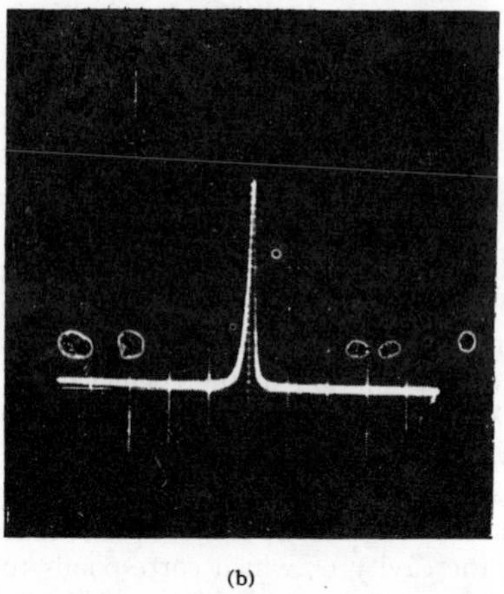

(b)

Fig. 1. Effect of change of nuclear polarization on maser amplifier gain. (a) rf off; power gain—15 db; (b) rf on; power gain—35 db.

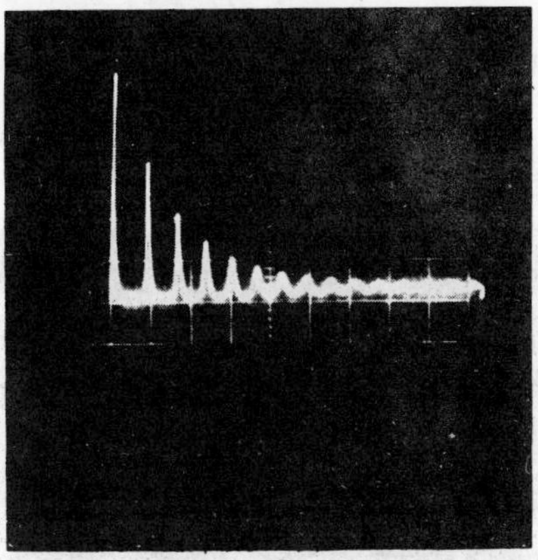

(a)

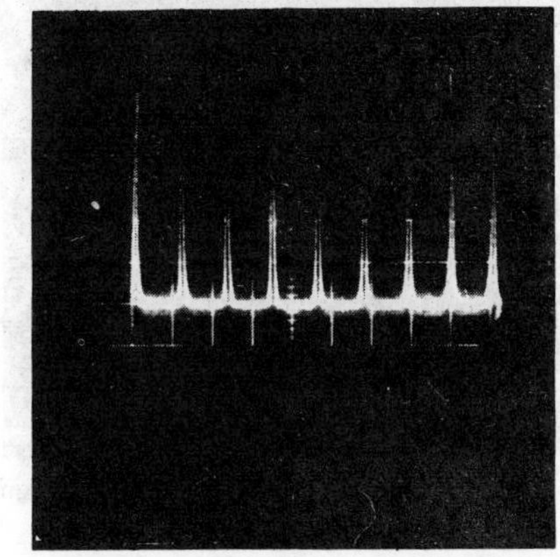

(b)

FIG. 2. Effect of change of nuclear polarization on the behavior of maser oscillator. (a) rf off; cw mode of operation; (b) rf on; relaxation mode of operation.

our experimental conditions.[4] Under conditions of marginal saturation of the pumping transition, this may lead to substantial decrease in magnetic Q, as noted in the foregoing.

These considerations suggest that the recovery of a solid-state maser device from saturation, or from fluctuations in pumping power, is characterized in general by two time constants. There is rapid recovery, of the order of 0.1 sec, determined by spin-lattice relaxation; and slow recovery, of the order of seconds, determined by nuclear-electronic relaxation. These effects have been observed experimentally. The latter effect, of course, becomes significant only when the on-period of the saturating signal, or variations in the degree of saturation of the pumping transition, are on a time scale comparable to that of nuclear relaxation.

In conclusion, we would like to conjecture that the observed increase in gain of the maser amplifier resulting from the application of rf power may be used to advantage in detecting weak nuclear resonances as well as in studies of ENDOR-type effects. In essence, the effect on the electron system produced by resonant pumping of the nuclear system, is amplified by the practically noiseless maser amplifier. When a high degree of regeneration is used, a small change in the magnetic Q results in a very considerable change in gain, or output, as attested by Figs. 1(a) and 1(b), and the corresponding calculation. A disadvantage of this method is, when using ruby, that maser action cannot be obtained in the vicinity of $\theta=0°$, whereas nuclear resonance effects are conveniently observed at that orientation. Presumably, this can be remedied by using a paramagnetic material, such as iron-doped sapphire, which permits maser action at the above orientation.

We are grateful to Professor C. Kikuchi and Professor G. Hok for many valuable discussions and helpful suggestions. We are appreciative of competent technical assistance rendered by A. Birko.

* This work was conducted by Project MICHIGAN under Department of the Army Contract administered by the U. S. Army Signal Corps.

† Now with the Scientific Laboratories, Ford Motor Company, Dearborn, Michigan.

[1] J. A. Cowen, W. R. Schafer, and R. D. Spence, Phys. Rev. Letters **3**, 13 (1959).

[2] Erb, Montchane, and Überfeld, Compt. rend. **246**, 2121 and 3051 (1958).

[3] M. Abraham, M. A. H. McCausland, and F. N. H. Robinson, Phys. Rev. Letters **2**, 449 (1959).

[4] R. W. Terhune, J. Lambe, G. Makhov, and L. G. Cross, Phys. Rev. Letters (to be published).

J. Phys. Soc. Japan **16** (1961) 2592~2593

Transient Phenomena in Ruby Maser

By Fujio Saito

Fundamental Research Laboratory,
Nippon Electric Company, Kawasaki,

(Received July 29, 1961)

Transient phenomena of maser oscillation were observed in an X-band three-level ruby maser and measurements on time lag at oscillation were made.

The $-3/2\leftrightarrow+1/2$ or $+1/2\leftrightarrow-3/2$ transition was used for pumping and the $+1/2\leftrightarrow-1/2$ transition was used for signal. The pumping and the signal frequencies were 24 kMc/sec and 9.4 kMc/sec respectively.

A ruby single crystal used in the experiments, containing 0.05% of Cr^{+++}, was about 1 cm^3. Because of large dielectric constant of ruby, most of the electromagnetic energy in the maser cavity was concentrated to the crystal, which might be considered as if it was a resonator itself. The energy concentration to the crystal and consequent decrease of wall loss of the cavity gave the filling factor very close to 100% and the loaded Q of about 10000.

In our experiments, the pumping microwave was chopped by applying square wave voltage to the reflector of the pumping klystron and the corresponding oscillation signal was displayed on a cathode ray tube. A photograph of typical oscillation signal is shown in Fig. 1.

When the pumping microwave was suddenly applied at $t=0$, the oscillation did not build up from $t=0$ but from $t=t_d$ with time lag t_d and reached to steady state with transient amplitude modulation similar to damped oscillation.

Similar phenomena to ours have been reported by Feher et al[1], Chester et al[2] and Kemp[3] for two-level maser and by Kikuchi et al[4] and Statz and de Mars[5] for three-level maser. Theoretical studies on these transient phenomena have been made by Singer et al[6][7], Yariv et al[8] and Kemp[9] for two-level maser and by Statz and de Mars[5] for three-level maser. These theories seem to well describe the principal aspects of the phenomena after building up of oscillation. There have been, however, no experimental and theoretical works on the time lag before building up of oscillation as we mentioned above.

We have measured t_d as a function of the pumping power P (peak value) and the recurrence frequency f of the modulating square wave.

When either P or f decreased, t_d increased, while the shape and duration of the transient amplitude modulation did not change remarkably. The amplitude of the oscillation signal decreased with decrease of P. When the temperature T was lowered from 4.2°K to 2°K, t_d increased slightly but other characteristics did not change. In all cases, the absolute values of t_d were order of few hundreds microseconds.

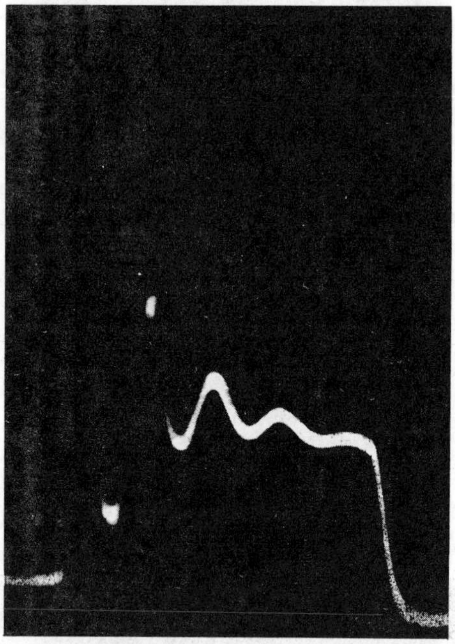

Fig. 1. A photograph of typical oscillation signal.

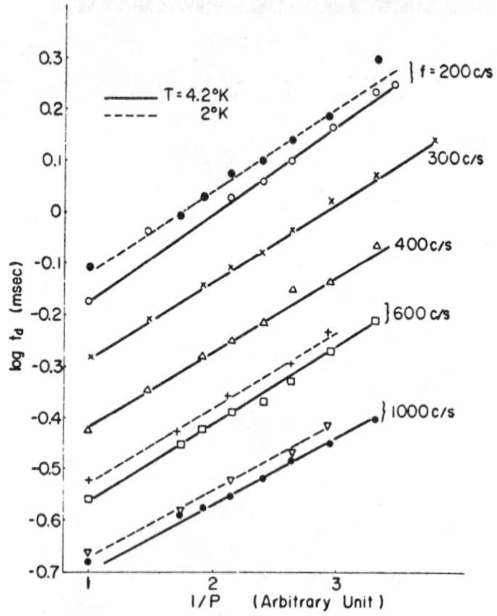

Fig. 2. The plots of $\log t_d$ vs $1/P$ for various values of f at $T=4.2$°K and 2°K.

The results of measurements on t_d are shown in Fig. 2, where $\log t_d$ is plotted as a function of $1/P$ for various values of f at $T=4.2$°K and 2°K.

From the results, it follows that $\log t_d$ is a linear function of $1/P$. From usual rate equations, we obtain the time lag as

$$t_d = -\frac{1}{2W_p}\ln\left(\frac{\Delta n - \Delta n(\infty)^*}{\Delta n(0) - \Delta n(\infty)}\right), \qquad (1)$$

where $\Delta n(t)$ is the population difference between $+1/2$ and $-1/2$ levels before building up of oscillation and Δn^* is the threshold value of $\Delta n(t)$ for oscillation to occur and W_p is the transition probability for the pumping transition.

For sufficiently high pumping power, $\Delta n(0)$, $\Delta n(\infty)$ and Δn^* are independent of P so that t_d is proportional to $1/W_p$ and consequently $1/P$. This result does not agree with the experimental facts and a more detailed consideration is required.

The author wishes to thank Dr. Y. Ishikawa and Dr. K. Hayashi for their kind advice and discussions.

References

1) G. Feher, J. P. Gordon, E. Buehler, E. A. Gere, and C. D. Thurmond; Phys. Rev. **109** (1958) 221.
2) P. F. Chester, P. E. Wagner, and J. G. Gastle, Jr.; Phys. Rev. **110** (1958) 281.
3) J. C. Kemp; Phys. Rev. Letters **7** (1961) 21.
4) C. Kikuchi, J. Lambe, G. Makhov, and R. W. Terhune; J. Appl. Phys. **30** (1959) 1061.
5) H. Statz and G. de Mars; "Quantum Electronics" Columbia University Press, N. Y., (1960) 530.
6) J. R. Singer; "Quantum Electronics" Columbia University Press, N. Y., (1960) 525.
7) J. R. Singer and S. Wang; Phys. Rev. Letters **6** (1961) 351.
8) A. Yariv, J. R. Singer, and J. Kemp; J. Appl. Phys. **30** (1959) 265.
9) J. C. Kemp; J. Appl. Phys. **30** (1959) 1451.

RELAXATION TIME AND MULTIPLE PUMPING EFFECTS IN MASERS*

A. SZABO

INTRODUCTION

A major disadvantage of present solid state masers is the requirement of operation at very low temperatures. The problem of increasing the operating temperature is twofold:

1. Pump relaxation times must be long enough so that saturation can be achieved with a reasonable amount of pump power.
2. Since the population difference contributing to maser action is inversely proportional to temperature, some means must be found to enhance this difference independently of temperature. This can be done by (i) increasing the ratio of pump-to-signal frequency, (ii) multiple pumping, and (iii) achieving large relaxation time ratios between certain of the transitions involved. The application of (ii) recently has resulted (Ditchfield and Forrester 1958) in maser operation at temperatures (~60° K) well above the usual liquid helium operating range.

In this note, we propose to examine maser operation under points (ii) and (iii) mentioned above. In particular a comparison will be made of systems (singly and multiply pumped) in which all relaxation times are equal, and those in which one specific relaxation time is much smaller than the others. The concept of an idler temperature will be introduced, and the effect on the latter temperature of shortening certain relaxation times and of multiple pumping will be discussed in relation to maser operation.

THREE-LEVEL MASER

Consider a three-level system where the transition $1 \leftrightarrow 3$ is saturated by radiation of frequency ν_p, the signal frequency ν_s corresponding to the transition $1 \leftrightarrow 2$. A figure of merit for the system acting as an amplifier is the

*Issued as N.R.C. No. 5425.

difference in populations between 2 and 1. An analysis similar to that of Schulz-DuBois *et al.* (1959) readily gives

$$(1) \qquad n_2 - n_1 = \frac{Nh\nu_\text{I}}{3kT}\left(\frac{R_{32} - \nu_s/\nu_\text{I}}{1 + R_{32}}\right), \qquad R_{32} = \frac{\tau_{21}}{\tau_{32}}$$

where N is the total population; ν_I is the idler frequency, $\nu_\text{I} = \nu_p - \nu_s$; τ_{21}, τ_{32} are the signal and idler relaxation times respectively; T is the absolute bath temperature; h is Planck's constant and k is Boltzmann's constant. In the derivation of the above equation and succeeding ones, relationships like $\tau_{21}/\tau_{12} = \exp(-h\nu_s/kT)$ are used, thus implicitly assuming that these relaxation time ratios remain the same under pumped conditions as at equilibrium. Also we assume all $h\nu$'s $\ll kT$. In terms of the idler temperature T_I defined by $n_3/n_2 = \exp(-h\nu_\text{I}/kT_\text{I})$, an alternate expression for $n_2 - n_1$ is

$$(2) \qquad n_2 - n_1 = \frac{Nh\nu_\text{I}}{3kT_\text{I}}.$$

From this equation it is seen that, in order to make $n_2 - n_1$ large, one possibility is to make T_I small. The other possibilities of making N or ν_I large will not be considered here except to say that in practice N cannot be advantageously increased much above a certain point (Bogle and Symmons 1959). Comparing equations (2) and (1) it is evident that the lowest possible temperature for T_I is bath temperature which occurs for $R_{32} \to \infty$. This result is, of course, to be expected since decreasing τ_{32} implies making better heat contact between the idler transition and lattice, or alternately, increasing τ_{21} lengthens the time of contact between the two, again forcing the idler to bath temperature.

MULTIPLE PUMPING

Another method of "cooling the idler" is by pumping between one of the idler levels and an additional level. The principle (Geusic *et al.* 1959) is illustrated in the energy level – population diagram shown in Fig. 1 and its application to a three-level maser is shown in Fig. 2. This method of pumping may be termed pull–pull pumping in analogy to the push–pull scheme described by Makhov *et al.* (1958). The other obvious variation would be push–push pumping (Meyer 1958) where the signal transition occurs between levels 3 and 4 and pumping is done at transitions 1 ↔ 2 and 2 ↔ 4.

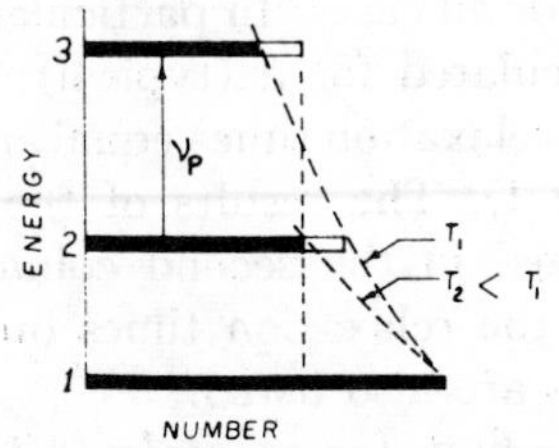

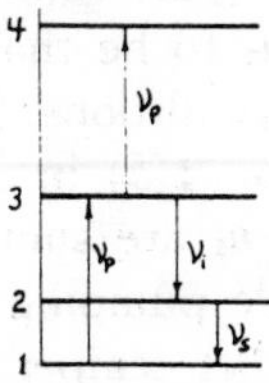

FIG. 1 (left). Cooling of transition 1 ↔ 2 by pumping transition 2 ↔ 3. T_1 is the bath temperature.
FIG. 2 (right). Application of the cooling principle shown in Fig. 1 to the three-level maser.

Analyzing the situation shown in Fig. 2, the rate equation for level 2 can be written

(3) $$\frac{dn_2}{dt} = -n_2(\omega_{21}+\omega_{23}+\omega_{24})+n_1\omega_{12}+n_3\omega_{32}+n_4\omega_{42}$$

where $\omega_{ij} = 1/\tau_{ij}$.

Under saturation conditions $n_1 = n_3 = n_4$, whence we obtain from (3), and the condition $\Sigma_i n_i = N$,

(4) $$n_2-n_1 = \frac{Nh\nu_i}{4kT}\left[\frac{R_{32}+2R_{42}+(\nu_s/\nu_i)(R_{42}-1)}{1+R_{32}+R_{42}}\right]$$

where

$$R_{j2} = \frac{\tau_{21}}{\tau_{j2}} \; (j = 3, 4).$$

Comparing the two situations (*a*) all *R*'s = 1, and (*b*) $R_{32} \to \infty$, i.e. signal to idler relaxation time ratio large, we observe that n_2-n_1 is the same in either case, namely

(5) $$n_2-n_1 = \frac{Nh\nu_i}{4kT} \text{ for all } R\text{'s} = 1 \text{ or } R_{32} \to \infty.$$

A way of interpreting this result is that the additional pumping between levels 3 and 4 cools the idler to bath temperature, and thus short-circuiting the idler to the bath by making $R_{32} \to \infty$ has no further effect on n_2-n_1. The relaxation time which can be advantageously decreased is τ_{42}. In the limit of $R_{42} \to \infty$ we get from (4)

(6) $$n_2-n_1 = \frac{Nh\nu_i}{4kT}[2+(\nu_s/\nu_i)].$$

A simple extension of the results to *m* levels shows that, in general, n_2-n_1 is largest for R_{m2} large.

To summarize the results, a comparison of maser operation under various pumping and relaxation time ratio conditions is given in Table I. Two relaxation time conditions are considered: (i) all relaxation times equal and (ii) the relaxation times optimized to give the largest n_2-n_1, i.e. $R_{m2} \to \infty$. As noted in column three, the parameter being compared is the bath temperature. N, ν_i, ν_s/ν_i, and n_2-n_1 are common for all cases. In particular we have chosen $\nu_s/\nu_i = \frac{1}{2}$ and n_2-n_1 to be that calculated for a (typical) three-level maser operating under the conditions: (i) all relaxation times equal and (ii) $T = 4.2°$ K (method of operation 1(*a*) in Table I). The results of the calculations for the normalized n_2-n_1 are summarized in the second column. To illustrate the effect of multiple pumping and the relaxation times on "idler cooling", the corresponding idler temperatures are also listed.

As an illustration of the results we find, for example (3(*b*)(i) of Table I), that a maser which has $m = 8$ and $R_{82} \to \infty$ can operate at 51.9° K and yield the same n_2-n_1 (or gain–bandwidth product) as a three-level maser

TABLE I

Comparison of single- and multiple-pumped masers for various relaxation time ratios

Method of operation	$(kT/Nh\nu_i)(n_2-n_1)$	$\nu_s/\nu_i = \frac{1}{2}$: Bath temperature for n_2-n_1 equivalent to 1(*a*) at 4.2° K, °K	Idler temperature, °K
1. Three-level			
(*a*) All relaxation times equal	$1/6[1-(\nu_s/\nu_i)]$	4.2	16.8
(*b*) $R_{32} \to \infty$	1/3	16.8	16.8
2. Four-level (pull–pull pumping)			
(*a*) All relaxation times equal	1/4	12.6	12.6
(*b*) $R_{42} \to \infty$	$1/4[2+(\nu_s/\nu_i)]$	31.5	12.6
3. *m*-Level ((*m*-2) fold–pull pumping)			
(*a*) All relaxation times equal			
(i) $m = 8$*	$1/8[3+(2\nu_s/\nu_i)]$	25.3	6.3
(ii) $m \to \infty$	$[1+(\nu_s/\nu_i)]$	75.6	0
(*b*) $R_{m2} \to \infty$			
(i) $m = 8$*	$1/8[6+(5\nu_s/\nu_i)]$	51.9	6.3
(ii) $m = 1500$, $\nu_i = 6000$ Mc		300	~0

*Largest known number of low-lying spin levels.

which has equal relaxation times and operates at 4.2° K, the pump and signal frequencies and the total spin population N being the same in both cases. It is apparent, however, that equivalent room temperature operation cannot be obtained except for unrealistic values of m. In general, similar results are obtained for the push–push and push–pull pumping schemes.

MASER OPERATION WITH LOW-FREQUENCY PUMPING

An examination of equation (4) shows that if $\tau_{21} \ll \tau_{32}, \tau_{42}$, then n_2-n_1 becomes negative, i.e. n_4-n_2 becomes positive if levels 1, 3, and 4 are saturated. Thus, under these conditions, maser operation can occur at frequency $\nu_p+\nu_i$ with pumping at a lower frequency ν_p. In the limit of $\tau_{21} \to 0$, we have $R_{32} \to 0$, $R_{42} \to 0$ so that

$$n_4-n_2 = \frac{Nh\nu_s}{4kT}. \tag{7}$$

In general, for m levels, the ratio of operating frequency to pump frequency increases with m; however, the population difference or efficiency of frequency multiplication decreases as $1/m$.

CONCLUSION

It is concluded that optimization of relaxation times combined with multiple pumping cannot by itself extend the operation of masers past the liquid nitrogen range and still result in performance comparable to that presently attainable at liquid helium temperatures with three-level masers. The only remaining possibility appears to be that of increasing the pump-to-signal frequency ratio.

A possible scheme of maser operation with pump frequency less than the signal frequency has been indicated for systems of four or more levels if certain relaxation time ratios are favorable. To achieve this operation, a rather high degree of control over the relaxation times is necessary. In practice, the impurity and self-doping schemes investigated by Scovil *et al.* (1957) and Schulz-DuBois *et al.* (1959) have been shown to result in a reduction of relaxation times of particular transitions by factors as large as 10. At present, however, such techniques are limited to a few materials and then only applicable under very special conditions. Presumably these restrictions will diminish as the cataloguing of host crystals along with their acceptable impurities continues, and a better understanding of the fundamental factors which control relaxation processes evolves.

BOGLE, G. S. and SYMMONS, H. F. 1959. Australian J. Phys. **12**, 1.
DITCHFIELD, C. R. and FORRESTER, P. A. 1958. Phys. Rev. Letters, **1**, 448.
GEUSIC, J. E., SCHULZ-DUBOIS, E. O., DE GRASSE, R. W., and SCOVIL, H. E. 1959. J. Appl. Phys. **30**, 1113.
MAKHOV, G., KIKUCHI, C., LAMBE, J., and TERHUNE, R. W. 1958. Phys. Rev. **109**, 1399.
MEYER, J. W. 1958. M.I.T. Report M37-32.
SCHULZ-DUBOIS, E. O., SCOVIL, H. E. D., and DE GRASSE, R. W. 1959. B.S.T.J. **38**, 335.
SCOVIL, H. E. D., FEHER, G., and SEIDEL, H. 1957. Phys. Rev. **105**, 762.

RECEIVED JULY 27, 1959.
DIVISION OF RADIO AND ELECTRICAL ENGINEERING,
NATIONAL RESEARCH COUNCIL,
OTTAWA, CANADA.

ELECTRON NUCLEAR DOUBLE RESONANCE EXPERIMENTS WITH RUBY*

R. W. Terhune, J. Lambe,† G. Makhov, and L. G. Cross
Willow Run Laboratories, The University of Michigan, Ann Arbor, Michigan
(Received January 14, 1960)

The polarization of nuclear spins throughout a crystal by saturation of an electron spin resonance of paramagnetic ions present as impurities has recently been reported.[1,2] We have observed an apparent inverse of this effect in ruby (Al_2O_3:0.05% Cr^{+++}), i.e., when the induced nuclear polarization is partially removed by saturating an aluminum nuclear spin resonance transition, a large decrease in the power absorbed by the electron spin resonance of the Cr^{+++} ions is observed. We have also observed effects associated with inducing transitions between the hyperfine levels of the chromium-53 ions.

Magnetic field modulation at 5 kc/sec was used to observe the edge of the ($+\frac{1}{2}\rightleftarrows-\frac{1}{2}$) electron spin resonance absorption line of ruby with a microwave power level about 20 db above saturation. The spectrum shown in Fig. 1 was then obtained by scanning the frequency of a low-power rf oscillator connected to a single turn of wire around the ruby sample. The five lines in the 3-Mc/sec region correspond very well with the nuclear magnetic resonance spectrum of the host aluminum nuclei in the crystal. The same dependence of the splitting between lines upon the angle of dc magnetic field and line width were observed both here and in the nuclear magnetic resonance spectra.

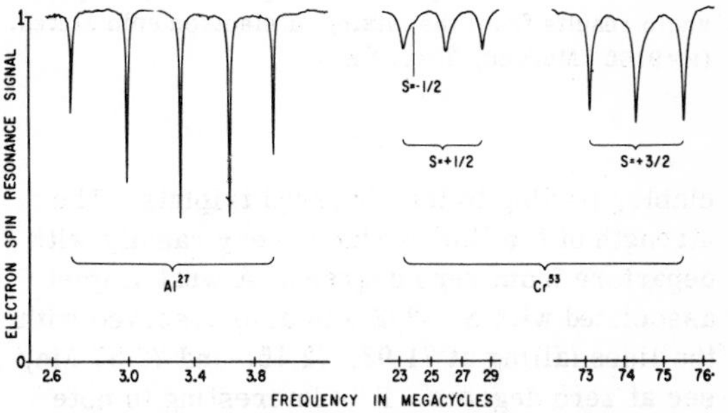

FIG. 1. Spectrum obtained by observing the ($+\frac{1}{2}\rightleftarrows-\frac{1}{2}$) electron spin resonance signal from ruby under saturation conditions and scanning the frequency of an rf generator connected to a coil around the crystal. ($H \cong 3285$ gauss, $\theta=0°$, $\nu=9160$ kMc/sec, $T=4.2°$K.)

The lines near 25 and 75 Mc/sec are associated with the $\vec{I}\cdot\vec{S}$ splitting of the chromium-53 ions[3] which have a nuclear spin of 3/2 and a natural abundance of 9.5%. The other isotopes of chromium all have zero nuclear spin. The +1/2 and +3/2 electron spin states are very close together at our operating point. As a result they interact strongly as the angle of the dc magnetic field is varied, causing large changes in the hyperfine splitting (Fig. 2). Also, the second order correction to their hyperfine splitting is appre-

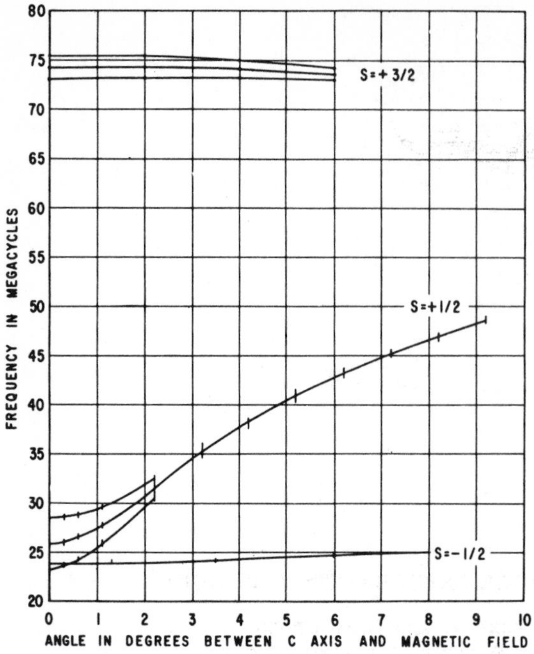

FIG. 2. Experimental data on angular dependence of the hyperfine splittings of the electron spin states of the Cr^{53} ion in ruby. The change in frequency with angle results from the mixing of electron spin states. (ν = 9160 kMc/sec, T = 4.2°K.)

ciable, leading to the observed triplets. The strength of the lines reduced very rapidly with departure from zero degrees. A weak triplet associated with $S = -3/2$ was also observed with the lines falling at 71.93, 72.15, and 72.37 Mc/sec at zero degrees. It is interesting to note that while all the Cr^{53} data were taken by observing the $S = -1/2$ to $+1/2$ transition, saturation of the hyperfine levels in the $S = +3/2$ state caused the largest changes in the electron spin resonance signal.

The strong effect of nuclear polarization on the electron spin resonance can easily be observed in ruby without applying rf. At microwave power level well above saturation, if one rapidly moves from one part of the resonance line to another a large transient with a decay time of about 5 seconds is observed. The same decay time is observed for the transient following removal of rf power sufficient to saturate one of the aluminum nuclear transitions. Further, the observed decay time of the aluminum nuclear polarization is also 5 seconds while T_1 for the electron spin resonance transition is approximately 0.2 second. The decay time of the effects associated with the chromium-53 nuclei was also near 5 seconds.

The effects of nuclear polarization upon the electron spin resonance signal were only observable when microwave power levels of the order of or greater than that needed to saturate the electron spin transition were used. When the electron spin resonance signal was observed at low microwave powers, the application of rf had no effect upon the signal. Further, when the signal was observed during the nuclear polarization relaxation time following a quick reduction in the microwave power level from above to well below saturation, only a 0.2-second time constant transient was observed. The application of rf power had no effect upon the transient, indicating that T_1 is independent of the nuclear polarization.

A decrease in microwave power absorption with the application of rf power was always observed. As a check, some observations were made using amplitude modulation of the microwaves rather than magnetic field modulation. Also, the amplitude of the magnetic field modulation was varied over a wide range with no significant effects being observed.

It does not seem that the effects reported here can be explained by any of the mechanisms proposed by Feher[4] to explain his observations in doped silicon. The slow relaxation after the removal of rf power would seem to indicate that the host nuclei play an important role in either the induced transition probabilities or relaxation mechanisms between electron spin states. If such were the case, in order to get an appreciable percentage effect in the electron system by saturating the nuclei, one would have to reduce the relative electronic polarization (N_i/N_j) to the same order as the nuclear polarization (n_k/n_l), i.e., $N_i/N_j \cong n_k/n_l$. This idea is consistent with our experimental results as the nuclear polarizations are increased by about a factor of[1] 40 and the electronic polarizations are decreased by about a factor of 100 under our experimental conditions, making the two comparable.

We have also studied the effect of rf upon maser action in ruby,[5] and have observed a number of additional very weak lines.

We wish to thank Professor C. Kikuchi for many helpful discussions.

*This work was supported by Project Michigan (administered by the U. S. Army Signal Corps), and by the Air Force Office of Scientific Research.

†Now with the Scientific Laboratory, Ford Motor Company, Dearborn, Michigan.

[1]J. A. Cowen, R. W. Schafer, and R. D. Spence, Phys. Rev. Letters 3, 13 (1959).

[2]M. Abraham, M. A. H. McCausland, and F. N. H. Robinson, Phys. Rev. Letters 2, 449 (1959).

[3]A. A. Manenkov and A. M. Prokhorov, Zhur. Eksp. i Teoret. Fiz. 31, 346 (1956) [translation: Soviet Phys.-JETP 4, 288 (1957)].

[4]G. Feher, Phys. Rev. 114, 1219 (1959); G. Feher and E. A. Gere, Phys. Rev. 114, 1245 (1959).

[5]G. Makhov, L. G. Cross, R. W. Terhune, and J. Lambe, J. Appl. Phys. (to be published).

Journal of Electronics and Control, Vol. 10, No. 1, p. 13, January 1961

Adiabatic Rapid Passage in Ruby at 8 mm Wavelengths†

By J. S. Thorp, J. H. Pace and D. F. Sampson
Physics Department, Royal Radar Establishment,
Malvern, Worcs

[Received November 10, 1960]

Abstract

An investigation of adiabatic rapid passage has been made in ruby at 8 mm wavelengths. Performance data are given on a two-level ruby maser operated both as a pulsed amplifier and as an oscillator at these wavelengths. When amplifying, values of gain and bandwidth of up to about 14 dB and 10 Mc/s at 1·4°K were obtained, giving root gain-bandwidth products of up to about 50 Mc/s. In preliminary experiments using the maser as an oscillator output powers of about 70 μW at 33·1 Gc/s were obtained at 1·4°K. The inversion technique used, which incorporates magnetic field modulation with the use of the crystal as a cavity, could be readily scaled to considerably higher frequencies.

§ 1. Introduction

When attempting to extend three-level maser techniques (Bloembergen 1956, Scovil *et al.* 1957, Kikuchi *et al.* 1959) to millimetre and sub-millimetre wavelengths difficulties are encountered because the pump frequency must in general be higher than that of the signal to be amplified and pumping valves of adequate power are not yet readily available in the required frequency range. This requirement has been avoided in two promising alternative approaches. In the first of these a favourable population difference is set up between suitable levels at a relatively low priming frequency and oscillation or amplification at a higher frequency is obtained by rapidly increasing the magnetic field. Experiments of this kind have been reported by Foner *et al.* (1960 a, b) and Hoskins and Birnbaum (1960) who performed a three-level saturation experiment in ruby at 9 Gc/s and, by using a pulsed solenoid to generate rapidly a much larger field, obtained oscillations at frequencies up to 70 Gc/s. In the second method use is made of cross-relaxation effects (Mims and McGee 1959, Bloembergen *et al.* 1959) to pump levels which are harmonically related to the priming source; by this means amplification at 10·5 Gc/s has been obtained using a 9·6 Gc/s pump (Arams 1960). Of these two approaches the former has the advantage that fewer restrictions are imposed on the maser material and operation at very short wavelengths should be possible if adequate magnetic fields are provided. In such a pulsed field maser the maximum population difference across the signal transition would be achieved by direct inversion of these levels

† Communicated by the Authors.

at the pump frequency. Population inversion by adiabatic rapid passage technique has been discussed in the literature (Combrisson *et al.* 1956, Singer 1959). The majority of electron spin resonance inversion experiments have been performed on materials having a single free electron, for example, phosphorus doped silicon and irradiated quartz, calcite, or magnesium oxide (Feher *et al.* 1958, Waters 1960, Bijl 1960), though some results have been reported on the more widely used maser materials such as potassium chromicyanide (Chester *et al.* 1960) and ruby (Hoskins 1959); these experiments were performed at frequencies up to only about 9 Gc/s and it was possible to mount a small sample in a tunable high Q cavity. At millimetre wavelengths, however, the high values of magnetic field required, which may reach about 100 kilogauss, impose severe limitations on the size of the magnet gap or solenoid which can be employed and this renders the use of a cavity system of this type difficult. The present approach incorporates magnetic field modulation with the use of the crystal as a cavity, and could be readily scaled to considerably higher frequencies.

§ 2. Apparatus and Technique

The experiments were conducted with a modified 8 mm microwave spectrometer, details of which have already been reported in connection with spin-lattice relaxation time measurements (Pace *et al.* 1960 a, b). The modifications necessary included the use of a tunable 8 mm power klystron

Fig. 1

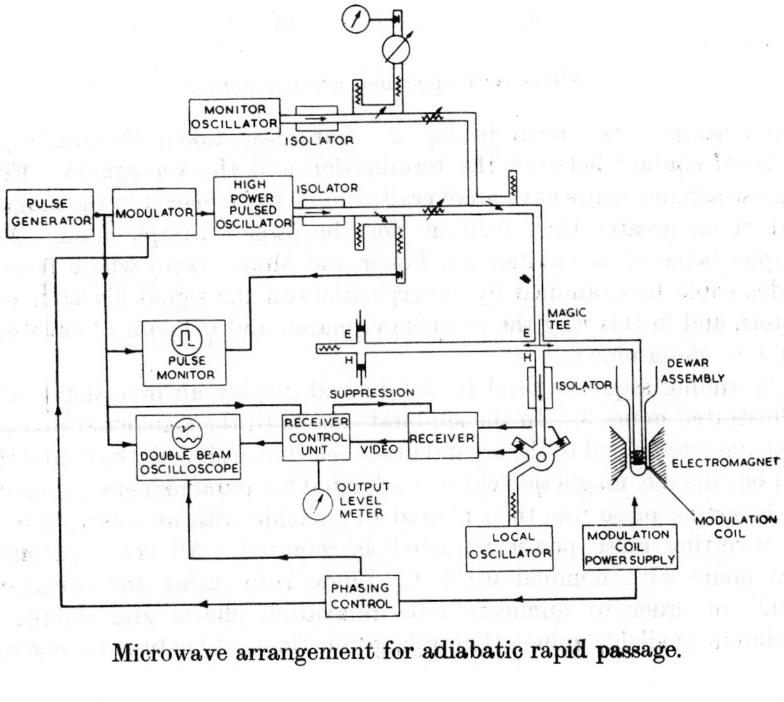

Microwave arrangement for adiabatic rapid passage.

(Elliot Type 8TFK2), the provision of a modulating field round the specimen, and the addition of a phasing control with which the inverting pulse could be made to occur at any point of the modulation cycle. A simplified block diagram of the microwave system is given in fig. 1. The modulating field was obtained from a coil mounted between the tails of the inner and outer dewars; this was cooled in liquid nitrogen and fields of up to about 1000 gauss at frequencies of up to about 1 kc/s could be obtained at the sample. The low-temperature assembly consisted of a straight length of silver plated cupro-nickel waveguide, of inside dimensions 0·140 in. × 0·280 in. and wall thickness 0·005 in., terminated either by a sample mounted on a plated plunger or by a shaped and silver

Fig. 2

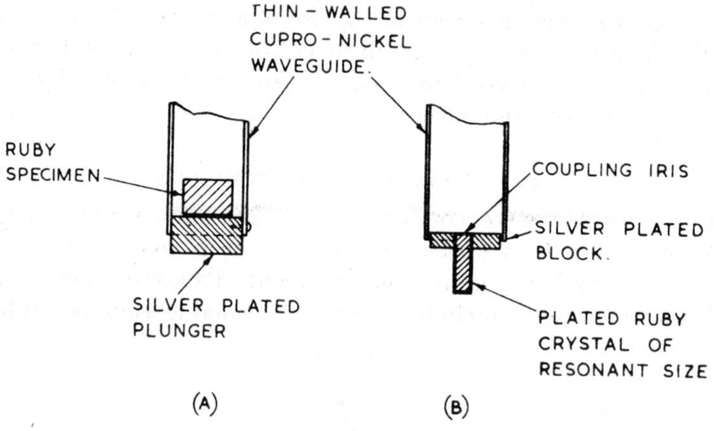

Alternative specimen arrangements.

plated sample, as shown in fig. 2. Care was taken to ensure good electrical contact between the termination and the waveguide. Either of these arrangements gave an overall volume to be placed in the magnetic field of no greater than 0·25 cm³ for the largest sample used. These samples behaved as cavities (cf. Foner and Momo 1960) whose resonant modes could be examined by superposition on the signal klystron mode pattern and in this way the frequency, match and Q factor of each mode could be determined.

The timing sequence used to obtain and display an inversion pattern is illustrated in fig. 3. In the simplest case both the signal and inverting klystrons were tuned to the crystal mode selected and, with the modulating field on, the d.c. magnetic field was adjusted for paramagnetic resonance; the inverting pulse was then phased to coincide with an absorption and the inverting pulse power adjusted as required. All the experiments were made with nominal 0·1% Cr Linde ruby using the orientation $\theta = 90°$ in order to minimize cross-relaxation effects and obtain the maximum available spin–lattice relaxation time. (Analysis by chemical

Fig. 3

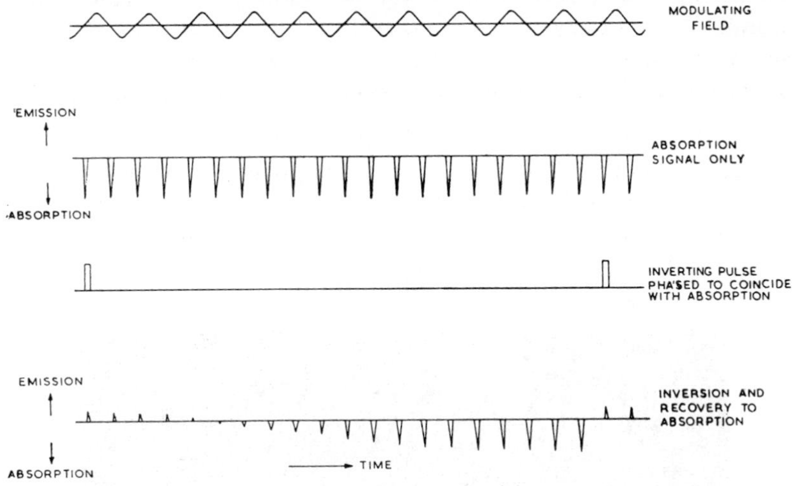

Sequence for inversion.

and spectrographic methods showed that the sample contained 0·05% Cr.) Typical conditions under which inversion of a first-order transition was observed at 1·4°K are given in table 1.

Table 1. Conditions for inversion of a first order ruby transition at 1·4°K

Crystal volume	0·03 cm³
Crystal mode Q factor	1000
Inverting pulse peak power	$\simeq$1 watt
Inverting pulse length	$\nless$120 microseconds
Inverting pulse p.r.f.	25 c/s
Signal power	$\simeq$0·5 microwatts
Signal frequency	33·87 Gc/s
D.C. magnetic field	10 425 gauss
Line width	20 gauss
Spin–lattice relaxation time	60 milliseconds
Modulating field amplitude	$\nless \pm 100$ gauss
Modulating field frequency	500 c/s

In this table the inverting pulse power quoted refers to the input to the cryostat. It was found that a minimum Q of about 700 was required for inversion and that the inverting power necessary decreased with increasing Q value. There was some freedom of choice of the sweep rate and inverting pulse length and power. It was noticeable that the minimum power required for inversion was only marginally greater than that needed for saturation; above this minimum level however the inversion efficiency increased with power and was still increasing at the maximum level of 3 watts available from the power klystron. The sweep rates required, about 2×10^5 gauss per second, are of the same order of magnitude as those reported by Hoskins for inversion in ruby at 9 Gc/s.

§ 3. Maser Performance

A number of experiments have been made to assess the performance of the system as a potential pulsed amplifier or oscillator for short millimetre wavelengths. The results of these are discussed below.

Fig. 4

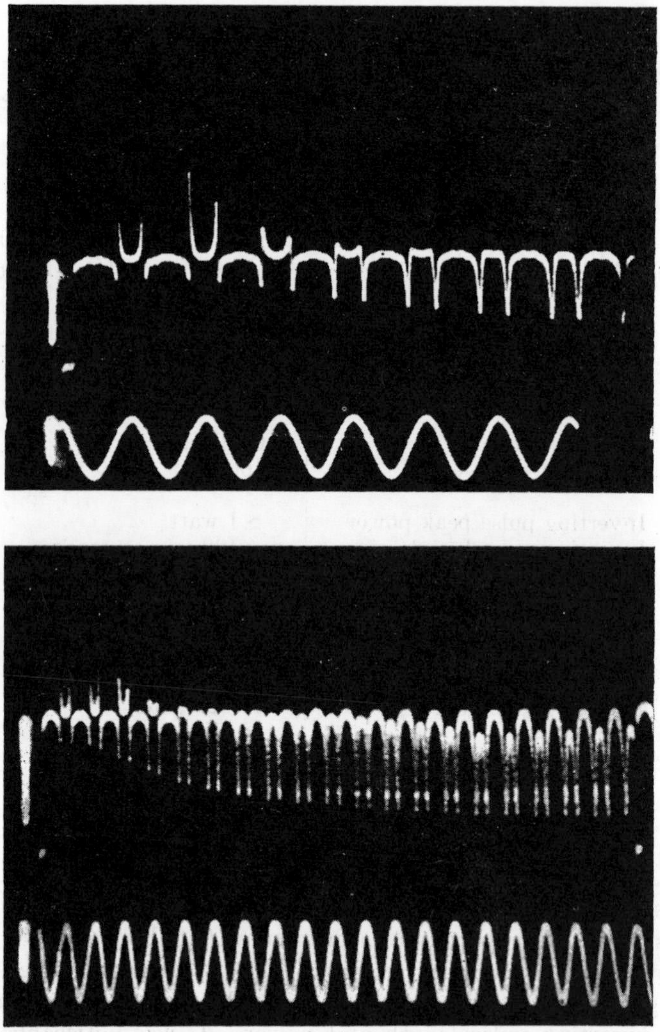

Typical inversion patterns showing (*a*), decrease in gain during inversion period and (*b*) inversion of part of a line followed by recovery to thermal equilibrium. Timing wave 500 c/s.

3.1. *Length of Inversion Period*

A typical inversion pattern is shown in fig. 4. To obtain this display the microwave bridge balance was adjusted so that the centre line. corresponding to zero input to the receiver, represented saturation while a downward going signal represented absorption and an upward signal amplification. In fig. 4 the modulating field frequency was 500 c/s, giving observations 1 millisecond apart. The period over which some inversion of population exists can be estimated directly from patterns of this kind. For a first-order transition at 1·4°K this period was about 6 milliseconds, and for a second-order transition about 14 milliseconds. The spin–lattice relaxation times for these transitions (Pace *et al.* 1960) are of the order of 60 milliseconds and 140 milliseconds respectively, and it thus appears that inversion periods of about one-tenth of the relaxation time can be obtained. Under the conditions of these experiments the duration of the inversion periods were unaffected by small changes in the power level of the signal klystron though it would be expected that at the much lower input signal levels which a maser would be used to detect in practice some increase in the length of the inversion period would be obtained. The variation of gain throughout this period is considered in a later section, but it can be noted immediately that this indicates that a pulsed amplifier having approximately constant gain for some microseconds with a recurrence frequency of about 25 c/s would be feasible.

3.2. *Inversion Efficiency*

Estimates of the inversion efficiency can also be made from these observations. The inversion efficiency is defined as the ratio of the

Fig. 5

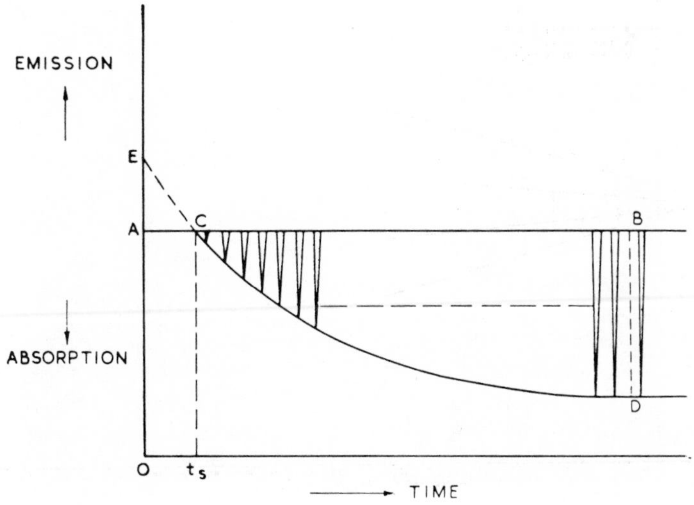

Derivation of inversion efficiency from inversion pattern.

number of spins available for amplication after inversion to the total number of absorbing spins before inversion. Figure 5 illustrates the derivation of the inversion efficiency from the inversion pattern. With the microwave bridge adjusted so that the input to the receiver is proportional to the absorption or emission due to the sample the line AB corresponds to zero input and represents saturation. Inversion occurs at a time $t=0$, and when t is several times T_1 it can be assumed that thermal equilibrium has been restored. (T_1 is the spin–lattice relaxation time.) At the point C, occurring at the measurable time t_s after inversion, the levels are saturated, and the curve CD represents the enevelope of the observed recovery from saturation to thermal equilibrium. Extrapolating this curve to $t=0$ gives the hypothetical decay curve from inversion to saturation in the absence of amplication. (The amplified signal abstracts energy from the inverted spin system and hence causes a faster decay rate than that due to normal spin–lattice relaxation). Thus the inversion efficiency is given by the ratio AE/BD which may readily be obtained from a log (amplitude) versus time plot derived from the observed recovery from saturation. In most experiments this was between about 10% and 20%: this is rather lower than the value of about 35% reported by Chester for chromicyanide at 9 G/cs and the difference is thought to be due to the limited inverting powers and Q factors available.

3.3. *Variation of Inverting Power with Order of Transition and Temperature*

In view of the difficulty in providing very high magnetic fields considerable advantage would be gained, particularly at the shorter wavelengths, if the higher order transitions which occur at lower fields could

Fig. 6

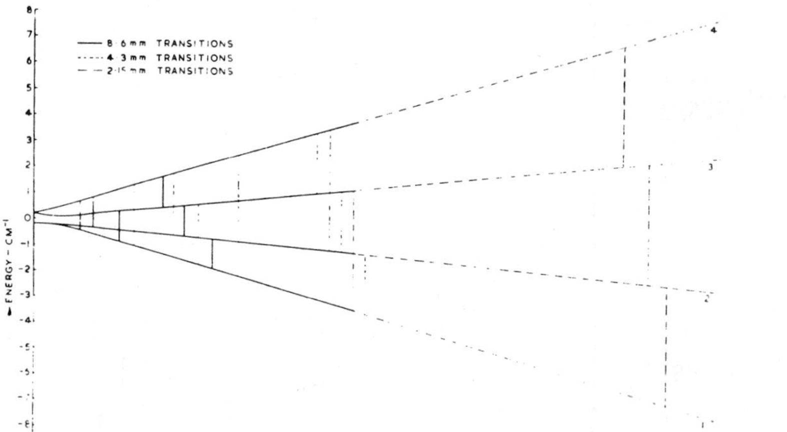

Energy level diagram for ruby at $\theta=90°$.

be utilized (fig. 6). It was possible to invert all the 8 mm transitions in the ruby spectrum at $\theta=90°$, both at 1·4°K and 4·2°K. In table 2 the minimum values of peak pulse power necessary for inversion of the various transitions are listed for two typical well matched crystal modes at 1·4°K; in these measurements the inverting pulse length was about 200 micro-seconds and the modulating field sweep rate about 2×10^5 gauss per second.

Table 2. Inverting powers for various transitions at 1·4°K.
Frequency = 33·5 Gc/s. V.S.W.R. at sample about 0·8

Transition		Inverting power (watts)	
Order	Field (kilogauss)	$Q=1000$	$Q=1660$
1–2	14·05	0·85	0·27
2–3	11·80	0·23	0·07
3–4	9·85	0·25	0·06
1–3	6·75	0·48	0·30
2–4	4·65	0·87	0·73
1–4	3·75	2·5	1·85

The minimum inverting power required for a given transition depends both on the Q of the mode being used and on the match. The higher-order transitions require greater inverting powers than the first order transitions but yield inversion periods about twice as long. It is interesting to note that the transition which required least inverting power is the 2–3 first-order line; this the transition for which, at the orientation $\theta=90°$ used, the transition probability is the greatest (Howarth 1958).

At 4·2°K the inverting powers required were rather larger than the corresponding values at 1·4°K, preliminary observations suggesting that for a given transition the inverting power necessary is approximately proportional to temperature in the helium range.

3.4. *Amplifier Characteristics*

Either stable simplification or self oscillation could be obtained after inversion depending on the loaded Q of the crystal mode and on the transition used. With Q factors lower than about 2000 amplification was obtained with all transitions: with Q factors above about 2500 oscillation was obtained with first-order transitions, but with intermediate values amplification was observed with some transitions and oscillation with others. Measurements of the gain of the system have been made under amplifying conditions by comparing the amplitudes of the detected signal at each successive sweep through resonance with the mean signal level between resonances.

Since the latter level was also the amplitude at saturation, i.e. unity gain, equating the resonance level to it by means of a variable attenuator in the input guide gave a direct measure of gain in the sample. This procedure was repeated for each successive cycle of amplification. Some typical results are given in table 3, in which the inverting and signal frequencies were both equal to 33·56 Gc/s and measurements were made over the first 5 milliseconds of the inversion periods using the same sample resonance for all transitions.

Table 3. Gain (dB) at millisecond intervals during inversion period for first and second order ruby transitions ; $\theta = 90°$, 1·4°K ; Mode $Q = 2240$

Transition	1 msec	Gain (dB) during inversion period			
		2 msec	3 msec	4 msec	5 msec
1–2	Oscillates	14·2	7·4	5·6	4·1
2–3	11·9	9·7	6·5	3·2	0·5
3–4	3·2	2·2	1·2	0·6	—
1–3	2·4	2·0	1·6	1·2	0·8
2–4	1·4	1·2	1·0	0·7	0·5

This shows that considerably higher gains can be obtained with some of the first-order transitions than with second-order lines, and that the rate of decay of gain with time is sufficiently slow to enable substantially constant gain to be achieved for periods of some tens of microseconds. For example, using the results given in table 3 for the 1–2 transition it can be seen that the change in gain over a 50 microsecond period occuring 2·5 milliseconds after inversion is only about 0·3 dB for a mean gain of about 10 dB. The low gain attained with second-order transitions is indicative of poor inversion efficiency, though it can be seen that under these conditions the gain falls off much more slowly and in fact some amplification can be obtained up to 14 milliseconds after inversion. During these gain measurements the inversion pattern observed (e.g. as in fig. 4 (*a*)) represented the superposition of many coincident traces and thus indicated that a high order of overall stability had been achieved for periods of some minutes.

Estimates of bandwidth were made by noting the change in frequency of the signal klystron required to reduce the gain by 3 dB on either side of the maximum. This was done for the first amplified signal for several transitions and the bandwidth obtained, which appeared to be roughly constant, was about 10 Mc/s. This figure gives a maximum observed root gain-bandwidth product of about 50 Mc/s at 1·4°K.

Amplification has also been obtained at frequencies above and below that of the inverting pulse. In one case a sample was prepared which had two fairly high Q modes about 0·7 Gc/s apart; with the inverting pulse frequency set on the lower resonance, at 33·5 Gc/s, amplification was observed at the higher mode frequency, 34·22 Gc/s for all the first and second-order transitions at 1·4°K. In another sample a mode separation of 2·1 Gc/s was available, though the lower resonance was outside the tuning range of the power klystron; the change in magnetic field of about 1000 gauss required to span these resonances could just be obtained with the modulating coil, and with the inverting pulse frequency set at 33·55 Gc/s amplification was observed at 31·40 Gc/s.

3.5. *Oscillator Characteristics*

Self-oscillation has been obtained after inversion of first-order transitions when a sufficiently high Q crystal mode was selected. In the present system the minimum Q value required for oscillation was about 2500 and emission has been observed as a pulse of about 25 microseconds duration occurring on the first passage after inversion through the field value corresponding to paramagnetic resonance. The frequency of the emission pulse was determined by the crystal resonance used and in preliminary measurements at 1·4°K the inverting pulse frequency was for convenience set to the same value. These measurements were made with a sample of volume 0·03 cm³ and a peak power output of about 70 microwatts at 33·1 Gc/s was obtained with a pulse recurrence frequency of 25 c/s, although the latter, limited by the circuitry available, was probably rather too fast to allow full recovery to thermal equilibrium to occur between successive inversions. The emission pulse could be made to occur at times of up to 2·2 milliseconds after inversion, by altering the modulation field frequency. Self-oscillation was also observed at 4·2°K.

Estimates of the energy available from the spin system under the conditions of this experiment indicated that a considerably larger power should have been obtainable; the difference between the calculated and observed powers suggests that only part of the sample was emitting.

§ 4. Extension to Shorter Wavelengths

The inversion technique developed using an electromagnet should be capable of extension to 4 and 2 mm wavelengths without radical alteration. It seems likely that the cryostat and crystal system could be directly scaled, and the general technique would be unchanged. The most difficult problem would be that of providing the magnetic fields required. Table 4 shows the approximate fields needed for 8, 4, and 2 mm operation in ruby at $\theta = 90°$.

Table 4. Approximate field requirements for 8, 4 and 2 mm operation in ruby at $\theta = 90°$

Transition	Magnetic field (kilogauss)		
	8·6 mm	4·3 mm	2·15 mm
1–2	14·45	26·8	51·1
2–3	12·15	24·8	49·6
3–4	10·45	22·8	47·5
1–3	6·95	13·3	25·8
2–4	4·90	11·3	23·8
1–4	3·85	8·15	16·5

Using first-order transitions 4 mm operation would be just possible within the limits of electromagnets, with which about 24 kilogauss should be attainable. It has been shown, however, that some gain can be obtained using second-order transitions, and under these conditions a pulsed 4 mm amplifier could be made using fields of less than 14 kilogauss which can readily be obtained with existing magnets. It can also be seen that with a 25 kilogauss electromagnet 2 mm operation could be obtained on the 1–3 and 2–4 transitions, but here pulsed field techniques appear to offer greater flexibility.

§ 5. Conclusions

A technique has been developed for inverting, at 8 mm wavelengths, the populations of any two levels in a multi-level system by adiabatic rapid passage. This incorporates the use of the sample as a resonant cavity, and magnetic field modulation, and has been applied to the study of inversion in 0·05% Cr ruby. At helium temperatures inverting pulse powers of from about 60 milliwatts to 3 watts and sweep rates of about 2×10^5 gauss per second are required. The system has been used both as a pulsed 8 mm two-level maser amplifier and as a pulsed oscillator. In the former case amplification can be obtained for approximately one tenth of the spin–lattice relaxation time, i.e. about 6 or 14 milliseconds for first and second-order transitions respectively. The gain and the bandwidth, for which typical observed values for the first amplified pulse were about 14 dB and 10 Mc/s, depend on the Q of the crystal resonance selected, the root gain bandwidth product being about 50 Mc/s. After inversion the gain decays with time, but amplification at substantially constant gain should be possible for a period of some tens of microseconds at any instant within the inversion period. In preliminary experiments using the system as an oscillator peak powers of about 70 μW were observed in pulses about 25 microseconds long. With minor modifications the technique should be suitable for extension to 4 and 2 mm wavelengths using electromagnets though it is probable that at these wavelengths a pulsed field approach would be more elegant.

Acknowledgments

We are indebted to the Chemical Inspectorate, Woolwich, for the analyses of the ruby samples.

This paper is published by permission of the Controller, H.M.S.O.

References

Arams, F. R., 1960, *Proc. Inst. Radio Engrs, N.Y.*, **48,** 108.

Bijl, D., 1960, Nottingham Conference on Solid State Microwave Amplifiers.

Bloembergen, N., 1956, *Phys. Rev.*, **104,** 324.

Bloembergen, N., Shapiro, S., Pershan, P. S., and Artman, J. O., 1959, *Phys. Rev.*, **114,** 445.

Chester, P. F., Wagner, P. E., and Castle, J. G., 1960, *Quantum Electronics* (New York : Columbia University Press).

COMBRISSON, J., HONIG, A., and TOWNES, C. H., 1956, *C.R. Acad. Sci., Paris*, **242,** 2451.
FEHER, G., GORDON, J. P., BUCHLER, E., GERE, E. A., and THURMOND, C. D 1958, *Phys. Rev.*, **109,** 221.
FONER, S., MOMO, L. R., MAYER, A., and MYERS, R. A., 1960 a, *Quantum Electronics* (New York : Columbia University Press); 1960 b, *J. appl. Phys.*, **31,** 443.
FONER, S., and MOMO, L. R., 1960, *J. appl. Phys.*, **31,** 742.
HOSKINS, R. H., 1959, *J. appl. Phys.*, **30,** 797.
HOSKINS, R. H., and BIRNBAUM, G., 1960, *Quantum Electronics* (New York : Columbia University Press).
HOWARTH, D. J., 1958, R.R.E. Memorandum No. 1525.
KIKUCHI, C., LAMBE, J., MAKHOV, G., and TERHUNE, R. W., 1959, *J. appl. Phys.*, **30,** 1061.
MIMS, W. B., and McGEE, J. D., 1959, *Proc. Inst. Radio Engrs. N.Y.*, **47,** 2120.
PACE, J. H., SAMPSON, D. F., and THORP, J. S., 1960 a, *Phys. Rev. Letters*, **4,** 18 ; 1960 b, *Proc. phys. Soc.*, **76,** 697 ; R.R.E. Memorandum No. 1693.
SCOVIL, H. E. D., FEHER, G., and SEIDEL, H., 1957, *Phys. Rev.*, **105,** 762.
SINGER, J. R., 1959, *Masers* (New York : John Wiley and Sons, Inc.).
WATERS, G., 1960, Nottingham Conference on Solid State Microwave Amplifiers.

Recovery Technique for Saturated Masers*

GUNTER K. WESSEL†, SENIOR MEMBER, IRE

Summary—**The practical application of masers is often hindered by saturation effects of the maser material. Any strong signal frequency (*e.g.*, the transmitter pulse of a radar system leaking into the maser) will cause saturation. This paralyzes the maser for a period of time, too long for most intended applications. In this report, a method is described which has been used in desaturating a four-level ruby maser.**

The saturation is caused by equalizing the populations of levels one, two, and three of the maser crystal by the leakage of the transmitter pulse, in addition to the action of the maser pump. The application of a desaturation pulse between levels one and four will then desaturate the maser, restoring the excess population density between levels two and one. In a cavity maser, full recovery of the amplification capabilities has been achieved within less than 1 msec after the maser has been saturated. Repetition rates up to 120 cps are tolerable.

Introduction

In recent years, the solid-state maser has been developed to a point of being applicable to many systems where an extremely low-noise microwave amplifier is required. Numerous important achievements in the maser field have been reported which make the maser a desirable preamplifier.

In some cases, however, the applicability of the maser is hindered by saturation effects due to strong pulses of the signal frequency. If the usual case of a radar system in which only one antenna is used for both the transmitter and the receiver is considered, the maser material may become saturated by leakage of the transmitter pulse into the maser. The pulse power which causes saturation may be as low as 10 to 100 μw in a ruby maser.

A saturated maser is not capable of amplifying the signal for a certain period of time—the recovery time. For most maser materials such as ruby, the recovery time is of the order of a few tenths of a second, much too long for most intended applications.

Several attempts to prevent or overcome saturation in the maser have been made or are under way. The conventional method is to use duplexers to prevent the transmitter power from reaching the receiver. However, unless a duplexer with extremely low insertion loss is employed, duplexers will generate too much noise to be tolerated in conjunction with a maser.

In the following, a method of desaturation is outlined using available maser materials.

Maser Operation and Saturation

Consider a material with suitably spaced internal energy levels. The essential requirement for the operation of a maser is an excess of population density of a higher energy level with respect to a lower one. Amplification of a signal of frequency ν_s occurs if the net stimulated emission is larger than the power required for overcoming the circuitry losses.

In a three-level maser,[1] the excess of population density is achieved by the application of a pumping power of frequency ν_p. Considering the lowest three energy levels in Fig. 1 for the three-level operation, the signal is applied between levels 1 and 2, and the pump between levels 1 and 3.

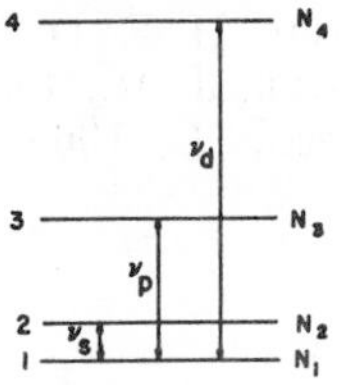

Fig. 1—Maser energy levels.

A strong pulse at the signal frequency ν_s will saturate the maser by nearly equalizing the populations N_1 and N_2 of the levels 1 and 2 in addition to the saturation caused by the pump. Therefore, all populations of the three involved levels become about equal in a saturated maser: $N_1 \approx N_2 \approx N_3$. Without the desaturation technique described below, amplification capabilities will be restored only within the recovery time.

Desaturation of a Saturated Maser

Maser materials such as ruby (where the paramagnetic atoms have spin 3/2) have four energy levels, one more than is necessary for the operation of a three-level maser. The fourth level is essential for the desaturation technique.

Suppose that the three-level maser is operated in a conventional way using the three lowest energy levels as shown in Fig. 1. The fourth level has then a higher energy and tends to achieve a lower population density than the other three levels according to Boltzmann's relation for temperature equilibrium.

Assuming that the fourth level is less populated at the time the maser becomes saturated, the desaturation of the maser is accomplished by the application of a pulse of frequency ν_d between levels 1 and 4. This desaturation pulse has to be strong enough to cause near equalization of the population N_1 and N_4. Level 2 is not affected by the application of the desaturating pulse.

Thus, a new population distribution results from the application of the desaturation pulse. The population

* Received by the PGED, March 28, 1960.
† General Electric Electronics Lab., Syracuse, N. Y.

[1] N. Bloembergen, "Proposal for a new type solid state maser," *Phys. Rev.*, vol. 104, pp. 324–327; October, 1956.

densities of level 1, and (by the continuous action of the pump) also level 3 are decreased with respect to the unchanged population of level 2. Therefore, the excess of population density of level 2 with respect to level 1, necessary for the maser operation, has been restored immediately after the application of the desaturating pulse. It is usually possible to adjust the CW pump so that the excess population remains constant during the interpulse time. This is a desirable feature resulting in the same gain of the maser at any time of the interpulse period.

The effective recovery time is given by the length of time of the desaturating pulse and can be kept small depending on the applied pulse peak power for obtaining saturation of levels 1 and 4.

The scheme outlined above will work only if the population N_4 is smaller than the populations of the lower levels at the time when the desaturation pulse is applied. After N_4 has been increased by the pulse, level 4 has to lose this increase of population by means of relaxation mechanisms in the time interval before the next desaturation pulse is applied. The amount of recovered population difference is, therefore, a function of the applied repetition rate of the pulses. Too high repetition rates will result in a loss of the maser operation recovery.

The Recovery Time

The recovery time is defined as the characteristic time associated with the gain recovery of the maser, saturated by a large signal, from zero to the factor $(1 - e^{-1})$ of the small signal gain.

In order to calculate the dependence of the recovery time on the relaxation times in a three-level maser, the following assumptions are made: the pump of frequency ν_p is strong enough to cause saturation between levels 1 and 3; the maser becomes saturated at the time $t = 0$ by the application of a strong signal of frequency ν_s between levels 1 and 2. Furthermore, it is assumed that the application of a small signal of the frequency ν_s, in addition to the strong (transmitter) signal, will change the population distribution so little by stimulated emission that this change can be neglected.

The sum of population densities must remain constant

$$N_1 + N_2 + N_3 = N \tag{1}$$

if only three levels are involved.

The rate of transition to level 2 is then:

$$\frac{dN_2}{dt} = -N_2(w_{21} + w_{23}) + N_1 w_{12} + N_3 w_{32}. \tag{2}$$

Introducing the pumping condition $N_1 = N_3$ and the boundary condition $t = 0$, $N_1 = N_2 = N_3 = N/3$, the solution of (2) for the excess population density $\Delta N = N_2 - N_1$ becomes

$$\Delta N = 3/2N \frac{(w_{12} + w_{32})(1 - e^{-t/\tau})}{2w_{21} + 2w_{23} + w_{32} + w_{12}} \tag{3}$$

with the recovery time

$$\tau = \frac{1}{w_{21} + w_{23} + w_{32}/2 + w_{12}/2}. \tag{4}$$

Eq. (4) relates the recovery time of a saturated maser to the individual transition probabilities of the material. The transition probability from level i to level j is related to the spin-lattice relaxation time T_1 by

$$w_{ij} = 1/[2T_1]_{ij}. \tag{5}$$

Making the very crude assumption that all the w's in (4) are equal, it follows that the recovery time of a saturated maser is two-thirds the spin-lattice relaxation time: $\tau = 2/3\ T_1$.

For the steady state ($t \to \infty$), (3) becomes identical with Bloembergen's[1] equation for the excess population density, assuming that

$$h\nu_{ij} \ll kT \quad \text{in} \quad w_{ij} = w_{ji} \exp\left[-\frac{h\nu_{ij}}{kT}\right]$$

$$\Delta N = \frac{Nh}{3kT} \frac{w_{32}\nu_{23} - w_{21}\nu_{12}}{w_{21} + w_{32}}. \tag{6}$$

The Desaturation Theory

In order to calculate the dependence of the recovery on the repetition rate in the four-level maser (Fig. 1), it is assumed that the maser has been fully saturated by a strong signal frequency pulse.

The desaturation technique has been discussed in detail above. The population distribution just before and immediately after the application of the desaturating pulse is as follows: before saturation,

$$N_1^* = N_2 = N_3^* \tag{7}$$

and

$$N_1^* + N_2 + N_3^* + N_4^* = N, \tag{8}$$

after desaturation,

$$N_1^0 = N_3^0 = N_4^0 \tag{9}$$

$$N_1^0 + N_2 + N_3^0 + N_4^0 = N. \tag{10}$$

The asterisks correspond to populations before the desaturation pulse is applied and the superscripts to populations immediately after that event.

The rate of transition to level 4 is

$$\frac{dN_4}{dt} = N_1(w_{14} + w_{24} + w_{34}) - N_4(w_{41} + w_{42} + w_{43}). \tag{11}$$

For the transition rates from the lower levels to level 4, the approximation is used in (11) that all of the lower levels are equally populated, which they actually are within a few per cent. Thus, with $N = 3N_1 + N_4$, and the boundary conditions (9) and (10) for $t = 0$, and (7) and (8) for $t = t_1 = 1/\nu_r - \Delta t$ (ν_r = repetition frequency;

Δt = length of desaturation pulse), the solution of 11 becomes

$$N_4^* = \frac{\alpha}{\beta} + \left(N_4^0 - \frac{\alpha}{\beta}\right)e^{-\beta t_1} \quad (12)$$

$$\alpha = \frac{N}{3}(w_{14} + w_{24} + w_{34}) \quad (13)$$

and

$$\beta = w_{41} + w_{42} + w_{43} + \frac{w_{14}}{3} + \frac{w_{24}}{3} + \frac{w_{34}}{3}. \quad (14)$$

This solution (12) is graphically shown in Fig. 2.

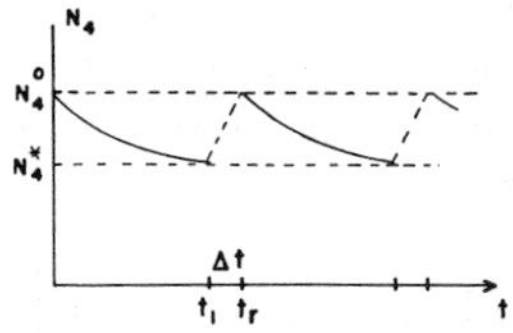

Fig. 2—Population density of level 4 as function of time.

After several periods $t_r = 1/\Delta\nu_r$ have transpired, the maser will be in such a quasi-steady state that the amount of excess population $\Delta N = N_2 - N_1^0$ gained by levels 1 and 3 is equal to the loss of population by level 4 during the time t_1

$$\Delta N = 1/2(N_4^0 - N_4^*). \quad (15)$$

The excess population density gained by the application of the desaturation pulse can now be obtained by calculating N_4^0 and N_4^*

$$\Delta N = \left[\frac{N - 4\dfrac{\alpha}{\beta}}{9 - e^{-\beta t_1}}\right](1 - e^{-\beta t_1}). \quad (16)$$

This excess population is available immediately after the application of the desaturating pulse. This means that the shortest time interval between the saturation of the maser and the complete recovery is the length Δt or the pulse itself; Δt can be kept as short as practical. The only requirement is that the pulse length and pulse peak power be large enough to produce saturation between levels 1 and 4.

Theoretical Performance

With the relations calculated above, the performance of the desaturation technique can be numerically predicted.

In order to calculate the relative excess population $\Delta N/N$ from (16), the following operational data are assumed:

liquid helium bath temperature $T = 2°K$
signal frequency $\nu_s = 2.5$ kMc
pump frequency $\nu_p = 12.6$ kMc
desaturation frequency $\nu_d = 23.8$ kMc
pulse length $\Delta t = 0.5$ msec
spin-lattice relaxation time $T_1 = 0.1$ second.

Furthermore, the transition probabilities are assumed to be equal: $w_{43} = w_{42} = w_{41} = w = 1/2\,T_1$. A special ruby crystal with the crystal axis perpendicular to the direction of growth was used in the desaturation experiments. For this crystal, the spin-lattice relaxation time $T_1 = 0.1$ second was measured at 2°K using several different measuring methods. For example, the recovery time of a saturated three-level maser was measured and the relaxation time ($T_1 = 0.11$ second) calculated according to the relation $T_1 = 3/2\,\tau$.

The results of the calculation of the relative excess population are given in Table I as function of the repetition rate.

TABLE I

Repetition rate (ν_r 1/second)	Relative Excess Population $\Delta N/N$
0	3.3 per cent
10	2.7
20	2.1
40	1.2
100	0.6
150	0.4

The values in Table I have to be compared to the relative excess population available in a conventional three-level maser. Assuming again equal relaxation times $w_{32} = w_{21}$, $\Delta N/N$ becomes 3.0 per cent according to (6). This comparison seems to indicate that full recovery is possible only for low repetition rates. However, by adjusting the signal coupling in the case of a cavity maser, the maser usually can be operated at considerably lower excess populations than 3 per cent, leading to reduced pumping power requirements than needed for full saturation of the two pump levels. Therefore, adjusting the maser, say to an operation of 0.5 per cent relative excess population, full recovery up to repetition rates of 120 cps can be achieved. The experiments described below verify this conclusion.

The Maser Material

In the work described below, pink ruby (Al_2O_3 doped with Cr) was used as maser material. In an external magnetic field, the chromium ions show a Zeeman effect with four energy levels as plotted in Fig. 3 for an angle of 90° between the dc magnetic field and the crystal axis. At a field of $H = 2.5$ kilo oersteds, an operating point can be found so that the signal frequency is at S band (2.49 kMc), the pumping frequency at X band (12.6 kMc), and the desaturation frequency at K band (23.8 kMc). In this region, all transitions between energy levels are allowed and maser operation can easily be obtained.

The alternate application of the desaturation pulse between levels 3 and 4, rather than 1 and 4, at a frequency of 11.2 kMc should lead to the same results.

The Apparatus

For the verification of the desaturation method, a transmitter pulse was fed into the maser; thereafter, the desaturation pulse and finally the echo as the signal pulse were applied.

It was necessary to employ a microwave cavity which is resonant at three frequencies—the signal at S band, the pump at X band, and the desaturation pulse at K band. These three frequencies must be tuned so that they correspond to resonance transitions in the maser material at the operating point.

A coax-type cavity, (Fig. 4,) was chosen and operated in the *TEM* mode of the S-band signal frequency. The length of the cavity (half wavelength) determined the resonance frequency of the cavity, and it was possible to make mechanical adjustments during operation in the following way: the upper half of the cavity was rigidly connected to the waveguides, whereas the lower half could be rotated by means of a threaded tuning rod. The rod was held by a nut on top of the dewar system. Every turn thus produced a change of length of the cavity amounting to the pitch of the thread. The change in frequency was not linear with the rotation of the lower half of the cavity because the ruby crystal in the lower half of the cavity was mounted asymmetrically.

In addition to the S-band resonance of the cavity, a great number of high-order modes in the X-band and K-band regions were observed. It was always possible to find an X-band and a K-band mode close enough to the resonance transition frequency of the material so that only a small mechanical adjustment of the cavity, in addition to the adjustment of the dc magnetic field, produced the operating condition.

The S-band signal frequency was coupled to the cavity from a coaxial line by means of a magnetic coupling loop whose position in the cavity could be adjusted from the outside. The X-band and K-band powers entered the cavity through coupling holes from X-band and K-band waveguides, respectively. The setup for the maser desaturation is schematically shown in Fig. 5. The desaturation power, the transmitter power, and signal power were produced by one K-band generator and two S-band generators, the latter ones tuned to the same frequency. All three

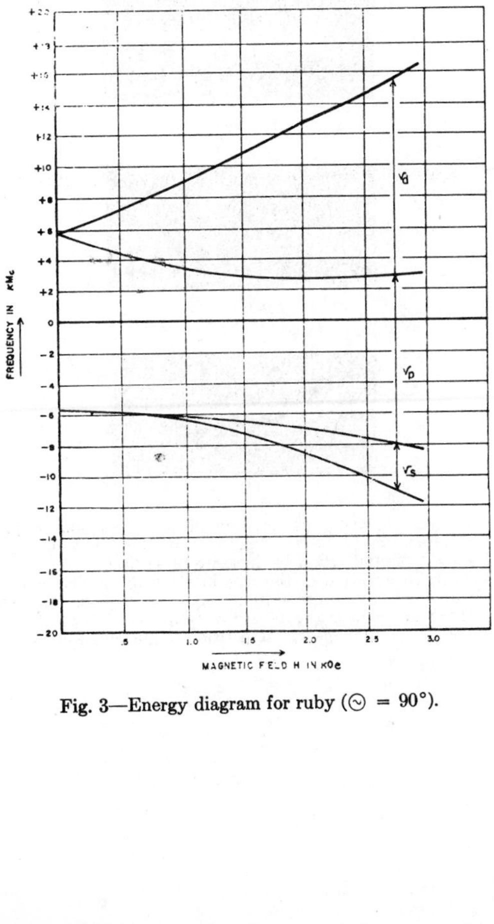

Fig. 3—Energy diagram for ruby (⊙ = 90°).

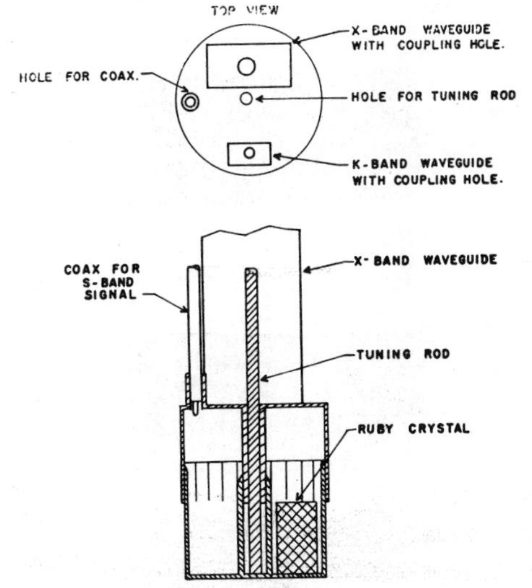

Fig. 4—Maser cavity.

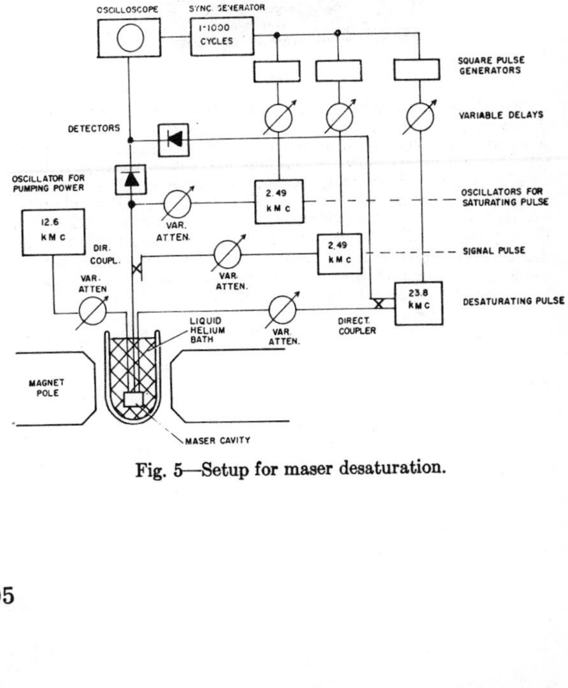

Fig. 5—Setup for maser desaturation.

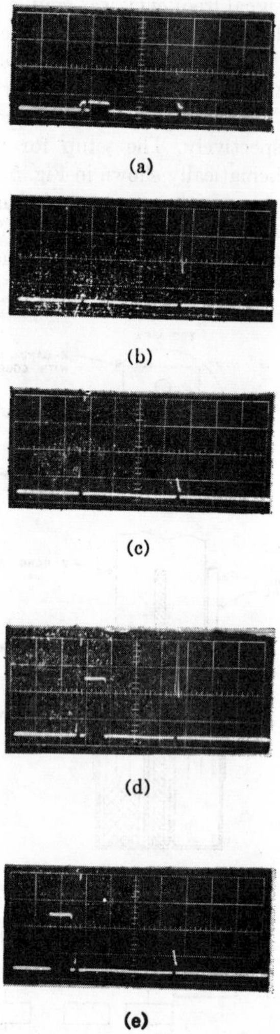

Fig. 6—Maser desaturation. (a) Saturating (transmitter) pulse, desaturating pulse, and signal pulse without maser action (CW *X*-band pump off). (b) Amplification of the signal pulse with the CW *X*-band pump switched on. The saturation pulse is reduced to a very low power; the desaturating pulse is off. (c) Loss of amplification of the signal pulse with unchanged *X*-band pump by increase of the saturating pulse to about 0.5 mw. (d) Restoration of the signal pulse amplification by the application of the desaturating pulse of about 2-mw pulse peak power. (e) Loss of signal pulse amplification by reversing the order of timing between saturating and desaturating pulses.

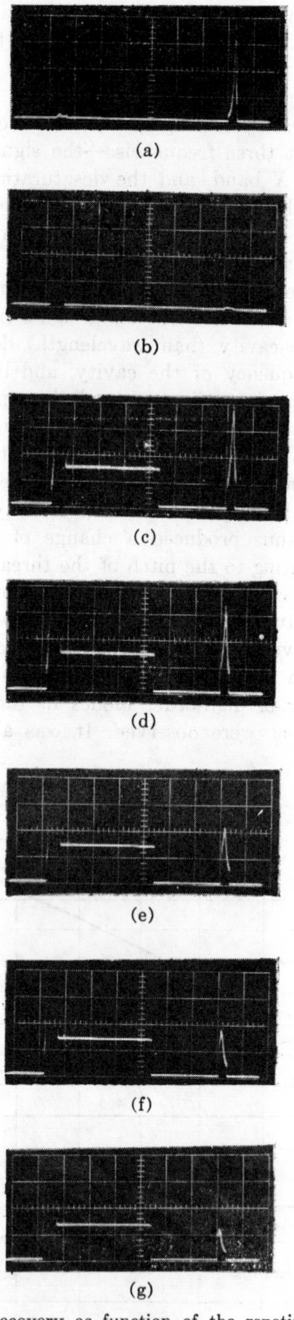

Fig. 7—Maser recovery as function of the repetition frequency. (a) Amplification of the signal pulse, using the CW *X*-band pump. (b) Loss of amplification by increase of saturating (transmitter) pulse. (c) Restoration of the amplification by application of the desaturating pulse at a repetition frequency of 35 cps. (d) Repetition frequency, 50 cps. (e) Repetition frequency, 75 cps. (f) Repetition frequency, 100 cps. (g) Repetition frequency, 150 cps.

generators were externally modulated by pulses from three square-pulse generators synchronized by a sync generator variable in frequency. The time delay between the pulses was adjusted by variable pulse delays.

The S-band signal pulse entered the coaxial line through a directional coupler, and the reflected power from the cavity was detected by a crystal detector and displayed on the screen of an oscilloscope. The sweep of the scope was also synchronized from the sync generator. The saturating S-band (transmitter) pulse entered the coaxial line between the maser and the crystal detector directly by means of a Tee, as shown in Fig. 5.

A portion of the desaturating pulse power was also detected and displayed on the oscilloscope, together with the two S-band pulses.

The Desaturation of the Maser

The desaturation demonstration is explained with the help of Fig. 6 in which pictures of the oscilloscope traces—microwave power as a function of time (in milliseconds per large unit)—are shown.

In Fig. 6(a), the timing of the following three pulses is displayed without any maser action: (from left to right) the saturating (transmitter) pulse, the desaturating pulse, and the signal pulse.

In order to produce amplification of the signal pulse, the desaturating pulse was switched off, the saturating pulse attenuated to a very low power, and the CW X-band pump switched on [Fig. 6(b)].

Saturation of the maser with the loss of amplification capabilities was then achieved by increasing the saturating pulse power [Fig. 6(c)].

Amplification of the signal could be completely restored by the application of the K-band desaturating pulse [Fig. 6(d)].

A valuable check of the correct functioning of the saturation and desaturating mechanisms was offered by the possibility of exchanging the timing order of the saturating and desaturating pulses so that the latter occurs first. In this case, one would not expect recovery of the amplification capabilities. The practical results followed the theory [Fig. 6(e)].

The dependence of the maser action recovery on the repetition rate is demonstrated in the series of oscilloscope pictures in Fig. 7. Again the microwave power is plotted as a function of time (in 0.2 msec per large unit.) The amplification of a signal pulse and the loss of amplification because of saturation by the saturating pulse are displayed again in Fig. 7(a) and (b), respectively.

In Fig. 7(c)-(g), the decrease of gain with increasing repetition rate can be observed for repetion rates up to 150 cps.

Optimizing all conditions for the maser operation and the desaturation, it was possible to achieve full recovery at repetition frequencies up to 120 cps. This may be the limit using this method. However, a repetition frequency of 120 cps is large enough for most applications where masers may be used.

To show in the figures the unamplified, as well as the amplified, signal without changing scales, the amplification power gain was adjusted relatively low. Stable gains of about 30 db could be obtained.

Because of the continuous action of the CW pump, the gain remained the same (within a few per cent) during the time period from the application of one desaturating pulse to the next. The effective recovery time, due to the length of the desaturating pulse, was about 0.7 msec. If necessary, this time could be reduced considerably by increasing the desaturating pulse peak power.

Conclusion

The desaturation of the maser described and analyzed in this paper shows the practicality of the method to recover amplification capabilities of a saturated maser within less than 1 msec.

The technique is now ready for application to any system with S-band signal frequency where saturation effects of the maser are a problem.

No difficulties in extending to higher or lower signal frequencies than S band are anticipated.

The desaturation method can be applied to available maser materials without the use of any noise-producing attenuating devices.

Repetition rates of over 100 cps are tolerable, provided that the maser can be operated with less-population density than available by application of the full saturating pump power. Otherwise, less gain after recovery will be available or lower repetition rates have to be used.

Reprinted from the IRE TRANSACTIONS OF THE PROFESSIONAL GROUP ON *ELECTRON DEVICES*
Volume ED-7, Number 4, October 1960

Optical Pumping of Microwave Masers*

H. HSU†, SENIOR MEMBER, IRE AND F. K. TITTEL‡

Summary—**The application of optical pumping techniques to microwave masers is discussed. It is shown that optical pumping appears to be promising for achieving low noise maser action at very high frequencies and at elevated temperatures. The analysis includes the treatment of optical pumping principles, noise considerations, pump power requirements and maximum signal frequencies. Potential advantages and limitations which can exist when using optical excitation are considered. Finally, the concepts and procedures developed in this paper are applied for illustrative purposes to evaluate the expected performance of a ruby maser.**

INTRODUCTION

INTEREST in applying optical pumping techniques to the development of quantum electronic devices has become apparent recently [1], [2], [3]. In particular, the successful demonstration of optically pumped microwave maser action in ruby using a ruby laser as the pump, by D. P. Devor, *et al.* [4], has paved the way for extending present maser technology. This paper is concerned with the requirements and predicted performance of an optically pumped maser. It will be shown that optical pumping methods can be used to achieve maser action with low effective noise characteristics at elevated operating temperatures or very high frequencies.

Although microwave pumped masers have been operated at liquid nitrogen and slightly higher temperatures for some time [5], [6], their performance is not satisfactory for two reasons. First, the gain-bandwidth product is inversely proportional to the temperature and, therefore, is low at elevated operating temperatures. Second, the excess noise temperature of a microwave pumped maser cannot be much lower than the actual bath or operating temperature of the device. However, as will be shown in this paper, by pumping at frequencies in the optical spectrum and at a favorable relaxation time ratio, it is possible to operate a maser without helium cooling while still keeping the noise and gain-bandwidth characteristics comparable to a conventional liquid helium cooled maser. In addition, the present lack of suitable pumping sources for masers operating at very high frequencies can be overcome by applying optical pumping techniques. Although the maser efficiency involved would be small, considerable practical advantages can be obtained.

In principle, the optically pumped maser is identical to conventional three-level masers which have been successfully operated at frequencies between 300 Mc/s and 96,000 Mc/s. The only basic difference is in the optical excitation process employed for obtaining a nonequilibrium distribution in the atomic population density. The basic limitations in the maser mechanism are the appropriate transition probabilities fixed by the inherent material constants. From a knowledge of the transition probabilities it is possible to determine the excess population in an upper state, the effective spin temperature and the pump power requirements of the maser. These properties are analyzed below. The particular case of ruby as the maser material will be considered because of its known optical and microwave properties for photon-spin interaction phenomena.

OPTICAL PUMPING PRINCIPLES

The concepts involved in the optically pumped microwave maser can be treated in a manner similar to an analysis by Bloembergen [7] for a three-level solid state maser. A suitable three-level configuration can be chosen (Fig. 1). The two lower energy levels 1 and 2,

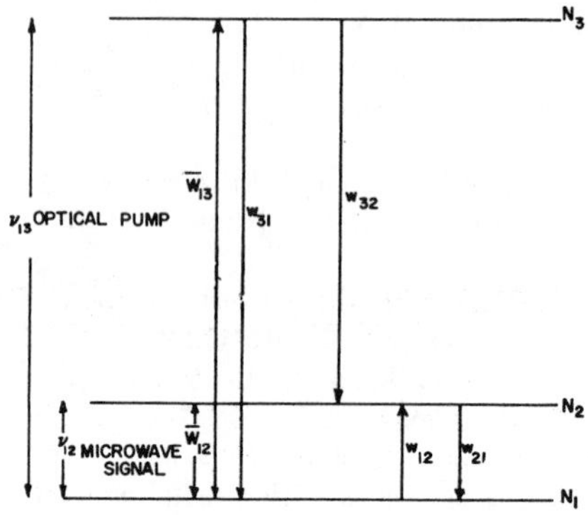

Fig. 1—Energy level diagram of three-level maser using optical pumping.

both belonging to the ground state, are separated by a microwave transition. The third level, 3, is separated from the other two by an optical transition. For such a system, the optical frequency involved is no longer small compared to kT/h at room temperature so that the transition probabilities for the relevant levels are given by

$$w_{12} = w_{21} \exp(-h\nu_{12}/kT) \approx w_{21}(1 - h\nu_{12}/kT)$$

while

$$w_{13} = w_{31} \exp(-h\nu_{31}/kT) \approx 0$$

* Received August 13, 1962. This work was supported in part by U. S. Army Signal Corps Contract No. DA-36-039-SC-87209.

† Department of Electrical Engineering, The Ohio State University, Columbus, Ohio. Formerly with Electronics Laboratory, General Electric Company, Syracuse, N. Y.

‡ Electronics Laboratory, General Electric Company, Syracuse, N. Y.

and

$$w_{23} = w_{32} \exp(-h\nu_{32}/kT) \approx 0$$

where the w's are the transition probabilities or inverse relaxation times for the specified levels. This information leads to the pertinent steady state maser rate equations for the maser and pump transitions as follows:

$$\frac{dN_2}{dT} = N_1\left(w_{21} - w_{21}\frac{h\nu_{12}}{kT} + \overline{W}_{12}\right) - N_2(w_{21} + \overline{W}_{21}) + N_3 w_{32} = 0 \quad (1)$$

and

$$\frac{dN_3}{dt} = N_1\overline{W}_{13} + N_2(0) - N_3(w_{31} + w_{32} + \overline{W}_{13}) = 0 \quad (2)$$

where the $\overline{W}$'s represent the appropriate induced optical and microwave transition probabilities and N_1, N_2, N_3 are the respective level population densities.

For incomplete saturation between levels 1 and 3, the excess population density can be calculated from (1) and (2), *i.e.*,

$$\frac{\Delta N}{N_1} \equiv \frac{N_2 - N_1}{N_1} = \left[\frac{w_{32}}{w_{21}}\cdot\frac{\overline{W}_{13}}{w_{31} + w_{32} + \overline{W}_{13}} - \frac{h\nu_{12}}{kT}\right] \cdot\left[1 + \frac{\overline{W}_{21}}{w_{21}}\right]^{-1} \quad (3)$$

The condition for stimulated emission is

$$\frac{w_{32}}{w_{21}} > \left(1 + \frac{w_{31} + w_{32}}{\overline{W}_{13}}\right)\frac{h\nu_{12}}{kT} \quad (4)$$

for $\Delta N > 0$. A simplified expression for (3) and (4) can be obtained by assuming saturation for the pump transition, *i.e.*, $\overline{W}_{13} \gg w_{13} + w_{32}$ or $N_1 = N_3$. Then, for (3),

$$\frac{\Delta N}{N_1} = \left(\frac{w_{32}}{w_{21}} - \frac{h\nu_{12}}{kT}\right)\left(1 + \frac{\overline{W}_{21}}{w_{21}}\right)^{-1} \quad (5)$$

and the corresponding condition for population inversion reduces from (4), to

$$\frac{w_{32}}{w_{21}} > \frac{h\nu_{12}}{kT}. \quad (6)$$

For a maser pumped optically and operating at 10 kMc/s and 300°K, (6) requires the ratio between the optical and microwave transition probabilities to be larger than 2×10^{-3}. For a practical system complete saturation may not be attained. In this case, as can be seen from (4), the required transition probability ratio for the maser material must be correspondingly higher.

It is interesting to compare (6) with the equivalent condition derived by Bloembergen [7] for stimulated emission at ν_{12} with microwave pumping, *i.e.*,

$$\frac{w_{32}}{w_{21}} > \frac{\nu_{12}}{\nu_{32}}. \quad (7)$$

The difference between (6) and (7) lies in the fact that (6) is valid when $h\nu_{32} \gg kT$ and (7) holds for $h\nu_{32} \ll kT$.

From (6) a limiting signal frequency can be defined as

$$\nu^0{}_{12} = \frac{w_{32}}{w_{21}}\cdot\frac{kT}{h}. \quad (8)$$

Above this frequency the maser ceases to function as a useful device, even with an infinite pumping power. It should be pointed out that the limiting frequency does not increase linearly with temperature, as it would appear in (8). In fact, ν_{12} is a complex function of temperature due to variations in the transition probabilities, particularly w_{21}.

By comparing (6) and (7), it is seen that the value of kT/h in an optically pumped maser is equivalent to ν_{32} in the microwave case because the population of the upper state will be completed depleted at $\nu_{32} > kT/h$. This relationship will also be apparent from the discussion on maser noise [see (12) and (13b)]. The comparison indicates that, as long as the pump frequency is sufficiently larger than kT/h, the advantages of optical pumping in a maser can be realized.

Maser Noise Consideration

Incoherent spontaneous emission of radiation from zero point energy fluctuations sets the lowest limit to maser noise. Noise calculations have been carried out by many authors [8], [9]. In the following, the merits of pumping optically will be discussed by considering only the noise contribution of the maser material.

The excess noise temperature (T_{ex}) is approximately equal to the abolute value of the negative temperature (T_m) which can be achieved by maser operation [10], *i.e.*

$$T_{ex} \approx |T_m|. \quad (9)$$

To determine the value of $|T_m|$, the degree of spin-level inversion is needed. Applying Boltzmann's distribution law to the quasi-equilibrium of a three-level maser and remembering that $kT \gg h\nu_{12}$ for microwaves, the negative temperature can be defined by

$$N_2 - N_1 \approx \frac{N_1 h\nu_{12}}{k|T_m|} \quad \text{or} \quad |T_m| = \frac{h\nu_{12}}{k\left(\frac{\Delta N}{N_1}\right)}. \quad (10)$$

In the case of the optically pumped maser, the relationship between the negative temperature and the operating temperature (T) is obtained from (3) and (10), *i.e.*,

$$|T_m| = T\left[1 + \frac{\overline{W}_{21}}{w_{21}}\right] \cdot\left[\frac{w_{32}}{w_{21}}\cdot\frac{kT}{h\nu_{12}}\frac{\overline{W}_{13}}{w_{31} + w_{32} + \overline{W}_{13}} - 1\right]^{-1}. \quad (11)$$

From the above expression, one may deduce that T_{ex} is increased for large values of signal power ($\overline{W}_{21}$) and $h\nu_{12}/kT$ while reduced for large pump power ($\overline{W}_{13}$) and transition probability ratio w_{32}/w_{21} Eq. (11) can be reduced to

$$|T_m| \approx T\left[\frac{w_{32}}{w_{21}}\cdot\frac{kT}{h\nu_{12}} - 1\right]^{-1} \quad (12)$$

if $\overline{W}_{13} \gg w_{31}+w_{32}$ and if $\overline{W}_{21} \ll w_{21}$ for small signal excitation.

In terms of the limiting signal frequency defined by (8), (12) can be written as

$$T_{ex} \approx T\left[\frac{\nu^0_{12}}{\nu_{12}} - 1\right]^{-1}. \quad (13)$$

In the limit of large gain, the excess noise temperature is further reduced to

$$T_{ex} \approx T\frac{\nu_{12}}{\nu^0_{12}} \quad (13a)$$

where

$$\frac{\nu^0_{12}}{\nu_{12}} \gg 1.$$

Thus, the excess noise temperature can be much lower than the operating temperature.

In the case of a microwave pumped maser having a signal transition at ν_{12}, the excess noise temperature can be obtained [10] by substituting the appropriate value of ΔN in (10).

$$|T_m| = T\frac{\nu_{12}(w_{21}+w_{32})}{w_{32}\nu_{32} - w_{21}\nu_{12}} \approx 2T\left(\frac{\nu_{32}}{\nu_{12}} - 1\right)^{-1}. \quad (13b)$$

Thus, with a microwave pump frequency not very much larger than the signal frequency, the excess noise temperature is of the order of the operating temperature. The merits of optical pumping over microwave pumping are apparent by comparing (13) or (13a) with (13b) and will be further demonstrated in the discussion of the ruby maser.

Pumping Requirements

In order to demonstrate the feasibility of applying optical pumping methods to masers, some consideration must be given to the pump power requirements for any proposed atomic system. For a three-level maser, these depend on the characteristic transition probabilities and linewidths.

In a conventional maser pumped with microwaves, all energy levels are not far from being equally populated, even at liquid helium temperature. Therefore, it is necessary to achieve near saturation of the pump level for the operation of the maser. For the optically pumped maser operated at elevated temperature, however, the situation is different. The populations of the signal levels are almost equal, whereas, the upper (pump) level is practically empty. Saturation of the pump level is not necessary for achieving the required excess population between the signal levels.

An order of magnitude estimate of pumping power requirements may be obtained by assuming that the entrant pump light of area (S) is totally absorbed by the maser material and that the linewidth of the pumping transition is $\Delta\nu$. The pump power requirement (P) becomes

$$P = \mu c S.\Delta\nu \quad (14)$$

where c is the velocity of light and μ is the radiation density per unit bandwidth of the pump light.

The value of μ can be calculated as follows. The relaxation process between the pump levels is assumed to be mostly due to spontaneous emission. Therefore,

$$w_{32} \cong w_{31} = A_{31}. \quad (14a)$$

Similarly,

$$\overline{W}_{13} = \mu B_{13} \quad (14b)$$

where A_{31} is the Einstein coefficient for the spontaneous emission and B_{13} is the coefficient for induced emission. The well-known Einstein relationships shows that the ratio of the probabilities for spontaneous and induced emission are related to each other as follows [11]:

$$\frac{A_{31}}{B_{13}} = 8\pi h\left[\frac{\nu_{13}}{c}\right]^3. \quad (14c)$$

(Note that $B_{13}=B_{31}$.) Combining (3) for the excess population $(\Delta N/N)$ with (14a–c), the energy density per unit bandwidth required for pumping the maser material becomes

$$\mu = \frac{16\pi h(\nu_{13/c})^3}{\frac{w_{32}}{w_{21}}\left(\frac{\Delta N}{N_1} + \frac{\nu_{12}}{kT}\right)^{-1} - 1}. \quad (15)$$

The required incident optical pump power is given by combining (14) and (15).

$$P = \frac{16\pi h S\Delta\nu \ \nu_{13}^3/c^2}{\frac{w_{32}}{w_{21}}\left(\frac{\Delta N}{N_1} + \frac{h\nu_{12}}{kT}\right)^{-1} - 1}. \quad (16)$$

As in the case for optimum noise performance, it is desirable to have a large transition probability ratio w_{32}/w_{21} in order to reduce the optical pump power.

From (16) it can be seen that the maximum signal frequency $(\nu_{12}{}^m)$ corresponding to a given excess population ratio $(\Delta N/N_1)$ and infinite pump power is

$$\nu_{12}{}^m = \left(\frac{w_{32}}{w_{21}} - \frac{\Delta N}{N_1}\right)\cdot\frac{kT}{h}. \quad (17)$$

When the excess population is reduced to zero, the maximum signal frequency reaches the limiting frequency $(\nu^0{}_{12})$ defined by (8).

Expected Performance of a Ruby Maser System

So far the analysis has been kept quite general. To illustrate the significance and implications of the previous discussion, it is appropriate to examine ruby ($Al_2O_3 : Cr^{3+}$) as an example of a particular maser material.

To determine the practical feasibility of an optically pumped ruby maser, the pump power requirements are examined. A typical excess population, $(\Delta N / N_1) = 0.1$ per cent, is assumed. The frequency of the exciting transition in ruby at 6929 Å is $\nu_{13} = 4.33 \times 10^{14}$ cps. for liquid nitrogen temperatures. If one considers a characteristic linewidth of 1 kMc/s and an incident beam of 0.3 cm^2 cross-sectional area, the pump radiation density and pump power can be calculated from (15) and (16) using the available experimental data of ruby, including the dependence of spin-lattice relaxation time on temperature and on chromium concentration [12] and the radiative lifetime for the optical transition [13]. The calculated pump power is plotted in Fig. 2 as a function of temperature for three different signal frequencies. The graph shows that optical pumping powers required for a ruby maser of the assumed properties are high but are in the realm of experimental techniques now available. Another interesting observation is the dependence of the signal frequency on the pump power. The lower limit of the signal frequency is set by the linewidth of the pumping transition because the pump fre-

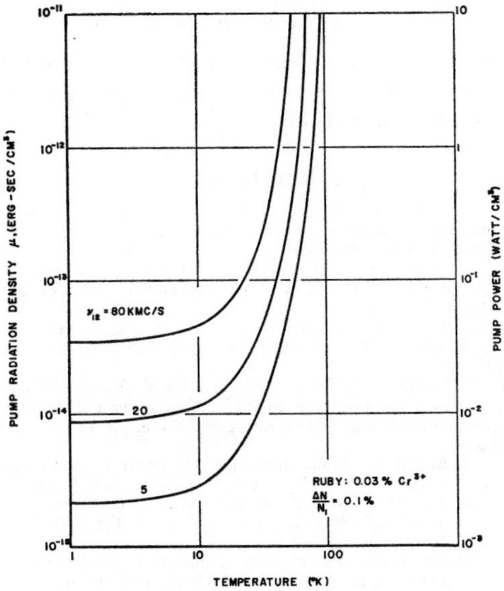

Fig. 2—Pump radiation density and power as a function of operating temperature for optically pumped ruby maser.

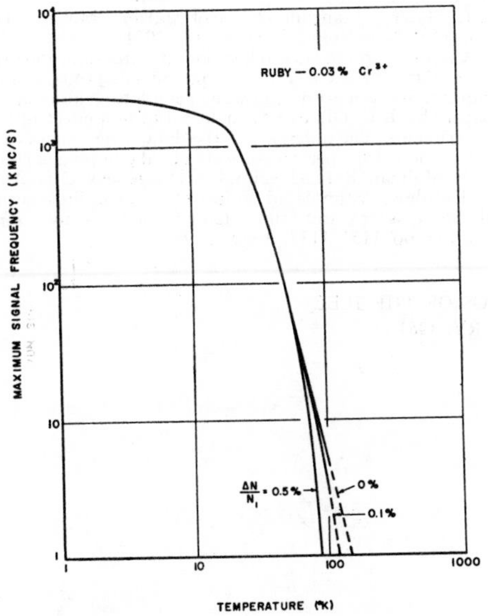

Fig. 3—Maximum signal frequency vs operating temperature for optically pumped ruby maser.

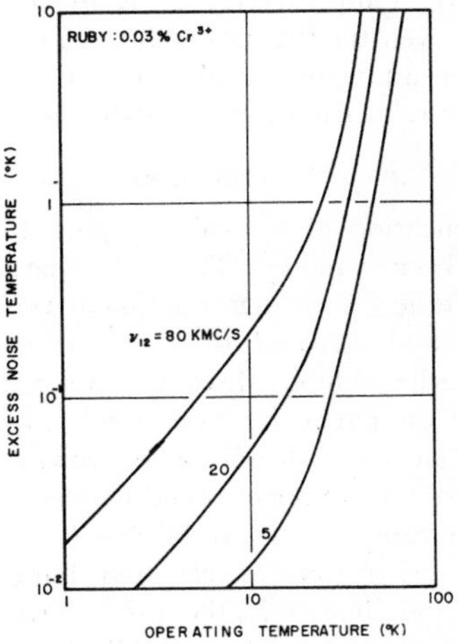

Fig. 4—Noise characteristics of optically pumped ruby maser.

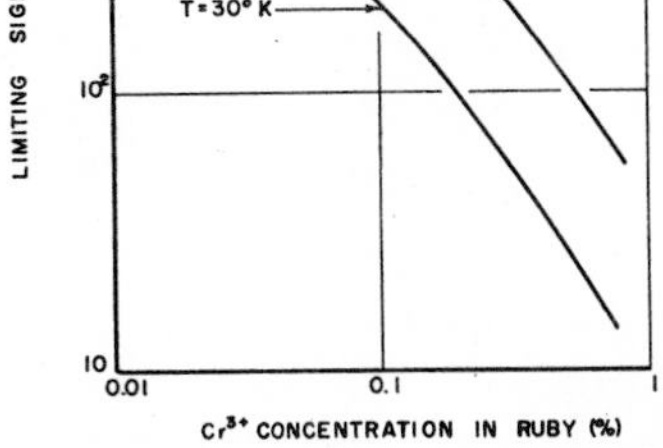

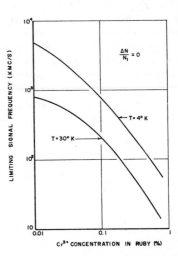

Fig. 5—Effect of operating temperature and chromium concentration in ruby on the upper limit of maser signal frequency.

quency must permit selective pumping in the ground state. From Fig. 2 it is evident that maser action achieved by optical pumping is feasible with ruby as the active material up to liquid nitrogen temperatures.

The dependence of the maximum microwave signal frequency on temperature and on excess population was calculated from (17) and is plotted in Fig. 3. From Fig. 3 and (13) it is possible to predict the maximum operating signal frequency and the excess noise temperature when using optical excitation. In Fig. 4 the predicted values for the excess noise temperature vs operating temperature (T) are shown graphically for three typical signal frequencies. For example, at a bath temperature of 50° K, the excess noise temperature of a ruby maser is 5.32° K for a signal frequency of 20 kMc/s and 1.23° K for a signal at 5 kMc/s.

Fig. 5 depicts the relationship of the limiting signal frequency and, hence indirectly, the noise and pump power as a function of chromium concentration for two characteristic temperatures. It is evident from this graph that even for the most dilute ruby crystal there is an upper limit for signal frequency owing to the reduction of relaxation time at high temperatures.

Conclusions

The application of optical pumping to microwave masers has been examined. This technique appears to be promising for low noise maser action at very high signal frequencies and elevated temperatures, provided the maser material exhibits favorable relaxation characteristics. In the particular case of ruby, low noise performance can be realized for microwave signals at temperatures up to that of liquid nitrogen. The discussion of the ruby maser establishes that a long spin lattice relaxation time at elevated temperatures for microwave frequencies is the prime criterion in the search for new materials suitable for an optically pumped maser. Likewise, a short radiative lifetime for the optical pump transition ($1/W_{32}$) is also a basic requirement in the choice of the pump transition. Since the required optical pump power varies with the third power of frequency, it is preferable to select an energy level scheme having a pump transition with the lowest available pump frequency (provided it is sufficiently larger than kT/h).

It should be pointed out that the effect of cross relaxation was neglected in the above analysis. In practice, cross-relaxation process may become significant, especially for high concentration materials at elevated temperatures. Furthermore, the accuracy of the maser rate equations becomes doubtful with cross relaxation. However, the calculated curves for ruby should indicate the trend in the pumping requirements and maser characteristics and provide a guide in the choice of suitable maser materials.

Acknowledgment

The authors are indebted to Dr. H. C. Rothenberg and Prof. G. K. Wessel for many enlightening discussions in the course of this work.

References

[1] H. H. Theissing, P. J. Caplan, F. A. Dieter, and N. Rabbiner "Optical pumping in crystals," *Phys. Rev. Lett.*, vol. 3, pp. 460–462; November 15, 1959.

[2] J. F. Ready and D. Chen, "Optimal pumping of masers using laser output," Proc. IRE (Correspondence), vol. 50, pp. 329–330; March, 1962.

[3] I. Weider, "Optical detection of paramagnetic resonance saturation in ruby," *Phys. Rev. Lett.*, vol. 3, pp. 468–470; November 15, 1959.

[4] D. P. Devor, I. J. D'Haenens, and C. K. Asawa, "Microwave generation in ruby due to population inversion produced by optical absorption," *Phys. Rev. Lett.*, vol. 8, pp. 432–435; June 1, 1962.

[5] T. H. Maiman, "Maser behavior: temperature and concentration effects," *J. Appl. Phys.*, vol. 31, pp. 222–223; January, 1960.

[6] C. R. Ditchfield and P. A. Forrester, "Maser action in the region of 60° K," *Phys. Rev. Lett.*, vol. 1, pp. 448–449; December 15, 1958.

[7] N. Bloenbergen, "Proposal for a new type solid state maser," *Phys. Rev.*, vol. 104, pp. 324–327; October 15, 1956.

[8] R. V. Pound, "Spontaneous emission and the noise figure of maser amplifiers," *Ann. Phys.*, vol. 1, pp. 24–32; April, 1957.

[9] J. P. Wittke, "Molecular amplification and generation of microwaves," Proc. IRE, vol. 45, pp. 291–316; March, 1957.

[10] J. R. Singer, "Masers," John Wiley and Sons, Inc., New York, N. Y., p. 112; 1959.

[11] J. C. Slater, "Quantum Theory of Matter," McGraw-Hill Book Co., Inc., New York, N. Y., p. 100; 1951.

[12] J. C. Gill, "Spin-lattice relaxation of chromium ions in ruby," *Proc. Phys. Soc.*, vol. 79, Pt. 1, pp. 58–68; January, 1962. This paper contains more accurate and complete results than previous papers by J. C. Gill due to slight saturation effect in his earlier experiments. The difference in the data is very significant in the calculation of the performance of optical pumping of ruby maser.

[13] T. H. Maiman, R. H. Hoskins, I. J. D'Haenens, C. K. Asawa, and V. Evtuhov, "Stimulated optical emission in fluorescent solids, II. Spectroscopy and stimulated emission in ruby," *Phys. Rev.*, vol. 123, pp. 1151–1157; August, 1961.

Reprinted from the PROCEEDINGS OF THE IEEE
VOL. 51, NO. 1, JANUARY, 1963

Optical Pumping of Masers Using Laser Output*

The possibility of optical pumping of masers has been considered previously[1] as a possible means of increasing the operating frequency range of masers. Sufficient power within the relatively narrow frequency range effective in pumping was not available at the time of these proposals. However, the development of lasers[2] has provided a source of high optical power concentrated within an extremely narrow bandwidth. Moreover the materials used as active laser materials generally contain the same type of paramagnetic ions that are suitable for maser use, so that the wavelength of laser emission can coincide with the useful absorption lines of the maser material.

We shall consider ruby in particular in this communication, since the energy levels in ruby have been thoroughly studied and since ruby has already been used as an active material for both masers and lasers. The rapid growth of the list of laser materials indicates that other materials more suitable for maser operation at extremely high frequencies will perhaps soon be available.

If the light from a ruby laser is focused on a ruby in a microwave cavity at helium temperature in a magnetic field, and the laser emission is thermally tuned[3] to the frequency of one Zeeman component of the ruby absorption, the lower sublevel of the Zeeman component will tend to be depopulated by absorption. If the light intensity is great, depopulation may occur fast enough to overcome the thermal processes leading to equilibrium and a population inversion may be attained. The line width of the ruby laser emission is of the order of 1 kMc, narrow enough that under suitable conditions we may consider absorption in only one of the ground state sublevels.

The energies of the sublevels of the ground state of ruby in a magnetic field have been studied in detail by Chang and Siegman.[4] If we number the ground state sublevels in order of increasing energy, we have five coupled differential equations of the form

$$\frac{dn_i}{dt} = -\sum_{j=1}^{4}{}' S_{ij}n_i + \sum_{j=1}^{4}{}' S_{ji}n_j - n_iB_{i5}\rho_{i5} + n_5B_{5i}\rho_{5i} + n_5 A_{5i}$$

where n_i is the population of level i, S_{ij} is the transition probability per unit time for thermal relaxation from level i to level j, level 5 is the upper level of the optical transition (assumed to be the lower sublevel of the $^2\bar{E}(E)$ state for our case), B_{kj} and A_{kj} are the Einstein A and B coefficients for transitions from level k to level j, and $\rho_{i5}=\rho_{5i}$ is the radiation density per unit frequency interval at a frequency corresponding to the transition between level i and level 5. Under our assumptions ρ_{i5} is nonzero for only one level i from which the optical transition takes place. Possible radiative transitions between the ground state sublevels and thermal transition from level 5 to the ground state sublevels are neglected. The Einstein A and B coefficients were estimated from the observed R_1 line absorption coefficient and fluorescent lifetime[5] and from the relative intensities of the different Zeeman components.[6] The thermal relaxation probabilities were estimated from the work of Gill[7] and from the Boltzmann distribution relations.

A currently realizable energy density from the output of a ruby laser operated to high input and cooled to the region where the relaxation oscillation spikes are suppressed is $\rho_{i5}=2\times 10/\text{cm}^3$, assuming a luminous flux density of 1 kw/cm².[5]

Using these data the set of coupled differential equations, along with the equation of conservation of total number of ions, was solved numerically for several different sets of parameters. The results for the case of magnetic field along the ruby c-axis, polarization of the laser light perpendicular to the c-axis, temperature 4.2°K, magnetic field equal to 3.2 kilogauss (energy difference between sublevels 2 and 3 equal to 6.4 kMc), and the laser output tuned to the Zeeman absorption component originating on sublevel 2 are shown in Fig. 1. The laser emission is assumed to begin at time zero and the total chromium ion concentration is normalized to unity. The effects of saturation of the optical transition are apparent. A significant population inversion is predicted between levels 3 and 2 for a period of several hundred microseconds. If the total chromium ion concentration is of the order of $10^{19}/\text{cm}^3$, an inversion of approximately $8\times 10^{17}/\text{cm}^3$ is predicted. This should be sufficient for observation of stimulated emission at 6.4 kMc. With suitable choice of the operating parameters, operation at much higher frequencies should be possible.

We are presently working on construction of apparatus to demonstrate this stimulated emission under the influence of ruby laser emission.

J. F. Ready
D. Chen
Dept. of Elec. Engrg.
University of Minnesota
Minneapolis, Minn.

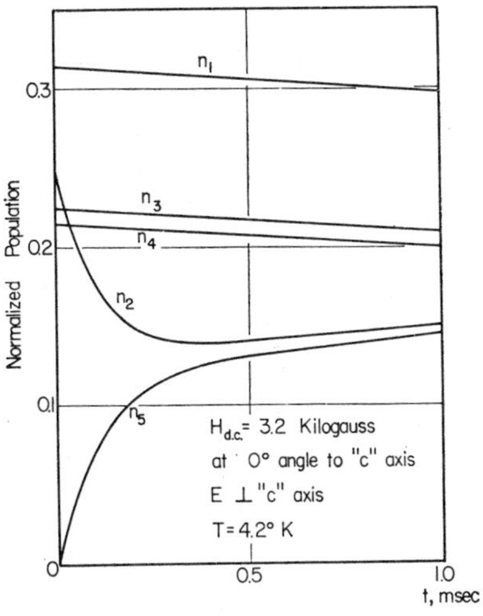

Fig. 1—Calculated populations of the four ruby ground state sublevels and the upper level of the optical absorption transition under the influence of ruby laser light, as a function of time.

* Received by the IRE, December 22, 1961. This work was supported in part by the University of Minnesota Graduate School Res. Grant 428-0800-8505-2.

[1] See, for example, H. H. Theissing, *et al.*, "Optical pumping in crystals," *Phys. Rev. Lett.*, vol. 3, pp. 460–462; November 15, 1959. See also, I. Wieder, "Optical detection of paramagnetic resonance saturation in ruby," *Ibid.*, pp. 468–470.

[2] T. H. Maiman, "Optical maser action in ruby," *Brit. Commun. and Electronics*, vol. 7, p. 674; September, 1960.
——, "Stimulated optical radiation in ruby," *Nature*, vol. 187, pp. 493–494; August, 1960.
R. J. Collins, *et al.*, "Coherence, narrowing, directionality, and relaxation oscillations in the light emission from ruby," *Phys. Rev. Lett.*, vol. 5, pp. 303–305; October 1, 1960.

[3] I. D. Abella and H. Z. Cummins, "Thermal tuning of ruby optical maser, *J. Appl. Phys.*, vol. 32, pp. 1177–1178; June, 1961.

[4] W. S. Chang and A. E. Siegman, "Characteristics of Ruby for Maser Applications," Stanford Electronics Labs., Stanford, Calif. Tech. Rept. No. 156–2; 1958.

[5] T. H. Maiman, *et al.*, "Stimulated optical emission in fluorescent solids II, spectroscopy and stimulated emission in ruby," *Phys. Rev.*, vol. 123, pp. 1151–1157; August, 1961.

[6] S. Sugano and I. Tsujikawa, "Absorption spectra in Cr^{3+} in Al_2O_3," *J. Appl. Soc. (Japan)*, vol. 13, pp. 899–910; August, 1958.

[7] J. C. Gill, "*Quantum Electronics*," C. H. Townes, Ed., Columbia University Press, New York, N. Y., 1960.

Reprinted from the PROCEEDINGS OF THE IRE
VOL. 50, NO. 3, MARCH, 1962

NOISE, THEORY AND MEASUREMENTS

The sources of noise in the thermionic electron tube amplifier arise from the random fluctuations in velocity and current density associated with the emission process, and the random character of the division of current among the grids and anode of a multi electrode tube. In the introduction we remarked that the noise temperature for low frequency triodes is nonetheless very good, varying from less than one degree Kelvin just above flicker noise frequencies to about 20° Kelvin at 20 megacycles. Microwave tubes have considerably more noise. The most compelling reason for the use of a paramagnetic ion low temperature microwave maser is its very low noise performance. This is due in part to the use of low temperatures and in part due to absence of the kind of noise arising from fluctuations in the electron beams. One approach to the theory of the noise is discussed in my Reviews of Modern Physics article in the front of this volume. Experimental results and other discussions of the theory follow.

System-Noise Measurement of a Solid-State Maser*

The effective input noise temperature[1] of a 2800-mc, three-level[2] solid-state maser of the reflection cavity type has previously been reported[3] to be less than 20°K, where this temperature refers to the maser cavity only, and not to the complete amplifier system. These first measurements were made with a room temperature isolator on the output side of the maser, which, because of the reciprocal nature of reflection-cavity masers, introduced about 300°K noise into the system. As a result, it was difficult to make a precise measurement of the relatively small amount of noise contributed by the maser itself. By combining a recently designed low-loss S-band circulator[4] with the maser, it has now been possible to form a complete amplifier system with an effective input noise temperature under 25°K.

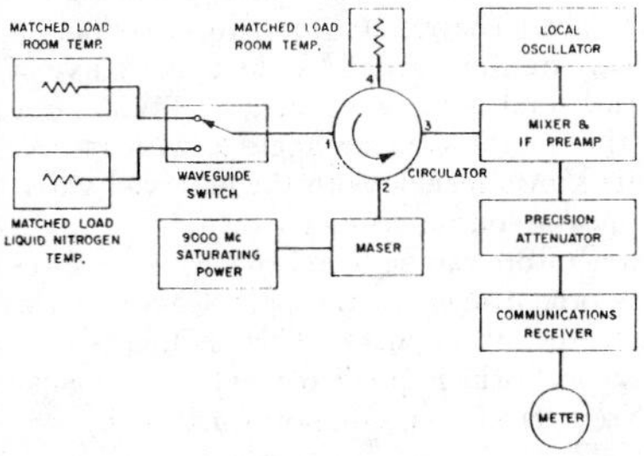

Fig. 1—Block diagram of instrumentation for noise measurement.

Fig. 1 shows the experimental arrangement used for the measurement. Port 1 of the circulator could be connected through the waveguide switch either to the matched load at room temperature or to the matched load at liquid nitrogen temperature, the loads having a vswr of 1.04 and 1.07, respectively, looking back through the switch. The maser, which was connected to port 2, has a voltage gain-bandwidth of about 1.8×10^6 sec^{-1}.[5] $K_3Co_{0.995}Cr_{0.005}(CN)_6$ is used as the paramagnetic salt and the operating temperature is 1.25°K. With 15 mw of 9000-mc saturating power, the external coupling at the amplifying frequency was adjusted to give a gain of the order of 30 db with 50-kc bandwidth. The receiver system connected to port 3 had an over-all noise figure of 8.5 db, the communications receiver being used to provide a bandwidth small in comparison with that of the maser. Port 4 was terminated by a matched load at room temperature with a vswr of 1.05.

By switching back and forth between the room temperature load and the liquid nitrogen temperature load at port 1, and measuring the ratio of the noise outputs with the precision attenuator, the noise temperature of the entire amplifier system was found to be 20 ± 5°K.

The sources of noise in the system other than the maser itself are the circulator, the maser input-output line, and the receiver. The circulator noise arises from:

1) Attenuation in transmission from port 1 to port 2,
2) Noise from the matched load at port 4 being reflected from port 1,
3) Noise from the matched load at port 4 being directly transmitted to port 2,
4) Noise from the receiver at port 3 being transmitted to port 2.

Since the isolation between ports 4 and 2 was greater than 35 db, and between ports 3 and 2 greater than 27 db, and because of the low vswr of the loads at port 1, the noise from sources 2), 3), and 4) combined is under 1°K. The insertion loss between ports 1 and 2 is 0.2 ± 0.1 in db, only a small part of which is reflective. Hence the noise arising from 1) is between 7 and 21°K.

The attenuation between port 2 of the circulator and the maser cavity is 0.4 ± 0.05 db, of which about 0.15 db is at room temperature and the rest occurs in the coaxial line leading down through the helium dewar to the cavity. This line, which is stainless steel for thermal insulation, was resilvered following the original maser noise measurements, but is still lossy. Depending on the assumptions made for the thermal distribution along the coaxial line,[3] the total noise generated between port 2 and the maser is between 7 and 23°K. (With special dewars to permit the use of S-band waveguide, almost all of this noise could be eliminated.) The third source of noise, the receiver at port 3, contributes less than 2°K because of the high gain of the maser.

From the above discussion it appears that the noise temperature of the maser proper must be very close to the theoretical value, which is about 2°K under the operating conditions used. In addition, the dissipative loss of the circulator is probably closer to the lower estimate of 0.1 db.

A. L. McWhorter
Lincoln Lab., Mass. Inst. Tech.
Lexington, Mass.
F. R. Arams
Airborne Instruments Lab., Inc.
Mineola, N. Y.

* Received by the IRE, January 20, 1958. The research reported in this document was supported jointly by the Army, Navy, and Air Force under contract with the Mass. Inst. Tech., Cambridge, Mass., and by the Dept. of Defense.

[1] The effective input noise temperature T_e is related to the noise figure F by the expression

$$T_e = 290(F - 1).$$

[2] N. Bloembergen, "Proposal for a new type solid state maser," *Phys. Rev.*, vol. 104, pp. 324–327; October 15, 1956.

[3] A. L. McWhorter, J. W. Meyer, and P. D. Strum, "Noise temperature measurement on a solid-state maser," *Phys. Rev.*, vol. 108, pp. 1642–1644; December 15, 1957.

[4] F. R. Arams and G. Krayer, "Design considerations for circulator maser systems," this issue, p. 912.

[5] A. L. McWhorter and J. W. Meyer, "A solid state maser amplifier," *Phys. Rev.*, vol. 109, pp. 312–318; January 15, 1958. The microwave cavity design of this experimental maser is far from ideal. A substantial improvement in bandwidth may be expected.

Reprinted from the PROCEEDINGS OF THE IRE
VOL. 46, NO. 5, MAY, 1958

Ultra-Low-Noise Measurements Using a Horn Reflector Antenna and a Traveling-Wave Maser

R. W. DeGrasse, D. C. Hogg, E. A. Ohm, and H. E. D. Scovil
Bell Telephone Laboratories, Inc., Murray Hill and Holmdel, New Jersey
(Received July 24, 1959)

A LOW-SKY-NOISE window exists in the region of a few centimeters wavelength.[1] The accuracy of an absolute sky temperature noise measurement is greatly improved by the use of an ultra-low-noise receiving system. We have combined a low-noise traveling-wave maser[2] and a low-noise horn reflector antenna[3] (low side-and-back-lobe pickup) into such a system, and have obtained an over-all system noise temperature (including sky noise) as low as 17.2°K with the antenna pointed vertically. The noise contribution of the atmosphere to this over-all noise temperature was found to be 2.5°K. The measurements performed at 5.65 kmc and utilizing a 20-mc band width were made on cool, clear winter nights from an elevated site (Crawford Hill) near Holmdel, New Jersey.

The experimental system consisted of the horn-reflector antenna, a 26 db directional coupler, used to introduce noise from an argon noise lamp, the traveling-wave maser, and a precision microwave attenuator. This was followed by a microwave superheterodyne receiver having excellent gain stability. The experimental data were taken by flashing the noise lamp, which increased the input noise temperature by about 25°K, and adding microwave attenuation to maintain the superheterodyne output noise level constant. With this technique the noise of the sky, antenna, TWM receiving system was determined—noise from the following stages does not affect the result. Also, since a maser gain as high as 40 db can be obtained, the following-stage noise contribution can be made negligible.

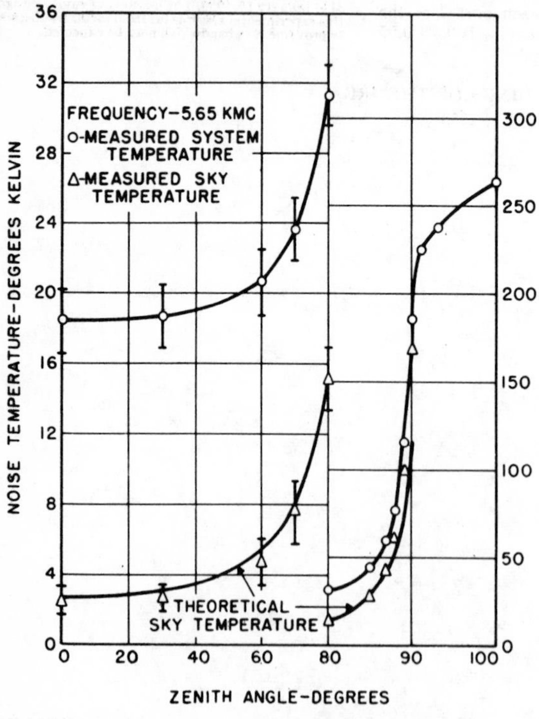

Fig. 1. Noise temperature *versus* antenna angle measured from the zenith—comparison of experimental data and theoretical sky temperature.

About 25 noise measurement runs were made with the antenna pointed near the zenith during a period of 2 days with a clear sky. Each measurement run consisted of a group of 10 individual measurements made over a period of about 5 minutes. The rms scatter within each group of 10 measurements was about 0.15°K. The lowest temperature so observed was 17.2°K and the highest 19.7°K while the mean of 25 runs was 18.5°K. These values are subject to attenuator, directional coupler, and noise lamp errors which result in an absolute accuracy of ±0.7°K.

Another set of measurement runs was made while changing the zenith angle of the antenna. The results, for two directions of antenna feed polarization, are summarized by the upper curve of Fig. 1 which shows the total sky, antenna, and TWM noise temperature as a function of the antenna angle θ, with respect to the zenith. The limits shown include both the observed variations and the absolute measurement accuracy.

The absolute sky temperature can be found to close tolerances by assuming that it is proportional to the path length of the antenna beam through the atmosphere. This assumption is consistent with the theory[1] which predicts that the angular variation of the sky noise is given to good approximation by

$$T_s = \frac{T_s(\theta=0)}{\cos\theta}; \quad \theta < 80°. \tag{1}$$

The measured system noise should therefore consist of two parts, a relatively constant term (antenna, wave guide, and maser) and an angular dependent term T_s given by (1). An analysis of the measured angular dependence of the system noise of Fig. 1 then gives the result that:

$$T_{\text{antenna, wave guide, and maser}} = 16.0 \pm 0.8°\text{K}$$
$$T_{\text{sky zenith}} = 2.5 \pm 0.75°\text{K}.$$

The zenith sky temperature is in agreement with the theory which predicts a value of 2.7°K.

The temperature contributions which stem from the wave guide, directional coupler, and antenna copper losses have been calculated to be 3.5±0.2°K; therefore the antenna and maser must contribute 12.5±1°K. From the data, it is estimated that radiation from the environment into the side and back lobes of the antenna contributes 2±1°K. Thus the maser temperature is estimated to be 10.5±2°K, which is in agreement with the measured temperature of a similar maser.[2]

Near the horizon the sky temperatures were found by subtracting the 16.3°K constant due to the antenna, wave guide, and maser from the observed system temperatures and these agreed well with the theoretical values, at least up to the point where the earth was intercepted by the 2-degree antenna beam width. These results are shown in the right-hand portion of Fig. 1. It is interesting to note that the zenith system temperature only doubles (from 19 to 38°K) when the antenna beam is as low as 7 degrees above the horizon.

Because of the low sky temperatures, it seems advisable to lower the receiving system noise temperature even further. It appears that by reduction of the coax and wave guide losses a noise temperature of less than 9°K could be realized with the present maser-antenna combination.

[1] D. C. Hogg, J. Appl. Phys. 30, 1417 (1959).
[2] DeGrasse, Schulz-DuBois, and Scovil, Bell System Tech. J. 38 (March, 1959).
[3] H. T. Friis and S. A. Schelkunoff, *Antennas, Theory and Practice* (John Wiley & Sons, Inc., New York, 1952), pp. 569–571.

ANNALS OF PHYSICS: 1, 24–32 (1957)

Spontaneous Emission and the Noise Figure of Maser Amplifiers

R. V. POUND

Lyman Laboratory, Harvard University

The Nyquist-Johnson formulation of the noise in circuits arising from thermal agitation is applied to circuit elements equivalent to and representing simple resonant absorption, such as occurs in paramagnetic materials or others having r-f line spectra. Such a model for a circuit resistance directly demonstrates the origin of the noise as spontaneous emission by excited particles, in complete analogy to black body radiation in free space. Extension of the conventional theorem to the domain of negative resistances at negative temperatures, as encountered in Maser amplifiers, is valid under circumstances of practical significance. Amplifiers of small noise figure can be made for frequencies ν such that $h\nu/kT_0$, where T_0 is the effective temperature of the signal source, is not large compared to unity. For example, an amplifier of high gain and noise figure less than 2 can be built if use is made of a medium describable by a negative effective temperature smaller, in absolute value, than T_0.

INTRODUCTION

The probability for spontaneous emission of radio-frequency radiation by particles in appropriate low lying excited states is very small. On the other hand such particles can emit electromagnetic radiation strongly when suitably stimulated. Beams or condensed aggregates containing such particles can, thereby, form the basis of practical regeneration of r-f electromagnetic energy. Amplifiers and oscillators based on this principle have been described by Gordon, Zeiger and Townes (*1*) who coined the acronym "Maser" to describe them. Other suggestions have been published by Bloembergen (*2*) and by Bassov and Prokhorov (*3*). Amplification of this kind of very limited magnitude was present on a transient basis in experiments reported to illustrate the existence of negative temperatures, in systems of interacting spins well "insulated" from their lattice (*4*). The usefulness of a method of amplification depends on such quantitative factors as the gain available, the bandwidths, and, especially, the noise figure (*5*). The purpose of this note is to put in view some of the factors affecting the noise figure of these devices; in particular, an aim is to demonstrate the applicability and utility of a wire circuit model for such consideration.

A CIRCUIT DESCRIPTION OF A RESONANT ABSORBER

It is well known that under conditions of thermal equilibrium, the equipartition theorem can be invoked to demonstrate that electrical circuits must possess noise currents and voltages of thermal origin. With each resistance $R(\nu)$, which may be dependent on frequency ν, must be associated a noise voltage generator, for example, such that the mean-squared noise voltage per unit frequency interval is given at temperature T by the Nyquist-Johnson formula

$$\langle e^2 \rangle_{\mathrm{Av}} = 4kTR(\nu). \tag{1}$$

It is well to keep in mind the fact that this representation is the transcription to circuit form of black body radiation and its origin is the spontaneous emission of radiation by particles in excited states. A direct connection between the circuit noise and black body radiation can be made by the well known model of a resistance, matched to the radiation resistance of an antenna which is immersed in black body radiation at temperature T (*5*). From the Rayleigh-Jeans approximation for the energy density in the radiation field, the requirement that there be no net power flow if the resistance is also at temperature T leads to Eq. (1) above. A value for $\langle e^2 \rangle_{\mathrm{Av}}$ valid for all values of $h\nu/kT$ can be written by use in such a model of the Planck radiation law,

$$\langle e^2 \rangle_{\mathrm{Av}} = 4h\nu R\,[\exp\,(h\nu/kT) - 1]^{-1}. \tag{2}$$

Suppose that a cavity is filled with a material that resonates at ν_0, the resonant frequency of the cavity, and further, suppose that the resulting absorption "line" has, per se, a normalized Lorentzian shape, such as is typical of collision broadening or radiation damping,

$$g(\nu) = 2T_2[1 + (2\pi(\nu - \nu_0)T_2)^2]^{-1}, \tag{3}$$

where T_2 has the dimensions of time and is chosen so as to agree with the conventions of the literature of nuclear magnetism. A wire circuit equivalent to the system is that of Fig. 1. The current generators i_S, i_N and the voltage generator

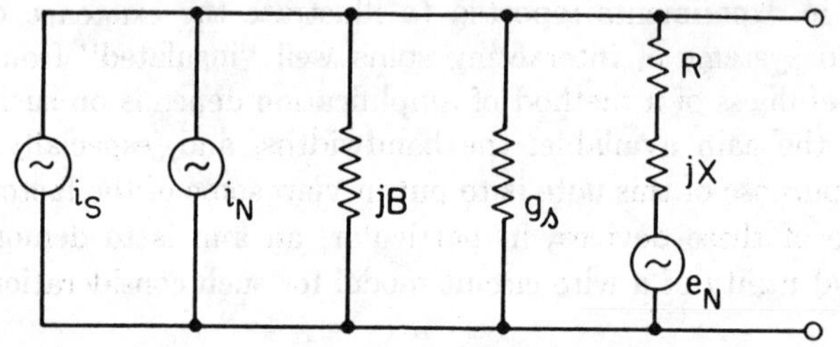

FIG. 1. A wire circuit equivalent to an r-f system including a resonant absorber.

e_N represent, respectively, a signal source and noise sources associated with the two parts of the circuit. The conductance g_s represents, at some point in the circuit, all the losses of the circuit other than the resonant absorbing atomic system. The susceptance jB, in the event that the frequency selectivity of the circuit arising elsewhere than in the absorber is dominated by that of a single cavity mode, is a linear function of frequency

$$B = 2(\nu - \nu_0)Qg_s/\nu_0 , \tag{4}$$

where Q is the conventional quality factor of that mode.

If the absorption at its peak is represented by δ, the ratio of power absorbed by the resonant absorber to $2\pi\nu$ times the energy stored in the circuit, the factor $Q\delta$ represents the ratio of the power absorbed in the absorber to that absorbed by the circuit losses. Therefore, the resistance R, representing the resonant absorption at its peak, is equal to $[g_s Q\delta]^{-1}$. The resonant character of the absorber is correctly simulated if the resistance R is made independent of frequency and the reactance jX is included to represent the dispersion of the medium. The quantity X has the value

$$X = 2\pi(\nu - \nu_0)T_2R \tag{5}$$

for the assumption covered by Eq. (3).

Suppose that the circuit conductance g_s is assumed to be at a temperature so low, compared to that of the absorber R, that the current in g_s caused by the noise current generator i_N, associated with g_s itself, can be ignored in comparison to the current produced by the noise voltage generator e_N associated with R. The power delivered to the circuit losses g_s from the absorber can then be computed. To do this one needs to integrate the mean-square of the current in g_s divided by g_s over all frequencies. One finds

$$P_{g_s} = \langle e^2\rangle_{\mathrm{Av}}\, g_s 2\pi\nu_0 Q\delta^2[4(1 + \delta Q)]^{-1}\{[1 + (2\pi\nu_0 T_2/Q)] + (\pi\nu_0 T_2/Q)^2\}^{-1/2} \tag{6}$$

In the event that $Q/\pi\nu_0 \ll T_2$, corresponding to a circuit of large width in frequency compared to the width of the resonance of the absorber, the expression becomes

$$P_{g_s} \approx \langle e^2\rangle_{\mathrm{Av}}\, g_s(Q\delta)^2[2(1 + \delta Q)T_2]^{-1}. \tag{7}$$

Putting $\langle e^2\rangle_{\mathrm{Av}}$ from Eq. (2) into this yields

$$P_{g_s} \approx 2h\nu_0(Q\delta)[(1 + \delta Q)T_2]^{-1}\,[\exp\,(h\nu_0/kT) - 1]^{-1}. \tag{8}$$

The factor $(1 + Q\delta)^{-1}$ measures the power gain G_0 of the circuit as a whole when the absorber is added, relative to the circuit without the absorber. The power gain G_0 is defined as the ratio of the power arising from i_s available from the terminals of the entire circuit to that available for the same current generator with δ made zero. For $\delta Q = 1$, for example, $G_0 = \frac{1}{2}$ and then P_{g_s} equals, for $(h\nu/kT) \ll 1$, kTB where B, the effective noise bandwidth of the circuit, is $(1/T_2)$. This bandwidth is twice the width characteristic of the absorber alone because of the critical coupling, $\delta Q = 1$. For $\delta \leq 0$, the power gain $G_0 \geq 1$, and the circuit is an amplifier. The noise power delivered to g_s is

$$P_{g_s} = 2h\nu_0(Q\delta)G_0\{T_2 [\exp (h\nu_0/kT) - 1]\}^{-1} \tag{9}$$

A more detailed examination of the absorption mechanism is required to identify δ. As an example, the resonance concerned might involve only two energy levels per particle, for which

$$\delta = W_{1\to2}(h\nu_0)(N_1 - N_2)/2\pi\nu_0 E \tag{10}$$

where E is the electromagnetic energy stored per unit volume, averaged over the circuit, and $W_{1\to2}$ is the transition probability from the lower state (1) whose population per unit volume is N_1, to the upper (2), whose corresponding population is N_2, induced by the presence of the radiation field. If the circuit were not filled with absorbing material a filling factor could be introduced in the usual manner but, for the purposes of the present discussion, there is no need for such additional complication. The difference $N_1 - N_2$ can be described in terms of the number of particles per unit volume in the upper state, N_2, and the effective temperature, $T_{\text{eff}} = h\nu_0/k \log (N_1/N_2)$, as

$$N_1 - N_2 = N_2 [\exp (h\nu_0/kT_{\text{eff}}) - 1]. \tag{11}$$

These substitutions into the above together with the discussion of $W_{1\to2}$ given below yield

$$P_{g_s} = 2\pi N_2 Q G_0(h\nu_0) \mid (1 \mid \mathbf{M}^+ \mid 2) \mid^2/\hbar \tag{12}$$

To obtain Eq. (12),

$$W_{1\to2} = \mid (1 \mid \mathcal{H}_1 \mid 2) \mid^2 g(\nu)/\hbar^2 \tag{13}$$

has been used for the transition probability, where $\mathcal{H}_1$ represents the interaction of the system with the field, and only a single linearly polarized field component has been allowed, representing a single mode in the resonator. The operator $\mathbf{M}^+$ could be either an electric or magnetic dipole moment operator. It is instructive to recognize, in Eq. (12), that all dependence on the temperature has vanished except that implicit in N_2 and in the factor G_0. The power represented in Eq. (12) is that resulting from *spontaneous emission*, delivered to the circuit with an efficiency that depends on the coupling conditions—as measured by G_0. Normally $G_0 < 1$ and some self-absorption occurs, but for $\delta < 0$, $G_0 > 1$ and there is, in the net, stimulated emission, leading for $\delta Q \leq -1$ to oscillation or self-sustained emission.

To demonstrate the appearance of the spontaneous emission explicitly, one can take the expression for the Einstein coefficient A for spontaneous emission in free space

$$A = 4 \mid (2 \mid \mathbf{M} \mid 1) \mid^2 / 3\hbar\lambda^3 \tag{14}$$

and recognize that the single mode cavity allows only one component of radiation field. For the present purposes

$$A_x = \mid (2 \mid \mathbf{M}^- \mid 1) \mid^2 / 3\hbar\lambda^3 = \mid (1 \mid \mathbf{M}^+ \mid 2) \mid^2 / 3\hbar\lambda^3$$

The cavity, having only a single mode actually at resonance with the system, enhances the spontaneous radiation rate by the factor (6)

$$S = 3\lambda^3 Q / 4\pi^2 \text{ (Volume)}. \tag{15}$$

This factor represents the ratio of the energy density in the cavity to that of a single field component in free space, at any temperature, or in the zero point vibrations that may be regarded as inducing the spontaneous emission. It is thereby seen that Eq. (12) can be written

$$P_{g_s} = G_0 S A_x \eta_2 (h\nu_0) \tag{16}$$

where η_2 is the total number of particles in the upper state, equal to ($N_2 \times$ Volume). The restriction to a circuit broad compared to the line width and filled with absorber simplifies the recognition of the factors G_0 and S but, clearly, similar results must be expected irrespective of such restrictions.

With the use of the modified Nyquist-Johnson formula, the power flow is given correctly even for $(h\nu/kT) \gg 1$ provided that the state of the system is correctly described only by N_1/N_2. The circuit model is entirely adequate to represent the "small signal" behavior of the system. The importance of stimulated absorption and emission relative to spontaneous emission together with interference effects among them are automatically taken into account. An important conclusion is that the possibility of a negative sign of T_{eff} does not invalidate the model. As far as algebra alone is concerned, trouble might be expected from the Nyquist-Johnson formula, which must yield a positive mean square, but the common sign of T_{eff} and R satisfies that requirement.

The validity of the noise formulation based on effective temperature is critically dependent on there being statistically no coherence in the states of the system. It is a property of aggregates of particles, constricted within dimensions smaller than the velocity of light c divided by the width of the frequency band $\Delta\nu$ associated with a radiative transition, that states having radiation rates per particle very different from those characteristic of single particles compatible with the representation above, can be produced (7). Clearly, any such coherent states are not properly described in the above manner, or by any temperature, negative or positive. If, for example, a system capable of amplification were initiated by an inversion of a net vector magnetic moment initially in equilibrium at temperature T_c, a small departure from exact inversion will lead to a radiation rate far above that of "thermal" origin. Quantitatively, it is easy to see from a classical model that, for thermal radiation to dominate, the angular departure from exact inversion would have to be less than $kT_c/h\nu N^{1/2}$, when N is the number of particles. This is true because the expectation value of a transverse moment that may be considered the origin of incoherent spontaneous emission would be $\sqrt{N}$ times the moment of an individual particle. For a small angle, the transverse moment due to imperfect inversion would equal the angle times the net moment of the system. On the other hand, any such enhanced radiation damps out through the influence of the forces producing internal equilibrium, as measured by T_2. The damping time is longer than T_2 because of the coupling to the circuit and, in practice, is the net time defined by the net amplifying bandwidth. It is the presence of this same relaxation that renders the assignment of a temperature to the spin system meaningful, however, and, therefore, a close connection is established between the applicability of the above noise calculations and the validity of an assignment of a negative temperature to the Maser system in a sense broader than that signifying only a ratio N_2/N_1.

In practice, the transient amplifier would experience, because of inexact inversion, some "ringing" as an after effect of that sensitizing operation, and it might not prove easy to reduce such ringing below thermal noise in the first few periods of reciprocal bandwidth. In steady state devices (*2*) the presence of strong "pumping" radiation, that mixes one of the states involved in the resonant transitions to be utilized with a third, must be rendered negligible by, similarly, the presence of a short relaxation time T_2 compared to the transition time produced by the pumping signal. For this example, too, the conditions allowing the assignment of a negative temperature to the system composed of two levels would seem to be satisfied.

It is, therefore, possible, subject to these restrictions, to represent not only the transfer characteristics for small signals but the noise properties as well, of both absorption circuits and Maser amplifiers, by the use of equivalent circuits made up of appropriate positive and negative resistances, and reactances, at appropriate positive or negative effective temperatures.

NOISE FIGURE CALCULATIONS

The above conclusions may easily be applied to the calculation of the noise figure of a typical Maser amplifier. Consider the circuit of Fig. 2. The ratio of signal power S_0 to noise power N_0 available in the frequency range between ν and $\nu + d\nu$ from the source is

$$\frac{dS_0}{dN_0} = \frac{i_s^2(\nu)[(\exp(h\nu/kT_0) - 1]d\nu}{4g_0 h\nu d\nu} \qquad (17)$$

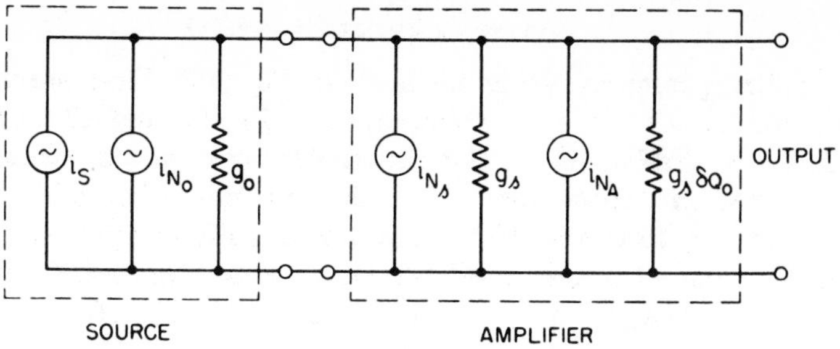

FIG. 2. An equivalent circuit useful for calculation of the noise figure of a Maser amplifier.

where T_0 is the effective temperature of the source g_0 and the ratio may be a function of frequency. The ratio of the signal power to the noise power, in the same frequency range, at the output of the Maser is

$$\frac{dS}{dN} = \frac{i_s^2}{4h\nu}\left\{\frac{g_0}{\exp(h\nu/kT_0) - 1} + \frac{g_s}{\exp(h\nu/kT_c) - 1} + \frac{g_s\delta Q_0}{\exp(-h\nu/\alpha kT_c) - 1}\right\}^{-1} \quad (18)$$

In this expression α is $(-T_{\mathrm{eff}}/T_c)$, T_c is the temperature of the losses of the cavity circuit, and Q_0 is the unloaded Q of the cavity circuit used for the amplifier. The noise figure F, which is, in general, a function of frequency and of the source temperature is, in the same frequency range,

$$F_{T_0}(\nu) = 1 + \frac{[\exp(h\nu/kT_0) - 1]}{[\exp(h\nu/kT_c) + 1]}\left\{(1 - G^{-1})\, x + \left[\frac{Q_{L1}}{P_0 - Q_{L1}}\right](1 + x)\right\} \quad (19)$$

where

$$x = [\exp(h\nu/kT_c) - 1][1 - \exp(-h\nu/\alpha kT_c)]^{-1}$$

and G is the power gain of the Maser, defined as the ratio of the signal power *available* from its output terminals to that *available* from the source itself and Q_{L1} is the Q of the cavity as loaded by the input circuit only, not including the unspecified output load. Note that the gain G defined here differs from G_0, above, because the cavity losses themselves are, here, assigned to the Maser.

In practice a net pass-band will be defined either by this circuit or by those following. In general, the reactive parts of the circuit and the selectivity of the succeeding amplifiers should be included and an effective over-all noise figure calculated by integration over all frequencies. If the bandwidth of the succeeding amplifiers is small, the over-all effective noise figure F_{T_0} can be set equal to $F_{T_0}(\nu)$ above.

CONCLUSIONS

Some summarizing remarks can be made about Eq. (19). First, suppose $h\nu/k$ is small compared to each of the three temperatures, T_0, T_c, and αT_c. Clearly, if $(T_c/T_0) \ll 1$, if $\alpha \sim 1$, as would result if the amplifying state were obtained as a transient effect from the application of a high level pulse of suitable duration (for a magnetic system to reverse M_0) to a system initially in equilibrium at T_c, and if $Q_{L1} \ll Q_0$, a noise figure approaching unity can be obtained. On the other hand, if $T_c = T_0$, and again if $\alpha = 1$, $F_{T_0} = 2 - G^{-1}$. This function ranges from 1 to 2 as G ranges from 1 to ∞.

It might be supposed that an over-all value close to 1 could be obtained for large net G by utilization of a cascade of amplifiers of small incremental gain each or, in the limit, a distributed device amplifying a running wave. Application of the cascade noise-figure formula

$$F_{12} = F_1 + (F_2 - 1)/G_1$$

demonstrates that, if the circuit losses represented by Q_0 are negligible in each stage, identical noise figure is obtained from a cascade of stages of similar T_c and α, with gains G_1, G_2, G_3, $\cdots$ as from a single stage of the same net gain, $G_1G_2G_3 \cdots$.

In circumstances where $(h\nu/kT_0) \gg 1$, Eq. (19) with $T_0 \sim T_c$ and $\alpha \sim 1$ leads to $F_{T_0} \gg 1$. This results not because greater noise is introduced by lowering T_0 but rather because the largeness of $(h\nu/kT_0)$ corresponds to extremely small noise in the signal source. The negative temperatures correspondingly near zero do not have correspondingly little thermal radiation, and, consequently, the large noise figure results from the quietness of the reference. The noise figure is least with the smallest value of α, corresponding to as *small* an absolute negative temperature as possible.

Circuit properties of the Maser are adequately represented by the equivalent negative resistance, so long as signal levels do not produce appreciable changes in the state of the system, in themselves. As is true generally with negative resistance or regenerative devices, the gain-bandwidth product is essentially a constant of the system. A singly resonant circuit that has a gain of ½, for example, without the addition of the radiant system, can be given a gain G with reduction of the bandwidth by the factor $1/2G$, corresponding to the net increase in operating resonant impedance in the presence of given reactive elements. The bandwidth can be increased by further loading of the circuit by, for example, the signal generator and compensating this by a correspondingly larger Maser system.

Attention may be called to a point in the noise properties that seems, from the circuit viewpoint, anomalous. The conclusion that power is delivered to the circuit losses by spontaneous emission processes was so independent of effective temperature that even a system with $N_1 = N_2$, which shows no absorption or no detectable circuit impedance, supplies the normal amount of noise power. In the equivalent circuit, R is infinite as is also $\langle e^2 \rangle_{Av}$. The power transfer found results from the fact that the coupled circuit allows the absorbing medium to relax to thermal equilibrium with the radiation in the circuit. The time constant for such relaxation is short compared to that which would arise from the coupling to radiation fields in free space (*6*). However, such power transfer can continue in accord with this same formula only if the system remains in statistical equilibrium internally, through some interaction between particles. Such an interaction is required to allow the system, on the average, to be described by N_1/N_2. From the interaction with the circuit alone, the particles develop in time with definite correlations that depend on the details of the field distribution of the circuit mode in the medium (*7*). The loss of energy cannot be ascribed to changes in N_1/N_2 alone except after the lapse of times comparable to T_2. Systems with adequately short internal time constants, corresponding to the interparticle interactions, could build up polarization through the interaction with the cavity in such a manner.

In summary, the solid state Maser, because of the feasibility of obtaining small negative effective temperatures, can offer much in improved noise figure for reception of signals from sources of low equivalent temperature, such as may occur in decimeter and centimeter wave bands. Similar analysis can be applied to devices utilizing beams of particles and, in them, the effective temperature is clearly a measure of the degree to which the beam is separated. In addition to the noise considered here and of concern for comparison to small signals, there may also be noise of the type that is proportional to the signal and that results from the fluctuations in the gain of the system. Usually the number of particles participating will be large and, therefore, the fractional fluctuations in output signal will be small.

RECEIVED: January 18, 1957.

REFERENCES

1. J. P. GORDON, H. J. ZEIGER, AND C. H. TOWNES, *Phys. Rev.* **99**, 1264 (1955).
2. N. BLOEMBERGEN, *Phys. Rev.* **104**, 324 (1956).
3. N. G. BASSOV AND A. M. PROKHOROV, *T. Exptl. Theoret. Phys.* (*USSR*) **27**, 431 (1954); *Proc. Acad. Sci.* (*USSR*) **101**, 37 (1945).
4. E. M. PURCELL AND R. V. POUND, *Phys. Rev.* **81**, 279 (1951).
5. J. L. LAWSON AND G. E. UHLENBECK, "Threshold Signals," Radiation Laboratory Series, Vol. 24, Chapter 5. McGraw-Hill, New York, 1950.
6. E. M. PURCELL, *Phys. Rev.* **69**, 681 (A) (1946).
7. R. H. DICKE, *Phys. Rev.* **93**, 99 (1954).

JOURNAL OF THE PHYSICAL SOCIETY OF JAPAN Vol. 12, No. 6, JUNE, 1957

Fluctuations in Amplification of Quanta with Application to Maser Amplifiers

By Koichi SHIMODA, Hidetosi TAKAHASI, and Charles H. TOWNES*

Department of Physics, Faculty of Science, University of Tokyo

(Received February 15, 1957)

Fluctuations in the amplification and absorption of waves by quantum processes are considered. Assuming for each quantum the probability (per unit time) a of producing another quantum, probability b of being absorbed, and assuming a probability c that a new quantum is introduced, a set of differential equations is obtained. By solving these equations, a complete expression for the probability of distribution of quanta is obtained, as well as expressions for the average values and fractional fluctuation.

The expressions developed are applied in particular to maser-type amplifiers, and certain fluctuations in the amplification of electromagnetic waves are pointed out which are important when their quantum character becomes significant. This condition can occur in maser-type amplifiers, where thermal and extraneous noises may be very small. For such an amplifier, a is proportional to the number of excited molecules, whereas b consists of a term proportional to the number of molecules in the ground state plus terms due to certain other losses. The noise temperature of a maser-type traveling-wave amplifier is the "effective temperature" $a(a-b)^{-1}h\nu/k$. In superregenerative and regenerative amplifiers using resonant cavities, the noise temperature is rather similar, if losses through the input coupling hole are excluded from b. In any case, the limiting noise for an ideal amplifier corresponds to a classical noise temperature of $h\nu/k$.

§ 1. Introduction

The intensity of a classical wave may increase or decrease continuously with time, or as the wave progresses. The intensity of a quantized wave, on the other hand, can change only by discrete amounts, and the extent of these changes is governed by probabilities. Hence a measurement of the number of quanta which it contains may give a variety of values. An evident example is a cosmic ray shower, in which a single initial electron may

* Fulbright Professor, May–Aug. 1956. Permanent address, Department of Physics, Columbia University.

produce other electrons as it progresses through matter. The expectation value for the number of particles in the shower after a certain path length may have some definite non-integral value, but the number of particles counted in the shower will of course be integral, and may have a wide variety of values. It is this general type of fluctuation, associated with quantum effects, with which the following discussion is primarily concerned.

A system involving stimulated emission and absorption of low energy photons by matter affords a particularly simple case for study of these fluctuations, since every such photon has the same energy, and the same probability per unit time of producing further absorption or emission. This case is also of interest because it allows discussion of the ultimate sensitivity of maser-type amplifiers, to which some application of the theory developed below will be made. However, the equation used and their solutions apply to certain simple cases of a variety of experiments, such as fluctuations in the number of mutants of some organism[1], in the growth of neutrons in fissionable material, in the multiplication of electrons by secondary emission, as well as variations in cosmic ray showers[2].

§ 2. Definitions and Fundamental Equations

Consider an initial number of particles, n, each of which has a probability per unit time, a, for producing another similar particle, and a probability per unit time, b, of being absorbed or destroyed. Also let c be the constant rate at which additional particles may be added from some unspecified source. If the total number of particles, m, could increase continuously, it would then follow the equation

$$\frac{dm}{dt}=(a-b)m+c\ , \tag{1}$$

with the initial condition, $m=n$ for $t=0$. Solution of this equation, corresponding to the change in intensity of a classical wave, is

$$m=\left(n+\frac{c}{a-b}\right)e^{(a-b)t}-\frac{c}{a-b}\ . \tag{2}$$

Hence the quantity $n+\frac{c}{a-b}$ increases or decreases exponentially with time. However, since m must be integral, equation (1) does not apply precisely*, and it is convenient to consider the probability $P_{n,m}(t)$ for having a total of m particles at a time t. Since $(am+c)P_{n,m}$ is the probability per unit time that the number of particles are increased from m to $m+1$ and $bmP_{n,m}$ the probability for a decrease from m to $m-1$, the $P_{n,m}$ are related by the set of differential equations

$$\begin{aligned}\frac{dP_{n,m}}{dt}=&-[(a+b)m+c]P_{n,m}\\&+[a(m-1)+c]P_{n,m-1}\\&+b(m+1)P_{n,m+1}\end{aligned} \tag{3}$$

with initial conditions that for $t=0$, $P_{n,m}=\delta_{nm}$ Evidently, this equation is satisfied by any probability distribution corresponding to an arbitrary initial state, although the initial condition may differ from that given above.

§ 3. Distributions when Absorption or Emission Occurs Alone

Since general solutions for the set of equations (3) are rather complicated, it is instructive to first consider solutions of the simplified cases when only emission or only absorption occurs ($b=0$ or $a=c=0$ respectively). For emission only,

$$\frac{dP_{n,m}}{dt}=-(am+c)P_{n,m}+[a(m-1)+c]P_{n,m-1}\ . \tag{4}$$

Solutions satisfying the initial conditions, $P_{n,m}=\delta_{nm}$ for $t=0$ are

$$\begin{aligned}P_{n,m}(t)=&\frac{\Gamma(m+c/a)}{(m-n)!\,\Gamma(n+c/a)}e^{-at(n+c/a)}\\&\times(1-e^{-at})^{m-n}\end{aligned} \tag{5a}$$

or

$$\begin{aligned}P_{n,m}=&\frac{\Gamma(m+c/a)}{(m-n)!\,\Gamma(n+c/a)}\left(\frac{1}{K}\right)^{n+c/a}\\&\times\left(1-\frac{1}{K}\right)^{m-n},\end{aligned} \tag{5b}$$

where $K=e^{at}$ is the classical growth or amplification factor from (2). When there is absorption or attenuation only,

$$P_{n,m}=\frac{n!}{m!\,(n-m)!}e^{-btm}(1-e^{-bt})^{n-m} \tag{6a}$$

or

* It will been seen below, in equation (11), that even when the number of particles is finite and does not increase continuously, the average number of particles still changes with time in precisely the same manner given by the classical expression.

$$P_{n,m}=\frac{n!}{m!\,(n-m)!}(K)^m(1-K)^{n-m} \tag{6b}$$

where $K=e^{-bt}$ is from (2) the classical attenuation factor.

After a very long time (6a) gives, as expected, a probability zero for finding any number of particles other than $m=0$. However, the asymptotic behavior of (5a) is more interesting. In the limit where e^{at} or K is very large,

$$P_{n,m}\rightarrow\frac{m^{n+c/a-1}e^{-m/K}}{K^{n+c/a}\,\Gamma(n+c/a)}\;. \tag{7}$$

This probability is a maximum when $m=K(n+c/a-1)$, but from it the average value of m can be shown to be $m=K(n+c/a)-c/a$, which is identical with the classical expression (2). Furthermore when K is so large that (7) is a good approximation, the distribution does not change shape, but is a function of $\frac{m}{K}=n+c/a-1$. The fluctuations then depend, after a large amplification, only on the number n of initial particles and on c/a, which is the number of new particles introduced during the time required for the amplification to increase by a factor e.

A special property of equation (6), or of (5) when $c/a=1$, is that an exponential probability distribution remains exponential after amplification or attenuation. The latter case $c/a=1$ is important, as will be shown below, for distributions of photons where c is due only to spontaneous emission. Let there be initially a probability $p_n(0)=(1-u_0)u_0^n$ that n particles are introduced, where $u_0<1$. The probability p_m of m particles after amplification is

$$\begin{aligned}p_m&=\sum_n P_{n,m}p_n(0)\\&=\frac{(1-u_0)}{K}\sum_n\frac{m!}{n!(m-n)!}\left(\frac{u_0}{K}\right)^n\left(1-\frac{1}{K}\right)^{m-n}\\&=\frac{(1-u_0)}{K}\left(\frac{K+u_0-1}{K}\right)^m.\end{aligned} \tag{8a}$$

This is just another exponential distribution with somewhat larger spread, since u_0 is replaced by $u=\frac{K+u_0-1}{K}$, and $u\geq u_0$ when $K\geq 1$. Equation (8a) can be written in the form

$$\frac{u}{1-u}=K\left(\frac{u_0}{1-u_0}+1\right)-1\;. \tag{8b}$$

Since $\frac{u_0}{1-u_0}$ and $\frac{u}{1-u}$ represent the average value of n and m respectively, (8b) means that the classical relation (2) is again satisfied for the average values.

Similarly, when attenuation occurs, a distribution $(1-u_0)u_0^n$ is changed into $(1-u)u^m$, where

$$u=\frac{Ku_0}{1-u_0(1-K)}\;. \tag{9a}$$

Here $u\leq u_0$ since now $K\leq 1$. (9a) may be written as

$$\frac{u}{1-u}=\frac{Ku_0}{1-u_0} \tag{9b}$$

which again corresponds to the classical relation (2) with $a=c=0$. When $c/a=0$ in expressions (6a) or (6b), an exponential distribution can be shown to again remain exponential after amplification, with exception of the unique case of $m=0$. The case of $m=0$ is exceptional when $c/a=0$, since its probability must remain constant, while probabilities for all other values of m may be changed by the effect of amplification. These properties will prove useful in a later section.

Expressions (5) and (6) giving the distribution in the number of particles are quite general in the sense that they do not depend on the particular mechanism of attenuation or amplification. Thus if a group of particles strike a partially reflecting surface, each particle having a probability K of being reflected, the probability that m particles in all are reflected is given by (6b). Expressions (5b) and (6b) do not include time as a parameter, but simply the total amplification or attenuation, and their validity can be shown not to depend on constant values of a or b. However, they do require that only emission or only absorption be present, and not both at once.

§ 4. The General Case — Moments of the Distribution and Average Fluctuations

When $K=1$, expressions (5b) and (6b) show that there is no change from the initial values of the probabilities. This is because no amplification or absorption has occurred, so no disturbances are introduced. However, the net amplification may also be unity in a system where both amplifying and absorbing processes occur simultaneously, and hence introduce fluctuations. Hence when neither a nor b is zero, equations (5) and (6) may need considerable modification. Since a general solution of (3) in this case is complex, it is convenient to examine first the various moments of the distribution and properties of the fluctuations which can be easily deduced from them.

Behavior of the average value of m, $\overline{m}=\sum_m mP_{n,m}$, can be obtained by multiplying equation (3) with m, summing over m, and making substitutions of the type,

$$\sum_m f(m)P_{n,m-1}=\sum_m f(m+1)P_{n,m}$$
$$\sum_m f(m)P_{n,m+1}=\sum_m f(m-1)P_{n,m}\,. \qquad (10)$$

This gives

$$\frac{d\overline{m}}{dt}=\overline{m}(a-b)+c\,. \qquad (11)$$

By a similar process, one obtains

$$\frac{d\overline{m^2}}{dt}=2(a-b)\overline{m^2}+(a+b+2c)\overline{m}+c \qquad (12)$$

$$\frac{d\overline{m^r}}{dt}=\sum_{s=1}^{r}\frac{r!}{s!\,(r-s)!}\{\overline{m^{r-s+1}}[a+(-1)^s b]+\overline{m^{r-s}}c\}\,. \qquad (13)$$

Solutions of (11) and (12) are

$$\overline{m}=\left(\overline{n}+\frac{c}{a-b}\right)e^{(a-b)t}-\frac{c}{a-b} \qquad (14)$$

$$\overline{m^2}=\left[\overline{n^2}-\frac{c(b+c)}{(a-b)^2}+\left(\overline{n}+\frac{c}{a-b}\right)\frac{(a+b+2c)}{a-b}\right]e^{2(a-b)t}$$
$$-\left(\overline{n}+\frac{c}{a-b}\right)\frac{(a+b+2c)}{a-b}e^{(a-b)t}+\frac{c(b+c)}{(a-b)^2}\,, \qquad (15)$$

where $\overline{n}$ and $\overline{n^2}$ are values of $\overline{m}$ and $\overline{m^2}$ respectively at $t=0$. The average or expectation value, $\overline{m}$, follows the same equation (2) which is obtained for a classical wave. It may be noted that when $\overline{n}=-\frac{c}{a-b}$ and $\overline{n^2}=\frac{c(b+c)}{(a-b)^2}$, $\overline{m}$ and $\overline{m^2}$ are constant. This equilibrium condition can occur only when $b>a$, and will be shown below to represent thermal equilibrium in the case of photons. Furthermore, if $b>a$, (14) and (15) show that $\overline{m}$ and $\overline{m^2}$ approach these equilibrium values after a long time.

The most significant quantity for a ready measure of fluctuations is $\frac{\overline{m^2}-\overline{m}^2}{\overline{m}^2}$. This is the square of what is usually called the coefficient of variation or more loosely the fractional fluctuation $\mathcal{E}$. $\mathcal{E}^2$ can be obtained from (14) and (15). If amplification occurs, so that $a>b$, then after a long time the first terms of expressions (14) and (15) are the only important ones. Neglecting other terms,

$$\mathcal{E}^2=\frac{\overline{m^2}-\overline{m}^2}{\overline{m}^2}=\frac{\overline{n}\left(\frac{a+b}{a-b}\right)+\frac{ac}{(a-b)^2}}{\left(\overline{n}+\frac{c}{a-b}\right)^2}+\frac{\overline{n^2}-\overline{n}^2}{\left(\overline{n}+\frac{c}{a-b}\right)^2}\,. \qquad (16)$$

A number of special cases are of interest. Suppose that there are a fixed number of initial particles n, and no new ones are added, i.e., $\overline{n^2}=\overline{n}^2$ and $c=0$. Then

$$\mathcal{E}=\frac{1}{\sqrt{n\left(\frac{a-b}{a+b}\right)}}\,. \qquad (17)$$

If amplification alone occurs ($b=0$), then $\mathcal{E}=n^{-1/2}$. The fluctuation $\mathcal{E}$ is not due to any uncertainty in the initial number n, but simply to fundamental processes in the amplification of particles. This fluctuation occurs also in amplification of an electromagnetic wave, even in the absence of thermal noise, and represents a lower limit to fluctuation of any amplifying process. If both emission and absorption occur, (17) shows that fluctuations may be appreciably larger than $n^{-1/2}$.

In many cases such fluctuations are negligible, particularly at low frequencies where the number of photons in thermal noise is large. Any degree of freedom of an electrical circuit has average energy kT and hence $kT/h\nu$

photons. Hence as long as $kT \gg h\nu$, and $(a-b)/(a+b)$ is not very small, fluctuations of this type will be negligible. On the other hand, the discussion of amplifiers of electromagnetic waves below will show that thermal noise at low frequencies is just the limiting case of the fluctuations discussed here when $kT/h\nu$ becomes large and $(a-b)/(a+b)$ becomes small as $h\nu/kT$.

A second special case of interest occurs when $c/(a-b) \gg \bar{n}$. Since $c/(a-b)$ is the number of new particles introduced during the time required for the amplification to increase by e, this condition represents the case where the initial number of particles can hardly be regarded as fixed, but is dominated by the entrance of $c/(a-b)$ new particles during the time required for an appreciable amplification. In this case

$$\varepsilon = \sqrt{\frac{a}{c}} . \tag{18}$$

Note that the fluctuations are determined not by $c/(a-b)$, the number of particles entering during time for amplification, but by c/a, the smaller number which enters during the time required for appreciable emission (or absorption if $a-b \ll a$, for then $b \approx a$).

§ 5. Complete Solution for the Distribution Function

Values of the first few moments of m may be all that is usually needed for practical purposes, and these can be conveniently calculated from the set of equations (13). However, a complete solution of (3) may be useful in some cases, and will be given in the following. The solution has been obtained for the general case of arbitrary values of a, b and c by use of a generating function. However, the cases $c=a$ and $c=0$, which have the special property mentioned above, can be dealt with in a somewhat different and more physical way. Since these are also quite important cases, they will be considered in some detail.

i) Case $c=a$

It has been shown above that, when $c=a$, the exponential form of probability distribution is invariant and that there is a linear relationship, (8b) or (9b), between the average numbers of quanta before and after either amplification alone or attenuation alone. Hence this invariance of an exponential distribution and the same type of linear relationship must remain valid for any combination of successive absorption and amplification and, as a limiting case, for simultaneous absorption and amplification. It may then be assumed that some solution of the fundamental differential equation

$$\frac{dp_m}{dt} = -[a(m+1)+bm]p_m + amp_{m-1} + b(m+1)p_{m+1} \tag{19}$$

has the form

$$p_m = (1-u)u^m . \tag{20}$$

Equation (19) is the form taken by (3) when $c=a$. When expression (20) is substituted into (19), a factor depending on m drops out from both sides of the equation, and a single equation independent of m is obtained:

$$\frac{du}{dt} = (1-u)(a-bu) .$$

Integration of this expression yields a linear relation between the average numbers of quanta, i.e.,

$$\frac{u}{1-u} = \frac{Ku_0}{1-u_0} + \frac{a}{a-b}(K-1) \tag{21}$$

where $K=e^{(a-b)t}$ is the classical amplification factor and u_0 is the initial value of u (for $t=0$).

Since (20) is the probability distribution corresponding to the initial distribution $(1-u_0)u_0^n$, we have

$$(1-u)u^m = \sum_n P_{n,m}(1-u_0)u_0^n \tag{22}$$

or

$$\sum_n P_{n,m}u_0^n = \frac{1-u}{1-u_0}u^m = \frac{(a-b)a^m(K-1)^m}{(aK-b)^{m+1}\left[1-\frac{b(K-1)}{aK-b}u_0\right]}\left[1+\frac{\frac{(a-b)^2Ku_0}{a(K-1)(aK-b)}}{1-\frac{b(K-1)}{aK-b}u_0}\right]^m \tag{23}$$

Since (23) holds for any u_0 (less than unity), it may be used to evaluate $P_{n,m}$ by expanding the right hand side in powers of u_0 and equating coefficients of u_0^n on each side of the equation. Such an expansion gives a convergent series when $u_0<1$, since always $\frac{b(K-1)}{aK-b}<1$. After carrying out the expansion, one obtains the probability distribution

$$P_{n,m}=\frac{(a-b)a^m b^n(K-1)^{m+n}}{(aK-b)^{m+n+1}}\sum_{j=0}^{m\text{ or }n}\frac{m!n!}{j!(m-j)!j!(n-j)!}\left[\frac{(a-b)^2K}{ab(K-1)^2}\right]^j. \tag{24}$$

Here the upper limit of the summation should be n for $n\leq m$ and m for $n\geq m$.

When $a=0$, expression (24) becomes $\frac{n!}{m!(n-m)!}K^m(1-K)^{n-m}$ for $n\geq m$, and 0 for $n<m$, in agreement with the previous result (6b). Similarly, when $b=0$, (24) becomes $\frac{m!}{(m-n)!n!}\times\frac{(K-1)^{m-n}}{K^{m+1}}$ for $m\geq n$, and 0 for $m<n$, in agreement with (5b) when $c=a$.

ii) Case $c=0$

It has already been shown that the same type of invariance of the exponential distribution holds also when $c=0$, with the exception of the case $m=0$. Accordingly, one can proceed in a way similar to that above for $c=a$, but with a few modifications. Since $m=0$ is exceptional, the probabilities may be written in the form

$$\begin{aligned} p_m&=\alpha(1-u)u^m \qquad (m\neq 0)\\ p_0&=1-\alpha u\,, \end{aligned} \tag{25}$$

using a positive parameter α. The lowest state $m=0$ is more or less populated than is required by the strictly exponential distribution according as $\alpha>1$ or $\alpha<1$. One again obtains the relation between u and u_0:

$$\frac{u}{1-u}=\frac{Ku_0}{1-u_0}+K-1 \tag{26}$$

which is identical with (8b). However, it should be noted that here the average number of quanta $\overline{m}$ is no longer $u/(1-u)$ but rather $\alpha u/(1-u)$ and the physical meaning of (26) is quite different. The proper equation for $\overline{m}$ is

$$\overline{m}=\frac{\alpha u}{1-u}=K\frac{\alpha_0 u_0}{1-u_0}\,, \tag{27}$$

where α_0 is the initial value of α at $t=0$. Note that (27) just corresponds to (14) when $c=0$. (27) may be used to determine the additional parameter α.

From these equations, one obtains after a little calculation for $m\neq 0$

$$\sum_{n=1}^{\infty}P_{n,m}u_0^n=\frac{(a-b)^2Ku[a(K-1)+(a-bK)u]^{m-1}}{[(aK-b)-b(K-1)u_0]^{m+1}} \tag{28}$$

and for $m=0$

$$\sum_{n=1}^{\infty}P_{n,0}u_0^n=\frac{b(K-1)u_0}{(aK-b)-b(K-1)u_0}\,.$$

Expansion of the right hand side gives

$$P_{n,m}=\frac{a^m b^n(K-1)^{m+n}}{(aK-b)^{m+n}}\sum_{j=0}^{m\text{ or }n}\frac{n!(m-1)!}{j!(n-j)!(j-1)!(m-j)!}\left[\frac{(a-b)^2K}{ab(K-1)^2}\right]^j. \tag{29}$$

iii) General Case

The form of $P_{m,n}$ for the general case might he conjectured from expressions (24) and (29), or it may be rigorously derived by use of a generating function. It is

$$P_{n,m}=\frac{(a-b)^{c/a}a^m b^n(K-1)^{m+n}}{(aK-b)^{m+n+c/a}}\sum_{j=0}^{m\text{ or }n}\frac{n!\Gamma(m+c/a)}{j!(n-j)!(m-j)!\Gamma(j+c/a)}\left[\frac{(a-b)^2K}{ab(K-1)^2}\right]^j, \tag{30}$$

where the sum is to m when $m\leq n$ or to n when $n\leq m$. The generating function and details of the derivation of (30) are given in the Appendix. Expression (30) holds for any positive values of K, a, b, and c. However, there are a number of special cases listed below which warrant separate consideration.

(a) Case $a=b$, $K=1$

Expression (30) holds for $K>1$ as well as for $K<1$. However, the equation cannot be used directly for the limiting case $K=1$, that is, the case with neither amplification nor attenuation. By the appropriate limiting process, $K=(a-b)t+1$ and $a\to b$, (30) can be brought to the following from

$$P_{n,m}=\frac{(at)^{m+n}}{(at+1)^{m+n+c/a}}\sum_{j=0}^{m\text{ or }n}\frac{n!\Gamma(m+c/a)}{j!(n-j)!(m-j)!\Gamma(j+c/a)}\left(\frac{1}{at}\right)^{2j}. \tag{31}$$

(b) Case $a=0$, $c\neq 0$

Another limiting case occurs when there is no amplification but a constant rate of generation of new quanta. Then

$$P_{n,m}=\frac{c^m(1-K)^{n+m}}{b^m}e^{-(1-K)c/b}\sum_{j=0}^{n\text{ or }m}\frac{n!}{j!(n-j)!(m-j)!}\left(\frac{bK}{c(1-K)^2}\right)^j. \tag{32}$$

(c) $K\to\infty$, $m\to\infty$, $K/m=$finite

The asymptotic behavior of (30) for large K and m is of special interest since such a case is related to a macroscopic observation of a small number of quanta by means of very large amplification, as in the case of photo-multiplier tubes, or perhaps in a maser amplifier.

The asymptotic form in this case is

$$P_{n,m}=\frac{1}{m}\left(\frac{a-b}{a}\frac{m}{K}\right)^{c/a}\left(\frac{b}{a}\right)^n\exp\left(-\frac{a-b}{a}\frac{m}{K}\right)\sum_{j=0}^{n}\frac{n!}{j!(n-j)!\Gamma(j+c/a)}\left[\frac{(a-b)^2}{ab}\frac{m}{K}\right]^j. \tag{33}$$

When $c=a$, the right hand side becomes a Laguerre polynomial and

$$P_{n,m}=\frac{a-b}{aK}\left(\frac{b}{a}\right)^n\exp\left(-\frac{a-b}{a}\frac{m}{K}\right)L_n\left[-\frac{(a-b)^2}{ab}\frac{m}{K}\right]. \tag{34}$$

When $a\gg b$, the highest term of the sum in (33) prevails and the distribution is nearly identical with the one given by (7). However, as the ratio b/a increases, the peak becomes broader and the value of $P_{n,m}$ does not vanish at $m=0$ corresponding to the fact that there is always some probability that all particles vanish during the process.

(d) Equilibrium

The distribution reaches an equilibrium after a long time only if $a<b$. $P_{n,m}$ may be evaluated in this case either by setting $dP_{n,m}/dt=0$ in the fundamental equation (3) and solving the equation by a mathematical induction, or by letting K approach zero in the general solution (30). This gives

$$P_{n,m}=(1-a/b)^{c/a}\frac{\Gamma(m+c/a)(a/b)^m}{m!\Gamma(c/a)} \tag{35}$$

which is independent of n and finite for all values of m, since $a<b$.

Finally, attention should be called to the generality of the expression of the type (30). In case $c=a$ and $c=0$, it can be shown that any succession of absorption and emission leaves the exponential form of distribution invariant and leads to a linear relation between $u/(1-u)$ and $u_0/(1-u_0)$. The expression contains two independent parameters K and a/b, and represents the most general linear relation between $u/(1-u)$ and $u_0/(1-u_0)$. Hence it follows that the forms (24) and (29) represent the general case involving any arbitrary succession of absorption, amplification, or mixture of both, provided appropriate values of K and a/b are used.

The same argument does not apply to the

general case represented by (30), but it will be shown in the appendix, that this is true even in this case, that is, when both a and b depend on time, but c/a remains constant.

§ 6. Applicability of Results to Maser-type Amplification

Equation (3) and solutions discussed above apply well to a group of photons which may increase or decrease in number as a result of normal absorption, stimulated emission, or spontaneous emission. Consider some atomic or molecular system which may exist in one of two nearby levels, between which photons may induce transitions. The probability of absorption of a photon by a molecule in the lower state is the same as that for emission stimulated by the photon from a molecule in the upper state. Under normal conditions, an ensemble of such molecules is in thermal equilibrium, there are more molecules in the lower than in the upper state, and hence the ensemble attenuates a wave packet of photons. However, spontaneous emission also occurs and is responsible for maintaining the thermal radiation of photons by the molecules. Moreover, if an abnormal ensemble can be created in which there are more molecules in the upper than in the lower state, a wave packet of photons passing through such an ensemble will be amplified rather than attenuated. This type of phenomenon occurs in a maser[3], and gives promise of allowing construction of amplifiers which are exceptionally free of noise. To show that equation (3) applies to such amplifiers, two somewhat idealized cases will be discussed.

Consider first a cavity with perfectly reflecting walls and containing molecules of the type described above with n_a molecules in the upper state and n_b in the lower state. For simplicity, suppose that the response of these molecules is independent of frequency over the range of frequencies considered, which includes the frequency of a normal mode of the cavity. If there are m photons of this frequency in the cavity, the probability of one of the photons being absorbed per unit time is proportional to m and to n_b or hence has the form Amn_b, where A is a constant. The probability per unit time for a photon to be produced by stimulated emission is correspondingly Amn_a.

Spontaneous emission may also provide new photons. When an excited atomic or molecular system interacts with one of the normal modes of an electromagnetic field in some enclosure, the probability for emission of a photon (of the same frequency as that of the normal mode) is proportional to $n+1$, where n is the number of quanta present in the mode. The finite probability for emission when $n=0$ represents spontaneous emission, or the effect of zero-point fluctuations of the electromagnetic field which have one-half the energy of one quantum. Hence the spontaneous emission is given by An_a.

From the above, it may be seen that the number of photons in a perfectly reflecting cavity containing molecules of the type discussed will follow equations (3) with $a=An_a$, $b=An_b$, and $c=a$. If the walls are not perfectly reflecting, but absorb and emit photons, they may be replaced in principle by perfectly reflecting walls and a suitable number of molecules n_a and n_b in the upper and lower states. Hence, with appropriate modification of the effective number of molecules involved, a cavity with absorbing walls is equivalent to the case with perfectly reflecting walls already considered. If there is a coupling hole in the cavity, this allows photons to escape and corresponds simply to an increase in n_b or in b provided no new photons enter through the coupling hole. If a signal is introduced through the coupling hole, this corresponds to an increase in c, the rate of introduction of new photons, so that $c>a$. However, as will be seen below, some care must be taken to allow for possible interference of the waves of incoming and outgoing photons in this case.

As a second example, consider a packet of m photons traveling along a waveguide filled with material containing the molecules in question with a density n_a of molecules in the upper state and a density n_b in the lower state. For simplicity, let the wave associated with the m photons be a packet of constant amplitude and finite length, with Δt the time required for the entire packet to pass a given point in the waveguide. Now the probability of one of the photons being absorbed per unit time is again proportional to m and to n_b, or $A'mn_b$. The probability per unit time for production of a photon by stimulated emission is correspondingly $A'mn_a$. Again for simplicity, the molecular systems will be assumed to respond uniformly over a wide range of frequencies so that A' is independent of frequencies to be considered.

The ratio of induced emission to spontaneous emission may be seen from the discussion above to be determined by the ratio of the energy density associated with photons to twice that of zero-point fluctuations of the normal modes which have appropriate frequencies to produce emission.

A waveguide may be considered an enclosure, and the energy density of normal modes calculated, by assuming it has some arbitrary long length. Or, such a calculation may be circumvented by use of the well known relation for the power flow P of noise along a waveguide.

$$P=kT\Delta\nu\ , \tag{36}$$

where $\Delta\nu$ is the bandwidth to which the amplifying system responds. Since each normal mode has energy kT (when $kT\gg h\nu$, which may be assumed for this derivation), and each mode may be considered as two traveling waves moving in opposite directions, it can be seen from (36) that the power which might be considered to flow in one direction due to zero-point vibration is

$$P_0=\frac{h\nu\Delta\nu}{2}\ .$$

The power flow due to the wave packet of m photons is $\frac{mh\nu}{\Delta t}$. Now a wave packet of duration Δt has a frequency spectrum with the power per unit bandwith given as a function of frequency by

$$\Phi(\nu)d\nu=\Phi(\nu_0)\left[\frac{\sin(\nu-\nu_0)\pi\Delta t}{(\nu-\nu_0)\pi\Delta t}\right]^2 d\nu\ . \tag{37}$$

Integration of (37) gives the total power flow and allows evalution of $\Phi(\nu_0)$

$$\frac{mh\nu}{\Delta t}=\int\Phi(\nu)d\nu=\frac{\Phi(\nu_0)}{\Delta t}$$

since $\int_{-\infty}^{\infty}\frac{\sin^2 x}{x^2}dx=\pi$. Hence the ratio of stimulated to spontaneous emission at the frequency ν is

$$r=\frac{\Phi(\nu)\Delta\nu}{2P_0}=\frac{\Phi(\nu)}{h\nu}=m\left[\frac{\sin(\nu-\nu_0)\pi\Delta t}{(\nu-\nu_0)\pi\Delta t}\right]^2.$$

Under the optimum condition, which occurs when $\nu=\nu_0$, $r=m$. Thus if the stimulated emission is given by $A'mn_a$ as indicated above, the spontaneous emission is $A'n_a$. This corresponds to the case $c=a$ in (3). If emission and absorption of photons by the waveguide walls occur, they may be again regarded as due to some equivalent number of absorbing or emitting molecules, so that the above discussion applies, but with modified numbers n_a and n_b of molecules in the two states.

Photons in Equilibrium

If there is an equilibrium distribution of particles, so that $dP_{n,m}/dt=0$ for all $P_{n,m}$, then according to (35)

$$P_{n,m}=(1-a/b)^{c/a}\frac{\Gamma(m+c/a)}{m!\Gamma(c/a)}(a/b)^m\ .$$

If new photons are introduced into the system only as a result of spontaneous or stimulated emission then, as shown above, $c/a=1$, and (35) becomes

$$P_{n,m}=(1-a/b)(a/b)^m\ . \tag{39}$$

This is just the probability distribution for thermal equilibrium of photons with the molecules, since $a/b=e^{-h\nu/kT}$ where T is the temperature of the molecules.

§ 7. Fluctuations in a Traveling-wave Maser

Fluctuations in an amplifier of the maser type may now be related to the coefficients a, b, and c. In many cases, fluctuations which determine the limiting sensitivity of such an amplifier depend only on the ratio a/b, which is conveniently expressed in terms of an effective temperature T_e defined by

$$\frac{a}{b}=\exp\left(\frac{-h\nu}{kT_e}\right)\ . \tag{40}$$

Here $h\nu$ is the energy gap between upper and lower levels and k is Boltzmann's constant. T_e may be positive or negative depending on the relative magnitude of a and b, but the fluctuations are primarily dependent on the absolute value of T_e.

Consider first the waveguide case, where for amplification to occur $a>b$. From (16), if exactly n photons are introduced into the amplifier, after a large amplification a measure of the fractional fluctuation is

$$\varepsilon^2=\frac{\overline{m^2}-\overline{m}^2}{\overline{m}^2}=\frac{n\left(\frac{a+b}{a-b}\right)+\frac{ac}{(a-b)^2}}{[n+c/(a-b)]^2}\ . \tag{41}$$

Since in the present case $c=a$,

$$\mathcal{E}^2=\frac{n\dfrac{1+e^{h\nu/kT_e}}{1-e^{h\nu/kT_e}}+\dfrac{1}{(1-e^{h\nu/kT_e})^2}}{[n+(1-e^{h\nu/kT_e})^{-1}]^2}\,. \tag{42}$$

If $h\nu/k|T_e|\gg 1$, (42) becomes

$$\mathcal{E}^2\approx\frac{1}{n+1} \tag{43}$$

and the probability distribution is given by (7) with $c=a$, or

$$P_{n,m}\approx\frac{1}{K}\left(\frac{m}{K}\right)^n\frac{e^{-m/K}}{n!} \tag{44}$$

Equation (43) and (44) represent the behavior of a perfect amplifier, where the absolute value of the temperature approaches zero and only emission processes occur ($b\to 0$). In this case there remain fluctuations due to quantum effects. The fractional variations which occur approach zero when the number of quanta to be amplified is large, which is normally the case for very low frequencies. It should be noted that the effective temperature need not be actually zero to approach a perfect amplifier, but $k|T_e|$ must be small compared with the energy $h\nu$ of one quantum. In the case of 1-centimeter radiation, $k|T_e|=h\nu$ when $|T_e|\approx 1.5°\mathrm{K}$. $|T_e|$ in an ammonia maser[3], for example, can be smaller than this value, since ammonia molecules in a well focused beam flowing into the cavity are predominantly in the upper inversion state and $a\gg b$.

In the other extreme case where a is almost equal to b, or $h\nu/k|T_e|\ll 1$,

$$\mathcal{E}^2\approx\frac{2nh\nu/k|T_e|+1}{(nh\nu/k|T_e|+1)^2}\,. \tag{45}$$

A measure of the minimum detectable number of quanta under such conditions can be obtained from the equations (14) or (21). After large amplification

$$\overline{m}=\left(\overline{n}+\frac{a}{a-b}\right)K \tag{46}$$

where K is the classical amplification factor $e^{(a-b)t}$. For the signal to equal background noise

$$n_{\min}=\frac{a}{a-b}\approx\frac{k|T_e|}{h\nu}\,, \tag{47}$$

if $a\approx b$ or $h\nu/k|T_e|\ll 1$. This value represents just the magnitude of thermal noise at a temperature $|T_e|$. The thermal power level in the same time interval Δt as the input signal may be expressed by $P_t=k|T_e|\Delta\nu_e$, where $\Delta\nu_e$, the effective bandwidth corresponding to the length of wave packet of the signal, is $1/(\Delta t)$ by (37). The thermal noise level in terms of number of photons in time Δt is then

$$n_t=\frac{P_t\Delta t}{h\nu}=\frac{k|T_e|}{h\nu}\,.$$

Thus the signal level which doubles the background output of an amplifier has just the magnitude of the usual thermal noise at temperature $|T_e|$. From (45), if the number of photons is s times the thermal noise level, $n=sk|T_e|/h\nu$, the fluctuation is given by

$$\mathcal{E}^2=\frac{2s+1}{(s+1)^2}\,. \tag{48}$$

Hence the signal level must be considerably larger than $k|T_e|/h\nu$ before the fractional fluctuations become small.

The probability distribution for this case is obtained from (34) as

$$P_{n,m}=\frac{1}{m_0}e^{-(s+m/m_0)}I_0\left(2\sqrt{\frac{m}{m_0}s}\right). \tag{49}$$

where m_0 is the average number of quanta for the background noise only, and I_0 is the modified Bessel function of order zero. Note that equations (48) and (49) agree precisely with the classical expressions for the fluctuation of power for the waves obtained by superposition of a sinusoidal wave and a thermal noise.

It is important to note that $|T_e|$ may have very little to do with any ordinary idea of the temperature of the amplifying system. Suppose, for example, that the waveguide walls are at absolute zero temperature, but absorb photons. Suppose also that the material inside the waveguide is at a very small negative temperature, so that for it $b=0$, and one might expect to have an ideal amplifier. However, absorption of photons by the waveguide adds to the net value of b, and if this absorption is of sufficient size, the entire system may have b almost equal to a, so that $|T_e|$ would be extremely large and the amplifier very noisy.

§8. Regenerative Amplifier Using a Cavity

In the case of a resonant microwave cavity containing amplifying materials, the same equations (14) and (15) for $\overline{m}$ and $\overline{m^2}$ apply, but their physical significance is somewhat different. m then represents the total number of photons in the cavity, which does not give directly the magnitude of the energy delivered by the amplifier. Furthermore, if a signal is fed into the cavity continuously, c must represent both this signal and spontaneous emission. Two general types of operation of an amplifier using a cavity are important:

1) Superregenerative amplification where $a>b$ and amplification results from an exponentially increasing pulse initiated by the signal. The exponentially increasing pulse is quenched, and the build-up from the input signal is then repeated in a so-called quenching cycle.

2) Stable amplification where $a<b$. This gives continuous amplification without any exponential build-up.

Consider first the case of a stable amplifier made up of a perfectly conducting cavity with input and output coupling holes and containing material with active molecules or atoms which responds uniformly to electromagnetic radiation at all frequencies of interest. If photons are put into the cavity, they will be absorbed in the material or escape from the input coupling holes. They may also stimulate emission and create new photons. As a result, their average number $\overline{m}$ will decay (since $a<b$) in accordance with the expression

$$-\frac{d\overline{m}}{dt}=(b-a)\overline{m}=(b_u+b_i+b_o-a)\overline{m}\ , \qquad (50)$$

where b_u represents loss in the material, b_i and b_o losses through the input and output coupling holes respectively. The loaded Q for the cavity is easily shown to be $Q=2\pi\nu/(b-a)$. Similarly the unloaded Q, and Q's for the coupling holes are $Q_u=2\pi\nu/(b_u-a)$, $Q_i=2\pi\nu/b_i$, and $Q_o=2\pi\nu/b_o$. Here Q_u may be negative, since the active material would have $a>b$ to provide amplification or the equivalent of a negative resistance.

Assume now an input signal of power P_i per unit frequency interval. Standard theory for cavity resonators, which may be extended to the case where Q_u is negative, gives for the power per unit bandwidth emerging from the output

$$P_o=P_i\frac{2\pi\nu QR(\nu)}{Q_iQ_o}\ , \qquad (51)$$

where $R(\nu)$ is the resonant expression

$$R(\nu)=\left(\frac{1}{2\pi\nu Q}\right)\frac{1}{\left(\frac{1}{2Q}\right)^2+\left(\frac{\nu-\nu_0}{\nu_0}\right)^2} \qquad (52)$$

with ν_0 the resonance frequency of the cavity. Similarly, power reflected back to the input waveguide is

$$P_r=P_i\frac{2\pi\nu QR(\nu)}{4}\left[\left(\frac{1}{Q}-\frac{2}{Q_i}\right)^2+4\left(\frac{\nu-\nu_0}{\nu_0}\right)^2\right] \qquad (53)$$

and the energy stored in the cavity as a result of the input signal is

$$W_i=P_i\frac{Q}{Q_i}R(\nu)\ . \qquad (54)$$

The gain of this type of amplifier is, from (51)

$$G=\frac{P_o}{P_i}=\frac{2\pi\nu Q}{Q_iQ_o}R(\nu) \qquad (55)$$

which becomes

$$G=\frac{4Q^2}{Q_iQ_o}=\frac{4b_ib_o}{(b-a)^2} \qquad (56)$$

at the resonance frequency, $\nu=\nu_0$.

It is important now to note the difference in the reemission of an input signal from the cavity, and the escape of spontaneous emission from the coupling holes. If the input signal is a long train of coherent waves $\left(\varDelta\nu<\frac{\nu_0}{2Q}\right)$, then there is an interference between the wave which is reflected from the input coupling hole without entering the cavity, and that which enters the cavity and is reemitted from the input hole. For example, in the case of a "matched" input, where $1/Q=2/Q_i$, equation (53) shows that there is no power reflected from the input when $\nu=\nu_0$. Hence in this case none of the power W_i accumulated in the cavity can escape from the input hole, which might lead one to suppose that $b_i=0$. However, the spontaneous emission within the cavity undergoes no interference of this type and is emitted from the input according to the value $b_i=\frac{2\pi\nu}{Q_i}$ indicated above. Because of these same interference effects, it is also not immediately clear what values of c should be attributed to the input signal. There are $P_i/h\nu$ photon/sec. per unit bandwidth flowing towards the cavity input, but since the wave reflected directly from the input is indistinguishable from that reemitted from the cavity through the input coupling, the number of photons actually entering the cavity is subject to various interpretations.

For use of equation (3) and its solutions, the effective value of c corresponding to a certain input power P_i is the rate at which photons would have to be released in the cavity to produce an equivalent total number of photons or an equivalent power output. Now if c_i photons/sec. are released within the cavity, it can be shown by standard methods that they produce the total output power which is $h\nu c_i \frac{Q}{Q_o}$. Letting this power equal the total output power due to the input as given by (51), the equivalent rate of introduction of photons by the input signal is

$$c_i = \int P_0(\nu)d\nu = \frac{2\pi P_i}{hQ_i} = \frac{P_i b_i}{h\nu} . \tag{57}$$

Fluctuations in the power output may now be obtained from expressions (14) and (15). The result is somewhat different from that of equation (16) because, in the case of a stable amplifier, $a < b$ and the exponentials in (14) and (15) decrease with time so that, under constant conditions

$$\overline{m} = \frac{c}{b-a} ,$$

$$\overline{m^2} = \frac{c(b+c)}{(b-a)^2} ,$$

$$\mathcal{E}^2 = \frac{\overline{m^2} - \overline{m}^2}{\overline{m}^2} = \frac{b}{c} . \tag{58}$$

Substituting appropriate values into (58) one has

$$\mathcal{E}^2 = \frac{b}{a+c_i} = \frac{b}{a + \frac{2\pi P_i}{hQ_i}} . \tag{59}$$

Here it is assumed that P_i is constant over the frequency range for which $R(\nu)$ is of appreciable magnitude. For an amplifying system of reasonably large gain, $a \approx b$, so that

$$\mathcal{E}^2 = \frac{1}{1 + \frac{2\pi P_i}{ahQ_i}} \tag{60}$$

and for $\mathcal{E}$ to be small, $\frac{2\pi P_i}{ahQ_i} \gg 1$.

As in the waveguide amplifier, there are background noise fluctuations due to spontaneous emission even when no signal is present. For the output power to be doubled as a result of an input signal, c_i must equal a, or from (57)

$$\frac{2\pi P_i}{hQ_i} = a . \tag{61}$$

In terms of a noise temperature T_n for the amplifier, this gives

$$P_i = kT_n = \frac{ahQ_i}{2\pi} = \frac{ah\nu}{b_i} . \tag{62}$$

Since $b = b_i + b_u + b_o$, and $a \approx b$ for large amplification, (62) becomes

$$T_n = \frac{bh\nu}{k(b - b_u - b_o)} . \tag{63}$$

An effective temperature $T_e (<0)$ for the molecular system can be defined which includes all gains and losses except those due to the input coupling, that is

$$\frac{a}{b_u + b_o} = \exp\left(-\frac{h\nu}{k|T_e|}\right) . \tag{64}$$

Hence, when $h\nu \ll k|T_e|$, the noise temperature (63) is simply

$$T_n = |T_e| \tag{65}$$

and if $h\nu \gg k|T_e|$, the limiting noise temperature becomes, from (63) and (64),

$$T_n = \frac{h\nu}{k} . \tag{66}$$

Now a noise temperature $T_n = h\nu/k$ is based on the classical assumption that the flow of power per unit bandwidth is $kT\Delta\nu$. An amplifier with this ideal noise temperature is capable, as is the ideal waveguide amplifier, to "detect a single photon." This may be demonstrated from the fact that the noise temperature $h\nu/k$ corresponds to a rate of power flow $h\nu\Delta\nu$ in a bandwidth $\Delta\nu$, or to $\Delta\nu$ quanta per unit time. But an amplifier of bandwidth $\Delta\nu$ can amplify a pulse of minimum length $1/\Delta\nu$ which would then contain just one photon at this minimum detectable power level.*

From (63) and (64), it may be noted that the lowest noise temperature is obtained for an amplifier by making the output coupling very small, and that the limiting noise temperature when $b_o = 0$ just corresponds to the effective temperature of the active material. Furthermore, as in the case of a waveguide amplifier, additional coupling holes or losses in the cavity can produce a very high noise temperature even when the cavity and its active material are at low temperatures. Of course it is also possible to dispense with the output coupling entirely and use the wave reflected from the input as the amplified signal.

* This does not mean the possibility of unambiguously observing a single photon as an individual pulse.

§ 9. Superregenerative Amplifier Using a Cavity

To consider the noise properties of a super-regenerative cavity amplifier, assume that the rate of induced emission a is zero until time $t=0$, when suddenly a is made larger than b so that an exponential build-up of energy in the cavity is begun. There are on the average n photons in the cavity at $t=0$. Then equation (14) describes the growth of the number of photons in the cavity during the amplification period. For large gain $(a-b)t \gg 1$ and the average number of photons in the cavity after amplification lasting time t_1 is

$$\overline{m}=\left(\overline{n}+\frac{c_i}{a-b}+\frac{a}{a-b}\right)e^{(a-b)t_1}, \qquad (67)$$

where c_i is again given by (57). Since the initial number of photons n is determined by the input power before $t=0$, it is from equation (14) for $a=0$

$$\overline{n}=\frac{c_i}{b}, \qquad (68)$$

where a term with exponential decay factor may be neglected. Whether the contribution of initial number of photons due to input signal before $t=0$, or that of continuing flow of photons during build-up denominates depends on the relative size of $1/b$ and $1/(a-b)$, assuming c_i is same for $t<0$ and $t>0$.

Putting (68) into (67), one obtains

$$\overline{m}=\left[\frac{c_i}{b}+1\right]\frac{a}{a-b}e^{(a-b)t_1}. \qquad (69)$$

Or, if the the cavity is operated as a stable regenerative amplifier until $t=0$ with $a=a_0<b$ and after that a is suddenly increased so that $a>b$, $\overline{n}$ in equation (67) is given by

$$\overline{n}=\frac{1}{b-a_0}(c_i+a_0) \qquad (68a)$$

instead of (68). Then one obtains from (67)

$$\overline{m}=\frac{b(a-a_0)}{(a-b)(b-a_0)}\left[\frac{c_i}{b}+1\right]e^{(a-b)t_1} \qquad (69a)$$

The background noise due to spontaneous emission when no photon is introduced from coupling holes is given by the second term, +1, in the brackets of (69) and (69a). The threshold signal is that which gives the same amount of output or the same number of quanta $\overline{m}$ as the background noise. Then

$$\frac{c_i}{b}=1 \quad \text{or} \quad \frac{b_iP_i}{bh\nu}=1$$

and the noise temperature of the amplifier at the resonance is

$$T_n=\frac{P_i}{k}=\frac{h\nu}{k}\frac{b}{b_i}. \qquad (70)$$

It may be noted that the noise temperature in a superregenerative amplifier is essentially the same form as (63) in a regenerative amplifier, and that more detailed discussion is allowed by the application of general solutions developed in § 5.

The discussion of noise and the number of quanta in the cavity has dealt with a continuous range of frequencies. The amplifier gain of course varies with frequency, but in any small part of its bandwidth the signal to noise ratio is equivalent. The gain varies as

$$\left[\left(\frac{1}{2Q}\right)^2+\left(\frac{\nu-\nu_0}{\nu_0}\right)^2\right]^{-1}$$

and at maximum, $\nu=\nu_0$, it is

$$G=\frac{4ab_ib_0}{b(a-b)^2}e^{(a-b)t_1} \qquad (71)$$

for the case described by equation (69), and

$$G=\frac{4(a-a_0)b_ib_0}{(b-a_0)(a-b)^2}e^{(a-b)t_1} \qquad (71a)$$

for the case to which equation (69a) applies.

These results differ somewhat from the conclusions of Gordon, Zeiger, and Townes,[3] partly because the earlier work did not take into account spontaneous emission from the molecules. Although this random spontaneous emission is generally small compared with the stimulated emission occuring in the cavity, it is amplified and therefore may become an important source of noise. Consider, for example, a group of molecules which are entirely in the upper state. Let them be in a cavity made of lossless and hence non-radiative material and let no photons enter through the coupling hole. One might then suppose that no noise would exist in the cavity. This is true only if there is no spontaneous emission $(c=0)$. Actually $c=a$ and if the system is stable, the noise level is given by $\overline{m}=a/(b-a)$, which is equivalent to the input noise temperature $b/b_i\cdot(h\nu)/k$.

Other differences between the present results and those of Gordon, Zeiger, and Townes come from the fact that they consider effects of thermal radiation which may enter the amplifier through input or output coupling holes.

Although this type of noise is quite important in some cases, it is not fundamental to the amplification process, and has been neglected in the above discussion. Appropriate design of input and output circuits can in most cases prevent such noise which is not essentially associated with the signal from entering the amplifier.

Many varieties of design are possible for maser-type amplifiers, each of which needs analysis for a precise evaluation of sensitivity. However, the above results for certain idealized cases should indicate qualitatively the results which may be obtained, and illustrate the application to maser amplifiers of the general expressions for fluctuations developed in the former sections.

In conclusion we would like to acknowledge a helpful correspondence on the subject of noise between one of the authors and Mr. Marcel Muller.

Appendix. Derivation of Solution (30)*

The equation (3) will be solved here by use of a generating function for the most general case that a and b are functions of time and c/a is any positive constant.

The generating function for $P_{n,m}$ is very similar to (23) and is defined by

$$f_n=\sum_m P_{n,m}x^m. \quad \text{(A1)}$$

By substituting (A1) into (3), one obtains a partial differential equation satisfied by $f_n(x,t)$:

$$\frac{\partial f_n}{\partial t}=(1-x)(b-ax)\frac{\partial f_n}{\partial t}-c(1-x)f_n \quad \text{(A2)}$$

This is linear in f_n and may be solved by standard methods. The characteristic equation for (A2) is given by

$$\frac{-dx}{(1-x)(b-ax)}=dt=\frac{-df_n}{c(1-x)f_n} \quad \text{(A3)}$$

The desired solution of (A2) is obtained by solving (A3) with the initial conditions: $x=x_0$ and $f_n=x_0{}^n$ for $t=0$, and then eliminating x_0.

The equation (A3) may be solved by putting

$$y=\frac{1}{1-x} \quad \text{(A4)}$$

Then (A3) becomes

$$\frac{-dy}{(b-a)y+a}=dt=\frac{-ydf_n}{cf_n} \quad \text{(A5)}$$

The left part of the equation (A5) is

$$dy/dt=(a-b)y-a \quad \text{(A6)}$$

which is linear in y. The solution is given by

$$y=e^{\int(a-b)dt}\left(\int -ae^{-\int(a-b)dt}dt+y_0\right) \quad \text{(A7)}$$

where y_0 is the initial value of y for $t=0$, i.e.

$$y_0=\frac{1}{1-x_0}$$

Using the notations

$$K=e^{\int(a-b)dt}, \quad \text{(A8)}$$

$$G=K\int\frac{a}{K}dt, \quad \text{(A9)}$$

(A7) is written in the form

$$y=Ky_0-G \quad \text{(A10)}$$

Evidently, K is the classical amplification factor.

f_n is obtained from the right part of (A5), i.e.

$$\frac{1}{f_n}\frac{df_n}{dt}=-\frac{c}{y} \quad \text{(A11)}$$

By (A7), the equation takes the form

$$\frac{1}{f_n}\frac{df_n}{dt}=-\frac{c}{a}\frac{a}{K}\Big/\left(-\int\frac{a}{K}dt+y_0\right) \quad \text{(A12)}$$

Integrating (A12), one obtains

$$f_n=\left(-\int a/K\,dt+y_0\right)^{c/a}\times\text{const}$$

$$=(-G/K+y_0)^{c/a}\times\text{const.} \quad \text{(A13)}$$

Considering the initial condition $f=x_0{}^n=(1-1/y_0)^n$ at $t=0$, (A13) becomes

$$f_n=\left(1-\frac{G}{Ky_0}\right)^{c/a}\left(1-\frac{1}{y_0}\right)^n \quad \text{(A14)}$$

Eliminating y_0 by use of (A10), the generating function is finally given by

$$f_n=\left(\frac{y}{y+G}\right)^{c/a}\left(1-\frac{K}{y+G}\right)^n$$

$$=\left(\frac{1}{1+G(1-x)}\right)^{c/a}\left(\frac{1+(G-K)(1-x)}{1+G(1-x)}\right)^n \quad \text{(A15)}$$

Expansion of the numerator and denominator in powers of x gives

* A derivation similar to that indicated here was obtained independently by Dr. L. R. Walker and kindly communicated to one of the authors.

$$P_{n,m}=\frac{G^m(G-K+1)^n(K-1)^{m+n}}{(G+1)^{m+n+c/a}}$$
$$\times\sum_{j=0}^{m\text{ or }n}\frac{n!\,\Gamma(n+m+c/a-j)}{(n-j)!\,j!\,(m-j)!\,\Gamma(n+c/a)}\left[\frac{(G+1)(G-K)}{G(G-K+1)(K-1)^2}\right]^j. \tag{A16}$$

Or, if (A15) is put into a form like that of (23) and similarly expanded, one obtains a more convenient expression

$$P_{n,m}=\frac{G^m(G-K+1)^n(K-1)^{m+n}}{(G+1)^{m+n+c/a}}$$
$$\times\sum_{j=0}^{m\text{ or }n}\frac{n!}{j!\,(n-j)!\,(m-j)!}\frac{\Gamma(m+c/a)}{\Gamma(j+c/a)}\left[\frac{K}{G(G-K+1)}\right]^j. \tag{A17}$$

When a and b are constant, K and G are given by

$$K=e^{(a-b)t},$$
$$G=\frac{a}{a-b}(e^{(a-b)t}-1)=\frac{a}{a-b}(K-1) \tag{A18}$$

and substituting this into (A17), one obtains the expression (30) as a result.

References

1) D. E. Lee and C. A. Coulson: Journal of Genetics, **49** (1949) 264.
2) W. Furry: Phys. Rev. **52** (1937) 567.
3) J. P. Gordon, H. J. Zeiger and C. H. Townes: Phys. Rev. **99** (1955) 1264.

ERRATA

Fluctuations in Amplification of Quanta with Application to Maser Amplifiers, K. Shimoda, H. Takahasi and Charles H. Townes.

Page 688, below equation 7, correct to read:

the average value of m can be shown to be

$$\bar{m} = K(n + c/a)$$

Page 690, equation (18) should read:

$$\varepsilon = \sqrt{\frac{a}{c}}$$

Page 691, top line change to read:

since always $\frac{b(K - 1)}{aK - b} < 1$

Equ. (26) should read

$$\frac{u}{1-u} = \frac{Ku_o}{1-u_o} + (K - 1)\frac{a}{(a-b)} \tag{26}$$

Page 692, equation 34 should read

$$P_{n,m} = \frac{(a-b)}{(aK)} \left(\frac{b}{a}\right)^n \exp\left(- \frac{(a-b)}{aK} m\right) L_n\left[- \frac{(a-b)^2 m}{abK}\right]$$

Page 695 equation 46 should read:

$$\bar{m} = \left(\bar{n} + \frac{a}{a-b}\right)K \tag{46}$$

Page 695 above equation 49 correct to read: is obtained from (34) as

page 697, paragraph below equation 50 last line correct to read:

$a > b$.

Page 698, above equation 68a correct to read:

$a > b$, $\bar{n}$ in equation (67) is given by

Page 698, left side, bottom of page correct to read:

$$\frac{a_i}{b} = 1$$

Page 699, equation A9 correct to read:

$$G = K\int \frac{a\,dt}{K} \tag{A9}$$

page 697, equation (57) should read:

$$c_i = \frac{2\pi P_i}{hQ_i} = \frac{P_i b_i}{h\nu}$$

Noise in Maser Amplifiers—Theory and Experiment*

J. P. GORDON† AND L. D. WHITE†, MEMBER, IRE

Summary—This paper contains a theoretical treatment of noise in maser amplifiers and the results of experimental measurements of the noise of an ammonia beam maser. The concept of "effective input noise temperature" is defined and used. The theoretical treatment obtains an equivalent microwave circuit and derives expressions for the gain and effective input noise temperature of both reflection and transmission-type masers. The experimental measurements yielded values of about 80°K for the effective input noise temperature of a reflection-type ammonia beam maser. The experimental values agree with those predicted by theory and the comparison of experiment and theory gives an upper limit of about 20°K for the magnitude of the "beam temperature."

INTRODUCTION

It has been realized for some time that maser amplifiers should be capable of very low noise operation.[1] Recently, several papers have given theoretical calculations[2–6] of the noise generated by "negative temperature" media, and predictions[2–7] of the noise figures of maser amplifiers. Also quite recently, experimental measurements of the noise figures of ammonia maser amplifiers[8–10] and of a solid-state maser amplifier[11] have been made. This paper reviews the theory of maser amplifiers, using an equivalent microwave circuit. This theory applies to two-level masers and also to three-level types in which noise introduced by the pumping source can be ignored. The term "effective input noise temperature"[12] is defined. This term is quite useful in describing very low noise amplifiers and gives a more immediate idea of the quality of the amplifier than does the usual description in terms of noise figure. Experimental values for the effective input noise temperature of an ammonia maser are given and are compared with those obtained from theory. From this comparison an upper limit for the beam temperature is obtained.

EFFECTIVE INPUT NOISE TEMPERATURE

The "effective input noise temperature,"[12] $T_n(f)$, is defined here as the temperature of the input termination which results at frequency f in output noise power per unit bandwidth double that which would occur if the same input termination were at absolute zero. The effective noise temperature is related to the noise figure $F(f)$ of the amplifier with the same input by $T_n(f) = [F(f) - 1]$ 290°K. The average effective input noise temperature $\overline{T}_n$ is defined as the temperature of the input termination which results in a total noise power output double that which would exist if the same input termination were at absolute zero. The average effective input noise temperature is related to the spot effective input noise temperature by

$$\overline{T}_n = \frac{\int T_n(f)G(f)df}{\int G(f)df}$$

where $G(f)$ is the power gain of the amplifier. Also, $\overline{T}_n = [\overline{F} - 1]$ 290°K, where $\overline{F}$ is the average noise figure. This concept of effective input noise temperature becomes particularly valuable in applications in which both the effective input noise temperature of the amplifier and the noise temperature of the input load (*e.g.*, an antenna looking at the sky) are less than room temperature.

For convenience, it is assumed in the following that the input termination is matched to the input waveguide.

THEORY OF NOISE IN A CAVITY MASER AMPLIFIER

In this section the noise output of a cavity maser amplifier is considered in detail, using the approach of the microwave circuit. The sources of noise include the

* Original manuscript received by the IRE, April 3, 1958; revised manuscript received, May 27, 1958.

† Bell Telephone Labs., Inc., Murray Hill, N. J.

[1] J. P. Gordon, H. J. Zeiger, and C. H. Townes, "Molecular microwave oscillator and new hyperfine structure in the microwave spectrum of NH_3," *Phys. Rev.* vol. 95, pp. 282–284; July 1, 1954.
———, "The maser—new type of microwave amplifier, frequency standard, and spectrometer," *Phys. Rev.*, vol. 99, pp. 1264–1274; August 15, 1955.

[2] K. Shimoda, H. Takahasi, and C. H. Townes, "Fluctuations in amplification of quanta with application of maser amplifiers," *J. Phys. Soc., Japan*, vol. 12, pp. 686–700; June, 1957.

[3] J. P. Wittke, "Molecular amplification and generation of microwaves," PROC. IRE, vol. 45, pp. 291–316; March, 1957.

[4] R. V. Pound, "Spontaneous emission and the noise figure of maser amplifiers," *Ann. Phys.*, vol. 1, pp. 24–32; April, 1957.

[5] M. W. Muller, "Noise in a molecular amplifier," *Phys. Rev.*, vol. 106, pp. 8–12; April 1, 1957.

[6] M. W. P. Strandberg, "Inherent noise of quantum-mechanical amplifiers," *Phys. Rev.*, vol. 106, pp. 617–620; May 15, 1957.

[7] J. C. Helmer and M. W. Muller, to be published.

[8] J. C. Helmer, "Maser noise measurement," *Phys. Rev.*, vol. 107, p. 902; August 1, 1957.

[9] L. E. Alsop, J. A. Giordmaine, C. H. Townes, and T. C. Wang, "Measurement of noise in a maser amplifier," *Phys. Rev.*, vol. 107, pp. 1450–1451; September 1, 1957.

[10] J. P. Gordon and L. D. White, "Experimental determination of the noise figure of an ammonia maser," *Phys. Rev.*, vol. 107, pp. 1728–1729; September 15, 1957.

[11] A. L. McWhorter, J. W. Meyer, and P. D. Strum, "Noise temperature measurement on a solid state maser," *Phys. Rev.*, vol. 108, pp. 1642–1644; December 15, 1957.

[12] The wording "effective input noise temperature" was chosen after consultation with H. A. Haus. Recently, Subcommittee 7.9 of the IRE approved for the same term a definition similar to that used here. The concept underlying these definitions has been utilized previously. In the analysis of noise in conventional amplifiers, $(F-1)$ has played an important part and has been designated the excess noise figure, and $(F-1)\cdot 290$°K has been termed the excess noise (temperature). (For example, see D. T. McCoy, "Present and future capabilities of microwave crystal receivers," PROC. IRE vol. 46, pp. 61–66; January, 1958.) Also, in dealing with maser noise this concept has been used, being called "noise temperature" by others[2,11] and "effective noise temperature" by the authors.[10]

amplifying medium and a number of sources of thermal noise; the cavity walls, the input circuit, the output circuit in the two-port case, and losses in the cavity caused by the presence of the amplifying medium, *e.g.*, dielectric losses in the case of a solid sample or, as was pointed out by Muller and Helmer,[8] absorption due to background ammonia gas in the case of the ammonia beam maser. Noise due to statistical fluctuations in the number of amplifying particles is usually negligible. For example, in the ammonia beam maser, fluctuations amount to about one part in 10^5 (there are about 10^{10} molecules in the cavity at any time), and this would be expected to cause gain fluctuations less than 0.1 per cent in a maser amplifier operating at about 20-db gain. Both transmission and reflection-type operation are treated theoretically, although experimental results are given only for the reflection type. It is shown that in most cases the reflection type is better in noise figure as well as in gain-bandwidth product. Finally, the possibility of a traveling-wave maser is mentioned. It is superior to either type of cavity maser if the necessary gain can be obtained.

Consider first the general maser amplifier (Fig. 1) utilizing a resonant cavity. The cavity is coupled by two waveguides, labeled 1 and 2 for input and output respectively, and contains the "negative temperature" amplifying medium. Let there be a circulator on the cavity input so that the power returning from the cavity in waveguide 1 is separated from the input signal power. Furthermore, let there be an isolator in the output waveguide so that a constant matched load is presented to the cavity. Each of the circuit elements has some definite temperature and, if lossy, is a generator of thermal noise. Let Q_1 and Q_2 be equal to the ratio of the energy stored in the cavity to the energy per radian which emerges from the cavity into the input and output waveguides, respectively.

Consider now an equivalent circuit for the maser. At the outset no circuit losses except that of the cavity, represented by Q_c, and the backward loss of the isolator are included. The losses of the circulator and other input circuitry are taken into account later. First, replace the lossy cavity by a lossless one of the same resonant frequency to which a matched waveguide is appended through a suitable coupling (Fig. 2). The temperature of the load in this waveguide is equal to the temperature of the cavity. As for the amplifying medium, it can be shown directly from Maxwell's equations that the effect of its complex susceptibility,[13] $\chi=\chi'-i\chi''$, is to

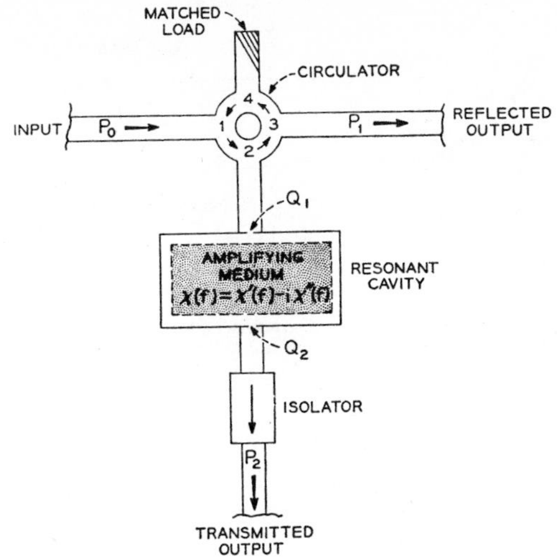

Fig. 1—Schematic diagram of a maser amplifier using a resonant cavity. Both transmitted and reflected power are indicated.

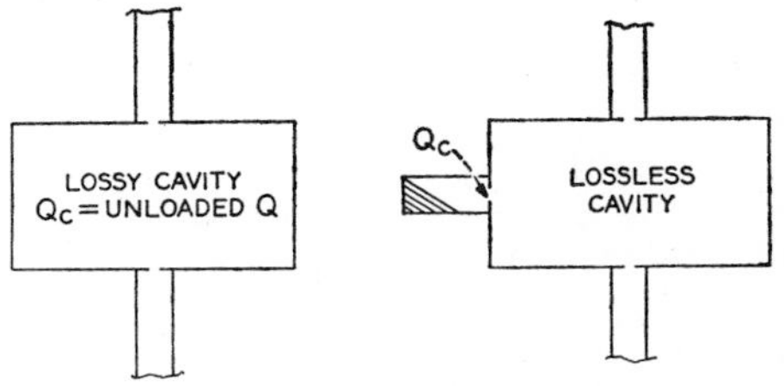

(a) (b)

Fig. 2—(a) A lossy cavity. (b) Equivalent circuit for lossy cavity.

change the apparent Q and resonant frequency of the cavity. The impedance of the cavity plus medium measured at frequency f is equal to that of a cavity whose resonant frequency differs from that of the actual cavity by the fractional amount $\Delta f/f_c=\frac{1}{2}\eta\,\chi'(f)$, and whose losses differ by an amount $\Delta(1/Q)=\eta\,\chi''(f)$. f_c is the resonant frequency of the loaded cavity without medium; η is the filling factor[14] and is unity when the medium completely fills the cavity.

According to the results of Slater's[15] analysis, an equivalent microwave circuit may be obtained through replacement of the amplifying medium by another waveguide, whose coupling to the cavity is proportional to the sample susceptibility. This waveguide is terminated at the "plane of the detuned short" by an admittance Y whose frequency dependence is that of the sample resonance. Let χ_m be the maximum absolute value of the imaginary part of the sample susceptibility, and let $g(f)$ and $b(f)$ be line shape factors such that $\chi'=\chi_m b(f)$ and $\chi''=\chi_m g(f)$. The equivalent circuit

[13] The electric susceptibility, $\chi(f)$, at frequency f is defined by $P(f)\cdot\exp i2\pi ft=\chi(f)\cdot\epsilon_0\cdot E(f)\cdot\exp i2\pi ft$, where $P(f)$ is the polarization produced by the electric field $E(f)$. χ' and χ'' are related to each other through the Kronig-Kramers relations. See J. H. Van Vleck, "Propagation of Short Radio Waves," M.I.T. Rad. Lab. Ser., McGraw-Hill Book Co., Inc., New York, N. Y., vol. 13, D. E. Kerr, ed., p. 642; 1951.
H. Fröhlich, "Theory of Dielectrics," Clarendon Press, Oxford, Eng.; ch. 1, sec. 2; 1949.
A. M. Portis, "Electronic structure of *F* centers: saturation of the spin resonance," *Phys. Rev.*, vol. 91, pp. 1071–1078; September 1, 1953.

$$= \int_{\text{sample}} E^2\,d(\text{vol}) \Big/ \int_{\text{cavity}} E^2\,d(\text{vol})$$

for the case of an electric dipole transition. For the magnetic dipole case B replaces E.

[15] J. C. Slater, "Microwave Electronics," D. Van Nostrand Co., Inc., New York, N. Y., ch. 4; 1950.

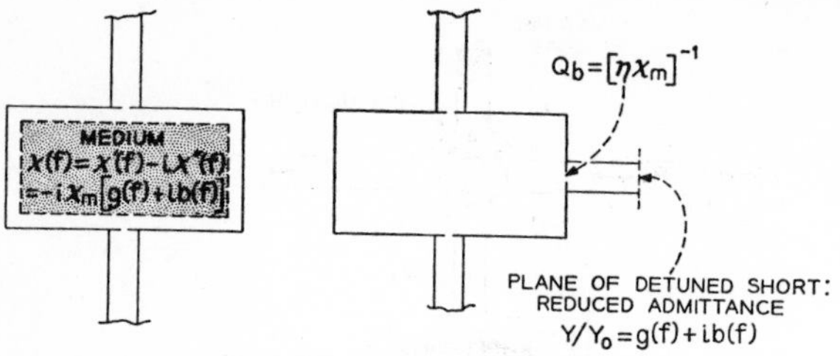

(a) (b)

Fig. 3—(a) Resonant cavity with amplifying medium. (b) Equivalent circuit for cavity with amplifying medium.

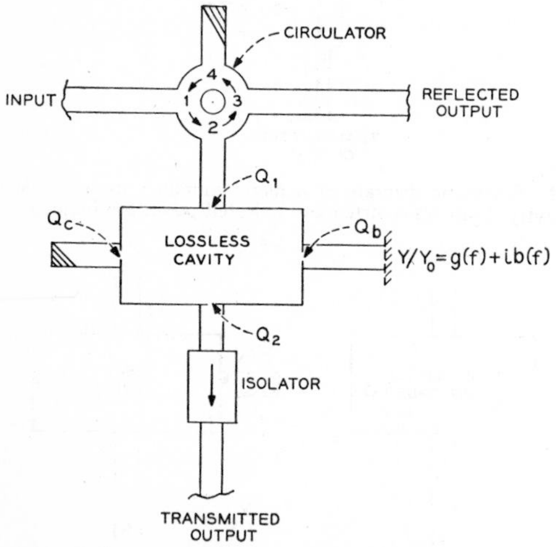

Fig. 4—Complete equivalent circuit for maser amplifier.

(Fig. 3) is then obtained by letting the coupling be $Q_b = 1/\eta\chi_m$ and the reduced admittance be $y_b = g(f) + ib(f)$, where $y_b = Y/Y_0$, and Y_0 is the characteristic admittance of the guide. Positive values of g represent absorption; negative values, emission. From the definition of χ_m note that the maximum absolute value of g is always unity, and that this occurs at the center of the sample resonance. The complete equivalent circuit, then, is as given in Fig. 4.

The sources of noise in the maser amplifier now are easily discernible. Noise power traveling toward the cavity is generated by the load in each waveguide. The output isolator is considered to be an integral part of the amplifier, and therefore the noise it radiates toward the cavity is included in the analysis. This noise power is a full kT_i per unit bandwidth, corresponding to the infinite attenuation in the backward direction which the isolator is assumed to possess. T_i is the isolator's temperature. The circulator contributes noise only if it is lossy and/or if it sees a mismatch looking toward the input. Circulator loss is considered later; it is assumed mismatches can be avoided. The amplifying medium also contributes noise. It has been shown by Pound[4] that the noise generator associated with a negative resistance (in this case a negative admittance) follows the Johnson-Nyquist formulation just as for the positive resistance. Thus, for $|T_b| \gg hf/k$, noise power per unit bandwidth of amount $kT_b g(f)$[16] is incident on the cavity from this noise source, where T_b is the "temperature" (negative) of the amplifying medium,[2] defined by $T_b = -hf/k \ln (n_a/n_b)$, where n_a and n_b are the populations of the upper and lower quantum energy levels responsible for the amplification. This is the same relationship between the level populations and temperature which holds for thermodynamic equilibrium at positive temperature. Dielectric losses in the sample, if any, should be added to the cavity loss in the types of maser in which the sample is permanently affixed to the cavity and takes up the cavity temperature. In the beam-type maser there is no dielectric loss; however, background gas causes some absorption. This absorption should be added similarly to the cavity loss since the molecules responsible for it have bounced, for the most part, at least once off the walls of the cavity, and so have acquired nearly the temperature of the cavity. The relative importance of each noise source is determined by its temperature and the size of the coupling by which it is attached to the cavity.

The calculations necessary to obtain gain and noise figure are quite straightforward from this point. First, however, it is convenient to define some useful symbols:

$$Q_L \equiv \left(\frac{1}{Q_c} + \frac{1}{Q_1} + \frac{1}{Q_2}\right)^{-1}, \text{ loaded cavity } Q,$$

$\beta = Q_L/Q_b$, beam strength parameter (this factor approaches unity for high gain),

$$D(f) \equiv 4Q_L^2\left[\frac{1}{4}\left(\frac{1}{Q_L} + \frac{g(f)}{Q_b}\right)^2 + \left(\frac{f-f_c}{f_c} + \frac{b(f)}{2Q_b}\right)^2\right],$$

resonant term

$$= (1 + \beta g(f))^2 + \left(\frac{f-f_c}{\Delta f_c} + \beta b(f)\right)^2,$$

where $\Delta f_c = f_c/2Q_L$ is the half width at half maximum of the cavity resonance. The input power P_0 per unit bandwidth, causes a reflection of amount[17]

$$P_r = P_0\left[1 - \frac{4Q_L^2}{DQ_1}\left(\frac{1}{Q_c} + \frac{1}{Q_2} + \frac{g}{Q_b}\right)\right]$$

and also a transmission into waveguide 2 of magnitude

$$P_t = P_0 4Q_L^2/Q_1Q_2D.$$

Similar equations obtain for the noise power originating from each of the noise sources. Adding up the contributions from all the different independent sources, the power P_1 per unit bandwidth which emerges from the input is

[16] For $|T_b| \lesssim hf/k$ the exact expression, $g(f) \cdot hf/[\exp(hf/kT_b) - 1]$, must be used.

[17] The explicit frequency dependence of $g(f)$, $b(f)$, and $D(f)$ is omitted from here on, and the simple forms g, b, and D used.

$$P_1 = P_0\left[1 - \frac{4Q_L^2}{DQ_1}\left(\frac{1}{Q_c} + \frac{1}{Q_2} + \frac{g}{Q_b}\right)\right] + \frac{4Q_L^2}{DQ_1}\left[\frac{kT_c}{Q_c} + \frac{kT_i}{Q_2} + \frac{kT_{bg}}{Q_b}\right]$$

where T_c is the temperature of the cavity. Similarly, the power P_2 per unit bandwidth emerging into waveguide 2 is

$$P_2 = P_0 4Q_L^2/Q_1Q_2D + kT_i\left[1 - \frac{4Q_L^2}{DQ_2}\left(\frac{1}{Q_c} + \frac{1}{Q_1} + \frac{g}{Q_b}\right)\right] + \frac{4Q_L^2}{DQ_2}\left[\frac{kT_c}{Q_c} + \frac{kT_{bg}}{Q_b}\right].$$

Now that the basic formulas have been obtained, the gain, bandwidth, noise figure, and relative merit for the transmission and reflection type masers can be evaluated. Also, these results can be compared with the experimental data.

Bandwidth of the amplifier, at high gain, is mainly determined by the resonant term D. At frequencies near the midband of the maser, g and b may be approximated by $g=-1$ and $b=(f-f_b)/\Delta f_b$, where f_b and Δf_b are, respectively, the center frequency and half width at half maximum of the amplifying resonance. For both reflected power and transmitted power, the difference B between half-power frequencies is approximately

$$B \approx 2(1-\beta)\left[\frac{1}{\Delta f_c} + \frac{\beta}{\Delta f_b}\right]^{-1}.$$

The effective input noise temperature $T_n(f)$ is obtained by setting P_0 equal to $kT_n(f)$ and equating the part of P_1 or P_2 originating from this noise source to the combined power per unit bandwidth from the other noise sources. When dealing with the one-port maser, Q_2 is set equal to infinity to eliminate the second waveguide.

The effective input noise temperature for the one-port maser is

$$T_n(f) = \frac{\frac{4Q_L^2}{Q_1D}\left[\frac{T_c}{Q_c} + g\frac{T_b}{Q_b}\right]}{1 - \frac{4Q_L^2}{Q_1D}\left[\frac{1}{Q_c} + g\frac{1}{Q_b}\right]}. \quad (1)$$

At resonance ($f=f_c=f_b$) the effective input noise temperature, $T_{n,0}$, may be expressed as

$$T_{n,0} = \frac{(\sqrt{G_0}+1)^2}{G_0}\left[T_c\frac{Q_1}{Q_c} + |T_b|\frac{Q_1}{Q_b}\right] \quad (2)$$

where G_0 is the power gain at resonance, given by

$$G_0 = \frac{P_r}{P_0} = 1 + \frac{4Q_L^2}{Q_1(1-\beta)^2}\left[\frac{1}{Q_b} - \frac{1}{Q_c}\right]. \quad (3)$$

For the transmission-type maser at resonance

$$T_{n,0} = T_c\frac{Q_1}{Q_c} + |T_b|\frac{Q_1}{Q_b} + T_i\left[\left(\frac{Q_1}{Q_2}\right)^{1/2} - \frac{1}{\sqrt{G_0}}\right]$$

and

$$G_0 = \frac{4Q_L^2}{Q_1Q_2(1-\beta)^2}.$$

One further consideration is in order, namely the effect of loss in the input circuit. This loss has two bad effects: it attenuates the signal and at the same time it introduces some noise. The effective input noise temperature T_n' of the resulting amplifier is increased over that of the maser proper, becoming

$$T_n' = [T_n + T_L(L-1)/L]L \quad (4)$$

where L is the loss (reciprocal of the gain) and T_L is the temperature of the element which introduces the loss. The effect of input loss may be important in maser amplifiers, especially the reflection type where the required circulator may introduce as much as a few tenths of a db of loss.

Contemplation of the above results reveals the following facts, assuming the same sample in both reflection and transmission-type operation.

1) For the same value of the loaded cavity Q, and thus the same bandwidth, the gain of the reflection type is 6 db greater than the maximum gain of the transmission type, which is obtained by setting $Q_1=Q_2$. Also, contributions to the effective input noise temperature from the amplifying material and the cavity walls are higher for the transmission-type maser; they are about twice as large in the case $Q_1=Q_2$.
2) For reasonably low noise operation and at the same time high gain, it is essential to cool the isolator of the transmission-type amplifier to a low temperature, whereas the circulator of the reflection type need not be cooled if its loss is kept small.
3) For minimum noise operation, it is necessary to cool the input circuit and the resonant cavity for either type of maser.

A word about the possible operation of a traveling-wave maser amplifier is appropriate at this point. The instability and loss in bandwidth, which are common to all types of regenerative amplifiers at high gain, are largely overcome by this method, and its noise properties are similar to those of the cavity maser. However, for some types of amplifying media, *e.g.*, gases, it is very difficult to produce the high concentration of field which is necessary in such a device to obtain useful gain in a reasonable volume.

Experimental Procedure

The aim of the experiment was to measure the effective input noise temperature of an ammonia maser and to compare this experimental value with theory.

A block diagram of the apparatus used in making the noise measurements is shown in Fig. 5. With the exception of the liquid nitrogen cooled load, all of the microwave plumbing, including the masers' cavities, was at room temperature. Each maser was similar to that described by Gordon, Zeiger, and Townes[1] and was of the reflection type. The cavities were operated in the TM_{010} mode. A circulator separated each maser's output from its input. The effective input noise temperature to be measured was that of the first maser. The coupling of its cavity was increased until sufficient gain was achieved with the strongest available beam. A considerable overcoupling, $(Q_1/Q_e<1)$, resulted, giving an expected effective input noise temperature much less than the cavity temperature [see (2)]. The amplification of the first maser was modulated[18] on and off at 35 cps by a square-wave transverse electric field within the cavity. To obtain this field the cavity was split longitudinally and a voltage was applied between the two halves. The resulting inhomogeneous field turned the maser OFF by broadening the ammonia resonance and shifting its peak to the extent that the effects of the beam became negligible. The second maser functioned as a CW low noise RF amplifier. The local oscillator klystron was stabilized with a dc Pound stabilizer circuit.[19] The IF amplifier operated at 70 mc and had a bandwidth of 2.5 mc. The time constant of the dc filter following the lock-in amplifier was about one second.

Measurements were made of the change in RF attenuation A that followed the second maser required to keep the recorder deflection constant as the temperature of the nonreflecting input termination was changed from one known temperature T'' to another, T'. This change in termination temperature was accomplished by inserting 20 db of room temperature attenuation between the cold load and the circulator. From these measurements alone an approximate value (within a few per cent) for the effective input noise temperature of the maser plus its input circuitry may be calculated. Measurements also were made of the loss L and the temperature T_L of the loss between the input termination and the maser cavity. From the combined measurements, an approximate value T_n^* may be obtained for the effective input noise temperature of the maser itself. A more exact determination of the effective input noise temperature T_n requires a knowledge of the relative amount of power leaving the maser when off.

[18] R. H. Dicke, "The measurement of thermal radiation at microwave frequencies," *Rev. Sci. Instr.*, vol. 17, pp. 268–275; July, 1946. This method of modulating the desired signal has a theoretical sensitivity for given IF bandwidth and dc filter time constant comparable to that obtained by making CW measurements. However, in practice, better sensitivity usually is obtained with the modulation technique because it is less sensitive to slow gain fluctuations in the superheterodyne receiver.

[19] R. V. Pound, "Frequency stabilization of microwave oscillators," PROC. IRE, vol. 35, pp. 1405–1415; December, 1947.

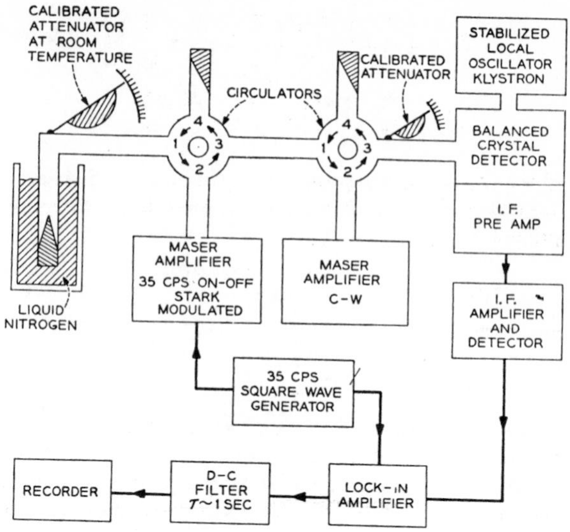

Fig. 5—Block diagram of apparatus.

The difference between T_n and T_n^* is of the order of T_n/G_0, and was obtained from measurements of the maser gain[20] when on G_0, the maser gain when off $G°$, and the temperature of the cavity T_c.

Interpretation of Data

Before considering the actual case, consider an ideal case which yields a simpler relationship between the effective input noise temperature and the measured quantities. Assume that there was zero noise power leaving the maser when it was off, that the second maser's gain was high, and that the bandwidth of the second maser was much narrower than that of the first. In this case, the change A in RF attenuation following the second maser required to keep the recorder deflection constant as the temperature of the first maser's input termination was changed from T'' to T' is related to the effective input noise temperature $T_n'(f_2)$ of the combination of the maser and its input circuitry by

$$\frac{T_n'(f_2) + T''}{T_n'(f_2) + T'} = A, \tag{5}$$

where f_2 is the center frequency of the second maser. The effective input noise temperature $T_n(f_2)$ of the maser itself would be related to the above quantities and to the loss L and temperature T_L of the circuitry between the input termination and the maser by (4), or by

$$\frac{T_n(f_2) + T''/L + T_L(L-1)/L}{T_n(f_2) + T'/L + T_L(L-1)/L} = A. \tag{6}$$

[20] The signal used for the gain measurement was derived from that of the local oscillator by a 70 mc modulator and a sideband filter.

Though not stated explicitly, (5) and (6) also assume that both masers were acting as linear amplifiers, which assumption should be valid at the power levels of operation.

The assumptions that the noise leaving the maser when off was zero, and that the second maser's bandwidth was much narrower than that of the first, were only approximately correct. As a result, (5) and (6) are no longer exact. However, for purposes of comparing experiment and theory it is convenient to use a quantity T_n^* defined by a relation similar to (6):

$$\frac{T_n^* + T''/L + T_L(L-1)/L}{T_n^* + T'/L + T_L(L-1)/L} = A. \qquad (7)$$

Thus, T_n^* is a number which may be experimentally determined with no knowledge of the maser's characteristics.

A theoretical value for T_n^* may be obtained from measurements of the maser's characteristics and the frequency dependence of the amplification between the (first) maser and the IF detector. The recorder deflection was a function of the difference between the power arriving at the detector when the maser was on, P, and that arriving at the detector when the maser was off, P°. This difference is

$$P - P^\circ = k\int_0^\infty ([T_n + T/L + T_L(L-1)/L]G - [T_n^\circ + T/L + T_L(L-1)/L]G^\circ)G_2'df.$$

T is the temperature of the input termination, T_n° and G°, respectively, are the effective input noise temperature and gain of the maser when it is off, and G_2' is the power gain between the output of the first maser and the IF detector. Equating this power difference for the case of the input termination at the temperature T'' with that for the input termination at T' and the RF attenuation changed by A, and arranging the terms into the form of (7), yields for the theoretical value of T_n^*

$$T_n^* = \frac{\int_0^\infty [T_nG - T_c(1-G^\circ)]G_2df}{\int_0^\infty (G - G^\circ)G_2df}, \qquad (8)$$

where G_2 has the frequency dependence of the amplification between the first maser and the IF detector. A is assumed constant over the frequency range of interest. In (8), $T_c(1-G^\circ)$ has been substituted for $T_n^\circ G^\circ$. This is a valid substitution because the effects of the beam were negligible when the maser was off and thus G° is the reflection coefficient of the cavity. In our case, a sufficiently accurate evaluation of (8) is possible, even though the exact frequency dependence of G and G_2 is unknown. In the frequency region where the gain of the first maser is a few db or more, the ratio of $T_nG - T_c(1-G^\circ)$ to $G - G^\circ$ is very nearly independent of frequency. Furthermore, the contribution to (8) from outside this region is negligible (see Appendix I). Thus, (8) reduces to

$$T_n^* = \frac{T_nG - T_c(1-G^\circ)}{G - G^\circ} = \frac{T_{n,0}G_0 - T_c(1-G^\circ)}{G_0 - G^\circ} \qquad (9)$$

with an estimated uncertainty in T_n^* of about 1 per cent, arising from lack of exact knowledge of the shape of the ammonia resonance. For these equations to hold, it is required that the resonant frequency of the maser cavity, the resonant frequency of the ammonia beam, and the center frequency of the second maser be identical; it is sufficient if these frequencies are close enough to each other for good operation.

Eq. (9) combined with (2) yields a theoretical value of T_n^* depending only upon the maser's characteristics. This theoretical value may be compared with the experimental value given by (7). However, since the effective input noise temperature is of more interest than T_n^*, (7) and (9) were combined to give the following expression for the experimental value of $T_{n,0}$:

$$T_{n,0} = \left[\frac{AT' - T''}{1-A}\frac{1}{L} - T_L\frac{L-1}{L}\right]\left(1 - \frac{G^\circ}{G_0}\right) + T_c\frac{1-G^\circ}{G_0}; \qquad (10)$$

and this experimental value was compared with the theoretical value of $T_{n,0}$ as given by (2).

Results

Three separate sets of measurements were made. The results are summarized in Table I as follows.

TABLE I

RESULTS

Date	T_{room} °K	A	L	G°	G_0	T_n Experimental	T_n Theoretical
June 10, 1957	300	2.00 ±0.05	1.172 ±0.027	0.473 ±0.011	50 ±5	81 ±18	77 ±3
June 25, 1957	307	2.04 ±0.14	1.177 ±0.014	0.505 ±0.030	45 ±7	78 ±30	75 ±7
July 18, 1957	304	1.95 ±0.05	1.232 ±0.020	0.513 ±0.013	71 ±7	74 ±16	68 ±3

$T'' = (T_{room} - 2)$ °K
$T' = 77$°K
$T_L = T_c = T_{room}$

The results of June 10, 1957, and July 18, 1957 have been reported previously.[10] In that report, the experimental and theoretical values of the effective input noise temperature were only approximate; the experimental numbers were the T_n^* of the present paper, and the theoretical numbers did not include the contribution of the background ammonia.

The experimental values given in Table I for the effective input noise temperature T_n of the maser, *i.e.*, cavity plus medium, were obtained from (10).

The theoretical values of the effective input noise temperature were calculated from (2) with $1/Q_c$ representing the losses both in the cavity walls and in the background ammonia. The "temperature" of the beam was negative and probably much smaller in absolute magnitude than hf/k. As a result, in (2) $|T_b|$ should be replaced by $hf/k = 1.1°K$. The contribution to the effective input noise temperature by the background ammonia was estimated to be 3.4°K (see Appendix II). The calculation of the theoretical value was based on measurements of the cavity temperature, the reflection coefficient of the cavity with no beam, the midband maser gain, and the pressure of the background ammonia.

The experimental and theoretical values for the effective input noise temperature of the maser agree well within the experimental error. The contribution of the beam to the maser noise was too small to be measured. However, an upper limit of approximately 20°K can be placed on the absolute value of the beam temperature

Appendix I

The difference in power per unit bandwidth between maser on and maser off is much larger in the frequency region of high gain than in the "tail" of the ammonia resonance. However, the effect of the tail on T_n^* may be significant, depending upon the frequency dependence of the gain G_2 following the maser. For example, if G_2 is constant over a frequency region which is large compared to the width of the cavity resonance, evaluation of (8) yields

$$T_n^* = T_{n,0}\,\beta\,\frac{(Q_c/Q_b) - 1}{(Q_c/Q_b) - \beta}$$

where it is assumed that the ammonia resonance has a Lorentz shape, *i.e.*, $g = -1/[1+((f-f_b)/\Delta f_b)^2]$. Using values of $\beta(\sim 0.8)$ and $Q_c/Q_b(\sim 5)$ appropriate to the maser as operated gives $T_n^* \sim (3/4)T_{n,0}$. The frequency region responsible for most of this difference between T_n^* and $T_{n,0}$ is the tail of the ammonia resonance. The exact line shape of the actual resonance is not known. However, enough is known to be able to state that the relative contribution to T_n^* from the tail of the resonance is the same order of magnitude as the contribution from the tail of a Lorentz-shaped line. In the actual experiment G_2, determined by the product of the second maser and the IF amplifier gains, was strongly peaked. In the vicinity of the ammonia resonance G_2 was more than 30 db larger than in the tail. Thus the contribution to T_n^* from the tail was negligible.

Appendix II

Eq. (2) can be extended to include the contribution, $\Delta T_{n,0}$, to the effective input noise temperature from the background ammonia gas. The loss, $1/Q_{gas}$, due to these stray ammonia molecules is simply added to the cavity loss, giving $\Delta T_{n,0} = [(\sqrt{G_0}+1)^2/G_0]T_cQ_1/Q_{gas}$. An estimate of $1/Q_{gas}$ may be made from the known absorption coefficient of the ammonia 3-3 line, $\alpha = 7.9 \times 10^{-4}$ cm^{-1}; the background pressure p of ammonia in the cavity chamber; the gas pressure p_0 at which molecule-molecule collisions and molecule-wall collisions make equal contributions to the line width, and the free space wavelength λ_0. The appropriate relationship for the case $p \ll p_0$ is

$$\frac{1}{Q_{gas}} \cong \frac{\alpha\lambda_0 p}{2\pi p_0}.$$

Taking values approximating the experimental conditions,

$$p_0 = 1 \times 10^{-3} \text{ mm Hg}$$
$$p = 3 \times 10^{-5} \text{ mm Hg}$$
$$\lambda_0 = 1.25 \text{ cm},$$

yields $1/Q_{gas} \cong 1.8 \times 10^{-6}$. The resulting contribution to the effective noise temperature is $\Delta T_{n,0} \cong 3.4°K$, where the values $Q_1 = 1800$, $G_0 = 50$, and $T_c = 300°K$ have been assumed.

Acknowledgment

The authors gratefully acknowledge many helpful discussions with Prof. C. H. Townes, Dr. R. Kompfner and Dr. C. F. Quate; circulator components and advice on circulator construction from Dr. E. H. Turner and Dr. E. A. Ohm; considerable experimental assistance from J. M. Dziedzic and J. J. Wiegand; and some valuable comments from the unknown reviewers.

DATE DUE

GAYLORD			PRINTED IN U.S.A.